Company for Furniture Hardware,
Development, Production, Service

Häfele America Co.
3901 Cheyenne Drive, P.O. Box 4000
Archdale, NC 27263
Phone: (910) 889-2322
Fax: (910) 431-3973 or (910) 431-3831

HÄFELE

Agreement and Application for Credit

- please print or type -

For the purpose of obtaining merchandise from HÄFELE AMERICA CO. (Seller), the following statement is made by the Applicant, intending that the Seller should rely on same as correct.

Name of Applicant ....
Trade Name, if any ....
Billing Address ....
City .... State .... Zip ....
Shipping Address ....
City .... State .... Zip ....
Telephone .... Fax ....
Type of Business .... Years in Business: ....
Sole Proprietorship [ ] Federal Tax No. Number of Employees: ....
Partnership [ ] (or Social Security No.) Estimated credit line
Corporation [ ] .... required: ....

LIST ALL OWNERS, OFFICERS OR GENERAL PARTNERS

1. Name .... Soc. Sec.# ....
   Address ....
   Phone .... Title. ....
2. Name .... Soc. Sec.# ....
   Address ....
   Phone .... Title. ....
3. Name .... Soc. Sec.# ....
   Address ....
   Phone .... Title. ....

TRADE REFERENCES (List only active vendors, no credit cards)

1. Name .... Phone: ....
   Address .... Fax: ....
   City .... State .... Zip ....
2. Name .... Phone: ....
   Address .... Fax: ....
   City .... State .... Zip ....
3. Name .... Phone: ....
   Address .... Fax: ....
   City .... State .... Zip ....

Please turn

Bank Reference of Applicant

Name . . . . Checking Acct.# . . . .
Address . . . . Savings Acct.# . . . .
City/St . . . . Phone: . . . .
Person to contact . . . . Fax:. . . . .

Bank Reference of Guarantor(s)

Name . . . . Checking Acct.# . . . .
Address . . . . Savings Acct.# . . . .
City/St . . . . Phone: . . . .
Person to contact . . . . Fax:. . . . .

TERMS OF AGREEMENT AND APPLICATION FOR CREDIT

In consideration of Seller's extension of credit to Applicant, Applicant agrees to pay under the terms of this Agreement and Application for Credit (the "Agreement") when due (a) all debts, liabilities and obligations, now existing or hereafter coming into existence; (b) a service charge not to exceed 1 1/2% per month, or 18% per annum, (or the maximum allowable contract rate under applicable law) on the unpaid balance of any account or other Obligations (the "Service Charge"); and (c) reasonable attorneys' fees, costs and expenses incurred in connection with the collection and enforcement, or any attempts at collection and enforcement, of such debts, liabilities or obligations of Applicant, by or through any attorney, all of (a), (b) and (c) shall be referred to as the "Obligations".

Applicant agrees to pay for all goods purchased in compliance with the prevailing terms of Seller. If Applicant fails to comply with Seller's prevailing terms or any of the provisions of this Agreement, Seller may declare the unpaid balance on this account immediately due and payable. In this event, Applicant agrees to pay such balance upon demand or Seller may, in the manner and as provided by applicable law, retake the goods or pursue any further remedy provided by applicable law.

Applicant hereby authorizes the use of this document, or a facsimile thereof, as consent for the release of credit information to Seller by the above-listed Trade and Bank References.

Applicant certifies that the statements on this Agreement are true, correct and complete, and that they have been made in order to obtain credit from Häfele America Co.

If more than one person shall execute this Agreement, the term "undersigned" shall mean all parties executing this Agreement, and any liability under this Agreement shall be joint and several.

Applicant has executed this Agreement under seal, this the . . . . day of . . . . , 19 . . . .

IF CORPORATION (must be signed and sealed by a duly authorized officer)

. . . .
Name of Corporation

By: . . . .
Name of Officer — Title

Corporate Seal

. . . .
Signature of Officer

IF INDIVIDUAL OR SOLE PROPRIETORSHIP

. . . . (Seal)

IF LIMITED PARTNERSHIP OR GENERAL PARTNERSHIP
(must be signed by all general partners)

. . . .
Name of Partnership

By: . . . . By. . . . .
Print Name of General Partner — Print Name of General Partner

. . . .
Signature of General Partner — Signature of General Partner

Company for Furniture Hardware.
Development, Production, Service.

Häfele America Co.
3901 Cheyenne Dr.
Archdale, NC 27263
Phone (910) 889-2322
FAX (910) 431-3831

HÄFELE

Dear Customer,

It is my pleasure to present The Complete Häfele, your comprehensive guide to Häfele's growing line of products and services.

Needless to say, we encourage you to use The Complete Häfele as a buyer's guide for selecting and ordering Häfele products. But at the same time, we want you to think of our catalog as a sourcebook of ideas.

As you will notice, we have streamlined our layout to enhance the stimulation of great ideas. Each product is conveniently grouped with its technical data, specifying information and suggested applications, al on the same page.

Over the past few years, our product line has experienced tremendous growth, matched only by our commitment to please our customers. As you can see from this new catalog, Häfele has spared no effort to maximize customer satisfaction. You will also be happy to discover that our service has kept pace with our growth -- from technical support to accurate, timely shipment of each order, Häfele continues to excel.

However, products are not the only things Häfele delivers. Take training, for example. Häfele operates a fleet of mobile training units. These state-of-the-art workshops on wheels crisscross North America, bringing hands-on product demonstrations to your doorstep. Häfele also delivers applications solutions. Our sales and technical support staff brings a wealth of experience to the equation. Their main job is working with you to turn experience into profitable solutions.

Generations have come to rely on Häfele quality. The tradition continues. Our performance and delivery standards recently earned us ISO 9002 certification. We are proud to display the coveted ISO seal, a symbol of highest quality standards.

I am confident you will find this latest edition of The Complete Häfele to be both practical and informative -- a gold mine of ideas.

We look forward to working with you.

Sincerely,

Wolfgang Häfele

Wolfgang Häfele
President

AFMA · AWI architectural woodwork institute · AMERICAN SOCIETY OF FURNITURE DESIGNERS · AWFS ASSOCIATION OF WOODWORKING & FURNISHINGS SUPPLIERS · BIFMA INTERNATIONAL · KCMA · PROUD MEMBER OF nasfm NATIONAL ASSOCIATION OF STORE FIXTURE MANUFACTURERS · Member NGA National Glass Association

Table Of Contents

A detailed illustrated product guide, complete with page numbers appears on the first page of each product group.

HÄFELE

How to contact Häfele

For your ordering convenience, Häfele maintains a number of Regional Service Centers. Please contact the one nearest you.

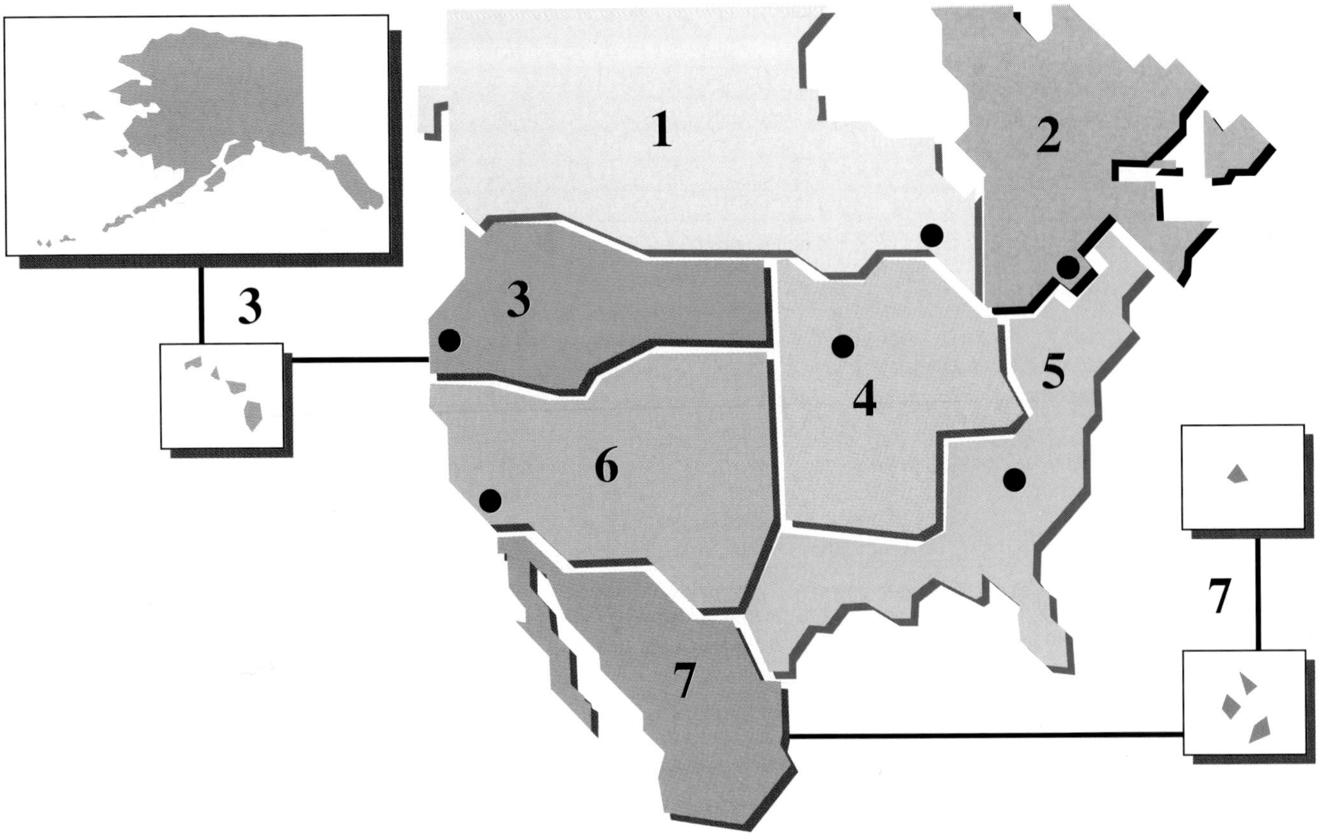

Häfele Headquarters
3901 Cheyenne Drive
P.O. Box 4000
Archdale, NC 27263
USA
(800) 423-3531 phone
(910) 431-3831 FAX

1. Häfele Service Center
Toronto, Canada
6345 Netherhart Road
Unit 1-3
Mississauga, Ontario L5T 1B8
Canada
(800) 423-3531 phone
(905) 564-0690 FAX

2. Häfele Service Center
Montréal, Canada
8558-A Boulevard Pie IX
Montréal, Québec H1Z 4G2
Canada
(800) 423-3531 phone
(514) 593-4472 FAX

3. Häfele Service Center
San Francisco, California
Suite 9
151 Vermont Street
San Francisco, CA 94103
USA
(800) 423-3531 phone
(415) 241-9824 FAX

4. Häfele Service Center
Chicago, Illinois
Suite 101
2340 S. Arlington Heights Rd.
Arlington Heights, IL 60005
USA
(800) 423-3531 phone
(847) 364-4073 FAX

5. Häfele Service Center
High Point, North Carolina
3901 Cheyenne Drive
P.O. Box 4000
Archdale, NC 27263
USA
(800) 423-3531 phone
(910) 431-3831 FAX

6. Häfele Service Center
Los Angeles, California
16926-A South Keegan Ave.
Carson, CA 90746
USA
(800) 423-3531 phone
(310) 632-3713 FAX

7. Häfele Service Center
Mexico/Caribbean
3901 Cheyenne Drive
P.O. Box 4000
Archdale, NC 27263
USA
(800) 325-6209 phone
(910) 431-6833 FAX

How to contact Häfele On-Line

For your 24-hour convenience, Häfele has added

PC-Link
Now you can place an order or retrieve information at any time, from any time zone.

Orders and Info via PC Link
Looking for an easy way to place orders? And retrieve current net price information without being limited to regular business hours?

Just enter the Häfele catalog number and quantity. PC-LINK will provide net pricing and inventory information at any time, around the clock, seven days a week. The merchandise is reserved immediately on receipt of order. Every order is acknowledged by fax within one hour during the normal business day.

System Requirements
PC with Windows 95 operating system and a modem.

Your Next Step
Fax a brief message to:

Häfele Teleservice
3901 Cheyenne Drive
Archdale, NC 27263 USA
Tel: 910-889-2322
Fax: 910-431-3831

❑ Häfele will immediately send you an application form. Fill out the application and fax it back to Häfele Teleservice. The Häfele Teleservice Team will contact you to schedule installation.

❑ Häfele will provide the following:
- -Diskettes containing the software
- -Detailed user instructions
- -Card with your customer and PIN numbers
- -Mouse pad

You can now place an order or retrieve information at any time, regardless of time zone.

Electronic Data Interchange via Mailbox
As a customer or supplier, are you in contact with Häfele on a daily basis? Do you have EDI translator software linked to your data processing system? And a mailbox?

EDI-LINK is now available for exchanging order, invoice and product information between you and Häfele. Data transmission via EDI (Electronic Data Interchange) is based on the ANSI X12 Standard.

System Requirements
EDI translator software and access to a mailbox.

Your Next Step
Fax a brief message to:

Häfele Teleservice
3901 Cheyenne Drive
Archdale, NC 27263 USA
Tel: 910-889-2322
Fax: 910-431-3831

❑ Häfele will immediately send you an application form. Fill out the application and fax it back to Häfele Teleservice.

The Häfele EDI-LINK Teleservice Team will contact your MIS.

How to get the most from The Complete Häfele

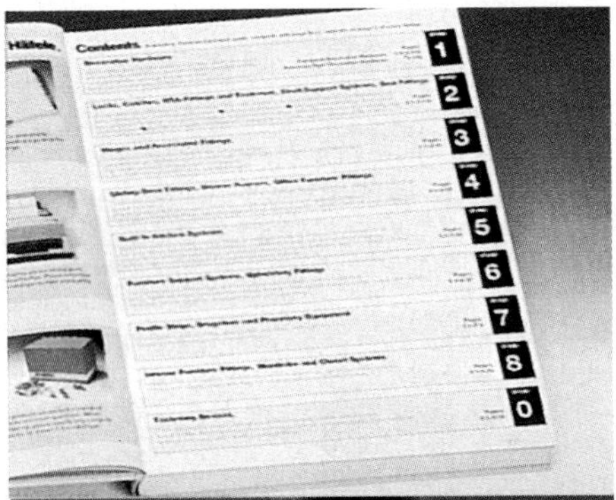

Finding the right product:
The Complete Häfele catalog contains literally thousands of products. The Contents page is arranged by product groups. If you know the name of the product, use the *Name Index* to find the correct page. If you know the catalog number, use the *Number Index*.

Call Häfele:
Can't find what you are looking for? We probably have it. Just call us. Need help selecting the right product for your particular application, or need price information? Don't hesitate to call us. We are always happy to help.

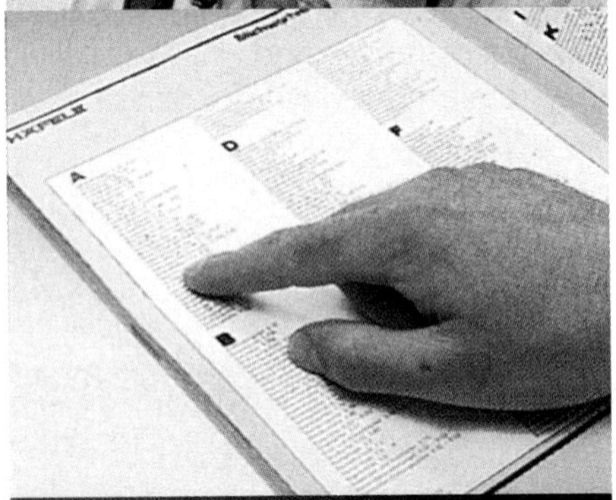

Häfele Catalog Numbers
Häfele catalog numbers contain eight-digits, e.g. 803.40.996. These numbers are designed to ensure you order exactly what you want. You will notice some catalog numbers contain an "X," e.g. 365.10.30X. The "X" indicates a variable such as size or color, which will need to be specified by you. Many Häfele products are custom designed and manufactured. If you have a special need, please do not hesitate to ask.

Packaging:
All Häfele products are packaged in standard units (minimum quantities) to ensure prompt, safe shipment. Please order only complete packaging units.

Häfele ISO Certification

Häfele America Co. has received International Standards Organization (ISO) certification from Underwriters Laboratories, Inc. This certifies that Häfele has been found in compliance with ISO 9002 for international quality standards.

Häfele is one of the few companies of its kind to achieve ISO Certification. Although earning this certification requires compliance with a number of different standards, the process focuses on development and implementation of controlled systems. This guarantees that every customer will receive the same high level of product and service quality from Häfele with every transaction. Our mission is to provide products, solutions, and service to the customer's complete satisfaction.

UNDERWRITERS LABORATORIES INC.

CERTIFICATE OF REGISTRATION

ISO 9000

HÄFELE AMERICA CO.

3901 Cheyenne Drive
Archdale, NC 27263

Underwriters Laboratories Inc.® (UL) issues this certificate to the Firm named above, after assessing the Firm's quality system and finding it in compliance with

ISO 9002:1994

EN ISO 9002:1994; BS EN ISO 9002:1994; ANSI/ASQC Q9002:1994

for the following scope of registration

5072 (US) : Hardware

The distribution of furniture and cabinet hardware, lighting components and fittings. The packaging and kitting of hardware to customer specifications.

This quality system registration is included in UL's Directory of Registered Firms and applies to the provision of goods and/or services as specified in the scope of registration from the address(es) shown above. By issuance of this certificate the firm represents that it will maintain its registration in accordance with the applicable requirements. This certificate is not transferable and remains the property of Underwriters Laboratories Inc. ®.

File Number: A2596
Volume: 1
Issue Date: August 5, 1996
Revision Date: August 13, 1996
Renewal Date: August 5, 1998

S. Joe Bhatia
Vice President
Follow-Up Services

REGISTERED FIRM

UL® REGISTERED FIRM

HÄFELE

Sales Service

Turning problems into solutions

Häfele salespeople have one job – to provide you with solutions.

Want to create something using a totally new approach? Your Häfele salesperson has the solution.

Want a very small quantity of product, or very large? Your Häfele salesperson has the solution.

Need a critical product immediately? Your Häfele salesperson has the solution.

Whether on the road, in the office or out on a sales call, no matter how tough the task, your Häfele sales representative has the solution for you.

Furniture Hardware
The
Complete
Häfele

HÄFELE

Regional Sales Managers

Support and Service

Häfele recognizes that no two markets are alike in terms of geography, infrastructure and customer base. This means differences in product and service requirements from region to region.

Each Häfele Regional Sales Manager is responsible for ensuring that these differences are adequately addressed.

With their in-depth knowledge of both product and region, Regional Sales Managers are the perfect resources to deliver a planned response to regional diversity.

To ensure thorough coverage, each Regional Sales Manager is supported by a well-trained traveling sales consultant force, plus inside sales staff.

For special product or service requirements, contact our Häfele Regional Sales Manager directly.

Marketing Directors

Industry Experts

Häfele Product Managers follow industry issues and trends in order to anticipate customer needs. Häfele has a Product Manager on staff who is THE expert for each key industry. Whether you produce home furniture, kitchen cabinets, store fixtures, or any other related product made of wood, the Häfele Product Manager will provide expert advice in response to your hardware needs.

Bottom line: Häfele can provide exactly what you need for your specific situation . . . at a very competitive price.

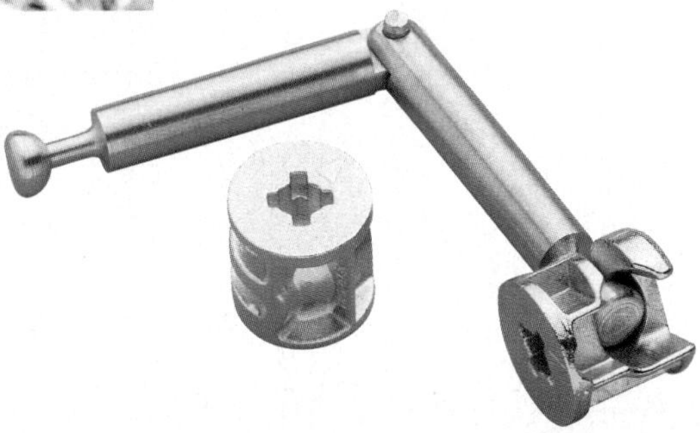

HÄFELE

Hardware Application Consultants

Hands-on Custom Solutions

No product can live up to its full potential without optimal application.

That is the reason Häfele employs a staff of European-trained woodworking technicians who study your materials, designs and production methods to devise the most economical way to produce your particular product.

Backed by its many years of experience, only Häfele provides this level of custom service. From prototype to shop drawings, all the way through to full-blown cutting list, these technicians provide you with start-to-finish service. Our consultants' only job is to make our products right for you.

HÄFELE

Comprehensive Educational Programs

Information transfer – to you

Häfele's commitment to education and training is underscored by the presence of a full-time Product Trainer on our staff. Our Product Trainer provides continuing education for our personnel in-house. In addition, he is available for on-site customer or trade show seminars, and directs our famous fleet of Häfele "mobile hands-on classrooms." Six buses tour all of North America, training woodworkers from any size business in use of the latest products, applications and technologies.

These buses are fully-functional, self-contained demonstration workshops. They are staffed by some of Häfele's most proficient craftsmen whose primary job is to communicate knowledge. Häfele solutions arrive Special Delivery.

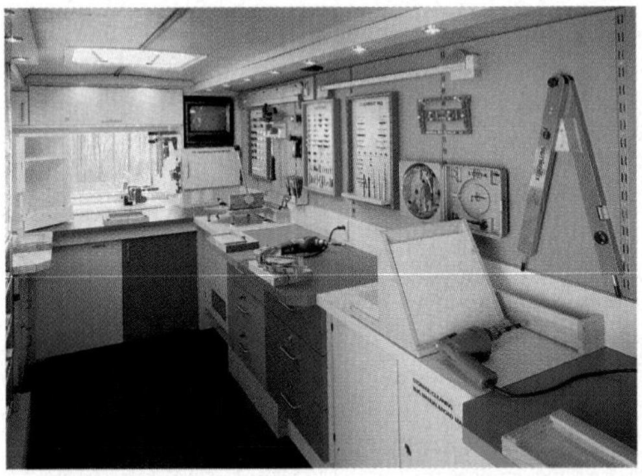

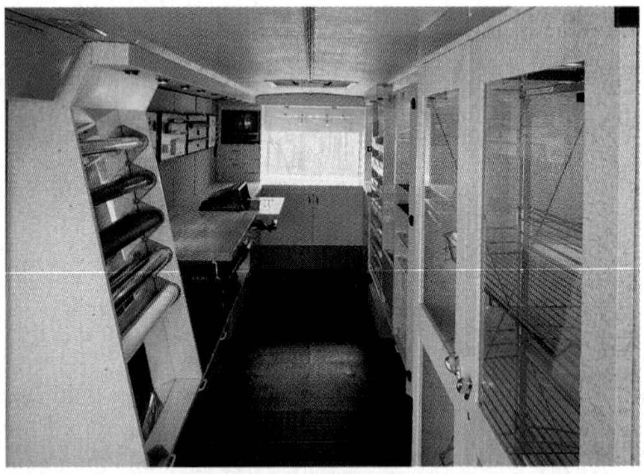

HÄFELE

Product Design and Engineering

Innovation / Standards

Our staff of Designers and Engineers is committed to ongoing development of new products which give customers intelligent productivity enhancements. Design and Engineering works hand-in-hand with Marketing to make these products available to each customer, primarily through our catalog and sales force.

Design and Engineering also joins forces with Häfele's Production Plants to develop and produce custom-made hardware for a wide range of different applications. A vital element in this collaborative process is maintaining a close, interactive relationship between our technical staff and the customer.

Finally, in order to ensure product quality and consistency, Häfele works almost exclusively with factories and distribution centers which are ISO 9000-compliant.

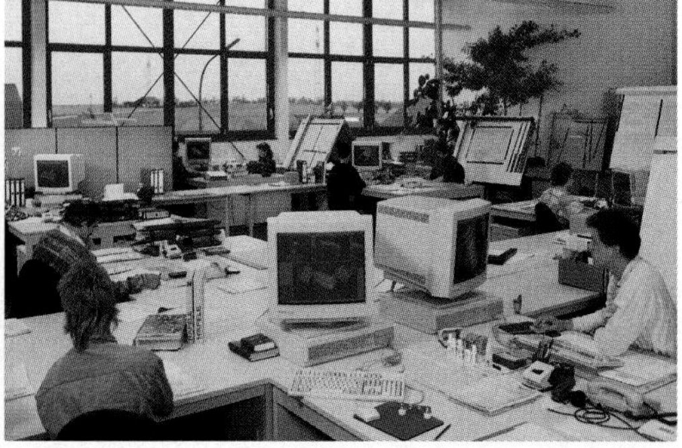

end cap with flat head and screw-in
necting pin to plug into kitchen rail.
c alloy
Packing: 1 pc.
Cat. No.
polished
520.73.220
e matt
520.73.024
ss polished
520.73.828
matt

HÄFELE

Architectural Consulting Group

Solutions in Design and Application

Häfele architectural hardware consultants specialize in working with architects, designers, engineers, builders, developers and contractors worldwide. This group is responsible for developing detailed product specifications, in addition to personally supervising product installation on-site. The group ensures consistency in quality, delivery and service for both domestic and international projects.

The Architectural Consulting Group is supported by trained woodworking technicians who are tasked with ensuring correct application of hardware at the millwork shop. Together, they make up the team which guarantees ultimate customer satisfaction. The Architectural Consulting Group for North America is based at Häfele's Chicago Service Center.

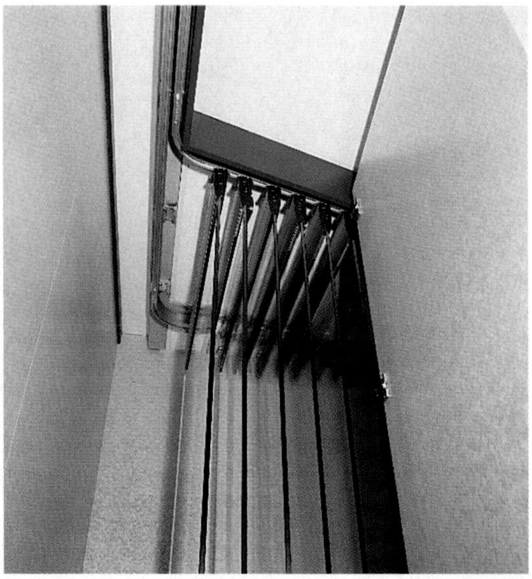

HÄFELE

Distribution

Getting it right, getting it out

Of all the members of Häfele's Service Team, Distribution most clearly epitomizes our commitment to consistency and continuity. Shipping from an inventory of over 18,000 different products has earned Häfele an enviable reputation for speed, accuracy and reliability. Tens of thousands of satisfied customers throughout North America are the proof.

Our state-of-the-art high-rise distribution center boasts over 40,000 computerized storage bins with plenty of space for all our products. Supported by Häfele-proprietary software, our highly-skilled staff directs and monitors the distribution process from start to finish. They make sure each order is filled accurately and shipped on time.

Häfele Service Facilities in North America

Häfele Distribution Center
Archdale, NC

Häfele Service Center
Los Angeles, CA

Häfele Service Center
San Francisco, CA

Häfele Service Center
Chicago, IL

Häfele Service Center
Toronto, Canada

Häfele Service Center
Montréal, Canada

Häfele Production Facilities in Germany

Häfele Distribution Center
Nagold, Germany

Häfele Jettingen Plant
Jettingen, Germany

Häfele Berlin Plant
Berlin, Germany

Schneider Kenzingen Plant
Kenzingen, Germany

Call 1-800-423-3531 anywhere in the US and Canada

Product Guide - Decorative Hardware

HÄFELE

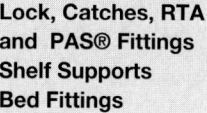

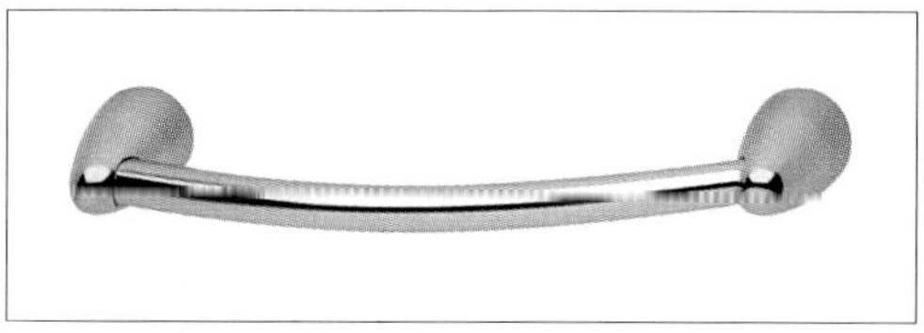

Brass Handles
Pages **1.4 - 1.29**

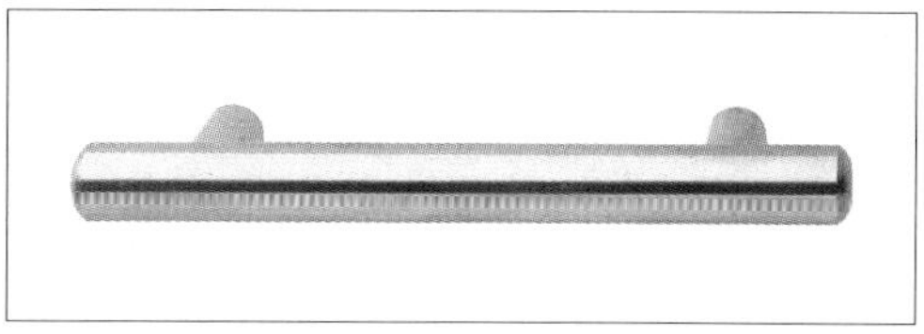

Stainless Steel Handles
Pages **1.30 - 1.34**

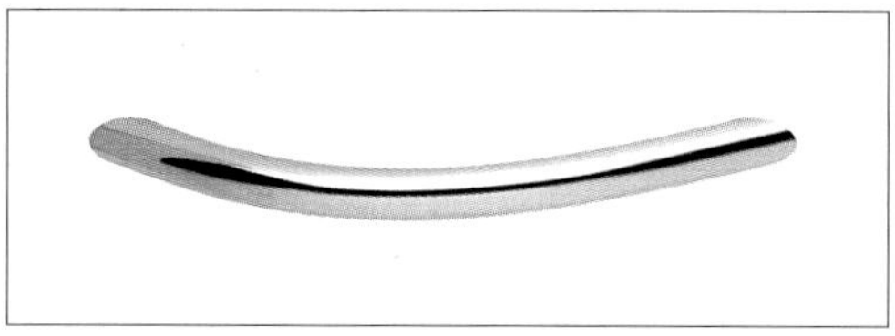

Steel Handles
Pages **1.35 - 1.42**

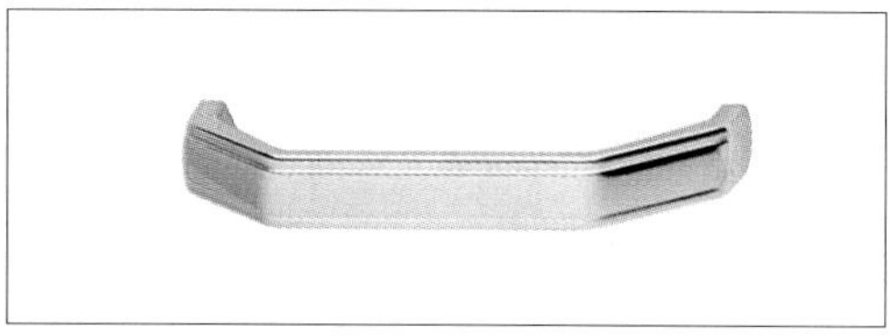

Zinc Handles
Page **1.43 - 1.146**

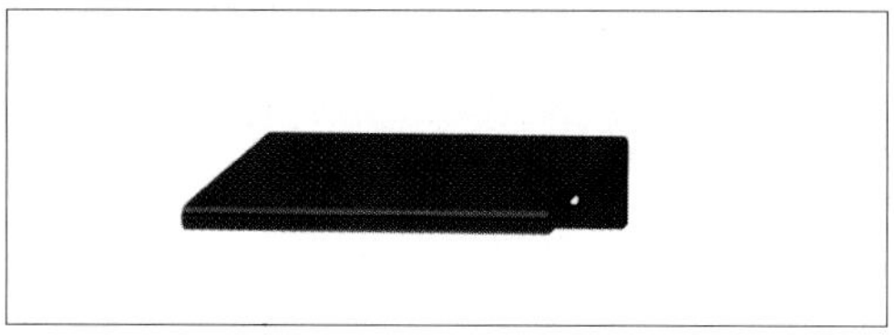

Aluminum Handles
Pages **1.147 - 1.149**

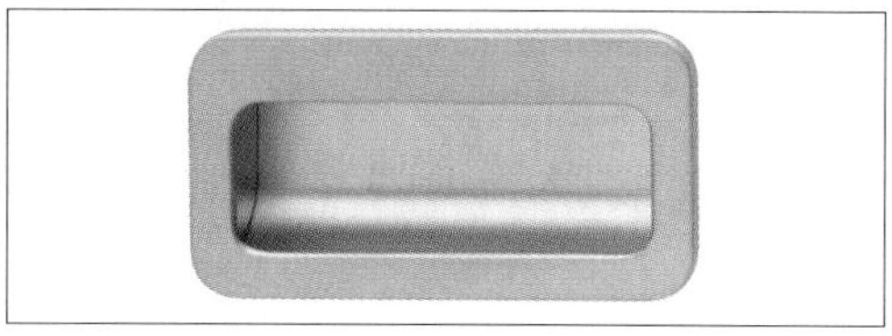

Flush Handles
Pages **1.150 - 1.175**

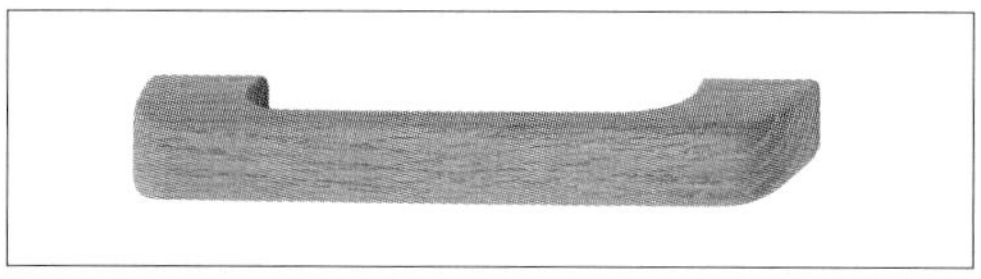

Wood Handles
Pages **1.164 - 1.175**

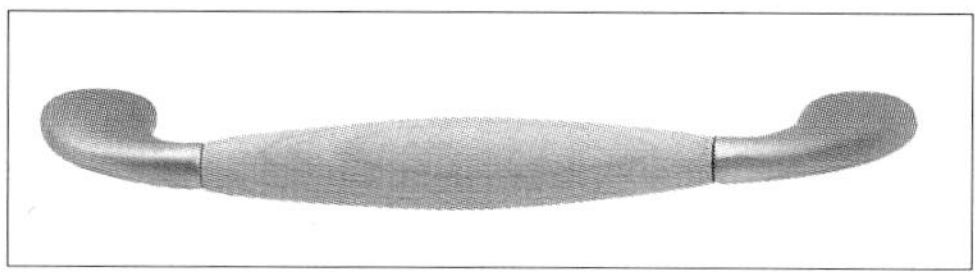

Wood Handles Combinations
Pages **1.176 - 1.179**

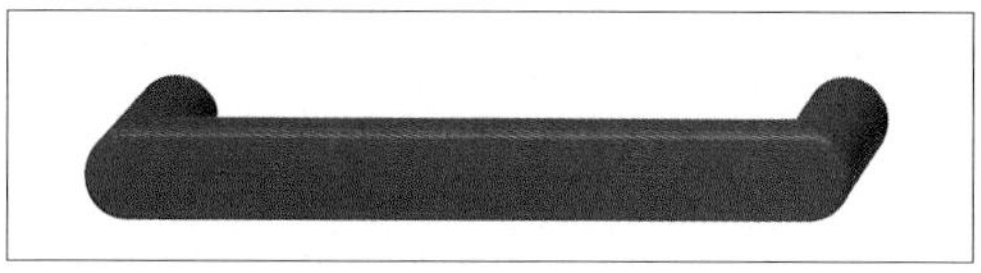

Plastic and Nylon Handles
Pages **1.180 - 1.200**

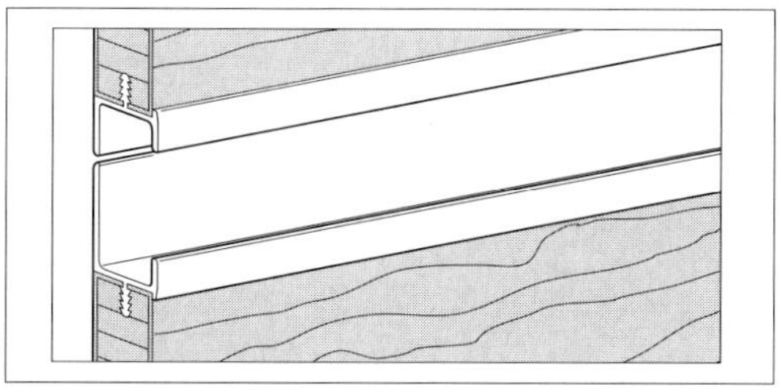

Continuous Pulls
Page **1.256 - 1.258**

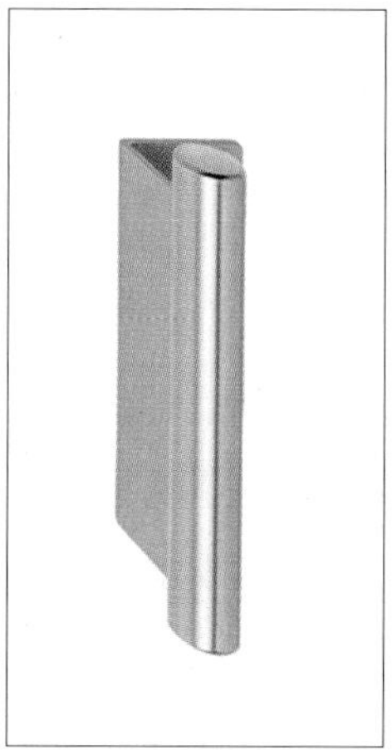

Sliding Door Pulls
Page **1.130**

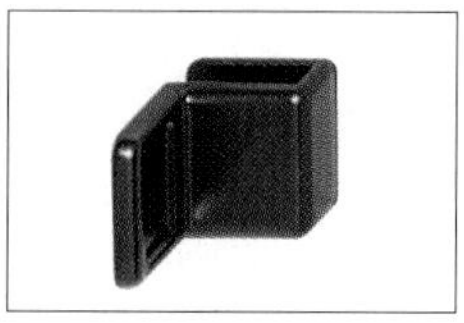

Glass Door Pulls
Page **1.129**

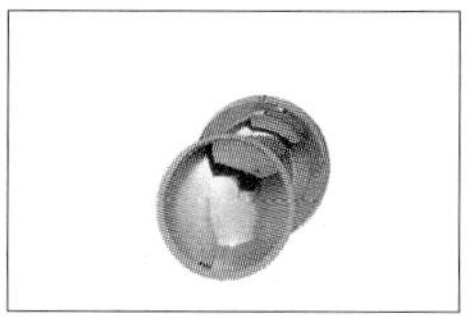

Brass Knobs
Pages **1.201 - 1.219**

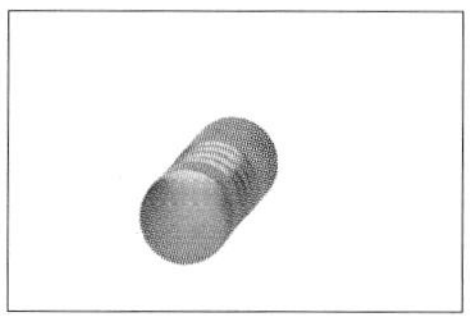

Stainless Steel Knobs
Pages **1.220**

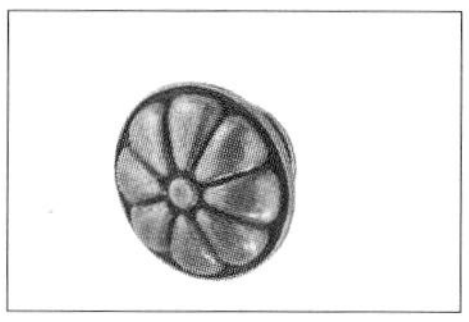

Zinc Knobs
Pages **1.221-1.234**

Ceramic Knobs
Pages **1.235 - 1.238**

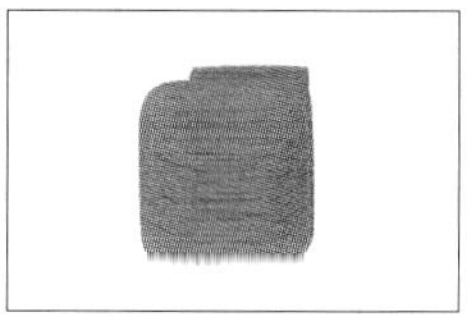

Wood Knobs
Pages **1.239 - 1.247**

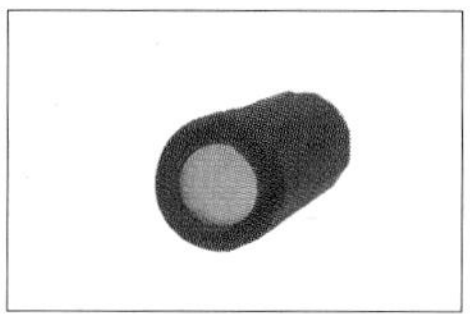

Plastic and Nylon Knobs
Pages **1.248 - 1. 255**

Wood Ornaments
Pages **1.259 - 1.267**

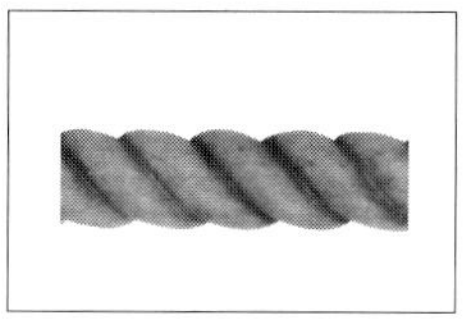

Wood Mouldings
Pages **1.268 - 1.274**

HÄFELE

Combination Brass Knobs and Handles

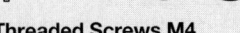

Threaded Screws M4
Combined slot, suitable for flat or cross blades
Finish: steel, zinc-plated

Length	Cat. No.
10 mm	022.35.109
12 mm	022.35.127
15 mm	022.35.154
18 mm	022.35.181
20 mm	022.35.207
22 mm	022.35.225
23 mm	022.35.234
25 mm	022.35.252
28 mm	022.35.289
30 mm	022.35.305
35 mm	022.35.350
38 mm	022.35.387
40 mm	022.35.403
45 mm	022.35.458
50 mm	022.35.501
60 mm	022.35.609

Packing: 100 and 1000 pcs.

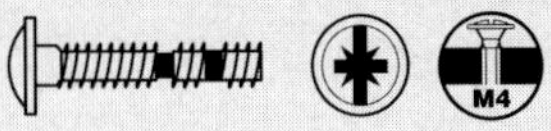

Threaded Breakoff Screw M4
Combined slot, suitable for flat or cross blades
Finish: steel, zinc-plated

Length	Cat. No.
1 3/4" x 3/4"	022.35.887

Packing: 100 and 1000 pcs.

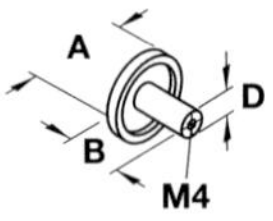

Base: polished and lacquered
Insert: chrome polished plated

Size A x B	Base D	Cat. No.
24 x 23	9	137.69.812
32 x 25	10	137.69.821

Packing: 10 pcs.

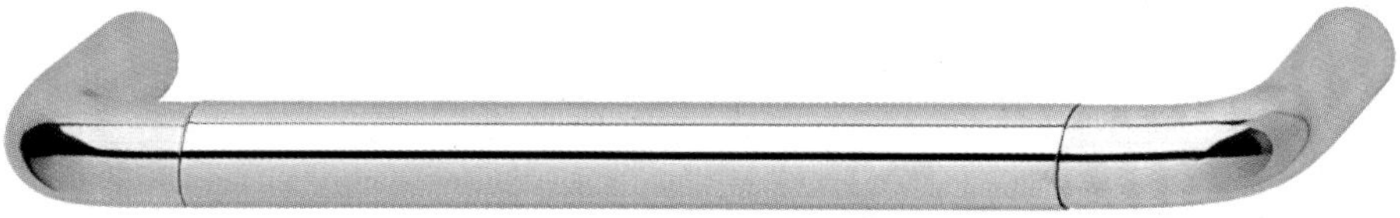

Ends: polished and lacquered
Insert: chrome polished plated

Size A x B	Dimensions C	Cat. No.
74 x 35	64	117.45.805
106 x 35	96	117.45.814
138 x 35	128	117.45.823
170 x 35	160	117.45.832

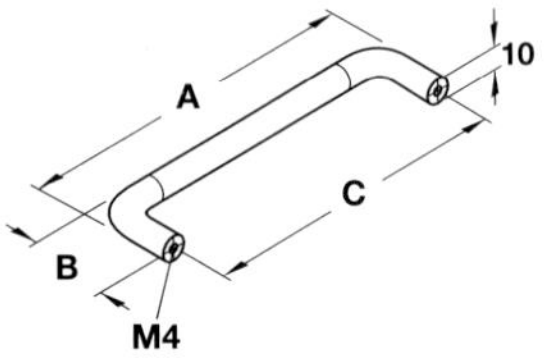

Packing: 10 pcs.

Dimensional data not binding.
We reserve the right to alter specifications without notice.

Combination Handles and Knobs

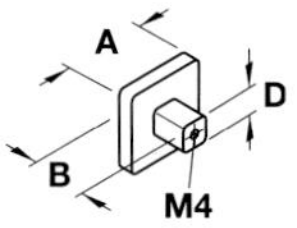

Base: brass polished and lacquered
Insert: brass chrome plated polished

Size A x B	Base D	Cat. No.
24 x 24	10 x 10	137.66.811
32 x 32	12 x 12	137.66.820
38 x 38	15 x 15	137.66.839

Packing: 10 pcs.

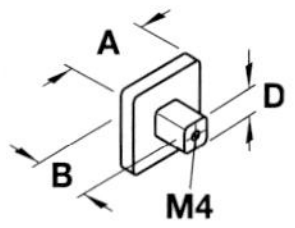

Base: brass polished and lacquered
Insert: brass black nickel plated

Size A x B	Base D	Cat. No.
24 x 24	10 x 10	137.66.857
32 x 32	12 x 12	137.66.866
38 x 38	15 x 15	137.66.875

Packing: 10 pcs.

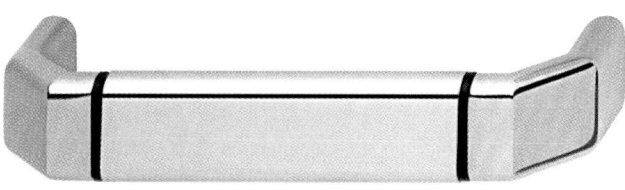

Ends: zinc brass polished
Center: brass chrome plated polished

Size A x B	Dimension C	Cat. No.
72 x 28	64	102.62.816
104 x 28	96	102.62.825
135 x 28	128	102.62.834

Packing: 10 pcs.

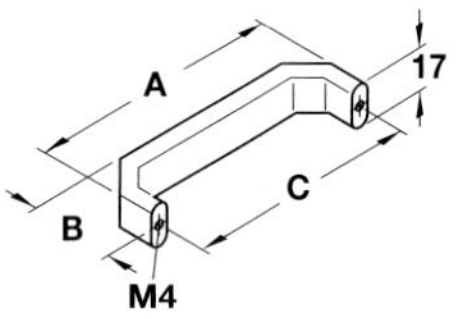

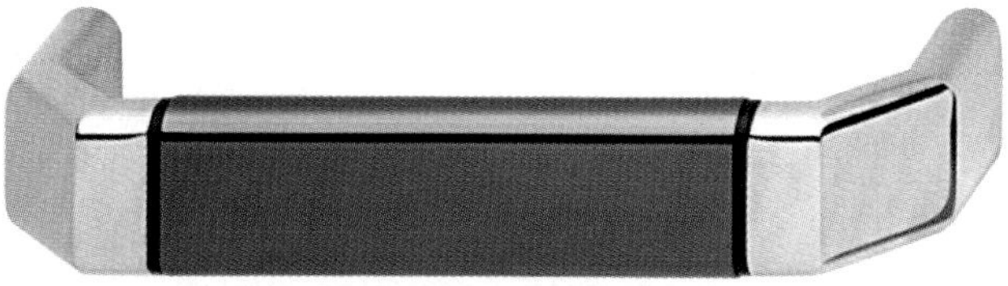

Ends: zinc brass polished brass
Center: brass black nickel plated

Size A x B	Dimension C	Cat. No.
72 x 28	64	102.62.852
104 x 28	96	102.62.861
135 x 28	128	102.62.870

Packing: 10 pcs.

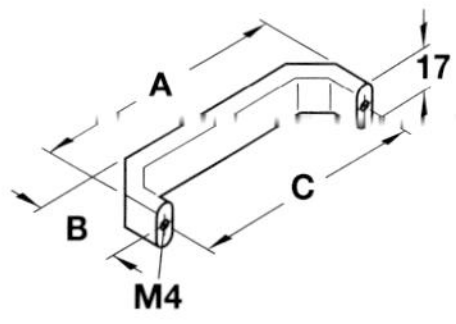

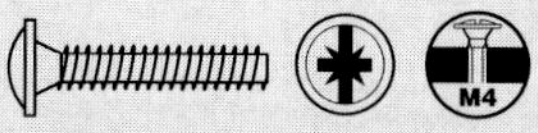

Threaded Screws M4
Combined slot, suitable for flat or cross blades
Finish: steel, zinc-plated

Length	Cat. No.
10 mm	022.35.109
12 mm	022.35.127
15 mm	022.35.154
18 mm	022.35.181
20 mm	022.35.207
22 mm	022.35.225
23 mm	022.35.234
25 mm	022.35.252
28 mm	022.35.289
30 mm	022.35.305
35 mm	022.35.350
38 mm	022.35.387
40 mm	022.35.403
45 mm	022.35.458
50 mm	022.35.501
60 mm	022.35.609

Packing: 100 and 1000 pcs.

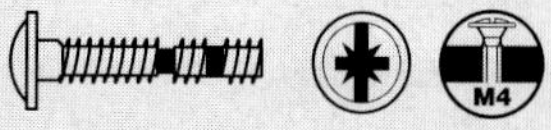

Threaded Breakoff Screw M4
Combined slot, suitable for flat or cross blades
Finish: steel, zinc-plated

Length	Cat. No.
1 3/4" x 3/4"	022.35.887

Packing: 100 and 1000 pcs.

Dimensional data not binding.
We reserve the right to alter specifications without notice.

HÄFELE

Brass Handles

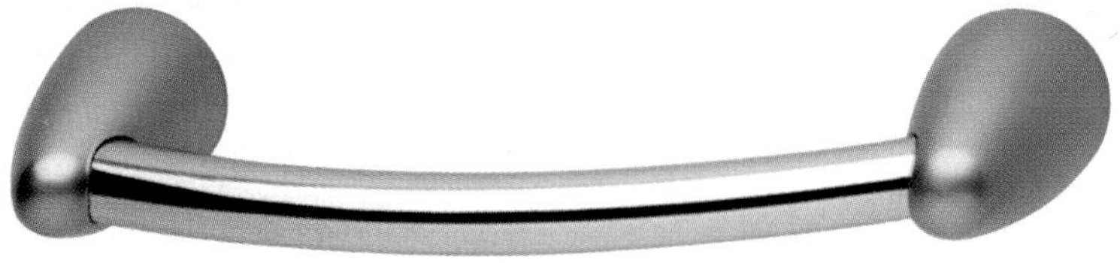

Ends: chrome plated matt
Center: chrome plated polished

Cat. No.	103.20.420

Packing: 25 pcs.

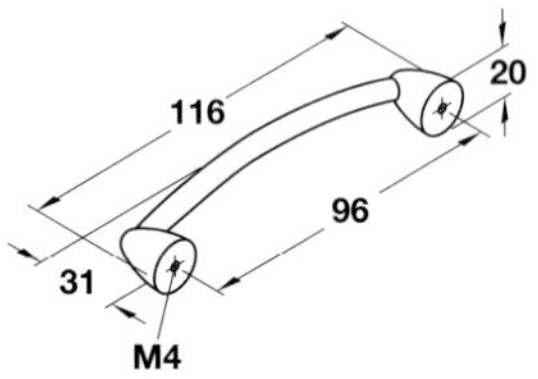

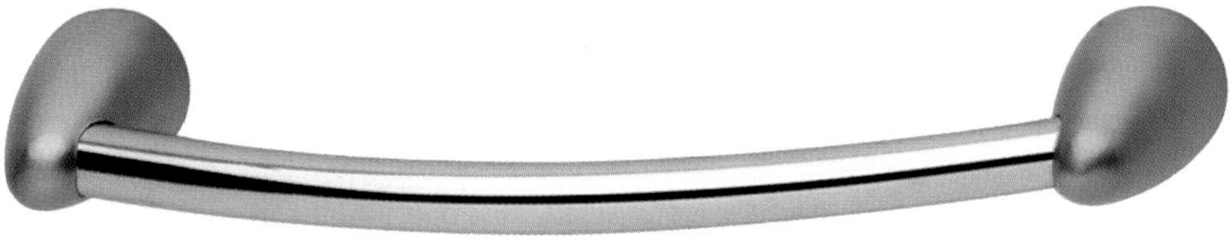

Ends: chrome plated matt
Center: chrome plated polished

Cat. No.	103.20.421

Packing: 25 pcs.

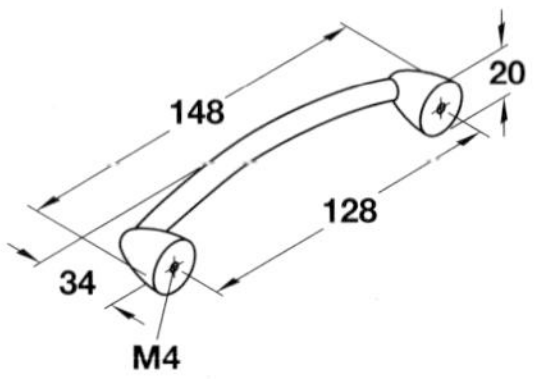

Ends: polished and lacquered
Center: chrome plated polished

Size A x B	Dimension C	Cat. No.
116 x 31	96	103.20.820
148 x 34	128	103.20.821

Packing: 25 pcs.

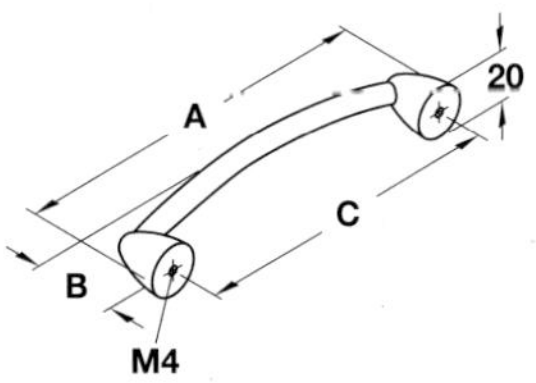

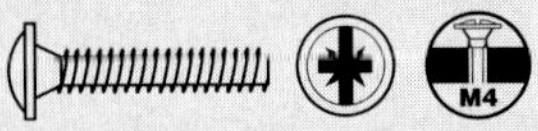

Threaded Screws M4
Combined slot, suitable for flat or cross blades
Finish: steel, zinc-plated

Length	Cat. No.
10 mm	022.35.109
12 mm	022.35.127
15 mm	022.35.154
18 mm	022.35.181
20 mm	022.35.207
22 mm	022.35.225
23 mm	022.35.234
25 mm	022.35.252
28 mm	022.35.289
30 mm	022.35.305
35 mm	022.35.350
38 mm	022.35.387
40 mm	022.35.403
45 mm	022.35.458
50 mm	022.35.501
60 mm	022.35.609

Packing: 100 and 1000 pcs.

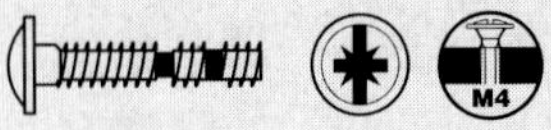

Threaded Breakoff Screw M4
Combined slot, suitable for flat or cross blades
Finish: steel, zinc-plated

Length	Cat. No.
1 3/4" x 3/4"	022.35.887

Packing: 100 and 1000 pcs.

Brass Handles

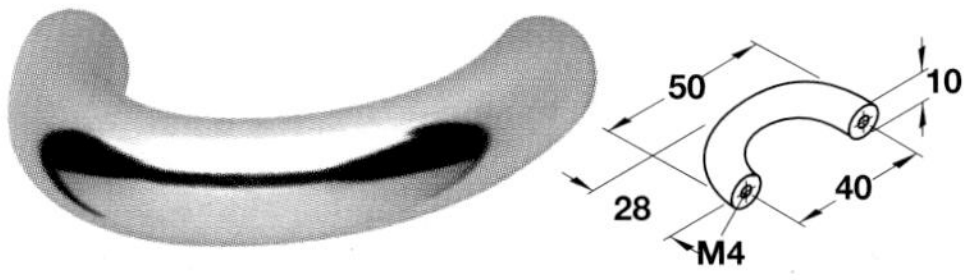

Chrome plated polished

Catalog No.	116.35.215

Packing: 25 pcs.

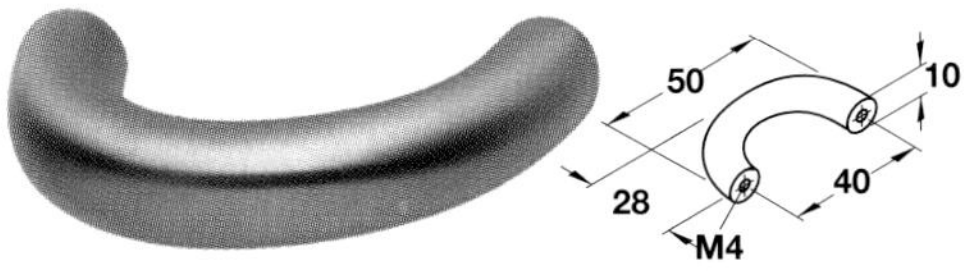

Nickel plated matt

Catalog No.	116.35.617

Packing: 25 pcs.

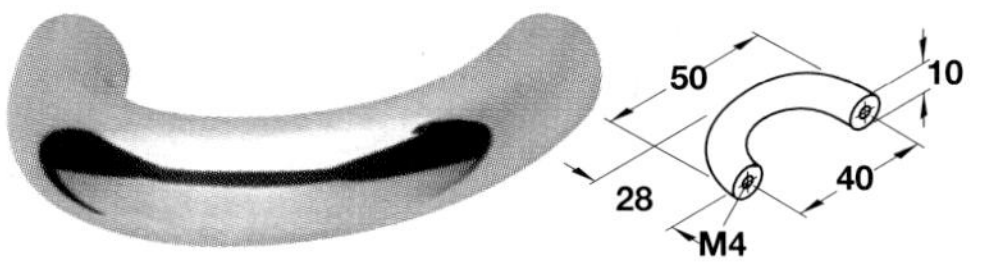

Polished

Catalog No.	116.35.813

Packing: 25 pcs.

Threaded Screws M4
Combined slot, suitable for flat or cross blades

Finish: steel, zinc-plated

Length	Cat. No.
10 mm	022.35.109
12 mm	022.35.127
15 mm	022.35.154
18 mm	022.35.181
20 mm	022.35.207
22 mm	022.35.225
23 mm	022.35.234
25 mm	022.35.252
28 mm	022.35.289
30 mm	022.35.305
35 mm	022.35.350
38 mm	022.35.387
40 mm	022.35.403
45 mm	022.35.458
50 mm	022.35.501
60 mm	022.35.609

Packing: 100 and 1000 pcs.

Threaded Breakoff Screw M4
Combined slot, suitable for flat or cross blades

Finish: steel, zinc-plated

Length	Cat. No.
1 3/4" x 3/4"	022.35.887

Packing: 100 and 1000 pcs.

HÄFELE

Brass Wire Handles

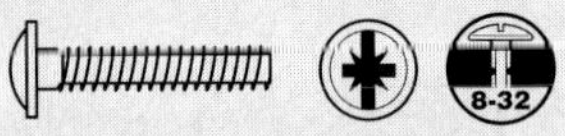

Threaded Screws 8-32
Combined slot, suitable for flat or cross blades
Finish: steel, yellow chromated

Length	Cat. No.
22 mm	022.25.229
25 mm	022.25.256
32 mm	022.25.327
38 mm	022.25.381
45 mm	022.25.452

Packing: 100 and 1000 pcs.

Threaded Breakoff Screw 8-32
Combined slot, suitable for flat or cross blades
Finish: steel, yellow chromated

Length	Cat. No.
1 3/4" x 3/4"	022.25.881

Packing: 100 and 1000 pcs.

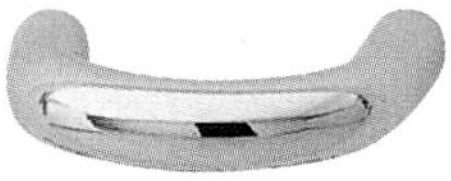

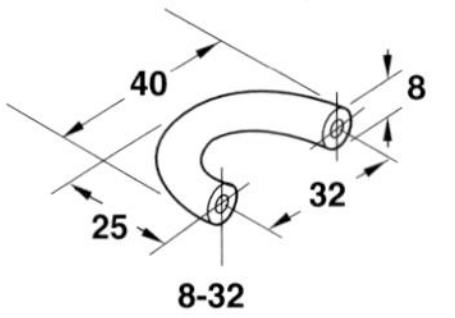

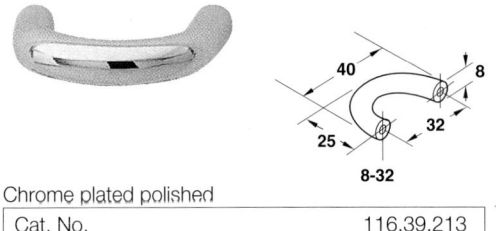

Chrome plated polished

Cat. No.	116.39.213

Packing: 50 pcs. (with 8-32 x 25 mm fastening screws)

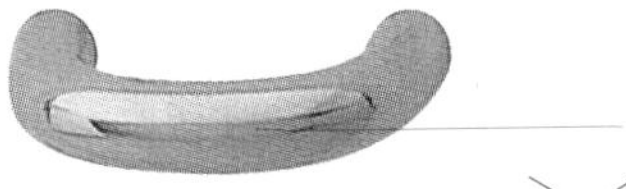

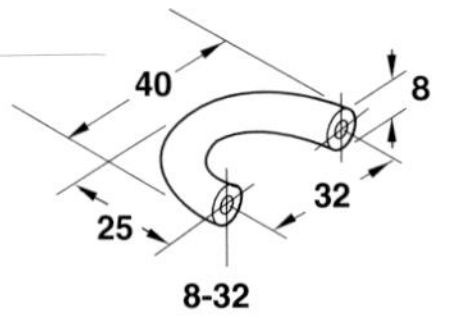

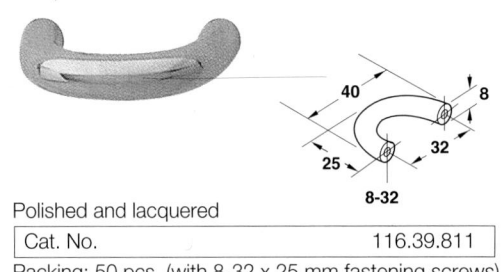

Polished and lacquered

Cat. No.	116.39.811

Packing: 50 pcs. (with 8-32 x 25 mm fastening screws)

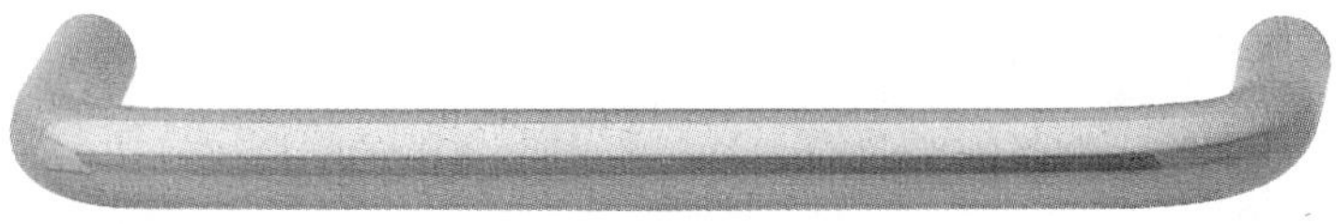

Nickel matt

Cat. No.	116.39.651

Packing: 50 pcs. (with 8-32 x 25 mm fastening screws)

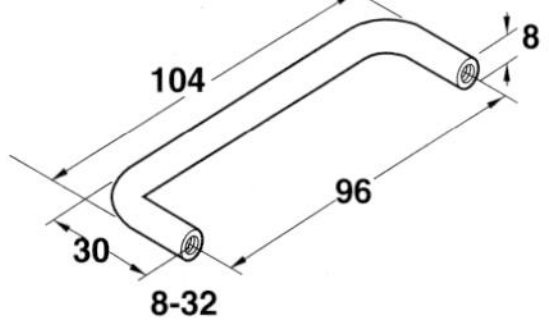

Dimensional data not binding.
We reserve the right to alter specifications without notice.

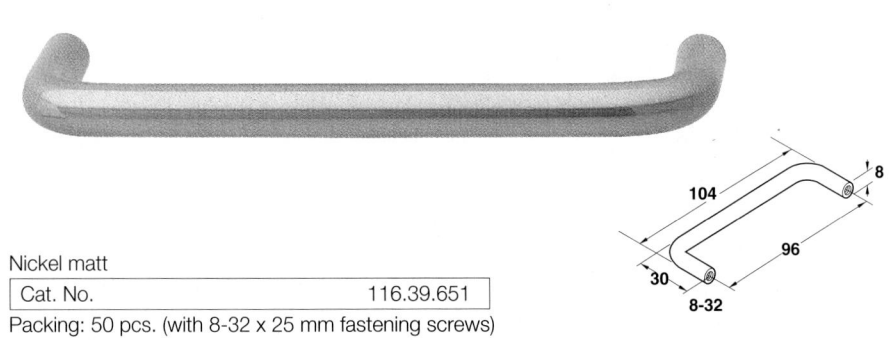

Brass Wire Handles

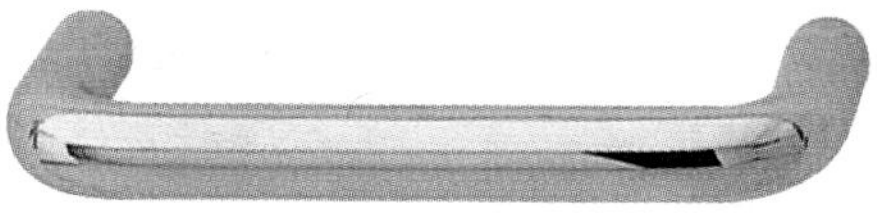

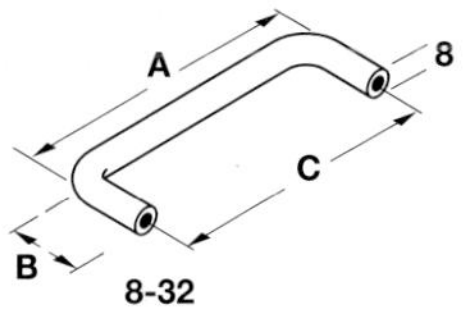

Chrome plated polished

Size A x B	Hole Spacing C	Cat. No.
72 x 30 mm	64 mm	116.39.222
84 x 30 mm	76 mm (3")	116.39.231
97 x 30 mm	89 mm (3.5")	116.39.240
104 x 30 mm	96 mm	116.39.259
110 x 30 mm	102 mm (4")	116.39.268
135 x 30 mm	127mm (5")	116.39.277

Packing: 50 pcs. (including 8-32 x 25 mm mounting scews)

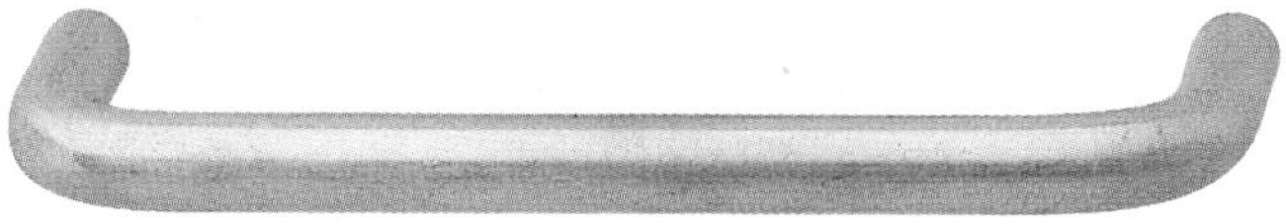

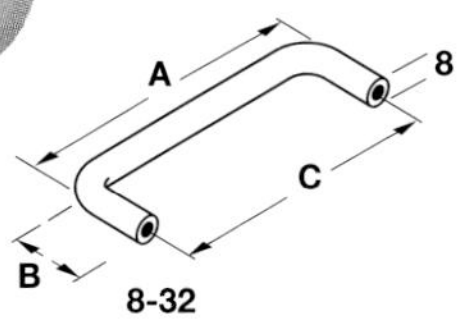

Chrome plated matt

Size A x B	Hole Spacing C	Cat. No.
84 x 30 mm	76mm (3")	116.39.437
97 x 30 mm	89 mm (3.5)	116.39.446
104 x 30 mm	96 mm	116.39.455
110 x 30 mm	101mm (4")	116.39.464
135 x 30 mm	5" (127mm)	116.39.473

Packing: 50 pcs. (including 8-32 x 25 mm mounting scews)

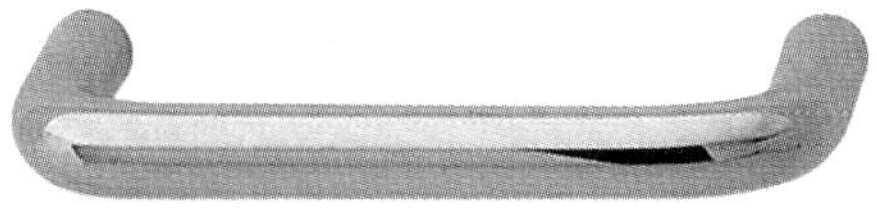

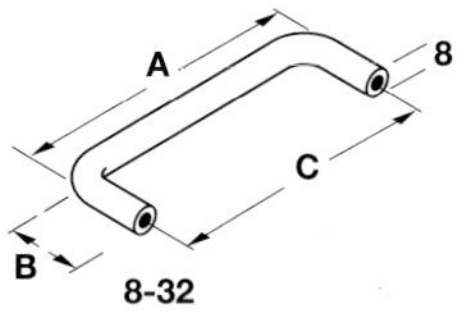

Polished and lacquered

Size A x B	Hole Spacing C	Cat. No.
72 x 30 mm	64 mm	116.39.820
84 x 30 mm	76 mm (3")	116.39.839
97 x 30 mm	89 mm (3.5")	116.39.848
104 x 30 mm	96 mm	116.39.857
110 x 30 mm	102 mm (4")	116.39.866
135 x 35 mm	127 mm (5")	116.39.875

Packing: 50 pcs. (including 8-32 x 25 mm mounting scews)

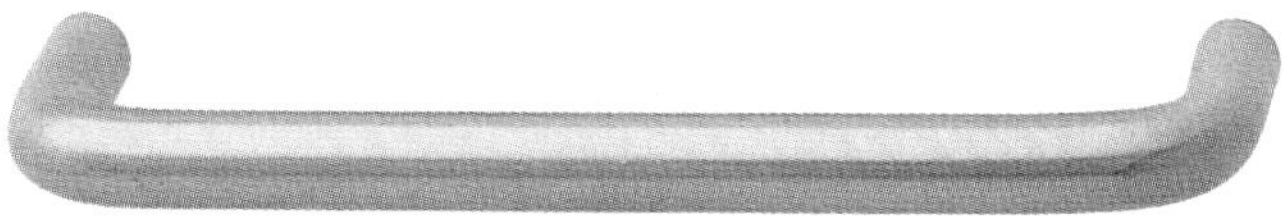

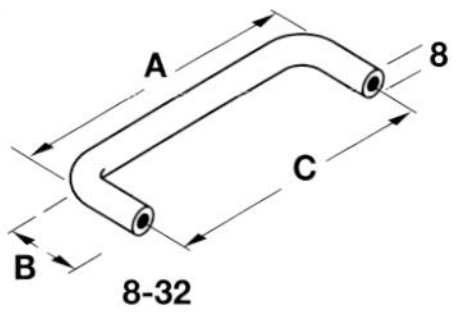

Matt

Size A x B	Hole Spacing C	Cat. No.
84 x 30 mm	76mm (3")	116.39.535
97 x 30 mm	89mm (3.5")	116.39.544
104 x 30 mm	96 mm	116.39.553
110 x 30 mm	102 mm (4")	116.39.562
135 x 30mm	127 mm (5")	116.39.571

Packing: 50 pcs. (including 8-32 x 25 mm mounting scews)

Decorative Hardware 1

Threaded Screws 8-32

Combined slot, suitable for flat or cross blades

Finish: steel, yellow chromated

Length	Cat. No.
22 mm	022.25.229
25 mm	022.25.256
32 mm	022.25.327
38 mm	022.25.381
45 mm	022.25.452

Packing: 100 and 1000 pcs.

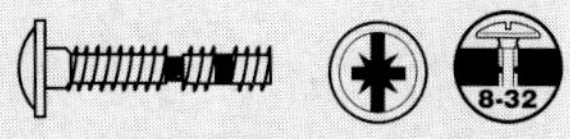

Threaded Breakoff Screw 8-32

Combined slot, suitable for flat or cross blades

Finish: steel, yellow chromated

Length	Cat. No.
1 3/4" x 3/4"	022.25.881

Packing: 100 and 1000 pcs.

Dimensional data not binding.
We reserve the right to alter specifications without notice.

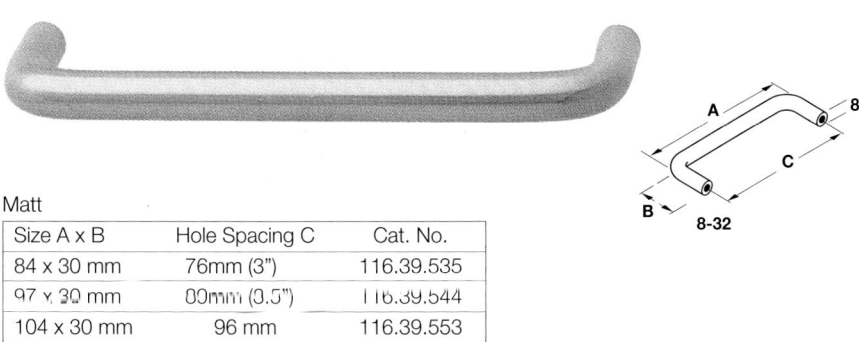

HÄFELE

1 Decorative Hardware

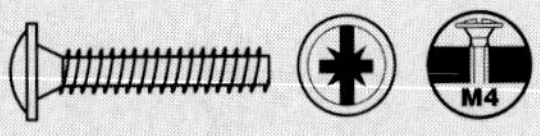

Threaded Screws M4
Combined slot, suitable for flat or cross blades
Finish: steel, zinc-plated

Length	Cat. No.
10 mm	022.35.109
12 mm	022.35.127
15 mm	022.35.154
18 mm	022.35.181
20 mm	022.35.207
22 mm	022.35.225
23 mm	022.35.234
25 mm	022.35.252
28 mm	022.35.289
30 mm	022.35.305
35 mm	022.35.350
38 mm	022.35.387
40 mm	022.35.403
45 mm	022.35.458
50 mm	022.35.501
60 mm	022.35.609

Packing: 100 and 1000 pcs.

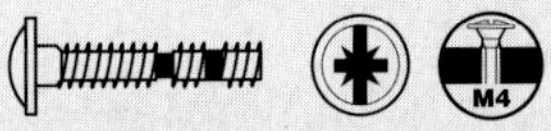

Threaded Breakoff Screw M4
Combined slot, suitable for flat or cross blades
Finish: steel, zinc-plated

Length	Cat. No.
1 3/4" x 3/4"	022.35.887

Packing: 100 and 1000 pcs.

Dimensional data not binding. We reserve the right to alter specifications without notice.

Brass Handles

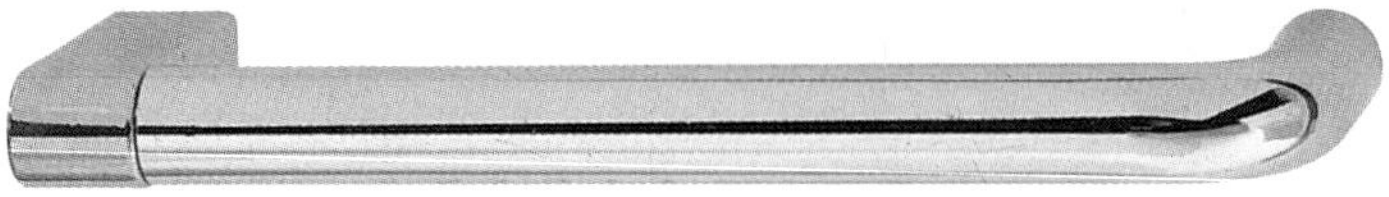

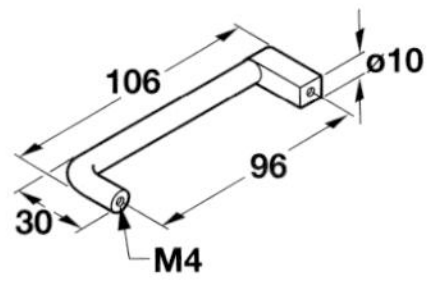

Chrome polished w/gold polished feet

Cat. No.	117.11.201

Packing: 25 pcs.

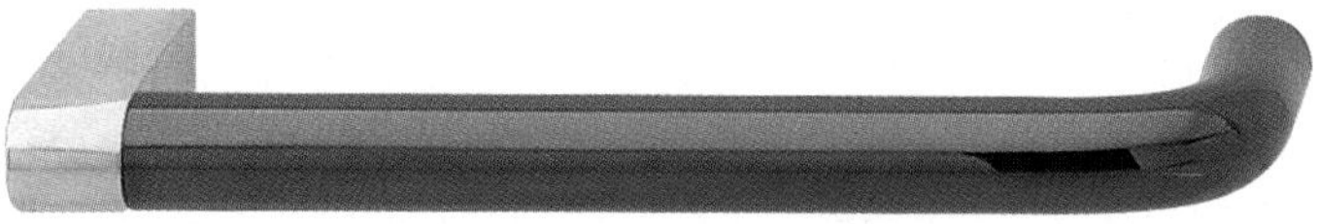

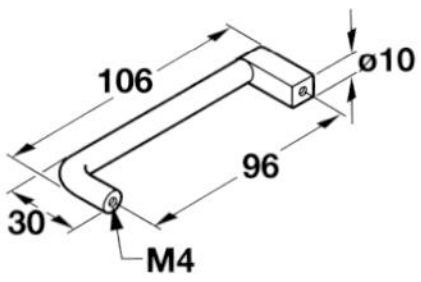

Black nickel w/gold polished feet

Cat. No.	117.11.309

Packing: 25 pcs.

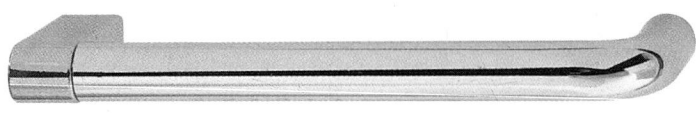

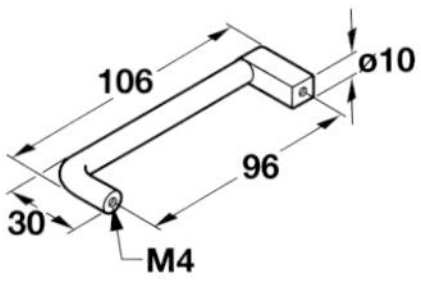

White w/chrome polished feet

Cat. No.	117.11.701

Packing: 25 pcs.

Brass Handles

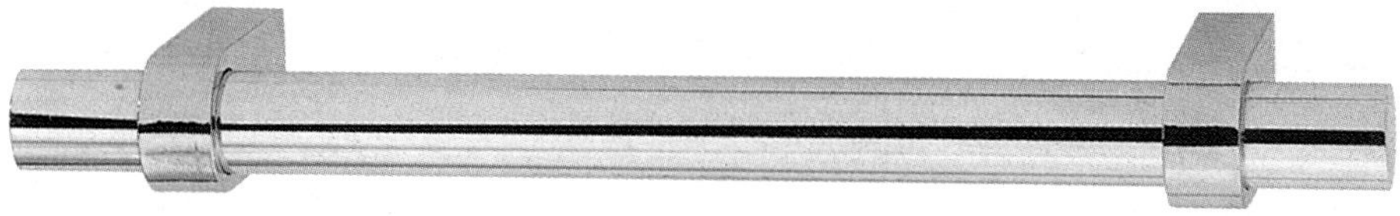

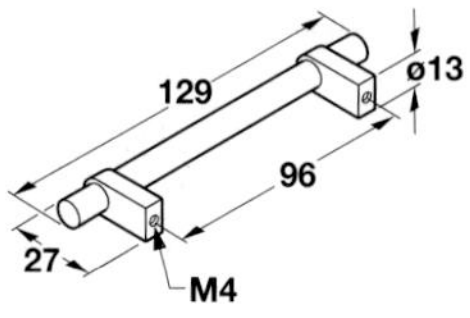

Feet: gold polished
Handle: Chrome polished

Cat. No.	117.44.200

Packing: 25 pcs.

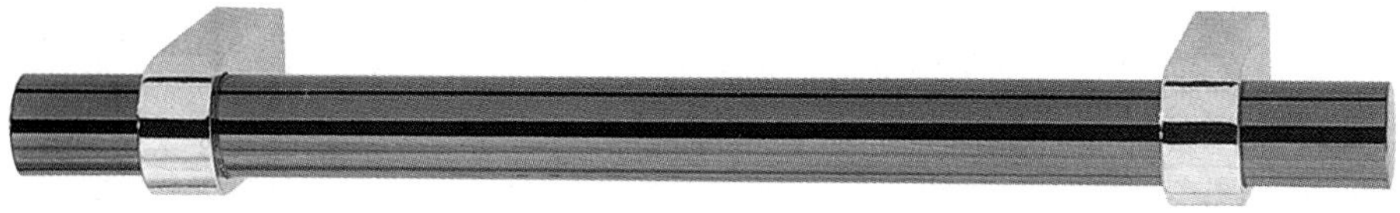

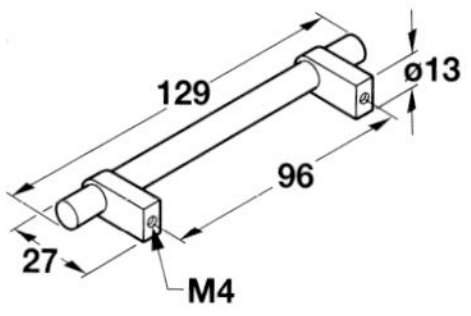

Feet: gold polished
Handle: Black nickel

Cat. No.	117.44.308

Packing: 25 pcs.

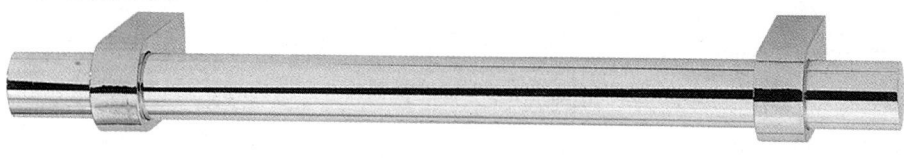

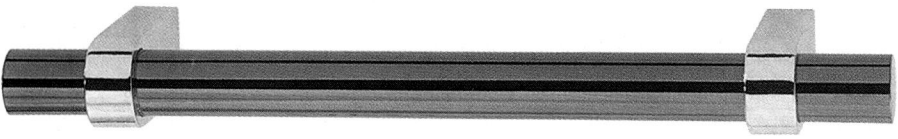

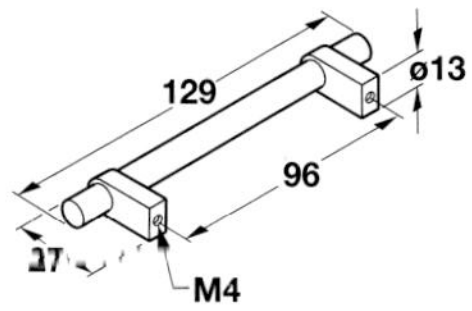

Feet: chrome polished
Handle: White

Cat. No.	117.44.700

Packing: 25 pcs.

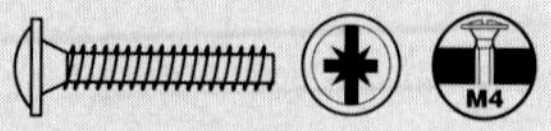

Threaded Screws M4
Combined slot, suitable for flat or cross blades
Finish: steel, zinc-plated

Length	Cat. No.
10 mm	022.35.109
12 mm	022.35.127
15 mm	022.35.154
18 mm	022.35.181
20 mm	022.35.207
22 mm	022.35.225
23 mm	022.35.234
25 mm	022.35.252
28 mm	022.35.289
30 mm	022.35.305
35 mm	022.35.350
38 mm	022.35.387
40 mm	022.35.403
45 mm	022.35.458
50 mm	022.35.501
60 mm	022.35.609

Packing: 100 and 1000 pcs.

Threaded Breakoff Screw M4
Combined slot, suitable for flat or cross blades
Finish: steel, zinc-plated

Length	Cat. No.
1 3/4" x 3/4"	022.35.887

Packing: 100 and 1000 pcs.

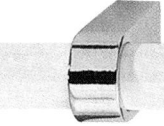

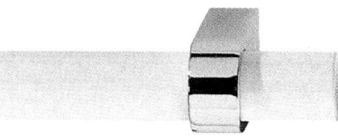

HÄFELE

Brass Handles

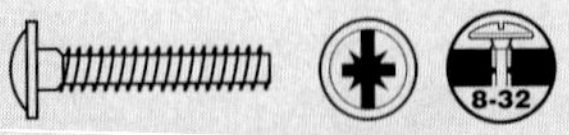

Threaded Screws 8-32
Combined slot, suitable for flat or cross blades
Finish: steel, yellow chromated

Length	Cat. No.
22 mm	022.25.229
25 mm	022.25.256
32 mm	022.25.327
38 mm	022.25.381
45 mm	022.25.452

Packing: 100 and 1000 pcs.

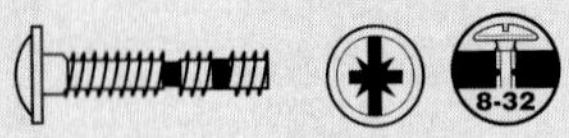

Threaded Breakoff Screw 8-32
Combined slot, suitable for flat or cross blades
Finish: steel, yellow chromated

Length	Cat. No.
1 3/4" x 3/4"	022.25.881

Packing: 100 and 1000 pcs.

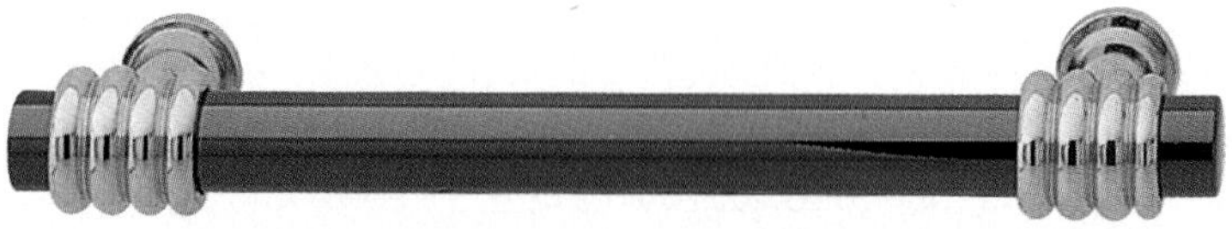

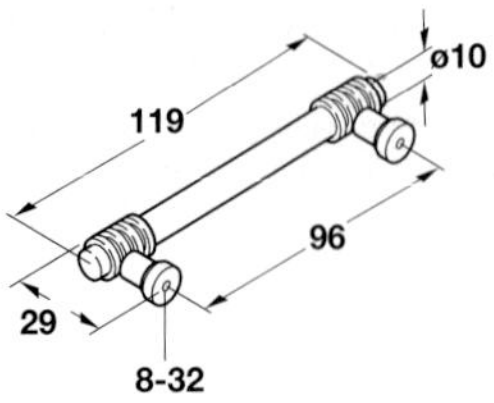

Center section: black nickel plated
Feet: polished and lacquered

Cat. No.	117.18.308

Packing: 25 pcs.

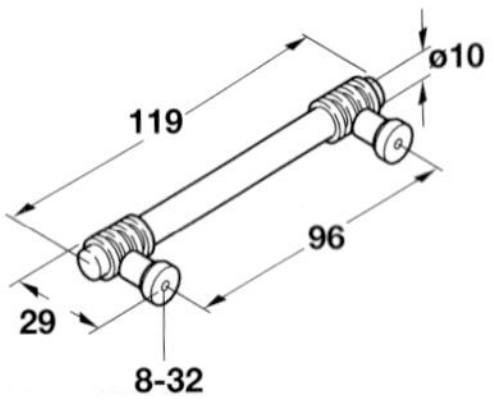

Center section: polished and lacquered
Feet: chrome polished

Cat. No.	117.18.808

Packing: 25 pcs.

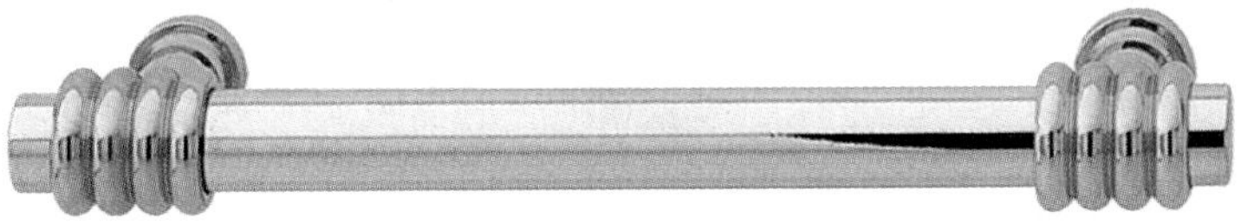

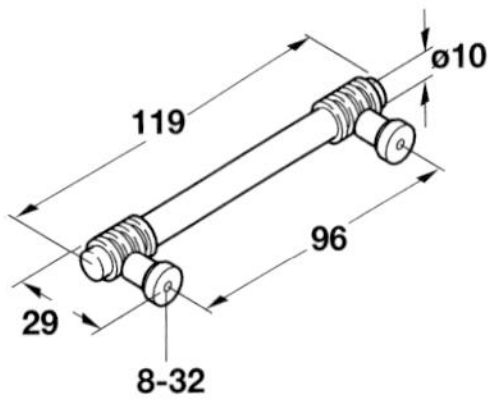

Center section: chrome polished
Feet: polished and lacquered

Cat. No.	117.18.200

Packing: 25 pcs.

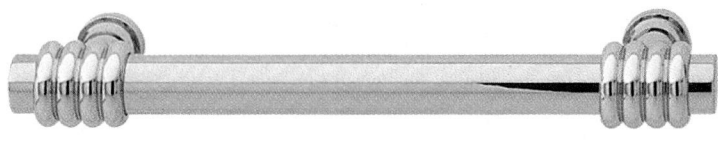

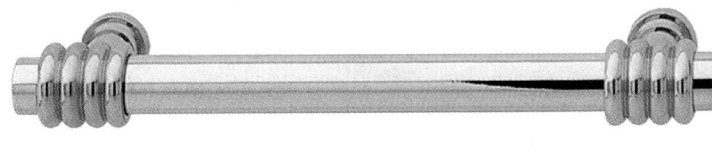

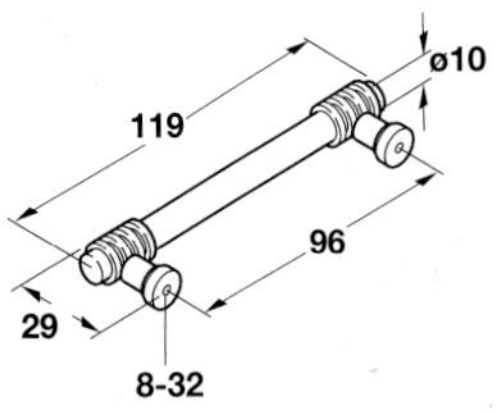

Center section: white
Feet: polished and lacquered

Cat. No.	117.18.700

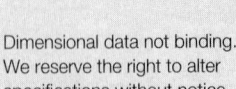

Packing: 25 pcs.

Dimensional data not binding.
We reserve the right to alter specifications without notice.

Brass Handles

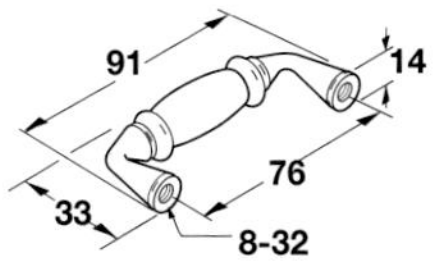

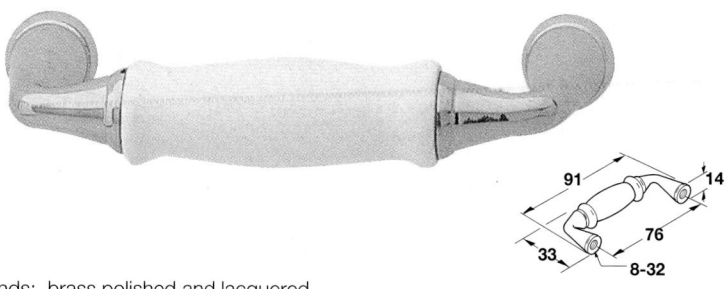

Ends: brass polished and lacquered
Center: white ceramic

Cat. No.	107.11.805

Packing: 25 pcs.

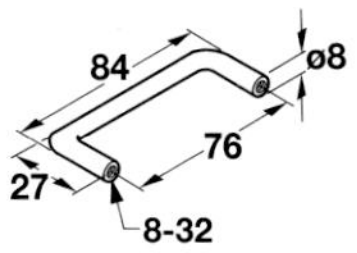

Chrome polished/brass polished & laquered

Cat. No.	117.34.204

Packing: 25 pcs.

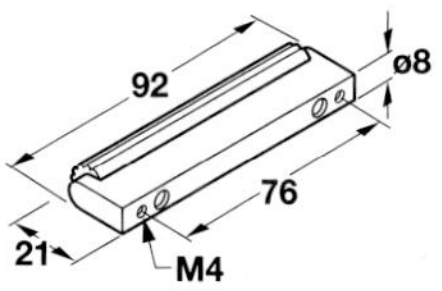

Top: polished and lacquered
Base: black nickel

Cat. No.	102.93.302

Packing: 25 pcs.

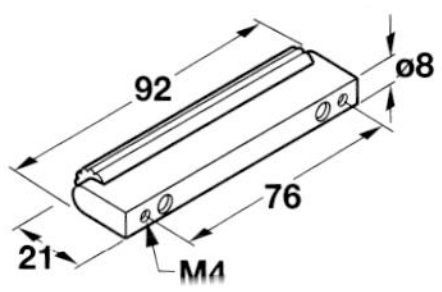

Top: black nickel
Base: chrome polished

Cat. No.	102.93.204

Packing: 25 pcs.

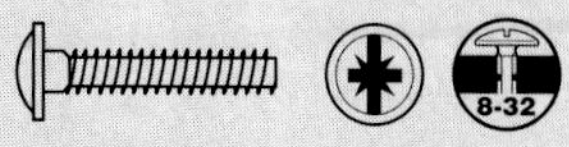

Threaded Screws 8-32
Combined slot, suitable for flat or cross blades
Finish: steel, yellow chromated

Length	Cat. No.
22 mm	022.25.229
25 mm	022.25.256
32 mm	022.25.327
38 mm	022.25.381
45 mm	022.25.452

Packing: 100 and 1000 pcs.

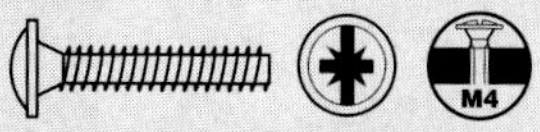

Threaded Screws M4
Combined slot, suitable for flat or cross blades
Finish: steel, zinc-plated

Length	Cat. No.
10 mm	022.35.109
12 mm	022.35.127
15 mm	022.35.154
18 mm	022.35.181
20 mm	022.35.207
22 mm	022.35.225
23 mm	022.35.234
25 mm	022.35.252
28 mm	022.35.289
30 mm	022.35.305
35 mm	022.35.350
38 mm	022.35.387
40 mm	022.35.403
45 mm	022.35.458
50 mm	022.35.501
60 mm	022.35.609

Packing: 100 and 1000 pcs.

Dimensional data not binding.
We reserve the right to alter specifications without notice.

HÄFELE

Brass Handles

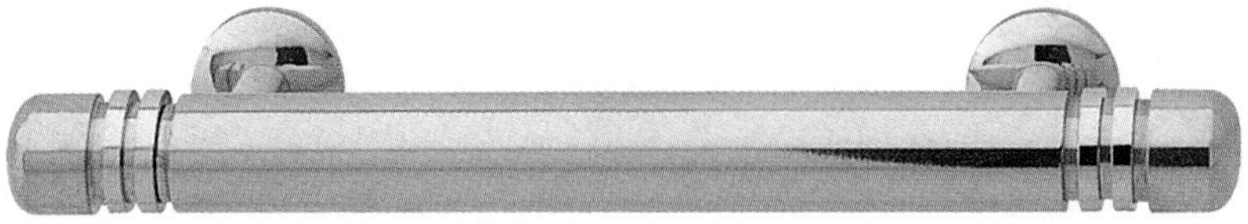

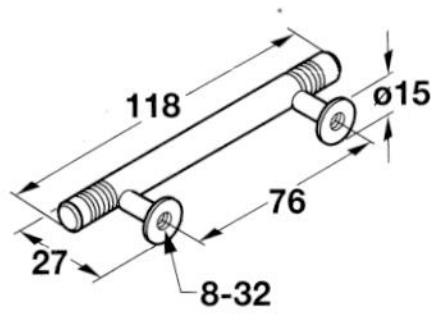

Handle: polished and lacquered
Rings: chrome polished

Cat. No.	117.33.805

Packing: 25 pcs.

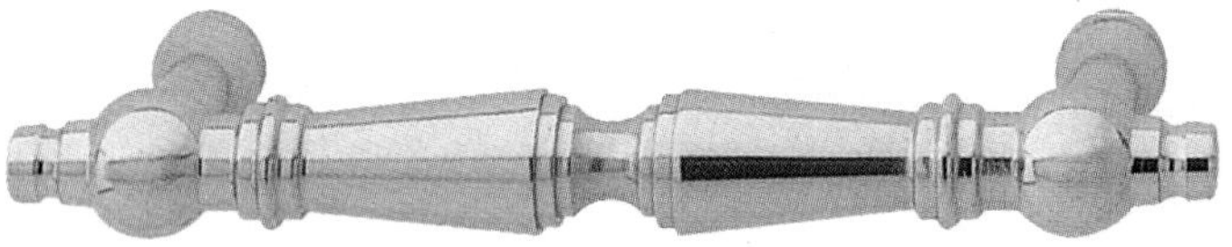

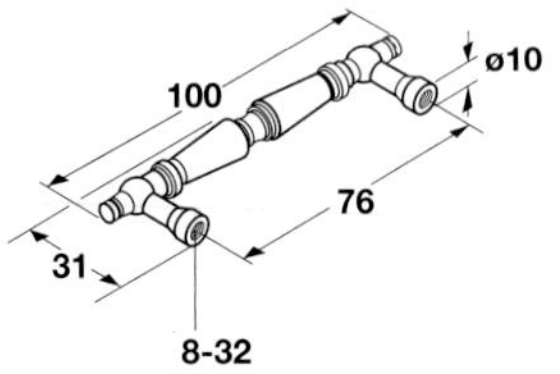

Polished and lacquered

Cat. No.	117.32.808

Packing: 25 pcs.

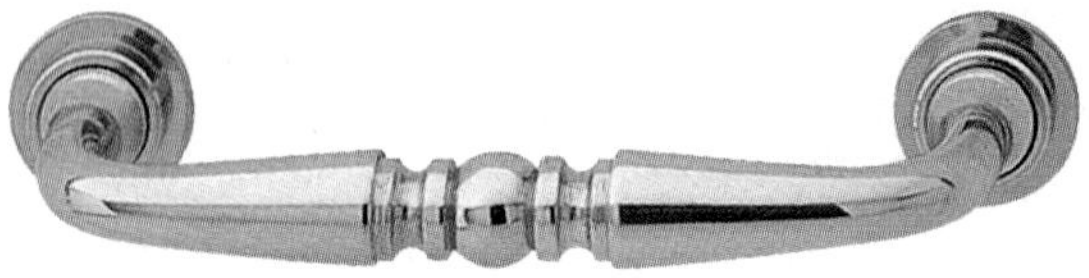

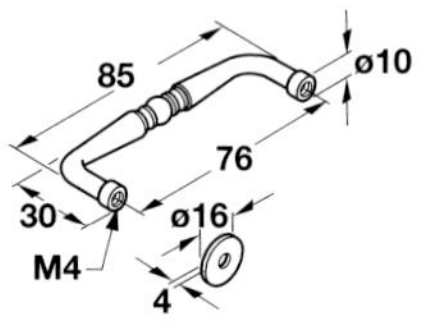

Polished and lacquered

Cat. No.	121.88.804

Packing: 25 pcs.

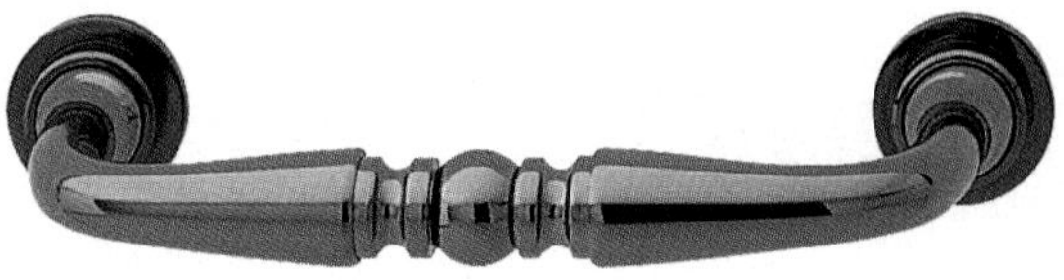

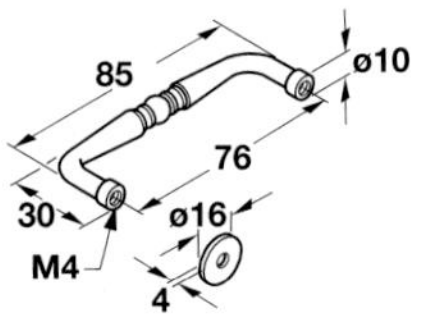

Black nickel polished

Cat. No.	121.88.304

Packing: 25 pcs.

Threaded Screws 8-32
Combined slot, suitable for flat or cross blades
Finish: steel, yellow chromated

Length	Cat. No.
22 mm	022.25.229
25 mm	022.25.256
32 mm	022.25.327
38 mm	022.25.381
45 mm	022.25.452

Packing: 100 and 1000 pcs.

Threaded Screws M4
Combined slot, suitable for flat or cross blades
Finish: steel, zinc-plated

Length	Cat. No.
10 mm	022.35.109
12 mm	022.35.127
15 mm	022.35.154
18 mm	022.35.181
20 mm	022.35.207
22 mm	022.35.225
23 mm	022.35.234
25 mm	022.35.252
28 mm	022.35.289
30 mm	022.35.305
35 mm	022.35.350
38 mm	022.35.387
40 mm	022.35.403
45 mm	022.35.458
50 mm	022.35.501
60 mm	022.35.609

Packing: 100 and 1000 pcs.

Brass handles

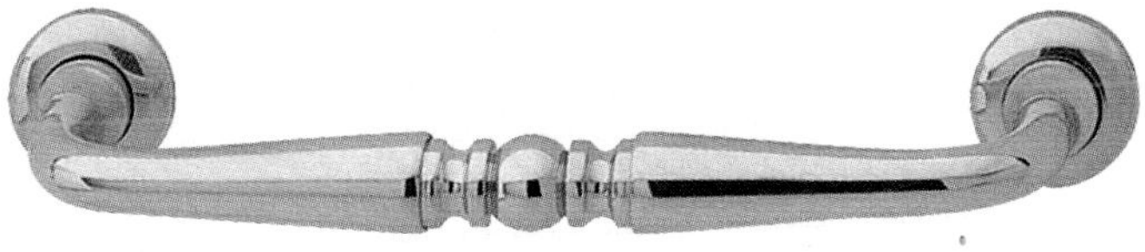

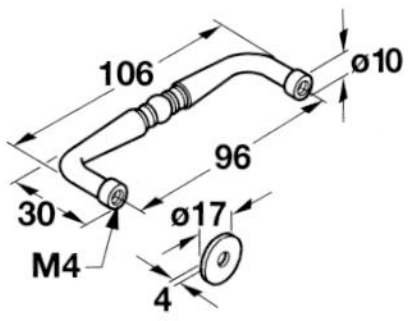

Polished and lacquered

Cat. No.	121.88.868

Packing: 25 pcs.

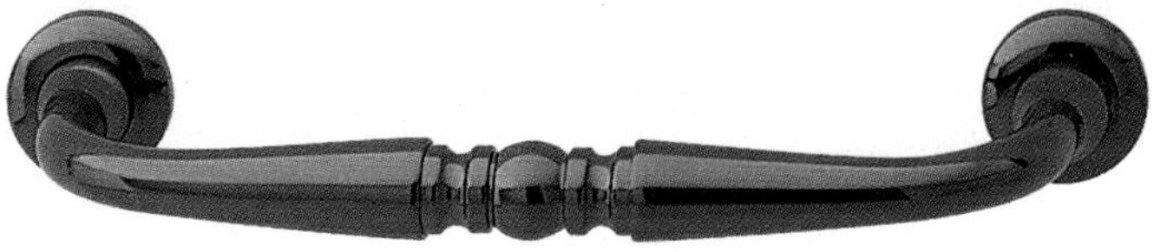

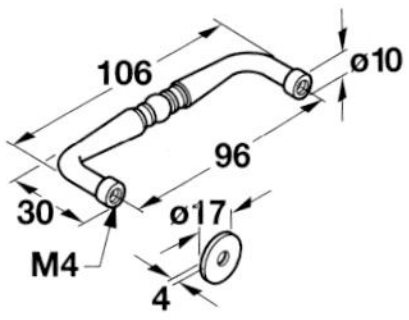

Black nickel

Cat. No.	121.88.368

Packing: 25 pcs.

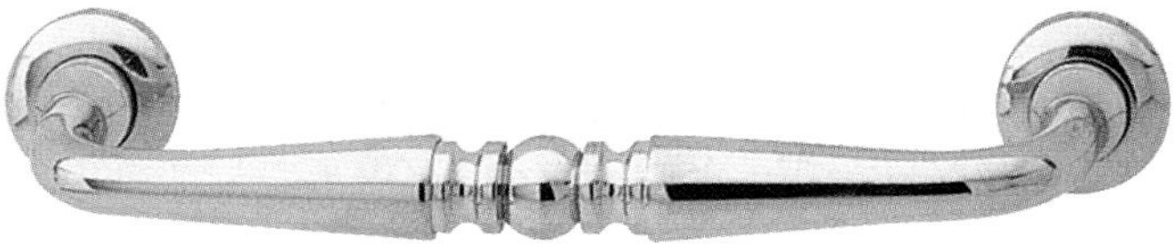

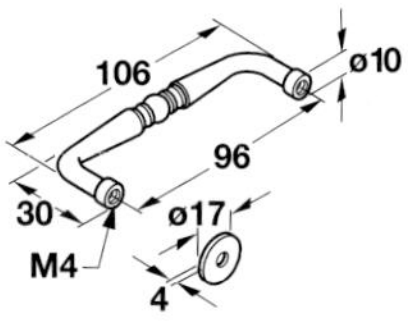

Polished chrome

Cat. No.	121.88.260

Packing: 25 pcs.

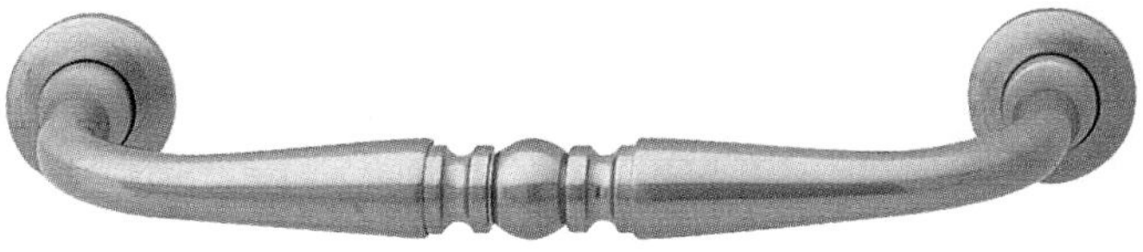

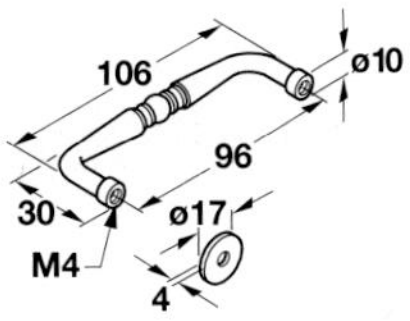

Nickel matt

Cat. No.	121.88.662

Packing: 25 pcs.

- Two rosettes provided per handle

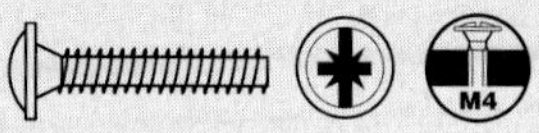

Threaded Screws M4
Combined slot, suitable for flat or cross blades

Finish: steel, zinc-plated

Length	Cat. No.
10 mm	022.35.109
12 mm	022.35.127
15 mm	022.35.154
18 mm	022.35.181
20 mm	022.35.207
22 mm	022.35.225
23 mm	022.35.234
25 mm	022.35.252
28 mm	022.35.289
30 mm	022.35.305
35 mm	022.35.350
38 mm	022.35.387
40 mm	022.35.403
45 mm	022.35.458
50 mm	022.35.501
60 mm	022.35.609

Packing: 100 and 1000 pcs.

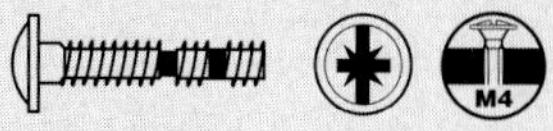

Threaded Breakoff Screw M4
Combined slot, suitable for flat or cross blades

Finish: steel, zinc-plated

Length	Cat. No.
1 3/4" x 3/4"	022.35.887

Packing: 100 and 1000 pcs.

Brass handles

Threaded Screws M4
Combined slot, suitable for flat or cross blades
Finish: steel, zinc-plated

Length	Cat. No.
10 mm	022.35.109
12 mm	022.35.127
15 mm	022.35.154
18 mm	022.35.181
20 mm	022.35.207
22 mm	022.35.225
23 mm	022.35.234
25 mm	022.35.252
28 mm	022.35.289
30 mm	022.35.305
35 mm	022.35.350
38 mm	022.35.387
40 mm	022.35.403
45 mm	022.35.458
50 mm	022.35.501
60 mm	022.35.609

Packing: 100 and 1000 pcs.

Countersunk wood screws
Finish: brass, unfinished

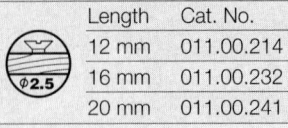

	Length	Cat. No.
	12 mm	011.00.214
	16 mm	011.00.232
	20 mm	011.00.241

Packing: 200 pcs.

Dimensional data not binding.
We reserve the right to alter specifications without notice.

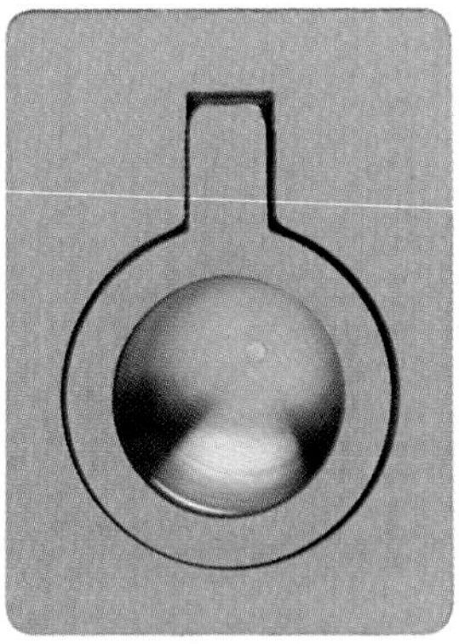

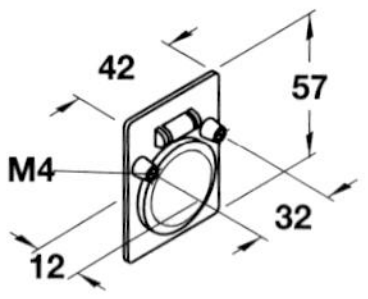

Brass ground

Catalog No.	161.11.550

Packing: 25 pcs.

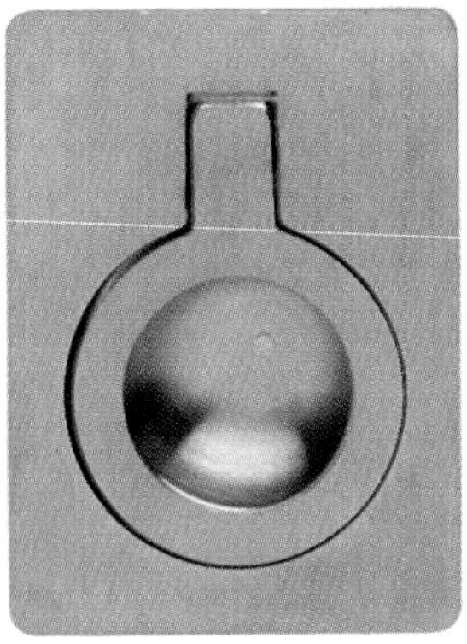

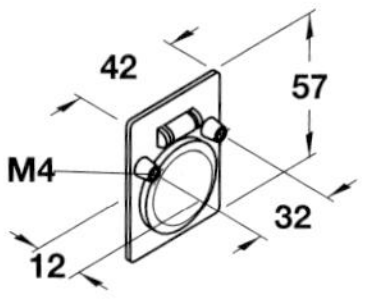

Brass nickel plated matt

Catalog No.	161.11.658

Packing: 25 pcs.

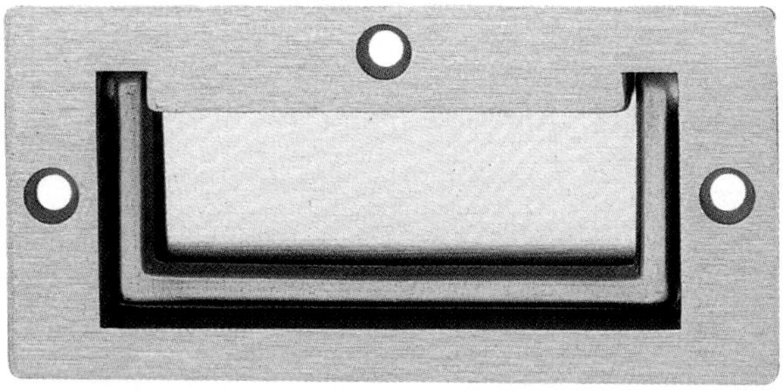

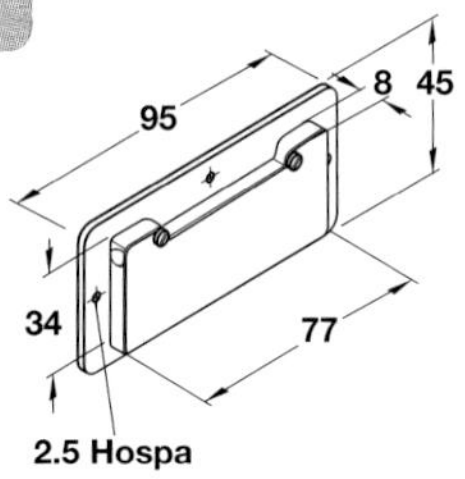

Brass ground

Catalog No.	161.10.526

Packing: 25 pcs.

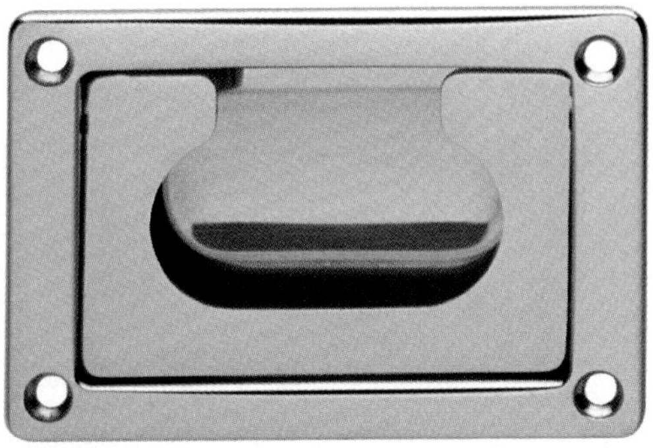

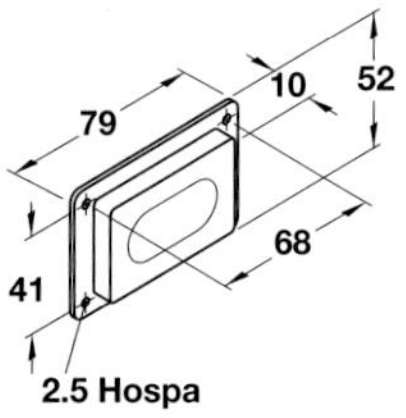

Brass polished

Catalog No.	161.03.825

Packing: 25 pcs.

Brass Handles

HÄFELE

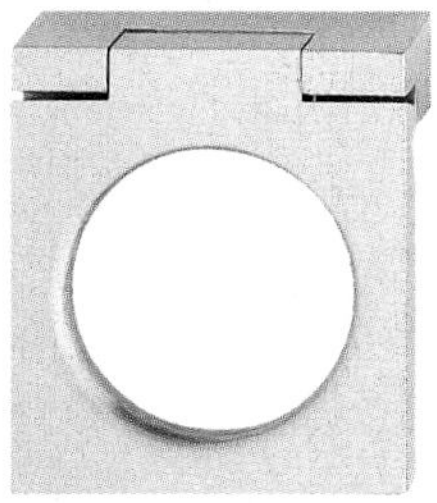

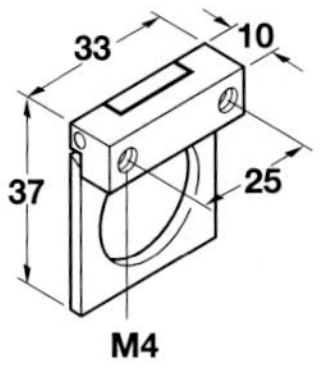

Nickel plated matt

Cat. No.	106.34.643

Packing: 25 pcs.

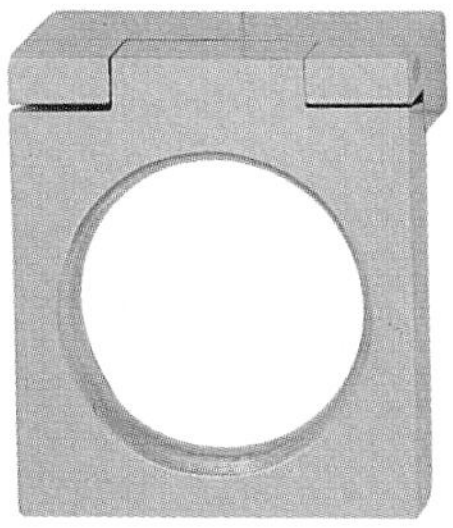

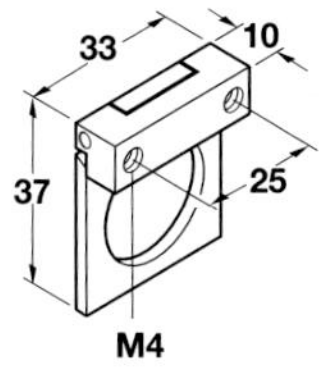

Matt

Cat. No.	106.34.545

Packing: 10 pcs.

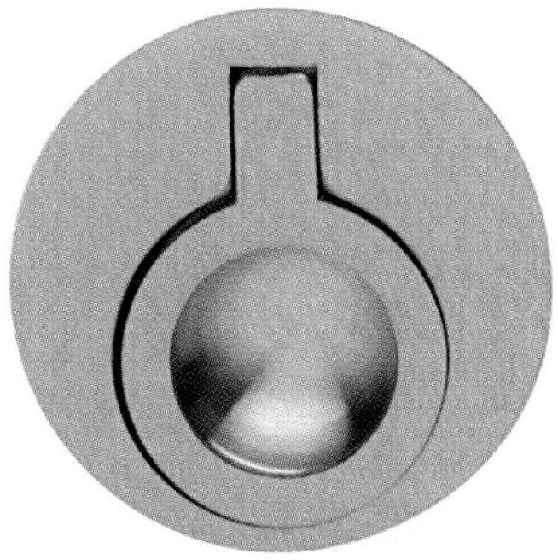

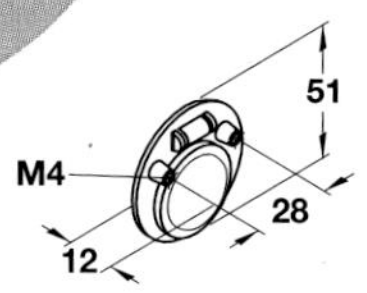

Brass ground

Catalog No.	101.12.557

Packing: 25 pcs.

Decorative Hardware **1**

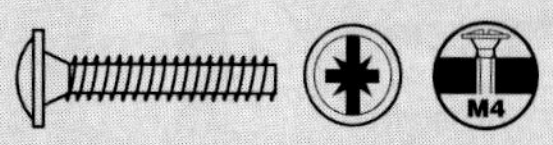

Threaded Screws M4
Combined slot, suitable for flat or cross blades

Finish: steel, zinc-plated

Length	Cat. No.
10 mm	022.35.109
12 mm	022.35.127
15 mm	022.35.154
18 mm	022.35.181
20 mm	022.35.207
22 mm	022.35.225
23 mm	022.35.234
25 mm	022.35.252
28 mm	022.35.289
30 mm	022.35.305
35 mm	022.35.350
38 mm	022.35.387
40 mm	022.35.403
45 mm	022.35.458
50 mm	022.35.501
60 mm	022.35.609

Packing: 100 and 1000 pcs.

Threaded Breakoff Screw M4
Combined slot, suitable for flat or cross blades

Finish: steel, zinc-plated

Length	Cat. No.
1 3/4" x 3/4"	022.35.887

Packing: 100 and 1000 pcs.

HÄFELE

Brass handles

Threaded Screws 8-32
Combined slot, suitable for flat or cross blades
Finish: steel, yellow chromated

Length	Cat. No.
22 mm	022.25.229
25 mm	022.25.256
32 mm	022.25.327
38 mm	022.25.381
45 mm	022.25.452

Packing: 100 and 1000 pcs.

Threaded Breakoff Screw 8-32
Combined slot, suitable for flat or cross blades
Finish: steel, yellow chromated

Length	Cat. No.
1 3/4" x 3/4"	022.25.881

Packing: 100 and 1000 pcs.

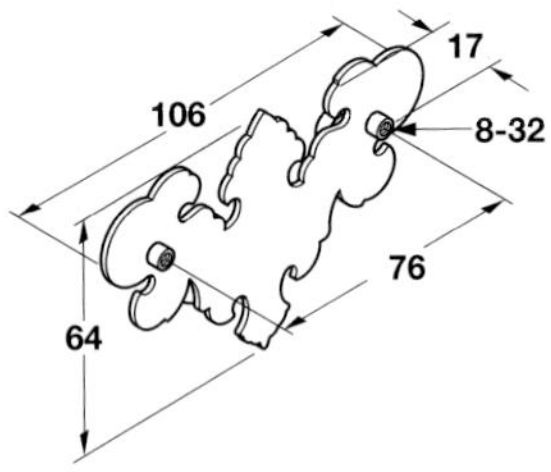

Polished and lacquered

Cat. No.	122.26.800

Packing: 25 pcs.

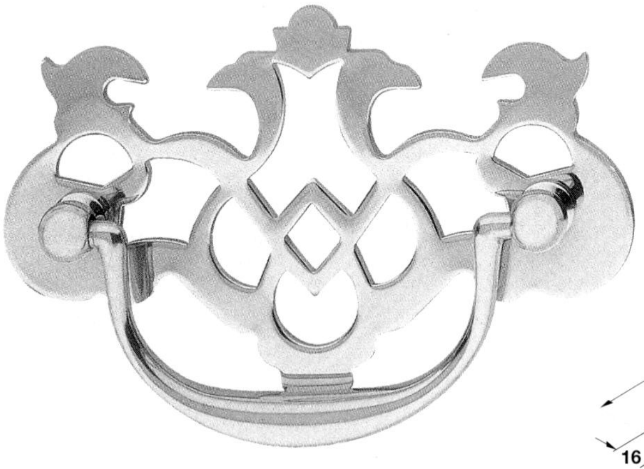

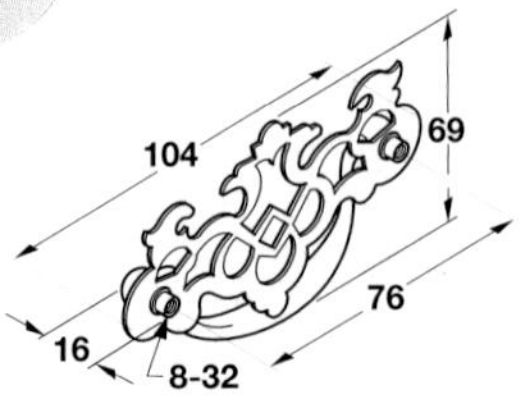

Polished and lacquered

Cat. No.	122.09.808

Packing: 25 pcs.

Dimensional data not binding.
We reserve the right to alter specifications without notice.

Brass Handles

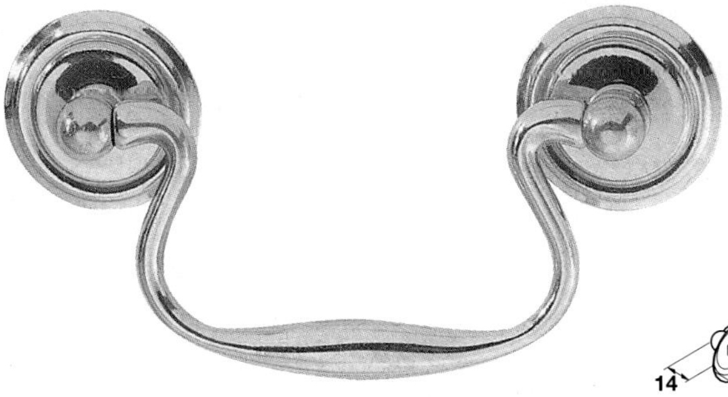

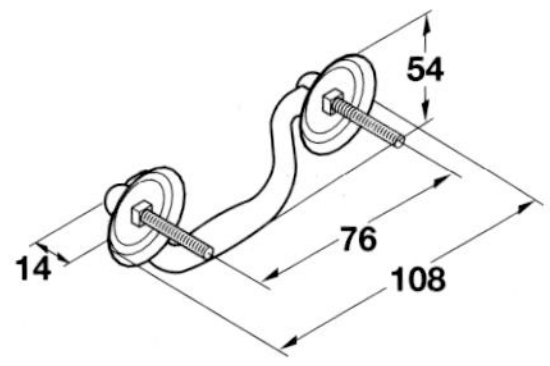

Polished and lacquered

Cat. No.	120.13.811

Packing: 25 pcs. (mounting hardware provided)

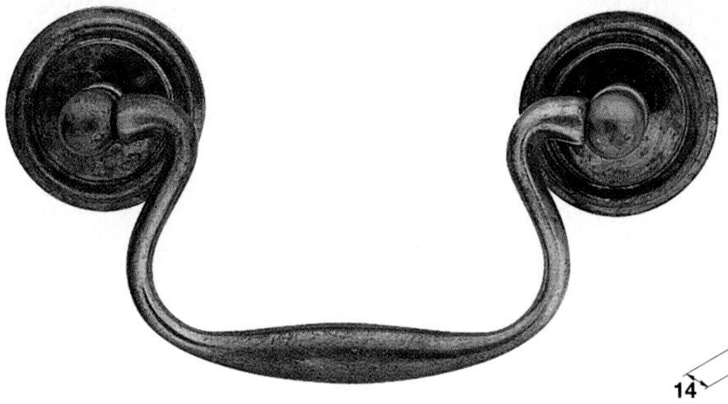

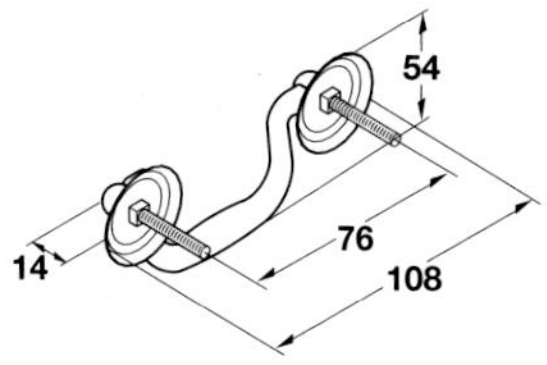

Antique brass

Cat. No.	120.13.115

Packing: 25 pcs. (mounting hardware provided)

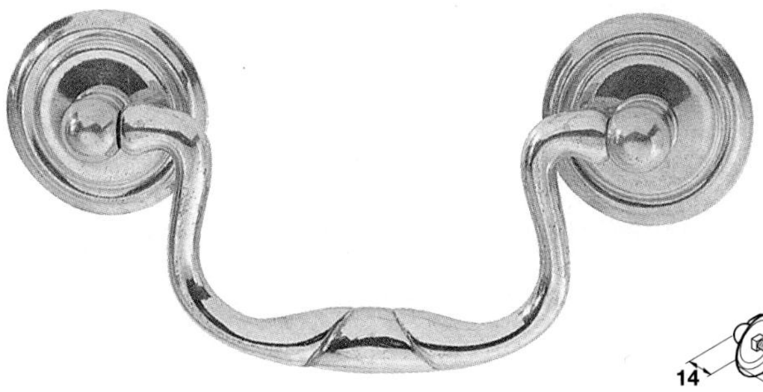

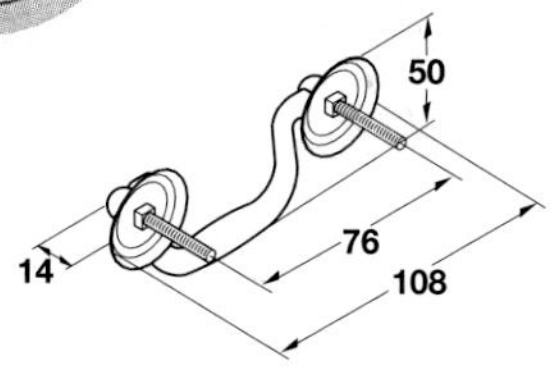

Polished and lacquered

Cat. No.	120.12.814

Packing: 25 pcs. (mounting hardware provided)

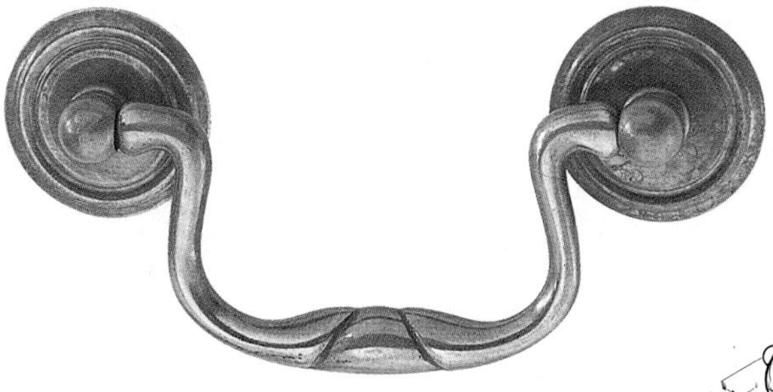

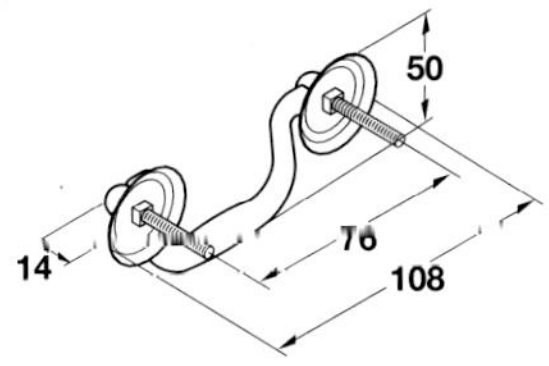

Antique brass

Cat. No.	120.12.118

Packing: 25 pcs. (mounting hardware provided)

- Handles are provided with bolt and nut for attachment to doors or drawers for panels up to 3/4" thick.

HÄFELE

Brass Handles

• Handles are provided with bolt and nut for attachment to doors or drawers for panels up to 3/4" thick.

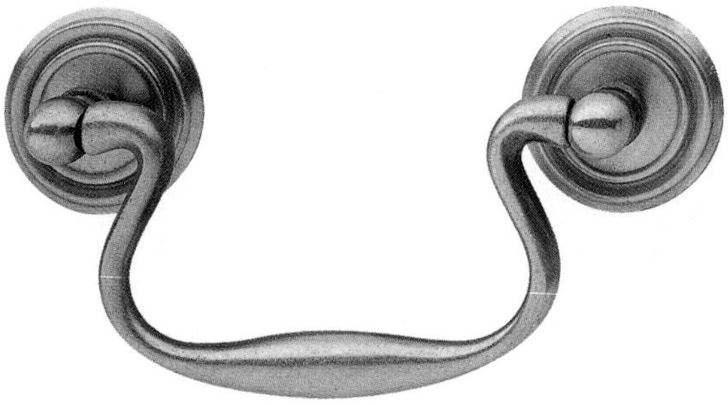
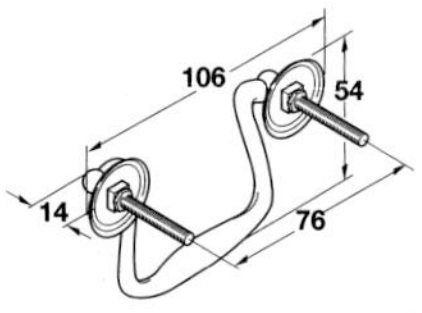

Old English brass

Cat. No.	122.10.114

Packing: 25 pcs. (mounting hardware provided)

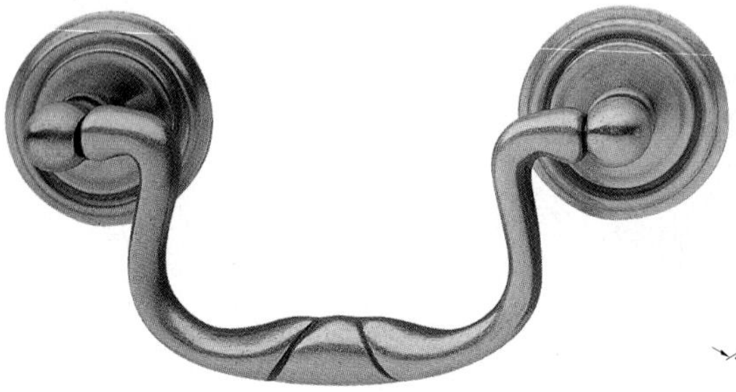
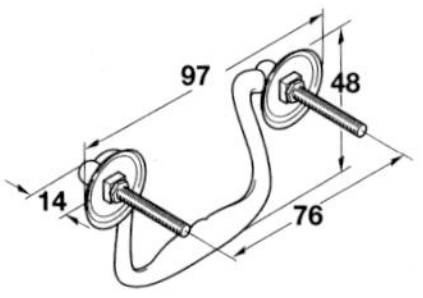

Old English brass

Cat. No.	122.10.123

Packing: 25 pcs. (mounting hardware provided)

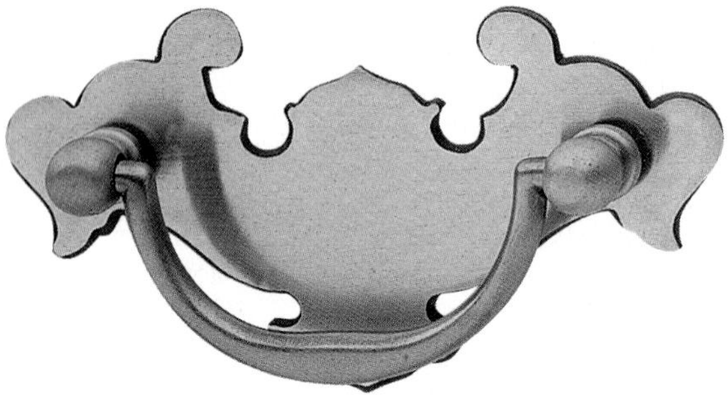
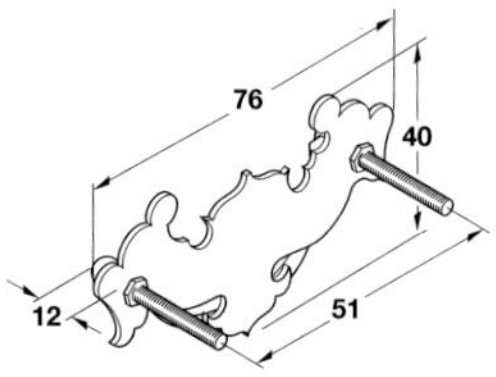

Old English brass

Cat. No.	122.11.111

Packing: 25 pcs. (mounting hardware provided)

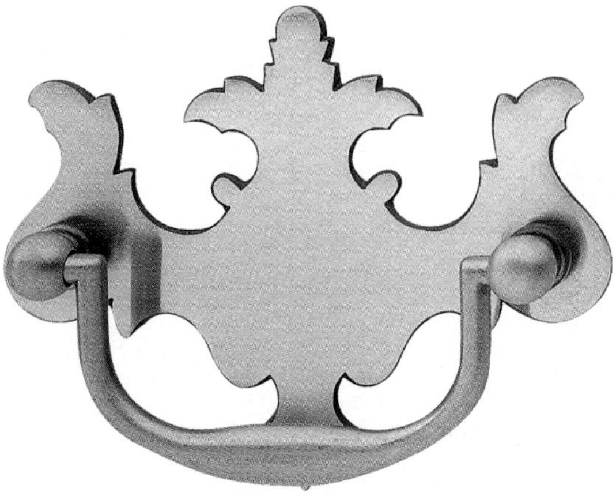
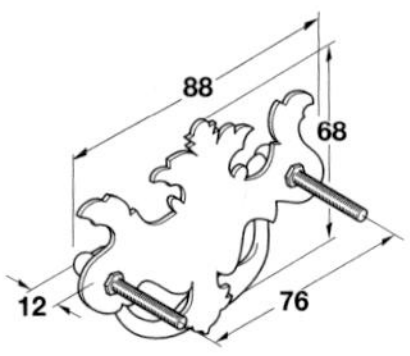

Old English brass

Cat. No.	122.11.120

Packing: 25 pcs. (mounting hardware provided)

Brass Handles

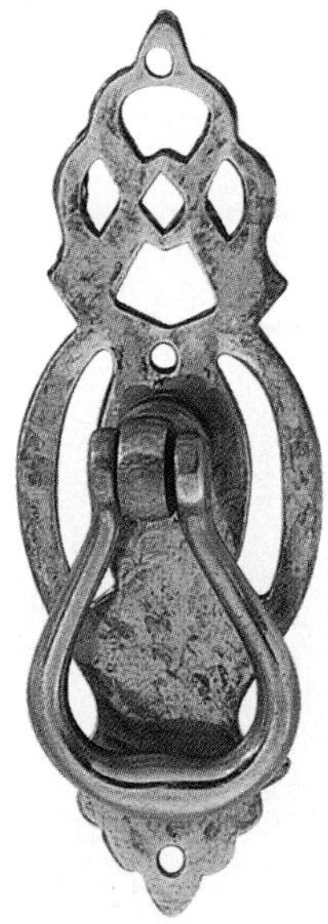

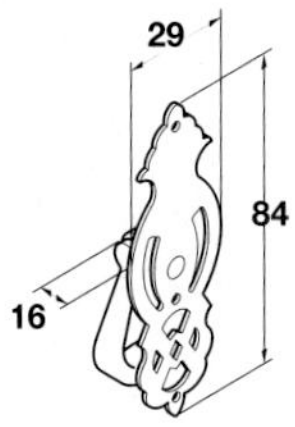

Polished and lacquered

Cat. No.	121.98.855

Packing: 25 pcs.

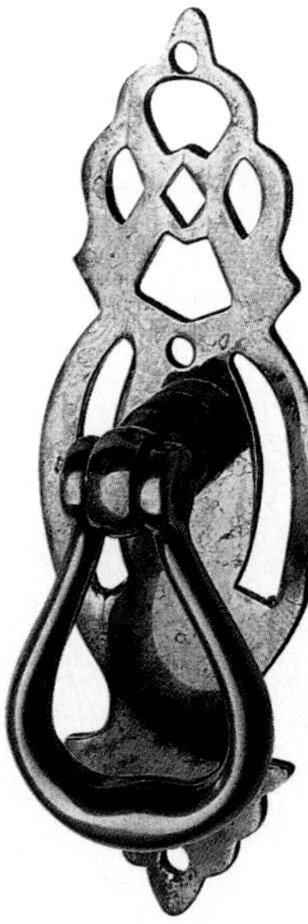

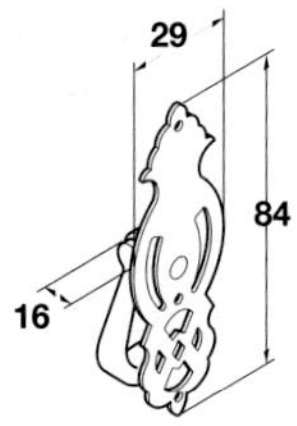

Antique brass

Cat. No.	121.98.159

Packing: 25 pcs.

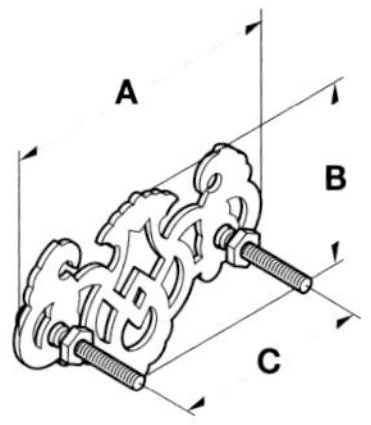

Polished and lacquered

Size A x B	Dimension C	Cat. No.
76 x 50	53 mm	121.98.819
92 x 63	58 mm	121.98.828

Packing: 25 pcs. (mounting hardware provided)

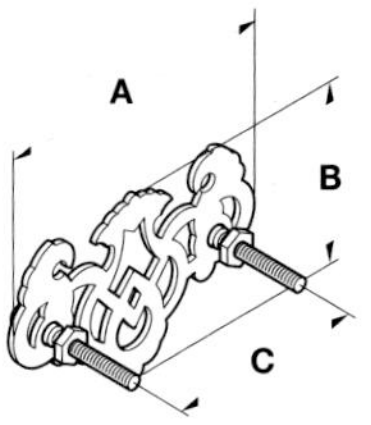

Antique brass

Size A x B	Dimension C	Cat. No.
76 x 50	53 mm	121.98.113
92 x 63	58 mm	121.98.122

Packing: 25 pcs. (mounting hardware provided)

Round-head Metal Pins
Ø 0.9 mm

Finish: steel, brass-plated

Ø 0.9	Length	Cat. No.
	11 mm	076.40.119

Packing: 7400 pcs.

- Handles noted with mounting hardware are provided with bolt and nut for attachment to doors or drawers for panels up to 3/4" thick.

HÄFELE

Brass Handles

1 Decorative Hardware

Round-head Metal Pins
Ø 0.9 mm

Finish: steel, brass-plated

Length	Cat. No.
11 mm	076.40.119

Packing: 7400 pcs.

- Handles noted with mounting hardware are provided with bolt and nut for attachment to doors or drawers for panels up to 3/4" thick.

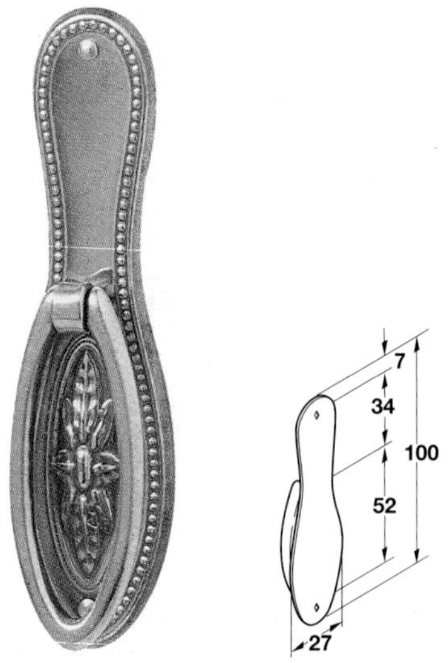

Old English brass

Cat. No.	122.16.125

Packing: 25 each

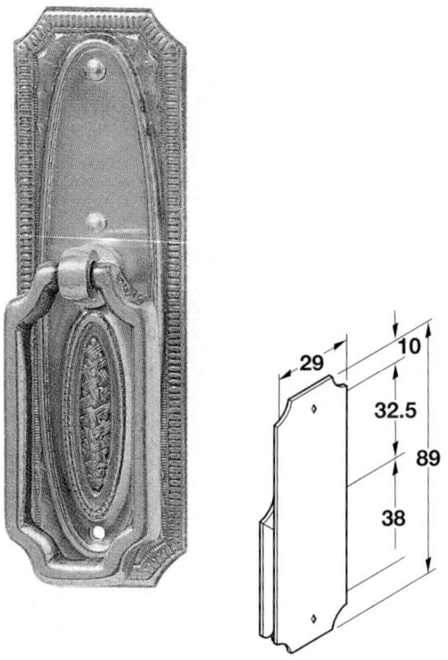

Old English brass

Cat. No.	122.16.116

Packing: 25 each

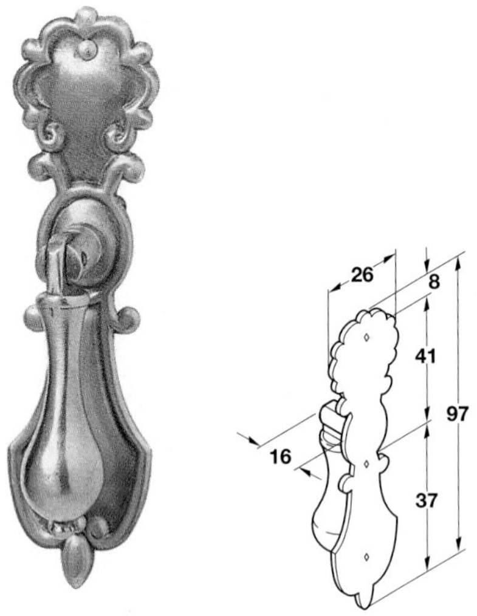

Old English brass

Cat. No.	122.17.113

Packing: 25 each

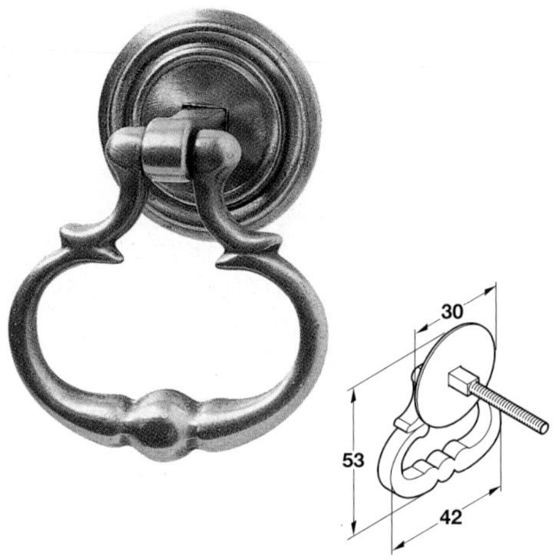

Old English brass

Cat. No.	122.14.112

Packing: 25 each (mounting hardware provided)

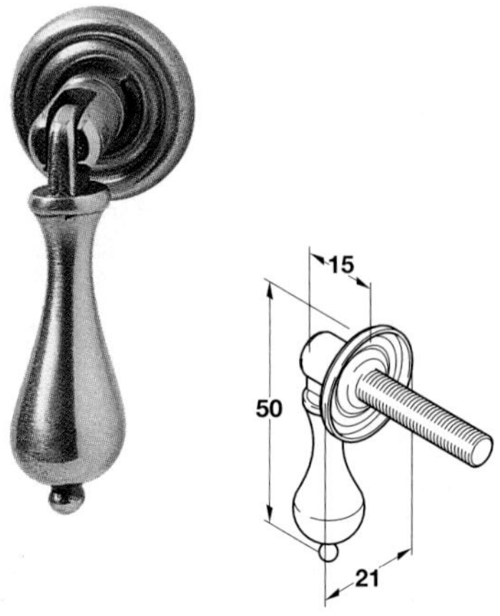

Old English brass

Cat. No.	122.14.121

Packing: 25 each (mounting hardware provided)

Dimensional data not binding. We reserve the right to alter specifications without notice.

Brass handles

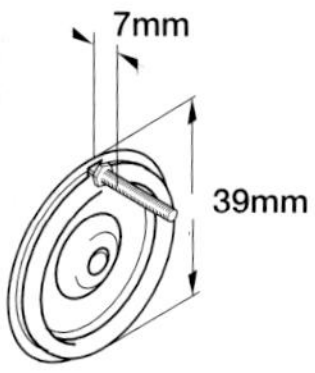

Old English brass

Cat. No.	122.15.128

Packing: 25 pcs. (including mounting hardware)

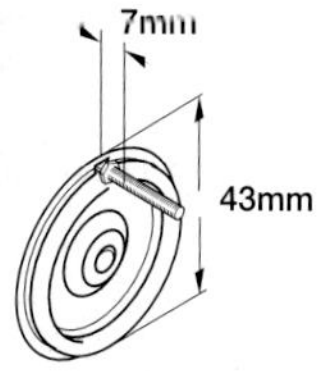

Old English brass

Cat. No.	122.15.137

Packing: 25 pcs. (including mounting hardware)

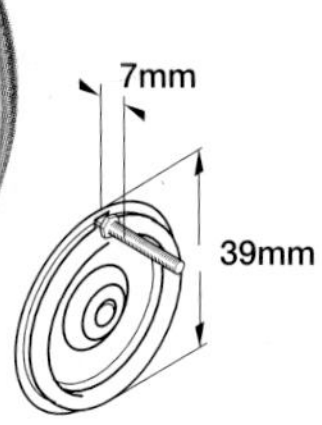

Old English brass

Cat. No.	122.15.119

Packing: 25 pcs. (including mounting hardware)

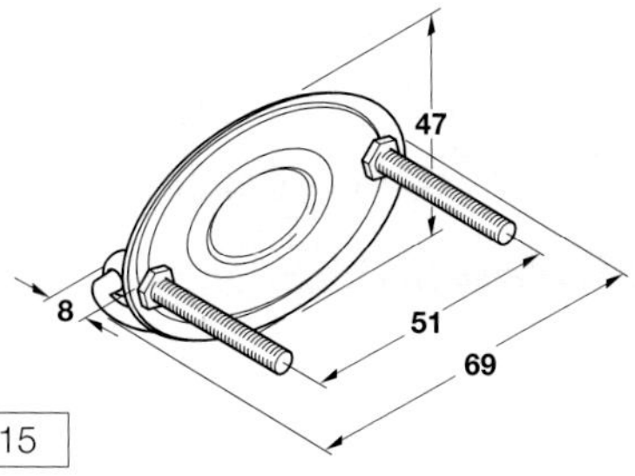

Old English brass

Cat. No.	122.13.115

Packing: 25 pcs. (including mounting hardware)

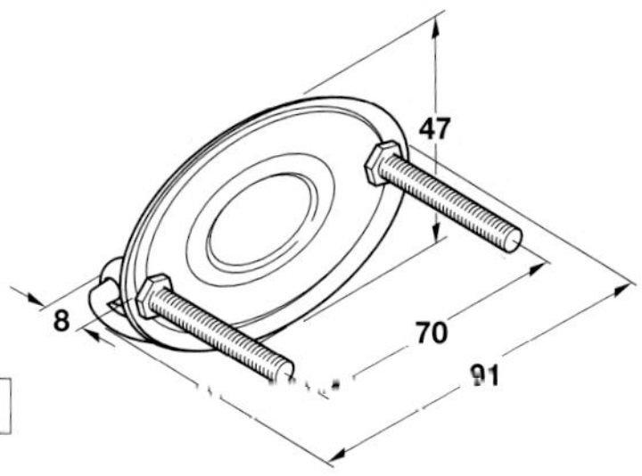

Old English brass

Cat. No.	122.13.124

Packing: 25 pcs. (including mounting hardware)

- Handles are provided with bolt and nut for attachment to doors or drawers for panels up to 3/4" thick.

HÄFELE

Brass handles

- Handles are provided with bolt and nut for attachment to doors or drawers for panels up to 3/4" thick.

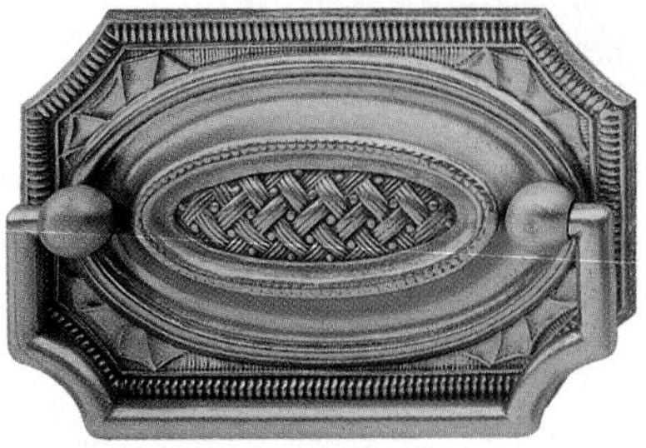

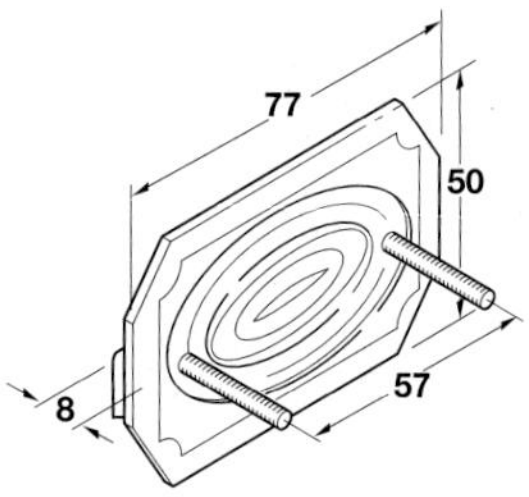

Old English brass

Cat. No.	122.12.118

Packing: 25 each (mounting hardware provided)

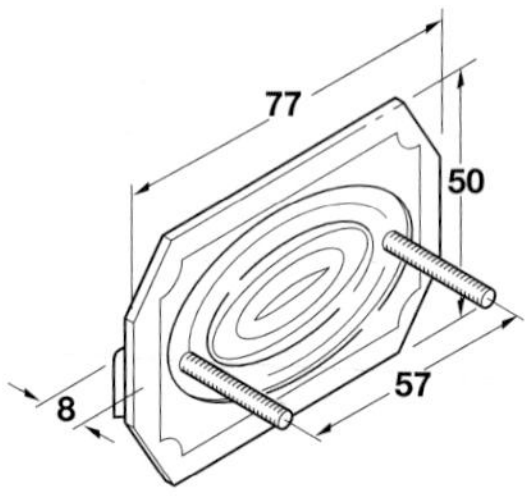

Old English brass

Cat. No.	122.12.127

Packing: 25 each (mounting hardware provided)

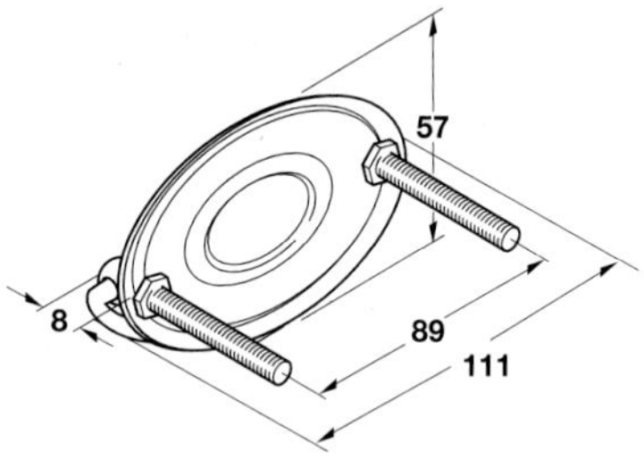

Old English brass

Cat. No.	122.13.133

Packing: 25 each (mounting hardware provided)

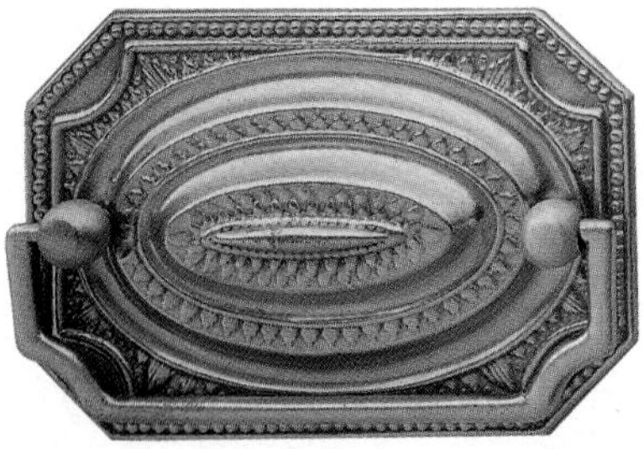

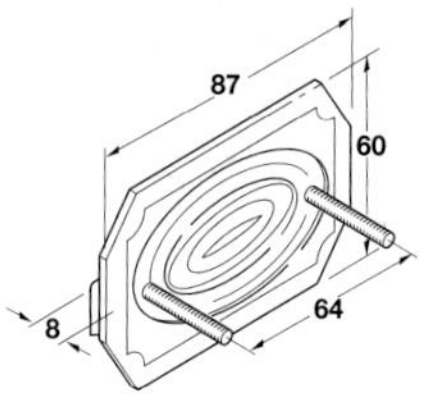

Old English brass

Cat. No.	122.12.136

Packing: 25 each (mounting hardware provided)

Solid Brass Knobs

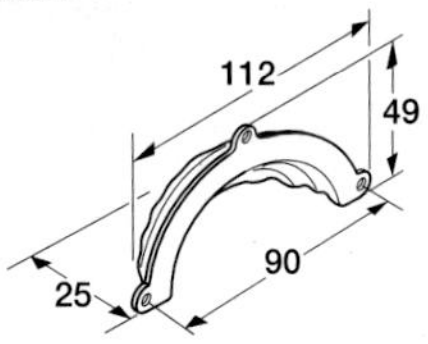

Polished and lacquered

Cat. No.	151.06.804

Packing: 25 pcs. (fixing screws provided)

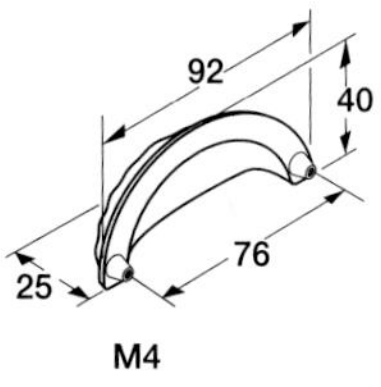

Polished and lacquered

Cat. No.	151.08.808

Packing: 25 pcs. (fixing screws provided)

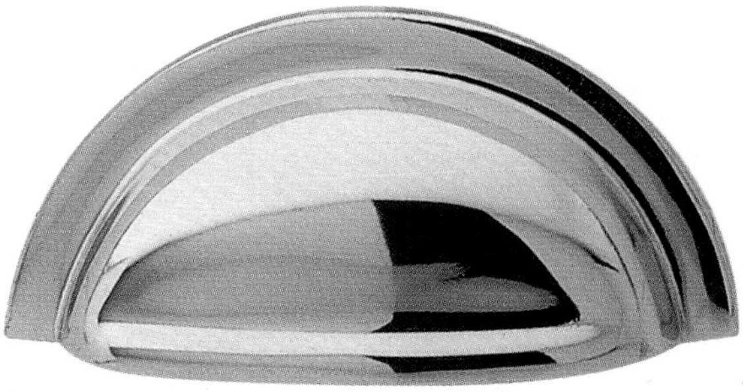

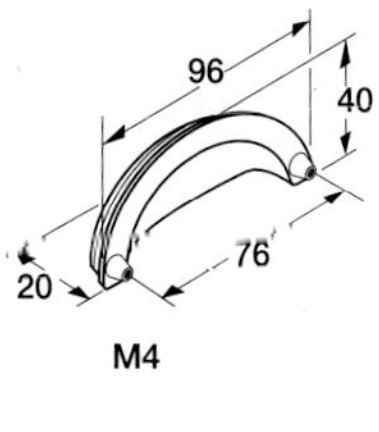

Polished and lacquered

Cat. No.	151.07.801

Packing: 25 pcs. (fixing screws provided)

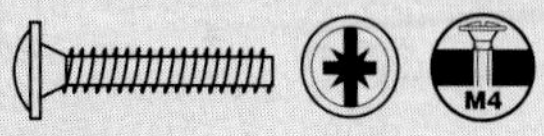

Threaded Screws M4
Combined slot, suitable for flat or cross blades

Finish: steel, zinc-plated

Length	Cat. No.
10 mm	022.35.109
12 mm	022.35.127
15 mm	022.35.154
18 mm	022.35.181
20 mm	022.35.207
22 mm	022.35.225
23 mm	022.35.234
25 mm	022.35.252
28 mm	022.35.289
30 mm	022.35.305
35 mm	022.35.350
38 mm	022.35.387
40 mm	022.35.403
45 mm	022.35.458
50 mm	022.35.501
60 mm	022.35.609

Packing: 100 and 1000 pcs.

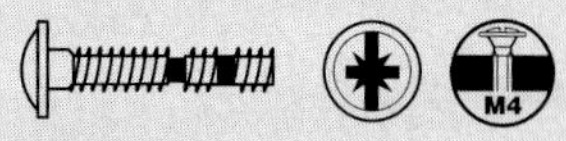

Threaded Breakoff Screw M4
Combined slot, suitable for flat or cross blades

Finish: steel, zinc-plated

Length	Cat. No.
1 3/4" x 3/4"	022.35.887

Packing: 100 and 1000 pcs.

Dimensional data not binding.
We reserve the right to alter specifications without notice.

HÄFELE

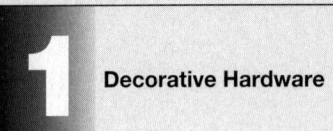

Brass Tray Handle

1 Decorative Hardware

- Mounts on tray sides, providing a sturdy easy grip method of holding tray

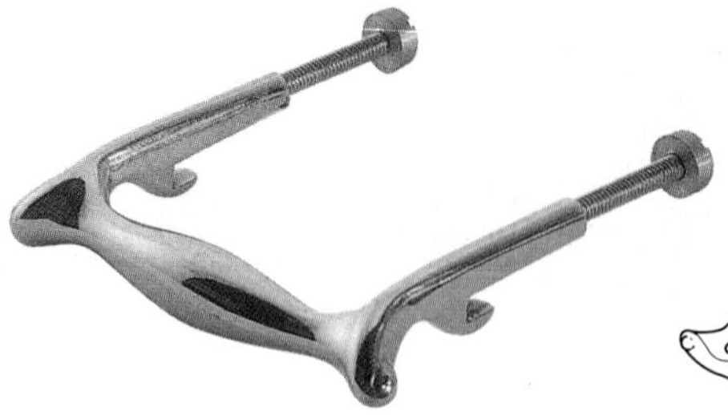

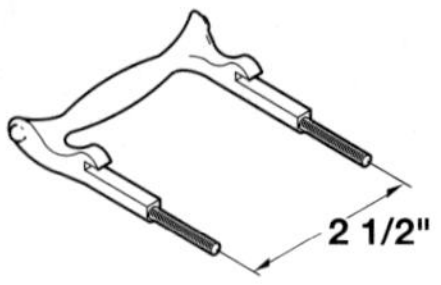

Polished and lacquered

Cat. No.	120.14.809

Packing: 1 pc.

Dimensional data not binding. We reserve the right to alter specifications without notice.

Zinc–Plastic Handle

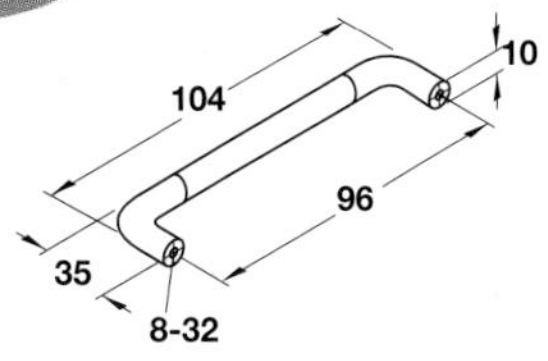

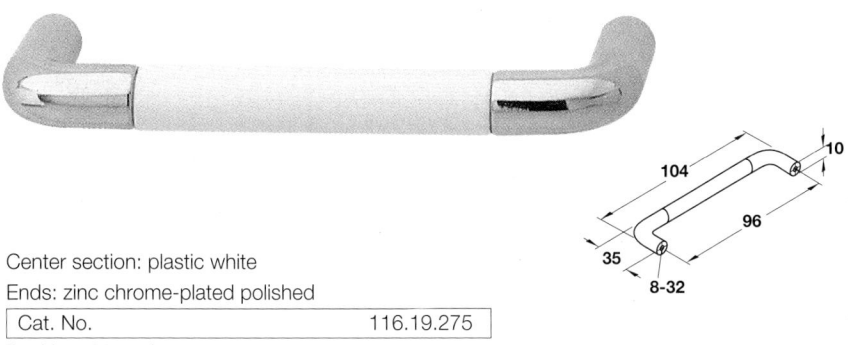

Center section: plastic transparent
Ends: zinc chrome-plated polished

Cat. No.	116.19.202

Packing: 25 each.

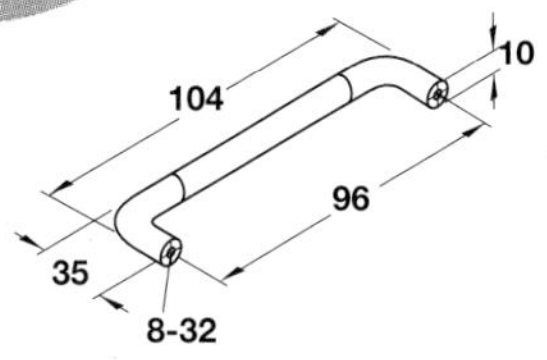

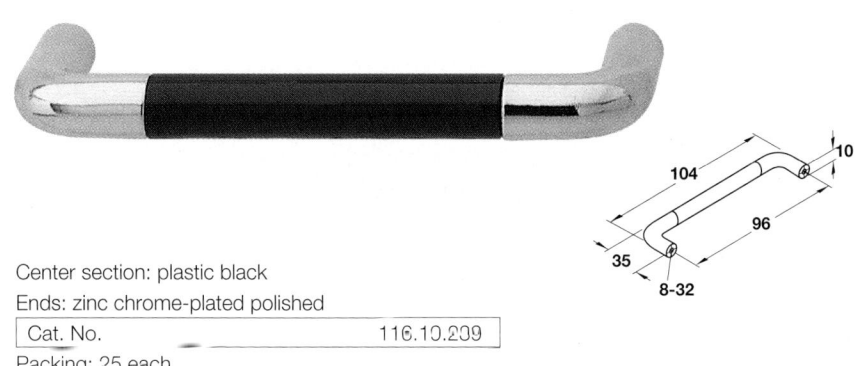

Center section: plastic white
Ends: zinc chrome-plated polished

Cat. No.	116.19.275

Packing: 25 each

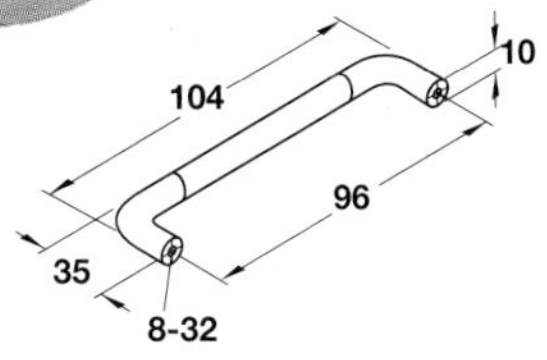

Center section: plastic black
Ends: zinc chrome-plated polished

Cat. No.	116.10.209

Packing: 25 each

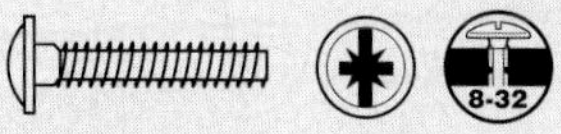

Threaded Screws 8-32
Combined slot, suitable for flat or cross blades
Finish: steel, yellow chromated

Length	Cat. No.
22 mm	022.25.229
25 mm	022.25.256
32 mm	022.25.327
38 mm	022.25.381
45 mm	022.25.452

Packing: 100 and 1000 pcs.

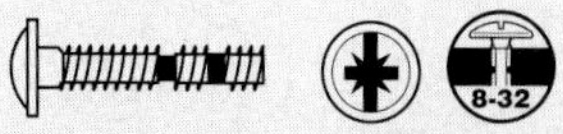

Threaded Breakoff Screw 8-32
Combined slot, suitable for flat or cross blades
Finish: steel, yellow chromated

Length	Cat. No.
1 3/4" x 3/4"	022.25.881

Packing: 100 and 1000 pcs.

Dimensional data not binding.
We reserve the right to alter specifications without notice.

HÄFELE

Zinc–Plastic Handle

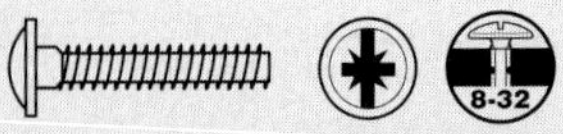

Threaded Screws 8-32
Combined slot, suitable for flat or cross blades
Finish: steel, yellow chromated

Length	Cat. No.
22 mm	022.25.229
25 mm	022.25.256
32 mm	022.25.327
38 mm	022.25.381
45 mm	022.25.452

Packing: 100 and 1000 pcs.

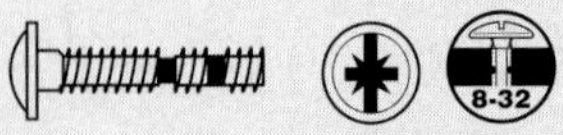

Threaded Breakoff Screw 8-32
Combined slot, suitable for flat or cross blades
Finish: steel, yellow chromated

Length	Cat. No.
1 3/4" x 3/4"	022.25.881

Packing: 100 and 1000 pcs.

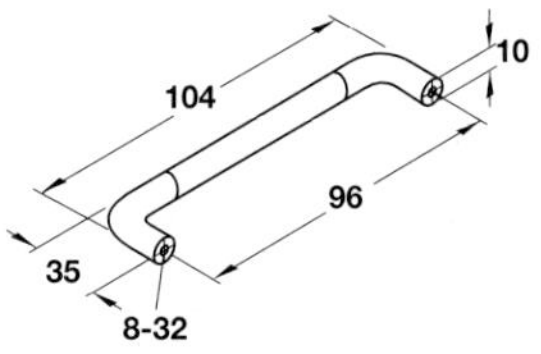

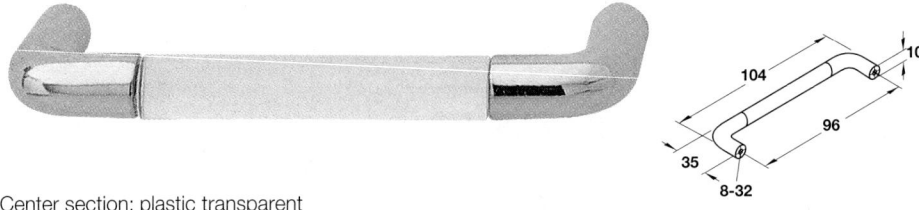

Center section: plastic transparent
Ends: zinc brass polished plated

Cat. No.	116.19.800

Packing: 25 each

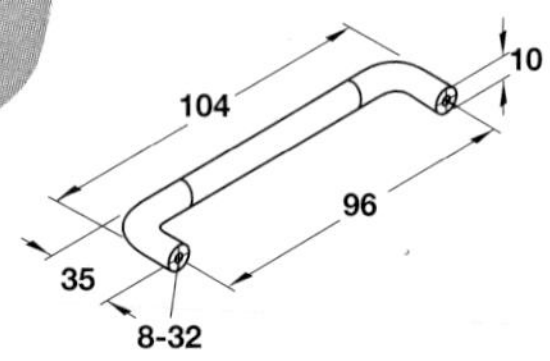

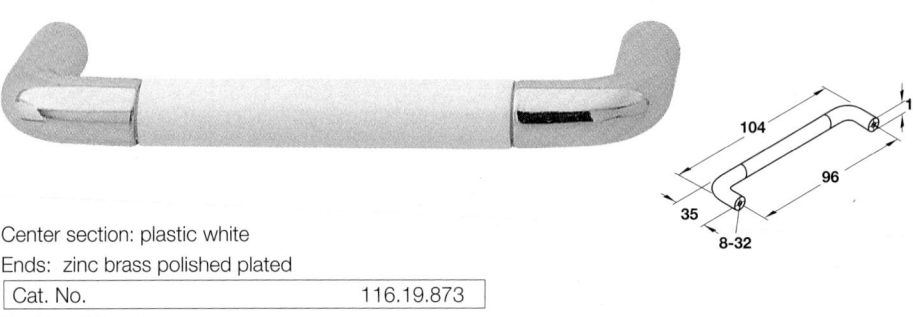

Center section: plastic white
Ends: zinc brass polished plated

Cat. No.	116.19.873

Packing: 25 each

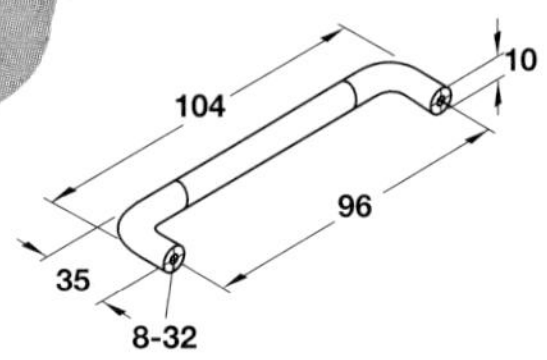

Center section: plastic black
Ends: zinc brass polished plated

Cat. No.	116.19.837

Packing: 25 each

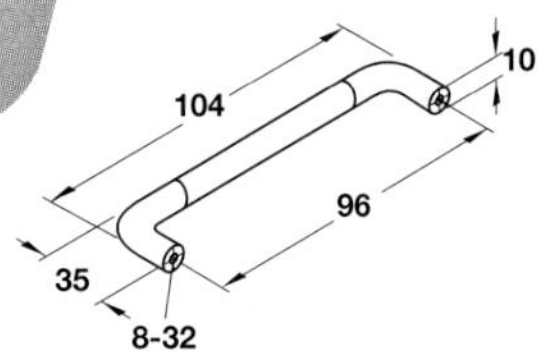

Center section: red oak unifinished
Ends: zinc brass polished plated

Cat. No.	116.19.944

Packing: 25 each

Brass/Steel Handle

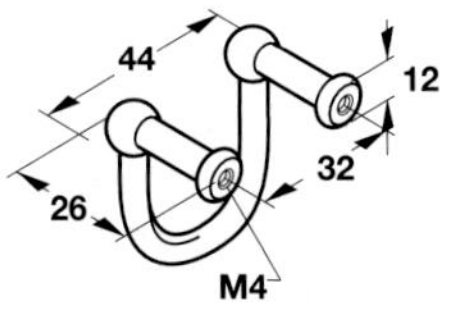

Feet: brass polished and lacquered
Handle: steel chrome plated polished

Cat. No.	103.23.820

Packing: 25 pcs.

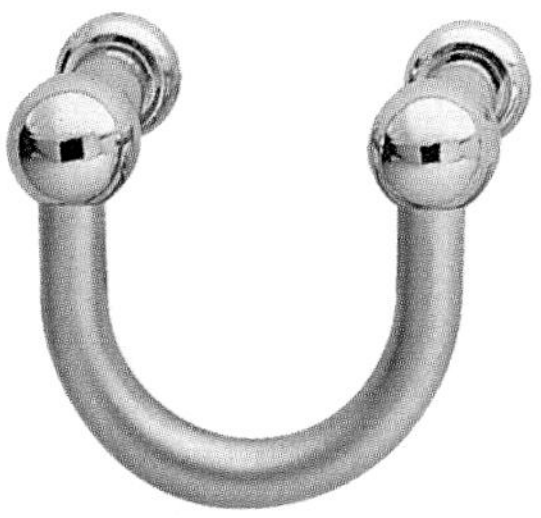

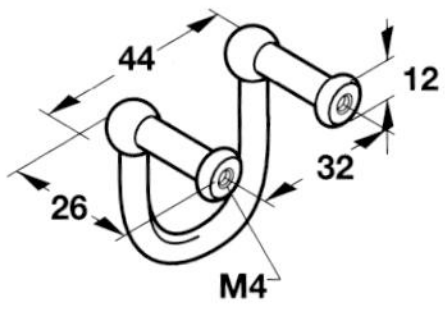

Feet: brass chrome plated polished
Handle: steel matt chrome plated

Cat. No.	103.23.240

Packing: 25 pcs.

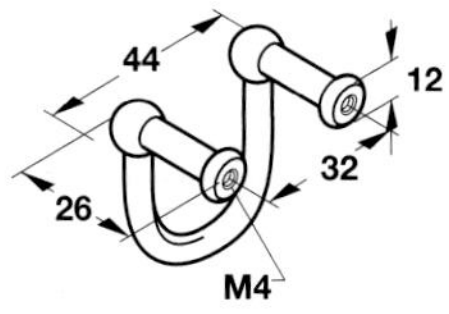

Feet: brass chrome plated polished
Handle: Steel chrome plated polished

Cat. No.	103.23.220

Packing: 25 pcs.

Threaded Screws M4

Combined slot, suitable for flat or cross blades

Finish: steel, zinc-plated

Length	Cat. No.
10 mm	022.35.109
12 mm	022.35.127
15 mm	022.35.154
18 mm	022.35.181
20 mm	022.35.207
22 mm	022.35.225
23 mm	022.35.234
25 mm	022.35.252
28 mm	022.35.289
30 mm	022.35.305
35 mm	022.35.350
38 mm	022.35.387
40 mm	022.35.403
45 mm	022.35.458
50 mm	022.35.501
60 mm	022.35.609

Packing: 100 and 1000 pcs.

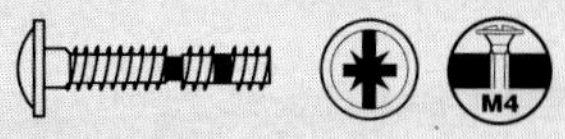

Threaded Breakoff Screw M4

Combined slot, suitable for flat or cross blades

Finish: steel, zinc-plated

Length	Cat. No.
1 3/4" x 3/4"	022.35.887

Packing: 100 and 1000 pcs.

Dimensional data not binding.
We reserve the right to alter specifications without notice.

HÄFELE

Brass/Steel Handle

1 Decorative Hardware

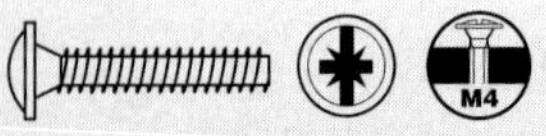

Threaded Screws M4
Combined slot, suitable for flat or cross blades
Finish: steel, zinc-plated

Length	Cat. No.
10 mm	022.35.109
12 mm	022.35.127
15 mm	022.35.154
18 mm	022.35.181
20 mm	022.35.207
22 mm	022.35.225
23 mm	022.35.234
25 mm	022.35.252
28 mm	022.35.289
30 mm	022.35.305
35 mm	022.35.350
38 mm	022.35.387
40 mm	022.35.403
45 mm	022.35.458
50 mm	022.35.501
60 mm	022.35.609

Packing: 100 and 1000 pcs.

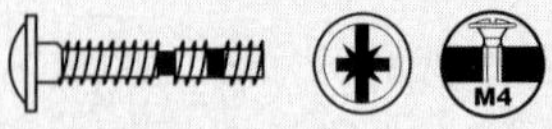

Threaded Breakoff Screw M4
Combined slot, suitable for flat or cross blades
Finish: steel, zinc-plated

Length	Cat. No.
1 3/4" x 3/4"	022.35.887

Packing: 100 and 1000 pcs.

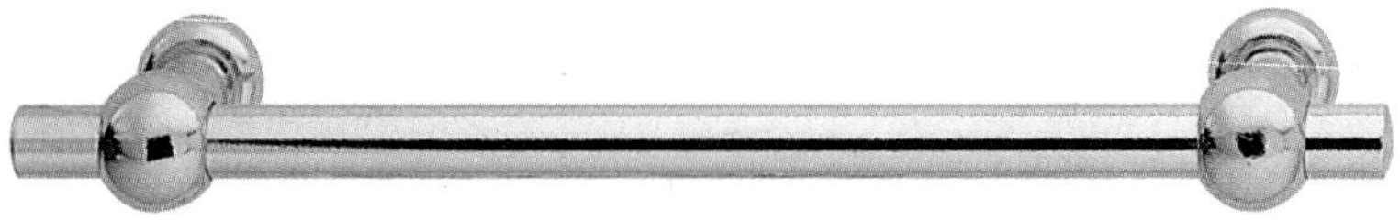

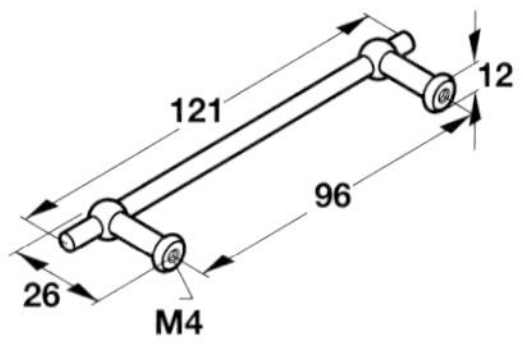

Feet: brass polished and lacquered
Handle: steel chrome plated polished

Cat. No.	103.24.821

Packing: 25 pcs.

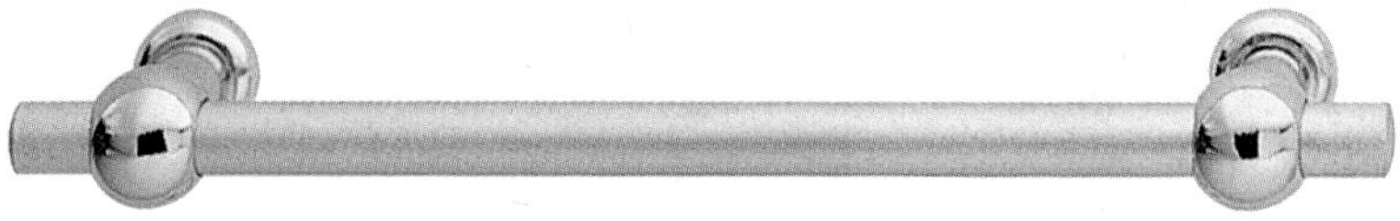

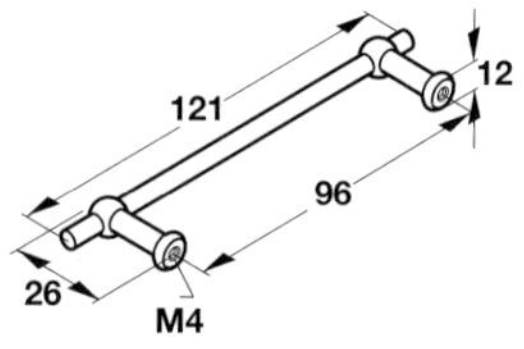

Feet: brass chrome plated polished
Handle: steel chrome plated matt

Cat. No.	103.24.241

Packing: 25 pcs.

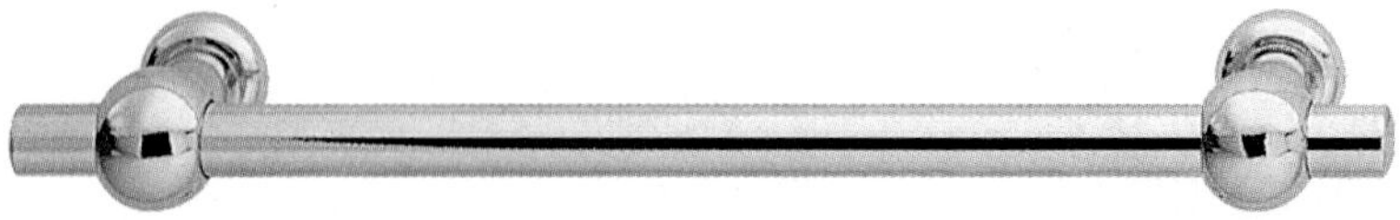

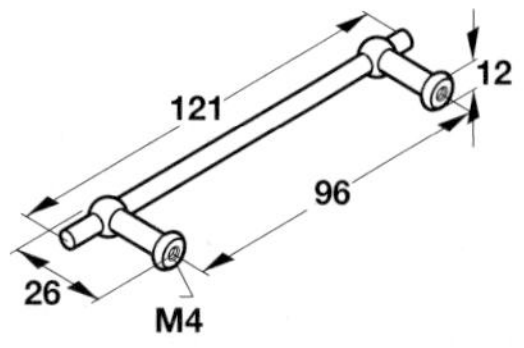

Feet: brass chrome plated polished
Handle: steel chrome polished

Cat. No.	103.24.221

Packing: 25 pcs.

Dimensional data not binding.
We reserve the right to alter specifications without notice.

Brass/Steel Handle

HÄFELE

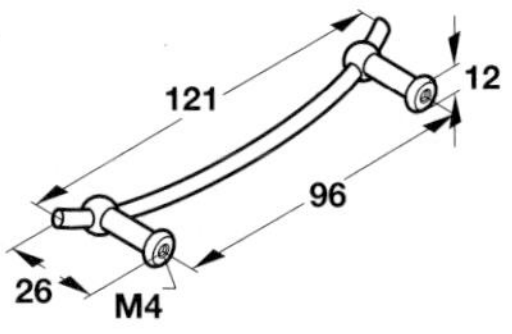

Feet: brass polished and lacquered
Handle: Steel chrome plated polished

Cat. No.	103.23.821

Packing: 25 pcs.

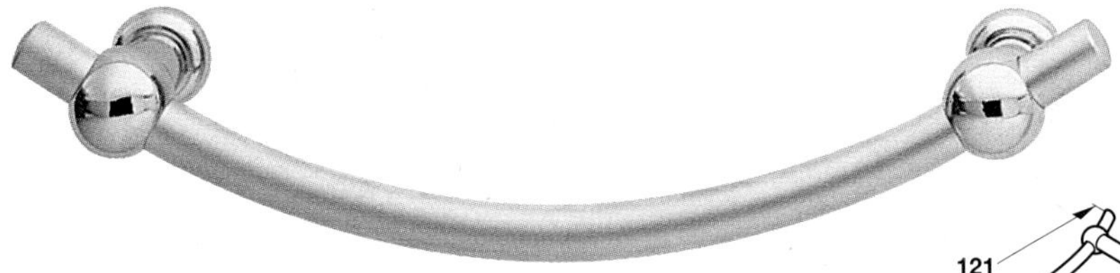

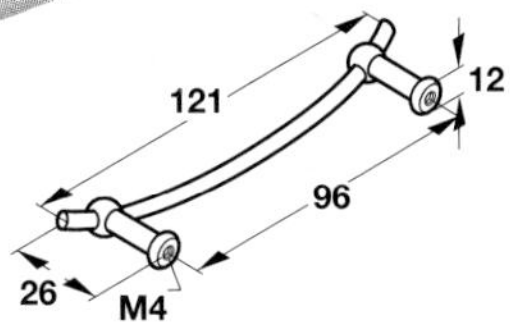

Feet: brass chrome plated polished
Handle: steel chrome plated matt

Cat. No.	103.23.241

Packing: 25 pcs.

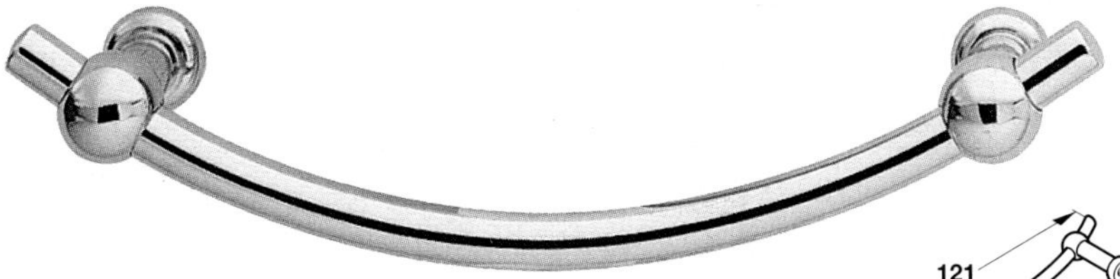

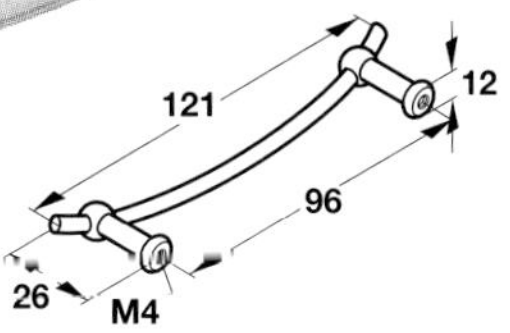

Feet: brass chrome plated polished
Handle: steel chrome plated polished

Cat. No.	103.23.221

Packing: 25 pcs.

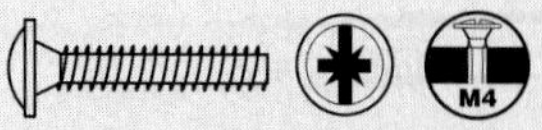

Threaded Screws M4
Combined slot, suitable for flat or cross blades

Finish: steel, zinc-plated

Length	Cat. No.
10 mm	022.35.109
12 mm	022.35.127
15 mm	022.35.154
18 mm	022.35.181
20 mm	022.35.207
22 mm	022.35.225
23 mm	022.35.234
25 mm	022.35.252
28 mm	022.35.289
30 mm	022.35.305
35 mm	022.35.350
38 mm	022.35.387
40 mm	022.35.403
45 mm	022.35.458
50 mm	022.35.501
60 mm	022.35.609

Packing: 100 and 1000 pcs.

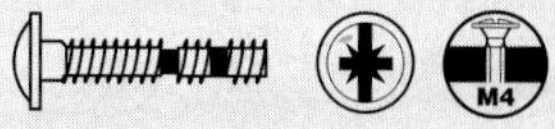

Threaded Breakoff Screw M4
Combined slot, suitable for flat or cross blades

Finish: steel, zinc-plated

Length	Cat. No.
1 3/4" x 3/4"	022.35.887

Packing: 100 and 1000 pcs.

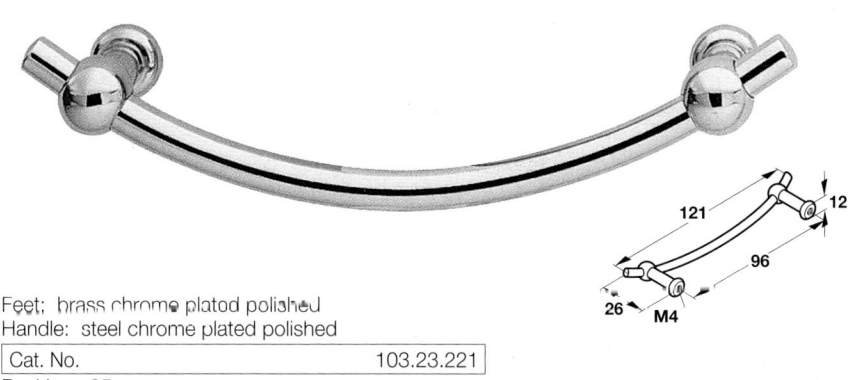

HÄFELE

Stainless steel handles

Threaded Screws M4
Combined slot, suitable for flat or cross blades

Finish: steel, zinc-plated

Length	Cat. No.
10 mm	022.35.109
12 mm	022.35.127
15 mm	022.35.154
18 mm	022.35.181
20 mm	022.35.207
22 mm	022.35.225
23 mm	022.35.234
25 mm	022.35.252
28 mm	022.35.289
30 mm	022.35.305
35 mm	022.35.350
38 mm	022.35.387
40 mm	022.35.403
45 mm	022.35.458
50 mm	022.35.501
60 mm	022.35.609

Packing: 100 and 1000 pcs.

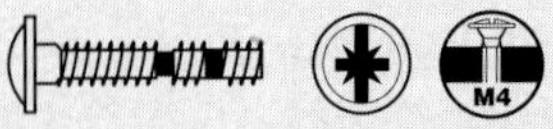

Threaded Breakoff Screw M4
Combined slot, suitable for flat or cross blades

Finish: steel, zinc-plated

Length	Cat. No.
1 3/4" x 3/4"	022.35.887

Packing: 100 and 1000 pcs.

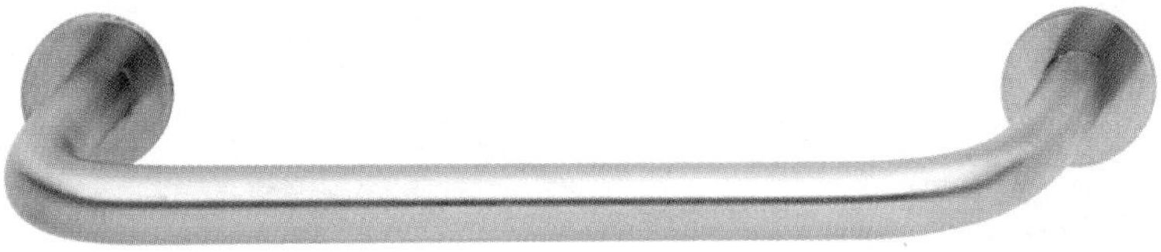

Matt

Size A x B	Dimension C	Catalog No.
90 x 32	82	116.10.209
104 x 32	96	116.10.227
120 x 34	112	116.10.218

Packing: 25 pcs.

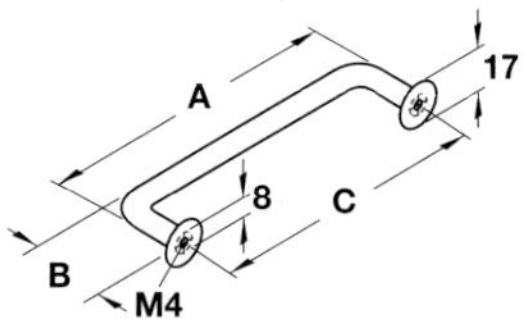

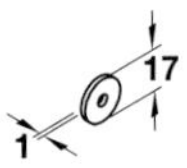

Matt

Catalog No.	116.10.094

Packing: 10 pcs.

Matt, brushed

Size A x B	Dimension C	Catalog No.
70 x 30	64	116.11.626
102 x 30	96	116.11.635
134 x 30	128	116.11.644
198 x 30	192	116.11.662
262 x 30	256	116.11.671
294 x 30	288	116.11.680
358 x 30	352	116.11.715

Packing: 10 pcs.

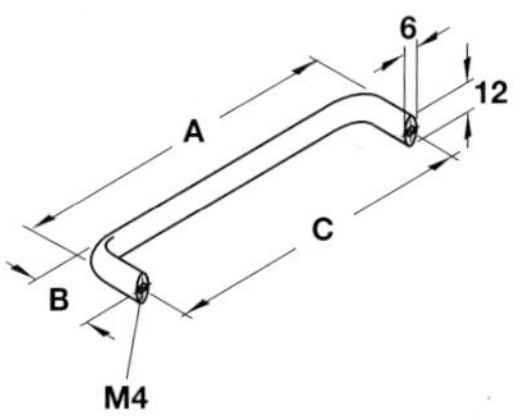

Stainless Steel Handles

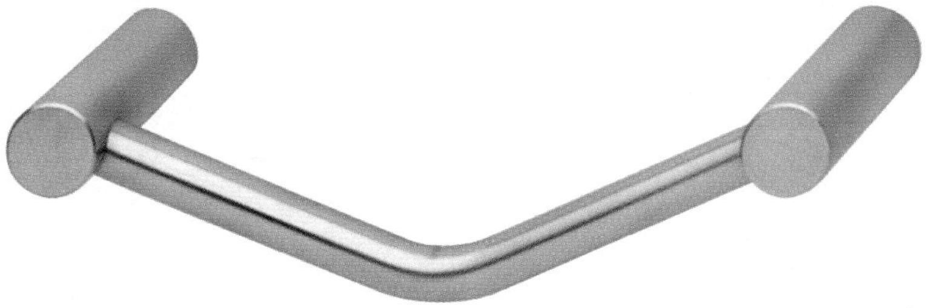

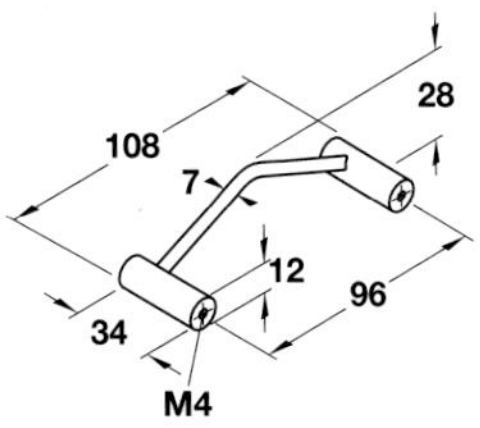

Matt

Cat. No.	115.58.610

Packing: 1 pc.

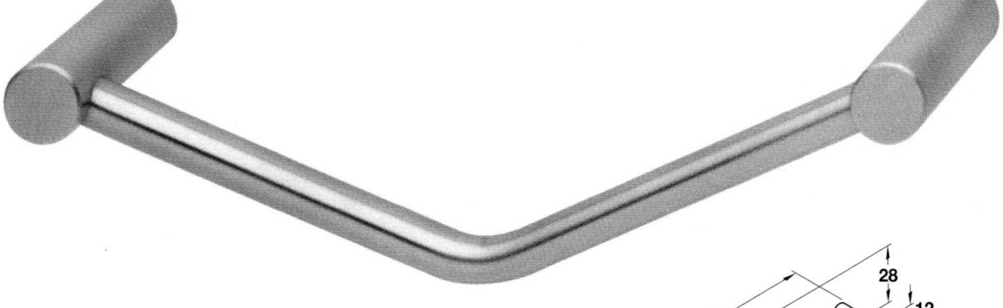

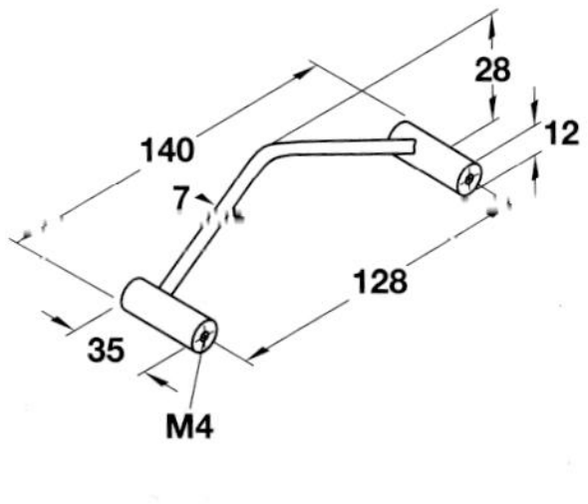

Matt

Cat. No.	115.58.620

Packing: 1 pc.

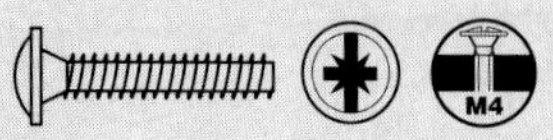

Threaded Screws M4
Combined slot, suitable for flat or cross blades

Finish: steel, zinc-plated

Length	Cat. No.
10 mm	022.35.109
12 mm	022.35.127
15 mm	022.35.154
18 mm	022.35.181
20 mm	022.35.207
22 mm	022.35.225
23 mm	022.35.234
25 mm	022.35.252
28 mm	022.35.289
30 mm	022.35.305
35 mm	022.35.350
38 mm	022.35.387
40 mm	022.35.403
45 mm	022.35.458
50 mm	022.35.501
60 mm	022.35.609

Packing: 100 and 1000 pcs.

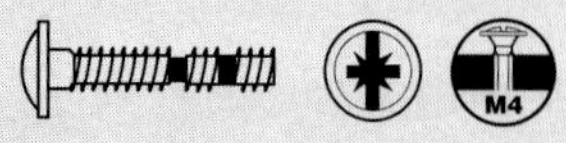

Threaded Breakoff Screw M4
Combined slot, suitable for flat or cross blades

Finish: steel, zinc-plated

Length	Cat. No.
1 3/4" x 3/4"	022.35.887

Packing: 100 and 1000 pcs.

HÄFELE

Stainless steel handles

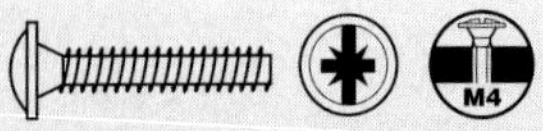

Threaded Screws M4
Combined slot, suitable for flat or cross blades

Finish: steel, zinc-plated

Length	Cat. No.
10 mm	022.35.109
12 mm	022.35.127
15 mm	022.35.154
18 mm	022.35.181
20 mm	022.35.207
22 mm	022.35.225
23 mm	022.35.234
25 mm	022.35.252
28 mm	022.35.289
30 mm	022.35.305
35 mm	022.35.350
38 mm	022.35.387
40 mm	022.35.403
45 mm	022.35.458
50 mm	022.35.501
60 mm	022.35.609

Packing: 100 and 1000 pcs.

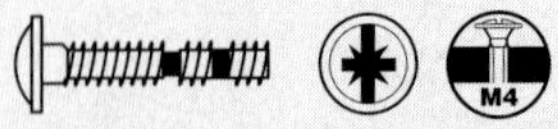

Threaded Breakoff Screw M4
Combined slot, suitable for flat or cross blades

Finish: steel, zinc-plated

Length	Cat. No.
1 3/4" x 3/4"	022.35.887

Packing: 100 and 1000 pcs.

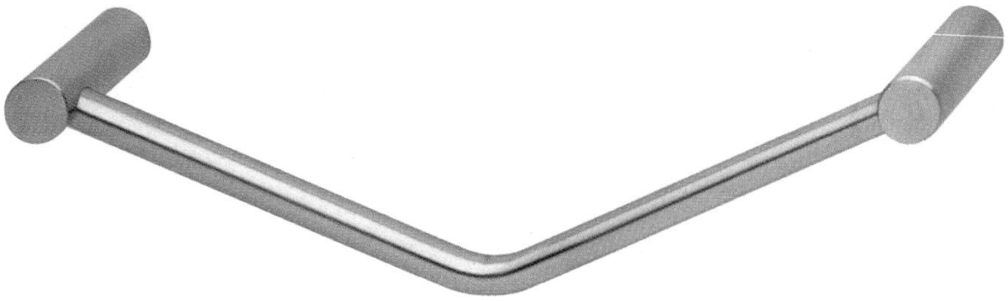

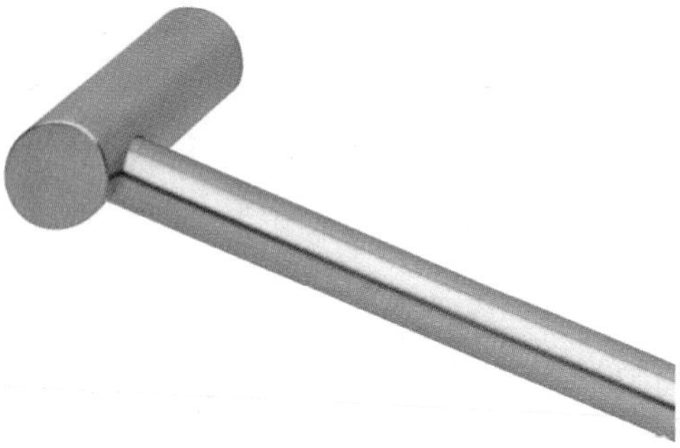

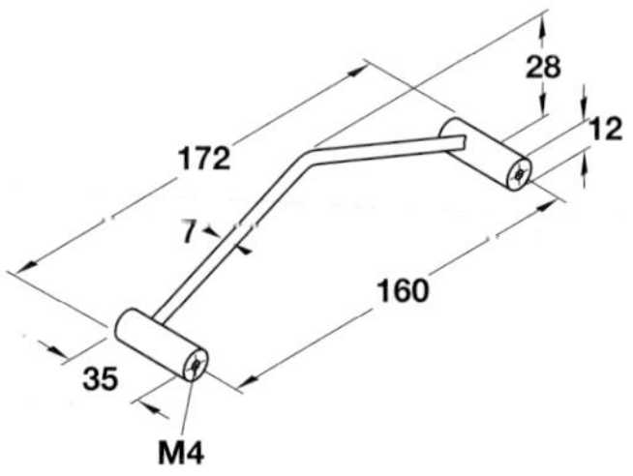

Matt

Cat. No.	115.58.630

Packing: 1 pc.

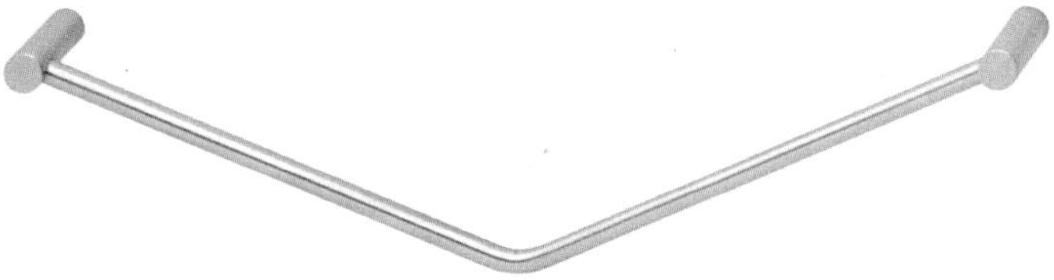

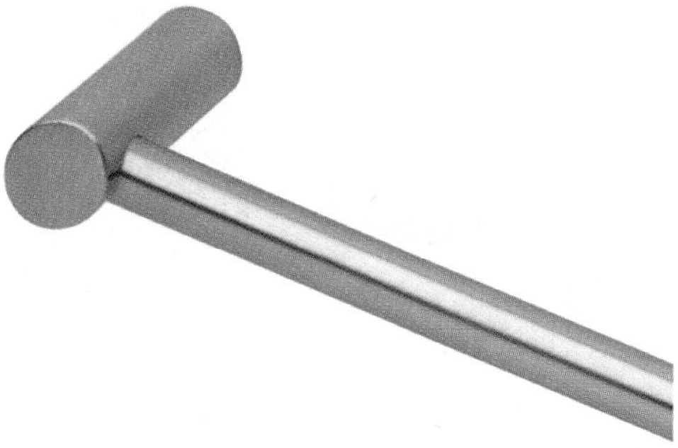

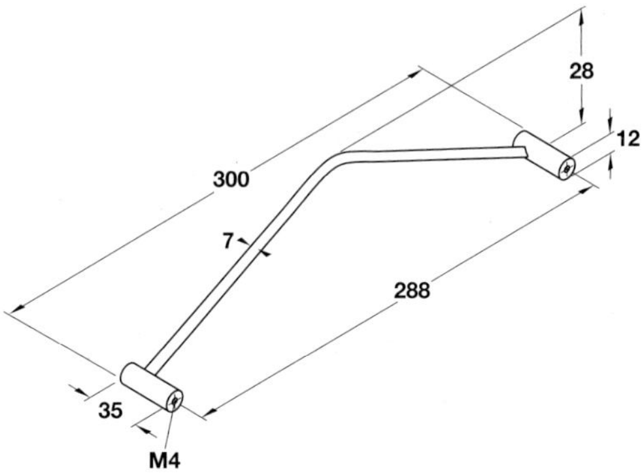

Matt

Cat. No.	115.58.650

Packing: 1 pc.

Dimensional data not binding.
We reserve the right to alter specifications without notice.

Stainless Steel Handles

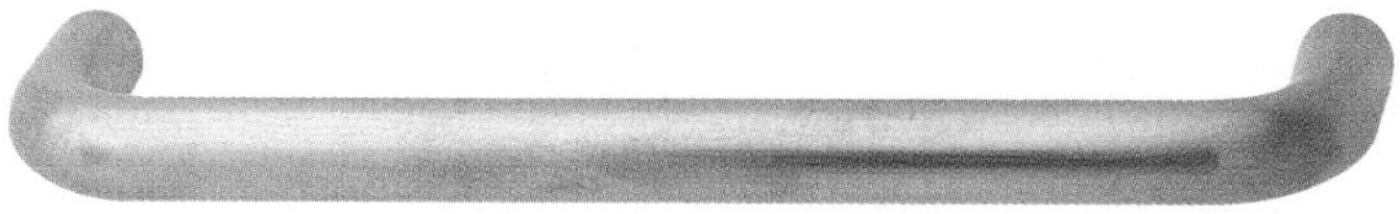

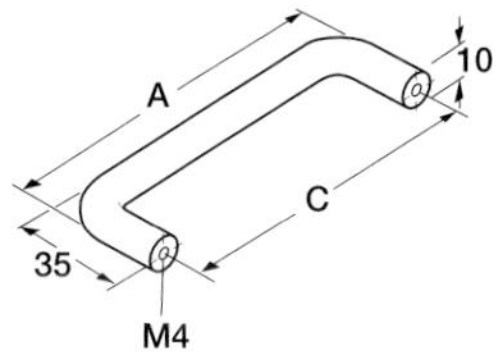

Matt

Size A	Dimension C	Cat. No.
106	96	115.61.601
138	128	115.61.602
170	160	115.61.603
202	192	115.61.604
234	224	115.61.605
266	256	115.61.606
298	288	115.61.607
362	352	115.61.608

Packing: 10 pcs.

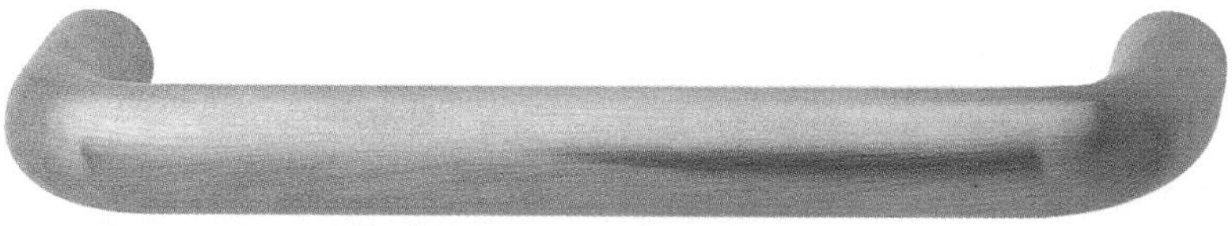

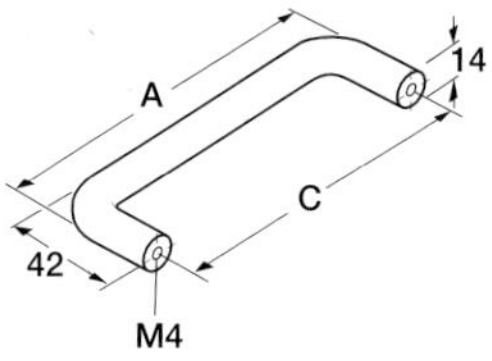

Matt

Size A	Dimension C	Cat. No.
110	96	117.50.610
142	128	117.50.620
174	160	117.50.630
238	224	117.50.640
334	320	117.50.650

Packing: 10 pcs.

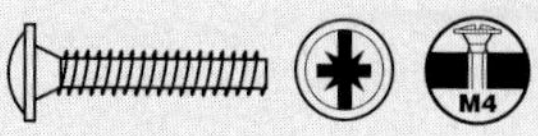

Threaded Screws M4
Combined slot, suitable for flat or cross blades

Finish: steel, zinc-plated

Length	Cat. No.
10 mm	022.35.109
12 mm	022.35.127
15 mm	022.35.154
18 mm	022.35.181
20 mm	022.35.207
22 mm	022.35.225
23 mm	022.35.234
25 mm	022.35.252
28 mm	022.35.289
30 mm	022.35.305
35 mm	022.35.350
38 mm	022.35.387
40 mm	022.35.403
45 mm	022.35.458
50 mm	022.35.501
60 mm	022.35.609

Packing: 100 and 1000 pcs.

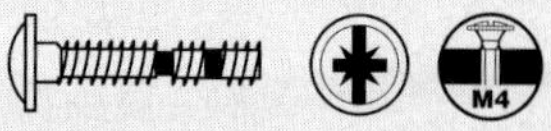

Threaded Breakoff Screw M4
Combined slot, suitable for flat or cross blades

Finish: steel, zinc-plated

Length	Cat. No.
1 3/4" x 3/4"	022.35.887

Packing: 100 and 1000 pcs.

HÄFELE

Stainless Steel Handles

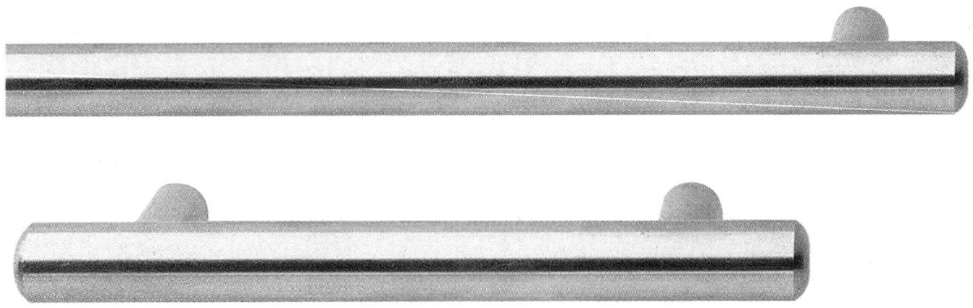

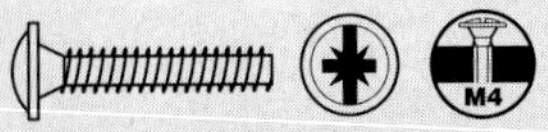

Threaded Screws M4
Combined slot, suitable for flat or cross blades

Finish: steel, zinc-plated

Length	Cat. No.
10 mm	022.35.109
12 mm	022.35.127
15 mm	022.35.154
18 mm	022.35.181
20 mm	022.35.207
22 mm	022.35.225
23 mm	022.35.234
25 mm	022.35.252
28 mm	022.35.289
30 mm	022.35.305
35 mm	022.35.350
38 mm	022.35.387
40 mm	022.35.403
45 mm	022.35.458
50 mm	022.35.501
60 mm	022.35.609

Packing: 100 and 1000 pcs.

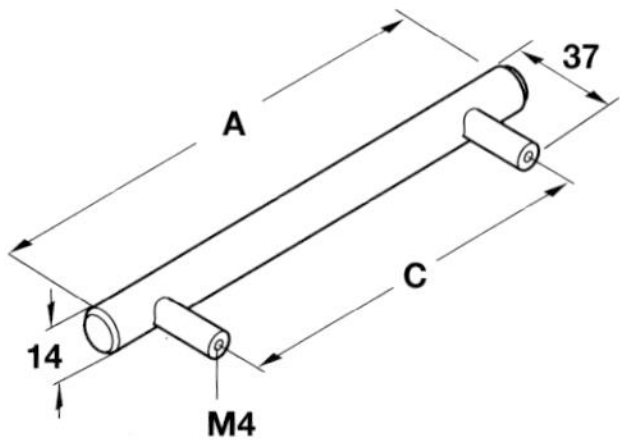

Matt

Size A	Dimension C	Cat. No.
146	96	117.05.600
178	128	117.05.610
242	192	117.05.620
274	224	117.05.630
370	320	117.05.640
530	480	117.05.650
722	672	117.05.660
946	896	117.05.670
1202	1152	117.05.680
1456	1408	117.05.690

Packing: 1 pc. (for attachment to door or drawer fastening screw required = thickness of panel plus 28 mm).

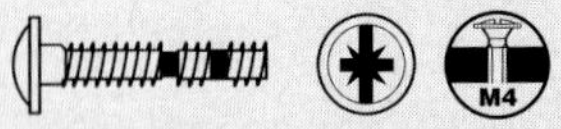

Threaded Breakoff Screw M4
Combined slot, suitable for flat or cross blades

Finish: steel, zinc-plated

Length	Cat. No.
1 3/4" x 3/4"	022.35.887

Packing: 100 and 1000 pcs.

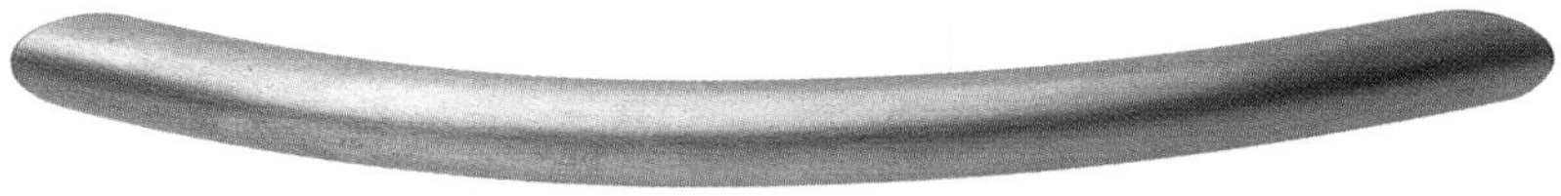

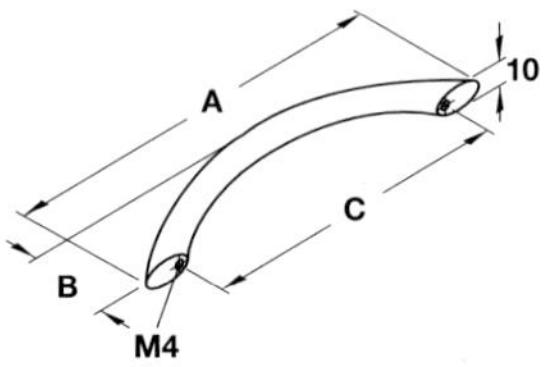

Matt

Size A x B	Dimension C	Cat. No.
116 x 28	96	115.60.601
156 x 30	128	115.60.602
189 x 32	160	115.60.603

Packing: 10 pcs.

Dimensional data not binding. We reserve the right to alter specifications without notice.

Steel handles

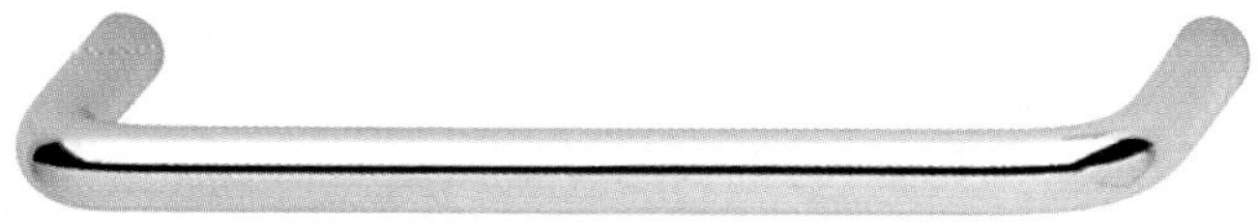

Chrome plated polished

Size A x B	Dimension C	Catalog No.
71 x 28	64	116.07.211
103 x 28	96	116.07.220
119 x 28	112	116.07.239
199 x 28	192	116.07.248

Packing: 25 pcs.

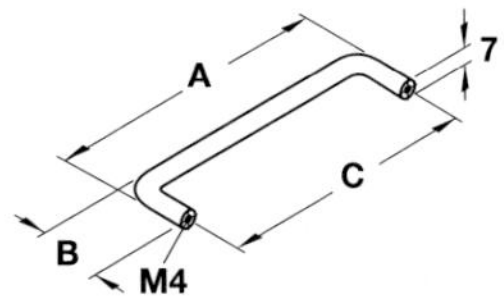

Nickel plated matt

Size A x B	Dimension C	Catalog No.
71 x 28	64	116.07.613
103 x 28	96	116.07.622
119 x 28	112	116.07.631
199 x 28	192	116.07.640

Packing: 25 pcs.

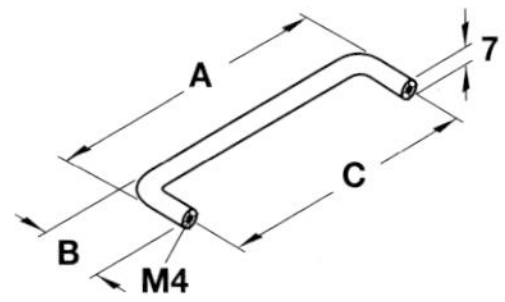

White

Size A x B	Dimension C	Catalog No.
71 x 28	64	116.07.711
103 x 28	96	116.07.720

Packing: 25 pcs.

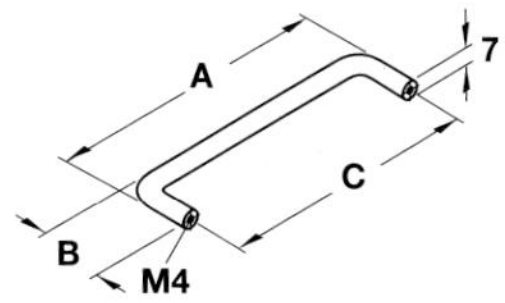

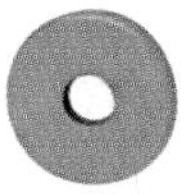

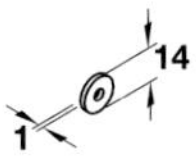

Brass chrome plated polished

Catalog No.	116.06.796

Packing: 50 pcs.

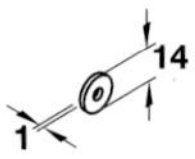

Brass nickel plated matt

Catalog No.	116.06.698

Packing: 50 pcs.

Decorative Hardware **1**

Threaded Screws M4
Combined slot, suitable for flat or cross blades

Finish: steel, zinc-plated

Length	Cat. No.
10 mm	022.35.109
12 mm	022.35.127
15 mm	022.35.154
18 mm	022.35.181
20 mm	022.35.207
22 mm	022.35.225
23 mm	022.35.234
25 mm	022.35.252
28 mm	022.35.289
30 mm	022.35.305
35 mm	022.35.350
38 mm	022.35.387
40 mm	022.35.403
45 mm	022.35.458
50 mm	022.35.501
60 mm	022.35.609

Packing: 100 and 1000 pcs.

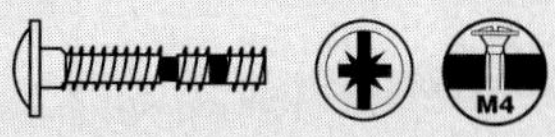

Threaded Breakoff Screw M4
Combined slot, suitable for flat or cross blades

Finish: steel, zinc-plated

Length	Cat. No.
1 3/4" x 3/4"	022.35.887

Packing: 100 and 1000 pcs.

Dimensional data not binding.
We reserve the right to alter specifications without notice.

HÄFELE

Steel handles

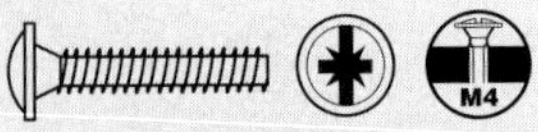

Threaded Screws M4
Combined slot, suitable for flat or cross blades

Finish: steel, zinc-plated

Length	Cat. No.
10 mm	022.35.109
12 mm	022.35.127
15 mm	022.35.154
18 mm	022.35.181
20 mm	022.35.207
22 mm	022.35.225
23 mm	022.35.234
25 mm	022.35.252
28 mm	022.35.289
30 mm	022.35.305
35 mm	022.35.350
38 mm	022.35.387
40 mm	022.35.403
45 mm	022.35.458
50 mm	022.35.501
60 mm	022.35.609

Packing: 100 and 1000 pcs.

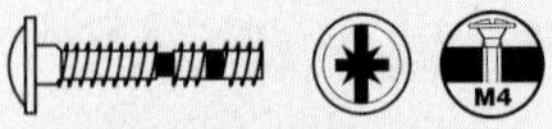

Threaded Breakoff Screw M4
Combined slot, suitable for flat or cross blades

Finish: steel, zinc-plated

Length	Cat. No.
1 3/4" x 3/4"	022.35.887

Packing: 100 and 1000 pcs.

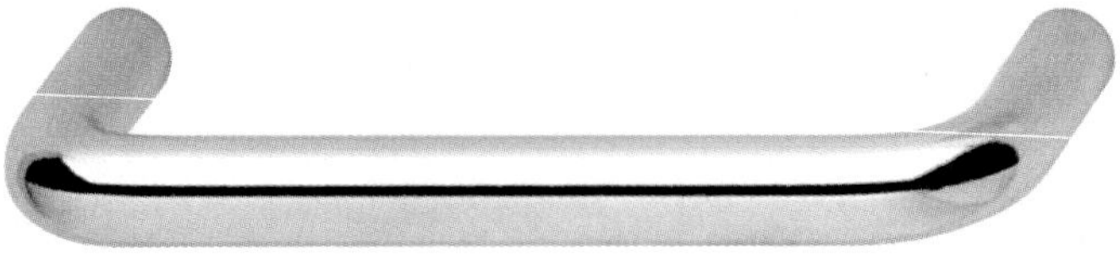

Chrome plated, polished

Size A x B	Dimension C	Cat. No.
74 x 35	64	116.09.206
106 x 35	96	116.09.215
138 x 35	128	116.09.288
170 x 35	160	116.09.242
202 x 35	192	116.09.260
298 x 35	288	116.09.279
362 x 35	352	116.09.297

Packing: 25 pcs.

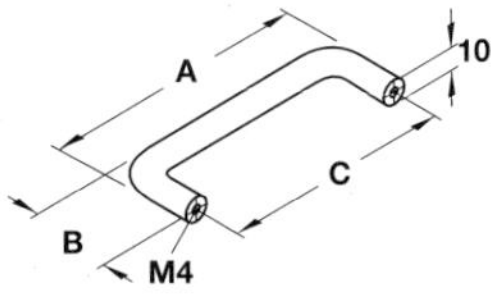

Nickel matt

Gross A x B	Dimension C	Cat. No.
74 x 35	64	116.09.608
106 x 35	96	116.09.617
138 x 35	128	116.09.680
170 x 35	160	116.09.644
202 x 35	192	116.09.662
298 x 35	288	116.09.671
362 x 35	352	116.09.699

Packing: 25 pcs.

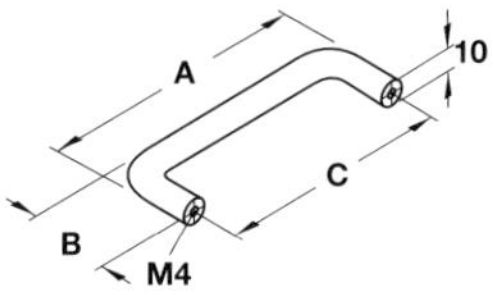

Chrome plated polished

Catalog No.	116.30.256

Packing: 25 pcs.

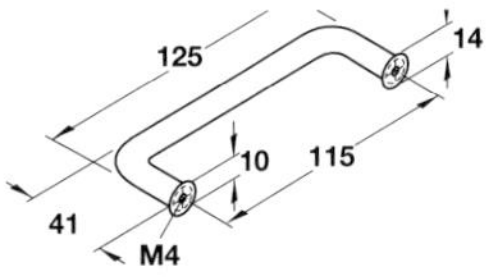

Dimensional data not binding.
We reserve the right to alter specifications without notice.

Steel handles

White

Size A x B	Dimension C	Catalog No.
106 x 35	96	116.09.715
138 x 35	128	116.09.788
298 x 35	288	116.09.770

Packing: 25 pcs.

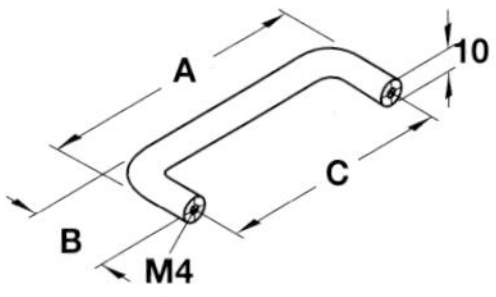

Black matt

Size A x B	Dimension C	Catalog No.
170 x 35	160	116.09.340
202 x 35	192	116.09.368
298 x 35	288	116.09.377
362 x 35	352	116.09.395

Packing: 25 pcs

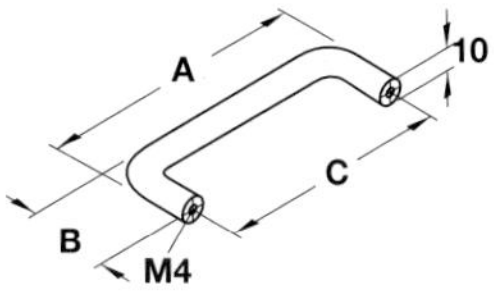

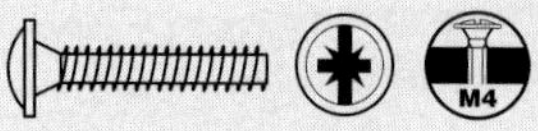

Threaded Screws M4
Combined slot, suitable for flat or cross blades
Finish: steel, zinc-plated

Length	Cat. No.
10 mm	022.35.109
12 mm	022.35.127
15 mm	022.35.154
18 mm	022.35.181
20 mm	022.35.207
22 mm	022.35.225
23 mm	022.35.234
25 mm	022.35.252
28 mm	022.35.289
30 mm	022.35.305
35 mm	022.35.350
38 mm	022.35.387
40 mm	022.35.403
45 mm	022.35.458
50 mm	022.35.501
60 mm	022.35.609

Packing: 100 and 1000 pcs.

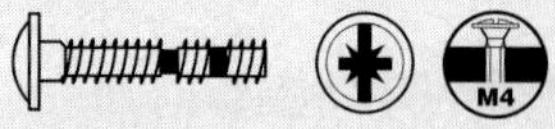

Threaded Breakoff Screw M4
Combined slot, suitable for flat or cross blades
Finish: steel, zinc-plated

Length	Cat. No.
1 3/4" x 3/4"	022.35.887

Packing: 100 and 1000 pcs.

HÄFELE

Steel handles

1 Decorative Hardware

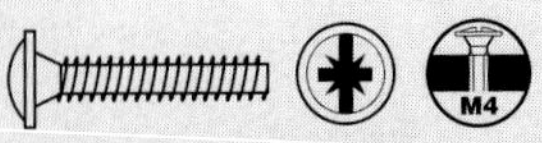

Threaded Screws M4

Combined slot, suitable for flat or cross blades

Finish: steel, zinc-plated

Length	Cat. No.
10 mm	022.35.109
12 mm	022.35.127
15 mm	022.35.154
18 mm	022.35.181
20 mm	022.35.207
22 mm	022.35.225
23 mm	022.35.234
25 mm	022.35.252
28 mm	022.35.289
30 mm	022.35.305
35 mm	022.35.350
38 mm	022.35.387
40 mm	022.35.403
45 mm	022.35.458
50 mm	022.35.501
60 mm	022.35.609

Packing: 100 and 1000 pcs.

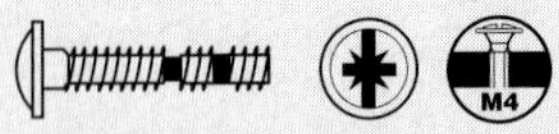

Threaded Breakoff Screw M4

Combined slot, suitable for flat or cross blades

Finish: steel, zinc-plated

Length	Cat. No.
1 3/4" x 3/4"	022.35.887

Packing: 100 and 1000 pcs.

*96 mm and 128 mm are packed 25 per box. All others are 10 pcs. per box.

Black nickel plated

Size A x B	Dimension C	Cat. No.
116 x 28	96	117.31.920
156 x 30	128	117.31.936
189 x 32	160	117.31.940
221 x 36	192	117.31.954
324 x 40	288	117.31.972
393 x 41	352	117.31.980

Packing: 10 and 25 pcs.*

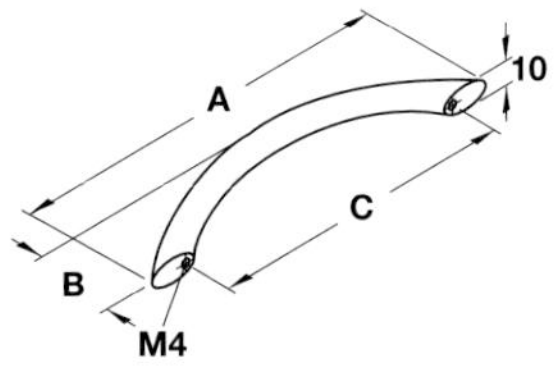

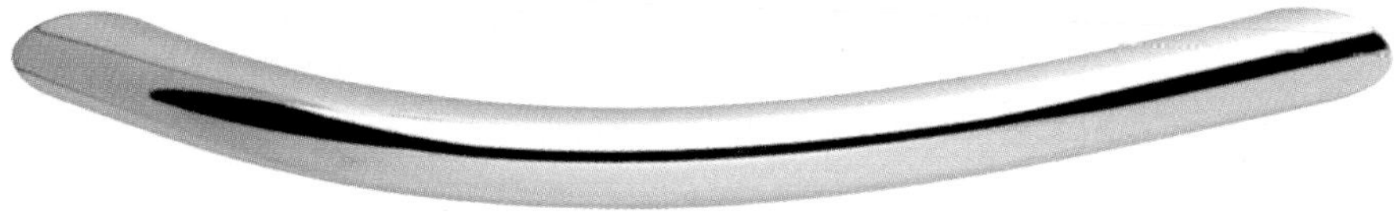

Chrome polished

Size A x B	Dimension C	Cat. No.
116 x 28	96	117.31.221
156 x 30	128	117.31.230
189 x 32	160	117.31.249
221 x 36	192	117.31.258
324 x 40	288	117.31.276
393 x 41	352	117.31.285

Packing: 10 and 25 pcs.*

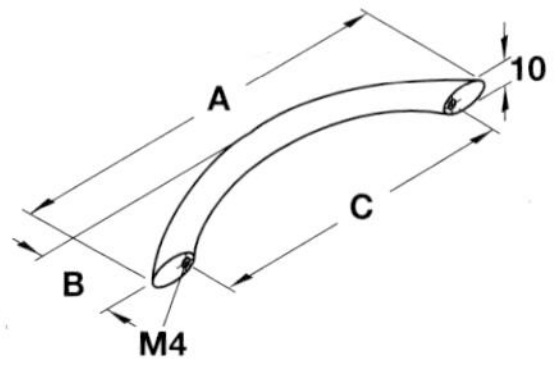

Chrome matt

Size A x B	Dimension C	Cat. No.
156 x 30	128	117.31.436
221 x 36	192	117.31.454
324 x 40	288	117.31.472

Packing: 10 and 25 pcs.*

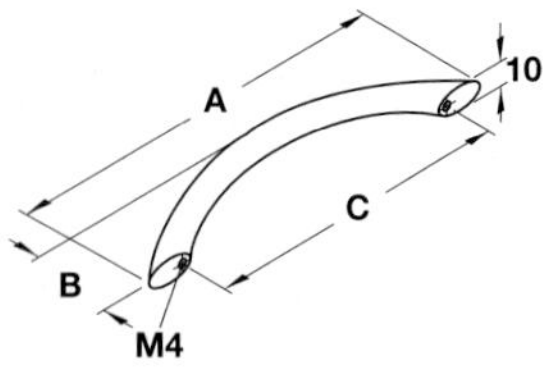

Dimensional data not binding. We reserve the right to alter specifications without notice.

Steel Handles

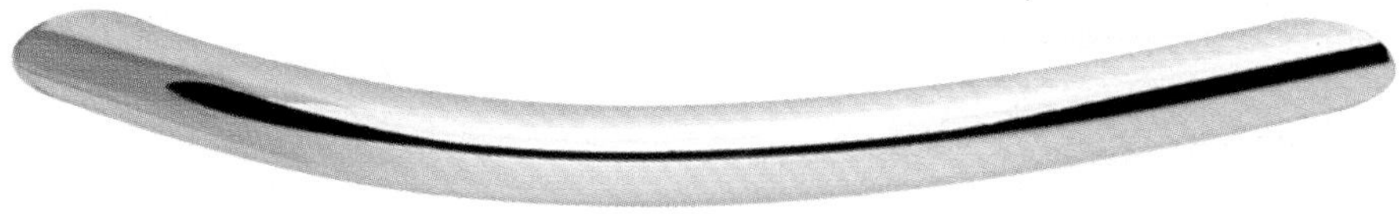

Gold plated polished

Size A x B	Dimension C	Catalog No.
116 x 28	96	117.31.829
156 x 30	128	117.31.838
189 x 32	160	117.31.847
221 x 36	192	117.31.856
324 x 40	288	117.31.874
393 x 41	352	117.31.883

Packing: 10 and 25 pcs.*

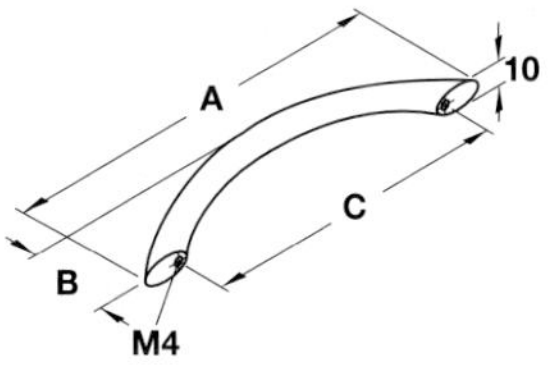

Black matt

Size A x B	Dimension C	Catalog No.
116 x 28	96	117.31.320
156 x 30	128	117.31.330
189 x 32	160	117.31.340
221 x 36	192	117.31.350
324 x 40	288	117.31.370
393 x 41	352	117.31.380

Packing: 10 and 25 pcs.*

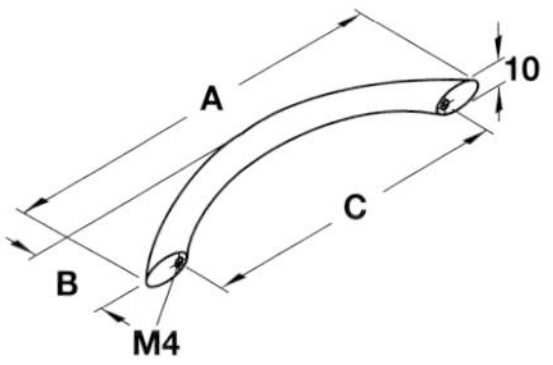

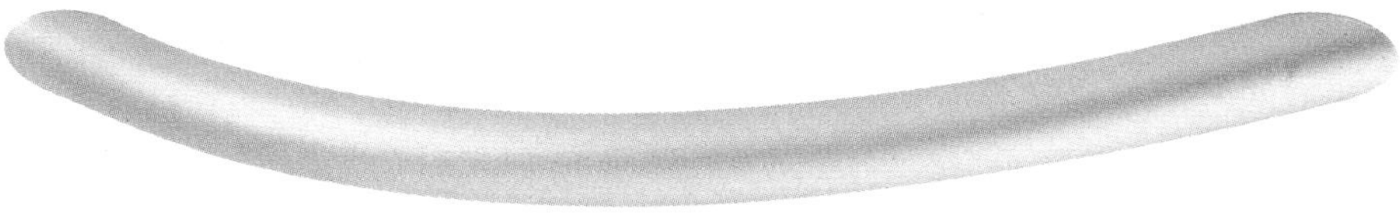

Nickel plated matt

Size A x B	Dimension C	Catalog No.
116 x 28	96	117.31.623
156 x 30	128	117.31.632
189 x 32	160	117.31.640
221 x 36	192	117.31.650
324 x 40	288	117.31.678
393 x 41	352	117.31.680

Packing: 10 and 25 pcs.*

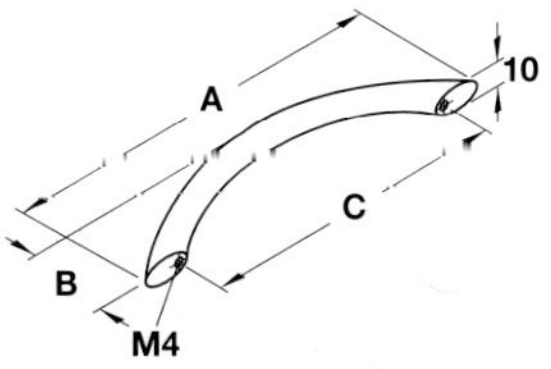

Decorative Hardware 1

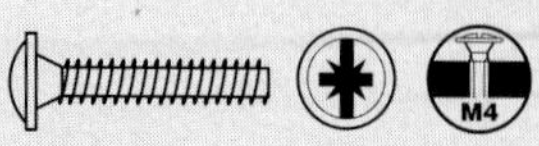

Threaded Screws M4
Combined slot, suitable for flat or cross blades

Finish: steel, zinc-plated

Length	Cat. No.
10 mm	022.35.109
12 mm	022.35.127
15 mm	022.35.154
18 mm	022.35.181
20 mm	022.35.207
22 mm	022.35.225
23 mm	022.35.234
25 mm	022.35.252
28 mm	022.35.289
30 mm	022.35.305
35 mm	022.35.350
38 mm	022.35.387
40 mm	022.35.403
45 mm	022.35.458
50 mm	022.35.501
60 mm	022.35.609

Packing: 100 and 1000 pcs.

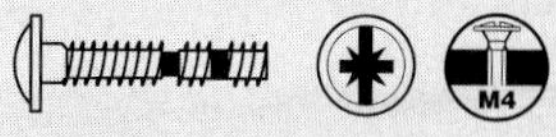

Threaded Breakoff Screw M4
Combined slot, suitable for flat or cross blades

Finish: steel, zinc-plated

Length	Cat. No.
1 3/4" x 3/4"	022.35.887

Packing: 100 and 1000 pcs.

*96 and 128 mm are packed 25 per box. All other are 10 pcs. per box.

Dimensional data not binding. We reserve the right to alter specifications without notice.

HÄFELE

Steel handles

Matt nickel

Cat. No.	166.19.600

Packing: 25 pcs.

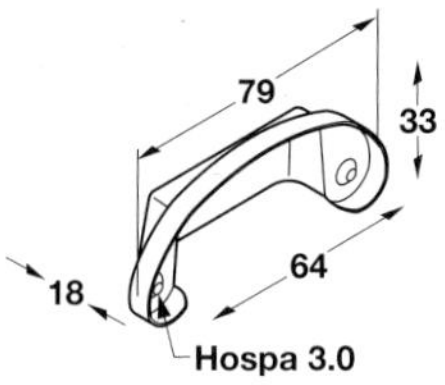

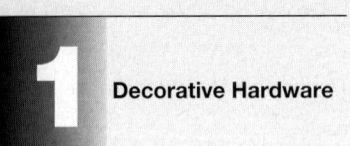

Hospa Raised Head Countersunk Screws
Pozi Recess

Finish: steel, nickel-plated

Length	Cat. No.
15 mm	015.55.531
17 mm	015.55.540
20 mm	015.55.559

Packing: 1000 pcs.

Metal Handles

Aluminum silver colored anodized

Cat. No.	124.22.936

Packing: 25 pcs.

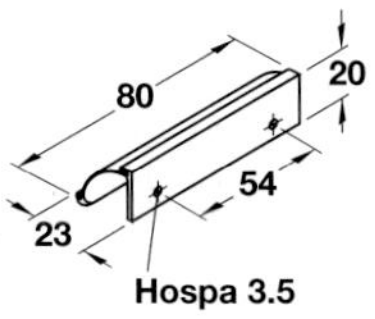

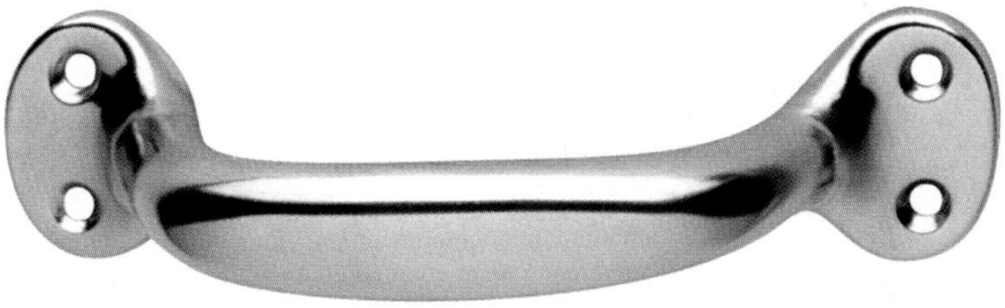

Sheet steel nickel plated polished

Size A x B	Screw Size	Diameter C	Cat. No.
85 x 25	2.5	69	162.00.721
115 x 32	3.0	99	162.00.730

Packing: 25 pcs.

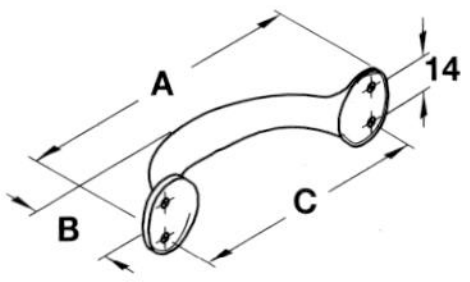

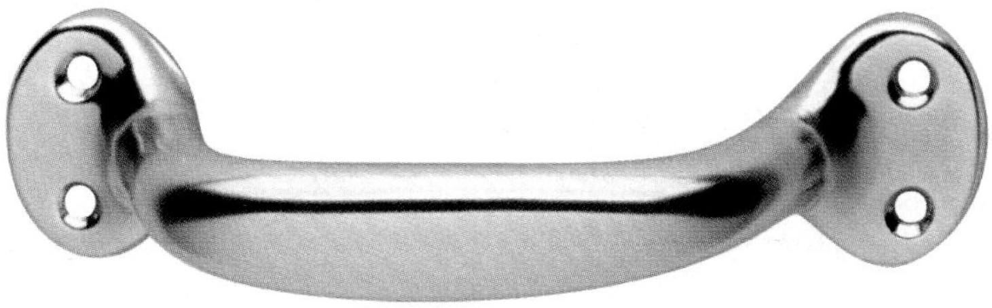

Sheet steel gold plated polished

Size A x B	Screw Size	Diameter C	Cat. No.
85 x 25	2.5	69	162.00.525
115 x 32	3.0	99	162.00.534

Packing: 25 pcs.

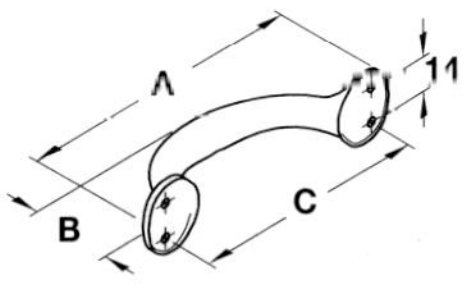

Raised Head Countersunk wood screw

Finish: brass, unfinished

	Length	Cat. No.
⌀2,5	12 mm	011.20.216
	16 mm	011.20.234
	20 mm	011.20.243

Packing: 200 pcs.

Raised Head Countersunk wood screw

Finish: brass, nickel-plated

	Length	Cat. No.
⌀2,5	12 mm	011.24.214
	16 mm	011.24.232
	20 mm	011.24.241

Packing: 200 pcs.

Raised Head Countersunk wood screw

Finish: brass, unfinished

	Length	Cat. No.
⌀3.0	12 mm	011.20.412
	16 mm	011.20.430
	20 mm	011.20.449

Packing: 200 pcs.

Raised Head Countersunk wood screw

Finish: brass, nickel-plated

	Length	Cat. No.
⌀3.0	12 mm	011.24.410
	16 mm	011.24.438
	20 mm	011.24.447

Packing: 200 pcs.

Countersunk wood screws

Finish: brass, nickel-plated

	Length	Cat. No.
⌀3.5	16 mm	011.04.525
	20 mm	011.04.534
	25 mm	011.04.543

Packing: 200 pcs.

HÄFELE

Plastic and metal label frames

Round-head Metal Pins
Ø 1.6 mm

Finish: steel, nickel-plated

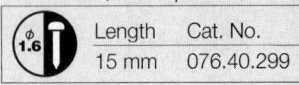

ϕ 1.6 Length	Cat. No.
15 mm	076.40.299

Packing: 2000 pcs.

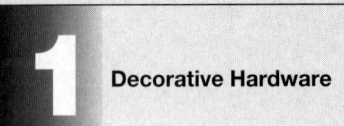

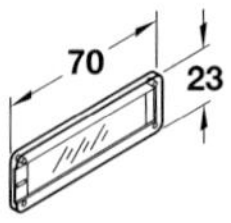

Plastic transparent

Label Size	Window Size	Cat. No.
63 x 14	57 x 13	168.01.460

Packing: 100 pcs.

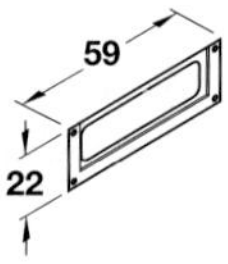

Sheet steel, nickel plated

Label Size	Window Size	Cat. No.
50 x 14	46 x 10	168.00.712

Packing: 25 pcs.

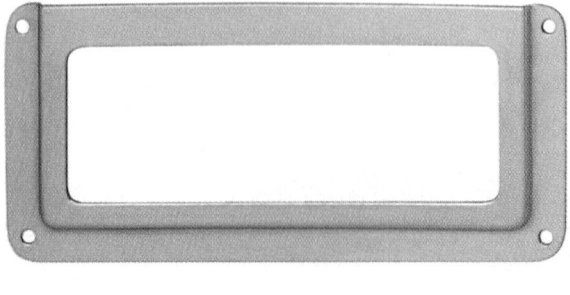

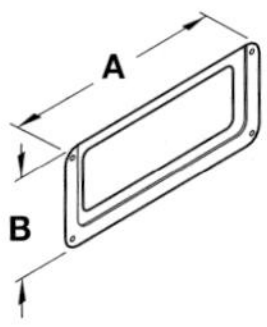

Sheet steel, nickel plated

Size A x B	Label Size	Window Size	Cat. No.
69 x 35	57 x 28	52 x 22	168.02.761
93 x 41	79 x 31	72 x 25	168.02.770
100 x 58	81 x 46	75 x 38	168.02.789

Packing: 25 pcs.

Zinc Handles

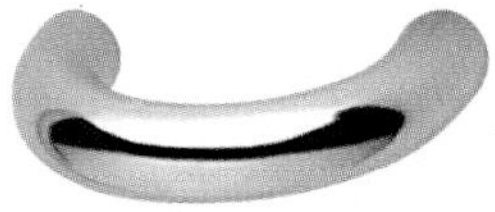
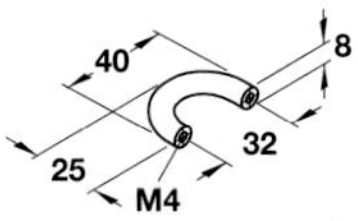

Chrome plated polished

Catalog No.	104.62.209

Packing: 25 pcs.

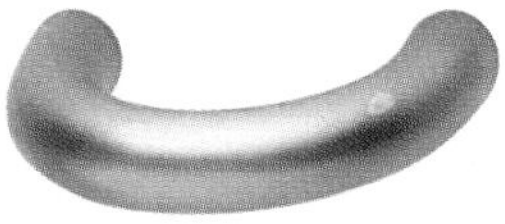
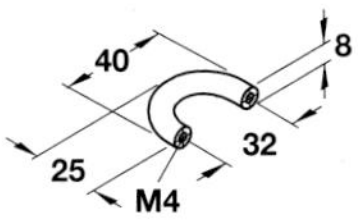

Nickel plated matt

Catalog No.	104.62.601

Packing: 25 pcs.

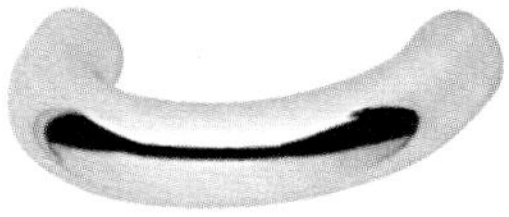
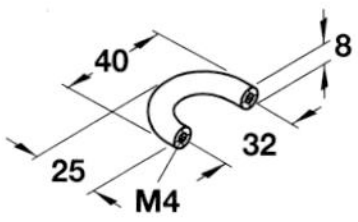

Gold plated polished

Catalog No.	104.62.807

Packing: 25 pcs.

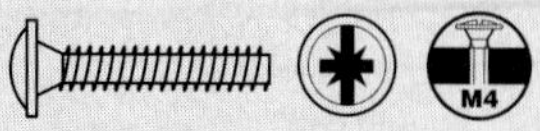

Threaded Screws M4
Combined slot, suitable for flat or cross blades
Finish: steel, zinc-plated

Length	Cat. No.
10 mm	022.35.109
12 mm	022.35.127
15 mm	022.35.154
18 mm	022.35.181
20 mm	022.35.207
22 mm	022.35.225
23 mm	022.35.234
25 mm	022.35.252
28 mm	022.35.289
30 mm	022.35.305
35 mm	022.35.350
38 mm	022.35.387
40 mm	022.35.403
45 mm	022.35.458
50 mm	022.35.501
60 mm	022.35.609

Packing: 100 and 1000 pcs.

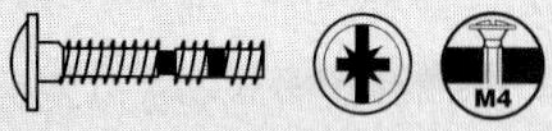

Threaded Breakoff Screw M4
Combined slot, suitable for flat or cross blades
Finish: steel, zinc-plated

Length	Cat. No.
1 3/4" x 3/4"	022.35.887

Packing: 100 and 1000 pcs.

HÄFELE

Zinc Handles

Threaded Screws M4
Combined slot, suitable for flat or cross blades

Finish: steel, zinc-plated

Length	Cat. No.
10 mm	022.35.109
12 mm	022.35.127
15 mm	022.35.154
18 mm	022.35.181
20 mm	022.35.207
22 mm	022.35.225
23 mm	022.35.234
25 mm	022.35.252
28 mm	022.35.289
30 mm	022.35.305
35 mm	022.35.350
38 mm	022.35.387
40 mm	022.35.403
45 mm	022.35.458
50 mm	022.35.501
60 mm	022.35.609

Packing: 100 and 1000 pcs.

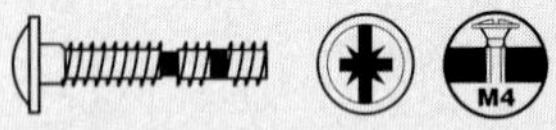

Threaded Breakoff Screw M4
Combined slot, suitable for flat or cross blades

Finish: steel, zinc-plated

Length	Cat. No.
1 3/4" x 3/4"	022.35.887

Packing: 100 and 1000 pcs.

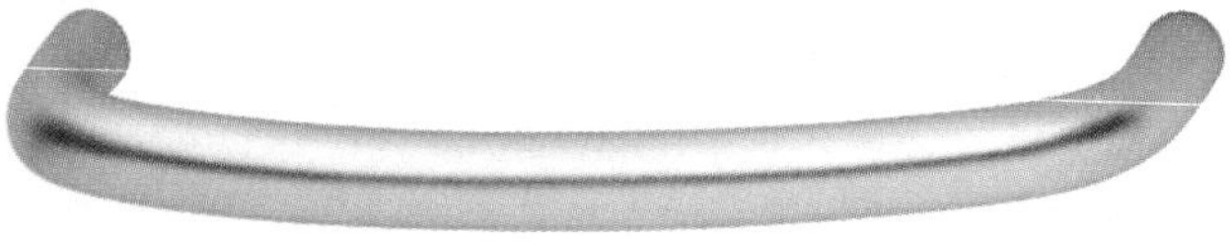

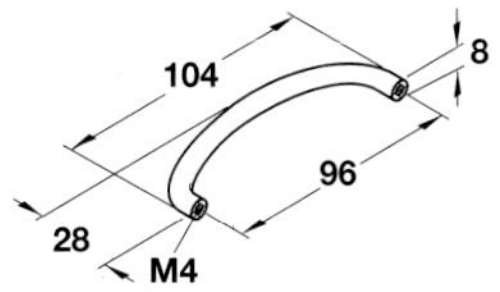

Nickel plated matt

Catalog No.	116.24.623

Packing: 25 pcs.

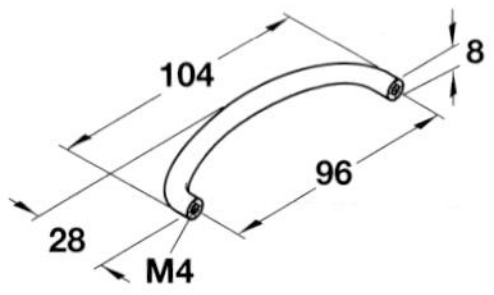

White

Catalog No.	116.24.721

Packing: 25 pcs.

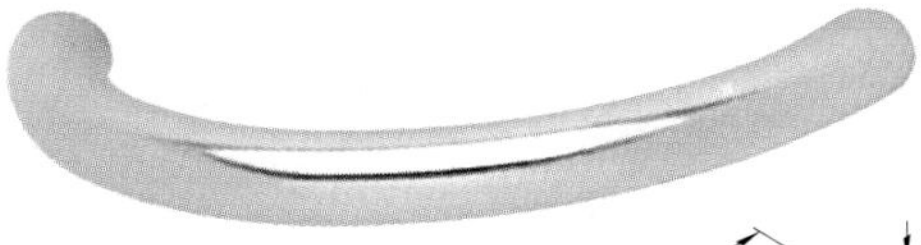

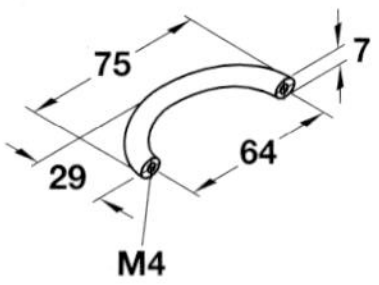

Chrome plated polished

Cat. No.	103.17.200

Packing: 25 pcs.

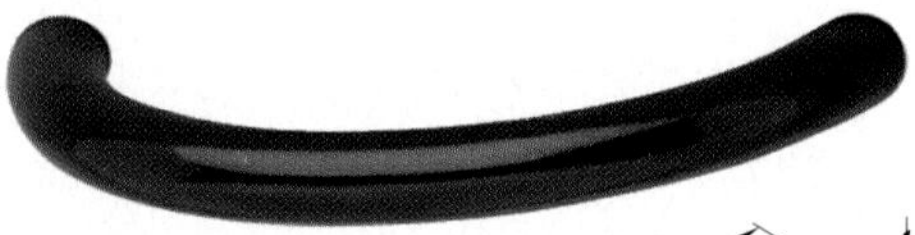

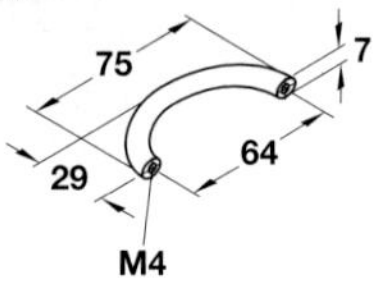

Black gloss

Cat. No.	103.17.300

Packing: 25 pcs.

Zinc Handles

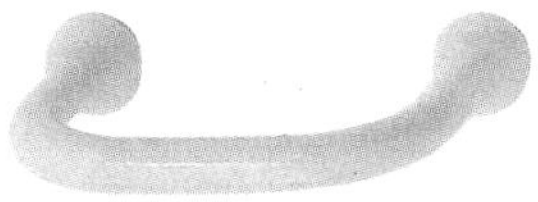
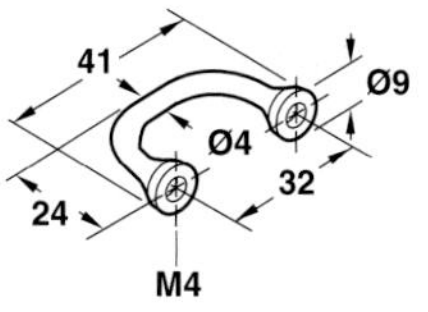

White

Cat. No.	116.32.714

Packing: 25 pcs.

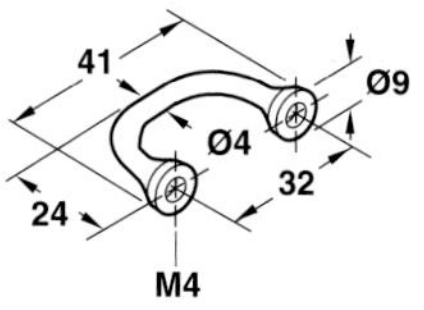

Black

Cat. No.	116.32.312

Packing: 25 pcs.

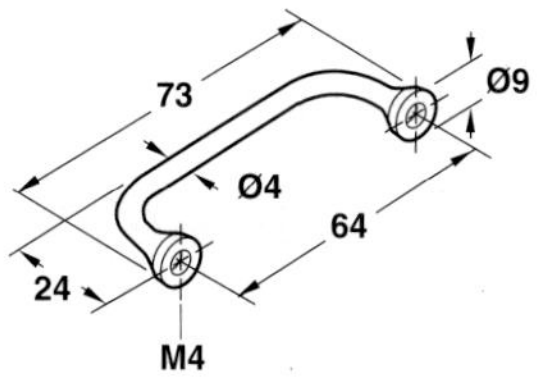

White

Cat. No.	116.32.723

Packing: 25 pcs.

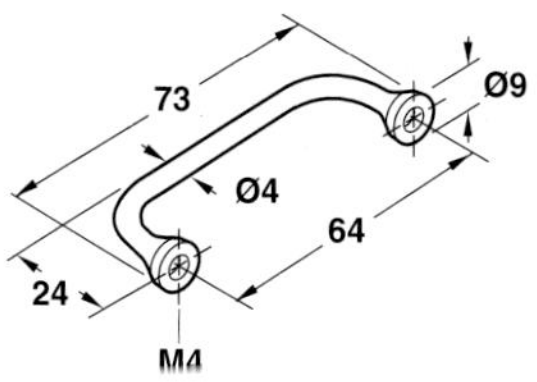

Black

Cat. No.	116.32.321

Packing: 25 pcs.

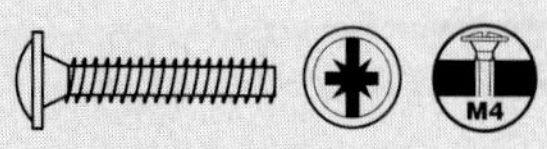

Threaded Screws M4
Combined slot, suitable for flat or cross blades

Finish: steel, zinc-plated

Length	Cat. No.
10 mm	022.35.109
12 mm	022.35.127
15 mm	022.35.154
18 mm	022.35.181
20 mm	022.35.207
22 mm	022.35.225
23 mm	022.35.234
25 mm	022.35.252
28 mm	022.35.289
30 mm	022.35.305
35 mm	022.35.350
38 mm	022.35.387
40 mm	022.35.403
45 mm	022.35.458
50 mm	022.35.501
60 mm	022.35.609

Packing: 100 and 1000 pcs.

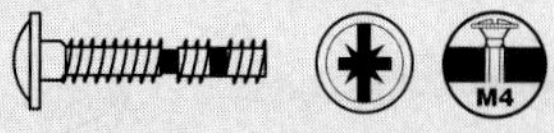

Threaded Breakoff Screw M4
Combined slot, suitable for flat or cross blades

Finish: steel, zinc-plated

Length	Cat. No.
1 3/4" x 3/4"	022.35.887

Packing: 100 and 1000 pcs.

HÄFELE

Zinc Handles

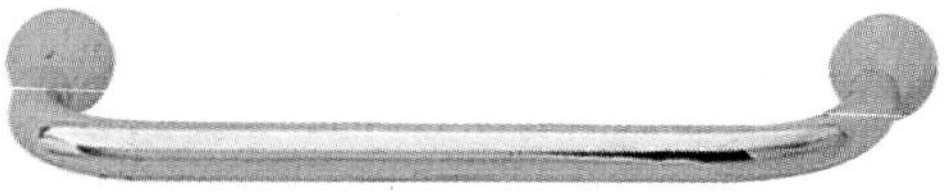

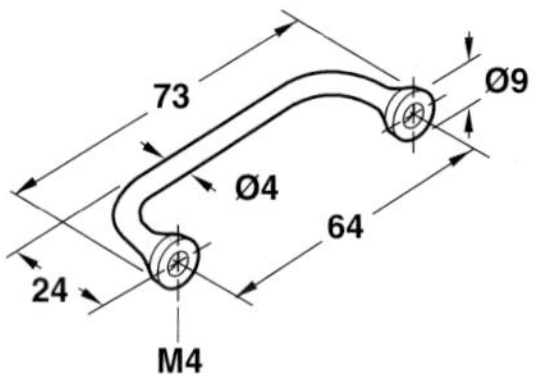

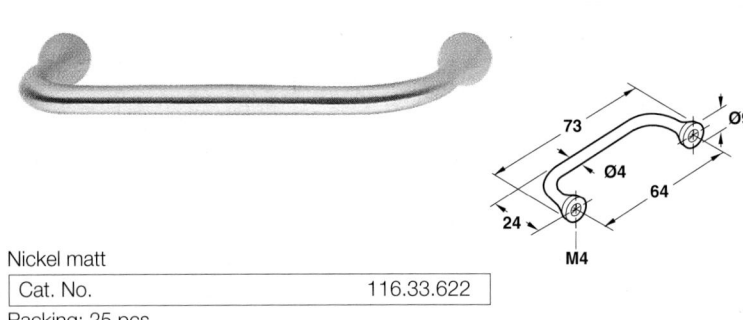

Chrome polished

Cat. No.	116.33.220

Packing: 25 pcs.

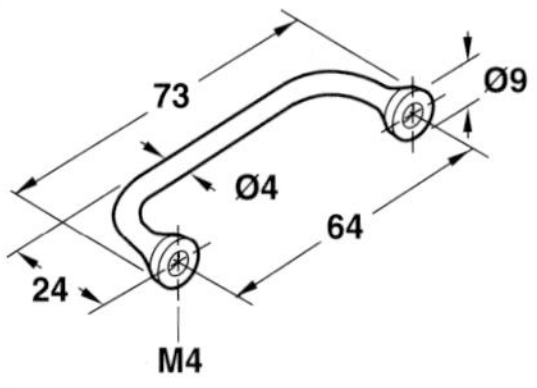

Nickel matt

Cat. No.	116.33.622

Packing: 25 pcs.

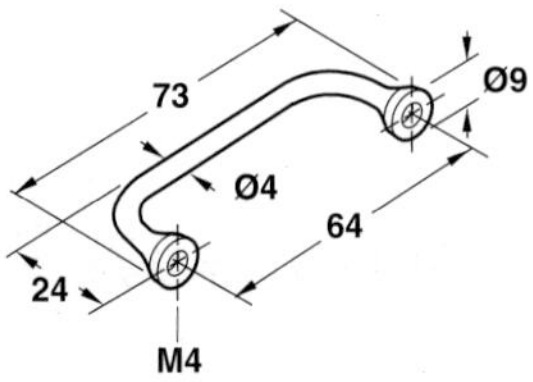

Gold colored polished

Cat. No.	116.33.828

Packing: 25 pcs.

Threaded Screws M4
Combined slot, suitable for flat or cross blades

Finish: steel, zinc-plated

Length	Cat. No.
10 mm	022.35.109
12 mm	022.35.127
15 mm	022.35.154
18 mm	022.35.181
20 mm	022.35.207
22 mm	022.35.225
23 mm	022.35.234
25 mm	022.35.252
28 mm	022.35.289
30 mm	022.35.305
35 mm	022.35.350
38 mm	022.35.387
40 mm	022.35.403
45 mm	022.35.458
50 mm	022.35.501
60 mm	022.35.609

Packing: 100 and 1000 pcs.

Threaded Breakoff Screw M4
Combined slot, suitable for flat or cross blades

Finish: steel, zinc-plated

Length	Cat. No.
1 3/4" x 3/4"	022.35.887

Packing: 100 and 1000 pcs.

Zinc Handles

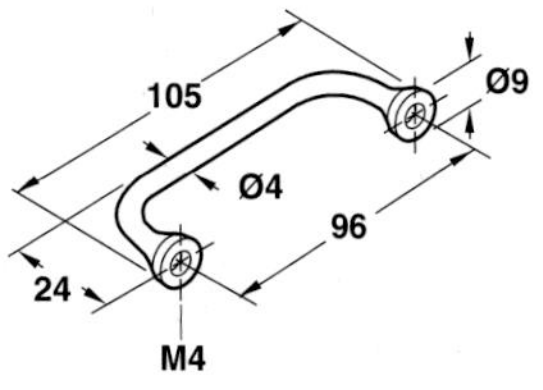

Nickel matt

Cat. No.	116.33.631

Packing: 25 pcs.

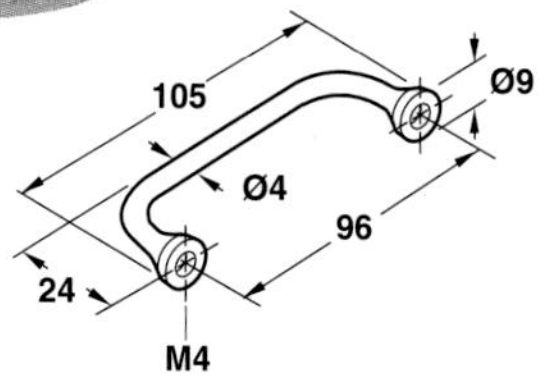

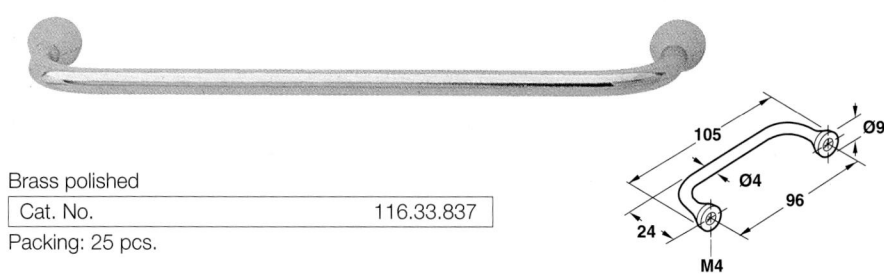

Brass polished

Cat. No.	116.33.837

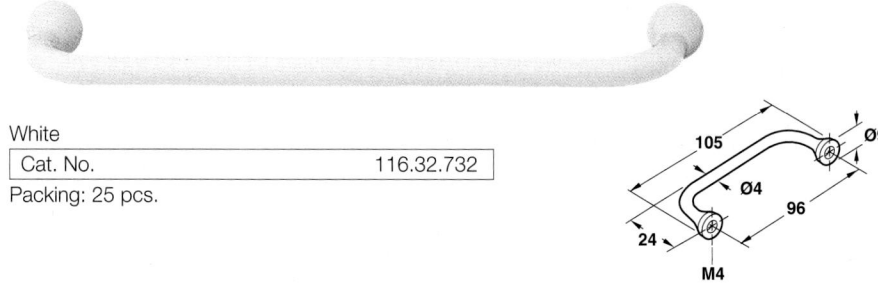

Packing: 25 pcs.

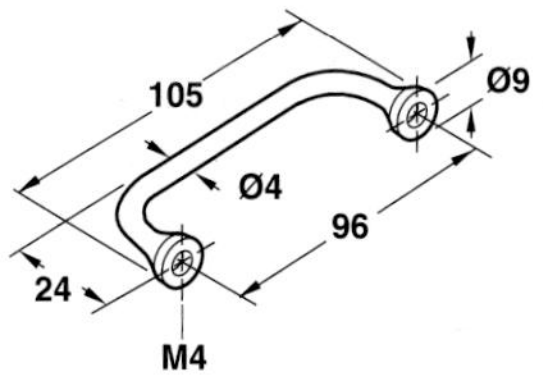

White

Cat. No.	116.32.732

Packing: 25 pcs.

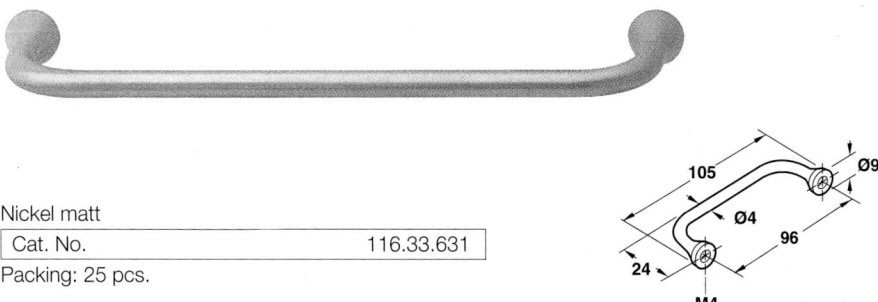

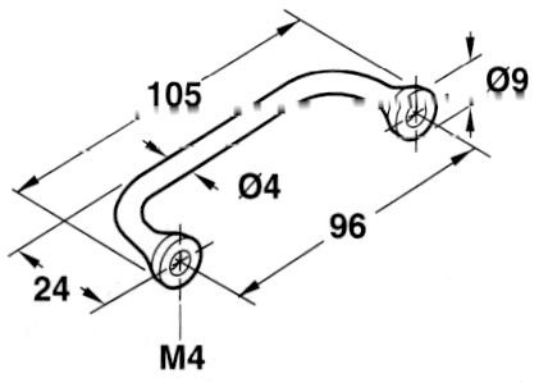

Black

Cat. No.	116.32.330

Packing: 25 pcs.

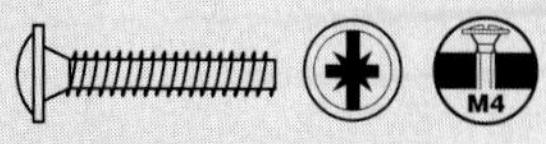

Threaded Screws M4
Combined slot, suitable for flat or cross blades

Finish: steel, zinc-plated

Length	Cat. No.
10 mm	022.35.109
12 mm	022.35.127
15 mm	022.35.154
18 mm	022.35.181
20 mm	022.35.207
22 mm	022.35.225
23 mm	022.35.234
25 mm	022.35.252
28 mm	022.35.289
30 mm	022.35.305
35 mm	022.35.350
38 mm	022.35.387
40 mm	022.35.403
45 mm	022.35.458
50 mm	022.35.501
60 mm	022.35.609

Packing: 100 and 1000 pcs.

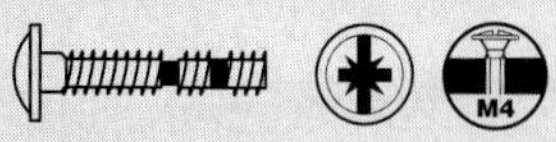

Threaded Breakoff Screw M4
Combined slot, suitable for flat or cross blades

Finish: steel, zinc-plated

Length	Cat. No.
1 3/4" x 3/4"	022.35.887

Packing: 100 and 1000 pcs.

HÄFELE

Zinc Handles

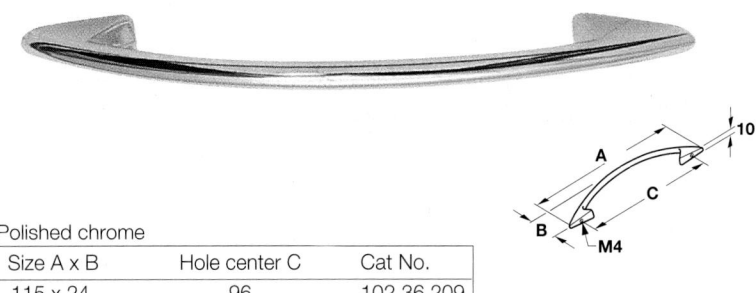

Threaded Screws M4
Combined slot, suitable for flat or cross blades

Finish: steel, zinc-plated

Length	Cat. No.
10 mm	022.35.109
12 mm	022.35.127
15 mm	022.35.154
18 mm	022.35.181
20 mm	022.35.207
22 mm	022.35.225
23 mm	022.35.234
25 mm	022.35.252
28 mm	022.35.289
30 mm	022.35.305
35 mm	022.35.350
38 mm	022.35.387
40 mm	022.35.403
45 mm	022.35.458
50 mm	022.35.501
60 mm	022.35.609

Packing: 100 and 1000 pcs.

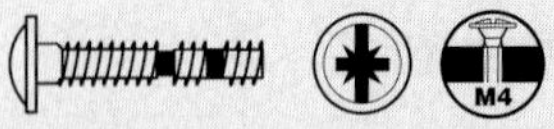

Threaded Breakoff Screw M4
Combined slot, suitable for flat or cross blades

Finish: steel, zinc-plated

Length	Cat. No.
1 3/4" x 3/4"	022.35.887

Packing: 100 and 1000 pcs.

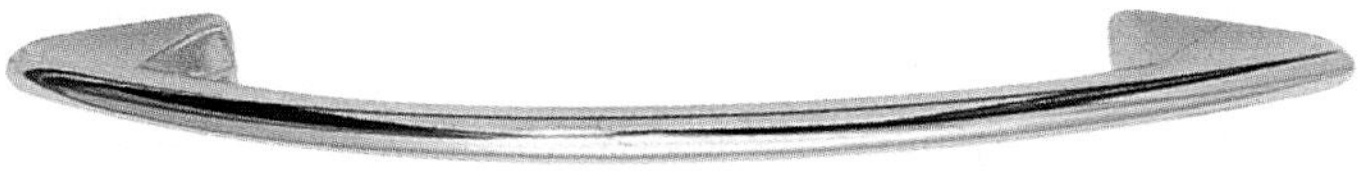

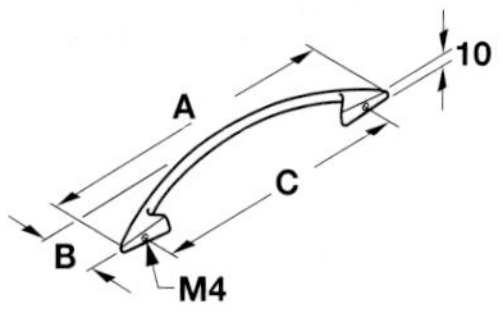

Polished chrome

Size A x B	Hole center C	Cat No.
115 x 24	96	102.36.209
155 x 24	128	102.36.210

Packing: 25 pcs.

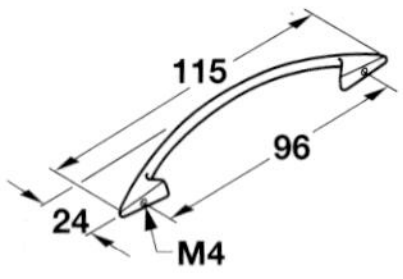

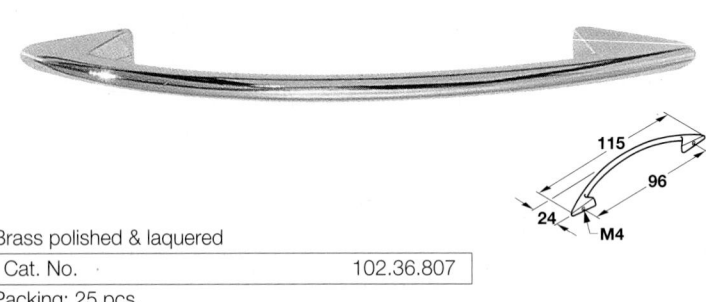

Brass polished & laquered

Cat. No.	102.36.807

Packing: 25 pcs.

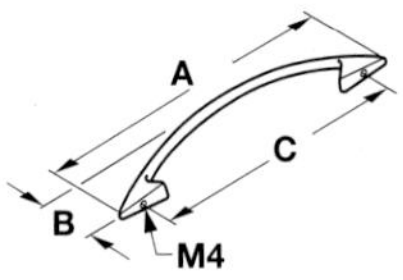

Black matt

Size A x B	Hole center C	Cat No.
115 x 24	96	102.36.307
155 x 24	128	102.36.310

Packing: 25 pcs.

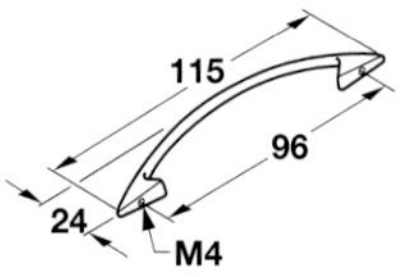

Nickel matt

Cat. No.	102.36.600

Packing: 25 pcs.

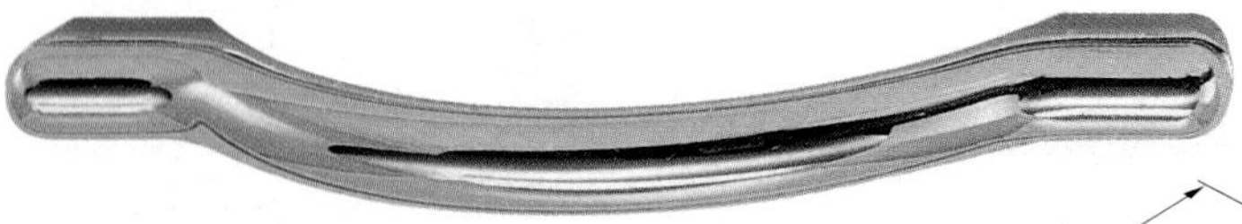

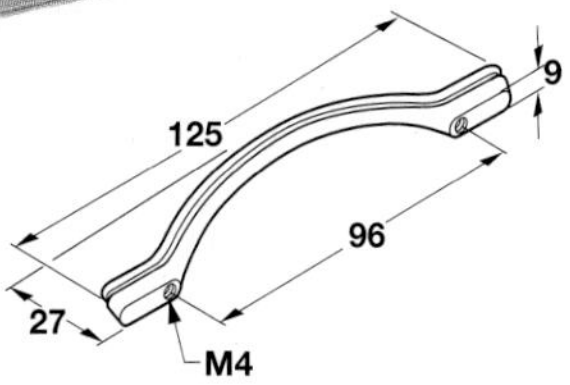

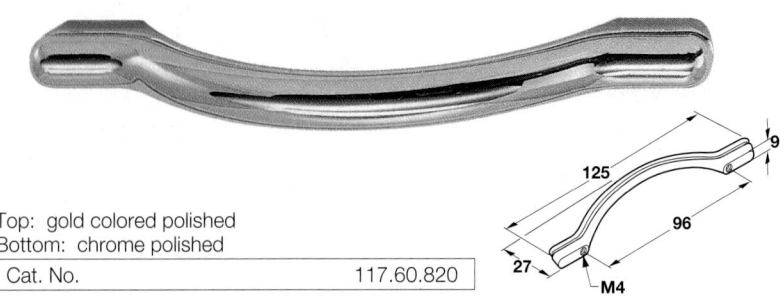

Top: gold colored polished
Bottom: chrome polished

Cat. No.	117.60.820

Packing: 25 pcs.

Dimensional data not binding.
We reserve the right to alter specifications without notice.

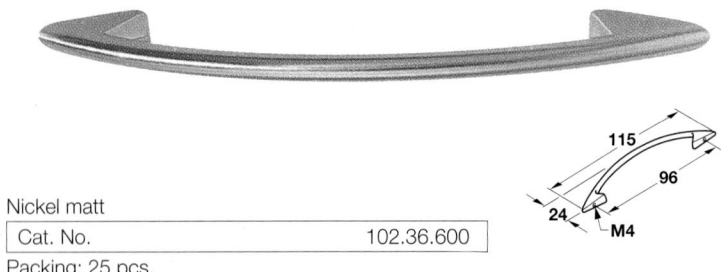

Zinc Handles

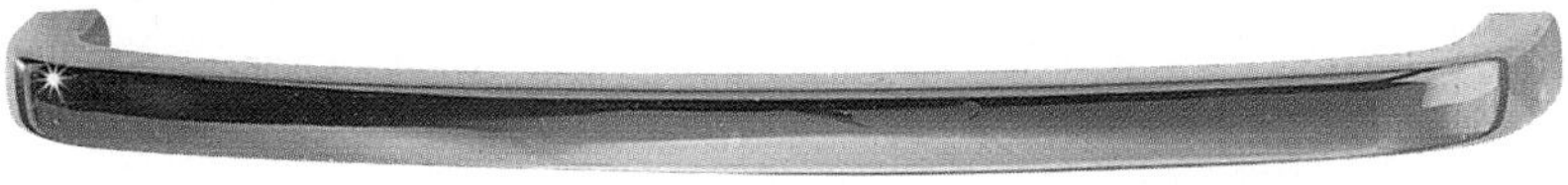

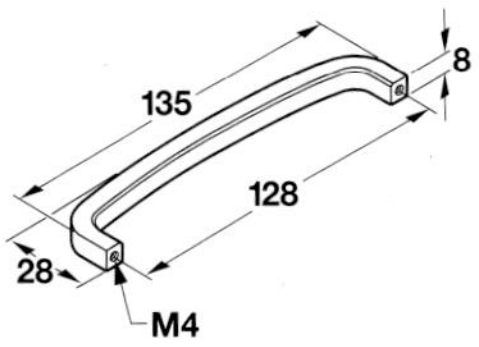

Black nickel-plated

Cat. No.	117.14.300

Packing: 25 pcs.

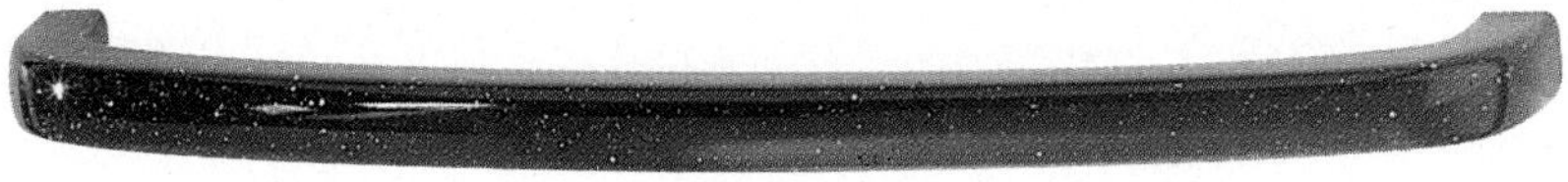

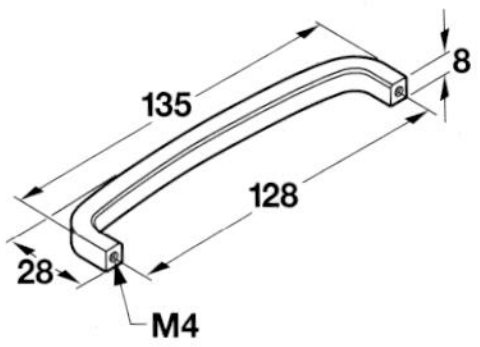

Black marble epoxy

Cat. No.	117.14.319

Packing: 25 pcs.

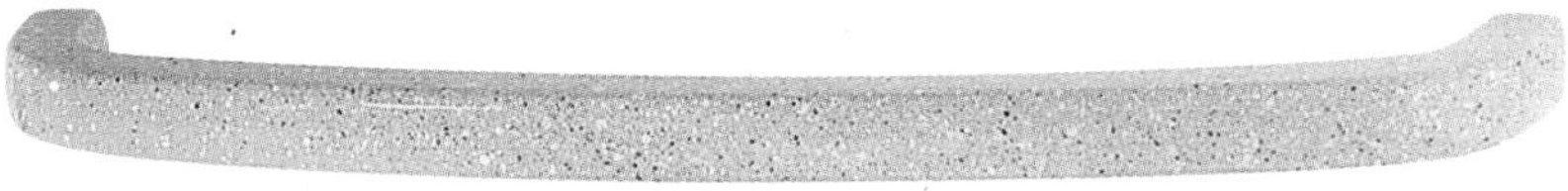

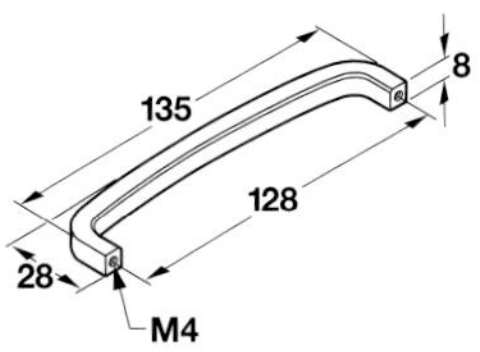

Grey marble epoxy

Cat. No.	117.14.506

Packing: 25 pcs.

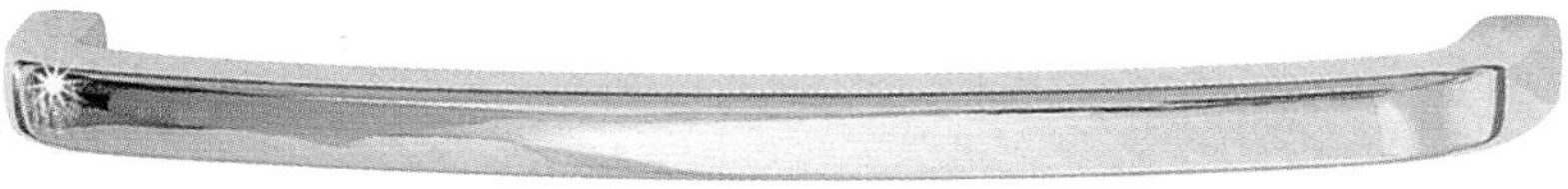

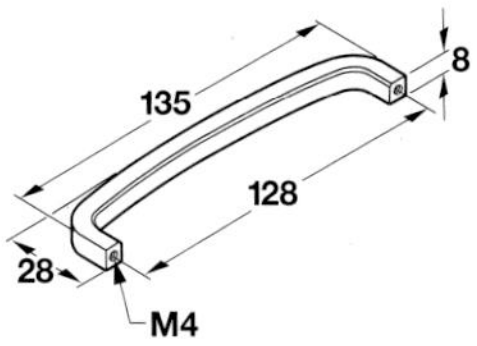

Gold polished & laquered

Cat. No.	117.14.800

Packing: 25 pcs.

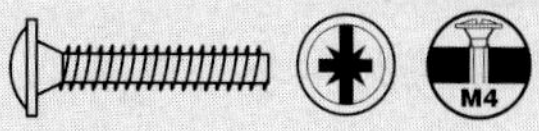

Threaded Screws M4
Combined slot, suitable for flat or cross blades
Finish: steel, zinc-plated

Length	Cat. No.
10 mm	022.35.109
12 mm	022.35.127
15 mm	022.35.154
18 mm	022.35.181
20 mm	022.35.207
22 mm	022.35.225
23 mm	022.35.234
25 mm	022.35.252
28 mm	022.35.289
30 mm	022.35.305
35 mm	022.35.350
38 mm	022.35.387
40 mm	022.35.403
45 mm	022.35.458
50 mm	022.35.501
60 mm	022.35.609

Packing: 100 and 1000 pcs.

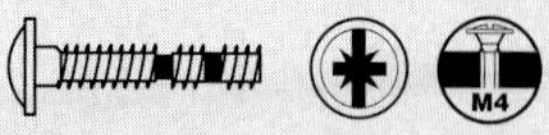

Threaded Breakoff Screw M4
Combined slot, suitable for flat or cross blades
Finish: steel, zinc-plated

Length	Cat. No.
1 3/4" x 3/4"	022.35.887

Packing: 100 and 1000 pcs.

Dimensional data not binding.
We reserve the right to alter specifications without notice.

HÄFELE

Zinc Handles

1 Decorative Hardware

Threaded Screws M4
Combined slot, suitable for flat or cross blades
Finish: steel, zinc-plated

Length	Cat. No.
10 mm	022.35.109
12 mm	022.35.127
15 mm	022.35.154
18 mm	022.35.181
20 mm	022.35.207
22 mm	022.35.225
23 mm	022.35.234
25 mm	022.35.252
28 mm	022.35.289
30 mm	022.35.305
35 mm	022.35.350
38 mm	022.35.387
40 mm	022.35.403
45 mm	022.35.458
50 mm	022.35.501
60 mm	022.35.609

Packing: 100 and 1000 pcs.

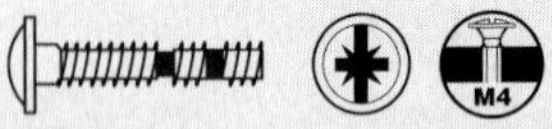

Threaded Breakoff Screw M4
Combined slot, suitable for flat or cross blades
Finish: steel, zinc-plated

Length	Cat. No.
1 3/4" x 3/4"	022.35.887

Packing: 100 and 1000 pcs.

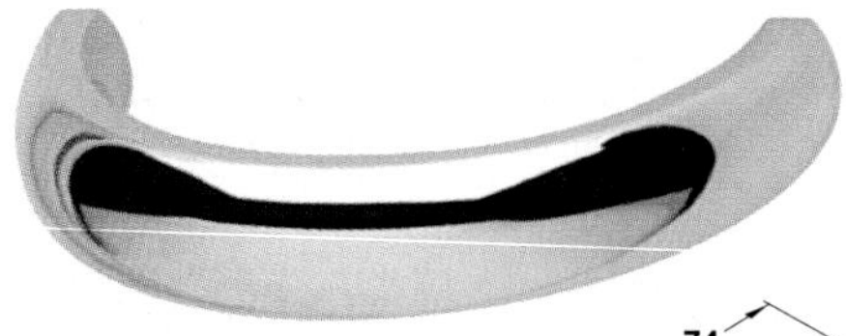

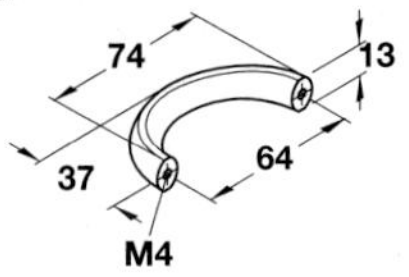

Chrome plated polished

Cat. No.	116.21.220

Packing: 25 pcs.

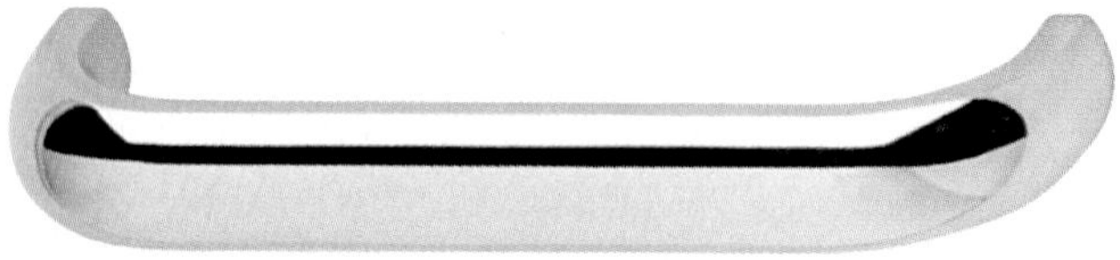

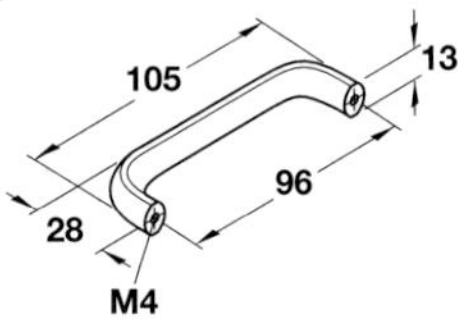

Chrome plated polished

Cat. No.	116.21.239

Packing: 25 pcs.

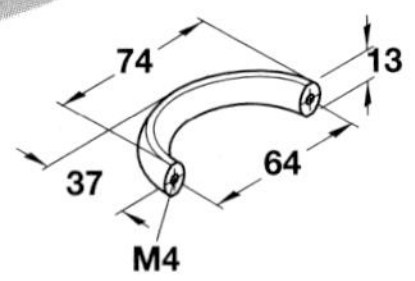

Gold colored polished

Cat. No.	116.21.828

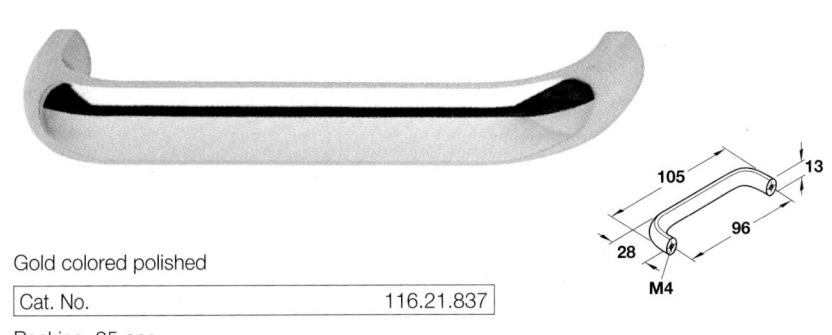

Packing: 25 pcs.

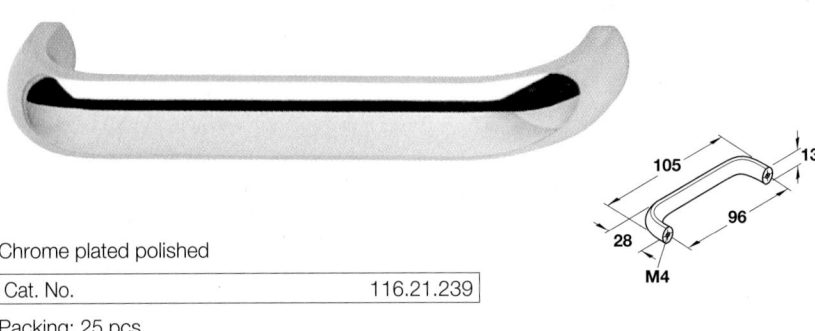

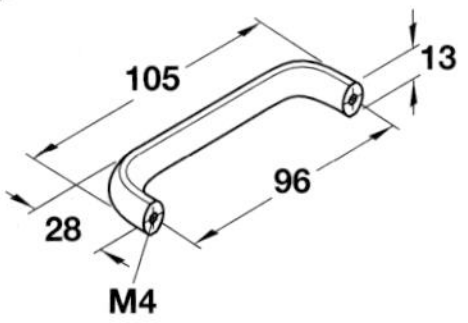

Gold colored polished

Cat. No.	116.21.837

Packing: 25 pcs.

Dimensional data not binding.
We reserve the right to alter specifications without notice.

Zinc Handles

HÄFELE

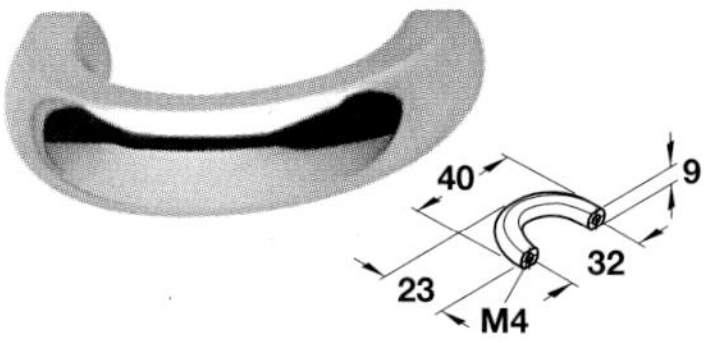

Chrome plated polished

Catalog No.	116.22.218

Packing: 25 pcs.

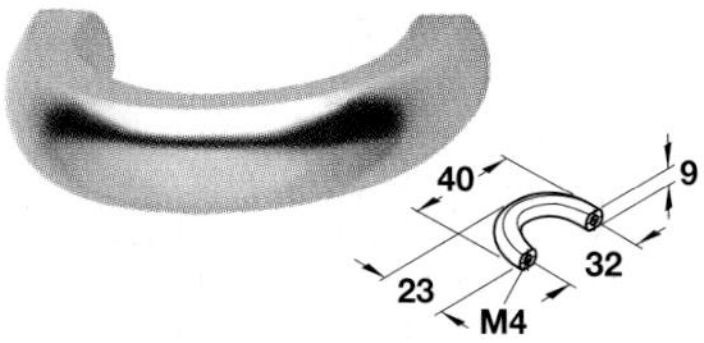

Nickel plated matt

Catalog No.	116.22.610

Packing: 25 pcs.

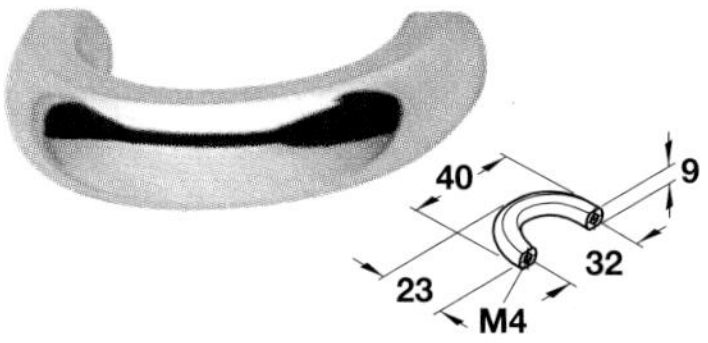

Gold colored polished

Catalog No.	116.22.816

Packing: 25 pcs.

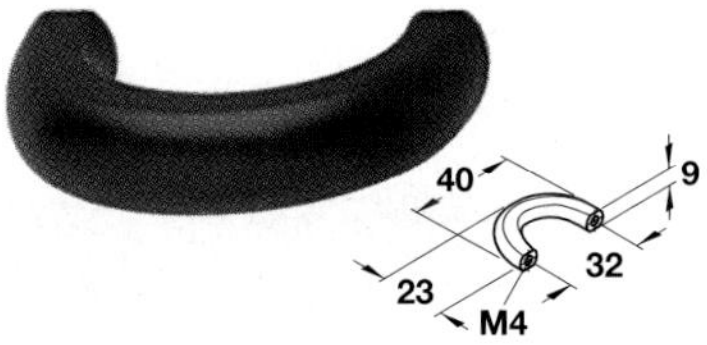

Black matt

Catalog No.	116.22.316

Packing: 25 pcs.

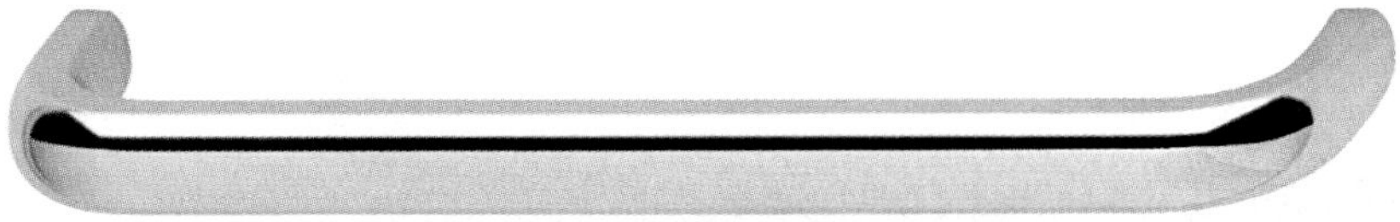

Chrome plated polished

Size A x B	Width W	Dimension C	Catalog No.
72 x 23	9	64	116.22.227
104 x 25	9	96	116.22.236
136 x 27	10	128	116.22.245

Packing: 25 pcs.

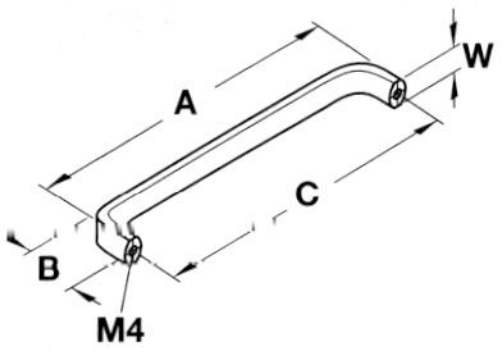

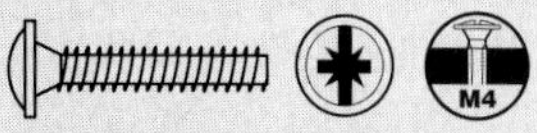

Threaded Screws M4
Combined slot, suitable for flat or cross blades

Finish: steel, zinc-plated

Length	Cat. No.
10 mm	022.35.109
12 mm	022.35.127
15 mm	022.35.154
18 mm	022.35.181
20 mm	022.35.207
22 mm	022.35.225
23 mm	022.35.234
25 mm	022.35.252
28 mm	022.35.289
30 mm	022.35.305
35 mm	022.35.350
38 mm	022.35.387
40 mm	022.35.403
45 mm	022.35.458
50 mm	022.35.501
60 mm	022.35.609

Packing: 100 and 1000 pcs.

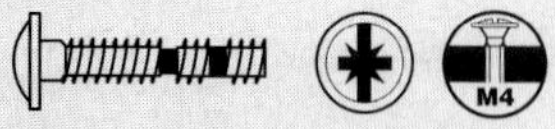

Threaded Breakoff Screw M4
Combined slot, suitable for flat or cross blades

Finish: steel, zinc-plated

Length	Cat. No.
1 3/4" x 3/4"	022.35.887

Packing: 100 and 1000 pcs.

HÄFELE

Zinc handles

Threaded Screws M4
Combined slot, suitable for flat or cross blades

Finish: steel, zinc-plated

Length	Cat. No.
10 mm	022.35.109
12 mm	022.35.127
15 mm	022.35.154
18 mm	022.35.181
20 mm	022.35.207
22 mm	022.35.225
23 mm	022.35.234
25 mm	022.35.252
28 mm	022.35.289
30 mm	022.35.305
35 mm	022.35.350
38 mm	022.35.387
40 mm	022.35.403
45 mm	022.35.458
50 mm	022.35.501
60 mm	022.35.609

Packing: 100 and 1000 pcs.

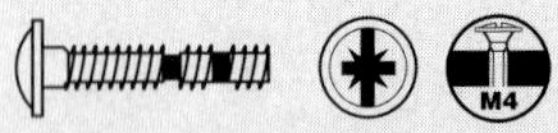

Threaded Breakoff Screw M4
Combined slot, suitable for flat or cross blades

Finish: steel, zinc-plated

Length	Cat. No.
1 3/4" x 3/4"	022.35.887

Packing: 100 and 1000 pcs.

Nickel plated matt

Size A x B	Width W	Dimension C	Catalog No.
72 x 23	9	64	116.22.629
104 x 25	9	96	116.22.638
136 x 27	10	128	116.22.647

Packing: 25 pcs.

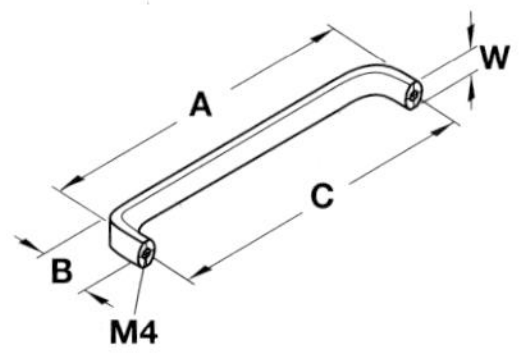

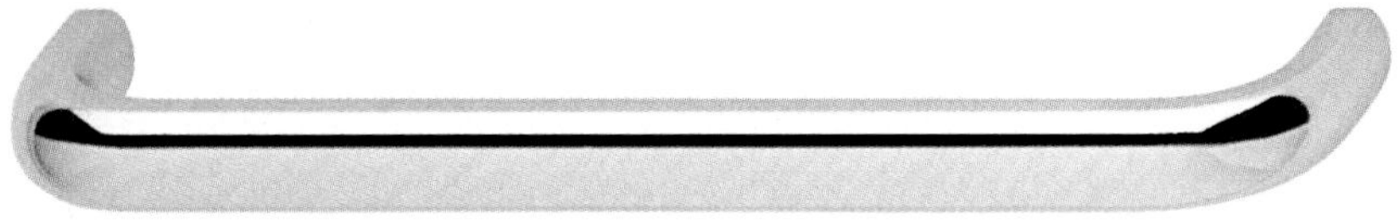

Gold plated, polished

Size A x B	Width W	Dimension C	Catalog No.
72 x 23	9	64	116.22.825
104 x 25	9	96	116.22.834
136 x 27	10	128	116.22.843

Packing: 25 pcs.

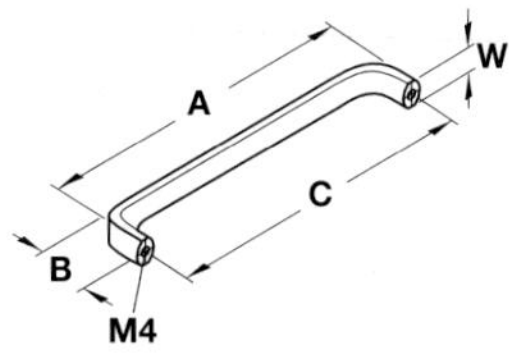

White

Size A x B	Width W	Dimension C	Catalog No.
104 x 25	9	96	116.22.736
136 x 27	10	128	116.22.745

Packing: 25 pcs.

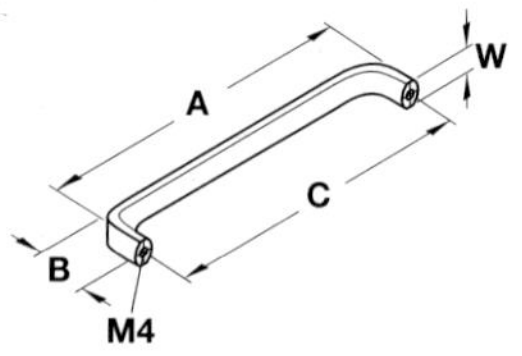

Black matt

Size A x B	Width W	Dimension C	Catalog No.
104 x 25	9	96	116.22.334
136 x 27	10	128	116.22.343

Packing: 25 pcs.

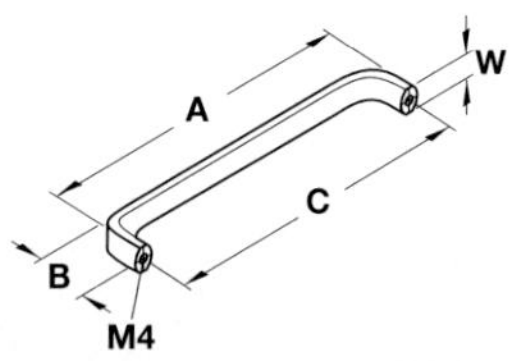

Zinc Handles

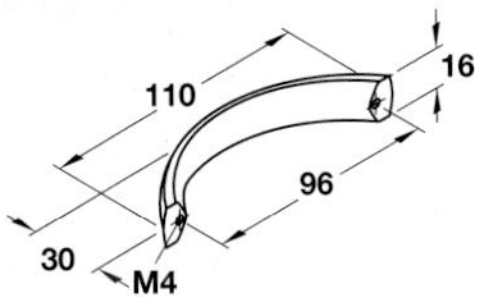

Nickel plated

Cat. No.	103.01.310

Packing: 25 pcs.

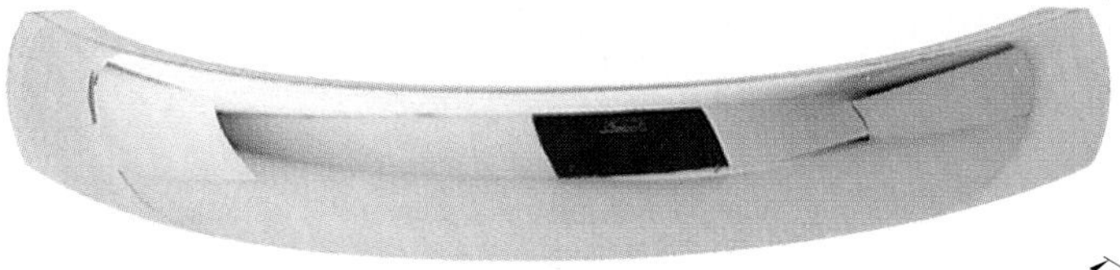

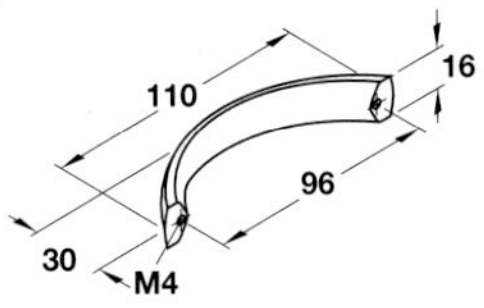

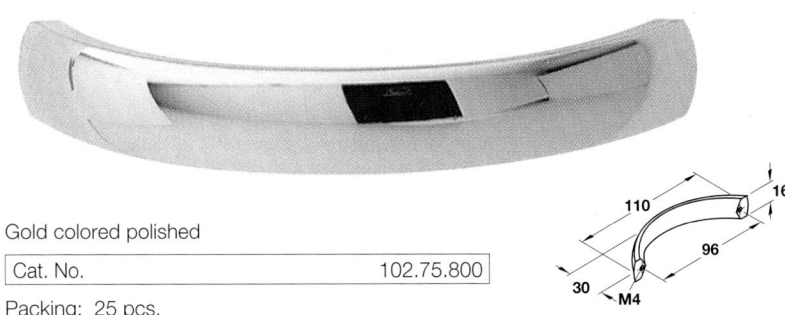

Gold colored polished

Cat. No.	102.75.800

Packing: 25 pcs.

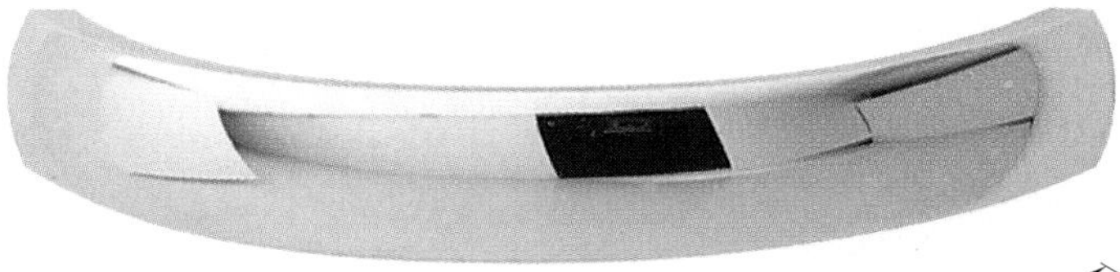

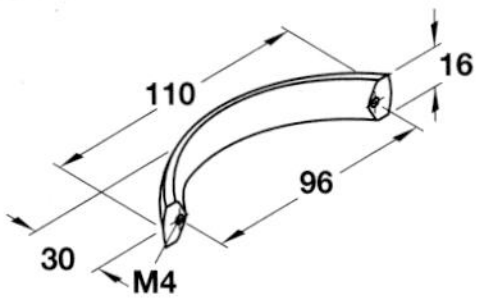

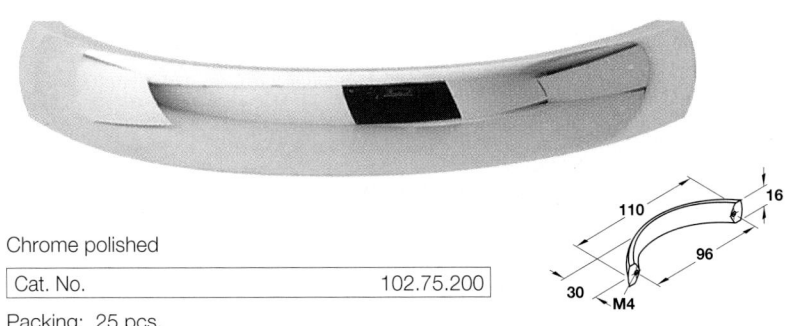

Chrome polished

Cat. No.	102.75.200

Packing: 25 pcs.

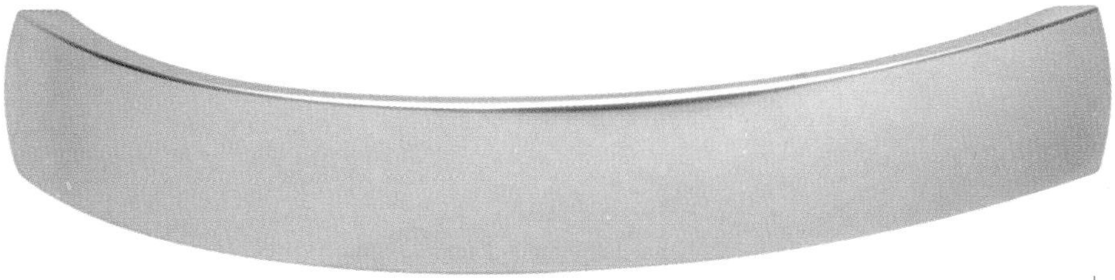

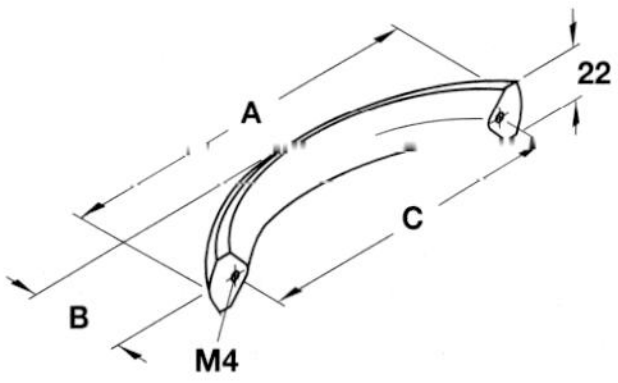

Chrome plated matt

Size A x B	Dimension C	Cat. No.
118 x 30	96	102.64.418
150 x 34	128	102.64.427

Packing: 25 pcs.

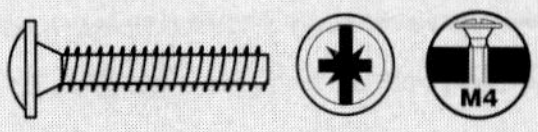

Threaded Screws M4
Combined slot, suitable for flat or cross blades

Finish: steel, zinc-plated

Length	Cat. No.
10 mm	022.35.109
12 mm	022.35.127
15 mm	022.35.154
18 mm	022.35.181
20 mm	022.35.207
22 mm	022.35.225
23 mm	022.35.234
25 mm	022.35.252
28 mm	022.35.289
30 mm	022.35.305
35 mm	022.35.350
38 mm	022.35.387
40 mm	022.35.403
45 mm	022.35.458
50 mm	022.35.501
60 mm	022.35.609

Packing: 100 and 1000 pcs.

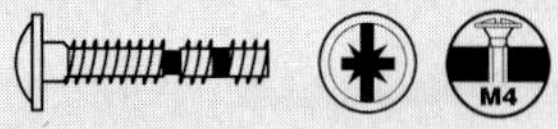

Threaded Breakoff Screw M4
Combined slot, suitable for flat or cross blades

Finish: steel, zinc-plated

Length	Cat. No.
1 3/4" x 3/4"	022.35.887

Packing: 100 and 1000 pcs.

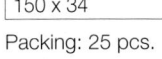

Dimensional data not binding. We reserve the right to alter specifications without notice.

HÄFELE

Zinc Handles

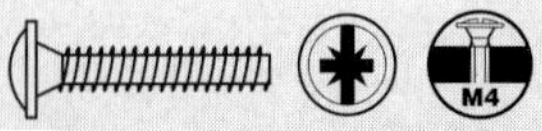

Threaded Screws M4
Combined slot, suitable for flat or cross blades

Finish: steel, zinc-plated

Length	Cat. No.
10 mm	022.35.109
12 mm	022.35.127
15 mm	022.35.154
18 mm	022.35.181
20 mm	022.35.207
22 mm	022.35.225
23 mm	022.35.234
25 mm	022.35.252
28 mm	022.35.289
30 mm	022.35.305
35 mm	022.35.350
38 mm	022.35.387
40 mm	022.35.403
45 mm	022.35.458
50 mm	022.35.501
60 mm	022.35.609

Packing: 100 and 1000 pcs.

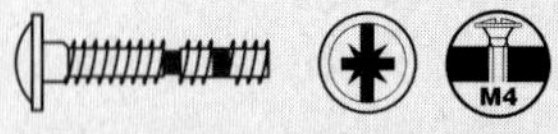

Threaded Breakoff Screw M4
Combined slot, suitable for flat or cross blades

Finish: steel, zinc-plated

Length	Cat. No.
1 3/4" x 3/4"	022.35.887

Packing: 100 and 1000 pcs.

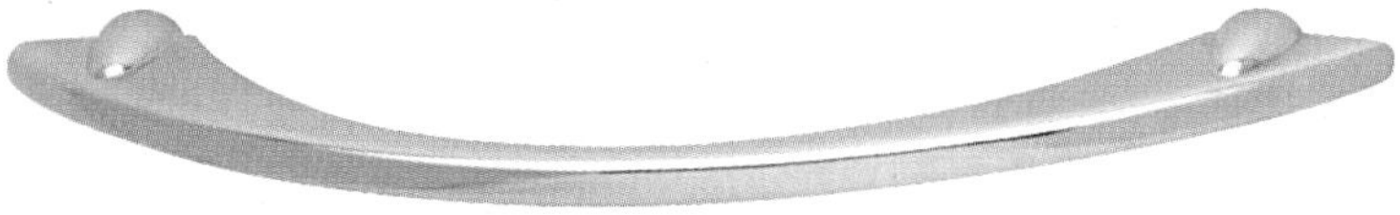

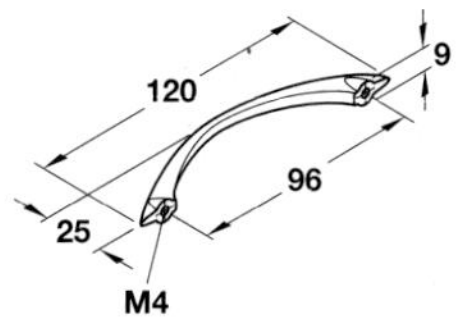

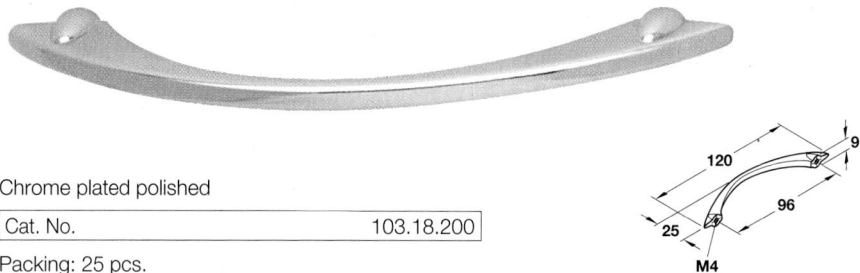

Chrome plated polished

Cat. No.	103.18.200

Packing: 25 pcs.

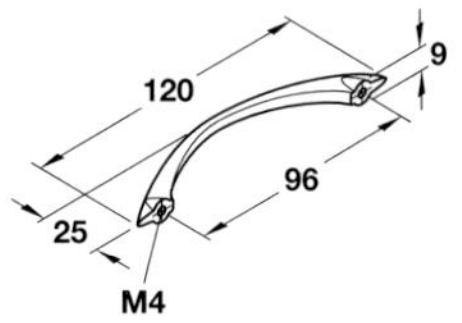

Gold colored polished

Cat. No.	103.18.800

Packing: 25 pcs.

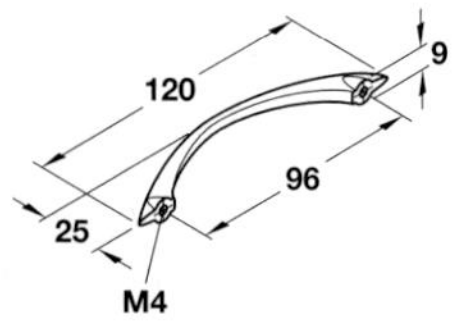

Black gloss

Cat. No.	103.18.300

Packing: 25 pcs.

Dimensional data not binding.
We reserve the right to alter specifications without notice.

Zinc Handles

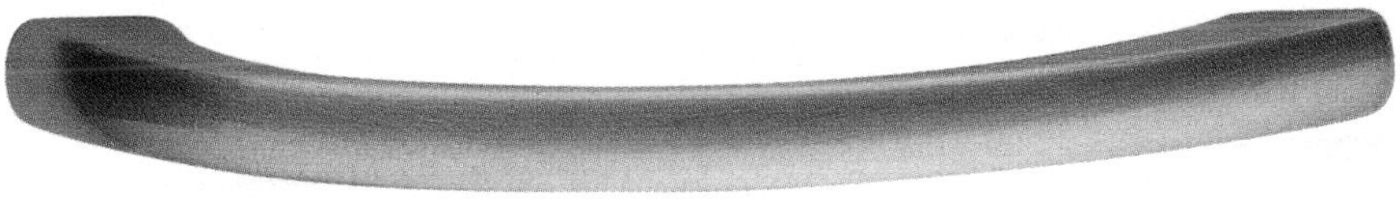

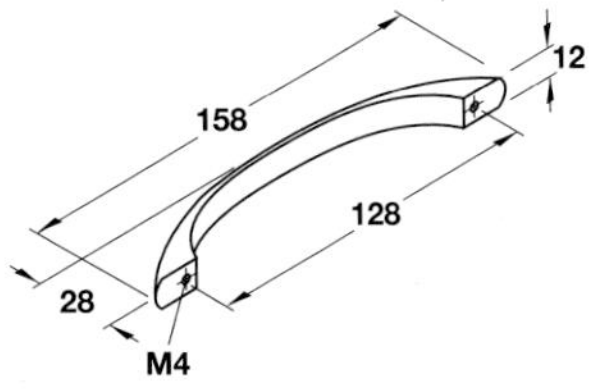

Stainless steel finish

Cat. No.	102.47.953

Packing: 25 pcs.

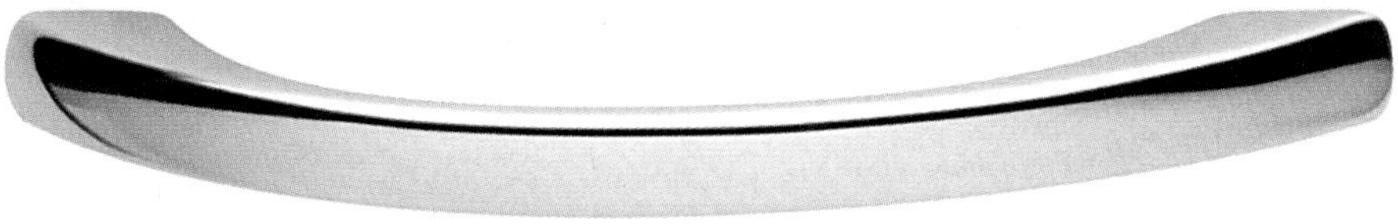

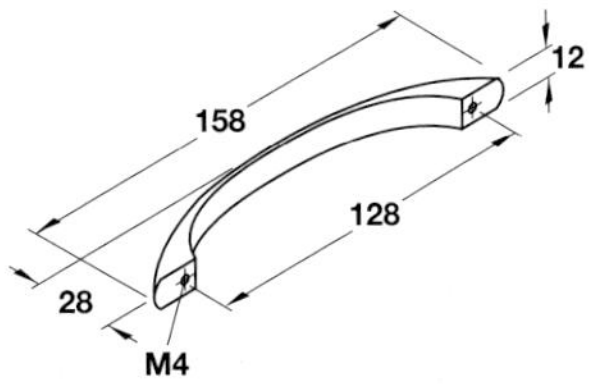

Chrome plated polished

Cat. No.	102.47.202

Packing: 25 pcs.

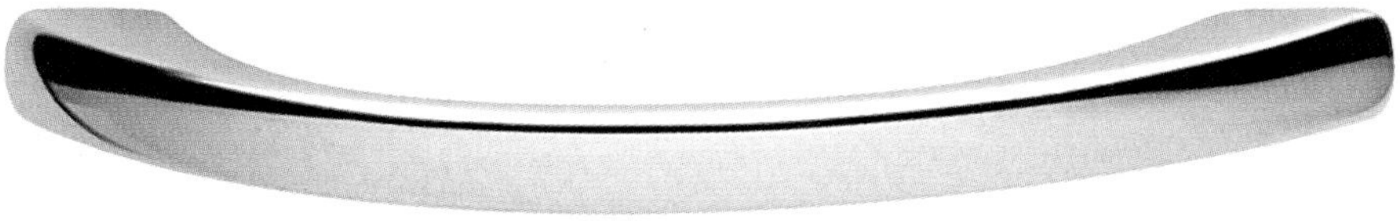

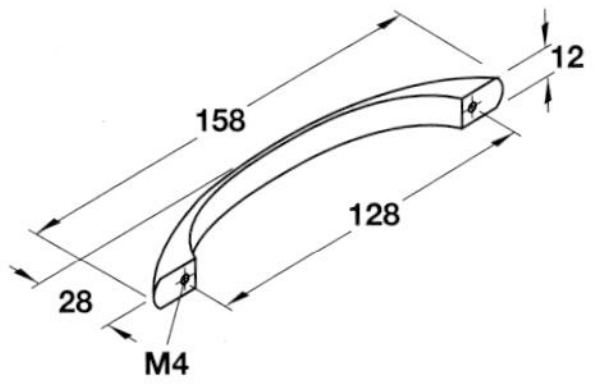

Gold colored polished

Cat. No.	102.47.800

Packing: 25 pcs.

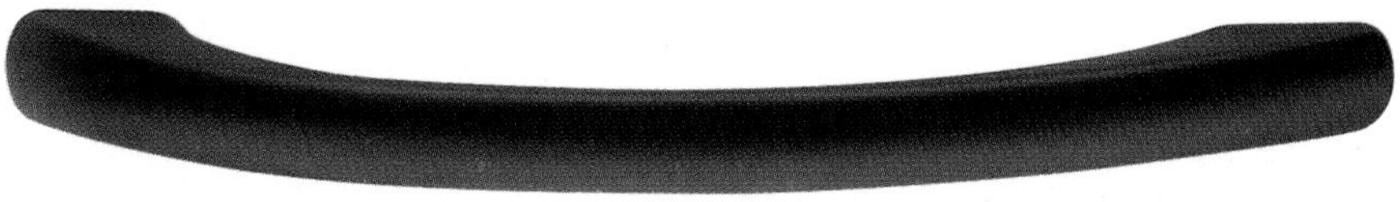

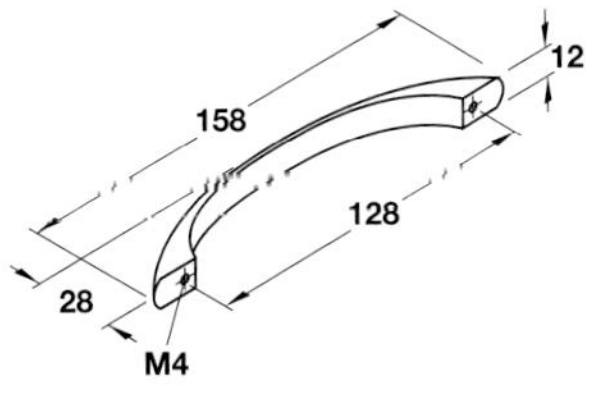

Black matt

Cat. No.	102.47.319

Packing: 25 pcs.

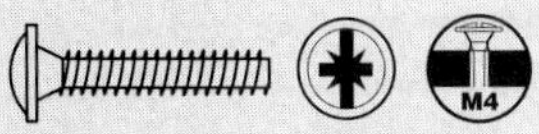

Threaded Screws M4
Combined slot, suitable for flat or cross blades
Finish: steel, zinc-plated

Length	Cat. No.
10 mm	022.35.109
12 mm	022.35.127
15 mm	022.35.154
18 mm	022.35.181
20 mm	022.35.207
22 mm	022.35.225
23 mm	022.35.234
25 mm	022.35.252
28 mm	022.35.289
30 mm	022.35.305
35 mm	022.35.350
38 mm	022.35.387
40 mm	022.35.403
45 mm	022.35.458
50 mm	022.35.501
60 mm	022.35.609

Packing: 100 and 1000 pcs.

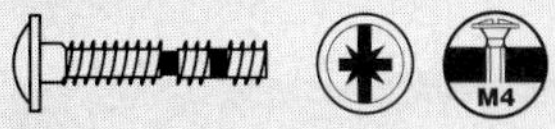

Threaded Breakoff Screw M4
Combined slot, suitable for flat or cross blades
Finish: steel, zinc-plated

Length	Cat. No.
1 3/4" x 3/4"	022.35.887

Packing: 100 and 1000 pcs.

HÄFELE

Zinc Handles

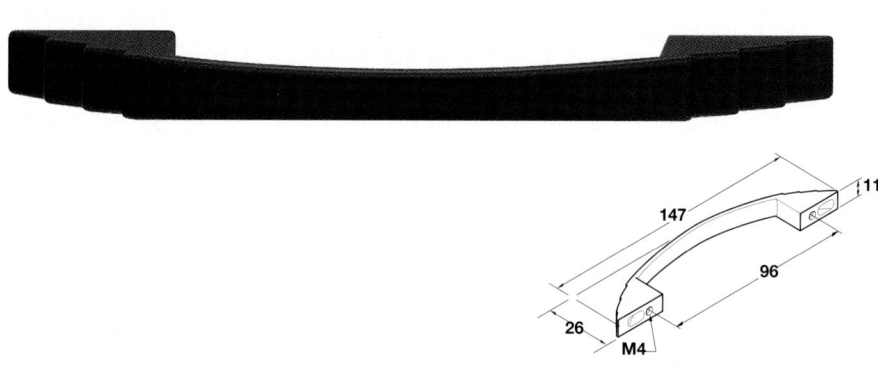

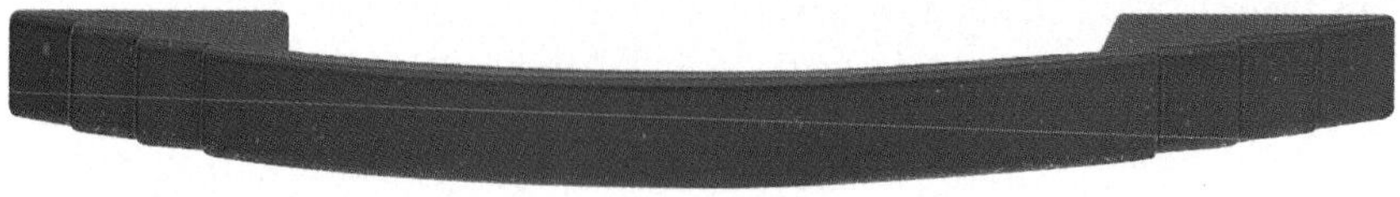

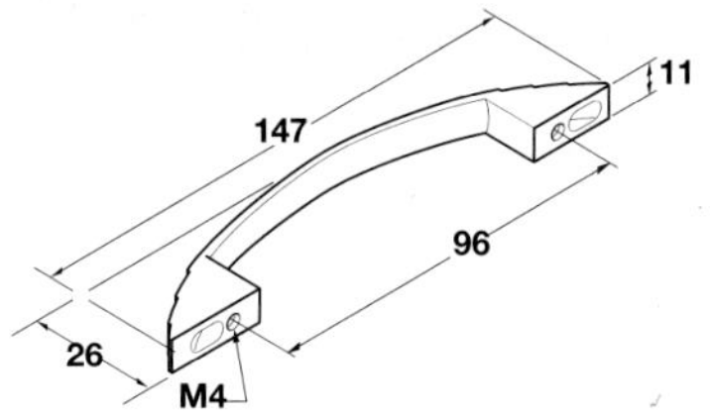

Water blue epoxy

Cat. No.	117.76.830

Packing: 25 pcs.

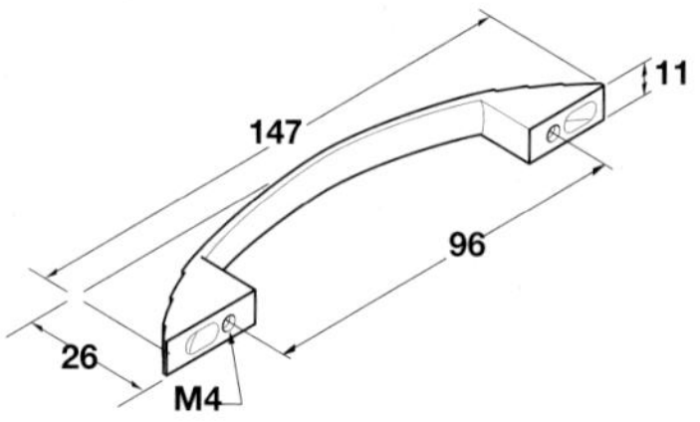

Matt black

Cat. No.	117.76.350

Packing: 25 pcs.

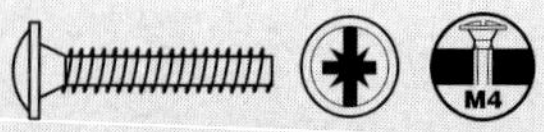

Threaded Screws M4
Combined slot, suitable for flat or cross blades

Finish: steel, zinc-plated

Length	Cat. No.
10 mm	022.35.109
12 mm	022.35.127
15 mm	022.35.154
18 mm	022.35.181
20 mm	022.35.207
22 mm	022.35.225
23 mm	022.35.234
25 mm	022.35.252
28 mm	022.35.289
30 mm	022.35.305
35 mm	022.35.350
38 mm	022.35.387
40 mm	022.35.403
45 mm	022.35.458
50 mm	022.35.501
60 mm	022.35.609

Packing: 100 and 1000 pcs.

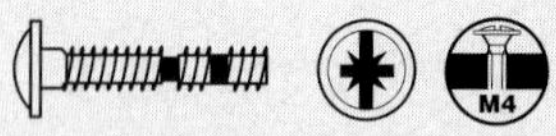

Threaded Breakoff Screw M4
Combined slot, suitable for flat or cross blades

Finish: steel, zinc-plated

Length	Cat. No.
1 3/4" x 3/4"	022.35.887

Packing: 100 and 1000 pcs.

Dimensional data not binding.
We reserve the right to alter specifications without notice.

Zinc Handles

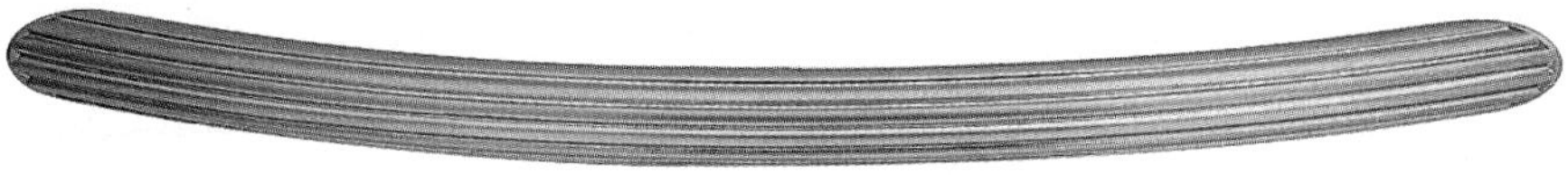

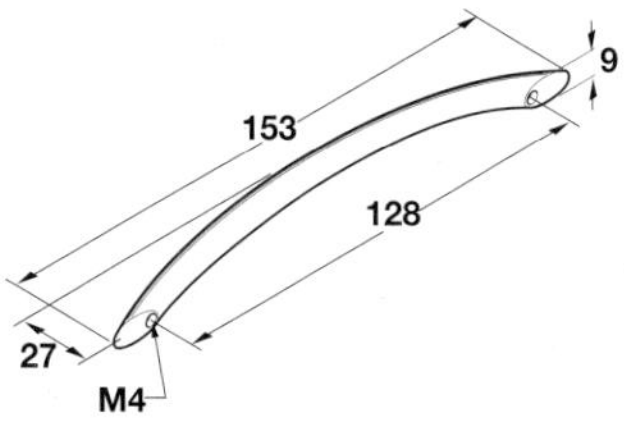

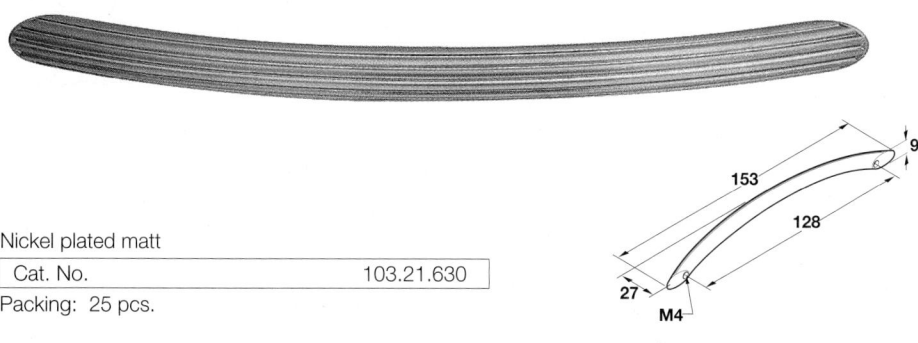

Nickel plated matt

Cat. No.	103.21.630

Packing: 25 pcs.

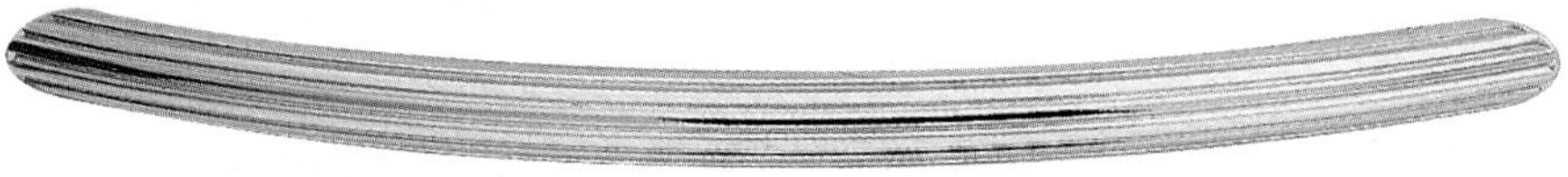

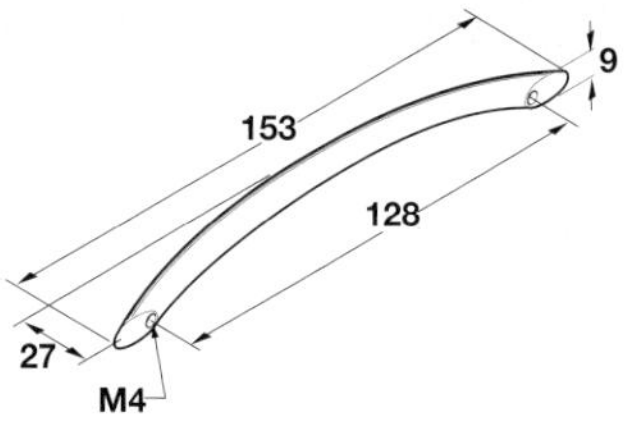

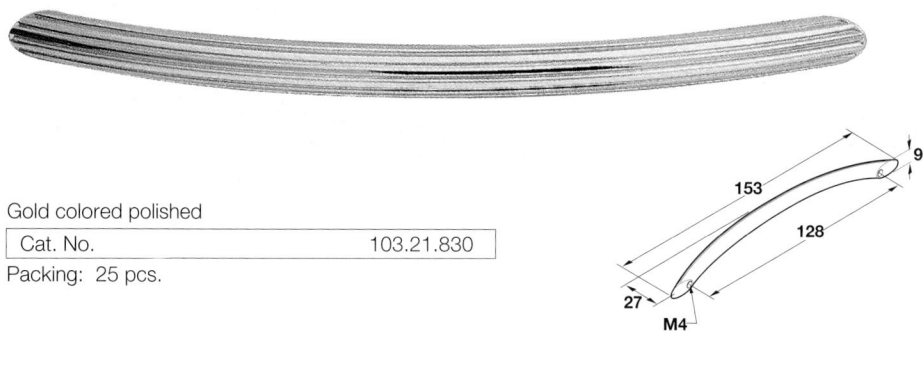

Gold colored polished

Cat. No.	103.21.830

Packing: 25 pcs.

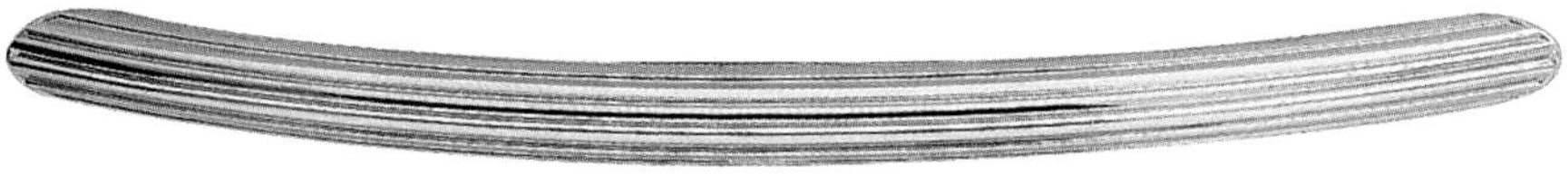

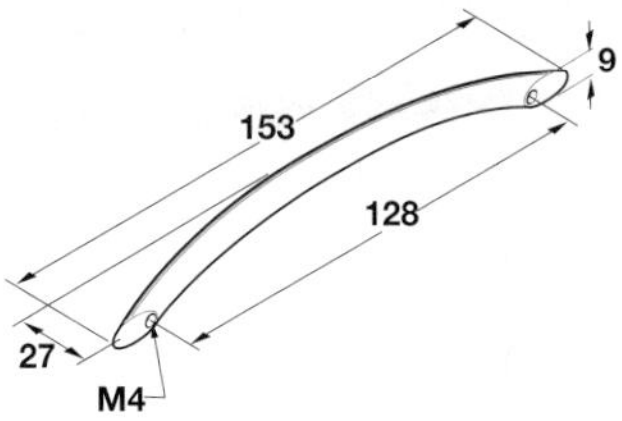

Polished chrome

Cat. No.	103.21.230

Packing: 25 pcs.

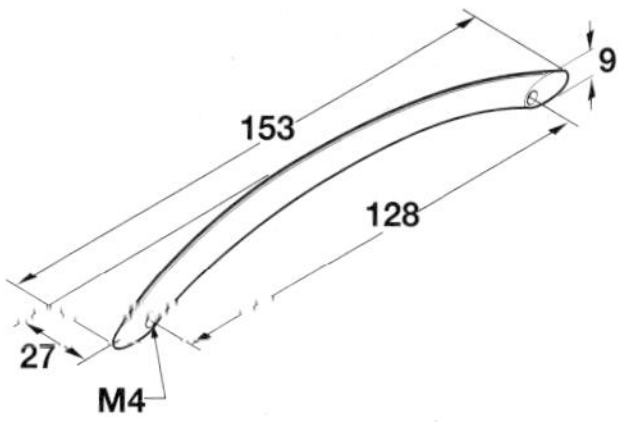

Black matt

Cat. No.	103.21.330

Packing: 25 pcs.

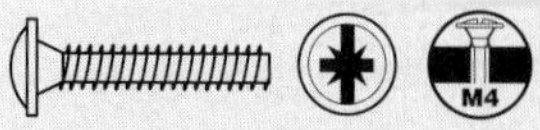

Threaded Screws M4
Combined slot, suitable for flat or cross blades

Finish: steel, zinc-plated

Length	Cat. No.
10 mm	022.35.109
12 mm	022.35.127
15 mm	022.35.154
18 mm	022.35.181
20 mm	022.35.207
22 mm	022.35.225
23 mm	022.35.234
25 mm	022.35.252
28 mm	022.35.289
30 mm	022.35.305
35 mm	022.35.350
38 mm	022.35.387
40 mm	022.35.403
45 mm	022.35.458
50 mm	022.35.501
60 mm	022.35.609

Packing: 100 and 1000 pcs.

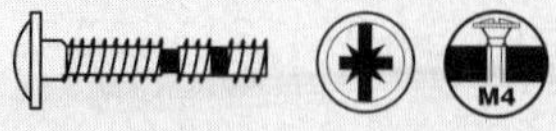

Threaded Breakoff Screw M4
Combined slot, suitable for flat or cross blades

Finish: steel, zinc-plated

Length	Cat. No.
1 3/4" x 3/4"	022.35.887

Packing: 100 and 1000 pcs.

Dimensional data not binding.
We reserve the right to alter specifications without notice.

HÄFELE

Zinc Handles

1 Decorative Hardware

Threaded Screws M4
Combined slot, suitable for flat or cross blades
Finish: steel, zinc-plated

Length	Cat. No.
10 mm	022.35.109
12 mm	022.35.127
15 mm	022.35.154
18 mm	022.35.181
20 mm	022.35.207
22 mm	022.35.225
23 mm	022.35.234
25 mm	022.35.252
28 mm	022.35.289
30 mm	022.35.305
35 mm	022.35.350
38 mm	022.35.387
40 mm	022.35.403
45 mm	022.35.458
50 mm	022.35.501
60 mm	022.35.609

Packing: 100 and 1000 pcs.

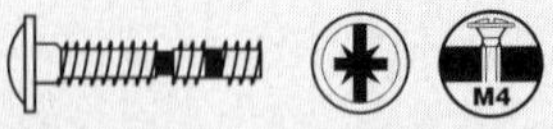

Threaded Breakoff Screw M4
Combined slot, suitable for flat or cross blades
Finish: steel, zinc-plated

Length	Cat. No.
1 3/4" x 3/4"	022.35.887

Packing: 100 and 1000 pcs.

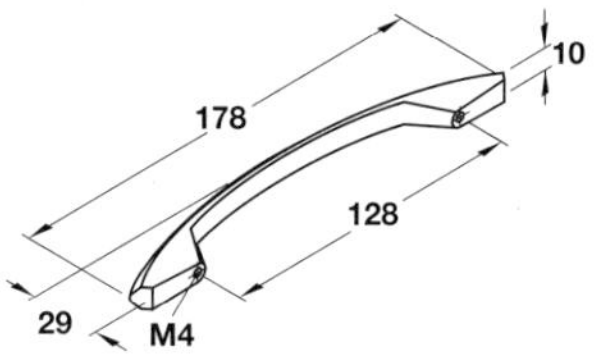

White

Cat. No.	102.78.700

Packing: 25 pcs.

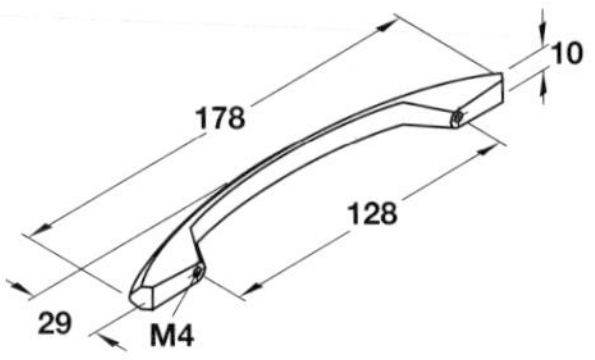

Black matt

Cat. No.	102.78.300

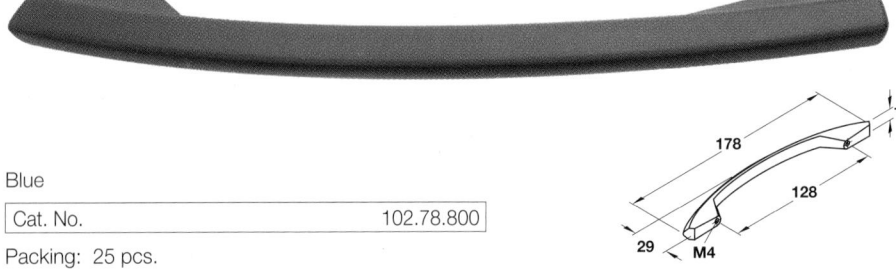

Packing: 25 pcs.

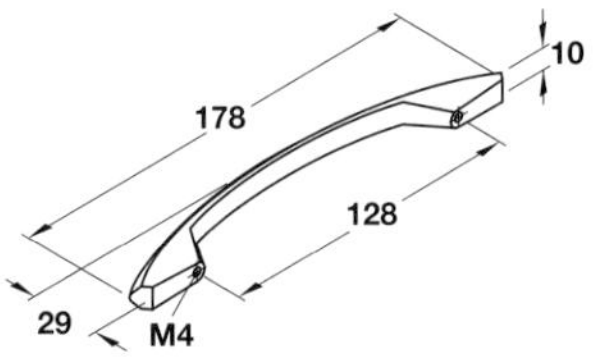

Blue

Cat. No.	102.78.800

Packing: 25 pcs.

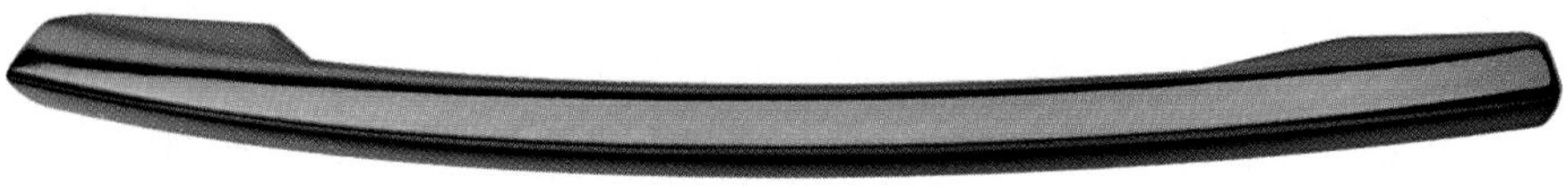

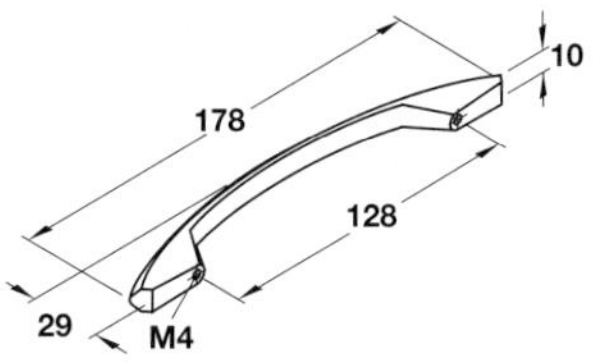

Black nickel plated

Cat. No.	102.78.310

Packing: 25 pcs.

Dimensional data not binding.
We reserve the right to alter specifications without notice.

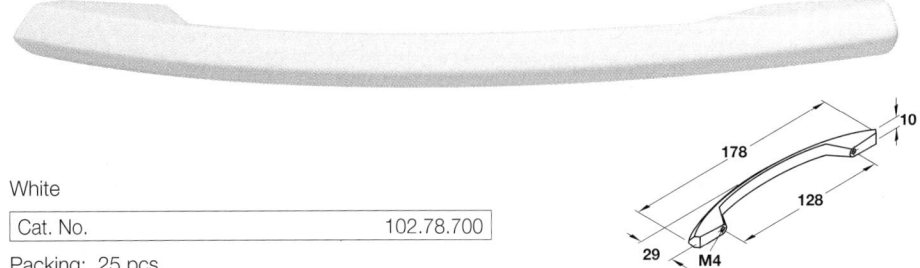

Zinc Handles

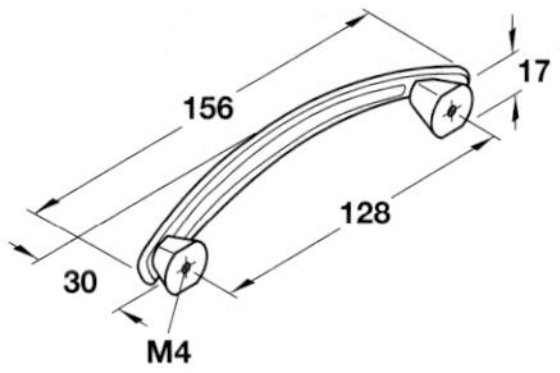

Feet: black gloss
Handle: metallic gray

Cat. No.	117.57.538

Packing: 25 pcs.

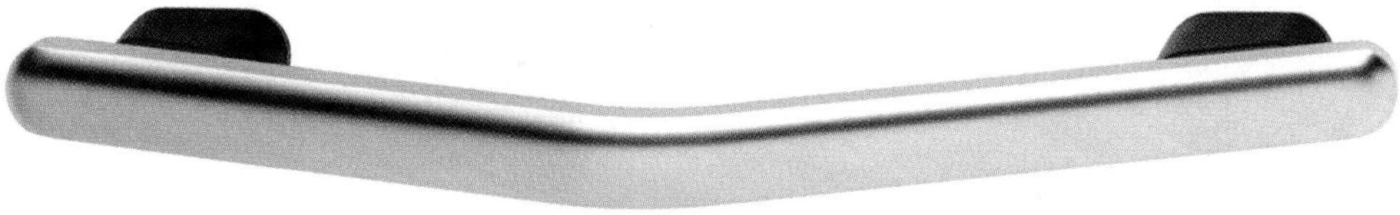

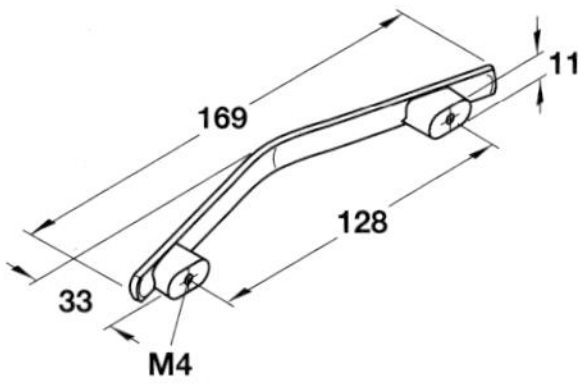

Feet: black matt
Handle: nickel matt

Cat. No.	117.58.633

Packing: 25 pcs.

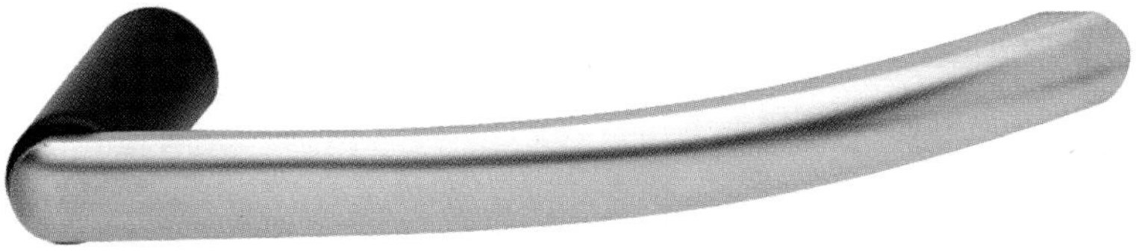

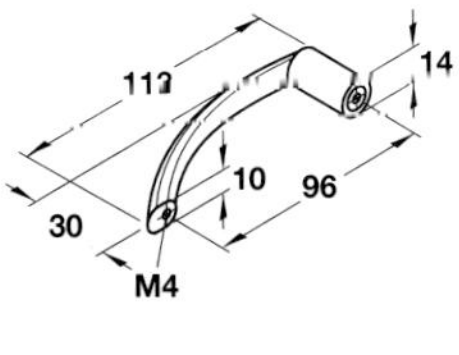

Feet: black matt
Handle: nickel matt

Cat. No.	117.59.621

Packing: 25 pcs.

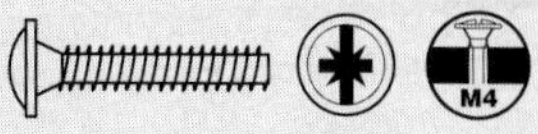

Threaded Screws M4
Combined slot, suitable for flat or cross blades
Finish: steel, zinc-plated

Length	Cat. No.
10 mm	022.35.109
12 mm	022.35.127
15 mm	022.35.154
18 mm	022.35.181
20 mm	022.35.207
22 mm	022.35.225
23 mm	022.35.234
25 mm	022.35.252
28 mm	022.35.289
30 mm	022.35.305
35 mm	022.35.350
38 mm	022.35.387
40 mm	022.35.403
45 mm	022.35.458
50 mm	022.35.501
60 mm	022.35.609

Packing: 100 and 1000 pcs.

Threaded Breakoff Screw M4
Combined slot, suitable for flat or cross blades
Finish: steel, zinc-plated

Length	Cat. No.
1 3/4" x 3/4"	022.35.887

Packing: 100 and 1000 pcs.

HÄFELE

Zinc and Wood Handles

Threaded Screws M4
Combined slot, suitable for flat or cross blades

Finish: steel, zinc-plated

Length	Cat. No.
10 mm	022.35.109
12 mm	022.35.127
15 mm	022.35.154
18 mm	022.35.181
20 mm	022.35.207
22 mm	022.35.225
23 mm	022.35.234
25 mm	022.35.252
28 mm	022.35.289
30 mm	022.35.305
35 mm	022.35.350
38 mm	022.35.387
40 mm	022.35.403
45 mm	022.35.458
50 mm	022.35.501
60 mm	022.35.609

Packing: 100 and 1000 pcs.

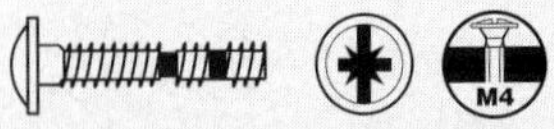

Threaded Breakoff Screw M4
Combined slot, suitable for flat or cross blades

Finish: steel, zinc-plated

Length	Cat. No.
1 3/4" x 3/4"	022.35.887

Packing: 100 and 1000 pcs.

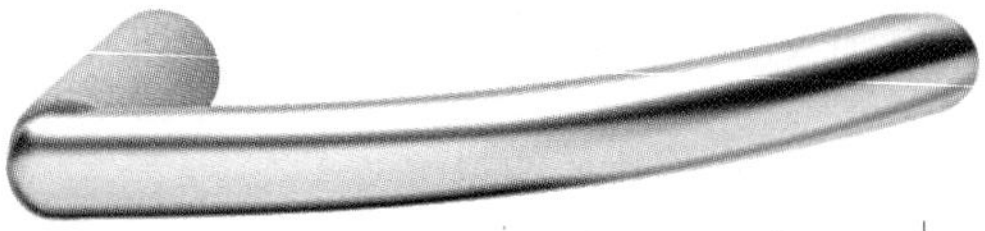

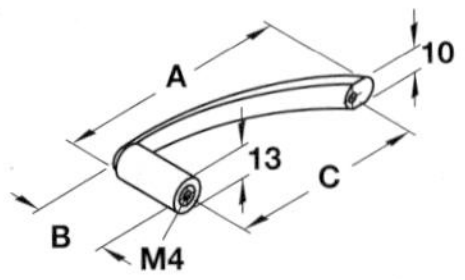

Foot: beech lacquered
Handle: zinc plated matt

Size A x B	Dimension C	Cat. No.
112 x 30	96	103.03.633
144 x 30	128	103.03.634

Packing: 25 pcs.

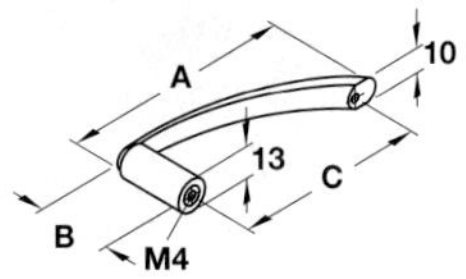

Foot: beech lacquered
Handle: zinc black matt

Size A x B	Dimension C	Cat. No.
112 x 30	96	103.03.333
144 x 30	128	103.03.334

Packing: 25 pcs.

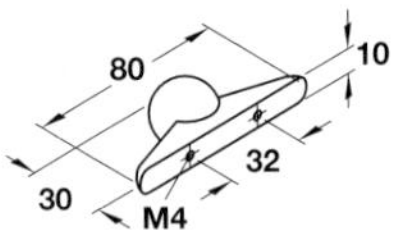

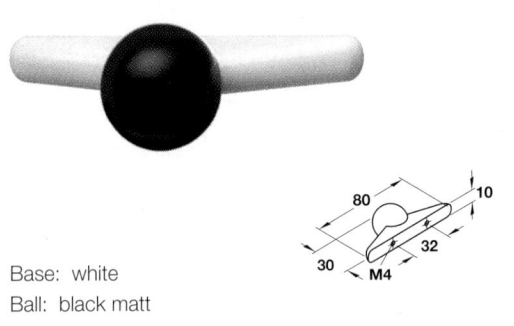

Base: white
Ball: black matt

Cat. No.	103.09.730

Packing: 25 pcs.

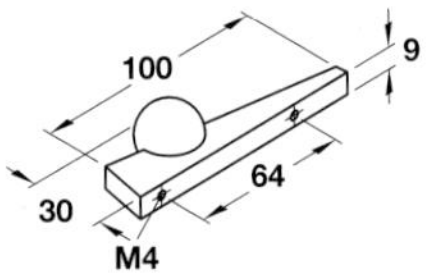

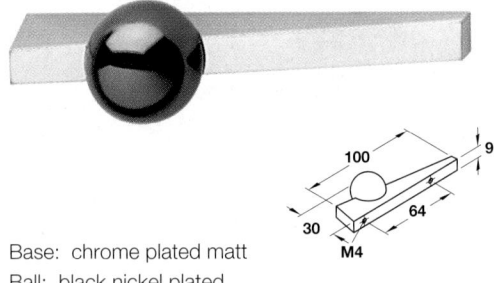

Base: chrome plated matt
Ball: black nickel plated

Cat. No.	103.08.230

Packing: 25 pcs.

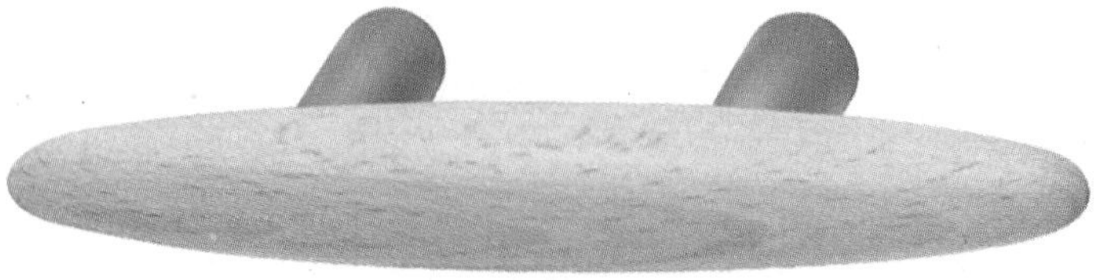

Feet: brass, nickel plated matt
Handle: beech lacquered

Cat. No.	194.22.360

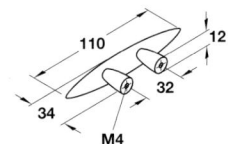

Packing: 25 pcs.

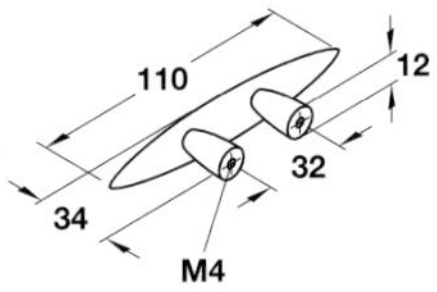

Dimensional data not binding. We reserve the right to alter specifications without notice.

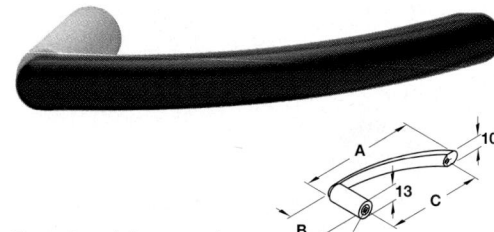

Zinc Handles

Matt black

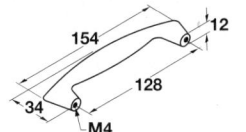

Cat. No.	104.17.330

Packing: 25 pcs.

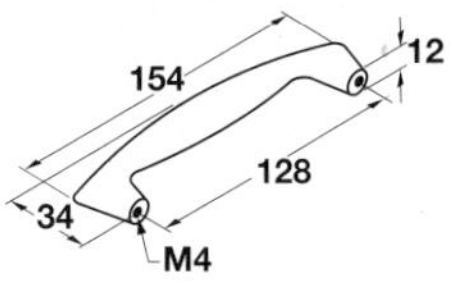

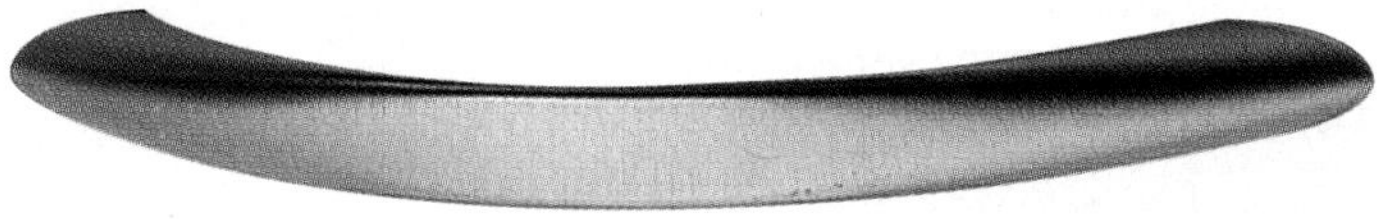

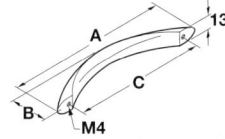

Matt stainless finish

A x B	Dimension C	Cat. No.
154 x 27	128	117.95.630
231 x 30	192	117.95.631

Packing: 25 pcs.

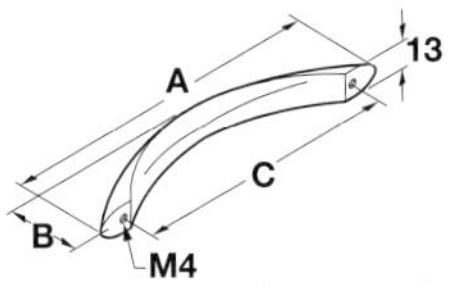

Matt black

A x B	Dimension C	Cat. No.
154 x 27	128	117.95.330
231 x 30	192	117.95.331

Packing: 10 pcs.

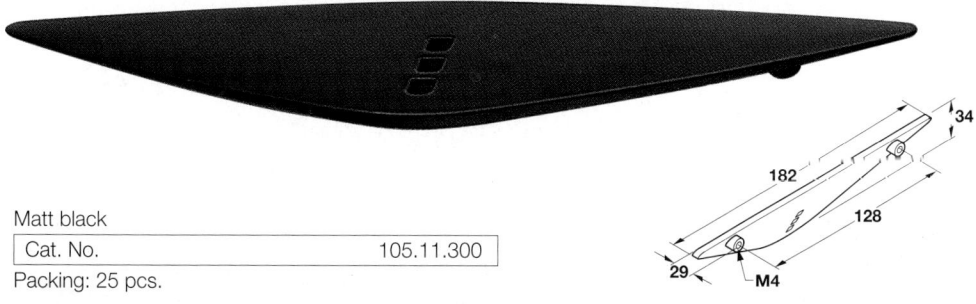

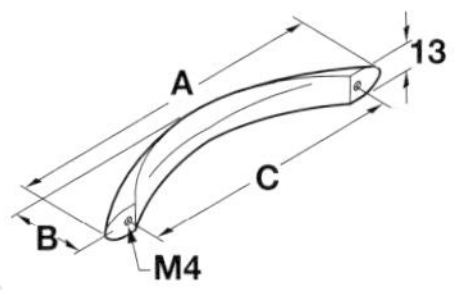

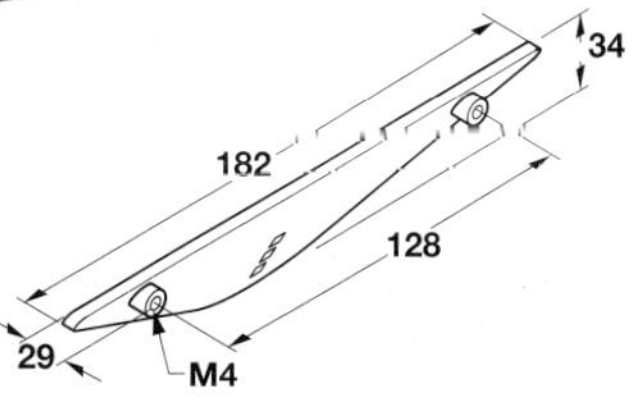

Matt black

Cat. No.	105.11.300

Packing: 25 pcs.

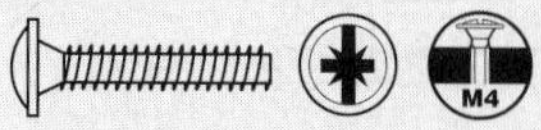

Threaded Screws M4
Combined slot, suitable for flat or cross blades

Finish: steel, zinc-plated

Length	Cat. No.
10 mm	022.35.109
12 mm	022.35.127
15 mm	022.35.154
18 mm	022.35.181
20 mm	022.35.207
22 mm	022.35.225
23 mm	022.35.234
25 mm	022.35.252
28 mm	022.35.289
30 mm	022.35.305
35 mm	022.35.350
38 mm	022.35.387
40 mm	022.35.403
45 mm	022.35.458
50 mm	022.35.501
60 mm	022.35.609

Packing: 100 and 1000 pcs.

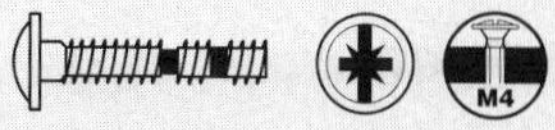

Threaded Breakoff Screw M4
Combined slot, suitable for flat or cross blades

Finish: steel, zinc-plated

Length	Cat. No.
1 3/4" x 3/4"	022.35.887

Packing: 100 and 1000 pcs.

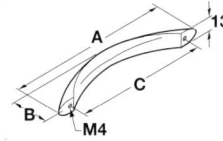

HÄFELE

Zinc Handles

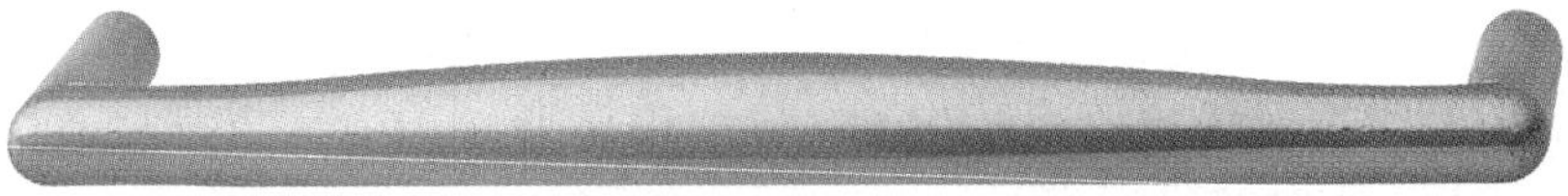

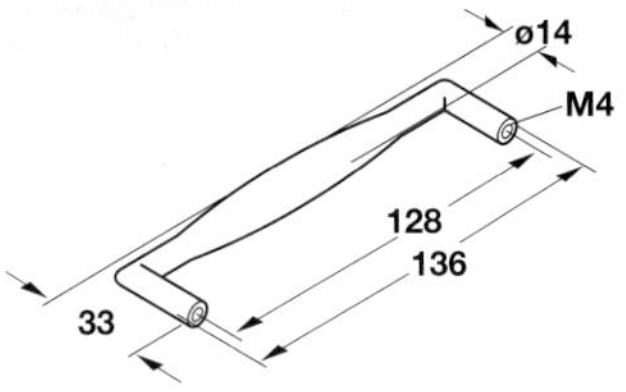

Stainless steel finish

Cat. No.	102.81.620

Packing: 25 pcs.

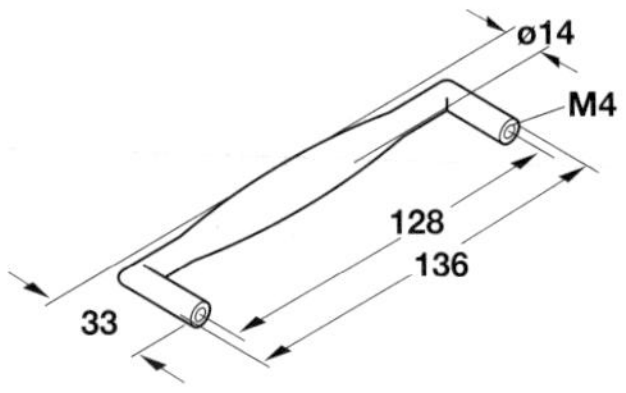

Black matt

Cat. No.	102.81.320

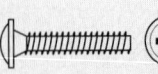

Packing: 25 pcs.

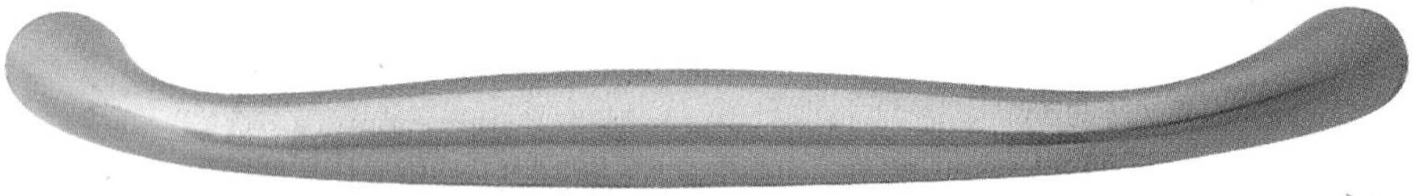

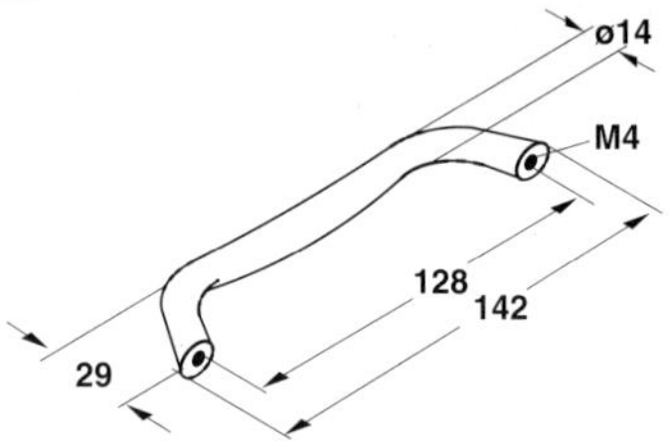

Stainless steel finish

Cat. No.	102.22.600

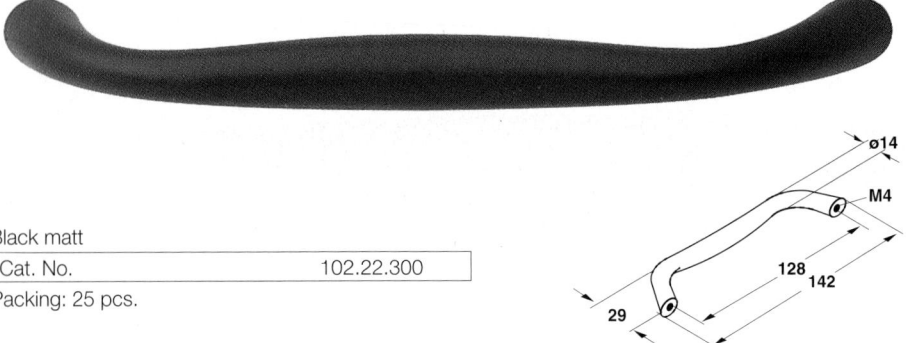

Packing: 25 pcs.

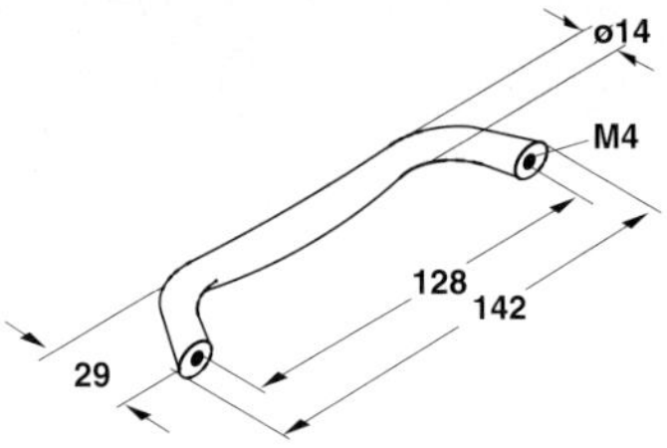

Black matt

Cat. No.	102.22.300

Packing: 25 pcs.

Threaded Screws M4
Combined slot, suitable for flat or cross blades

Finish: steel, zinc-plated

Length	Cat. No.
10 mm	022.35.109
12 mm	022.35.127
15 mm	022.35.154
18 mm	022.35.181
20 mm	022.35.207
22 mm	022.35.225
23 mm	022.35.234
25 mm	022.35.252
28 mm	022.35.289
30 mm	022.35.305
35 mm	022.35.350
38 mm	022.35.387
40 mm	022.35.403
45 mm	022.35.458
50 mm	022.35.501
60 mm	022.35.609

Packing: 100 and 1000 pcs.

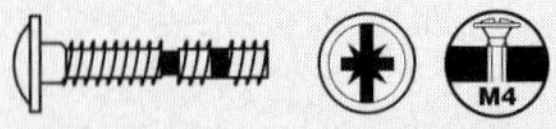

Threaded Breakoff Screw M4
Combined slot, suitable for flat or cross blades

Finish: steel, zinc-plated

Length	Cat. No.
1 3/4" x 3/4"	022.35.887

Packing: 100 and 1000 pcs.

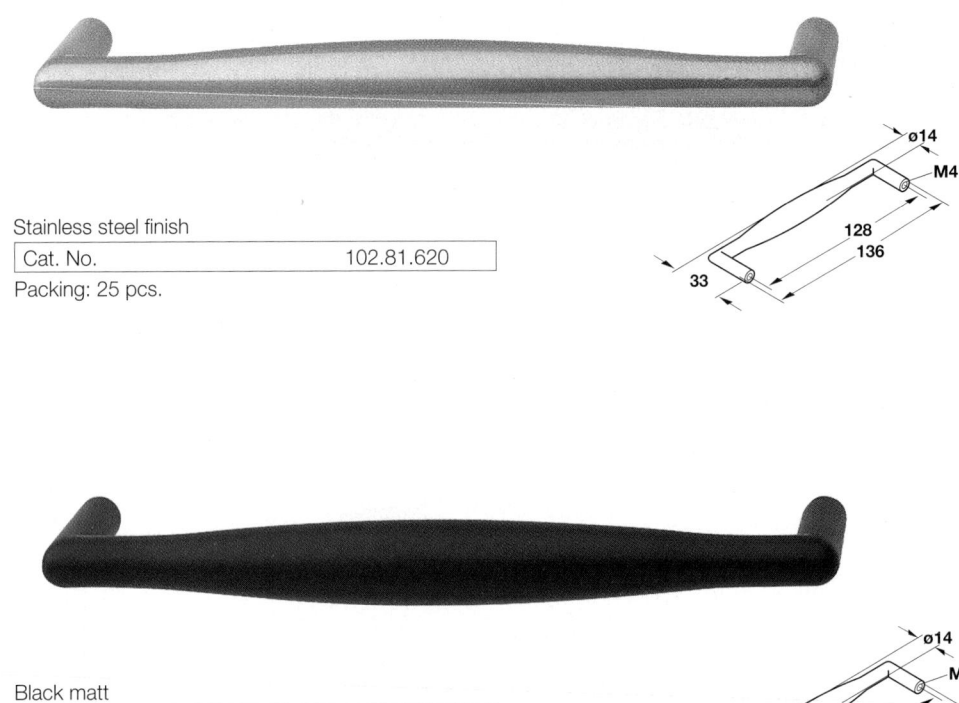

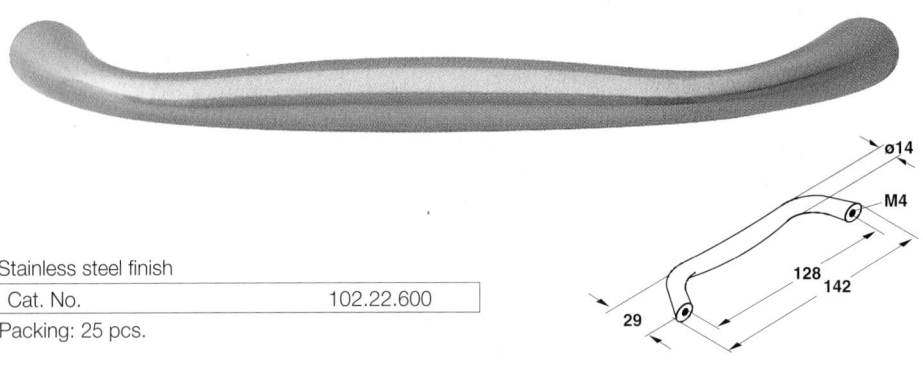

Zinc Handles

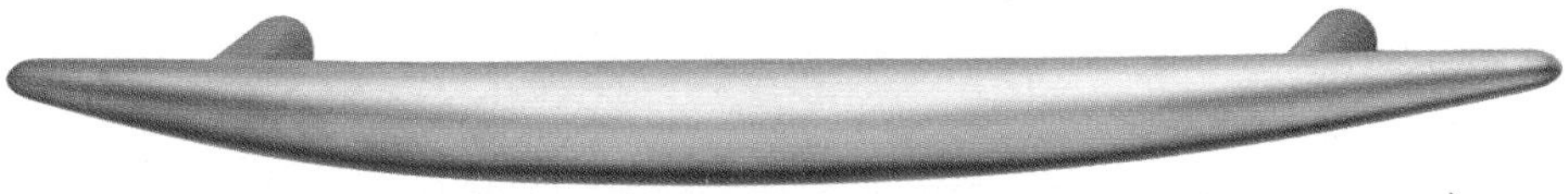

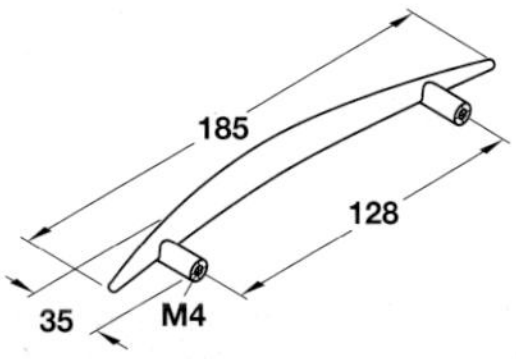

Stainless steel finish

Cat. No.	102.71.959

Packing: 25 pcs.

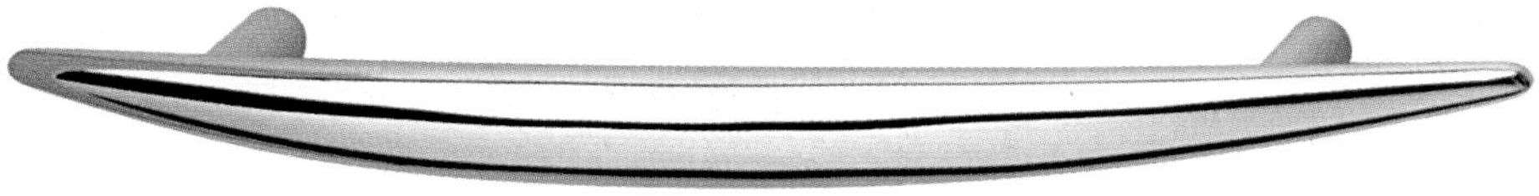

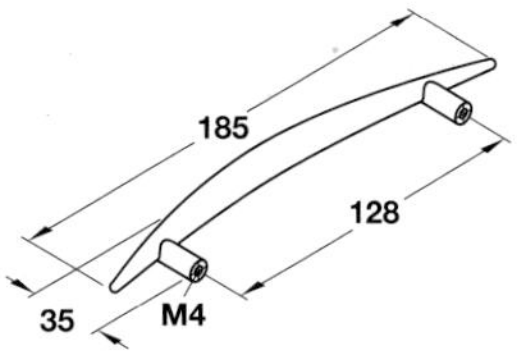

Chrome polish

Cat. No.	102.71.200

Packing: 25 pcs.

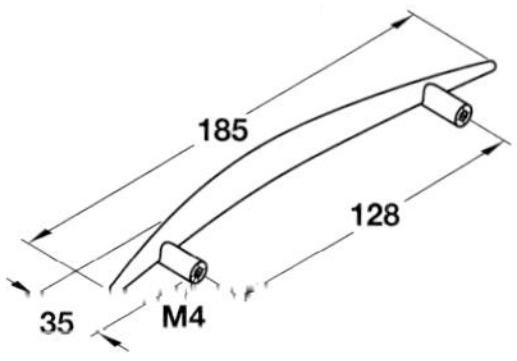

Black matt

Cat. No.	102.71.300

Packing: 25 pcs.

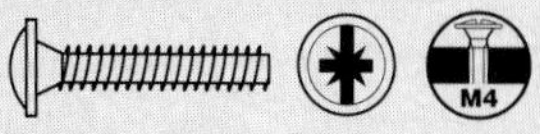

Threaded Screws M4
Combined slot, suitable for flat or cross blades
Finish: steel, zinc-plated

Length	Cat. No.
10 mm	022.35.109
12 mm	022.35.127
15 mm	022.35.154
18 mm	022.35.181
20 mm	022.35.207
22 mm	022.35.225
23 mm	022.35.234
25 mm	022.35.252
28 mm	022.35.289
30 mm	022.35.305
35 mm	022.35.350
38 mm	022.35.387
40 mm	022.35.403
45 mm	022.35.458
50 mm	022.35.501
60 mm	022.35.609

Packing: 100 and 1000 pcs.

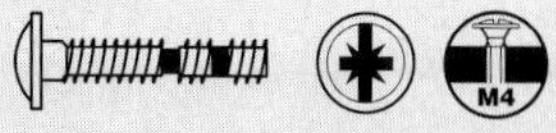

Threaded Breakoff Screw M4
Combined slot, suitable for flat or cross blades
Finish: steel, zinc-plated

Length	Cat. No.
1 3/4" x 3/4"	022.35.887

Packing: 100 and 1000 pcs.

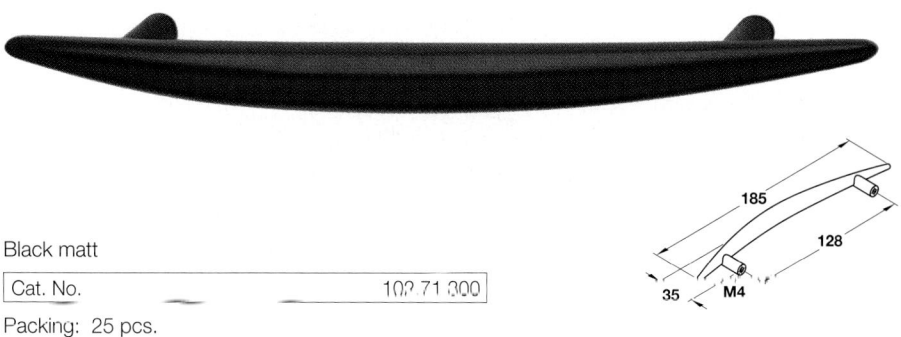

HÄFELE

Zinc handles

1 Decorative Hardware

Threaded Screws M4
Combined slot, suitable for flat or cross blades
Finish: steel, zinc-plated

Length	Cat. No.
10 mm	022.35.109
12 mm	022.35.127
15 mm	022.35.154
18 mm	022.35.181
20 mm	022.35.207
22 mm	022.35.225
23 mm	022.35.234
25 mm	022.35.252
28 mm	022.35.289
30 mm	022.35.305
35 mm	022.35.350
38 mm	022.35.387
40 mm	022.35.403
45 mm	022.35.458
50 mm	022.35.501
60 mm	022.35.609

Packing: 100 and 1000 pcs.

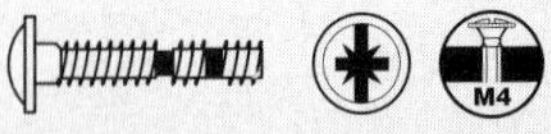

Threaded Breakoff Screw M4
Combined slot, suitable for flat or cross blades
Finish: steel, zinc-plated

Length	Cat. No.
1 3/4" x 3/4"	022.35.887

Packing: 100 and 1000 pcs.

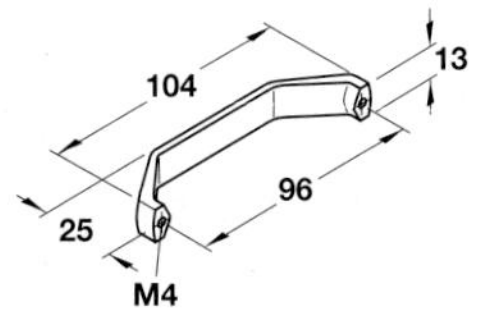

White

Cat. No.	102.59.720

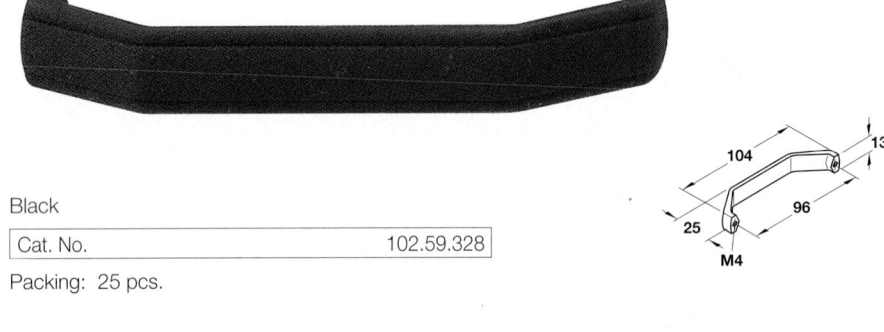

Packing: 25 pcs.

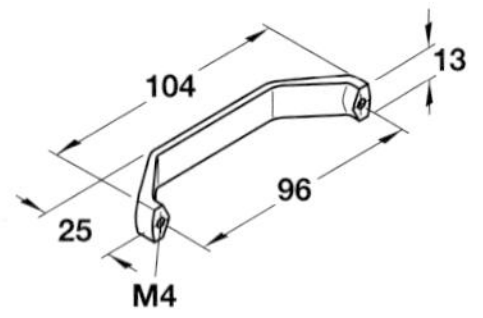

Black

Cat. No.	102.59.328

Packing: 25 pcs.

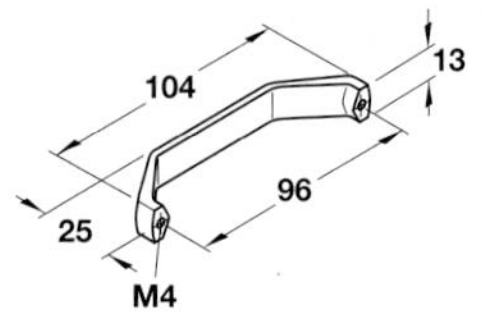

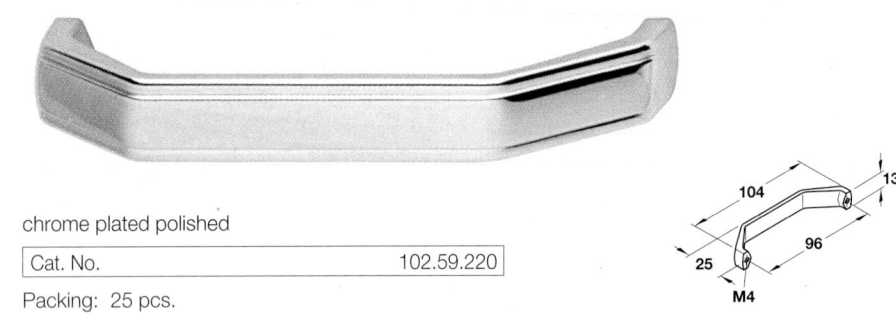

chrome plated polished

Cat. No.	102.59.220

Packing: 25 pcs.

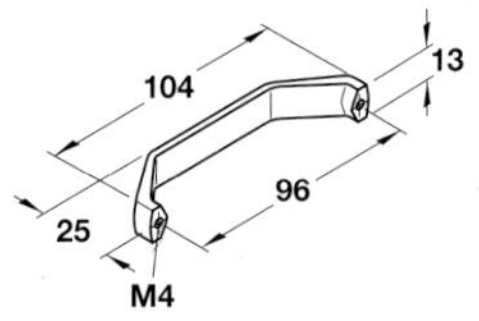

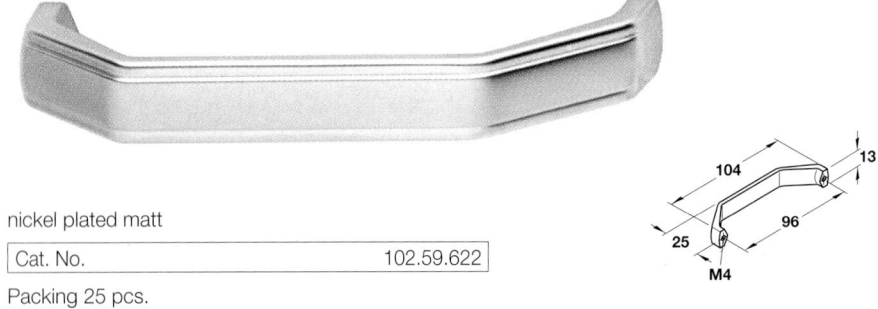

nickel plated matt

Cat. No.	102.59.622

Packing 25 pcs.

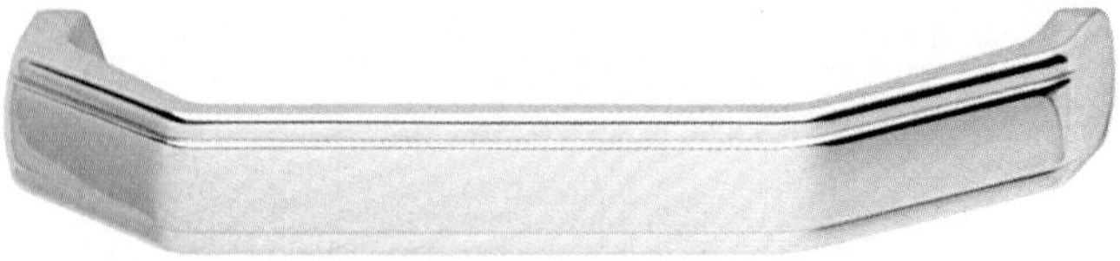

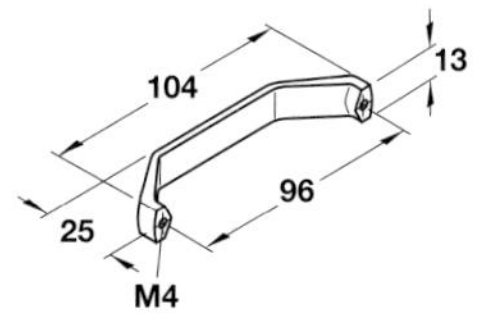

gold plated polished

Size A x B	Dimension C	Cat. No.
104 x 25	96	102.59.828
137 x 26	128	102.59.837

Packing: 25 pcs.

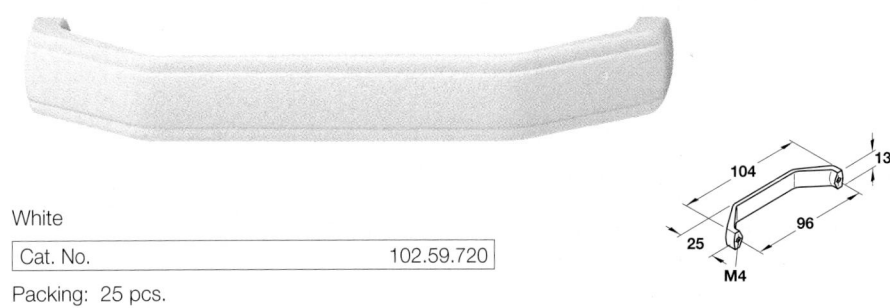

Zinc Handles

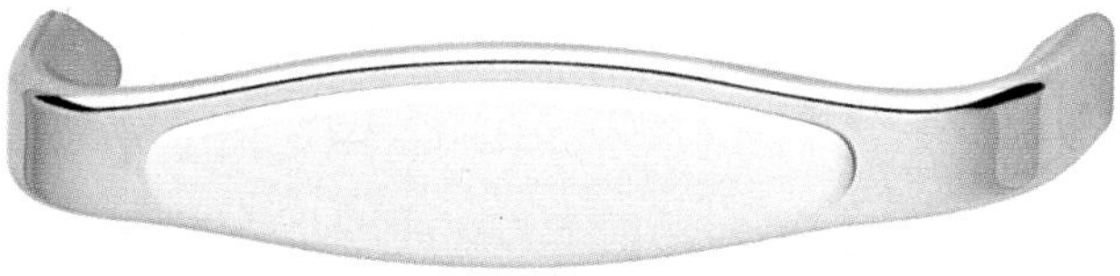

Handle: chrome plated polished
Insert: white

Cat. No.	102.61.266

Packing: 25 pcs.

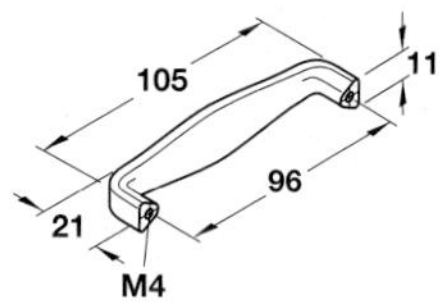

Handle: chrome plated polished
Insert: chrome plated matt

Cat. No.	102.61.275

Packing: 25 pcs.

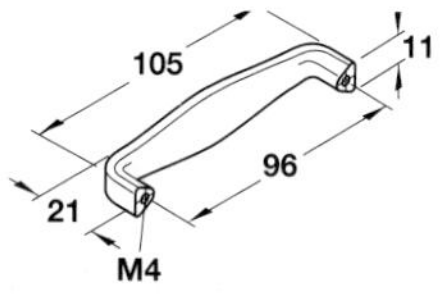

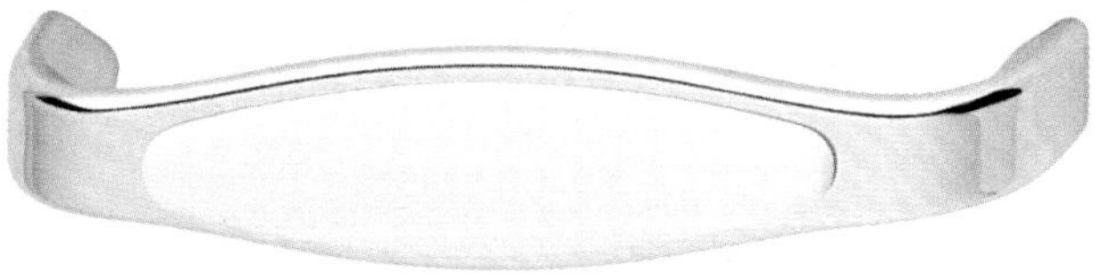

Handle: gold colored polished
Insert: white

Cat. No.	102.61.864

Packing: 25 pcs.

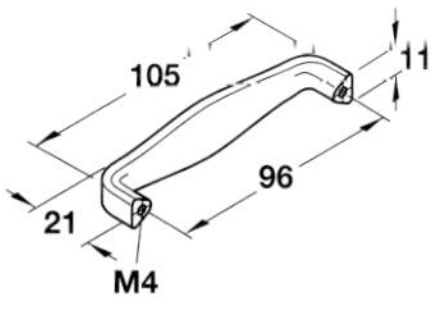

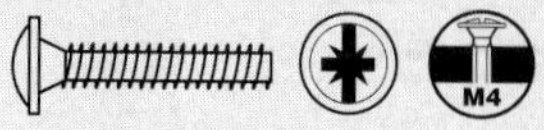

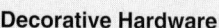

Threaded Screws M4
Combined slot, suitable for flat or cross blades
Finish: steel, zinc-plated

Length	Cat. No.
10 mm	022.35.109
12 mm	022.35.127
15 mm	022.35.154
18 mm	022.35.181
20 mm	022.35.207
22 mm	022.35.225
23 mm	022.35.234
25 mm	022.35.252
28 mm	022.35.289
30 mm	022.35.305
35 mm	022.35.350
38 mm	022.35.387
40 mm	022.35.403
45 mm	022.35.458
50 mm	022.35.501
60 mm	022.35.609

Packing: 100 and 1000 pcs.

Threaded Breakoff Screw M4
Combined slot, suitable for flat or cross blades
Finish: steel, zinc-plated

Length	Cat. No.
1 3/4" x 3/4"	022.35.887

Packing: 100 and 1000 pcs.

Dimensional data not binding.
We reserve the right to alter specifications without notice.

HÄFELE

Zinc Handles

1 Decorative Hardware

Threaded Screws M4
Combined slot, suitable for flat or cross blades

Finish: steel, zinc-plated

Length	Cat. No.
10 mm	022.35.109
12 mm	022.35.127
15 mm	022.35.154
18 mm	022.35.181
20 mm	022.35.207
22 mm	022.35.225
23 mm	022.35.234
25 mm	022.35.252
28 mm	022.35.289
30 mm	022.35.305
35 mm	022.35.350
38 mm	022.35.387
40 mm	022.35.403
45 mm	022.35.458
50 mm	022.35.501
60 mm	022.35.609

Packing: 100 and 1000 pcs.

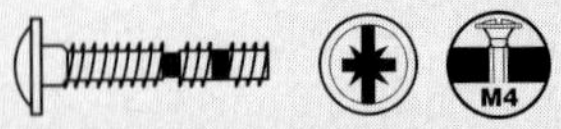

Threaded Breakoff Screw M4
Combined slot, suitable for flat or cross blades

Finish: steel, zinc-plated

Length	Cat. No.
1 3/4" x 3/4"	022.35.887

Packing: 100 and 1000 pcs.

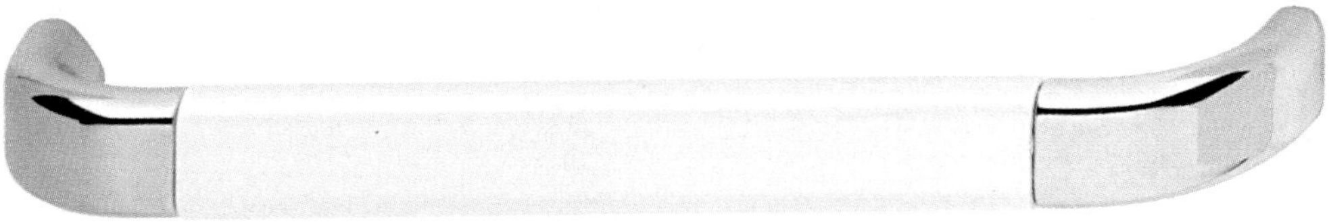

Ends: chrome polished
Center: white

Cat. No.	117.36.217

Packing: 25 pcs.

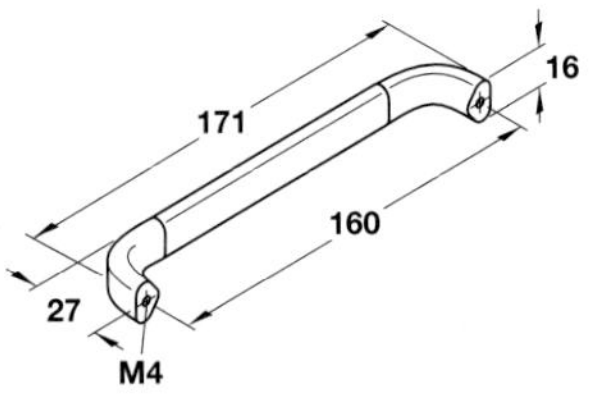

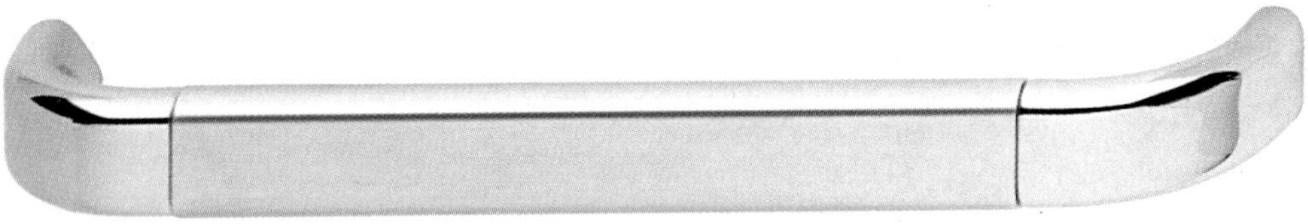

Ends: chrome polished
Center: chrome plated matt

Cat. No.	117.36.226

Packing: 25 pcs.

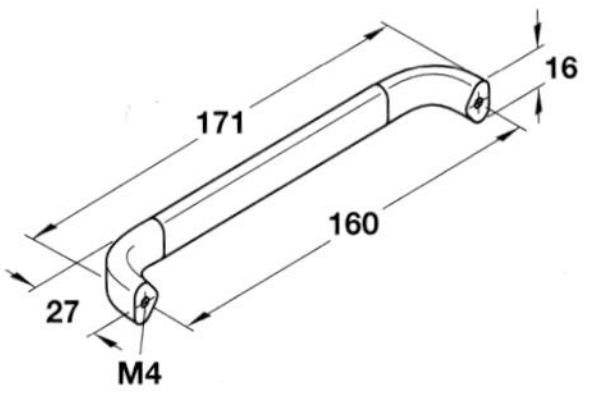

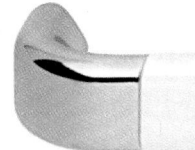

Ends: gold colored polished
Center: white

Cat. No.	117.36.815

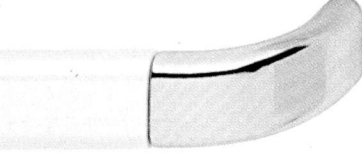

Packing: 25 pcs.

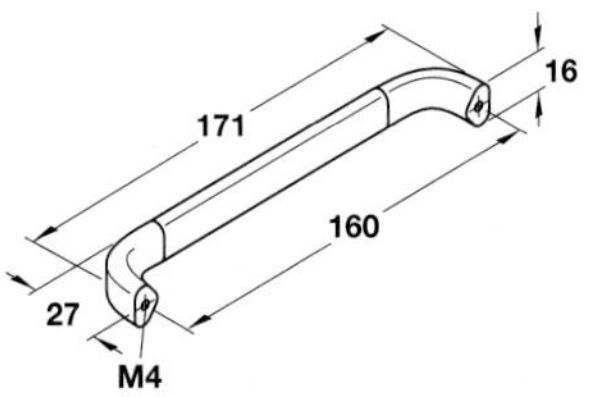

HÄFELE

Zinc Handles

Chrome plated

Size A x B	Width W	Dimension C	Cat. No.
124 x 23	10	96	102.60.223
158 x 25	11	128	102.60.232

Packing: 25 pcs.

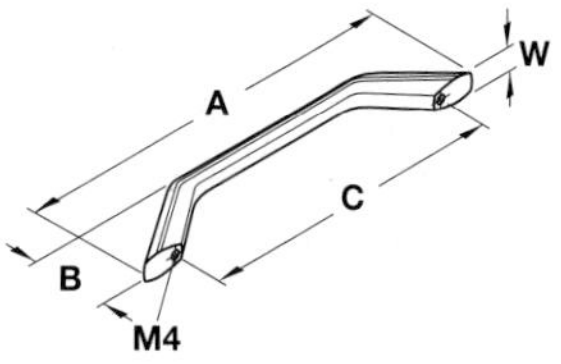

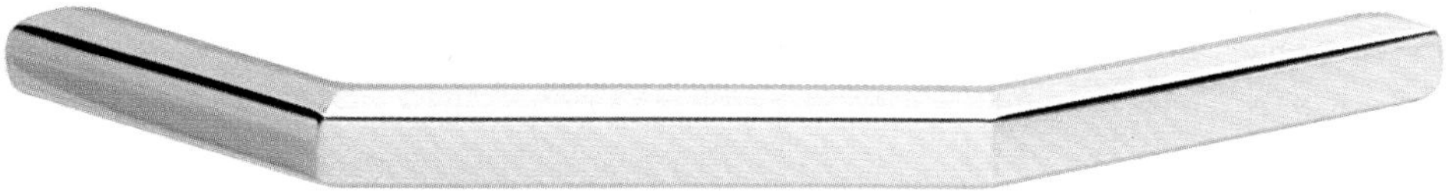

Gold plated polished

Size A x B	Wdith W	Dimension C	Cat. No.
124 x 23	10	96	102.60.821
158 x 25	11	128	102.60.830

Packing: 25 pcs.

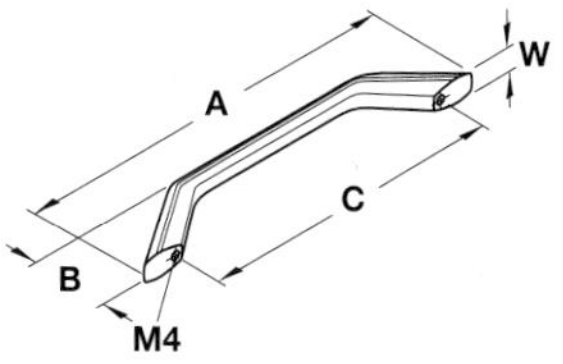

White matt

Cat. No.	117.28.733

Packing: 25 pcs.

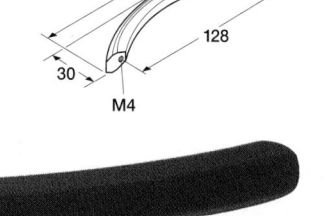

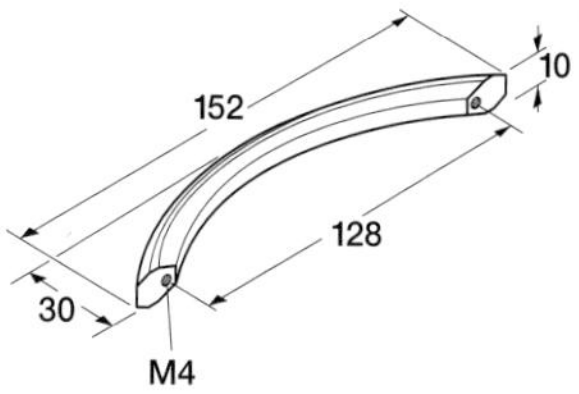

Black matt

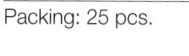

Cat. No.	117.28.331

Packing: 25 pcs.

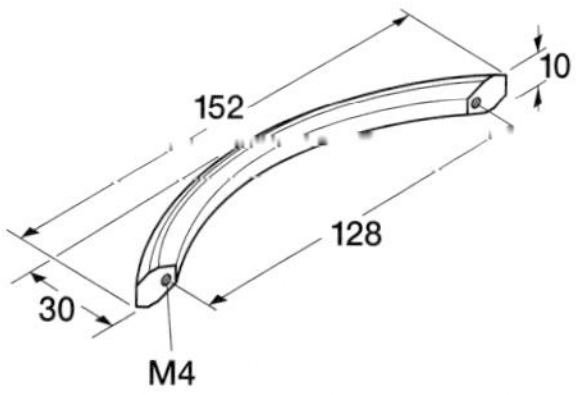

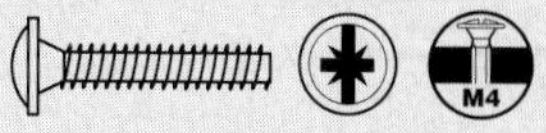

Threaded Screws M4
Combined slot, suitable for flat or cross blades

Finish: steel, zinc-plated

Length	Cat. No.
10 mm	022.35.109
12 mm	022.35.127
15 mm	022.35.154
18 mm	022.35.181
20 mm	022.35.207
22 mm	022.35.225
23 mm	022.35.234
25 mm	022.35.252
28 mm	022.35.289
30 mm	022.35.305
35 mm	022.35.350
38 mm	022.35.387
40 mm	022.35.403
45 mm	022.35.458
50 mm	022.35.501
60 mm	022.35.609

Packing: 100 and 1000 pcs.

Threaded Breakoff Screw M4
Combined slot, suitable for flat or cross blades

Finish: steel, zinc-plated

Length	Cat. No.
1 3/4" x 3/4"	022.35.887

Packing: 100 and 1000 pcs.

Dimensional data not binding.
We reserve the right to alter specifications without notice.

HÄFELE

Zinc handles

Threaded Screws M4
Combined slot, suitable for flat or cross blades
Finish: steel, zinc-plated

Length	Cat. No.
10 mm	022.35.109
12 mm	022.35.127
15 mm	022.35.154
18 mm	022.35.181
20 mm	022.35.207
22 mm	022.35.225
23 mm	022.35.234
25 mm	022.35.252
28 mm	022.35.289
30 mm	022.35.305
35 mm	022.35.350
38 mm	022.35.387
40 mm	022.35.403
45 mm	022.35.458
50 mm	022.35.501
60 mm	022.35.609

Packing: 100 and 1000 pcs.

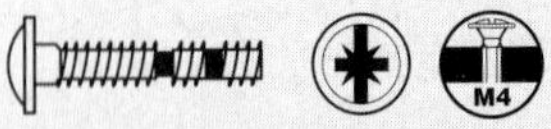

Threaded Breakoff Screw M4
Combined slot, suitable for flat or cross blades
Finish: steel, zinc-plated

Length	Cat. No.
1 3/4" x 3/4"	022.35.887

Packing: 100 and 1000 pcs.

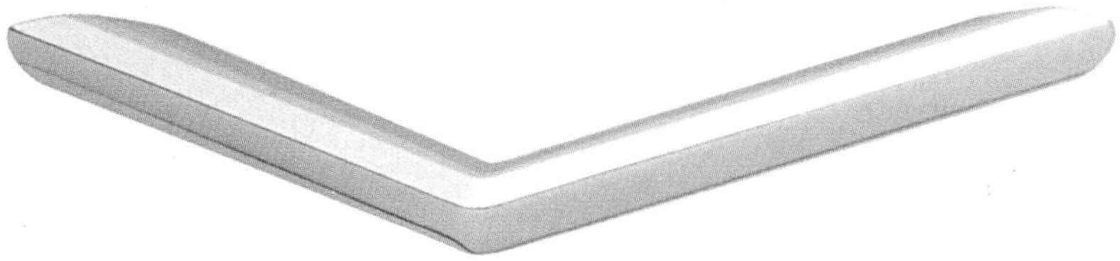

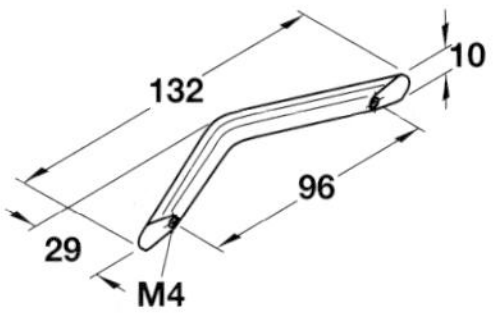

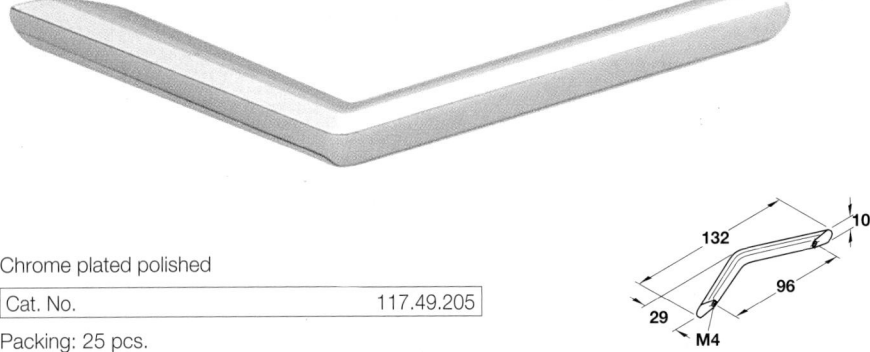

Chrome plated polished

Cat. No.	117.49.205

Packing: 25 pcs.

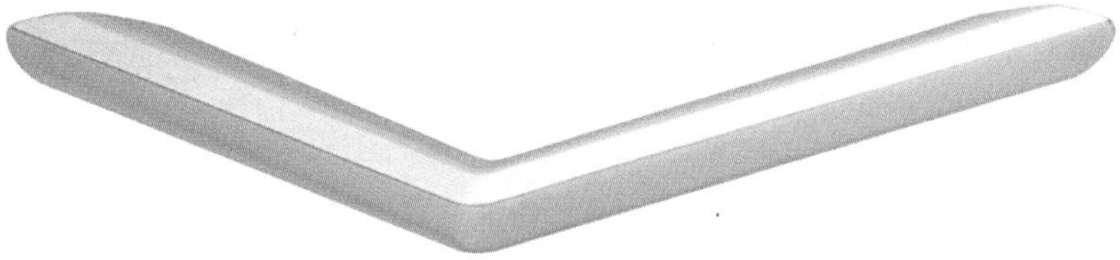

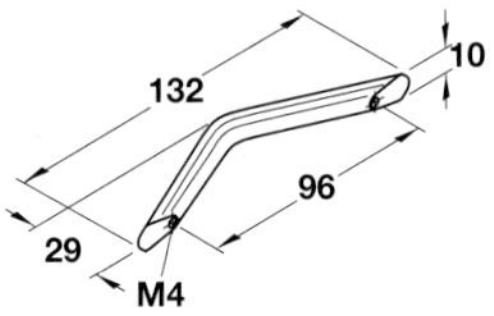

Chrome plated matt

Cat. No.	117.49.401

Packing: 25 pcs.

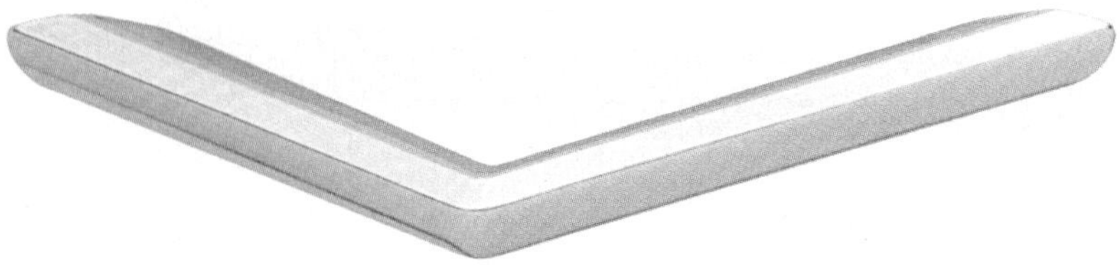

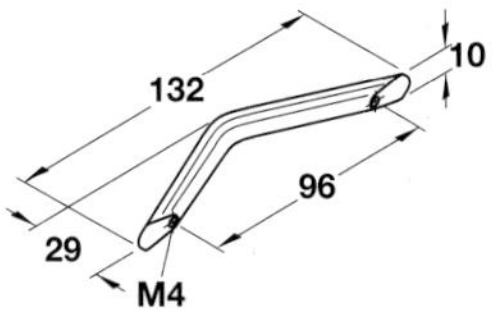

Gold colored polished

Cat. No.	117.49.803

Packing: 25 pcs.

Zinc handles

Nickel plated matt

Cat. No.	102.41.611

Packing: 25 pcs.

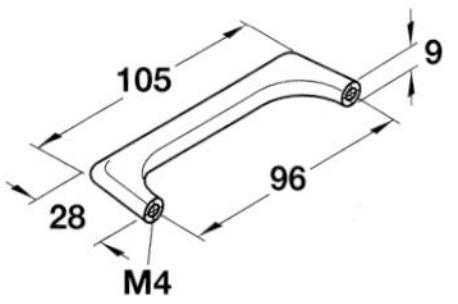

Chrome plated polished

Cat. No.	102.42.216

Packing: 25 pcs.

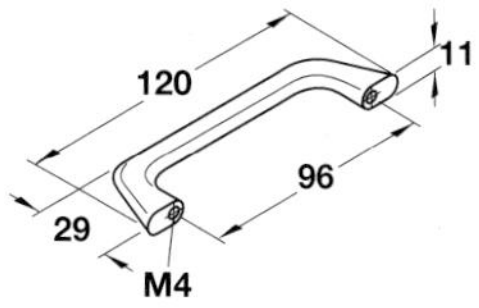

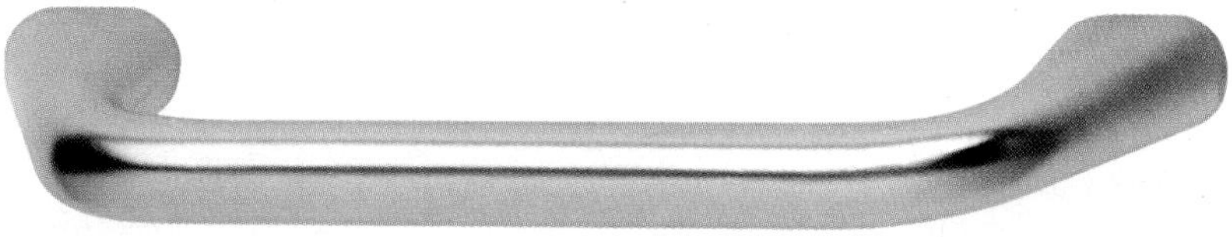

Nickel plated matt

Cat. No.	102.42.618

Packing: 25 pcs.

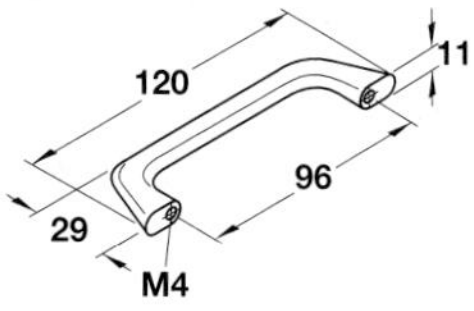

Gold colored polished

Cat. No.	102.42.814

Packing: 25 pcs.

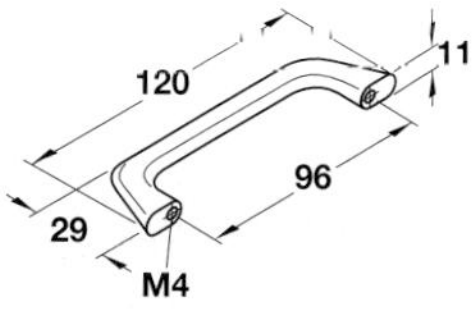

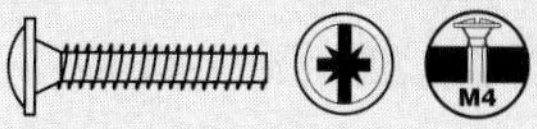

Threaded Screws M4
Combined slot, suitable for flat or cross blades
Finish: steel, zinc-plated

Length	Cat. No.
10 mm	022.35.109
12 mm	022.35.127
15 mm	022.35.154
18 mm	022.35.181
20 mm	022.35.207
22 mm	022.35.225
23 mm	022.35.234
25 mm	022.35.252
28 mm	022.35.289
30 mm	022.35.305
35 mm	022.35.350
38 mm	022.35.387
40 mm	022.35.403
45 mm	022.35.458
50 mm	022.35.501
60 mm	022.35.609

Packing: 100 and 1000 pcs.

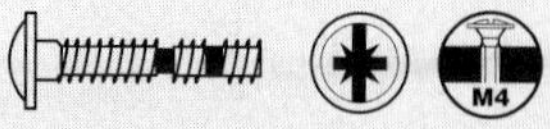

Threaded Breakoff Screw M4
Combined slot, suitable for flat or cross blades
Finish: steel, zinc-plated

Length	Cat. No.
1 3/4" x 3/4"	022.35.887

Packing: 100 and 1000 pcs.

HÄFELE

Zinc Handles

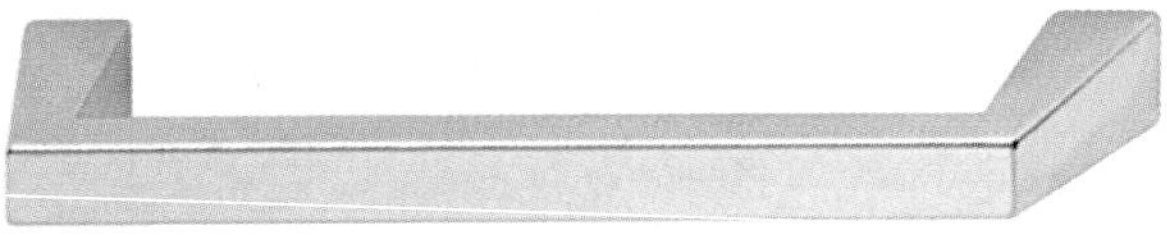

Chrome plated polished

Size A x B	Dimension C	Catalog No.
80 x 22	70	102.17.259
100 x 23	90	102.17.213
125 x 23	115	102.17.286

Packing: 25 pcs.

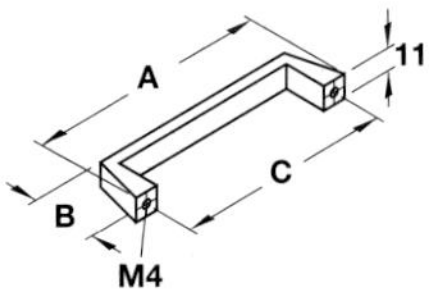

Nickel plated matt

Catalog No.	102.17.400

Packing: 25 pcs.

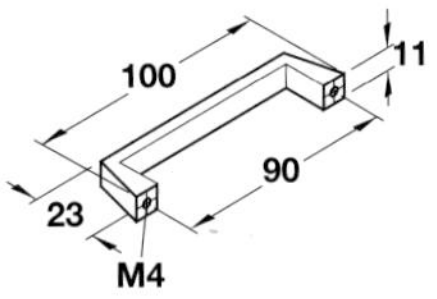

Gold colored polished

Catalog No.	102.17.802

Packing: 25 pcs.

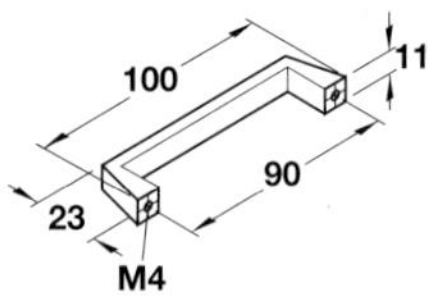

Black matt

Size A x B	Dimension C	Catalog No.
80 x 22	70	102.17.357
100 x 23	90	102.17.302

Packing: 25 pcs.

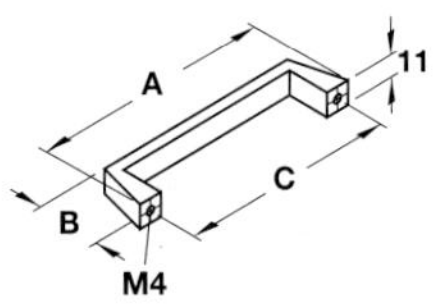

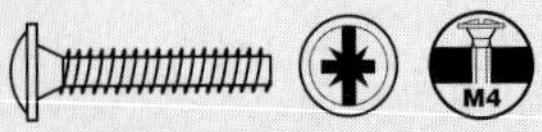

Threaded Screws M4

Combined slot, suitable for flat or cross blades

Finish: steel, zinc-plated

Length	Cat. No.
10 mm	022.35.109
12 mm	022.35.127
15 mm	022.35.154
18 mm	022.35.181
20 mm	022.35.207
22 mm	022.35.225
23 mm	022.35.234
25 mm	022.35.252
28 mm	022.35.289
30 mm	022.35.305
35 mm	022.35.350
38 mm	022.35.387
40 mm	022.35.403
45 mm	022.35.458
50 mm	022.35.501
60 mm	022.35.609

Packing: 100 and 1000 pcs.

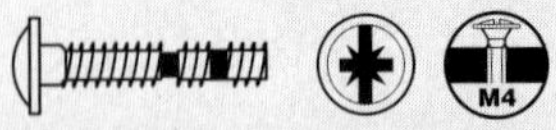

Threaded Breakoff Screw M4

Combined slot, suitable for flat or cross blades

Finish: steel, zinc-plated

Length	Cat. No.
1 3/4" x 3/4"	022.35.887

Packing: 100 and 1000 pcs.

Dimensional data not binding. We reserve the right to alter specifications without notice.

Zinc Handles

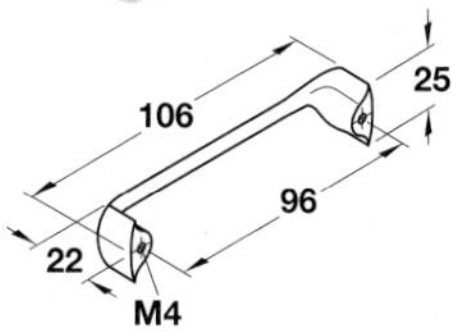

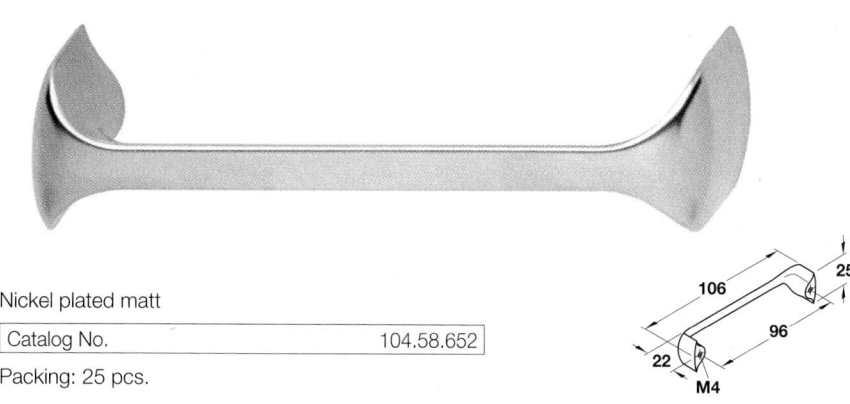

Nickel plated matt

Catalog No.	104.58.652

Packing: 25 pcs.

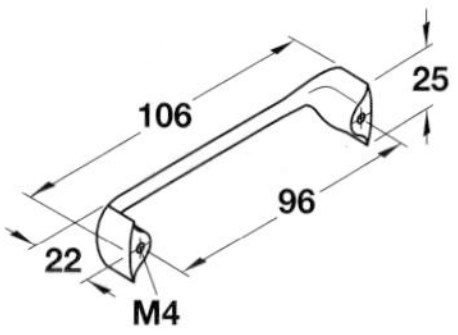

Gold colored polished

Catalog No.	104.58.858

Packing: 25 pcs.

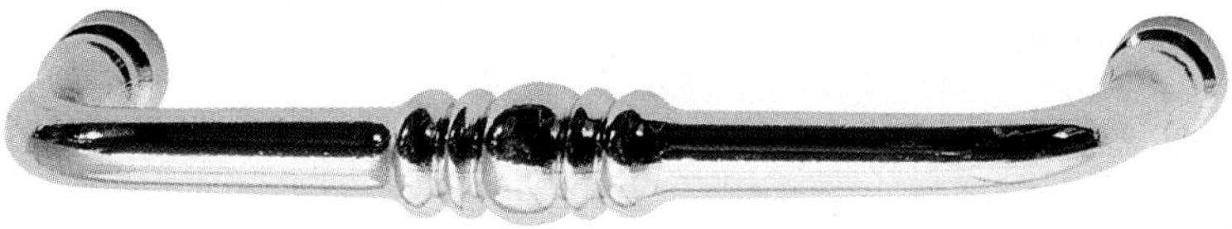

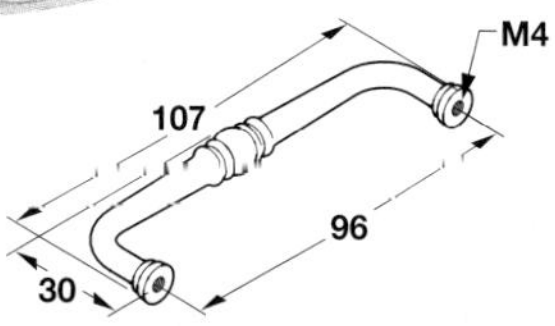

Gold polished

Cat. No.	121.64.822

Packing: 25 pcs.

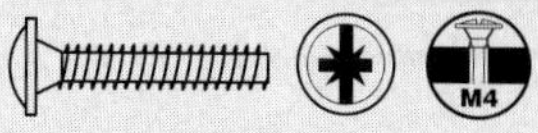

Threaded Screws M4
Combined slot, suitable for flat or cross blades
Finish: steel, zinc-plated

Length	Cat. No.
10 mm	022.35.109
12 mm	022.35.127
15 mm	022.35.154
18 mm	022.35.181
20 mm	022.35.207
22 mm	022.35.225
23 mm	022.35.234
25 mm	022.35.252
28 mm	022.35.289
30 mm	022.35.305
35 mm	022.35.350
38 mm	022.35.387
40 mm	022.35.403
45 mm	022.35.458
50 mm	022.35.501
60 mm	022.35.609

Packing: 100 and 1000 pcs.

Threaded Breakoff Screw M4
Combined slot, suitable for flat or cross blades
Finish: steel, zinc-plated

Length	Cat. No.
1 3/4" x 3/4"	022.35.887

Packing: 100 and 1000 pcs.

Dimensional data not binding. We reserve the right to alter specifications without notice.

HÄFELE

Zinc Handles

Threaded Screws M4
Combined slot, suitable for flat or cross blades
Finish: steel, zinc-plated

Length	Cat. No.
10 mm	022.35.109
12 mm	022.35.127
15 mm	022.35.154
18 mm	022.35.181
20 mm	022.35.207
22 mm	022.35.225
23 mm	022.35.234
25 mm	022.35.252
28 mm	022.35.289
30 mm	022.35.305
35 mm	022.35.350
38 mm	022.35.387
40 mm	022.35.403
45 mm	022.35.458
50 mm	022.35.501
60 mm	022.35.609

Packing: 100 and 1000 pcs.

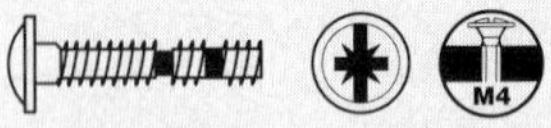

Threaded Breakoff Screw M4
Combined slot, suitable for flat or cross blades
Finish: steel, zinc-plated

Length	Cat. No.
1 3/4" x 3/4"	022.35.887

Packing: 100 and 1000 pcs.

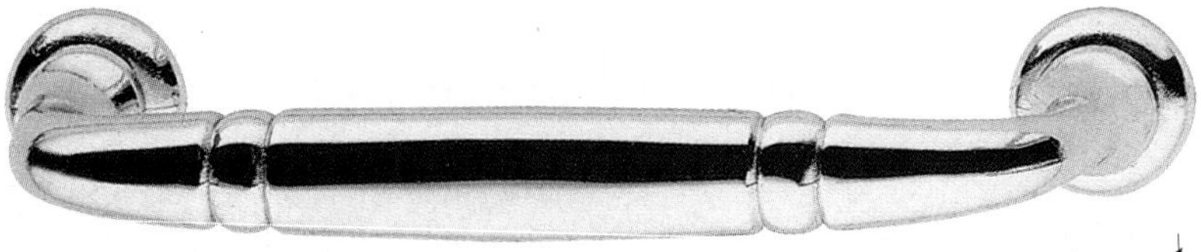

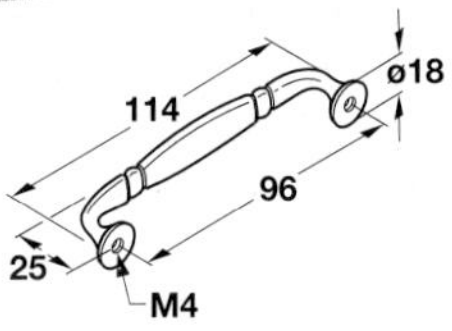

Brass polished & lacquered

Cat. No.	121.46.806

Packing: 25 pcs.

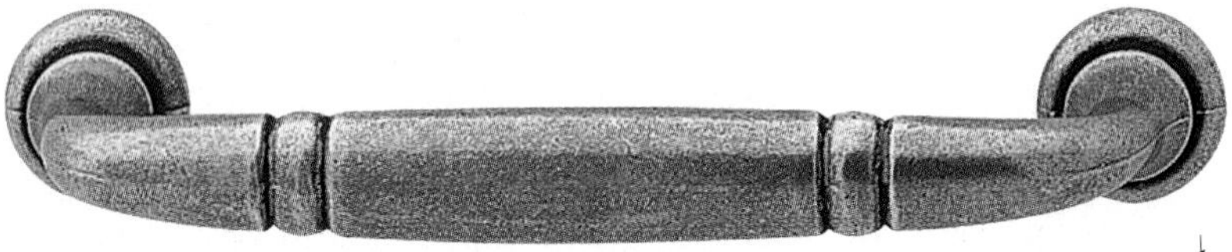

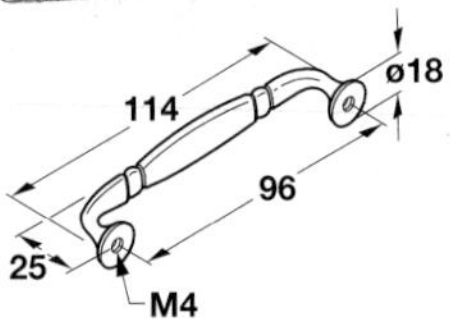

Antique bronze

Cat. No.	121.46.100

Packing: 25 pcs.

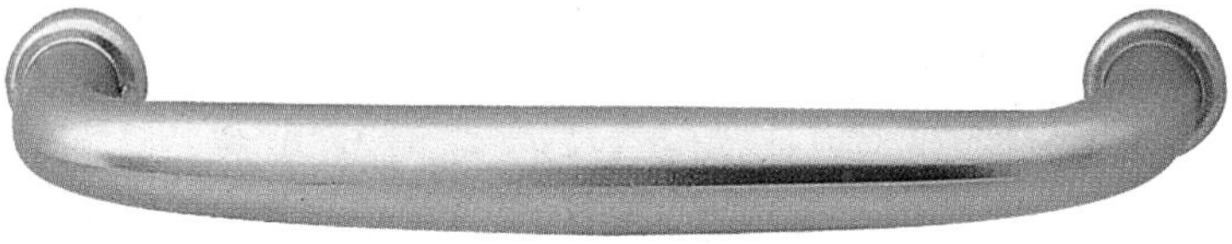

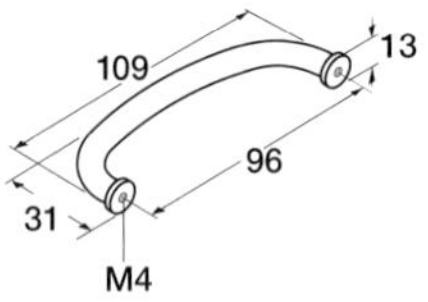

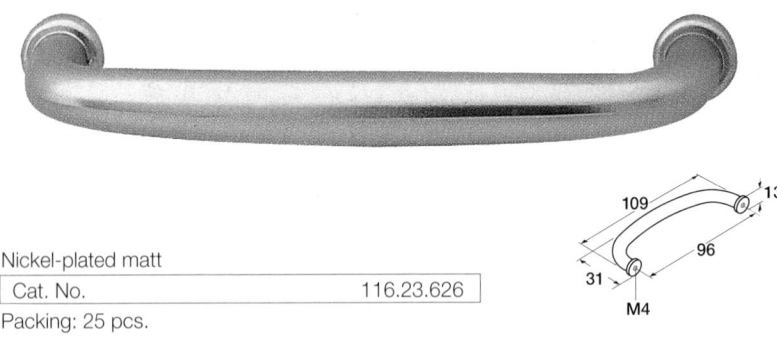

Nickel-plated matt

Cat. No.	116.23.626

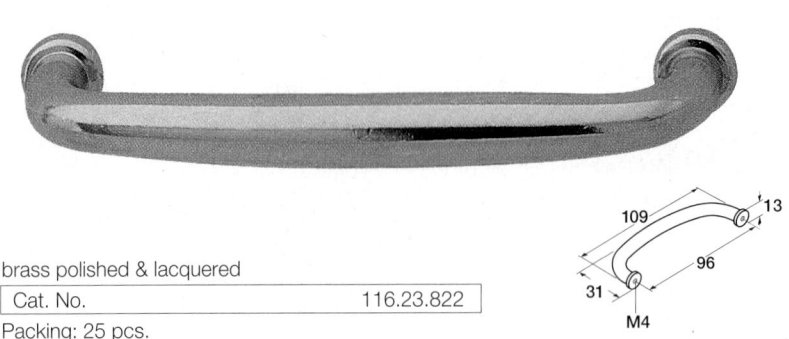

Packing: 25 pcs.

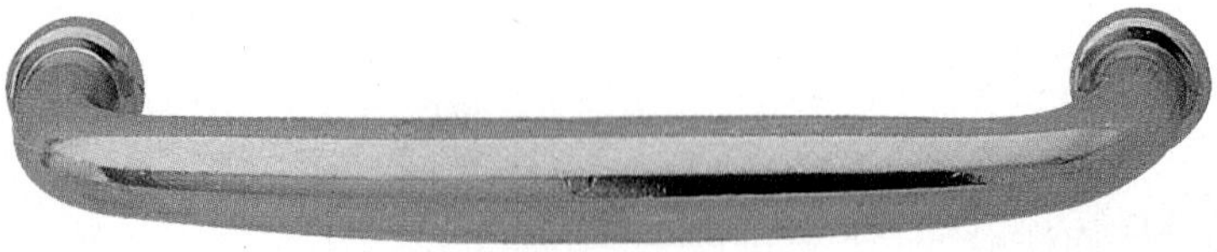

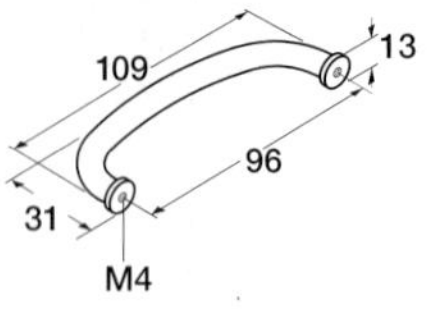

brass polished & lacquered

Cat. No.	116.23.822

Packing: 25 pcs.

Dimensional data not binding. We reserve the right to alter specifications without notice.

Zinc Handles

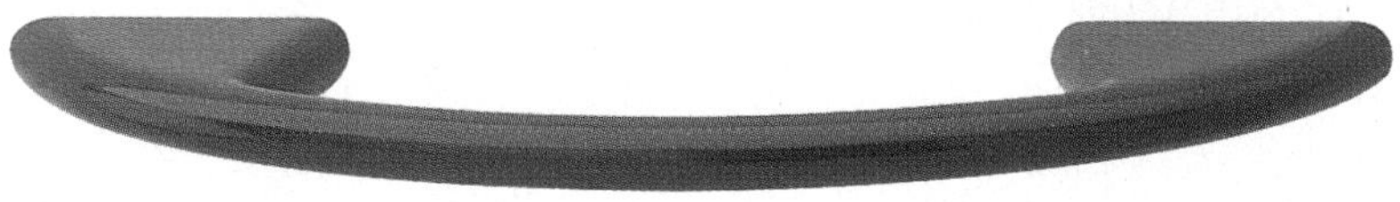

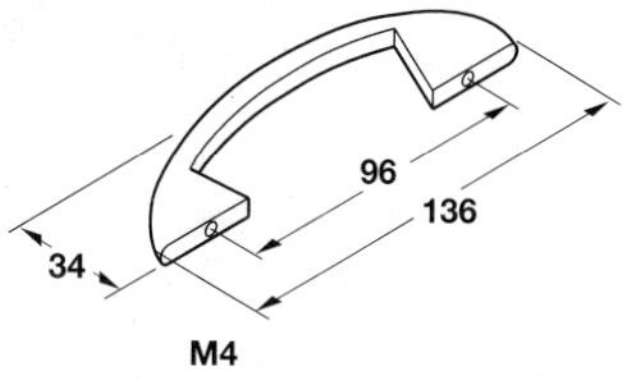

Metallic gray

Cat. No.	102.49.304

Packing: 25 each

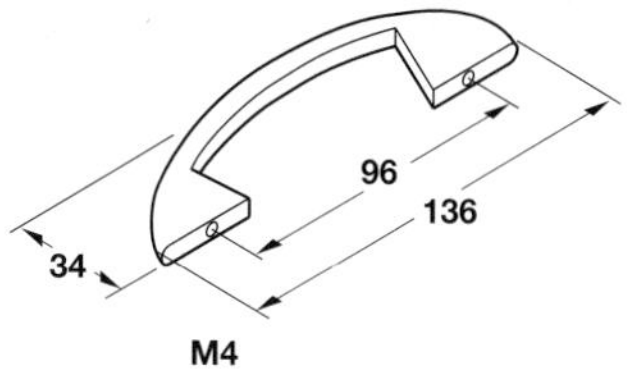

Silver metallic

Cat. No.	102.49.402

Packing: 25 each

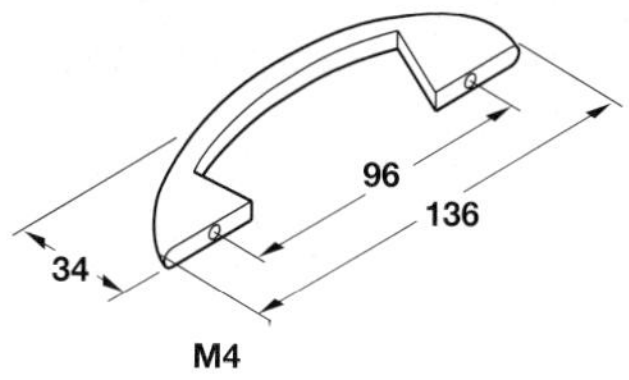

Black matt

Cat. No.	102.49.300

Packing: 25 each

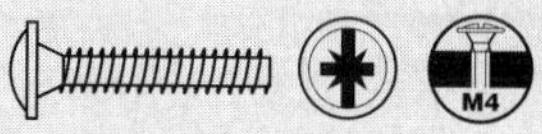

Threaded Screws M4
Combined slot, suitable for flat or cross blades
Finish: steel, zinc-plated

Length	Cat. No.
10 mm	022.35.109
12 mm	022.35.127
15 mm	022.35.154
18 mm	022.35.181
20 mm	022.35.207
22 mm	022.35.225
23 mm	022.35.234
25 mm	022.35.252
28 mm	022.35.289
30 mm	022.35.305
35 mm	022.35.350
38 mm	022.35.387
40 mm	022.35.403
45 mm	022.35.458
50 mm	022.35.501
60 mm	022.35.609

Packing: 100 and 1000 pcs.

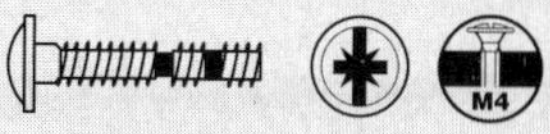

Threaded Breakoff Screw M4
Combined slot, suitable for flat or cross blades
Finish: steel, zinc-plated

Length	Cat. No.
1 3/4" x 3/4"	022.35.887

Packing: 100 and 1000 pcs.

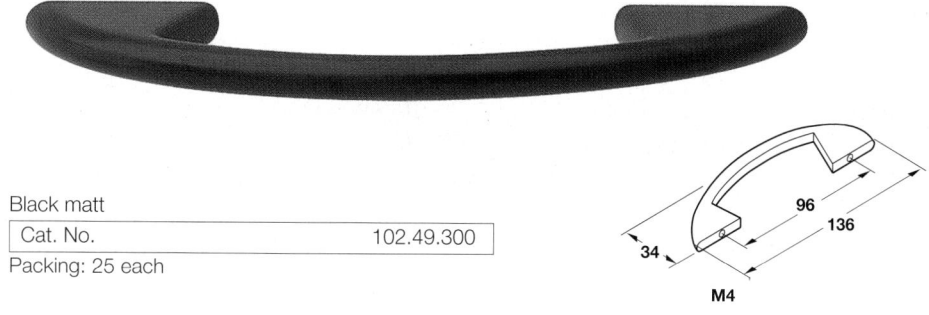

HÄFELE

Zinc Handles

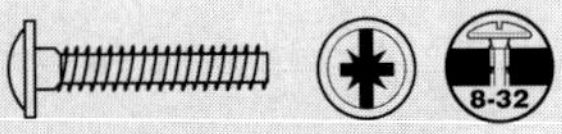

Threaded Screws 8-32
Combined slot, suitable for flat or cross blades

Finish: steel, yellow chromated

Length	Cat. No.
22 mm	022.25.229
25 mm	022.25.256
32 mm	022.25.327
38 mm	022.25.381
45 mm	022.25.452

Packing: 100 and 1000 pcs.

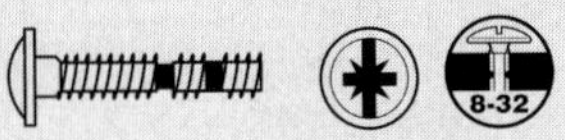

Threaded Breakoff Screw 8-32
Combined slot, suitable for flat or cross blades

Finish: steel, yellow chromated

Length	Cat. No.
1 3/4" x 3/4"	022.25.881

Packing: 100 and 1000 pcs.

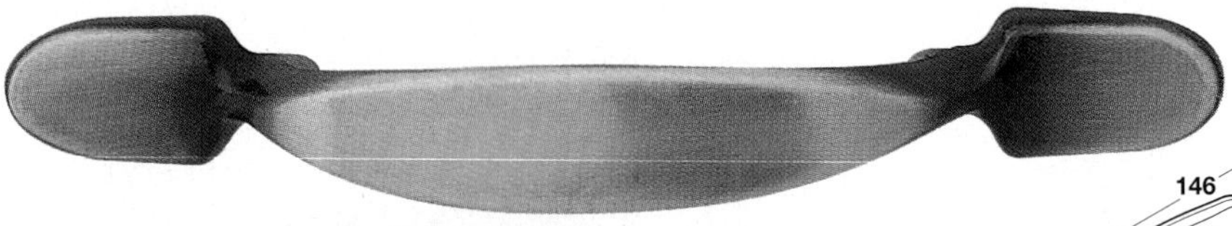

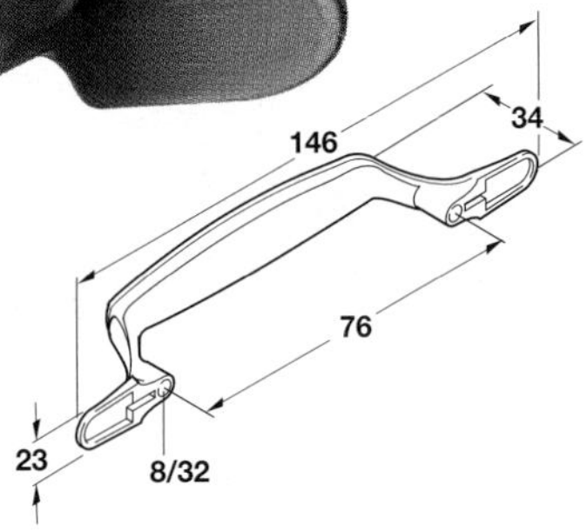

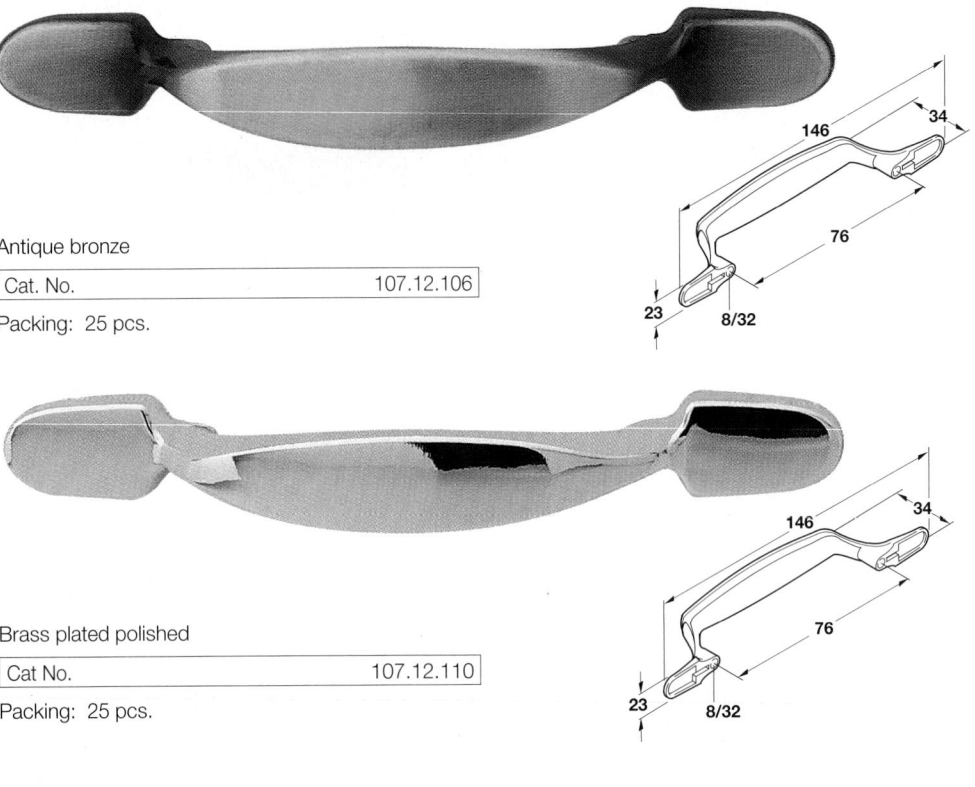

Antique bronze

Cat. No.	107.12.106

Packing: 25 pcs.

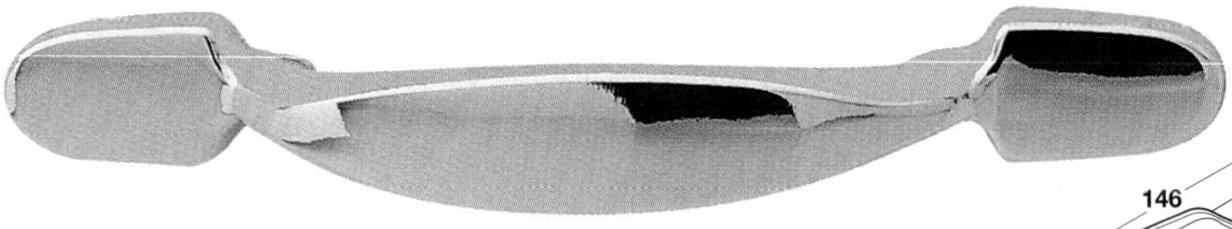

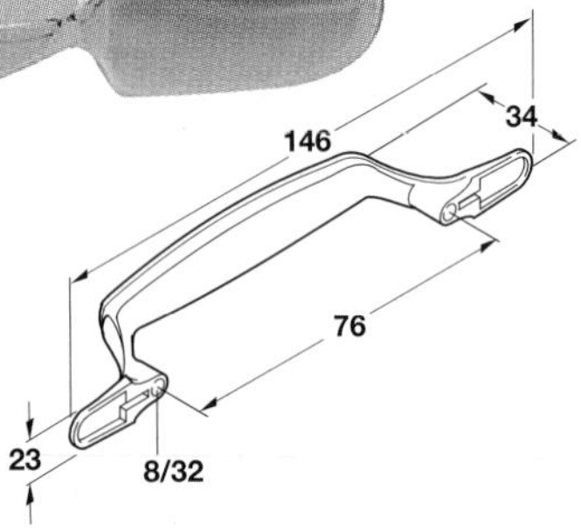

Brass plated polished

Cat No.	107.12.110

Packing: 25 pcs.

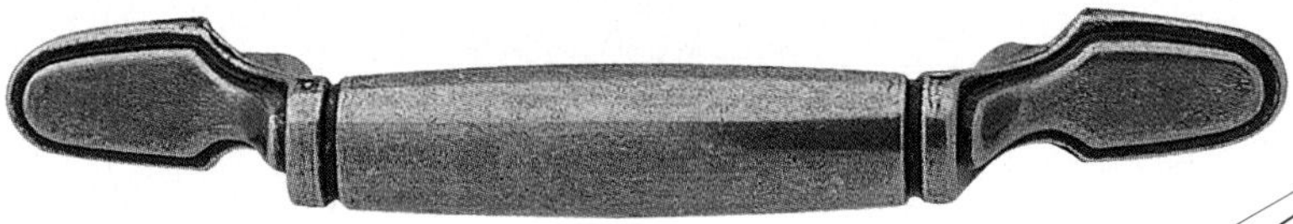

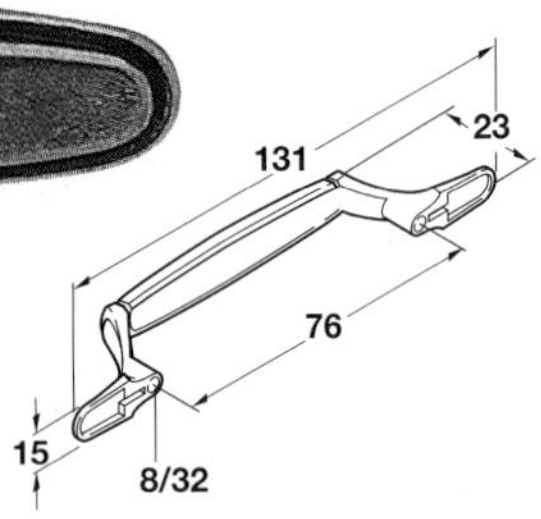

Antique english

Cat No.	107.13.112

Packing: 25 pcs.

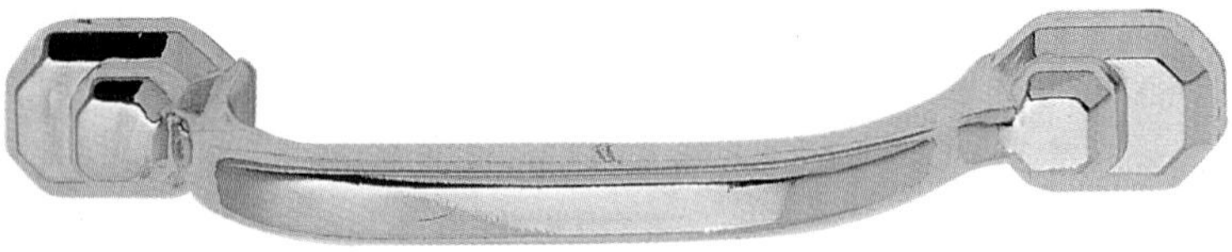

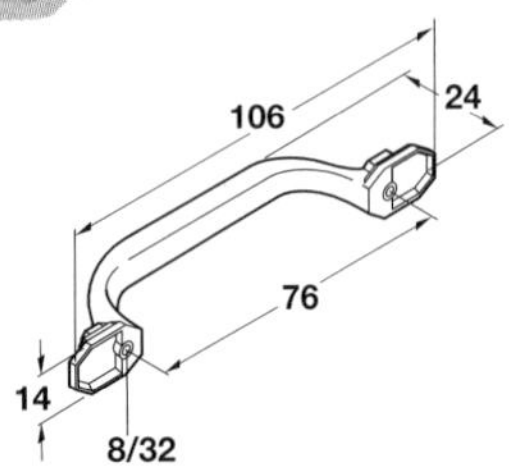

Brass plated polished

Cat No.	122.04.803

Packing: 25 pcs.

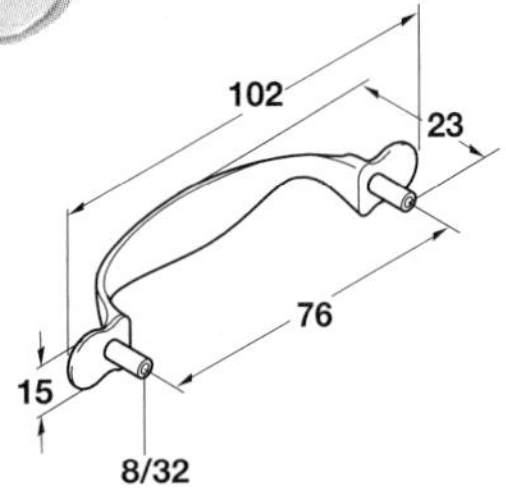

Brass plated polished

Cat No.	122.03.800

Packing: 25 pcs.

Dimensional data not binding.
We reserve the right to alter specifications without notice.

Zinc Handles

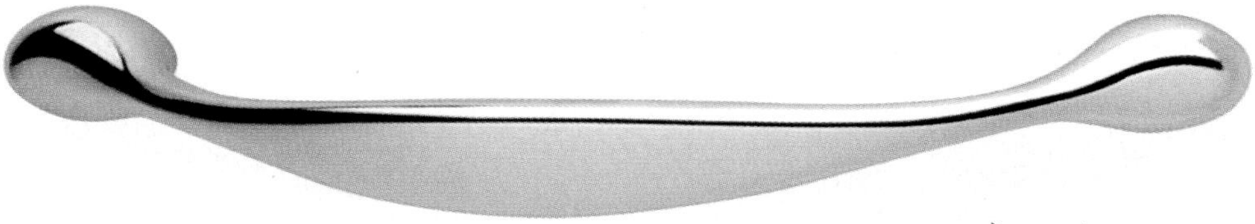

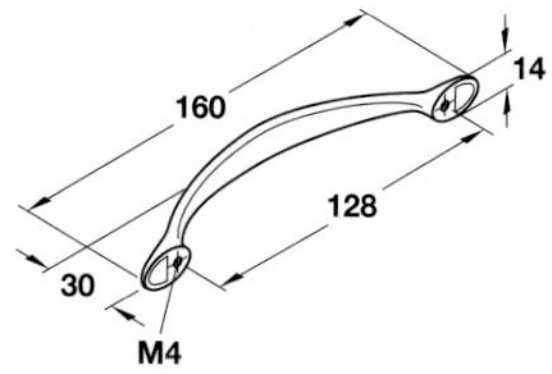

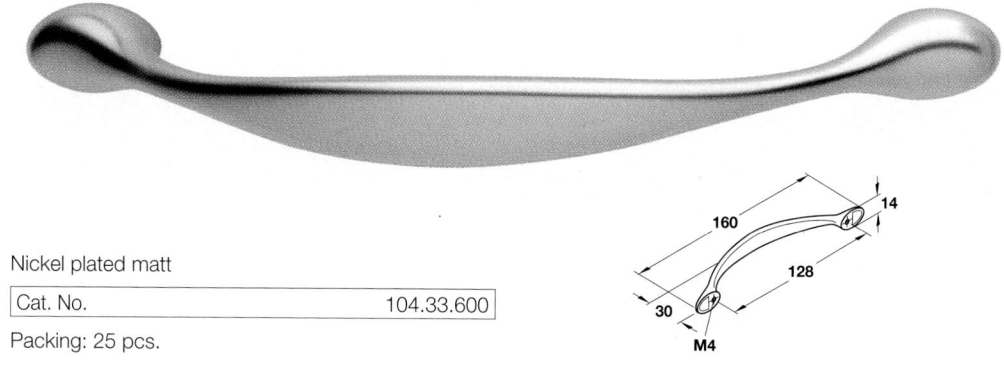

Chrome plated polished

Cat. No.	104.33.200

Packing: 25 pcs.

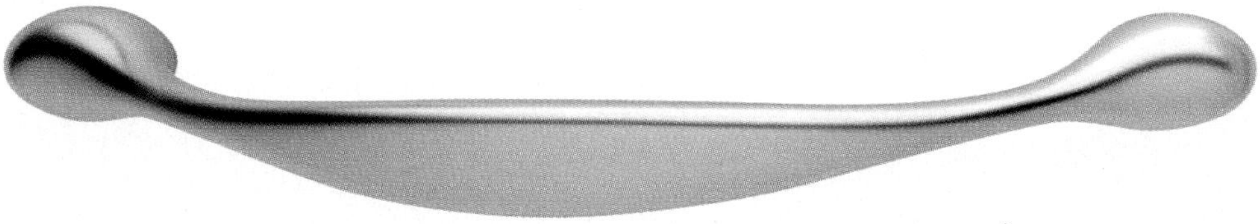

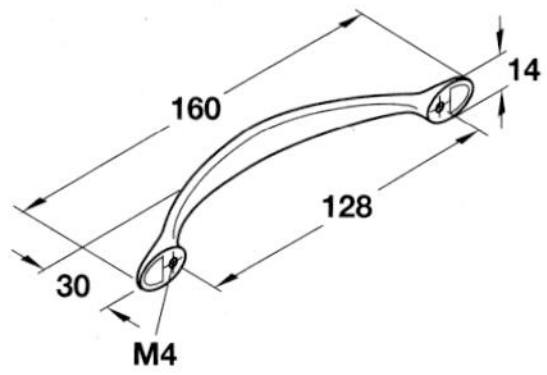

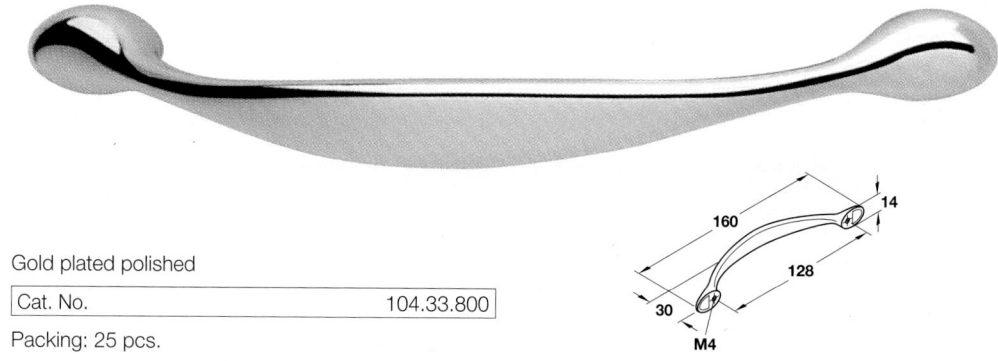

Nickel plated matt

Cat. No.	104.33.600

Packing: 25 pcs.

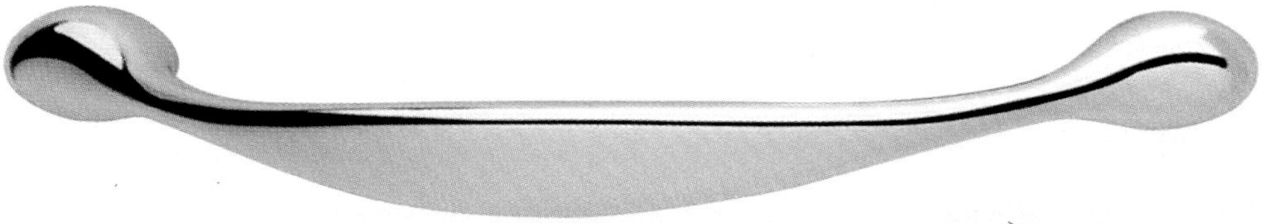

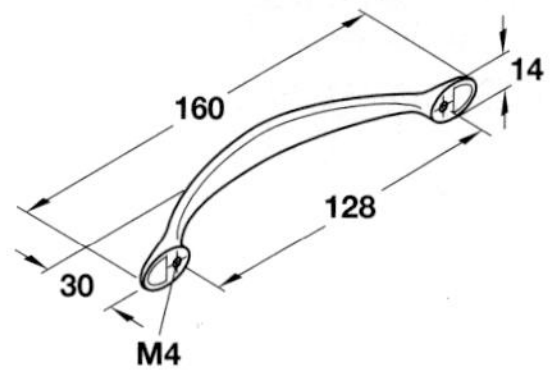

Gold plated polished

Cat. No.	104.33.800

Packing: 25 pcs.

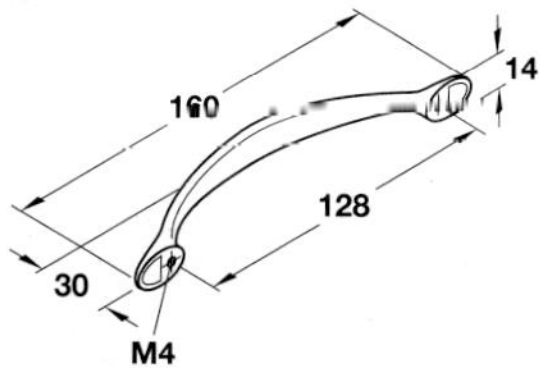

Black matt

Cat. No.	104.33.300

Packing: 25 pcs.

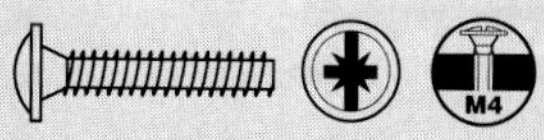

Threaded Screws M4
Combined slot, suitable for flat or cross blades

Finish: steel, zinc-plated

Length	Cat. No.
10 mm	022.35.109
12 mm	022.35.127
15 mm	022.35.154
18 mm	022.35.181
20 mm	022.35.207
22 mm	022.35.225
23 mm	022.35.234
25 mm	022.35.252
28 mm	022.35.289
30 mm	022.35.305
35 mm	022.35.350
38 mm	022.35.387
40 mm	022.35.403
45 mm	022.35.458
50 mm	022.35.501
60 mm	022.35.609

Packing: 100 and 1000 pcs.

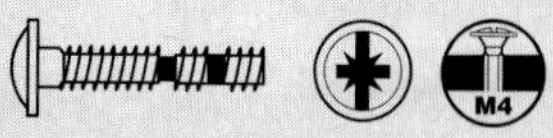

Threaded Breakoff Screw M4
Combined slot, suitable for flat or cross blades

Finish: steel, zinc-plated

Length	Cat. No.
1 3/4" x 3/4"	022.35.887

Packing: 100 and 1000 pcs.

HÄFELE

Zinc Handles

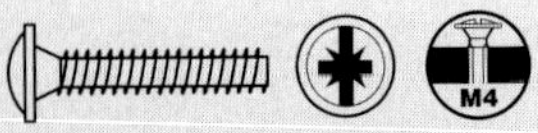

Threaded Screws M4
Combined slot, suitable for flat or cross blades

Finish: steel, zinc-plated

Length	Cat. No.
10 mm	022.35.109
12 mm	022.35.127
15 mm	022.35.154
18 mm	022.35.181
20 mm	022.35.207
22 mm	022.35.225
23 mm	022.35.234
25 mm	022.35.252
28 mm	022.35.289
30 mm	022.35.305
35 mm	022.35.350
38 mm	022.35.387
40 mm	022.35.403
45 mm	022.35.458
50 mm	022.35.501
60 mm	022.35.609

Packing: 100 and 1000 pcs.

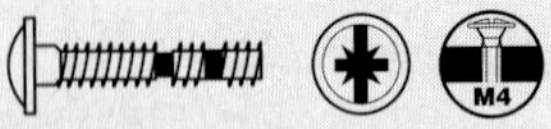

Threaded Breakoff Screw M4
Combined slot, suitable for flat or cross blades

Finish: steel, zinc-plated

Length	Cat. No.
1 3/4" x 3/4"	022.35.887

Packing: 100 and 1000 pcs.

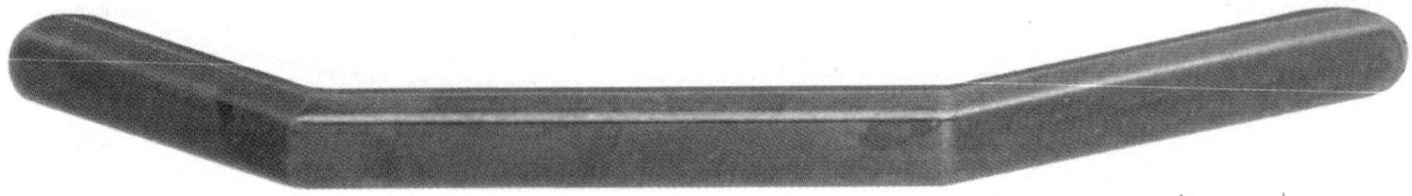

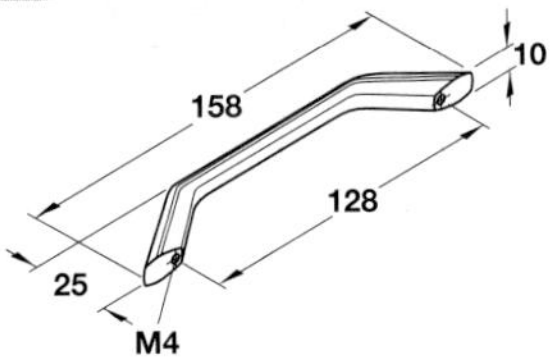

Copper

Cat. No.	102.60.030

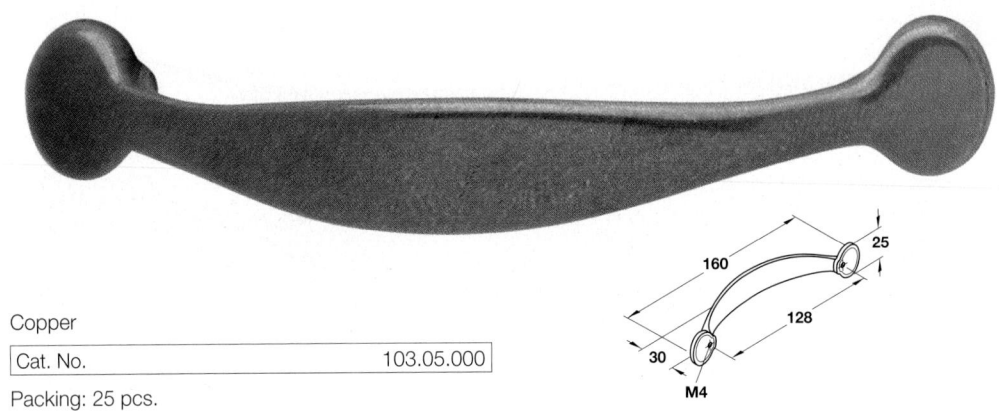

Packing: 25 pcs.

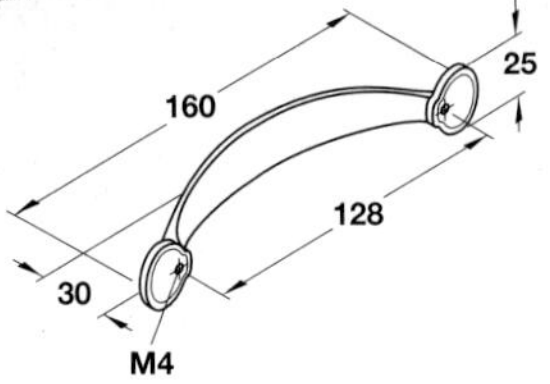

Copper

Cat. No.	103.05.000

Packing: 25 pcs.

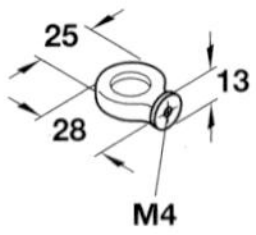

Copper

Cat. No.	134.58.000

Packing: 25 pcs.

Zinc Handles

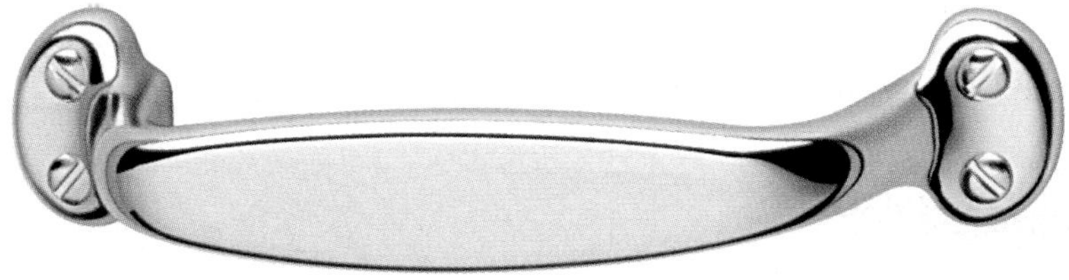

Chrome plated polished

Cat. No.	103.06.200

Packing: 25 pcs.

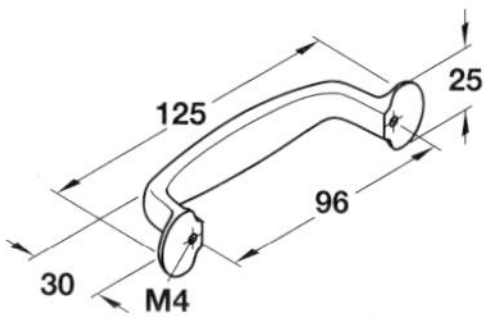

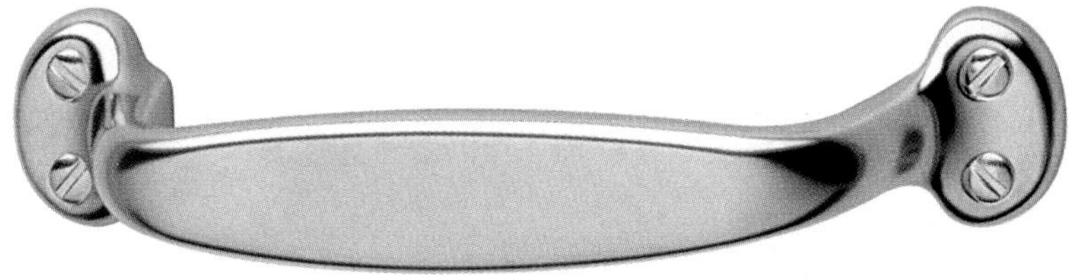

Nickel plated matt

Cat. No.	103.06.600

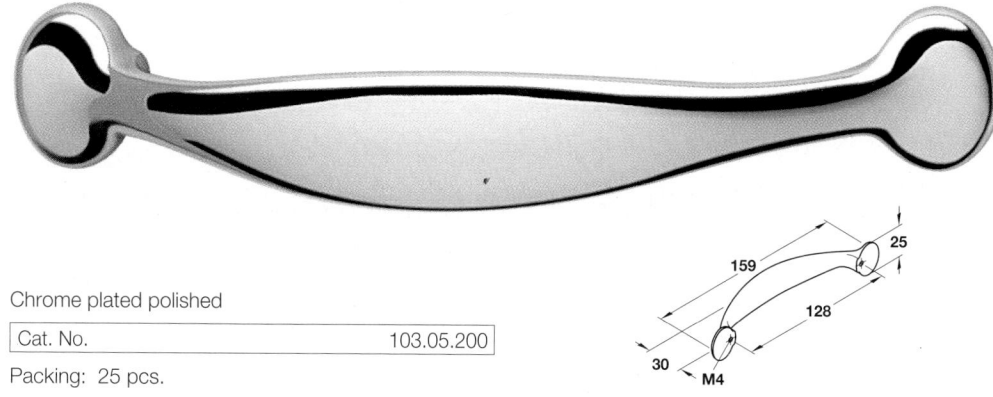

Packing: 25 pcs.

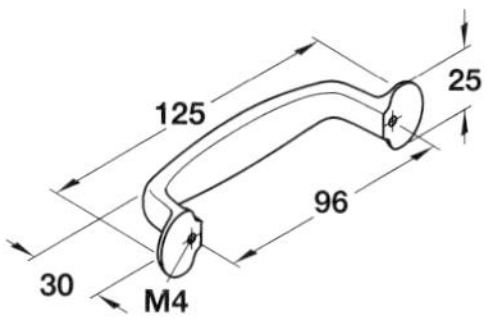

Chrome plated polished

Cat. No.	103.05.200

Packing: 25 pcs.

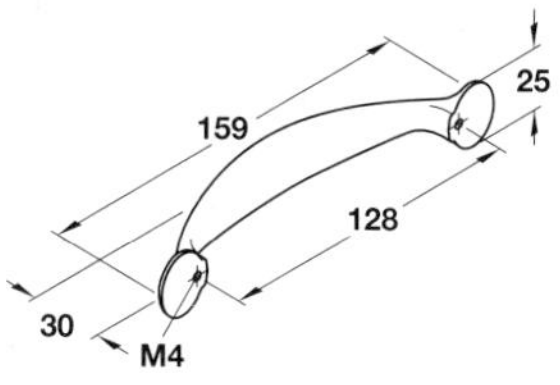

Nickel plated matt

Cat. No.	103.05.600

Packing: 25 pcs.

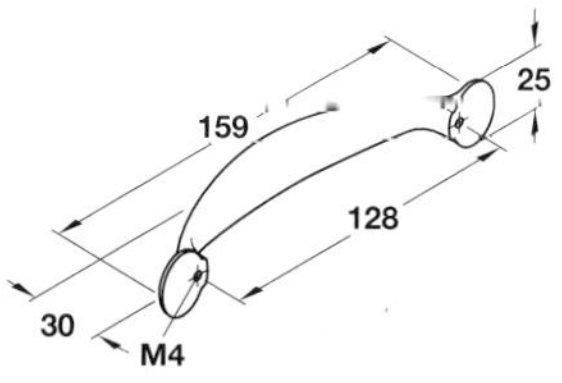

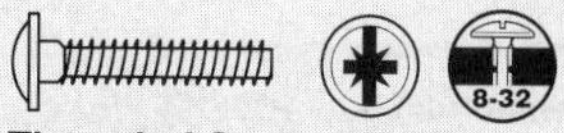

Threaded Screws 8-32
Combined slot, suitable for flat or cross blades

Finish: steel, yellow chromated

Length	Cat. No.
22 mm	022.25.229
25 mm	022.25.256
32 mm	022.25.327
38 mm	022.25.381
45 mm	022.25.452

Packing: 100 and 1000 pcs.

Threaded Screws M4
Combined slot, suitable for flat or cross blades

Finish: steel, zinc-plated

Length	Cat. No.
10 mm	022.35.109
12 mm	022.35.127
15 mm	022.35.154
18 mm	022.35.181
20 mm	022.35.207
22 mm	022.35.225
23 mm	022.35.234
25 mm	022.35.252
28 mm	022.35.289
30 mm	022.35.305
35 mm	022.35.350
38 mm	022.35.387
40 mm	022.35.403
45 mm	022.35.458
50 mm	022.35.501
60 mm	022.35.609

Packing: 100 and 1000 pcs.

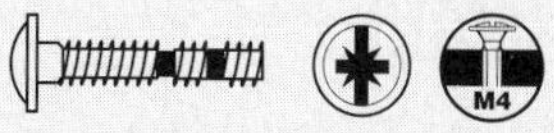

Threaded Breakoff Screw M4
Combined slot, suitable for flat or cross blades

Finish: steel, zinc-plated

Length	Cat. No.
1 3/4" x 3/4"	022.35.887

Packing: 100 and 1000 pcs.

Dimensional data not binding.
We reserve the right to alter specifications without notice.

HÄFELE

Zinc Handles

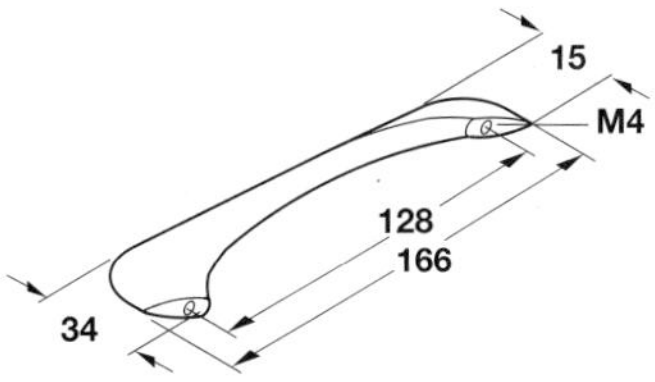

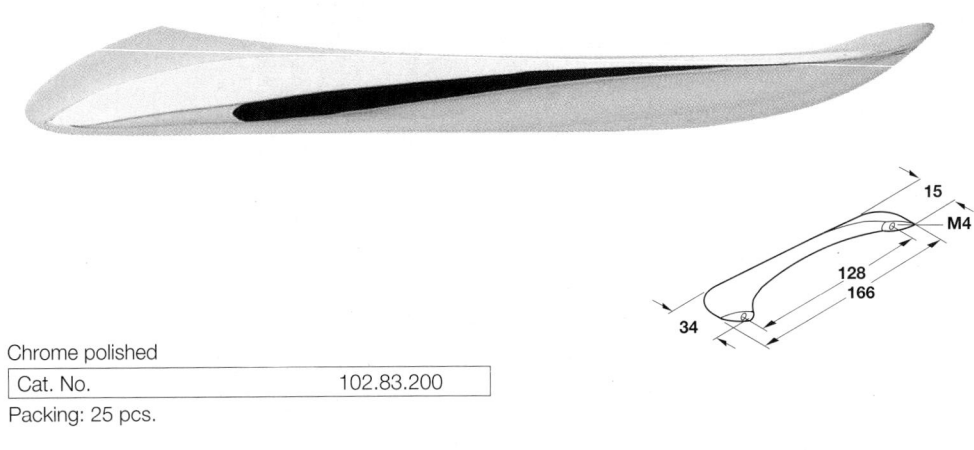

Chrome polished

Cat. No.	102.83.200

Packing: 25 pcs.

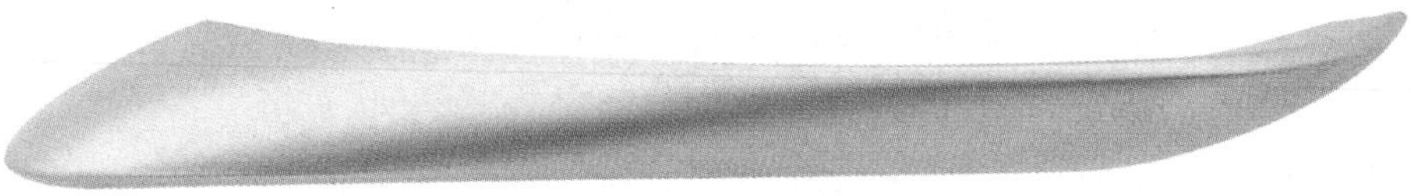

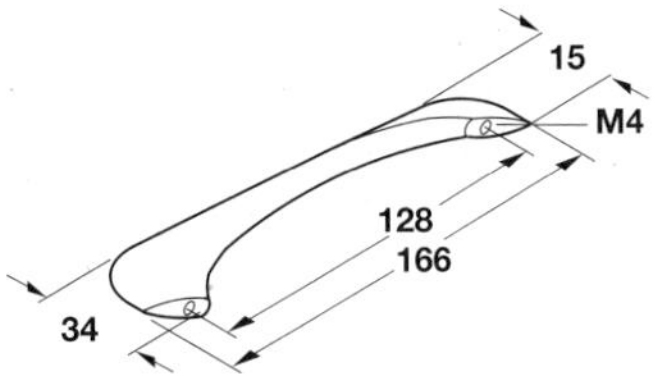

Nickel matt

Cat. No.	102.83.600

Packing: 25 pcs.

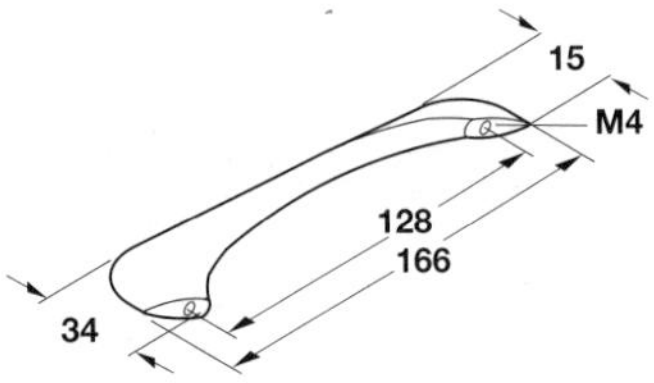

Gold colored polished

Cat. No.	102.83.800

Packing: 25 pcs.

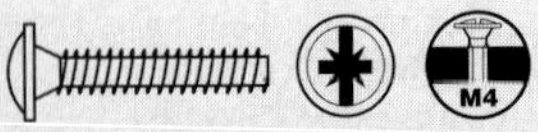

Threaded Screws M4
Combined slot, suitable for flat or cross blades

Finish: steel, zinc-plated

Length	Cat. No.
10 mm	022.35.109
12 mm	022.35.127
15 mm	022.35.154
18 mm	022.35.181
20 mm	022.35.207
22 mm	022.35.225
23 mm	022.35.234
25 mm	022.35.252
28 mm	022.35.289
30 mm	022.35.305
35 mm	022.35.350
38 mm	022.35.387
40 mm	022.35.403
45 mm	022.35.458
50 mm	022.35.501
60 mm	022.35.609

Packing: 100 and 1000 pcs.

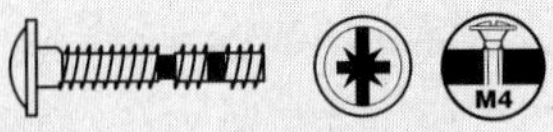

Threaded Breakoff Screw M4
Combined slot, suitable for flat or cross blades

Finish: steel, zinc-plated

Length	Cat. No.
1 3/4" x 3/4"	022.35.887

Packing: 100 and 1000 pcs.

Zinc Handles

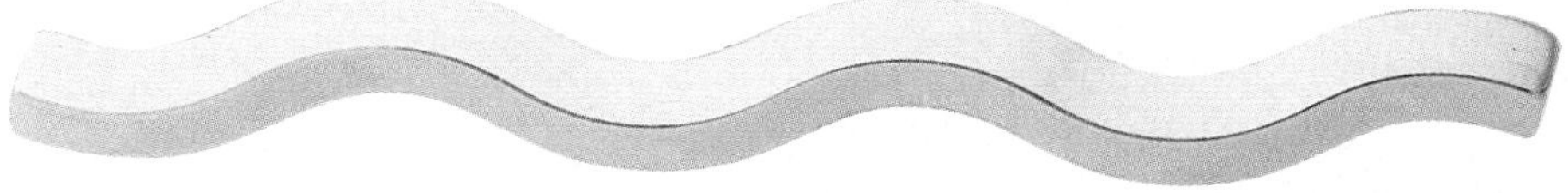

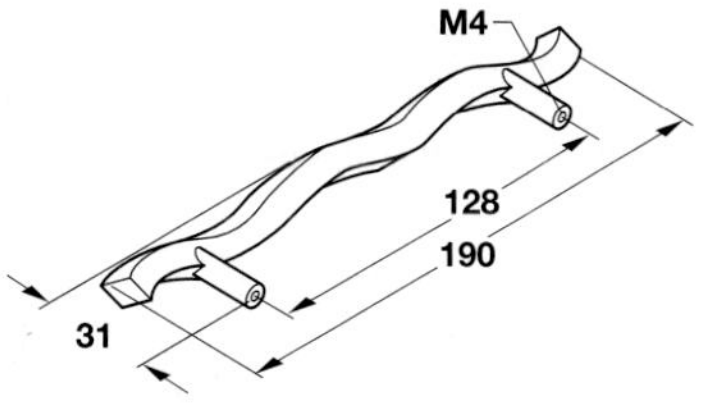

Chrome polished

Cat. No.	103.32.220

Packing: 25 pcs.

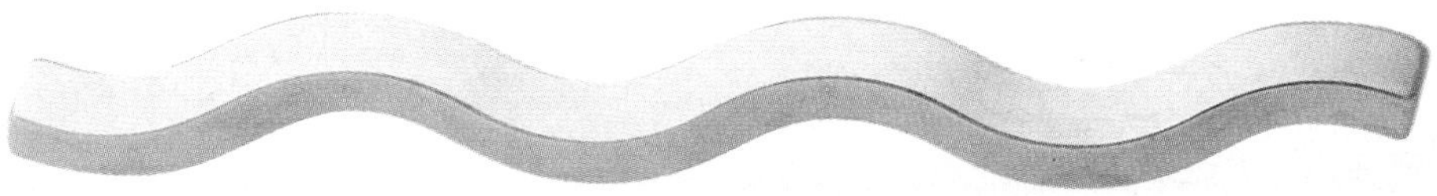

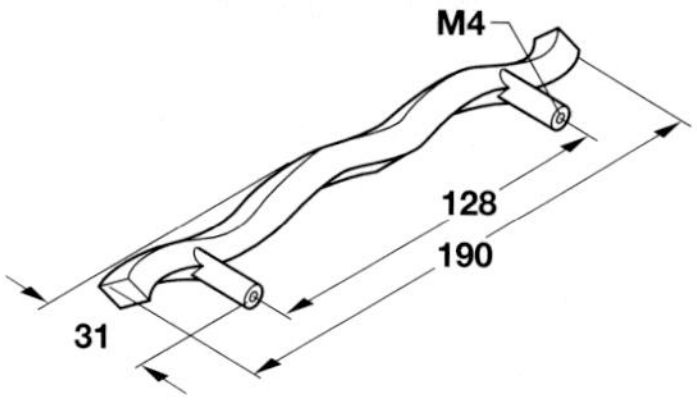

Nickel plated matt

Cat. No.	103.32.620

Packing: 25 pcs.

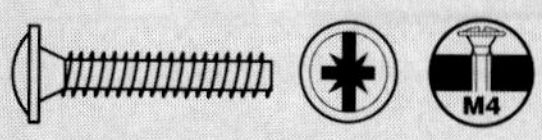

Threaded Screws M4
Combined slot, suitable for flat or cross blades

Finish: steel, zinc-plated

Length	Cat. No.
10 mm	022.35.109
12 mm	022.35.127
15 mm	022.35.154
18 mm	022.35.181
20 mm	022.35.207
22 mm	022.35.225
23 mm	022.35.234
25 mm	022.35.252
28 mm	022.35.289
30 mm	022.35.305
35 mm	022.35.350
38 mm	022.35.387
40 mm	022.35.403
45 mm	022.35.458
50 mm	022.35.501
60 mm	022.35.609

Packing: 100 and 1000 pcs.

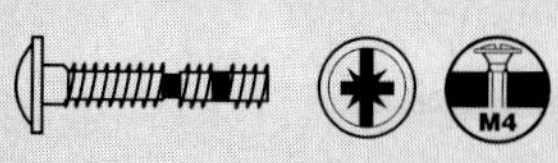

Threaded Breakoff Screw M4
Combined slot, suitable for flat or cross blades

Finish: steel, zinc-plated

Length	Cat. No.
1 3/4" x 3/4"	022.35.887

Packing: 100 and 1000 pcs.

HÄFELE

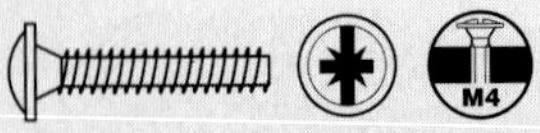

Threaded Screws M4

Combined slot, suitable for flat or cross blades

Finish: steel, zinc-plated

Length	Cat. No.
10 mm	022.35.109
12 mm	022.35.127
15 mm	022.35.154
18 mm	022.35.181
20 mm	022.35.207
22 mm	022.35.225
23 mm	022.35.234
25 mm	022.35.252
28 mm	022.35.289
30 mm	022.35.305
35 mm	022.35.350
38 mm	022.35.387
40 mm	022.35.403
45 mm	022.35.458
50 mm	022.35.501
60 mm	022.35.609

Packing: 100 and 1000 pcs.

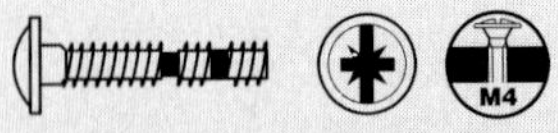

Threaded Breakoff Screw M4

Combined slot, suitable for flat or cross blades

Finish: steel, zinc-plated

Length	Cat. No.
1 3/4" x 3/4"	022.35.887

Packing: 100 and 1000 pcs.

Zinc Handles

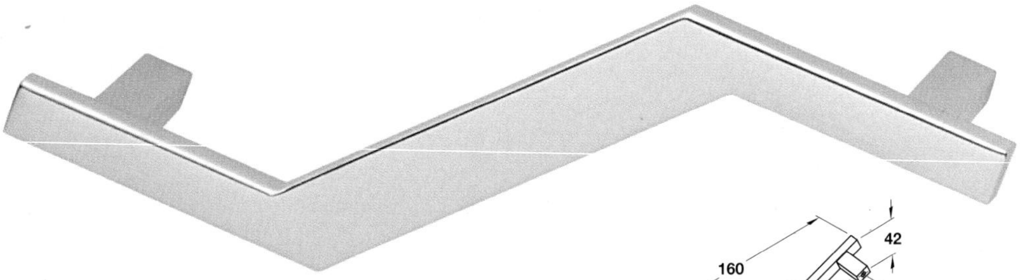

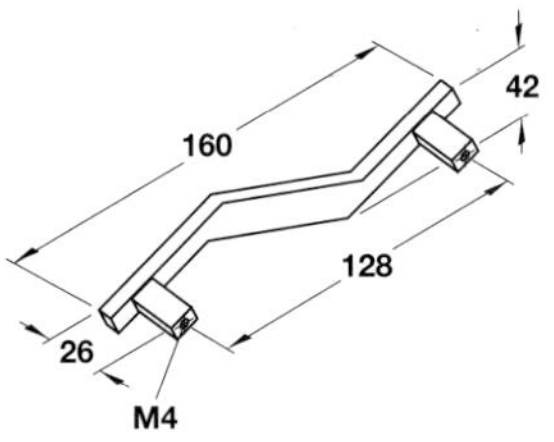

Chrome plated polished

Cat. No.	103.16.200

Packing: 25 pcs.

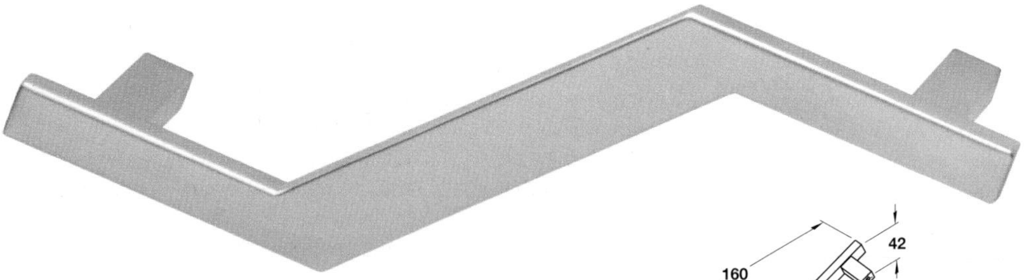

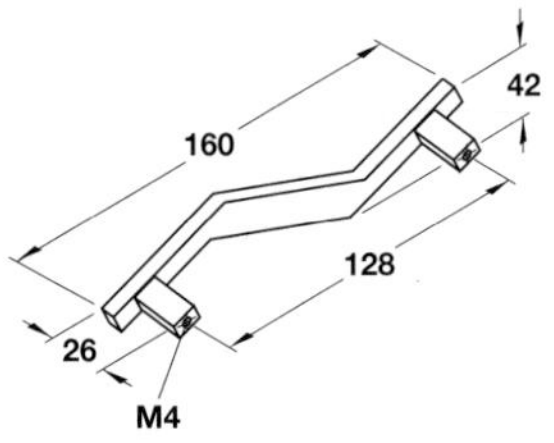

Nickel plated matt

Cat. No.	103.16.600

Packing: 25 pcs.

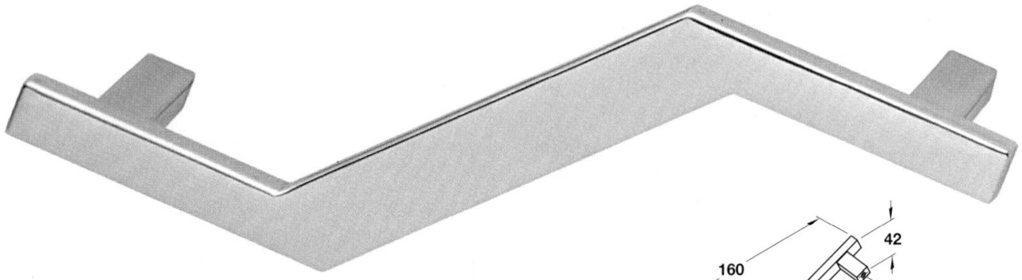

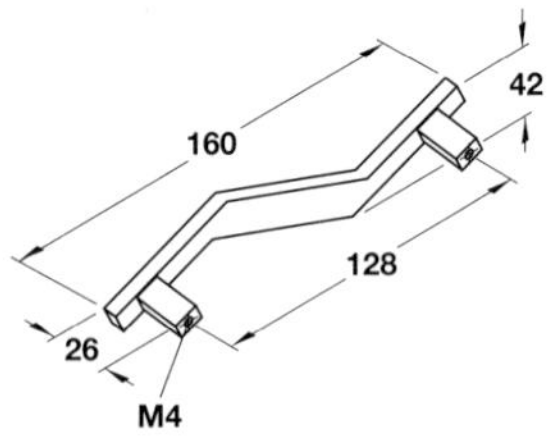

Gold colored polished

Cat. No.	103.16.800

Packing: 25 pcs.

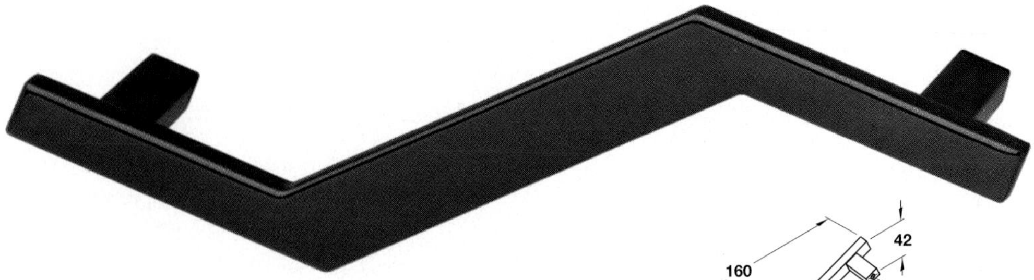

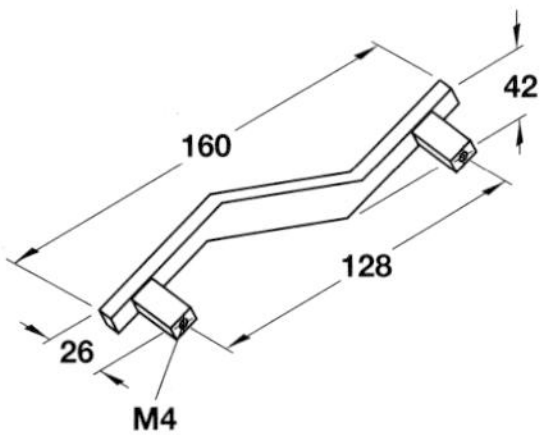

Black gloss

Cat. No.	103.16.300

Packing: 25 pcs.

Zinc Handles

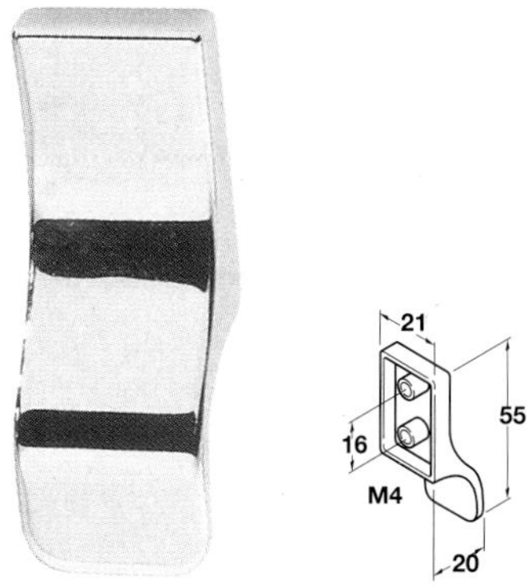

Polished chrome

Cat. No.	104.39.200

Packing: 25 pcs.

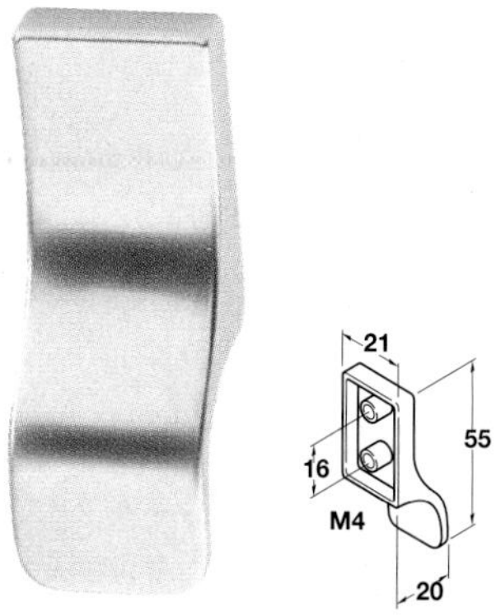

Matt chrome plated

Cat. No.	104.39.406

Packing: 25 pcs.

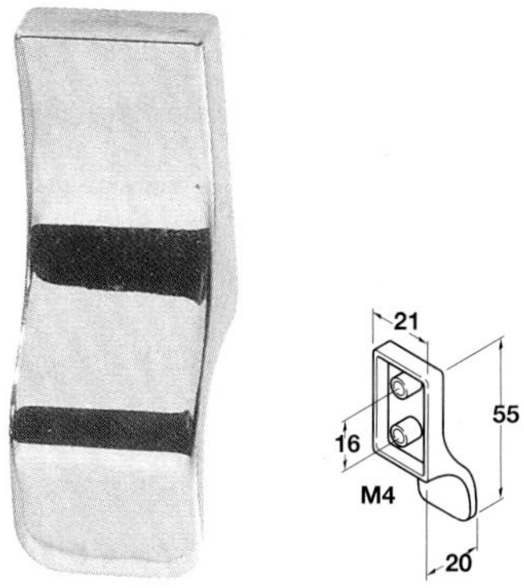

Gold plated polished

Cat. No.	104.39.808

Packing: 25 pcs.

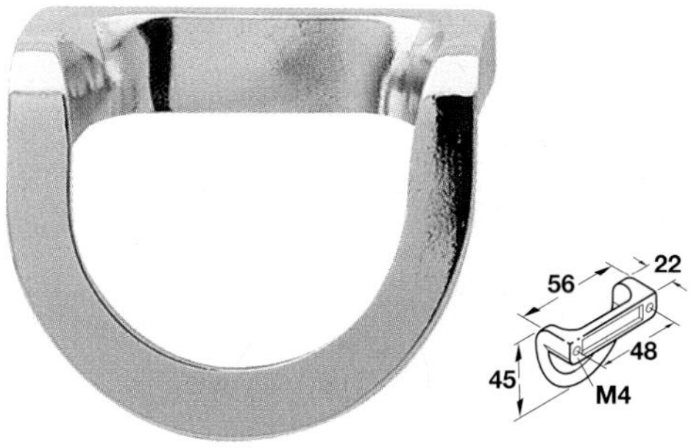

Chrome plated polished

Cat. No.	104.92.207

Packing: 25 pcs.

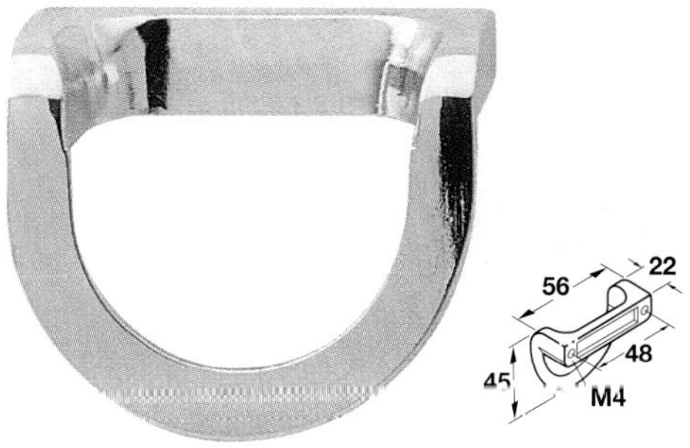

Gold colored polished

Cat. No.	104.92.805

Packing: 25 pcs.

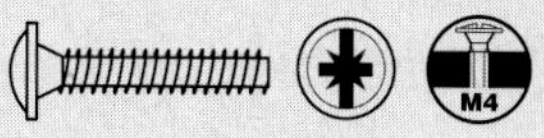

Threaded Screws M4
Combined slot, suitable for flat or cross blades

Finish: steel, zinc-plated

Length	Cat. No.
10 mm	022.35.109
12 mm	022.35.127
15 mm	022.35.154
18 mm	022.35.181
20 mm	022.35.207
22 mm	022.35.225
23 mm	022.35.234
25 mm	022.35.252
28 mm	022.35.289
30 mm	022.35.305
35 mm	022.35.350
38 mm	022.35.387
40 mm	022.35.403
45 mm	022.35.458
50 mm	022.35.501
60 mm	022.35.609

Packing: 100 and 1000 pcs.

Threaded Breakoff Screw M4
Combined slot, suitable for flat or cross blades

Finish: steel, zinc-plated

Length	Cat. No.
1 3/4" x 3/4"	022.35.887

Packing: 100 and 1000 pcs.

Zinc Handles

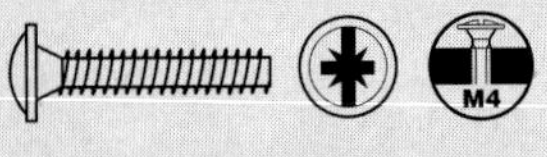

Threaded Screws M4
Combined slot, suitable for flat or cross blades
Finish: steel, zinc-plated

Length	Cat. No.
10 mm	022.35.109
12 mm	022.35.127
15 mm	022.35.154
18 mm	022.35.181
20 mm	022.35.207
22 mm	022.35.225
23 mm	022.35.234
25 mm	022.35.252
28 mm	022.35.289
30 mm	022.35.305
35 mm	022.35.350
38 mm	022.35.387
40 mm	022.35.403
45 mm	022.35.458
50 mm	022.35.501
60 mm	022.35.609

Packing: 100 and 1000 pcs.

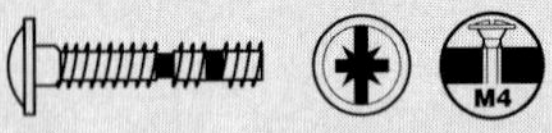

Threaded Breakoff Screw M4
Combined slot, suitable for flat or cross blades
Finish: steel, zinc-plated

Length	Cat. No.
1 3/4" x 3/4"	022.35.887

Packing: 100 and 1000 pcs.

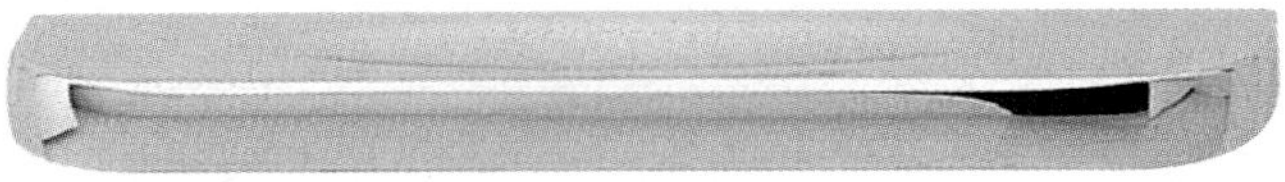

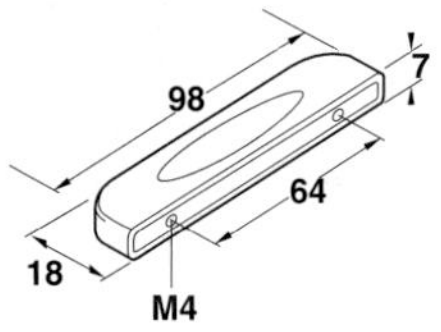

Polished chrome

Cat. No.	105.34.200

Packing: 25 pcs.

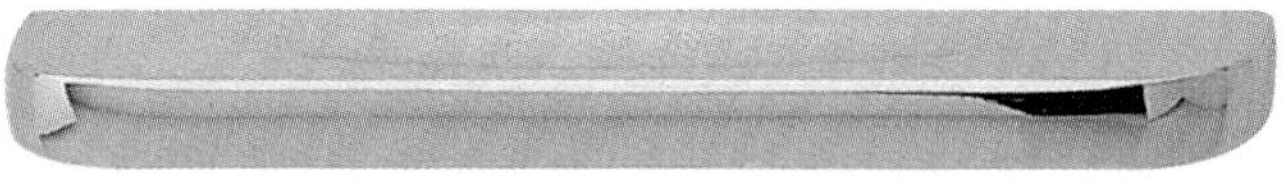

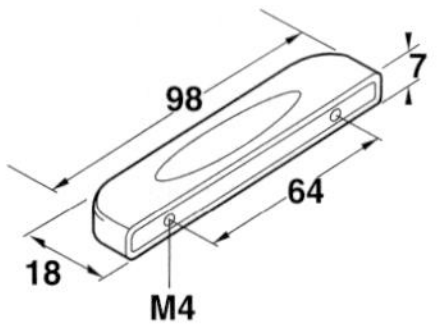

Polished brass

Cat. No.	105.34.808

Packing: 25 pcs.

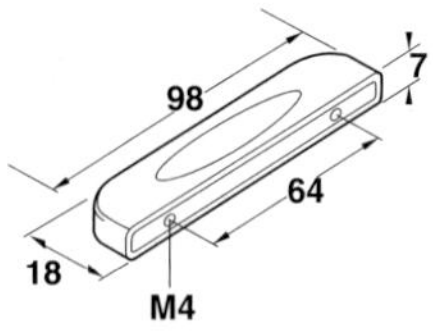

Satin nickel

Cat. No.	105.34.602

Packing: 25 pcs.

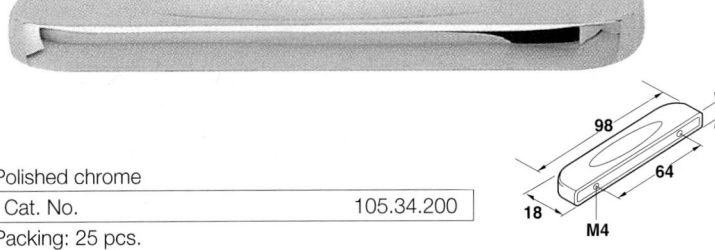

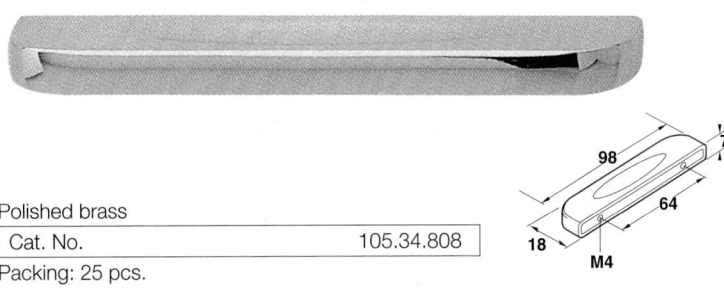

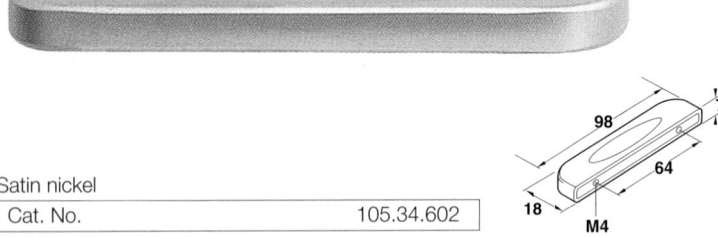

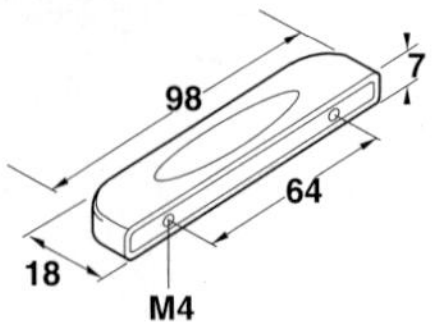

Black

Cat. No.	105.34.353

Packing: 25 pcs.

Zinc Handles

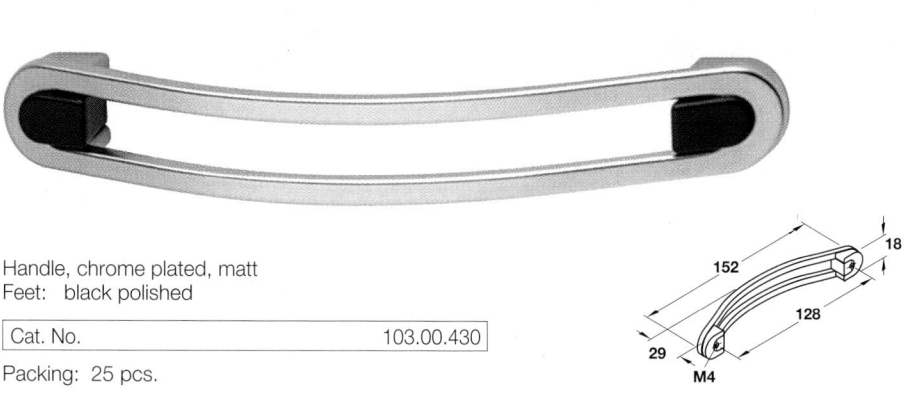

Handle, black polished
Feet: chrome plated, matt

Cat. No.	103.00.340

Packing: 25 pcs.

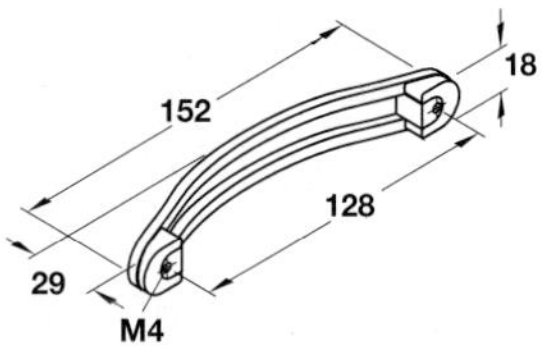

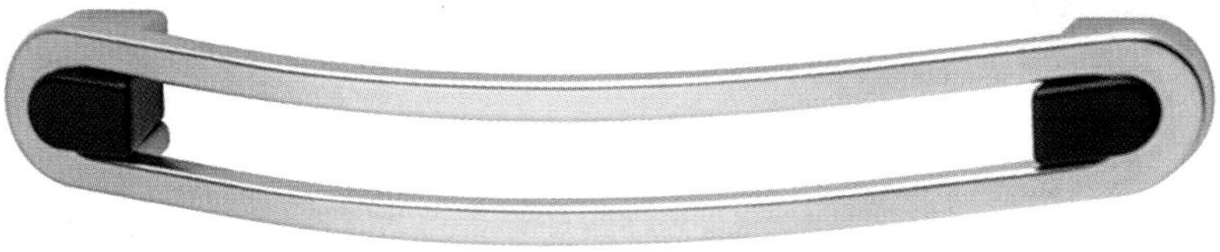

Handle, chrome plated, matt
Feet: black polished

Cat. No.	103.00.430

Packing: 25 pcs.

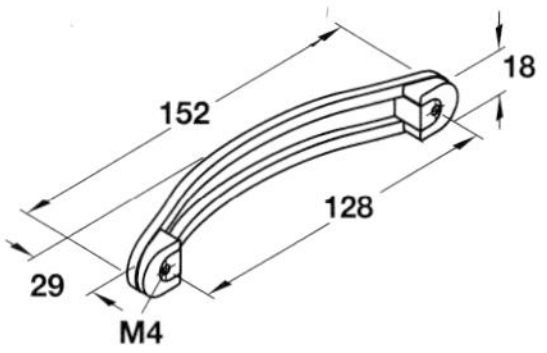

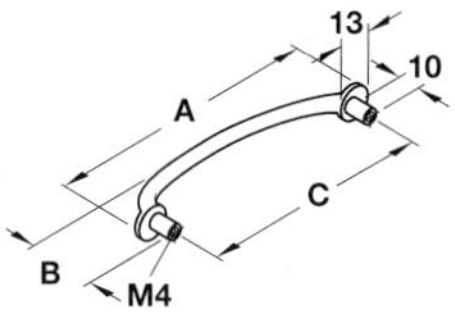

Black polished

Size A x B	Dimension C	Cat. No.
80 x 35	64	116.20.310
110 x 38	96	116.20.320

Packing: 25 pcs.

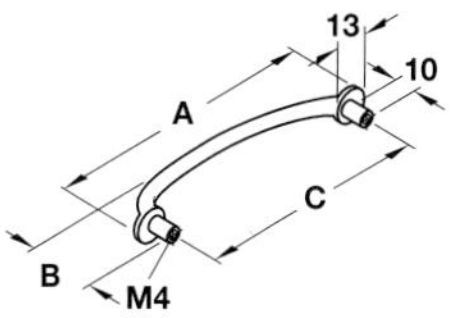

Chrome plated, polished

Size A x B	Dimension C	Cat. No.
80 x 35	64	116.20.210
110 x 38	96	116.20.220

Packing: 25 pcs.

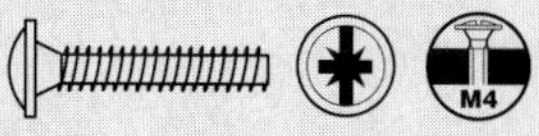

Threaded Screws M4
Combined slot, suitable for flat or cross blades
Finish: steel, zinc-plated

Length	Cat. No.
10 mm	022.35.109
12 mm	022.35.127
15 mm	022.35.154
18 mm	022.35.181
20 mm	022.35.207
22 mm	022.35.225
23 mm	022.35.234
25 mm	022.35.252
28 mm	022.35.289
30 mm	022.35.305
35 mm	022.35.350
38 mm	022.35.387
40 mm	022.35.403
45 mm	022.35.458
50 mm	022.35.501
60 mm	022.35.609

Packing: 100 and 1000 pcs.

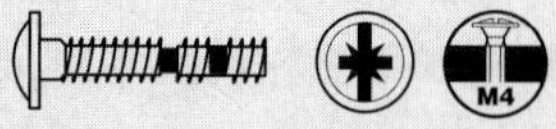

Threaded Breakoff Screw M4
Combined slot, suitable for flat or cross blades
Finish: steel, zinc-plated

Length	Cat. No.
1 3/4" x 3/4"	022.35.887

Packing: 100 and 1000 pcs.

HÄFELE

Zinc Handles and Knobs

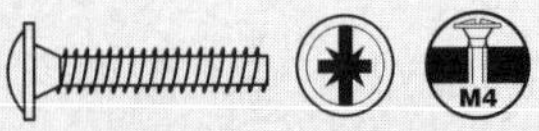

Threaded Screws M4
Combined slot, suitable for flat or cross blades
Finish: steel, zinc-plated

Length	Cat. No.
10 mm	022.35.109
12 mm	022.35.127
15 mm	022.35.154
18 mm	022.35.181
20 mm	022.35.207
22 mm	022.35.225
23 mm	022.35.234
25 mm	022.35.252
28 mm	022.35.289
30 mm	022.35.305
35 mm	022.35.350
38 mm	022.35.387
40 mm	022.35.403
45 mm	022.35.458
50 mm	022.35.501
60 mm	022.35.609

Packing: 100 and 1000 pcs.

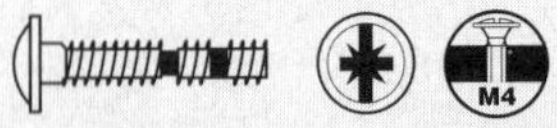

Threaded Breakoff Screw M4
Combined slot, suitable for flat or cross blades
Finish: steel, zinc-plated

Length	Cat. No.
1 3/4" x 3/4"	022.35.887

Packing: 100 and 1000 pcs.

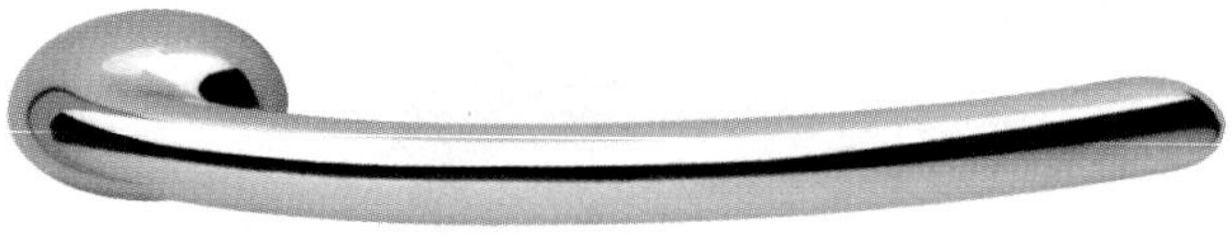

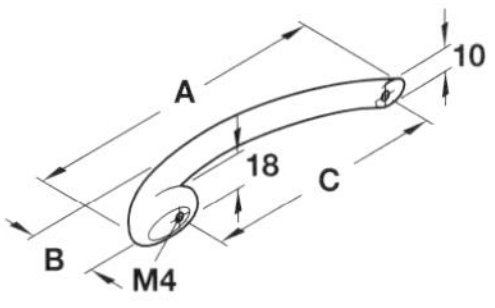

Nickel plated polished

Size A x B	Dimension C	Cat. No.
126 x 27	96	117.85.701
160 x 29	128	117.85.710

Packing: 25 pcs.

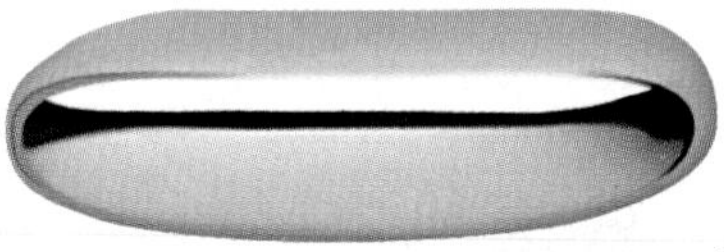

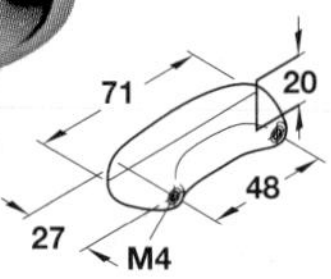

Nickel plated polished

Cat. No.	104.16.710

Packing: 25 pcs.

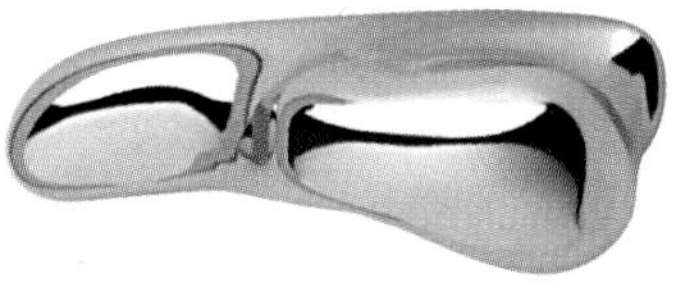

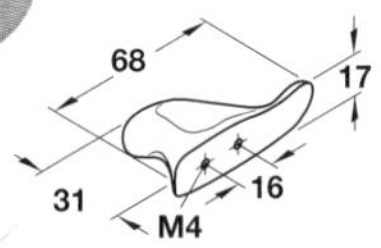

Nickel plated polished/left

Cat. No.	104.20.702

Packing: 25 pcs.

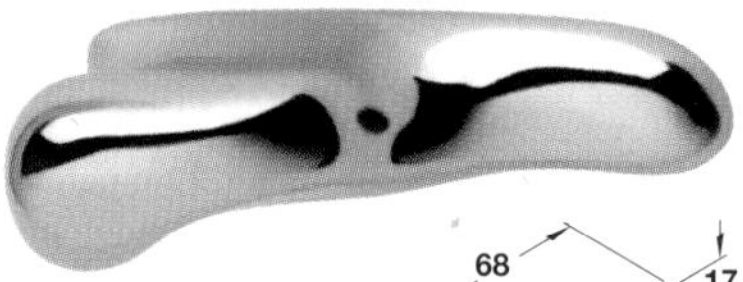

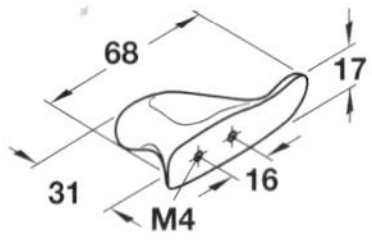

Nickel plated polished/right

Cat. No.	104.20.701

Packing: 25 pcs.

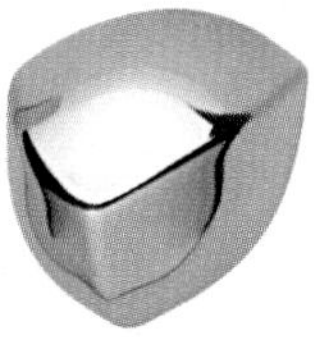

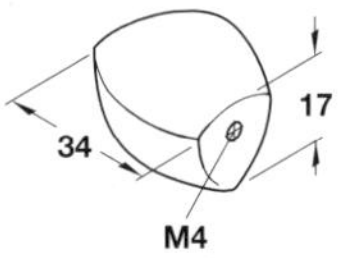

Nickel plated polished

Cat. No.	137.68.700

Packing: 25 pcs.

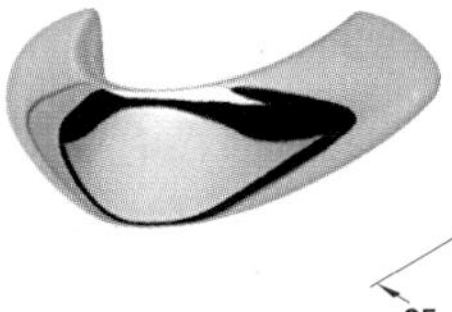

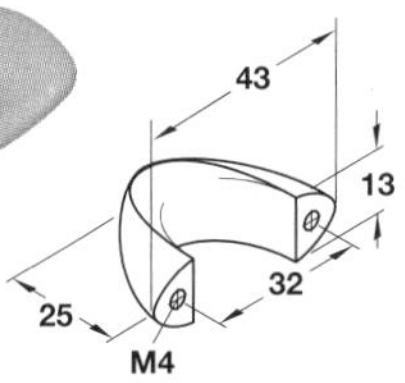

Chrome plated polished

Cat. No.	117.95.210

Packing: 25 pcs.

Zinc Cast Resin Handle

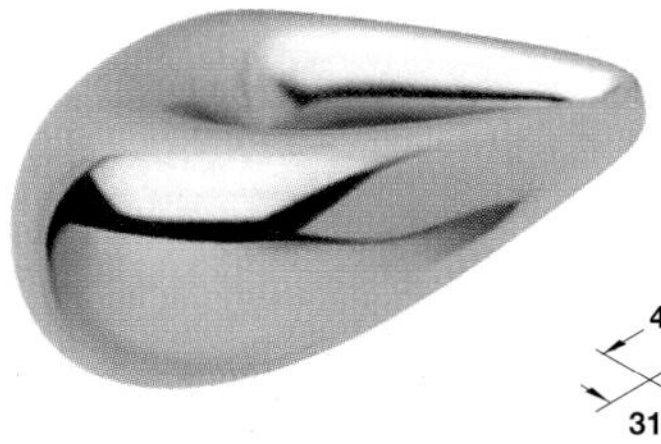

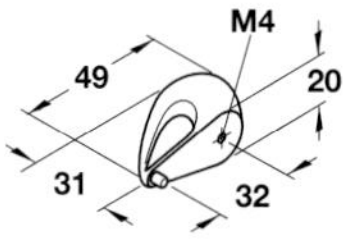

Zinc nickel plated polished

Cat. No.	104.11.702

Packing: 25 pcs.

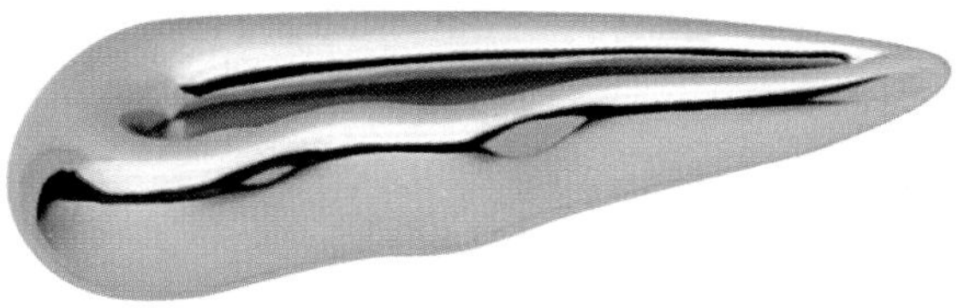

Zinc nickel plated polished

Cat. No.	104.12.709

Packing: 25 pcs.

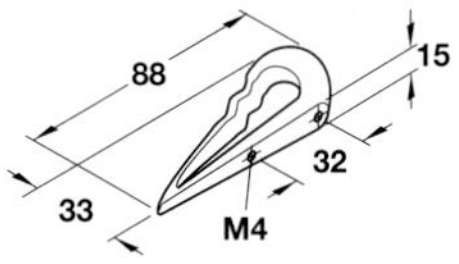

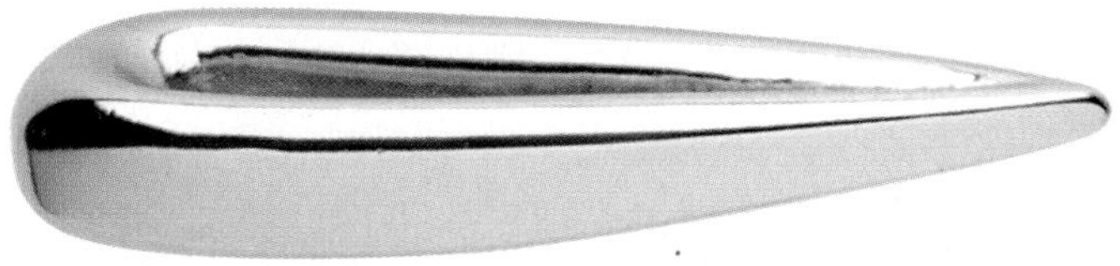

Zinc nickel plated polished

Cat. No.	104.10.705

Packing: 25 pcs.

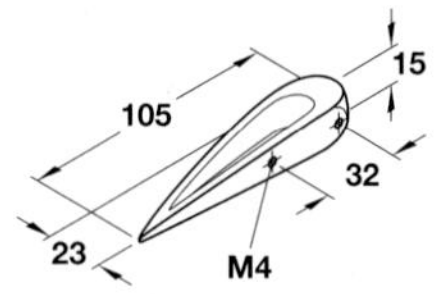

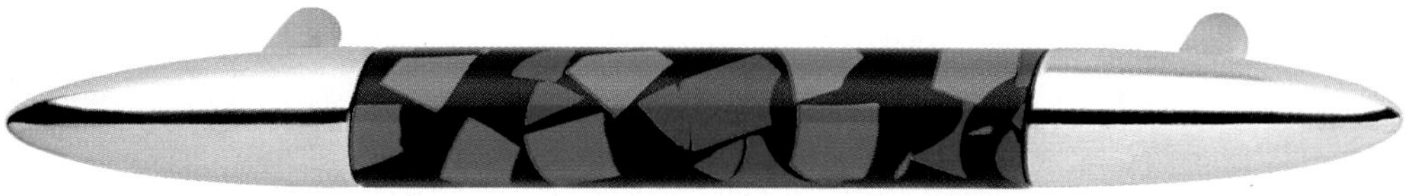

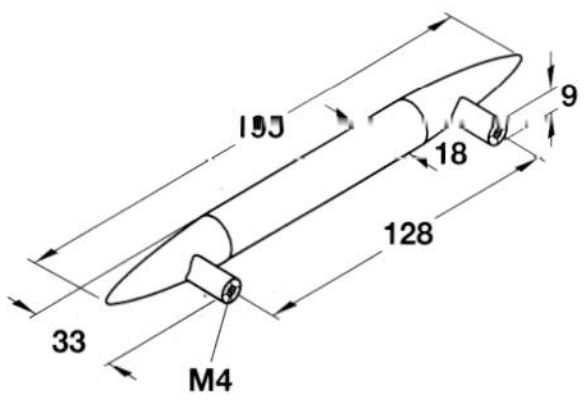

End: Zinc nickel plated polished
Center: Cast resin mosiac blue

Cat. No.	128.34.785

Packing: 25 pcs.

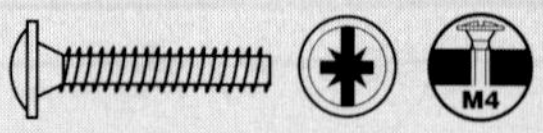

Threaded Screws M4
Combined slot, suitable for flat or cross blades

Finish: steel, zinc-plated

Length	Cat. No.
10 mm	022.35.109
12 mm	022.35.127
15 mm	022.35.154
18 mm	022.35.181
20 mm	022.35.207
22 mm	022.35.225
23 mm	022.35.234
25 mm	022.35.252
28 mm	022.35.289
30 mm	022.35.305
35 mm	022.35.350
38 mm	022.35.387
40 mm	022.35.403
45 mm	022.35.458
50 mm	022.35.501
60 mm	022.35.609

Packing: 100 and 1000 pcs.

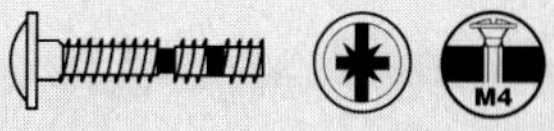

Threaded Breakoff Screw M4
Combined slot, suitable for flat or cross blades

Finish: steel, zinc-plated

Length	Cat. No.
1 3/4" x 3/4"	022.35.887

Packing: 100 and 1000 pcs.

Zinc Handles

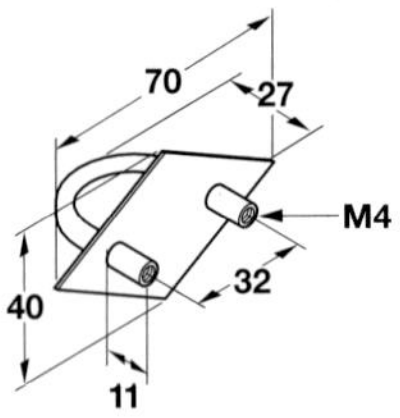

Handle: steel cable with clear plastic cover
Backplate: zinc matt nickel

Cat. No.	105.57.600

Packing: 10 pcs.

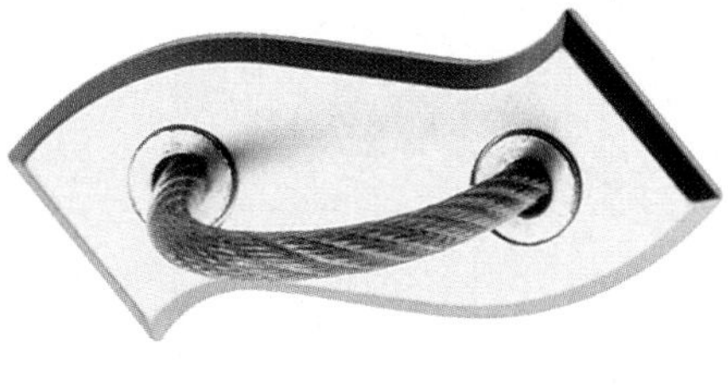

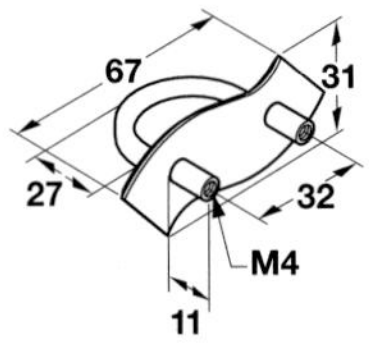

Handle: steel cable with clear plastic cover
Backplate: zinc matt nickel

Cat. No.	105.58.600

Packing: 10 pcs.

Threaded Screws M4

Combined slot, suitable for flat or cross blades

Finish: steel, zinc-plated

Length	Cat. No.
10 mm	022.35.109
12 mm	022.35.127
15 mm	022.35.154
18 mm	022.35.181
20 mm	022.35.207
22 mm	022.35.225
23 mm	022.35.234
25 mm	022.35.252
28 mm	022.35.289
30 mm	022.35.305
35 mm	022.35.350
38 mm	022.35.387
40 mm	022.35.403
45 mm	022.35.458
50 mm	022.35.501
60 mm	022.35.609

Packing: 100 and 1000 pcs.

Threaded Breakoff Screw M4

Combined slot, suitable for flat or cross blades

Finish: steel, zinc-plated

Length	Cat. No.
1 3/4" x 3/4"	022.35.887

Packing: 100 and 1000 pcs.

Dimensional data not binding.
We reserve the right to alter specifications without notice.

Zinc handles

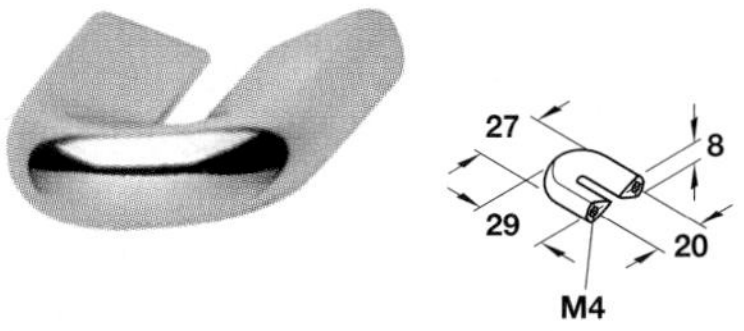

Chrome plated polished

Cat. No.	105.39.205

Packing: 25 pcs.

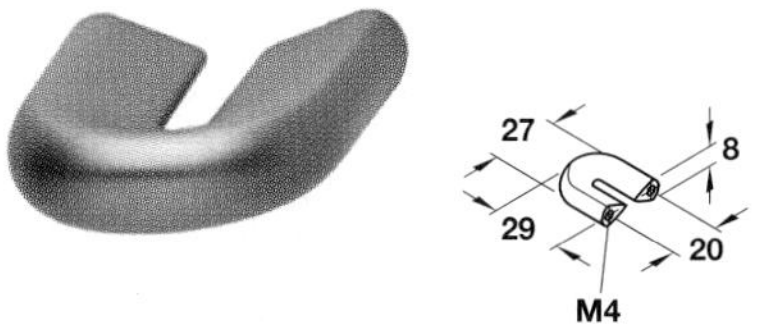

Chrome plated matt

Cat. No.	105.39.401

Packing: 25 pcs.

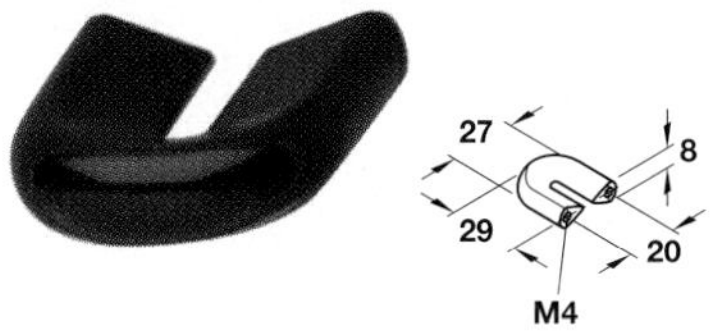

Black polished

Cat. No.	105.39.303

Packing: 25 pcs.

HÄFELE

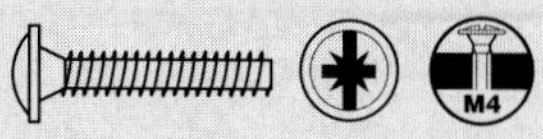

Threaded Screws M4
Combined slot, suitable for flat or cross blades

Finish: steel, zinc-plated

Length	Cat. No.
10 mm	022.35.109
12 mm	022.35.127
15 mm	022.35.154
18 mm	022.35.181
20 mm	022.35.207
22 mm	022.35.225
23 mm	022.35.234
25 mm	022.35.252
28 mm	022.35.289
30 mm	022.35.305
35 mm	022.35.350
38 mm	022.35.387
40 mm	022.35.403
45 mm	022.35.458
50 mm	022.35.501
60 mm	022.35.609

Packing: 100 and 1000 pcs.

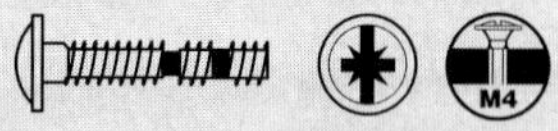

Threaded Breakoff Screw M4
Combined slot, suitable for flat or cross blades

Finish: steel, zinc-plated

Length	Cat. No.
1 3/4" x 3/4"	022.35.887

Packing: 100 and 1000 pcs.

HÄFELE

Zinc Handles

Threaded Screws M4
Combined slot, suitable for flat or cross blades
Finish: steel, zinc-plated

Length	Cat. No.
10 mm	022.35.109
12 mm	022.35.127
15 mm	022.35.154
18 mm	022.35.181
20 mm	022.35.207
22 mm	022.35.225
23 mm	022.35.234
25 mm	022.35.252
28 mm	022.35.289
30 mm	022.35.305
35 mm	022.35.350
38 mm	022.35.387
40 mm	022.35.403
45 mm	022.35.458
50 mm	022.35.501
60 mm	022.35.609

Packing: 100 and 1000 pcs.

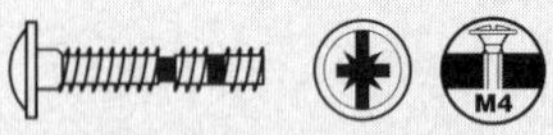

Threaded Breakoff Screw M4
Combined slot, suitable for flat or cross blades
Finish: steel, zinc-plated

Length	Cat. No.
1 3/4" x 3/4"	022.35.887

Packing: 100 and 1000 pcs.

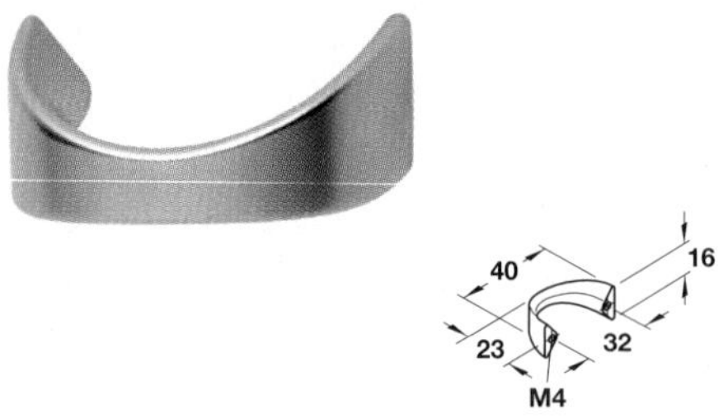

Nickel plated matt

Catalog No.	105.26.600

Packing: 25 pcs.

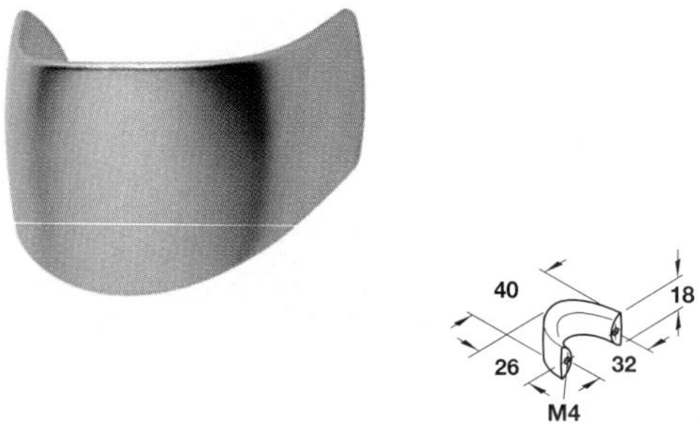

Nickel plated matt

Catalog No.	104.93.606

Packing: 25 pcs.

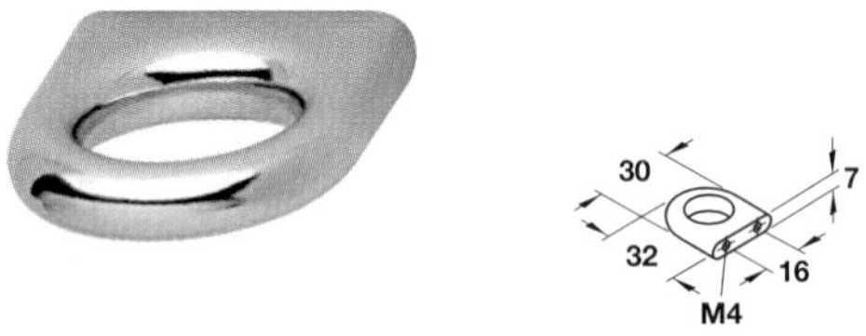

Chrome plated polished

Catalog No.	105.25.201

Packing: 25 pcs.

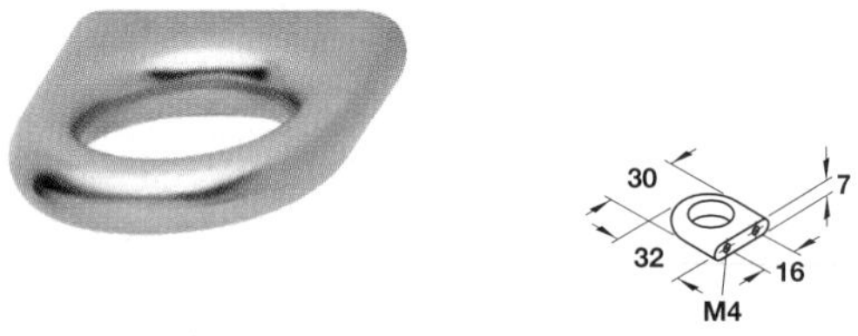

Nickel plated matt

Catalog No.	105.25.603

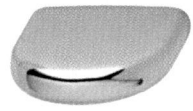

Packing: 25 pcs.

Chrome plated polished

Catalog No.	105.20.206

Packing: 25 pcs.

Nickel plated matt

Catalog No.	105.20.608

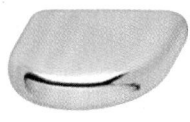

Packing: 25 pcs.

Gold colored polished

Catalog No.	105.20.804

Packing: 25 pcs.

Zinc Handles

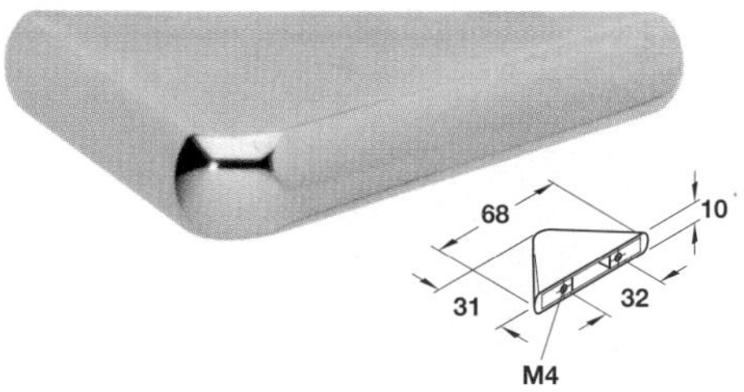

Chrome plated polished

Cat. No.	105.37.201

Packing: 25 pcs.

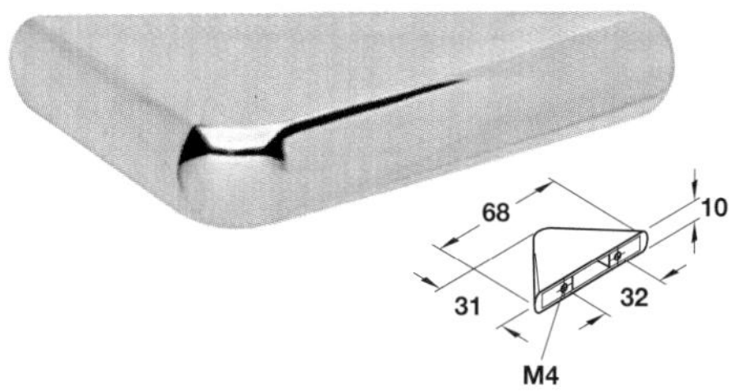

Gold colored polished

Cat. No.	105.37.800

Packing: 25 pcs.

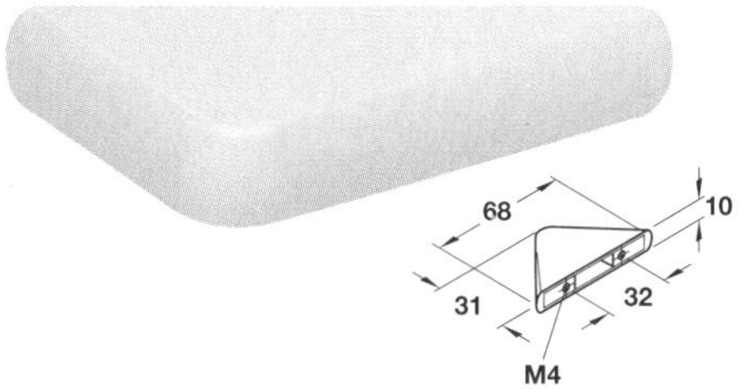

White

Cat. No.	105.37.701

Packing: 25 pcs.

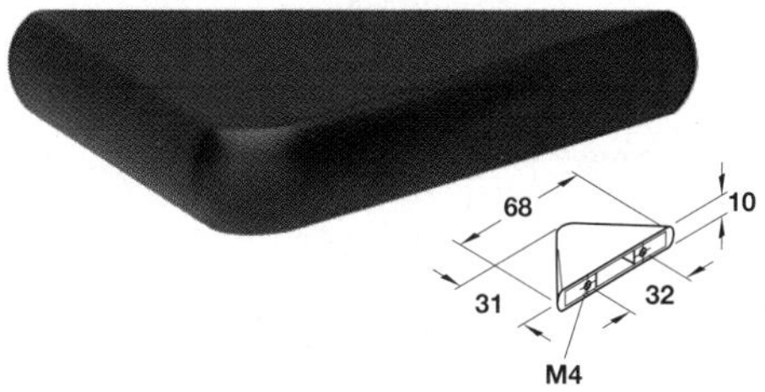

Black matt

Cat. No.	105.37.309

Packing: 25 pcs.

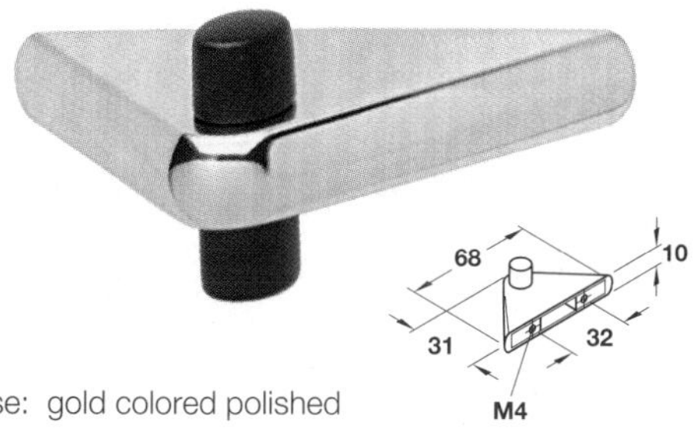

Base: gold colored polished
Post: black

Cat. No.	105.36.803

Packing: 25 pcs.

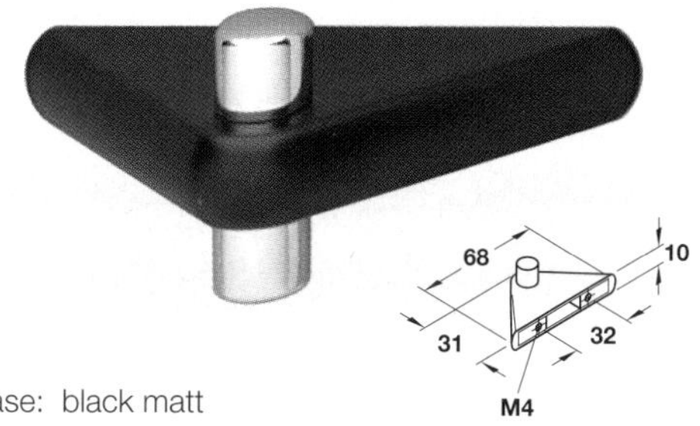

Base: black matt
Post: chrome plated polished

Cat. No.	105.36.302

Packing: 25 pcs.

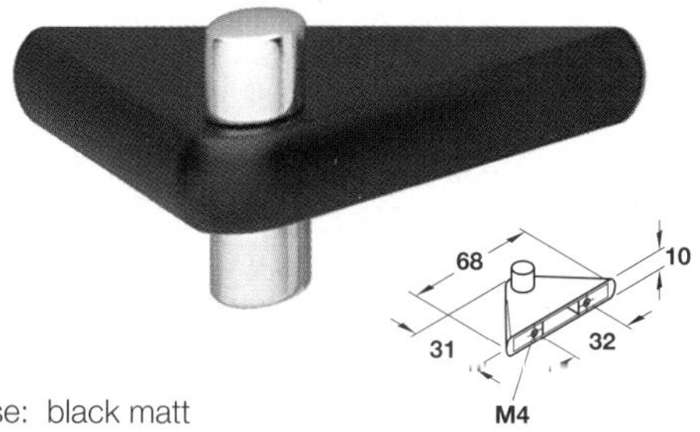

Base: black matt
Post: gold colored polished

Cat. No.	105.36.310

Packing: 25 pcs.

Threaded Screws M4
Combined slot, suitable for flat or cross blades
Finish: steel, zinc-plated

Length	Cat. No.
10 mm	022.35.109
12 mm	022.35.127
15 mm	022.35.154
18 mm	022.35.181
20 mm	022.35.207
22 mm	022.35.225
23 mm	022.35.234
25 mm	022.35.252
28 mm	022.35.289
30 mm	022.35.305
35 mm	022.35.350
38 mm	022.35.387
40 mm	022.35.403
45 mm	022.35.458
50 mm	022.35.501
60 mm	022.35.609

Packing: 100 and 1000 pcs.

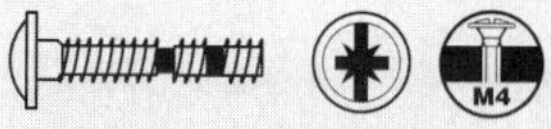

Threaded Breakoff Screw M4
Combined slot, suitable for flat or cross blades
Finish: steel, zinc-plated

Length	Cat. No.
1 3/4" x 3/4"	022.35.887

Packing: 100 and 1000 pcs.

HÄFELE

Zinc handles

Threaded Screws M4
Combined slot, suitable for flat or cross blades
Finish: steel, zinc-plated

Length	Cat. No.
10 mm	022.35.109
12 mm	022.35.127
15 mm	022.35.154
18 mm	022.35.181
20 mm	022.35.207
22 mm	022.35.225
23 mm	022.35.234
25 mm	022.35.252
28 mm	022.35.289
30 mm	022.35.305
35 mm	022.35.350
38 mm	022.35.387
40 mm	022.35.403
45 mm	022.35.458
50 mm	022.35.501
60 mm	022.35.609

Packing: 100 and 1000 pcs.

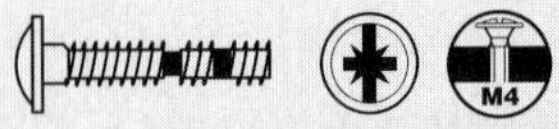

Threaded Breakoff Screw M4
Combined slot, suitable for flat or cross blades
Finish: steel, zinc-plated

Length	Cat. No.
1 3/4" x 3/4"	022.35.887

Packing: 100 and 1000 pcs.

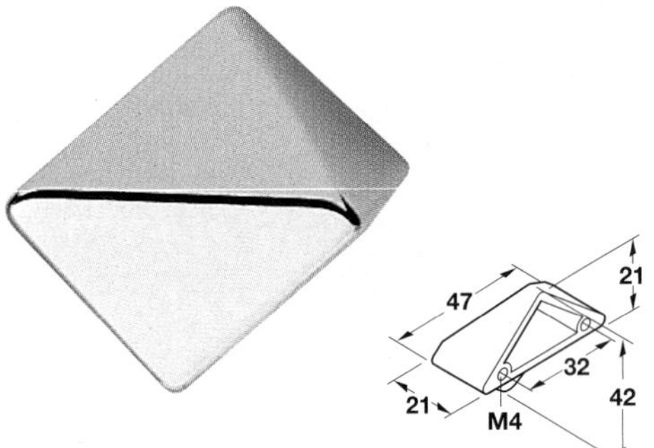

Chrome polished

Cat. No.	104.44.200

Packing: 25 pcs.

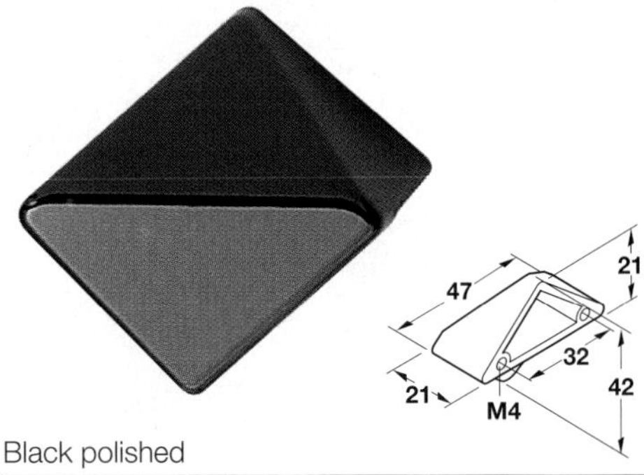

Black polished

Cat. No.	104.44.300

Packing: 25 pcs.

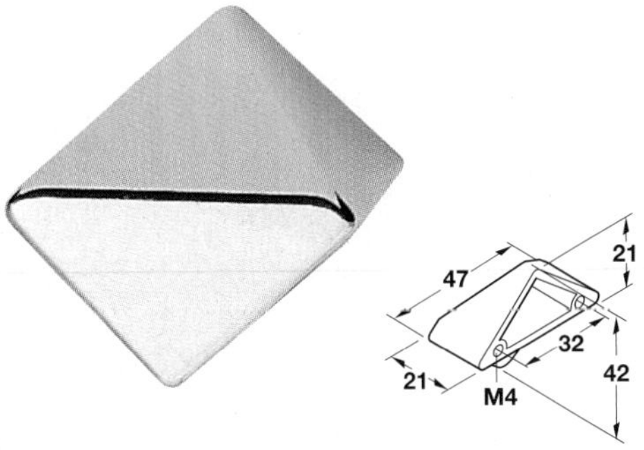

Brass polished

Cat. No.	104.44.800

Packing: 25 pcs.

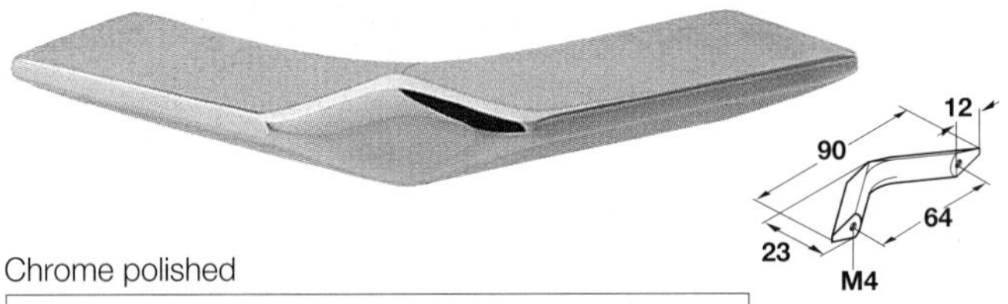

Chrome polished

Cat. No.	102.68.201

Packing: 25 pcs.

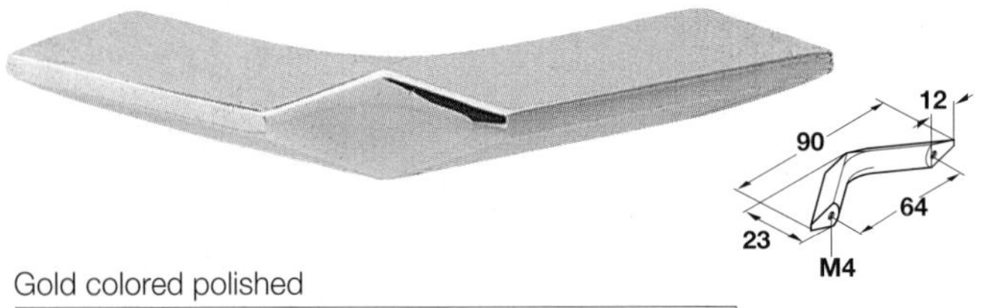

Gold colored polished

Cat. No.	102.68.800

Packing: 25 pcs.

Dimensional data not binding.
We reserve the right to alter specifications without notice.

Metal Handles

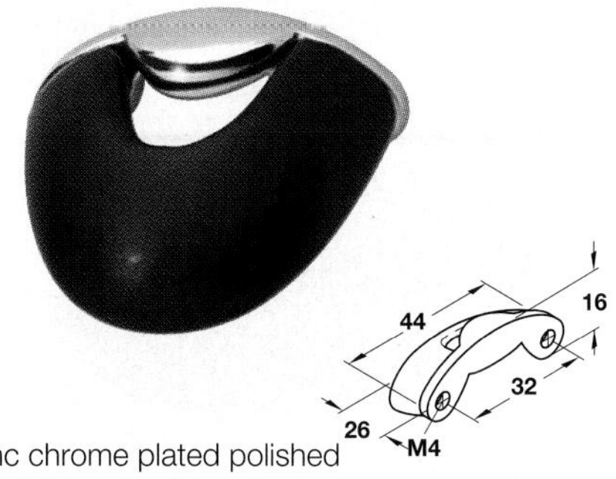

Base, zinc chrome plated polished
Handle, zinc black matt

Cat. No.	103.07.230

Packing: 25 pcs.

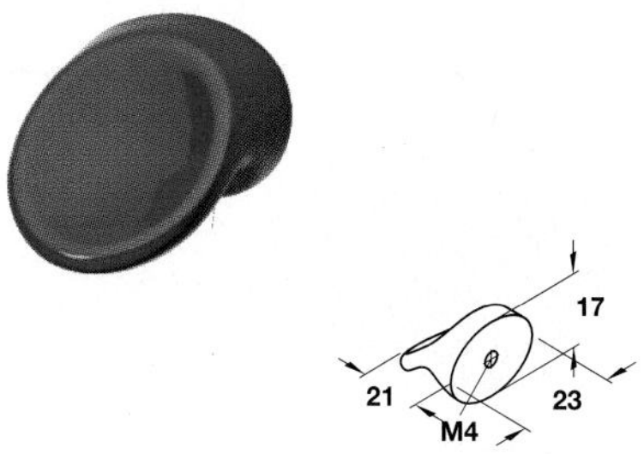

Zinc, blue

Cat. No.	138.55.800

Packing: 25 pcs.

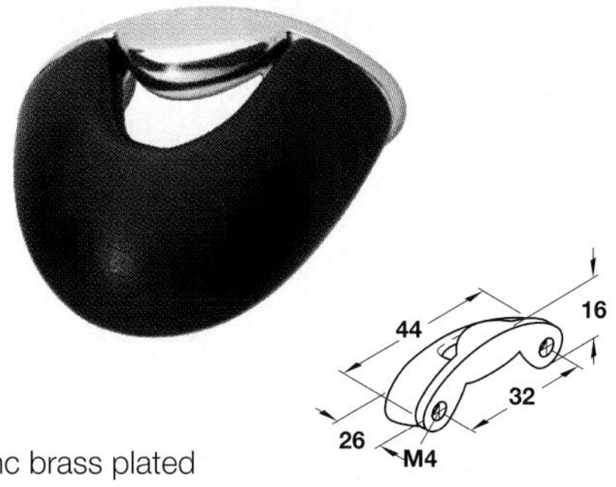

Base: Zinc brass plated
Handle: zinc black matt

Cat. No.	103.07.830

Packing: 25 pcs.

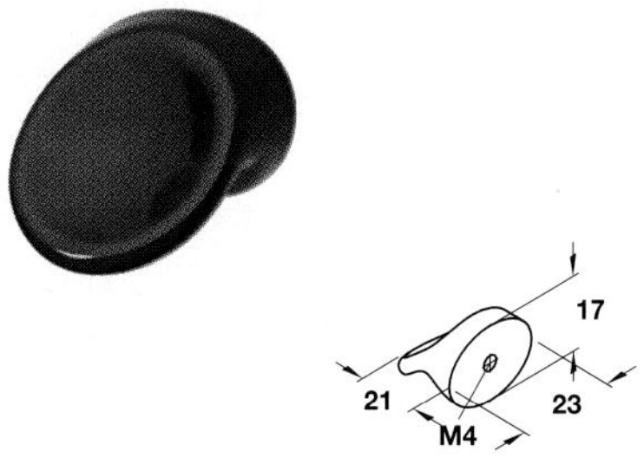

Zinc, red

Cat. No.	138.55.900

Packing: 25 pcs.

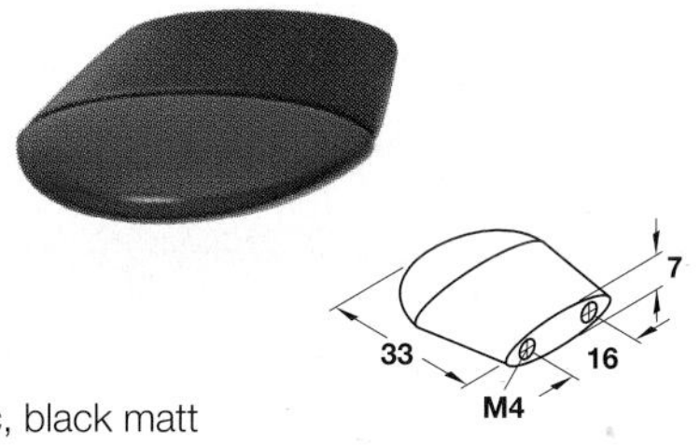

Base: plastic, black matt
Top: zinc, blue

Cat. No.	137.76.360

Packing: 25 pcs.

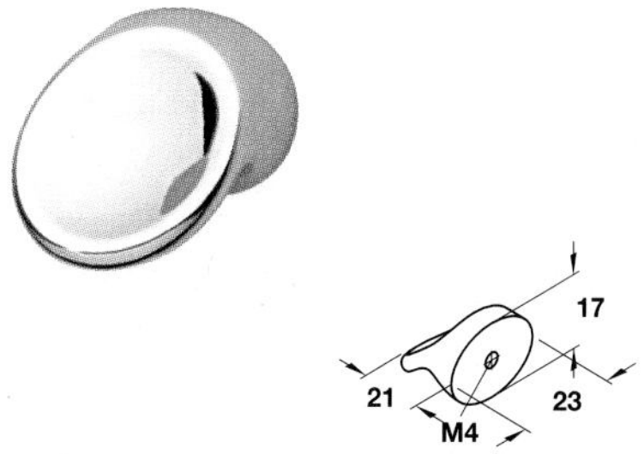

Zinc, chrome plated polished

Cat. No.	138.55.200

Packing: 25 pcs.

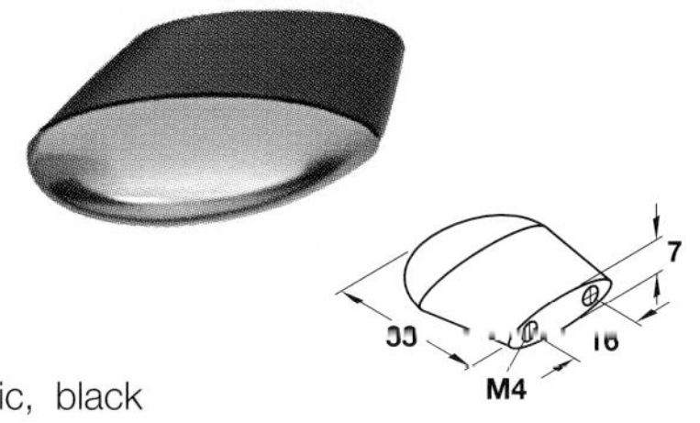

Base: plastic, black
Top: zinc nickel plated matt

Cat. No.	137.76.380

Packing: 25 pcs.

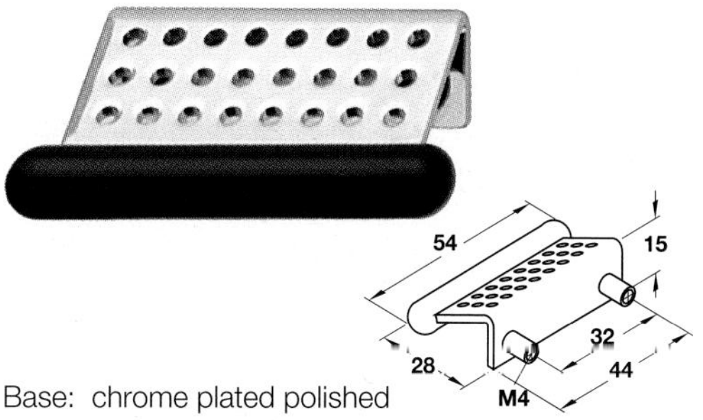

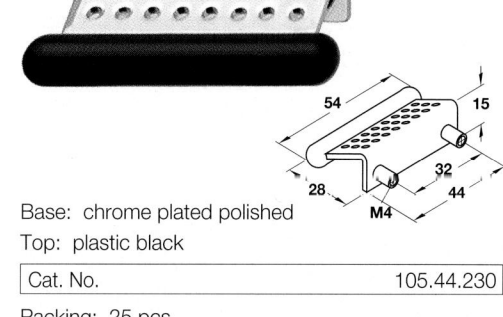

Base: chrome plated polished
Top: plastic black

Cat. No.	105.44.230

Packing: 25 pcs.

Decorative Hardware 1

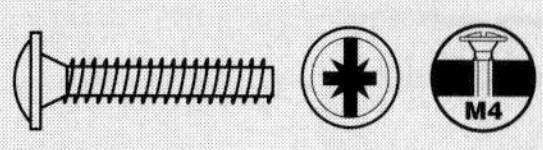

Threaded Screws M4
Combined slot, suitable for flat or cross blades
Finish: steel, zinc-plated

Length	Cat. No.
10 mm	022.35.109
12 mm	022.35.127
15 mm	022.35.154
18 mm	022.35.181
20 mm	022.35.207
22 mm	022.35.225
23 mm	022.35.234
25 mm	022.35.252
28 mm	022.35.289
30 mm	022.35.305
35 mm	022.35.350
38 mm	022.35.387
40 mm	022.35.403
45 mm	022.35.458
50 mm	022.35.501
60 mm	022.35.609

Packing: 100 and 1000 pcs.

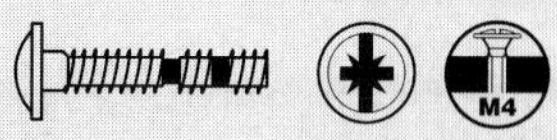

Threaded Breakoff Screw M4
Combined slot, suitable for flat or cross blades
Finish: steel, zinc-plated

Length	Cat. No.
1 3/4" x 3/4"	022.35.887

Packing: 100 and 1000 pcs.

Zinc Handles

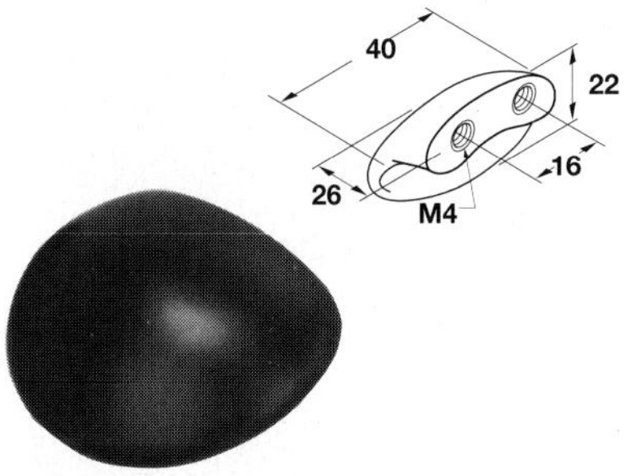

Black matt

Cat. No.	105.49.310

Packing: 25 pcs.

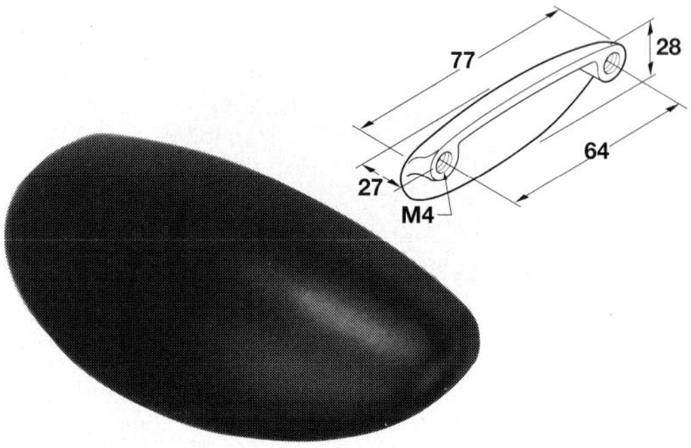

Black matt

Cat. No.	105.49.320

Packing: 25 pcs.

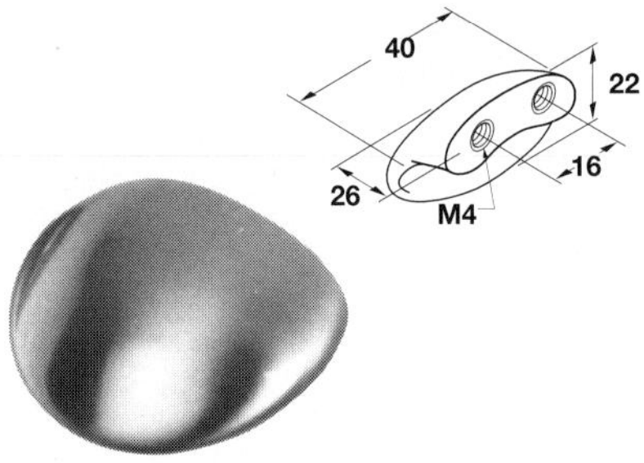

Nickel plated matt

Cat. No.	105.49.610

Packing: 25 pcs.

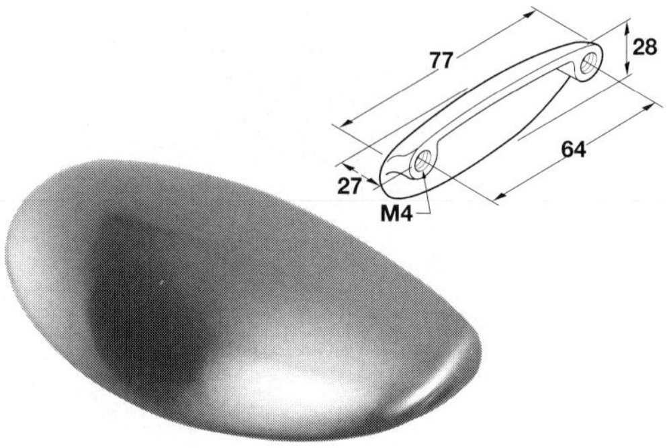

Nickel plated matt

Cat. No.	105.49.620

Packing: 25 pcs.

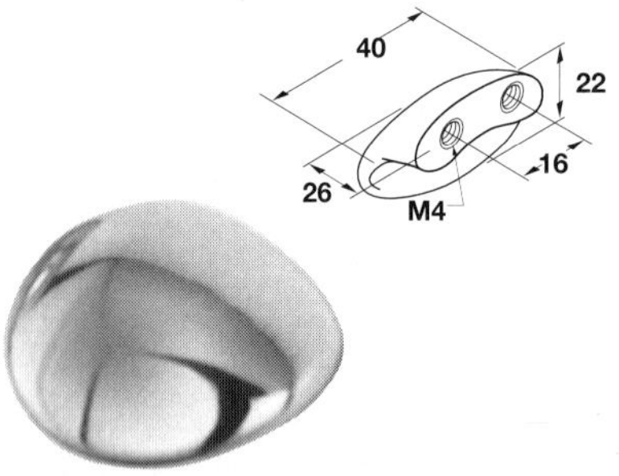

Chrome polished

Cat. No.	105.49.210

Packing: 25 pcs.

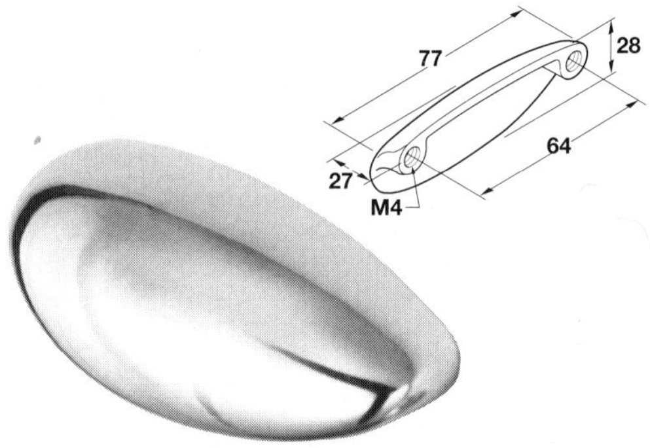

Chrome polished

Cat. No.	105.49.220

Packing: 25 pcs.

Threaded Screws M4
Combined slot, suitable for flat or cross blades

Finish: steel, zinc-plated

Length	Cat. No.
10 mm	022.35.109
12 mm	022.35.127
15 mm	022.35.154
18 mm	022.35.181
20 mm	022.35.207
22 mm	022.35.225
23 mm	022.35.234
25 mm	022.35.252
28 mm	022.35.289
30 mm	022.35.305
35 mm	022.35.350
38 mm	022.35.387
40 mm	022.35.403
45 mm	022.35.458
50 mm	022.35.501
60 mm	022.35.609

Packing: 100 and 1000 pcs.

Threaded Breakoff Screw M4
Combined slot, suitable for flat or cross blades

Finish: steel, zinc-plated

Length	Cat. No.
1 3/4" x 3/4"	022.35.887

Packing: 100 and 1000 pcs.

Zinc Handles

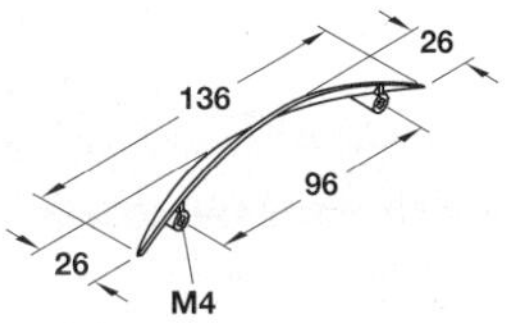

Nickel matt

Cat. No.	105.47.600

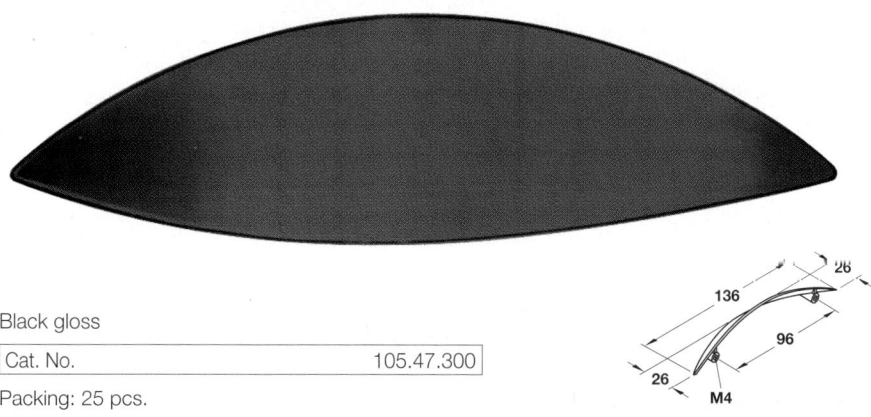

Packing: 25 pcs.

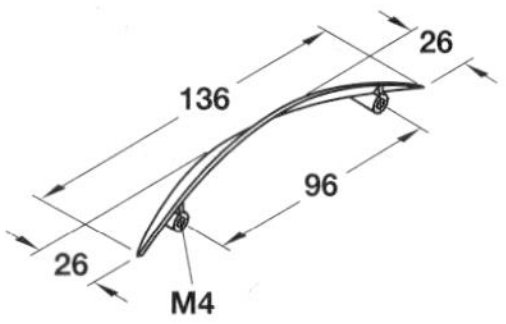

Blue

Cat. No.	105.47.800

Packing: 25 pcs.

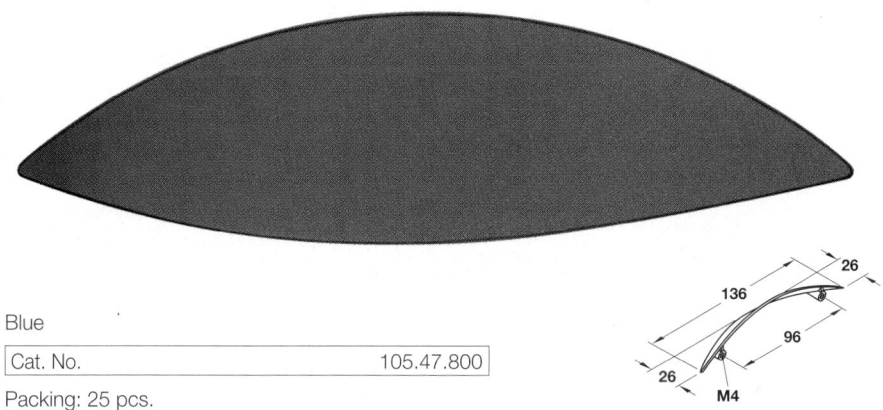

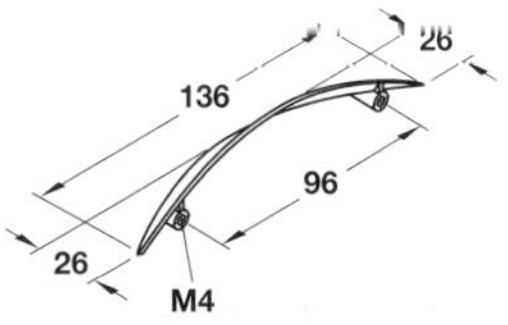

Black gloss

Cat. No.	105.47.300

Packing: 25 pcs.

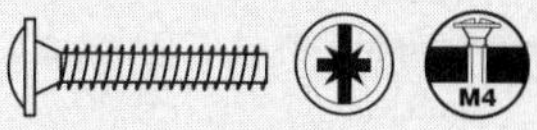

Threaded Screws M4
Combined slot, suitable for flat or cross blades

Finish: steel, zinc-plated

Length	Cat. No.
10 mm	022.35.109
12 mm	022.35.127
15 mm	022.35.154
18 mm	022.35.181
20 mm	022.35.207
22 mm	022.35.225
23 mm	022.35.234
25 mm	022.35.252
28 mm	022.35.289
30 mm	022.35.305
35 mm	022.35.350
38 mm	022.35.387
40 mm	022.35.403
45 mm	022.35.458
50 mm	022.35.501
60 mm	022.35.609

Packing: 100 and 1000 pcs.

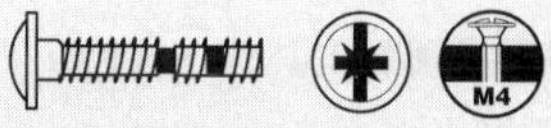

Threaded Breakoff Screw M4
Combined slot, suitable for flat or cross blades

Finish: steel, zinc-plated

Length	Cat. No.
1 3/4" x 3/4"	022.35.887

Packing: 100 and 1000 pcs.

HÄFELE

Zinc handles

1 Decorative Hardware

Threaded Screws M4
Combined slot, suitable for flat or cross blades

Finish: steel, zinc-plated

Length	Cat. No.
10 mm	022.35.109
12 mm	022.35.127
15 mm	022.35.154
18 mm	022.35.181
20 mm	022.35.207
22 mm	022.35.225
23 mm	022.35.234
25 mm	022.35.252
28 mm	022.35.289
30 mm	022.35.305
35 mm	022.35.350
38 mm	022.35.387
40 mm	022.35.403
45 mm	022.35.458
50 mm	022.35.501
60 mm	022.35.609

Packing: 100 and 1000 pcs.

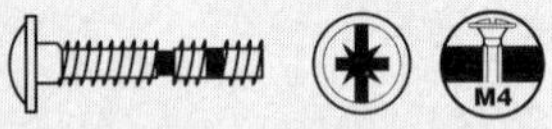

Threaded Breakoff Screw M4
Combined slot, suitable for flat or cross blades

Finish: steel, zinc-plated

Length	Cat. No.
1 3/4" x 3/4"	022.35.887

Packing: 100 and 1000 pcs.

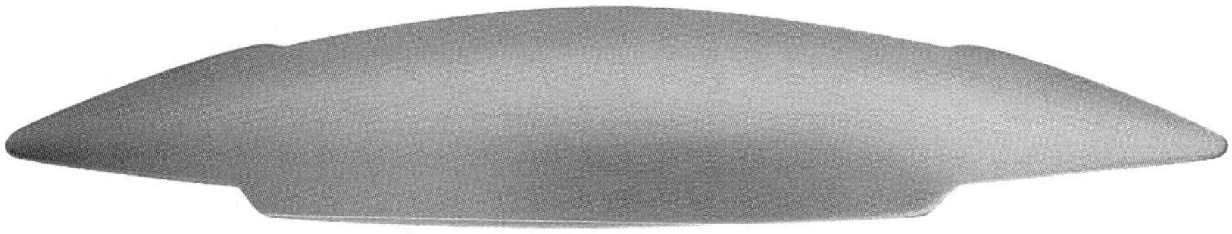

Nickel plated matt

Cat. No.	105.50.600

Packing: 25 pcs.

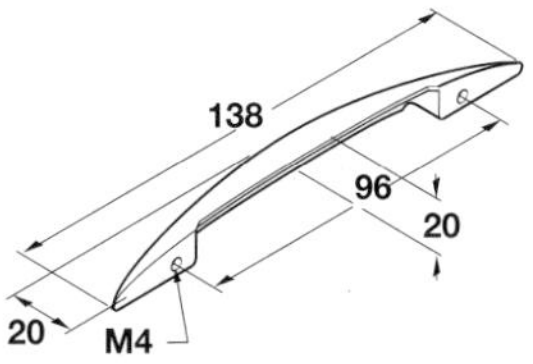

Black matt

Cat. No.	105.50.300

Packing: 25 pcs.

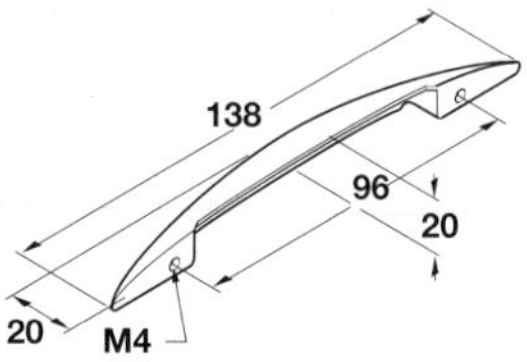

Black matt

Cat. No.	104.19.300

Packing: 25 pcs.

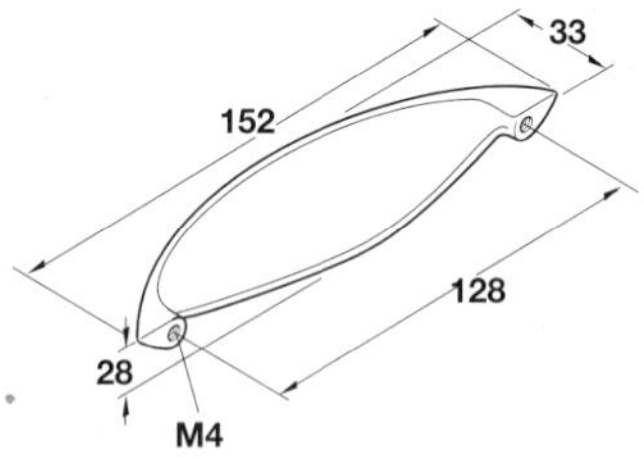

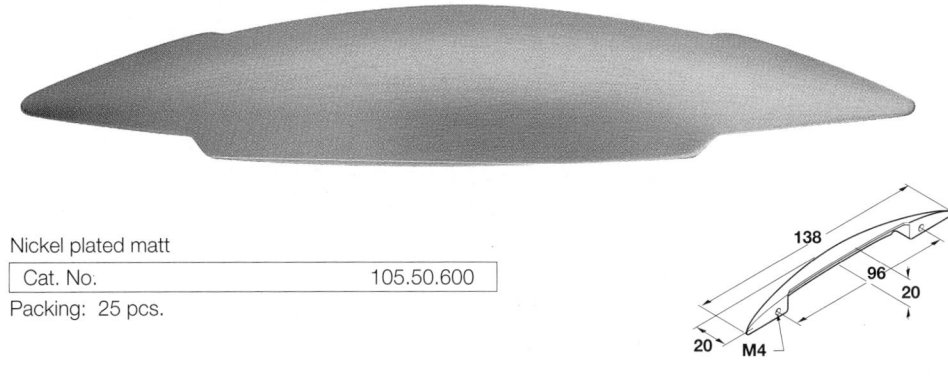

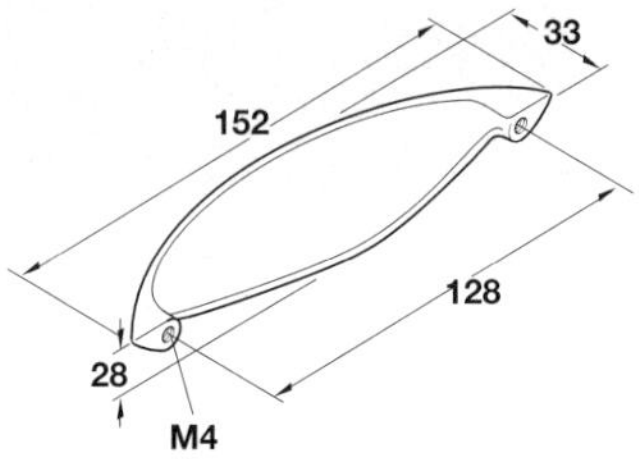

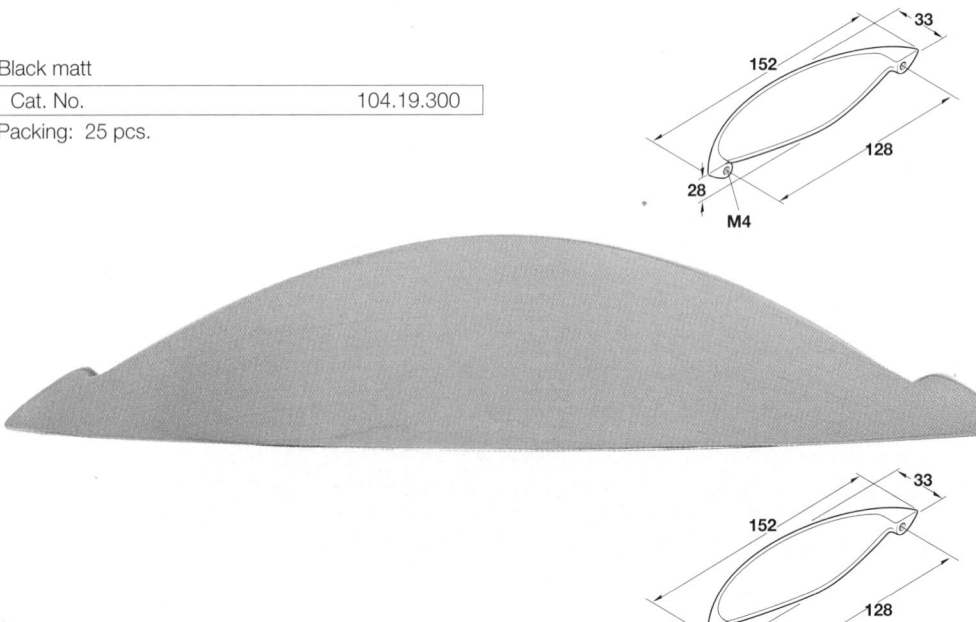

Steel satin chrome

Cat. No.	104.19.404

Packing: 25 pcs.

Dimensional data not binding.
We reserve the right to alter specifications without notice.

Zinc handles

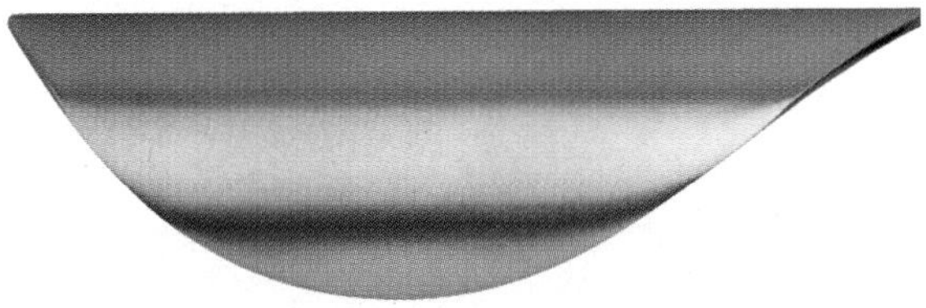

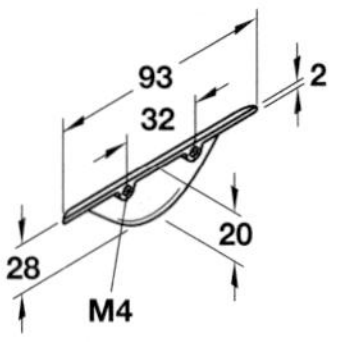

Nickel plated matt

Cat. No.	105.46.600

Packing: 25 pcs.

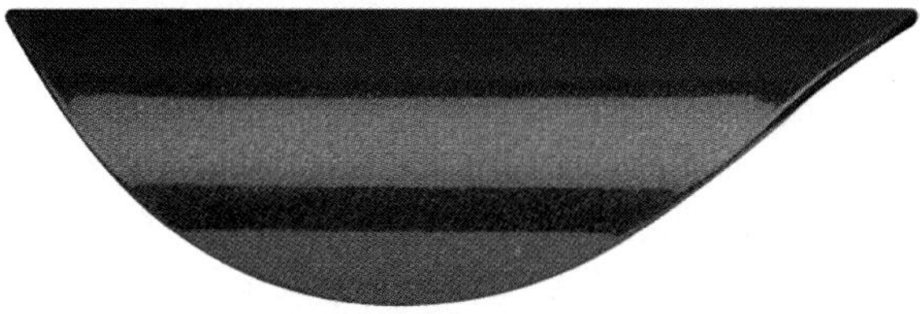

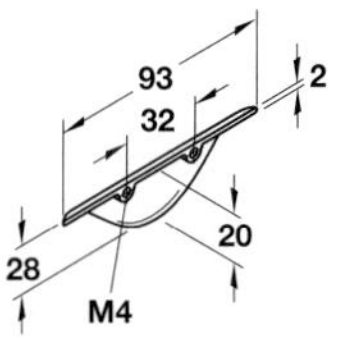

Blue

Cat. No.	105.46.800

Packing: 25 pcs.

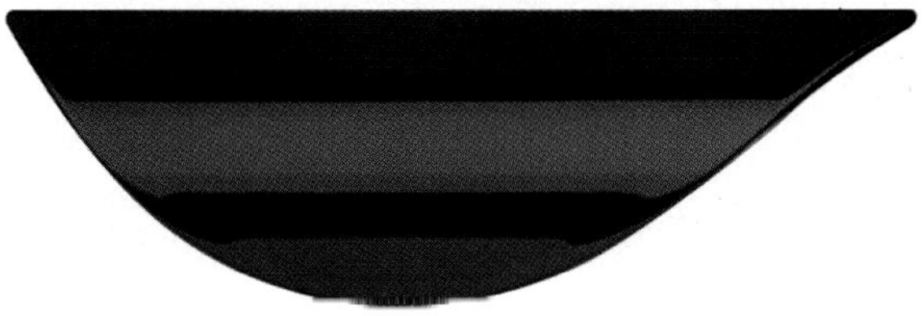

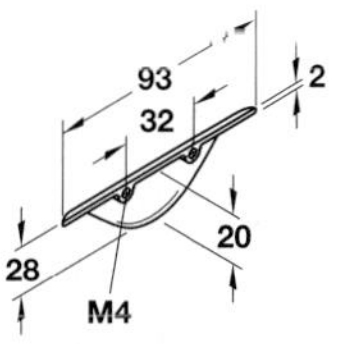

Black gloss

Cat. No.	105.46.300

Packing: 25 pcs.

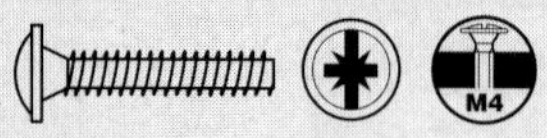

Threaded Screws M4
Combined slot, suitable for flat or cross blades
Finish: steel, zinc-plated

Length	Cat. No.
10 mm	022.35.109
12 mm	022.35.127
15 mm	022.35.154
18 mm	022.35.181
20 mm	022.35.207
22 mm	022.35.225
23 mm	022.35.234
25 mm	022.35.252
28 mm	022.35.289
30 mm	022.35.305
35 mm	022.35.350
38 mm	022.35.387
40 mm	022.35.403
45 mm	022.35.458
50 mm	022.35.501
60 mm	022.35.609

Packing: 100 and 1000 pcs.

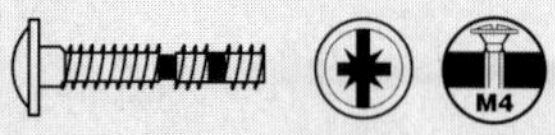

Threaded Breakoff Screw M4
Combined slot, suitable for flat or cross blades
Finish: steel, zinc-plated

Length	Cat. No.
1 3/4" x 3/4"	022.35.887

Packing: 100 and 1000 pcs.

Zinc Handles

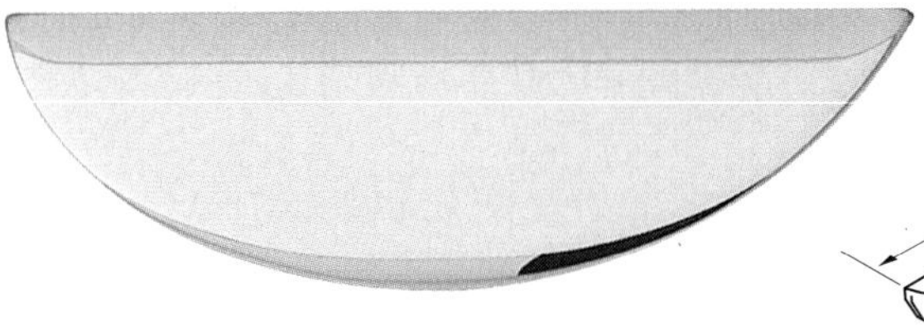

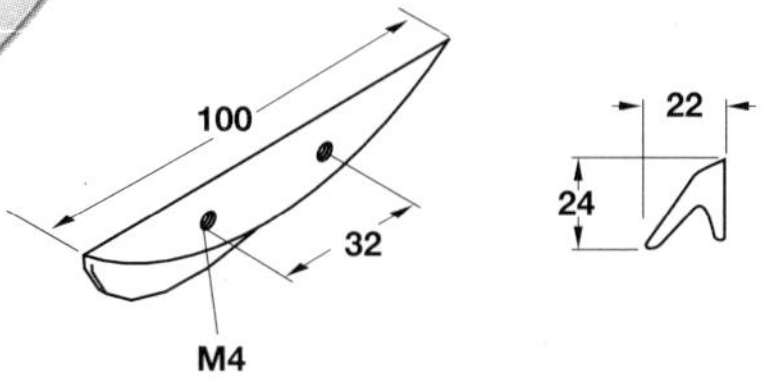

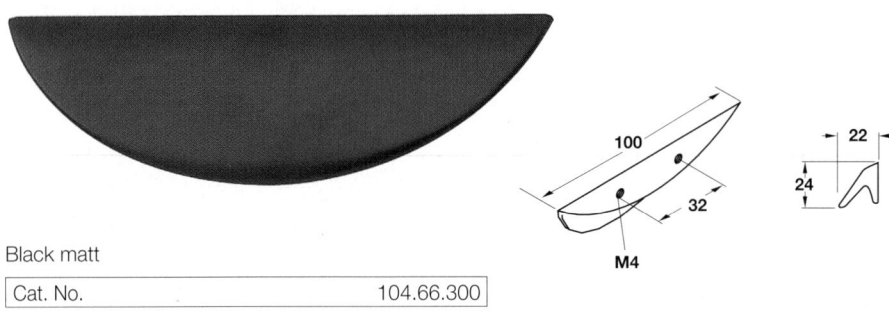

Chrome polished

Cat. No.	104.66.200

Packing: 25 pcs.

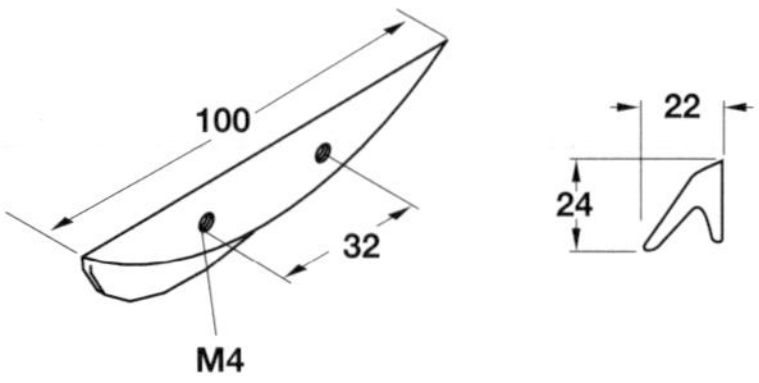

Black matt

Cat. No.	104.66.300

Packing: 25 pcs.

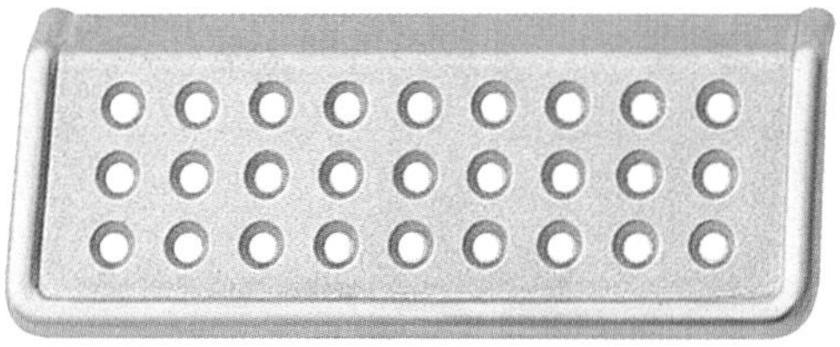

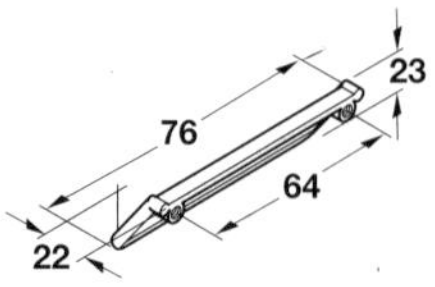

Matt nickel

Cat. No.	105.45.610

Packing: 25 pcs.

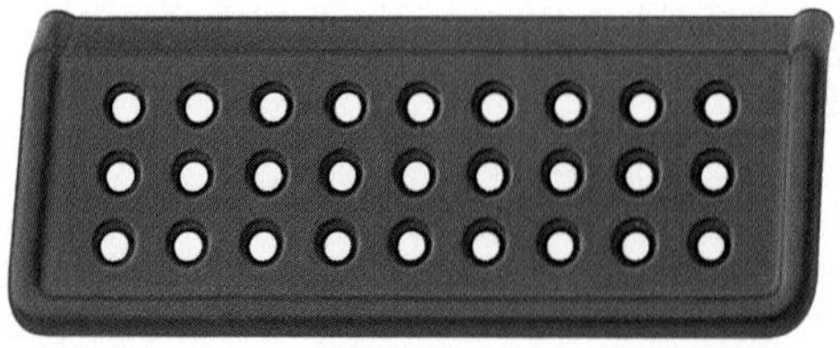

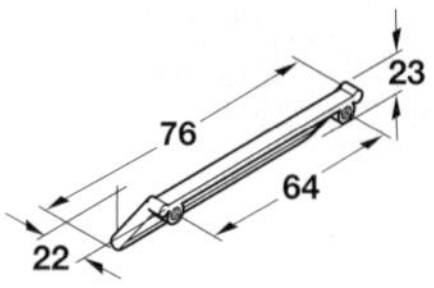

Matt black

Cat. No.	105.45.310

Packing: 25 pcs.

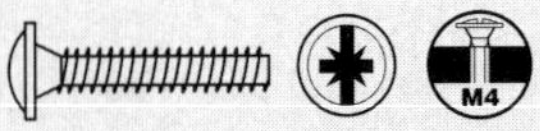

Threaded Screws M4
Combined slot, suitable for flat or cross blades

Finish: steel, zinc-plated

Length	Cat. No.
10 mm	022.35.109
12 mm	022.35.127
15 mm	022.35.154
18 mm	022.35.181
20 mm	022.35.207
22 mm	022.35.225
23 mm	022.35.234
25 mm	022.35.252
28 mm	022.35.289
30 mm	022.35.305
35 mm	022.35.350
38 mm	022.35.387
40 mm	022.35.403
45 mm	022.35.458
50 mm	022.35.501
60 mm	022.35.609

Packing: 100 and 1000 pcs.

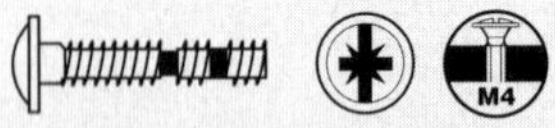

Threaded Breakoff Screw M4
Combined slot, suitable for flat or cross blades

Finish: steel, zinc-plated

Length	Cat. No.
1 3/4" x 3/4"	022.35.887

Packing: 100 and 1000 pcs.

Zinc Handles

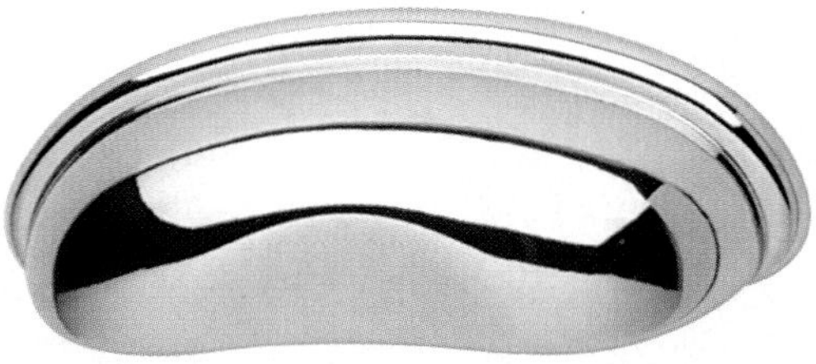

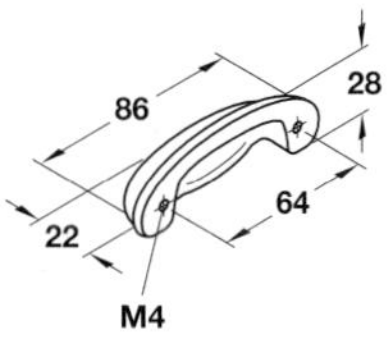

Chrome plated polished

Cat. No.	105.55.200

Packing: 25 pcs.

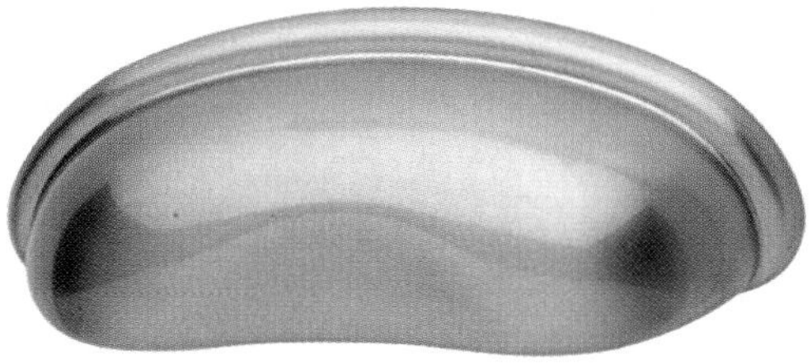

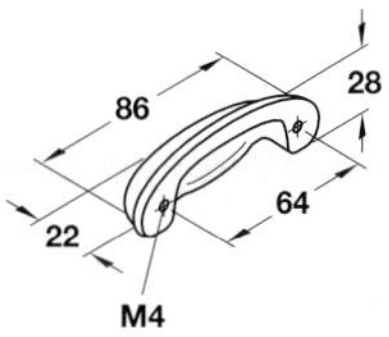

Nickel matt

Cat. No.	105.55.600

Packing: 25 pcs.

Threaded Screws M4
Combined slot, suitable for flat or cross blades

Finish: steel, zinc-plated

Length	Cat. No.
10 mm	022.35.109
12 mm	022.35.127
15 mm	022.35.154
18 mm	022.35.181
20 mm	022.35.207
22 mm	022.35.225
23 mm	022.35.234
25 mm	022.35.252
28 mm	022.35.289
30 mm	022.35.305
35 mm	022.35.350
38 mm	022.35.387
40 mm	022.35.403
45 mm	022.35.458
50 mm	022.35.501
60 mm	022.35.609

Packing: 100 and 1000 pcs.

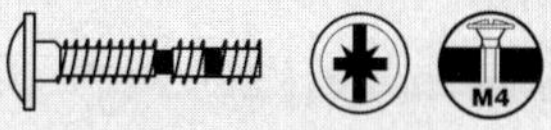

Threaded Breakoff Screw M4
Combined slot, suitable for flat or cross blades

Finish: steel, zinc-plated

Length	Cat. No.
1 3/4" x 3/4"	022.35.887

Packing: 100 and 1000 pcs.

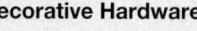

HÄFELE

Zinc Handles

Threaded Screws M4
Combined slot, suitable for flat or cross blades

Finish: steel, zinc-plated

Length	Cat. No.
10 mm	022.35.109
12 mm	022.35.127
15 mm	022.35.154
18 mm	022.35.181
20 mm	022.35.207
22 mm	022.35.225
23 mm	022.35.234
25 mm	022.35.252
28 mm	022.35.289
30 mm	022.35.305
35 mm	022.35.350
38 mm	022.35.387
40 mm	022.35.403
45 mm	022.35.458
50 mm	022.35.501
60 mm	022.35.609

Packing: 100 and 1000 pcs.

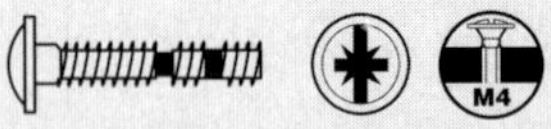

Threaded Breakoff Screw M4
Combined slot, suitable for flat or cross blades

Finish: steel, zinc-plated

Length	Cat. No.
1 3/4" x 3/4"	022.35.887

Packing: 100 and 1000 pcs.

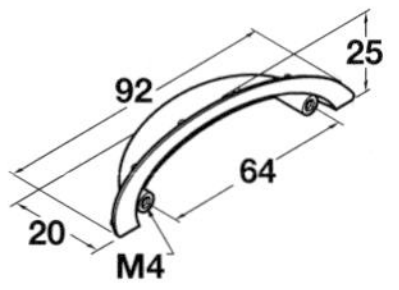

Gold colored polished

Cat. No.	166.17.806

Packing: 25 pcs.

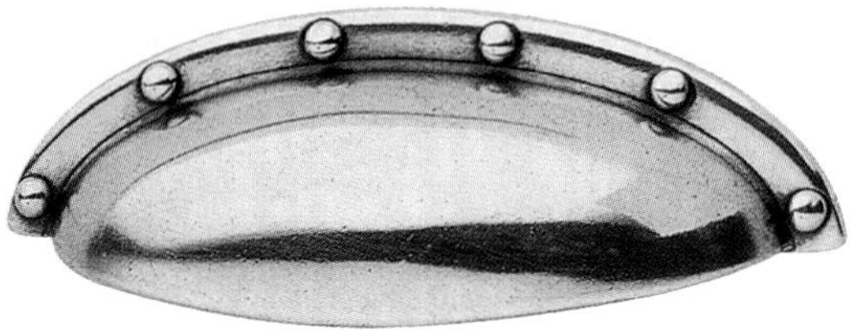

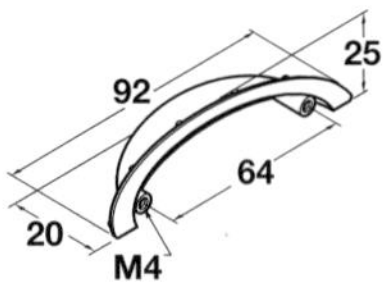

Polished bronze

Cat. No.	166.17.100

Packing: 25 pcs.

Zinc Handles

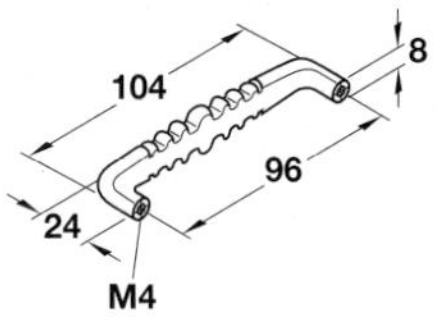

Antique tin

Cat. No.	121.02.902

Packing: 25 pcs.

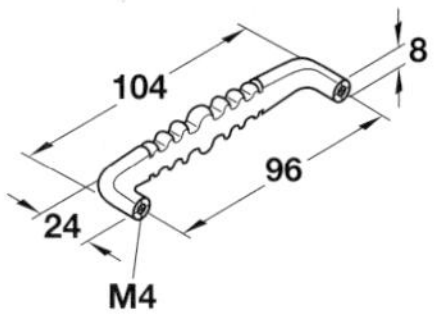

Bronzed and brushed

Cat. No.	121.02.108

Packing: 25 pcs.

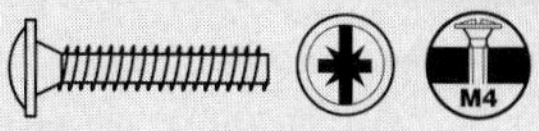

Threaded Screws M4
Combined slot, suitable for flat or cross blades

Finish: steel, zinc-plated

Length	Cat. No.
10 mm	022.35.109
12 mm	022.35.127
15 mm	022.35.154
18 mm	022.35.181
20 mm	022.35.207
22 mm	022.35.225
23 mm	022.35.234
25 mm	022.35.252
28 mm	022.35.289
30 mm	022.35.305
35 mm	022.35.350
38 mm	022.35.387
40 mm	022.35.403
45 mm	022.35.458
50 mm	022.35.501
60 mm	022.35.609

Packing: 100 and 1000 pcs.

Threaded Breakoff Screw M4
Combined slot, suitable for flat or cross blades

Finish: steel, zinc-plated

Length	Cat. No.
1 3/4" x 3/4"	022.35.887

Packing: 100 and 1000 pcs.

HÄFELE

Zinc handles

- Matching back plates available.

Threaded Screws M4
Combined slot, suitable for flat or cross blades
Finish: steel, zinc-plated

Length	Cat. No.
10 mm	022.35.109
12 mm	022.35.127
15 mm	022.35.154
18 mm	022.35.181
20 mm	022.35.207
22 mm	022.35.225
23 mm	022.35.234
25 mm	022.35.252
28 mm	022.35.289
30 mm	022.35.305
35 mm	022.35.350
38 mm	022.35.387
40 mm	022.35.403
45 mm	022.35.458
50 mm	022.35.501
60 mm	022.35.609

Packing: 100 and 1000 pcs.

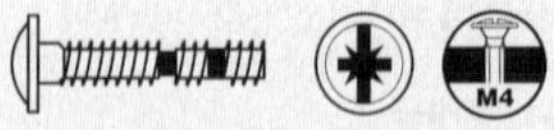

Threaded Breakoff Screw M4
Combined slot, suitable for flat or cross blades
Finish: steel, zinc-plated

Length	Cat. No.
1 3/4" x 3/4"	022.35.887

Packing: 100 and 1000 pcs.

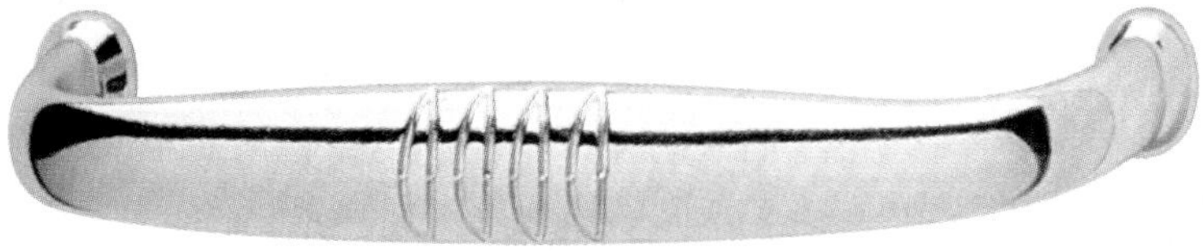

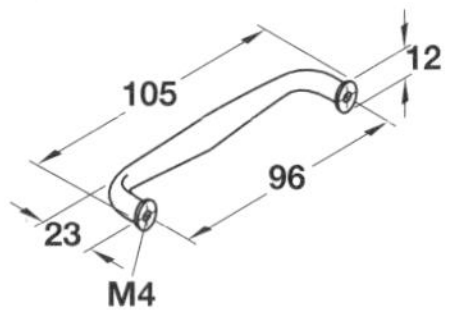

Gold colored polished

Catalog No.	102.55.802

Packing: 25 pcs.

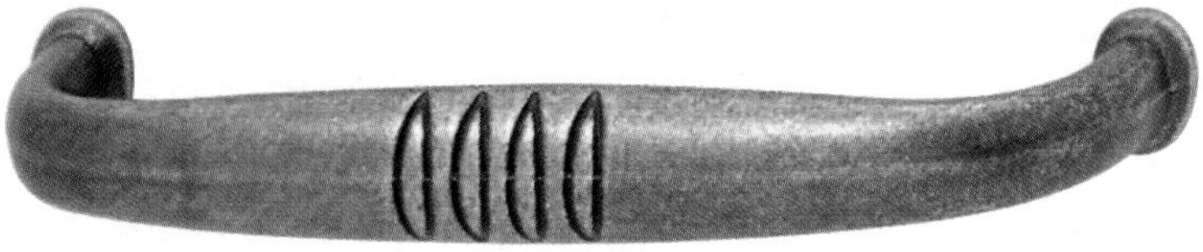

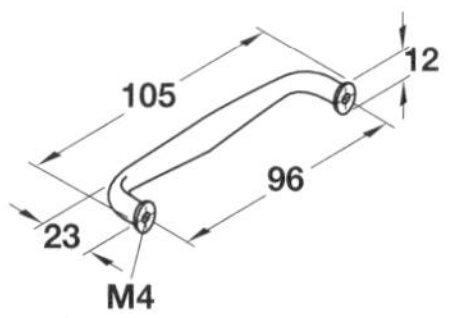

Brass antique

Catalog No.	102.55.106

Packing: 25 pcs.

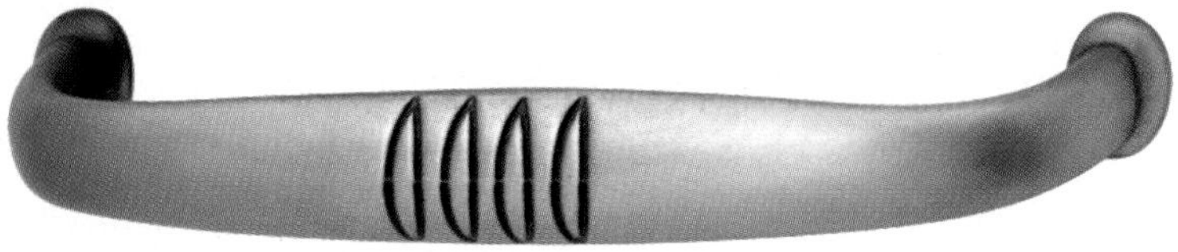

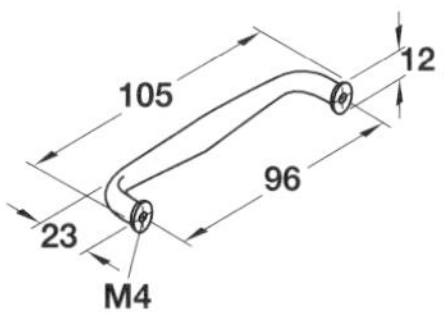

Antique tin plated

Catalog No.	102.55.900

Packing: 25 pcs.

Dimensional data not binding. We reserve the right to alter specifications without notice.

Zinc backplates

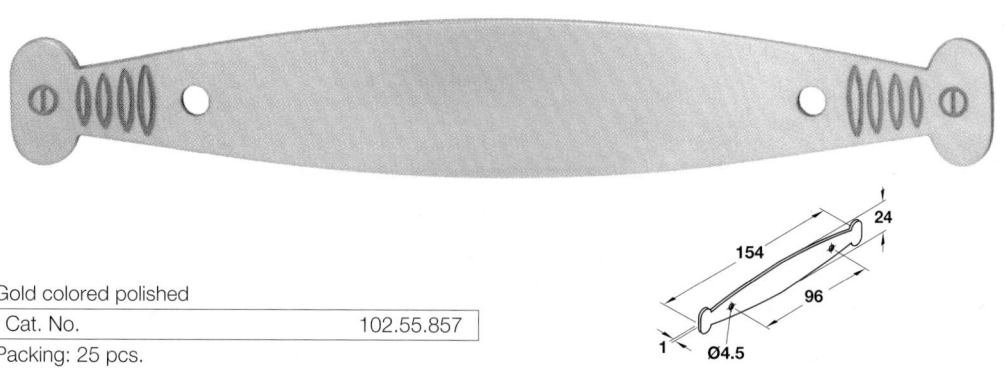

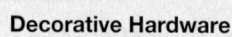

Gold colored polished

Cat. No.	102.55.857

Packing: 25 pcs.

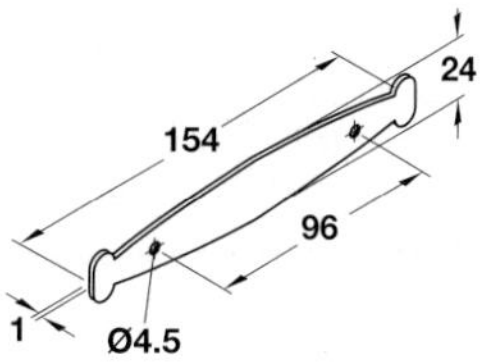

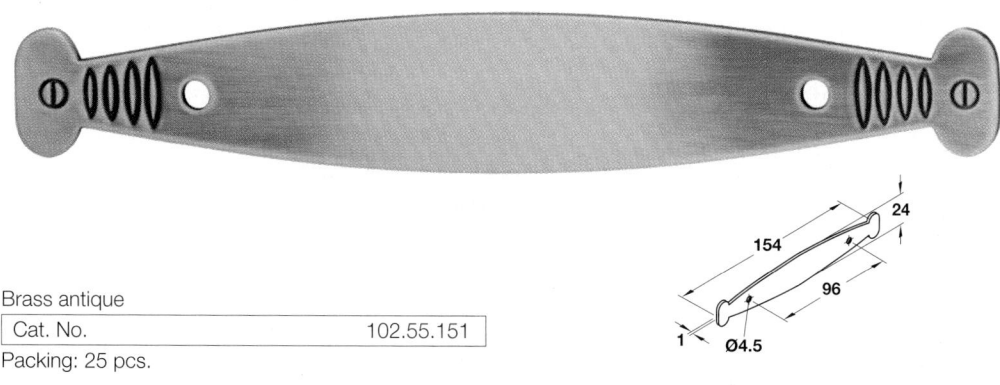

Brass antique

Cat. No.	102.55.151

Packing: 25 pcs.

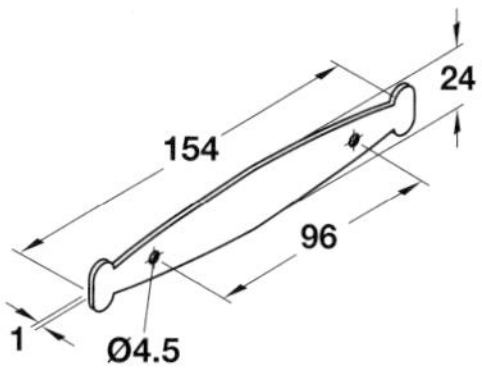

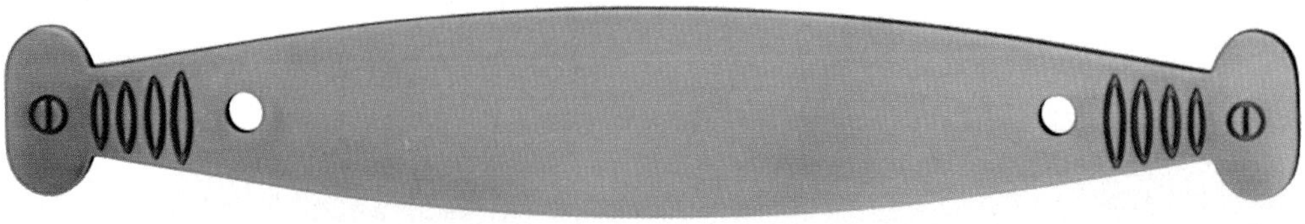

Antique tin plated

Cat. No.	102.55.955

Packing: 25 pcs.

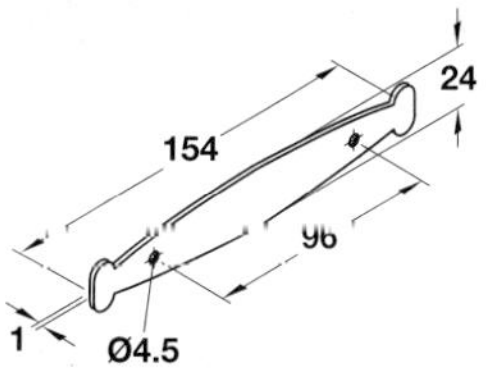

- Backplates can be used with handles 102.55. on preceding page.

Dimensional data not binding. We reserve the right to alter specifications without notice.

HÄFELE

Zinc Handles and Backplate

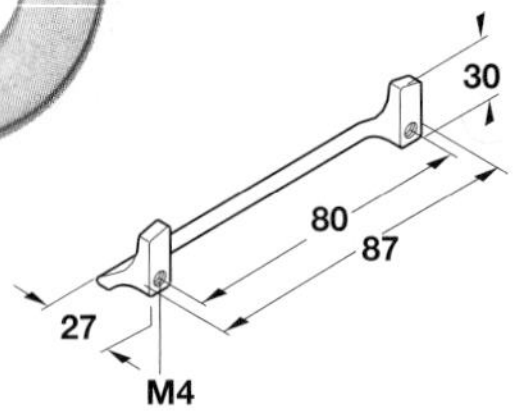

Nickel plated matt

Cat. No.	103.95.600

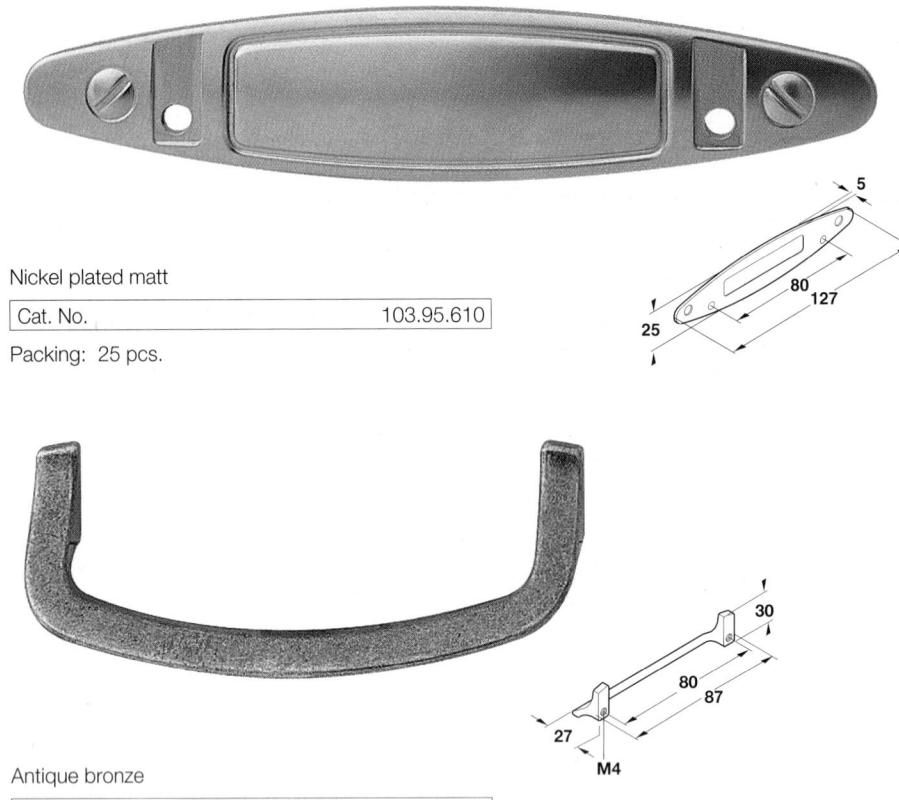

Packing: 25 pcs.

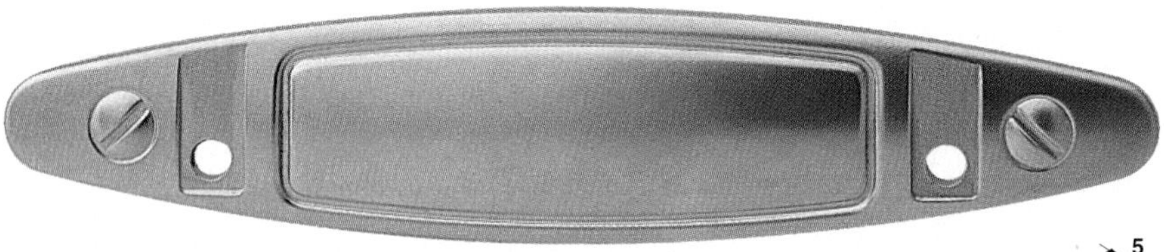

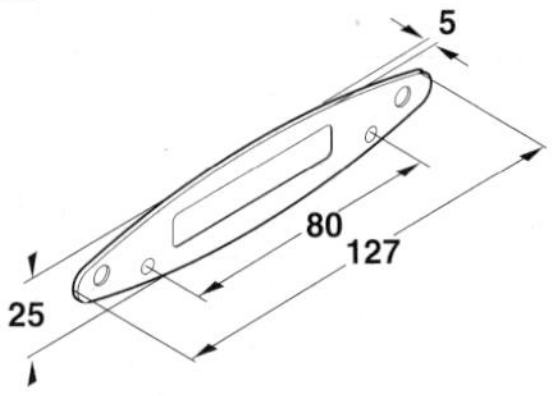

Nickel plated matt

Cat. No.	103.95.610

Packing: 25 pcs.

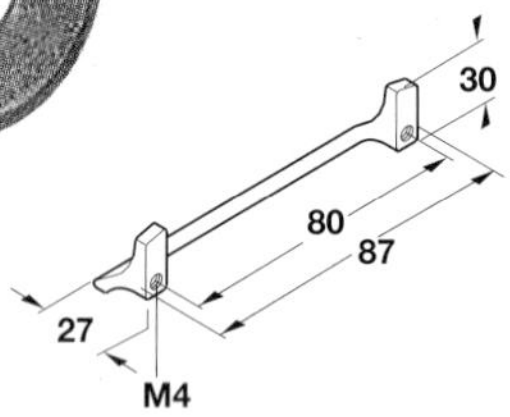

Antique bronze

Cat. No.	103.95.100

Packing: 25 pcs.

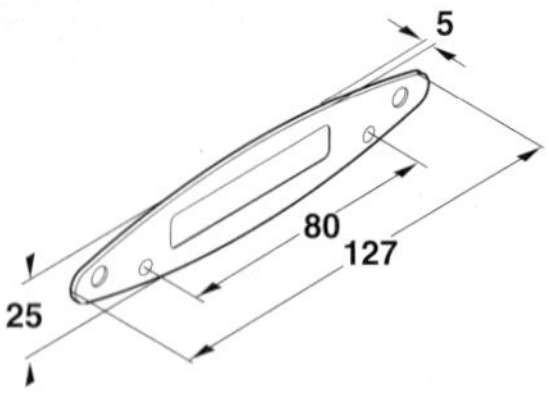

Antique bronze

Cat. No.	103.95.110

Packing: 25 pcs.

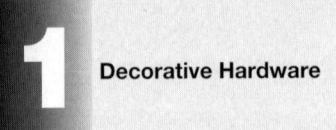

Threaded Screws M4
Combined slot, suitable for flat or cross blades

Finish: steel, zinc-plated

Length	Cat. No.
10 mm	022.35.109
12 mm	022.35.127
15 mm	022.35.154
18 mm	022.35.181
20 mm	022.35.207
22 mm	022.35.225
23 mm	022.35.234
25 mm	022.35.252
28 mm	022.35.289
30 mm	022.35.305
35 mm	022.35.350
38 mm	022.35.387
40 mm	022.35.403
45 mm	022.35.458
50 mm	022.35.501
60 mm	022.35.609

Packing: 100 and 1000 pcs.

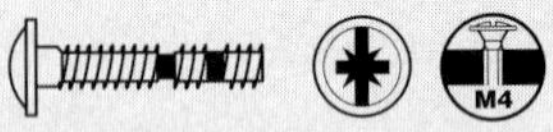

Threaded Breakoff Screw M4
Combined slot, suitable for flat or cross blades

Finish: steel, zinc-plated

Length	Cat. No.
1 3/4" x 3/4"	022.35.887

Packing: 100 and 1000 pcs.

Handle can be used with matching backplate

Dimensional data not binding. We reserve the right to alter specifications without notice.

Zinc handles

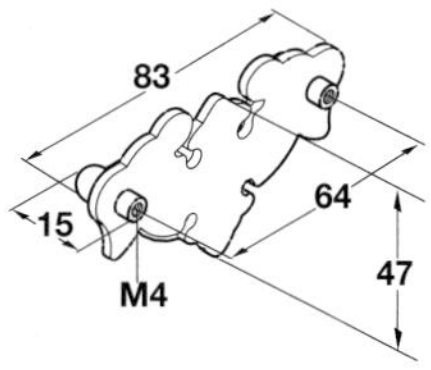

Antique bronze

Cat. No.	122.39.100

Packing: 25 pcs.

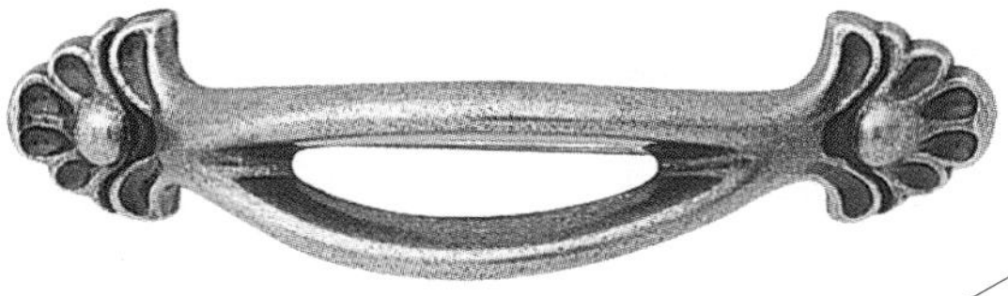

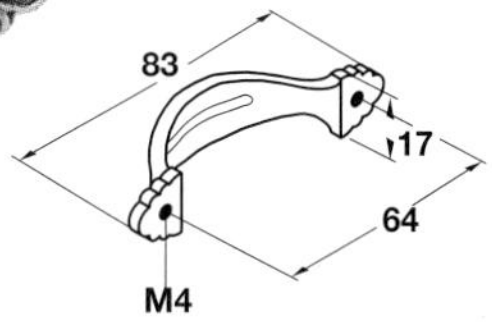

Antique bronze

Cat. No.	122.42.100

Packing: 25 pcs.

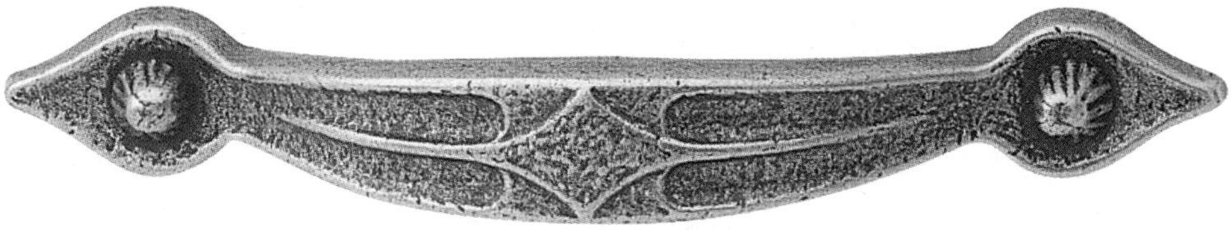

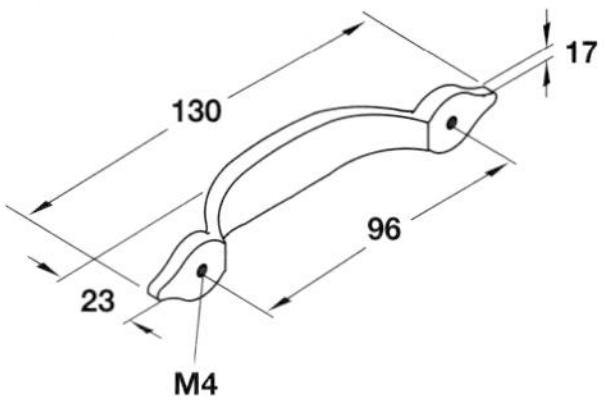

Antique bronze

Cat. No.	122.40.100

Packing: 25 pcs.

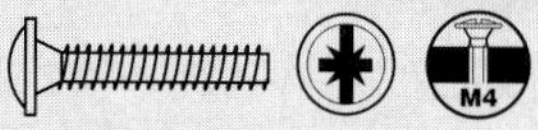

Threaded Screws M4
Combined slot, suitable for flat or cross blades

Finish: steel, zinc-plated

Length	Cat. No.
10 mm	022.35.109
12 mm	022.35.127
15 mm	022.35.154
18 mm	022.35.181
20 mm	022.35.207
22 mm	022.35.225
23 mm	022.35.234
25 mm	022.35.252
28 mm	022.35.289
30 mm	022.35.305
35 mm	022.35.350
38 mm	022.35.387
40 mm	022.35.403
45 mm	022.35.458
50 mm	022.35.501
60 mm	022.35.609

Packing: 100 and 1000 pcs.

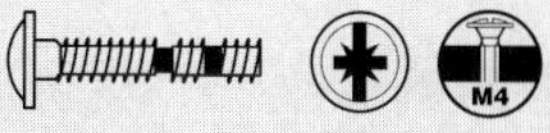

Threaded Breakoff Screw M4
Combined slot, suitable for flat or cross blades

Finish: steel, zinc-plated

Length	Cat. No.
1 3/4" x 3/4"	022.35.887

Packing: 100 and 1000 pcs.

HÄFELE

Zinc Handles

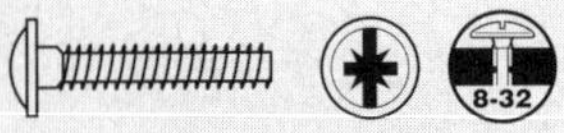

Threaded Screws 8-32
Combined slot, suitable for flat or cross blades

Finish: steel, yellow chromated

Length	Cat. No.
22 mm	022.25.229
25 mm	022.25.256
32 mm	022.25.327
38 mm	022.25.381
45 mm	022.25.452

Packing: 100 and 1000 pcs.

Threaded Screws M4
Combined slot, suitable for flat or cross blades

Finish: steel, zinc-plated

Length	Cat. No.
10 mm	022.35.109
12 mm	022.35.127
15 mm	022.35.154
18 mm	022.35.181
20 mm	022.35.207
22 mm	022.35.225
23 mm	022.35.234
25 mm	022.35.252
28 mm	022.35.289
30 mm	022.35.305
35 mm	022.35.350
38 mm	022.35.387
40 mm	022.35.403
45 mm	022.35.458
50 mm	022.35.501
60 mm	022.35.609

Packing: 100 and 1000 pcs.

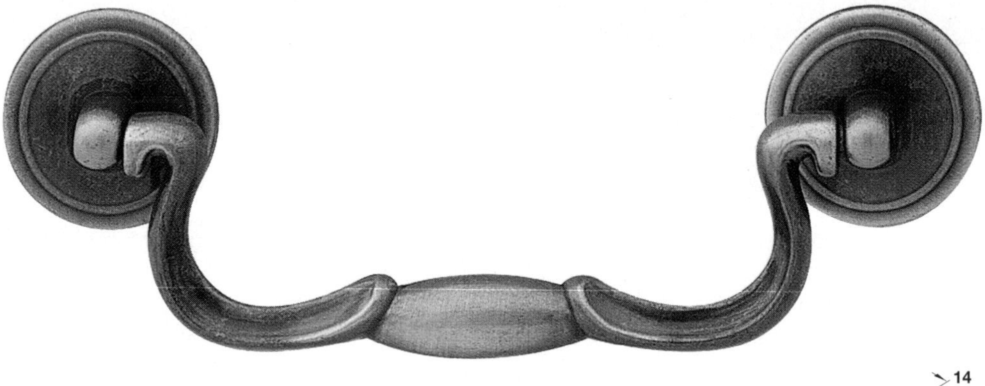

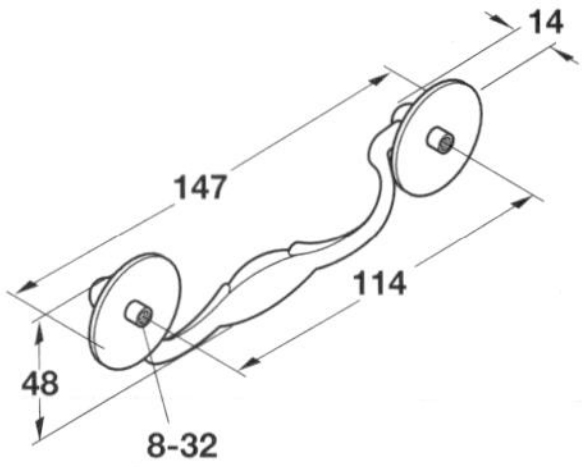

Antique bonze

Cat. No.	118.30.103

Packing: 25 pcs.

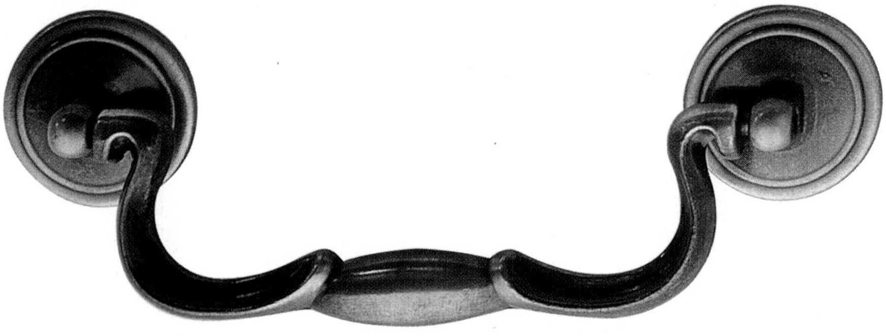

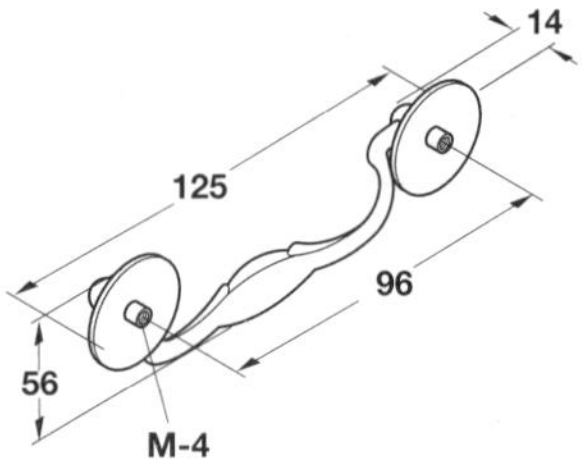

Satin antique

Cat. No.	118.22.101

Packing: 25 pcs.

Dimensional data not binding.
We reserve the right to alter specifications without notice.

Zinc Handles

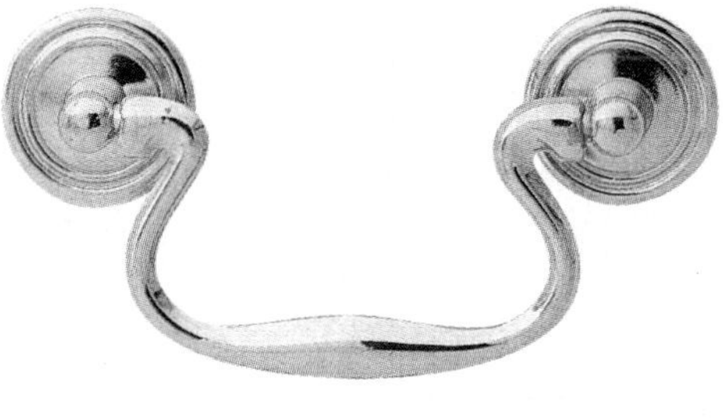

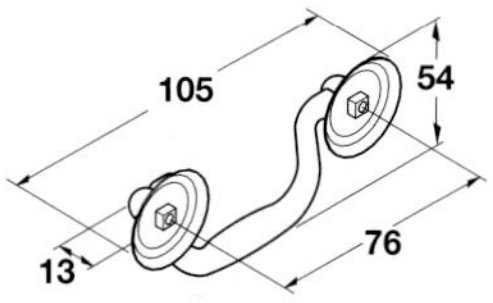

Gold colored polished

Cat. No.	120.55.800

Packing: 25 pcs.

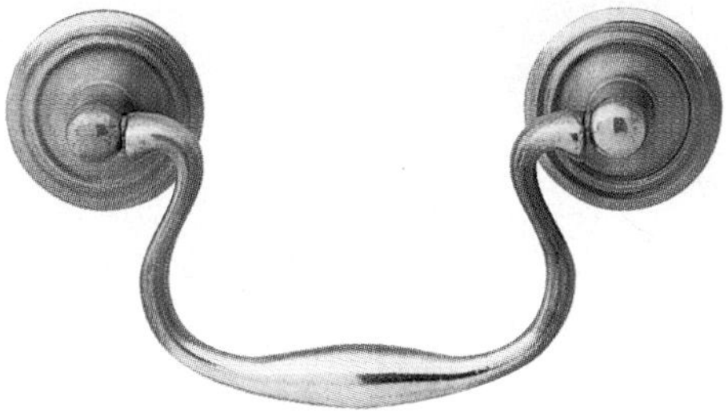

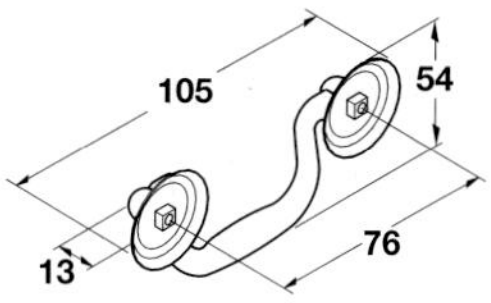

Antique english

Cat. No.	120.55.100

Packing: 25 pcs.

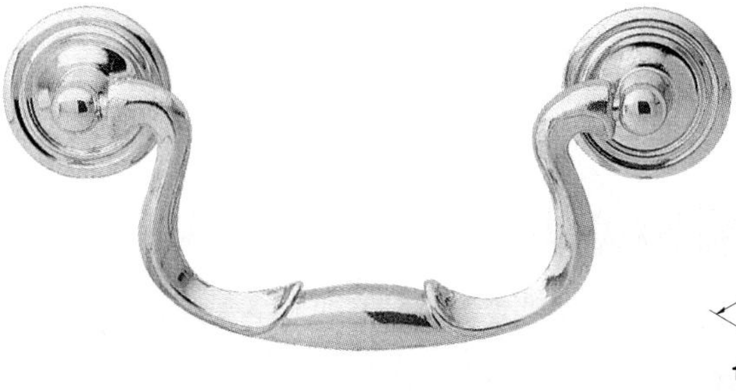

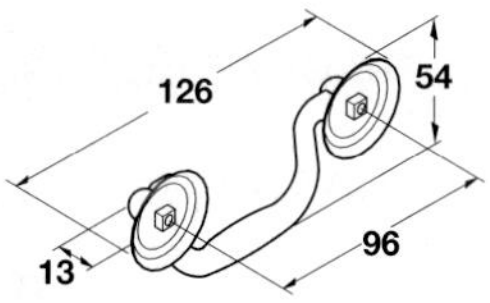

Gold colored polished

Cat. No.	120.56.800

Packing: 25 pcs.

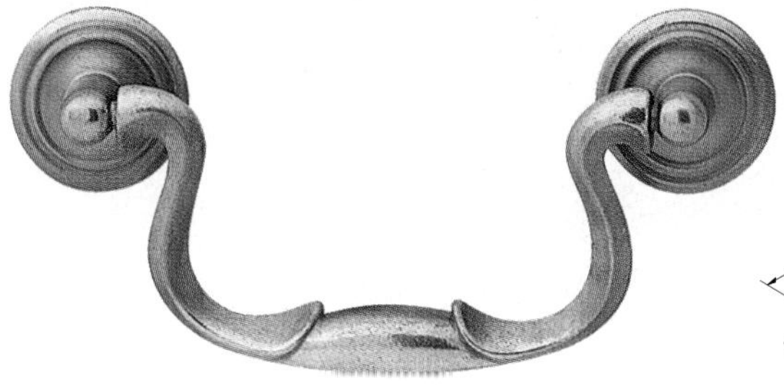

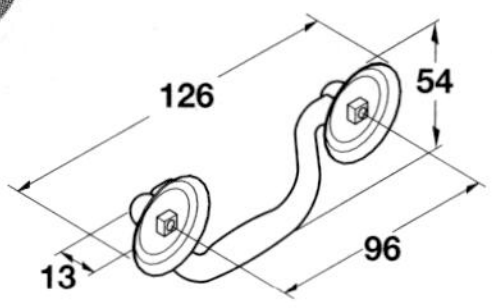

Antique english

Cat. No.	120.56.100

Packing: 25 pcs.

Threaded Screws M4
Combined slot, suitable for flat or cross blades

Finish: steel, zinc-plated

Length	Cat. No.
10 mm	022.35.109
12 mm	022.35.127
15 mm	022.35.154
18 mm	022.35.181
20 mm	022.35.207
22 mm	022.35.225
23 mm	022.35.234
25 mm	022.35.252
28 mm	022.35.289
30 mm	022.35.305
35 mm	022.35.350
38 mm	022.35.387
40 mm	022.35.403
45 mm	022.35.458
50 mm	022.35.501
60 mm	022.35.609

Packing: 100 and 1000 pcs.

Threaded Breakoff Screw M4
Combined slot, suitable for flat or cross blades

Finish: steel, zinc-plated

Length	Cat. No.
1 3/4" x 3/4"	022.35.887

Packing: 100 and 1000 pcs.

HÄFELE

Zinc Handles

1 Decorative Hardware

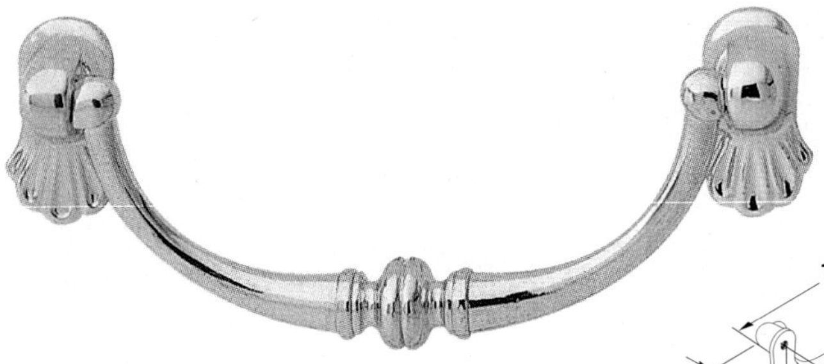
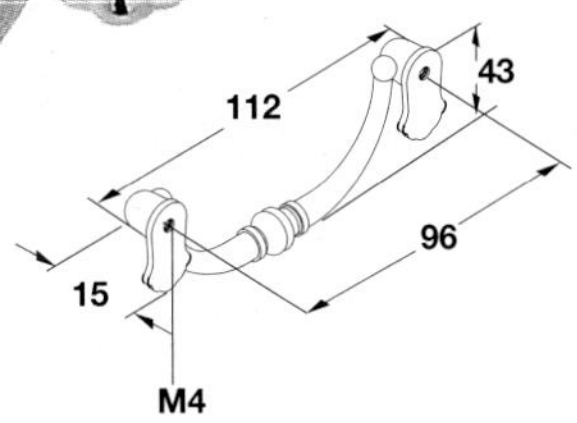

Gold colored polished

Cat. No.	120.57.800

Packing: 25 pcs.

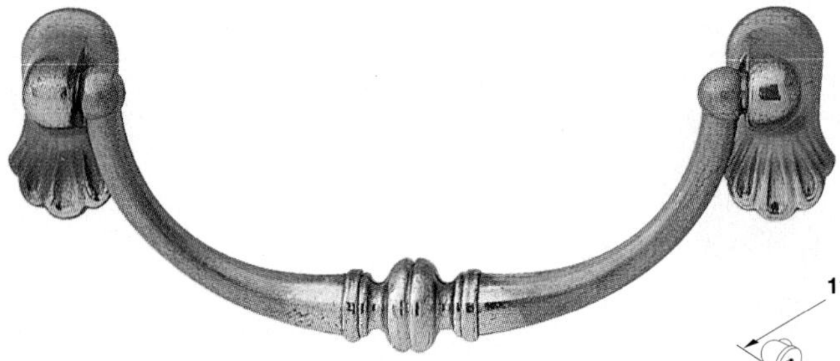
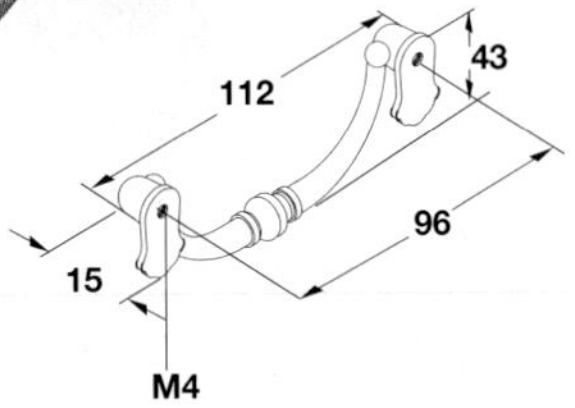

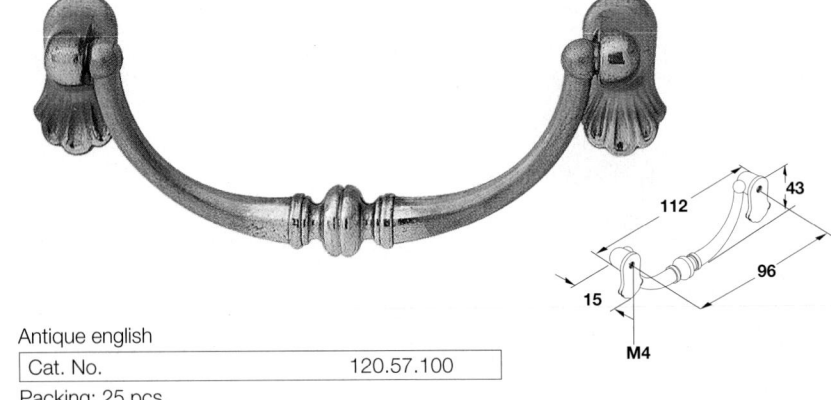

Antique english

Cat. No.	120.57.100

Packing: 25 pcs.

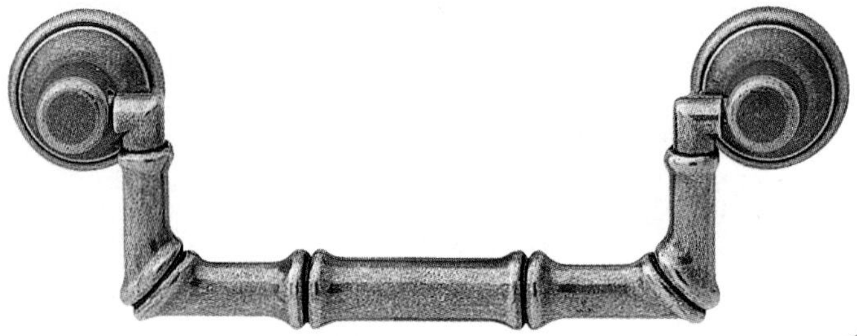
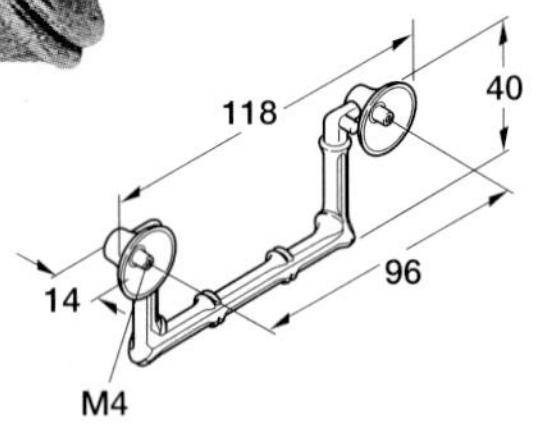

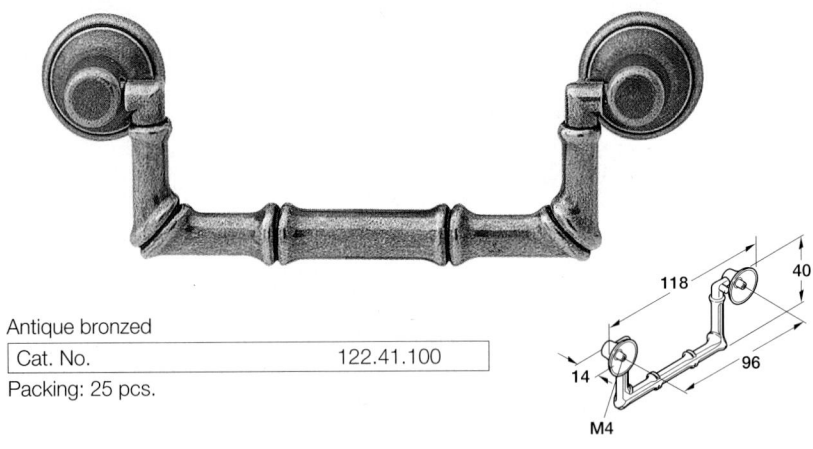

Antique bronzed

Cat. No.	122.41.100

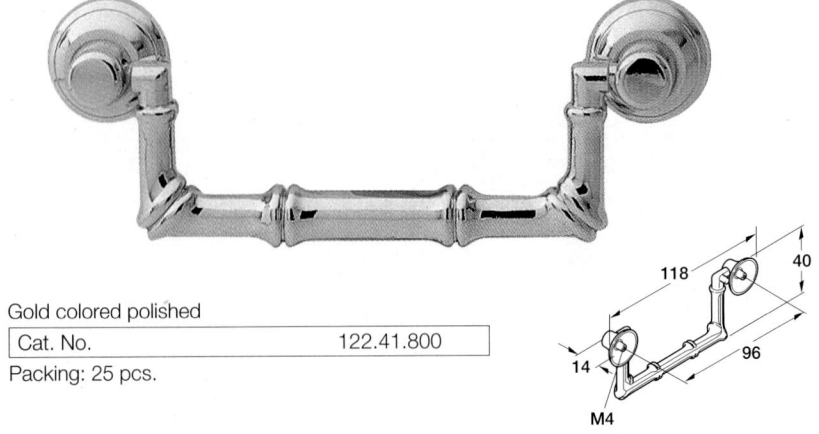

Packing: 25 pcs.

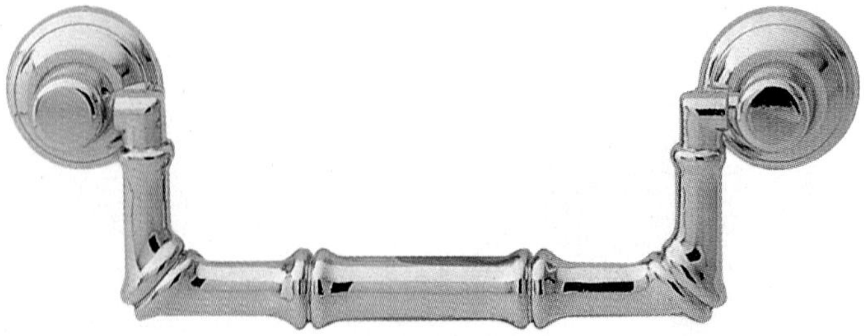
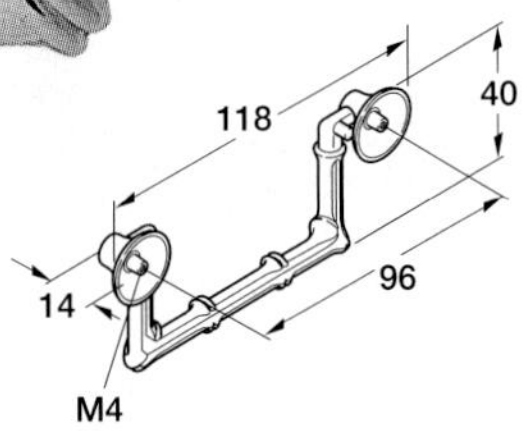

Gold colored polished

Cat. No.	122.41.800

Packing: 25 pcs.

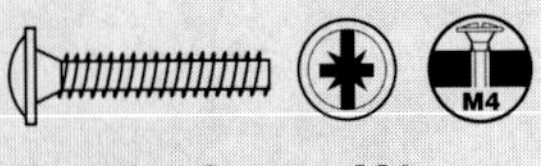

Threaded Screws M4
Combined slot, suitable for flat or cross blades
Finish: steel, zinc-plated

Length	Cat. No.
10 mm	022.35.109
12 mm	022.35.127
15 mm	022.35.154
18 mm	022.35.181
20 mm	022.35.207
22 mm	022.35.225
23 mm	022.35.234
25 mm	022.35.252
28 mm	022.35.289
30 mm	022.35.305
35 mm	022.35.350
38 mm	022.35.387
40 mm	022.35.403
45 mm	022.35.458
50 mm	022.35.501
60 mm	022.35.609

Packing: 100 and 1000 pcs.

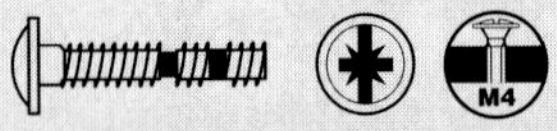

Threaded Breakoff Screw M4
Combined slot, suitable for flat or cross blades
Finish: steel, zinc-plated

Length	Cat. No.
1 3/4" x 3/4"	022.35.887

Packing: 100 and 1000 pcs.

Dimensional data not binding.
We reserve the right to alter specifications without notice.

Zinc Knobs and Handles

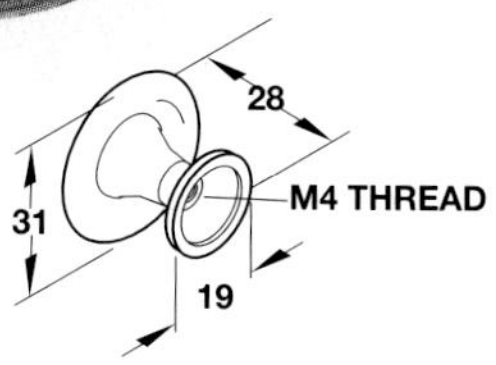

Antique english

Cat. No.	120.61.100

Packing: 25 pcs.

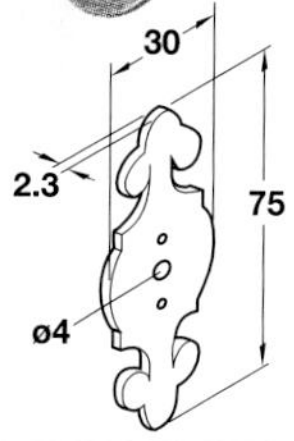

Antique english

Cat. No.	120.61.190

Packing: 25 pcs.

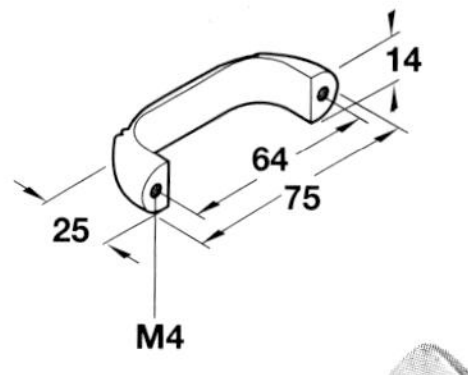

Antique english

Cat. No.	120.58.100

Packing: 25 pcs.

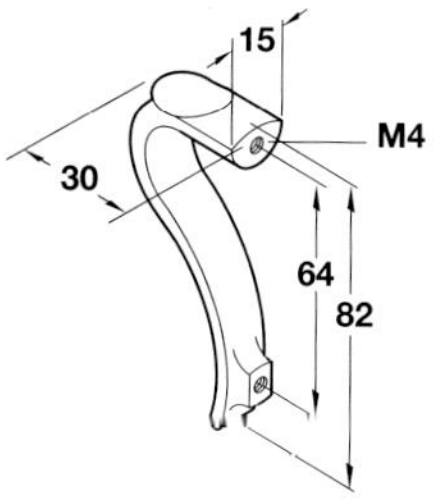

Antique english

Cat. No.	120.59.100

Packing: 25 pcs.

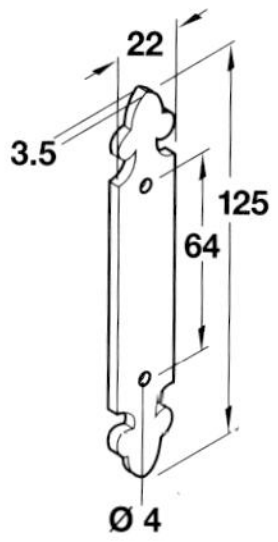

Antique english

Cat. No.	120.59.190

Packing: 25 pcs.

HÄFELE

Decorative Hardware **1**

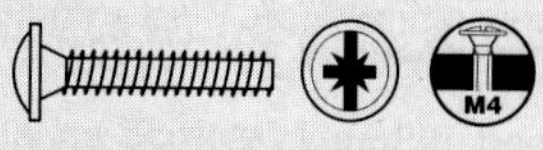

Threaded Screws M4
Combined slot, suitable for flat or cross blades

Finish: steel, zinc-plated

Length	Cat. No.
10 mm	022.35.109
12 mm	022.35.127
15 mm	022.35.154
18 mm	022.35.181
20 mm	022.35.207
22 mm	022.35.225
23 mm	022.35.234
25 mm	022.35.252
28 mm	022.35.289
30 mm	022.35.305
35 mm	022.35.350
38 mm	022.35.387
40 mm	022.35.403
45 mm	022.35.458
50 mm	022.35.501
60 mm	022.35.609

Packing: 100 and 1000 pcs.

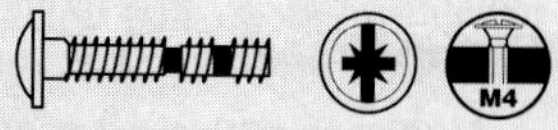

Threaded Breakoff Screw M4
Combined slot, suitable for flat or cross blades

Finish: steel, zinc-plated

Length	Cat. No.
1 3/4" x 3/4"	022.35.887

Packing: 100 and 1000 pcs.

Backplate can be used with either handle.

Dimensional data not binding. We reserve the right to alter specifications without notice.

HÄFELE

Zinc Knobs and Handles

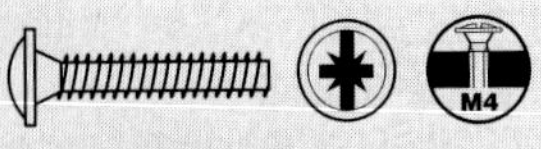

Threaded Screws M4
Combined slot, suitable for flat or cross blades

Finish: steel, zinc-plated

Length	Cat. No.
10 mm	022.35.109
12 mm	022.35.127
15 mm	022.35.154
18 mm	022.35.181
20 mm	022.35.207
22 mm	022.35.225
23 mm	022.35.234
25 mm	022.35.252
28 mm	022.35.289
30 mm	022.35.305
35 mm	022.35.350
38 mm	022.35.387
40 mm	022.35.403
45 mm	022.35.458
50 mm	022.35.501
60 mm	022.35.609

Packing: 100 and 1000 pcs.

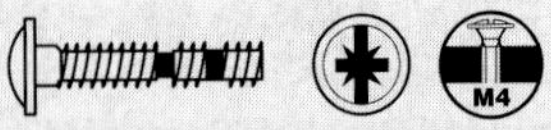

Threaded Breakoff Screw M4
Combined slot, suitable for flat or cross blades

Finish: steel, zinc-plated

Length	Cat. No.
1 3/4" x 3/4"	022.35.887

Packing: 100 and 1000 pcs.

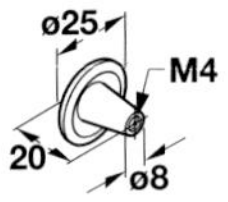

Antique bronze

Cat. No.	122.20.101

Packing: 25 pcs.

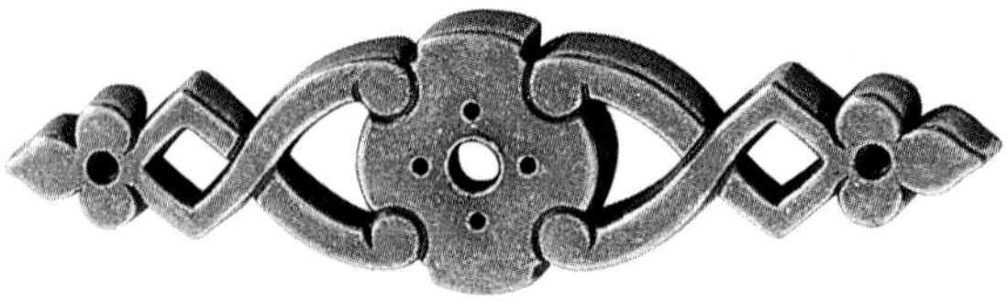

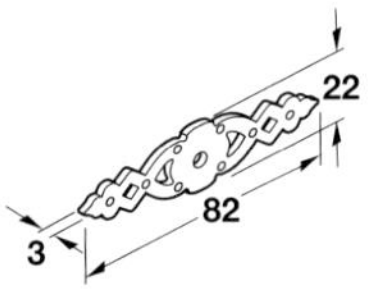

Antique bronze

Cat. No.	122.21.108

Packing: 25 pcs.

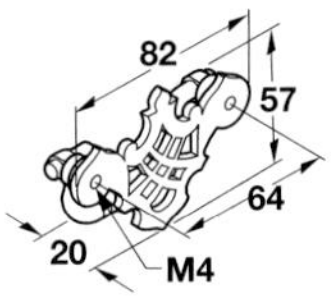

Antique bronze

Cat. No.	121.89.114

Packing: 25 pcs.

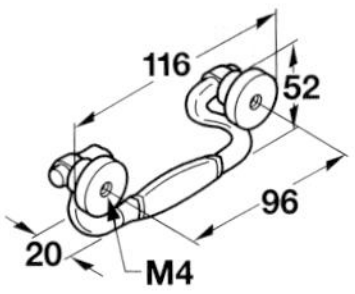

Antique bronze

Cat. No.	122.18.129

Packing: 25 pcs.

Zinc knobs and handles

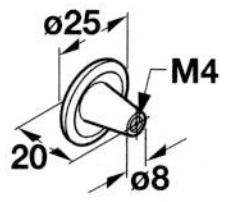

Gold colored/polished

Cat. No.	122.20.807

Packing: 25 pcs.

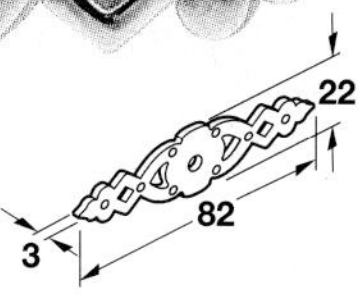

Gold colored/polished

Cat. No.	122.21.804

Packing: 25 pcs.

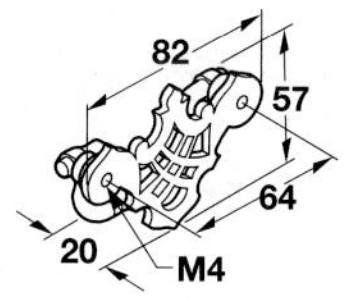

Gold colored/polished

Cat. No.	121.89.810

Packing: 25 pcs.

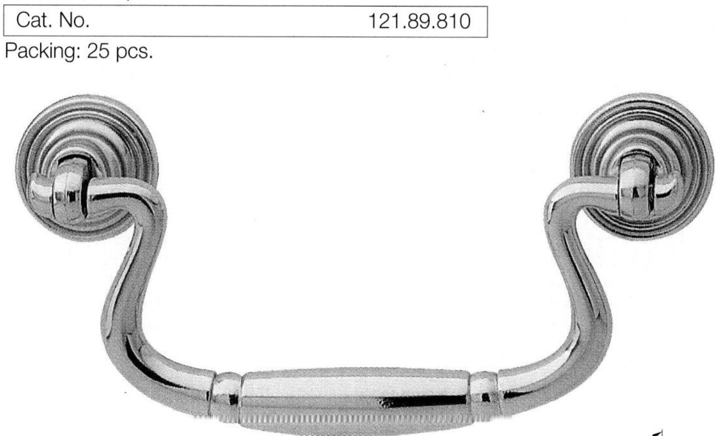
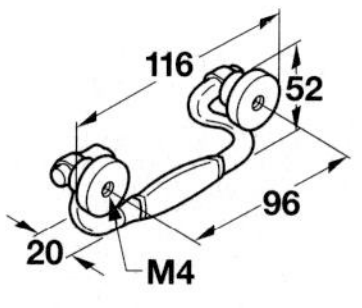

Gold colored/polished

Cat. No.	122.18.825

Packing: 25 pcs.

Threaded Screws M4
Combined slot, suitable for flat or cross blades

Finish: steel, zinc-plated

Length	Cat. No.
10 mm	022.35.109
12 mm	022.35.127
15 mm	022.35.154
18 mm	022.35.181
20 mm	022.35.207
22 mm	022.35.225
23 mm	022.35.234
25 mm	022.35.252
28 mm	022.35.289
30 mm	022.35.305
35 mm	022.35.350
38 mm	022.35.387
40 mm	022.35.403
45 mm	022.35.458
50 mm	022.35.501
60 mm	022.35.609

Packing: 100 and 1000 pcs.

Threaded Breakoff Screw M4
Combined slot, suitable for flat or cross blades

Finish: steel, zinc-plated

Length	Cat. No.
1 3/4" x 3/4"	022.35.887

Packing: 100 and 1000 pcs.

HÄFELE

Zinc Drop Handles

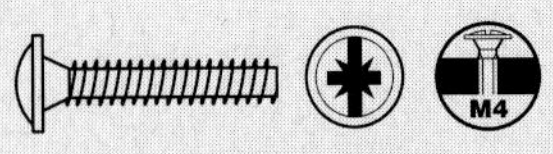

Threaded Screws M4
Combined slot, suitable for flat or cross blades

Finish: steel, zinc-plated

Length	Cat. No.
10 mm	022.35.109
12 mm	022.35.127
15 mm	022.35.154
18 mm	022.35.181
20 mm	022.35.207
22 mm	022.35.225
23 mm	022.35.234
25 mm	022.35.252
28 mm	022.35.289
30 mm	022.35.305
35 mm	022.35.350
38 mm	022.35.387
40 mm	022.35.403
45 mm	022.35.458
50 mm	022.35.501
60 mm	022.35.609

Packing: 100 and 1000 pcs.

Threaded Breakoff Screw M4
Combined slot, suitable for flat or cross blades

Finish: steel, zinc-plated

Length	Cat. No.
1 3/4" x 3/4"	022.35.887

Packing: 100 and 1000 pcs.

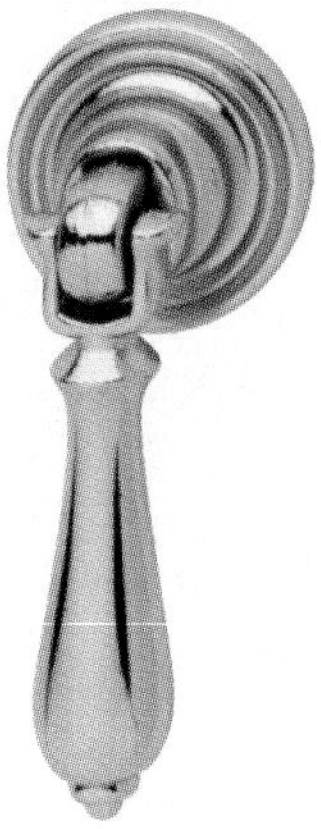

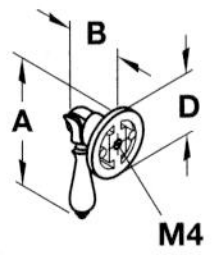

Gold plated polished

Size A x B	Dimension D	Cat. No.
48 x 20	22	120.17.864
55 x 19	25	120.17.873

Packing: 25 pcs.

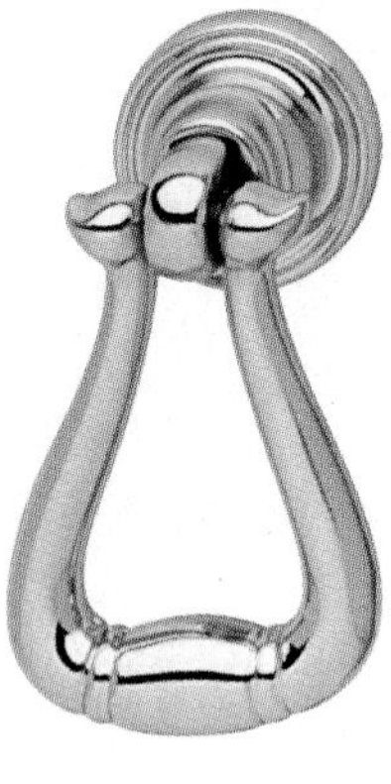

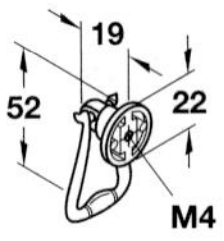

Gold plated polished

Cat. No.	120.17.855

Packing: 25 pcs.

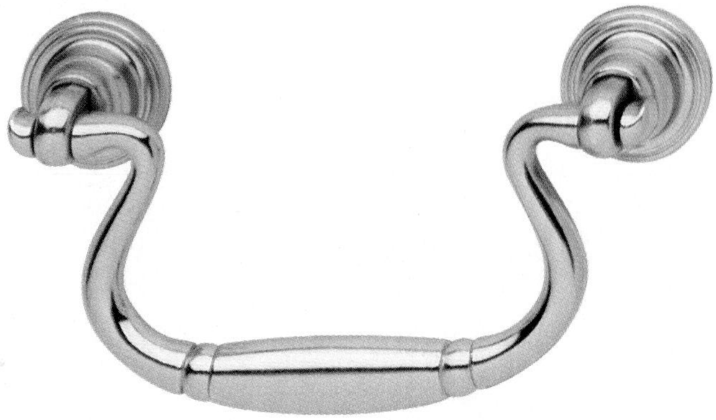

Gold plated polished

Size A x B	Height H	Dimension C	Cat. No.
86 x 19	42	64	120.17.819
102 x 19	45	80	120.17.828

Packing: 25 pcs.

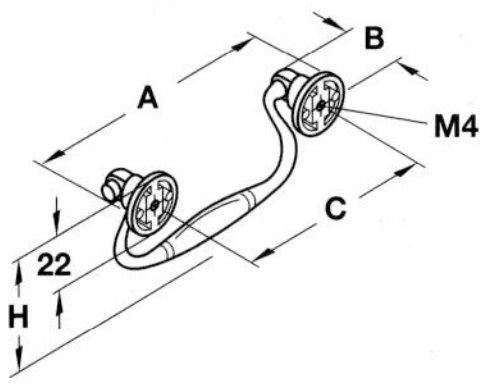

Dimensional data not binding.
We reserve the right to alter specifications without notice.

Antique Zinc Fitting Sets

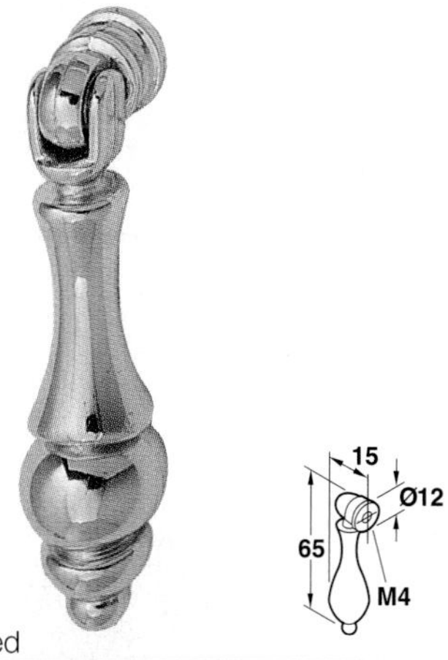

Gold colored polished

Cat. No.	121.05.850

Packing: 25 pcs.

Bronzed and brushed

Cat. No.	121.05.154

Packing: 25 pcs.

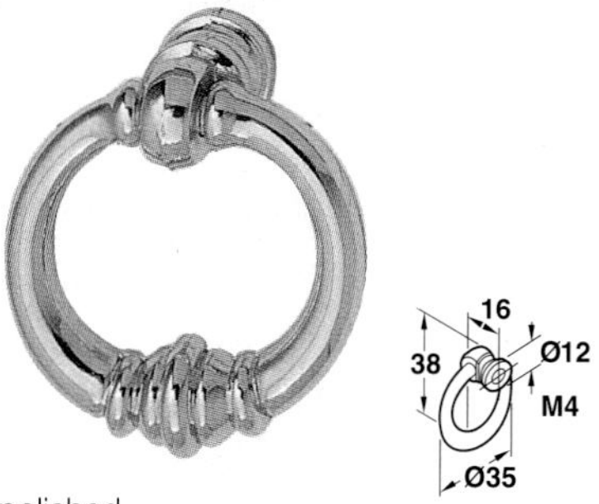

Gold colored polished

Cat. No.	121.19.809

Packing: 25 pcs.

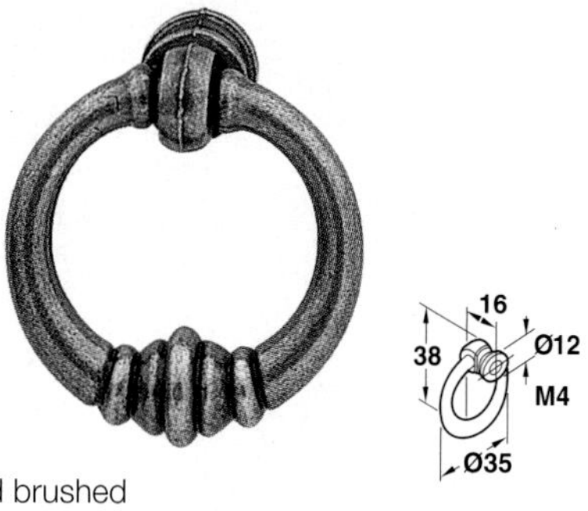

Bronzed and brushed

Cat. No.	121.19.103

Packing: 25 pcs.

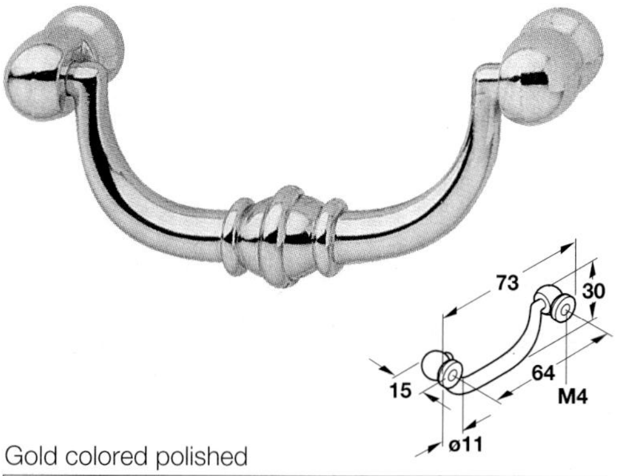

Gold colored polished

Cat. No.	121.18.811

Packing: 25 pcs.

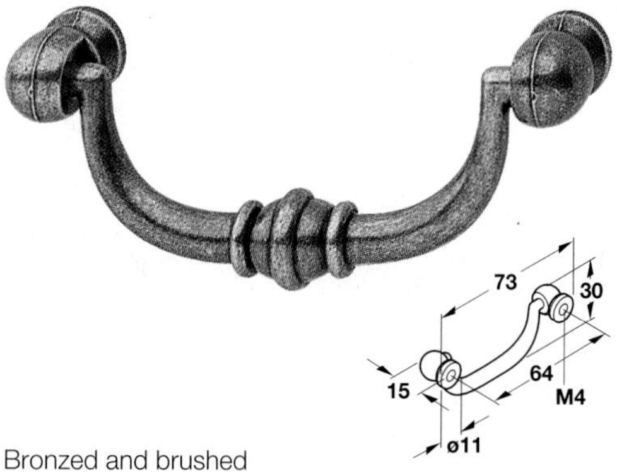

Bronzed and brushed

Cat. No.	121.18.115

Packing: 25 pcs.

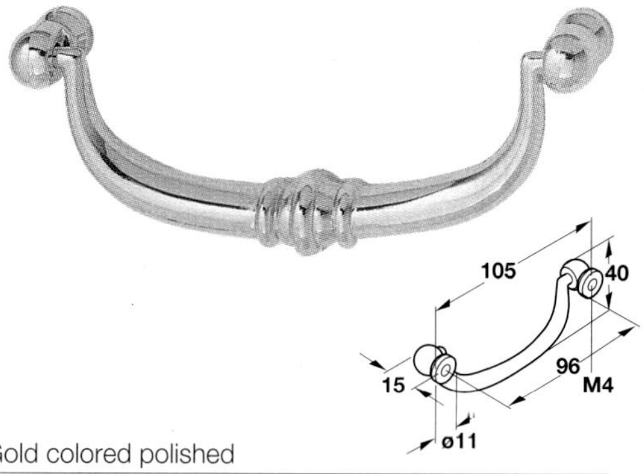

Gold colored polished

Cat. No.	121.18.820

Packing: 25 pcs.

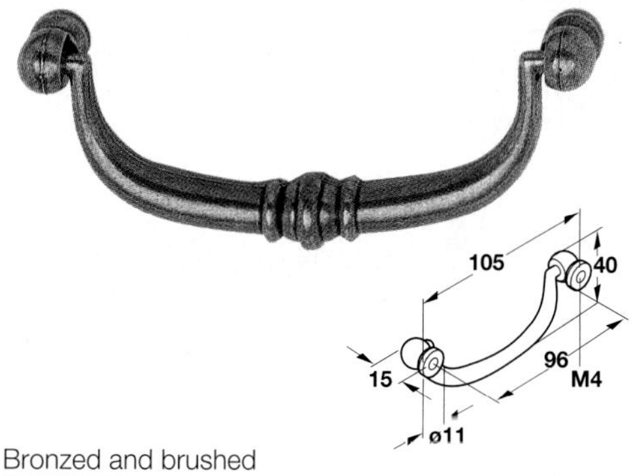

Bronzed and brushed

Cat. No.	121.18.124

Packing: 25 pcs.

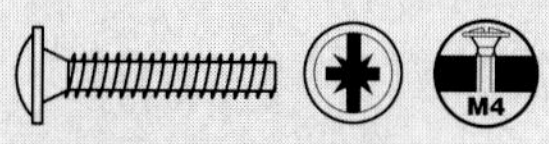

Threaded Screws M4
Combined slot, suitable for flat or cross blades
Finish: steel, zinc-plated

Length	Cat. No.
10 mm	022.35.109
12 mm	022.35.127
15 mm	022.35.154
18 mm	022.35.181
20 mm	022.35.207
22 mm	022.35.225
23 mm	022.35.234
25 mm	022.35.252
28 mm	022.35.289
30 mm	022.35.305
35 mm	022.35.350
38 mm	022.35.387
40 mm	022.35.403
45 mm	022.35.458
50 mm	022.35.501
60 mm	022.35.609

Packing: 100 and 1000 pcs.

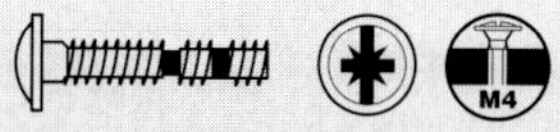

Threaded Breakoff Screw M4
Combined slot, suitable for flat or cross blades
Finish: steel, zinc-plated

Length	Cat. No.
1 3/4" x 3/4"	022.35.887

Packing: 100 and 1000 pcs.

Dimensional data not binding. We reserve the right to alter specifications without notice.

HÄFELE

Zinc Handles and Knobs

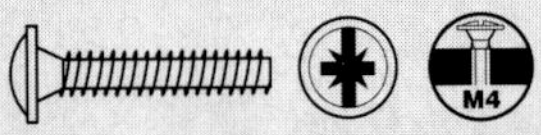

Threaded Screws M4
Combined slot, suitable for flat or cross blades

Finish: steel, zinc-plated

Length	Cat. No.
10 mm	022.35.109
12 mm	022.35.127
15 mm	022.35.154
18 mm	022.35.181
20 mm	022.35.207
22 mm	022.35.225
23 mm	022.35.234
25 mm	022.35.252
28 mm	022.35.289
30 mm	022.35.305
35 mm	022.35.350
38 mm	022.35.387
40 mm	022.35.403
45 mm	022.35.458
50 mm	022.35.501
60 mm	022.35.609

Packing: 100 and 1000 pcs.

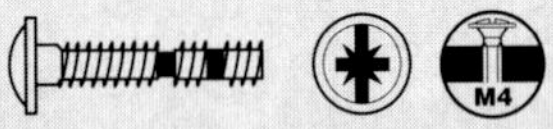

Threaded Breakoff Screw M4
Combined slot, suitable for flat or cross blades

Finish: steel, zinc-plated

Length	Cat. No.
1 3/4" x 3/4"	022.35.887

Packing: 100 and 1000 pcs.

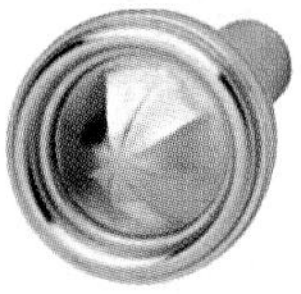

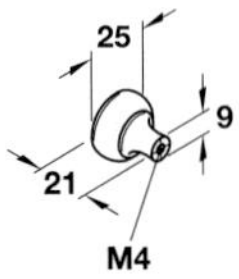

Gold plated polished

Cat. No.	120.20.816

Packing: 25 pcs.

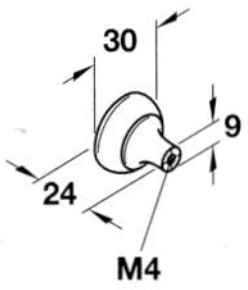

Gold plated polished

Cat. No.	120.20.825

Packing: 25 pcs.

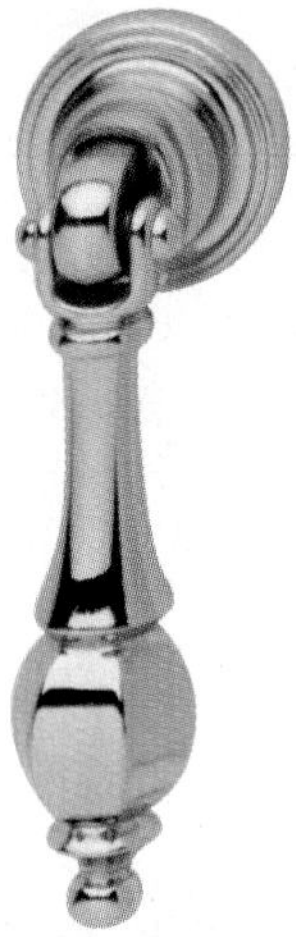

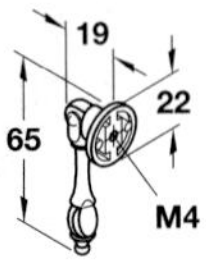

Gold plated polished

Cat. No.	120.18.861

Packing: 25 pcs.

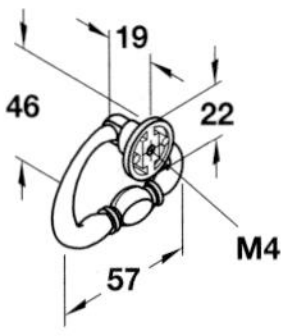

Gold plated polished

Cat. No.	120.18.852

Packing: 25 pcs.

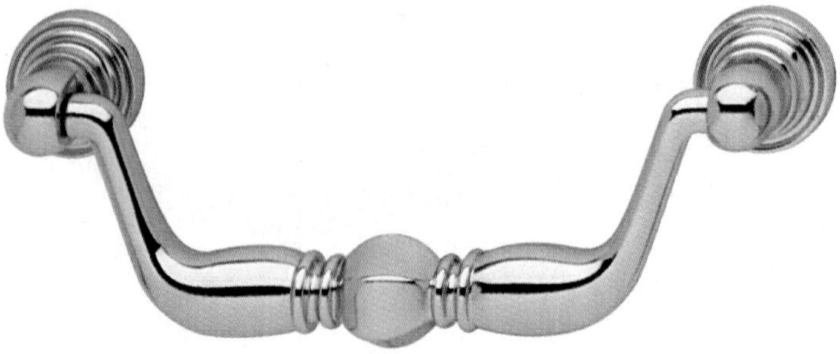

Gold plated polished

Size A x B	Height H	Dimension C	Cat. No.
83 x 16	30	64	121.01.816
115 x 16	40	96	121.01.825

Packing: 25 pcs.

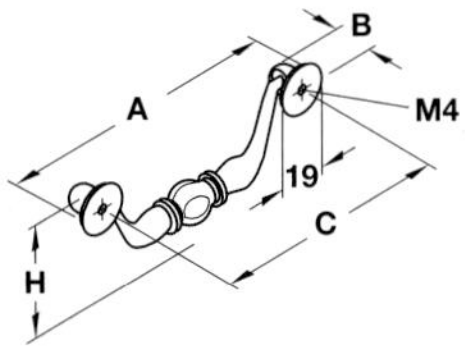

Dimensional data not binding.
We reserve the right to alter specifications without notice.

Zinc Knobs and Handles

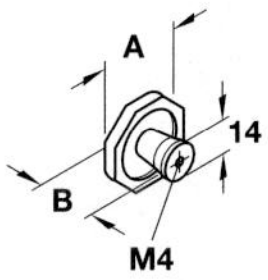

Gold colored polished

Size A x B	Cat. No.
27 x 20	121.63.825
33 x 21	121.63.834

Packing: 25 pcs.

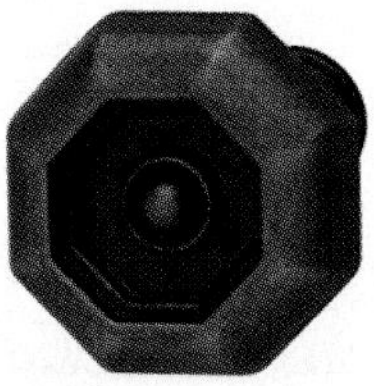

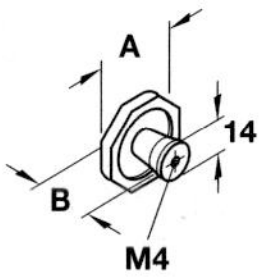

Bronzed & brushed

Size A x B	Cat. No.
27 x 20	121.63.129
33 x 21	121.63.138

Packing: 25 pcs.

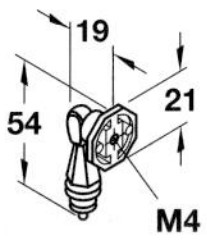

Gold colored polished

Cat. No.	121.62.855

Packing: 25 pcs.

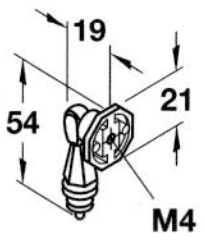

Bronzed & brushed

Cat. No.	121.62.159

Packing: 25 pcs.

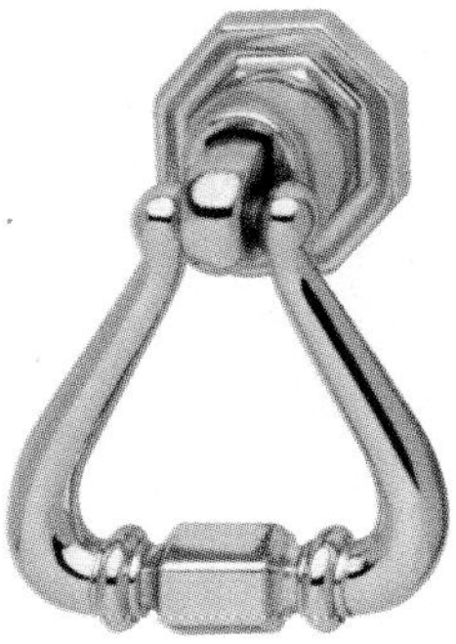

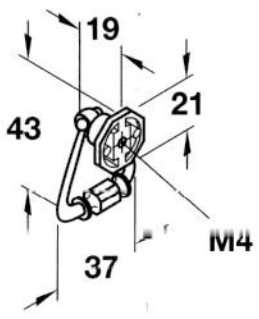

Gold colored polished

Cat. No.	121.62.800

Packing: 25 pcs.

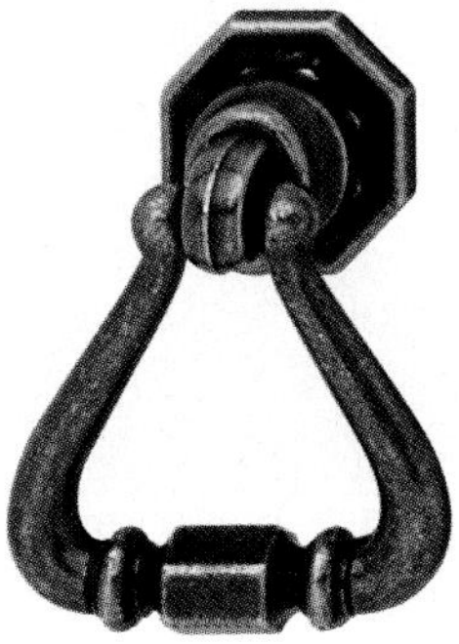

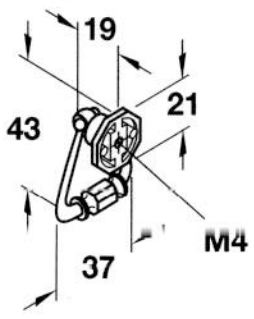

Bronzed & brushed

Cat. No.	121.62.104

Packing: 25 pcs.

Threaded Screws M4
Combined slot, suitable for flat or cross blades

Finish: steel, zinc-plated

Length	Cat. No.
10 mm	022.35.109
12 mm	022.35.127
15 mm	022.35.154
18 mm	022.35.181
20 mm	022.35.207
22 mm	022.35.225
23 mm	022.35.234
25 mm	022.35.252
28 mm	022.35.289
30 mm	022.35.305
35 mm	022.35.350
38 mm	022.35.387
40 mm	022.35.403
45 mm	022.35.458
50 mm	022.35.501
60 mm	022.35.609

Packing: 100 and 1000 pcs.

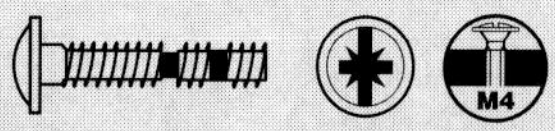

Threaded Breakoff Screw M4
Combined slot, suitable for flat or cross blades

Finish: steel, zinc-plated

Length	Cat. No.
1 3/4" x 3/4"	022.35.887

Packing: 100 and 1000 pcs.

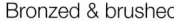

HÄFELE

Zinc handles

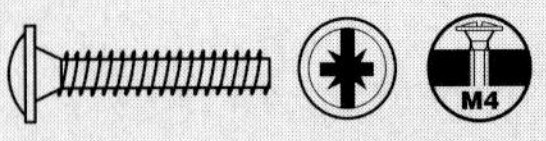

Threaded Screws M4
Combined slot, suitable for flat or cross blades

Finish: steel, zinc-plated

Length	Cat. No.
10 mm	022.35.109
12 mm	022.35.127
15 mm	022.35.154
18 mm	022.35.181
20 mm	022.35.207
22 mm	022.35.225
23 mm	022.35.234
25 mm	022.35.252
28 mm	022.35.289
30 mm	022.35.305
35 mm	022.35.350
38 mm	022.35.387
40 mm	022.35.403
45 mm	022.35.458
50 mm	022.35.501
60 mm	022.35.609

Packing: 100 and 1000 pcs.

Threaded Breakoff Screw M4
Combined slot, suitable for flat or cross blades

Finish: steel, zinc-plated

Length	Cat. No.
1 3/4" x 3/4"	022.35.887

Packing: 100 and 1000 pcs.

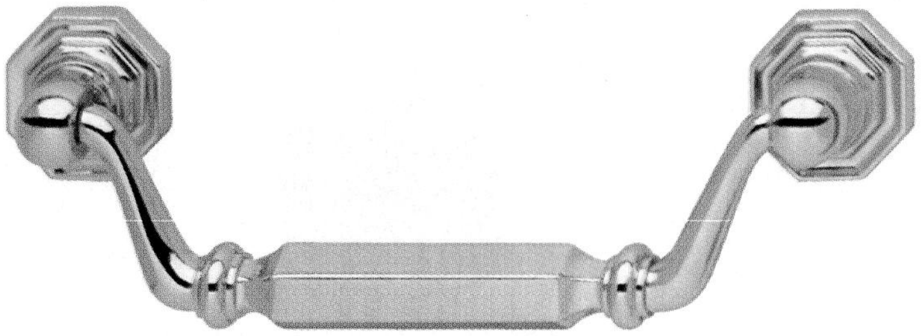

Gold colored polished

Size A x B	Height H	Dimension C	Cat. No.
101 x 15	32	80	121.61.812
117 x 15	35	96	121.61.821

Packing: 25 pcs.

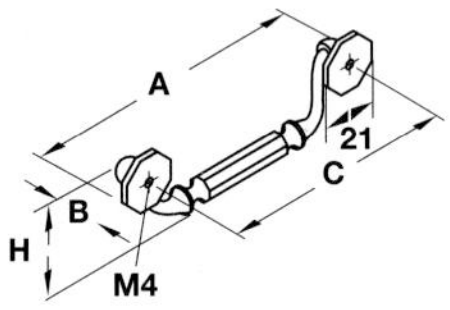

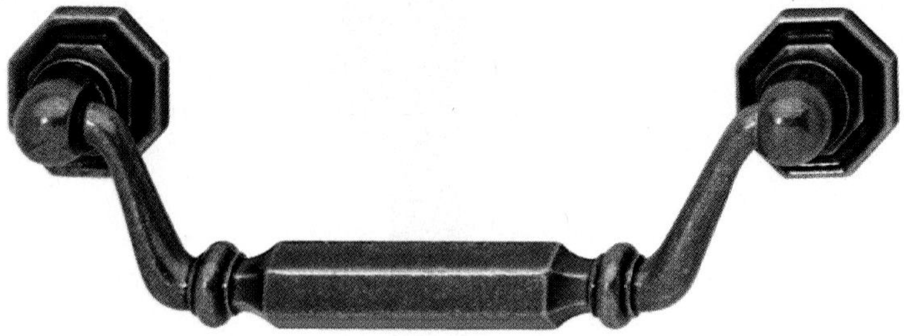

Bronzed and Brushed

Size A x B	Height H	Dimension C	Cat. No.
101 x 15	32	80	121.61.116
117 x 15	35	96	121.61.125

Packing: 25 pcs.

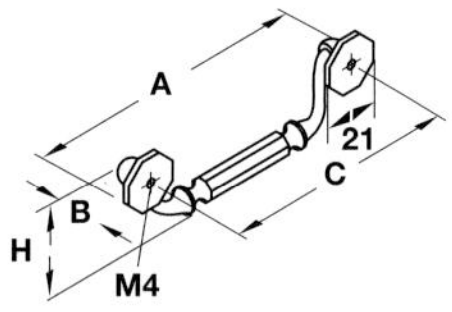

Dimensional data not binding.
We reserve the right to alter specifications without notice.

Zinc handles

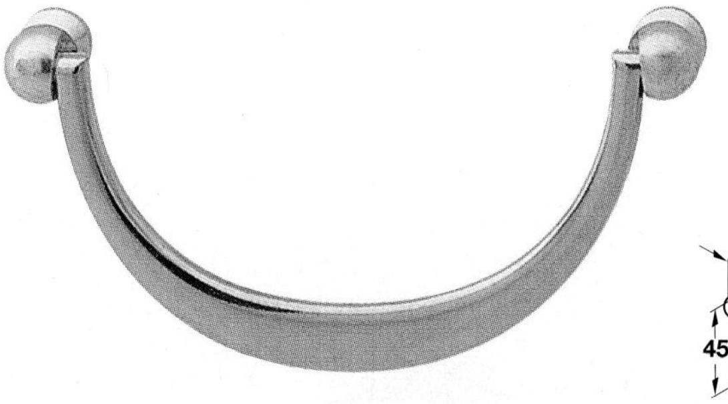

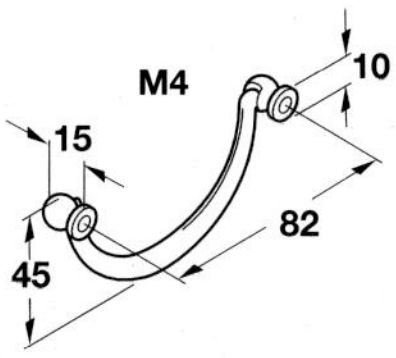

Gold colored polished

Cat. No.	118.01.835

Packing: 25 each

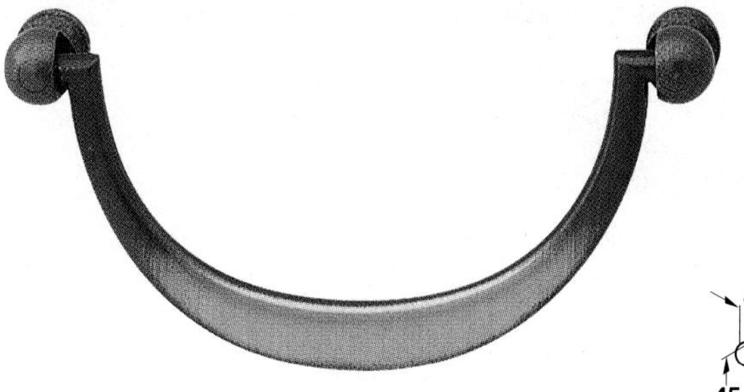

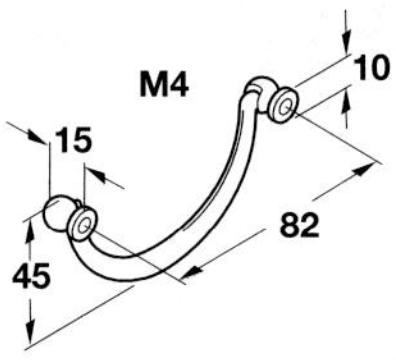

Bronzed and brushed

Cat. No.	118.01.139

Packing: 25 each

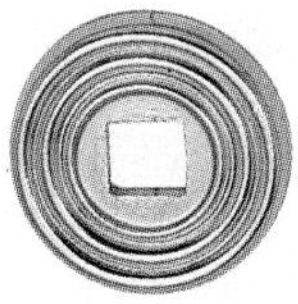

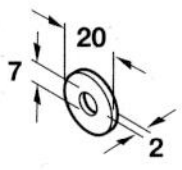

Gold colored polished

Cat. No.	118.01.899

Packing: 25 each

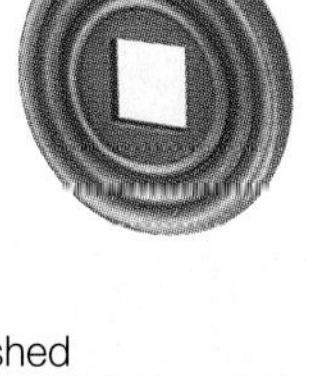

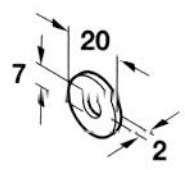

Bronzed and brushed

Cat. No.	118.01.193

Packing: 25 each

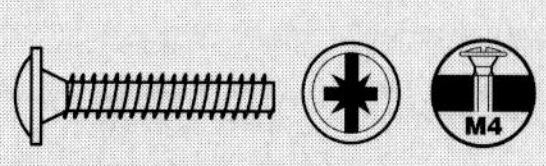

Threaded Screws M4
Combined slot, suitable for flat or cross blades

Finish: steel, zinc-plated

Length	Cat. No.
10 mm	022.35.109
12 mm	022.35.127
15 mm	022.35.154
18 mm	022.35.181
20 mm	022.35.207
22 mm	022.35.225
23 mm	022.35.234
25 mm	022.35.252
28 mm	022.35.289
30 mm	022.35.305
35 mm	022.35.350
38 mm	022.35.387
40 mm	022.35.403
45 mm	022.35.458
50 mm	022.35.501
60 mm	022.35.609

Packing: 100 and 1000 pcs.

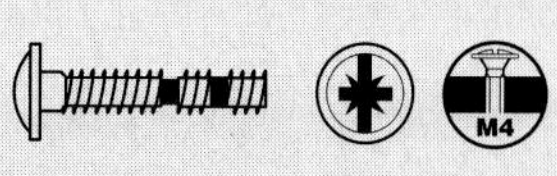

Threaded Breakoff Screw M4
Combined slot, suitable for flat or cross blades

Finish: steel, zinc-plated

Length	Cat. No.
1 3/4" x 3/4"	022.35.887

Packing: 100 and 1000 pcs.

Dimensional data not binding.
We reserve the right to alter specifications without notice.

HÄFELE

Zinc Drop Handles

Threaded Screws M4
Combined slot, suitable for flat or cross blades
Finish: steel, zinc-plated

Length	Cat. No.
10 mm	022.35.109
12 mm	022.35.127
15 mm	022.35.154
18 mm	022.35.181
20 mm	022.35.207
22 mm	022.35.225
23 mm	022.35.234
25 mm	022.35.252
28 mm	022.35.289
30 mm	022.35.305
35 mm	022.35.350
38 mm	022.35.387
40 mm	022.35.403
45 mm	022.35.458
50 mm	022.35.501
60 mm	022.35.609

Packing: 100 and 1000 pcs.

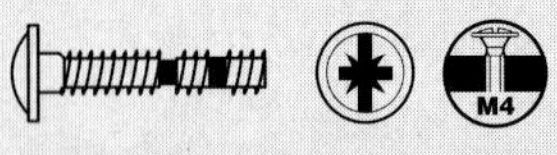

Threaded Breakoff Screw M4
Combined slot, suitable for flat or cross blades
Finish: steel, zinc-plated

Length	Cat. No.
1 3/4" x 3/4"	022.35.887

Packing: 100 and 1000 pcs.

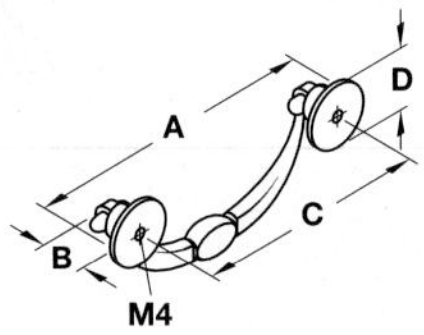

Antique bronze

Size A x B x D	Dimension C	Cat. No.
86 x 20 x 22	64	118.71.111
102 x 20 x 22	80	118.71.121
120 x 20 x 25	96	118.71.131

Packing: 25 pcs.

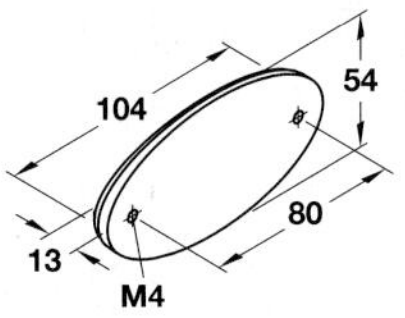

Antique bronze

Cat. No.	118.70.121

Packing: 25 pcs.

Dimensional data not binding.
We reserve the right to alter specifications without notice.

Zinc Drop Handles

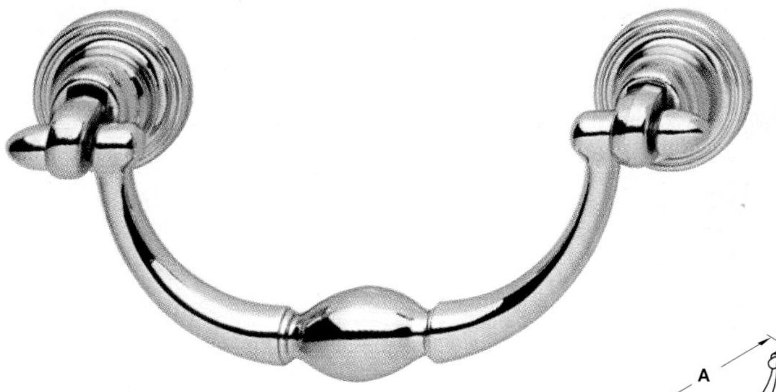

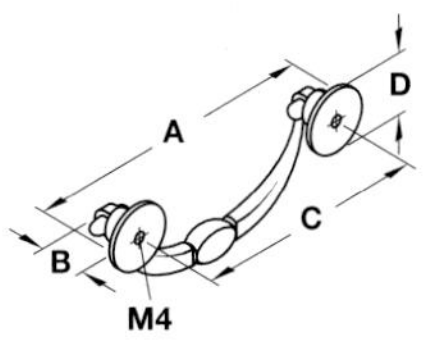

Gold colored polished

Size A x B x D	Dimension C	Cat. No.
86 x 20 x 22	64	118.71.810
102 x 20 x 22	80	118.71.820
120 x 20 x 25	96	118.71.830

Packing: 25 pcs.

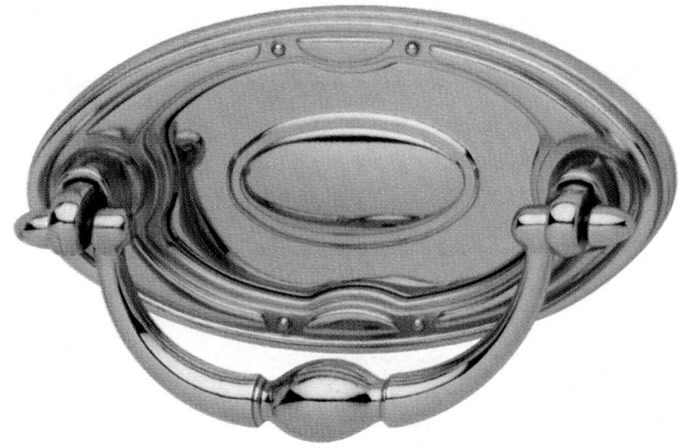

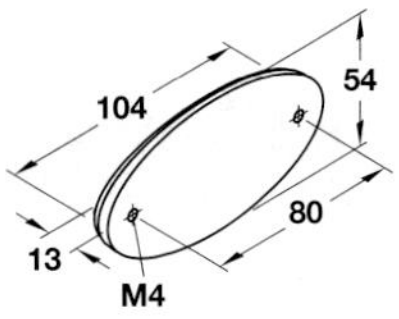

Gold colored polished

Cat. No.	118.70.820

Packing: 25 pcs.

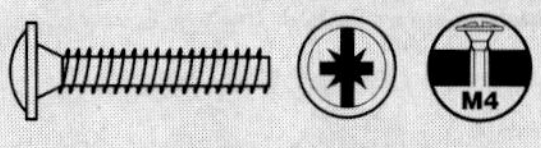

Threaded Screws M4
Combined slot, suitable for flat or cross blades

Finish: steel, zinc-plated

Length	Cat. No.
10 mm	022.35.109
12 mm	022.35.127
15 mm	022.35.154
18 mm	022.35.181
20 mm	022.35.207
22 mm	022.35.225
23 mm	022.35.234
25 mm	022.35.252
28 mm	022.35.289
30 mm	022.35.305
35 mm	022.35.350
38 mm	022.35.387
40 mm	022.35.403
45 mm	022.35.458
50 mm	022.35.501
60 mm	022.35.609

Packing: 100 and 1000 pcs.

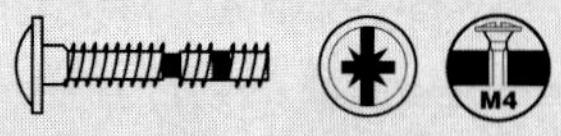

Threaded Breakoff Screw M4
Combined slot, suitable for flat or cross blades

Finish: steel, zinc-plated

Length	Cat. No.
1 3/4" x 3/4"	022.35.887

Packing: 100 and 1000 pcs.

HÄFELE

Zinc Knobs and Handles

Threaded Screws M4
Combined slot, suitable for flat or cross blades

Finish: steel, zinc-plated

Length	Cat. No.
10 mm	022.35.109
12 mm	022.35.127
15 mm	022.35.154
18 mm	022.35.181
20 mm	022.35.207
22 mm	022.35.225
23 mm	022.35.234
25 mm	022.35.252
28 mm	022.35.289
30 mm	022.35.305
35 mm	022.35.350
38 mm	022.35.387
40 mm	022.35.403
45 mm	022.35.458
50 mm	022.35.501
60 mm	022.35.609

Packing: 100 and 1000 pcs.

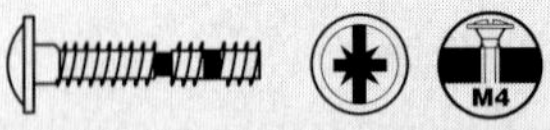

Threaded Breakoff Screw M4
Combined slot, suitable for flat or cross blades

Finish: steel, zinc-plated

Length	Cat. No.
1 3/4" x 3/4"	022.35.887

Packing: 100 and 1000 pcs.

Dimensional data not binding.
We reserve the right to alter specifications without notice.

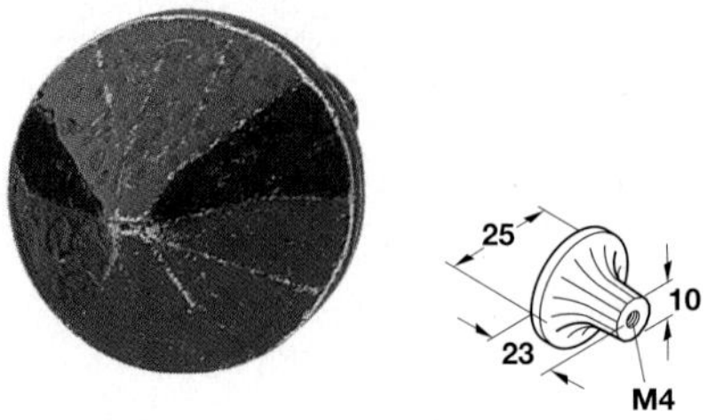

Black antique

Cat. No.	120.97.320

Packing: 25 pcs.

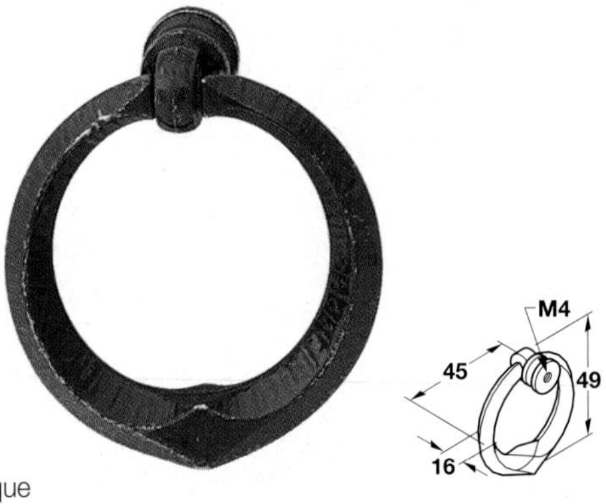

Black antique

Cat. No.	120.95.320

Packing: 25 pcs.

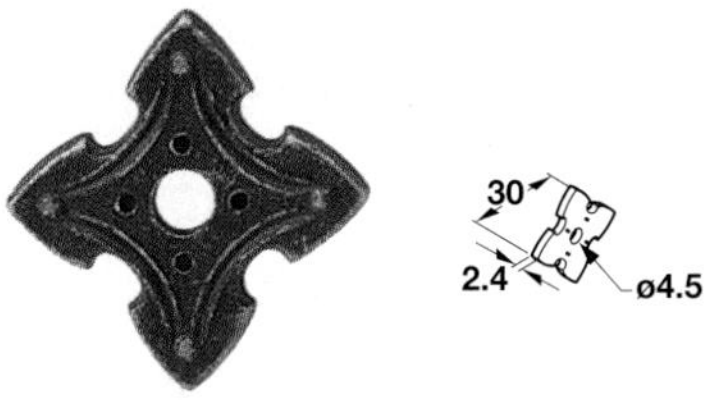

Black antique

Cat. No.	120.94.390

Packing: 25 pcs.

Black antique

Cat. No.	120.94.320

Packing: 25 pcs.

Zinc Knobs and Handles

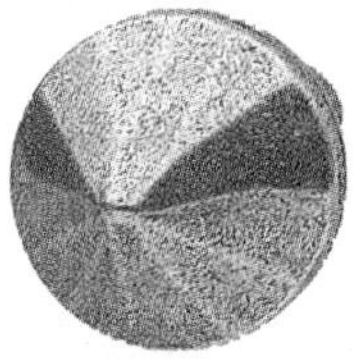
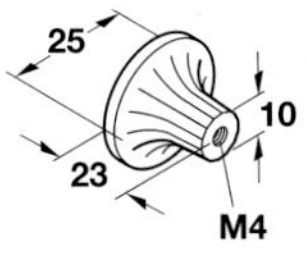

Pewter

Cat. No.	120.97.920

Packing: 25 pcs.

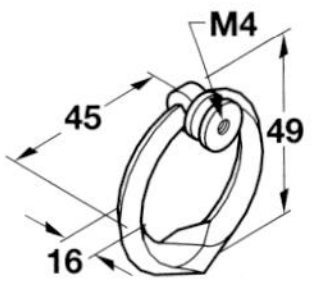

Pewter

Cat. No.	120.95.920

Packing: 25 pcs.

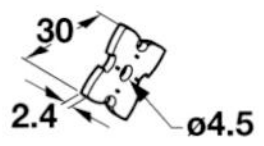

Pewter

Cat. No.	120.94.990

Packing: 25 pcs.

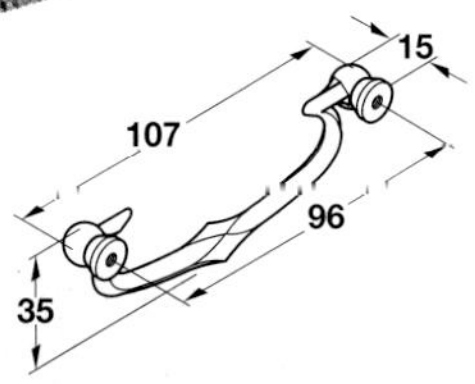

Pewter

Cat. No.	120.94.920

Packing: 25 pcs.

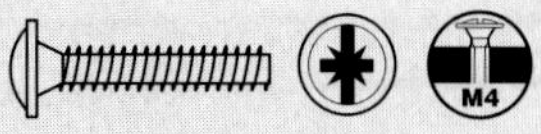

Threaded Screws M4
Combined slot, suitable for flat or cross blades

Finish: steel, zinc-plated

Length	Cat. No.
10 mm	022.35.109
12 mm	022.35.127
15 mm	022.35.154
18 mm	022.35.181
20 mm	022.35.207
22 mm	022.35.225
23 mm	022.35.234
25 mm	022.35.252
28 mm	022.35.289
30 mm	022.35.305
35 mm	022.35.350
38 mm	022.35.387
40 mm	022.35.403
45 mm	022.35.458
50 mm	022.35.501
60 mm	022.35.609

Packing: 100 and 1000 pcs.

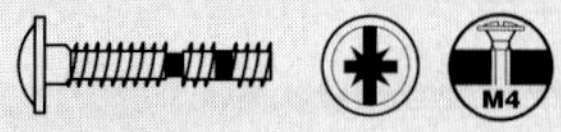

Threaded Breakoff Screw M4
Combined slot, suitable for flat or cross blades

Finish: steel, zinc-plated

Length	Cat. No.
1 3/4" x 3/4"	022.35.887

Packing: 100 and 1000 pcs.

HÄFELE

Iron Handles and Knobs

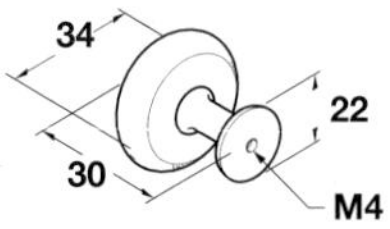

Pewter

Cat. No.	120.32.900

Packing: 25 pcs.

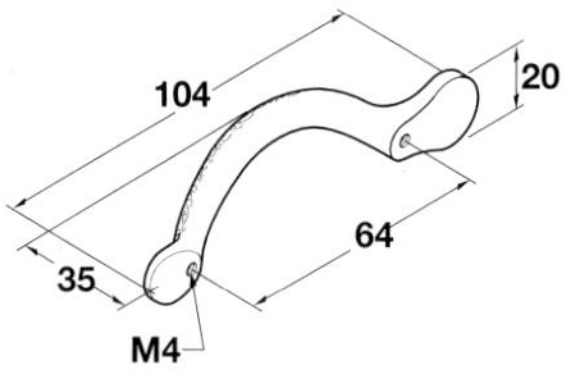

Pewter

Cat. No.	120.33.900

Packing: 25 pcs.

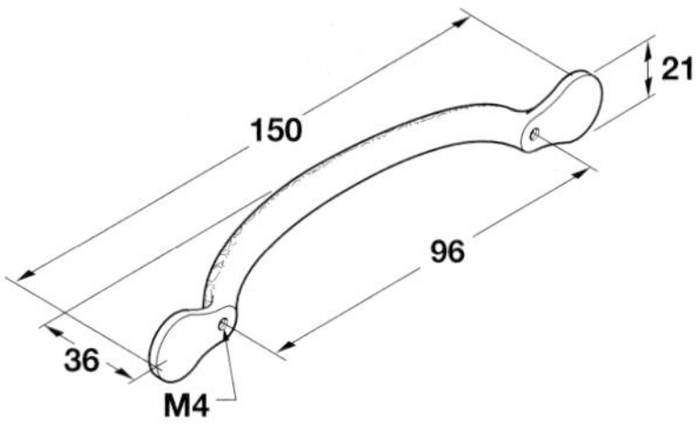

Pewter

Cat. No.	120.34.900

Packing: 25 pcs.

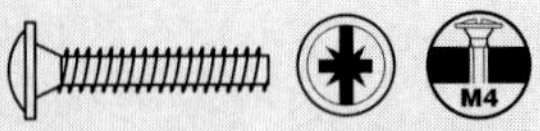

Threaded Screws M4
Combined slot, suitable for flat or cross blades

Finish: steel, zinc-plated

Length	Cat. No.
10 mm	022.35.109
12 mm	022.35.127
15 mm	022.35.154
18 mm	022.35.181
20 mm	022.35.207
22 mm	022.35.225
23 mm	022.35.234
25 mm	022.35.252
28 mm	022.35.289
30 mm	022.35.305
35 mm	022.35.350
38 mm	022.35.387
40 mm	022.35.403
45 mm	022.35.458
50 mm	022.35.501
60 mm	022.35.609

Packing: 100 and 1000 pcs.

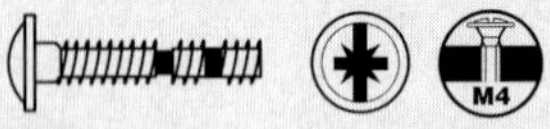

Threaded Breakoff Screw M4
Combined slot, suitable for flat or cross blades

Finish: steel, zinc-plated

Length	Cat. No.
1 3/4" x 3/4"	022.35.887

Packing: 100 and 1000 pcs.

Iron Handles and Knobs

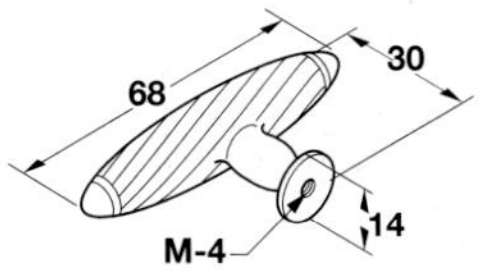

Pewter

Cat. No.	120.37.900

Packing: 25 pcs.

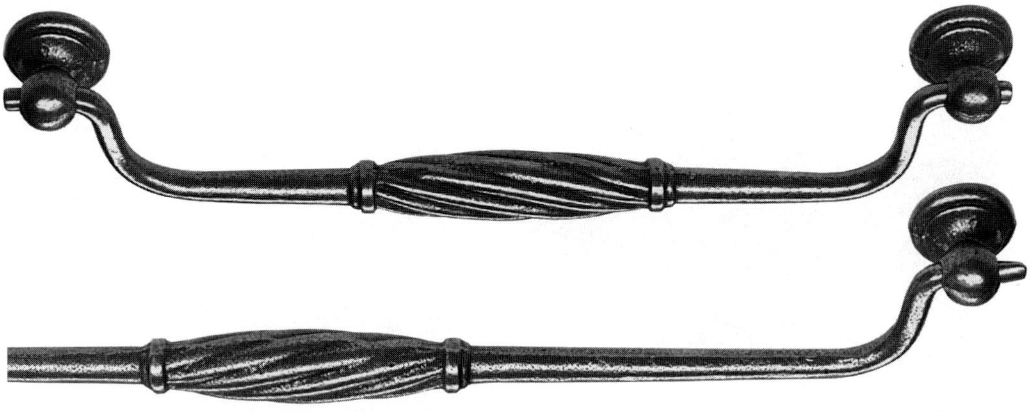

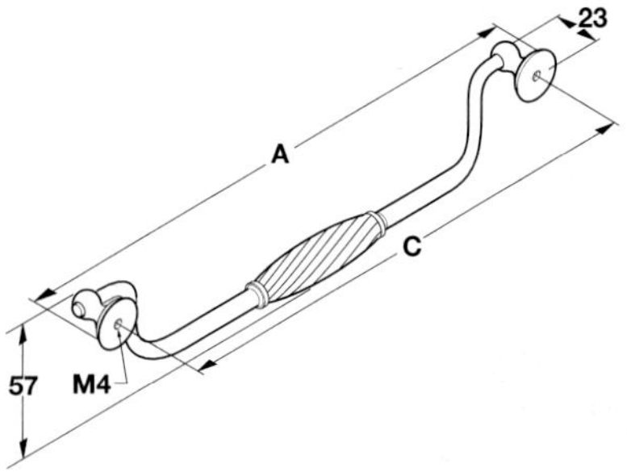

Pewter

Length A	Dimension C	Cat. No.
146	128	120.38.900
242	224	120.38.910
338	320	120.38.920

Packing: 25 pcs.

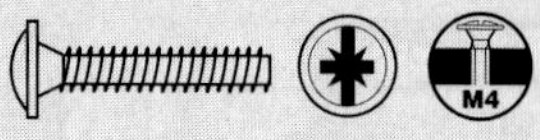

Threaded Screws M4
Combined slot, suitable for flat or cross blades

Finish: steel, zinc-plated

Length	Cat. No.
10 mm	022.35.109
12 mm	022.35.127
15 mm	022.35.154
18 mm	022.35.181
20 mm	022.35.207
22 mm	022.35.225
23 mm	022.35.234
25 mm	022.35.252
28 mm	022.35.289
30 mm	022.35.305
35 mm	022.35.350
38 mm	022.35.387
40 mm	022.35.403
45 mm	022.35.458
50 mm	022.35.501
60 mm	022.35.609

Packing: 100 and 1000 pcs.

Threaded Breakoff Screw M4
Combined slot, suitable for flat or cross blades

Finish: steel, zinc-plated

Length	Cat. No.
1 3/4" x 3/4"	022.35.887

Packing: 100 and 1000 pcs.

Dimensional data not binding.
We reserve the right to alter specifications without notice.

HÄFELE

Zinc Handles

1 Decorative Hardware

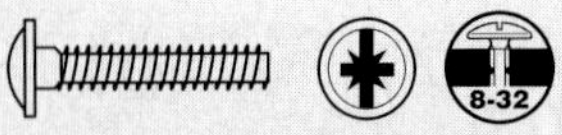

Threaded Screws 8-32
Combined slot, suitable for flat or cross blades
Finish: steel, yellow chromated

Length	Cat. No.
22 mm	022.25.229
25 mm	022.25.256
32 mm	022.25.327
38 mm	022.25.381
45 mm	022.25.452

Packing: 100 and 1000 pcs.

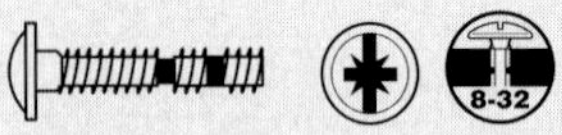

Threaded Breakoff Screw 8-32
Combined slot, suitable for flat or cross blades
Finish: steel, yellow chromated

Length	Cat. No.
1 3/4" x 3/4"	022.25.881

Packing: 100 and 1000 pcs.

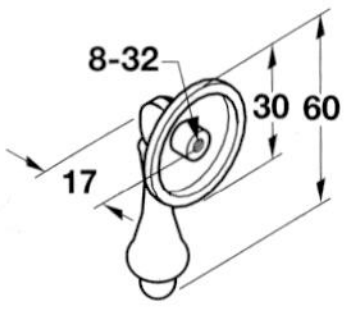

Antique brass

Cat. No.	122.29.100

Packing: 25 pcs.

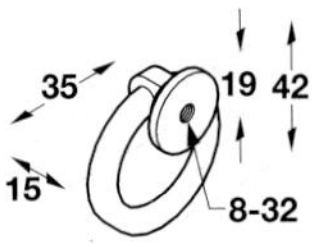

Burnished Brass

Cat. No.	122.28.100

Packing: 25 pcs.

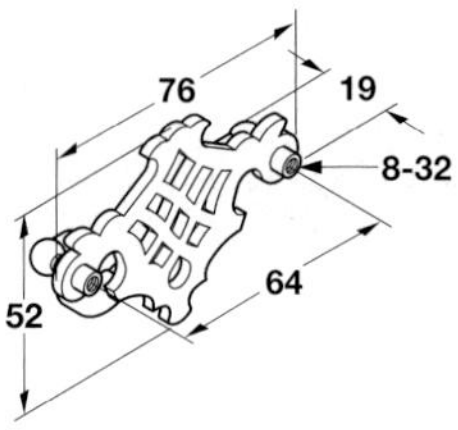

Burnished Brass

Cat. No.	122.34.100

Packing: 25 pcs.

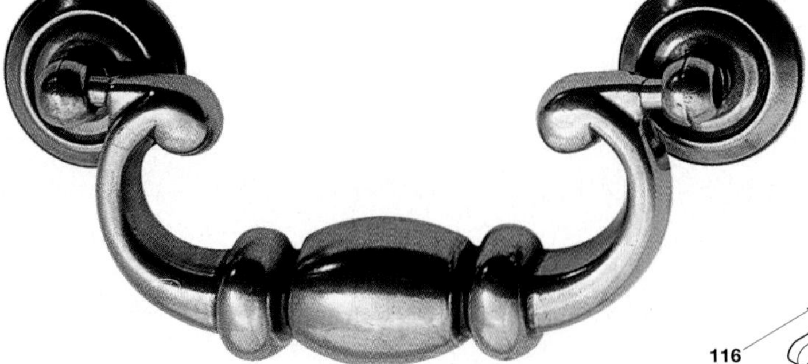

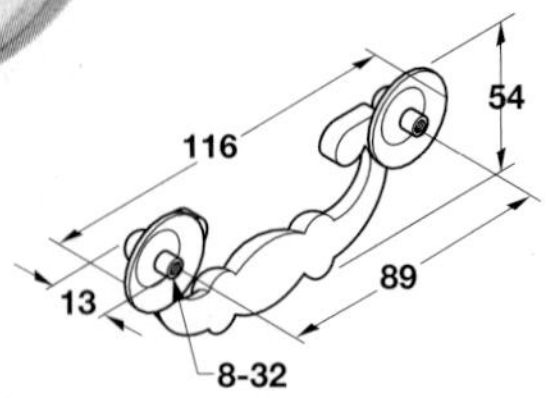

Burnished Brass

Cat. No.	122.27.100

Packing: 25 pcs.

Zinc Handles

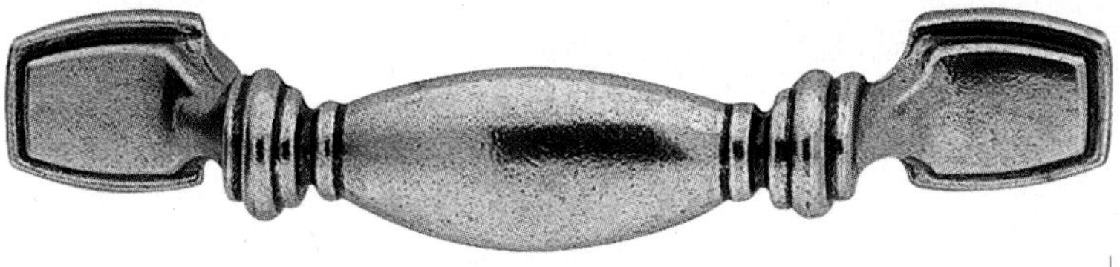

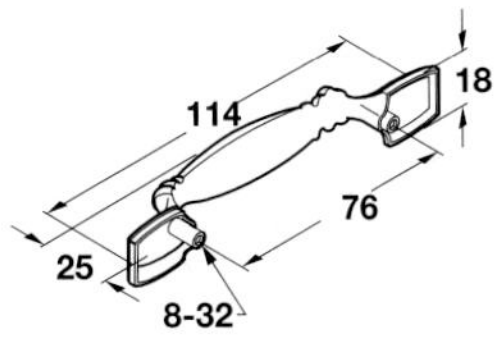

Zinc, regency brass

Cat. No.	122.07.500

Packing: 25 pcs.

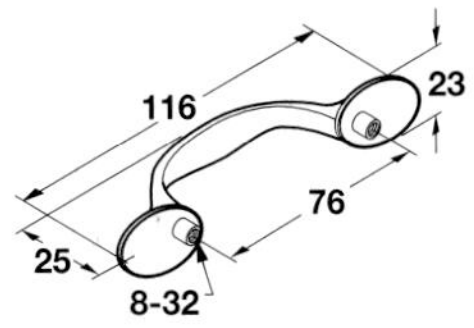

Zinc, regency brass

Cat. No.	122.06.503

Packing: 25 pcs.

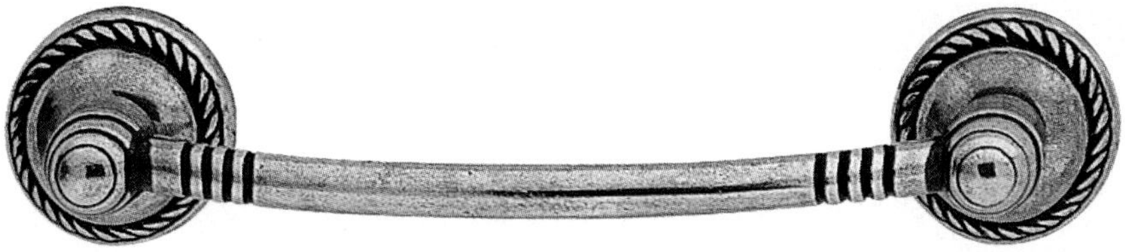

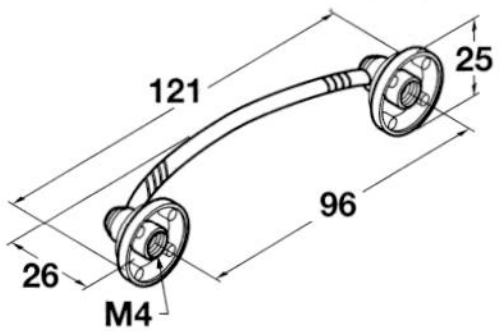

Polished bronze

Cat. No.	121.45.121

Packing: 25 pcs.

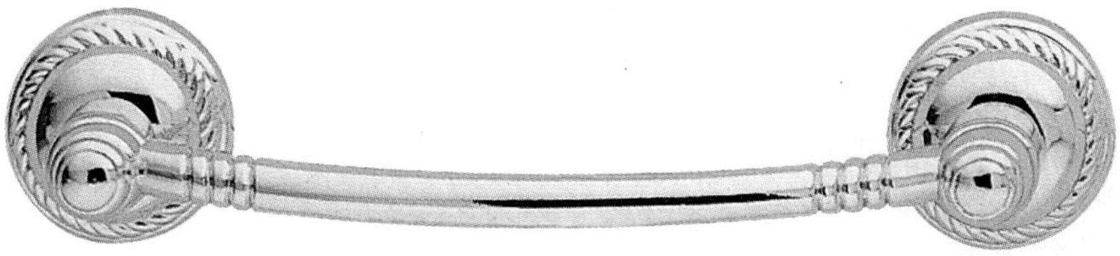

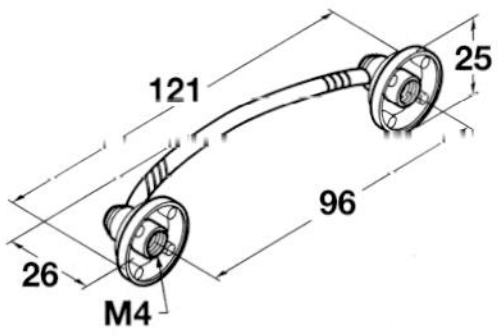

Brass plated polished

Cat. No.	121.45.821

Packing: 25 pcs.

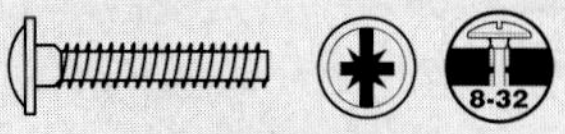

Threaded Screws 8-32
Combined slot, suitable for flat or cross blades

Finish: steel, yellow chromated

Length	Cat. No.
22 mm	022.25.229
25 mm	022.25.256
32 mm	022.25.327
38 mm	022.25.381
45 mm	022.25.452

Packing: 100 and 1000 pcs.

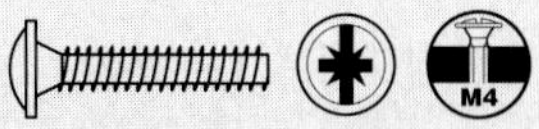

Threaded Screws M4
Combined slot, suitable for flat or cross blades

Finish: steel, zinc-plated

Length	Cat. No.
10 mm	022.35.109
12 mm	022.35.127
15 mm	022.35.154
18 mm	022.35.181
20 mm	022.35.207
22 mm	022.35.225
23 mm	022.35.234
25 mm	022.35.252
28 mm	022.35.289
30 mm	022.35.305
35 mm	022.35.350
38 mm	022.35.387
40 mm	022.35.403
45 mm	022.35.458
50 mm	022.35.501
60 mm	022.35.609

Packing: 100 and 1000 pcs.

Dimensional data not binding.
We reserve the right to alter specifications without notice.

HÄFELE

Zinc/Ceramic and Wood Handle Combination

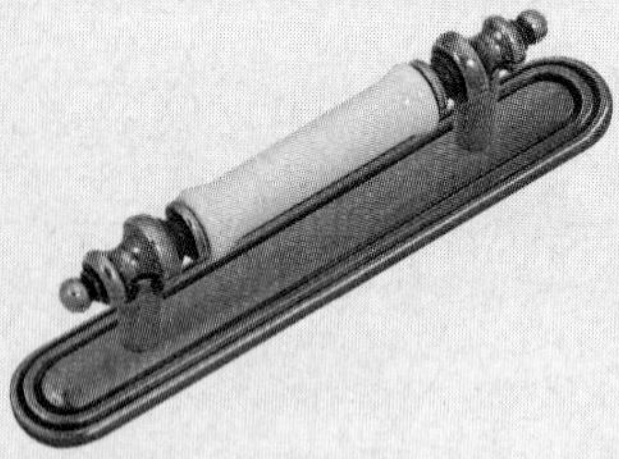

- Backplate can be used with handles shown.

Threaded Screws 8-32
Combined slot, suitable for flat or cross blades

Finish: steel, yellow chromated

Length	Cat. No.
22 mm	022.25.229
25 mm	022.25.256
32 mm	022.25.327
38 mm	022.25.381
45 mm	022.25.452

Packing: 100 and 1000 pcs.

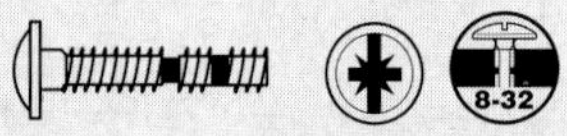

Threaded Breakoff Screw 8-32
Combined slot, suitable for flat or cross blades

Finish: steel, yellow chromated

Length	Cat. No.
1 3/4" x 3/4"	022.25.881

Packing: 100 and 1000 pcs.

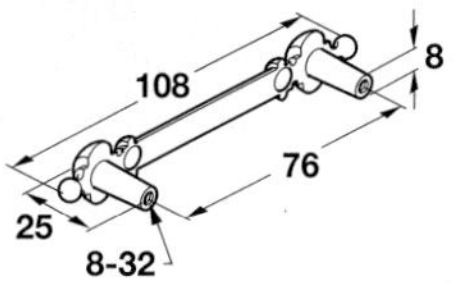

Zinc, regency brass

Cat. No.	122.08.507

Packing: 25 pcs.

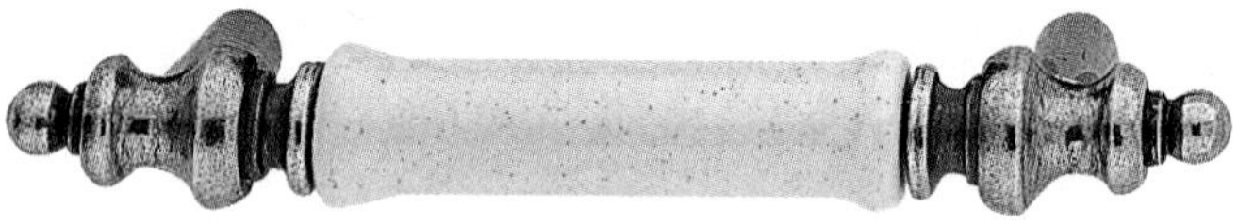

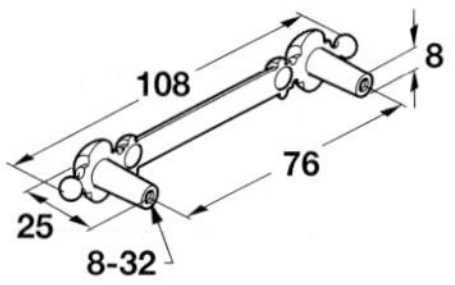

Ends: zinc, regency brass
Center: ceramic, oatmeal almond

Cat. No.	107.17.503

Packing: 25 pcs.

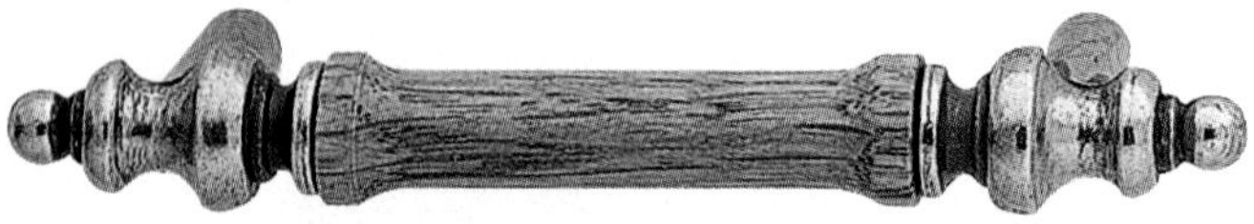

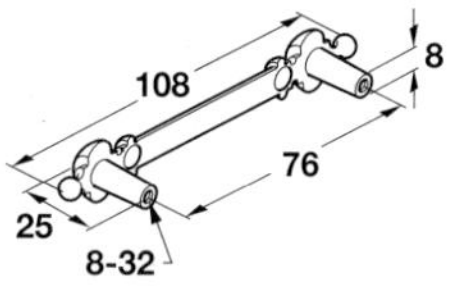

Socket: zinc, regency brass
Center: oak stained

Cat. No.	107.16.506

Packing: 25 pcs.

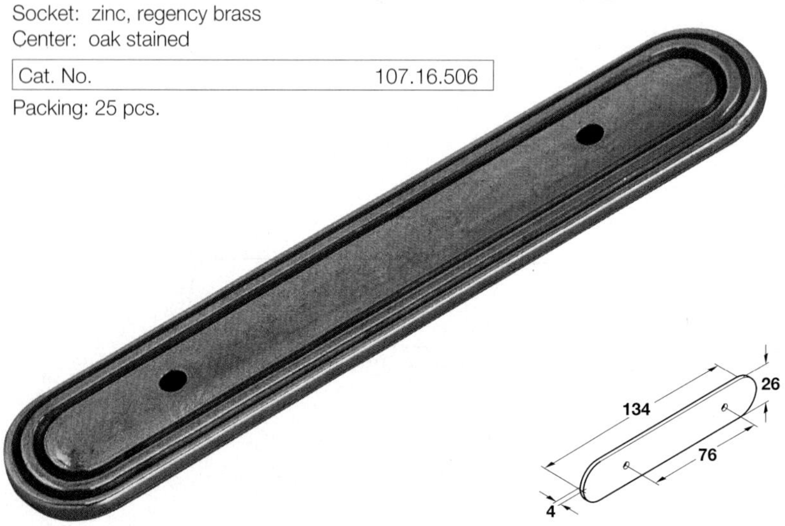

Zinc, regency brass

Cat. No.	122.05.506

Packing: 25 pcs.

Dimensional data not binding. We reserve the right to alter specifications without notice.

Zinc Handles with Wood Centers

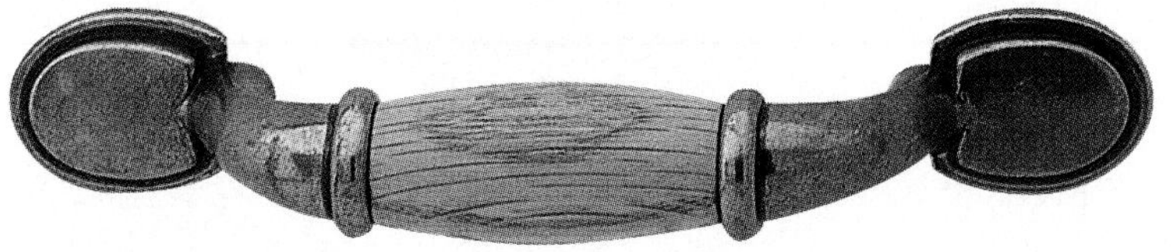

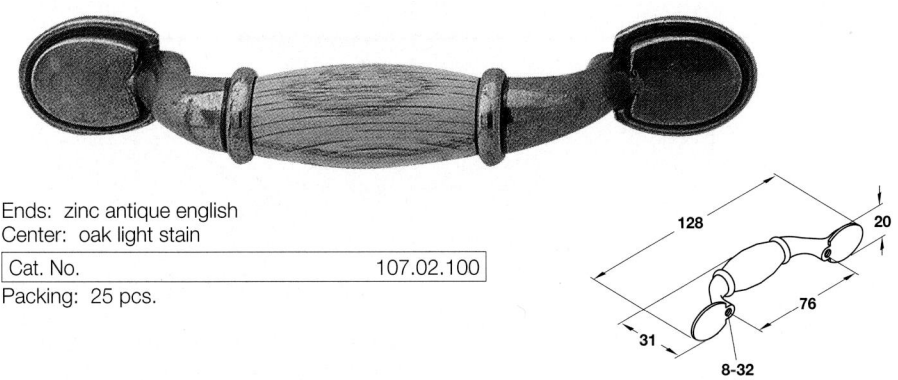

Ends: zinc antique english
Center: oak light stain

Cat. No.	107.02.100

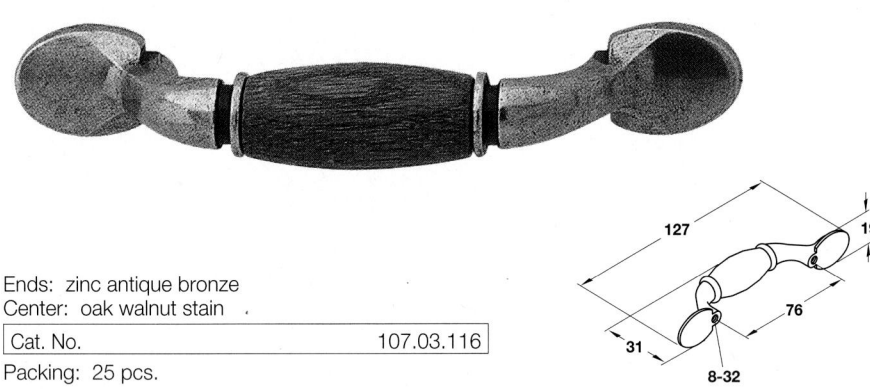

Packing: 25 pcs.

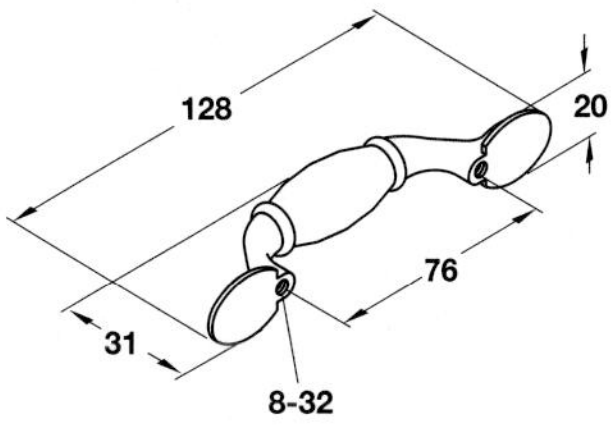

Ends: zinc antique bronze
Center: oak walnut stain

Cat. No.	107.03.116

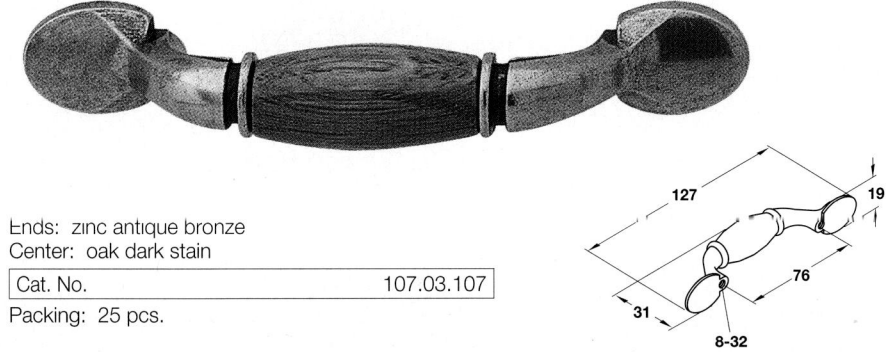

Packing: 25 pcs.

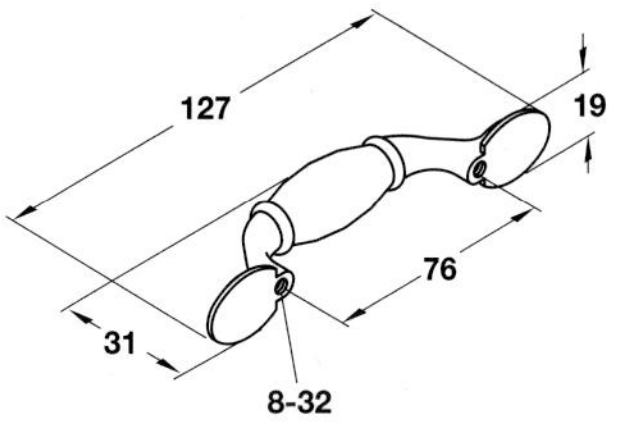

Ends: zinc antique bronze
Center: oak dark stain

Cat. No.	107.03.107

Packing: 25 pcs.

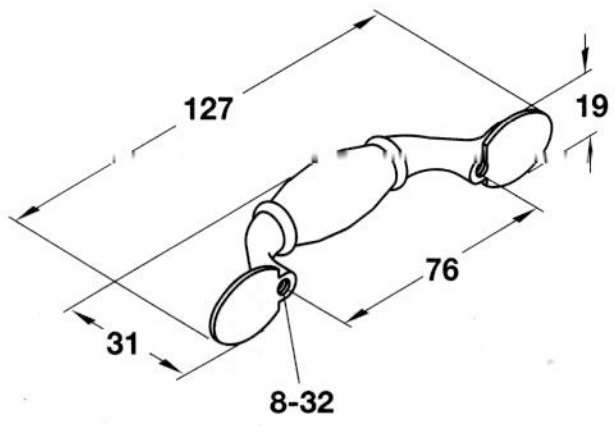

Threaded Screws 8-32
Combined slot, suitable for flat or cross blades

Finish: steel, yellow chromated

Length	Cat. No.
22 mm	022.25.229
25 mm	022.25.256
32 mm	022.25.327
38 mm	022.25.381
45 mm	022.25.452

Packing: 100 and 1000 pcs.

Threaded Breakoff Screw 8-32
Combined slot, suitable for flat or cross blades

Finish: steel, yellow chromated

Length	Cat. No.
1 3/4" x 3/4"	022.25.881

Packing: 100 and 1000 pcs.

Dimensional data not binding.
We reserve the right to alter specifications without notice.

HÄFELE

Zinc Handles with Ceramic Centers

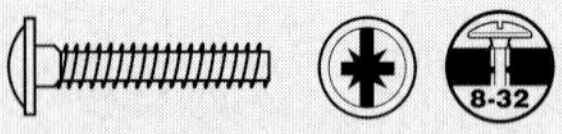

Threaded Screws 8-32
Combined slot, suitable for flat or cross blades
Finish: steel, yellow chromated

Length	Cat. No.
22 mm	022.25.229
25 mm	022.25.256
32 mm	022.25.327
38 mm	022.25.381
45 mm	022.25.452

Packing: 100 and 1000 pcs.

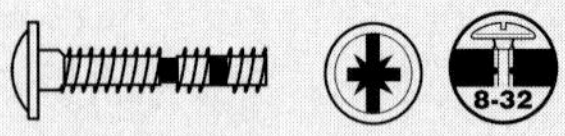

Threaded Breakoff Screw 8-32
Combined slot, suitable for flat or cross blades
Finish: steel, yellow chromated

Length	Cat. No.
1 3/4" x 3/4"	022.25.881

Packing: 100 and 1000 pcs.

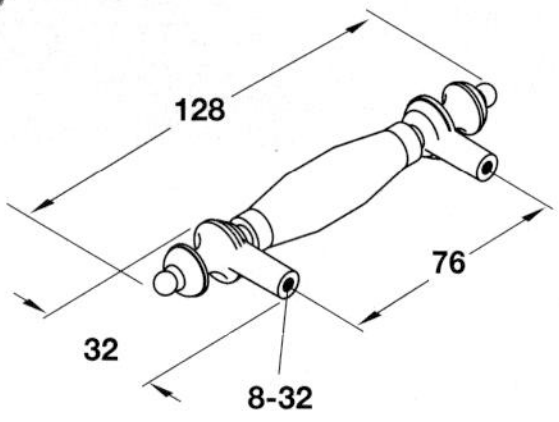

Ends: zinc antique bronze
Center: ceramic white

Cat. No.	107.10.504

Packing: 25 pcs.

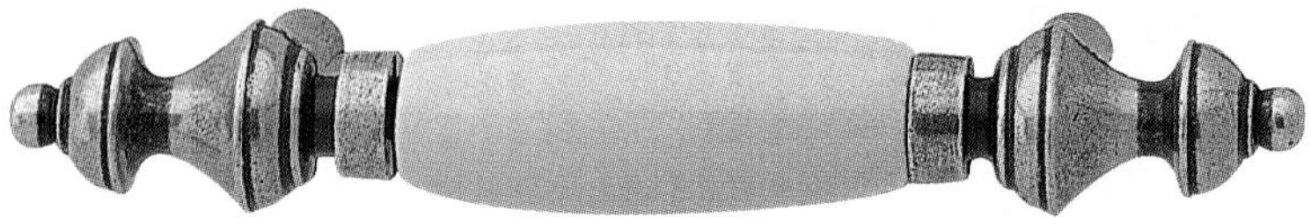

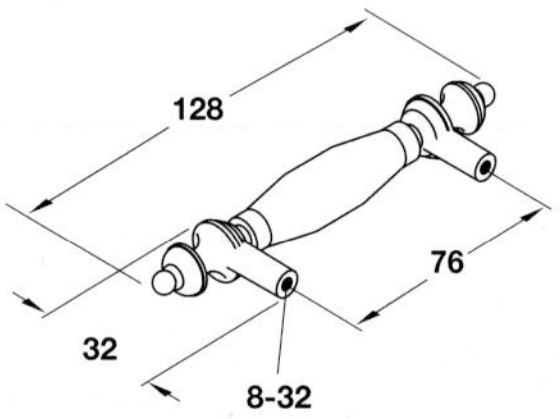

Ends: zinc antique bronze
Center: ceramic almond

Cat. No.	107.10.102

Packing: 25 pcs.

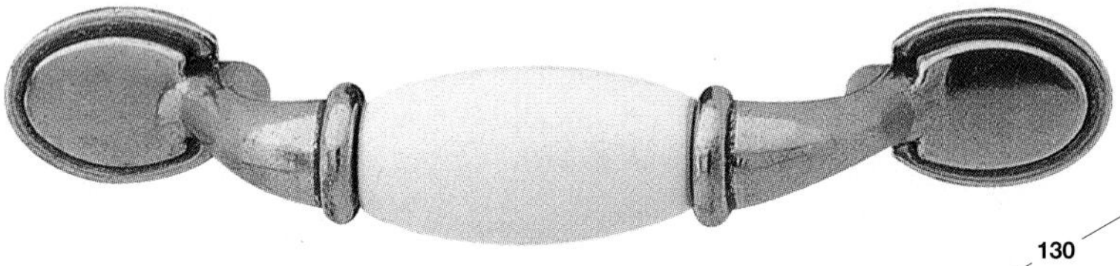

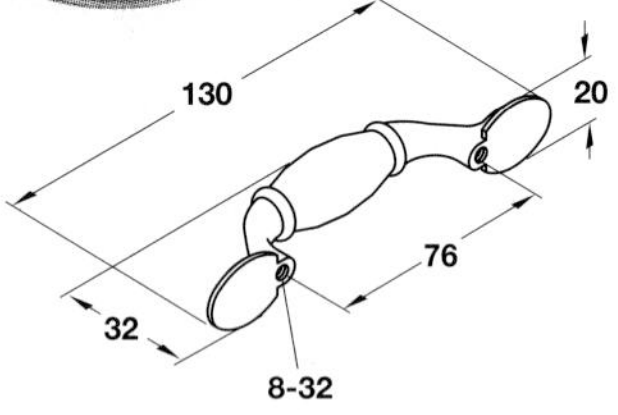

Ends: zinc antique bronze
Center: ceramic white

Cat. No.	107.01.103

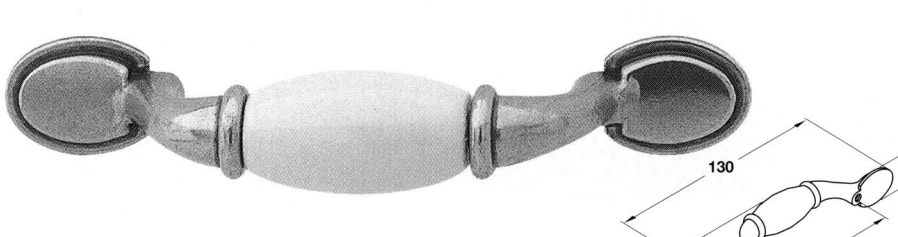

Packing: 25 pcs.

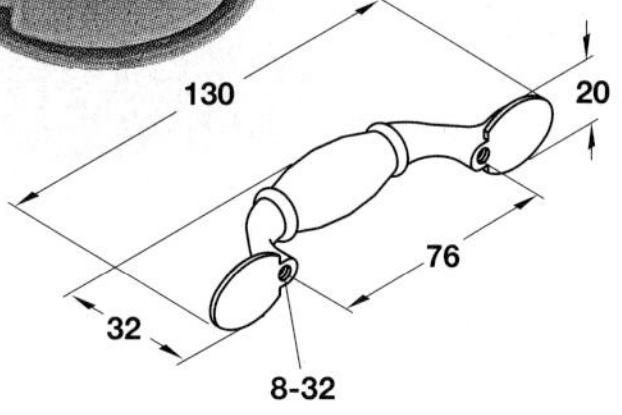

Ends: zinc antique bronze
Center: ceramic almond

Cat. No.	107.00.106

Packing: 25 pcs.

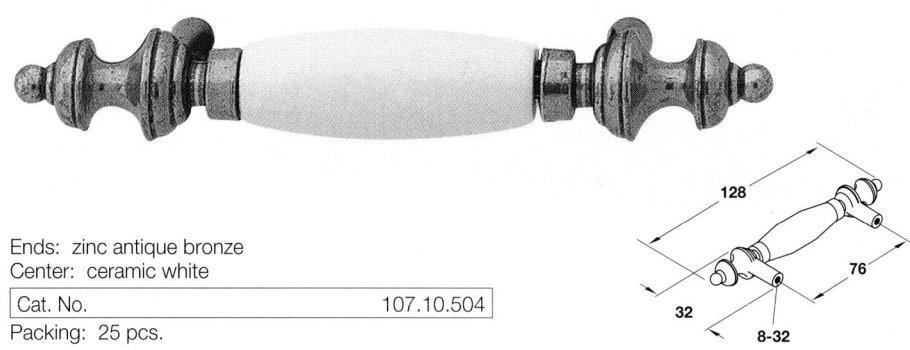

Zinc Glass Door Pulls

HÄFELE

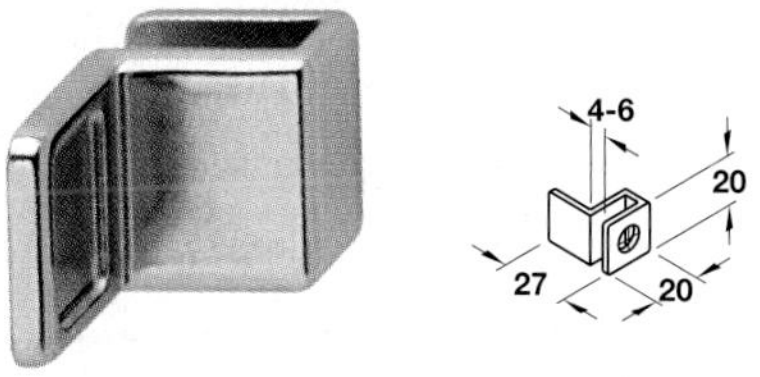

Nickel matt

Cat. No.	154.22.607

Packing: 25 pcs.

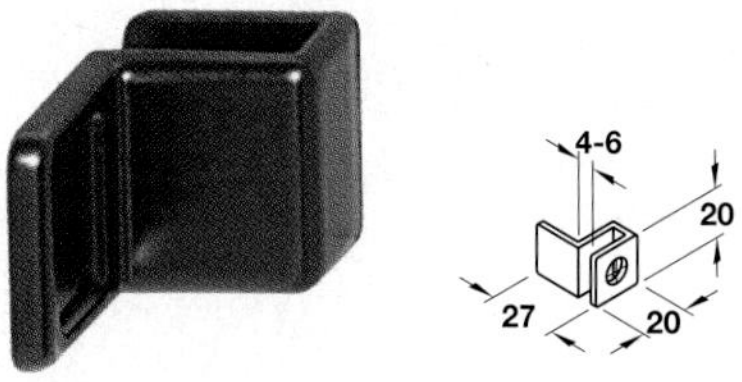

Black matt

Cat. No.	154.22.303

Packing: 25 pcs.

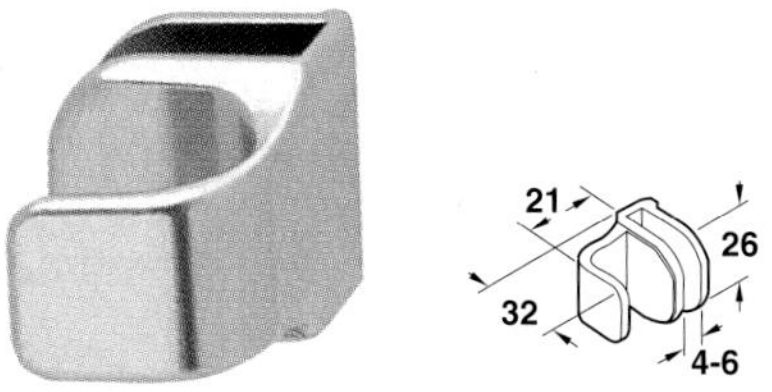

Nickel matt

Cat. No.	154.18.701

Packing: 20 pcs.

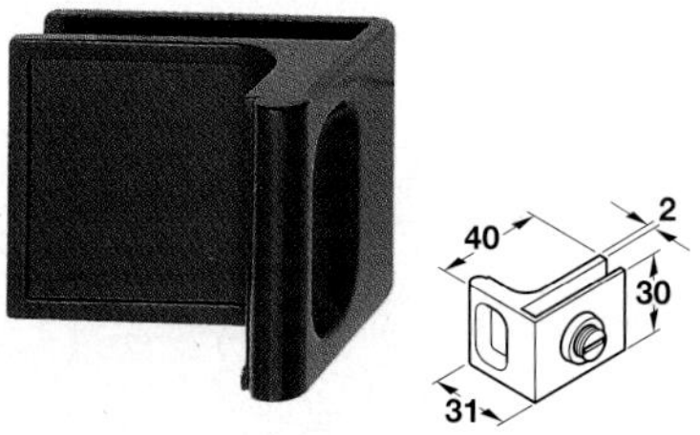

Black matt

Cat. No.	154.25.310

Packing: 25 pcs.

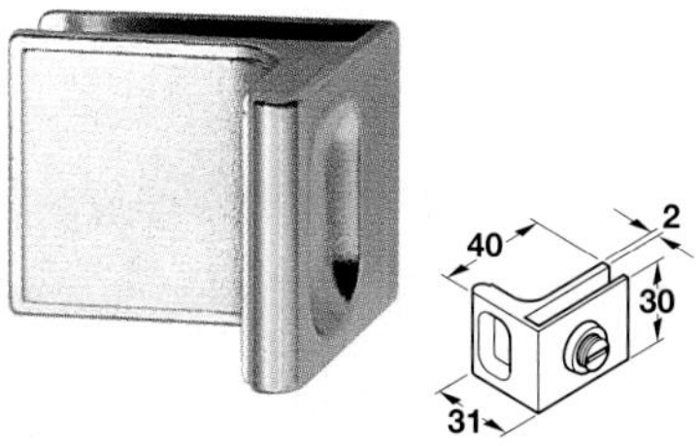

Chrome plated polished textured matt

Cat. No.	154.25.210

Packing: 20 pcs.

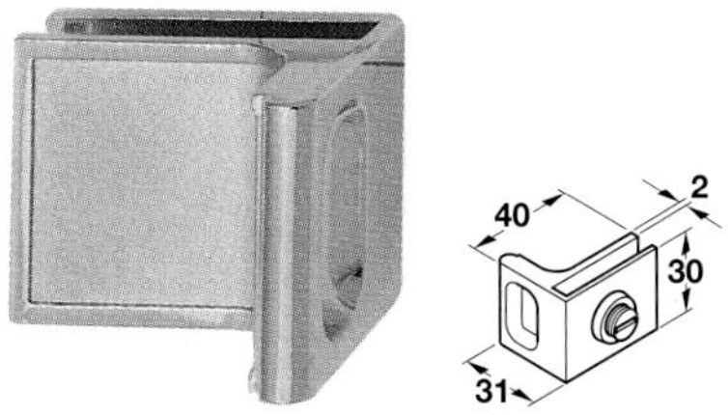

Nickel plated polished texture matt

Cat. No.	154.25.610

Packing: 25 pcs.

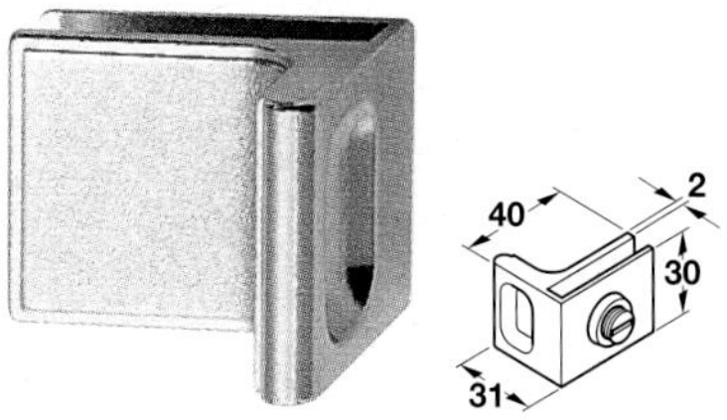

Brass plated polished textured matt

Cat. No.	154.25.810

Packing: 20 pcs.

Decorative Hardware **1**

- Handle for glass doors up to 5mm thick maximum.

Dimensional data not binding. We reserve the right to alter specifications without notice.

HÄFELE

Zinc Handles

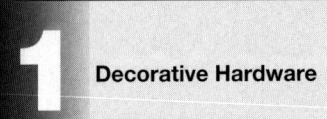

Hospa Pan Head Screws
Pozi Recess

Finish: steel, zinc-plated

Length	Cat. No.
13 mm	015.71.811
15 mm	015.71.820
17 mm	015.71.839
20 mm	015.71.848
25 mm	015.71.857
30 mm	015.71.866
35 mm	015.71.875
40 mm	015.71.884
45 mm	015.71.893

Packing: 100 and 1000 pcs.

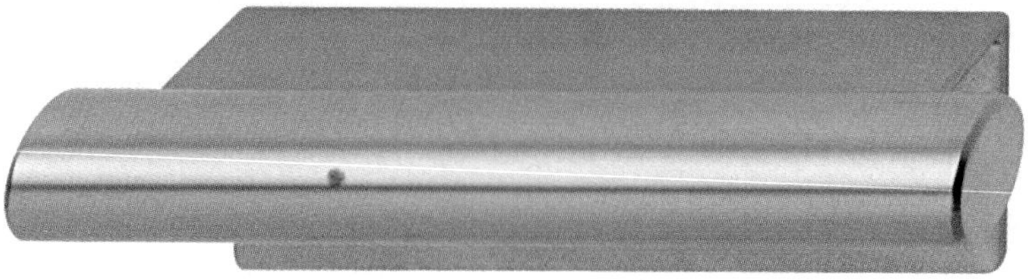

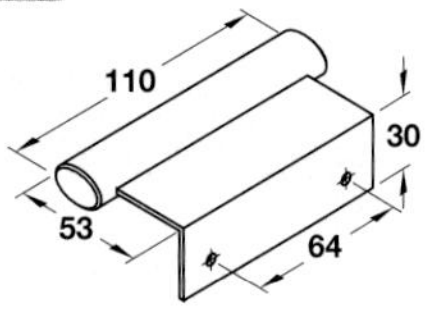

Nickel matt

Cat. No.	103.99.610

Packing: 25 pcs.

Dimensional data not binding.
We reserve the right to alter specifications without notice.

Metal and plastic handles

HÄFELE

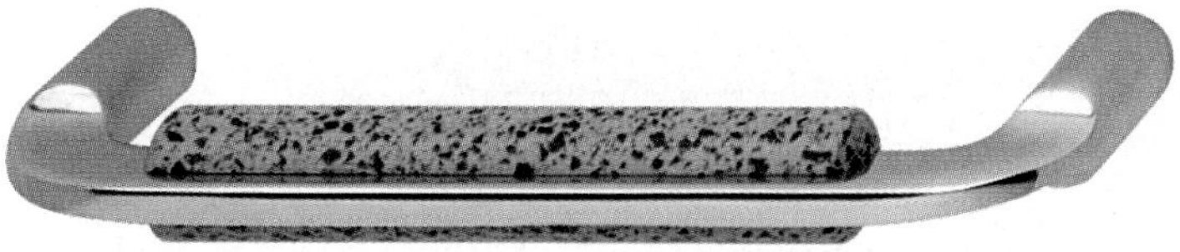

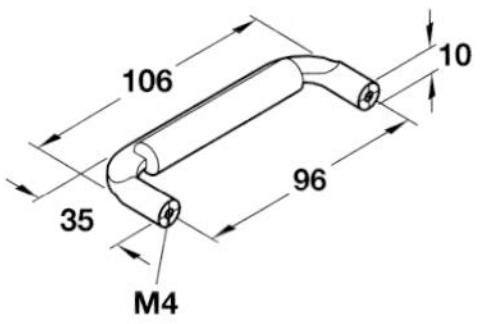

Chrome plated polished/gray

Cat. No.	103.19.250

Packing: 25 pcs.

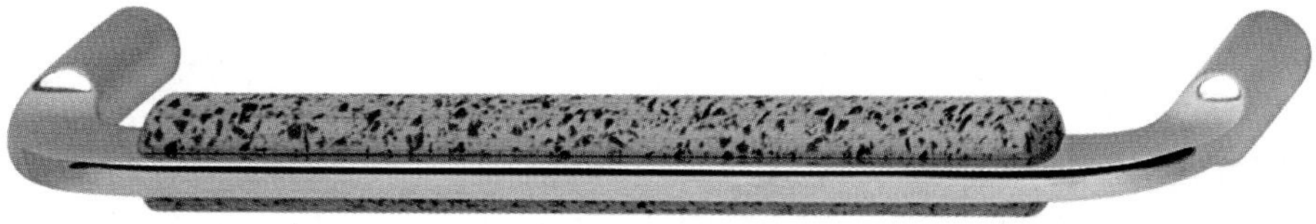

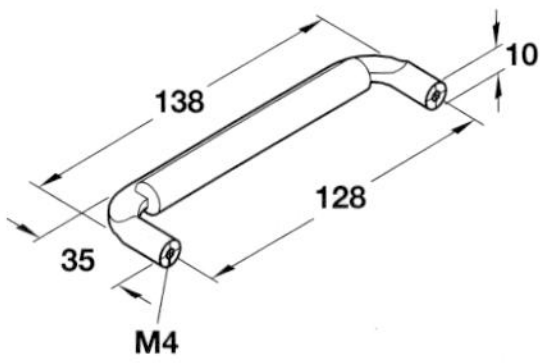

Chrome plated polished/gray

Cat. No.	103.19.251

Packing: 25 pcs.

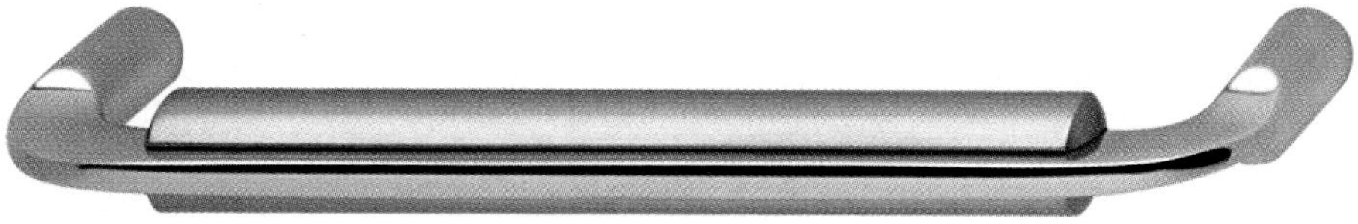

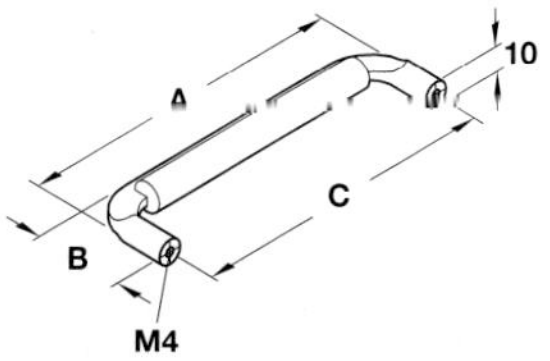

Chrome plated polished/Chrome plated matt

Size A x B	Dimension C	Cat. No.
106 x 35	96	103.19.240
138 x 35	128	103.19.241

Packing: 25 pcs.

Decorative Hardware 1

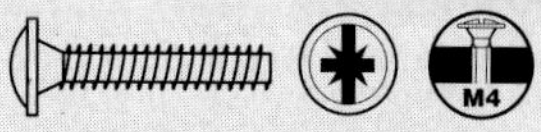

Threaded Screws M4
Combined slot, suitable for flat or cross blades
Finish: steel, zinc-plated

Length	Cat. No.
10 mm	022.35.109
12 mm	022.35.127
15 mm	022.35.154
18 mm	022.35.181
20 mm	022.35.207
22 mm	022.35.225
23 mm	022.35.234
25 mm	022.35.252
28 mm	022.35.289
30 mm	022.35.305
35 mm	022.35.350
38 mm	022.35.387
40 mm	022.35.403
45 mm	022.35.458
50 mm	022.35.501
60 mm	022.35.609

Packing: 100 and 1000 pcs.

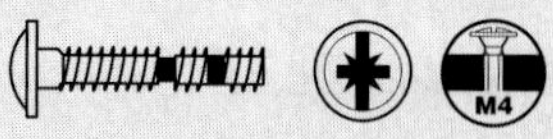

Threaded Breakoff Screw M4
Combined slot, suitable for flat or cross blades
Finish: steel, zinc-plated

Length	Cat. No.
1 3/4" x 3/4"	022.35.887

Packing: 100 and 1000 pcs.

HÄFELE

Metal and plastic handles

Threaded Screws M4
Combined slot, suitable for flat or cross blades
Finish: steel, zinc-plated

Length	Cat. No.
10 mm	022.35.109
12 mm	022.35.127
15 mm	022.35.154
18 mm	022.35.181
20 mm	022.35.207
22 mm	022.35.225
23 mm	022.35.234
25 mm	022.35.252
28 mm	022.35.289
30 mm	022.35.305
35 mm	022.35.350
38 mm	022.35.387
40 mm	022.35.403
45 mm	022.35.458
50 mm	022.35.501
60 mm	022.35.609

Packing: 100 and 1000 pcs.

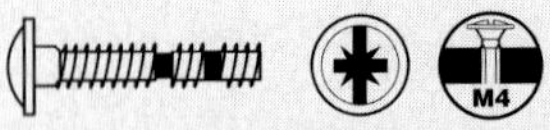

Threaded Breakoff Screw M4
Combined slot, suitable for flat or cross blades
Finish: steel, zinc-plated

Length	Cat. No.
1 3/4" x 3/4"	022.35.887

Packing: 100 and 1000 pcs.

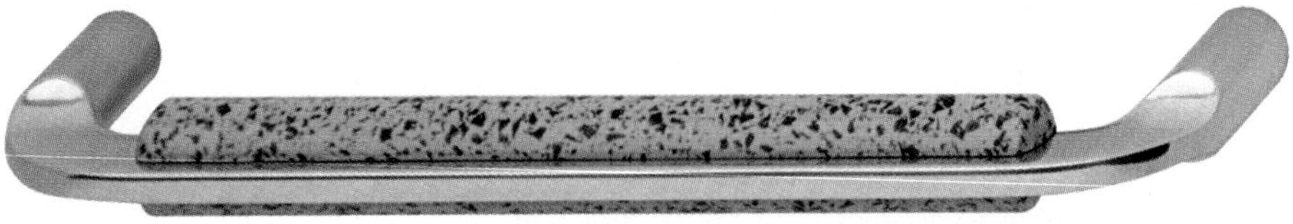

Gold colored polished/gray

Size A x B	Dimension C	Cat. No.
106 x 35	96	103.19.850
138 x 35	128	103.19.851

Packing: 25 pcs.

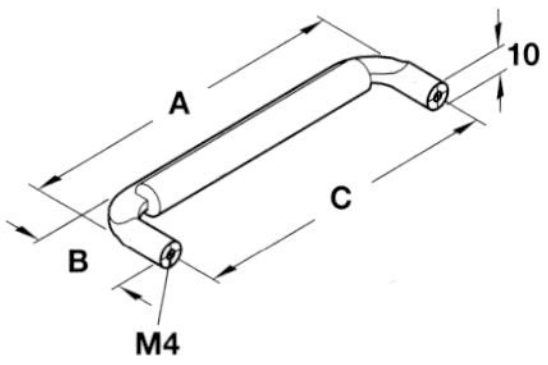

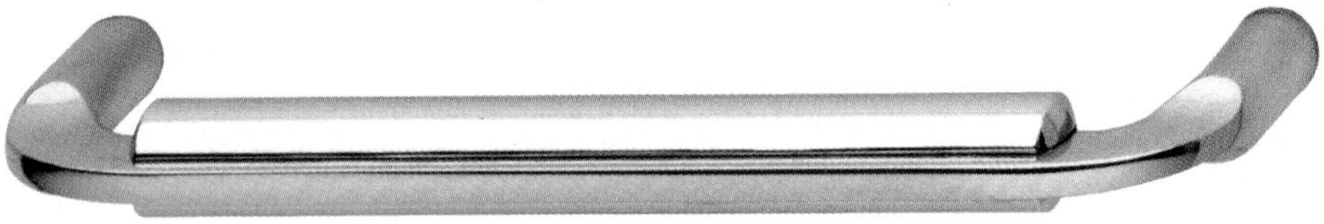

Gold colored polished/Chrome plated polished

Size A x B	Dimension C	Cat. No.
106 x 35	96	103.19.820
138 x 35	128	103.19.821

Packing: 25 pcs.

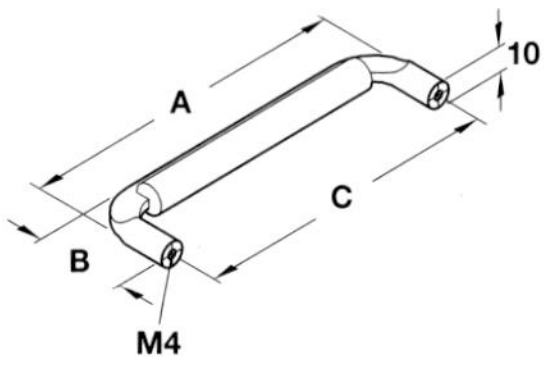

Dimensional data not binding.
We reserve the right to alter specifications without notice.

Zinc/steel handles

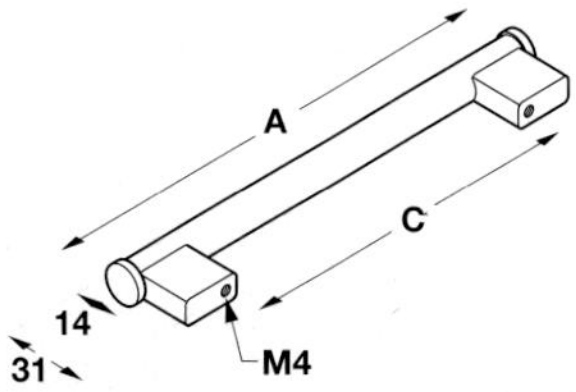

Feet/Ends: Zinc, matt chrome
Handle: Steel, matt chrome

Size A x B	Dimension C	Cat. No.
168 x 31mm	128	117.26.400
264 x 31mm	224	117.25.401

Packing: 25 pcs.

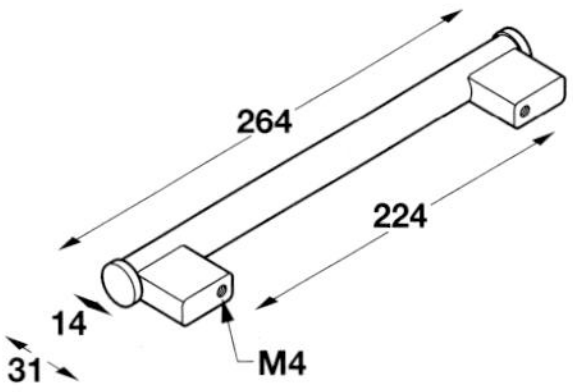

Feet/Ends: Zinc gold polished
Handle: Steel, chrome polished

Cat. No.	117.25.821

Packing: 25 pcs.

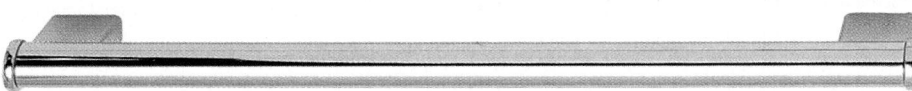

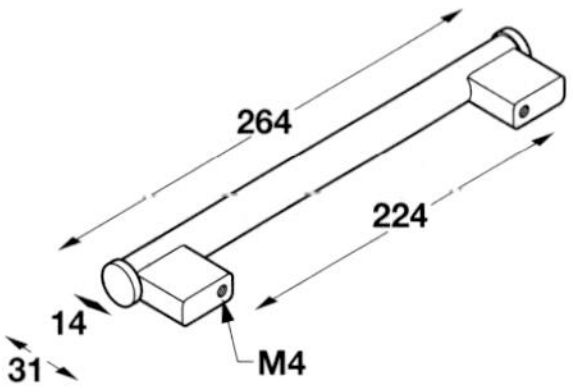

Feet/Ends: Zinc, gold polished
Handle: Steel white

Cat. No.	117.25.812

Packing: 25 pcs.

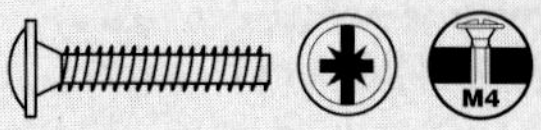

Threaded Screws M4
Combined slot, suitable for flat or cross blades
Finish: steel, zinc-plated

Length	Cat. No.
10 mm	022.35.109
12 mm	022.35.127
15 mm	022.35.154
18 mm	022.35.181
20 mm	022.35.207
22 mm	022.35.225
23 mm	022.35.234
25 mm	022.35.252
28 mm	022.35.289
30 mm	022.35.305
35 mm	022.35.350
38 mm	022.35.387
40 mm	022.35.403
45 mm	022.35.458
50 mm	022.35.501
60 mm	022.35.609

Packing: 100 and 1000 pcs.

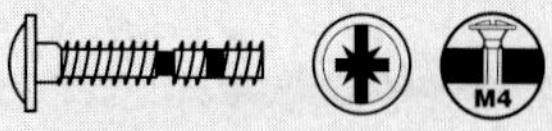

Threaded Breakoff Screw M4
Combined slot, suitable for flat or cross blades
Finish: steel, zinc-plated

Length	Cat. No.
1 3/4" x 3/4"	022.35.887

Packing: 100 and 1000 pcs.

HÄFELE

Zinc/Steel Handles

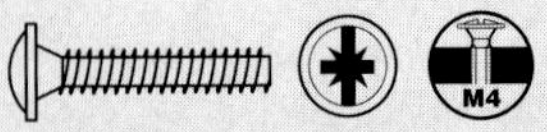

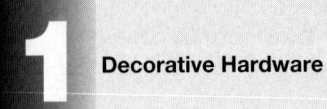

Threaded Screws M4
Combined slot, suitable for flat or cross blades

Finish: steel, zinc-plated

Length	Cat. No.
10 mm	022.35.109
12 mm	022.35.127
15 mm	022.35.154
18 mm	022.35.181
20 mm	022.35.207
22 mm	022.35.225
23 mm	022.35.234
25 mm	022.35.252
28 mm	022.35.289
30 mm	022.35.305
35 mm	022.35.350
38 mm	022.35.387
40 mm	022.35.403
45 mm	022.35.458
50 mm	022.35.501
60 mm	022.35.609

Packing: 100 and 1000 pcs.

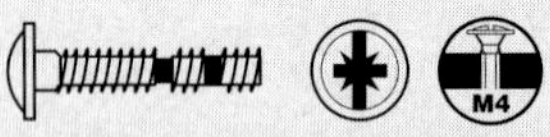

Threaded Breakoff Screw M4
Combined slot, suitable for flat or cross blades

Finish: steel, zinc-plated

Length	Cat. No.
1 3/4" x 3/4"	022.35.887

Packing: 100 and 1000 pcs.

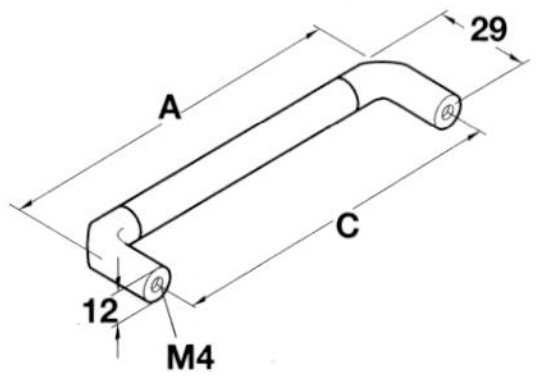

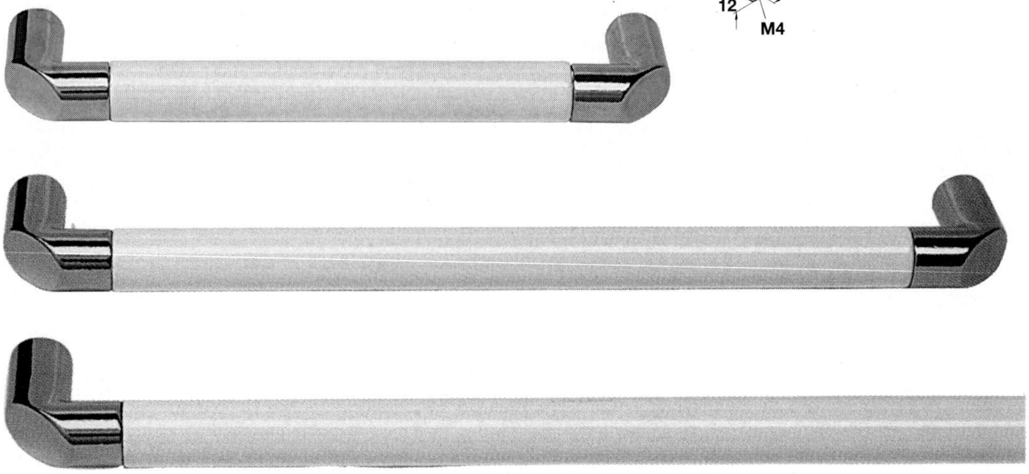

Ends: zinc chrome plated polished
Center: steel white

Size A	Dimension C	Cat. No.
132	128	117.71.216
288	192	117.71.243
324	288	117.71.261

Packing: 25 pcs.

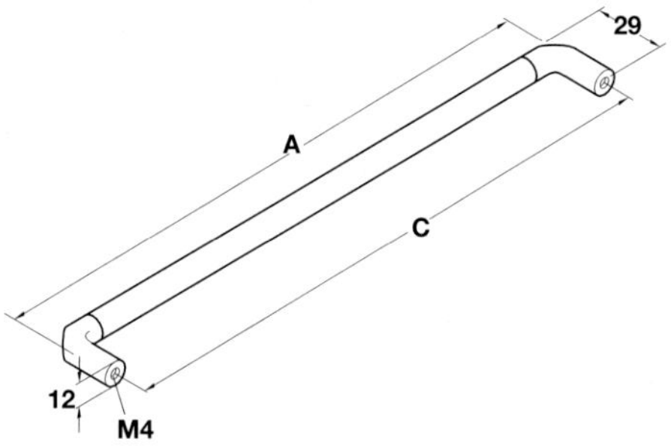

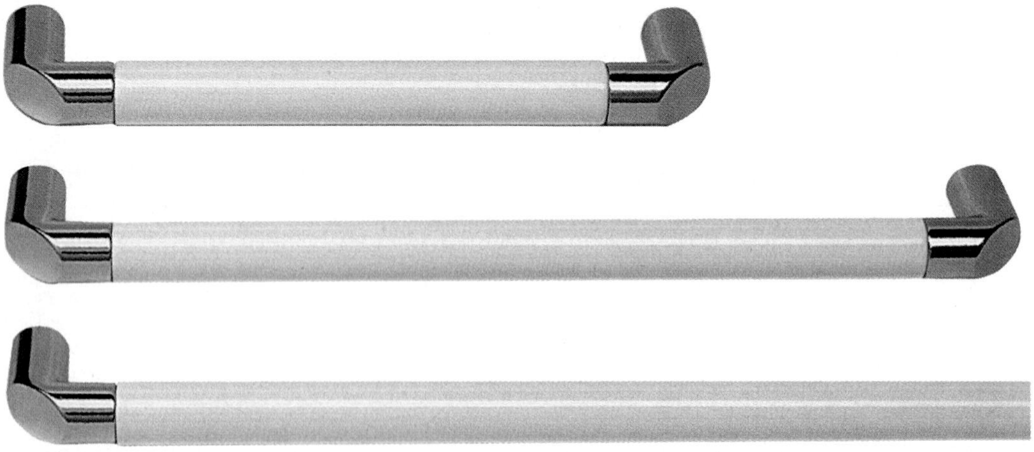

Ends: zinc gold colored polished
Center steel white

Size A	Dimension C	Cat. No.
132	128	117.71.814
228	192	117.71.841
324	288	117.71.869

Packing: 25 pcs.

Zinc/steel handles

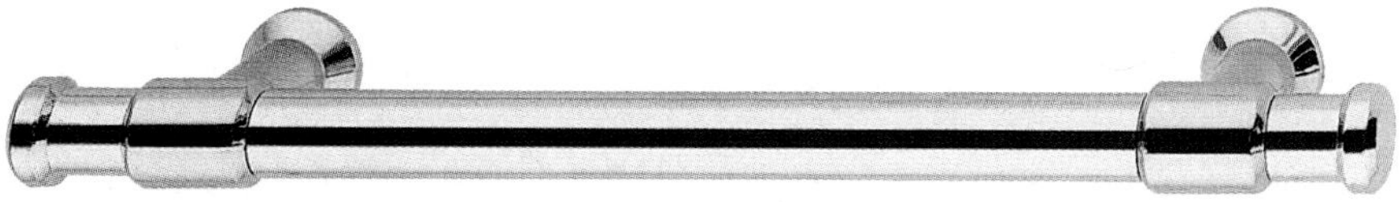

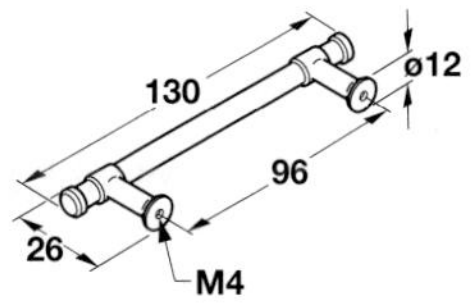

Handle: chrome polished
Feet: gold colored polished

Cat. No.	117.48.824

Packing: 25 pcs.

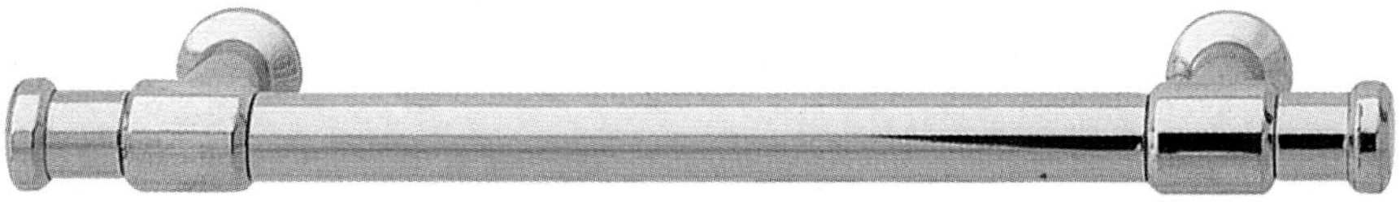

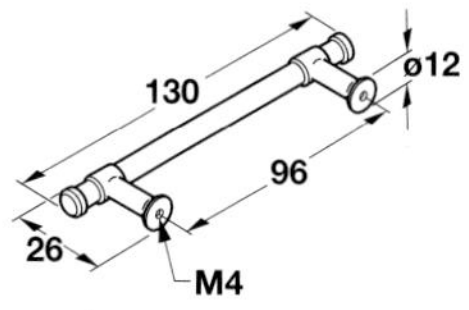

Handle: gold colored polished
Feet: chrome polished

Cat. No.	117.48.226

Packing: 25 pcs.

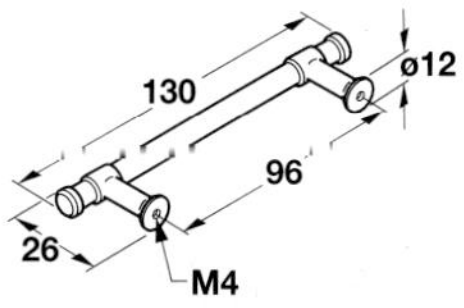

Handle: steel chrome polished
Foot: white

Cat. No.	117.48.726

Packing: 25 pcs.

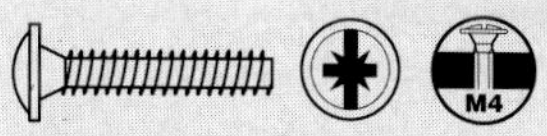

Threaded Screws M4
Combined slot, suitable for flat or cross blades
Finish: steel, zinc-plated

Length	Cat. No.
10 mm	022.35.109
12 mm	022.35.127
15 mm	022.35.154
18 mm	022.35.181
20 mm	022.35.207
22 mm	022.35.225
23 mm	022.35.234
25 mm	022.35.252
28 mm	022.35.289
30 mm	022.35.305
35 mm	022.35.350
38 mm	022.35.387
40 mm	022.35.403
45 mm	022.35.458
50 mm	022.35.501
60 mm	022.35.609

Packing: 100 and 1000 pcs.

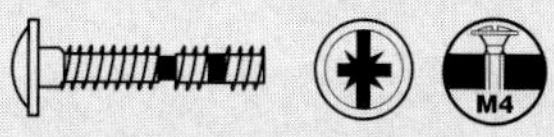

Threaded Breakoff Screw M4
Combined slot, suitable for flat or cross blades
Finish: steel, zinc-plated

Length	Cat. No.
1 3/4" x 3/4"	022.35.887

Packing: 100 and 1000 pcs.

HÄFELE

Zinc/steel handles

Threaded Screws M4
Combined slot, suitable for flat or cross blades
Finish: steel, zinc-plated

Length	Cat. No.
10 mm	022.35.109
12 mm	022.35.127
15 mm	022.35.154
18 mm	022.35.181
20 mm	022.35.207
22 mm	022.35.225
23 mm	022.35.234
25 mm	022.35.252
28 mm	022.35.289
30 mm	022.35.305
35 mm	022.35.350
38 mm	022.35.387
40 mm	022.35.403
45 mm	022.35.458
50 mm	022.35.501
60 mm	022.35.609

Packing: 100 and 1000 pcs.

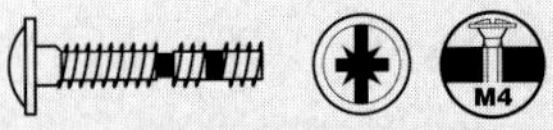

Threaded Breakoff Screw M4
Combined slot, suitable for flat or cross blades
Finish: steel, zinc-plated

Length	Cat. No.
1 3/4" x 3/4"	022.35.887

Packing: 100 and 1000 pcs.

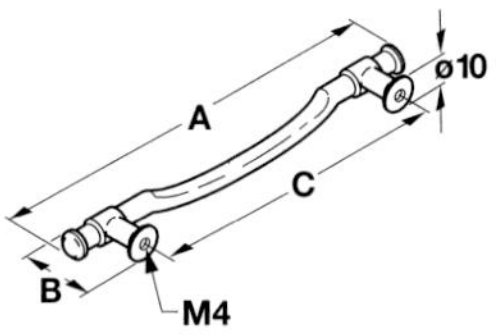

Feet: gold colored polished
Handle: steel chrome polished

Size A x B	Dimension C	Cat. No.
122 x 26	96	117.42.813
153 x 30	128	117.42.822

Packing: 25 pcs.

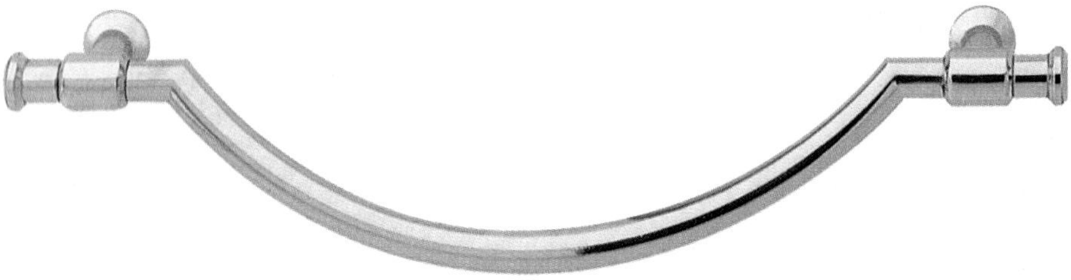

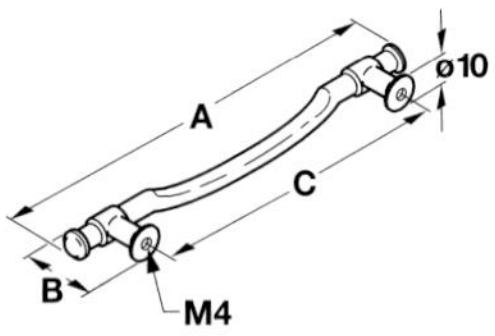

Feet: zinc chrome polished
Handle: steel gold colored polished

Size A x B	Dimension C	Cat. No.
122 x 26	96	117.42.215
153 x 30	128	117.42.224

Packing: 25 pcs.

Zinc steel handles

Ends: zinc chrome polished
Center: steel white

Cat. No.	117.46.268

Packing: 25 pcs.

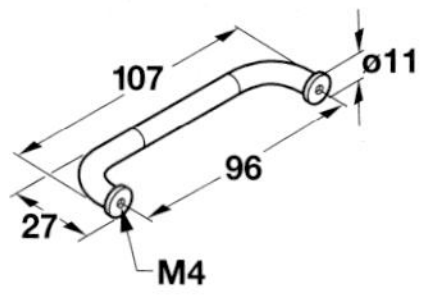

Ends: zinc gold colored polished
Center: steel white

Cat. No.	117.46.722

Packing: 25 pcs.

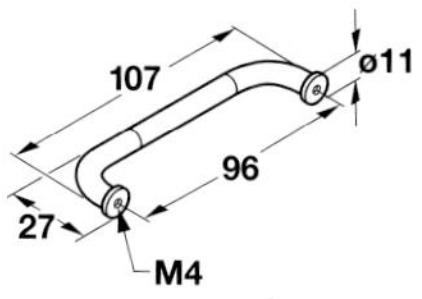

Ends: zinc gold colored polished
Center: steel chrome polished

Cat. No.	117.46.820

Packing: 25 pcs.

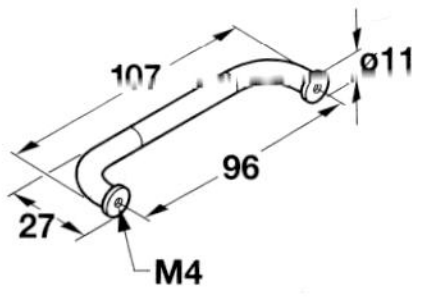

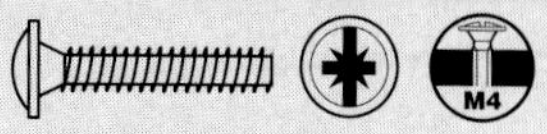

Threaded Screws M4
Combined slot, suitable for flat or cross blades
Finish: steel, zinc-plated

Length	Cat. No.
10 mm	022.35.109
12 mm	022.35.127
15 mm	022.35.154
18 mm	022.35.181
20 mm	022.35.207
22 mm	022.35.225
23 mm	022.35.234
25 mm	022.35.252
28 mm	022.35.289
30 mm	022.35.305
35 mm	022.35.350
38 mm	022.35.387
40 mm	022.35.403
45 mm	022.35.458
50 mm	022.35.501
60 mm	022.35.609

Packing: 100 and 1000 pcs.

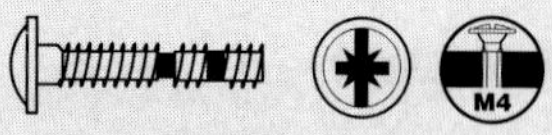

Threaded Breakoff Screw M4
Combined slot, suitable for flat or cross blades
Finish: steel, zinc-plated

Length	Cat. No.
1 3/4" x 3/4"	022.35.887

Packing: 100 and 1000 pcs.

Dimensional data not binding.
We reserve the right to alter specifications without notice.

HÄFELE

Zinc/Steel Handles

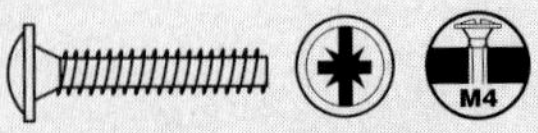

Threaded Screws M4
Combined slot, suitable for flat or cross blades
Finish: steel, zinc-plated

Length	Cat. No.
10 mm	022.35.109
12 mm	022.35.127
15 mm	022.35.154
18 mm	022.35.181
20 mm	022.35.207
22 mm	022.35.225
23 mm	022.35.234
25 mm	022.35.252
28 mm	022.35.289
30 mm	022.35.305
35 mm	022.35.350
38 mm	022.35.387
40 mm	022.35.403
45 mm	022.35.458
50 mm	022.35.501
60 mm	022.35.609

Packing: 100 and 1000 pcs.

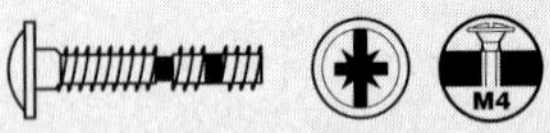

Threaded Breakoff Screw M4
Combined slot, suitable for flat or cross blades
Finish: steel, zinc-plated

Length	Cat. No.
1 3/4" x 3/4"	022.35.887

Packing: 100 and 1000 pcs.

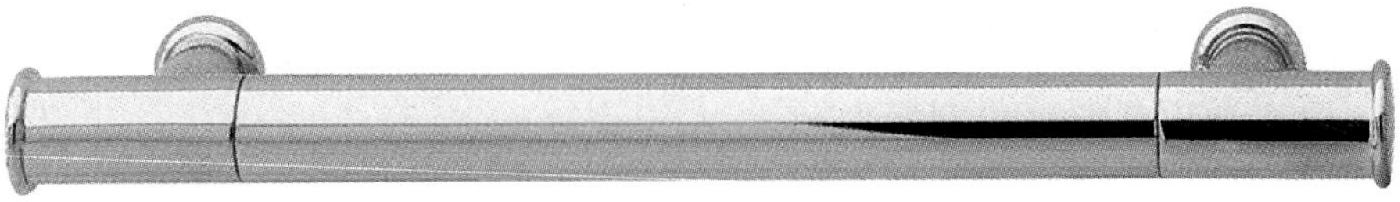

Ends: zinc polished chrome
Center: steel polished chrome

Cat. No.	116.01.237

Packing: 25 pcs.

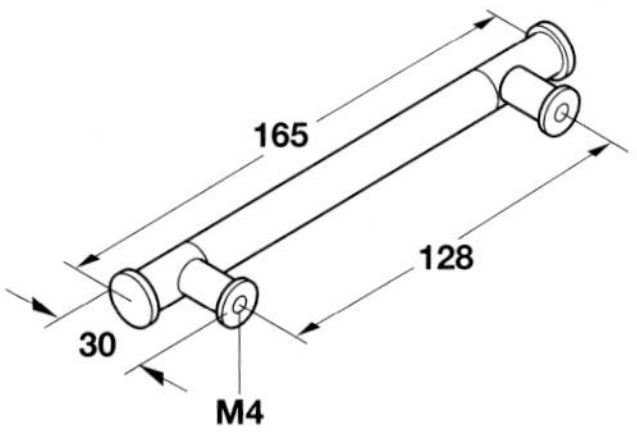

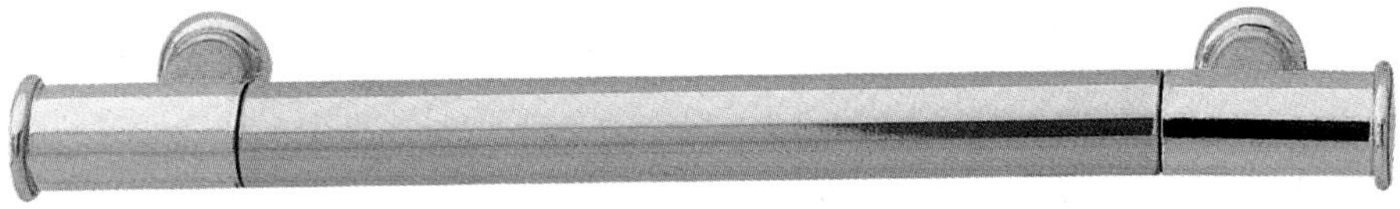

Ends: zinc brass polished
Center: steel brass polished

Cat. No.	116.01.835

Packing: 25 pcs.

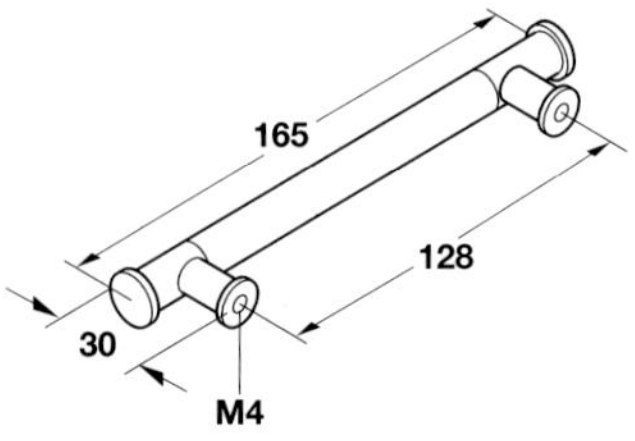

Dimensional data not binding.
We reserve the right to alter specifications without notice.

Zinc/Steel Handles

Ends: zinc chrome plated polished
Center: steel white

Cat. No.	116.13.200

Packing: 25 pcs.

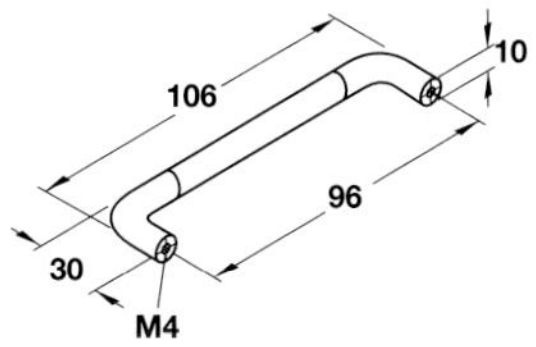

White/rings: black

Cat. No.	116.13.719

Packing: 25 pcs.

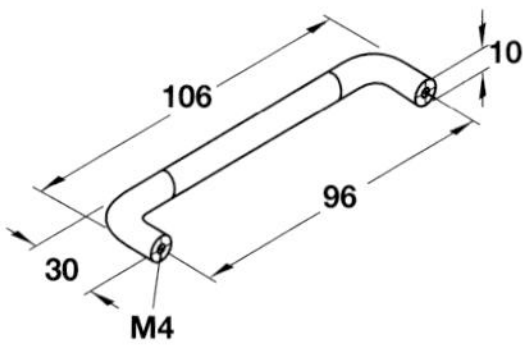

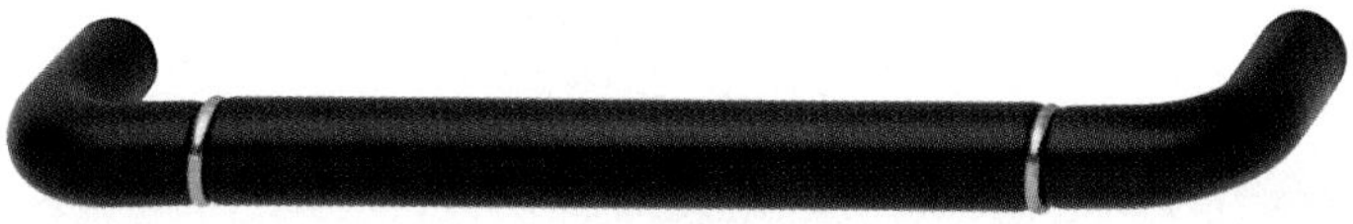

Black/rings: gold plated polished

Cat. No.	116.13.317

Packing: 25 pcs.

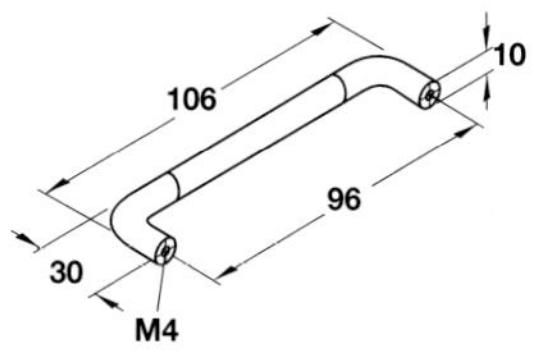

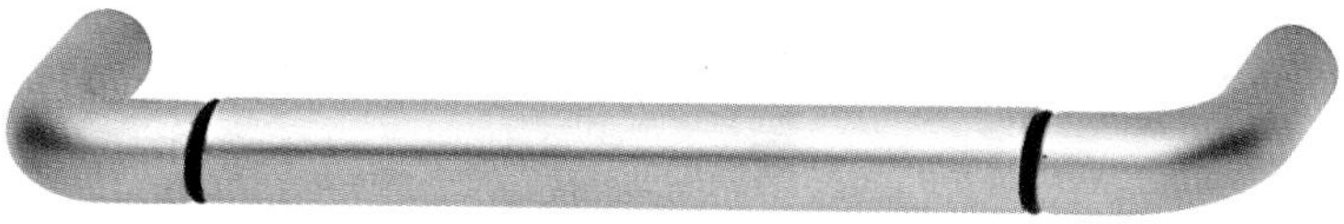

Nickel plated matt/rings: black

Cat. No.	116.13.675

Packing: 25 pcs.

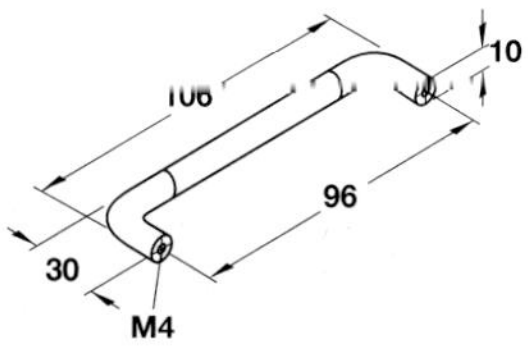

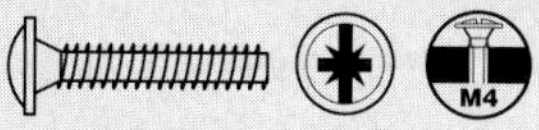

Threaded Screws M4
Combined slot, suitable for flat or cross blades

Finish: steel, zinc-plated

Length	Cat. No.
10 mm	022.35.109
12 mm	022.35.127
15 mm	022.35.154
18 mm	022.35.181
20 mm	022.35.207
22 mm	022.35.225
23 mm	022.35.234
25 mm	022.35.252
28 mm	022.35.289
30 mm	022.35.305
35 mm	022.35.350
38 mm	022.35.387
40 mm	022.35.403
45 mm	022.35.458
50 mm	022.35.501
60 mm	022.35.609

Packing: 100 and 1000 pcs.

Threaded Breakoff Screw M4
Combined slot, suitable for flat or cross blades

Finish: steel, zinc-plated

Length	Cat. No.
1 3/4" x 3/4"	022.35.887

Packing: 100 and 1000 pcs.

HÄFELE

Zinc/steel handles

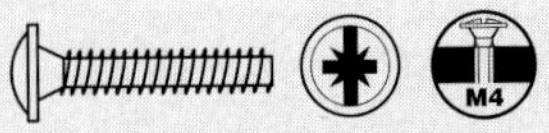

Threaded Screws M4
Combined slot, suitable for flat or cross blades
Finish: steel, zinc-plated

Length	Cat. No.
10 mm	022.35.109
12 mm	022.35.127
15 mm	022.35.154
18 mm	022.35.181
20 mm	022.35.207
22 mm	022.35.225
23 mm	022.35.234
25 mm	022.35.252
28 mm	022.35.289
30 mm	022.35.305
35 mm	022.35.350
38 mm	022.35.387
40 mm	022.35.403
45 mm	022.35.458
50 mm	022.35.501
60 mm	022.35.609

Packing: 100 and 1000 pcs.

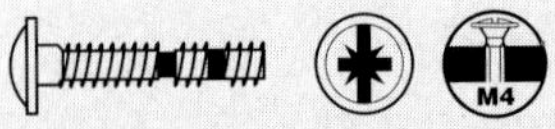

Threaded Breakoff Screw M4
Combined slot, suitable for flat or cross blades
Finish: steel, zinc-plated

Length	Cat. No.
1 3/4" x 3/4"	022.35.887

Packing: 100 and 1000 pcs.

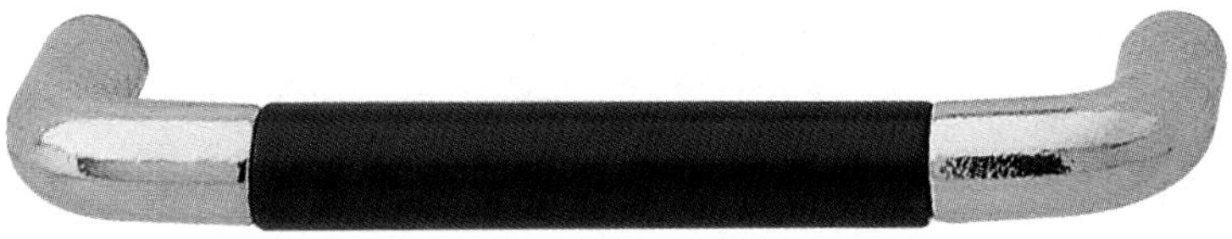

Ends: zinc gold colored polished
Center: steel black matt

Cat. No.	116.13.817

Packing: 25 pcs.

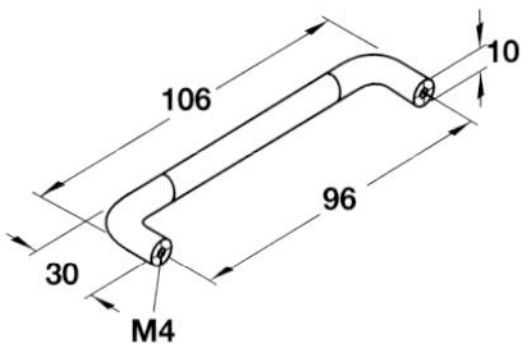

Ends: zinc chrome polished
Center: steel black matt

Cat. No.	116.13.255

Packing: 25 pcs.

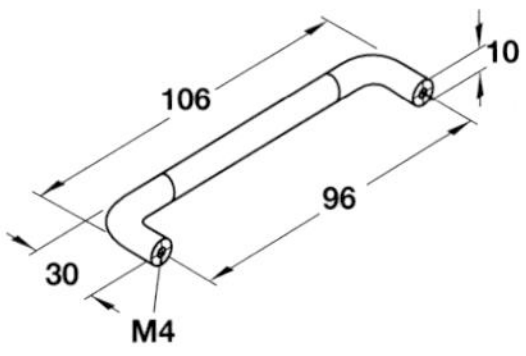

Ends: zinc black matt
Center: steel chrome polished

Cat. No.	116.13.335

Packing: 25 pcs.

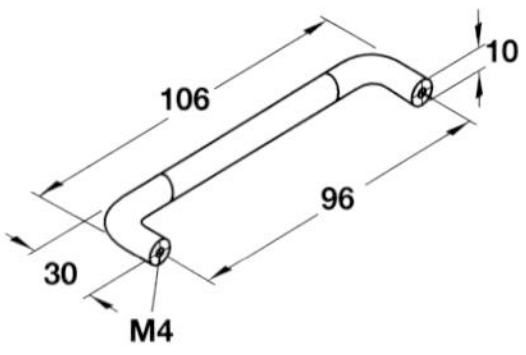

Ends: zinc black matt
Center: steel white

Cat. No.	116.13.308

Packing: 25 pcs.

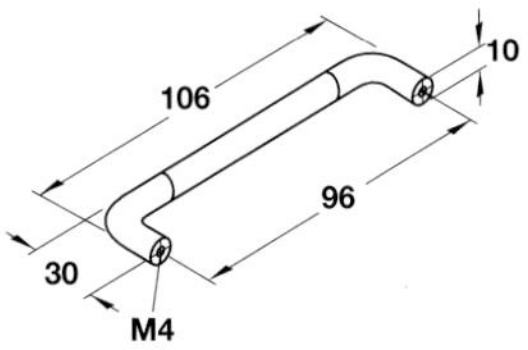

Zinc/Steel Handles

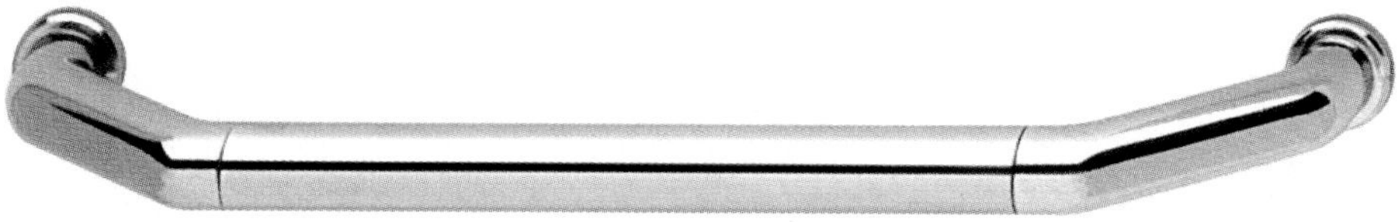

Ends: gold colored polished
Center chrome plated polished

Size A x B	Dimension C	Cat. No.
107 x 27	96	117.47.827
139 x 27	128	117.47.836

Packing: 25 pcs.

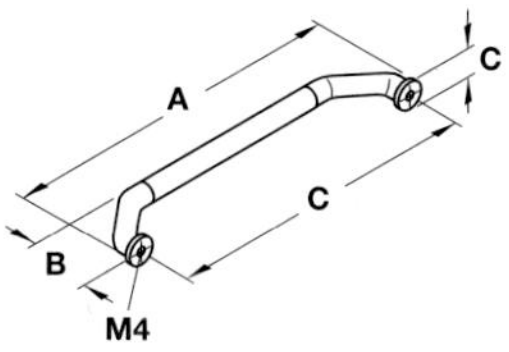

Ends: gold colored polished
Center steel black polished

Size A x B	Dimension C	Cat. No.
107 x 27	96	117.47.925
139 x 27	128	117.47.934

Packing: 25 pcs.

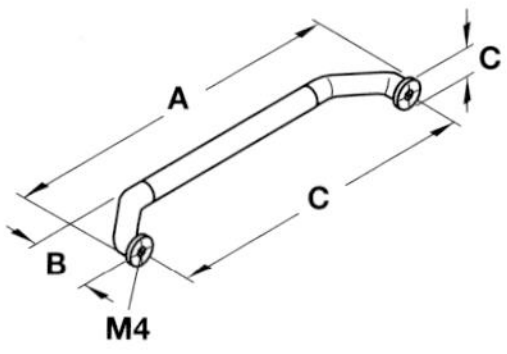

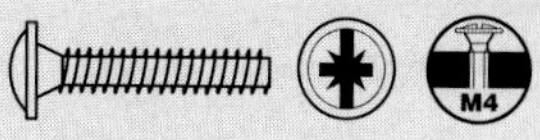

Threaded Screws M4
Combined slot, suitable for flat or cross blades
Finish: steel, zinc-plated

Length	Cat. No.
10 mm	022.35.109
12 mm	022.35.127
15 mm	022.35.154
18 mm	022.35.181
20 mm	022.35.207
22 mm	022.35.225
23 mm	022.35.234
25 mm	022.35.252
28 mm	022.35.289
30 mm	022.35.305
35 mm	022.35.350
38 mm	022.35.387
40 mm	022.35.403
45 mm	022.35.458
50 mm	022.35.501
60 mm	022.35.609

Packing: 100 and 1000 pcs.

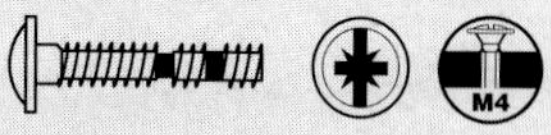

Threaded Breakoff Screw M4
Combined slot, suitable for flat or cross blades
Finish: steel, zinc-plated

Length	Cat. No.
1 3/4" x 3/4"	022.35.887

Packing: 100 and 1000 pcs.

Dimensional data not binding.
We reserve the right to alter specifications without notice.

HÄFELE

Zinc Handles with Plastic Inserts

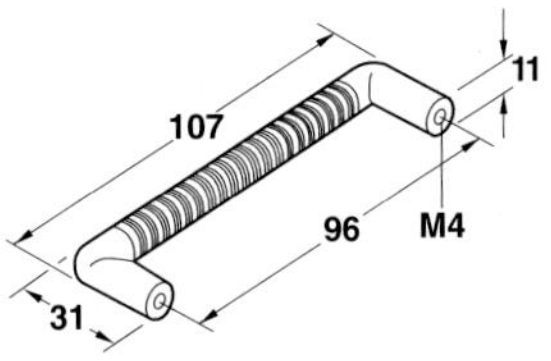

Ends: red
Center section: black

Cat. No.	116.18.938

Packing: 25 each

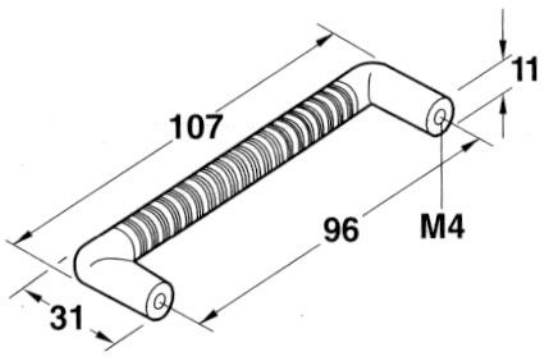

Ends: white
Center section: black

Cat. No.	116.18.732

Packing: 25 pcs.

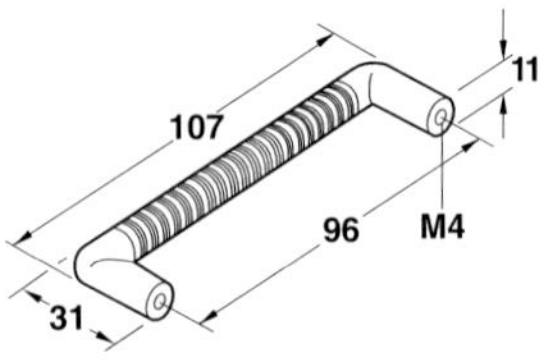

Ends: black
Center section: black

Cat. No.	116.18.330

Packing: 25 pcs.

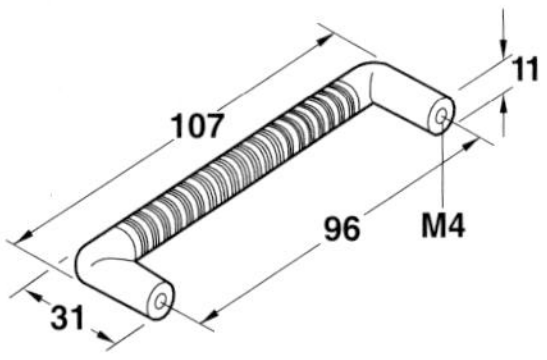

Ends: grey
Center section: grey

Cat. No.	116.18.536

Packing: 25 pcs.

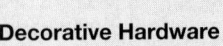

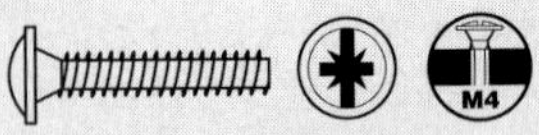

Threaded Screws M4
Combined slot, suitable for flat or cross blades
Finish: steel, zinc-plated

Length	Cat. No.
10 mm	022.35.109
12 mm	022.35.127
15 mm	022.35.154
18 mm	022.35.181
20 mm	022.35.207
22 mm	022.35.225
23 mm	022.35.234
25 mm	022.35.252
28 mm	022.35.289
30 mm	022.35.305
35 mm	022.35.350
38 mm	022.35.387
40 mm	022.35.403
45 mm	022.35.458
50 mm	022.35.501
60 mm	022.35.609

Packing: 100 and 1000 pcs.

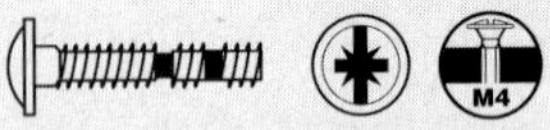

Threaded Breakoff Screw M4
Combined slot, suitable for flat or cross blades
Finish: steel, zinc-plated

Length	Cat. No.
1 3/4" x 3/4"	022.35.887

Packing: 100 and 1000 pcs.

Dimensional data not binding. We reserve the right to alter specifications without notice.

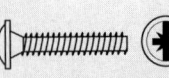

Metal combinations

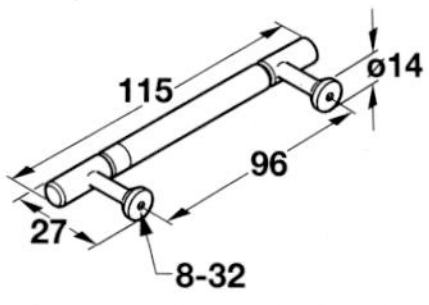

Ends: brass gold colored polished
Center: acrylic clear

Cat. No.	107.14.806

Packing: 25 pcs.

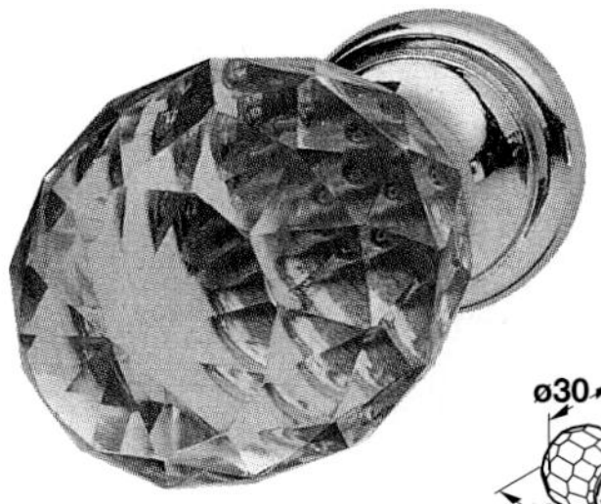

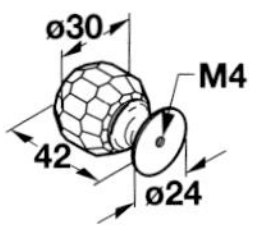

Base: zinc gold colored polished
Knob: crystal clear

Cat. No.	138.72.800

Packing: 25 pcs.

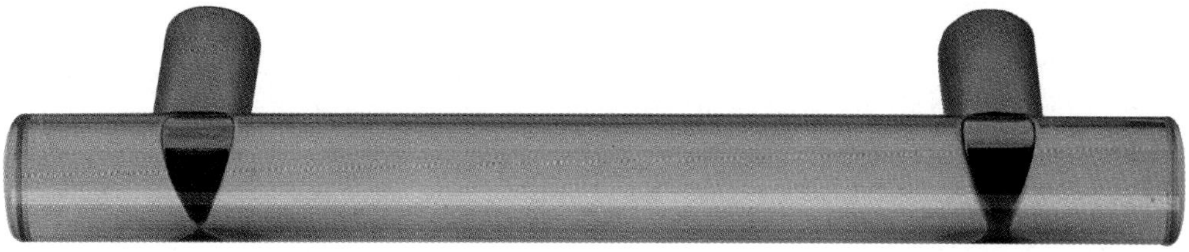

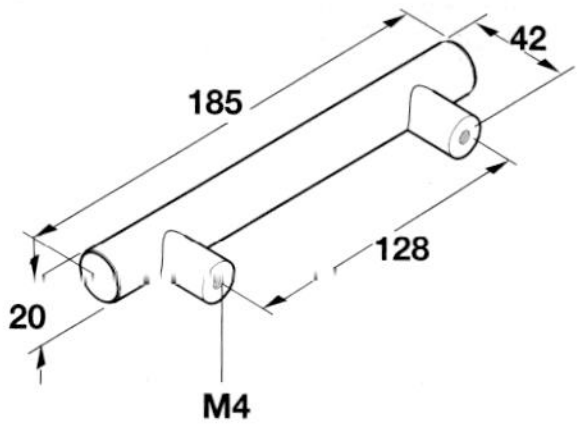

Handle: glass clear
Feet: brass chrome polished

Overall dia.	Center to center	Cat. No.
33	128	117.70.200

Packing: 25 pcs.

HÄFELE

Decorative Hardware 1

Threaded Screws 8-32
Combined slot, suitable for flat or cross blades
Finish: steel, yellow chromated

Length	Cat. No.
22 mm	022.25.229
25 mm	022.25.256
32 mm	022.25.327
38 mm	022.25.381
45 mm	022.25.452

Packing: 100 and 1000 pcs.

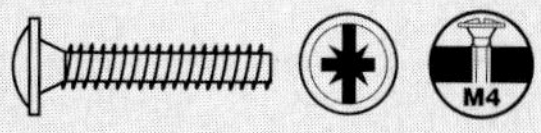

Threaded Screws M4
Combined slot, suitable for flat or cross blades
Finish: steel, zinc-plated

Length	Cat. No.
10 mm	022.35.109
12 mm	022.35.127
15 mm	022.35.154
18 mm	022.35.181
20 mm	022.35.207
22 mm	022.35.225
23 mm	022.35.234
25 mm	022.35.252
28 mm	022.35.289
30 mm	022.35.305
35 mm	022.35.350
38 mm	022.35.387
40 mm	022.35.403
45 mm	022.35.458
50 mm	022.35.501
60 mm	022.35.609

Packing: 100 and 1000 pcs.

Dimensional data not binding.
We reserve the right to alter specifications without notice.

HÄFELE

Metal and Thermoplastic Handles

Threaded Screws M4
Combined slot, suitable for flat or cross blades
Finish: steel, zinc-plated

Length	Cat. No.
10 mm	022.35.109
12 mm	022.35.127
15 mm	022.35.154
18 mm	022.35.181
20 mm	022.35.207
22 mm	022.35.225
23 mm	022.35.234
25 mm	022.35.252
28 mm	022.35.289
30 mm	022.35.305
35 mm	022.35.350
38 mm	022.35.387
40 mm	022.35.403
45 mm	022.35.458
50 mm	022.35.501
60 mm	022.35.609

Packing: 100 and 1000 pcs.

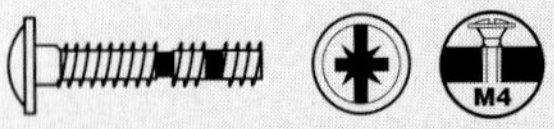

Threaded Breakoff Screw M4
Combined slot, suitable for flat or cross blades
Finish: steel, zinc-plated

Length	Cat. No.
1 3/4" x 3/4"	022.35.887

Packing: 100 and 1000 pcs.

Ends: zinc nickel, plated matt
Center: plastic mint matt

Cat. No.	128.35.601

Packing: 25 pcs.

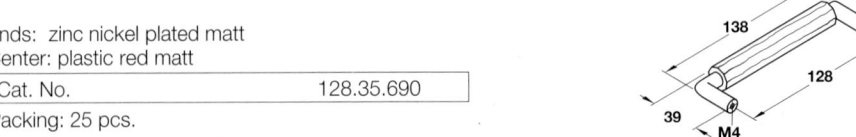

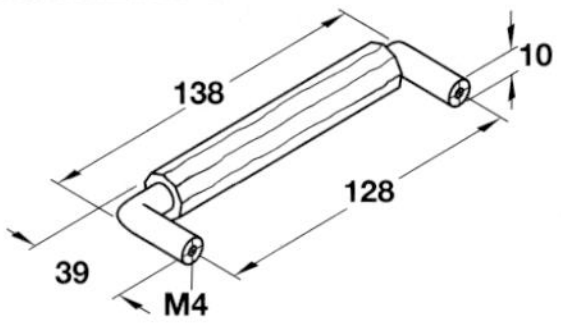

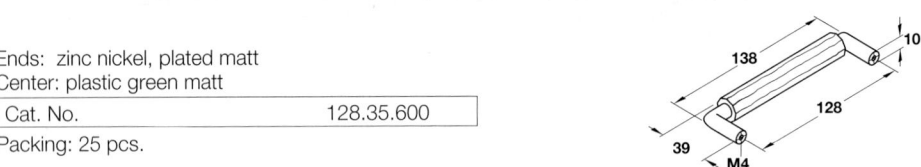

Ends: zinc nickel, plated matt
Center: plastic blue matt

Cat. No.	128.35.680

Packing: 25 pcs.

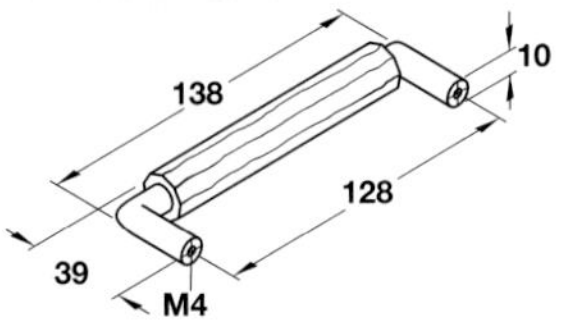

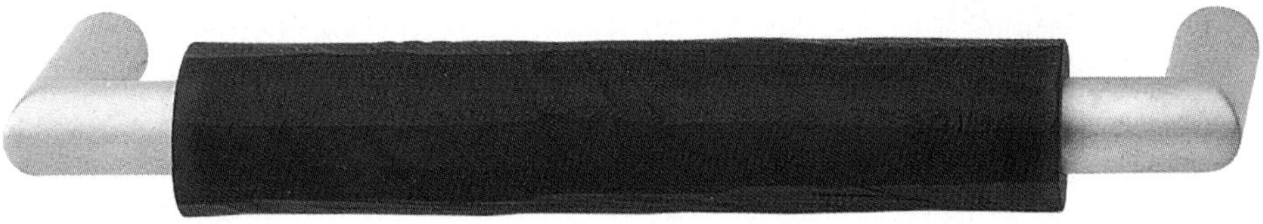

Ends: zinc nickel, plated matt
Center: plastic green matt

Cat. No.	128.35.600

Packing: 25 pcs.

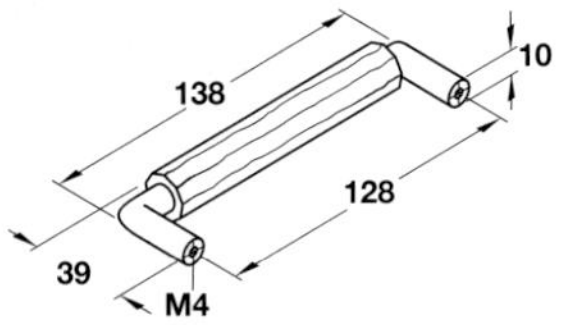

Ends: zinc nickel plated matt
Center: plastic red matt

Cat. No.	128.35.690

Packing: 25 pcs.

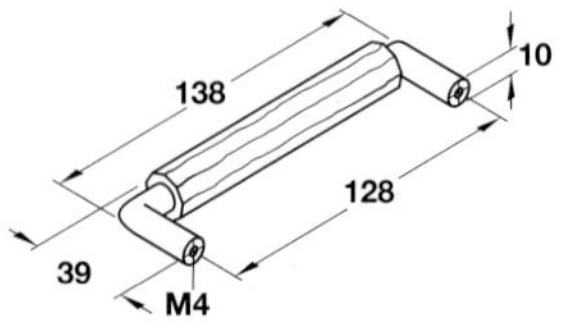

Ends: zinc nickel plated matt
Center: plastic black matt

Cat. No.	128.35.630

Packing: 25 pcs.

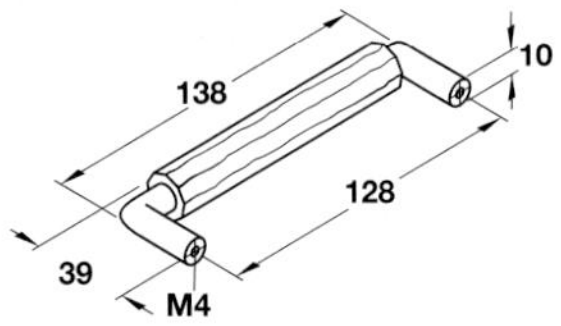

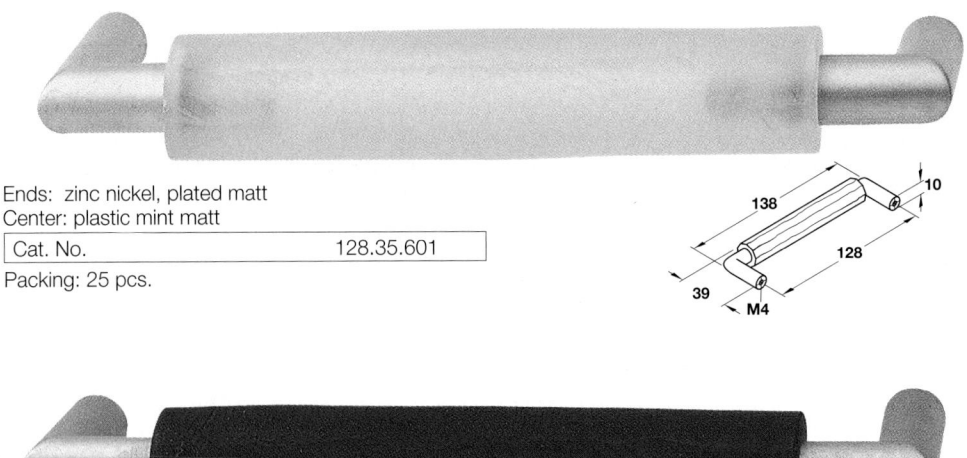

Steel Handles

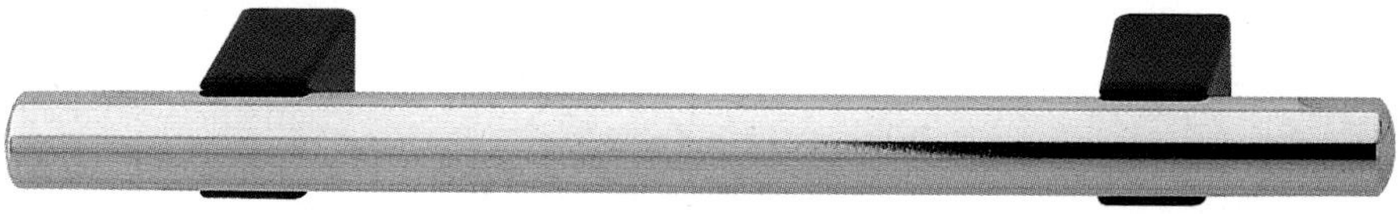

Handle: chrome polished
Pedestal: plastic black

Cat. No.	117.20.237

Packing: 25 pcs.

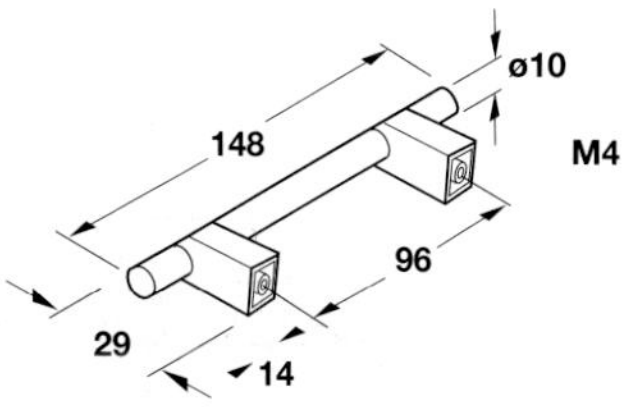

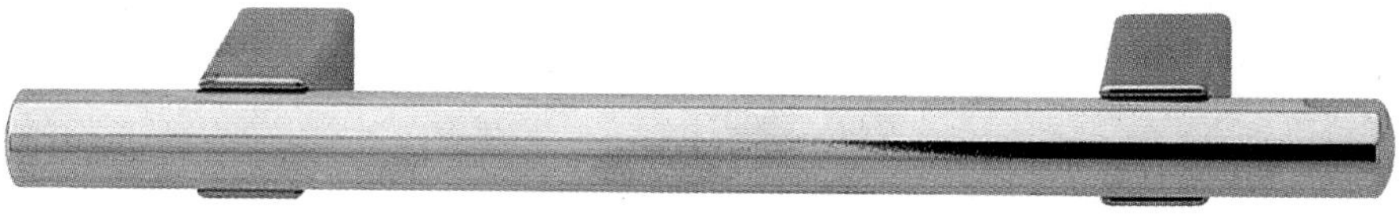

Handle: chrome polished
Pedestal: plastic chromium plated

Size A	Dimension C	Cat. No.
148	96mm	117.20.200
220	160mm	117.21.207

Packing: 25 pcs.

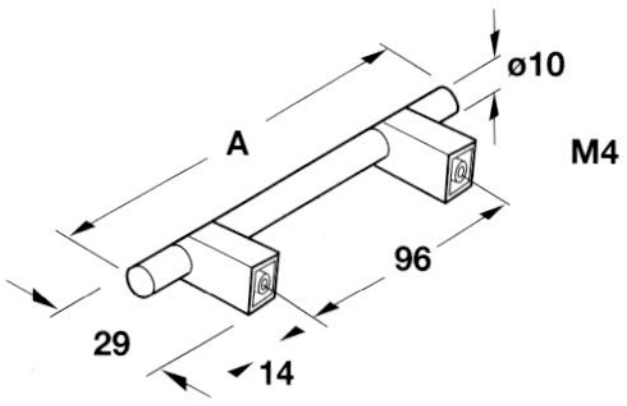

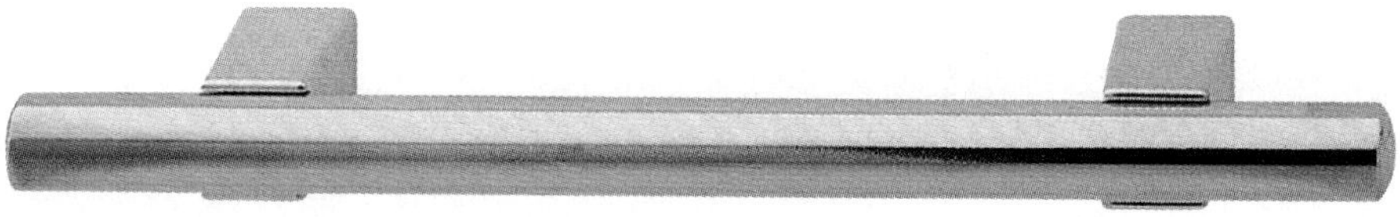

Handle: gold colored polished
Pedestal: plastic gold plated

Cat. No.	117.20.808

Packing: 25 pcs.

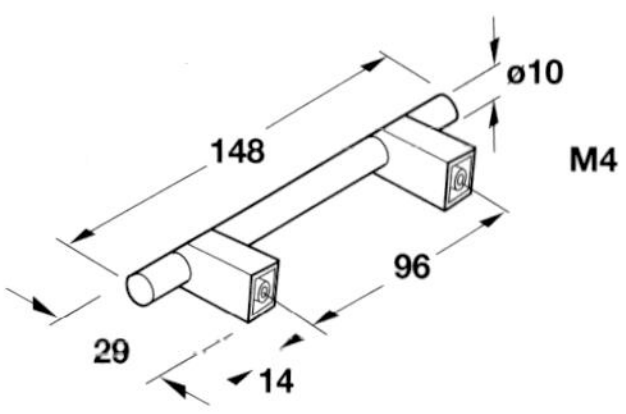

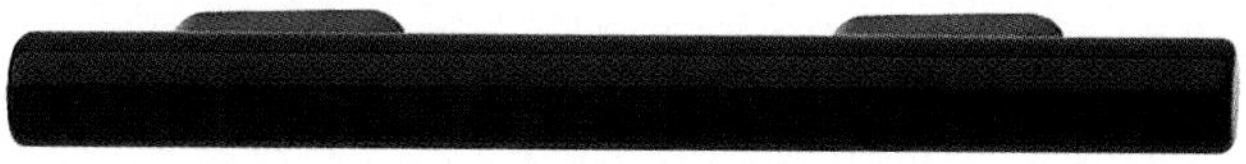

Center section: zinc black
Base: plastic black

Cat. No.	105.32.331

Packing: 25 pcs.

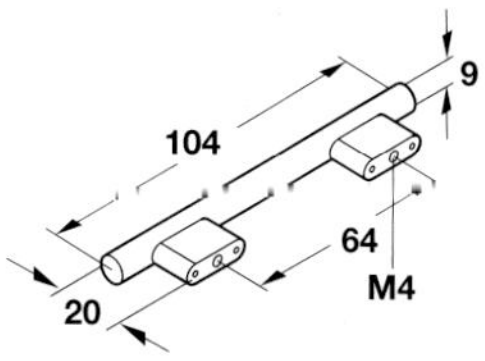

Decorative Hardware 1

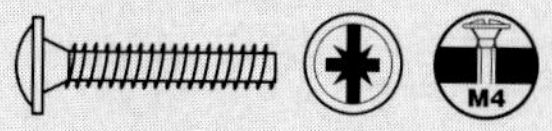

Threaded Screws M4
Combined slot, suitable for flat or cross blades
Finish: steel, zinc-plated

Length	Cat. No.
10 mm	022.35.109
12 mm	022.35.127
15 mm	022.35.154
18 mm	022.35.181
20 mm	022.35.207
22 mm	022.35.225
23 mm	022.35.234
25 mm	022.35.252
28 mm	022.35.289
30 mm	022.35.305
35 mm	022.35.350
38 mm	022.35.387
40 mm	022.35.403
45 mm	022.35.458
50 mm	022.35.501
60 mm	022.35.609

Packing: 100 and 1000 pcs.

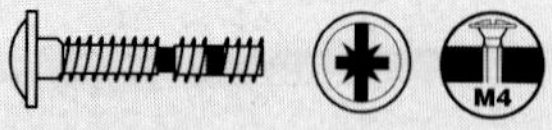

Threaded Breakoff Screw M4
Combined slot, suitable for flat or cross blades
Finish: steel, zinc-plated

Length	Cat. No.
1 3/4" x 3/4"	022.35.887

Packing: 100 and 1000 pcs.

Dimensional data not binding.
We reserve the right to alter specifications without notice.

HÄFELE

Zinc/Plastic Handles

1 Decorative Hardware

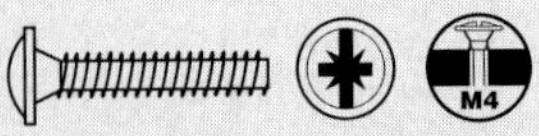

Threaded Screws M4
Combined slot, suitable for flat or cross blades
Finish: steel, zinc-plated

Length	Cat. No.
10 mm	022.35.109
12 mm	022.35.127
15 mm	022.35.154
18 mm	022.35.181
20 mm	022.35.207
22 mm	022.35.225
23 mm	022.35.234
25 mm	022.35.252
28 mm	022.35.289
30 mm	022.35.305
35 mm	022.35.350
38 mm	022.35.387
40 mm	022.35.403
45 mm	022.35.458
50 mm	022.35.501
60 mm	022.35.609

Packing: 100 and 1000 pcs.

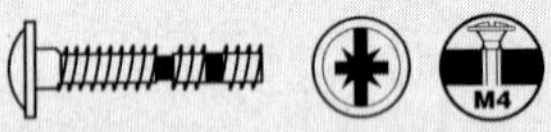

Threaded Breakoff Screw M4
Combined slot, suitable for flat or cross blades
Finish: steel, zinc-plated

Length	Cat. No.
1 3/4" x 3/4"	022.35.887

Packing: 100 and 1000 pcs.

Center section: metallic grey
Base: matt nickel

Cat. No.	115.05.605

Packing: 25 each

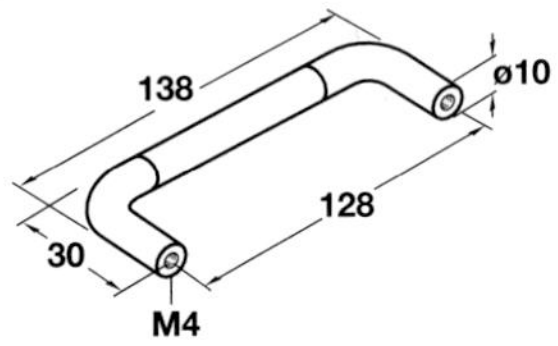

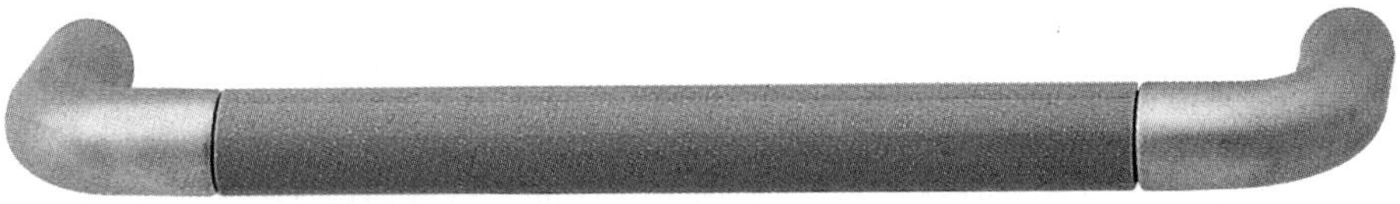

Center section: metallic mauve
Base: matt nickel

Cat. No.	115.05.614

Packing: 25 each

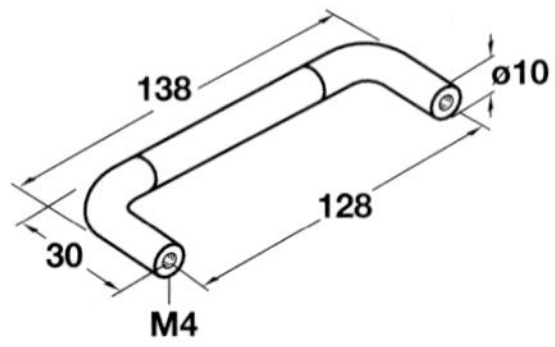

Dimensional data not binding.
We reserve the right to alter specifications without notice.

Aluminum Handles

Silver colored anodized

Size A x B	Dimension C	Catalog No.
106 x 35	96	116.05.922
138 x 35	128	116.05.931
234 x 35	224	116.05.959
298 x 35	288	116.05.977
362 x 35	352	116.05.995

Packing: 25 pcs.

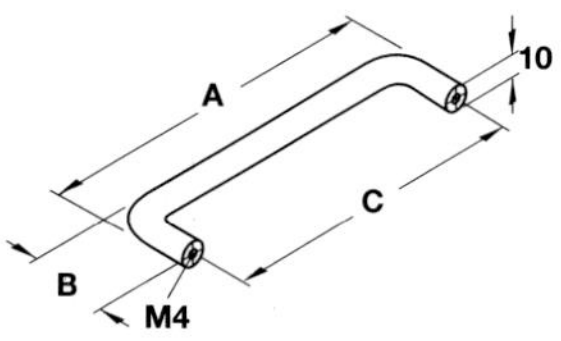

Light bronze anodized

Size A x B	Dimension C	Catalog No.
106 x 35	96	116.05.020
138 x 35	128	116.05.039
234 x 35	224	116.05.057

Packing: 25 pcs.

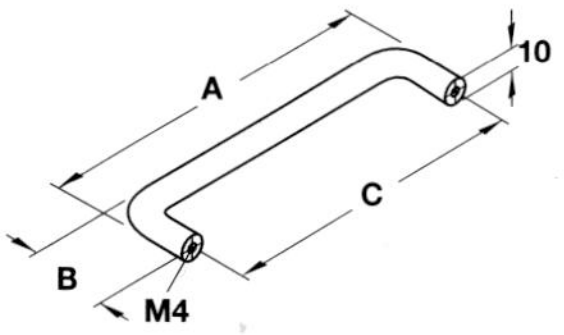

Dark bronze, anodized

Size A x B	Dimension C	Catalog No.
106 x 35	96	116.05.128
138 x 35	128	116.05.137
298 x 35	288	116.05.173

Packing: 25 pcs.

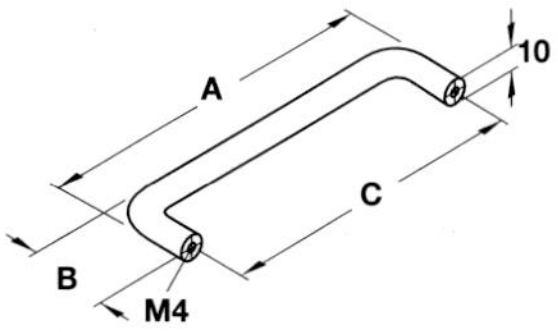

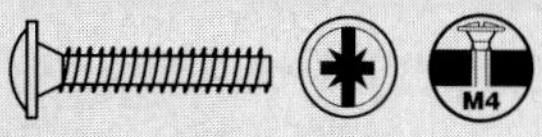

Threaded Screws M4
Combined slot, suitable for flat or cross blades

Finish: steel, zinc-plated

Length	Cat. No.
10 mm	022.35.109
12 mm	022.35.127
15 mm	022.35.154
18 mm	022.35.181
20 mm	022.35.207
22 mm	022.35.225
23 mm	022.35.234
25 mm	022.35.252
28 mm	022.35.289
30 mm	022.35.305
35 mm	022.35.350
38 mm	022.35.387
40 mm	022.35.403
45 mm	022.35.458
50 mm	022.35.501
60 mm	022.35.609

Packing: 100 and 1000 pcs.

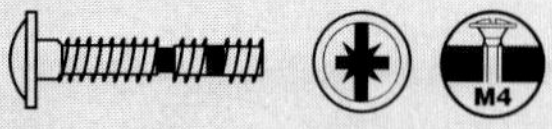

Threaded Breakoff Screw M4
Combined slot, suitable for flat or cross blades

Finish: steel, zinc-plated

Length	Cat. No.
1 3/4" x 3/4"	022.35.887

Packing: 100 and 1000 pcs.

Dimensional data not binding.
We reserve the right to alter specifications without notice.

HÄFELE

Aluminum Handles

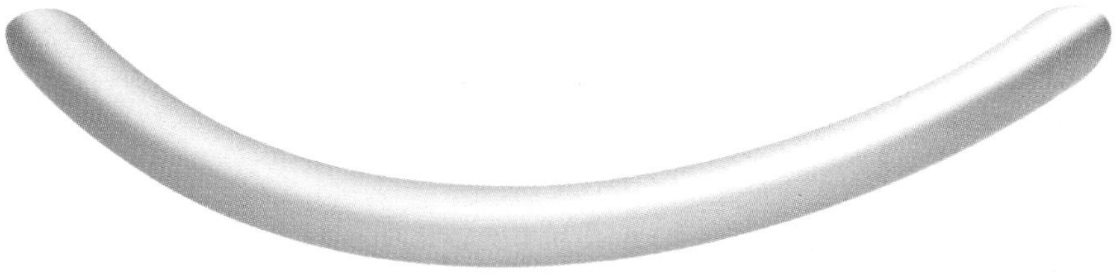

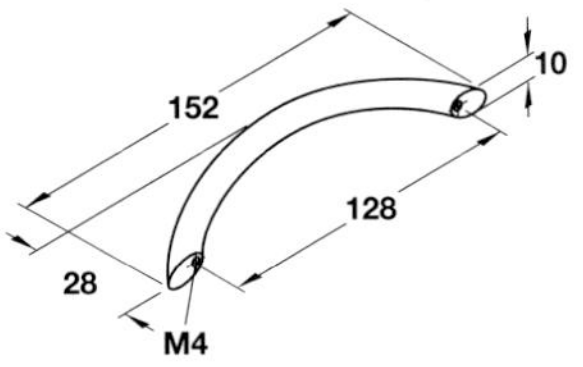

Silver anodized

Cat. No.	117.43.007

Packing: 25 pcs.

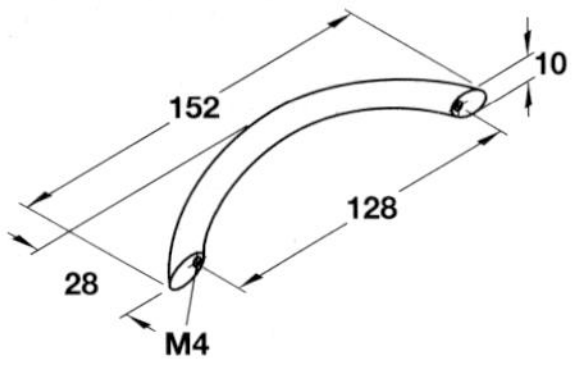

Black anodized matt

Cat. No.	117.43.301

Packing: 25 pcs.

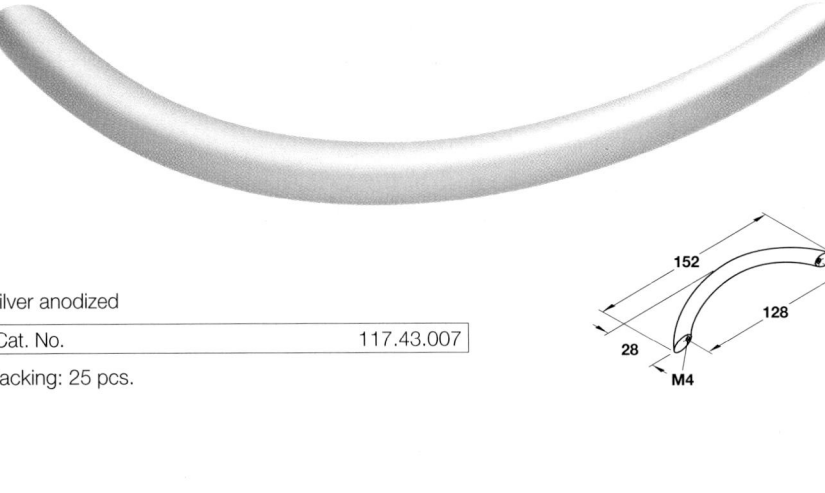

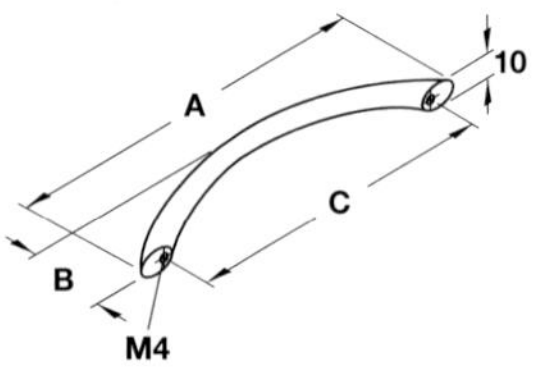

Silver anodized

Size A x B	Dimension C	Cat. No.
112 x 29	96	117.67.016
150 x 29	128	117.67.025

Packing: 25 pcs.

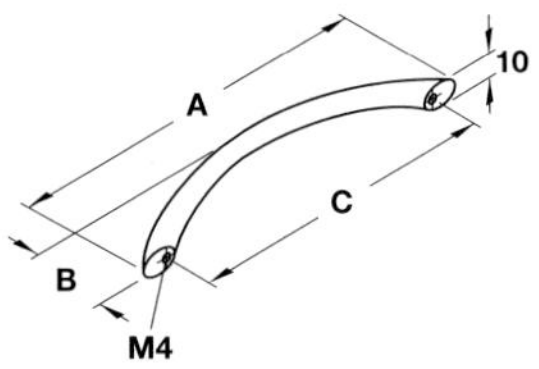

Black anodized matt

Size A x B	Dimension C	Cat. No.
112 x 29	96	117.67.310
150 x 29	128	117.67.329

Packing: 25 pcs.

Threaded Screws M4
Combined slot, suitable for flat or cross blades

Finish: steel, zinc-plated

Length	Cat. No.
10 mm	022.35.109
12 mm	022.35.127
15 mm	022.35.154
18 mm	022.35.181
20 mm	022.35.207
22 mm	022.35.225
23 mm	022.35.234
25 mm	022.35.252
28 mm	022.35.289
30 mm	022.35.305
35 mm	022.35.350
38 mm	022.35.387
40 mm	022.35.403
45 mm	022.35.458
50 mm	022.35.501
60 mm	022.35.609

Packing: 100 and 1000 pcs.

Threaded Breakoff Screw M4
Combined slot, suitable for flat or cross blades

Finish: steel, zinc-plated

Length	Cat. No.
1 3/4" x 3/4"	022.35.887

Packing: 100 and 1000 pcs.

Aluminum anodized handles

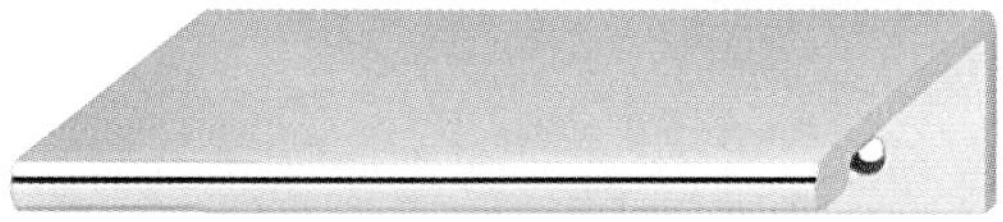

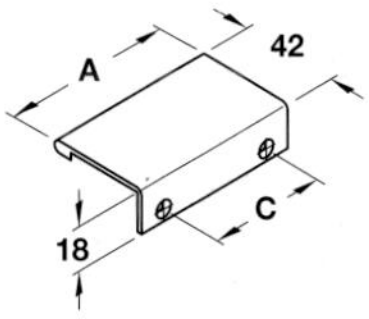

Chrome plated polished

Length A	Dimension C	Cat. No.
40	25	124.02.210
70	50	124.02.220

Packing: 25 pcs. (with #4 x 1/2" mounting screws)

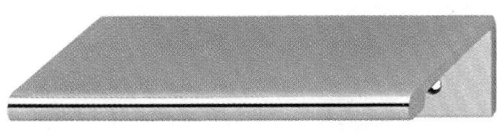

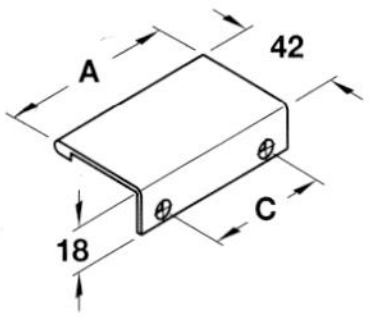

Black polished

Length A	Dimension C	Cat. No.
40	25	124.02.310
70	50	124.02.320

Packing: 25 pcs. (with #4 x 1/2" mounting screws)

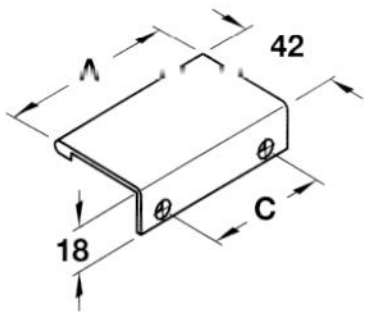

Gold colored polished

Length A	Dimension C	Cat. No.
40	25	124.02.810
70	50	124.02.820

Packing: 25 pcs. (with #4 x 1/2" mounting screws)

- Also available as a continuous pull handle in fixed lengths up to 1143 mm (45") on request. Cut to size minimum 100 pieces per size.

Dimensional data not binding. We reserve the right to alter specifications without notice.

HÄFELE

Zinc Flush Handles

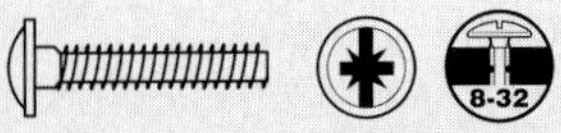

Threaded Screws 8-32
Combined slot, suitable for flat or cross blades

Finish: steel, yellow chromated

Length	Cat. No.
22 mm	022.25.229
25 mm	022.25.256
32 mm	022.25.327
38 mm	022.25.381
45 mm	022.25.452

Packing: 100 and 1000 pcs.

Threaded Screws M4
Combined slot, suitable for flat or cross blades

Finish: steel, zinc-plated

Length	Cat. No.
10 mm	022.35.109
12 mm	022.35.127
15 mm	022.35.154
18 mm	022.35.181
20 mm	022.35.207
22 mm	022.35.225
23 mm	022.35.234
25 mm	022.35.252
28 mm	022.35.289
30 mm	022.35.305
35 mm	022.35.350
38 mm	022.35.387
40 mm	022.35.403
45 mm	022.35.458
50 mm	022.35.501
60 mm	022.35.609

Packing: 100 and 1000 pcs.

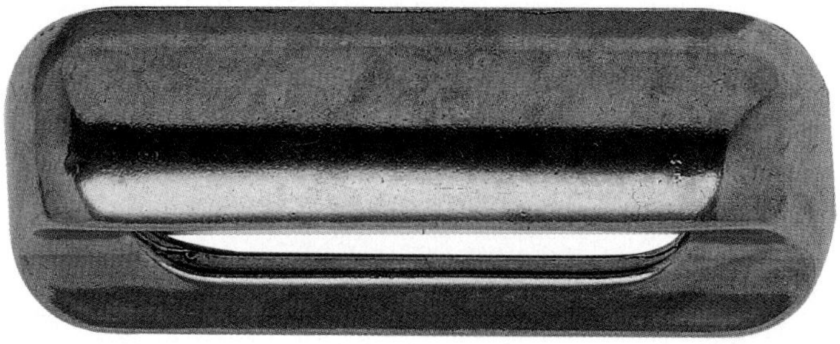

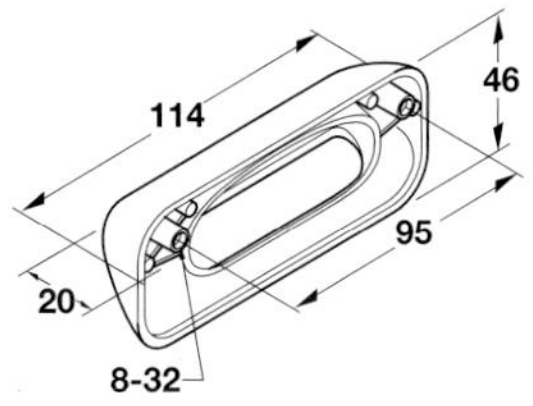

Regency brass

Cat. No.	151.30.100

Packing: 25 pcs.

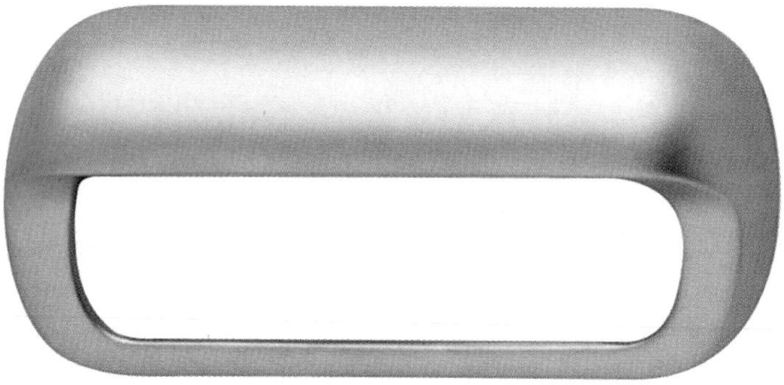

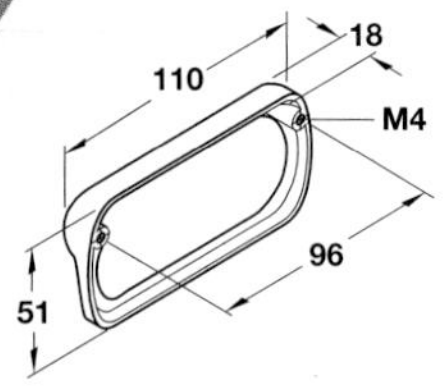

Chrome plated matt

Cat. No.	151.33.203

Packing: 25 pcs.

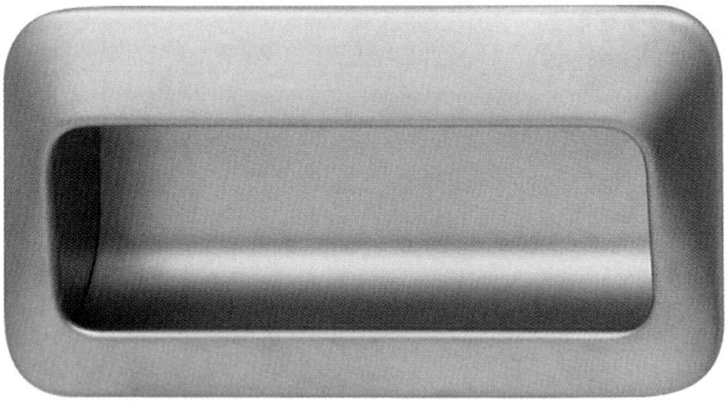

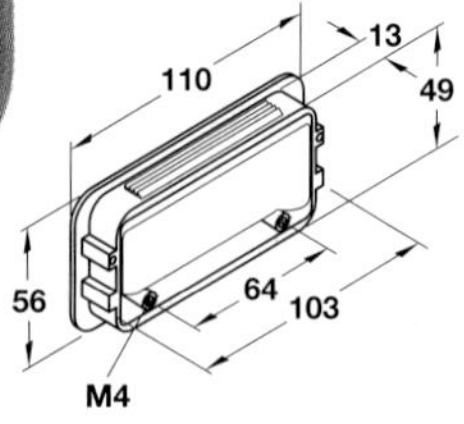

Chrome plated matt

Cat. No.	151.50.213

Packing: 25 pcs.

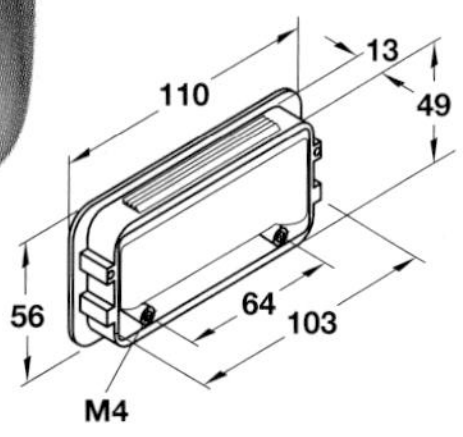

Nickel plated matt

Cat. No.	151.50.615

Packing: 25 pcs.

Dimensional data not binding.
We reserve the right to alter specifications without notice.

Zinc Flush Handles

HÄFELE

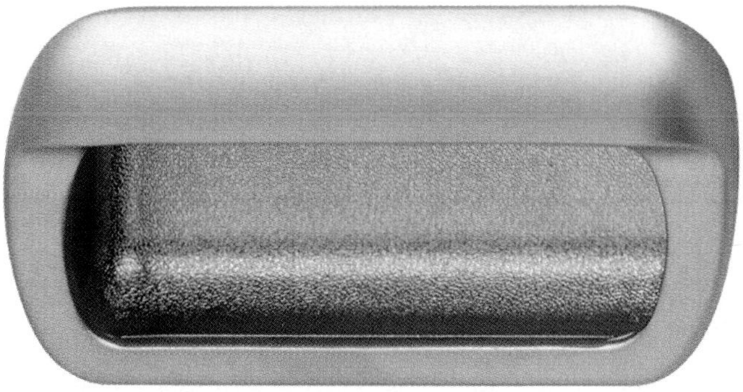

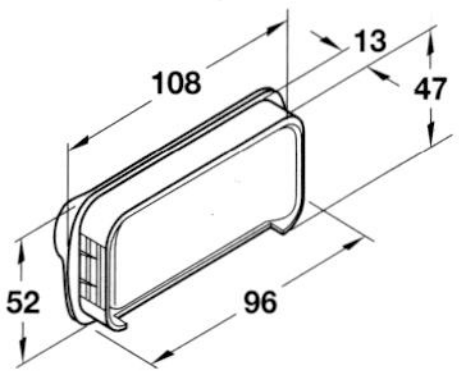

Chrome plated matt

Cat. No.	151.36.222

Packing: 25 pcs.

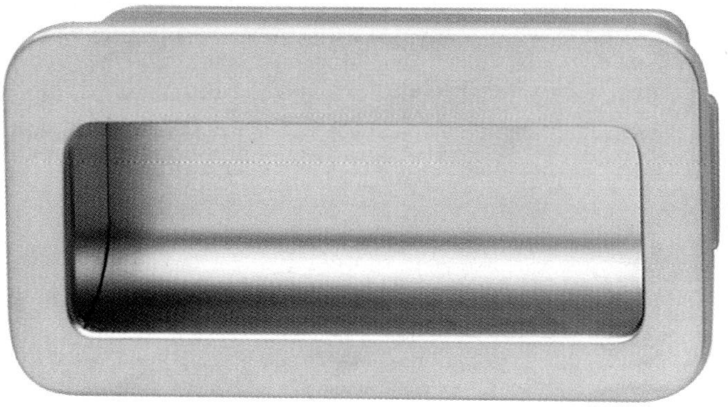

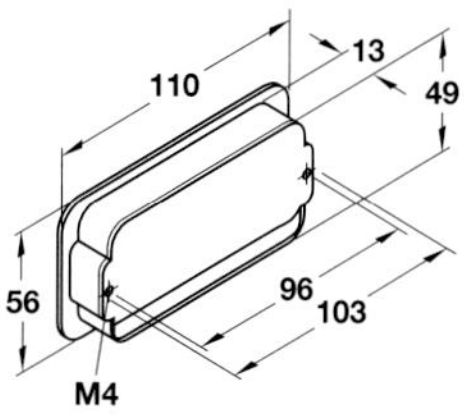

Chrome plated matt

Cat. No.	151.35.207

Packing: 25 pcs.

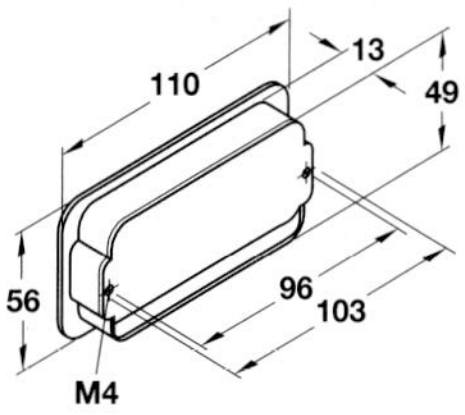

Chrome plated matt

Cat. No.	151.35.261

Packing 25: pcs.

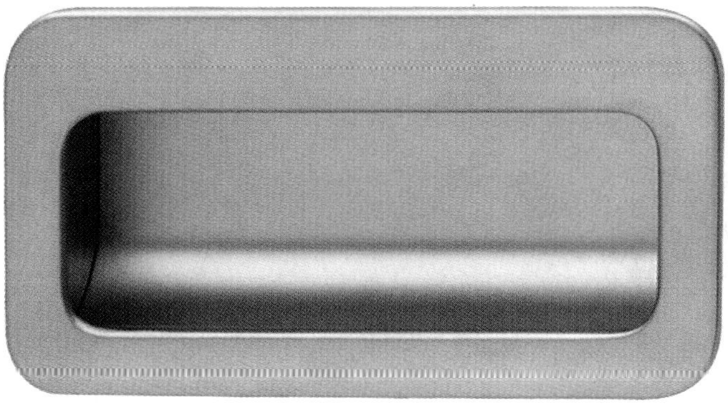

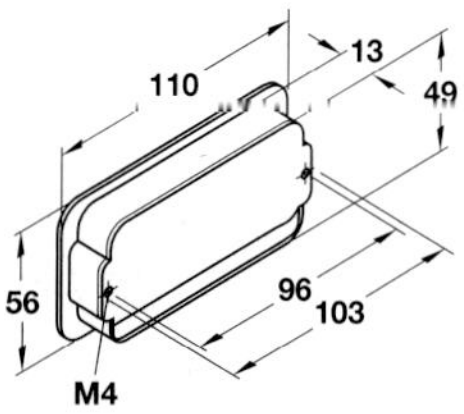

Nickel plated matt

Cat. No.	151.35.663

Packing: 25 pcs.

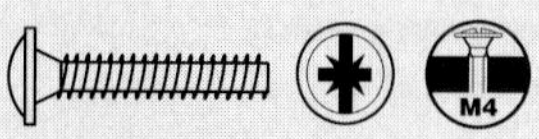

Threaded Screws M4
Combined slot, suitable for flat or cross blades

Finish: steel, zinc-plated

Length	Cat. No.
10 mm	022.35.109
12 mm	022.35.127
15 mm	022.35.154
18 mm	022.35.181
20 mm	022.35.207
22 mm	022.35.225
23 mm	022.35.234
25 mm	022.35.252
28 mm	022.35.289
30 mm	022.35.305
35 mm	022.35.350
38 mm	022.35.387
40 mm	022.35.403
45 mm	022.35.458
50 mm	022.35.501
60 mm	022.35.609

Packing: 100 and 1000 pcs.

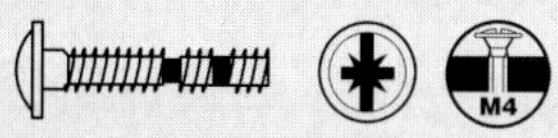

Threaded Breakoff Screw M4
Combined slot, suitable for flat or cross blades

Finish: steel, zinc-plated

Length	Cat. No.
1 3/4" x 3/4"	022.35.887

Packing: 100 and 1000 pcs.

Dimensional data not binding.
We reserve the right to alter specifications without notice.

HÄFELE

Metal Flush Handles

Round-head Metal Pins
Ø 0.9 mm

Finish: steel, nickel-plated

Length	Cat. No.
11 mm	076.40.217

Packing: 7400 pcs.

Round-head Metal Pins
Ø 0.9 mm

Finish: steel, brass-plated

Length	Cat. No.
11 mm	076.40.119

Packing: 7400 pcs.

Round-head Metal Pins
Ø 1.6 mm

Finish: steel, nickel-plated

Length	Cat. No.
15 mm	076.40.299

Packing: 2000 pcs.

Round-head Metal Pins
Ø 1.6 mm

Finish: steel, brass-plated

Length	Cat. No.
15 mm	076.40.191

Packing: 2150 pcs.

Brass nickel plated polished

Size A x B	Size C x D	Depth t	Cat. No.
75 x 32	69 x 26	9	151.01.710
100 x 39	93 x 32	11	151.01.729

Packing: 25 pcs.

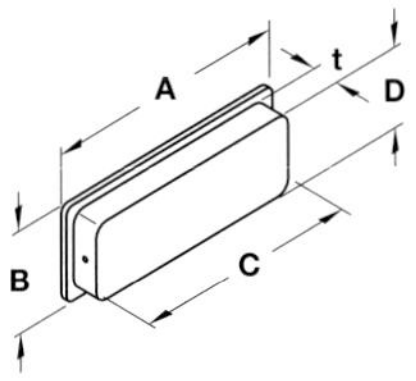

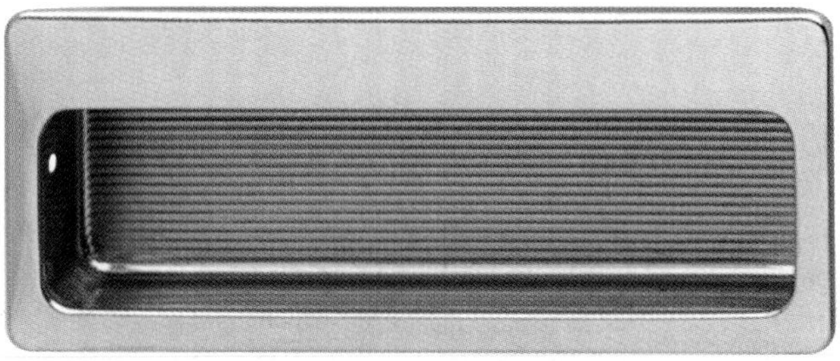

Brass polished/inside matt

Size A x B	Size C x D	Depth t	Cat. No.
75 x 32	69 x 26	9	151.01.818
100 x 39	93 x 32	11	151.01.827

Packing: 25 pcs.

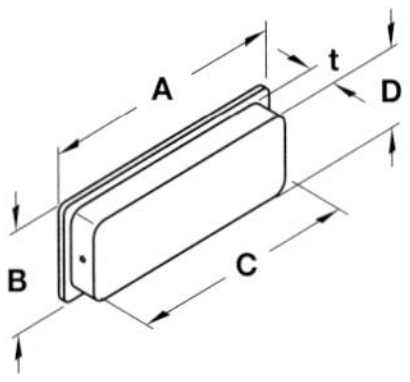

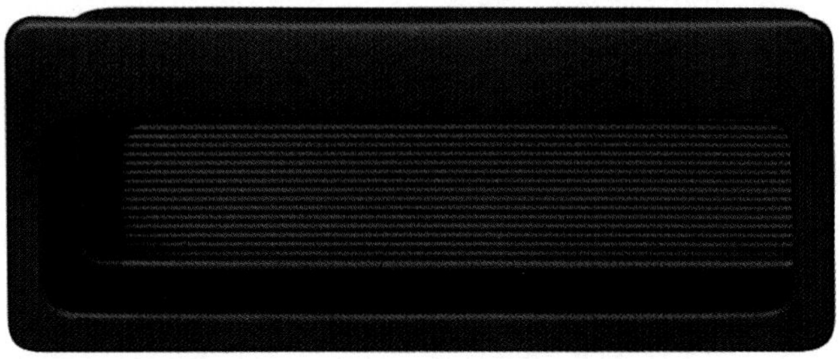

Steel black matt

Size A x B	Size C x D	Depth t	Cat. No.
75 x 32	69 x 26	9	151.00.311
100 x 39	93 x 32	11	151.00.320

Packing: 25 pcs.

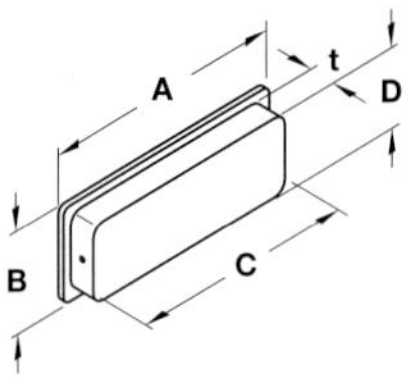

Zinc nickel plated matt
back aluminum, inside black

Cat. No.	151.09.609

Packing: 25 pcs.

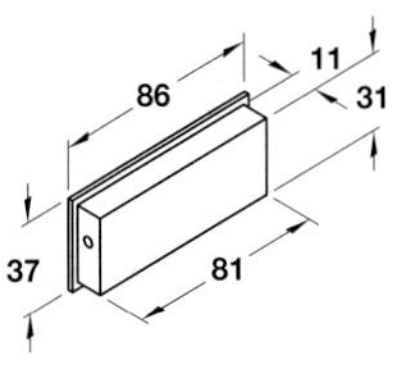

Dimensional data not binding.
We reserve the right to alter specifications without notice.

Metal Flush Handles

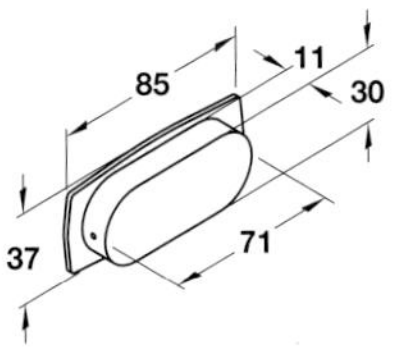

Brass, nickel plated matt
Back sheet steel; inside black

Cat. No.	151.12.606

Packing: 25 pcs.

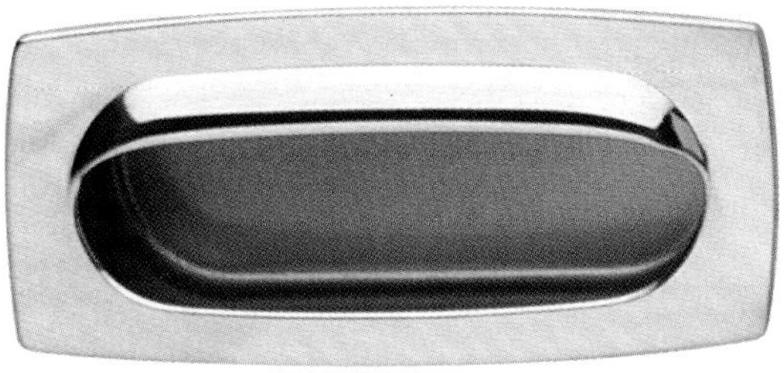

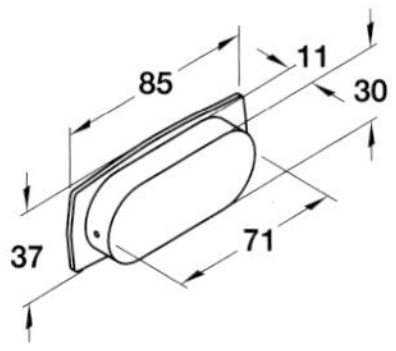

Brass polished
Back sheet steel; inside matt

Cat. No.	151.12.802

Packing: 25 pcs.

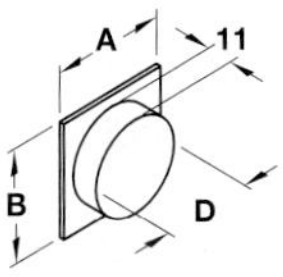

Brass, nickel plated, matt/ inside black

Size A x B	Diameter D	Cat. No.
47 x 47	39	151.04.613
57 x 57	47	151.04.622

Packing: 25 pcs.

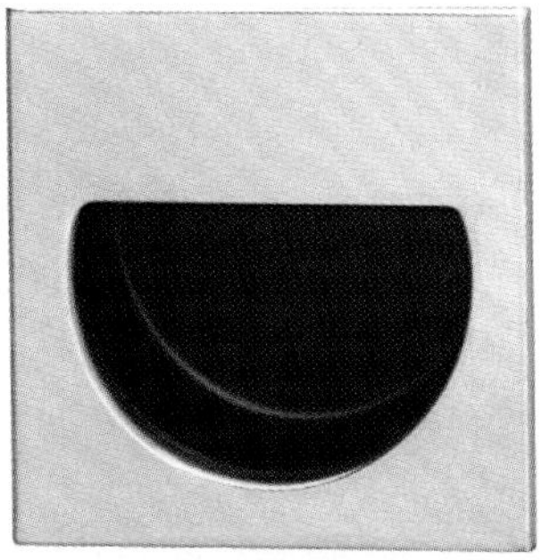

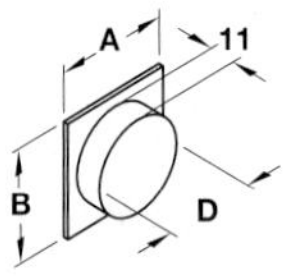

Brass polished/ inside black

Size A x B	Diameter D	Cat. No.
47 x 47	39	151.04.819
57 x 57	47	151.04.828

Packing: 25 pcs.

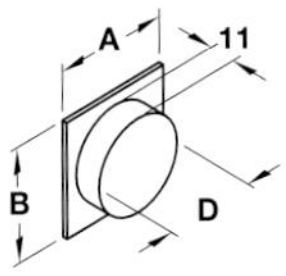

Brass black matt

Size A x B	Diameter D	Cat. No.
47 x 47	39	151.04.319
57 x 57	47	151.04.328

Packing: 25 pcs.

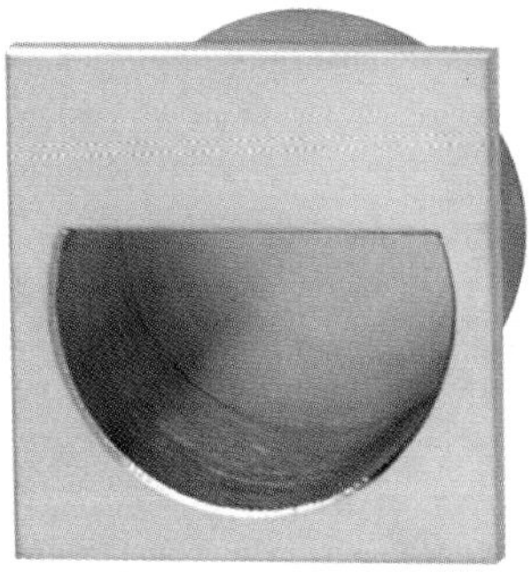

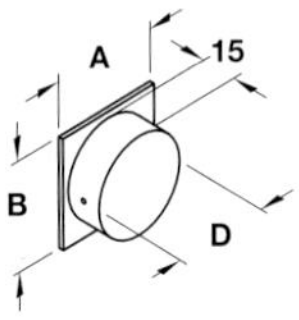

Brass, nickel plated, matt

Size A x B	Diameter D	Cat. No.
45 x 45	40	151.40.717
70 x 70	60	151.40.726

Packing: 25 pcs.

Round-head Metal Pins
Ø 0.9 mm

Finish: steel, nickel-plated

ø 0.9	Length	Cat. No.
	11 mm	076.40.217

Packing: 7400 pcs.

Round-head Metal Pins
Ø 0.9 mm

Finish: steel, brass-plated

ø 0.9	Length	Cat. No.
	11 mm	076.40.119

Packing: 7400 pcs.

Round-head Metal Pins
Ø 1.6 mm

Finish: steel, nickel-plated

ø 1.6	Length	Cat. No.
	15 mm	076.40.299

Packing: 2000 pcs.

Round-head Metal Pins
Ø 1.6 mm

Finish: steel, brass-plated

ø 1.6	Length	Cat. No.
	15 mm	076.40.191

Packing: 2150 pcs.

Dimensional data not binding.
We reserve the right to alter specifications without notice.

HÄFELE

Metal flush handles

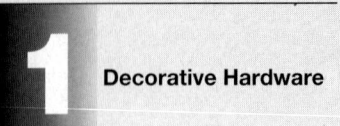

Round-head Metal Pins
Ø 0.9 mm

Finish: steel, nickel-plated

	Length	Cat. No.
Ø 0.9	11 mm	076.40.217

Packing: 7400 pcs.

Round-head Metal Pins
Ø 0.9 mm

Finish: steel, brass-plated

	Length	Cat. No.
Ø 0.9	11 mm	076.40.119

Packing: 7400 pcs.

Round-head Metal Pins
Ø 1.6 mm

Finish: steel, nickel-plated

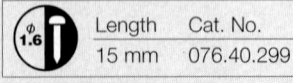

	Length	Cat. No.
Ø 1.6	15 mm	076.40.299

Packing: 2000 pcs.

Round-head Metal Pins
Ø 1.6 mm

Finish: steel, brass-plated

	Length	Cat. No.
Ø 1.6	15 mm	076.40.191

Packing: 2150 pcs.

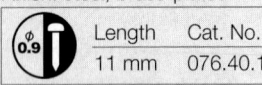

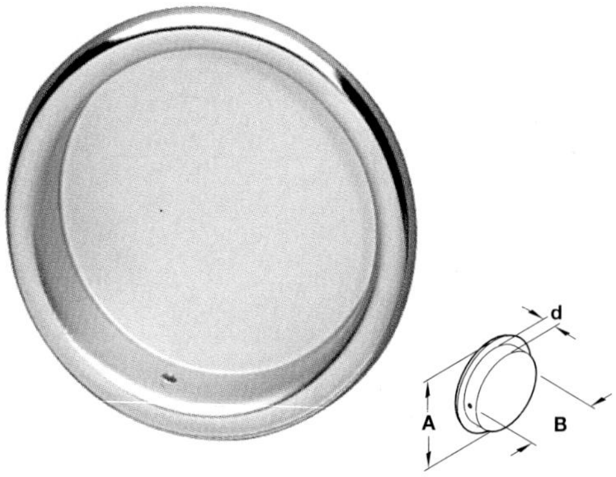

Sheet steel nickel plated polished/inside matt

Dimension A	Dimension B	Depth d	Cat. No.
30	25	7	153.20.715
40	33	8	153.20.724
55	45	8	153.20.733

Packing: 25 pcs.

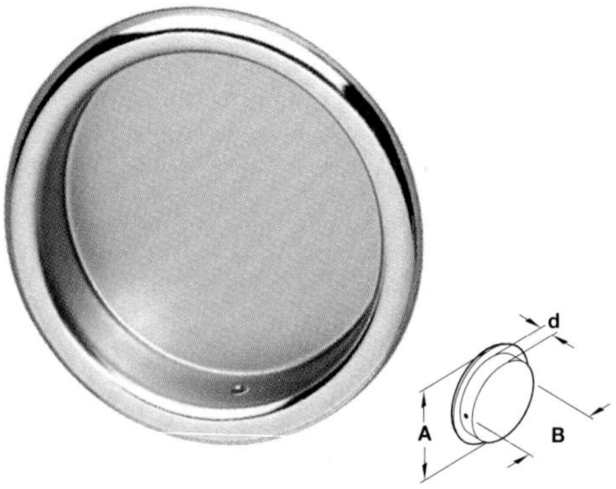

Sheet steel gold colored polished

Dimension A	Dimension B	Depth d	Cat. No.
30	25	7	153.20.519
40	33	8	153.20.528
55	45	8	153.20.537

Packing: 25 pcs.

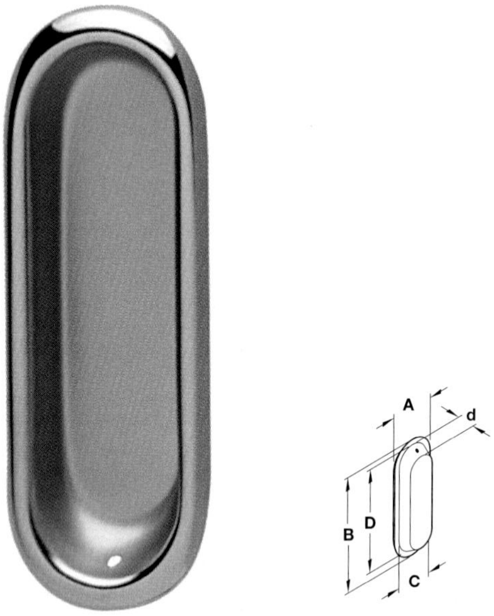

Sheet steel nickel plated polished/inside matt

Size A x B	Size C x D	Depth d	Cat. No.
25 x 75	18 x 68	7	152.00.727
32 x 88	23 x 77	8	152.00.736

Packing: 25 pcs.

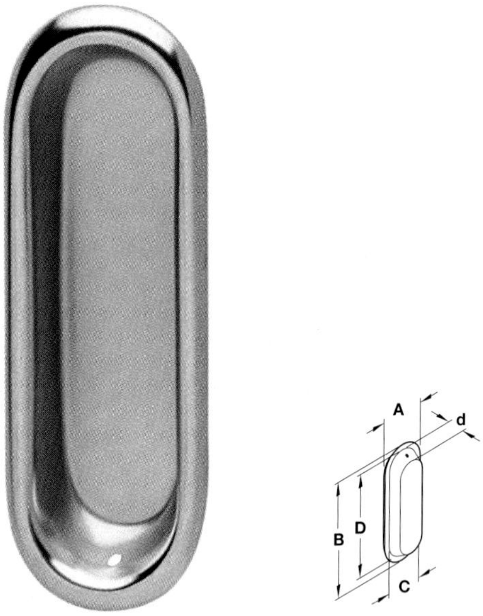

Sheet steel gold colored polished

SizeA x B	Size C x D	Depth d	Cat. No.
25 x 75	18 x 68	7	152.00.521
32 x 88	23 x 77	8	152.00.530

Packing: 25 pcs.

Dimensional data not binding.
We reserve the right to alter specifications without notice.

Metal Flush Handles

Zinc, chrome plated matt

Cat. No.	103.75.603

Packing: 25 pcs.

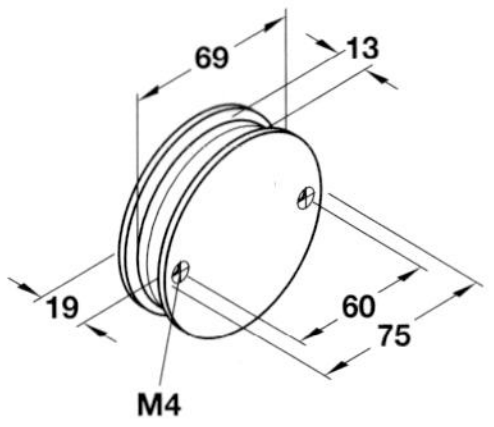

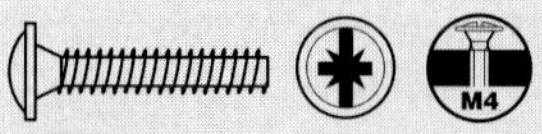

Threaded Screws M4
Combined slot, suitable for flat or cross blades

Finish: steel, zinc-plated

Length	Cat. No.
10 mm	022.35.109
12 mm	022.35.127
15 mm	022.35.154
18 mm	022.35.181
20 mm	022.35.207
22 mm	022.35.225
23 mm	022.35.234
25 mm	022.35.252
28 mm	022.35.289
30 mm	022.35.305
35 mm	022.35.350
38 mm	022.35.387
40 mm	022.35.403
45 mm	022.35.458
50 mm	022.35.501
60 mm	022.35.609

Packing: 100 and 1000 pcs.

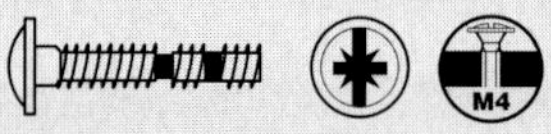

Threaded Breakoff Screw M4
Combined slot, suitable for flat or cross blades

Finish: steel, zinc-plated

Length	Cat. No.
1 3/4" x 3/4"	022.35.887

Packing: 100 and 1000 pcs.

HÄFELE

Wood Flush Handles

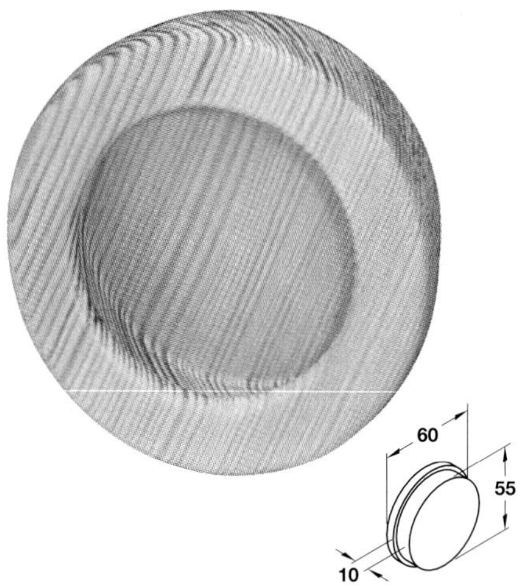

Pine

Cat. No.	191.67.009

Packing: 25 pcs.

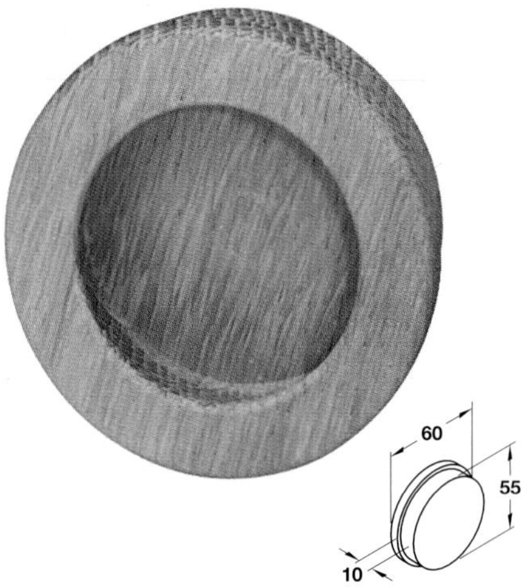

Oak

Cat. No.	191.67.401

Packing: 25 pcs.

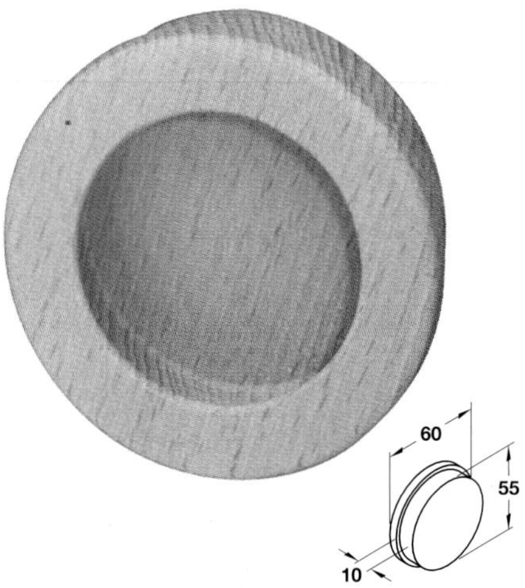

Beech

Cat. No.	191.67.303

Packing: 25 pcs.

Plastic Flush Handles

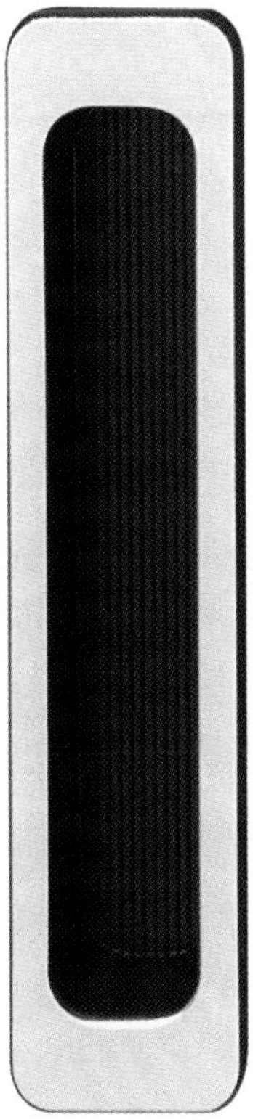

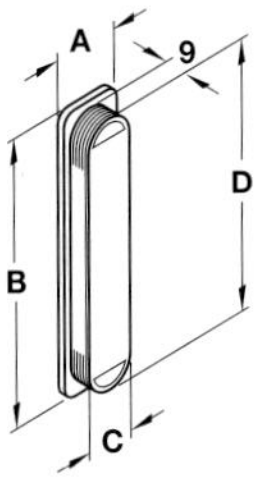

Plastic gold colored matt/inside dark brown

Size A x B	Size C x D	Cat. No.
26 x 116	20 x 110	158.43.526

Packing: 100 pcs.

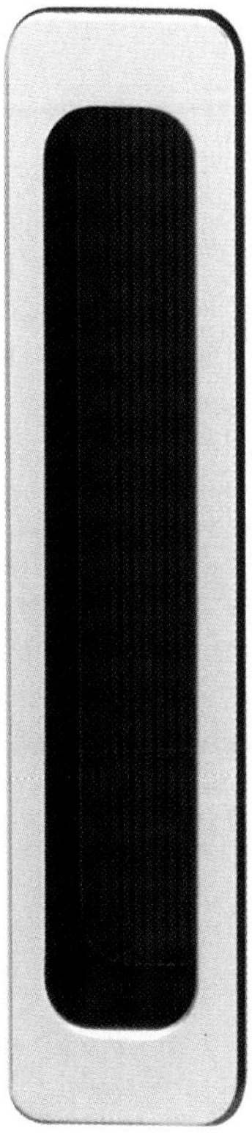

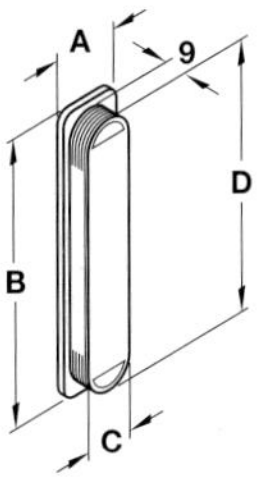

Plastic silver colored matt/inside black

Size A x B	Size C x D	Cat. No.
26 x 85	20 x 75	158.42.921
26 x 116	20 x 110	158.43.928

Packing: 100 pcs.

Plastic silver colored matt/inside black

Cat. No.	158.44.925

Packing: 100 pcs.

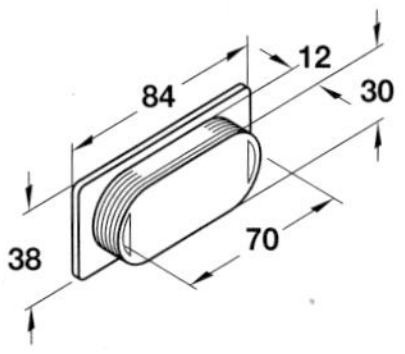

HÄFELE

HEWI Recessed Pulls

Countersunk wood screws
Finish: brass, unfinished

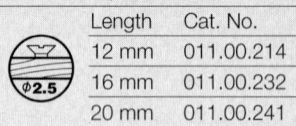

	Length	Cat. No.
⌀2.5	12 mm	011.00.214
	16 mm	011.00.232
	20 mm	011.00.241

Packing: 200 pcs.

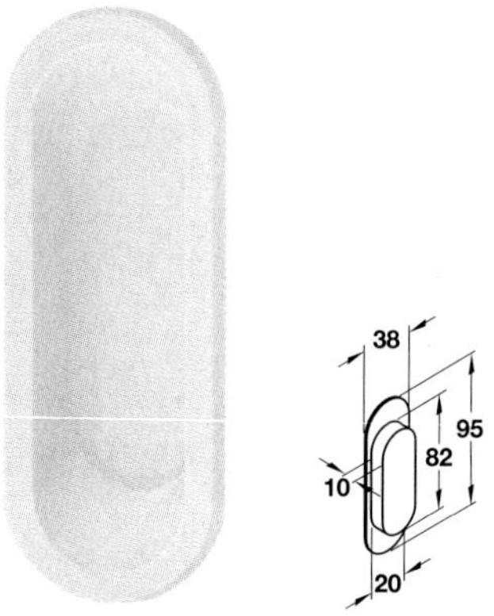

Nylon

Cat. No.	158.90.0..

Packing: 25 pcs.

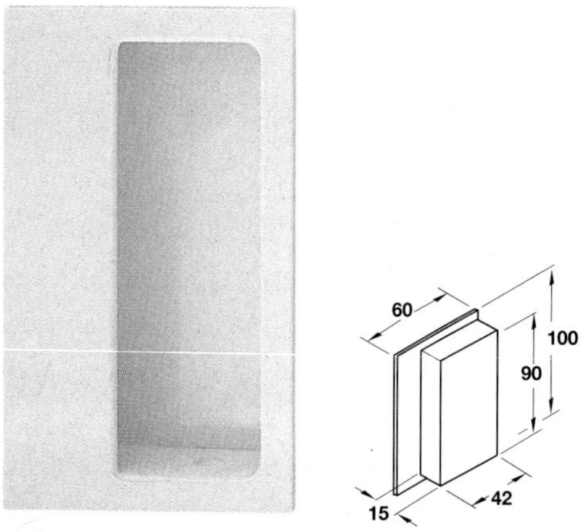

Nylon

Cat. No.	158.80.0..

Packing: 25 pcs.

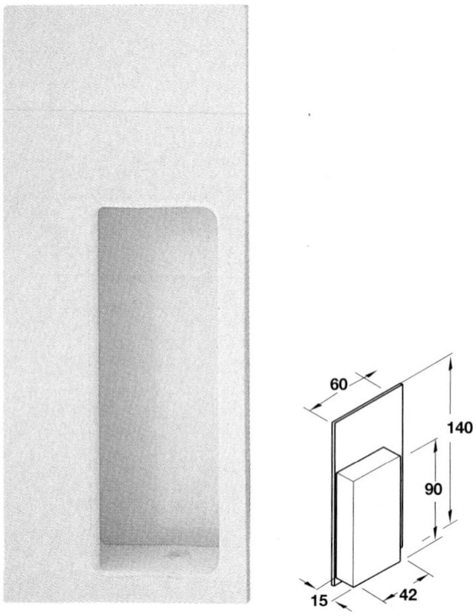

Nylon

Cat. No.	158.89.1..

Packing: 25 pcs.

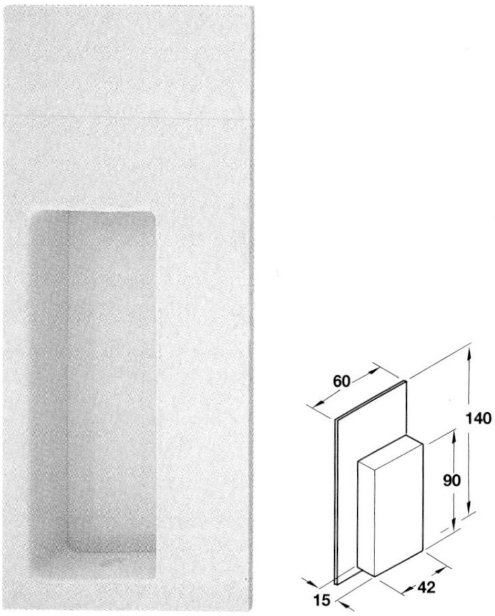

Nylon

Cat. No.	158.89.2..

Packing: 25 pcs.

Ordering tip: replace the decimals (. .) in the catalog number with the color number of your choice.

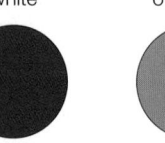

01 white	21 off white	20 grey	08 black	12 yellow	33 red
52 blue	06 green	09 dark brown	50 dark blue	30 dark red	60 dark green

Dimensional data not binding. We reserve the right to alter specifications without notice.

Dimensions in mm

HEWI Nylon Flush Pulls

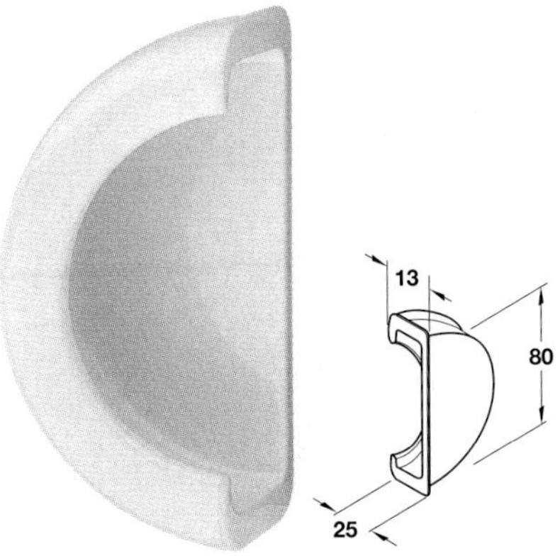

Nylon

Cat. No.	158.73.0..

Packing: 25 pcs.

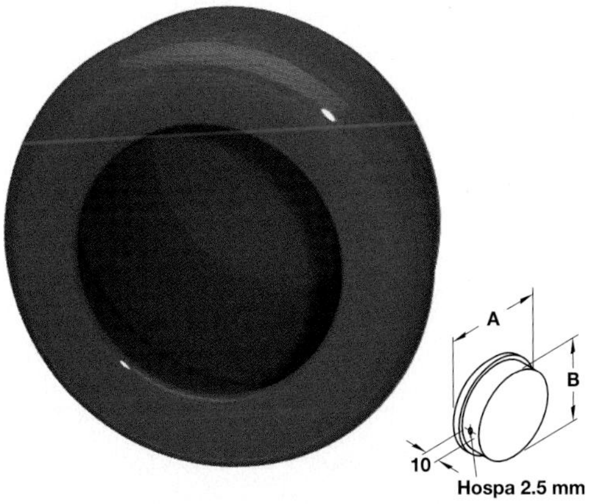

Nylon

Diameter A	Diameter B	Artikel-Nr.
60	55	158.80.1..
75	70	158.80.2..
90	85	158.80.3..

Packing: 25 pcs.

- When using 158.73.0 series in a pair, creates a full round.

Countersunk wood screws
Finish: brass, unfinished

	Length	Cat. No.
Φ2.5	12 mm	011.00.214
	16 mm	011.00.232
	20 mm	011.00.241

Packing: 200 pcs.

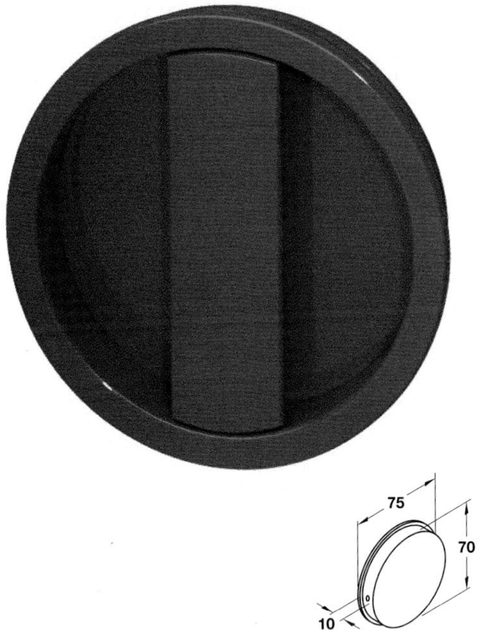

Nylon

Cat. No.	158.85.0..

Packing: 25 pcs.

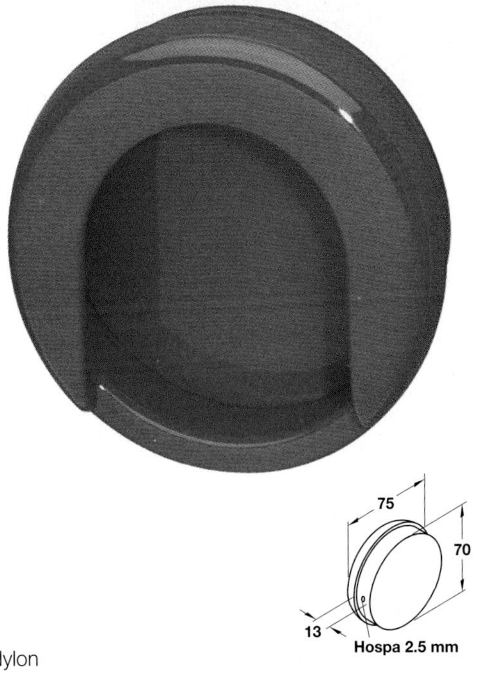

Nylon

Cat. No.	158.75.0..

Packing: 25 pcs.

Ordering tip: replace the decimals (. .) in the catalog number with the color number of your choice.

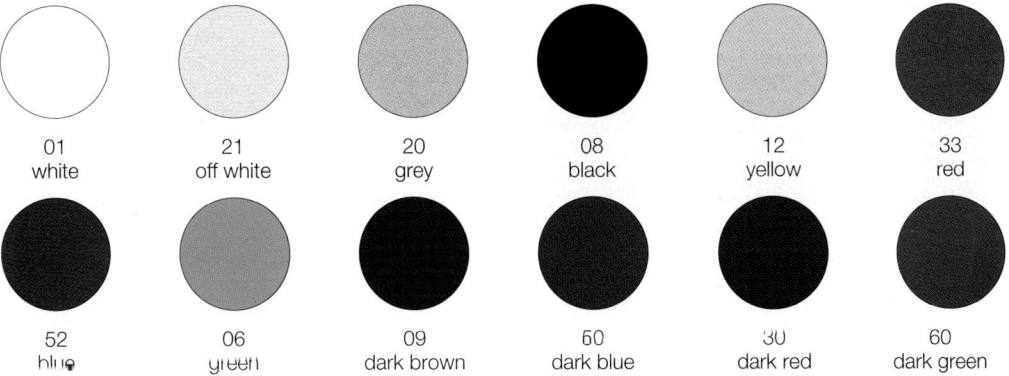

01 white
21 off white
20 grey
08 black
12 yellow
33 red
52 blue
06 green
09 dark brown
50 dark blue
30 dark red
60 dark green

Dimensional data not binding. We reserve the right to alter specifications without notice.

Dimensions in mm

HÄFELE

Plastic flush handles

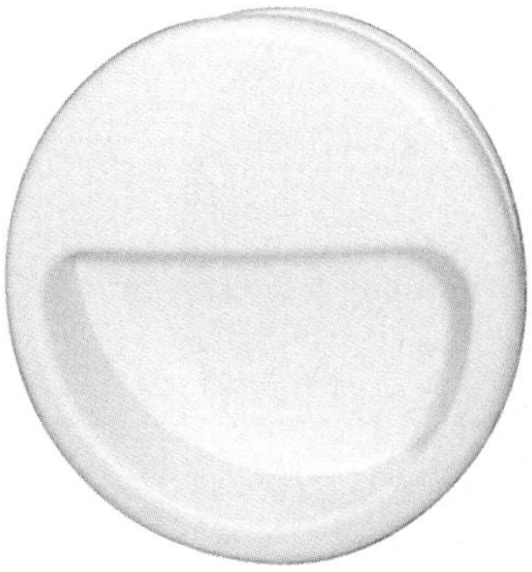

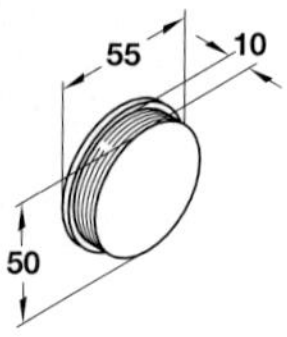

White

Cat. No.	158.23.702

Packing: 25 pcs.

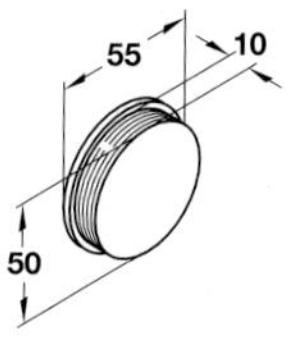

Chrome plated polished/inside black

Cat. No.	158.23.211

Packing: 25 pcs.

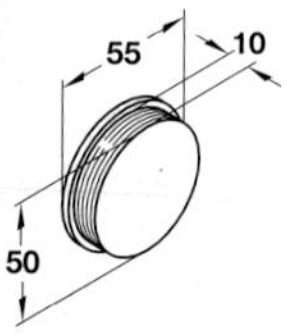

Black

Cat. No.	158.23.300

Packing: 25 pcs.

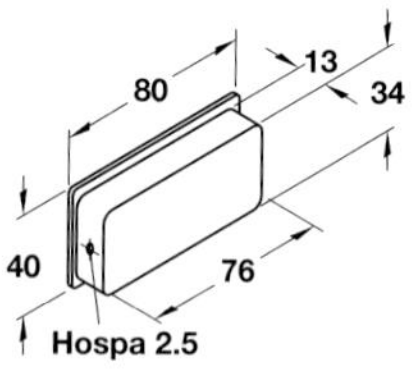

White

Cat. No.	129.57.701

Packing: 25 pcs.

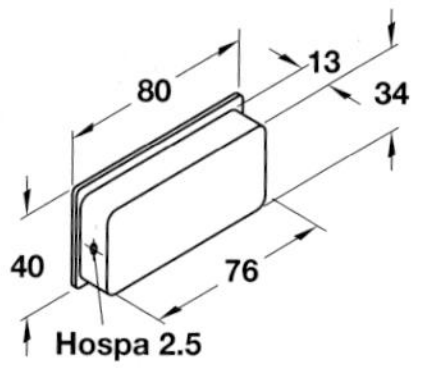

Black

Cat. No.	129.57.603

Packing: 25 pcs.

Countersunk wood screws
Finish: brass, unfinished

	Length	Cat. No.
⌀2.5	12 mm	011.00.214
	16 mm	011.00.232
	20 mm	011.00.241

Packing: 200 pcs.

Plastic Flush Handles

Black

Cat. No.	129.67.609

Packing: 25 pcs.

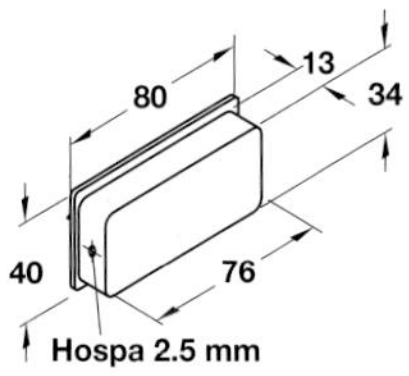

Light grey

Cat. No.	129.39.507

Packing: 25 pcs.

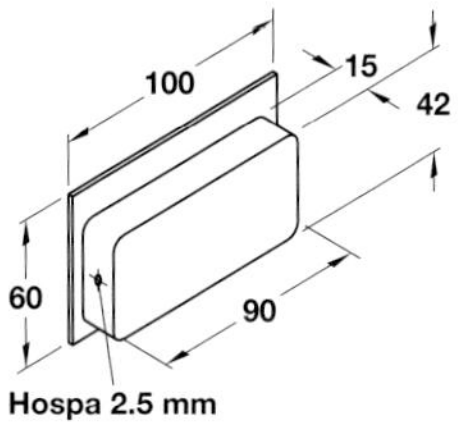

Black

Cat. No.	129.39.605

Packing: 25 pcs.

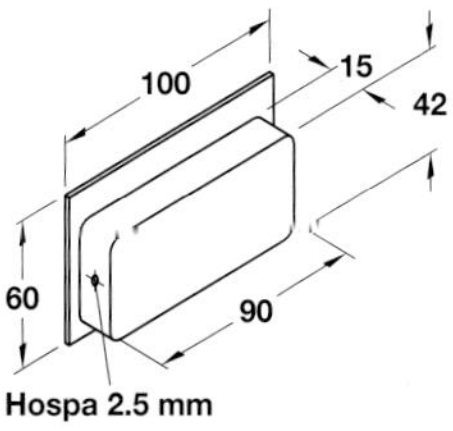

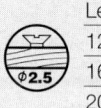

Countersunk wood screws
Finish: brass, unfinished

ϕ2.5	Length	Cat. No.
	12 mm	011.00.214
	16 mm	011.00.232
	20 mm	011.00.241

Packing: 200 pcs.

Dimensional data not binding.
We reserve the right to alter specifications without notice.

HÄFELE

Plastic Flush Handles

Round-head Metal Pins Ø 1.6 mm

Finish: steel, nickel-plated

Length	Cat. No.
15 mm	076.40.299

Packing: 2000 pcs.

Round-head Metal Pins Ø 1.6 mm

Finish: steel, brass-plated

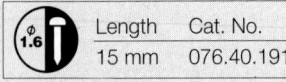

Length	Cat. No.
15 mm	076.40.191

Packing: 2150 pcs.

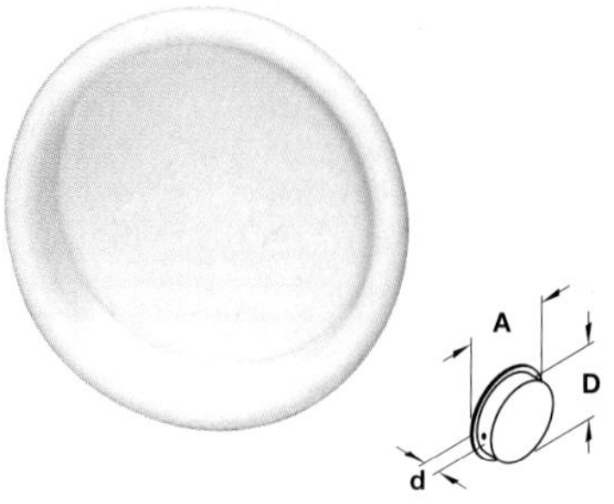

White

Diameter A	Diameter D	Depth d	Cat. No.
30	25	6	158.30.216
40	36	9	158.30.225

Packing: 25 pcs.

Black

Cat. No.	158.20.630

Packing: 50 pcs.

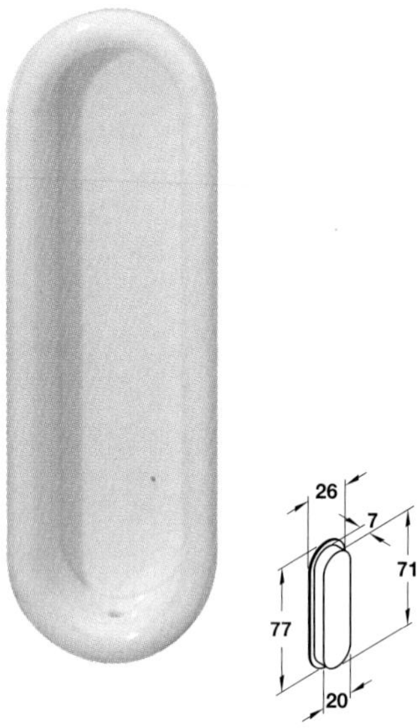

White

Cat. No.	158.03.737

Packing: 500 pcs.

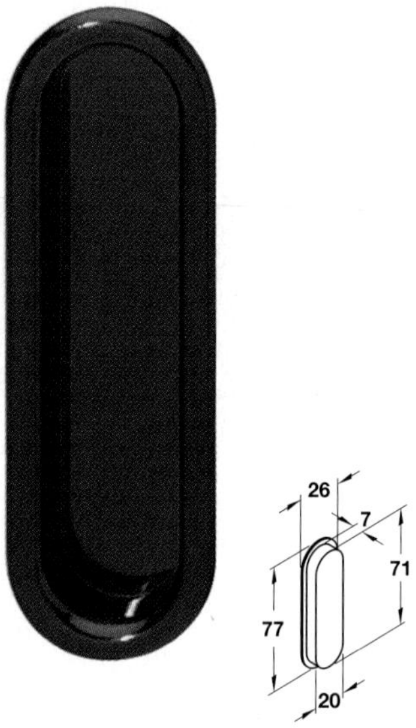

Black

Cat. No.	158.03.639

Packing: 500 pcs.

Plastic Flush Handles

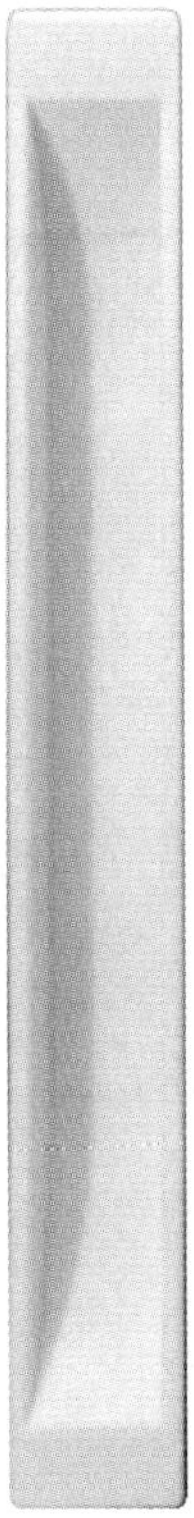

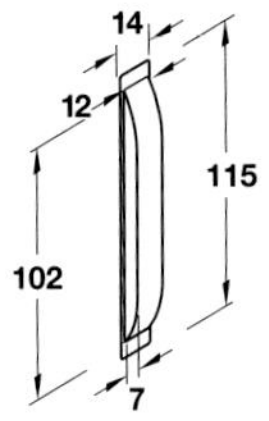

White

Cat. No.	158.05.704

Packing: 100 pcs.

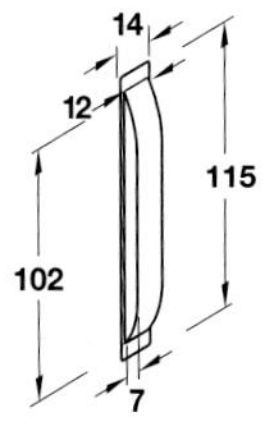

Brown

Cat. No.	158.05.106

Packing: 100 pcs.

HÄFELE

Wood Handles

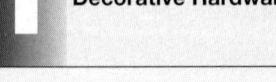

Threaded Screws 8-32
Combined slot, suitable for flat or cross blades
Finish: steel, yellow chromated

Length	Cat. No.
22 mm	022.25.229
25 mm	022.25.256
32 mm	022.25.327
38 mm	022.25.381
45 mm	022.25.452

Packing: 100 and 1000 pcs.

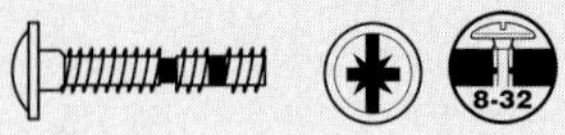

Threaded Breakoff Screw 8-32
Combined slot, suitable for flat or cross blades
Finish: steel, yellow chromated

Length	Cat. No.
1 3/4" x 3/4"	022.25.881

Packing: 100 and 1000 pcs.

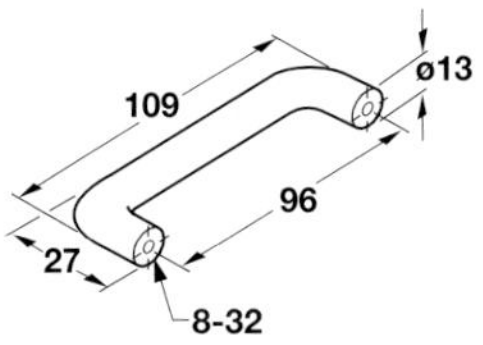

Maple

Cat. No.	193.41.121

Packing: 25 pcs.

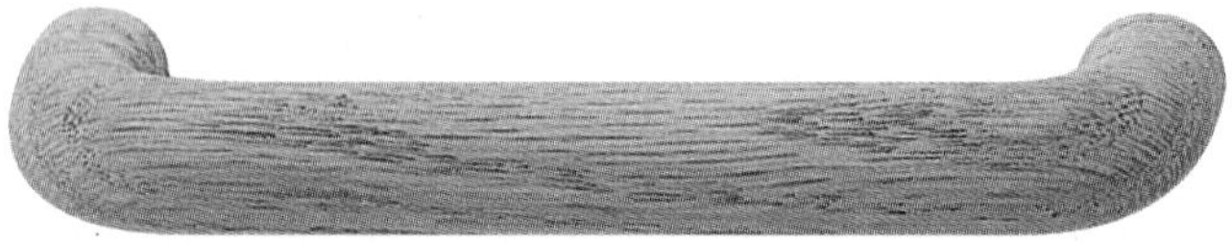

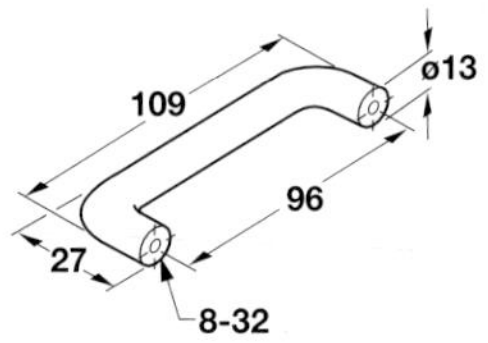

Red oak

Cat. No.	193.41.425

Packing: 25 pcs.

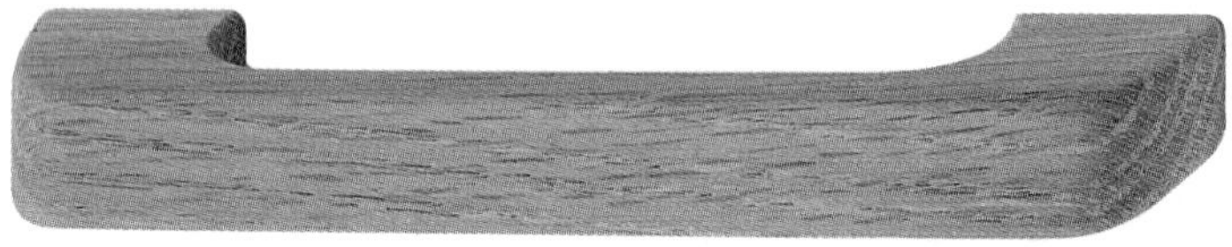

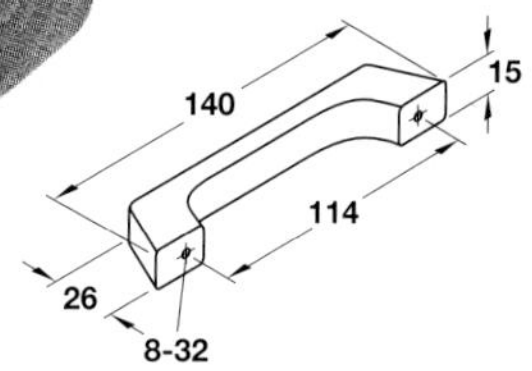

Red oak

Cat. No.	193.33.469

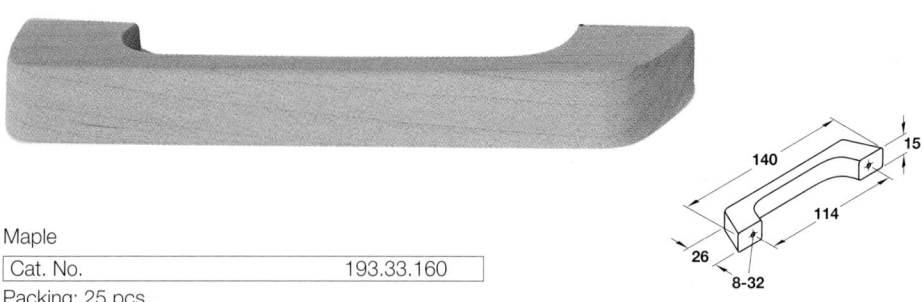

Packing: 25 pcs.

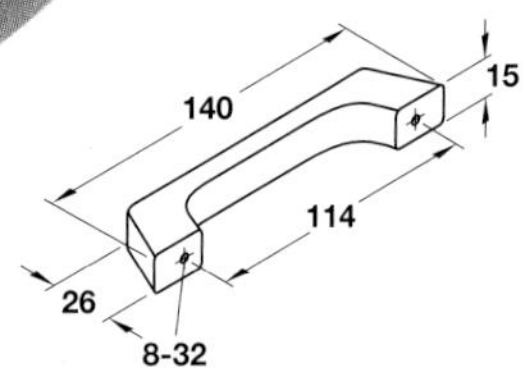

Maple

Cat. No.	193.33.160

Packing: 25 pcs.

Dimensional data not binding.
We reserve the right to alter specifications without notice.

Wood Handles

HÄFELE

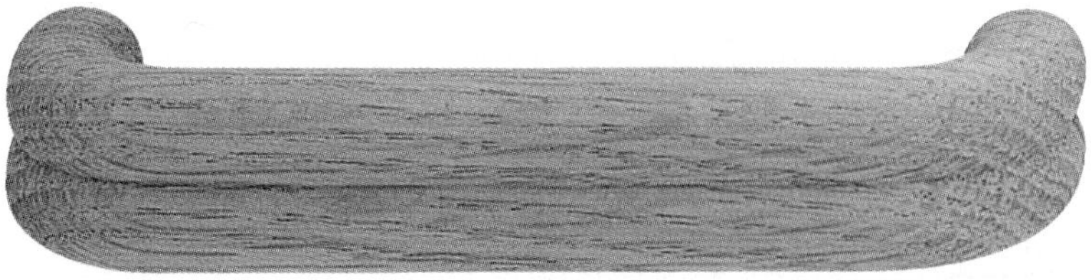

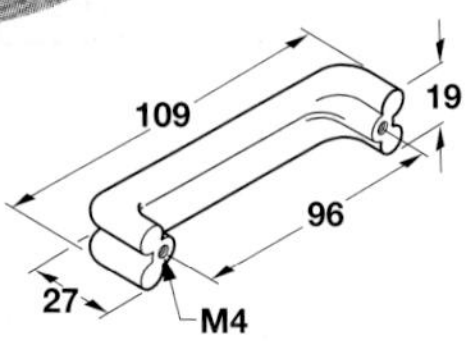

Red Oak

Cat. No.	193.65.452

Packing: 25 pcs.

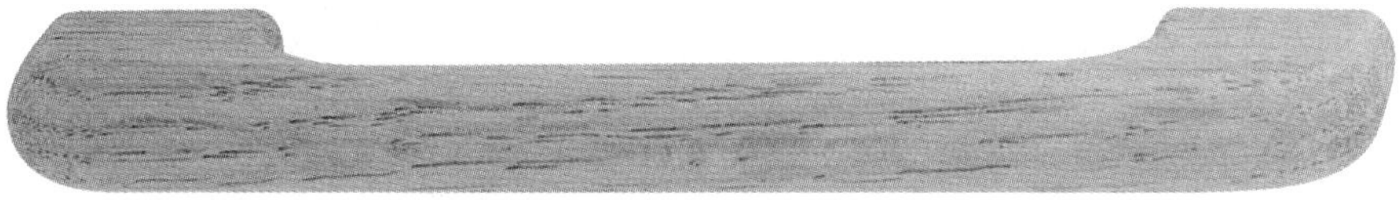

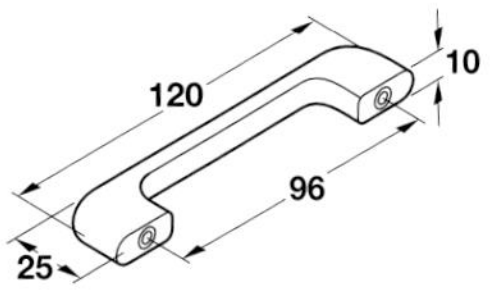

Red Oak

Cat. No.	193.64.455

Packing: 25 pcs.

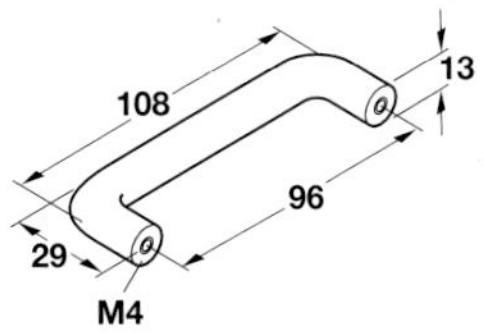

Red Oak

Cat. No.	193.41.470

Packing: 25 pcs.

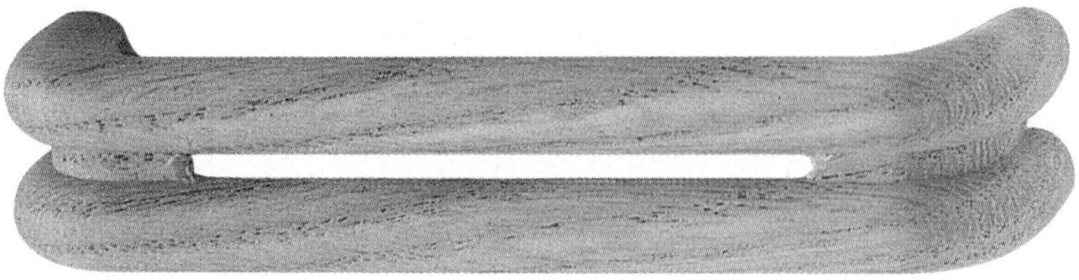

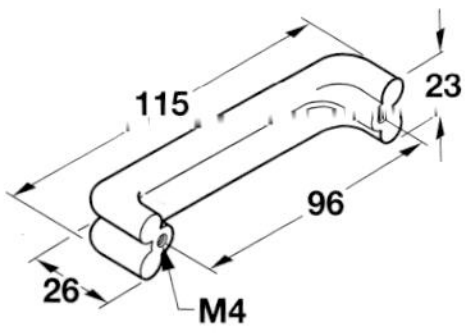

Red oak

Cat. No.	193.65.461

Packing: 25 pcs.

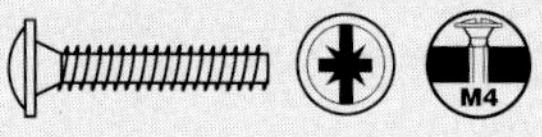

Threaded Screws M4
Combined slot, suitable for flat or cross blades

Finish: steel, zinc-plated

Length	Cat. No.
10 mm	022.35.109
12 mm	022.35.127
15 mm	022.35.154
18 mm	022.35.181
20 mm	022.35.207
22 mm	022.35.225
23 mm	022.35.234
25 mm	022.35.252
28 mm	022.35.289
30 mm	022.35.305
35 mm	022.35.350
38 mm	022.35.387
40 mm	022.35.403
45 mm	022.35.458
50 mm	022.35.501
60 mm	022.35.609

Packing: 100 and 1000 pcs.

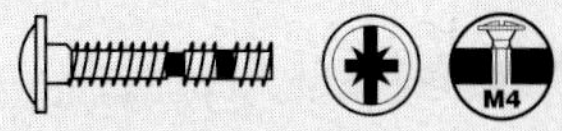

Threaded Breakoff Screw M4
Combined slot, suitable for flat or cross blades

Finish: steel, zinc-plated

Length	Cat. No.
1 3/4" x 3/4"	022.35.887

Packing: 100 and 1000 pcs.

Dimensional data not binding.
We reserve the right to alter specifications without notice.

HÄFELE

Wood handles

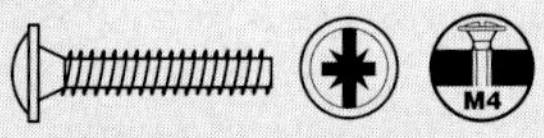

Threaded Screws M4
Combined slot, suitable for flat or cross blades

Finish: steel, zinc-plated

Length	Cat. No.
10 mm	022.35.109
12 mm	022.35.127
15 mm	022.35.154
18 mm	022.35.181
20 mm	022.35.207
22 mm	022.35.225
23 mm	022.35.234
25 mm	022.35.252
28 mm	022.35.289
30 mm	022.35.305
35 mm	022.35.350
38 mm	022.35.387
40 mm	022.35.403
45 mm	022.35.458
50 mm	022.35.501
60 mm	022.35.609

Packing: 100 and 1000 pcs.

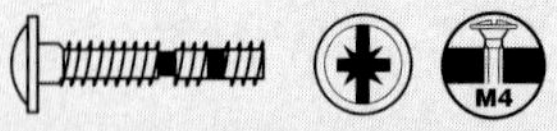

Threaded Breakoff Screw M4
Combined slot, suitable for flat or cross blades

Finish: steel, zinc-plated

Length	Cat. No.
1 3/4" x 3/4"	022.35.887

Packing: 100 and 1000 pcs.

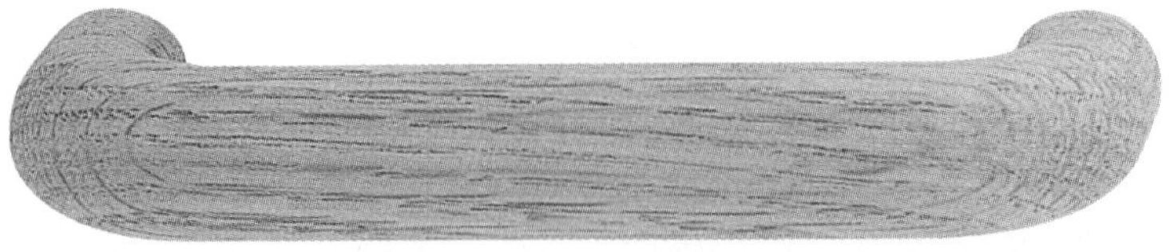

Red Oak

Cat. No.	193.34.475

Packing: 25 pcs.

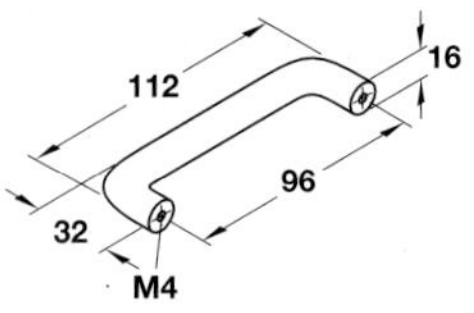

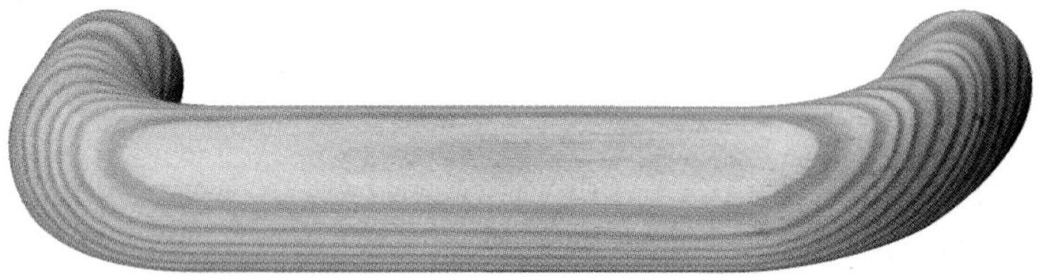

Pine

Cat. No.	193.34.028

Packing: 25 pcs.

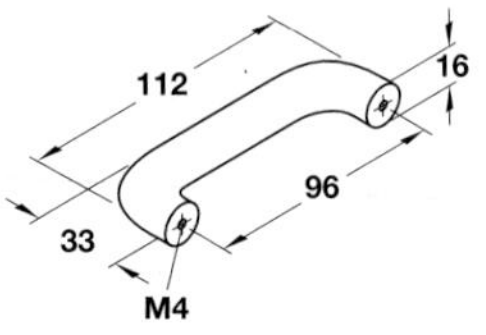

White oak

Cat. No.	193.34.420

Packing: 25 pcs.

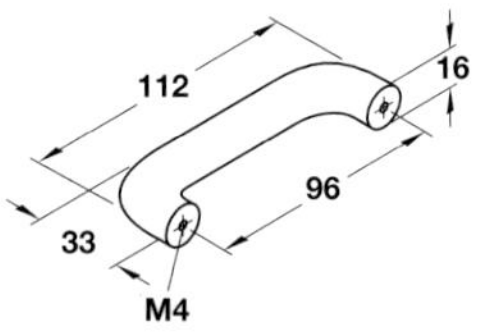

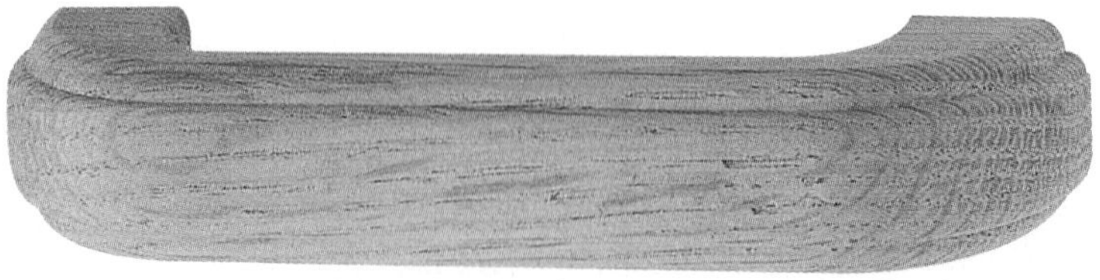

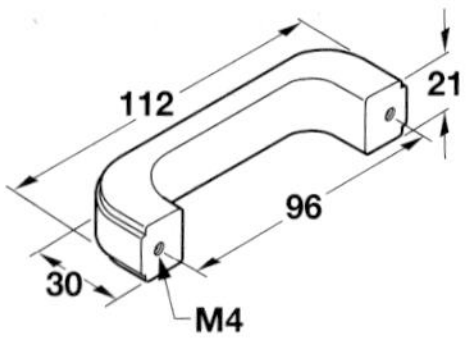

Red oak

Cat. No.	193.72.457

Packing: 25 pcs.

Dimensional data not binding.
We reserve the right to alter specifications without notice.

Wood handles

White Oak

Cat. No.	193.10.411

Packing: 25 pcs.

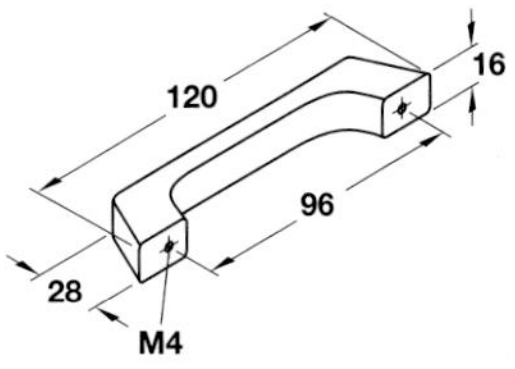

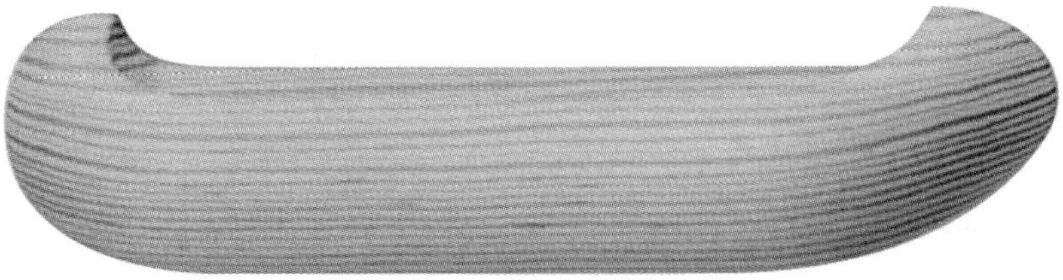

Pine

Cat. No.	193.54.002

Packing: 25 pcs.

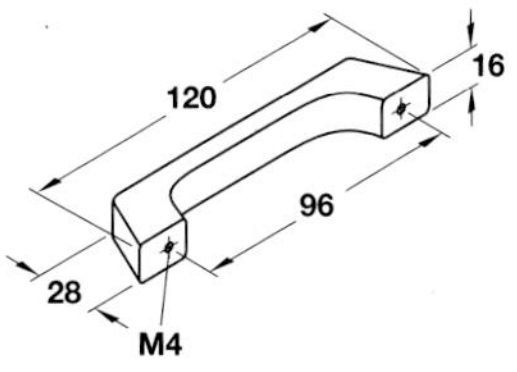

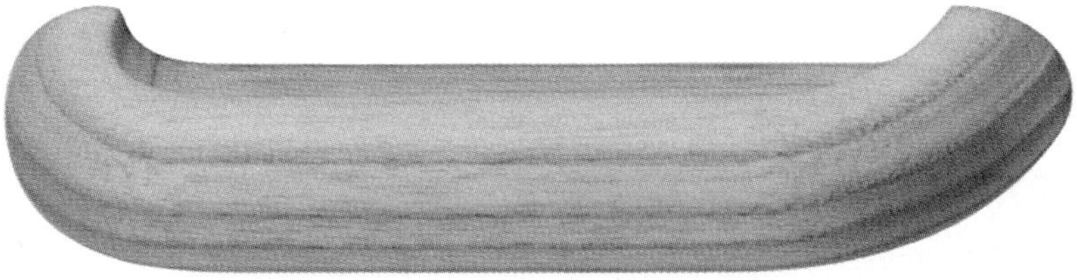

Ash

Cat. No.	193.54.502

Packing: 25 pcs.

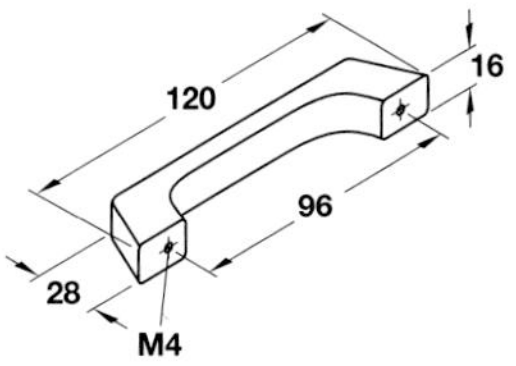

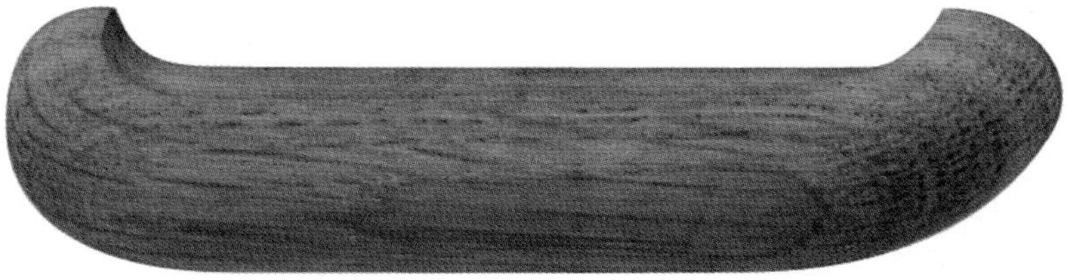

White oak

Cat. No.	193.54.404

Packing: 25 pcs.

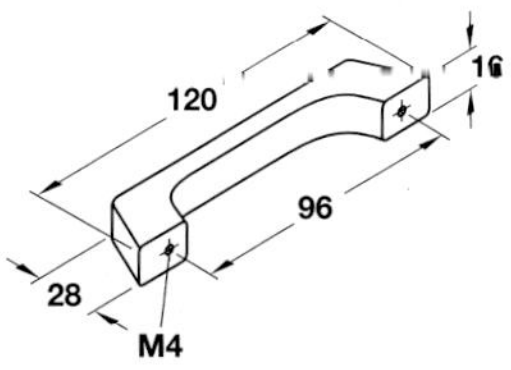

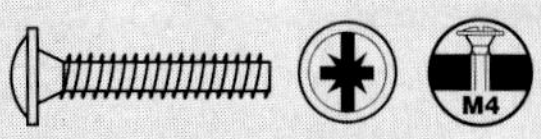

Threaded Screws M4
Combined slot, suitable for flat or cross blades

Finish: steel, zinc-plated

Length	Cat. No.
10 mm	022.35.109
12 mm	022.35.127
15 mm	022.35.154
18 mm	022.35.181
20 mm	022.35.207
22 mm	022.35.225
23 mm	022.35.234
25 mm	022.35.252
28 mm	022.35.289
30 mm	022.35.305
35 mm	022.35.350
38 mm	022.35.387
40 mm	022.35.403
45 mm	022.35.458
50 mm	022.35.501
60 mm	022.35.609

Packing: 100 and 1000 pcs.

Threaded Breakoff Screw M4
Combined slot, suitable for flat or cross blades

Finish: steel, zinc-plated

Length	Cat. No.
1 3/4" x 3/4"	022.35.887

Packing: 100 and 1000 pcs.

HÄFELE

Wood handles

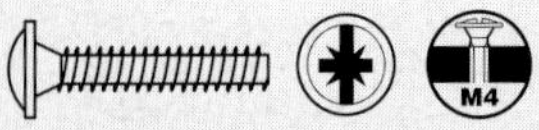

Threaded Screws M4
Combined slot, suitable for flat or cross blades
Finish: steel, zinc-plated

Length	Cat. No.
10 mm	022.35.109
12 mm	022.35.127
15 mm	022.35.154
18 mm	022.35.181
20 mm	022.35.207
22 mm	022.35.225
23 mm	022.35.234
25 mm	022.35.252
28 mm	022.35.289
30 mm	022.35.305
35 mm	022.35.350
38 mm	022.35.387
40 mm	022.35.403
45 mm	022.35.458
50 mm	022.35.501
60 mm	022.35.609

Packing: 100 and 1000 pcs.

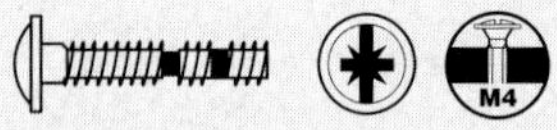

Threaded Breakoff Screw M4
Combined slot, suitable for flat or cross blades
Finish: steel, zinc-plated

Length	Cat. No.
1 3/4" x 3/4"	022.35.887

Packing: 100 and 1000 pcs.

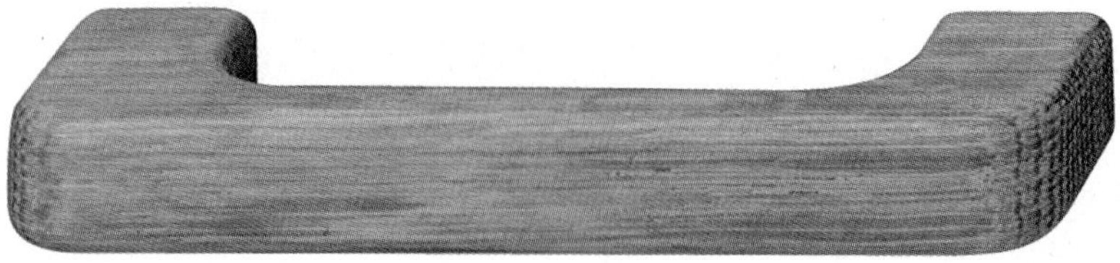

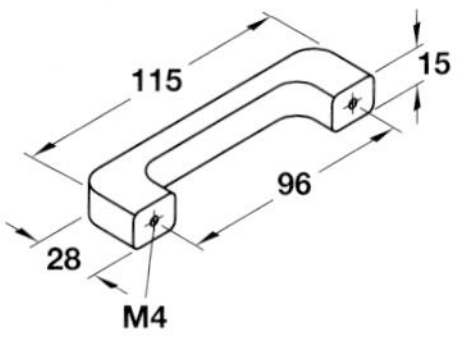

White oak

Cat. No.	193.13.403

Packing: 25 pcs.

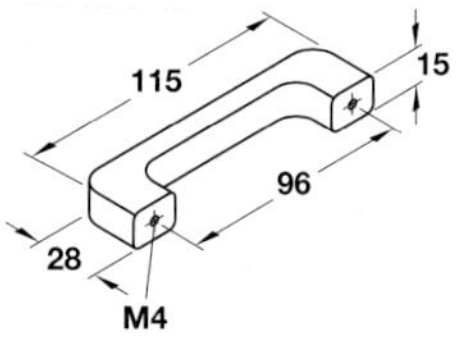

Beech

Cat. No.	193.13.305

Packing: 25 pcs.

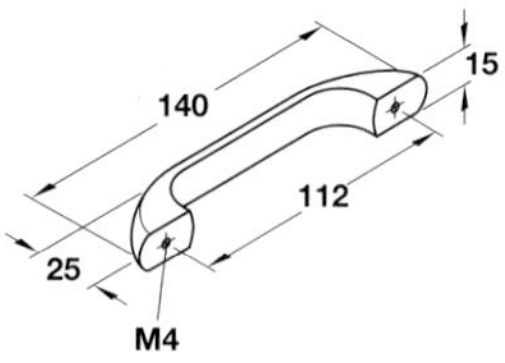

White oak

Cat. No.	193.15.407

Packing: 25 pcs.

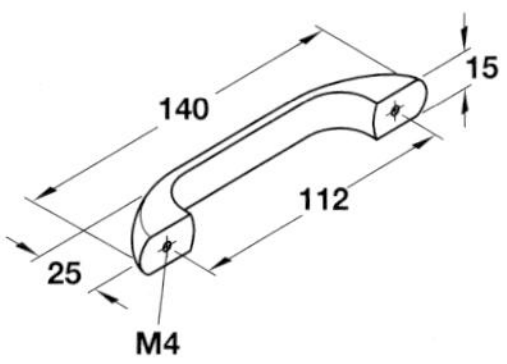

Beech

Cat. No.	193.15.309

Packing: 25 pcs.

Dimensional data not binding.
We reserve the right to alter specifications without notice.

Wood Handles

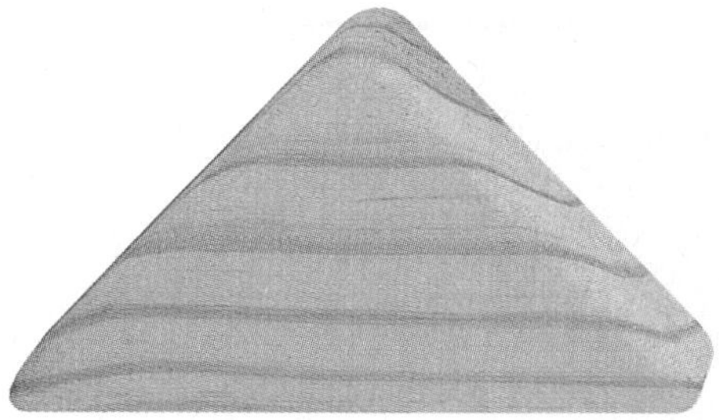

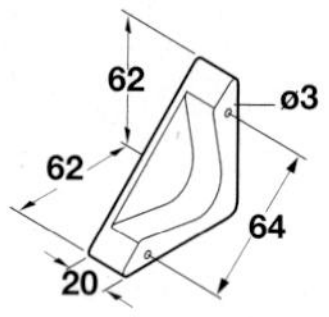

Pine

Cat. No.	193.23.007

Packing: 25 pcs.

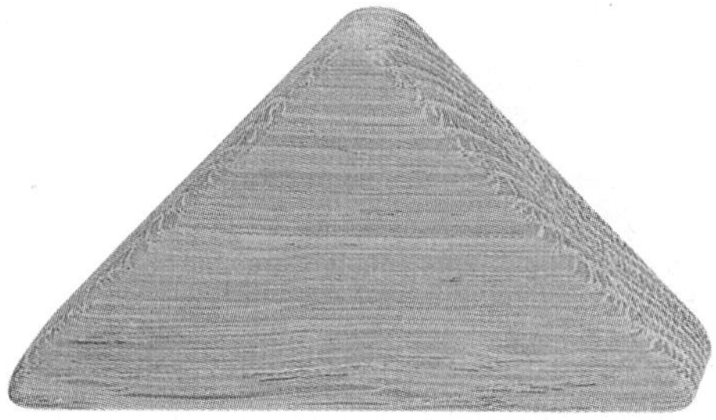

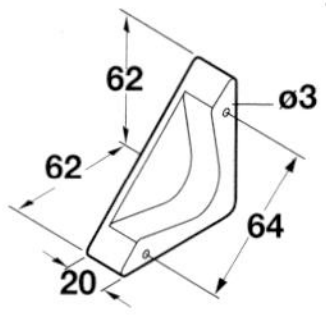

Red Oak

Cat. No.	193.23.409

Packing: 25 pcs.

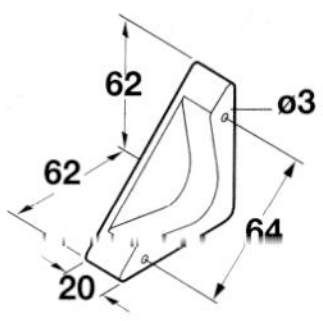

Beech black painted

Cat. No.	193.23.356

Packing: 25 pcs.

Hospa Pan Head Screws
Pozi Recess

Finish: steel, zinc-plated

Length	Cat. No.
13 mm	015.71.811
15 mm	015.71.820
17 mm	015.71.839
20 mm	015.71.848
25 mm	015.71.857
30 mm	015.71.866
35 mm	015.71.875
40 mm	015.71.884
45 mm	015.71.893

Packing: 1000 pcs.

HÄFELE

Wood Surface Mounted Handles

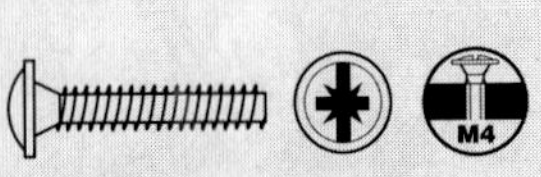

Threaded Screws M4

Combined slot, suitable for flat or cross blades

Finish: steel, zinc-plated

Length	Cat. No.
10 mm	022.35.109
12 mm	022.35.127
15 mm	022.35.154
18 mm	022.35.181
20 mm	022.35.207
22 mm	022.35.225
23 mm	022.35.234
25 mm	022.35.252
28 mm	022.35.289
30 mm	022.35.305
35 mm	022.35.350
38 mm	022.35.387
40 mm	022.35.403
45 mm	022.35.458
50 mm	022.35.501
60 mm	022.35.609

Packing: 100 and 1000 pcs.

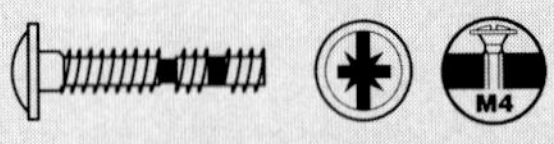

Threaded Breakoff Screw M4

Combined slot, suitable for flat or cross blades

Finish: steel, zinc-plated

Length	Cat. No.
1 3/4" x 3/4"	022.35.887

Packing: 100 and 1000 pcs.

Pine

Cat. No.	192.26.003

Packing: 25 pcs.

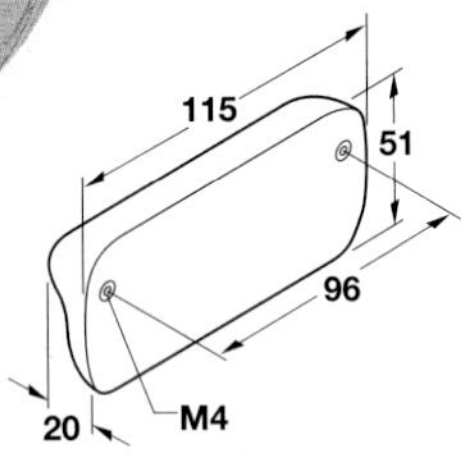

White oak

Cat. No.	192.26.405

Packing: 25 pcs.

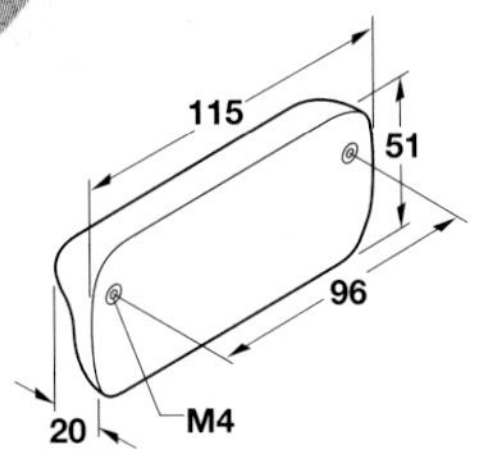

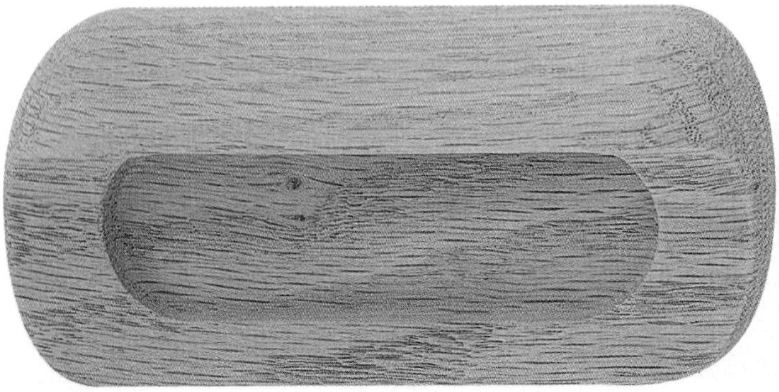

Red Oak

Cat. No.	192.26.450

Packing: 25 pcs.

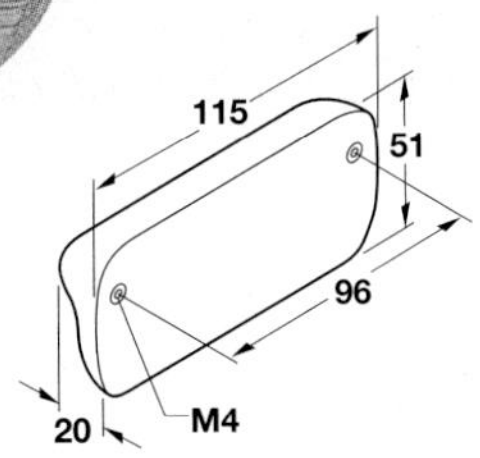

Dimensional data not binding.
We reserve the right to alter specifications without notice.

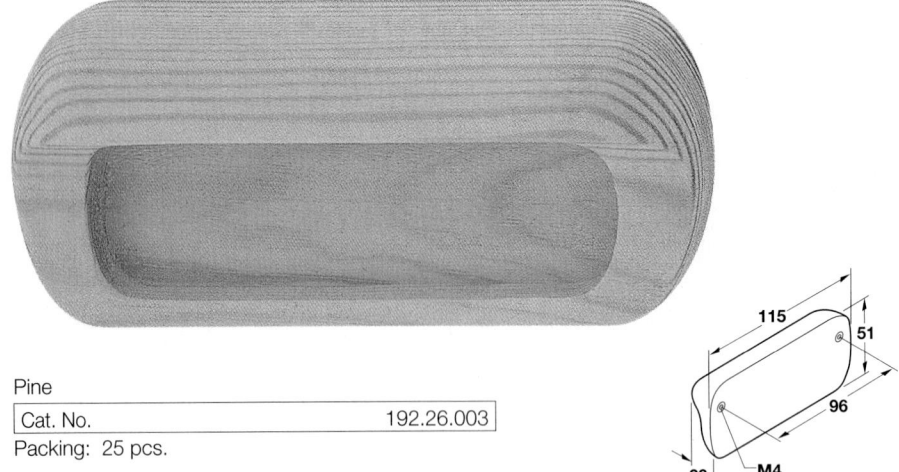

Wood surface mounted handles

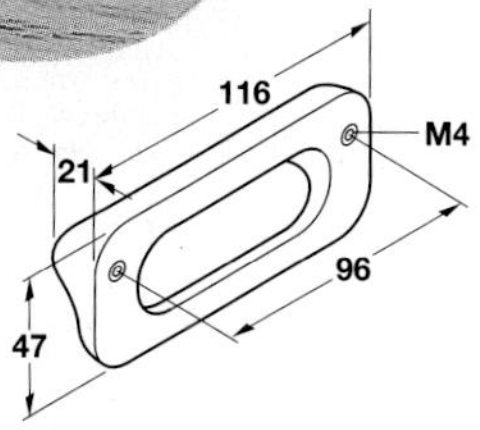

Red Oak

Cat. No.	192.48.456

Packing: 25 pcs.

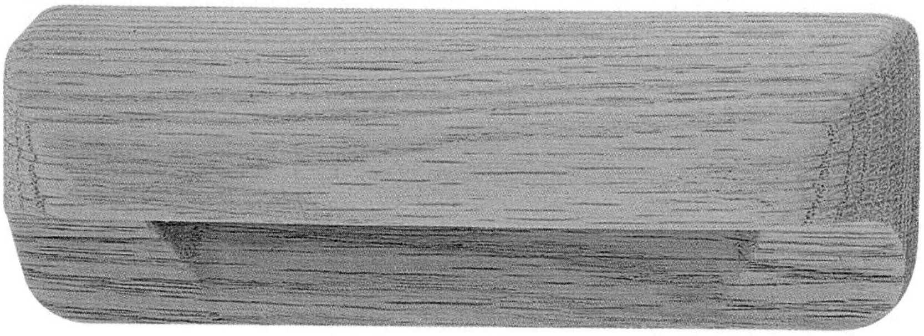

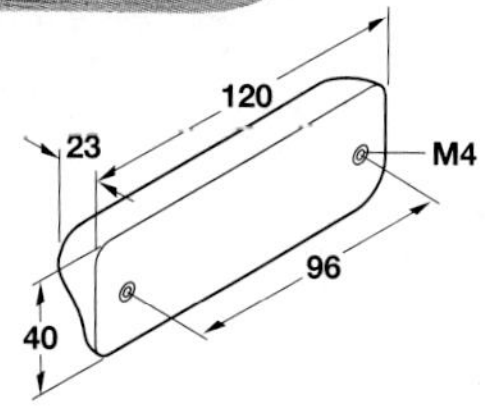

Red Oak

Cat. No.	192.49.453

Packing: 25 pcs.

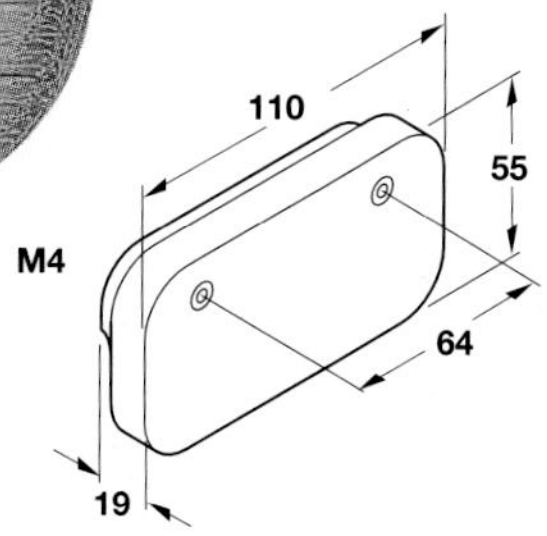

Red Oak

Cat. No.	192.25.453

Packing: 25 pcs.

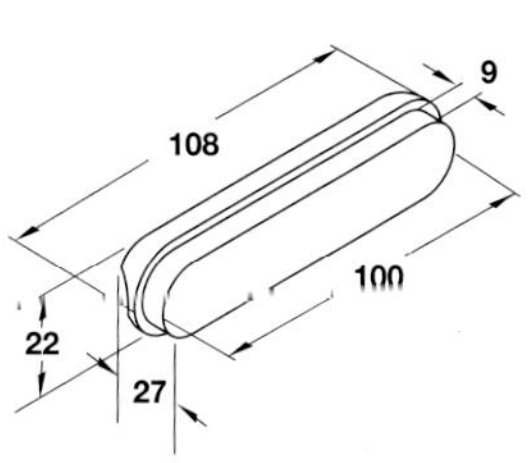

Red Oak

Cat. No.	192.06.476

Packing: 25 pcs.

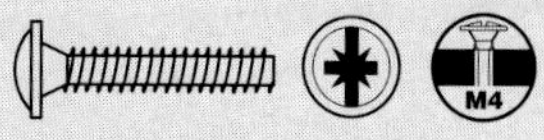

Threaded Screws M4
Combined slot, suitable for flat or cross blades
Finish: steel, zinc-plated

Length	Cat. No.
10 mm	022.35.109
12 mm	022.35.127
15 mm	022.35.154
18 mm	022.35.181
20 mm	022.35.207
22 mm	022.35.225
23 mm	022.35.234
25 mm	022.35.252
28 mm	022.35.289
30 mm	022.35.305
35 mm	022.35.350
38 mm	022.35.387
40 mm	022.35.403
45 mm	022.35.458
50 mm	022.35.501
60 mm	022.35.609

Packing: 100 and 1000 pcs.

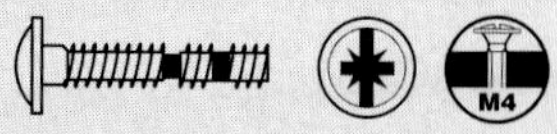

Threaded Breakoff Screw M4
Combined slot, suitable for flat or cross blades
Finish: steel, zinc-plated

Length	Cat. No.
1 3/4" x 3/4"	022.35.887

Packing: 100 and 1000 pcs.

HÄFELE

Wood handles

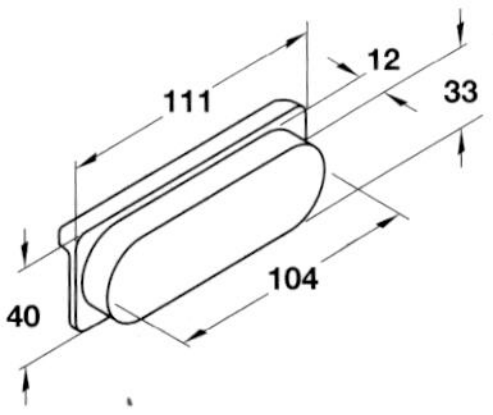

Beech

Cat. No.	192.45.300

Packing: 25 pcs.

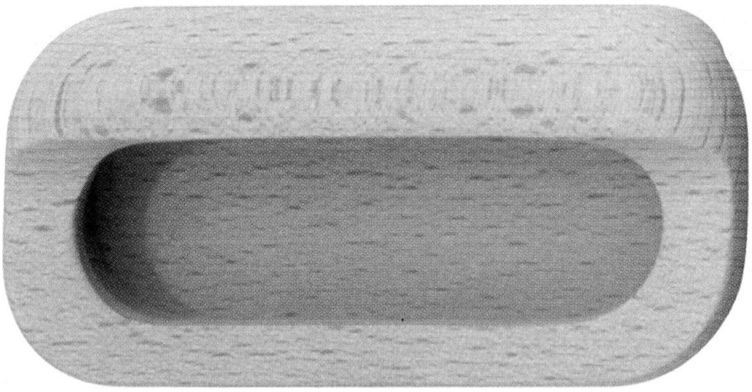

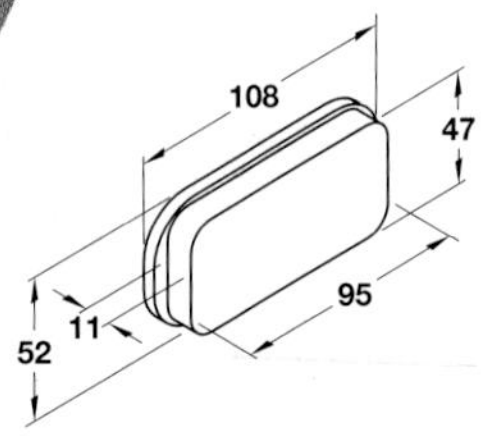

Beech

Cat. No.	192.20.300

Packing: 25 pcs.

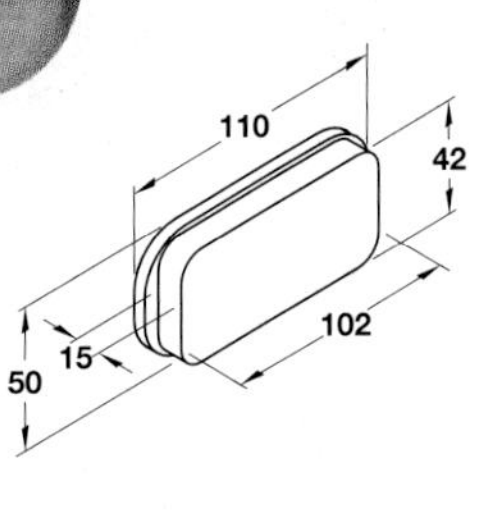

Beech

Cat. No.	192.29.300

Packing: 25 pcs.

Wood Flush Handles

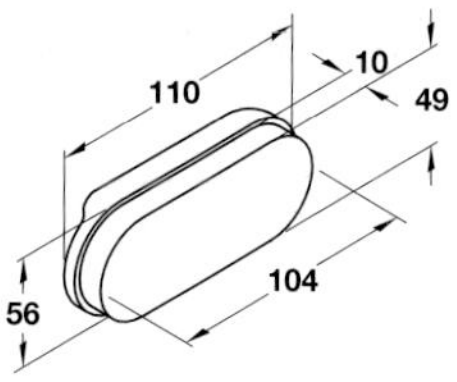

White oak

Cat. No.	192.43.415

Packing: 25 pcs.

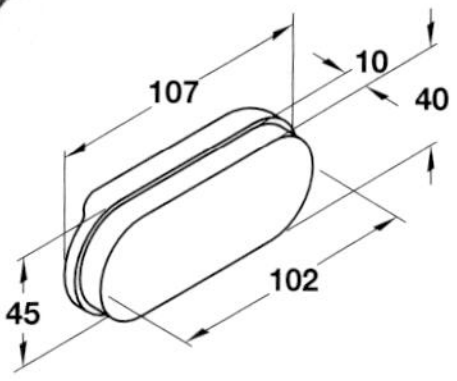

White oak

Cat. No.	192.22.407

Packing: 25 pcs.

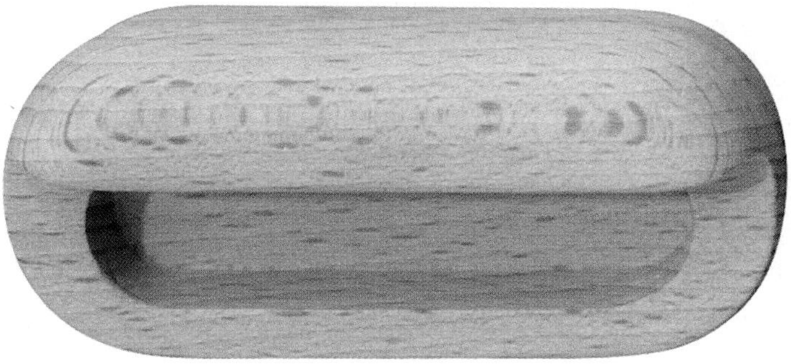

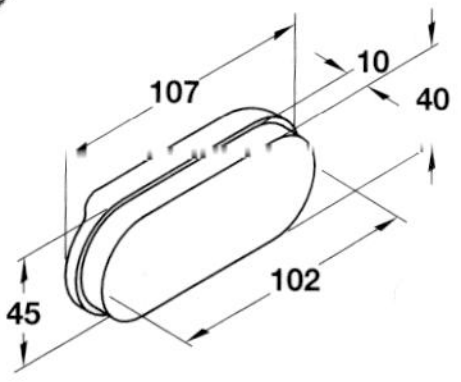

Beech

Cat. No.	192.22.309

Packing: 25 pcs.

Dimensional data not binding.
We reserve the right to alter specifications without notice.

HÄFELE

Wood flush handle

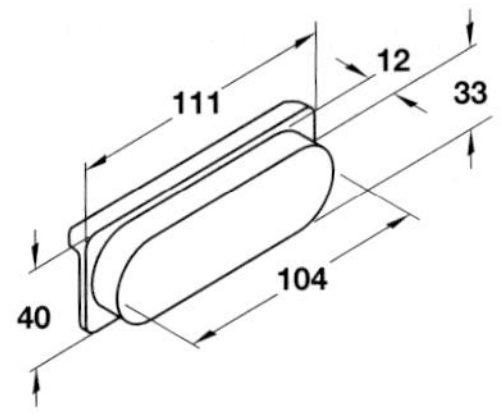

Red Oak

Cat. No.	192.45.455

Packing: 25 pcs.

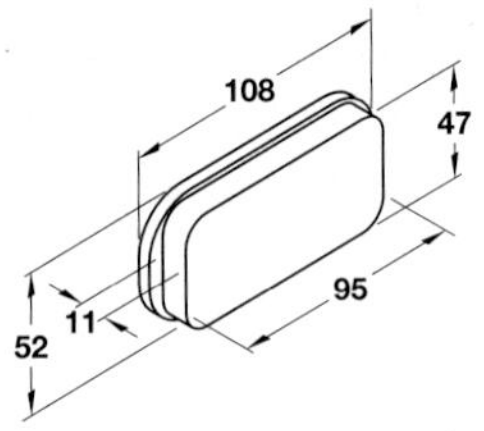

Red Oak

Cat. No.	192.20.458

Packing: 25 pcs.

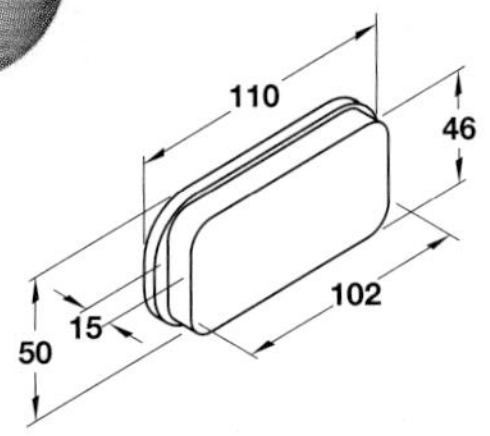

White oak

Cat. No.	192.29.406

Packing: 25 pcs.

Dimensional data not binding.
We reserve the right to alter specifications without notice.

Wood Flush Handles

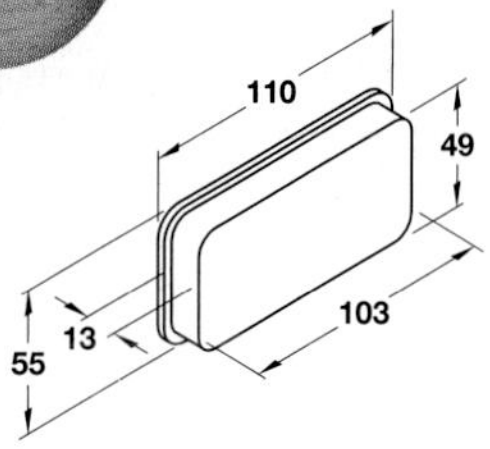

White oak

Cat. No.	192.41.402

Packing: 25 pcs.

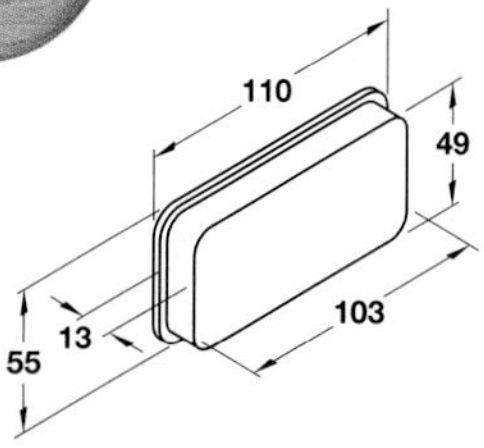

Beech

Cat. No.	192.41.304

Packing: 25 pcs.

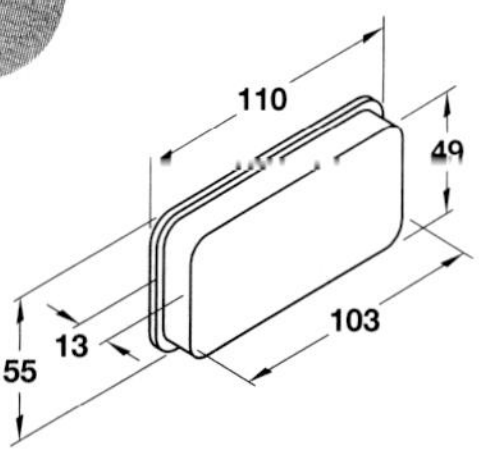

Red Oak

Cat. No.	192.41.457

Packing: 25 pcs.

Dimensional data not binding.
We reserve the right to alter specifications without notice.

HÄFELE

Wood and metal combinations

Threaded Screws M4
Combined slot, suitable for flat or cross blades

Finish: steel, zinc-plated

Length	Cat. No.
10 mm	022.35.109
12 mm	022.35.127
15 mm	022.35.154
18 mm	022.35.181
20 mm	022.35.207
22 mm	022.35.225
23 mm	022.35.234
25 mm	022.35.252
28 mm	022.35.289
30 mm	022.35.305
35 mm	022.35.350
38 mm	022.35.387
40 mm	022.35.403
45 mm	022.35.458
50 mm	022.35.501
60 mm	022.35.609

Packing: 100 and 1000 pcs.

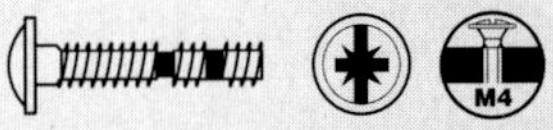

Threaded Breakoff Screw M4
Combined slot, suitable for flat or cross blades

Finish: steel, zinc-plated

Length	Cat. No.
1 3/4" x 3/4"	022.35.887

Packing: 100 and 1000 pcs.

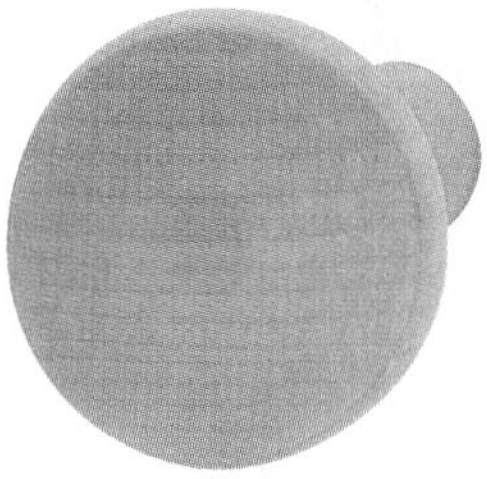

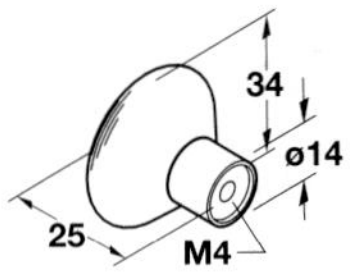

Knob: maple clear lacquered
Base: steel matt nickel

Cat. No.	132.79.680

Packing: 25 pcs.

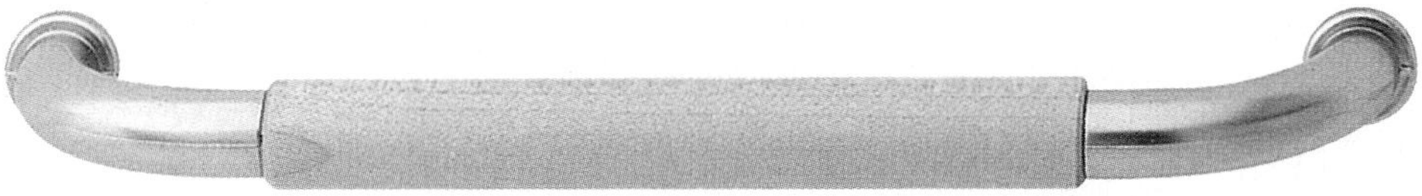

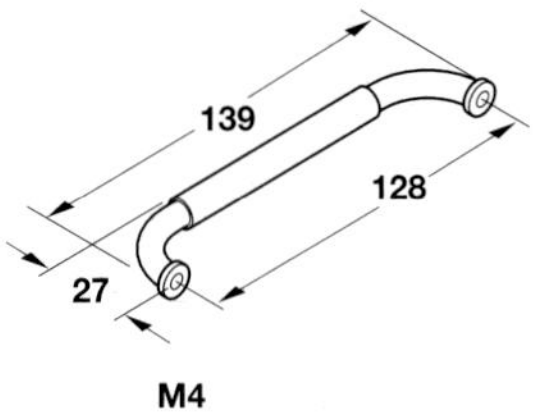

Handles: maple lacquered
Ends: zinc nickel plated matt

Cat. No.	103.59.610

Packing: 25 pcs.

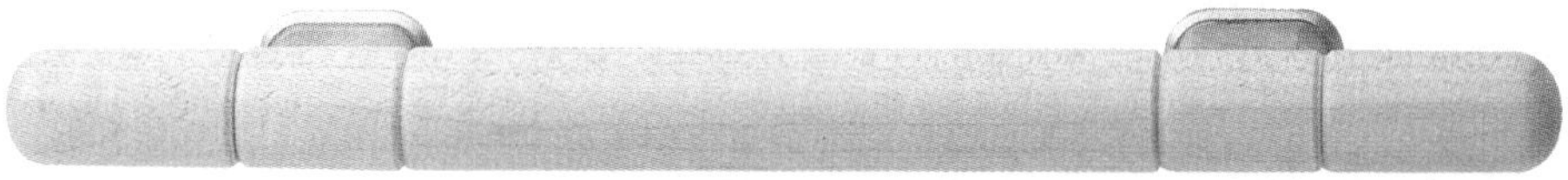

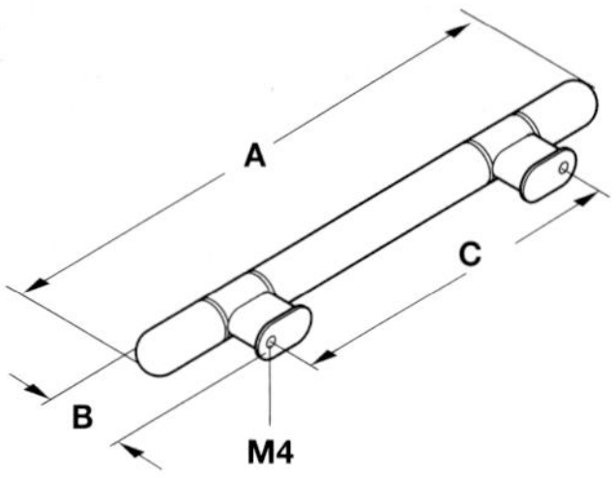

Handles: maple lacquered
Ends: zinc nickel plated matt

Size A x B	Dimension C	Cat. No.
196 x 30	128	193.98.410
238 x 30	160	193.98.411

Packing: 25 pcs.

Dimensional data not binding.
We reserve the right to alter specifications without notice.

Metal/Wood Handles and Knobs

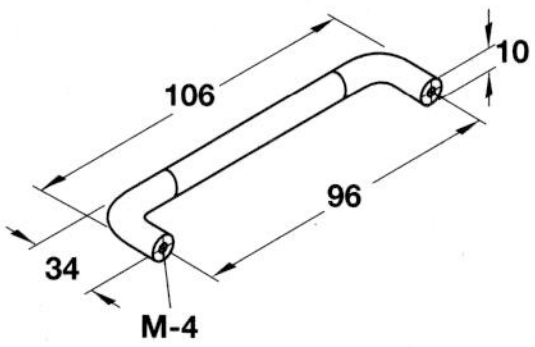

Insert: oak, laquered
Ends: zinc white

Cat. No.	116.13.728

Packing: 25 each

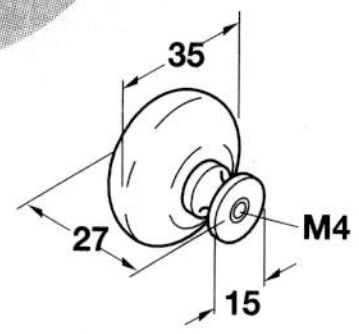

Knob: oak, laquered
Center/Base: zinc white

Cat. No.	195.09.409

Packing: 25 each

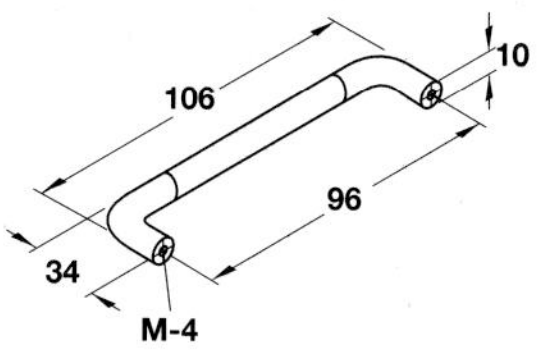

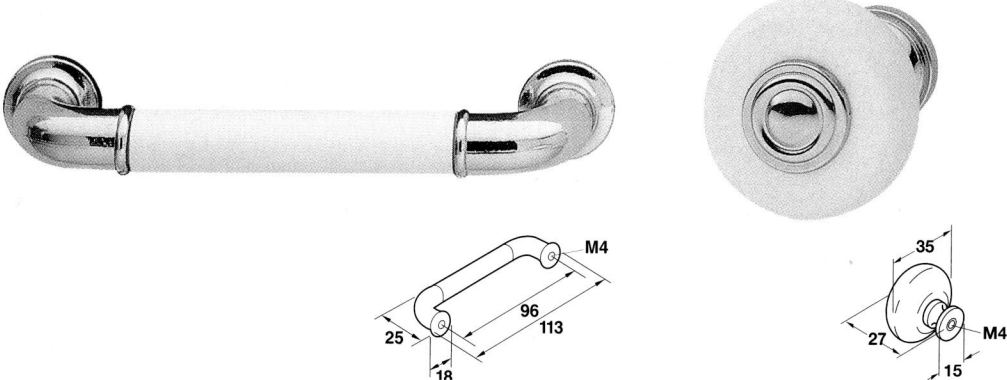

Insert: oak, laquered
Ends: zinc black

Cat. No.	116.13.326

Packing: 25 each

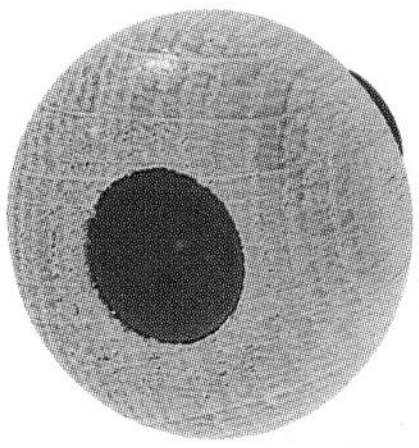

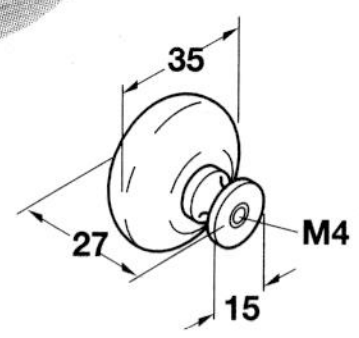

Knob: oak, laquered
Center/Base: zinc black

Cat. No.	195.09.418

Packing: 25 each

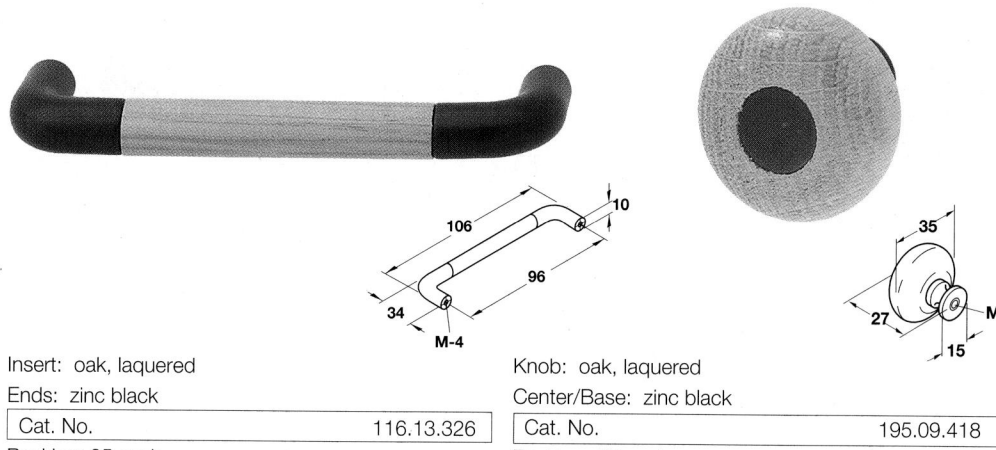

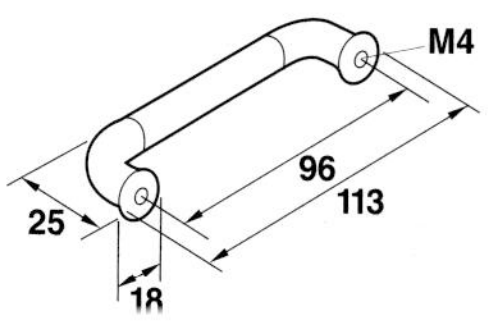

Insert: beech, white
Ends: zinc gold colored polished

Cat. No.	193.84.804

Packing: 25 pcs.

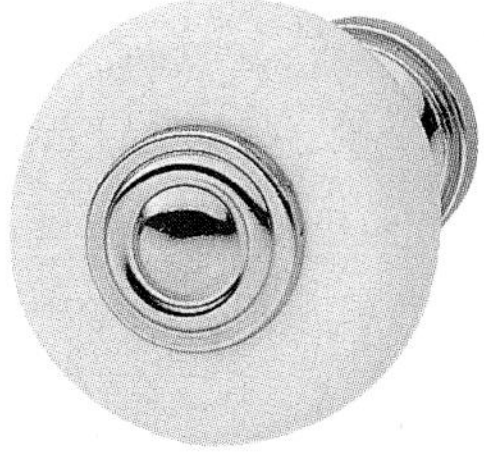

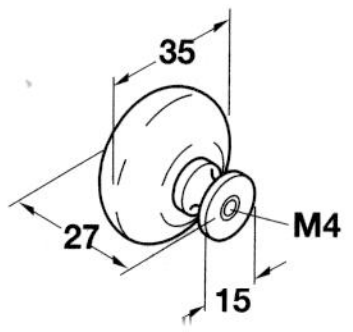

Knob: beech, white
Center/base: zinc gold colored polished

Cat. No.	195.08.715

Packing: 25 pcs.

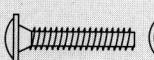

Threaded Screws M4
Combined slot, suitable for flat or cross blades
Finish: steel, zinc-plated

Length	Cat. No.
10 mm	022.35.109
12 mm	022.35.127
15 mm	022.35.154
18 mm	022.35.181
20 mm	022.35.207
22 mm	022.35.225
23 mm	022.35.234
25 mm	022.35.252
28 mm	022.35.289
30 mm	022.35.305
35 mm	022.35.350
38 mm	022.35.387
40 mm	022.35.403
45 mm	022.35.458
50 mm	022.35.501
60 mm	022.35.609

Packing: 100 and 1000 pcs.

Threaded Breakoff Screw M4
Combined slot, suitable for flat or cross blades
Finish: steel, zinc-plated

Length	Cat. No.
1 3/4" x 3/4"	022.35.887

Packing: 100 and 1000 pcs.

HÄFELE

Handles of Zinc and Wood

Threaded Screws M4
Combined slot, suitable for flat or cross blades
Finish: steel, zinc-plated

Length	Cat. No.
10 mm	022.35.109
12 mm	022.35.127
15 mm	022.35.154
18 mm	022.35.181
20 mm	022.35.207
22 mm	022.35.225
23 mm	022.35.234
25 mm	022.35.252
28 mm	022.35.289
30 mm	022.35.305
35 mm	022.35.350
38 mm	022.35.387
40 mm	022.35.403
45 mm	022.35.458
50 mm	022.35.501
60 mm	022.35.609

Packing: 100 and 1000 pcs.

Threaded Breakoff Screw M4
Combined slot, suitable for flat or cross blades
Finish: steel, zinc-plated

Length	Cat. No.
1 3/4" x 3/4"	022.35.887

Packing: 100 and 1000 pcs.

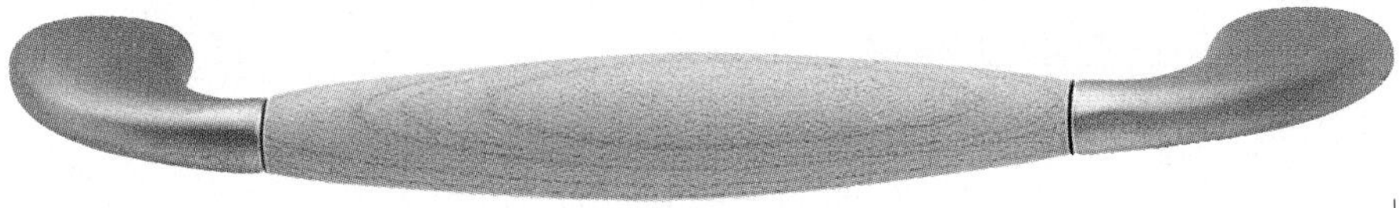

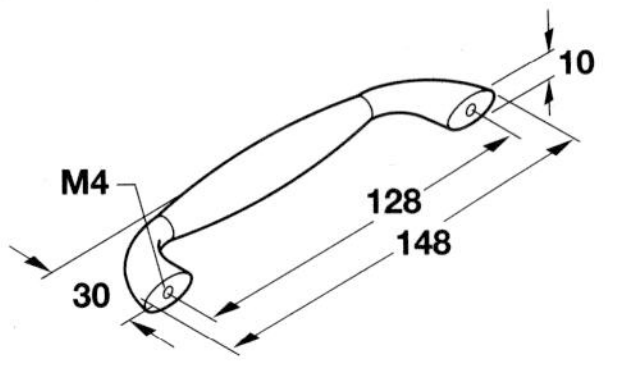

Ends: zinc nickel-plated matt
Center: maple lacquered

Cat. No.	103.14.680

Packing: 25 pcs.

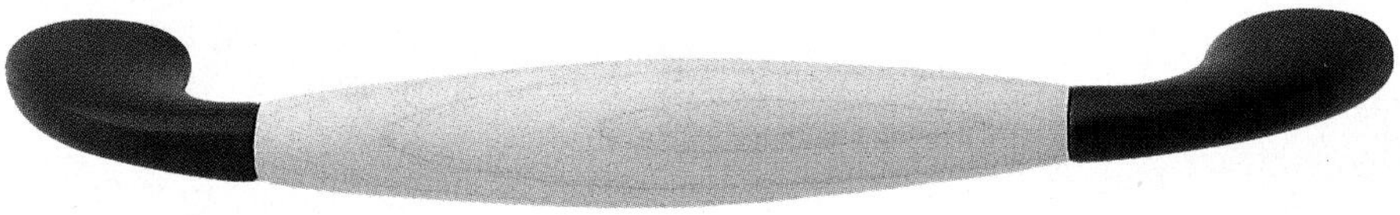

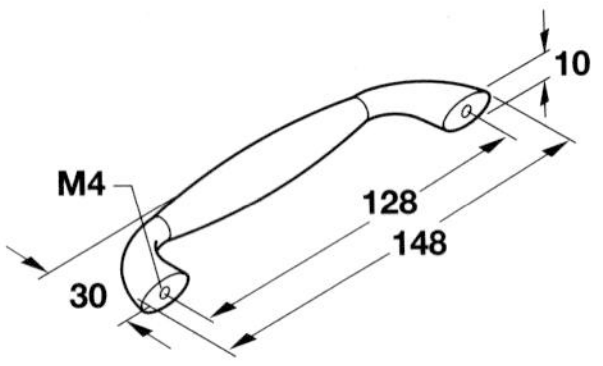

Ends: zinc black matt
Center: maple lacquered

Cat. No.	103.14.380

Packing: 25 pcs.

Dimensional data not binding.
We reserve the right to alter specifications without notice.

Combination Handles

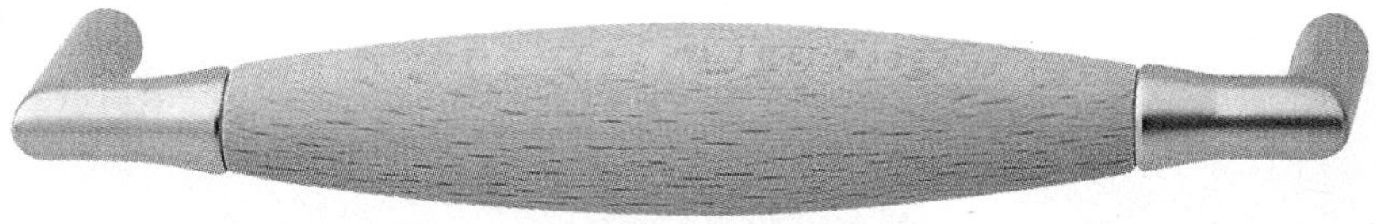

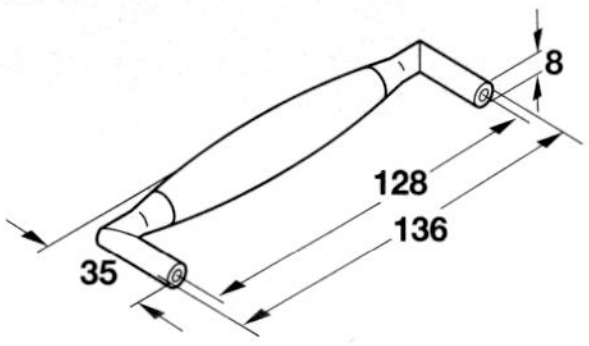

Center: beech lacquered
Ends: zinc nickel-plated matt

Cat. No.	103.58.630

Packing: 25 pcs.

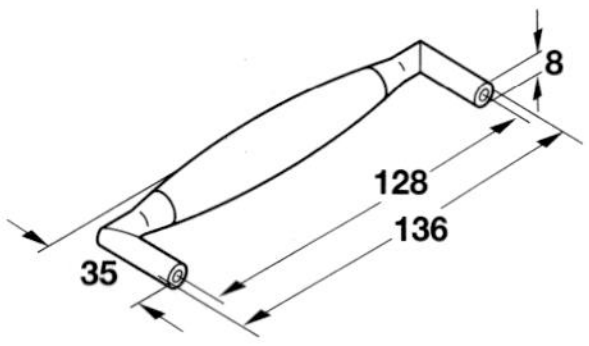

Center: thermoplastic black
Ends: zinc nickel-plated matt

Cat. No.	103.58.631

Packing: 25 pcs.

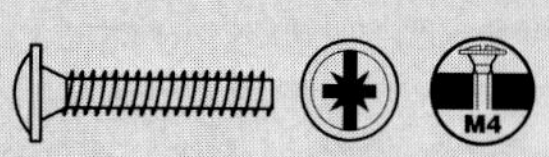

Threaded Screws M4
Combined slot, suitable for flat or cross blades

Finish: steel, zinc-plated

Length	Cat. No.
10 mm	022.35.109
12 mm	022.35.127
15 mm	022.35.154
18 mm	022.35.181
20 mm	022.35.207
22 mm	022.35.225
23 mm	022.35.234
25 mm	022.35.252
28 mm	022.35.289
30 mm	022.35.305
35 mm	022.35.350
38 mm	022.35.387
40 mm	022.35.403
45 mm	022.35.458
50 mm	022.35.501
60 mm	022.35.609

Packing: 100 and 1000 pcs.

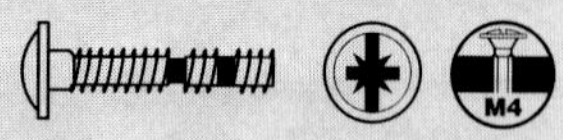

Threaded Breakoff Screw M4
Combined slot, suitable for flat or cross blades

Finish: steel, zinc-plated

Length	Cat. No.
1 3/4" x 3/4"	022.35.887

Packing: 100 and 1000 pcs.

HÄFELE

Plastic handles

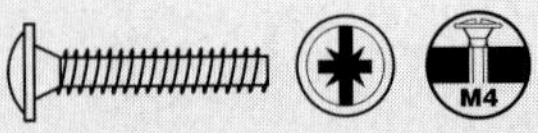

Threaded Screws M4
Combined slot, suitable for flat or cross blades
Finish: steel, zinc-plated

Length	Cat. No.
10 mm	022.35.109
12 mm	022.35.127
15 mm	022.35.154
18 mm	022.35.181
20 mm	022.35.207
22 mm	022.35.225
23 mm	022.35.234
25 mm	022.35.252
28 mm	022.35.289
30 mm	022.35.305
35 mm	022.35.350
38 mm	022.35.387
40 mm	022.35.403
45 mm	022.35.458
50 mm	022.35.501
60 mm	022.35.609

Packing: 100 and 1000 pcs.

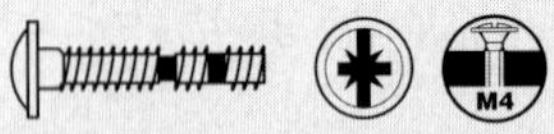

Threaded Breakoff Screw M4
Combined slot, suitable for flat or cross blades
Finish: steel, zinc-plated

Length	Cat. No.
1 3/4" x 3/4"	022.35.887

Packing: 100 and 1000 pcs.

Black matt

Cat. No.	128.01.300

Packing: 25 pcs.

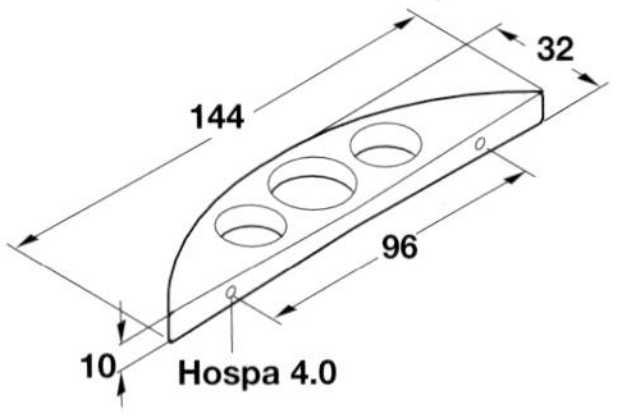

Black polished

Cat. No.	128.10.300

Packing: 25 pcs.

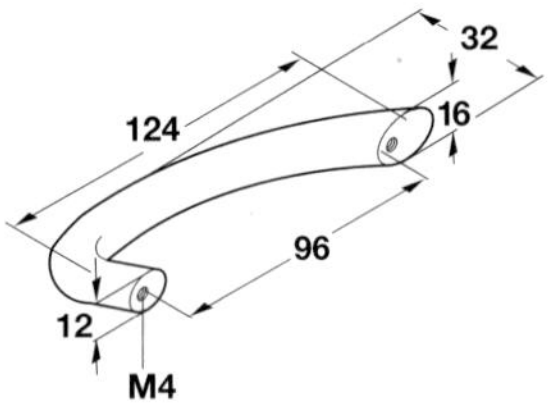

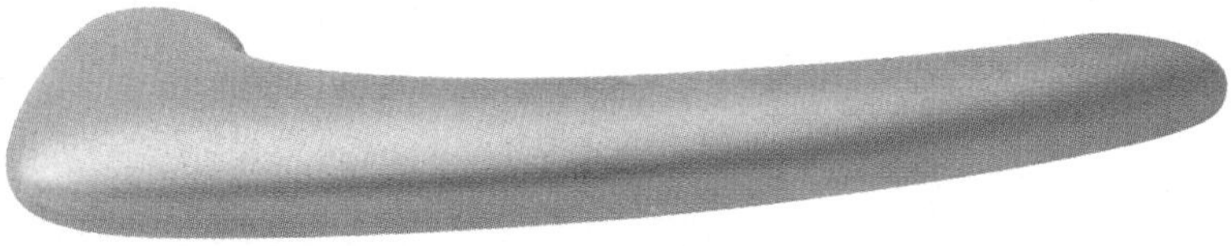

Thermoplastic nickel-plated matt

Cat. No.	129.85.600

Packing: 25 pcs.

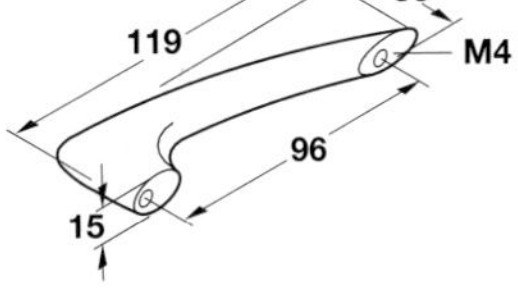

HEWI 10mm diameter Nylon handles

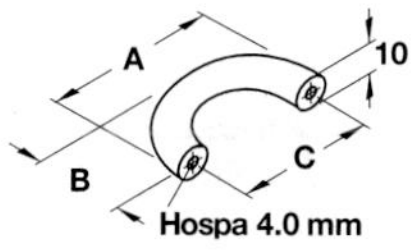

Nylon

Size A x B	Dimension C	Cat. No.
42 x 26	32	114.21.1..
50 x 30	40	114.21.2..
70 x 40	60	114.21.3..
74 x 42	64	114.21.4..

Packing: 25 pcs.

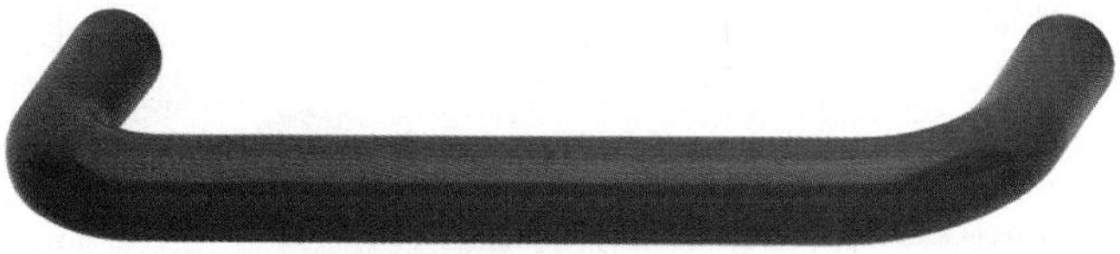

Nylon

Size A x B	Dimension C	Cat. No.
74 x 32	64	114.20.1..
80 x 32	70 (2¾")	114.20.2..
86 x 35	76 (3")	114.20.3..
99 x 35	89 (3½")	114.20.4..
106 x 35	96	114.20.5..
110 x 35	100 (4")	114.20.6..
138 x 35	128	114.20.7..
148 x 35	138	114.20.8..

Packing: 25 pcs.

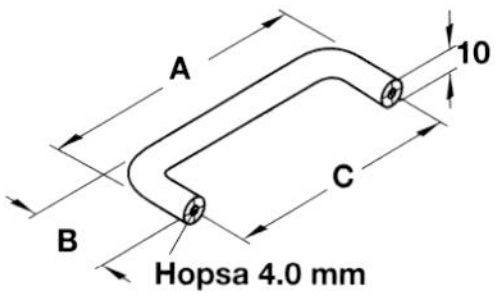

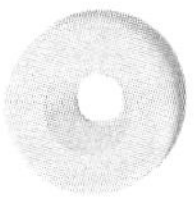

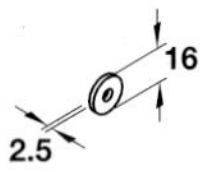

Nylon

for use with series	Cat. No.
114.20 & 114.21	114.29.1..

Packing: 50 pcs.

Ordering tip: replace the decimals (. .) in the catalog number with the color number of your choice.

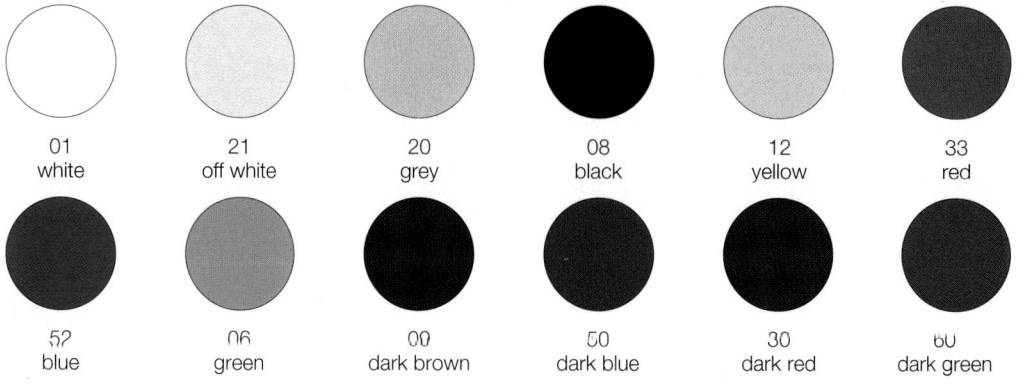

01 white	21 off white	20 grey	08 black	12 yellow	33 red
52 blue	06 green	00 dark brown	50 dark blue	30 dark red	60 dark green

Decorative Hardware 1

Hospa Pan Head Screws
Pozi Recess

Finish: steel, zinc-plated

Length	Cat. No.
13 mm	015.71.811
15 mm	015.71.820
17 mm	015.71.839
20 mm	015.71.848
25 mm	015.71.857
30 mm	015.71.866
35 mm	015.71.875
40 mm	015.71.884
45 mm	015.71.893

Packing: 1000 pcs.

Dimensional data not binding. We reserve the right to alter specifications without notice.

Dimensions in mm

HÄFELE

HEWI 13mm diameter Nylon handles

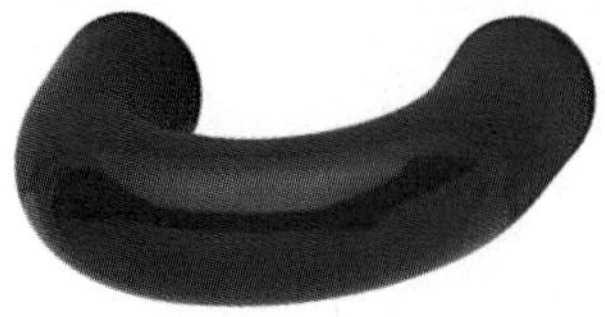

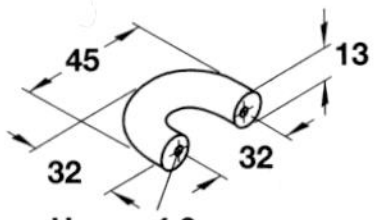

Nylon

Cat. No.	114.22.1..

Packing: 25 pcs.

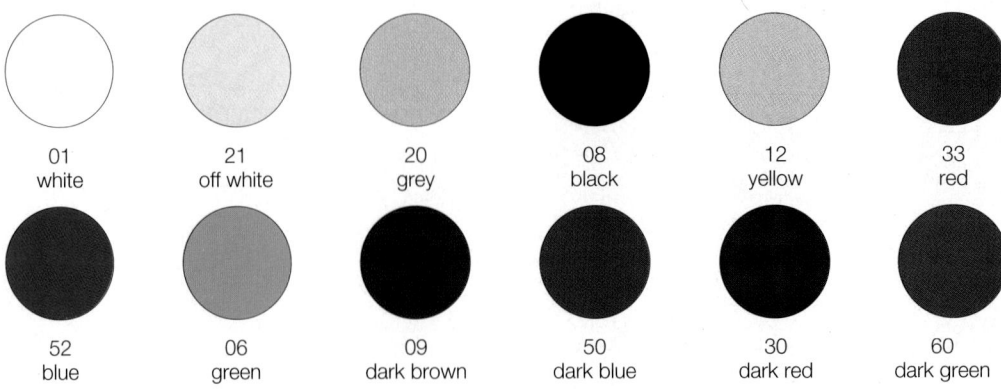

Size A x B	Dimension C	Cat. No.
109 x 38	96	114.22.2..
141 x 38	128	114.22.3..
205 x 38	192	114.22.4..
301 x 38	288	114.22.5..

Packing: 25 pcs.

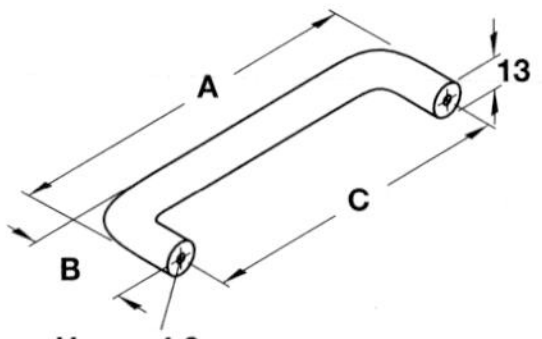

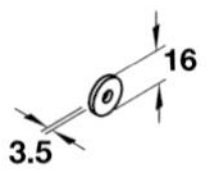

Nylon

for use with series	Cat. No.
114.22	114.29.2..

Packing: 50 pcs.

Ordering tip: replace the decimals (. .) in the catalog number with the color number of your choice.

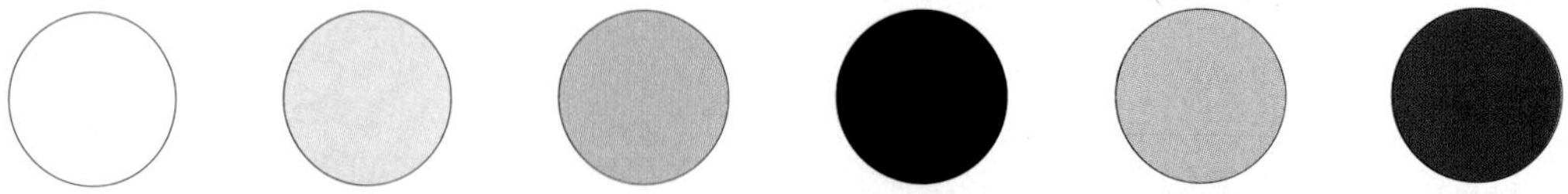

01 white	21 off white	20 grey	08 black	12 yellow	33 red

52 blue	06 green	09 dark brown	50 dark blue	30 dark red	60 dark green

Hospa Pan Head Screws
Pozi Recess
Finish: steel, zinc-plated

Length	Cat. No.
13 mm	015.71.811
15 mm	015.71.820
17 mm	015.71.839
20 mm	015.71.848
25 mm	015.71.857
30 mm	015.71.866
35 mm	015.71.875
40 mm	015.71.884
45 mm	015.71.893

Packing: 1000 pcs.

Dimensional data not binding. We reserve the right to alter specifications without notice.

Dimensions in mm

HÄFELE

HEWI 13mm Nylon handles

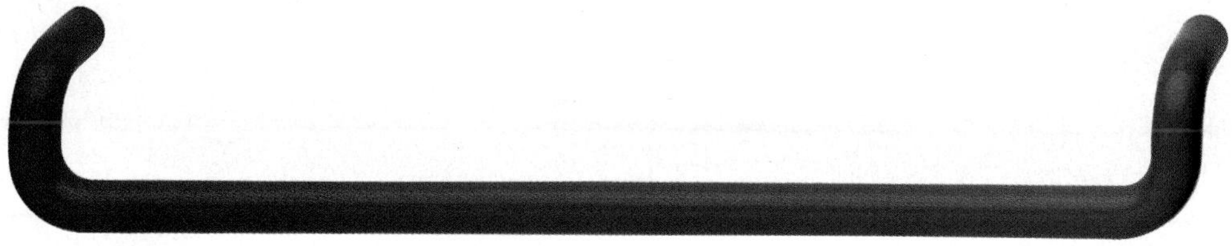

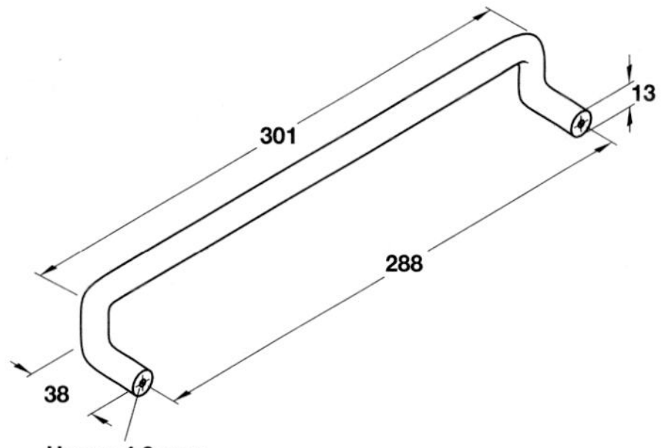

Nylon

Cat. No.	114.38.5..

Packing: 25 pcs.

Decorative Hardware 1

Hospa Pan Head Screws
Pozi Recess
Finish: steel, zinc-plated

Length	Cat. No.
13 mm	015.71.811
15 mm	015.71.820
17 mm	015.71.839
20 mm	015.71.848
25 mm	015.71.857
30 mm	015.71.866
35 mm	015.71.875
40 mm	015.71.884
45 mm	015.71.893

Packing: 1000 pcs.

Ordering tip: replace the asterisks (**) in the catalog number with the color number of your choice.

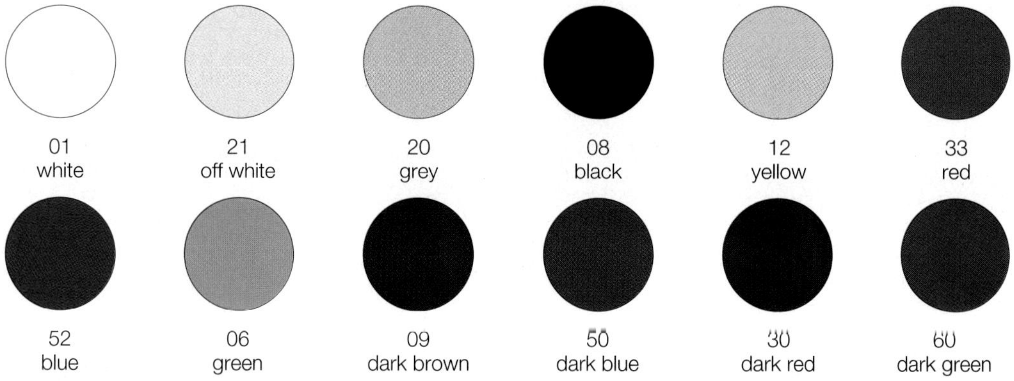

Dimensional data not binding.
We reserve the right to alter specifications without notice.

Dimensions in mm

HÄFELE

HEWI 16 and 20mm diameter Nylon handles

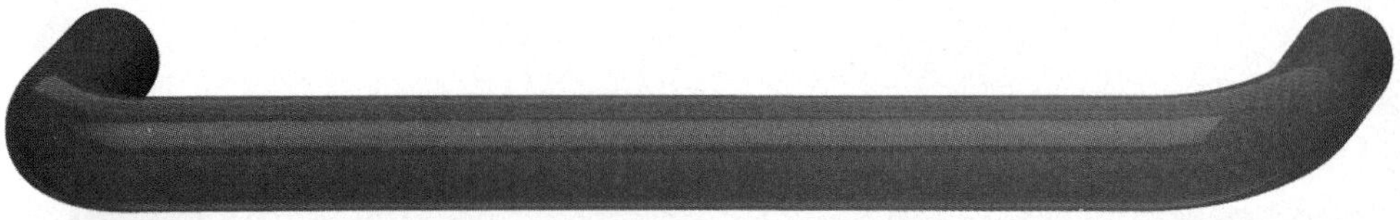

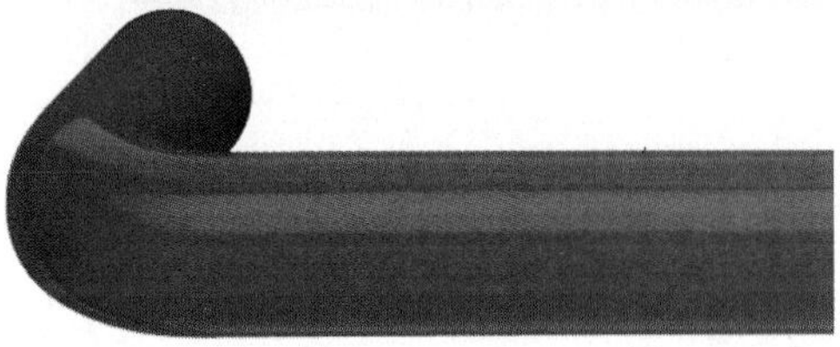

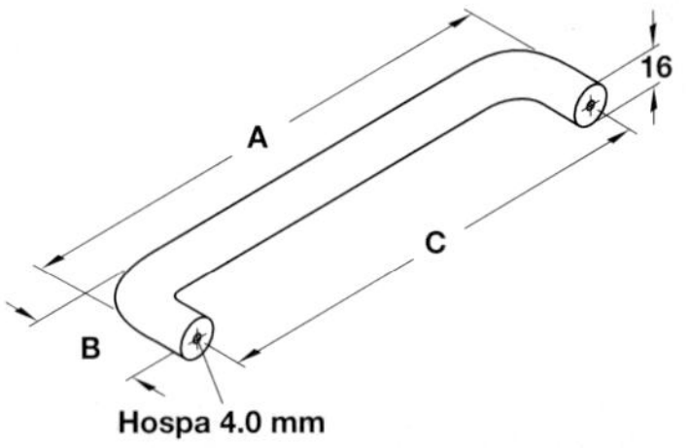

Nylon

Size A x B	Dimension C	Cat. No.
208 x 44	192	114.23.4..
304 x 44	288	114.23.5..

Packing: 1 pc.

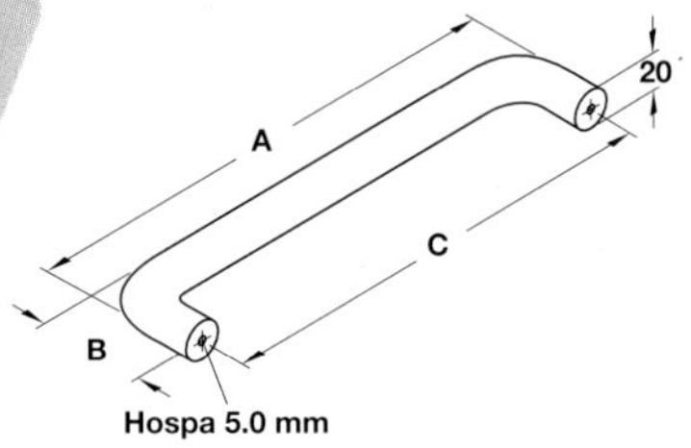

Nylon

Size A x B	Dimension C	Cat. No.
135 x 55	115	114.24.1..
270 x 55	250	114.24.2..

Packing: 1 pc.

Hospa Pan Head Screws
Pozi Recess
Finish: steel, zinc-plated

Length	Cat. No.
13 mm	015.71.811
15 mm	015.71.820
17 mm	015.71.839
20 mm	015.71.848
25 mm	015.71.857
30 mm	015.71.866
35 mm	015.71.875
40 mm	015.71.884
45 mm	015.71.893

Packing: 1000 pcs.

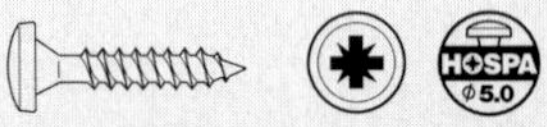

Hospa Pan Head Screws
Pozi Recess
Finish: steel, zinc-plated

Length	Cat. No.
20 mm	015.72.078
30 mm	015.72.096
50 mm	015.72.130

Packing: 1000 pcs.

Ordering tip: replace the decimals (. .) in the catalog number with the color number of your choice.

01 white	21 off white	20 grey	08 black	12 yellow	33 red
52 blue	06 green	09 dark brown	50 dark blue	30 dark red	60 dark green

Dimensional data not binding. We reserve the right to alter specifications without notice.

Dimensions in mm

HEWI 23mm diameter Nylon handles

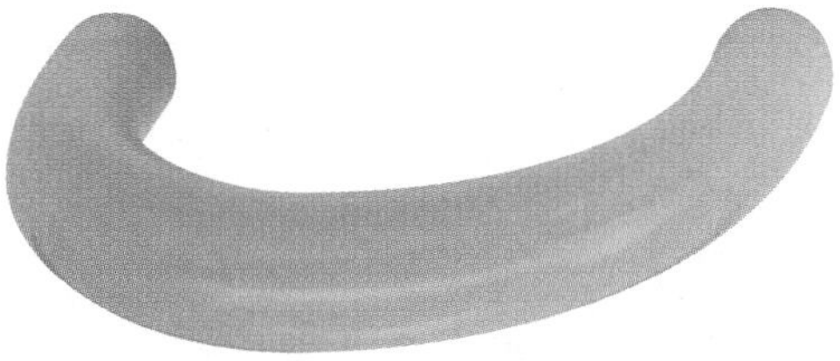

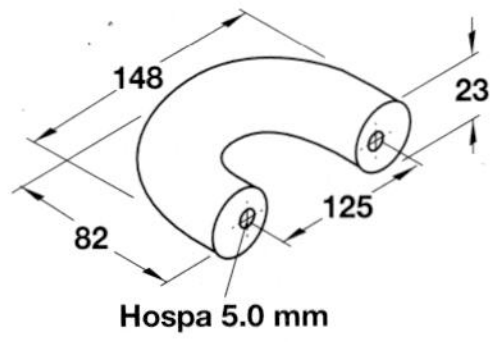

Nylon

Cat. No.	114.25.1..

Packing: 1 pc.

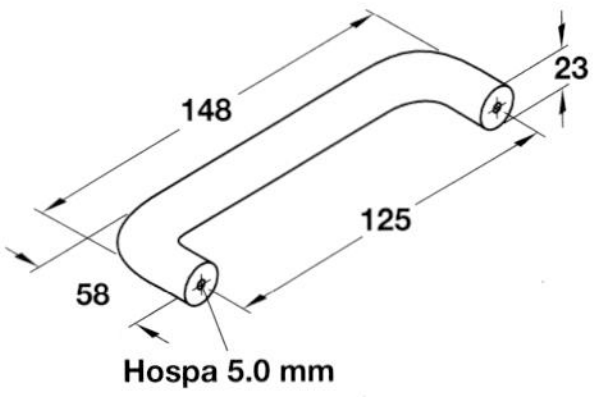

Cat. No.	114.25.2..

Packing: 1 pc.

Ordering tip: replace the decimals (. .) in the catalog number with the color number of your choice.

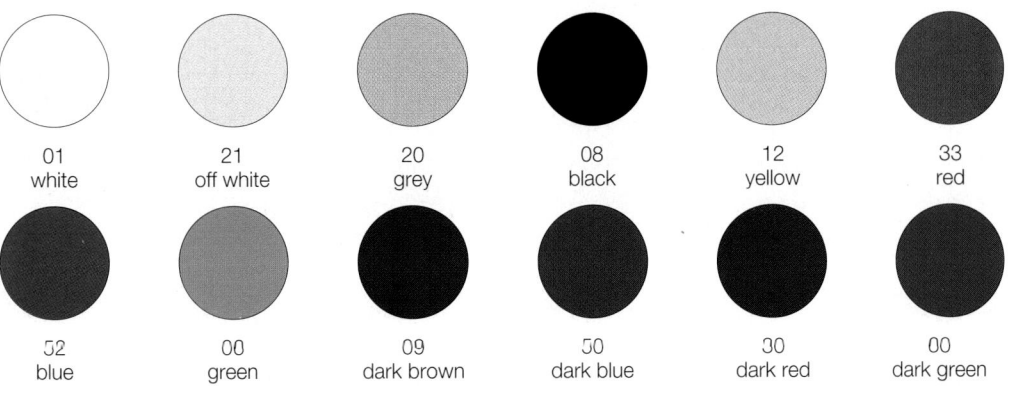

01 white	21 off white	20 grey	08 black	12 yellow	33 red
52 blue	00 green	09 dark brown	50 dark blue	30 dark red	00 dark green

Hospa Pan Head Screws
Pozi Recess

Finish: steel, zinc-plated

Length	Cat. No.
20 mm	015.72.078
30 mm	015.72.096
50 mm	015.72.130

Packing: 1000 pcs.

Dimensions in mm

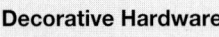

HÄFELE

HEWI Nylon Handles

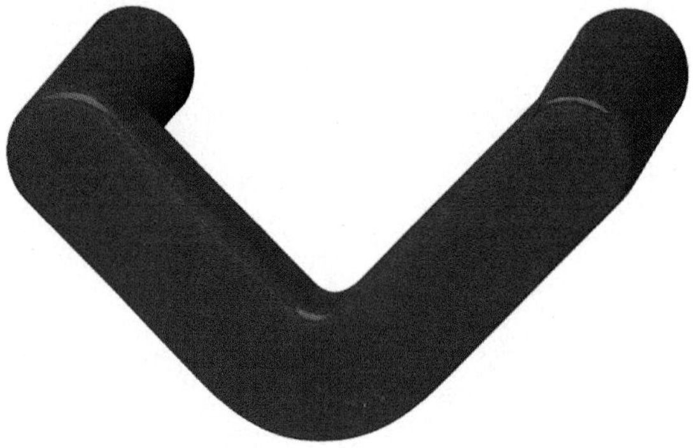

Cat. No.	114.28.1..

Packing: 1 pc.

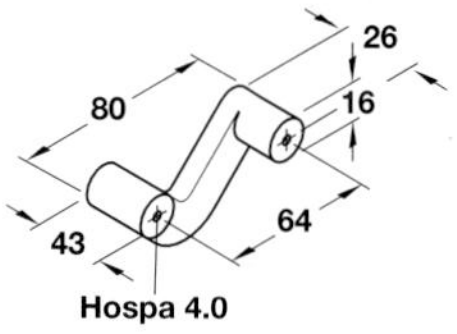

Size A x B	Dimension C	Cat. No.
112 x 26	96	114.27.2..
144 x 26	128	114.28.3..

Packing: 1 pc.

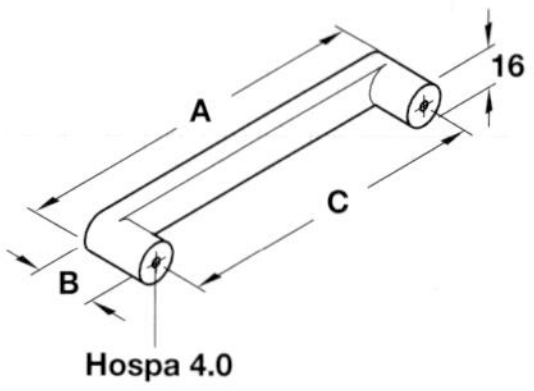

1 Decorative Hardware

Hospa Pan Head Screws
Pozi Recess
Finish: steel, zinc-plated

Length	Cat. No.
13 mm	015.71.811
15 mm	015.71.820
17 mm	015.71.839
20 mm	015.71.848
25 mm	015.71.857
30 mm	015.71.866
35 mm	015.71.875
40 mm	015.71.884
45 mm	015.71.893

Packing: 1000 pcs.

Ordering tip: replace the asterisks (**) in the catalog number with the color number of your choice.

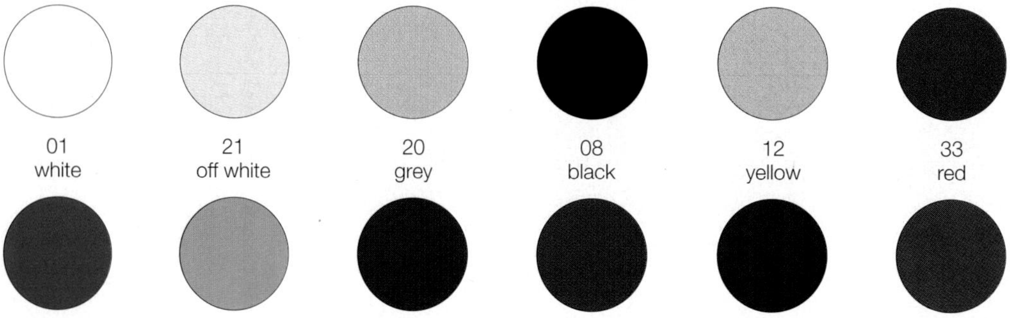

01 white	21 off white	20 grey	08 black	12 yellow	33 red
52 blue	06 green	09 dark brown	50 dark blue	30 dark red	60 dark green

Dimensional data not binding.
We reserve the right to alter specifications without notice.

Dimensions in mm

Plastic Handles for Laminate Inserts

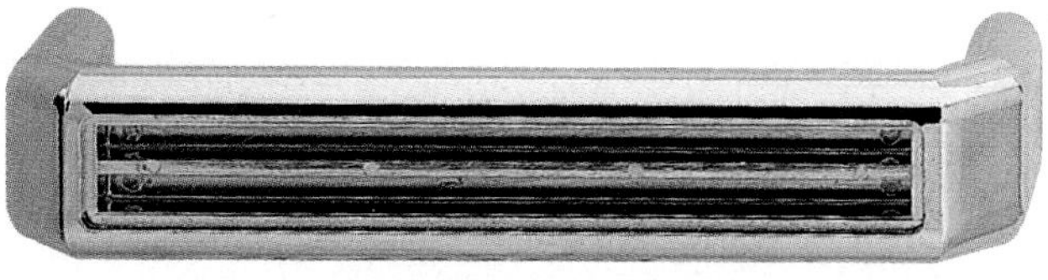

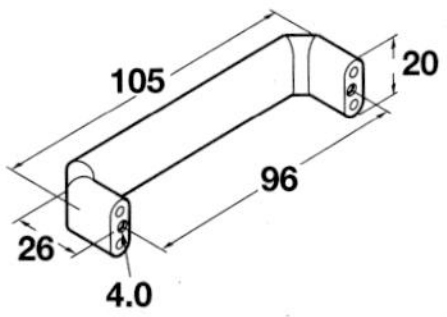

Chrome polished electroplated

Cat. No.	116.89.204

Packing: 100 pcs.

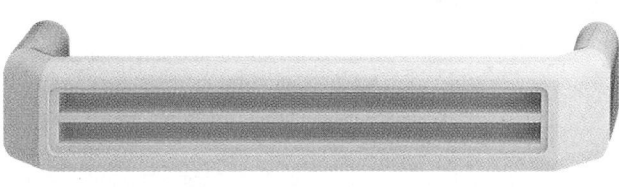

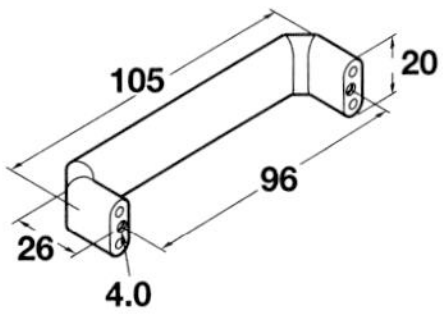

Black

Cat. No.	116.89.302

Packing: 100 pcs.

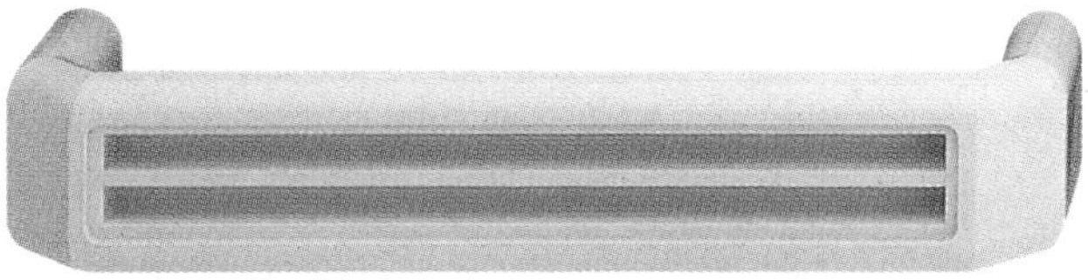

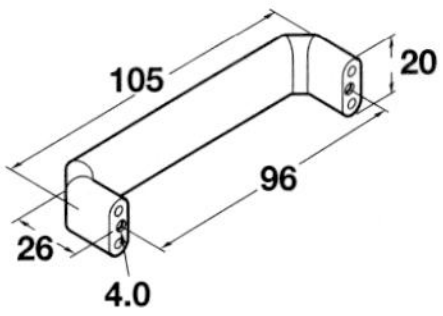

White

Cat. No.	116.89.704

Packing: 100 pcs.

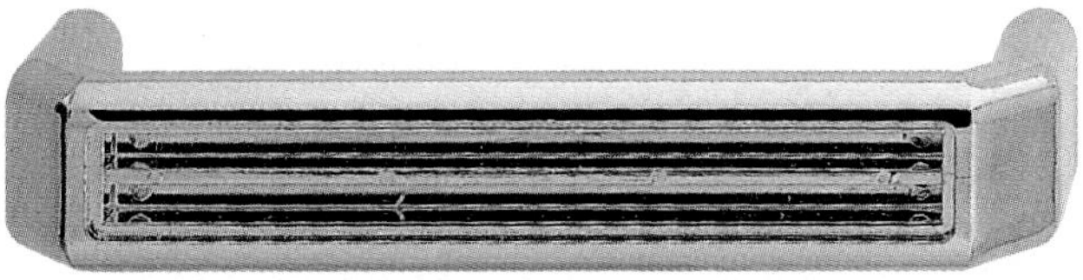

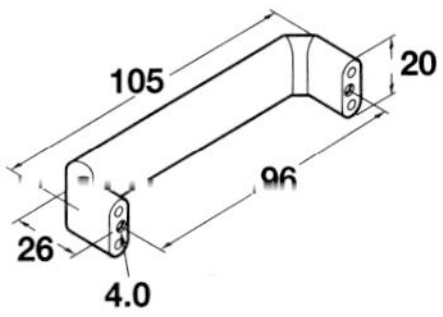

Gold polished electroplated

Cat. No.	116.89.802

Packing: 100 pcs.

Punch Press
for use with laminate up to 1/16"
Finish: Steel, black

Cat. No.	004.04.802

Packing: 1 pc.

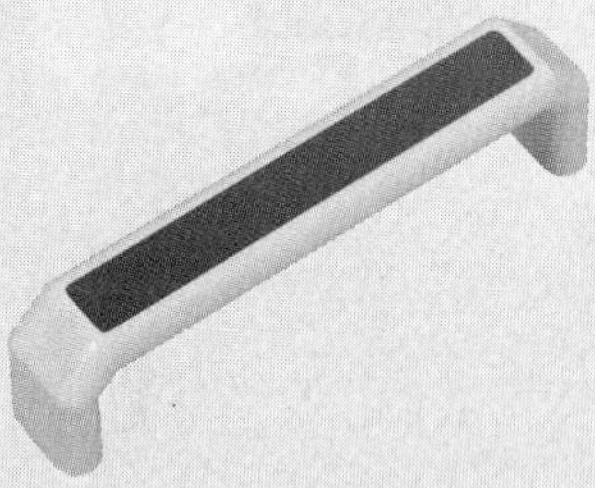

Make your own inserts with Punch Press sold separately.

Hospa Pan Head Screws
Pozi Recess
Finish: steel, zinc-plated

Length	Cat. No.
13 mm	015.71.811
15 mm	015.71.820
17 mm	015.71.839
20 mm	015.71.848
25 mm	015.71.857
30 mm	015.71.866
35 mm	015.71.875
40 mm	015.71.884
45 mm	015.71.893

Packing: 1000 pcs.

Dimensional data not binding.
We reserve the right to alter specifications without notice.

HÄFELE

Plastic Handles

Hospa Pan Head Screws
Pozi Recess
Finish: steel, zinc-plated

Length	Cat. No.
13 mm	015.71.811
15 mm	015.71.820
17 mm	015.71.839
20 mm	015.71.848
25 mm	015.71.857
30 mm	015.71.866
35 mm	015.71.875
40 mm	015.71.884
45 mm	015.71.893

Packing: 1000 pcs.

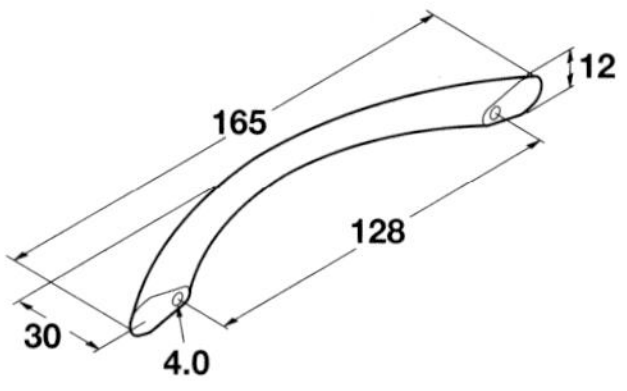

White gloss

Cat. No.	116.92.700

Packing: 100 pcs.

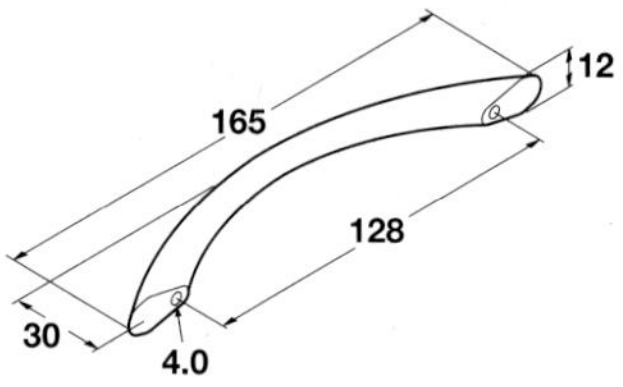

Black gloss

Cat. No.	116.92.300

Packing: 100 pcs.

Dimensional data not binding.
We reserve the right to alter specifications without notice.

Nylon handles

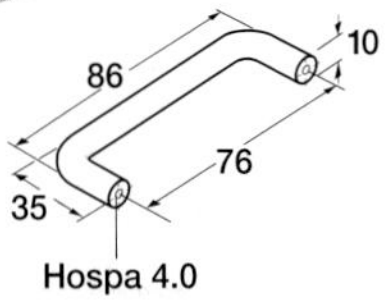

Nylon white

Cat. No.	116.80.701

Packing: 100 pcs.

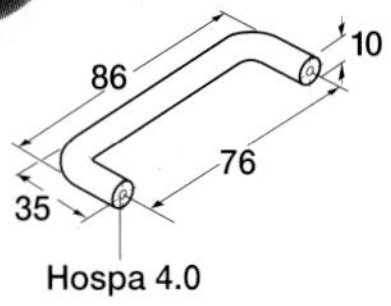

Nylon black

Cat. No.	116.80.309

Packing: 100 pcs.

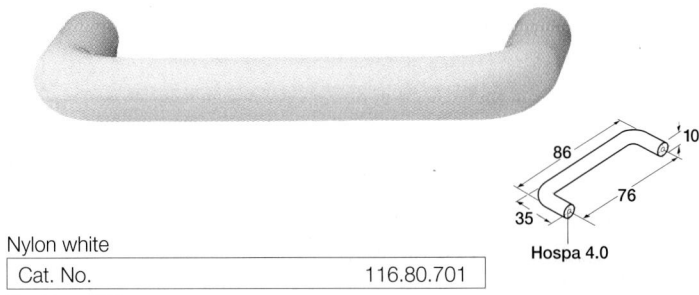

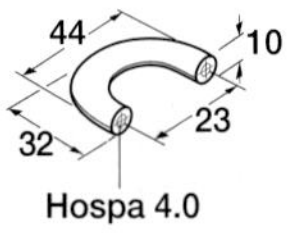

White

Cat. No.	116.54.701

Packing: 100 pcs.

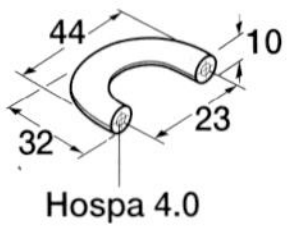

Black

Cat. No.	116.54.309

Packing: 100 pcs.

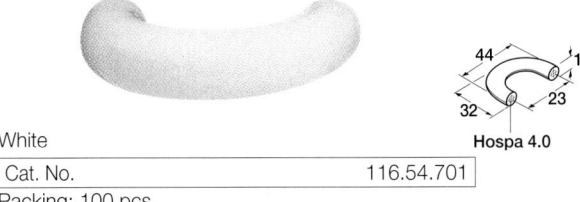

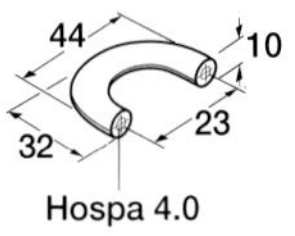

Almond

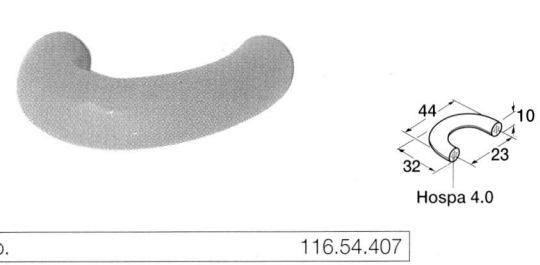

Cat. No.	116.54.407

Packing: 100 pcs.

Hospa Pan Head Screws
Pozi Recess

Finish: steel, zinc-plated

Length	Cat. No.
13 mm	015.71.811
15 mm	015.71.820
17 mm	015.71.839
20 mm	015.71.848
25 mm	015.71.857
30 mm	015.71.866
35 mm	015.71.875
40 mm	015.71.884
45 mm	015.71.893

Packing: 1000 pcs.

HÄFELE

1 Decorative Hardware

Hospa Pan Head Screws
Pozi Recess
Finish: steel, zinc-plated

Length	Cat. No.
13 mm	015.71.811
15 mm	015.71.820
17 mm	015.71.839
20 mm	015.71.848
25 mm	015.71.857
30 mm	015.71.866
35 mm	015.71.875
40 mm	015.71.884
45 mm	015.71.893

Packing: 1000 pcs.

Nylon Handles

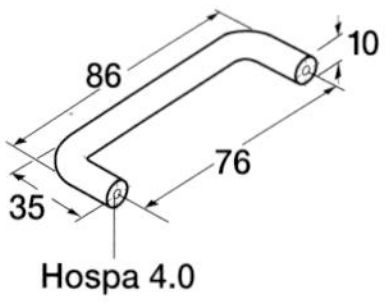

White

Size A x B	Dimension C	Cat. No.
74 x 33	64	116.55.708
106 x 35	96	116.56.705
138 x 35	128	116.57.702

Packing: 100 pcs.

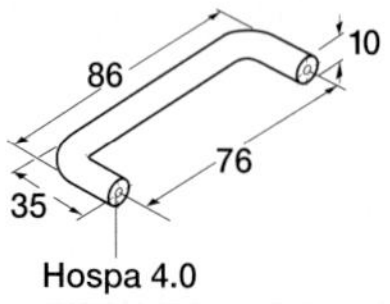

Almond

Size A x B	Dimension C	Cat. No.
74 x 33	64	116.55.404
106 x 35	96	116.56.401
138 x 35	128	116.57.408

Packing: 100 pcs.

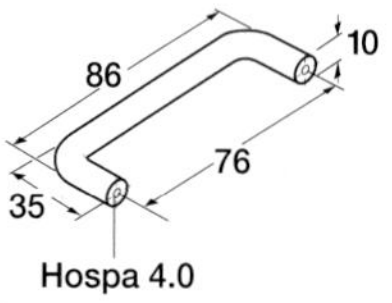

Black

Size A x B	Dimension C	Cat. No.
74 x 33	64	116.55.306
106 x 35	96	116.56.303
138 x 35	128	116.57.300

Packing: 100 pcs.

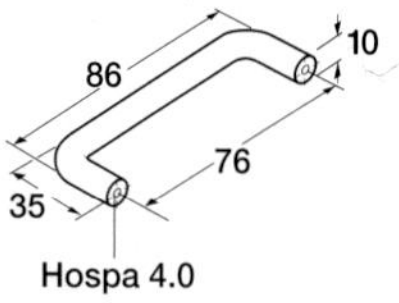

Red

Size A x B	Dimension C	Cat. No.
74 x 33	64	116.55.913
106 x 35	96	116.56.910
138 x 35	128	116.57.917

Packing: 100 pcs.

Nylon Handles

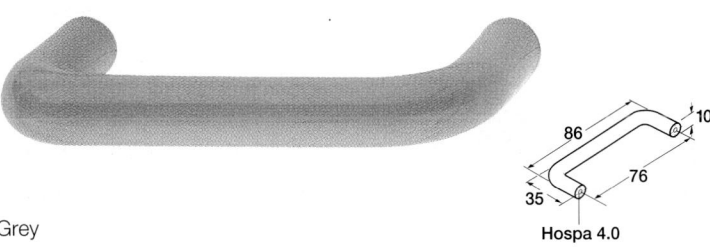

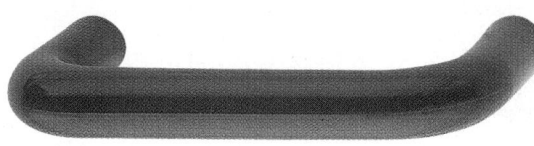

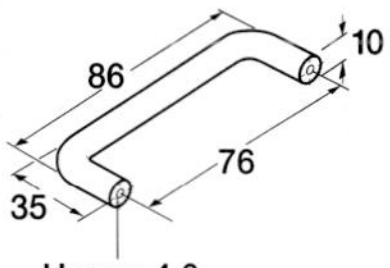

Hospa 4.0

Grey

Size A x B	Dimension C	Cat. No.
74 x 33	64	116.55.511
106 x 35	96	116.56.518
138 x 35	128	116.57.515

Packing: 100 pcs.

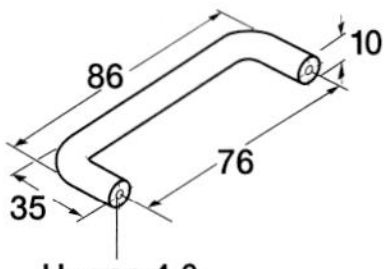

Hospa 4.0

Dark grey

Size A x B	Dimension C	Cat. No.
74 x 33	64	116.55.520
106 x 35	96	116.56.527
138 x 35	128	116.57.524

Packing: 100 pcs.

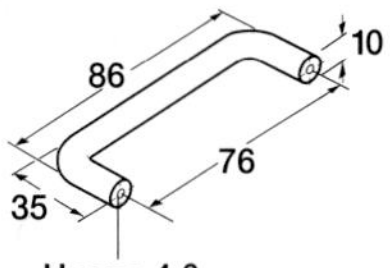

Hospa 4.0

Yellow

Size A x B	Dimension C	Cat. No.
74 x 33	64	116.55.600
106 x 35	96	116.56.607
138 x 35	128	116.57.604

Packing: 100 pcs.

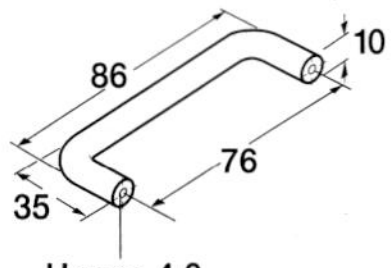

Hospa 4.0

Brown

Size A x B	Dimension C	Cat. No.
74 x 33	64	116.55.119
106 x 35	96	116.56.116
138 x 35	128	116.57.113

Packing: 100 pcs.

Hospa Pan Head Screws
Pozi Recess

Finish: steel, zinc-plated

Length	Cat. No.
13 mm	015.71.811
15 mm	015.71.820
17 mm	015.71.839
20 mm	015.71.848
25 mm	015.71.857
30 mm	015.71.866
35 mm	015.71.875
40 mm	015.71.884
45 mm	015.71.893

Packing: 1000 pcs.

HÄFELE

Nylon Handles

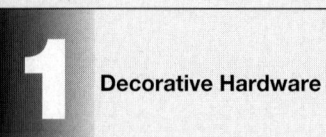

Hospa Pan Head Screws
Pozi Recess
Finish: steel, zinc-plated

Length	Cat. No.
13 mm	015.71.811
15 mm	015.71.820
17 mm	015.71.839
20 mm	015.71.848
25 mm	015.71.857
30 mm	015.71.866
35 mm	015.71.875
40 mm	015.71.884
45 mm	015.71.893

Packing: 1000 pcs.

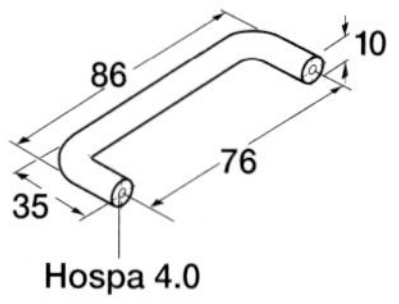

Dark brown

Size A x B	Dimension C	Cat. No.
74 x 33	64	116.55.128
106 x 35	96	116.56.125
138 x 35	128	116.57.122

Packing: 100 pcs.

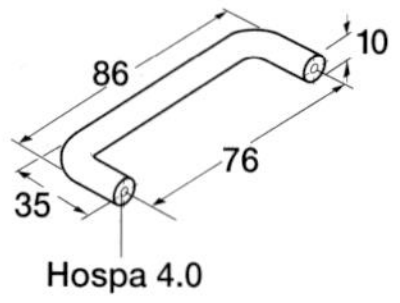

Green

Size A x B	Dimension C	Cat. No.
74 x 33	64	116.55.011
106 x 35	96	116.56.018
138 x 35	128	116.57.015

Packing: 100 pcs.

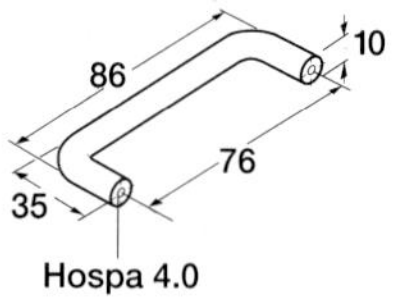

Blue

Size A x B	Dimension C	Cat. No.
74 x 33	64	116.55.815
106 x 35	96	116.56.812
138 x 35	128	116.57.819

Packing: 100 pcs.

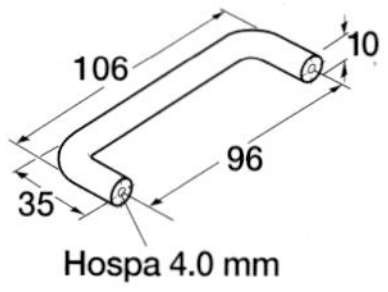

Light brown

Cat. No.	116.56.107

Packing: 100 pcs.

Dimensional data not binding.
We reserve the right to alter
specifications without notice.

Nylon Handles

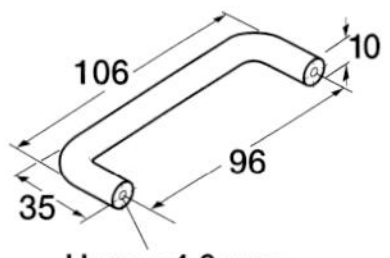

Pink

Cat. No.	116.56.901

Packing: 100 pcs.

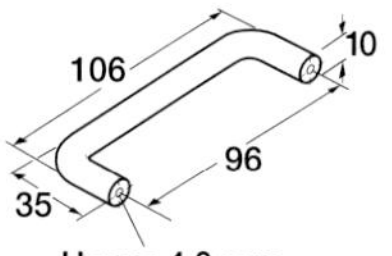

Dark blue

Cat. No.	116.56.849

Packing: 100 pcs.

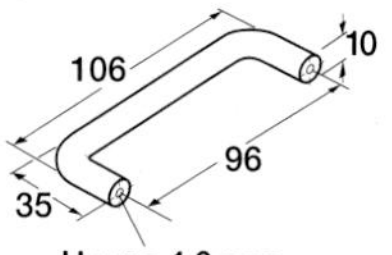

Dove grey

Cat. No.	116.56.545

Packing: 100 pcs.

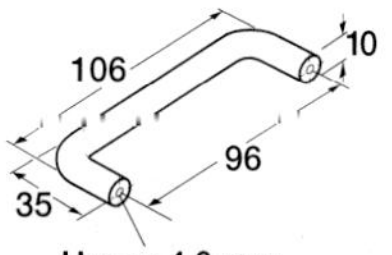

Dove blue

Cat. No.	116.56.858

Packing: 100 pcs.

Hospa Pan Head Screws
Pozi Recess

Finish: steel, zinc-plated

Length	Cat. No.
13 mm	015.71.811
15 mm	015.71.820
17 mm	015.71.839
20 mm	015.71.848
25 mm	015.71.857
30 mm	015.71.866
35 mm	015.71.875
40 mm	015.71.884
45 mm	015.71.893

Packing: 1000 pcs.

HÄFELE

Plastic Handles and Knobs

Hospa Pan Head Screws
Pozi Recess
Finish: steel, zinc-plated

Length	Cat. No.
13 mm	015.71.811
15 mm	015.71.820
17 mm	015.71.839
20 mm	015.71.848
25 mm	015.71.857
30 mm	015.71.866
35 mm	015.71.875
40 mm	015.71.884
45 mm	015.71.893

Packing: 1000 pcs.

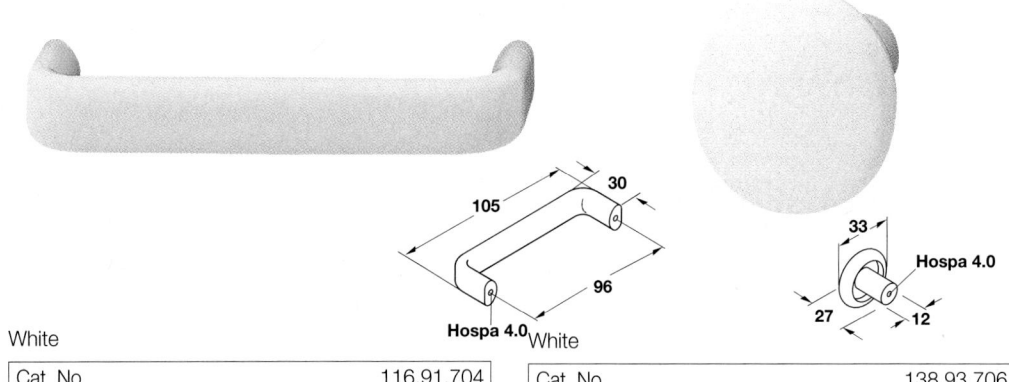

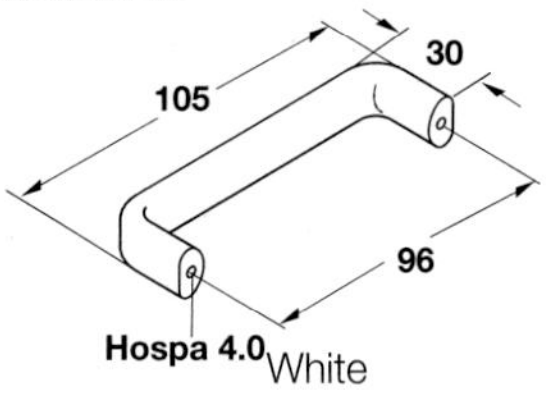

White

Cat. No.	116.91.704

Packing: 100 pcs.

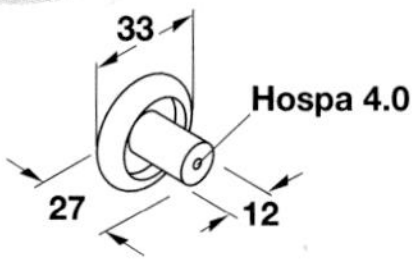

White

Cat. No.	138.93.706

Packing: 100 pcs.

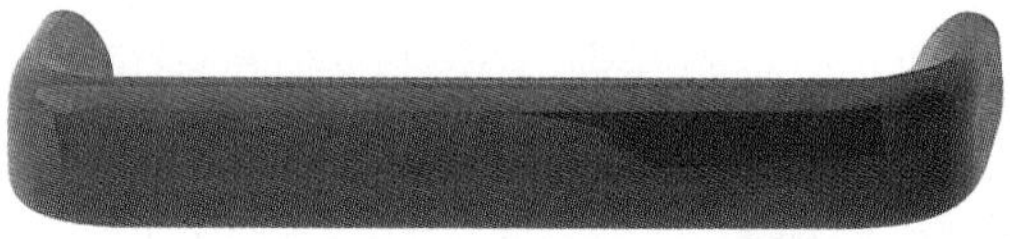
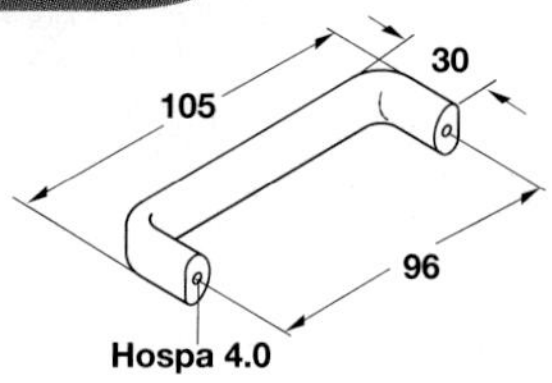

Red

Cat. No.	116.91.910

Packing: 100 pcs.

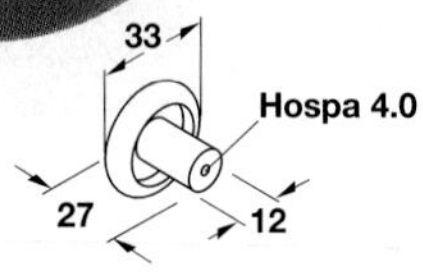

Red

Cat. No.	138.93.910

Packing: 100 pcs.

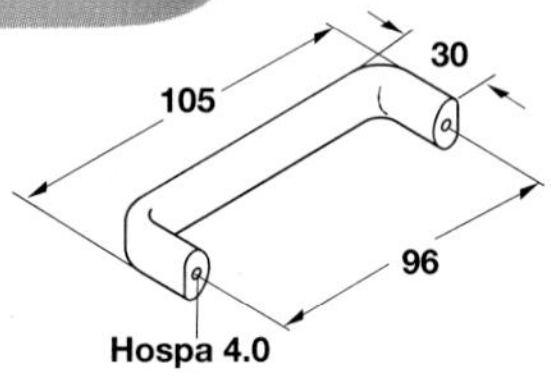

Light blue

Cat. No.	116.91.830

Packing: 100 pcs.

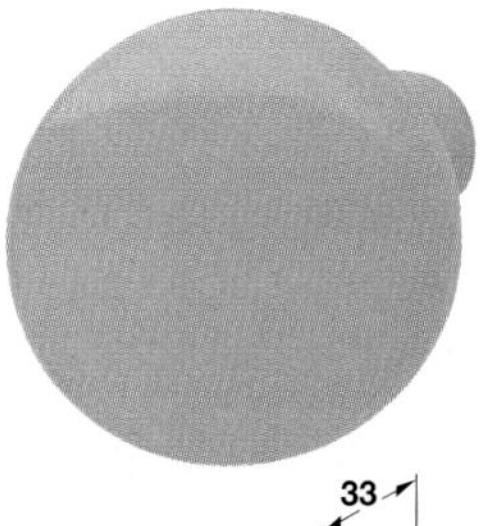
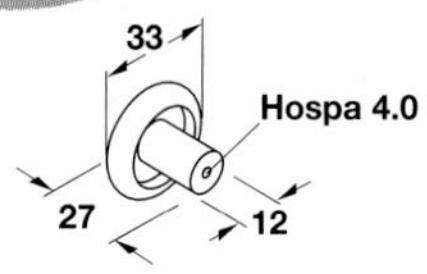

Light blue

Cat. No.	138.93.830

Packing: 100 pcs.

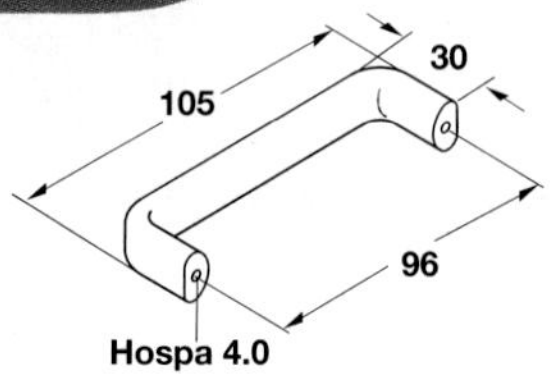

Blue

Cat. No.	116.91.800

Packing: 100 pcs.

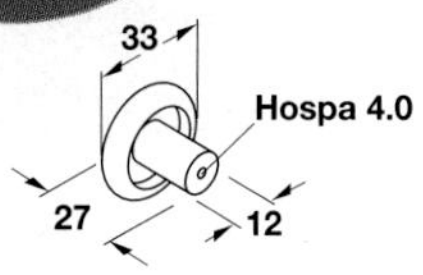

Blue

Cat. No.	138.93.800

Packing: 100 pcs.

Dimensional data not binding.
We reserve the right to alter specifications without notice.

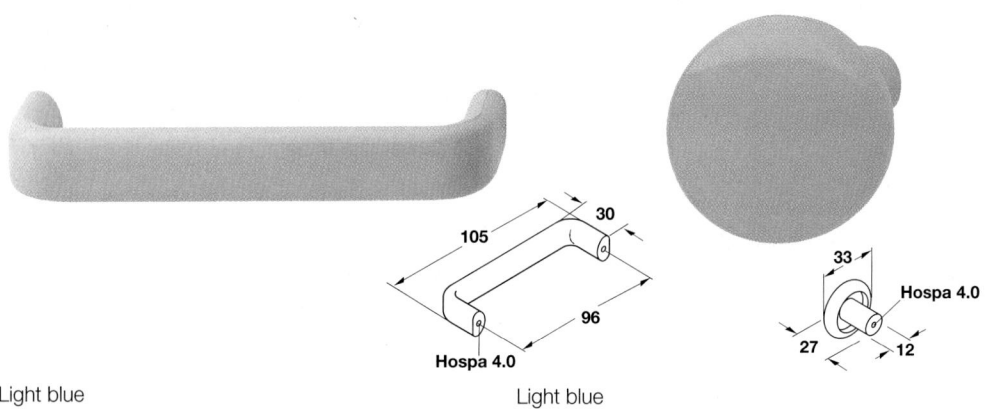

Plastic Handles and Knobs

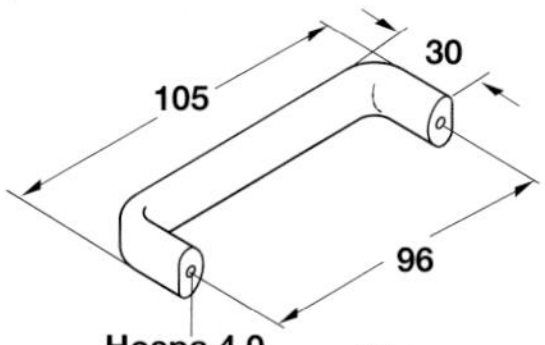

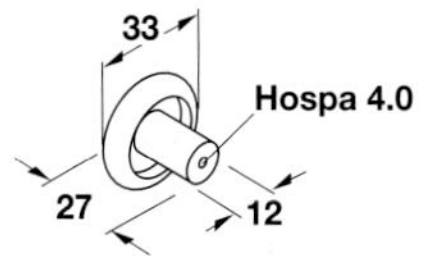

Lilac

Cat. No.	116.91.890

Packing: 100 pcs.

Lilac

Cat. No.	138.93.890

Packing: 100 pcs.

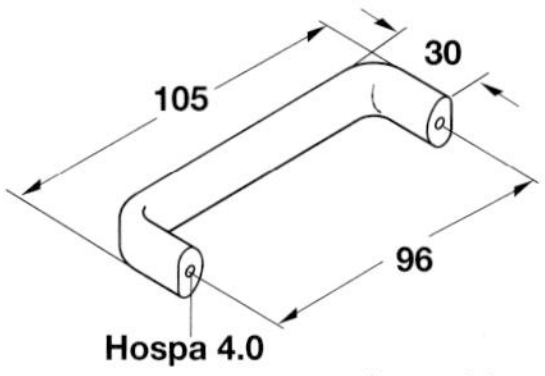

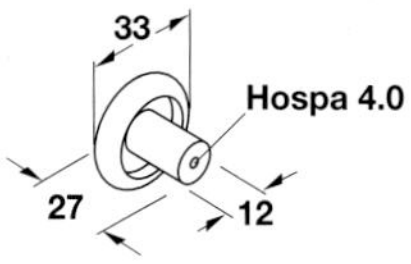

Aqua blue

Cat. No.	116.91.810

Packing: 100 pcs.

Aqua blue

Cat. No.	138.93.810

Packing: 100 pcs.

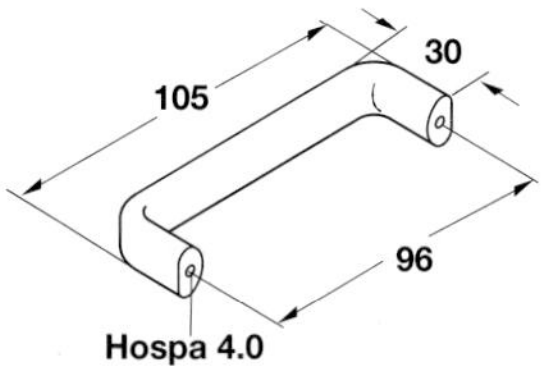

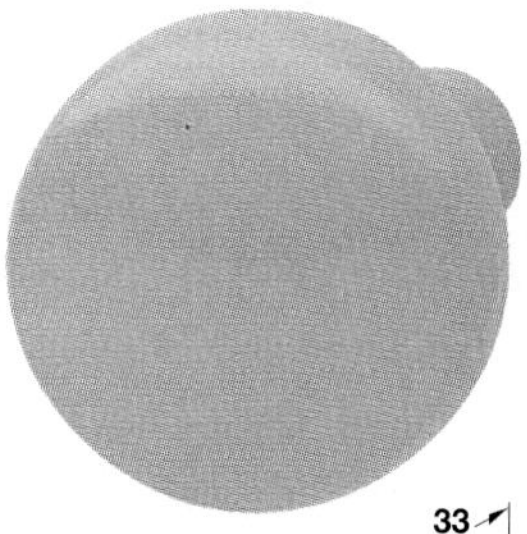

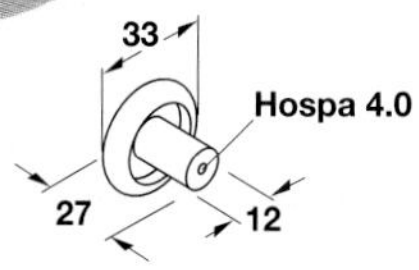

Peach

Cat. No.	116.91.940

Packing: 100 pcs.

Peach

Cat. No.	138.93.940

Packing: 100 pcs.

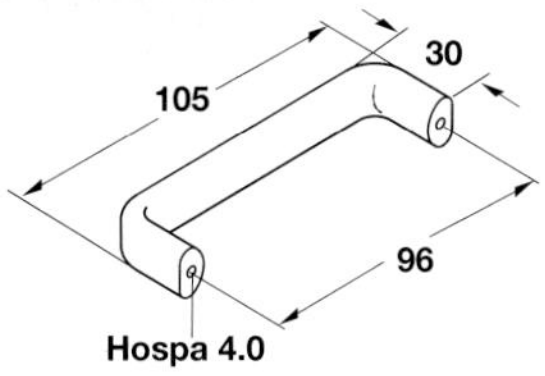

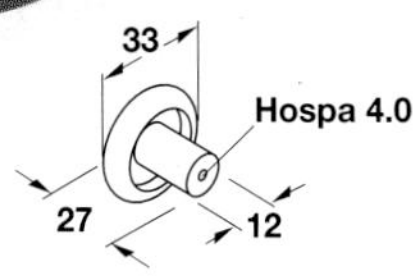

Green

Cat. No.	116.91.000

Packing: 100 pcs.

Green

Cat. No.	138.93.000

Packing: 100 pcs.

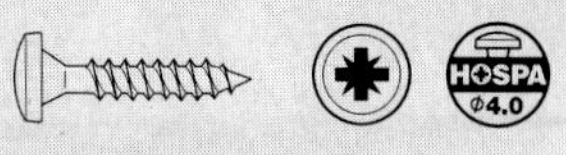

Hospa Pan Head Screws
Pozi Recess
Finish: steel, zinc-plated

Length	Cat. No.
13 mm	015.71.811
15 mm	015.71.820
17 mm	015.71.839
20 mm	015.71.848
25 mm	015.71.857
30 mm	015.71.866
35 mm	015.71.875
40 mm	015.71.884
45 mm	015.71.893

Packing: 1000 pcs.

HÄFELE

Plastic Handles with Knob

Hospa Pan Head Screws
Pozi Recess
Finish: steel, zinc-plated

Length	Cat. No.
13 mm	015.71.811
15 mm	015.71.820
17 mm	015.71.839
20 mm	015.71.848
25 mm	015.71.857
30 mm	015.71.866
35 mm	015.71.875
40 mm	015.71.884
45 mm	015.71.893

Packing: 1000 pcs.

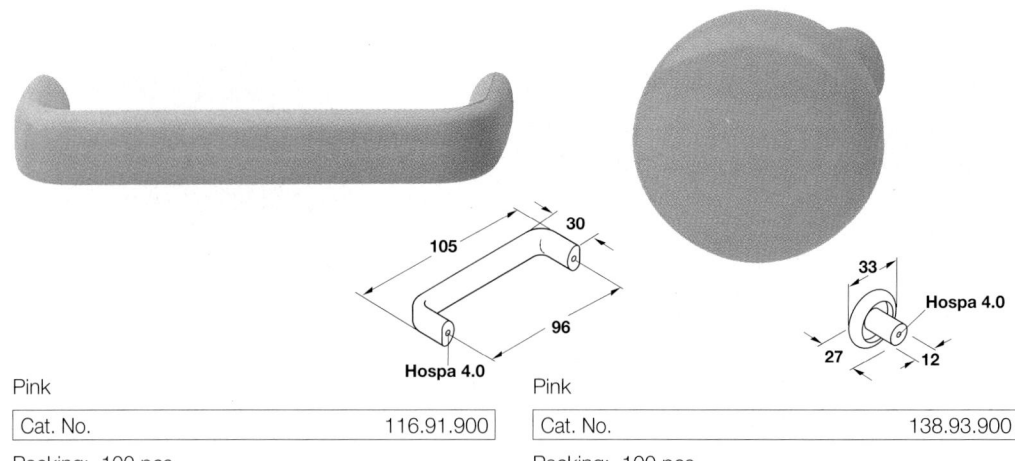

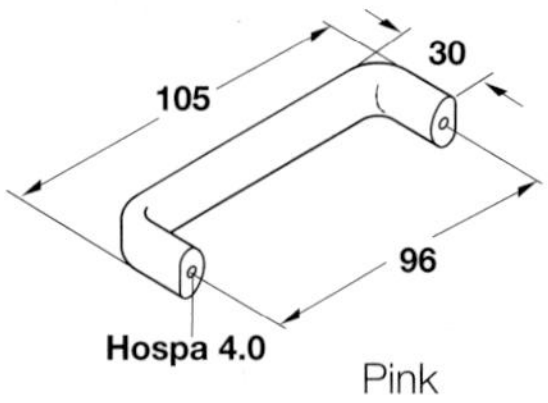

Pink

Cat. No.	116.91.900

Packing: 100 pcs.

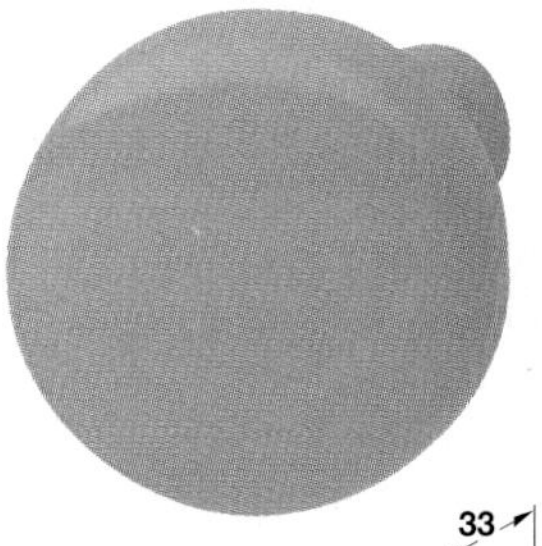
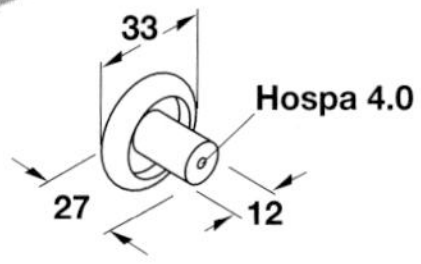

Pink

Cat. No.	138.93.900

Packing: 100 pcs.

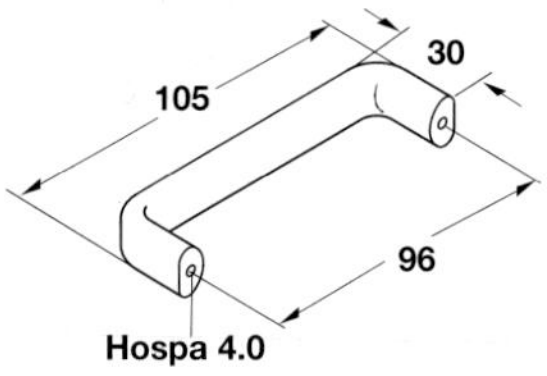

Opal green

Cat. No.	116.91.010

Packing: 100 pcs.

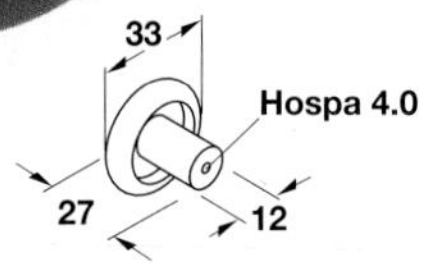

Opal green

Cat. No.	138.93.010

Packing: 100 pcs.

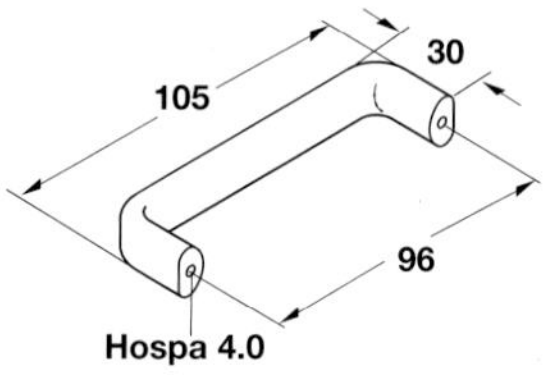

Blue steel

Cat. No.	116.91.840

Packing: 100 pcs.

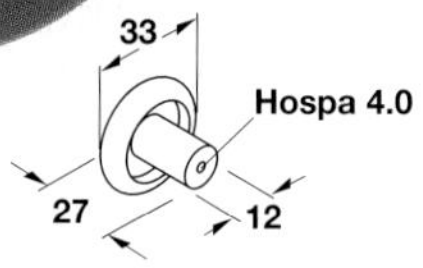

Blue steel

Cat. No.	138.93.840

Packing: 100 pcs.

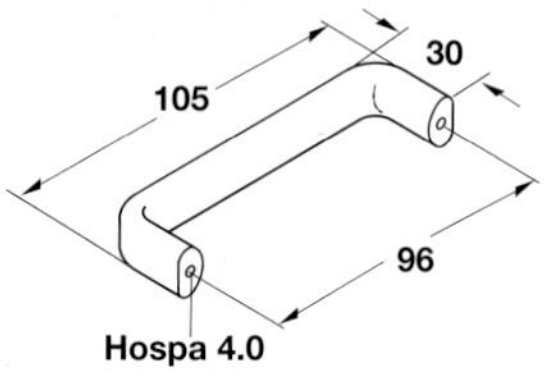

Purple blush

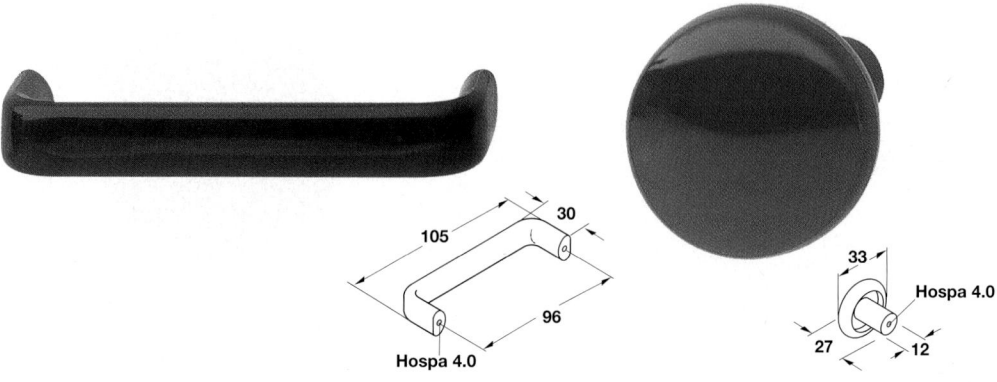

Cat. No.	116.91.960

Packing: 100 pcs.

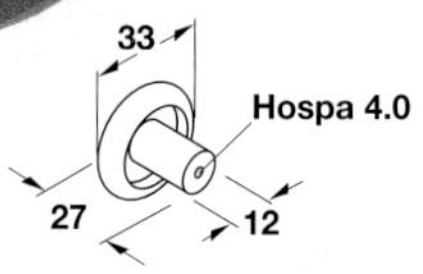

Purple blush

Cat. No.	138.93.860

Packing: 100 pcs.

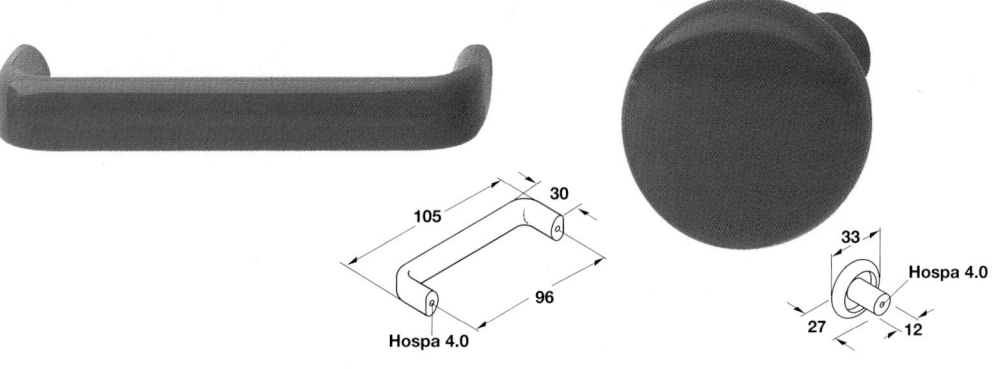

Plastic Handles and Knobs

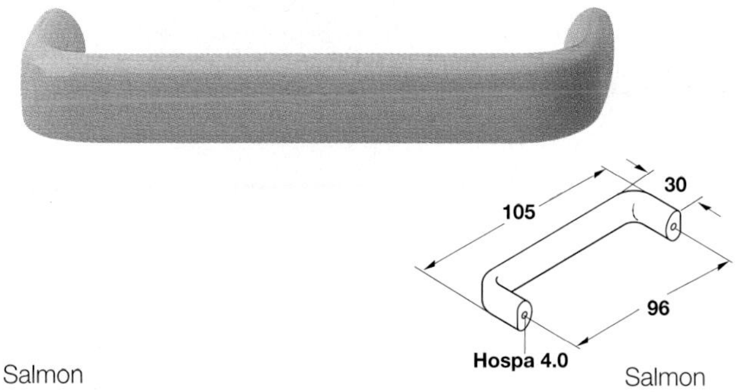

Salmon

Cat. No.	116.91.930

Packing: 100 pcs.

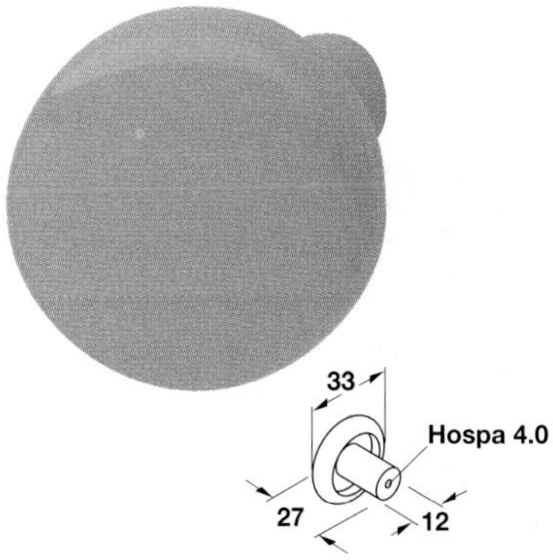

Salmon

Cat. No.	138.93.930

Packing: 100 pcs.

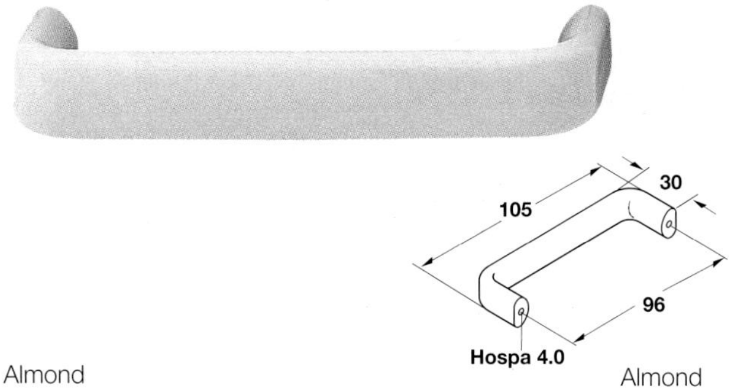

Almond

Cat. No.	116.91.401

Packing: 100 pcs.

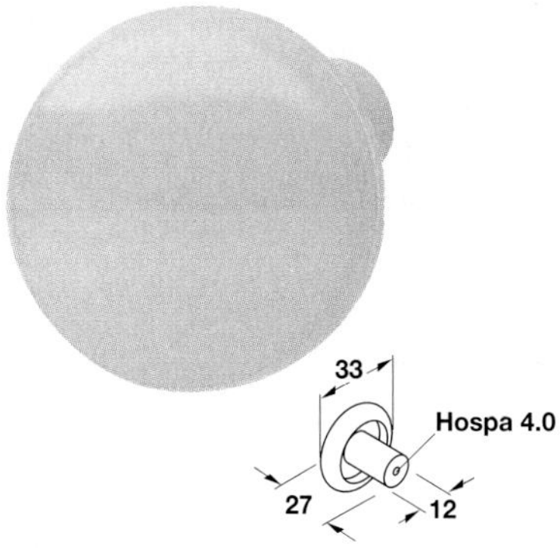

Almond

Cat. No.	138.93.401

Packing: 100 pcs.

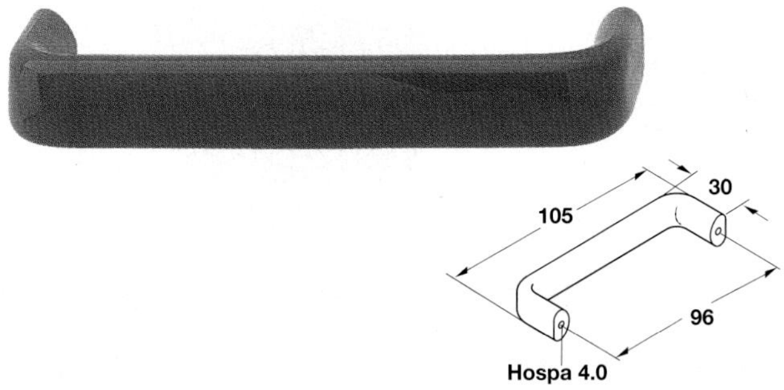

Raspberry

Cat. No.	116.91.970

Packing: 100 pcs.

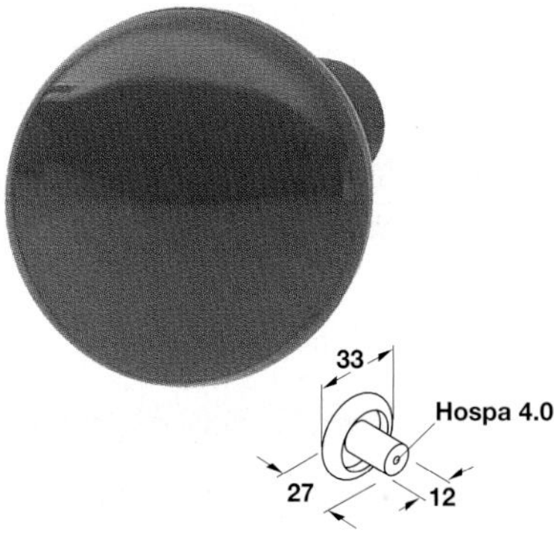

Raspberry

Cat. No.	138.93.970

Packing: 100 pcs.

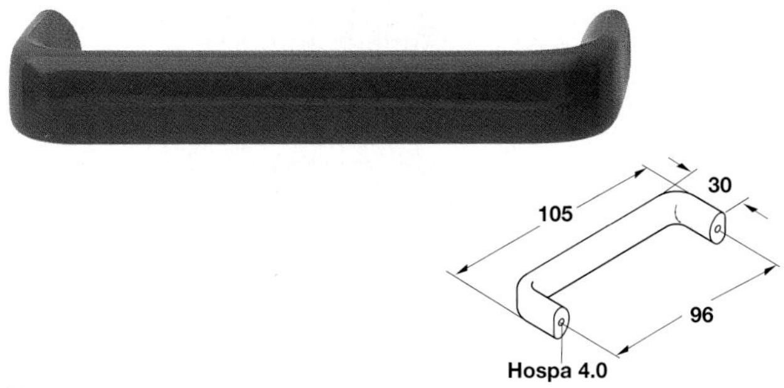

Hunter green

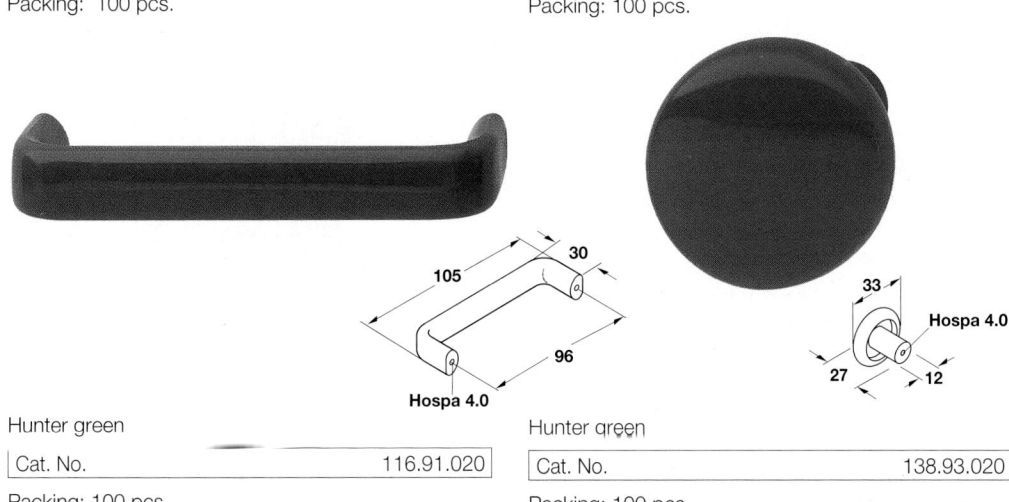

Cat. No.	116.91.020

Packing: 100 pcs.

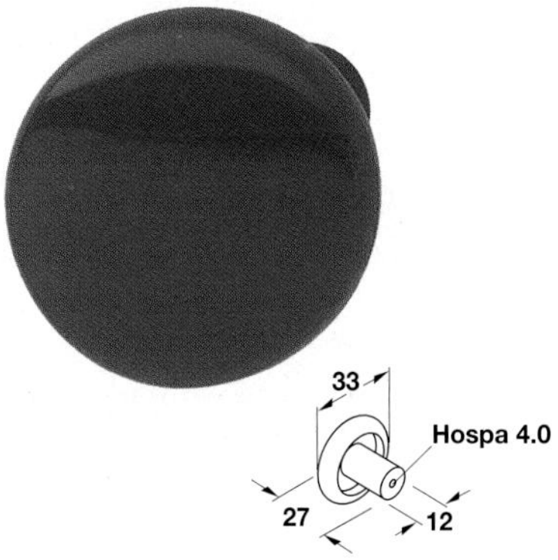

Hunter green

Cat. No.	138.93.020

Packing: 100 pcs.

Hospa Pan Head Screws
Pozi Recess
Finish: steel, zinc-plated

Length	Cat. No.
13 mm	015.71.811
15 mm	015.71.820
17 mm	015.71.839
20 mm	015.71.848
25 mm	015.71.857
30 mm	015.71.866
35 mm	015.71.875
40 mm	015.71.884
45 mm	015.71.893

Packing: 1000 pcs.

Dimensional data not binding.
We reserve the right to alter specifications without notice.

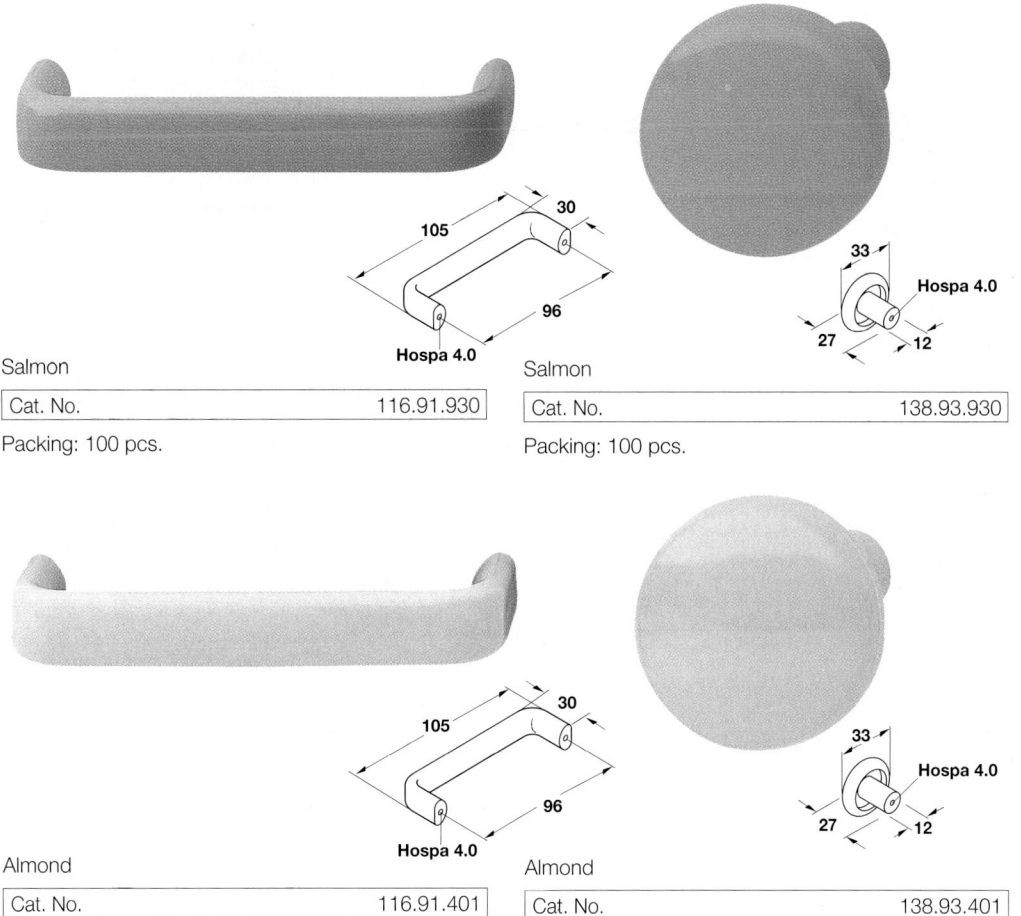

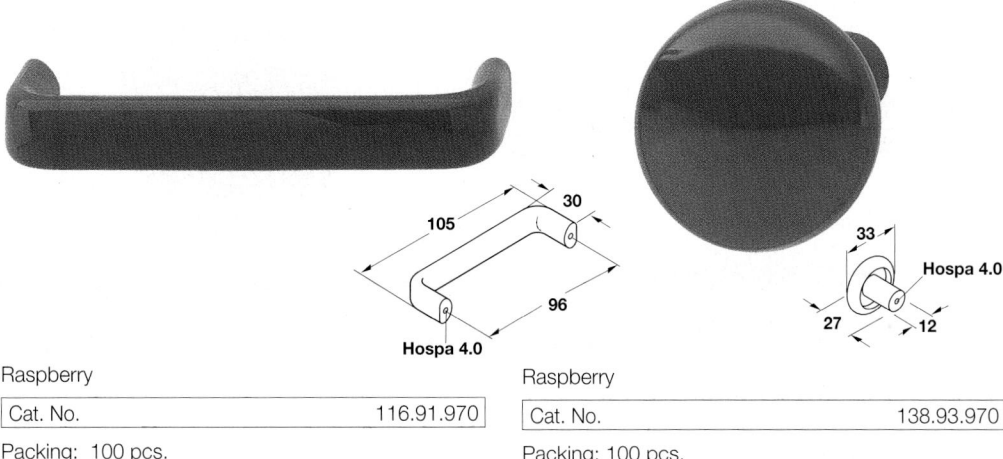

Plastic Handles and Knobs

Hospa Pan Head Screws
Pozi Recess
Finish: steel, zinc-plated

Length	Cat. No.
13 mm	015.71.811
15 mm	015.71.820
17 mm	015.71.839
20 mm	015.71.848
25 mm	015.71.857
30 mm	015.71.866
35 mm	015.71.875
40 mm	015.71.884
45 mm	015.71.893

Packing: 1000 pcs.

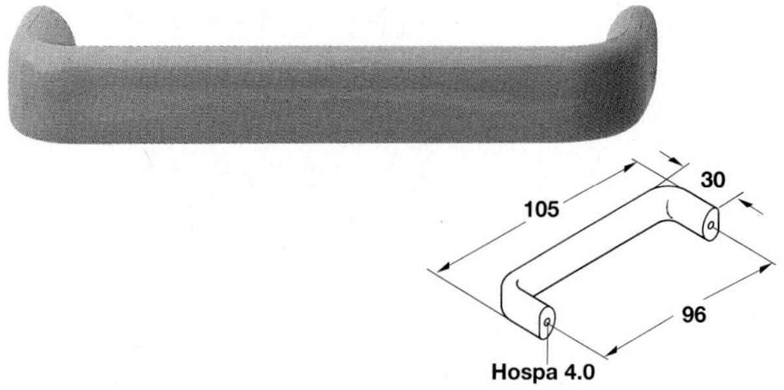

Grey

Cat. No.	116.91.500

Packing: 100 pcs.

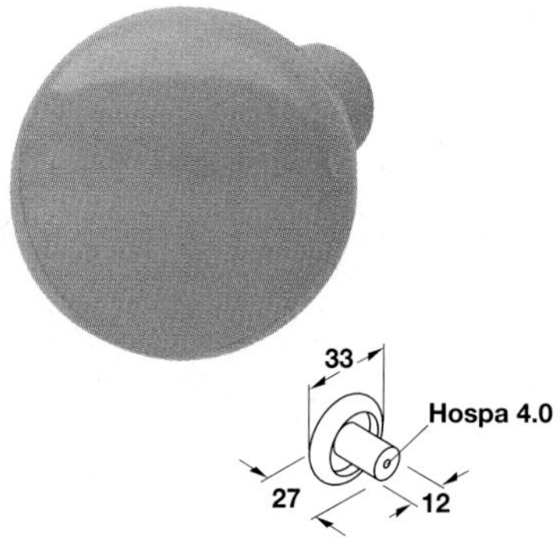

Grey

Cat. No.	138.93.500

Packing: 100 pcs.

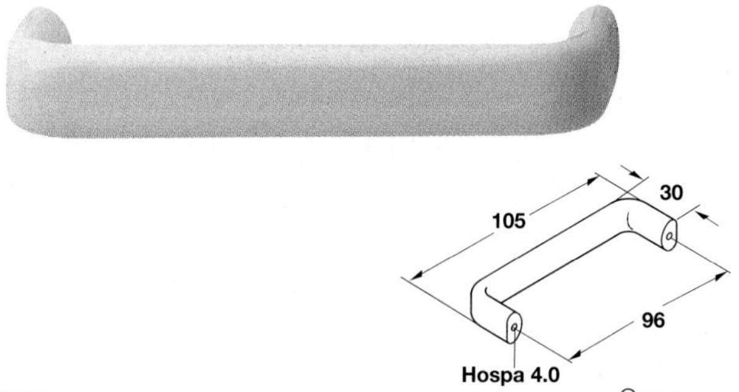

Creme

Cat. No.	116.91.400

Packing: 100 pcs.

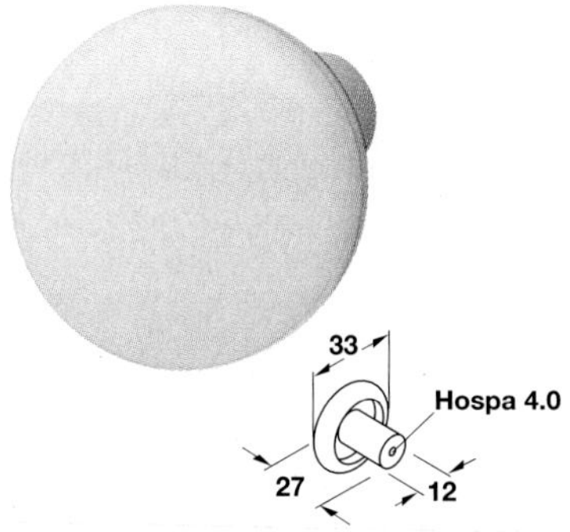

Creme

Cat. No.	138.93.402

Packing: 100 pcs.

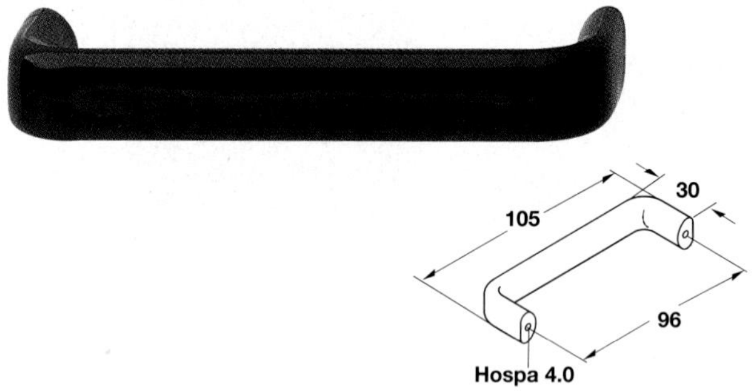

Brown

Cat. No.	116.91.100

Packing: 100 pcs.

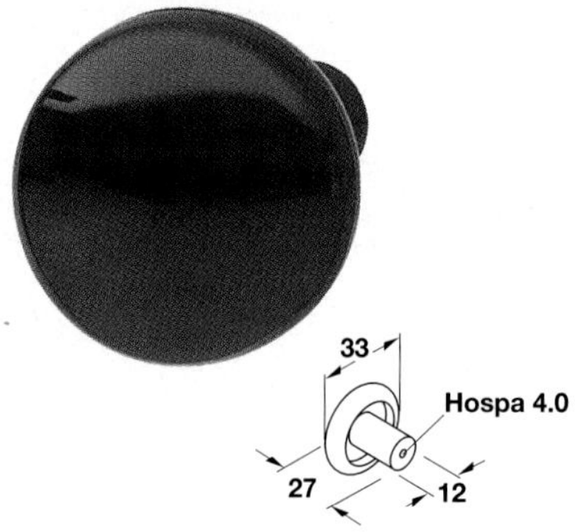

Brown

Cat. No.	138.93.100

Packing: 100 pcs.

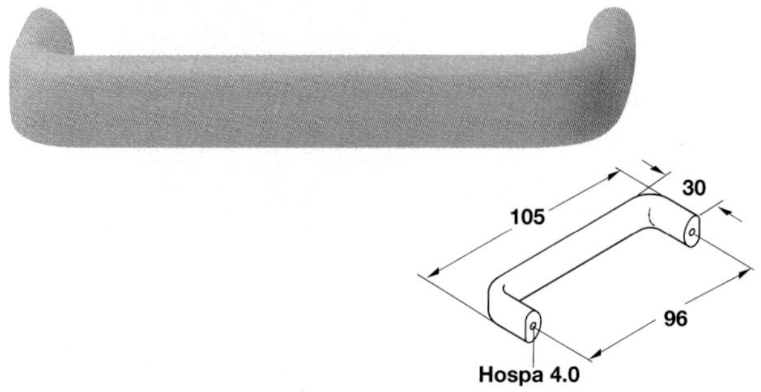

Yellow

Cat. No.	116.91.600

Packing: 100 pcs.

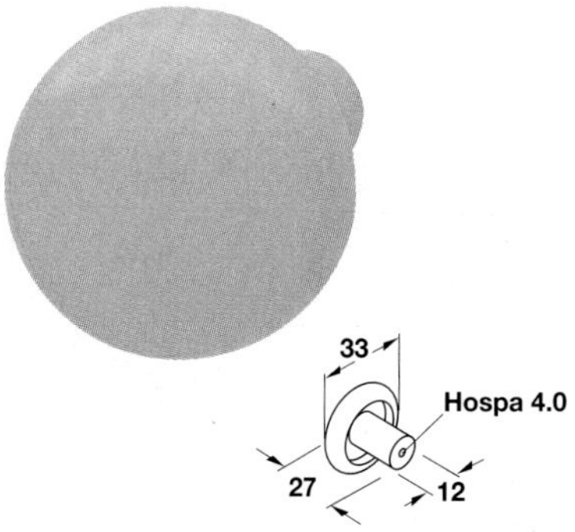

Yellow

Cat. No.	138.93.600

Packing: 100 pcs.

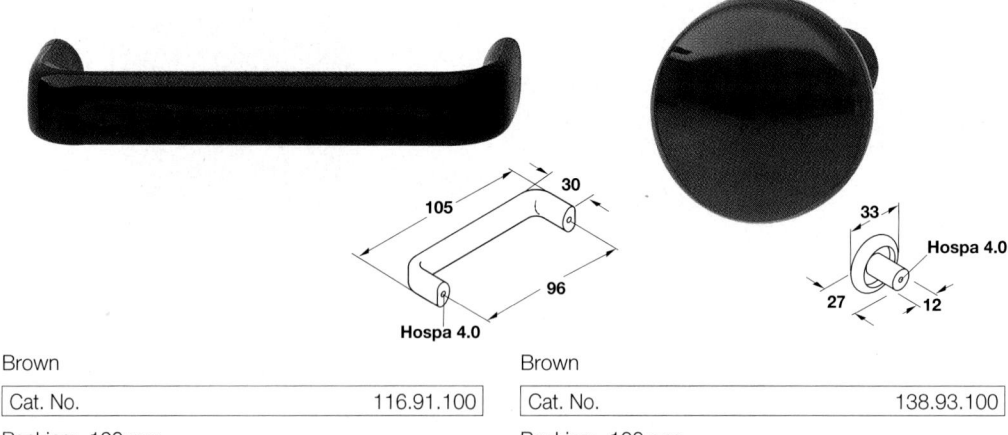

Plastic Handles and Knobs

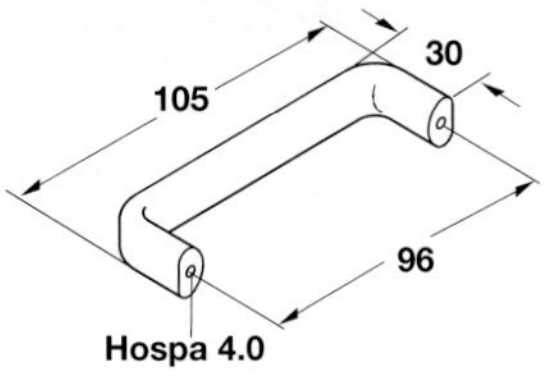

Black

Cat. No.	116.91.302

Packing: 100 pcs.

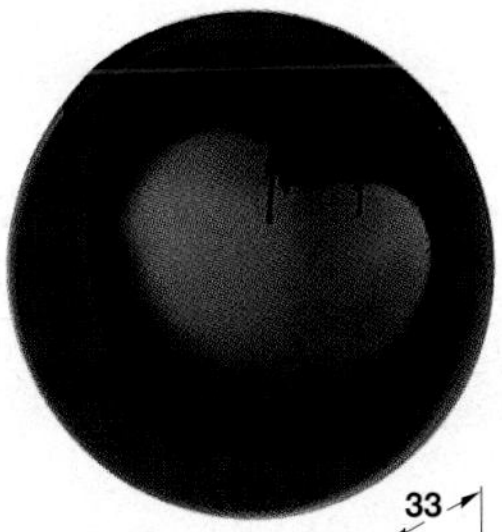

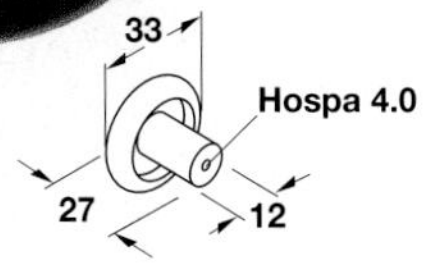

Black

Cat. No.	138.93.304

Packing: 100 pcs.

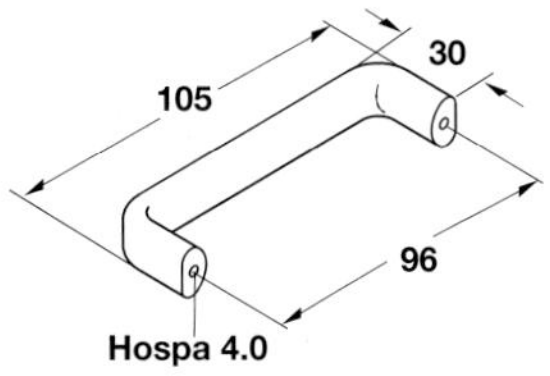

Aubergine

Cat. No.	116.91.950

Packing: 100 pcs.

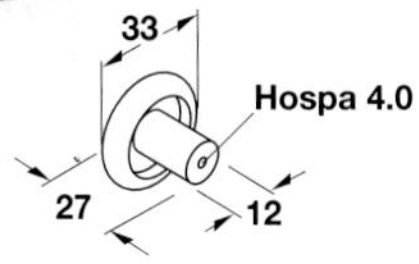

Aubergine

Cat. No.	138.93.950

Packing: 100 pcs.

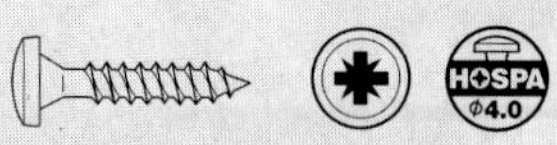

Hospa Pan Head Screws
Pozi Recess
Finish: steel, zinc-plated

Length	Cat. No.
13 mm	015.71.811
15 mm	015.71.820
17 mm	015.71.839
20 mm	015.71.848
25 mm	015.71.857
30 mm	015.71.866
35 mm	015.71.875
40 mm	015.71.884
45 mm	015.71.893

Packing: 1000 pcs.

HÄFELE

Rubber Handles

Threaded Screws M4
Combined slot, suitable for flat or cross blades
Finish: steel, zinc-plated

Length	Cat. No.
10 mm	022.35.109
12 mm	022.35.127
15 mm	022.35.154
18 mm	022.35.181
20 mm	022.35.207
22 mm	022.35.225
23 mm	022.35.234
25 mm	022.35.252
28 mm	022.35.289
30 mm	022.35.305
35 mm	022.35.350
38 mm	022.35.387
40 mm	022.35.403
45 mm	022.35.458
50 mm	022.35.501
60 mm	022.35.609

Packing: 100 and 1000 pcs.

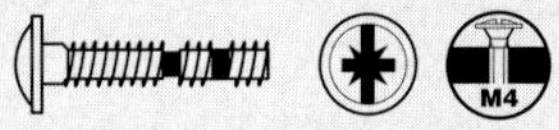

Threaded Breakoff Screw M4
Combined slot, suitable for flat or cross blades
Finish: steel, zinc-plated

Length	Cat. No.
1 3/4" x 3/4"	022.35.887

Packing: 100 and 1000 pcs.

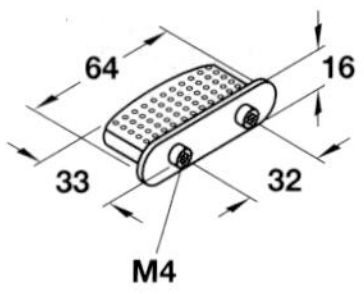

Black

Cat. No.	105.51.300

Packing: 25 pcs.

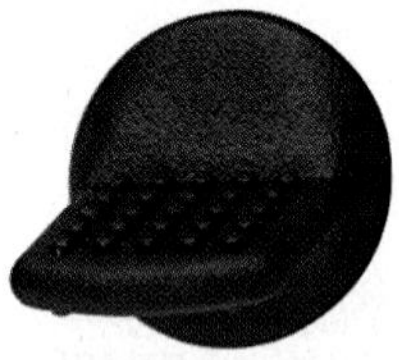
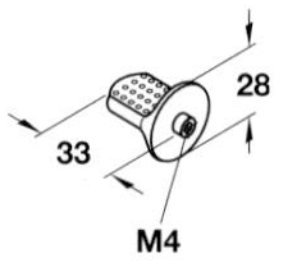

Black

Cat. No.	139.19.300

Packing: 25 pcs.

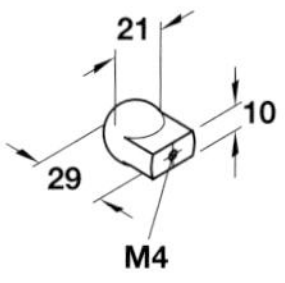

Black

Cat. No.	138.81.304

Packing: 25 pcs.

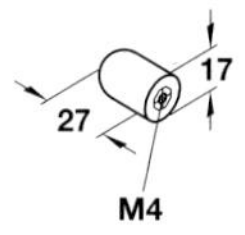

Black

Cat. No.	138.82.301

Packing: 25 pcs.

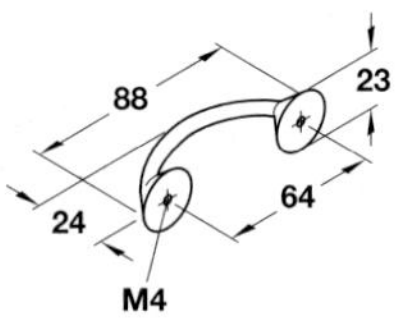

Black

Cat. No.	105.41.303

Packing: 25 pcs.

Dimensional data not binding. We reserve the right to alter specifications without notice.

Brass Knobs

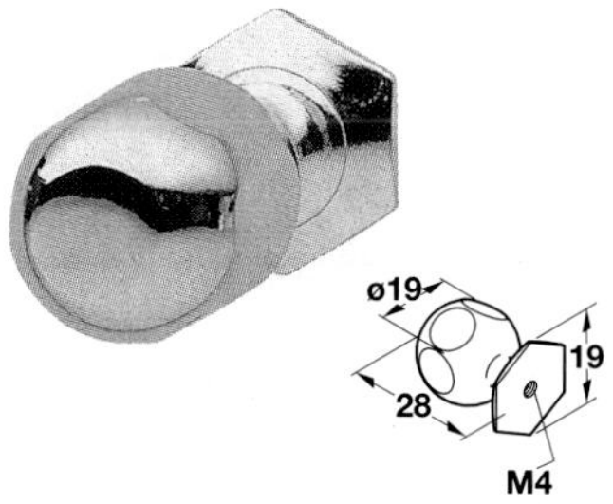

Polished and lacquered

Cat. No.	136.35.810

Packing: 25 pcs.

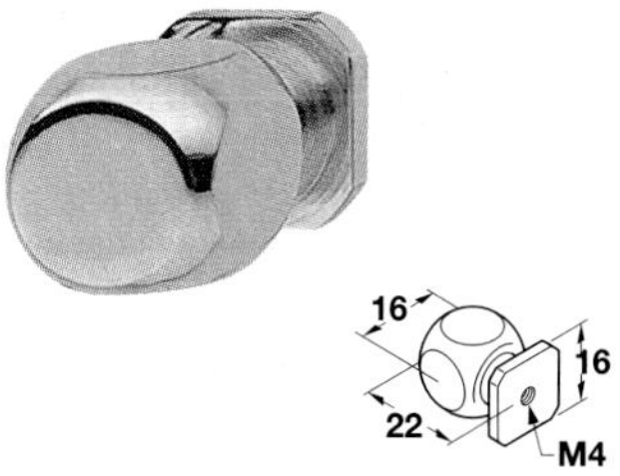

Polished and lacquered

Cat. No.	136.38.810

Packing: 25 pcs.

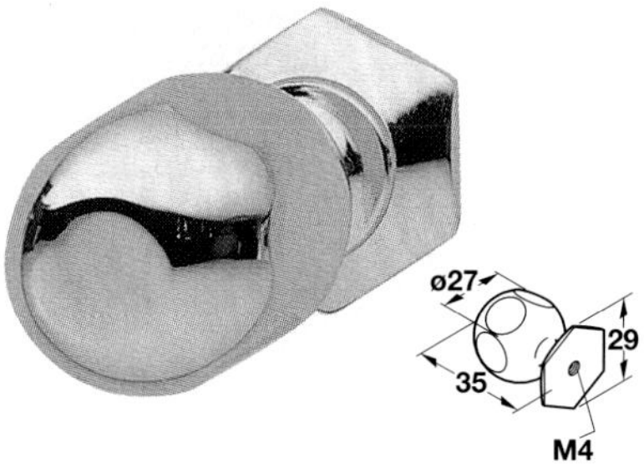

Polished and lacquered

Cat. No.	136.35.820

Packing: 25 pcs.

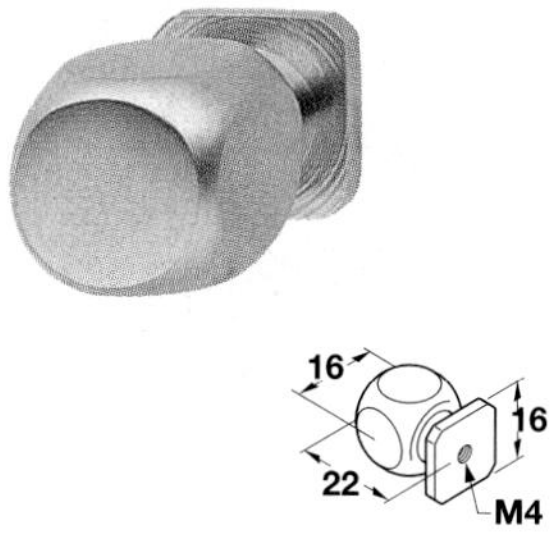

Matt nickel plated

Cat. No.	136.38.610

Packing: 25 pcs.

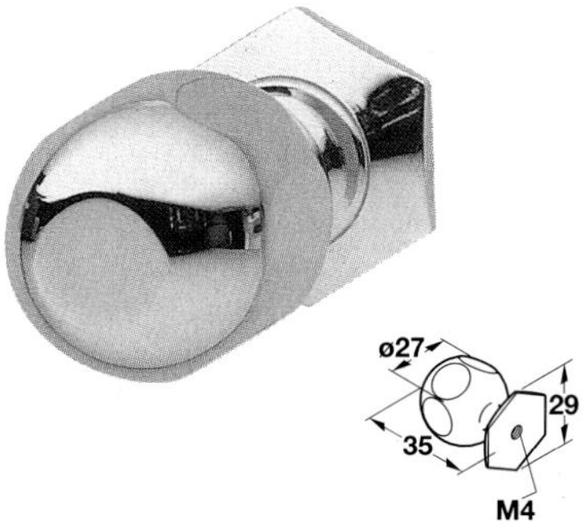

Chrome polished

Cat. No.	136.35.220

Packing: 25 pcs.

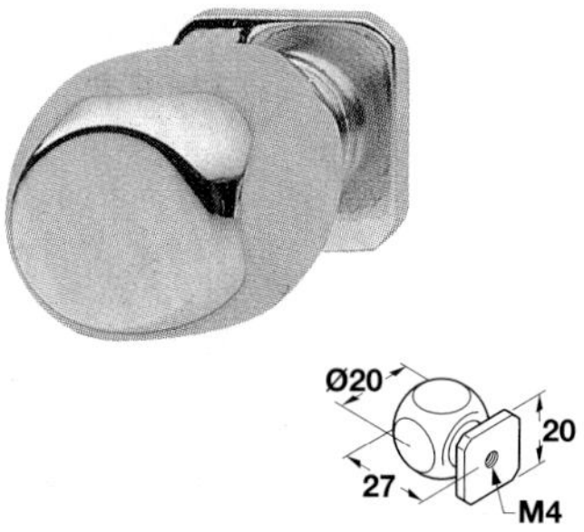

Polished and lacquered

Cat. No.	136.38.820

Packing: 25 pcs.

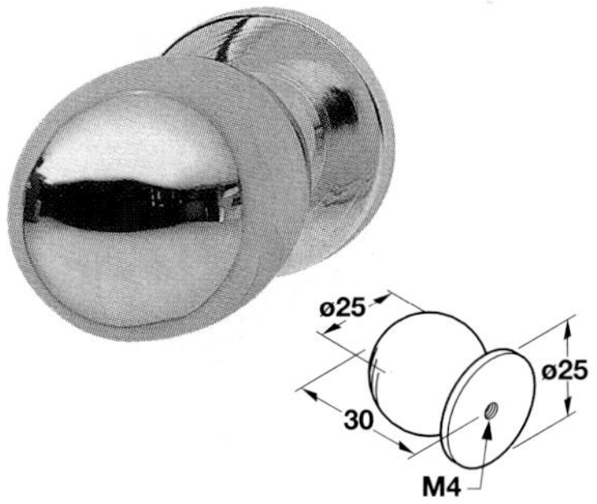

Polished and lacquered

Cat. No.	136.42.800

Packing: 25 pcs.

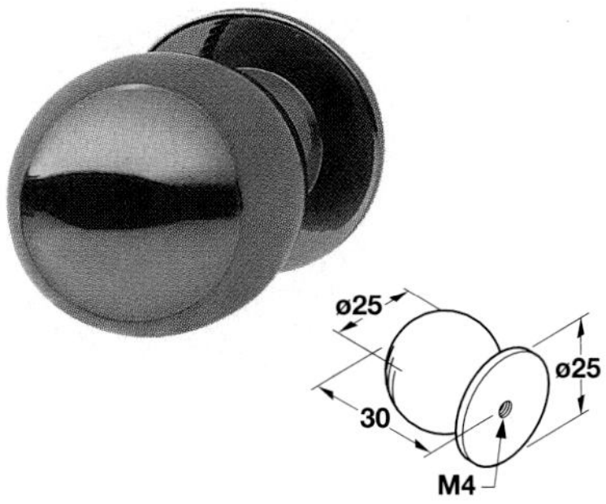

Black nickel plated

Cat. No.	136.42.300

Packing: 25 pcs.

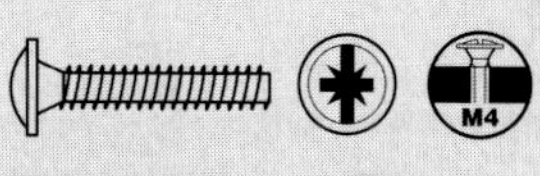

Threaded Screws M4
Combined slot, suitable for flat or cross blades
Finish: steel, zinc-plated

Length	Cat. No.
10 mm	022.35.109
12 mm	022.35.127
15 mm	022.35.154
18 mm	022.35.181
20 mm	022.35.207
22 mm	022.35.225
23 mm	022.35.234
25 mm	022.35.252
28 mm	022.35.289
30 mm	022.35.305
35 mm	022.35.350
38 mm	022.35.387
40 mm	022.35.403
45 mm	022.35.458
50 mm	022.35.501
60 mm	022.35.609

Packing: 100 and 1000 pcs.

Threaded Breakoff Screw M4
Combined slot, suitable for flat or cross blades
Finish: steel, zinc-plated

Length	Cat. No.
1 3/4" x 3/4"	022.35.887

Packing: 100 and 1000 pcs.

Brass Knobs

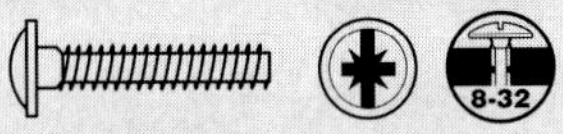

Threaded Screws 8-32

Combined slot, suitable for flat or cross blades

Finish: steel, yellow chromated

Length	Cat. No.
22 mm	022.25.229
25 mm	022.25.256
32 mm	022.25.327
38 mm	022.25.381
45 mm	022.25.452

Packing: 100 and 1000 pcs.

Threaded Screws M4

Combined slot, suitable for flat or cross blades

Finish: steel, zinc-plated

Length	Cat. No.
10 mm	022.35.109
12 mm	022.35.127
15 mm	022.35.154
18 mm	022.35.181
20 mm	022.35.207
22 mm	022.35.225
23 mm	022.35.234
25 mm	022.35.252
28 mm	022.35.289
30 mm	022.35.305
35 mm	022.35.350
38 mm	022.35.387
40 mm	022.35.403
45 mm	022.35.458
50 mm	022.35.501
60 mm	022.35.609

Packing: 100 and 1000 pcs.

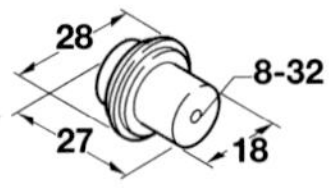

Ring: chrome polished
Center: polished and lacquered

Cat. No.	136.00.809

Packing: 25 pcs.

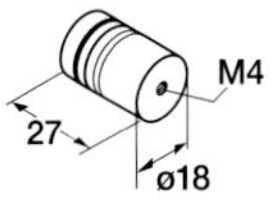

Top/base: chrome
Center: polished and laquered

Cat. No.	136.01.208

Packing: 25 pcs.

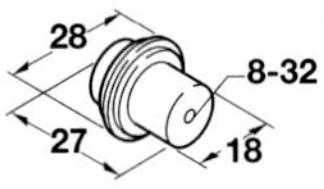

Ring: polished and lacquered
Center: black nickel plated

Cat. No.	136.00.830

Packing: 25 pcs.

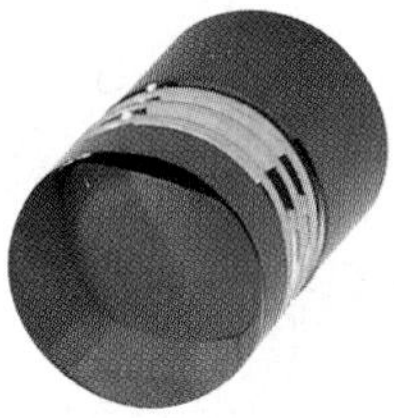

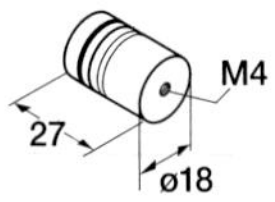

Top/base: black nickel
Center: polished and laquered

Cat. No.	136.01.306

Packing: 25 pcs.

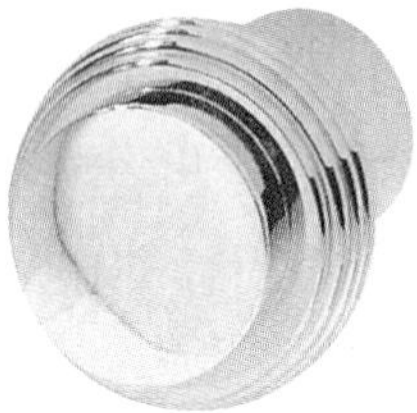

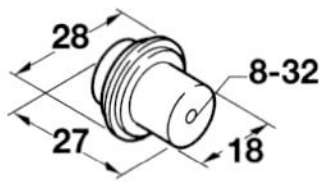

Ring: polished and lacquered
Center: chrome polished

Cat. No.	136.00.201

Packing: 25 pcs.

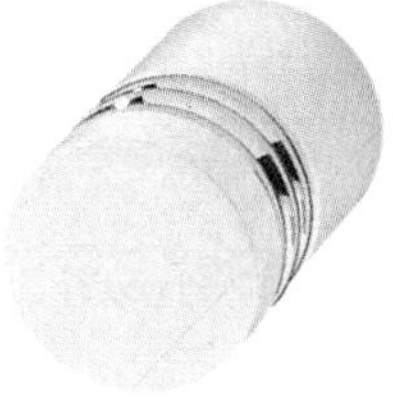

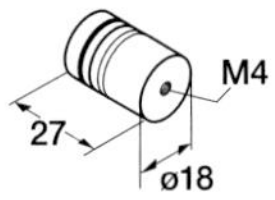

Top/base: white
Center: chrome polished

Cat. No.	136.01.708

Packing: 25 pcs.

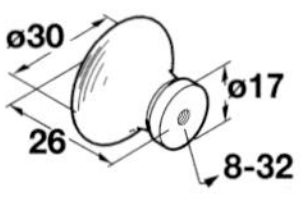

Base, polished and lacquered
Insert: chrome polished

Cat. No.	136.92.820

Packing: 25 pcs.

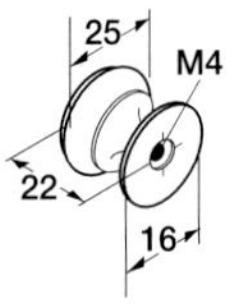

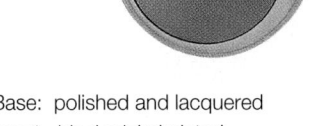

Base: polished and lacquered
Insert: black nickel plated

Cat. No.	137.50.804

Packing: 25 pcs.

Brass Knobs

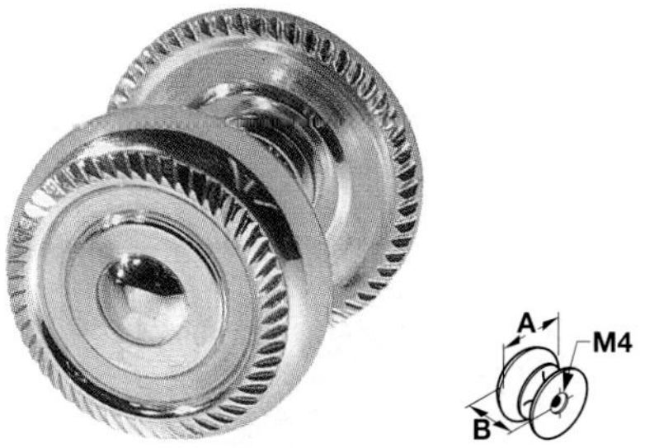

Polished & laquered

Size A x B	Cat. No.
32 x 30	137.59.834
25 x 25	137.59.825

Packing: 25 pcs.

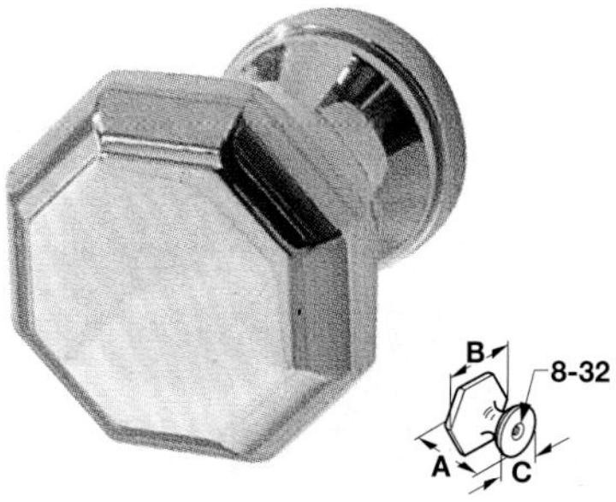

Polished & laquered

Size A x B x C	Cat. No.
28 x 36 x 19	137.62.813
24 x 27 x 18	137.62.804

Packing: 25 pcs.

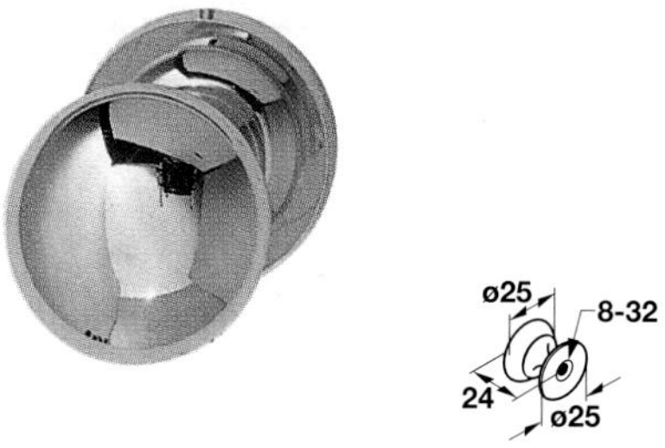

Polished & laquered

Cat. No.	137.64.808

Packing: 25 pcs.

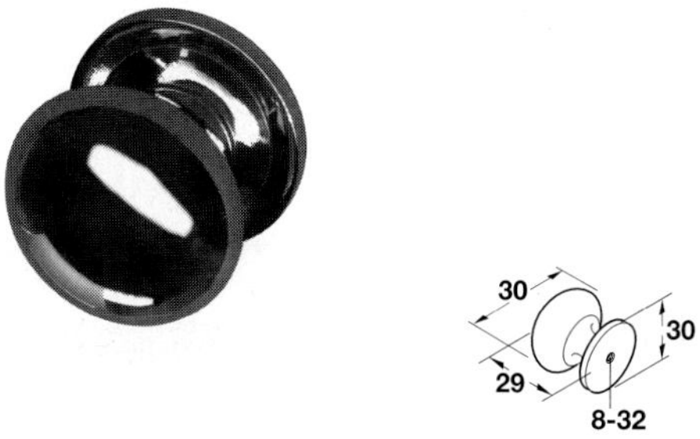

Polished and lacquered

Cat. No.	134.47.811

Packing: 25 pcs.

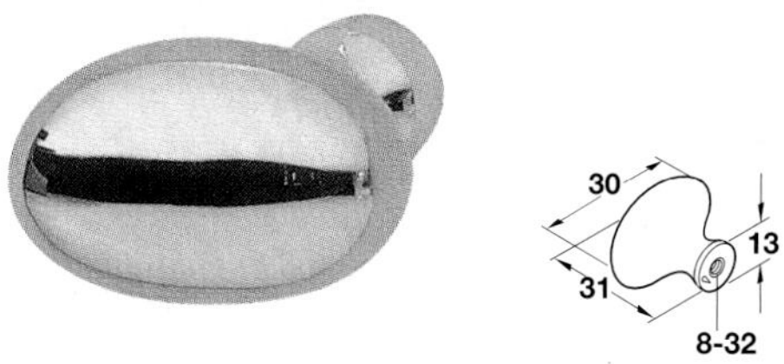

Polished and lacquered

Cat. No.	137.63.801

Packing: 25 pcs.

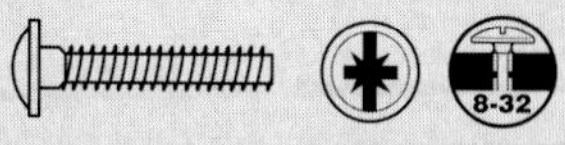

Threaded Screws 8-32
Combined slot, suitable for flat or cross blades

Finish: steel, yellow chromated

Length	Cat. No.
22 mm	022.25.229
25 mm	022.25.256
32 mm	022.25.327
38 mm	022.25.381
45 mm	022.25.452

Packing: 100 and 1000 pcs.

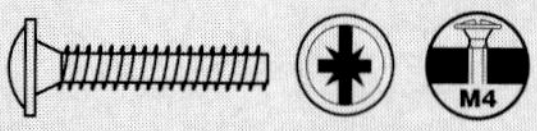

Threaded Screws M4
Combined slot, suitable for flat or cross blades

Finish: steel, zinc-plated

Length	Cat. No.
10 mm	022.35.109
12 mm	022.35.127
15 mm	022.35.154
18 mm	022.35.181
20 mm	022.35.207
22 mm	022.35.225
23 mm	022.35.234
25 mm	022.35.252
28 mm	022.35.289
30 mm	022.35.305
35 mm	022.35.350
38 mm	022.35.387
40 mm	022.35.403
45 mm	022.35.458
50 mm	022.35.501
60 mm	022.35.609

Packing: 100 and 1000 pcs.

HÄFELE

Brass knobs

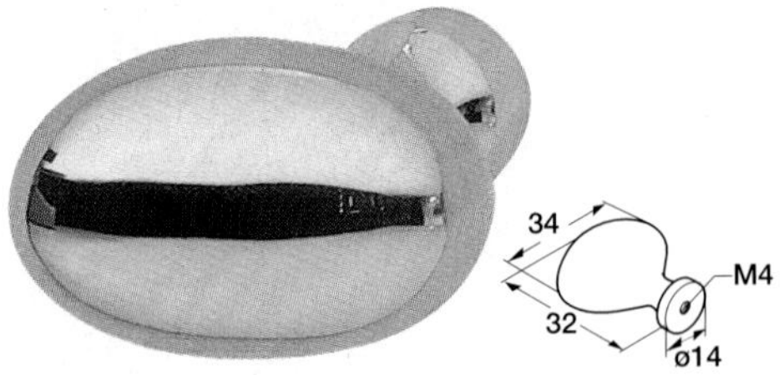

Polished and lacquered

Cat No.	137.42.802

Packing: 25 pcs.

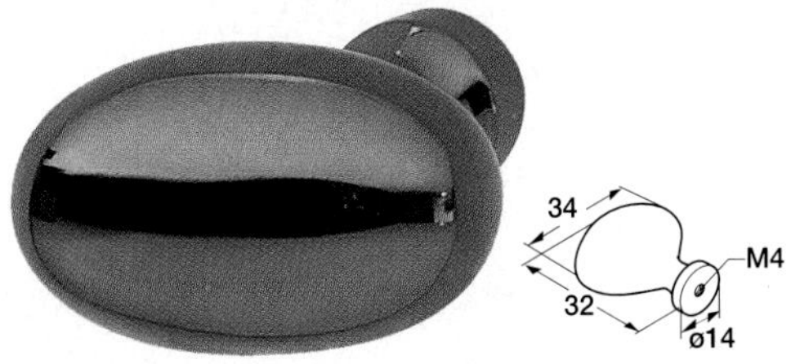

Black nickel plated

Cat No.	137.42.302

Packing: 25 pcs.

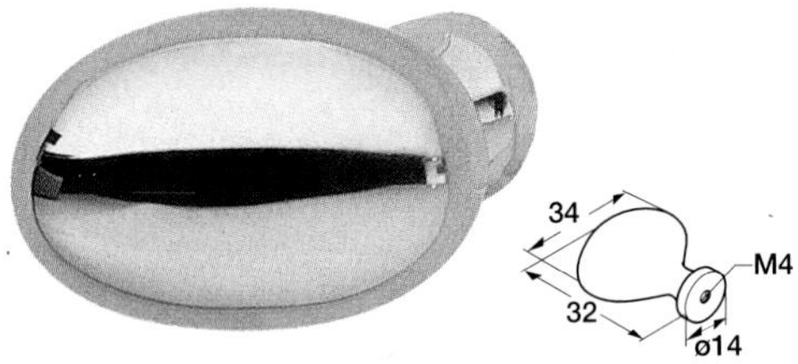

Chrome polished plated

Cat No.	137.42.204

Packing: 25 pcs.

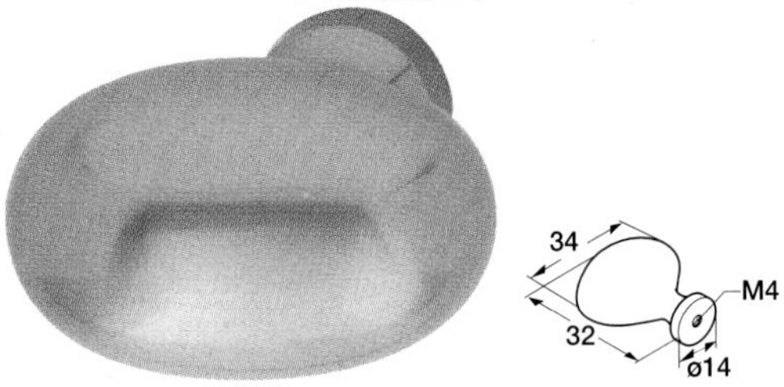

Nickel matt

Cat No.	137.42.606

Packing: 25 pcs.

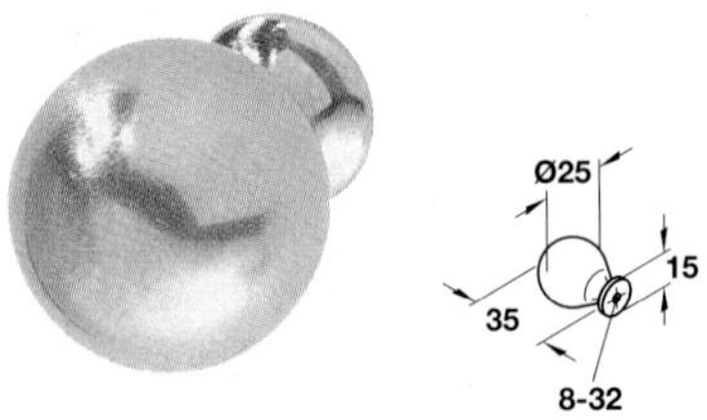

Nickel plated matt

Cat. No.	136.81.626

Packing: 25 pcs.

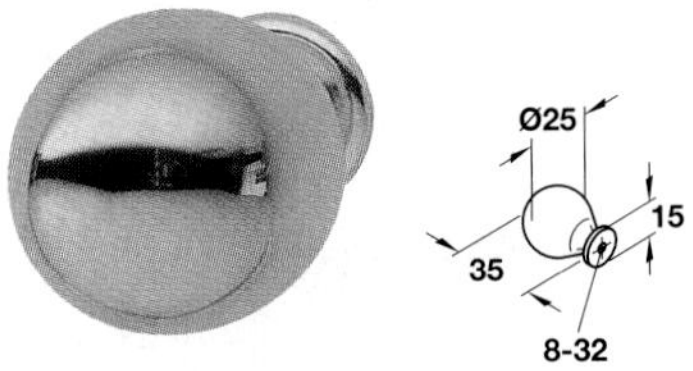

Polished and lacquered

Cat. No.	136.81.822

Packing: 25 pcs.

Threaded Screws 8-32
Combined slot, suitable for flat or cross blades
Finish: steel, yellow chromated

Length	Cat. No.
22 mm	022.25.229
25 mm	022.25.256
32 mm	022.25.327
38 mm	022.25.381
45 mm	022.25.452

Packing: 100 and 1000 pcs.

Threaded Screws M4
Combined slot, suitable for flat or cross blades
Finish: steel, zinc-plated

Length	Cat. No.
10 mm	022.35.109
12 mm	022.35.127
15 mm	022.35.154
18 mm	022.35.181
20 mm	022.35.207
22 mm	022.35.225
23 mm	022.35.234
25 mm	022.35.252
28 mm	022.35.289
30 mm	022.35.305
35 mm	022.35.350
38 mm	022.35.387
40 mm	022.35.403
45 mm	022.35.458
50 mm	022.35.501
60 mm	022.35.609

Packing: 100 and 1000 pcs.

Brass Knobs

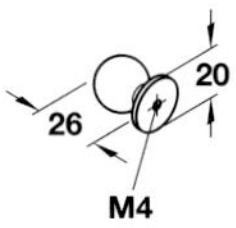

Blue

Cat. No.	137.82.810

Packing: 25 pcs.

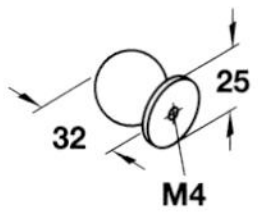

Blue

Cat. No.	137.82.820

Packing: 25 pcs.

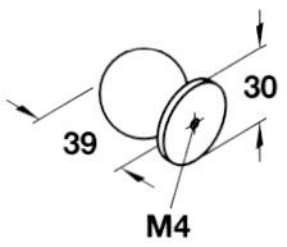

Blue

Cat. No.	137.82.830

Packing: 25 pcs.

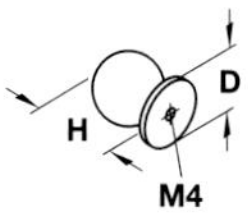

Chrome plated polished

Height H	Diameter D	Cat. No.
26	20	137.82.210
32	25	137.82.220
39	30	137.82.230

Packing: 25 pcs.

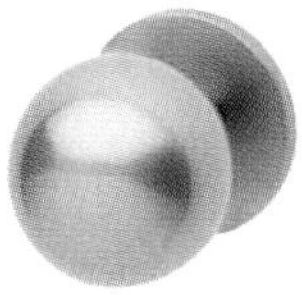
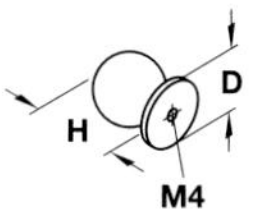

Nickel plated matt

Height H	Diameter D	Cat. No.
26	20	137.82.610
32	25	137.82.620
39	30	137.82.630

Packing: 25 pcs.

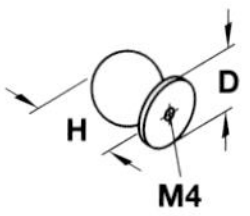

Black matt

Height H	Diameter D	Cat. No.
26	20	137.82.310
32	25	137.82.320
39	30	137.82.330

Packing: 25 pcs.

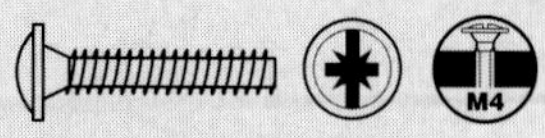

Threaded Screws M4
Combined slot, suitable for flat or cross blades

Finish: steel, zinc-plated

Length	Cat. No.
10 mm	022.35.109
12 mm	022.35.127
15 mm	022.35.154
18 mm	022.35.181
20 mm	022.35.207
22 mm	022.35.225
23 mm	022.35.234
25 mm	022.35.252
28 mm	022.35.289
30 mm	022.35.305
35 mm	022.35.350
38 mm	022.35.387
40 mm	022.35.403
45 mm	022.35.458
50 mm	022.35.501
60 mm	022.35.609

Packing: 100 and 1000 pcs.

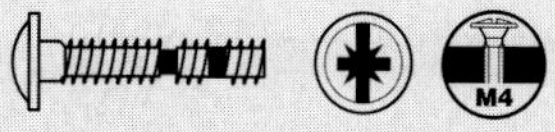

Threaded Breakoff Screw M4
Combined slot, suitable for flat or cross blades

Finish: steel, zinc-plated

Length	Cat. No.
1 3/4" x 3/4"	022.35.887

Packing: 100 and 1000 pcs.

HÄFELE

Brass Knobs

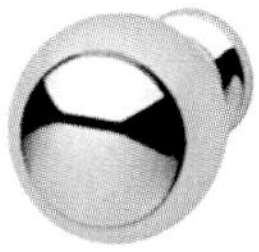
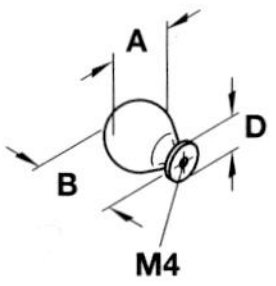

Chrome plated polished

Size A x B	Diameter D	Cat. No.
19 x 25	13	136.87.217
25 x 35	15	136.87.226

Packing: 25 pcs.

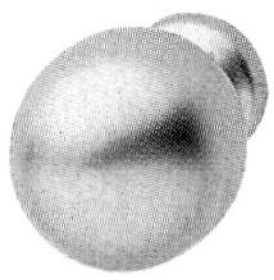
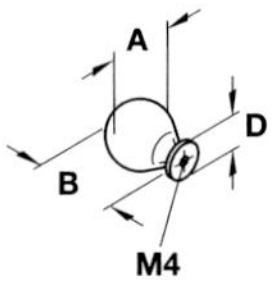

Nickel plated matt

Size A x B	Diameter D	Cat. No.
19 x 25	13	136.87.619
25 x 35	15	136.87.628

Packing: 25 pcs.

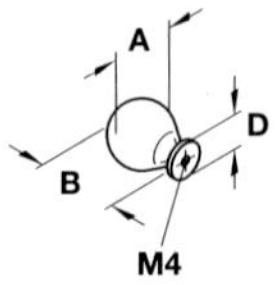

Polished and lacquered

Size A x B	Diameter D	Cat. No.
19 x 25	13	136.87.815
25 x 35	15	136.87.824

Packing: 25 pcs.

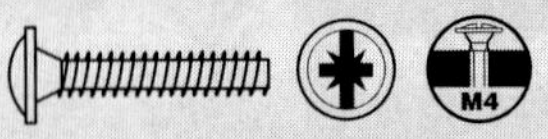

Threaded Screws M4
Combined slot, suitable for flat or cross blades
Finish: steel, zinc-plated

Length	Cat. No.
10 mm	022.35.109
12 mm	022.35.127
15 mm	022.35.154
18 mm	022.35.181
20 mm	022.35.207
22 mm	022.35.225
23 mm	022.35.234
25 mm	022.35.252
28 mm	022.35.289
30 mm	022.35.305
35 mm	022.35.350
38 mm	022.35.387
40 mm	022.35.403
45 mm	022.35.458
50 mm	022.35.501
60 mm	022.35.609

Packing: 100 and 1000 pcs.

Threaded Breakoff Screw M4
Combined slot, suitable for flat or cross blades
Finish: steel, zinc-plated

Length	Cat. No.
1 3/4" x 3/4"	022.35.887

Packing: 100 and 1000 pcs.

Brass Knobs and Backplates

HÄFELE

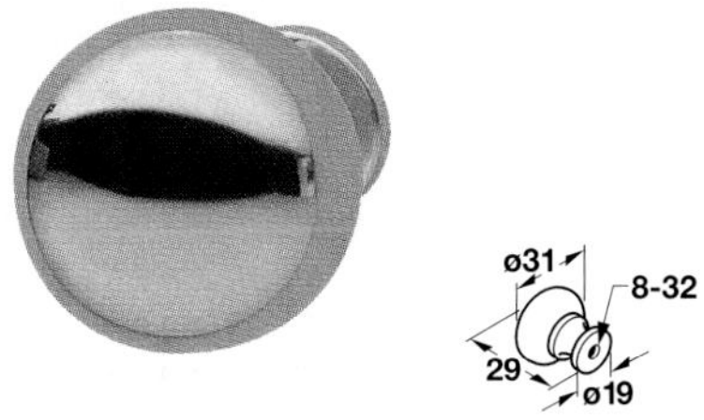

Copper polished

Cat. No.	134.42.010

Packing: 25 pcs.

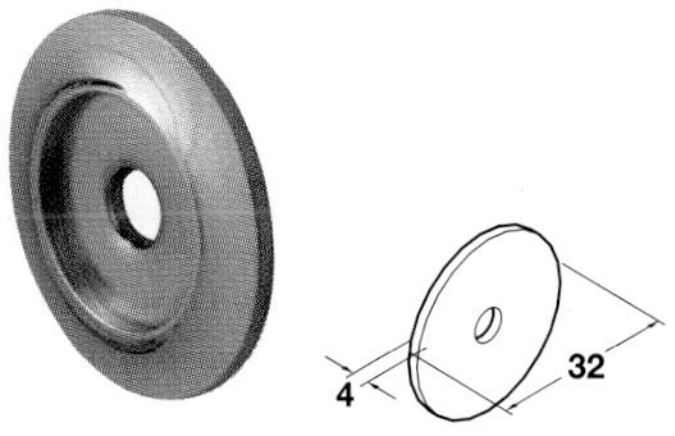

Copper polished

Cat. No.	134.42.090

Packing: 25 pcs.

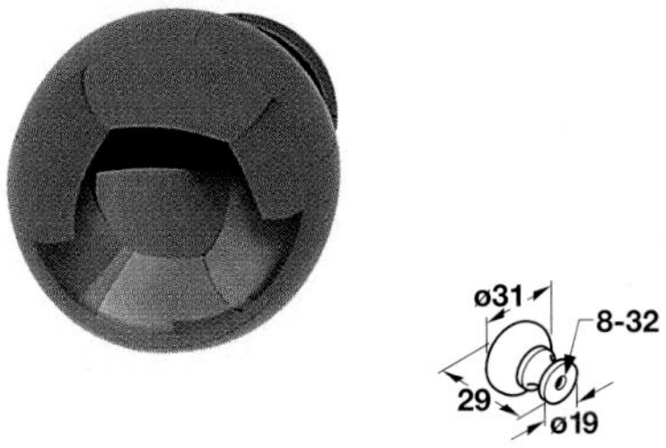

Black nickel plated

Cat. No.	134.42.316

Packing: 25 pcs.

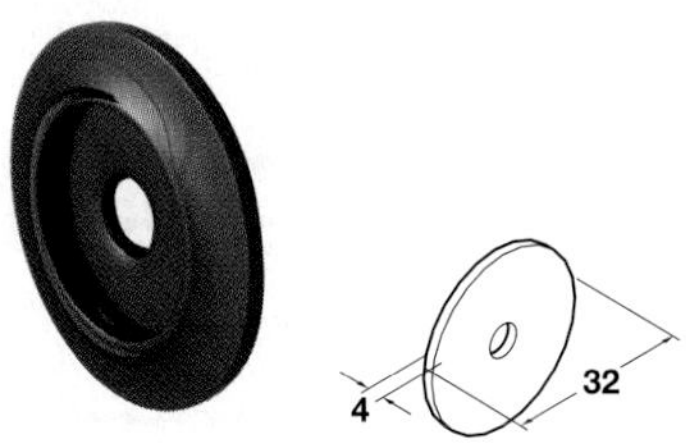

Black nickel plated

Cat. No.	134.42.390

Packing: 25 pcs.

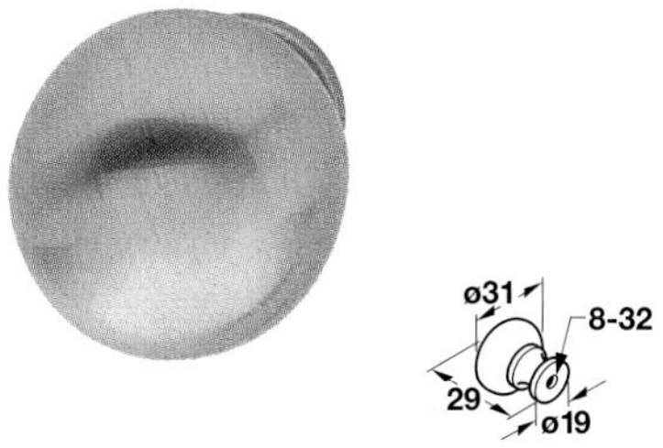

Nickel plated matt

Cat. No.	134.42.414

Packing: 25 pcs.

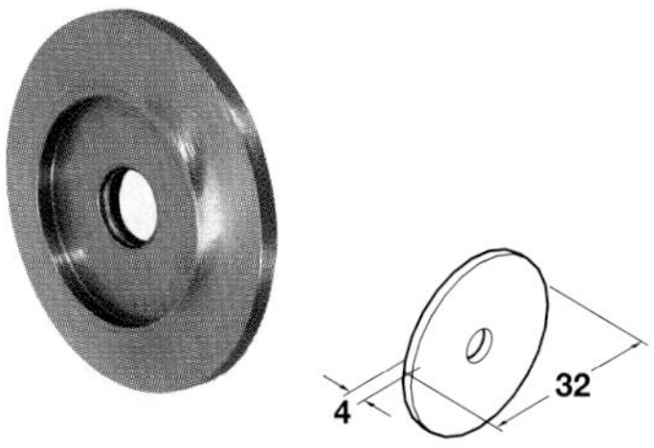

Nickel plated matt

Cat. No.	134.42.490

Packing: 25 pcs.

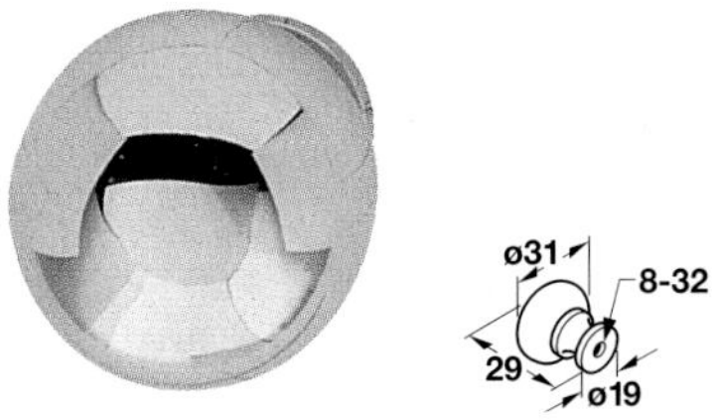

Polished chrome

Cat. No.	134.42.218

Packing: 25 pcs.

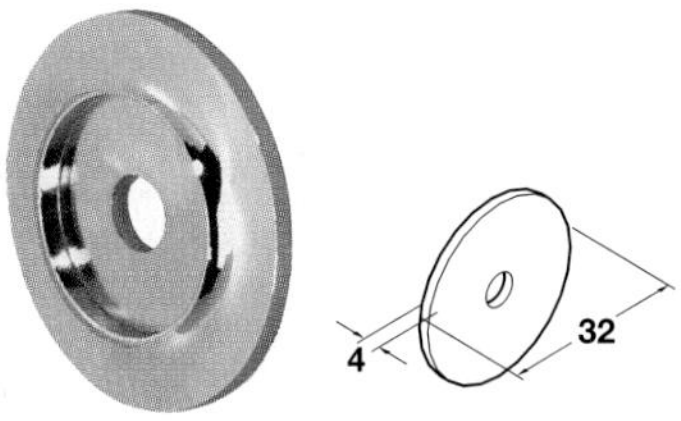

Polished chrome

Cat. No.	134.42.290

Packing: 25 pcs.

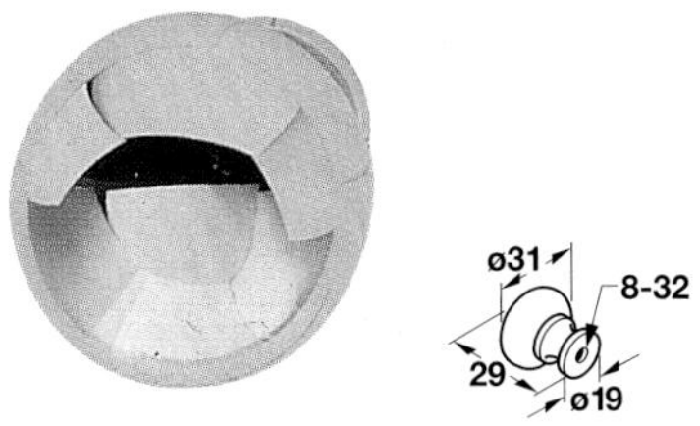

Polished and lacquered

Cat. No.	134.42.816

Packing: 25 pcs.

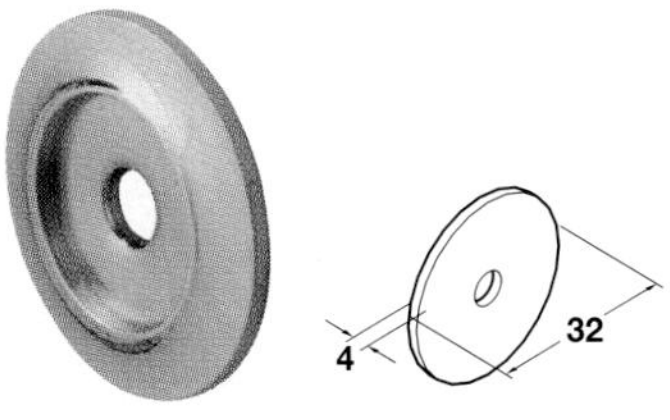

Polished and lacquered

Cat. No.	134.42.890

Packing: 25 pcs.

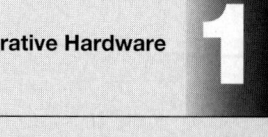

Decorative Hardware **1**

- **Backplates can be used with brass knobs shown**

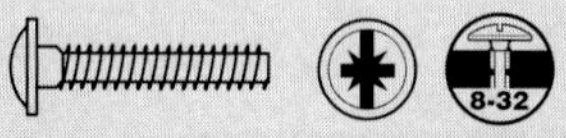

Threaded Screws 8-32
Combined slot, suitable for flat or cross blades

Finish: steel, yellow chromated

Length	Cat. No.
22 mm	022.25.229
25 mm	022.25.256
32 mm	022.25.327
38 mm	022.25.381
45 mm	022.25.452

Packing: 100 and 1000 pcs.

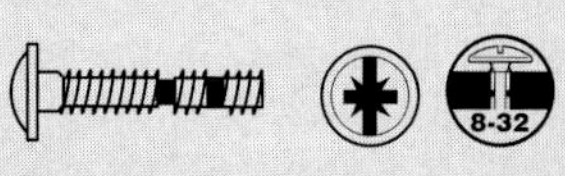

Threaded Breakoff Screw 8-32
Combined slot, suitable for flat or cross blades

Finish: steel, yellow chromated

Length	Cat. No.
1 3/4" x 3/4"	022.25.881

Packing: 100 and 1000 pcs.

Dimensional data not binding
We reserve the right to alter specifications without notice.

Brass backplates

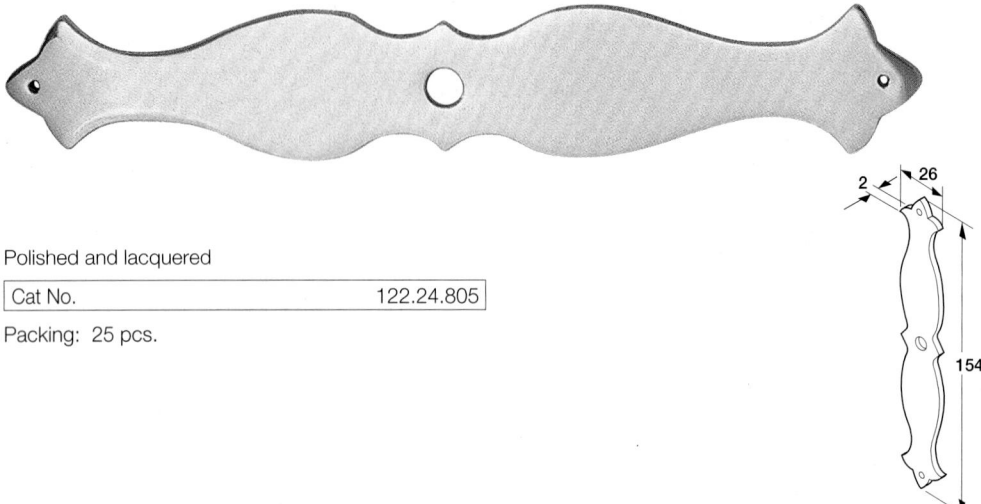

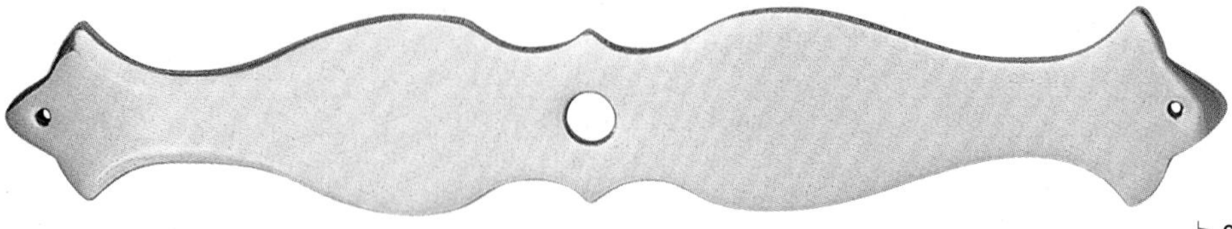

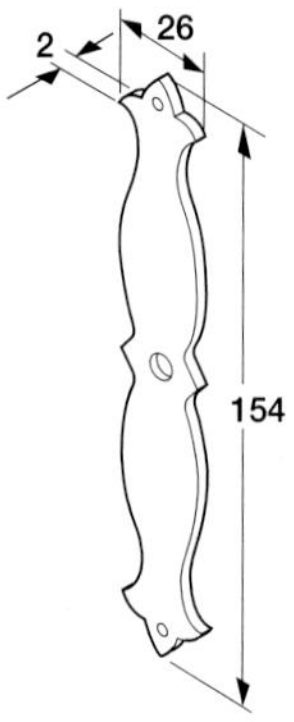

Polished and lacquered

Cat No.	122.24.805

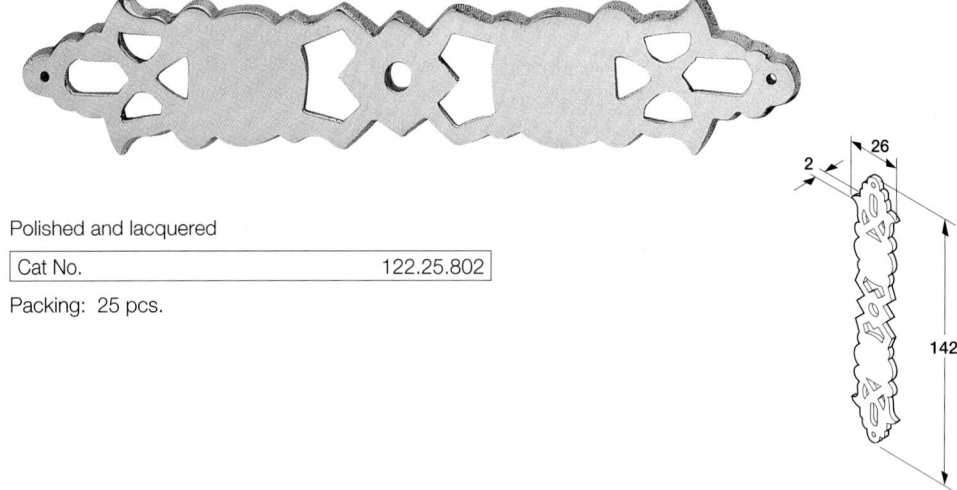

Packing: 25 pcs.

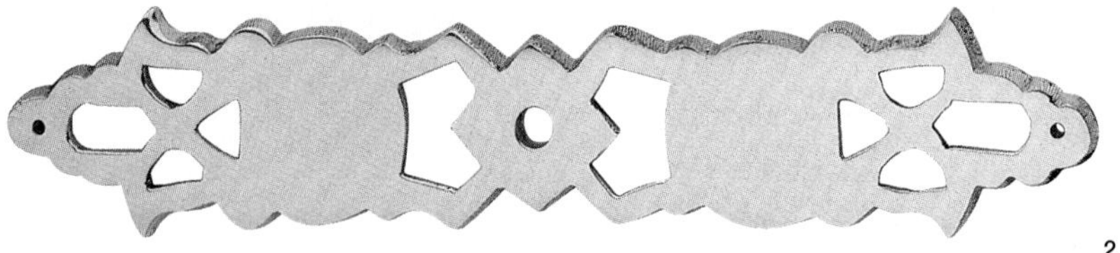

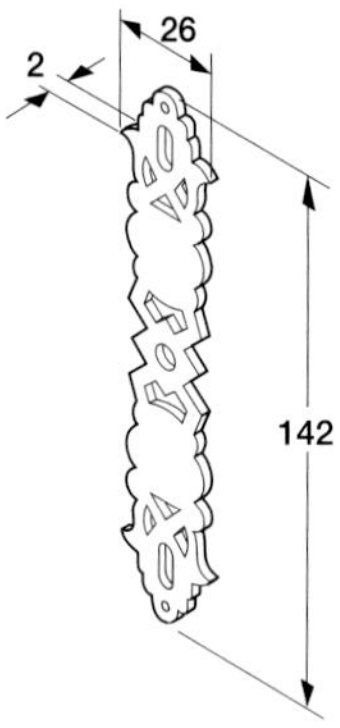

Polished and lacquered

Cat No.	122.25.802

Packing: 25 pcs.

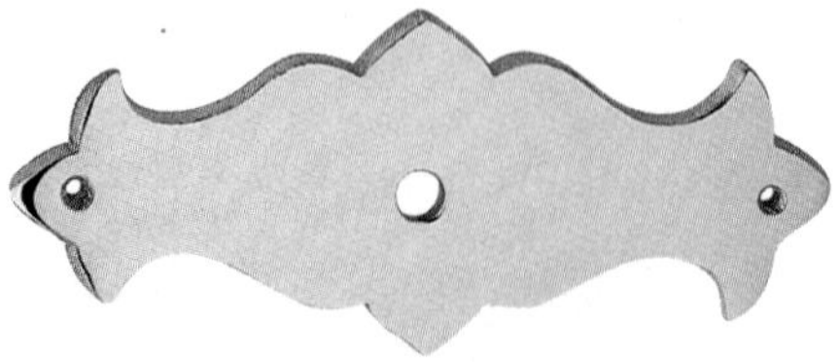

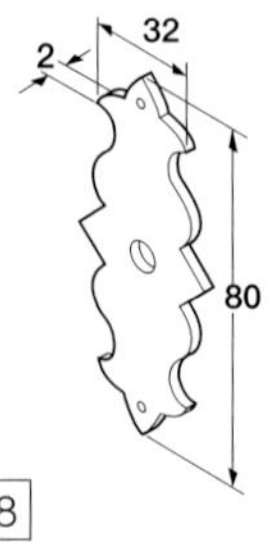

Polished and lacquered

Cat. No.	122.23.808

Packing: 25 pcs.

Hollow brass knobs

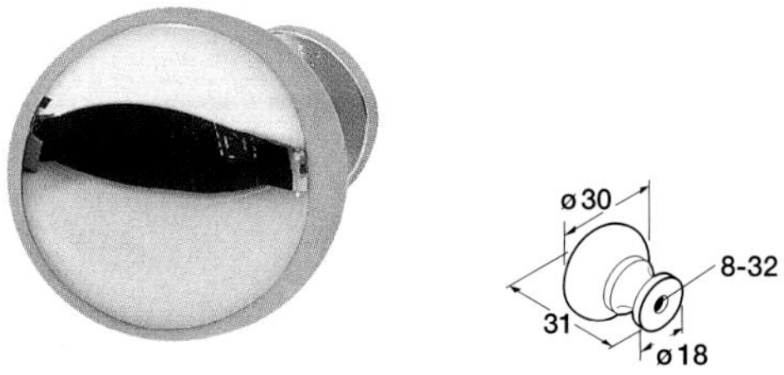

Polished chrome

Cat. No.	134.46.207

Packing: 25 pcs.

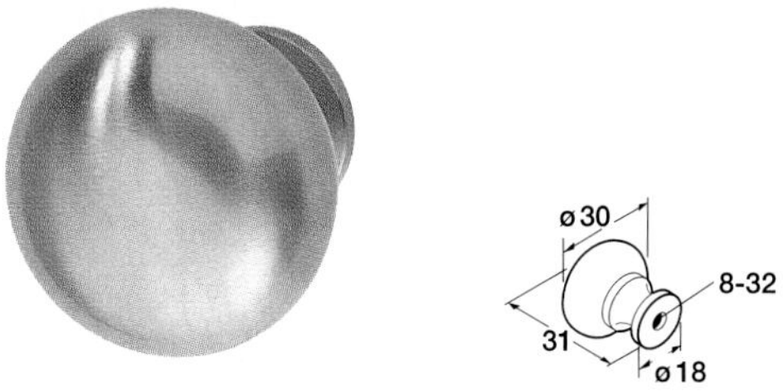

Satin chrome

Cat. No.	134.46.609

Packing: 25 pcs.

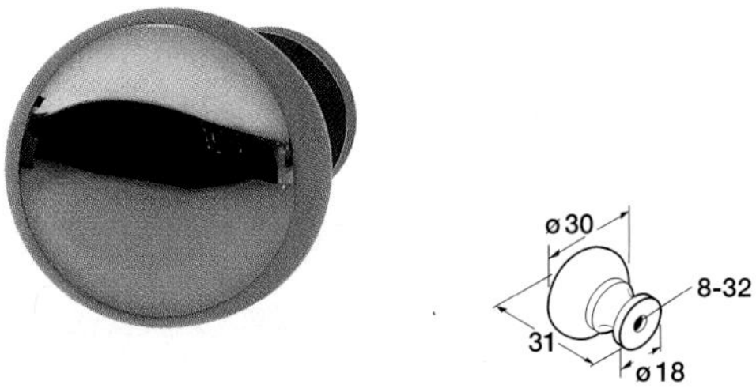

Black nickel

Cat. No.	134.46.305

Packing: 25 pcs.

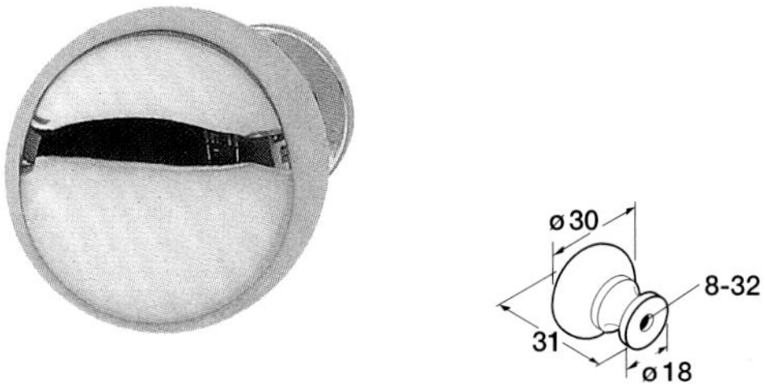

Polished and lacquered

Cat. No.	134.46.805

Packing: 25 pcs.

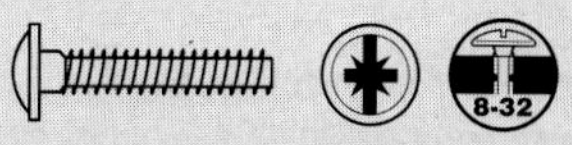

Threaded Screws 8-32
Combined slot, suitable for flat or cross blades
Finish: steel, yellow chromated

Length	Cat. No.
22 mm	022.25.229
25 mm	022.25.256
32 mm	022.25.327
38 mm	022.25.381
45 mm	022.25.452

Packing: 100 and 1000 pcs.

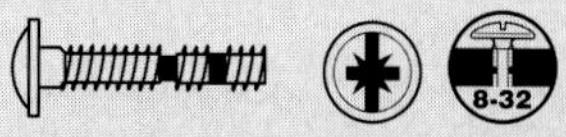

Threaded Breakoff Screw 8-32
Combined slot, suitable for flat or cross blades
Finish: steel, yellow chromated

Length	Cat. No.
1 3/4" x 3/4"	022.25.881

Packing: 100 and 1000 pcs.

HÄFELE

Brass Knobs

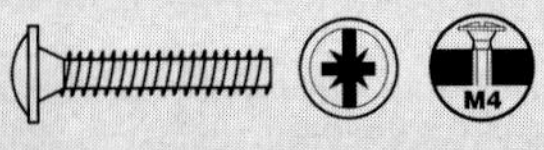

Threaded Screws M4

Combined slot, suitable for flat or cross blades

Finish: steel, zinc-plated

Length	Cat. No.
10 mm	022.35.109
12 mm	022.35.127
15 mm	022.35.154
18 mm	022.35.181
20 mm	022.35.207
22 mm	022.35.225
23 mm	022.35.234
25 mm	022.35.252
28 mm	022.35.289
30 mm	022.35.305
35 mm	022.35.350
38 mm	022.35.387
40 mm	022.35.403
45 mm	022.35.458
50 mm	022.35.501
60 mm	022.35.609

Packing: 100 and 1000 pcs.

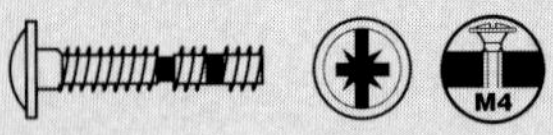

Threaded Breakoff Screw M4

Combined slot, suitable for flat or cross blades

Finish: steel, zinc-plated

Length	Cat. No.
1 3/4" x 3/4"	022.35.887

Packing: 100 and 1000 pcs.

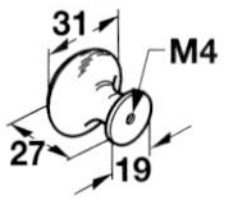

Brass polished/black marble epoxy

Cat. No.	137.43.836

Packing: 25 pcs.

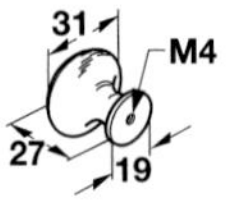

Brass polished/grey marble epoxy

Cat. No.	137.43.854

Packing: 25 pcs.

Brass Knob for Laminate Inserts

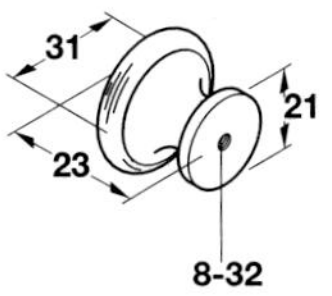

Chrome polished

Cat. No.	137.12.200

Packing: 25 pcs.

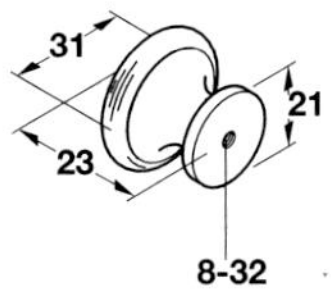

Polished & lacquered

Cat. No.	137.12.807

Packing: 25 pcs.

Punch Press
for use with laminate
up to 1 ¹⁄₁₆"
finish: steel, black

Cat. No.	004.04.820

packing: 1 pc

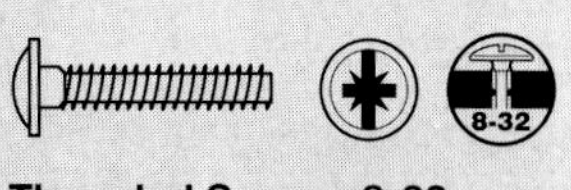

Threaded Screws 8-32
Combined slot, suitable for flat or cross blades

Finish: steel, yellow chromated

Length	Cat. No.
22 mm	022.25.229
25 mm	022.25.256
32 mm	022.25.327
38 mm	022.25.381
45 mm	022.25.452

Packing: 100 and 1000 pcs.

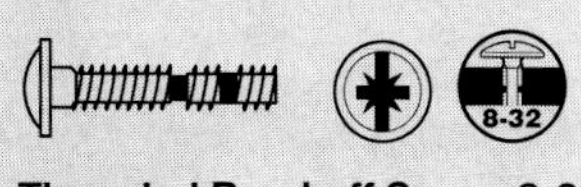

Threaded Breakoff Screw 8-32
Combined slot, suitable for flat or cross blades

Finish: steel, yellow chromated

Length	Cat. No.
1 3/4" x 3/4"	022.25.881

Packing: 100 and 1000 pcs.

Brass knobs

Threaded Screws M4
Combined slot, suitable for flat or cross blades

Finish: steel, zinc-plated

Length	Cat. No.
10 mm	022.35.109
12 mm	022.35.127
15 mm	022.35.154
18 mm	022.35.181
20 mm	022.35.207
22 mm	022.35.225
23 mm	022.35.234
25 mm	022.35.252
28 mm	022.35.289
30 mm	022.35.305
35 mm	022.35.350
38 mm	022.35.387
40 mm	022.35.403
45 mm	022.35.458
50 mm	022.35.501
60 mm	022.35.609

Packing: 100 and 1000 pcs.

Threaded Breakoff Screw M4
Combined slot, suitable for flat or cross blades

Finish: steel, zinc-plated

Length	Cat. No.
1 3/4" x 3/4"	022.35.887

Packing: 100 and 1000 pcs.

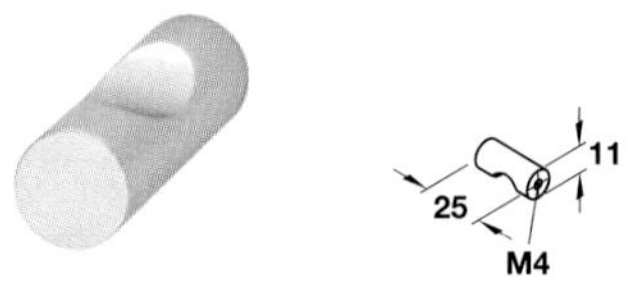

Chrome plated polished

Cat. No.	136.06.212

Packing: 25 pcs.

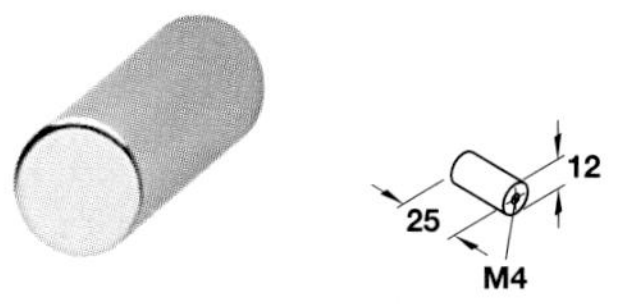

Chrome plated polished

Cat. No.	136.58.207

Packing: 25 pcs.

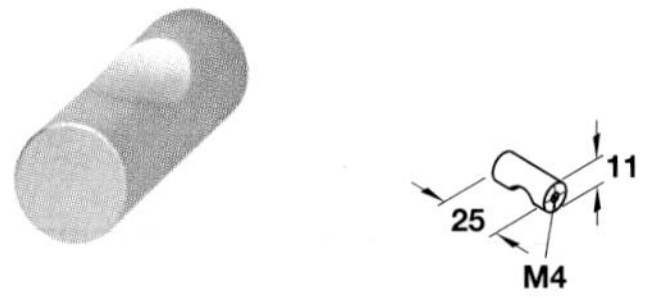

Nickel plated matt

Cat. No.	136.06.614

Packing: 25 pcs.

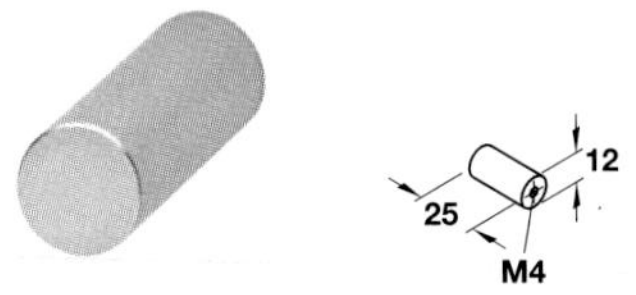

Nickel plated matt

Cat. No.	136.58.609

Packing: 25 pcs.

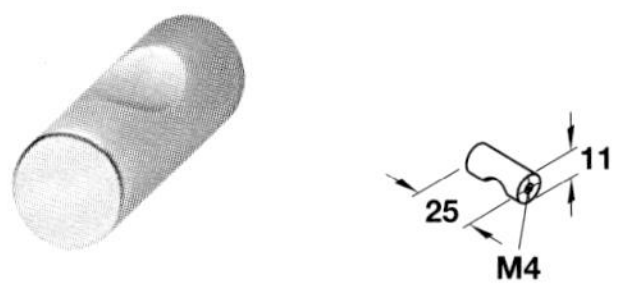

Polished

Cat. No.	136.06.810

Packing: 25 pcs.

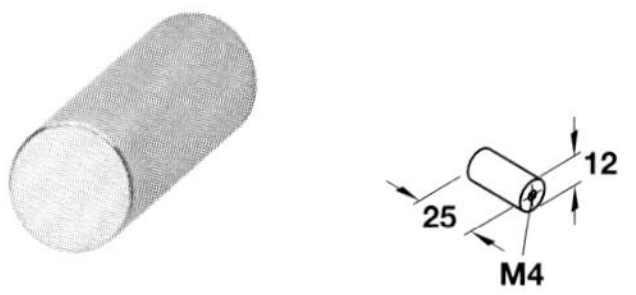

Polished

Cat. No.	136.58.805

Packing: 25 pcs.

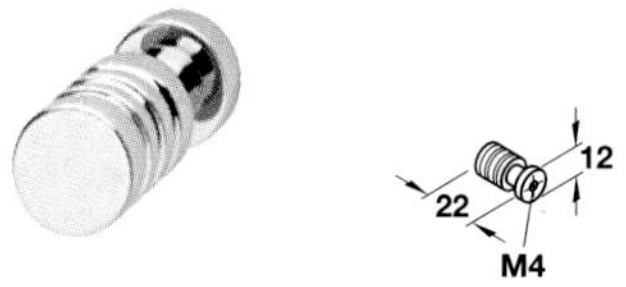

Chrome plated polished

Cat. No.	137.29.201

Packing: 25 pcs.

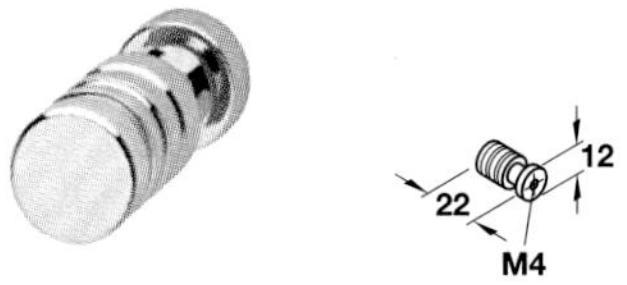

Polished

Cat. No.	137.29.809

Packing: 25 pcs.

Brass knobs

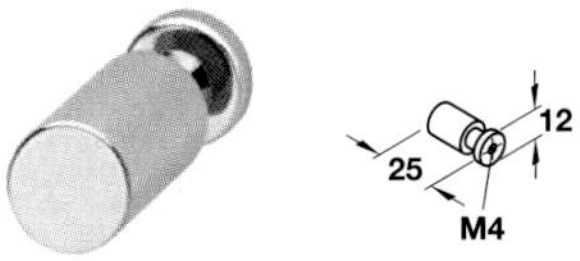

Chrome plated polished

Cat. No.	137.38.200

Packing: 25 pcs.

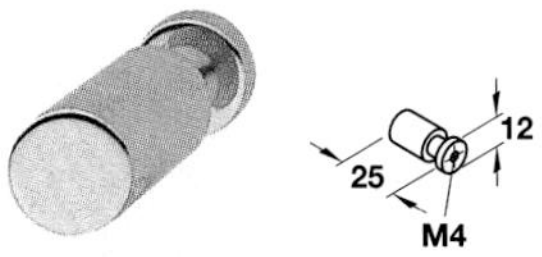

Polished and lacquered

Cat. No.	137.38.808

Packing: 25 pcs.

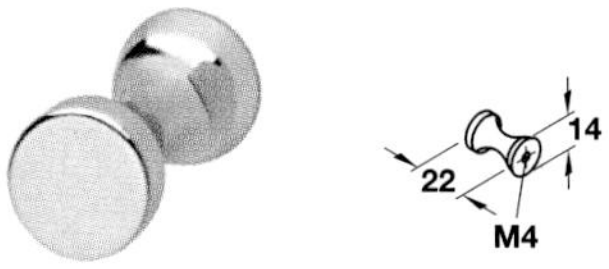

Chrome plated polished

Cat. No.	137.21.205

Packing: 25 pcs.

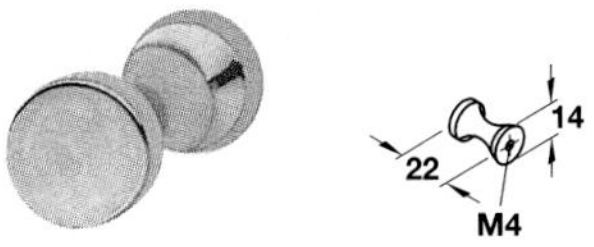

Polished and lacquered

Cat. No.	137.21.803

Packing: 25 pcs.

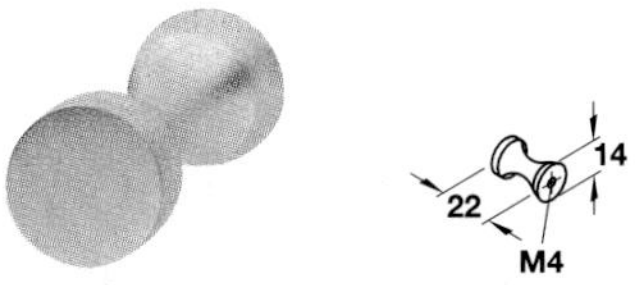

Matt

Cat. No.	137.21.500

Packing: 25 pcs.

HÄFELE

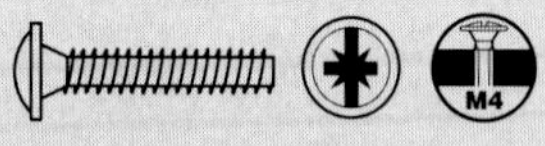

Threaded Screws M4
Combined slot, suitable for flat or cross blades
Finish: steel, zinc-plated

Length	Cat. No.
10 mm	022.35.109
12 mm	022.35.127
15 mm	022.35.154
18 mm	022.35.181
20 mm	022.35.207
22 mm	022.35.225
23 mm	022.35.234
25 mm	022.35.252
28 mm	022.35.289
30 mm	022.35.305
35 mm	022.35.350
38 mm	022.35.387
40 mm	022.35.403
45 mm	022.35.458
50 mm	022.35.501
60 mm	022.35.609

Packing: 100 and 1000 pcs.

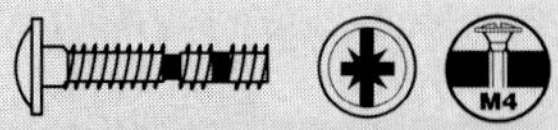

Threaded Breakoff Screw M4
Combined slot, suitable for flat or cross blades
Finish: steel, zinc-plated

Length	Cat. No.
1 3/4" x 3/4"	022.35.887

Packing: 100 and 1000 pcs.

Brass Knobs

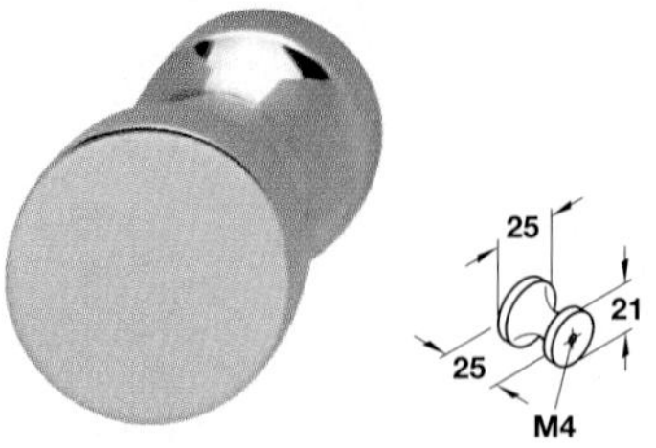

Chrome plated polished

Cat. No.	136.76.205

Packing: 25 pcs.

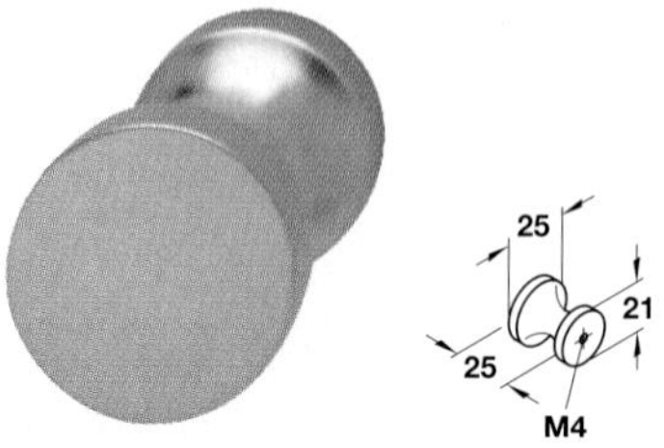

Nickel plated matt

Cat. No.	136.76.607

Packing: 25 pcs.

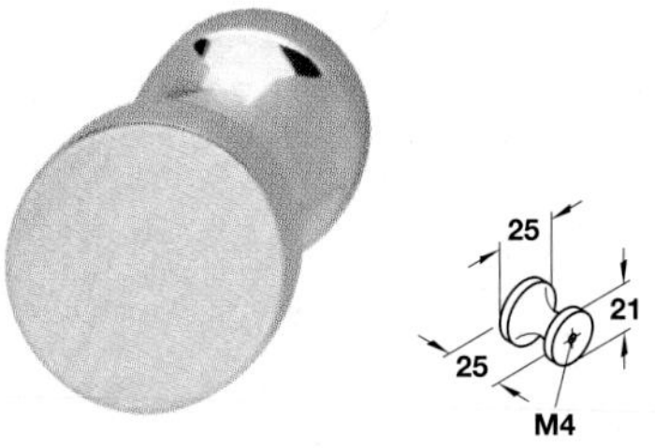

Polished and lacquered

Cat. No.	136.76.803

Packing: 25 pcs.

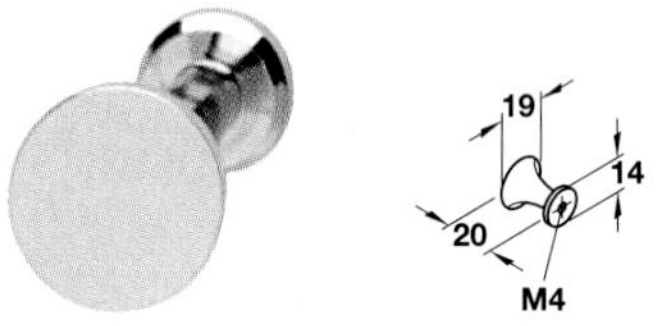

Chrome plated polished

Cat. No.	136.27.202

Packing: 25 pcs.

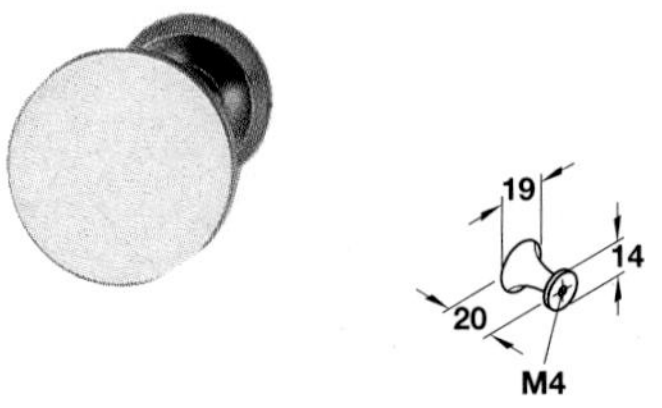

Nickel matt

Cat. No.	136.27.604

Packing: 25 pcs.

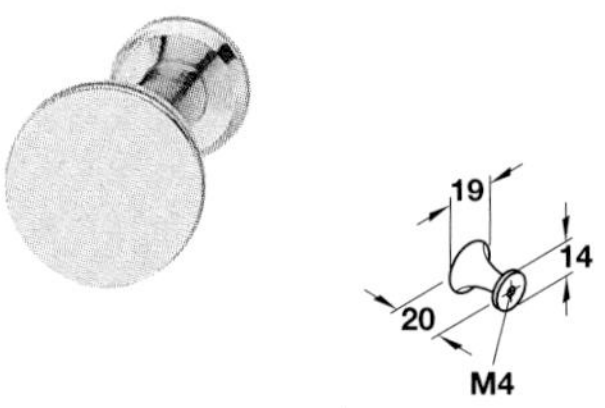

Polished and lacquered

Cat. No.	136.27.800

Packing: 25 pcs.

Threaded Screws M4
Combined slot, suitable for flat or cross blades

Finish: steel, zinc-plated

Length	Cat. No.
10 mm	022.35.109
12 mm	022.35.127
15 mm	022.35.154
18 mm	022.35.181
20 mm	022.35.207
22 mm	022.35.225
23 mm	022.35.234
25 mm	022.35.252
28 mm	022.35.289
30 mm	022.35.305
35 mm	022.35.350
38 mm	022.35.387
40 mm	022.35.403
45 mm	022.35.458
50 mm	022.35.501
60 mm	022.35.609

Packing: 100 and 1000 pcs.

Threaded Breakoff Screw M4
Combined slot, suitable for flat or cross blades

Finish: steel, zinc-plated

Length	Cat. No.
1 3/4" x 3/4"	022.35.887

Packing: 100 and 1000 pcs.

Dimensional data not binding.
We reserve the right to alter specifications without notice.

Brass Knobs

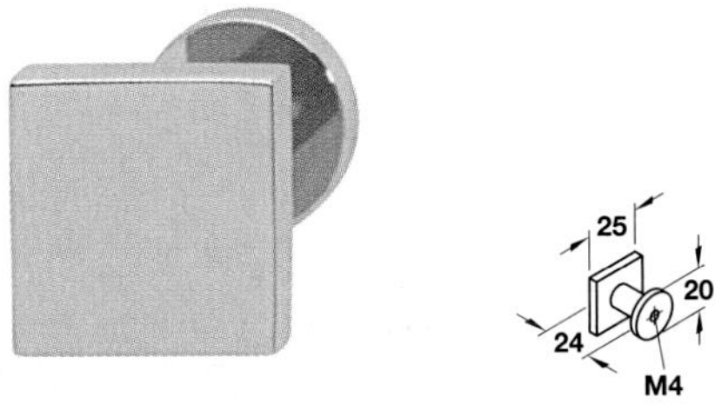

Chrome plated polished

Cat. No.	137.80.200

Packing: 25 pcs.

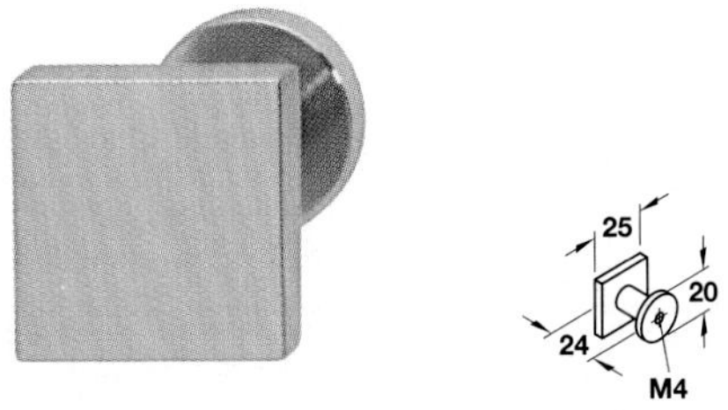

Brass polished

Cat. No.	137.80.800

Packing: 25 pcs.

Chrome plated polished

Cat. No.	137.81.200

Packing: 25 pcs.

Chrome plated matt

Cat. No.	137.81.400

Packing: 25 pcs.

Gold colored polished

Cat. No.	137.81.800

Packing: 25 pcs.

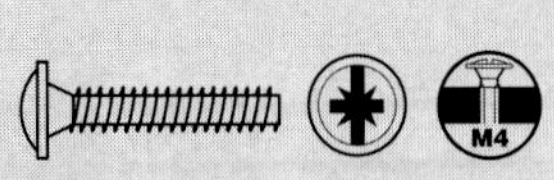

Threaded Screws M4
Combined slot, suitable for flat or cross blades
Finish: steel, zinc-plated

Length	Cat. No.
10 mm	022.35.109
12 mm	022.35.127
15 mm	022.35.154
18 mm	022.35.181
20 mm	022.35.207
22 mm	022.35.225
23 mm	022.35.234
25 mm	022.35.252
28 mm	022.35.289
30 mm	022.35.305
35 mm	022.35.350
38 mm	022.35.387
40 mm	022.35.403
45 mm	022.35.458
50 mm	022.35.501
60 mm	022.35.609

Packing: 100 and 1000 pcs.

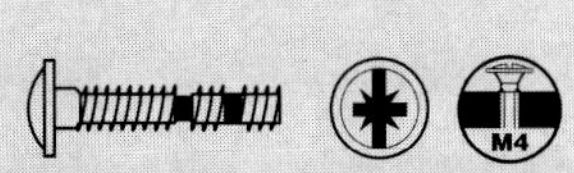

Threaded Breakoff Screw M4
Combined slot, suitable for flat or cross blades
Finish: steel, zinc-plated

Length	Cat. No.
1 3/4" x 3/4"	022.35.887

Packing: 100 and 1000 pcs.

HÄFELE

Brass Knobs

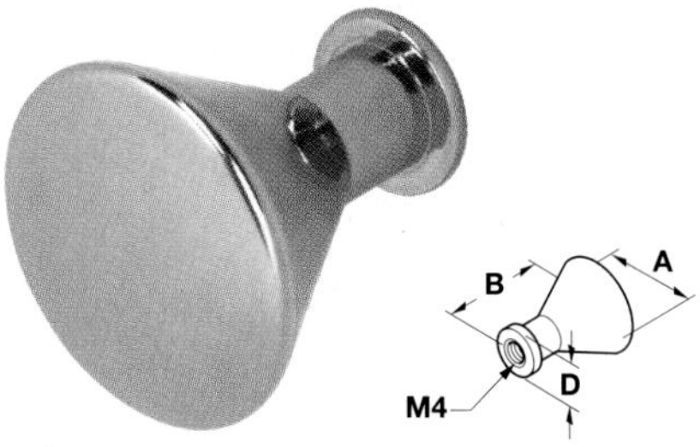

Chrome polished

Size A x B	Diameter D	Cat. No.
12 x 18	9	136.79.210
22 x 24	12	136.79.220
30 x 31	15	136.79.230

Packing: 25 pcs.

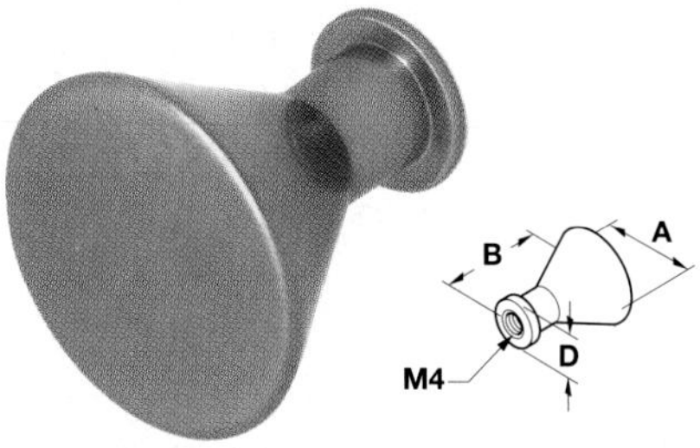

Nickel plated, matt

Size A x B	Diameter D	Cat. No.
12 x 18	9	136.79.610
22 x 24	12	136.79.620
30 x 31	15	136.79.630

Packing: 25 pcs.

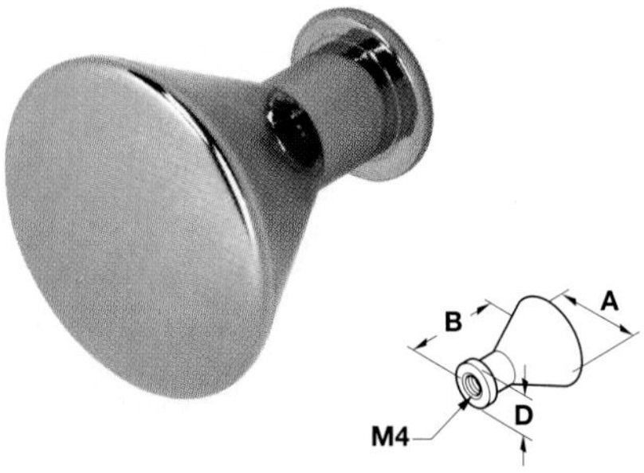

Gold colored polished

Size A x B	Diameter D	Cat. No.
12 x 18	9	136.79.810
22 x 24	12	136.79.820
30 x 31	15	136.79.830

Packing: 25 pcs.

1 Decorative Hardware

Threaded Screws M4
Combined slot, suitable for flat or cross blades

Finish: steel, zinc-plated

Length	Cat. No.
10 mm	022.35.109
12 mm	022.35.127
15 mm	022.35.154
18 mm	022.35.181
20 mm	022.35.207
22 mm	022.35.225
23 mm	022.35.234
25 mm	022.35.252
28 mm	022.35.289
30 mm	022.35.305
35 mm	022.35.350
38 mm	022.35.387
40 mm	022.35.403
45 mm	022.35.458
50 mm	022.35.501
60 mm	022.35.609

Packing: 100 and 1000 pcs.

Threaded Breakoff Screw M4
Combined slot, suitable for flat or cross blades

Finish: steel, zinc-plated

Length	Cat. No.
1 3/4" x 3/4"	022.35.887

Packing: 100 and 1000 pcs.

Dimensional data not binding.
We reserve the right to alter specifications without notice.

Brass Knobs

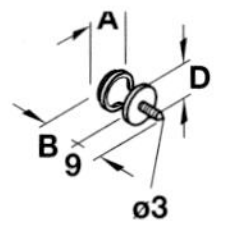

Polished

Size A x B	Diameter D	Cat. No.
12 x 11	12	137.31.827
14 x 13	14	137.31.845

Packing: 25 pcs.

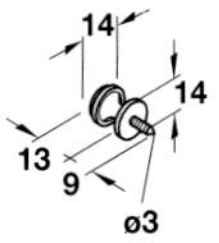

Chrome polished

Cat. No.	137.31.240

Packing: 25 pcs.

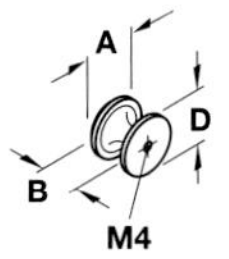

Polished

Size A x B	Diameter D	Cat. No.
19 x 16	19	137.31.863
22 x 18	22	137.31.872
25 x 22	25	137.31.881

Packing: 25 pcs.

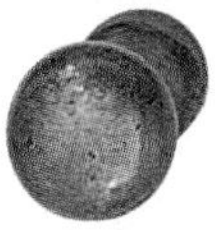
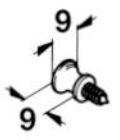

Antique

Cat. No.	120.15.119

Packing: 25 pcs.

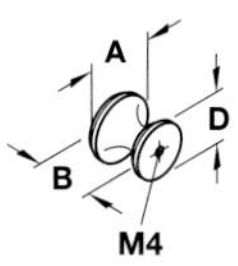

Polished

Size A x B	Diameter D	Cat. No.
20 x 17	18	137.32.815
25 x 22	21	137.32.824
30 x 25	24	137.32.833

Packing: 25 pcs.

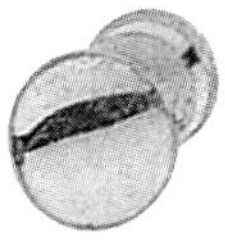
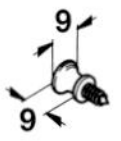

Polished

Cat. No.	120.15.815

Packing: 25 pcs.

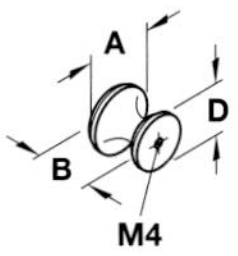

Bronzed and brushed

Size A x B	Diameter D	Cat. No.
20 x 17	18	137.32.119
25 x 22	21	137.32.128
30 x 25	24	137.32.137

Packing: 25 pcs.

Threaded Screws M4
Combined slot, suitable for flat or cross blades
Finish: steel, zinc-plated

Length	Cat. No.
10 mm	022.35.109
12 mm	022.35.127
15 mm	022.35.154
18 mm	022.35.181
20 mm	022.35.207
22 mm	022.35.225
23 mm	022.35.234
25 mm	022.35.252
28 mm	022.35.289
30 mm	022.35.305
35 mm	022.35.350
38 mm	022.35.387
40 mm	022.35.403
45 mm	022.35.458
50 mm	022.35.501
60 mm	022.35.609

Packing: 100 and 1000 pcs.

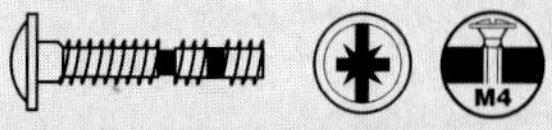

Threaded Breakoff Screw M4
Combined slot, suitable for flat or cross blades
Finish: steel, zinc-plated

Length	Cat. No.
1 3/4" x 3/4"	022.35.887

Packing: 100 and 1000 pcs.

HÄFELE

Brass Knobs

Threaded Screws M4
Combined slot, suitable for flat or cross blades
Finish: steel, zinc-plated

Length	Cat. No.
10 mm	022.35.109
12 mm	022.35.127
15 mm	022.35.154
18 mm	022.35.181
20 mm	022.35.207
22 mm	022.35.225
23 mm	022.35.234
25 mm	022.35.252
28 mm	022.35.289
30 mm	022.35.305
35 mm	022.35.350
38 mm	022.35.387
40 mm	022.35.403
45 mm	022.35.458
50 mm	022.35.501
60 mm	022.35.609

Packing: 100 and 1000 pcs.

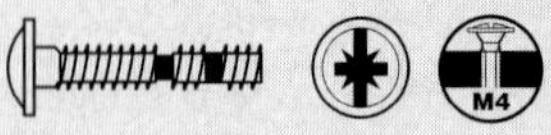

Threaded Breakoff Screw M4
Combined slot, suitable for flat or cross blades
Finish: steel, zinc-plated

Length	Cat. No.
1 3/4" x 3/4"	022.35.887

Packing: 100 and 1000 pcs.

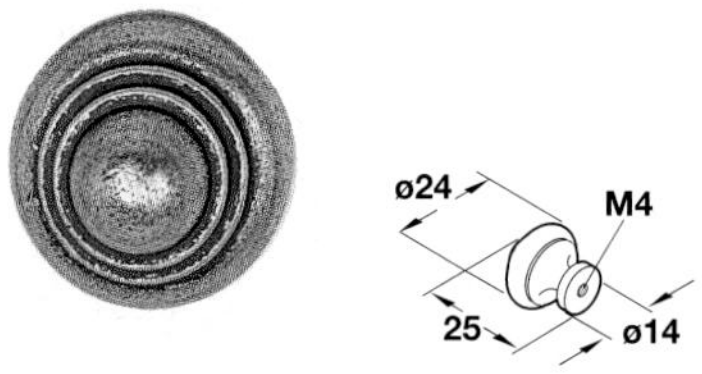

Tin antique plated

Cat. No.	134.31.902

Packing: 25 pcs.

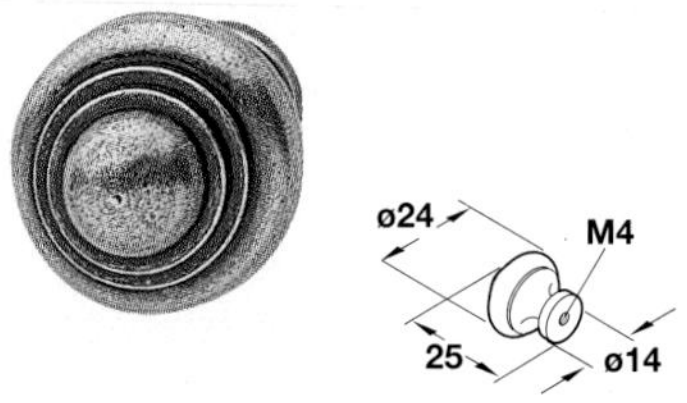

Bronzed and brushed

Cat. No.	134.31.108

Packing: 25 pcs.

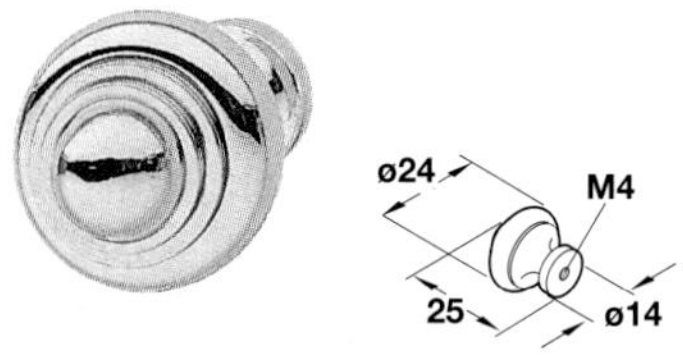

Polished and lacquered

Cat. No.	134.31.804

Packing: 25 pcs.

Dimensional data not binding.
We reserve the right to alter specifications without notice.

Brass Knobs

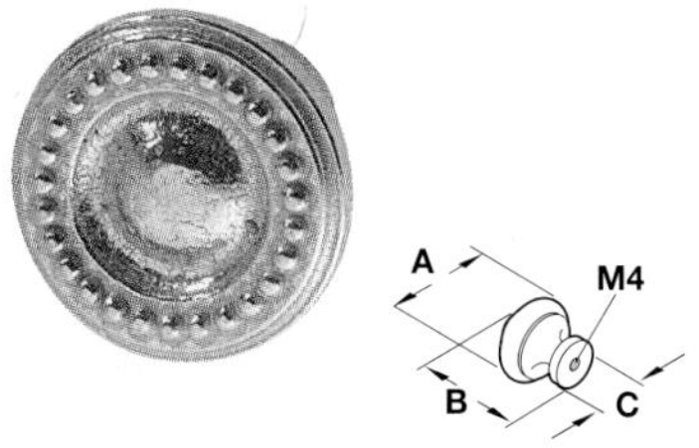

Polished and lacquered

Size A x B	Diameter C	Cat. No.
25 x 18	11	134.48.820
34 X 19	14	134.48.830

Packing: 25 pcs.

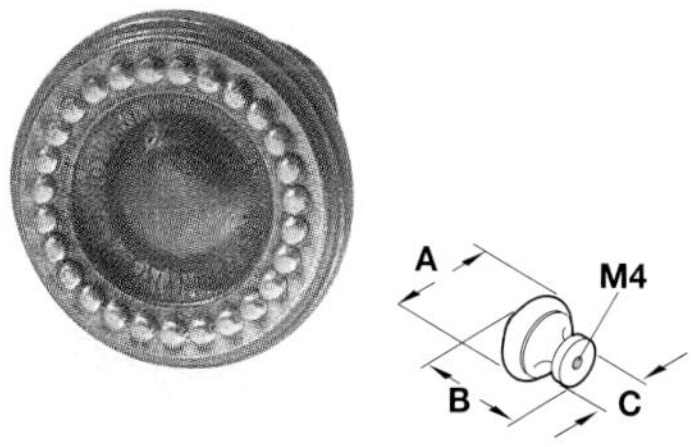

Bronzed and brushed

Size A x B	Diameter C	Cat. No.
25 x 18	11	134.48.120
34 x 19	14	134.48.130

Packing: 25 pcs.

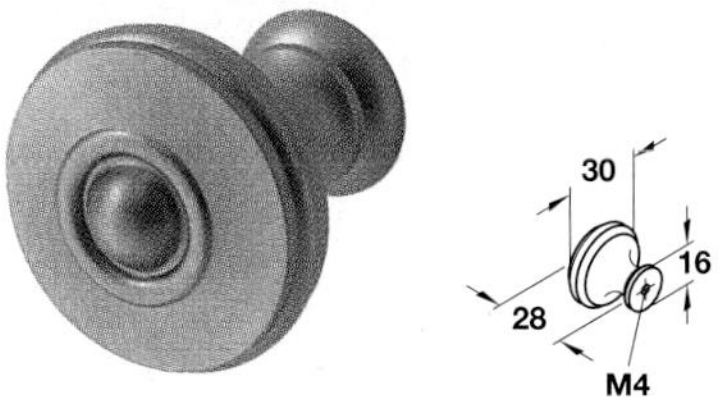

Tin antique

Cat No.	122.02.900

Packing: 25 pcs.

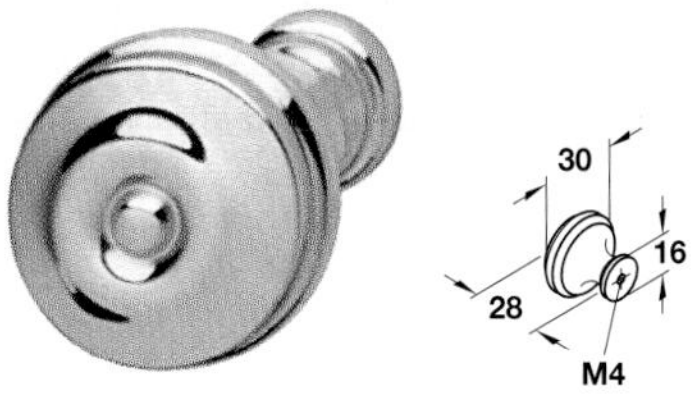

Polished and lacquered

Cat No.	121.57.827

Packing: 25 pcs.

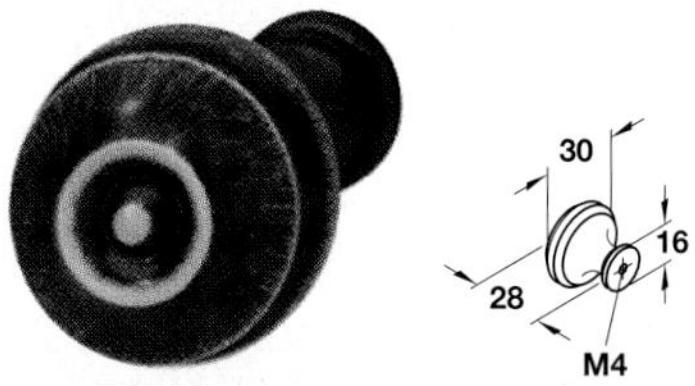

Bronzed and brushed

Cat. No.	121.57.121

Packing: 25 pcs.

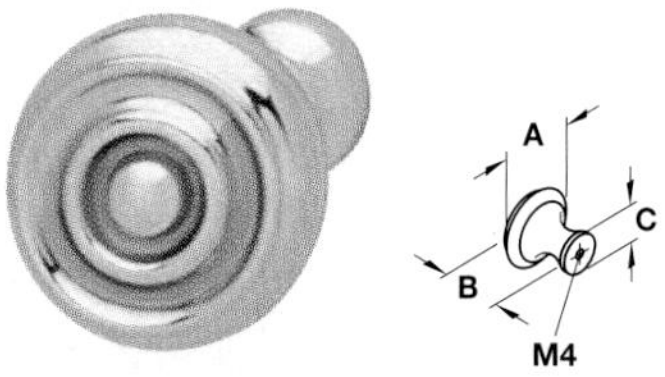

Polished and lacquered

Size A x B	Dimension C	Cat. No.
25 x 20	13	137.61.825
30 x 25	16	137.61.834
35 x 29	17	137.61.843
40 x 31	17	137.61.852

Packing: 25 pcs.

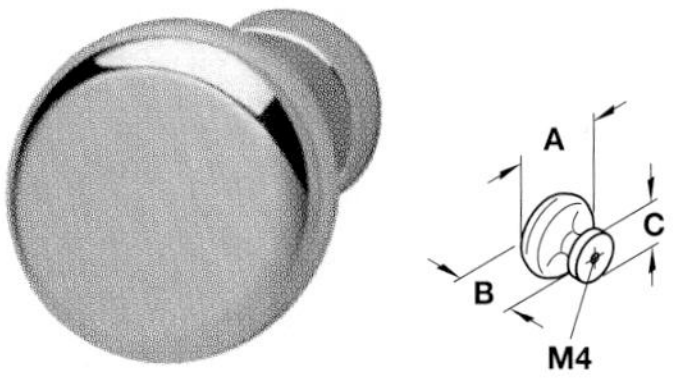

Polished and lacquered

Size A x B	Dimension C	Cat. No.
25 x 19	16	137.60.828
30 x 22	17	137.60.837
35 x 22	19	137.60.846

Packing: 25 pcs.

Decorative Hardware **1**

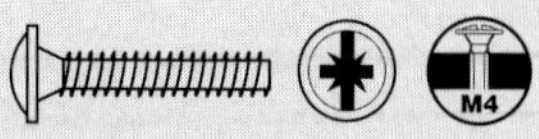

Threaded Screws M4
Combined slot, suitable for flat or cross blades
Finish: steel, zinc-plated

Length	Cat. No.
10 mm	022.35.109
12 mm	022.35.127
15 mm	022.35.154
18 mm	022.35.181
20 mm	022.35.207
22 mm	022.35.225
23 mm	022.35.234
25 mm	022.35.252
28 mm	022.35.289
30 mm	022.35.305
35 mm	022.35.350
38 mm	022.35.387
40 mm	022.35.403
45 mm	022.35.458
50 mm	022.35.501
60 mm	022.35.609

Packing: 100 and 1000 pcs.

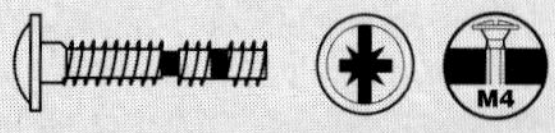

Threaded Breakoff Screw M4
Combined slot, suitable for flat or cross blades
Finish: steel, zinc-plated

Length	Cat. No.
1 3/4" x 3/4"	022.35.887

Packing: 100 and 1000 pcs.

Dimensional data not binding.
We reserve the right to alter specifications without notice.

Stainless Steel Knobs

Threaded Screws M4
Combined slot, suitable for flat or cross blades
Finish: steel, zinc-plated

Length	Cat. No.
10 mm	022.35.109
12 mm	022.35.127
15 mm	022.35.154
18 mm	022.35.181
20 mm	022.35.207
22 mm	022.35.225
23 mm	022.35.234
25 mm	022.35.252
28 mm	022.35.289
30 mm	022.35.305
35 mm	022.35.350
38 mm	022.35.387
40 mm	022.35.403
45 mm	022.35.458
50 mm	022.35.501
60 mm	022.35.609

Packing: 100 and 1000 pcs.

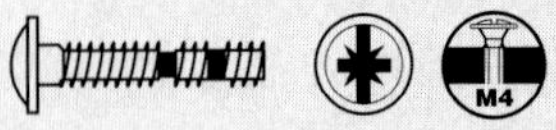

Threaded Breakoff Screw M4
Combined slot, suitable for flat or cross blades
Finish: steel, zinc-plated

Length	Cat. No.
1 3/4" x 3/4"	022.35.887

Packing: 100 and 1000 pcs.

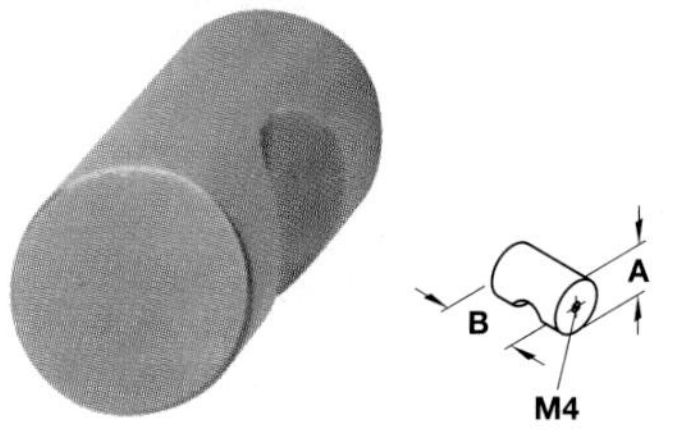

Brushed

Size A x B	Cat. No.
12 x 25	134.80.610
20 x 30	134.80.629

Packing: 25 pcs.

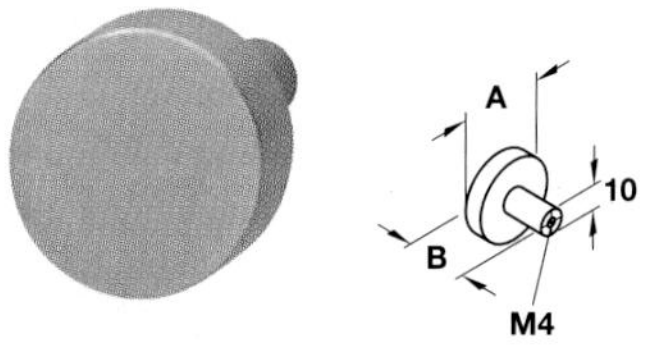

Brushed

Size A x B	Cat. No.
25 x 22	134.81.617
32 x 25	134.81.626

Packing: 25 pcs.

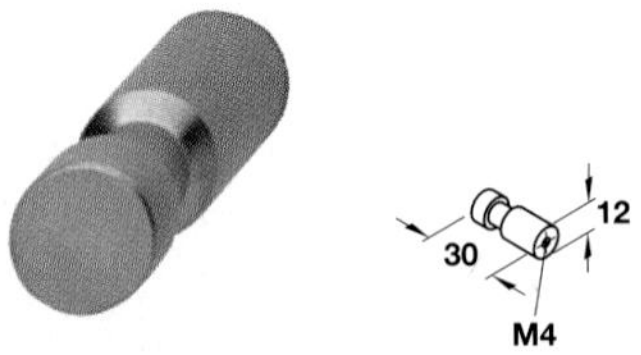

Brushed

Cat. No.	134.82.605

Packing: 25 pcs.

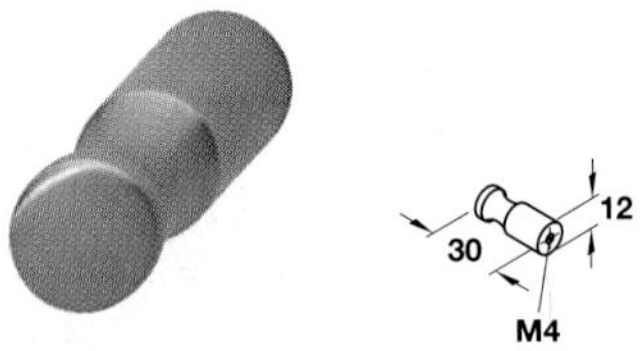

Brushed

Cat. No.	134.83.602

Packing: 25 pcs.

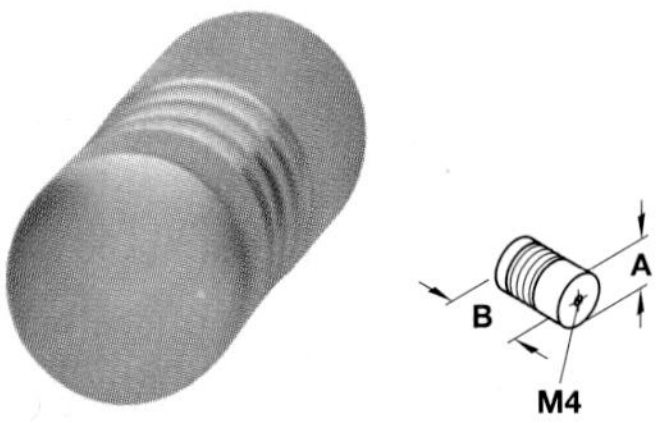

Brushed

Size A x B	Cat. No.
15 x 30	134.84.618
20 x 30	134.84.627

Packing: 25 pcs.

Zinc Knobs

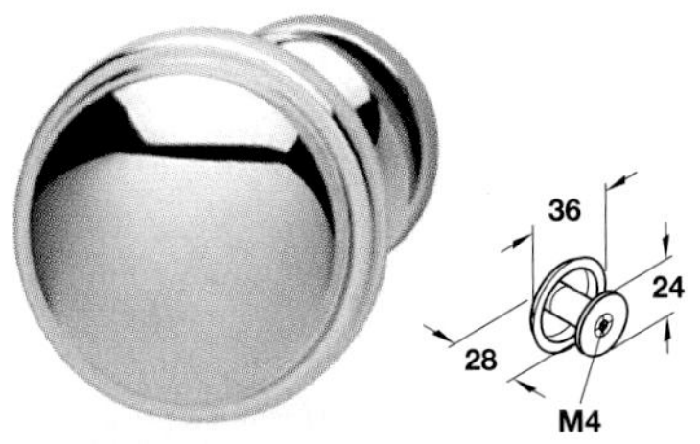

Chrome plated polished

Cat. No.	134.09.231

Packing: 25 pcs.

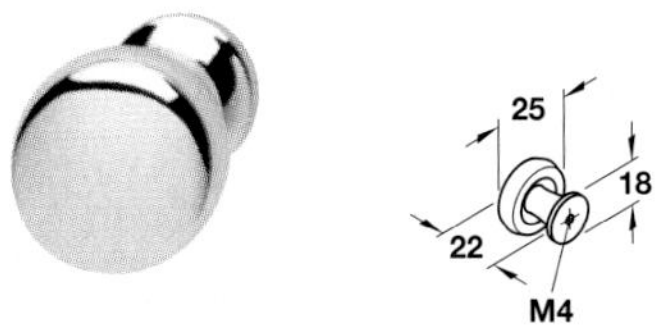

Chrome plated polished

Cat. No.	134.39.202

Packing: 25 pcs.

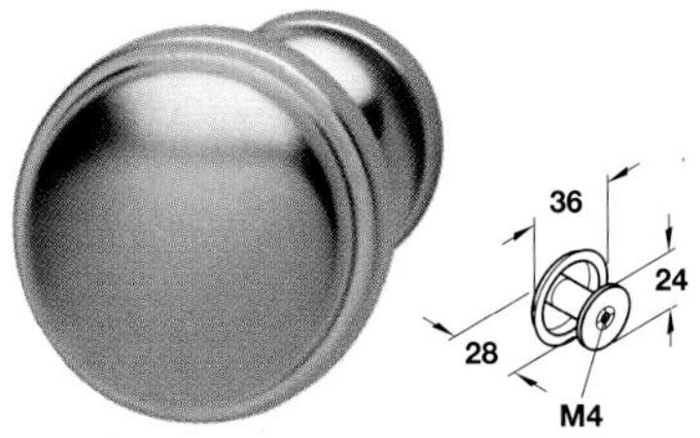

Nickel plated matt

Cat. No.	134.09.633

Packing: 25 pcs.

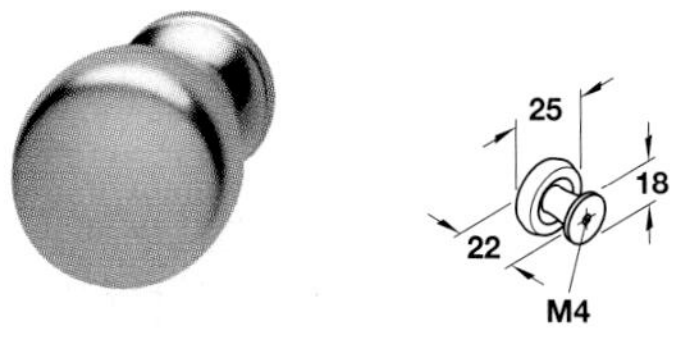

Nickel plated matt

Cat. No.	134.39.604

Packing: 25 pcs.

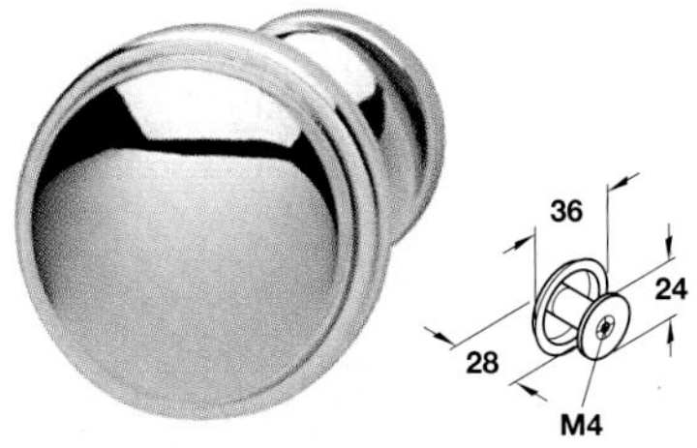

Gold plated polished

Cat. No.	134.09.839

Packing: 25 pcs.

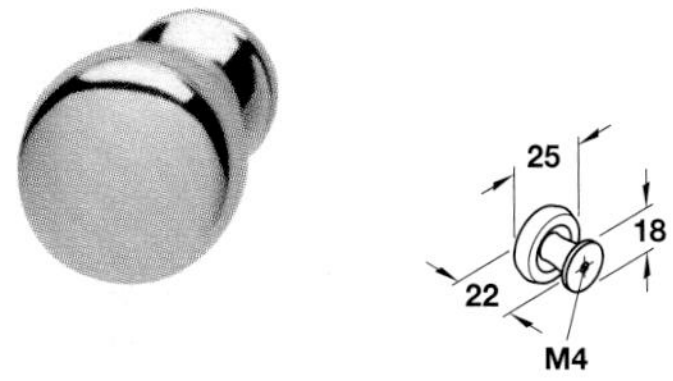

Gold plated polished

Cat. No.	134.39.800

Packing: 25 pcs.

HÄFELE

Threaded Screws M4
Combined slot, suitable for flat or cross blades
Finish: steel, zinc-plated

Length	Cat. No.
10 mm	022.35.109
12 mm	022.35.127
15 mm	022.35.154
18 mm	022.35.181
20 mm	022.35.207
22 mm	022.35.225
23 mm	022.35.234
25 mm	022.35.252
28 mm	022.35.289
30 mm	022.35.305
35 mm	022.35.350
38 mm	022.35.387
40 mm	022.35.403
45 mm	022.35.458
50 mm	022.35.501
60 mm	022.35.609

Packing: 100 and 1000 pcs.

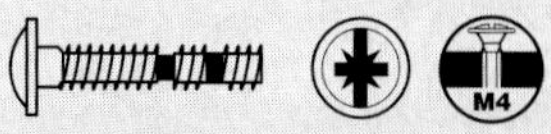

Threaded Breakoff Screw M4
Combined slot, suitable for flat or cross blades
Finish: steel, zinc-plated

Length	Cat. No.
1 3/4" x 3/4"	022.35.887

Packing: 100 and 1000 pcs.

Dimensional data not binding.
We reserve the right to alter specifications without notice.

HÄFELE

Zinc Knobs

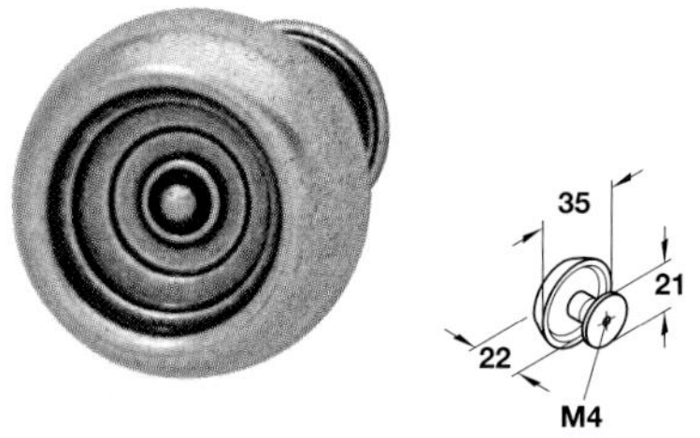

Antique tin plated

Cat. No.	121.06.928

Packing: 25 pcs.

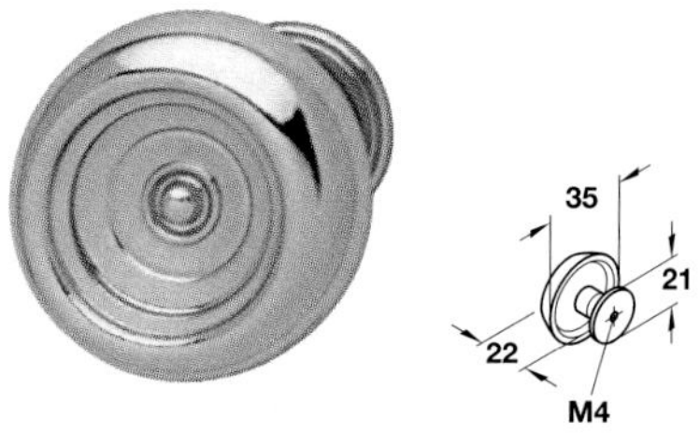

Gold plated polished

Cat. No.	121.06.820

Packing: 25 pcs.

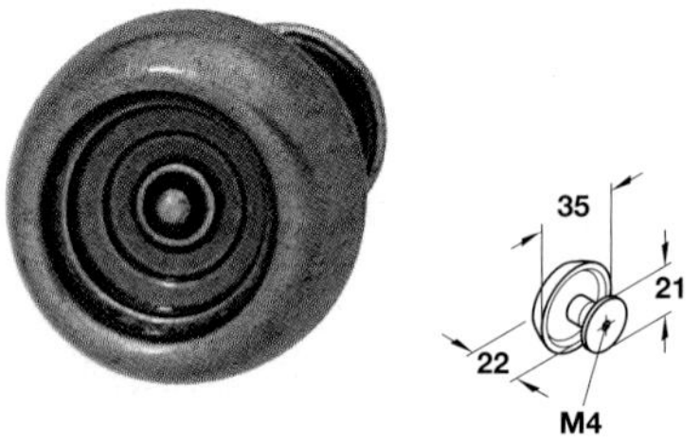

Bronzed and brushed

Cat. No.	121.06.124

Packing: 25 pcs.

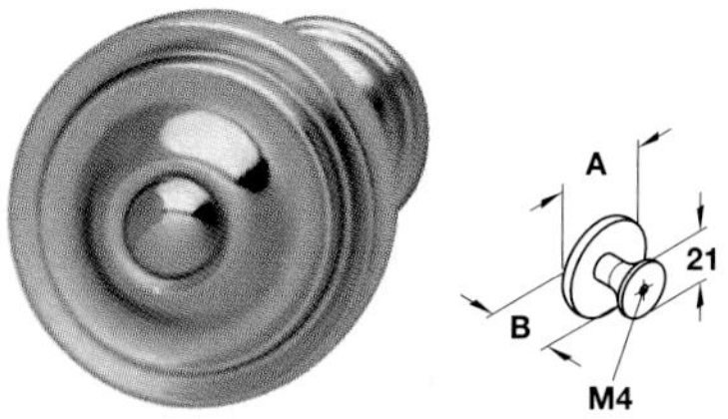

Gold plated polished

Size A x B	Cat. No.
30 x 22	134.33.817
36 x 26	134.33.826

Packing: 25 pcs.

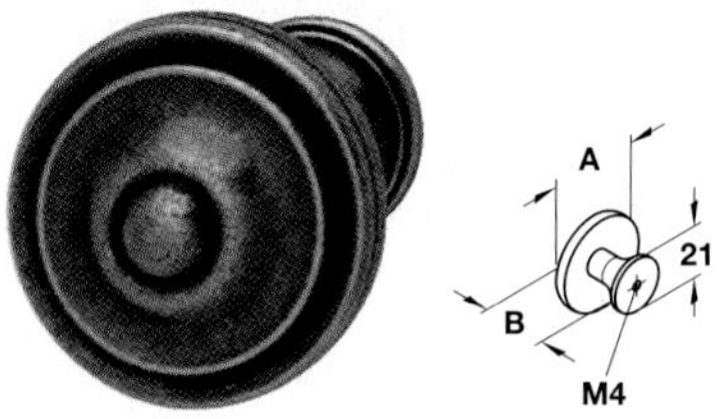

Bronzed & Brushed

Size A x B	Cat. No.
30 x 22	134.33.111
36 x 26	134.33.120

Packing: 25 pcs.

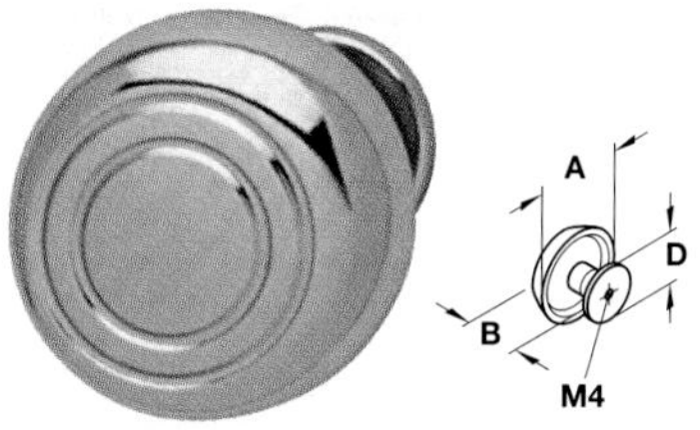

Gold plated polished

Size A x B	Diameter D	Cat. No.
28 x 21	21	134.35.811
36 x 24	21	134.35.820

Packing: 25 pcs.

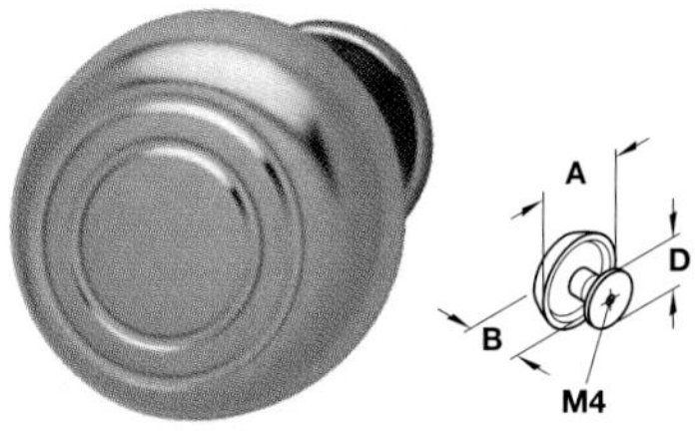

Nickel plated matt

Size A x B	Diameter D	Cat. No.
28 x 21	21	134.35.615
36 x 24	21	134.35.624

Packing: 25 pcs.

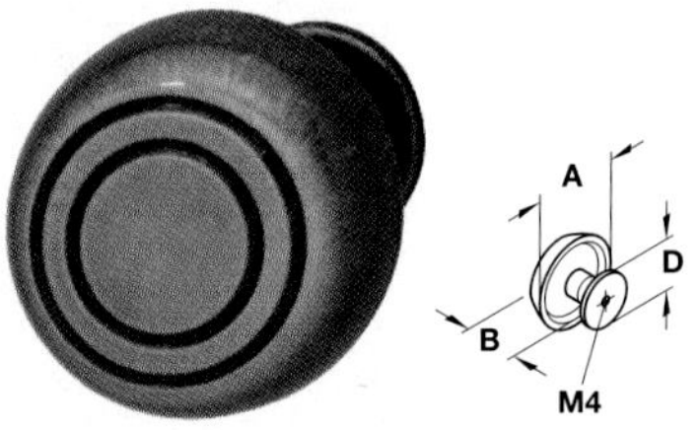

Bronzed and brushed

Size A x B	Diameter D	Cat. No.
28 x 21	21	134.35.115
36 x 24	21	134.35.124

Packing: 25 pcs.

Threaded Screws M4
Combined slot, suitable for flat or cross blades

Finish: steel, zinc-plated

Length	Cat. No.
10 mm	022.35.109
12 mm	022.35.127
15 mm	022.35.154
18 mm	022.35.181
20 mm	022.35.207
22 mm	022.35.225
23 mm	022.35.234
25 mm	022.35.252
28 mm	022.35.289
30 mm	022.35.305
35 mm	022.35.350
38 mm	022.35.387
40 mm	022.35.403
45 mm	022.35.458
50 mm	022.35.501
60 mm	022.35.609

Packing: 100 and 1000 pcs.

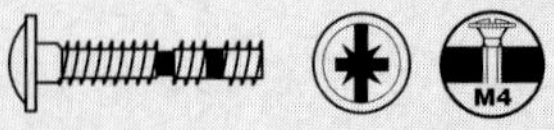

Threaded Breakoff Screw M4
Combined slot, suitable for flat or cross blades

Finish: steel, zinc-plated

Length	Cat. No.
1 3/4" x 3/4"	022.35.887

Packing: 100 and 1000 pcs.

Zinc Knobs

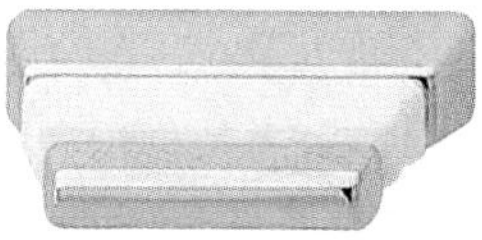

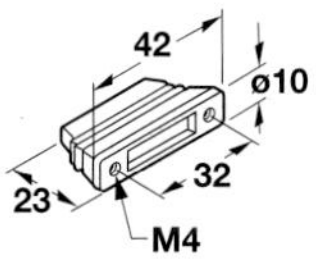

Chrome polished/white/chrome polished

Cat. No.	105.38.217

Packing: 25 pcs.

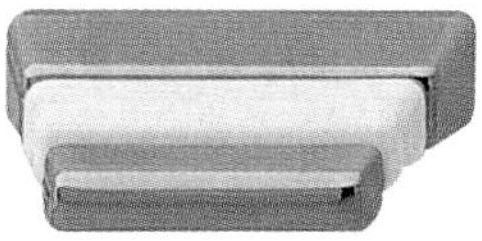

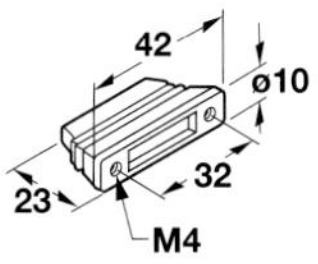

Gold polished/white/gold polished

Cat. No.	105.38.815

Packing: 25 pcs.

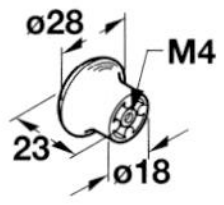

Base and center: chrome polished
Insert: gold colored polished

Cat. No.	122.22.212

Packing: 25 pcs.

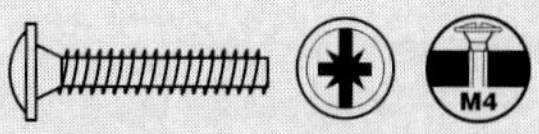

Threaded Screws M4
Combined slot, suitable for flat or cross blades
Finish: steel, zinc-plated

Length	Cat. No.
10 mm	022.35.109
12 mm	022.35.127
15 mm	022.35.154
18 mm	022.35.181
20 mm	022.35.207
22 mm	022.35.225
23 mm	022.35.234
25 mm	022.35.252
28 mm	022.35.289
30 mm	022.35.305
35 mm	022.35.350
38 mm	022.35.387
40 mm	022.35.403
45 mm	022.35.458
50 mm	022.35.501
60 mm	022.35.609

Packing: 100 and 1000 pcs.

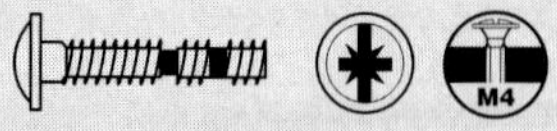

Threaded Breakoff Screw M4
Combined slot, suitable for flat or cross blades
Finish: steel, zinc-plated

Length	Cat. No.
1 3/4" x 3/4"	022.35.887

Packing: 100 and 1000 pcs.

HÄFELE

Zinc Knobs

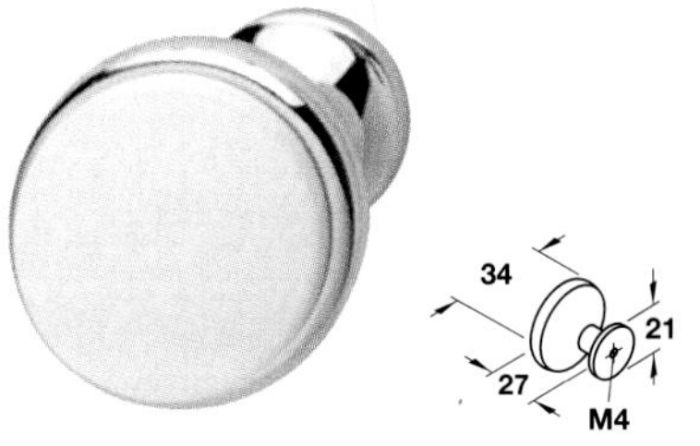

Base chrome plated, polished
Inset white

Cat. No.	134.07.219

Packing: 25 pcs.

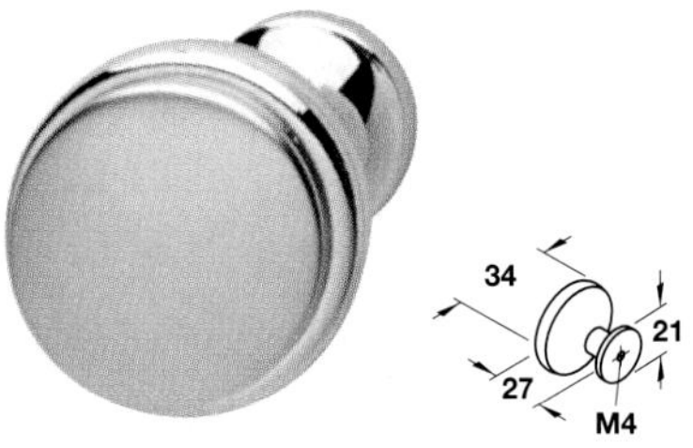

Base chrome plated, polished
Inset chrome plated, matte

Cat. No.	134.07.228

Packing: 25 pcs.

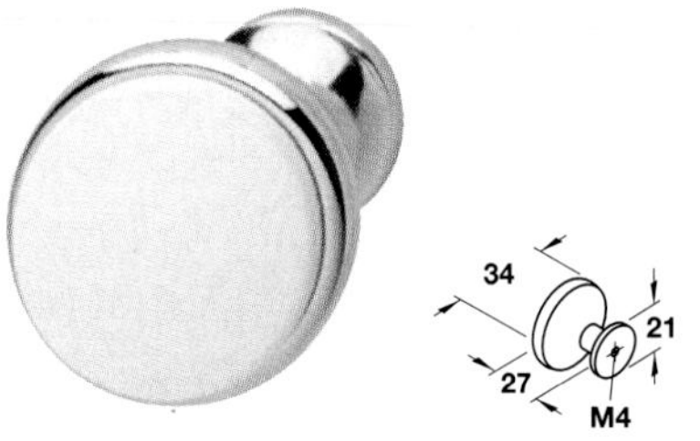

Base gold colored, polished
Inset white

Cat. No.	134.07.817

Packing: 25 pcs.

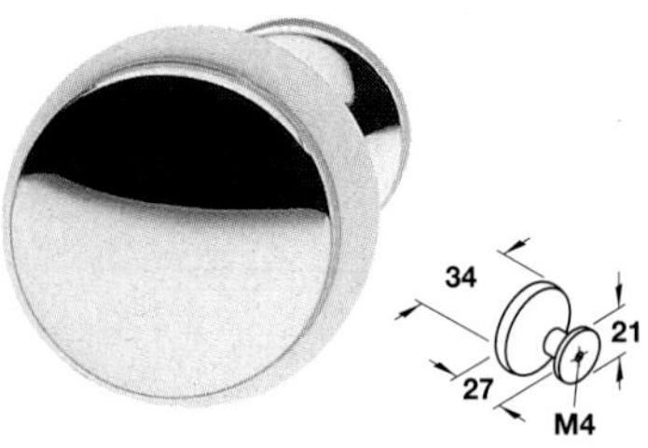

Chrome polished/white/chrome polished

Cat. No.	134.07.237

Packing: 25 pcs.

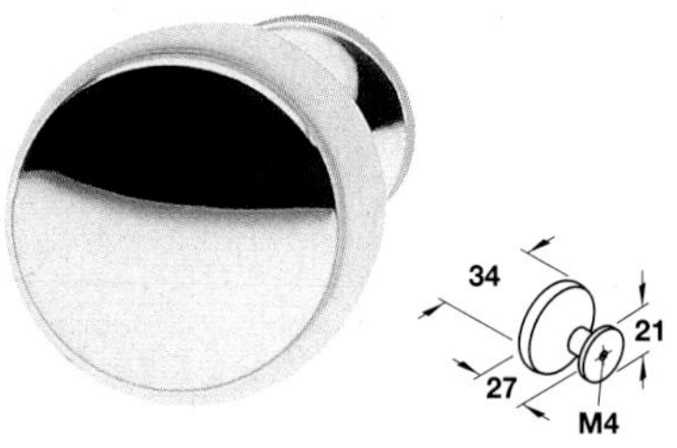

Gold polished/white/gold polished

Cat. No.	134.07.835

Packing: 25 pcs.

Threaded Screws M4
Combined slot, suitable for flat or cross blades
Finish: steel, zinc-plated

Length	Cat. No.
10 mm	022.35.109
12 mm	022.35.127
15 mm	022.35.154
18 mm	022.35.181
20 mm	022.35.207
22 mm	022.35.225
23 mm	022.35.234
25 mm	022.35.252
28 mm	022.35.289
30 mm	022.35.305
35 mm	022.35.350
38 mm	022.35.387
40 mm	022.35.403
45 mm	022.35.458
50 mm	022.35.501
60 mm	022.35.609

Packing: 100 and 1000 pcs.

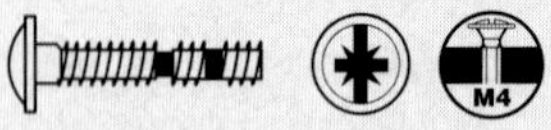

Threaded Breakoff Screw M4
Combined slot, suitable for flat or cross blades
Finish: steel, zinc-plated

Length	Cat. No.
1 3/4" x 3/4"	022.35.887

Packing: 100 and 1000 pcs.

Zinc Knobs

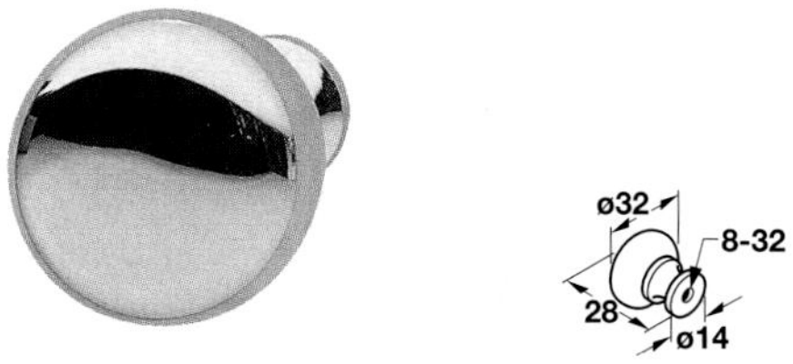

Polished chrome

Cat. No.	134.45.200

Packing: 25 pcs.

Black nickel

Cat. No.	134.45.308

Packing: 25 pcs.

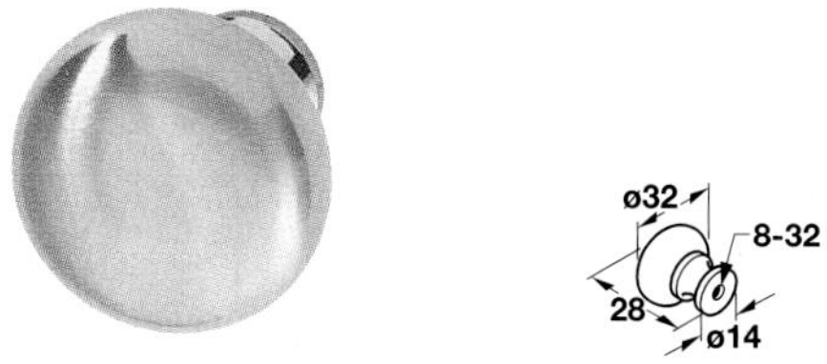

Nickel matt

Cat. No.	134.45.602

Packing: 25 pcs.

Brass polished

Cat. No.	134.45.808

Packing: 25 pcs.

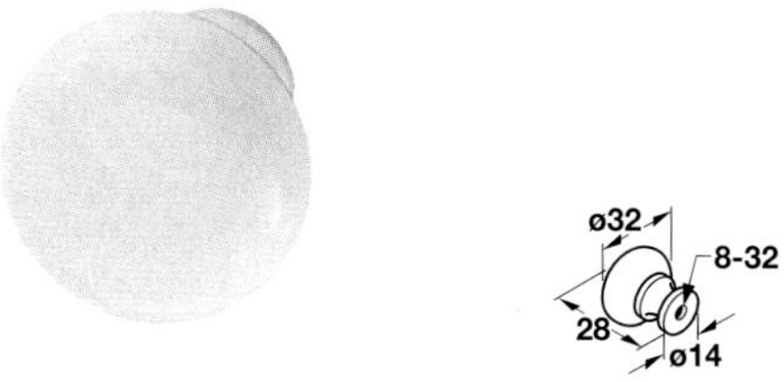

White

Cat. No.	134.44.712

Packing: 25 pcs.

Black matt

Cat. No.	134.44.310

Packing: 25 pcs.

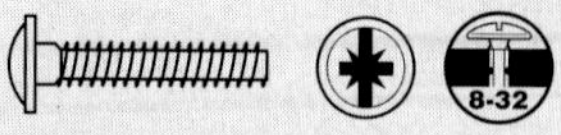

Threaded Screws 8-32
Combined slot, suitable for flat or cross blades

Finish: steel, yellow chromated

Length	Cat. No.
22 mm	022.25.229
25 mm	022.25.256
32 mm	022.25.327
38 mm	022.25.381
45 mm	022.25.452

Packing: 100 and 1000 pcs.

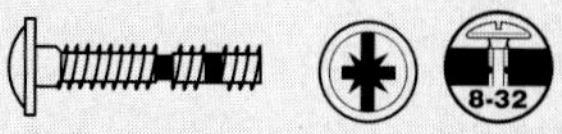

Threaded Breakoff Screw 8-32
Combined slot, suitable for flat or cross blades

Finish: steel, yellow chromated

Length	Cat. No.
1 3/4" x 3/4"	022.25.881

Packing: 100 and 1000 pcs.

Dimensional data not binding.
We reserve the right to alter specifications without notice.

HÄFELE

Zinc Knobs

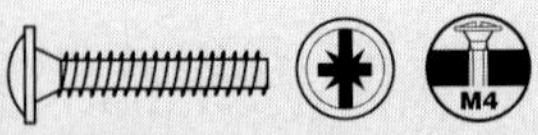

Threaded Screws M4
Combined slot, suitable for flat or cross blades
Finish: steel, zinc-plated

Length	Cat. No.
10 mm	022.35.109
12 mm	022.35.127
15 mm	022.35.154
18 mm	022.35.181
20 mm	022.35.207
22 mm	022.35.225
23 mm	022.35.234
25 mm	022.35.252
28 mm	022.35.289
30 mm	022.35.305
35 mm	022.35.350
38 mm	022.35.387
40 mm	022.35.403
45 mm	022.35.458
50 mm	022.35.501
60 mm	022.35.609

Packing: 100 and 1000 pcs.

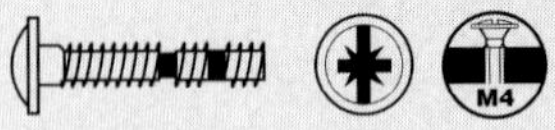

Threaded Breakoff Screw M4
Combined slot, suitable for flat or cross blades
Finish: steel, zinc-plated

Length	Cat. No.
1 3/4" x 3/4"	022.35.887

Packing: 100 and 1000 pcs.

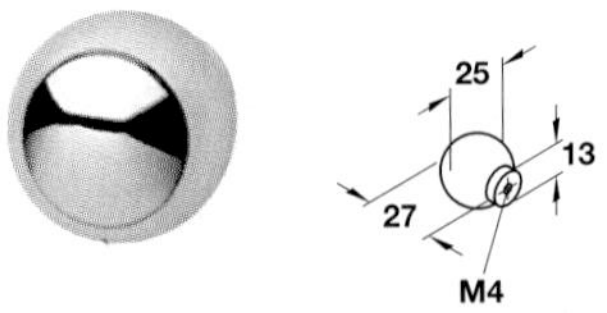

Chrome polished

Cat. No.	136.08.207

Packing: 25 pcs.

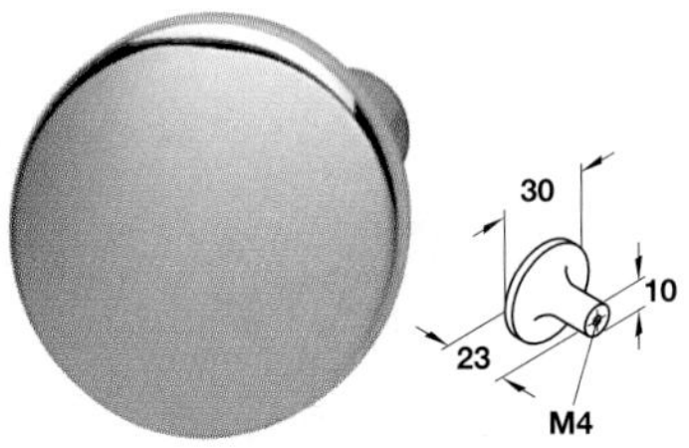

Chrome polished

Cat. No.	134.23.213

Packing: 25 pcs.

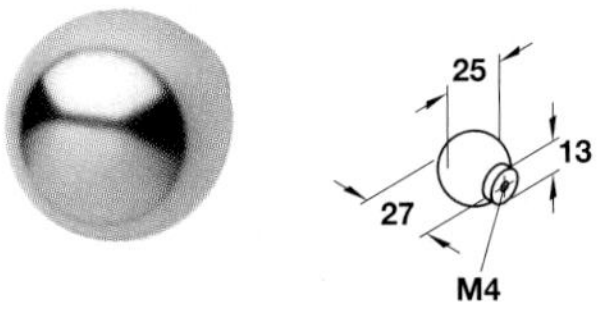

Nickel plated matt

Cat. No.	136.08.609

Packing: 25 pcs.

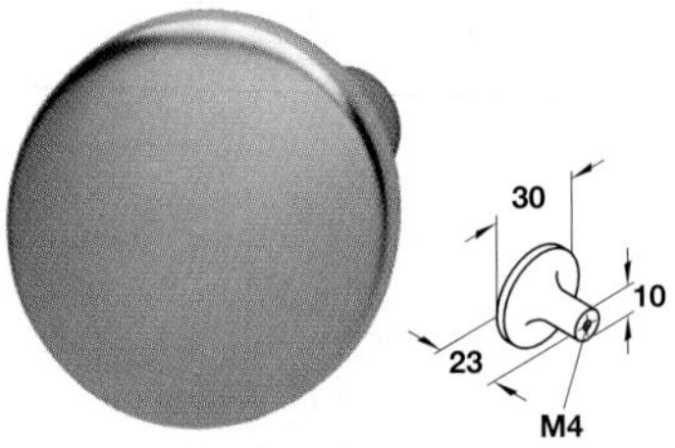

Nickel plated matt

Cat. No.	134.23.615

Packing: 25 pcs.

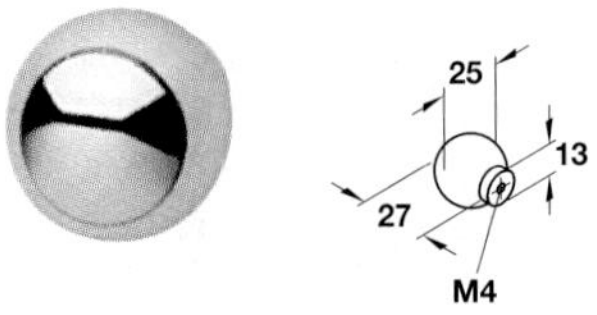

Gold plated polished

Cat. No.	136.08.805

Packing: 25 pcs.

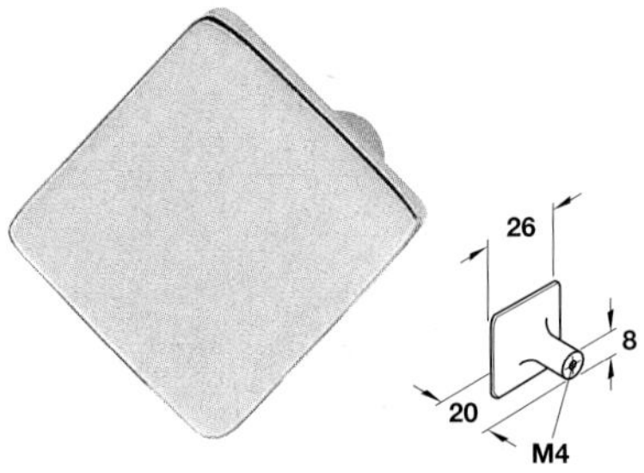

Chrome polished

Cat. No.	132.00.229

Packing: 25 pcs.

Dimensional data not binding.
We reserve the right to alter specifications without notice.

Zinc Knobs

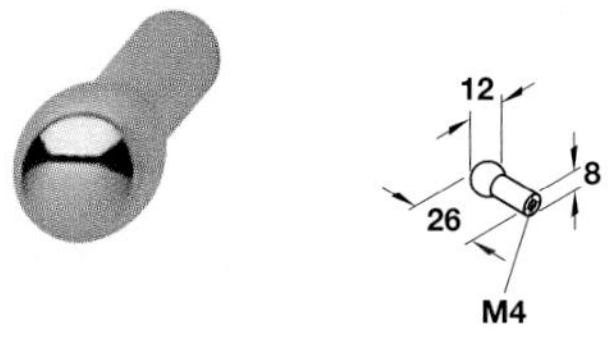

Chrome plated, polished

Cat. No.	136.09.204

Packing: 25 pcs.

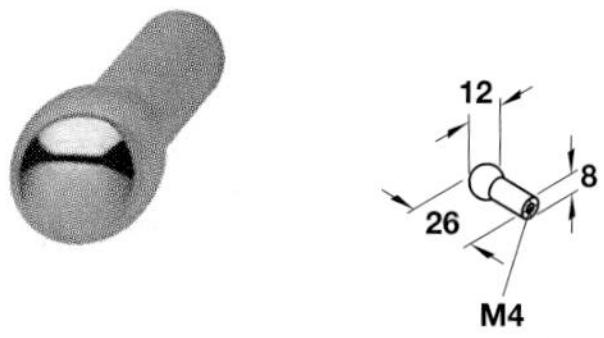

Gold colored, polished

Cat. No.	136.09.802

Packing: 25 pcs.

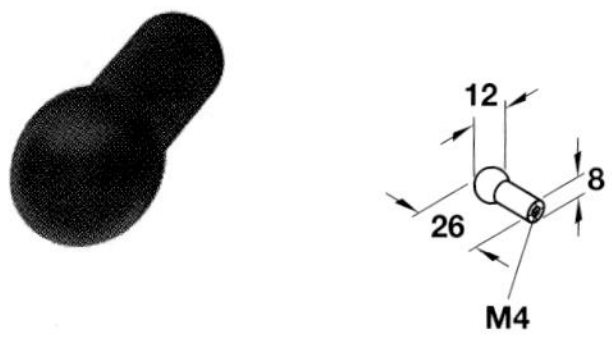

Black matt

Cat. No.	136.09.302

Packing: 25 pcs.

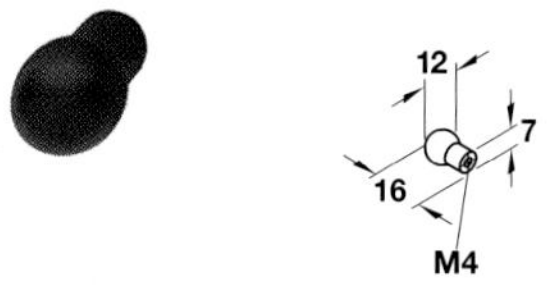

Black matt

Cat. No.	136.22.305

Packing: 25 pcs.

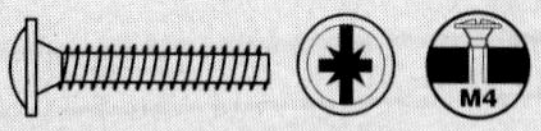

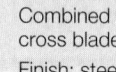

Threaded Screws M4
Combined slot, suitable for flat or cross blades
Finish: steel, zinc-plated

Length	Cat. No.
10 mm	022.35.109
12 mm	022.35.127
15 mm	022.35.154
18 mm	022.35.181
20 mm	022.35.207
22 mm	022.35.225
23 mm	022.35.234
25 mm	022.35.252
28 mm	022.35.289
30 mm	022.35.305
35 mm	022.35.350
38 mm	022.35.387
40 mm	022.35.403
45 mm	022.35.458
50 mm	022.35.501
60 mm	022.35.609

Packing: 100 and 1000 pcs.

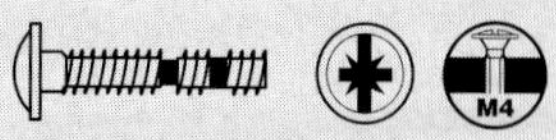

Threaded Breakoff Screw M4
Combined slot, suitable for flat or cross blades
Finish: steel, zinc-plated

Length	Cat. No.
1 3/4" x 3/4"	022.35.887

Packing: 100 and 1000 pcs.

HÄFELE

Zinc Knobs

Threaded Screws M4
Combined slot, suitable for flat or cross blades
Finish: steel, zinc-plated

Length	Cat. No.
10 mm	022.35.109
12 mm	022.35.127
15 mm	022.35.154
18 mm	022.35.181
20 mm	022.35.207
22 mm	022.35.225
23 mm	022.35.234
25 mm	022.35.252
28 mm	022.35.289
30 mm	022.35.305
35 mm	022.35.350
38 mm	022.35.387
40 mm	022.35.403
45 mm	022.35.458
50 mm	022.35.501
60 mm	022.35.609

Packing: 100 and 1000 pcs.

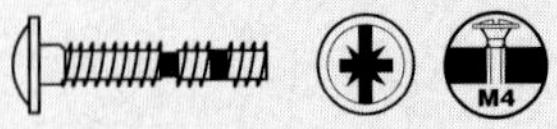

Threaded Breakoff Screw M4
Combined slot, suitable for flat or cross blades
Finish: steel, zinc-plated

Length	Cat. No.
1 3/4" x 3/4"	022.35.887

Packing: 100 and 1000 pcs.

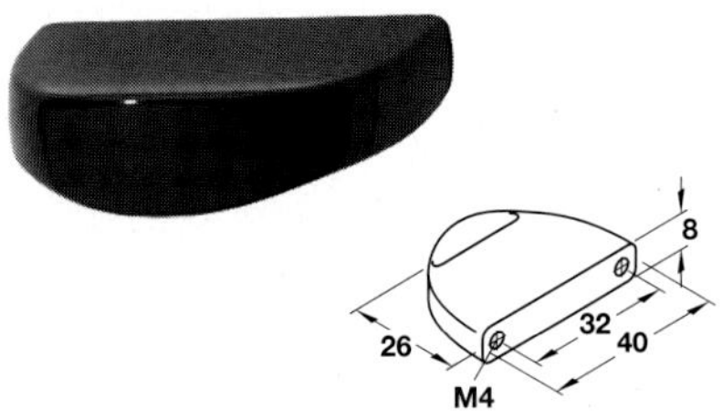

Zinc, black polished

Cat. No.	105.43.300

Packing: 25 pcs.

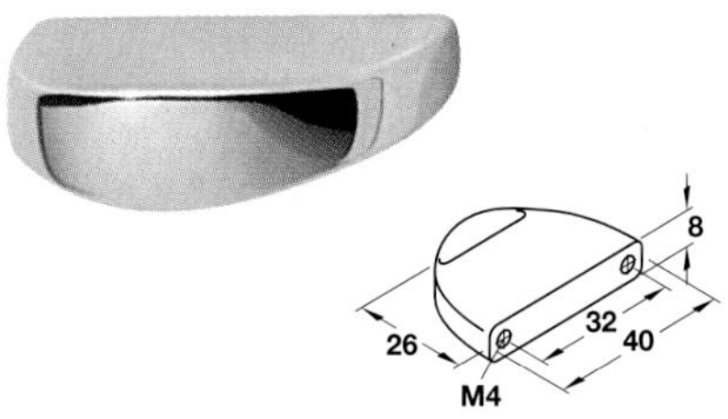

Zinc, chrome polished

Cat. No.	105.43.200

Packing: 25 pcs.

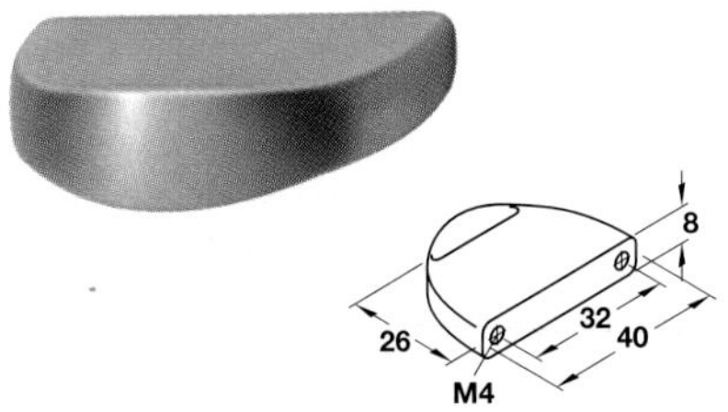

Zinc, chrome plated, matt

Cat. No.	105.43.400

Packing: 25 pcs.

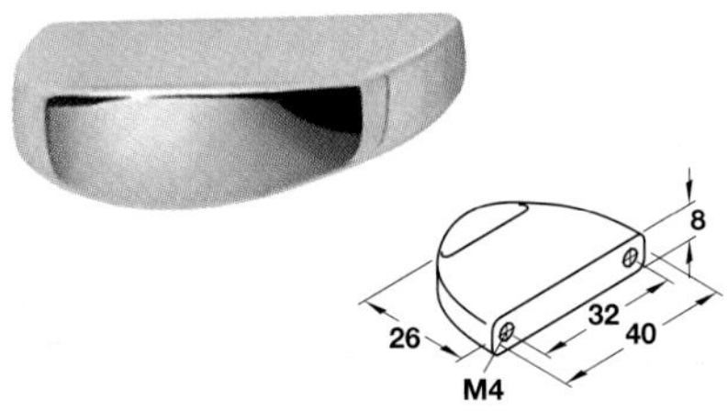

Zinc, gold plated

Cat. No.	105.43.800

Packing: 25 pcs.

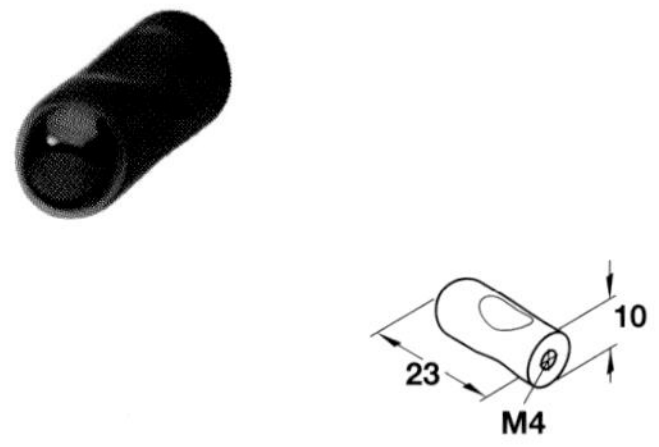

Zinc, black polished

Cat. No.	137.56.300

Packing: 25 pcs.

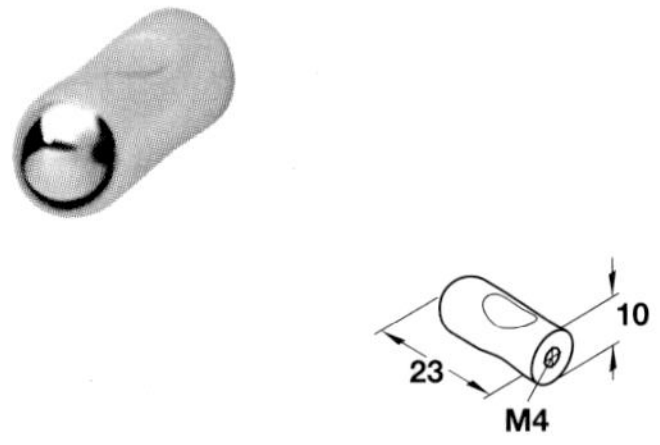

Zinc, chrome plated polished

Cat. No.	137.56.200

Packing: 25 pcs.

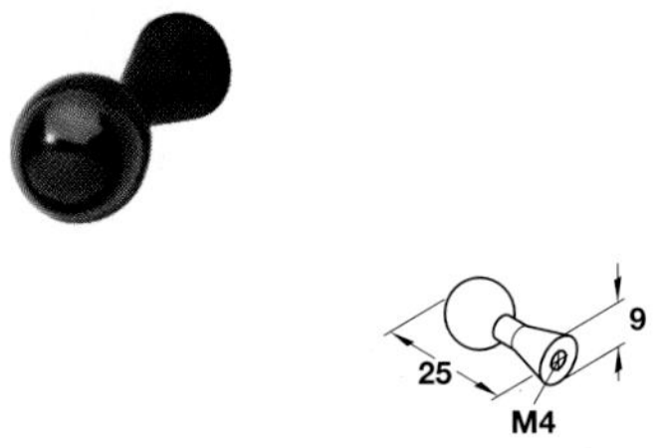

Brass, black polished

Cat. No.	137.57.300

Packing: 25 pcs.

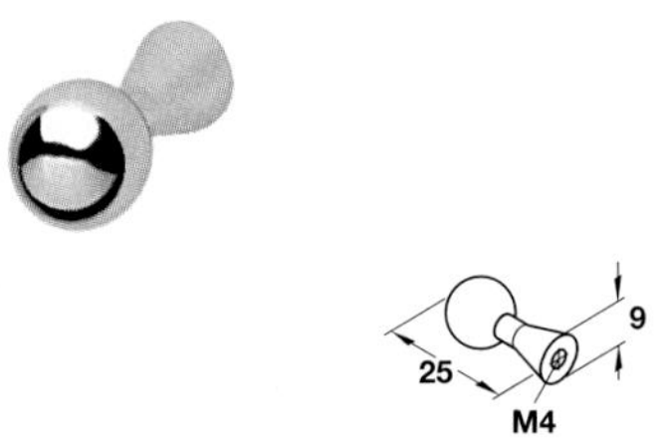

Brass, chrome plated polished

Cat. No.	137.57.200

Packing: 25 pcs.

Dimensional data not binding.
We reserve the right to alter specifications without notice.

Zinc Knobs

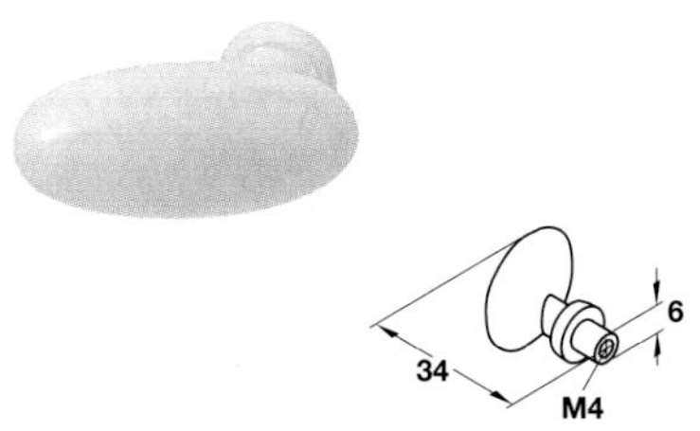

White

Cat. No.	137.13.700

Packing: 25 pcs.

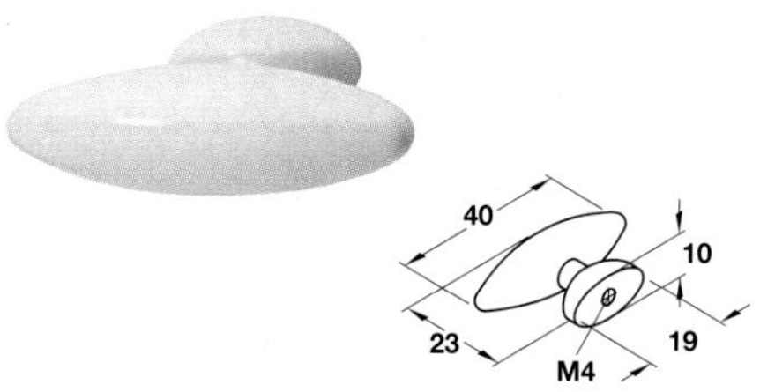

White

Cat. No.	137.55.700

Packing: 25 pcs.

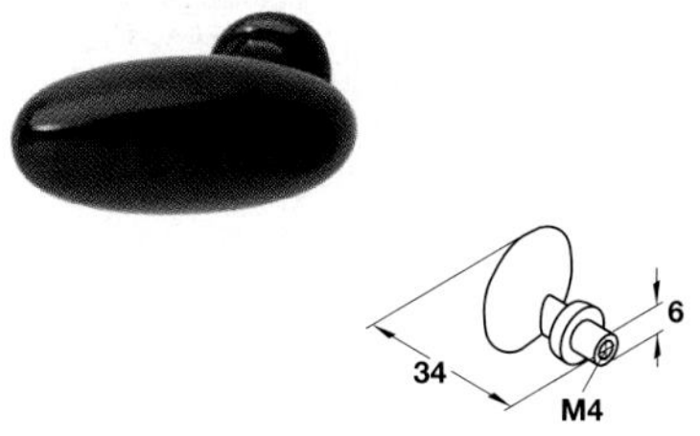

Black, polished

Cat. No.	137.13.300

Packing: 25 pcs.

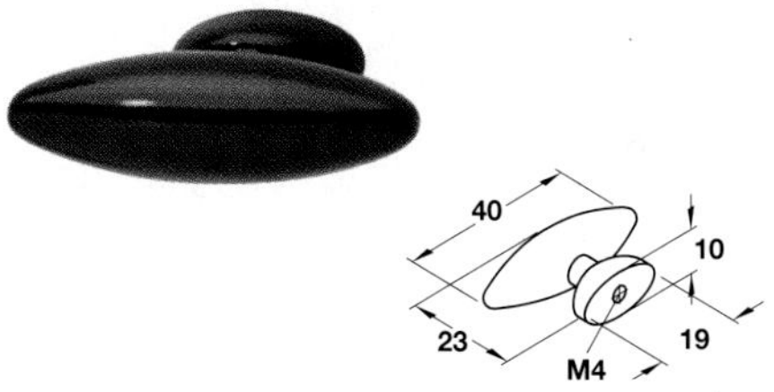

Black, polished

Cat. No.	137.55.300

Packing: 25 pcs.

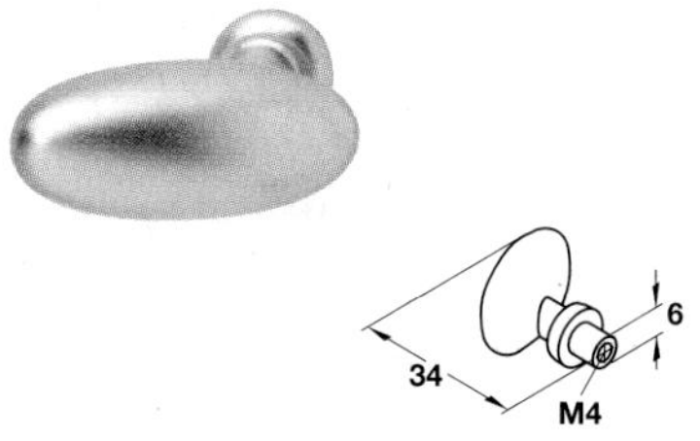

Chrome plated, matt

Cat. No.	137.13.400

Packing: 25 pcs.

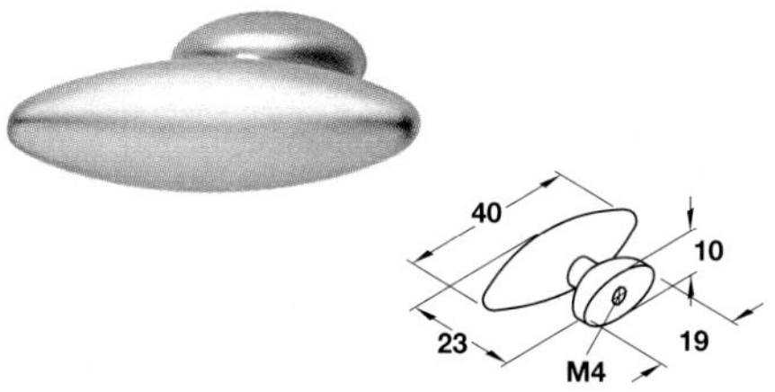

Chrome plated, matt

Cat. No.	137.55.400

Packing: 25 pcs.

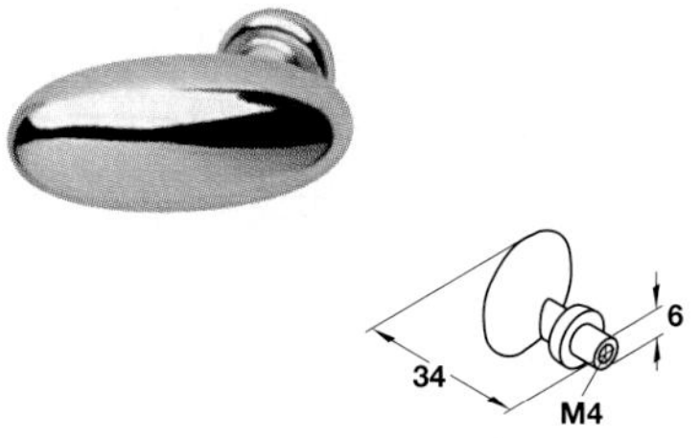

Gold colored, polished

Cat. No.	137.13.800

Packing: 25 pcs.

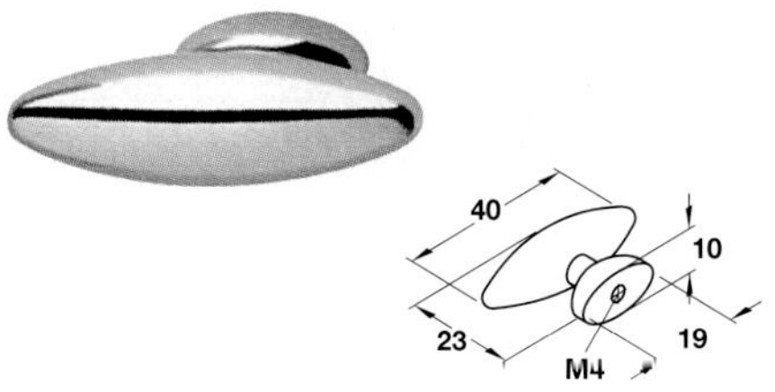

Gold colored, polished

Cat. No.	137.55.800

Packing: 25 pcs.

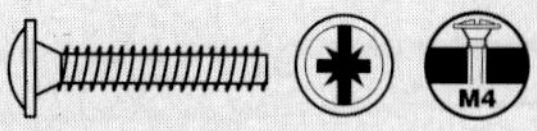

Threaded Screws M4
Combined slot, suitable for flat or cross blades

Finish: steel, zinc-plated

Length	Cat. No.
10 mm	022.35.109
12 mm	022.35.127
15 mm	022.35.154
18 mm	022.35.181
20 mm	022.35.207
22 mm	022.35.225
23 mm	022.35.234
25 mm	022.35.252
28 mm	022.35.289
30 mm	022.35.305
35 mm	022.35.350
38 mm	022.35.387
40 mm	022.35.403
45 mm	022.35.458
50 mm	022.35.501
60 mm	022.35.609

Packing: 100 and 1000 pcs.

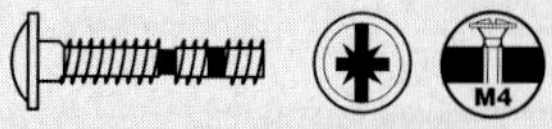

Threaded Breakoff Screw M4
Combined slot, suitable for flat or cross blades

Finish: steel, zinc-plated

Length	Cat. No.
1 3/4" x 3/4"	022.35.887

Packing: 100 and 1000 pcs.

HÄFELE

Zinc Knobs

Antique bronze

Cat. No.	121.07.103

Packing: 25 pcs.

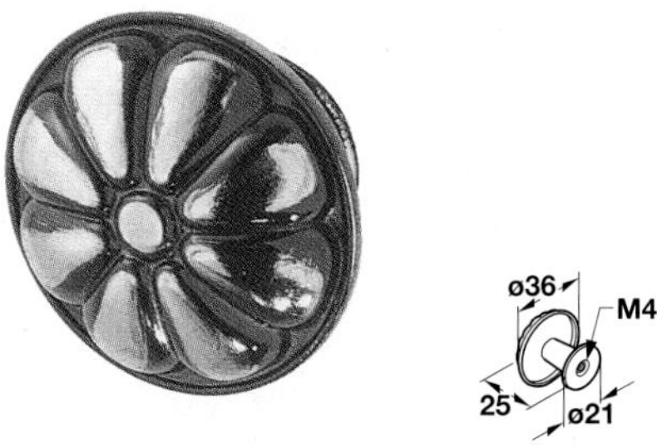

Antique brass polished

Cat. No.	121.07.005

Packing: 25 pcs.

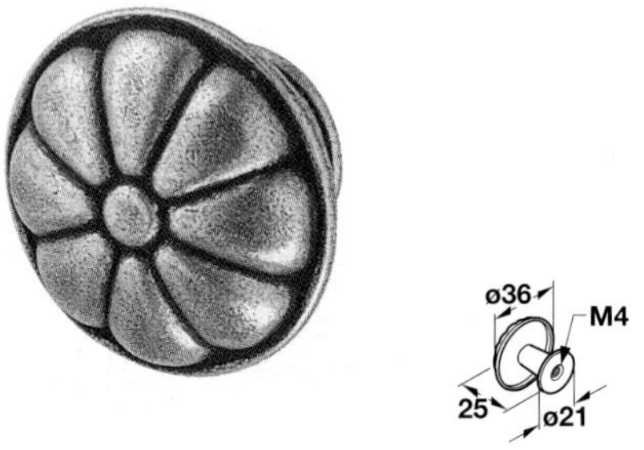

Antique pewter

Cat. No.	121.07.907

Packing: 25 pcs.

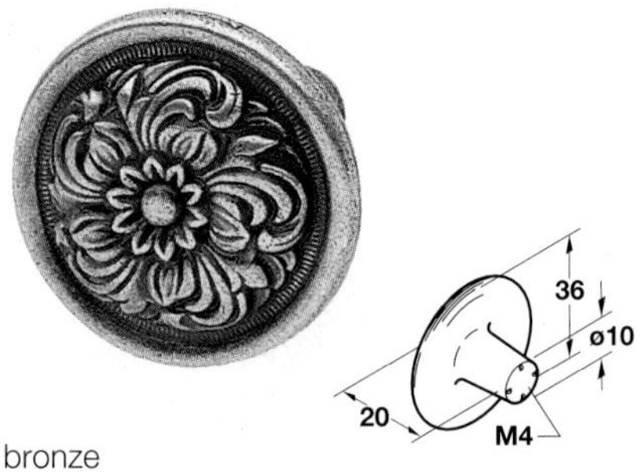

Antique bronze

Cat. No.	122.43.100

Packing: 25 pcs.

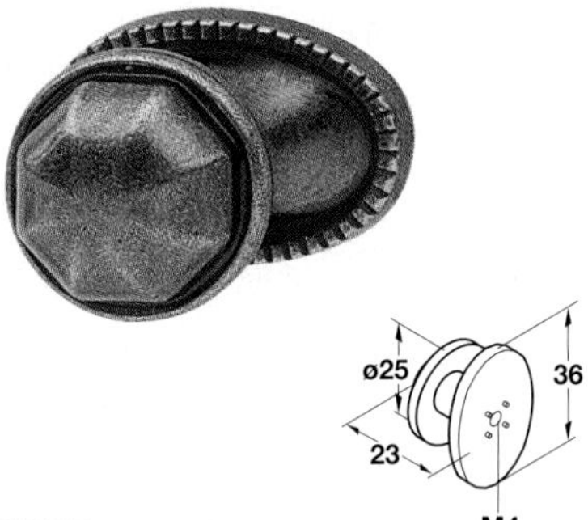

Antique bronze

Cat. No.	122.44.100

Packing: 25 pcs.

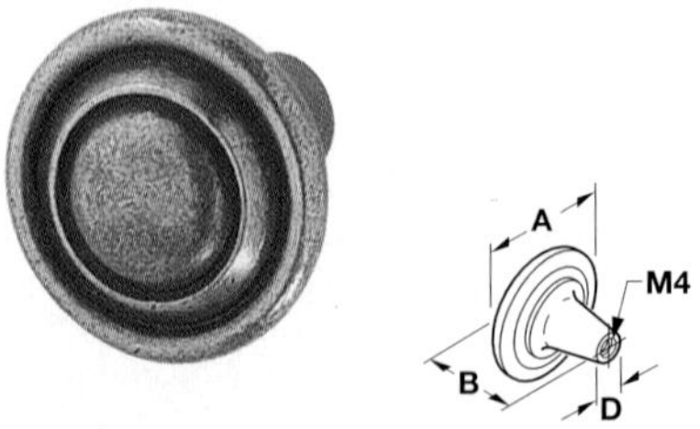

Antique bronze

Size A x B	Diameter D	Cat. No.
25 x 25	10	134.27.177
32 x 76	11	134.27.186

Packing: 25 pcs.

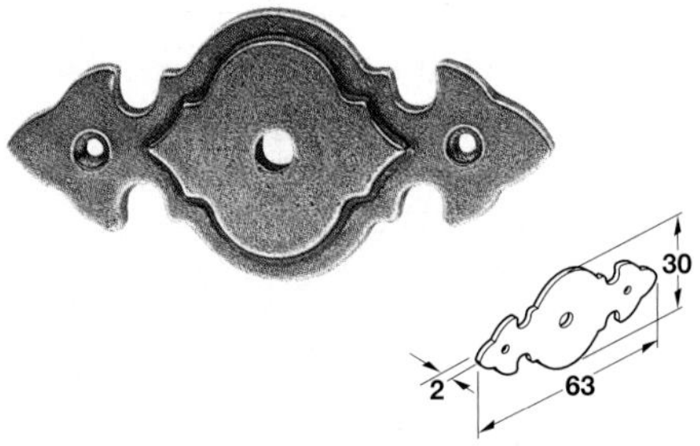

Antique bronze

Cat. No.	121.67.010

Packing: 25 pcs.

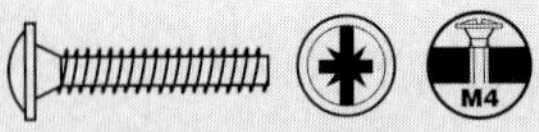

Threaded Screws M4
Combined slot, suitable for flat or cross blades
Finish: steel, zinc-plated

Length	Cat. No.
10 mm	022.35.109
12 mm	022.35.127
15 mm	022.35.154
18 mm	022.35.181
20 mm	022.35.207
22 mm	022.35.225
23 mm	022.35.234
25 mm	022.35.252
28 mm	022.35.289
30 mm	022.35.305
35 mm	022.35.350
38 mm	022.35.387
40 mm	022.35.403
45 mm	022.35.458
50 mm	022.35.501
60 mm	022.35.609

Packing: 100 and 1000 pcs.

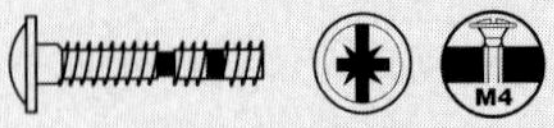

Threaded Breakoff Screw M4
Combined slot, suitable for flat or cross blades
Finish: steel, zinc-plated

Length	Cat. No.
1 3/4" x 3/4"	022.35.887

Packing: 100 and 1000 pcs.

Dimensional data not binding.
We reserve the right to alter specifications without notice.

Zinc knobs and backplates

HÄFELE

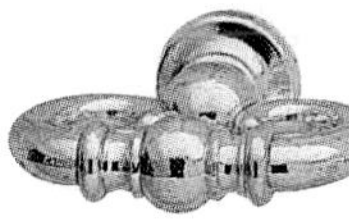

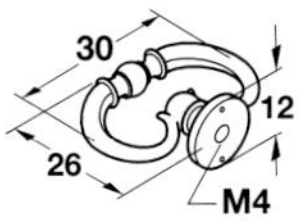

Gold colored polished

Cat. No.	120.60.800

Packing: 25 pcs.

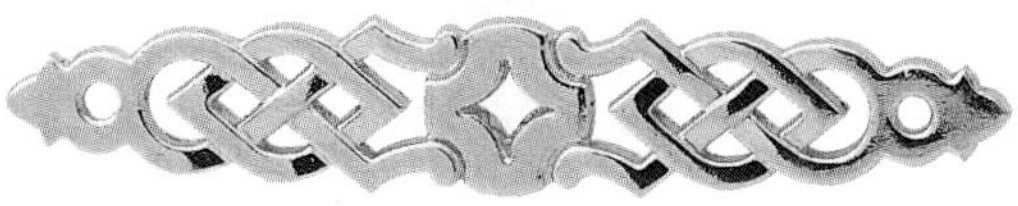

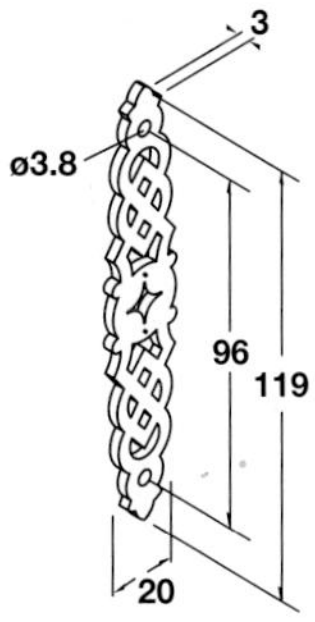

Gold colored polished

Cat. No.	120.60.890

Packing: 25 pcs.

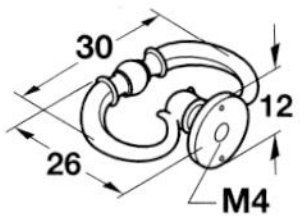

Antique english

Cat. No.	120.60.100

Packing: 25 pcs.

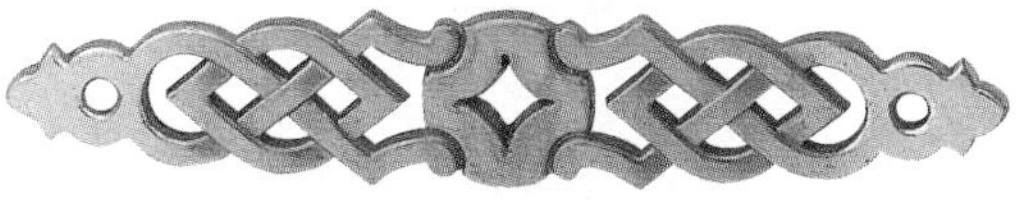

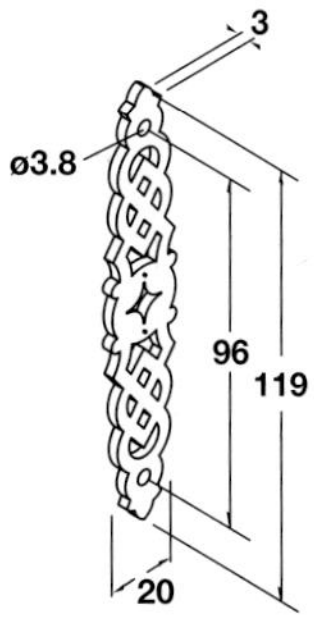

Antique english

Cat. No.	120.60.190

Packing: 25 pcs.

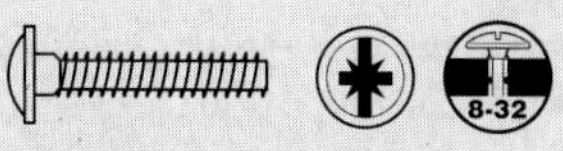

Threaded Screws 8-32
Combined slot, suitable for flat or cross blades

Finish: steel, yellow chromated

Length	Cat. No.
22 mm	022.25.229
25 mm	022.25.256
32 mm	022.25.327
38 mm	022.25.381
45 mm	022.25.452

Packing: 100 and 1000 pcs.

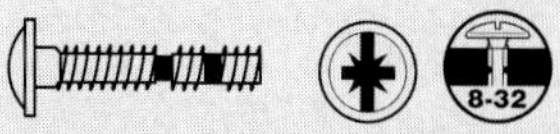

Threaded Breakoff Screw 8-32
Combined slot, suitable for flat or cross blades

Finish: steel, yellow chromated

Length	Cat. No.
1 3/4" x 3/4"	022.25.881

Packing: 100 and 1000 pcs.

Dimensional data not binding.
We reserve the right to alter specifications without notice.

Dimensions in mm

HÄFELE

Zinc handles and backplates

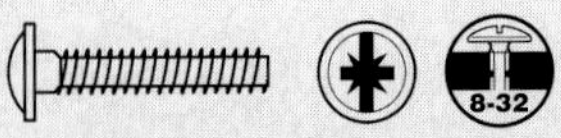

Threaded Screws 8-32
Combined slot, suitable for flat or cross blades
Finish: steel, yellow chromated

Length	Cat. No.
22 mm	022.25.229
25 mm	022.25.256
32 mm	022.25.327
38 mm	022.25.381
45 mm	022.25.452

Packing: 100 and 1000 pcs.

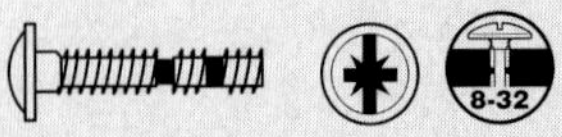

Threaded Breakoff Screw 8-32
Combined slot, suitable for flat or cross blades
Finish: steel, yellow chromated

Length	Cat. No.
1 3/4" x 3/4"	022.25.881

Packing: 100 and 1000 pcs.

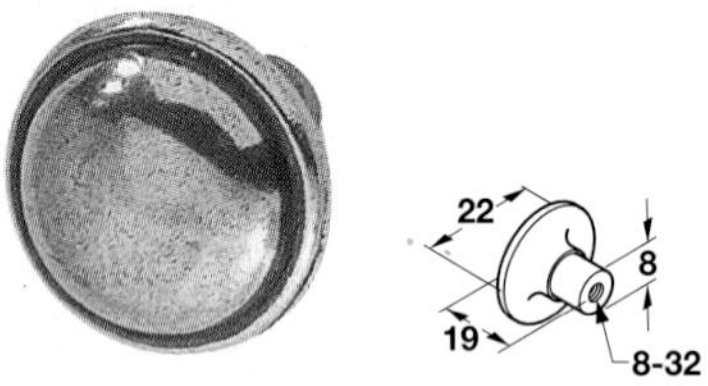

Burnished brass

Cat. No.	122.32.100

Packing: 25 pcs.

Burnished brass

Cat. No.	122.32.150

Packing: 25 pcs.

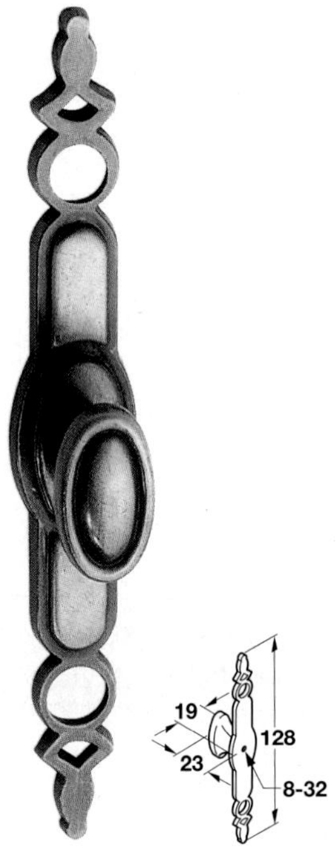

Antique english

Cat. No.	122.33.100

Packing: 25 pcs.

Dimensional data not binding.
We reserve the right to alter specifications without notice.

Zinc handles and backplates

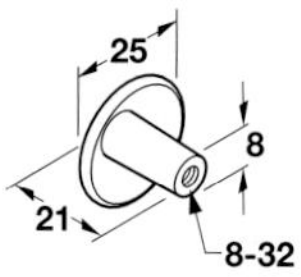

Burnished brass

Cat. No.	122.31.100

Packing: 25 pcs.

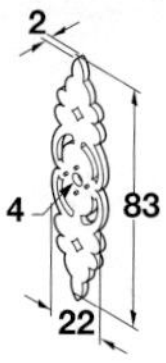

Burnished brass

Cat. No.	122.31.150

Packing: 25 pcs.

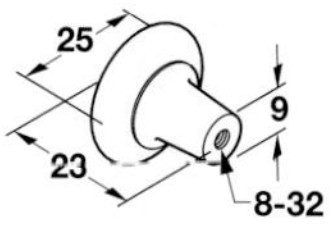

Burnished brass

Cat. No.	122.30.100

Packing: 25 pcs.

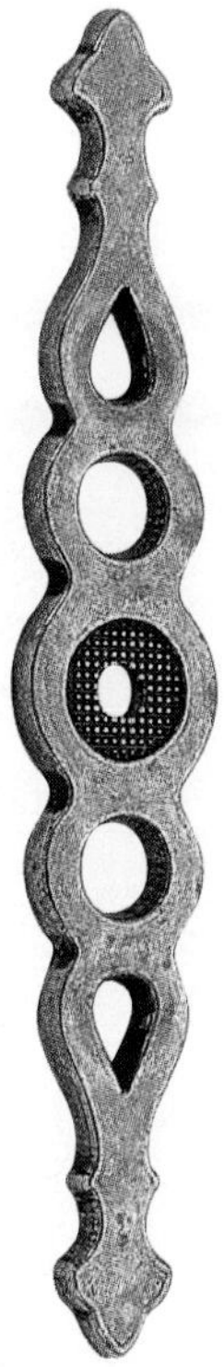

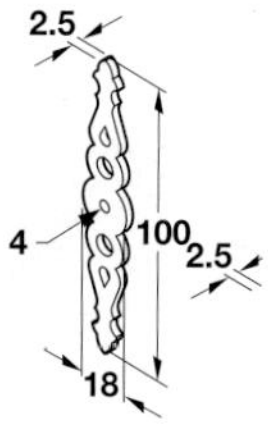

Burnished brass

Cat. No.	122.30.150

Packing: 25 pcs.

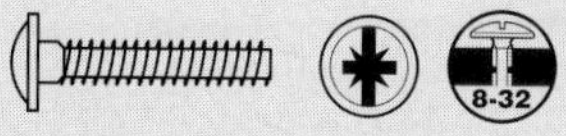

Threaded Screws 8-32
Combined slot, suitable for flat or cross blades

Finish: steel, yellow chromated

Length	Cat. No.
22 mm	022.25.229
25 mm	022.25.256
32 mm	022.25.327
38 mm	022.25.381
45 mm	022.25.452

Packing: 100 and 1000 pcs.

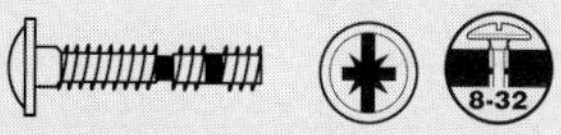

Threaded Breakoff Screw 8-32
Combined slot, suitable for flat or cross blades

Finish: steel, yellow chromated

Length	Cat. No.
1 3/4" x 3/4"	022.25.881

Packing: 100 and 1000 pcs.

HÄFELE

Zinc knobs

1 Decorative Hardware

- Knobs 122.36.100 and 122.35.100 can be used with optional backplate 122.35.150

Threaded Screws 8-32
Combined slot, suitable for flat or cross blades
Finish: steel, yellow chromated

Length	Cat. No.
22 mm	022.25.229
25 mm	022.25.256
32 mm	022.25.327
38 mm	022.25.381
45 mm	022.25.452

Packing: 100 and 1000 pcs.

Threaded Breakoff Screw 8-32
Combined slot, suitable for flat or cross blades
Finish: steel, yellow chromated

Length	Cat. No.
1 3/4" x 3/4"	022.25.881

Packing: 100 and 1000 pcs.

- Knob 134.59.800 can be used with backplate 122.36.850

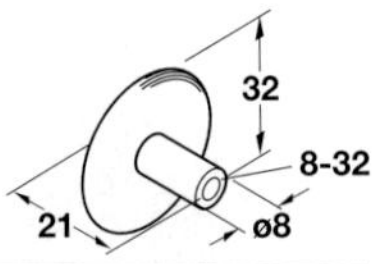

Burnished brass

Cat. No.	122.36.100

Packing: 25 pcs.

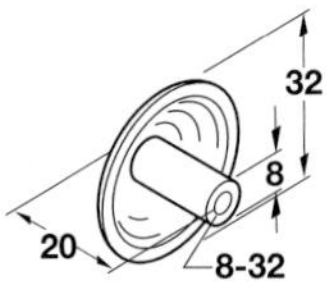

Burnished brass

Cat. No.	122.35.100

Packing: 25 pcs.

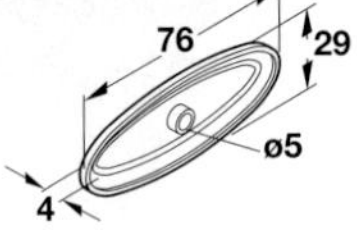

Burnished brass

Cat. No.	122.35.150

Packing: 50 pcs.

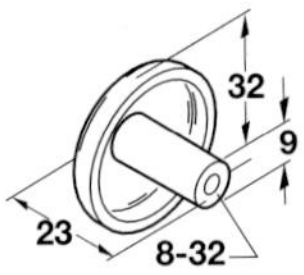

Brass plated

Cat. No.	136.32.500

Packing: 25 pcs.

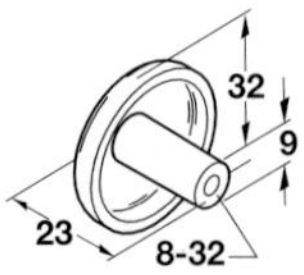

Antique brass plated

Cat. No.	136.32.100

Packing: 25 pcs.

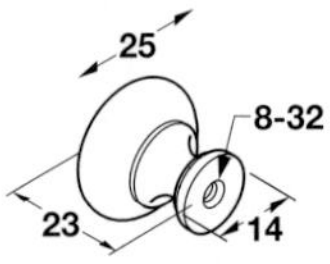

Brass, polished

Cat. No.	134.59.800

Packing: 25 pcs.

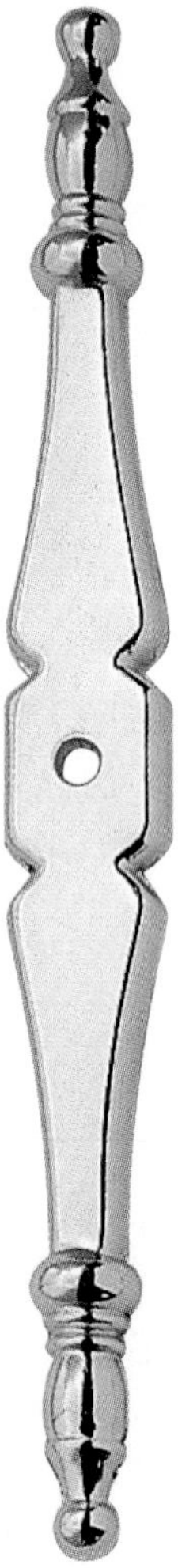
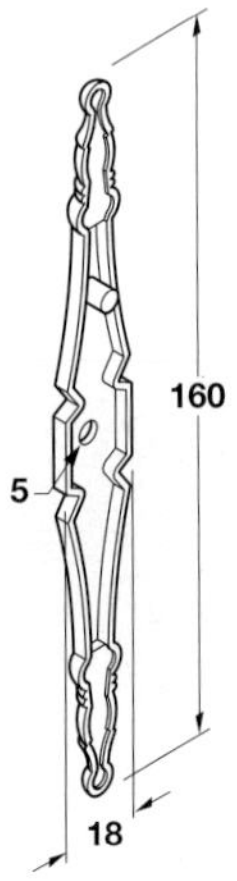

Brass polished

Cat. No.	122.36.850

Packing: 25 pcs.

Ceramic Knobs

White harmony, gold base

Cat. No.	130.43.760

Packing: 25 pcs.

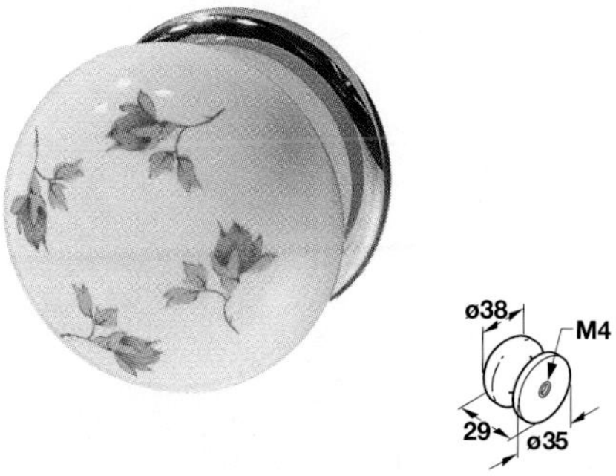

White spot rose/gold base

Cat. No.	130.43.751

Packing: 25 pcs.

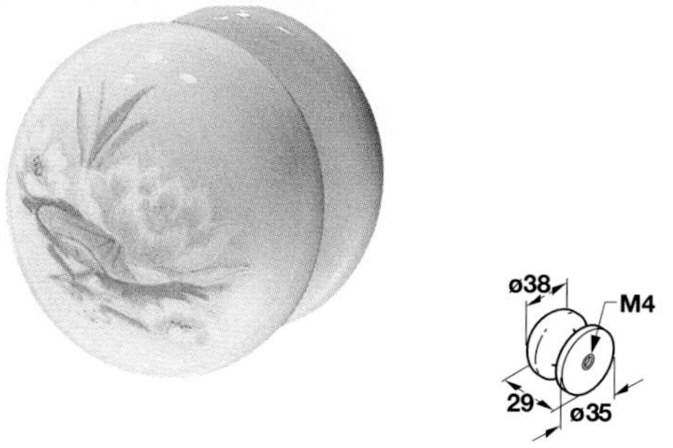

White waterlily

Cat. No.	130.43.733

Packing: 25 pcs.

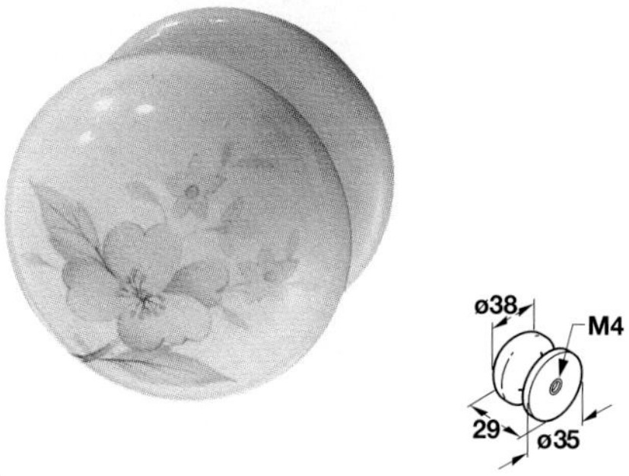

Beige/harmony

Cat. No.	130.43.411

Packing: 25 pcs.

White rosalind

Cat. No.	130.43.724

Packing: 25 pcs.

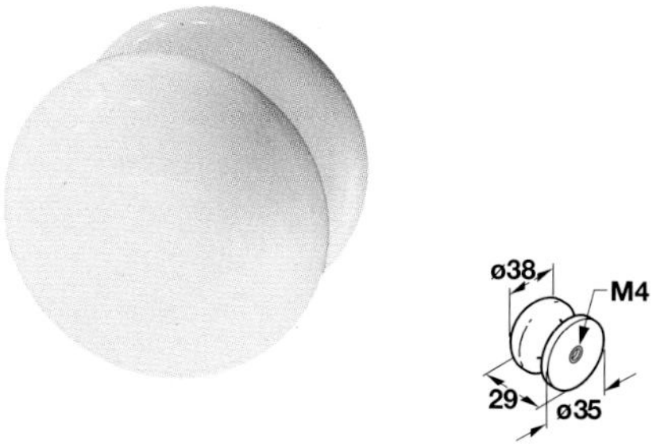

Ceramic, white

Cat. No.	130.43.706

Packing: 10 pcs.

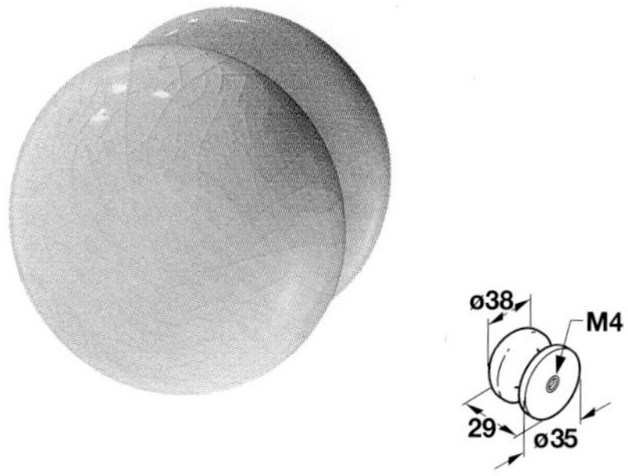

Ceramic, ivory, crackled

Cat. No.	130.43.206

Packing: 10 pcs.

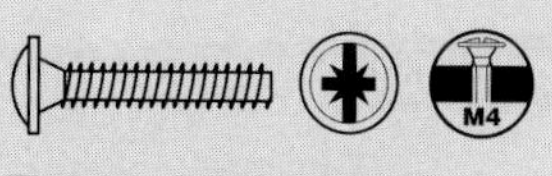

Threaded Screws M4
Combined slot, suitable for flat or cross blades

Finish: steel, zinc-plated

Length	Cat. No.
10 mm	022.35.109
12 mm	022.35.127
15 mm	022.35.154
18 mm	022.35.181
20 mm	022.35.207
22 mm	022.35.225
23 mm	022.35.234
25 mm	022.35.252
28 mm	022.35.289
30 mm	022.35.305
35 mm	022.35.350
38 mm	022.35.387
40 mm	022.35.403
45 mm	022.35.458
50 mm	022.35.501
60 mm	022.35.609

Packing: 100 and 1000 pcs.

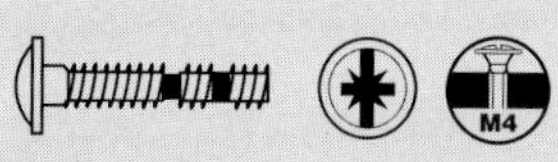

Threaded Breakoff Screw M4
Combined slot, suitable for flat or cross blades

Finish: steel, zinc-plated

Length	Cat. No.
1 3/4" x 3/4"	022.35.887

Packing: 100 and 1000 pcs.

HÄFELE

Ceramic Knobs

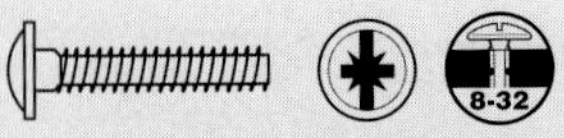

Threaded Screws 8-32
Combined slot, suitable for flat or cross blades

Finish: steel, yellow chromated

Length	Cat. No.
22 mm	022.25.229
25 mm	022.25.256
32 mm	022.25.327
38 mm	022.25.381
45 mm	022.25.452

Packing: 100 and 1000 pcs.

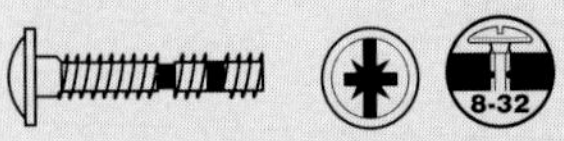

Threaded Breakoff Screw 8-32
Combined slot, suitable for flat or cross blades

Finish: steel, yellow chromated

Length	Cat. No.
1 3/4" x 3/4"	022.25.881

Packing: 100 and 1000 pcs.

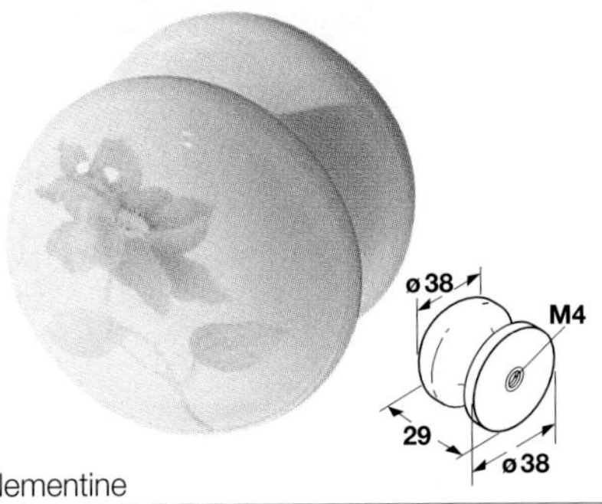

White/clementine

Cat. No.	130.44.776

Packing: 10 pcs.

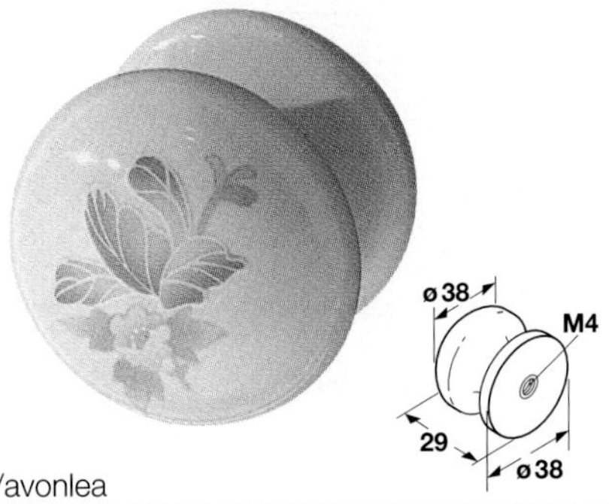

beige/avonlea

Cat. No.	130.44.418

Packing: 10 pcs.

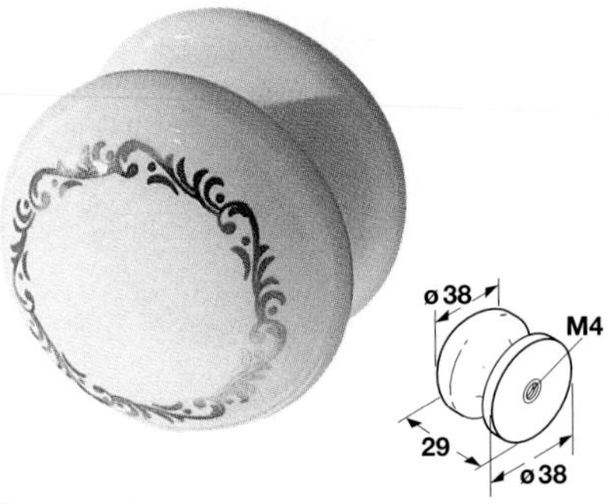

White/fraganaud

Cat. No.	130.44.712

Packing: 10 pcs.

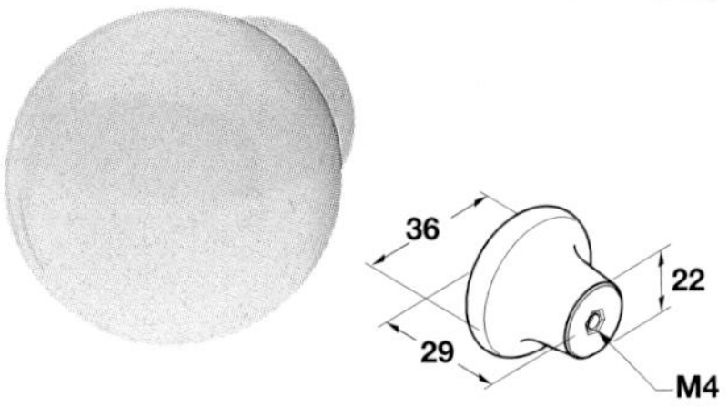

White

Cat. No.	130.14.705

Packing: 25 pcs.

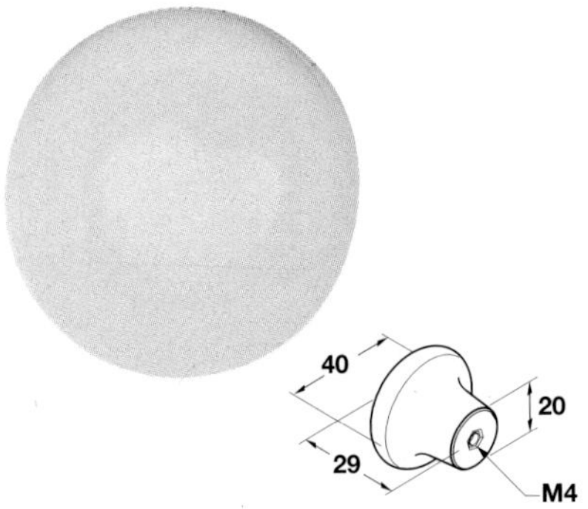

White

Cat. No.	130.13.708

Packing: 10 pcs.

Ceramic Knobs

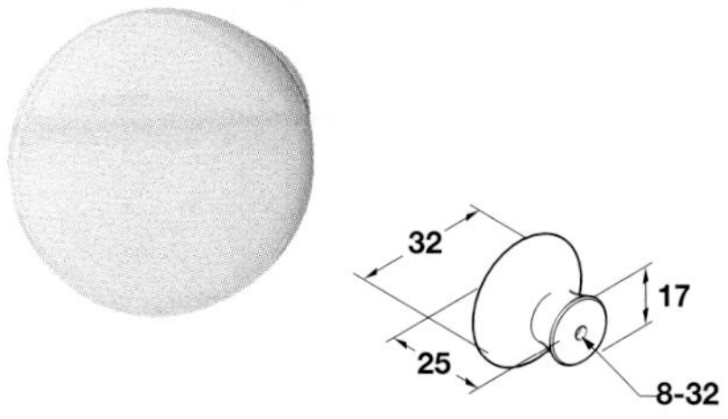

White

Cat. No.	130.08.707

Packing: 25 pcs.

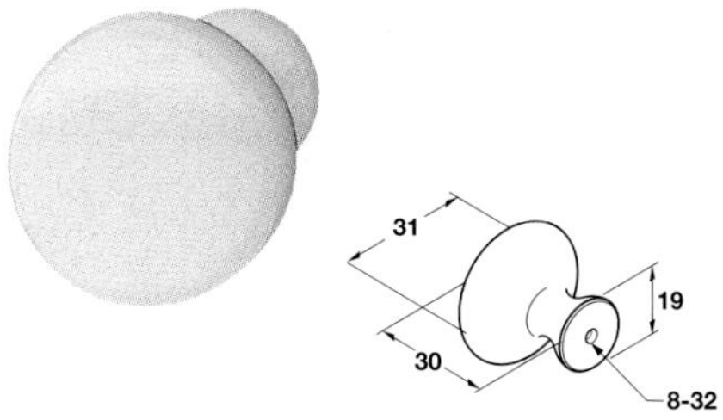

White

Cat. No.	130.25.700

Packing: 25 pcs.

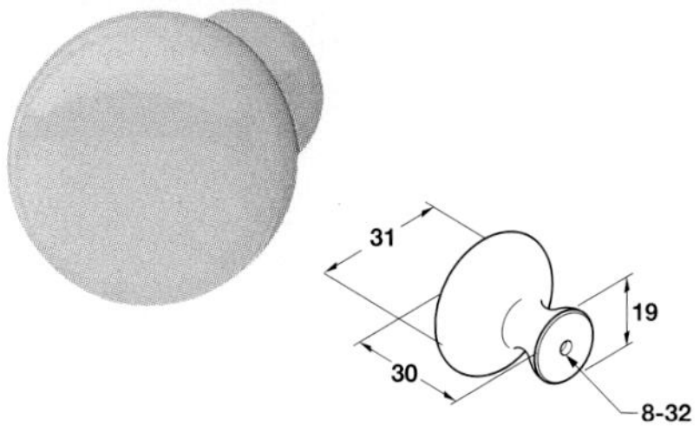

Almond

Cat. No.	130.25.400

Packing: 25 pcs.

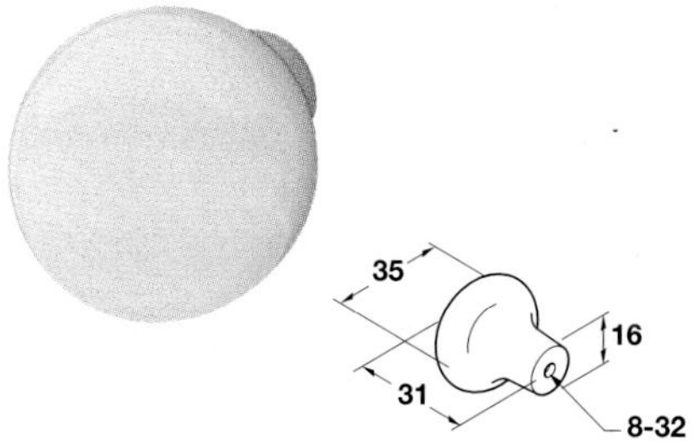

White

Cat. No.	130.23.700

Packing: 25 pcs.

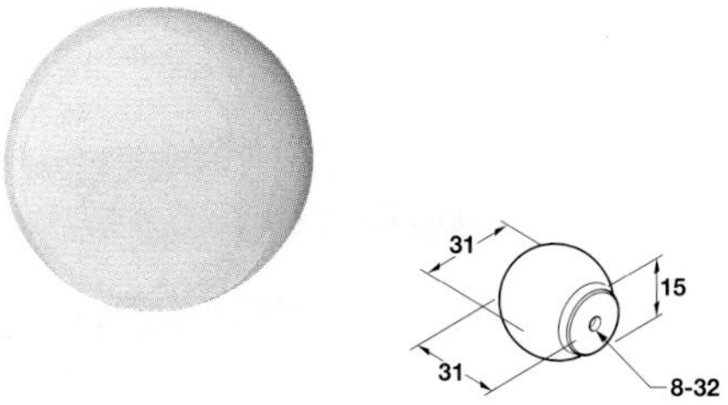

White

Cat. No.	130.24.700

Packing: 25 pcs.

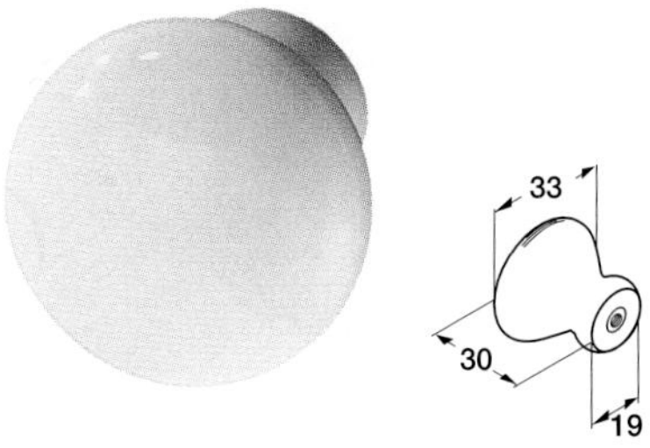

White

Cat. No.	130.07.700

Packing: 25 pcs.

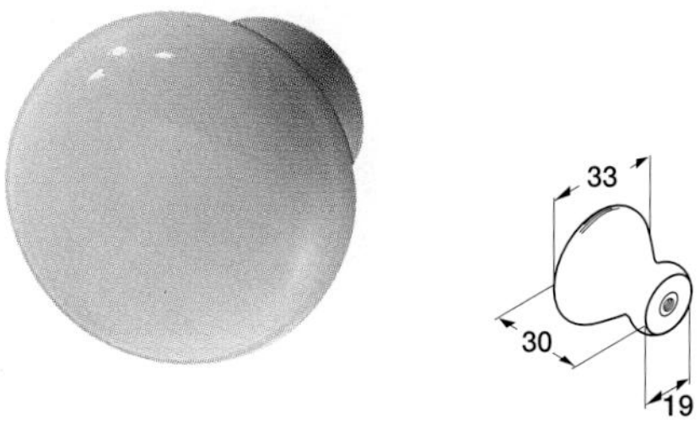

Almond

Cat. No.	130.07.406

Packing: 25 pcs.

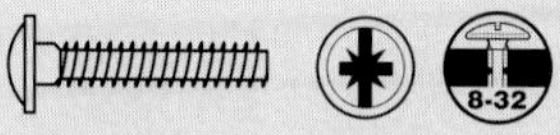

Threaded Screws 8-32
Combined slot, suitable for flat or cross blades

Finish: steel, yellow chromated

Length	Cat. No.
22 mm	022.25.229
25 mm	022.25.256
32 mm	022.25.327
38 mm	022.25.381
45 mm	022.25.452

Packing: 100 and 1000 pcs.

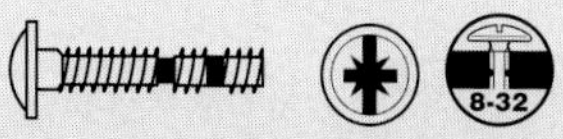

Threaded Breakoff Screw 8-32
Combined slot, suitable for flat or cross blades

Finish: steel, yellow chromated

Length	Cat. No.
1 3/4" x 3/4"	022.25.881

Packing: 100 and 1000 pcs.

HÄFELE

Ceramic and Zinc Knobs

Threaded Screws 8-32
Combined slot, suitable for flat or cross blades
Finish: steel, yellow chromated

Length	Cat. No.
22 mm	022.25.229
25 mm	022.25.256
32 mm	022.25.327
38 mm	022.25.381
45 mm	022.25.452

Packing: 100 and 1000 pcs.

Threaded Breakoff Screw 8-32
Combined slot, suitable for flat or cross blades
Finish: steel, yellow chromated

Length	Cat. No.
1 3/4" x 3/4"	022.25.881

Packing: 100 and 1000 pcs.

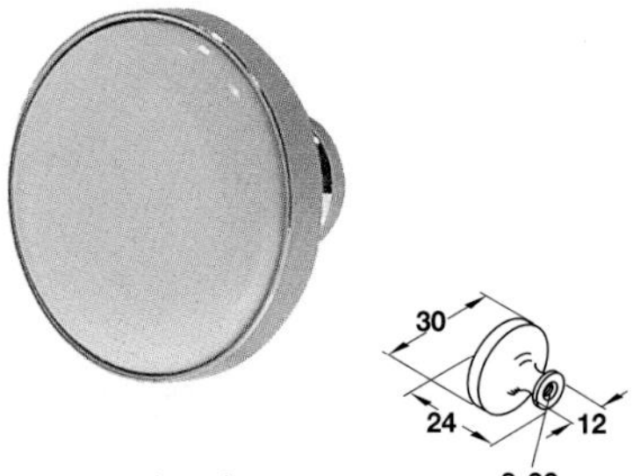

Base: zinc chrome plated
Inset: ceramic white

Cat. No.	132.69.270

Packing: 25 pcs.

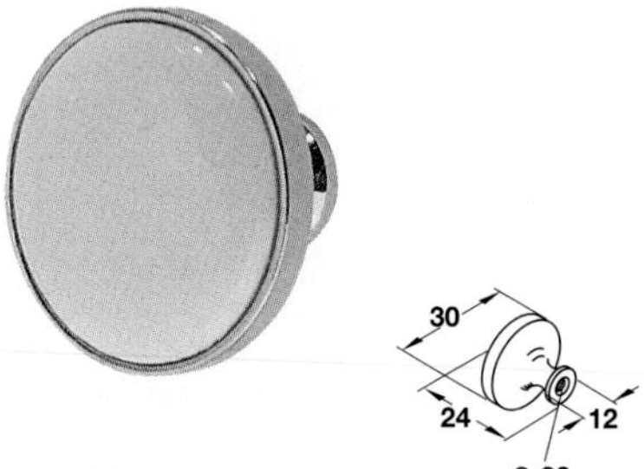

Base: zinc gold colored plated
Inset: ceramic white

Cat. No.	132.69.870

Packing: 25 pcs.

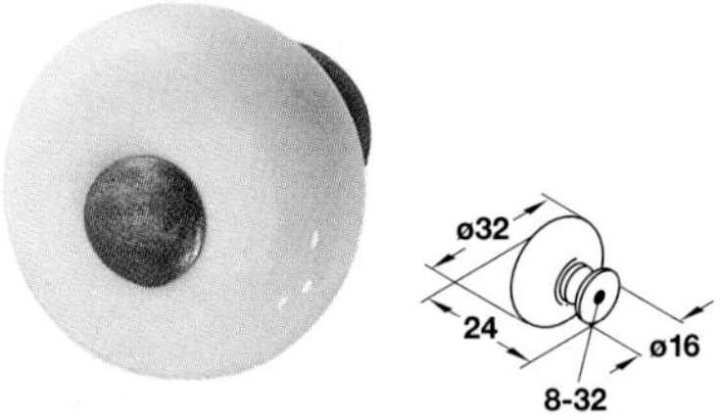

Ceramic: white
Base/insert: zinc antique bronze

Cat. No.	130.16.736

Packing: 25 pcs.

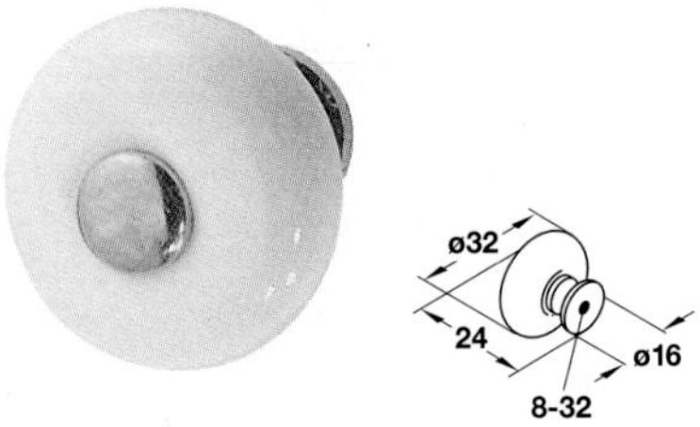

Ceramic: white
Base/insert: zinc polished brass

Cat. No.	130.16.834

Packing: 25 pcs.

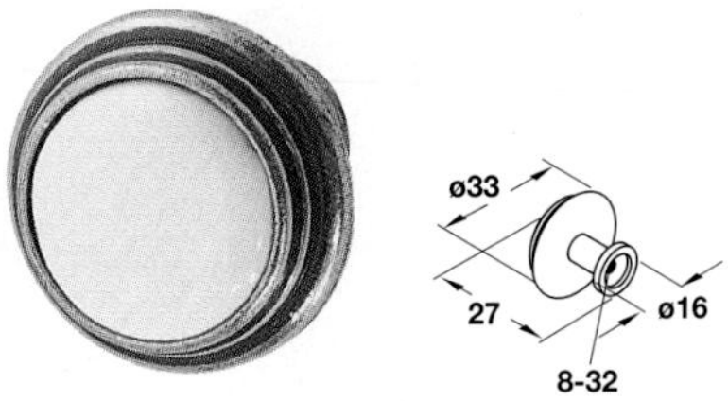

Ceramic: white
Base: zinc antique bronze

Cat. No.	132.70.105

Packing: 25 pcs.

Dimensional data not binding.
We reserve the right to alter specifications without notice.

Wood Knobs

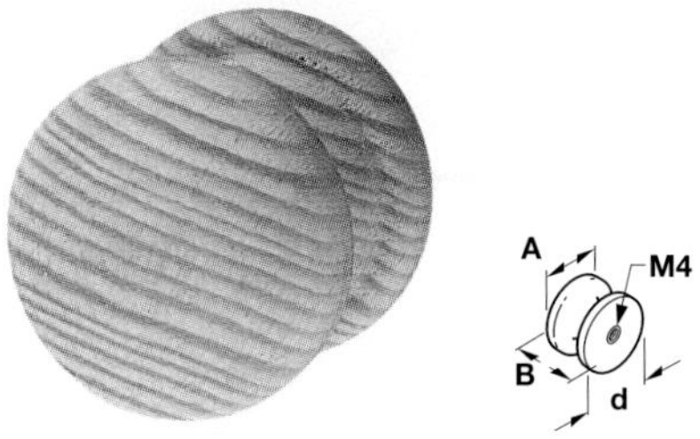

Pine

Size A x B	Diameter d	Cat. No.
34 x 26	34	196.04.016
38 x 30	38	196.04.007

Packing: 25 pcs.

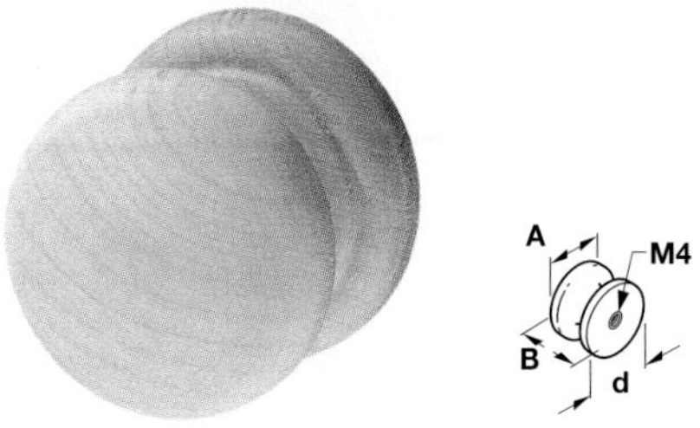

Maple

Size A x B	Diameter d	Cat. No.
34 x 26	34	196.04.114
38 x 30	38	196.04.105

Packing: 25 pcs.

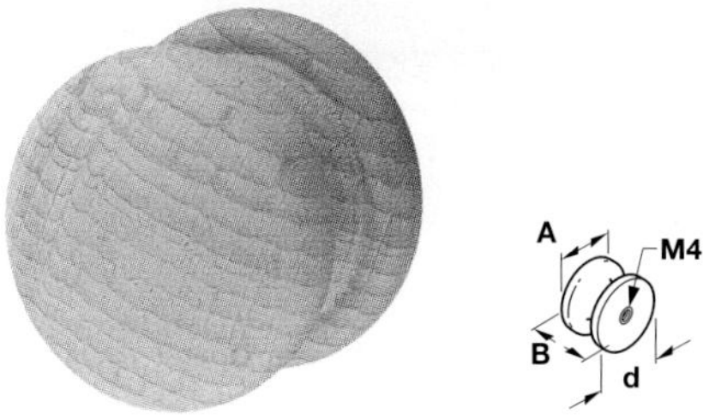

Beech

Size A x B	Diameter d	Cat. No.
34 x 26	34	196.04.310
38 x 30	38	196.04.301

Packing: 25 pcs.

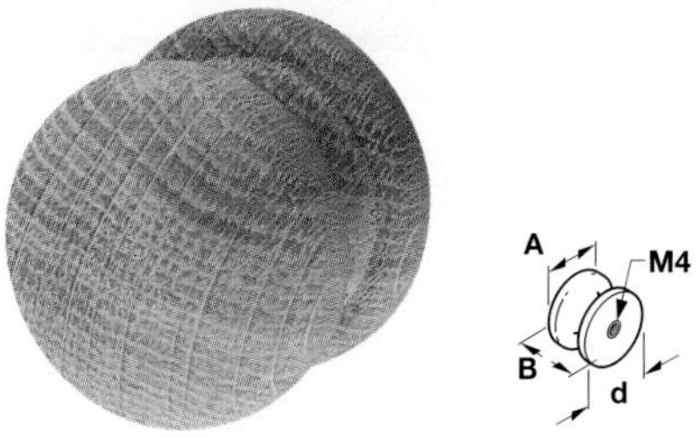

White oak

Size A x B	Diameter d	Cat. No.
34 x 26	34	196.04.418
38 x 30	38	196.04.409

Packing: 25 pcs.

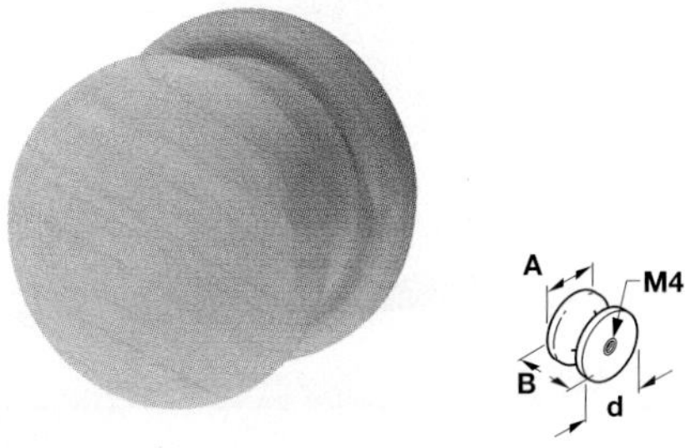

Cherry

Size A x B	Diameter d	Cat. No.
34 x 26	34	196.04.614
38 x 30	38	196.04.605

Packing: 25 pcs.

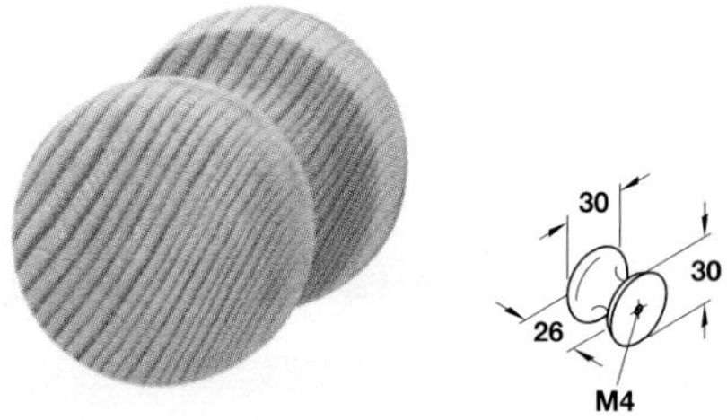

Pine

Cat. No.	196.54.016

Packing: 25 pcs.

White oak

Cat. No.	196.54.418

Packing: 25 pcs.

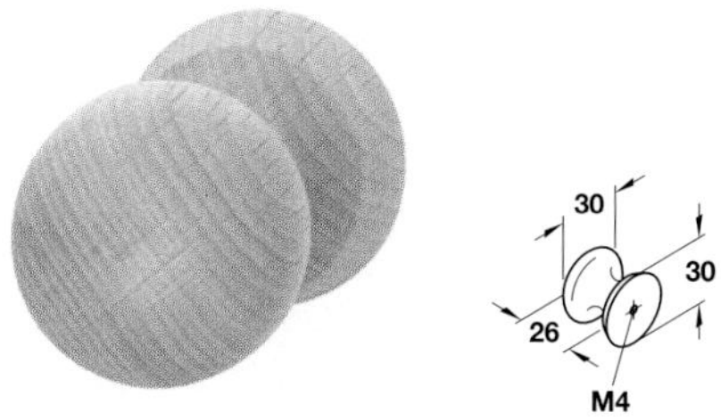

Beech

Cat. No.	196.54.310

Packing: 25 pcs.

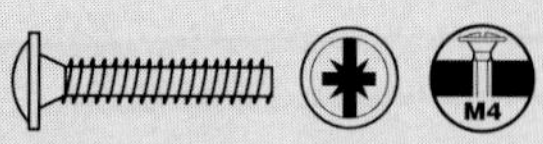

Threaded Screws M4
Combined slot, suitable for flat or cross blades

Finish: steel, zinc-plated

Length	Cat. No.
10 mm	022.35.109
12 mm	022.35.127
15 mm	022.35.154
18 mm	022.35.181
20 mm	022.35.207
22 mm	022.35.225
23 mm	022.35.234
25 mm	022.35.252
28 mm	022.35.289
30 mm	022.35.305
35 mm	022.35.350
38 mm	022.35.387
40 mm	022.35.403
45 mm	022.35.458
50 mm	022.35.501
60 mm	022.35.609

Packing: 100 and 1000 pcs.

Threaded Breakoff Screw M4
Combined slot, suitable for flat or cross blades

Finish: steel, zinc-plated

Length	Cat. No.
1 3/4" x 3/4"	022.35.887

Packing: 100 and 1000 pcs.

HÄFELE

Wood Knobs

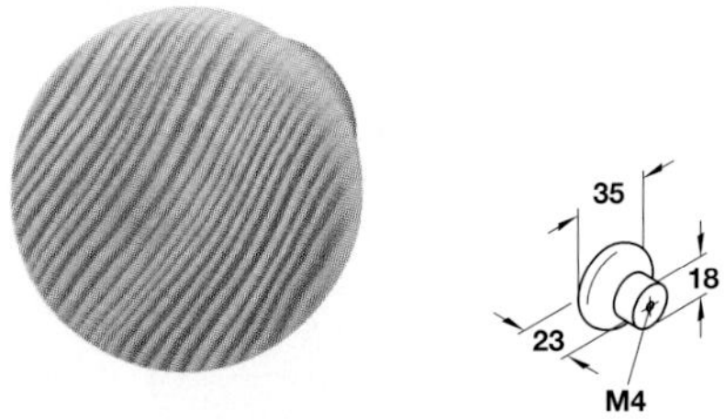

Pine

Cat. No.	196.75.006

Packing: 25 pcs.

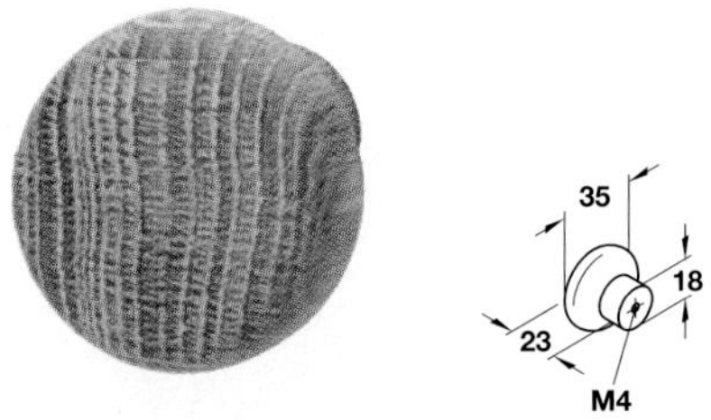

White oak

Cat. No.	196.75.408

Packing: 25 pcs.

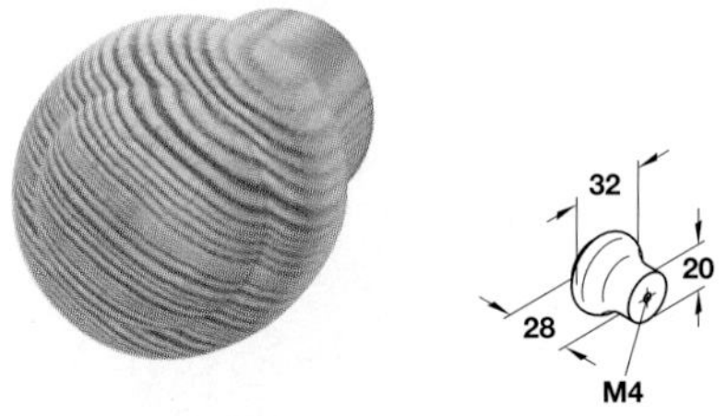

Pine

Cat. No.	196.76.003

Packing: 25 pcs.

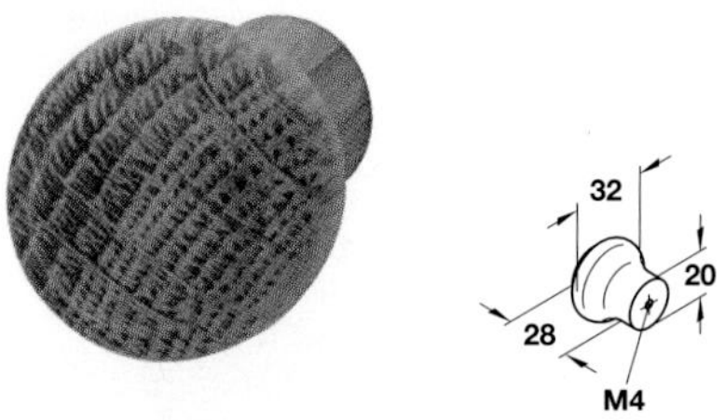

White oak

Cat. No.	196.76.405

Packing: 25 pcs.

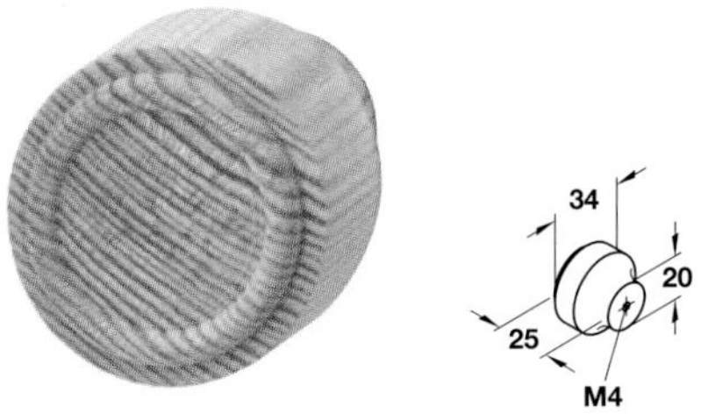

Pine

Cat. No.	196.77.000

Packing: 25 pcs.

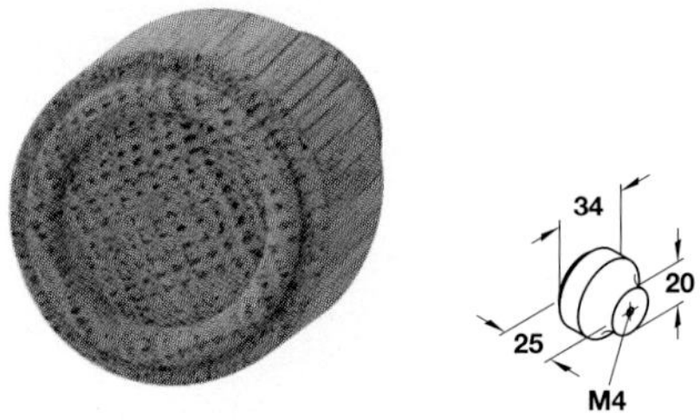

White oak

Cat. No.	196.77.402

Packing: 25 pcs.

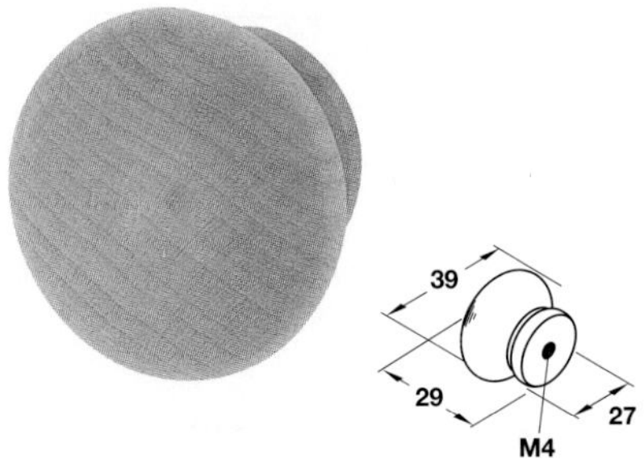

Maple

Cat. No.	196.08.400

Packing: 25 pcs.

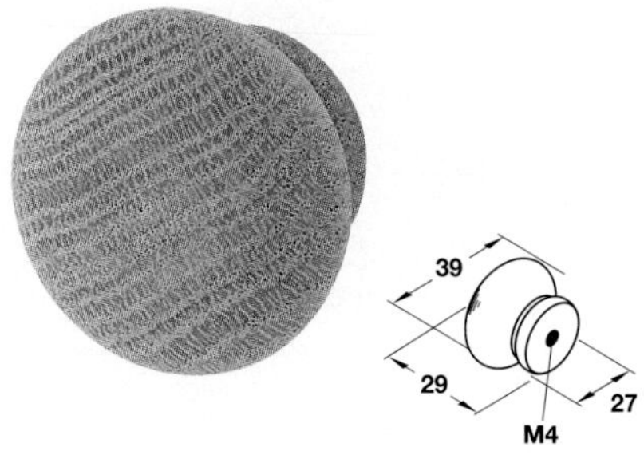

Red oak

Cat. No.	196.08.800

Packing: 25 pcs.

Threaded Screws M4
Combined slot, suitable for flat or cross blades

Finish: steel, zinc-plated

Length	Cat. No.
10 mm	022.35.109
12 mm	022.35.127
15 mm	022.35.154
18 mm	022.35.181
20 mm	022.35.207
22 mm	022.35.225
23 mm	022.35.234
25 mm	022.35.252
28 mm	022.35.289
30 mm	022.35.305
35 mm	022.35.350
38 mm	022.35.387
40 mm	022.35.403
45 mm	022.35.458
50 mm	022.35.501
60 mm	022.35.609

Packing: 100 and 1000 pcs.

Threaded Breakoff Screw M4
Combined slot, suitable for flat or cross blades

Finish: steel, zinc-plated

Length	Cat. No.
1 3/4" x 3/4"	022.35.887

Packing: 100 and 1000 pcs.

Wood Knobs - Flat Grain

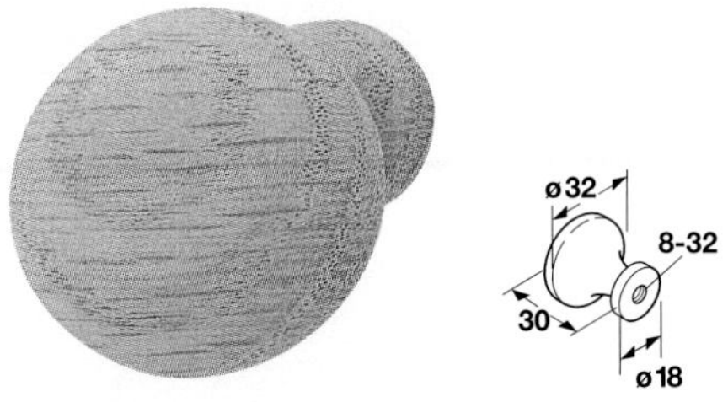

Red oak

Cat. No.	196.59.400

Packing: 25 pcs.

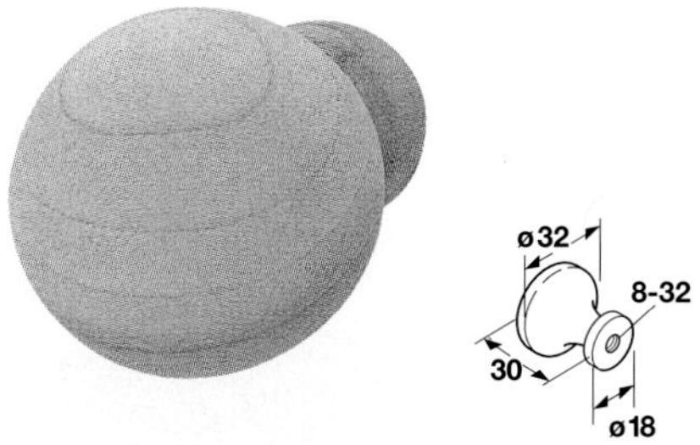

Maple

Cat. No.	196.59.100

Packing: 25 pcs.

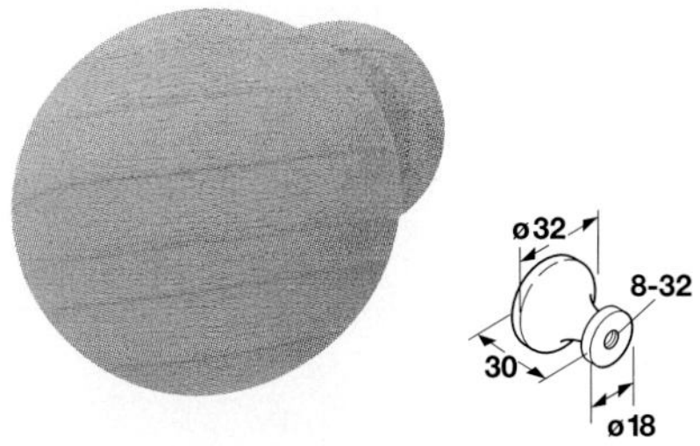

Cherry

Cat. No.	196.59.600

Packing: 25 pcs.

Threaded Screws 8-32
Combined slot, suitable for flat or cross blades
Finish: steel, yellow chromated

Length	Cat. No.
22 mm	022.25.229
25 mm	022.25.256
32 mm	022.25.327
38 mm	022.25.381
45 mm	022.25.452

Packing: 100 and 1000 pcs.

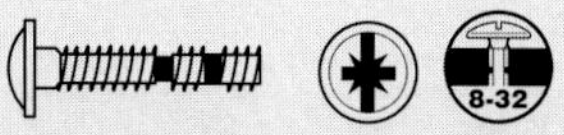

Threaded Breakoff Screw 8-32
Combined slot, suitable for flat or cross blades
Finish: steel, yellow chromated

Length	Cat. No.
1 3/4" x 3/4"	022.25.881

Packing: 100 and 1000 pcs.

HÄFELE

Wood knobs

1 Decorative Hardware

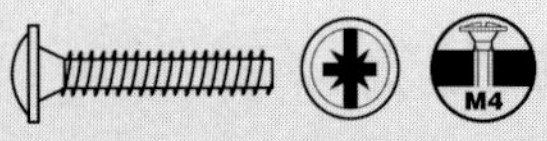

Threaded Screws M4
Combined slot, suitable for flat or cross blades
Finish: steel, zinc-plated

Length	Cat. No.
10 mm	022.35.109
12 mm	022.35.127
15 mm	022.35.154
18 mm	022.35.181
20 mm	022.35.207
22 mm	022.35.225
23 mm	022.35.234
25 mm	022.35.252
28 mm	022.35.289
30 mm	022.35.305
35 mm	022.35.350
38 mm	022.35.387
40 mm	022.35.403
45 mm	022.35.458
50 mm	022.35.501
60 mm	022.35.609

Packing: 100 and 1000 pcs.

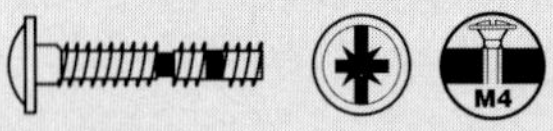

Threaded Breakoff Screw M4
Combined slot, suitable for flat or cross blades
Finish: steel, zinc-plated

Length	Cat. No.
1 3/4" x 3/4"	022.35.887

Packing: 100 and 1000 pcs.

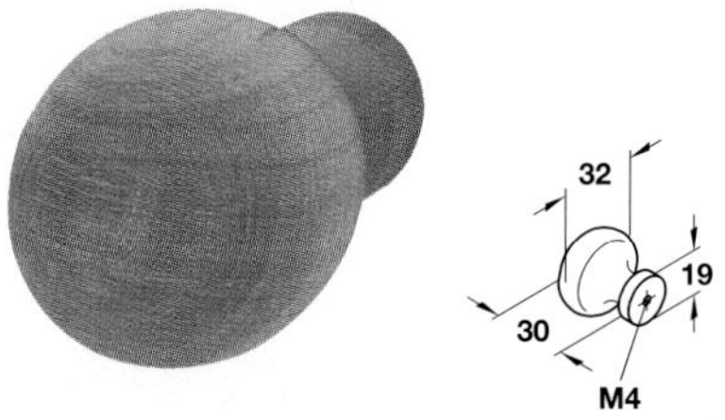

Maple

Cat. No.	196.74.107

Packing: 25 pcs.

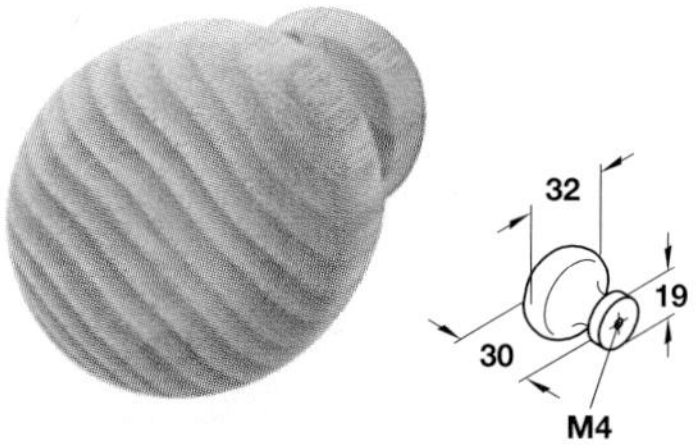

Ash

Cat. No.	196.74.509

Packing: 25 pcs.

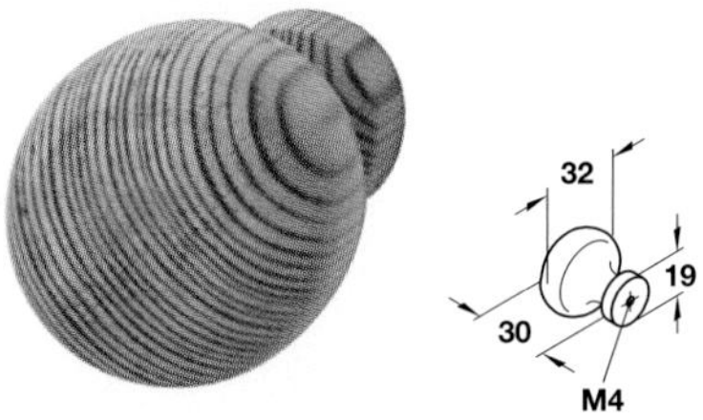

Pine

Cat. No.	196.74.009

Packing: 25 pcs.

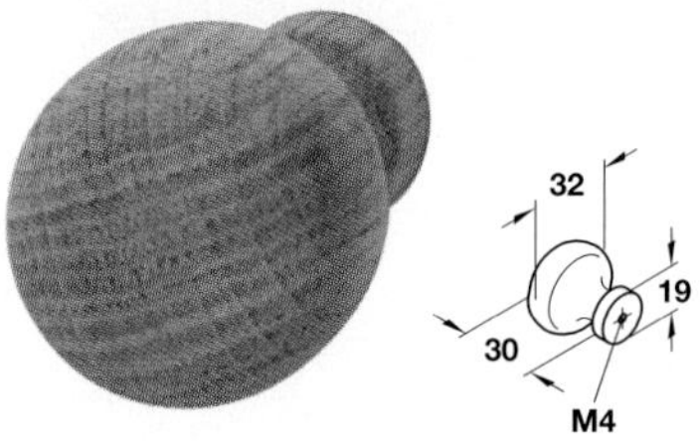

White oak

Cat. No.	196.74.401

Packing: 25 pcs.

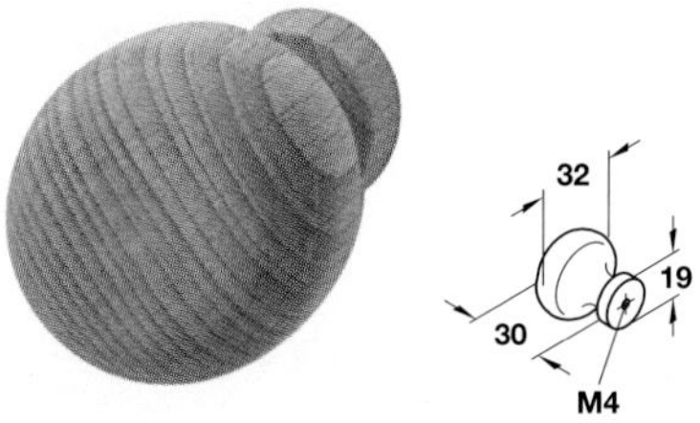

Beech

Cat. No.	196.74.303

Packing: 25 pcs.

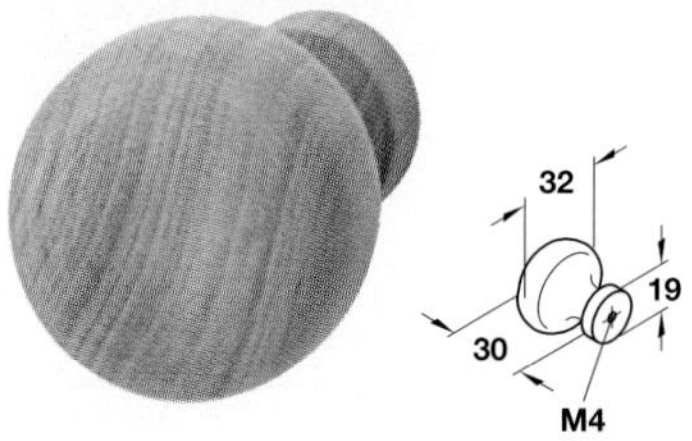

Cherry

Cat. No.	196.74.607

Packing: 25 pcs.

Wood Knobs

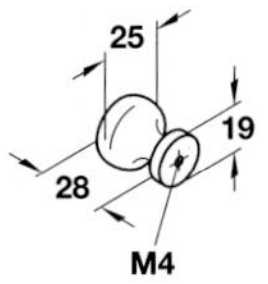

Pine

Cat. No.	196.49.006

Packing: 25 pcs.

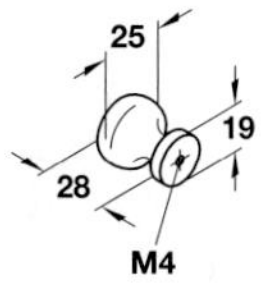

Maple

Cat. No.	196.49.104

Packing: 25 pcs.

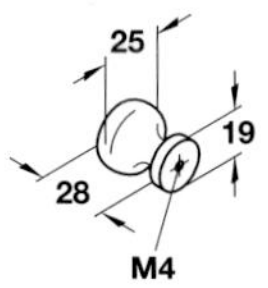

White oak

Cat. No.	196.49.408

Packing: 25 pcs.

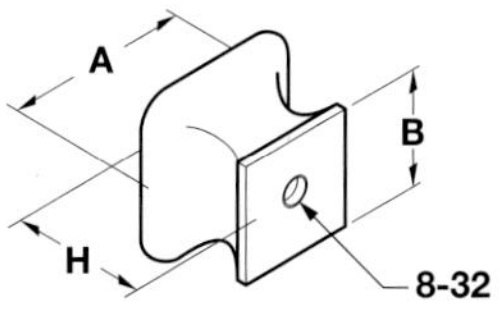

Red oak

Size A x B	Height H	Cat. No.
32 x 24	21	195.42.400
38 x 29	22	195.44.400
45 x 37	23	195.43.400

Packing: 25 pcs.

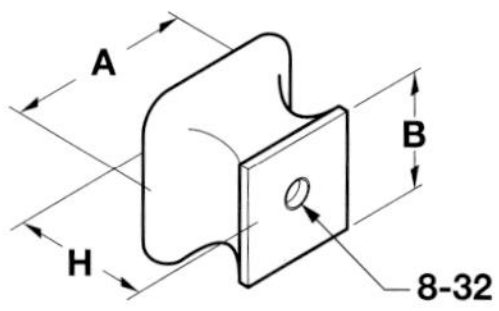

Maple

Size A x B	Height H	Cat. No.
32 x 24	21	195.42.800
38 x 29	22	195.44.800
45 x 37	23	195.43.800

Packing: 25 pcs.

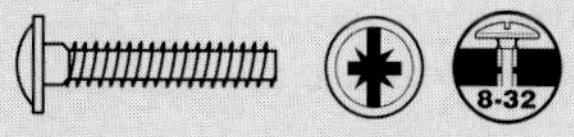

Threaded Screws 8-32
Combined slot, suitable for flat or cross blades

Finish: steel, yellow chromated

Length	Cat. No.
22 mm	022.25.229
25 mm	022.25.256
32 mm	022.25.327
38 mm	022.25.381
45 mm	022.25.452

Packing: 100 and 1000 pcs.

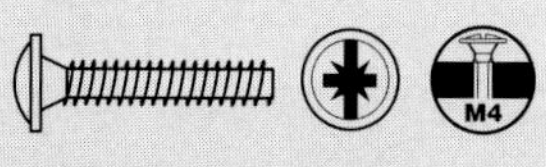

Threaded Screws M4
Combined slot, suitable for flat or cross blades

Finish: steel, zinc-plated

Length	Cat. No.
10 mm	022.35.109
12 mm	022.35.127
15 mm	022.35.154
18 mm	022.35.181
20 mm	022.35.207
22 mm	022.35.225
23 mm	022.35.234
25 mm	022.35.252
28 mm	022.35.289
30 mm	022.35.305
35 mm	022.35.350
38 mm	022.35.387
40 mm	022.35.403
45 mm	022.35.458
50 mm	022.35.501
60 mm	022.35.609

Packing: 100 and 1000 pcs.

Dimensional data not binding.
We reserve the right to alter specifications without notice.

HÄFELE

Wood Knobs

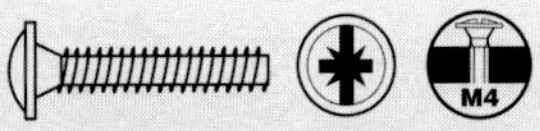

Threaded Screws M4
Combined slot, suitable for flat or cross blades
Finish: steel, zinc-plated

Length	Cat. No.
10 mm	022.35.109
12 mm	022.35.127
15 mm	022.35.154
18 mm	022.35.181
20 mm	022.35.207
22 mm	022.35.225
23 mm	022.35.234
25 mm	022.35.252
28 mm	022.35.289
30 mm	022.35.305
35 mm	022.35.350
38 mm	022.35.387
40 mm	022.35.403
45 mm	022.35.458
50 mm	022.35.501
60 mm	022.35.609

Packing: 100 and 1000 pcs.

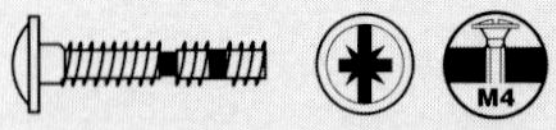

Threaded Breakoff Screw M4
Combined slot, suitable for flat or cross blades
Finish: steel, zinc-plated

Length	Cat. No.
1 3/4" x 3/4"	022.35.887

Packing: 100 and 1000 pcs.

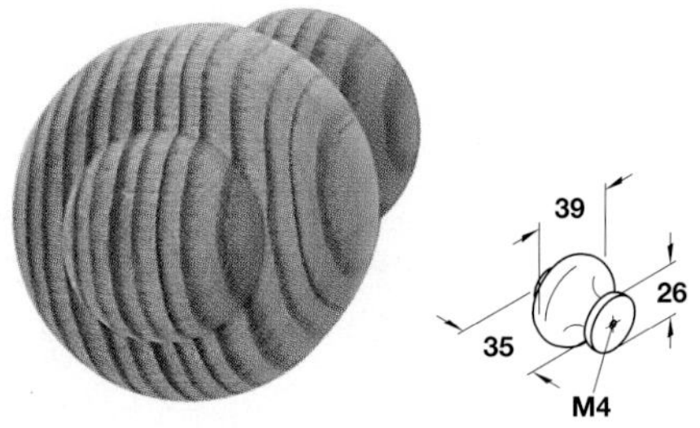

Pine

Cat. No.	196.50.027

Packing: 25 pcs.

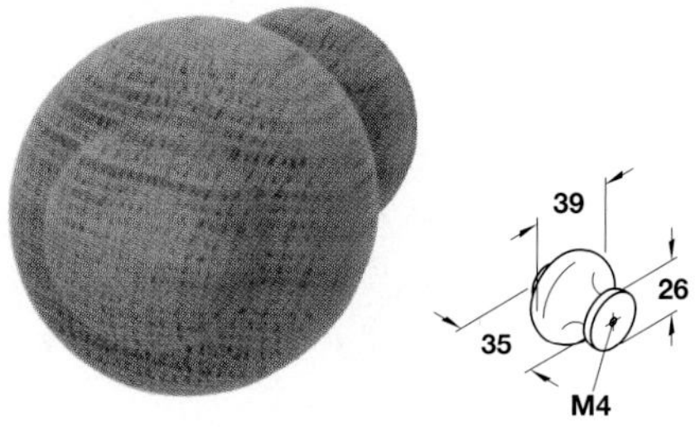

White oak

Cat. No.	196.50.429

Packing: 25 pcs.

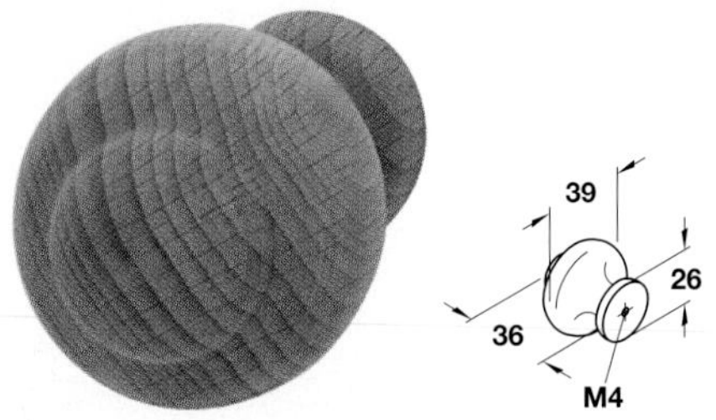

Beech

Cat. No.	196.50.321

Packing: 25 pcs.

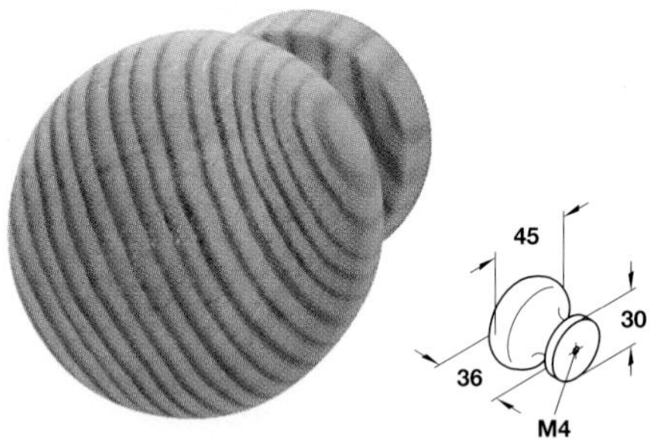

Pine

Cat. No.	196.66.007

Packing: 25 pcs.

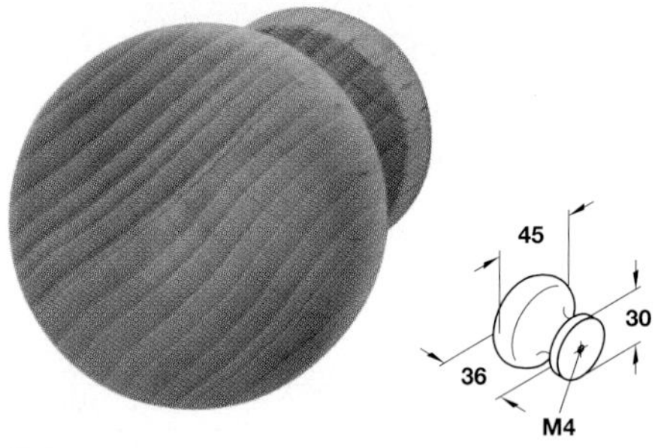

White Oak

Cat. No.	196.66.409

Packing: 25 pcs.

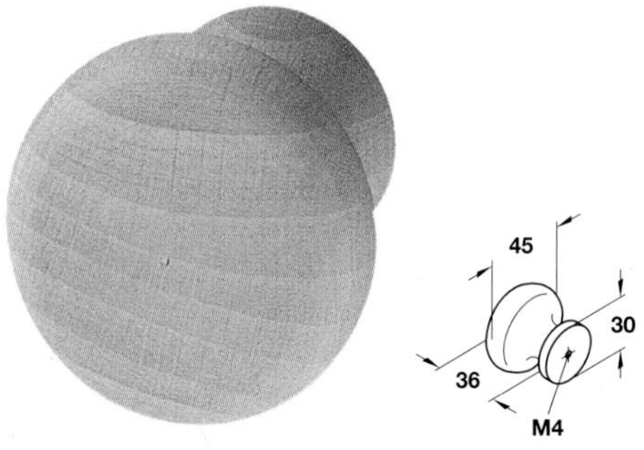

Beech

Cat. No.	196.66.301

Packing: 25 pcs.

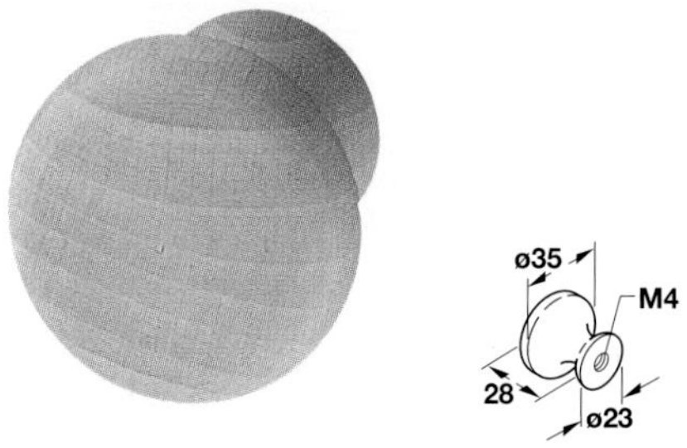

Beech

Cat. No.	196.66.310

Packing: 25 pcs.

Dimensional data not binding.
We reserve the right to alter specifications without notice.

Wood Knobs

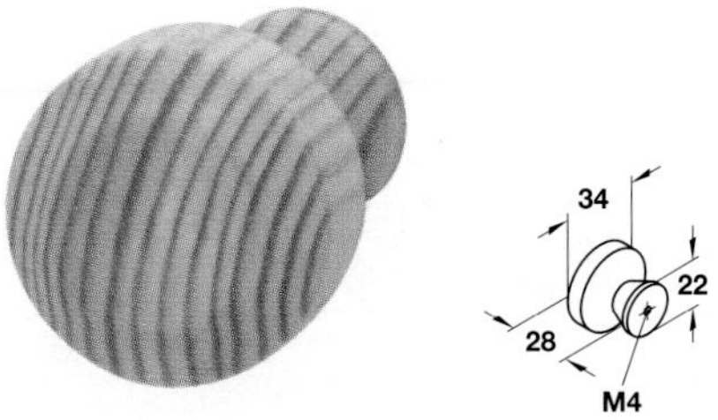

Pine

Cat. No.	196.58.005

Packing: 25 pcs.

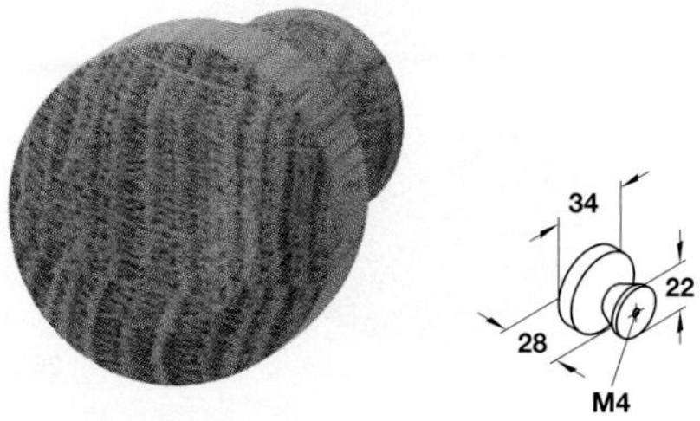

White oak

Cat. No.	196.58.407

Packing: 25 pcs.

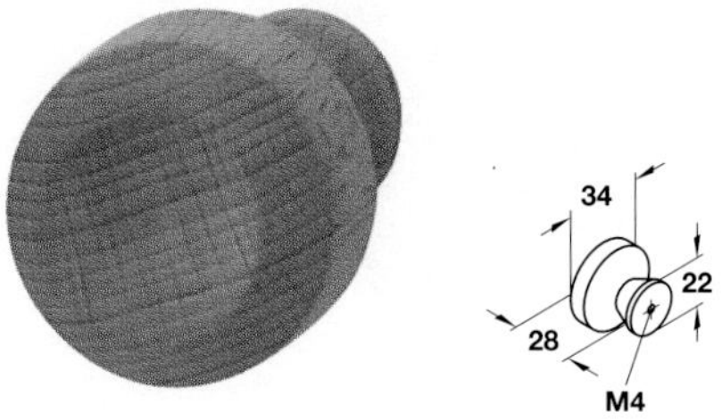

Beech

Cat. No.	196.58.309

Packing: 25 pcs.

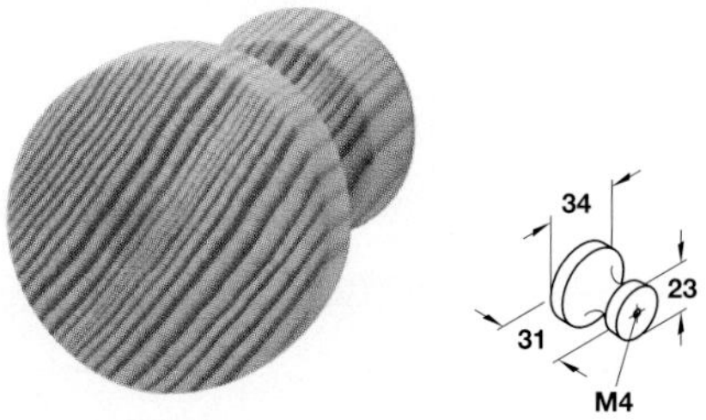

Pine

Cat. No.	196.57.008

Packing: 25 pcs.

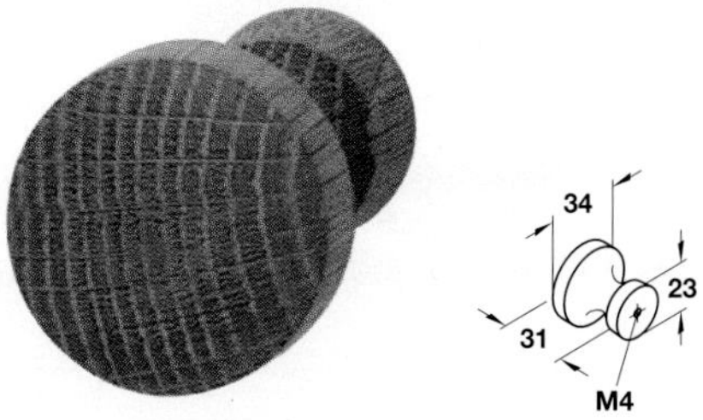

White Oak

Cat. No.	196.57.400

Packing: 25 pcs.

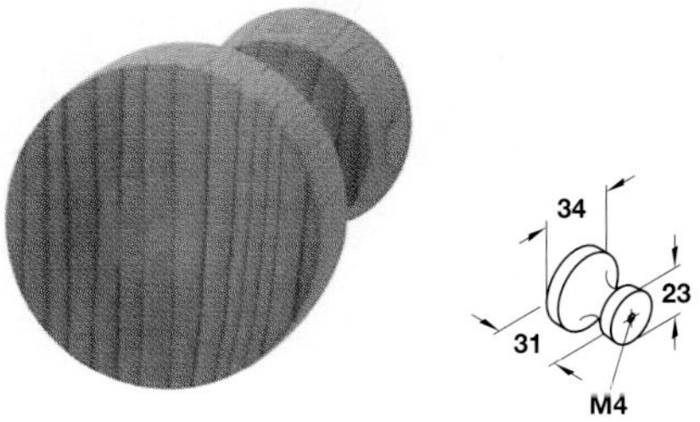

Beech

Cat. No.	196.57.302

Packing: 25 pcs.

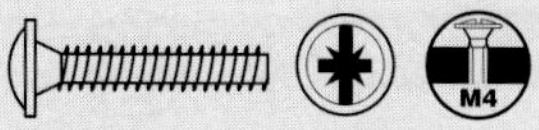

Threaded Screws M4
Combined slot, suitable for flat or cross blades

Finish: steel, zinc-plated

Length	Cat. No.
10 mm	022.35.109
12 mm	022.35.127
15 mm	022.35.154
18 mm	022.35.181
20 mm	022.35.207
22 mm	022.35.225
23 mm	022.35.234
25 mm	022.35.252
28 mm	022.35.289
30 mm	022.35.305
35 mm	022.35.350
38 mm	022.35.387
40 mm	022.35.403
45 mm	022.35.458
50 mm	022.35.501
60 mm	022.35.609

Packing: 100 and 1000 pcs.

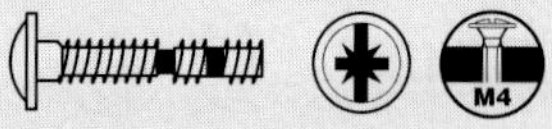

Threaded Breakoff Screw M4
Combined slot, suitable for flat or cross blades

Finish: steel, zinc-plated

Length	Cat. No.
1 3/4" x 3/4"	022.35.887

Packing: 100 and 1000 pcs.

HÄFELE

Wood knobs

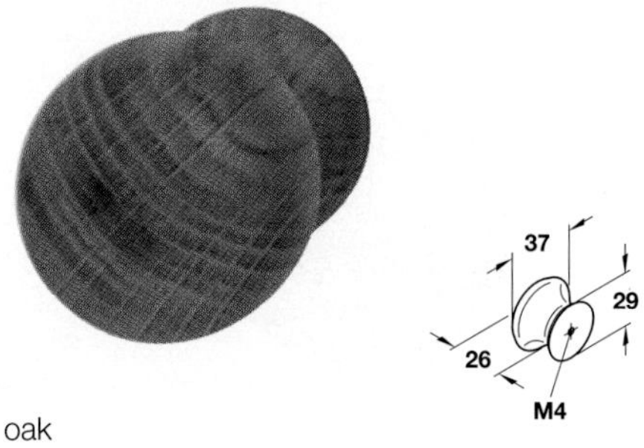

White oak

Cat. No.	196.41.420

Packing: 25 pcs.

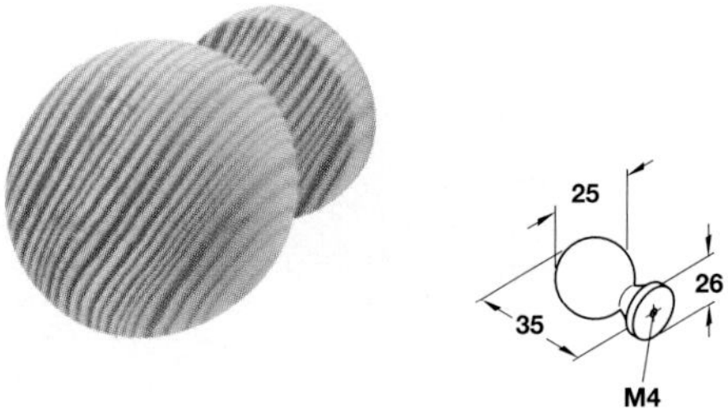

Pine

Cat. No.	196.56.001

Packing: 25 pcs.

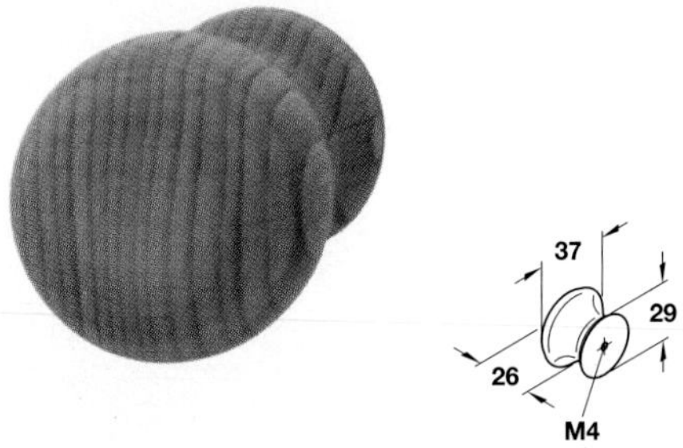

Beech

Cat. No.	196.41.322

Packing: 25 pcs.

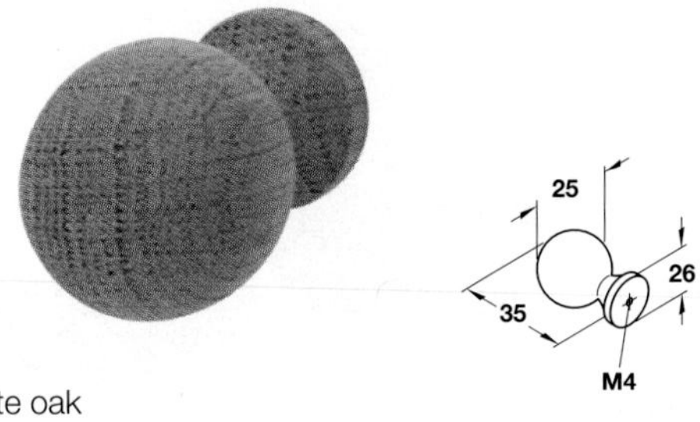

White oak

Cat. No.	196.56.403

Packing: 25 pcs.

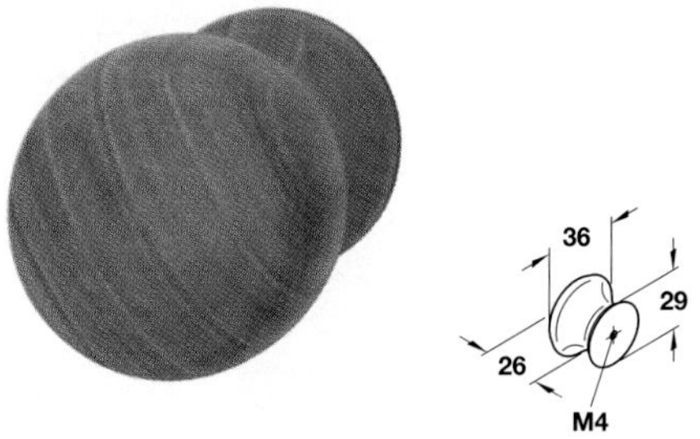

Cherry

Cat. No.	196.41.626

Packing: 25 pcs.

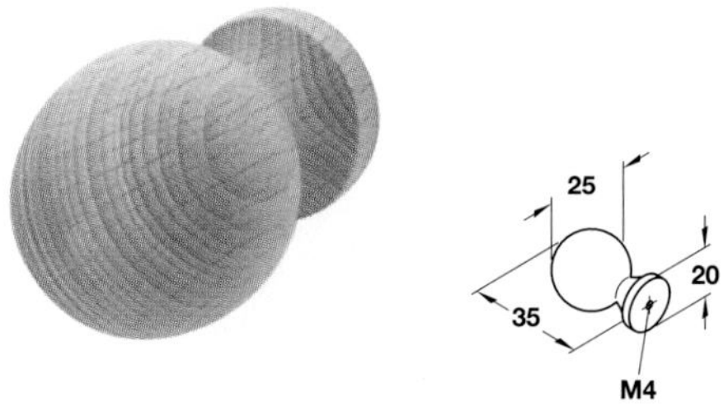

Beech

Cat. No.	196.56.305

Packing: 25 pcs.

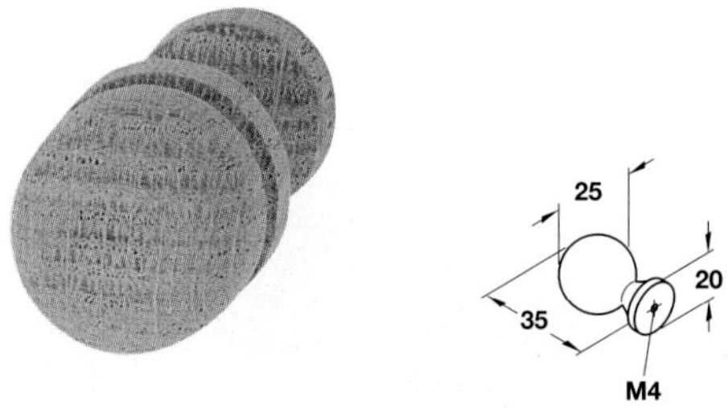

White oak

Cat. No.	196.52.423

Packing: 25 pcs.

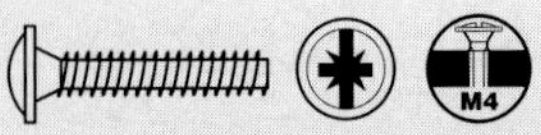

Threaded Screws M4
Combined slot, suitable for flat or cross blades
Finish: steel, zinc-plated

Length	Cat. No.
10 mm	022.35.109
12 mm	022.35.127
15 mm	022.35.154
18 mm	022.35.181
20 mm	022.35.207
22 mm	022.35.225
23 mm	022.35.234
25 mm	022.35.252
28 mm	022.35.289
30 mm	022.35.305
35 mm	022.35.350
38 mm	022.35.387
40 mm	022.35.403
45 mm	022.35.458
50 mm	022.35.501
60 mm	022.35.609

Packing: 100 and 1000 pcs.

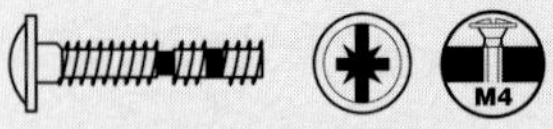

Threaded Breakoff Screw M4
Combined slot, suitable for flat or cross blades
Finish: steel, zinc-plated

Length	Cat. No.
1 3/4" x 3/4"	022.35.887

Packing: 100 and 1000 pcs.

Wood knobs with metal inserts

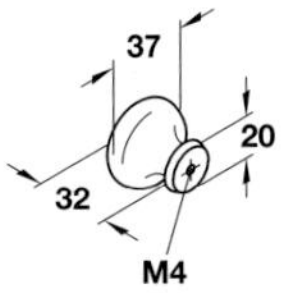

Knob: oak
Insert: zinc bronze & brushed

Cat. No.	196.88.496

Packing: 25 pcs.

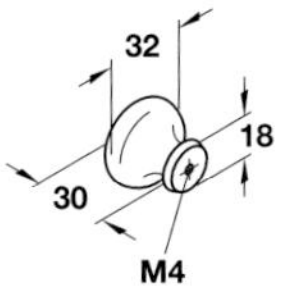

Knob: beech
Insert: zinc bronze & brushed

Cat. No.	196.88.361

Packing: 25 pcs.

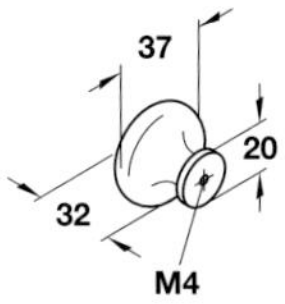

Knob: oak
Insert: zinc tin, antique

Cat. No.	196.88.478

Packing: 25 pcs.

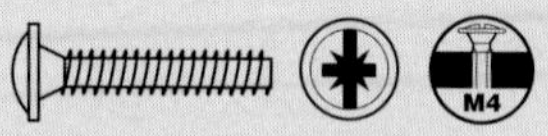

Threaded Screws M4
Combined slot, suitable for flat or cross blades
Finish: steel, zinc-plated

Length	Cat. No.
10 mm	022.35.109
12 mm	022.35.127
15 mm	022.35.154
18 mm	022.35.181
20 mm	022.35.207
22 mm	022.35.225
23 mm	022.35.234
25 mm	022.35.252
28 mm	022.35.289
30 mm	022.35.305
35 mm	022.35.350
38 mm	022.35.387
40 mm	022.35.403
45 mm	022.35.458
50 mm	022.35.501
60 mm	022.35.609

Packing: 100 and 1000 pcs.

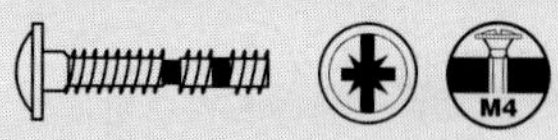

Threaded Breakoff Screw M4
Combined slot, suitable for flat or cross blades
Finish: steel, zinc-plated

Length	Cat. No.
1 3/4" x 3/4"	022.35.887

Packing: 100 and 1000 pcs.

HÄFELE

Plastics knobs

Threaded Screws M4
Combined slot, suitable for flat or cross blades
Finish: steel, zinc-plated

Length	Cat. No.
10 mm	022.35.109
12 mm	022.35.127
15 mm	022.35.154
18 mm	022.35.181
20 mm	022.35.207
22 mm	022.35.225
23 mm	022.35.234
25 mm	022.35.252
28 mm	022.35.289
30 mm	022.35.305
35 mm	022.35.350
38 mm	022.35.387
40 mm	022.35.403
45 mm	022.35.458
50 mm	022.35.501
60 mm	022.35.609

Packing: 100 and 1000 pcs.

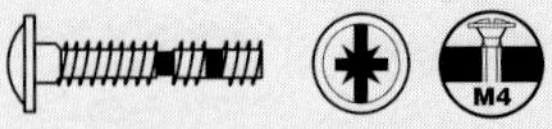

Threaded Breakoff Screw M4
Combined slot, suitable for flat or cross blades
Finish: steel, zinc-plated

Length	Cat. No.
1 3/4" x 3/4"	022.35.887

Packing: 100 and 1000 pcs.

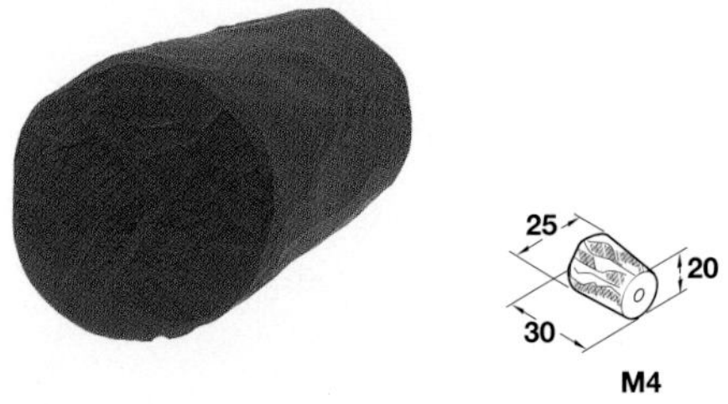

Red matt

Cat. No.	137.94.900

Packing: 25 pcs.

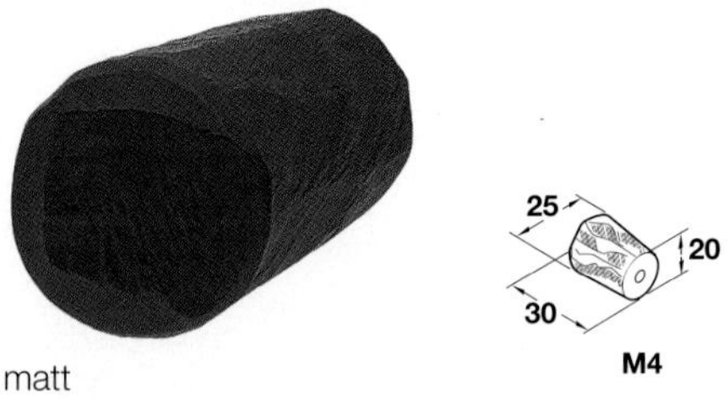

Black matt

Cat. No.	137.94.300

Packing: 25 pcs.

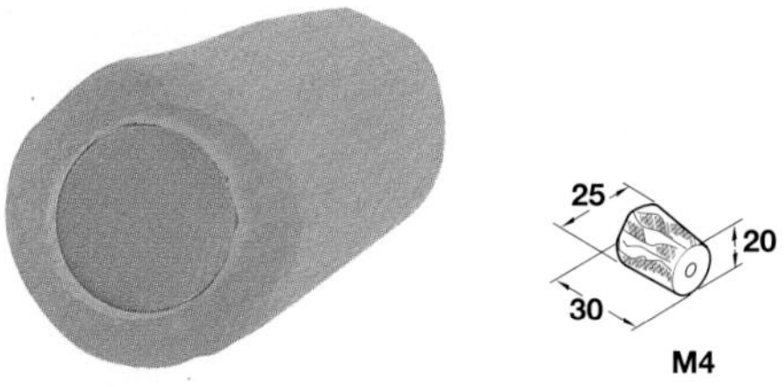

Knob: mint green
Center: zinc nickel matt

Cat. No.	137.94.060

Packing: 25 pcs.

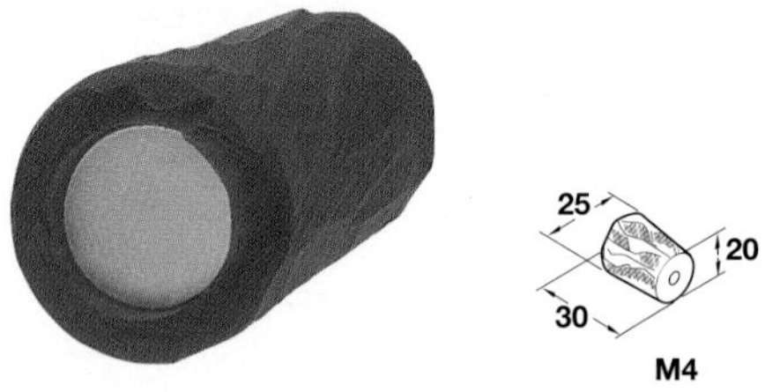

Knob: red matt
Center: zinc nickel matt

Cat. No.	137.94.960

Packing: 25 pcs.

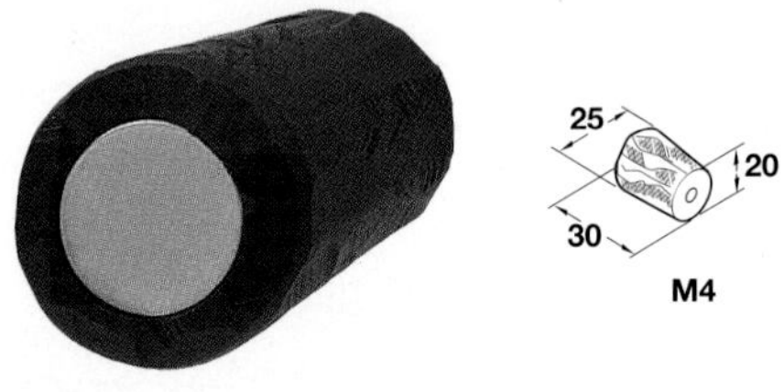

Knob: black matt
Center: zinc nickel matt

Cat. No.	137.94.360

Packing: 25 pcs.

Cast Resin Knobs

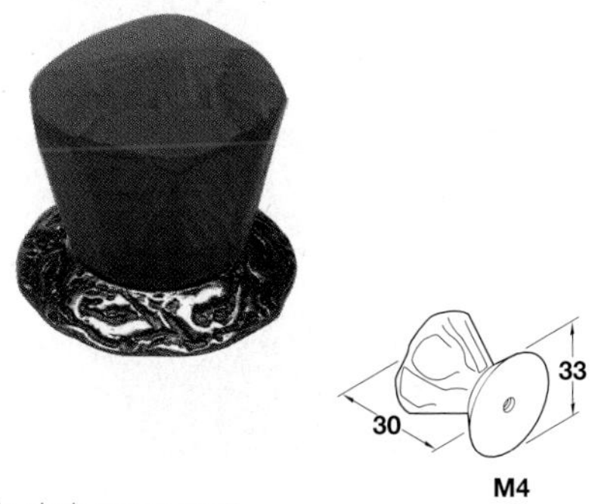

Knob: cast resin dark green matt
Rosette: brass antique

Cat. No.	138.58.805

Packing: 25 pcs.

Knob: cast resin black matt
Rosette: brass antique

Cat. No.	138.58.832

Packing: 25 pcs.

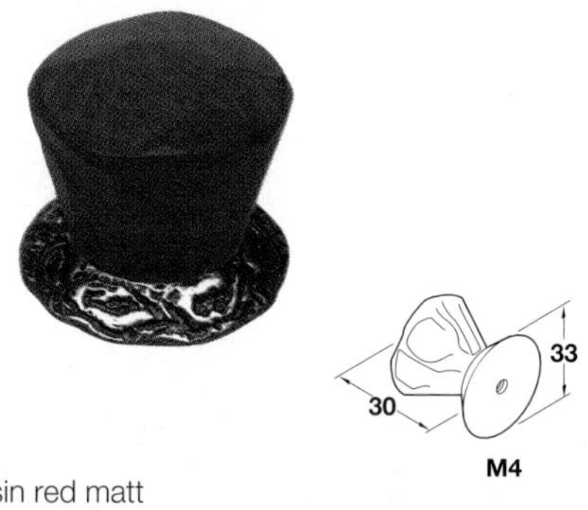

Knob: cast resin red matt
Rosette: brass antique

Cat. No.	138.58.896

Packing: 25 pcs.

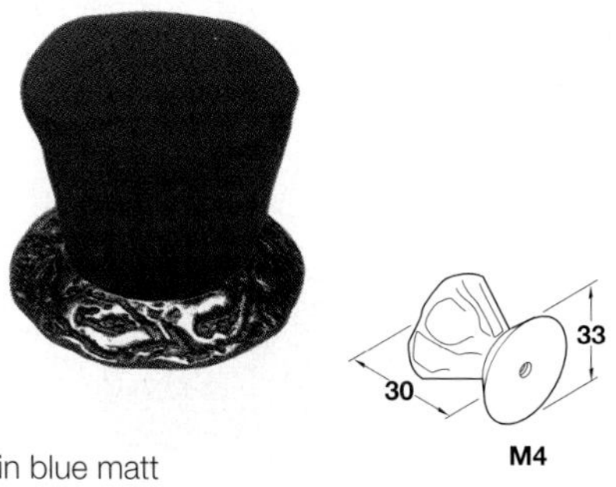

Knob: cast resin blue matt
Rosette: brass; antique

Cat. No.	138.58.887

Packing: 25 pcs.

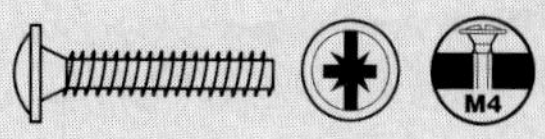

Threaded Screws M4
Combined slot, suitable for flat or cross blades
Finish: steel, zinc-plated

Length	Cat. No.
10 mm	022.35.109
12 mm	022.35.127
15 mm	022.35.154
18 mm	022.35.181
20 mm	022.35.207
22 mm	022.35.225
23 mm	022.35.234
25 mm	022.35.252
28 mm	022.35.289
30 mm	022.35.305
35 mm	022.35.350
38 mm	022.35.387
40 mm	022.35.403
45 mm	022.35.458
50 mm	022.35.501
60 mm	022.35.609

Packing: 100 and 1000 pcs.

Threaded Breakoff Screw M4
Combined slot, suitable for flat or cross blades
Finish: steel, zinc-plated

Length	Cat. No.
1 3/4" x 3/4"	022.35.887

Packing: 100 and 1000 pcs.

HÄFELE

Cast Resin Knobs

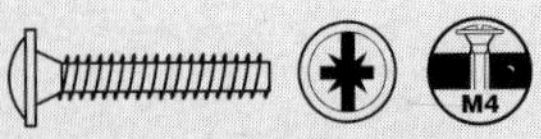

Threaded Screws M4
Combined slot, suitable for flat or cross blades
Finish: steel, zinc-plated

Length	Cat. No.
10 mm	022.35.109
12 mm	022.35.127
15 mm	022.35.154
18 mm	022.35.181
20 mm	022.35.207
22 mm	022.35.225
23 mm	022.35.234
25 mm	022.35.252
28 mm	022.35.289
30 mm	022.35.305
35 mm	022.35.350
38 mm	022.35.387
40 mm	022.35.403
45 mm	022.35.458
50 mm	022.35.501
60 mm	022.35.609

Packing: 100 and 1000 pcs.

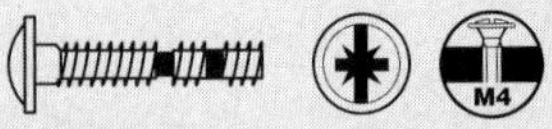

Threaded Breakoff Screw M4
Combined slot, suitable for flat or cross blades
Finish: steel, zinc-plated

Length	Cat. No.
1 3/4" x 3/4"	022.35.887

Packing: 100 and 1000 pcs.

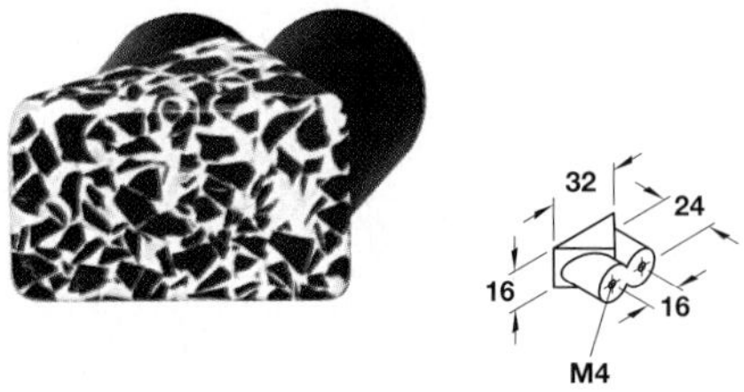

White/black

Cat. No.	138.14.303

Packing: 25 pcs.

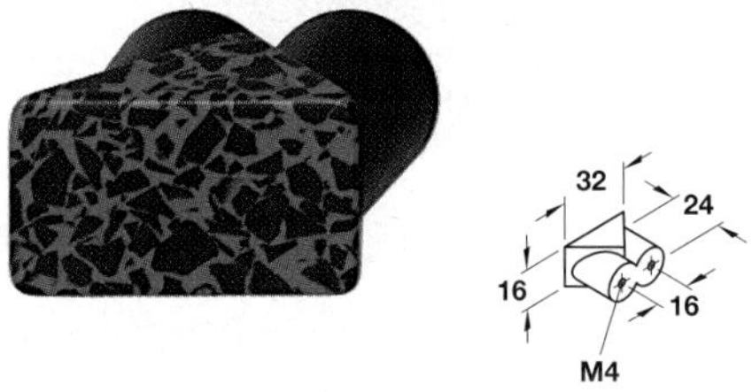

Blue/black

Cat. No.	138.14.367

Packing: 25 pcs.

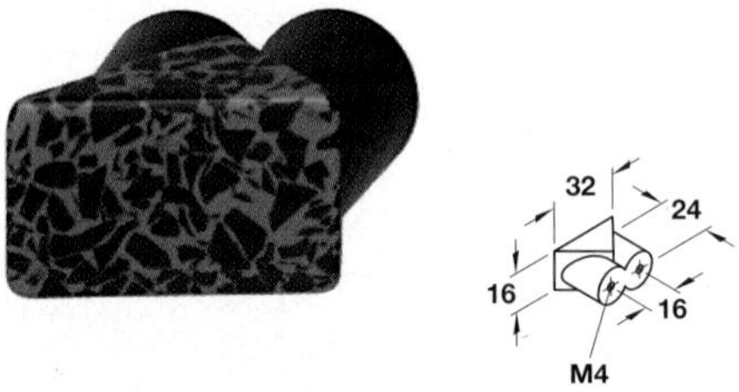

Grey/black

Cat. No.	138.14.312

Packing: 25 pcs.

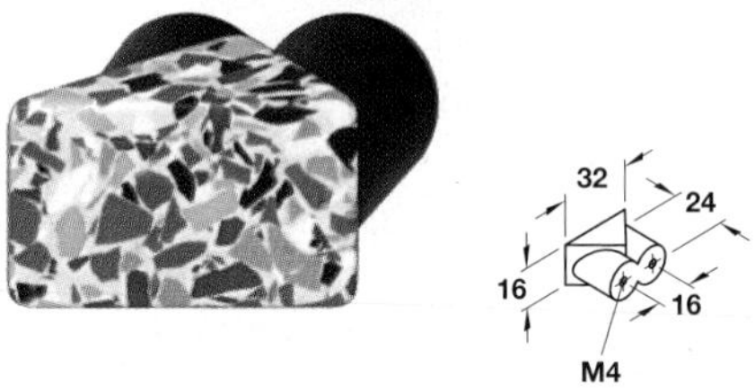

Multicolor

Cat. No.	138.14.349

Packing: 25 pcs.

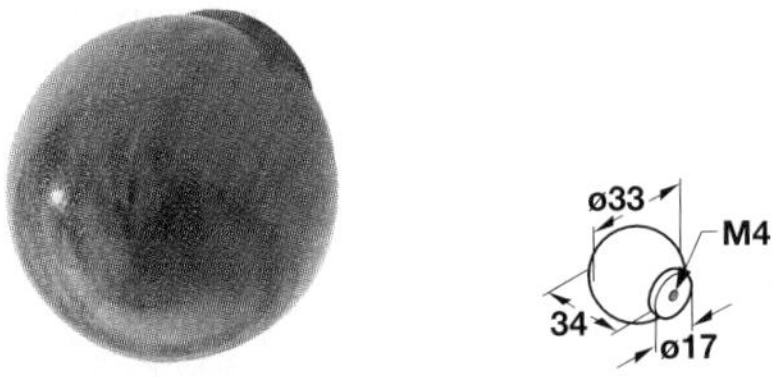

Green

Cat. No.	138.54.503

Packing: 25 pcs.

Blue

Cat. No.	138.54.003

Packing: 25 pcs.

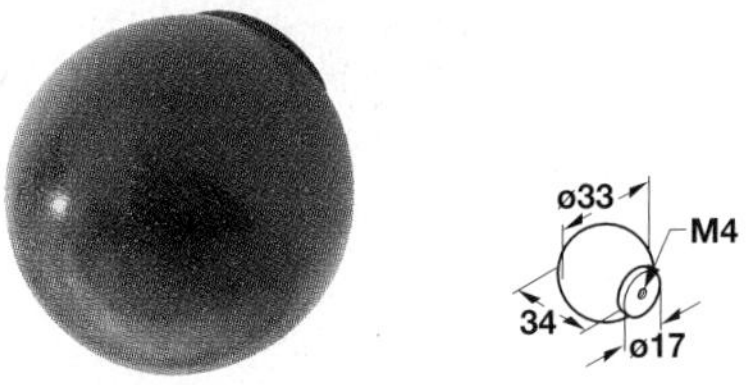

Rust

Cat. No.	138.54.101

Packing: 25 pcs.

Dimensional data not binding.
We reserve the right to alter specifications without notice.

Plastic Knobs for Laminate Inserts

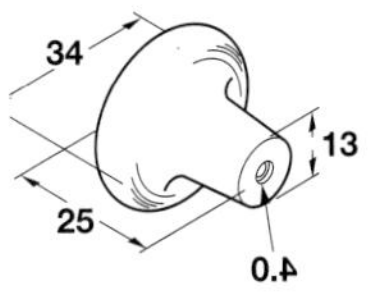

Chrome polished electroplated

Cat. No.	138.89.202

Packing: 100 pcs.

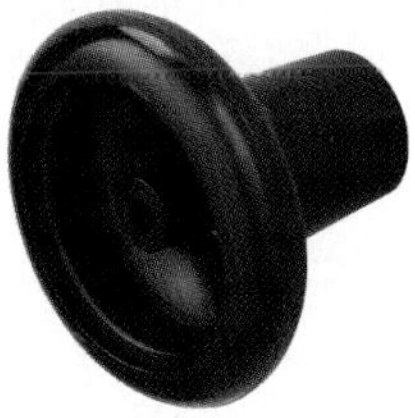
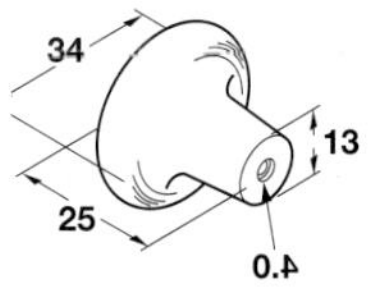

Black

Cat. No.	138.89.300

Packing: 100 pcs.

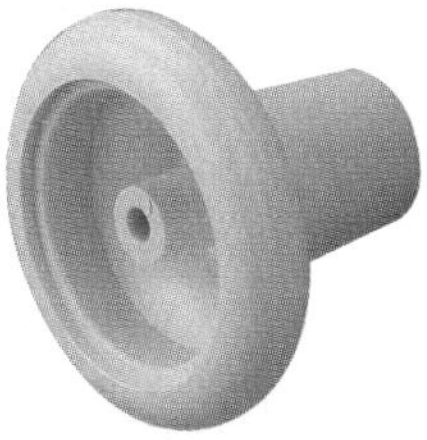
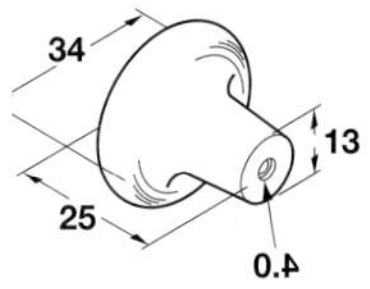

White

Cat. No.	138.89.702

Packing: 100 pcs.

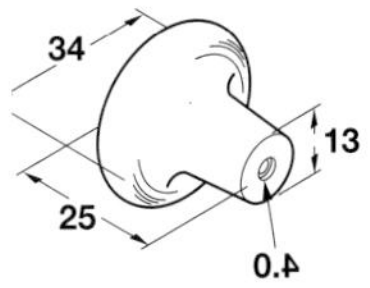

Gold polished electroplated

Cat. No.	138.89.800

Packing: 100 pcs.

Punch Press
for use with laminate up to 1/16"
Finish: Steel, black

Cat. No.	004.04.811

Packing: 1 pc.

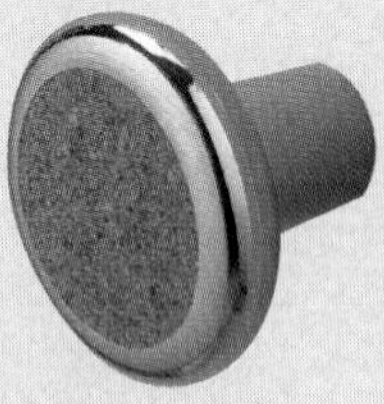

Make your own inserts with Punch Press sold separately.

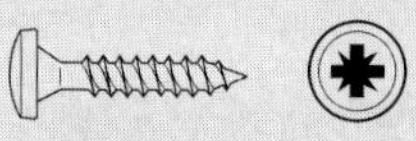

Hospa Pan Head Screws
Pozi Recess
Finish: steel, zinc-plated

Length	Cat. No.
13 mm	015.71.811
15 mm	015.71.820
17 mm	015.71.839
20 mm	015.71.848
25 mm	015.71.857
30 mm	015.71.866
35 mm	015.71.875
40 mm	015.71.884
45 mm	015.71.893

Packing: 1000 pcs.

HÄFELE

Plastic Knobs

1 Decorative Hardware

Threaded Screws M4
Combined slot, suitable for flat or cross blades
Finish: steel, zinc-plated

Length	Cat. No.
10 mm	022.35.109
12 mm	022.35.127
15 mm	022.35.154
18 mm	022.35.181
20 mm	022.35.207
22 mm	022.35.225
23 mm	022.35.234
25 mm	022.35.252
28 mm	022.35.289
30 mm	022.35.305
35 mm	022.35.350
38 mm	022.35.387
40 mm	022.35.403
45 mm	022.35.458
50 mm	022.35.501
60 mm	022.35.609

Packing: 100 and 1000 pcs.

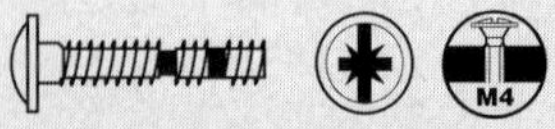

Threaded Breakoff Screw M4
Combined slot, suitable for flat or cross blades
Finish: steel, zinc-plated

Length	Cat. No.
1 3/4" x 3/4"	022.35.887

Packing: 100 and 1000 pcs.

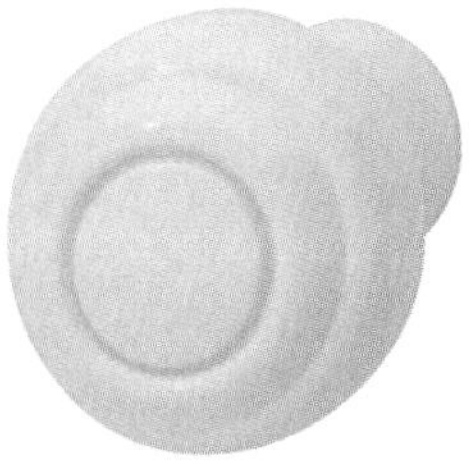

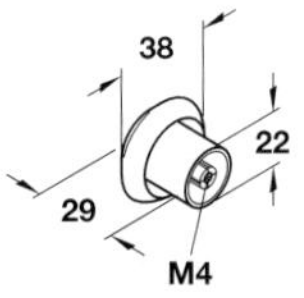

White

Cat. No.	138.30.709

Packing: 25 pcs.

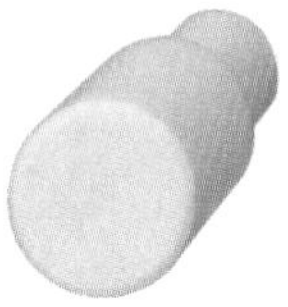

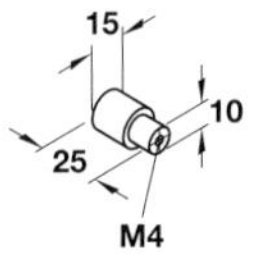

White

Cat. No.	138.44.703

Packing: 100 pcs.

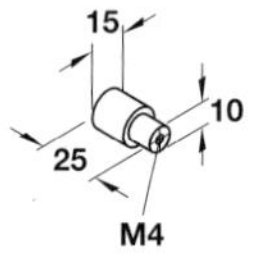

Black

Cat. No.	138.44.605

Packing: 100 pcs.

Dimensional data not binding.
We reserve the right to alter specifications without notice.

Plastic Knobs

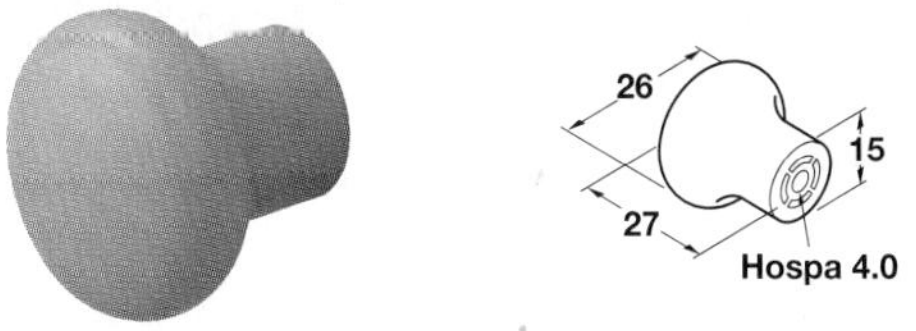

Almond matt

Cat. No.	136.75.400

Packing: 100 pcs.

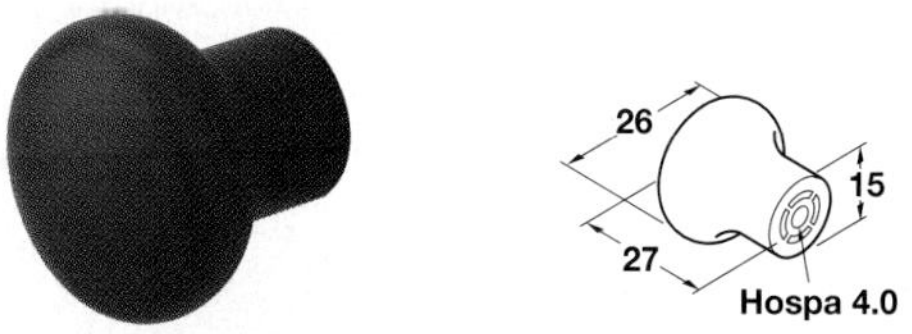

Dark green matt

Cat. No.	136.75.000

Packing: 100 pcs.

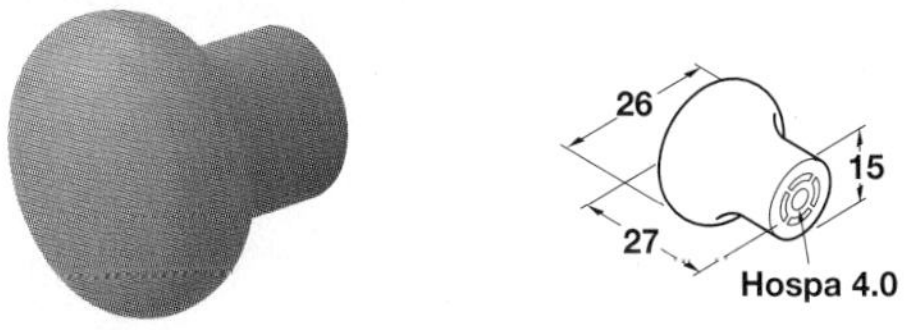

Pink matt

Cat. No.	136.75.902

Packing: 100 pcs.

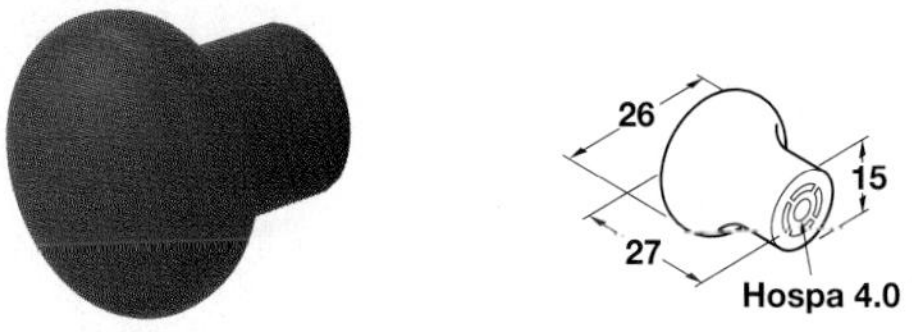

Red matt

Cat. No.	136.75.910

Packing: 100 pcs.

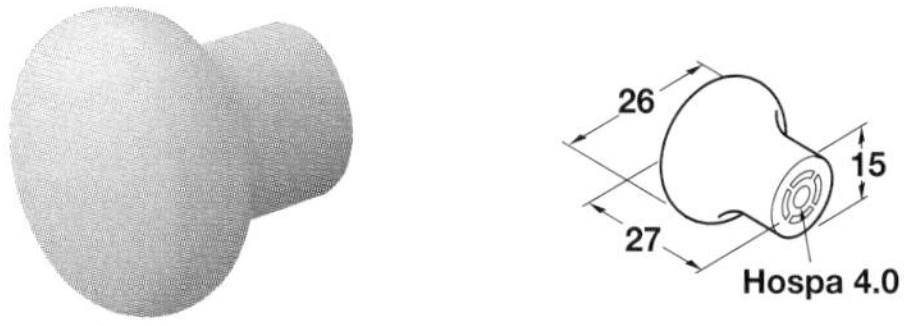

White matt

Cat. No.	136.75.700

Packing: 100 pcs.

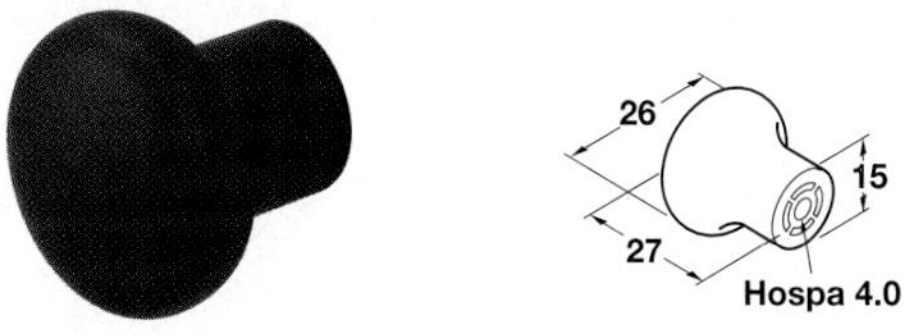

Black matt

Cat. No.	136.75.300

Packing: 100 pcs.

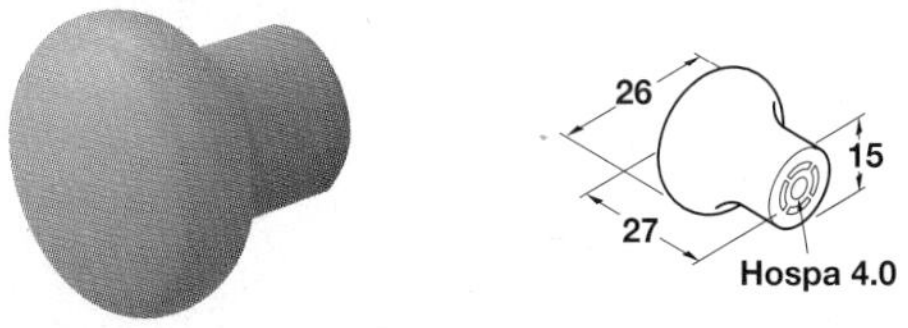

Yellow matt

Cat. No.	136.75.600

Packing: 100 pcs.

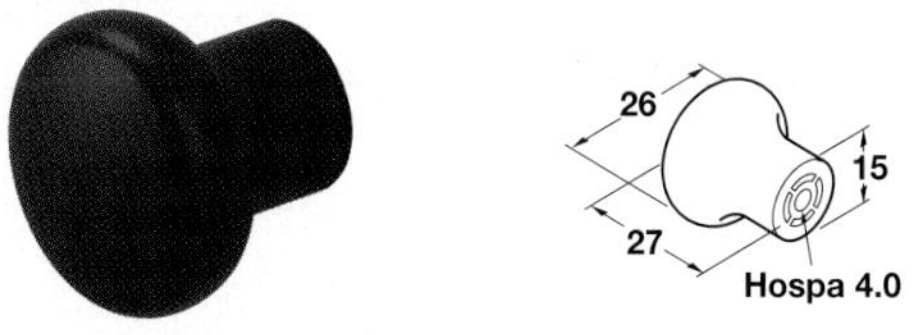

Dark burgundy matt

Cat. No.	136.75.921

Packing: 100 pcs.

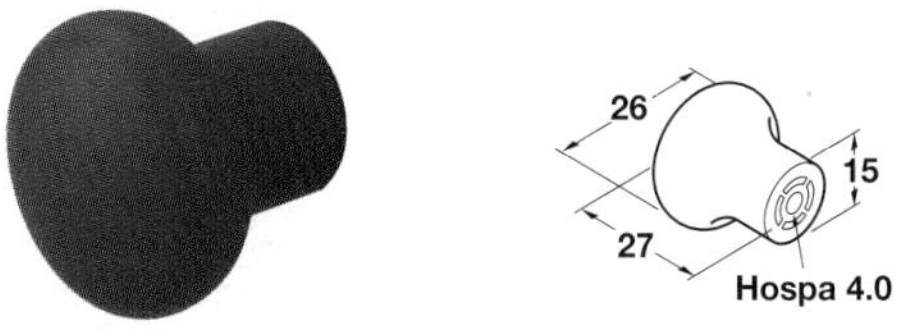

Blue matt

Cat. No.	136.75.801

Packing: 100 pcs.

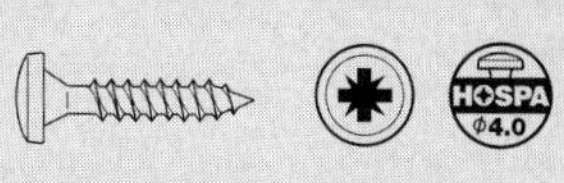

Hospa Pan Head Screws
Pozi Recess
Finish: steel, zinc-plated

Length	Cat. No.
13 mm	015.71.811
15 mm	015.71.820
17 mm	015.71.839
20 mm	015.71.848
25 mm	015.71.857
30 mm	015.71.866
35 mm	015.71.875
40 mm	015.71.884
45 mm	015.71.893

Packing: 1000 pcs.

HÄFELE

Aluminum Extruded Handles

- Length 2500 mm

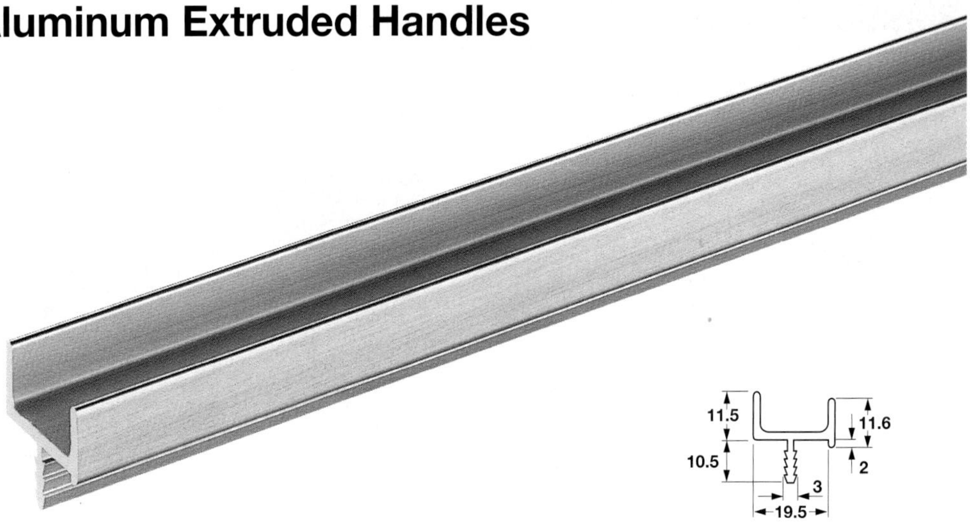

Silver colored

Cat No.	126.20.905

Packing: 1 pc.

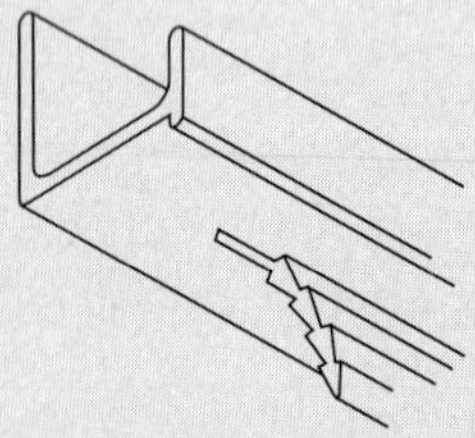

- Harpoon bar can be mortised for installation.

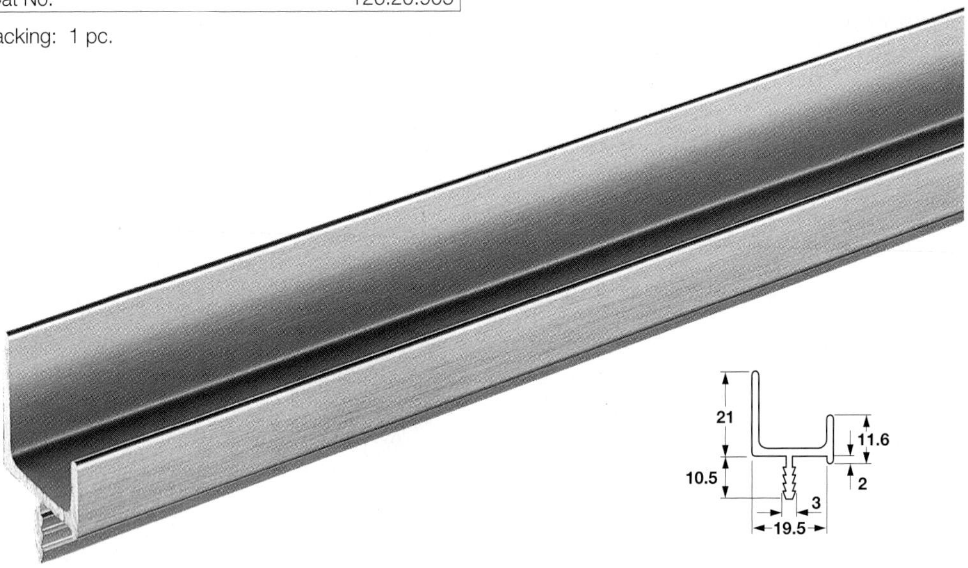

Silver colored

Cat No.	126.21.902

Packing: 1 pc.

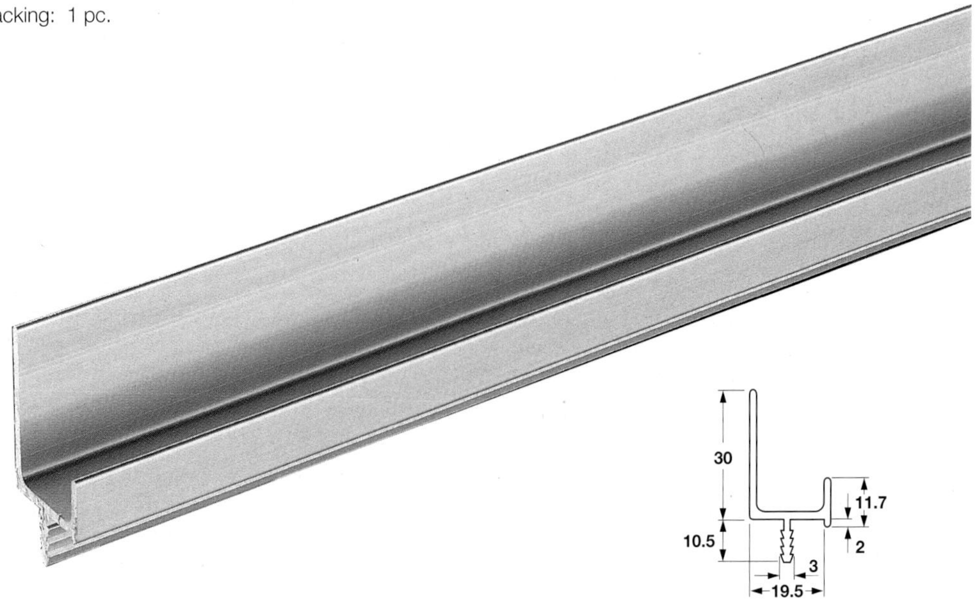

Silver colored

Cat. No.	126.22.909

Packing: 1 pc.

Dimensional data not binding.
We reserve the right to alter specifications without notice.

Anodized Aluminum Extruded Handles

HÄFELE

Decorative Hardware 1

- Length 2500 mm

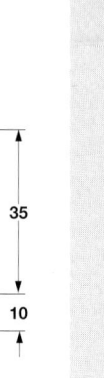

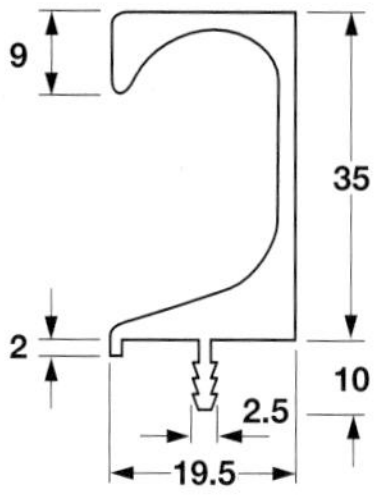

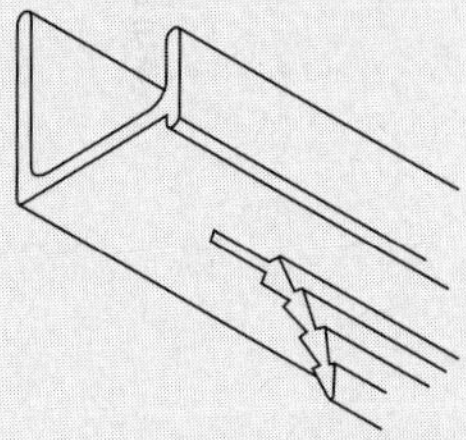

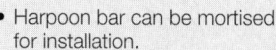

- Harpoon bar can be mortised for installation.

Black

Cat No.	126.27.306

Packing: 1 pc.

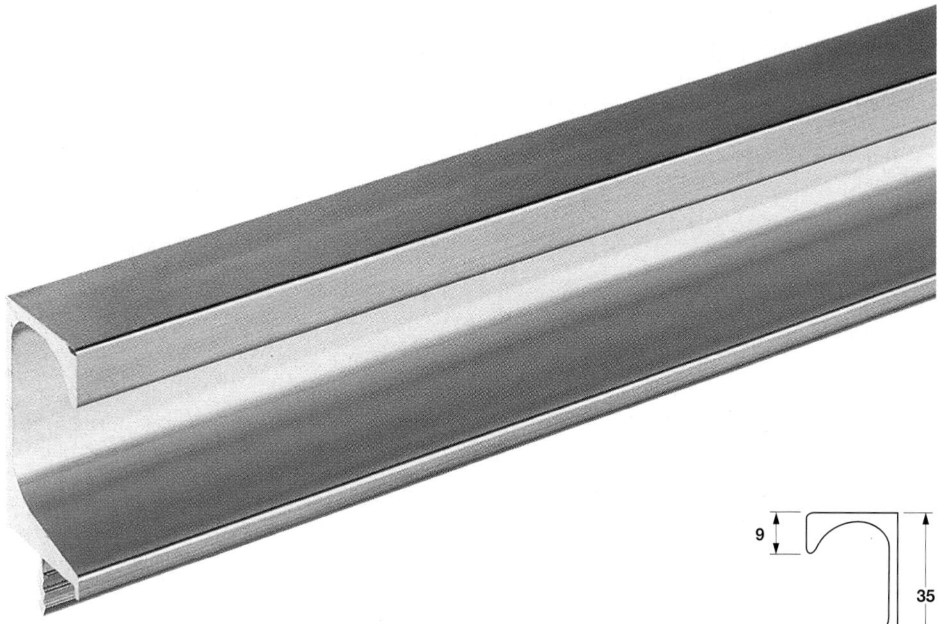

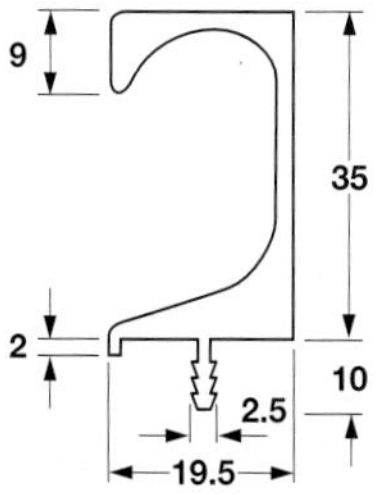

Silver colored

Cat No.	126.27.904

Packing: 1 pc.

Dimensional data not binding. We reserve the right to alter specifications without notice.

HÄFELE

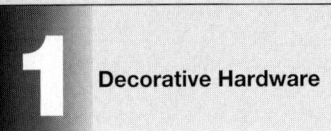

Contiuous Wooden Pulls

- Random length 5 to 10 feet.
- Other species can be produced from 2000 feet onward--inquire for details.

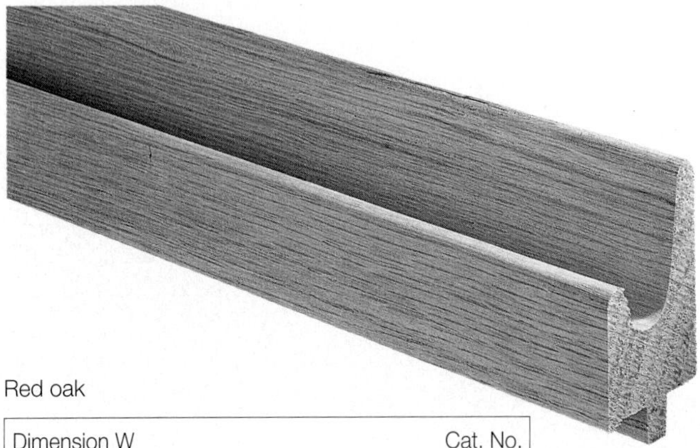

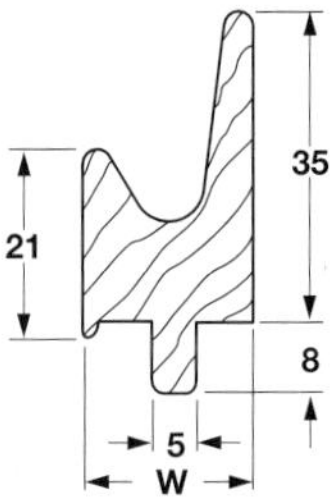

Red oak

Dimension W	Cat. No.
17.5	193.93.410
19.0	193.93.429

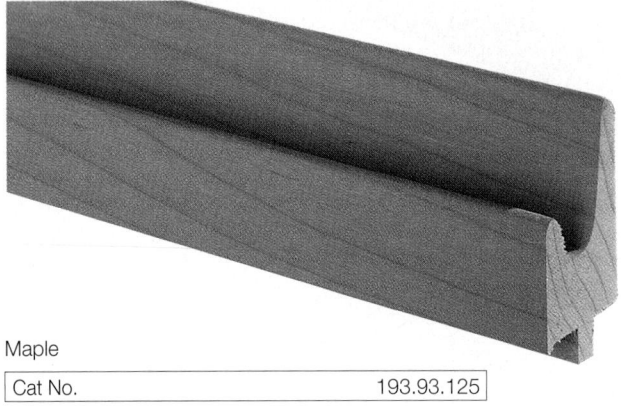

Packing: 250 ft.

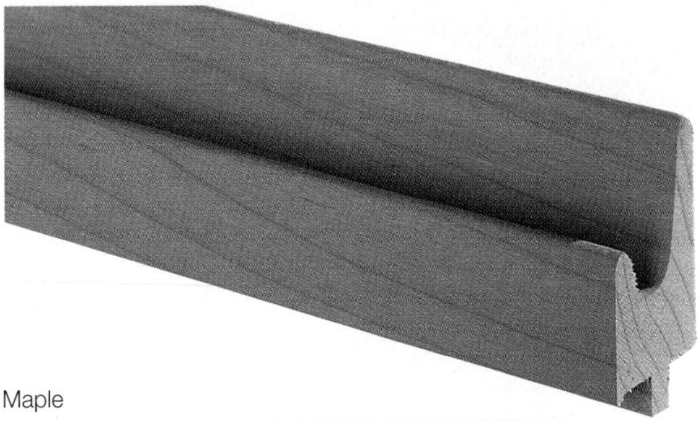

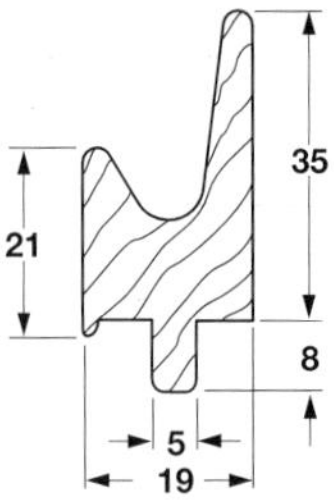

Maple

Cat No.	193.93.125

Packing: 250 ft.

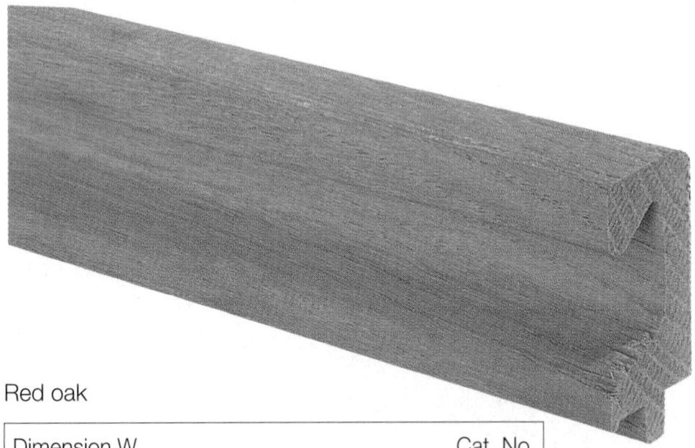

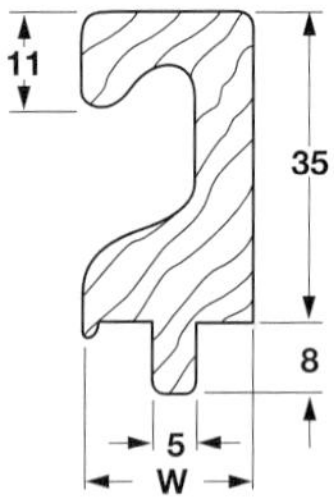

Red oak

Dimension W	Cat. No.
17.5	193.94.417
19.0	193.94.426

Packing: 250 ft.

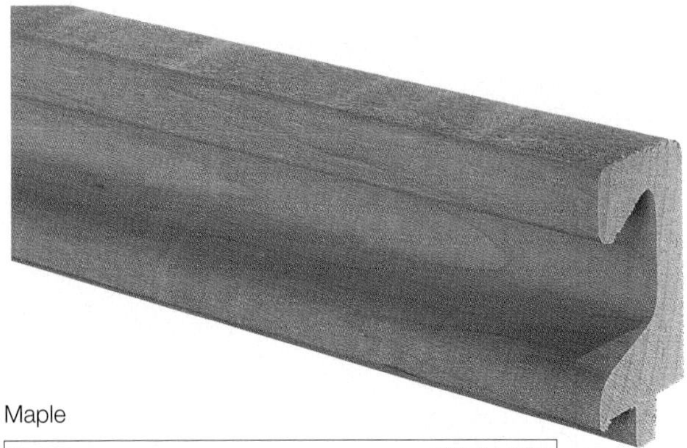

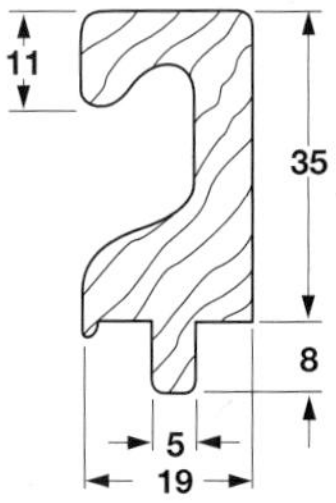

Maple

Cat No.	193.94.122

Packing: 250 ft.

Ornaments

1 11/16 x 1 11/16 x 3/16
Embossed Plywood

Finish	Cat. No.
Red Oak	194.78.414
White Hardwood	194.78.114

Packing: 10 pcs

4 1/2 x 2 3/8 x 7/32
Embossed Plywood

Finish	Cat. No.
Red Oak	194.78.415
White Hardwood	194.78.115

Packing: 10 pcs

2 1/8 x 2 1/8 x 7/32
Embossed Plywood

Finish	Cat. No.
Red Oak	194.78.412
White Hardwood	194.78.112

Packing: 10 pcs

3 x 3 x 7/32
Embossed Plywood

Finish	Cat. No.
Red Oak	194.78.413
White Hardwood	194.78.113

Packing: 10 pcs

1 x 1 x 7/32
Embossed Plywood

Finish	Cat. No.
Red Oak	194.78.411
White Hardwood	194.78.111

Packing: 10 pcs

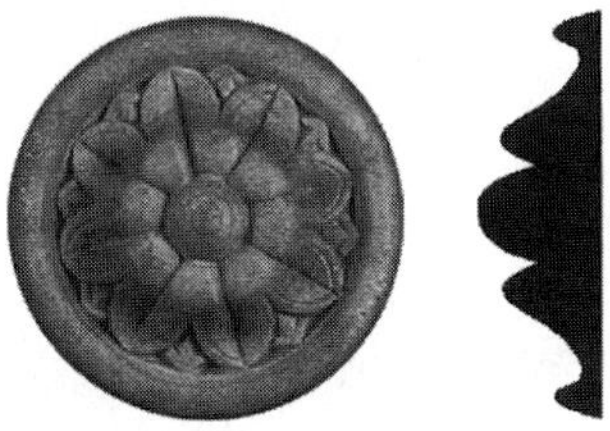

2 1/8 x 2 1/8 x 21/32
Maple Turned Embossed

Cat. No.	194.78.132

Packing: 10 pcs

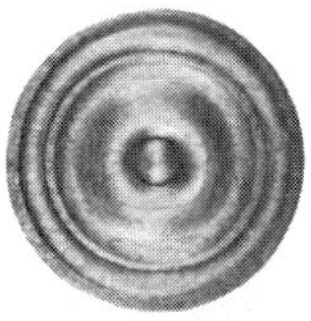

1 1/4 x 1 1/4 x 1/4
Turned

Finish	Cat. No.
Maple	194.78.128
Cherry	194.78.628

Packing: 25 pcs

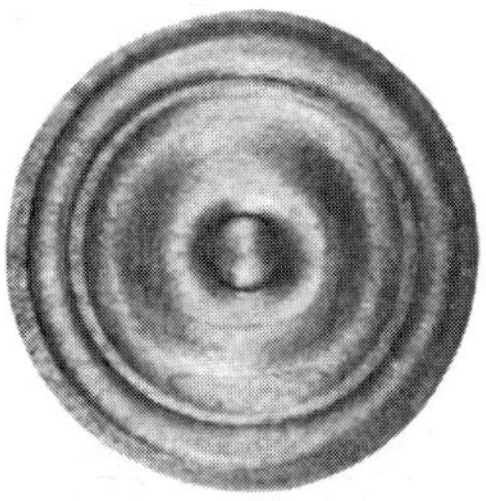

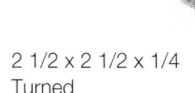

2 1/2 x 2 1/2 x 1/4
Turned

Finish	Cat. No.
Maple	194.78.129
Cherry	194.78.629

Packing: 25 pcs

Dimensions shown in inches

Easy to Apply
with woodworking glue
or small brad.

Other species available.
Minimum 250 piece order.
Ask for details.

HÄFELE

Ornaments

3 15/16 x 5/16
Beech Carved

Cat. No.	194.78.331

Packing: 10 pcs

5 1/2 x 2 11/32 x 9/32
Plywood Beech Carved

Cat. No.	194.78.330

Packing: 10 pcs

Easy to Apply
with woodworking glue
or small brad.

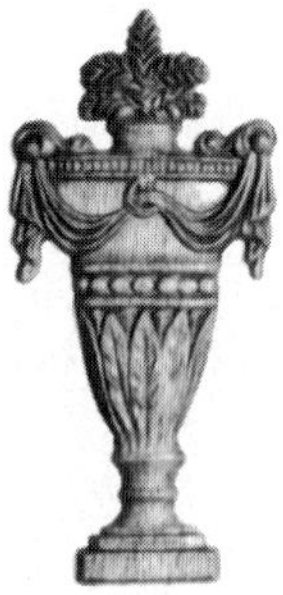

2 3/4 x 5 29/32 x 1/4
Plywood Beech Carved

Cat. No.	194.78.338

Packing: 10 pcs

4 29/32 x 4 11/32 x 1/4
Plywood Beech Carved

Cat. No.	194.78.339

Packing: 10 pcs

7/8 x 7/8 x 5/32
Plywood

Finish	Cat. No.
Red Oak	194.78.420
White Hardwood	194.78.120

Packing: 25 pcs

21/32 x 5 23/32 x 1/4
Plywood Beech Carved

Cat. No.	194.78.337

Packing: 10 pcs

**Other species available.
Minimum 250 piece order.
Ask for details.**

10 27/32 x 1 25/32 x 1/4
Plywood Beech Carved

Cat. No.	194.78.336

Packing: 10 pcs

Dimensional data not binding.
We reserve the right to alter
specifications without notice.

Dimensions shown in inches

Ornaments

2 11/32 x 2 9/16 x 1/4
Plywood Beech Carved

Cat. No.	194.78.334

Packing: 10 pcs

2 11/32 x 2 9/16 x 1/4
Beech Carved

Cat. No.	194.78.333

Packing: 10 pcs

3 1/4 x 2 15/16 x 11/32
Beech Carved

Cat. No.	194.78.335

Packing: 10 pcs

Easy to Apply
with woodworking glue
or small brad.

3 5/32 x 3 11/32 x 31/32
Beech Carved

Cat. No.	194.78.340

Packing: 10 pcs

Other species available.
Minimum 250 piece order.
Ask for details.

Dimensional data not binding.
We reserve the right to alter
specifications without notice.

Dimensions shown in inches

HÄFELE

Ornaments

1 9/16 x 3 15/16 x 11/32
Beech Carved

Cat. No.	194.78.341

Packing: 10 pcs

2 15/16 x 4 11/32 x 1 1/16
Beech Carved

Cat. No.	194.78.342

Packing: 10 pcs

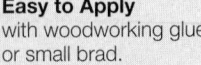

Easy to Apply
with woodworking glue
or small brad.

5 1/8 x 4 1/2 x 1 9/16
Beech Carved

Cat. No.	194.78.343

Packing: 10 pcs

Other species available.
Minimum 250 piece order.
Ask for details.

Dimensional data not binding.
We reserve the right to alter
specifications without notice.

Dimensions shown in inches

Ornaments

HÄFELE

4 1/2 x 4 1/2 x 7/32
Embossed Plywood

Finish	Cat. No.
Red Oak	194.78.421
White Hardwood	194.78.121

Packing: 25 pcs

5 13/32 x 1 7/16 x 7/32
Embossed Plywood

Finish	Cat. No.
Red Oak	194.78.419
White Hardwood	194.78.119

Packing: 25 pcs

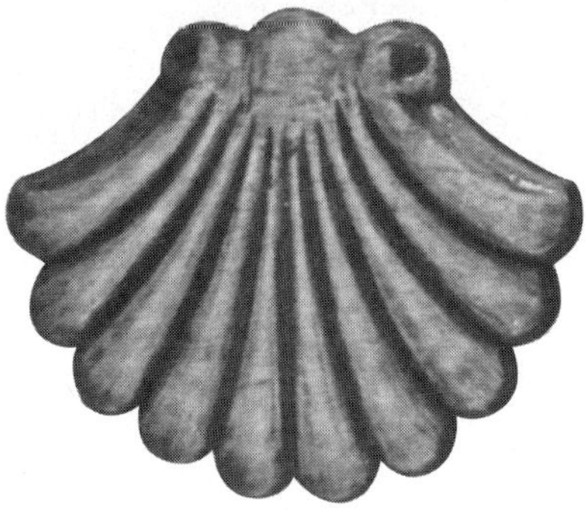

3 x 2 1/2 x 7/32
Embossed Plywood

Finish	Cat. No.
Red Oak	194.78.416
White Hardwood	194.78.116

Packing: 25 pcs

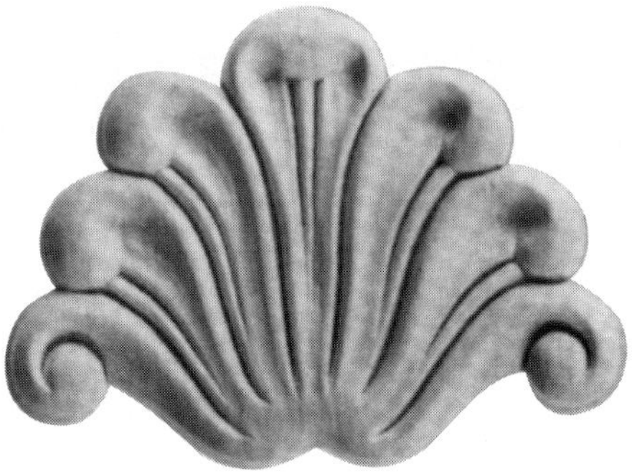

4 x 2 7/8 x 7/32
Embossed Plywood

Finish	Cat. No.
Red Oak	194.78.417
White Hardwood	194.78.117

Packing: 25 pcs

Easy to Apply with woodworking glue or small brad.

5 3/4 x 6 3/16 x 7/32
Embossed Plywood

Finish	Cat. No.
Red Oak	194.78.418
White Hardware	194.78.118

Packing: 25 pcs

Other species available. Minimum 250 piece order. Ask for details.

Dimensions shown in inches

Dimensional data not binding. We reserve the right to alter specifications without notice.

HÄFELE

Ornaments

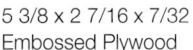

5 3/8 x 2 7/16 x 7/32
Embossed Plywood

Finish	Cat. No.
Red Oak	194.78.400
White Hardwood	194.78.100

Packing: 10 pcs

5 7/8 x 2 7/16 x 7/32
Embossed Plywood

Finish	Cat. No.
Red Oak	194.78.401
White Hardwood	194.78.101

Packing: 10 pcs

Easy to Apply
with woodworking glue
or small brad.

6 1/8 x 7/8 x 7/32
Embossed Plywood

Finish	Cat. No.
Red Oak	194.78.402
White Hardwood	194.78.102

Packing: 10 pcs

6 7/8 x 3 7/8 x 7/32
Embossed Plywood

Finish	Cat. No.
Red Oak	194.78.403
White Hardwood	194.78.103

Packing: 10 pcs

7 1/8 x 1 11/16 x 7/32
Embossed Plywood

Finish	Cat. No.
Red Oak	194.78.404
White Hardwood	194.78.104

Packing: 10 pcs

8 1/8 x 2 1/2 x 1/4
Embossed Plywood

Finish	Cat. No.
Red Oak	194.78.405
White Hardwood	194.78.105

Packing: 10 pcs

**Other species available.
Minimum 250 piece order.
Ask for details.**

8 5/32 x 1 15/16 x 7/32
Embossed Plywood

Finish	Cat. No.
Red Oak	194.78.406
White Hardwood	194.78.106

Packing: 10 pcs

8 7/8 x 2 x 7/32
Embossed Plywood

Finish	Cat. No.
Red Oak	194.78.407
White Hardwood	194.78.107

Packing: 10 pcs

Dimensions shown in inches

Dimensional data not binding.
We reserve the right to alter
specifications without notice.

Horizontal Ornaments

12 15/16 x 4 x 7/32
Embossed Plywood

Finish	Cat. No.
Red Oak	194.78.408
White Hardwood	194.78.108

Packing: 10 pcs

Easy to Apply
with woodworking glue
or small brad.

14 1/4 x 3 1/8 x 7/32
Embossed Plywood

Finish	Cat. No.
Red Oak	194.78.409
White Hardwood	194.78.109

Packing: 10 pcs

Other species available.
Minimum 250 piece order.
Ask for details.

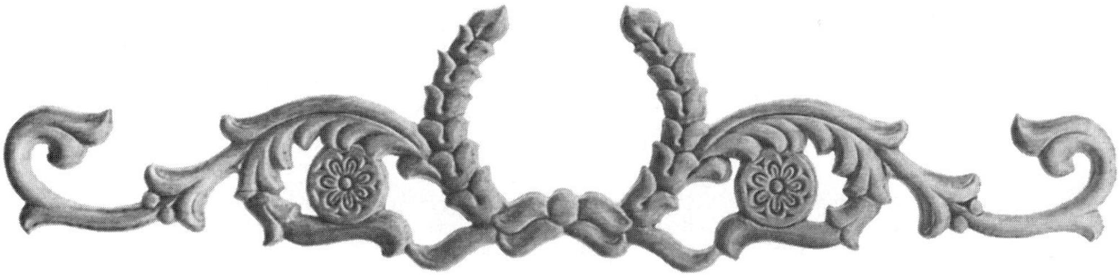

16 25/32 x 3 7/8 x 1/4
Embossed Plywood

Finish	Cat. No.
Red Oak	194.78.410
White Hardwood	104.70.110

Packing: 10 pcs

Dimensional data not binding.
We reserve the right to alter
specifications without notice.

Dimensions shown in inches

HÄFELE

Scrolls

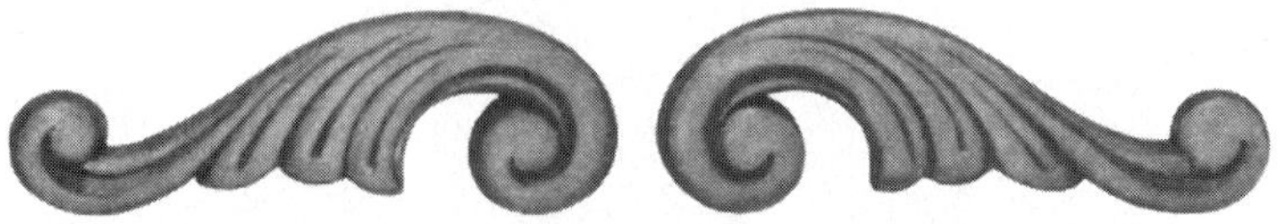

3 11/16 x 1 5/16 x 7/32
Embossed Plywood

Finish	Cat. No.
Red Oak	194.78.422
White Hardwood	194.78.122

Packing: 10 pair

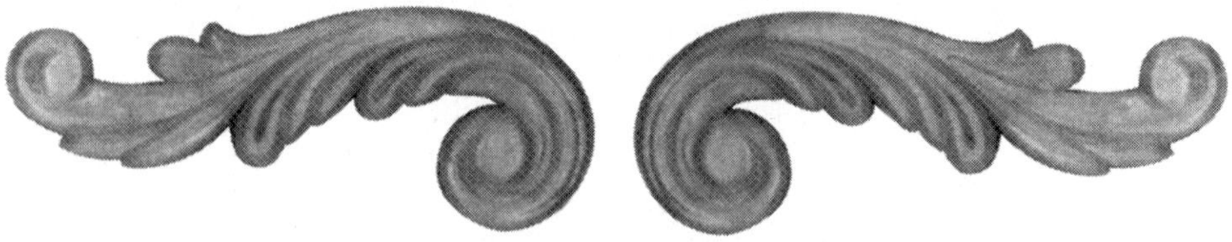

Easy to Apply
with woodworking glue
or small brad.

Dimensions given are per one side.

4 19/32 x 1 21/32 x 5/32
Embossed Plywood

Finish	Cat. No.
Red Oak	194.78.423
White Hardwood	194.78.123

Packing: 10 pair

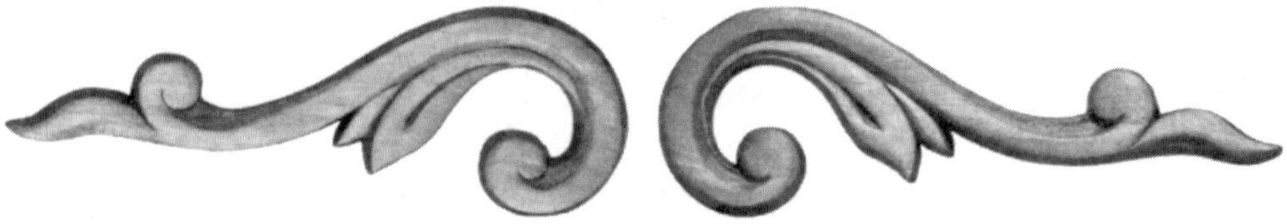

5 7/16 x 1 7/8 x 7/32
Embossed Plywood

Finish	Cat. No.
Red Oak	194.78.424
White Hardwood	194.78.124

Packing: 10 pair

Other species available.
Minimum 250 piece order.
Ask for details.

6 3/8 x 1 1/2 x 7/32
Embossed Plywood

Finish	Cat. No.
Red Oak	194.78.425
White Hardwood	194.78.125

Packing: 10 pair

Dimensions shown in inches

Scrolls

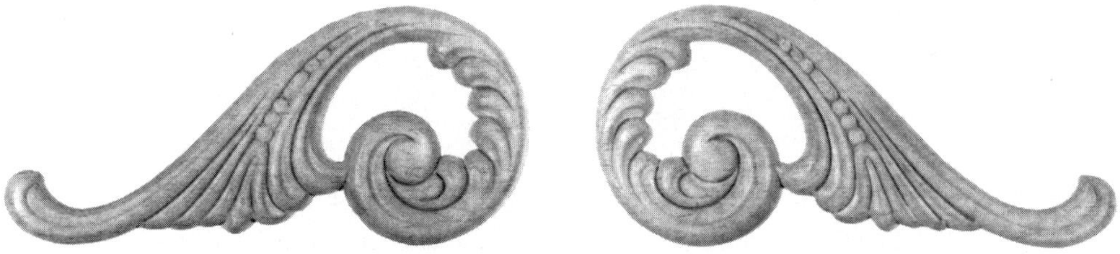

6 5/8 x 3 x 9/32
Embossed Plywood

Finish	Cat. No.
Red Oak	194.78.426
White Hardwood	194.78.126

Packing: 10 pair

Easy to Apply
with woodworking glue
or small brad.

Dimensions given are per one side.

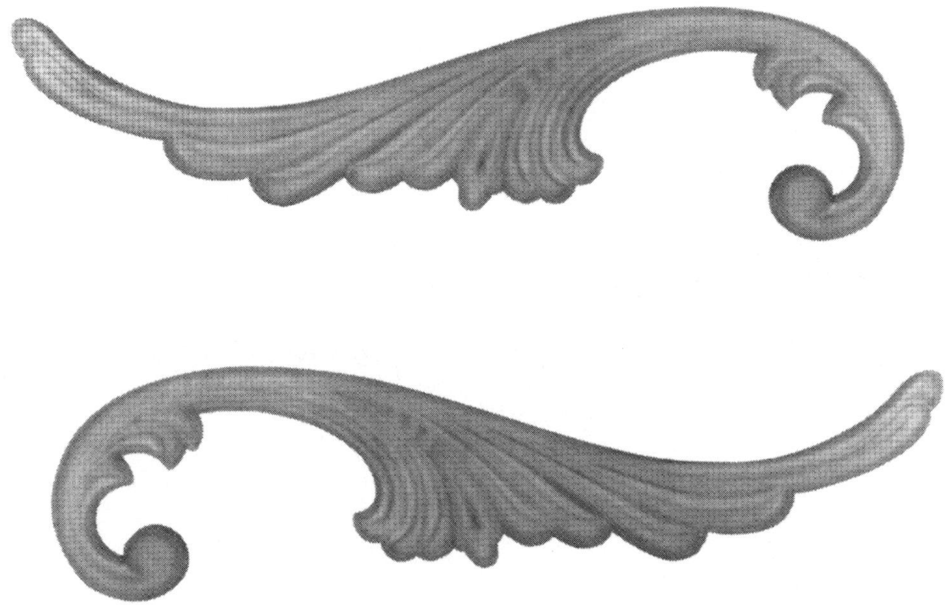

Other species available.
Minimum 250 piece order.
Ask for details.

9 5/16 x 2 1/4 x 9/32
Embossed Plywood

Finish	Cat. No.
Red Oak	194.78.427
White Hardwood	194.78.127

Packing: 10 pair

Dimensional data not binding.
We reserve the right to alter
specifications without notice.

Dimensions shown in inches

Corner Brackets and Rails

Laser-cut Precision

- Wood trim for application on furniture, cabinetry, book shelves, etc.
- Unfinished wood, ready to stain or paint.

Corner Bracket, solid
4 1/2 x 4 1/2 x 3/4

Finish	Cat. No.
Red Oak	194.78.444
Maple	194.78.144
Cherry	194.78.644
Hickory	194.78.441

Packing: 10 pcs

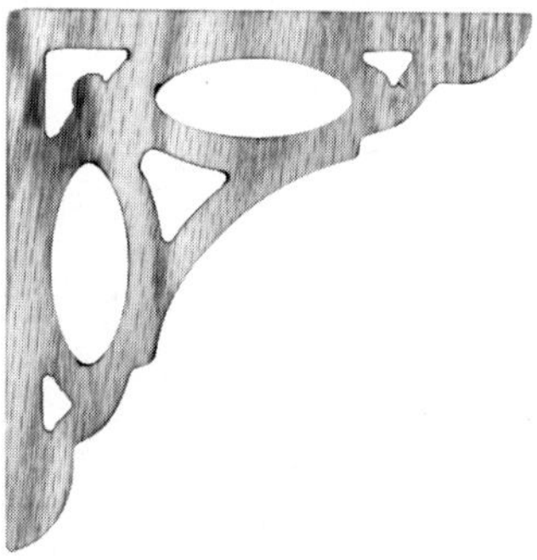

Corner Bracket with openings
4 1/2 x 4 1/2 x 3/4

Finish	Cat. No.
Red Oak	194.78.445
Maple	194.78.145
Cherry	194.78.645
Hickory	194.78.442

Packing: 10 pcs

25 x 5 x 3/4

Finish	Cat. No.
Red Oak	194.78.446
Maple	194.78.146
Cherry	194.78.646
Hickory	194.78.443

Packing: 10 pcs

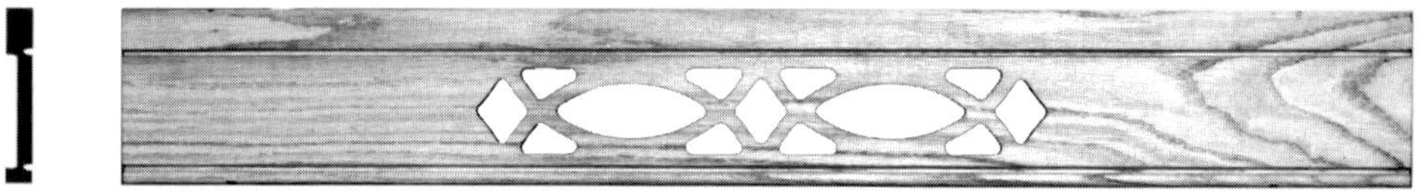

37 x 5 x 3/4

Finish	Cat. No.
Red Oak	194.78.447
Maple	194.78.147
Cherry	194.78.647
Hickory	194.78.449

Packing: 10 pcs

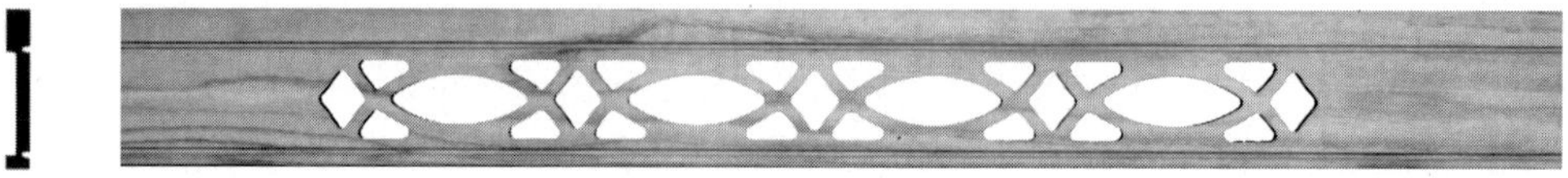

49 x 5 x 3/4

Finish	Cat. No.
Red Oak	194.78.448
Maple	194.78.148
Cherry	194.78.648
Hickory	194.78.440

Packing: 10 pcs

**Other species available.
Minimum 100 piece order.
Ask for details.**

Dimensional data not binding.
We reserve the right to alter specifications without notice.

Dimensions shown in inches

Wood Moulding

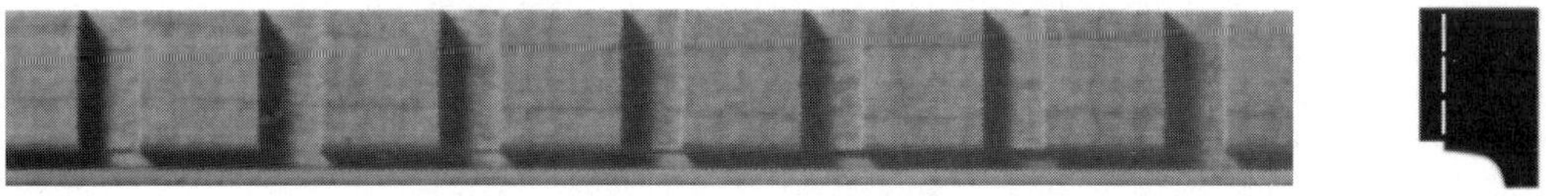

3/4 x 1/2 Thick x 96 Long

Finish	Cat. No.
Red Oak	194.79.400
Maple	194.79.100
Cherry	194.79.600
Hickory	194.79.407

Packing: 10 pcs

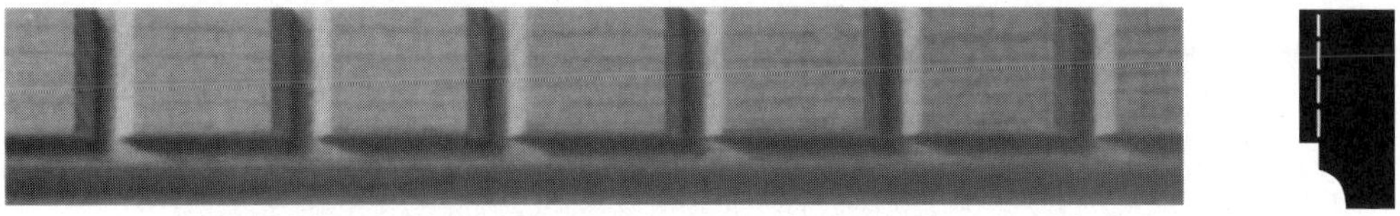

1 x 1/2 Thick x 96 Long

Finish	Cat. No.
Red Oak	194.79.401
Maple	194.79.101
Cherry	194.79.601
Hickory	194.79.408

Packing: 10 pcs

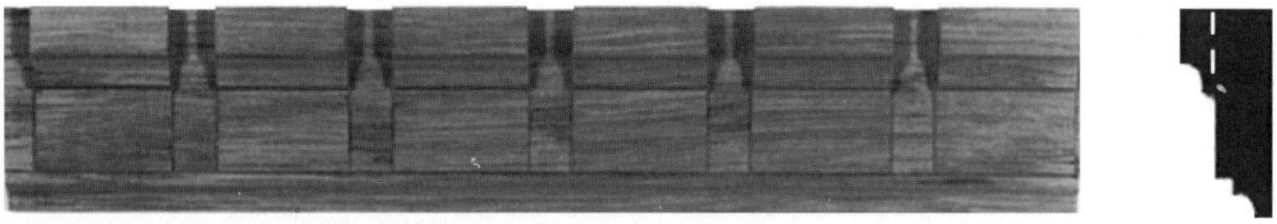

1 1/8 x 1/2 Thick x 96 Long

Finish	Cat. No.
Red Oak	194.79.402
Maple	194.79.102
Cherry	194.79.602

Packing: 10 pcs

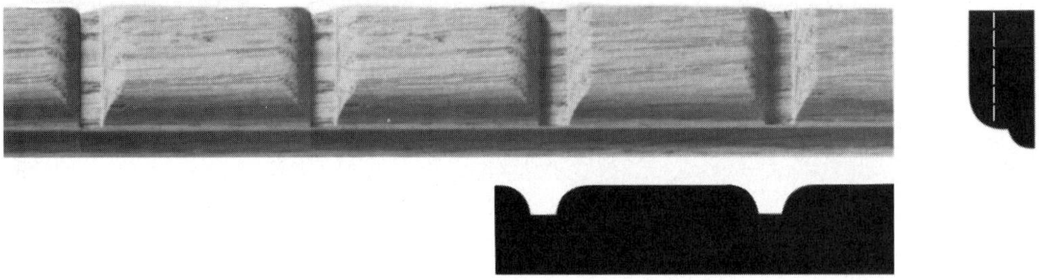

1 1/4 x 3/4 Thick x 96 Long

Finish	Cat. No.
Red Oak	194.79.403
Maple	194.79.103

Packing: 10 pcs

Dimensions shown in inches

Deep-carved solid wood moulding. Patterns to accent your furniture and cabinet designs.

Ready to stain or paint.

Easy to Apply
with woodworking glue or small brad.

Other species available. Minimum 1000 feet order. Ask for details.

Dimensional data not binding. We reserve the right to alter specifications without notice.

HÄFELE

Wood Moulding

1 Decorative Hardware

Solid wood moulding in patterns to accent your furniture and cabinet designs.

Ready to stain or paint.

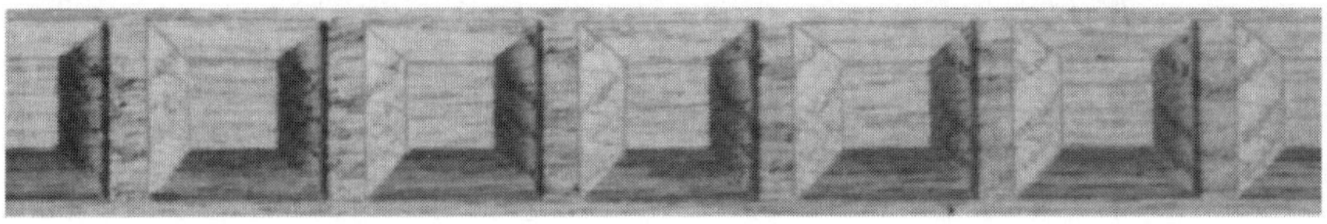

15/16 x 11/32 Thick x 96 Long

Finish	Cat. No.
Red Oak	194.79.404
Maple	194.79.104
Cherry	194.79.604

Packing: 10 pcs

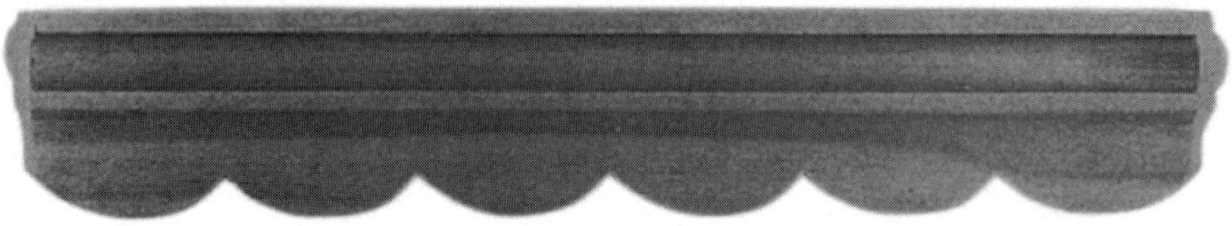

1 1/16 x 3/8 Thick x 96 Long

Finish	Cat. No.
Red Oak	194.79.405
Maple	194.79.105

Packing: 10 pcs

Easy to Apply

with woodworking glue
or small brad.

3/4 x 7/32 Thick x 96 Long
Maple Embossed

Cat. No.	194.79.113

Packing: 10 pcs

1 x 1/4 Thick x 96 Long
Maple Embossed

Cat. No.	194.79.114

Packing: 10 pcs

**Other species available.
Minimum 1000 feet order.
Ask for details.**

Dimensions shown in inches

Dimensional data not binding.
We reserve the right to alter
specifications without notice.

Wood Moulding

HÄFELE

1 3/8 x 1/4 Thick x 96 Long
Maple Embossed

Cat. No.	194.79.115

Packing: 10 pcs

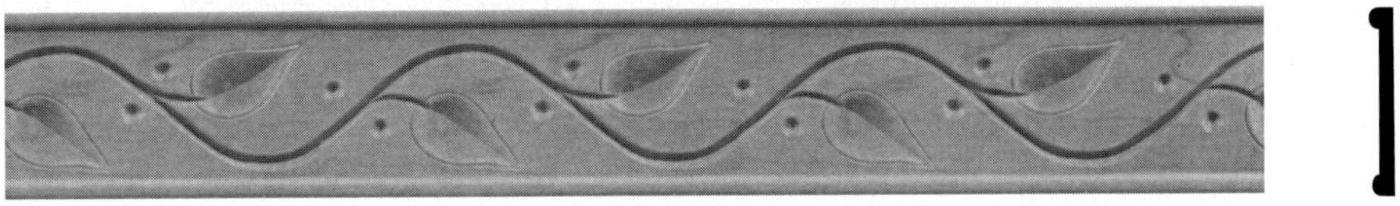

1 3/4 x 11/32 Thick x 96 Long
Maple Embossed

Cat. No.	194.79.116

Packing: 10 pcs

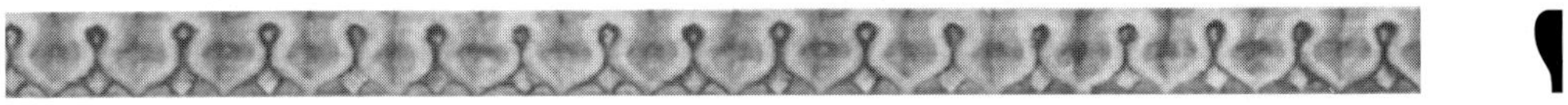

1/2 x 3/16 Thick x 96 Long
Maple Embossed

Cat. No.	194.79.112

Packing: 10 pcs

3/4 x 1/2 Thick x 96 Long
Embossed

Finish	Cat. No.
Maple	194.79.111
Red Oak	194.79.411

Packing: 10 pcs

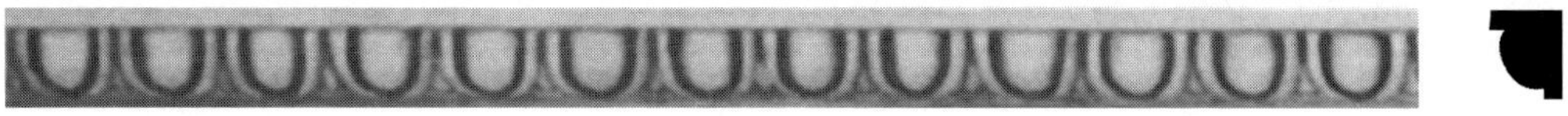

1/2 x 3/8 Thick x 96 Long
Maple Embossed

Cat. No.	194.79.110

Packing: 10 pcs

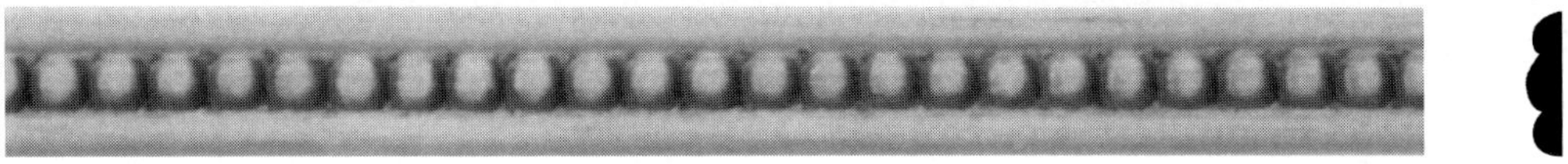

3/4 x 3/16 Thick x 96 Long
Maple Embossed

Cat. No.	194.79.109

Packing: 10 pcs

Dimensions shown in inches

Deep-carved solid wood moulding. Patterns to accent your furniture and cabinet designs.

Ready to stain or paint.

Easy to Apply
with woodworking glue or small brad.

Other species available. Minimum 250 feet order. Ask for details.

Dimensional data not binding. We reserve the right to alter specifications without notice.

HÄFELE

Wood Moulding

Embossed or deep-carved solid wood moulding. Patterns to accent your furniture and cabinet designs.

Ready to stain or paint.

Easy to Apply
with woodworking glue
or small brad.

Other species available.
Minimum 1000 feet order.
Ask for details.

7/32 x 1/8 Thick x 48 Long
Maple Embossed

Cat. No.	194.79.106

Packing: 10 pcs

1/2 x 1/4 Thick x 48 Long
Maple Embossed

Cat. No.	194.79.107

Packing: 10 pcs

1/4 x 1/4 Thick x 48 Long
Maple Embossed

Cat. No.	194.79.108

Packing: 10 pcs

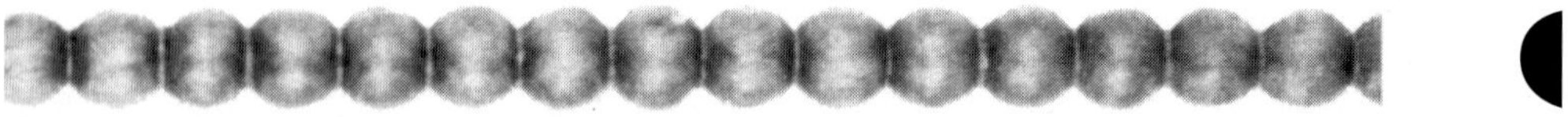

7/16 x 3/16 Thick x 48 Long
Beech Carved

Cat. No.	194.79.317

Packing: 10 pcs

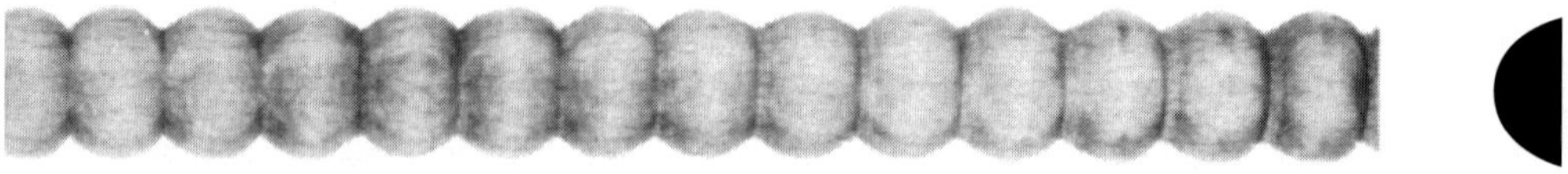

11/16 x 5/16 Thick x 48 Long
Beech Carved

Cat. No.	194.79.318

Packing: 10 pcs

15/32 x 7/32 Thick x 96 Long
Carved

Finish	Cat. No.
Beech	194.79.319
Cherry	194.79.619

Packing: 10 pcs

Dimensions shown in inches

Wood Moulding

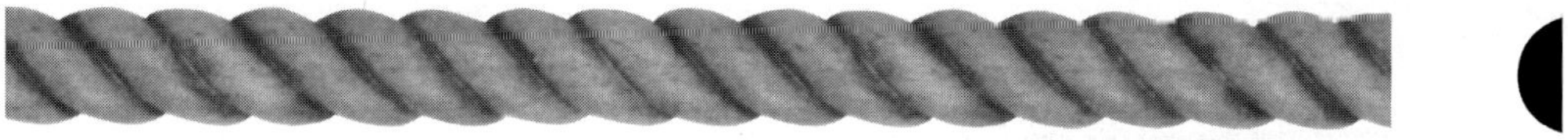

3/4 x 11/32 Thick x 96 Long
Carved

Finish	Cat. No.
Beech	194.79.320
Cherry	194.79.620

Packing: 10 pcs

11/16 x 5/16 Thick x 96 Long
Beech Carved

Cat. No.	194.79.321

Packing: 10 pcs

1 1/32 x 3/16 Thick x 96 Long
Beech Carved

Cat. No.	194.79.322

Packing: 10 pcs

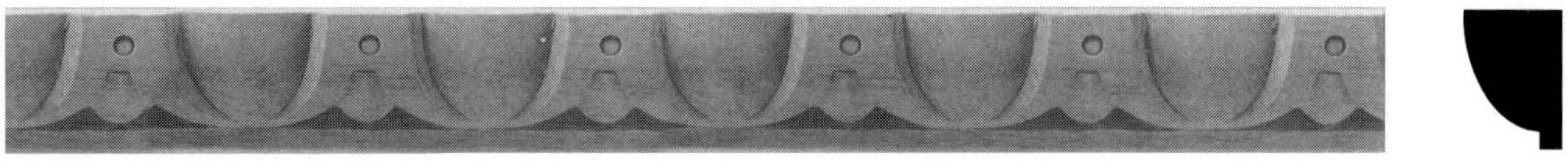

1 3/16 x 13/16 Thick x 96 Long
Ramin Carved

Cat. No.	194.79.123

Packing: 10 pcs

1/2 Wide x 1/4 Thick x 96 Long

Finish	Cat. No.
Maple	194.79.128
Cherry	194.79.628

Packing: 10 pcs

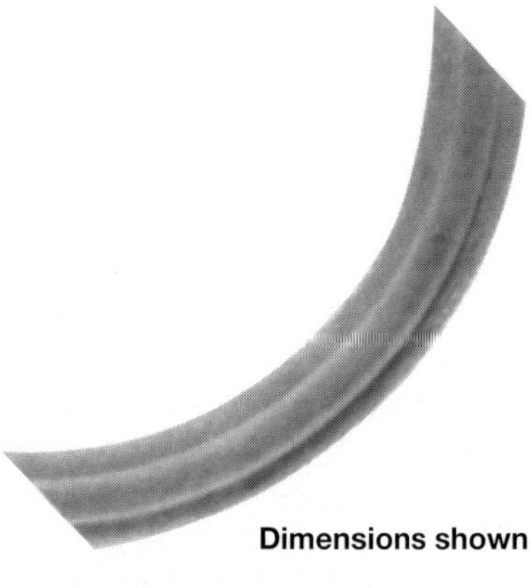

2 13/16 x 1/2 x 1/4; 1 3/4 Radius

Finish	Cat. No.
Maple	194.79.129
Cherry	194.79.629

Packing: 10 pcs

Dimensions shown in inches

Decorative Hardware **1**

Deep-carved solid wood moulding. Patterns to accent your furniture and cabinet designs.

Ready to stain or paint.

Easy to Apply
with woodworking glue
or small brad.

Other species available.
Minimum 1000 feet order.
Ask for details.

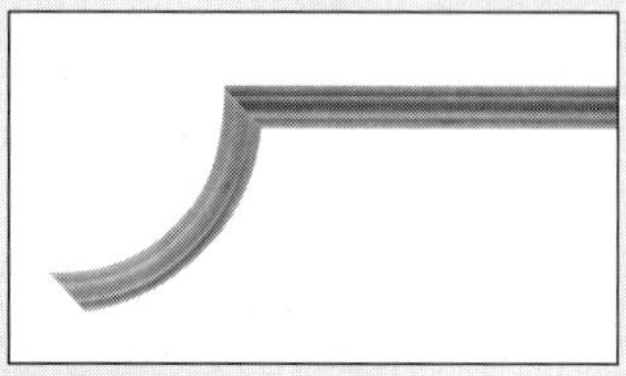

Radius with Moulding
allows for creative details
in cabinets.

Dimensional data not binding.
We reserve the right to alter
specifications without notice.

HÄFELE

Pliable Wood Moulding

Ready to stain or paint.

Easy to Apply
with woodworking glue
or small brad.

- for use on round or oval countertops and work surfaces. Profiles for round, curved and flat surfaces, etc.
- Pliable wood mouldings can be glued, nailed and finished like conventional wood mouldings.
- All pliable wood mouldings must be sealed on all sides at time of installation. A flat finish sealant is recommended.

  Moulding surfaces which come in contact with the furniture should be sealed by glue or other adhesives.

3/16 x 3/16 x 51.2"
Beech

Cat. No.	194.79.324

Packing: 10 pcs

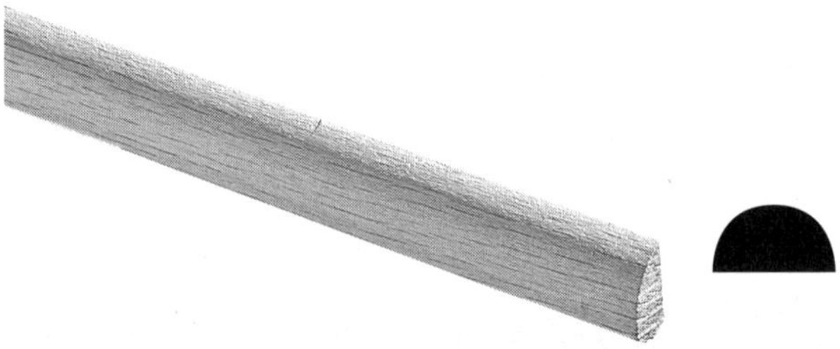

15/32 x 1/4 x 51.2"
Beech

Cat. No.	194.79.325

Packing: 10 pcs

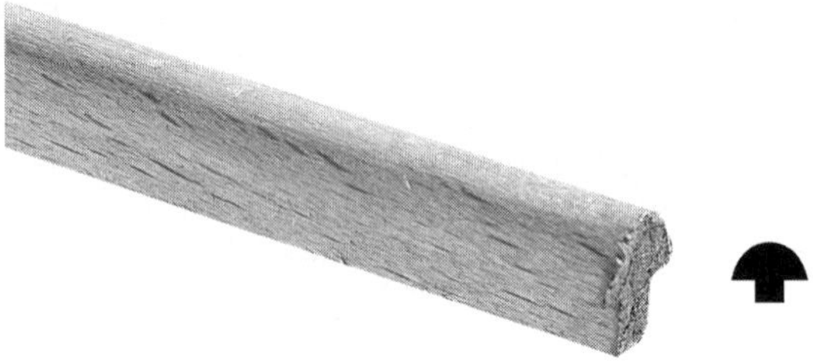

1/4 x 1/4 x 51.2"
Beech

Cat. No.	194.79.326

Packing: 10 pcs

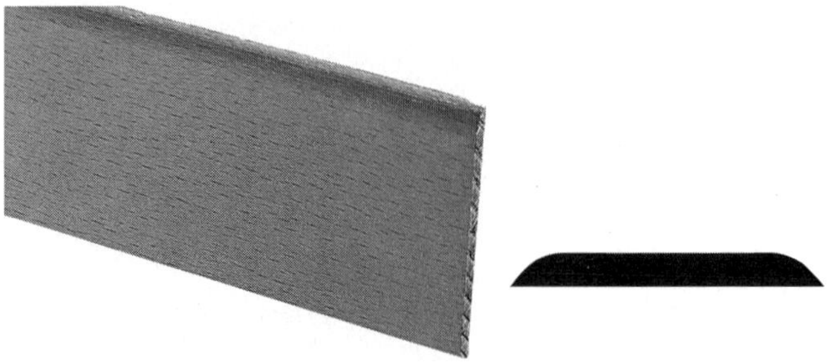

1 9/32 x 1/8 x 51.2"
Beech

Cat. No.	194.79.327

Packing: 10 pcs

Dimensional data not binding.
We reserve the right to alter specifications without notice.

Dimensions shown in inches

Gallery Rails

HÄFELE

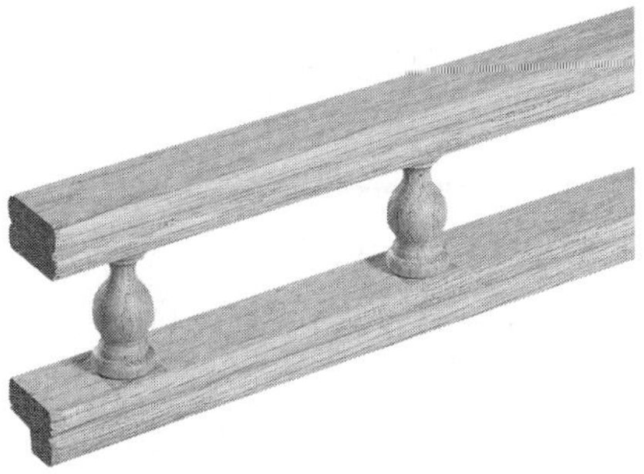

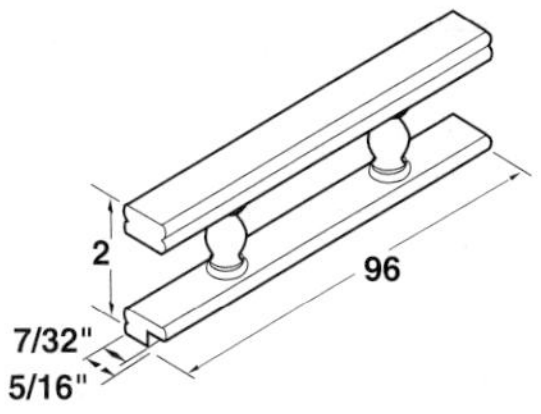

2 x 3/4 x 96
Red Oak

Cat. No.	522.92.420

Packing: 25 pcs

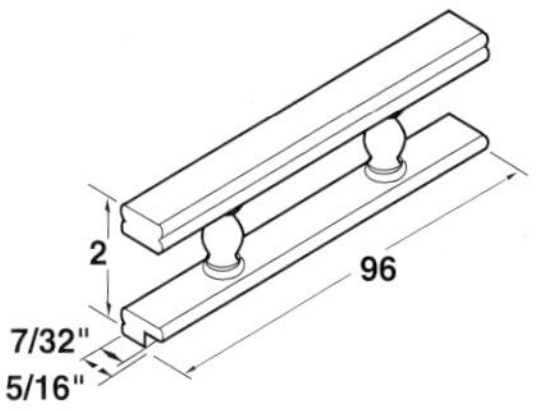

2 x 3/4 x 96
Poplar

Cat. No.	522.92.120

Packing: 25 pcs

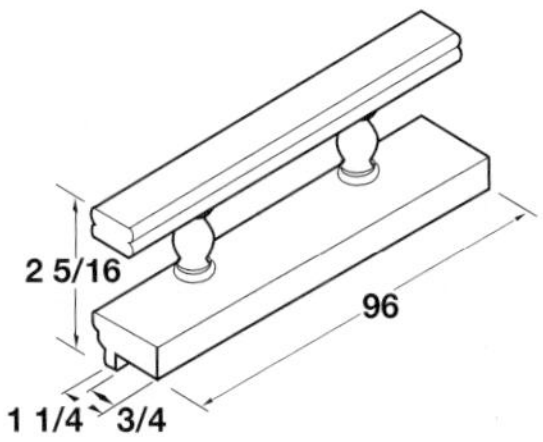

1 1/4 x 2 5/16 x 96
Red Oak

Cat. No.	522.92.430

Packing: 25 pcs

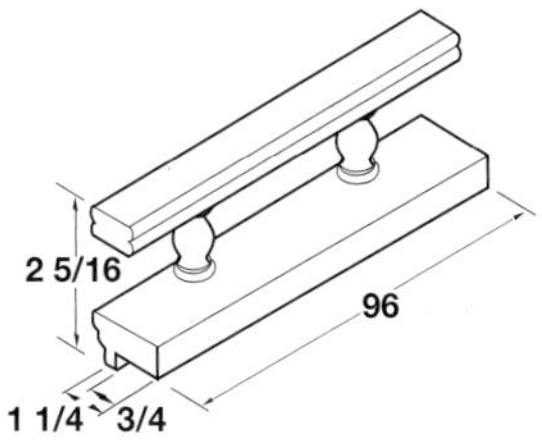

1 1/4 x 2 5/16 x 96
Poplar

Cat. No.	522.92.130

Packing: 25 pcs

Spindles are spaced 3" intervals.

Ready to finish.

Dimensional data not binding. We reserve the right to alter specifications without notice.

Dimensions in inches

HÄFELE

Gallery Rails and Corner Posts

Spindles are spaced 3" intervals.

Ready to finish.

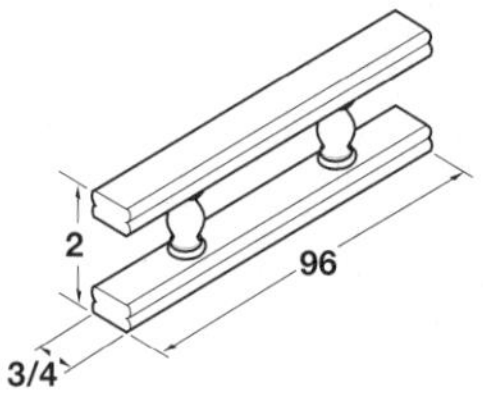

2 x 3/4 x 96
Red Oak

Cat. No.	522.92.410

Packing: 25 pcs

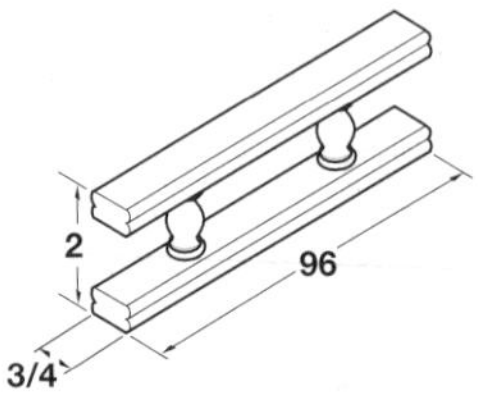

2 x 3/4 x 96
Poplar

Cat. No.	522.92.110

Packing: 25 pcs

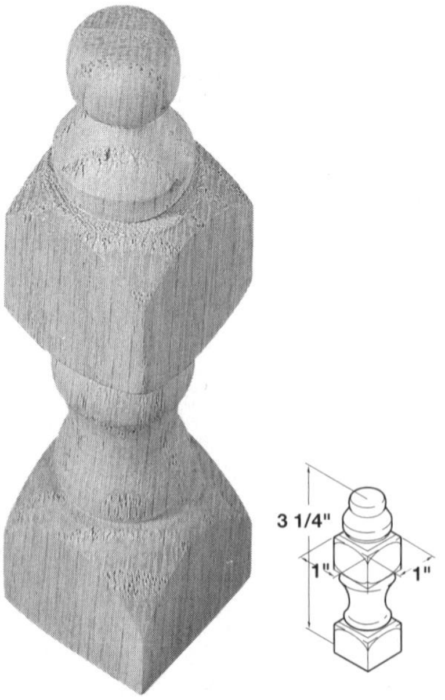

Red Oak

Cat. No.	522.92.490

Packing: 10 pcs

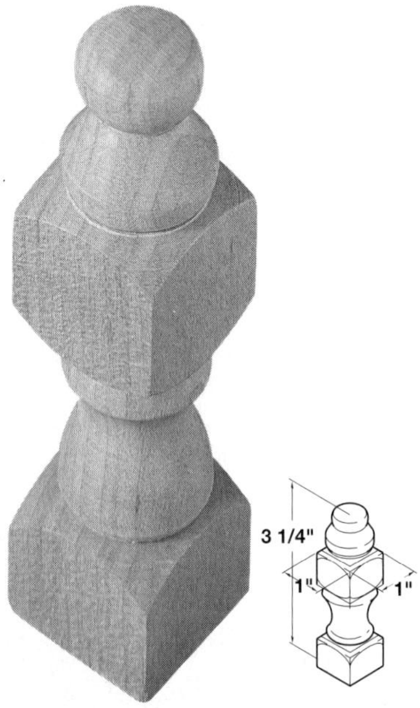

Maple

Cat. No.	522.92.190

Packing: 10 pcs

Dimensional data not binding.
We reserve the right to alter specifications without notice.

Dimensions shown in inches

Wood Dowel Rods

HÄFELE

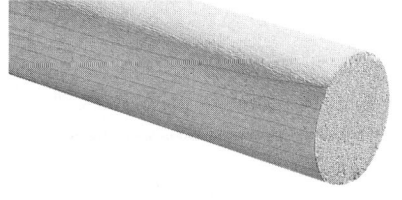

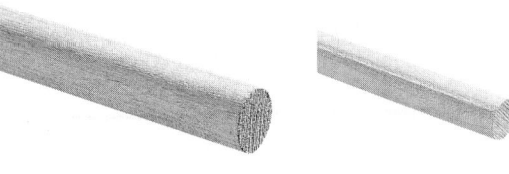

1/8" Diameter

Finish	Length	Cat. No.
Birch	36"	267.80.040
Birch	48"	267.80.045

Packing: 1 pc

3/16" Diameter

Finish	Length	Cat. No.
Birch	36"	267.80.090
Birch	48"	267.80.095

Packing: 1 pc

1/4" Diameter

Finish	Length	Cat. No.
Birch	36"	267.80.140
Oak	36"	267.81.140
Birch	48"	267.80.145

Packing: 1 pc

5/16" Diameter

Finish	Length	Cat. No.
Birch	36"	267.80.240
Birch	48"	267.80.245

Packing: 1 pc

3/8" Diameter

Finish	Length	Cat. No.
Birch	36"	267.80.340
Oak	36"	267.81.340
Birch	48"	267.80.345

Packing: 1 pc

7/16" Diameter

Finish	Length	Cat. No.
Birch	36"	267.80.540
Birch	48"	267.80.545

Packing: 1 pc

1/2" Diameter

Finish	Length	Cat. No.
Birch	36"	267.80.740
Oak	36"	267.81.740
Birch	48"	267.80.745

Packing: 1 pc

5/8" Diameter

Finish	Length	Cat. No.
Birch	36"	267.80.840
Oak	36"	267.81.840
Birch	48"	267.80.845

Packing: 1 pc

3/4" Diameter

Finish	Length	Cat. No.
Birch	36"	267.80.440
Oak	36"	267.81.440
Birch	48"	267.80.445

Packing: 1 pc

7/8" Diameter

Finish	Length	Cat. No.
Birch	36"	267.80.640
Oak	36"	267.81.640
Birch	48"	267.80.645

Packing: 1 pc

1" Diameter

Finish	Length	Cat. No.
Birch	36"	267.80.890
Oak	36"	267.81.890
Birch	48"	267.80.895

Packing: 1 pc

Perfect for use in

- **CD Racks**
- **Cabinet Dish holders**
- **Hampers**
- **Closet Rods**
- **Curtain Rods**
- **Racks**

Dimensions shown in inches

HÄFELE

Wood Plugs and Buttons

1 **Decorative Hardware**

- **Easy to apply with woodworking glue.**
- **For Use in any application requiring a complete wood finish look.**

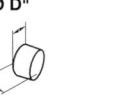

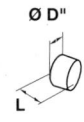

Round Head Plugs
Birch

Size D	Size L	Cat. No.
3/8	1/4	006.95.231
1/2	9/32	006.95.232

Packing: 5,000 pcs

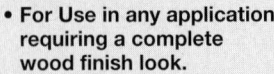

Flathead Plugs
Birch

Size D	Size L	Cat. No.
3/8	1/4	006.95.211
1/2	1/4	006.95.212

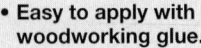

Packing: 5,000 pcs

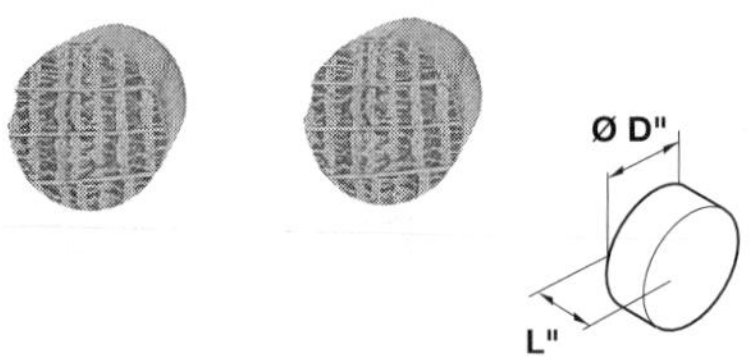

Flat Head Plugs
Red Oak

Size D	Size L	Cat. No.
3/8	1/4	006.95.121
1/2	1/4	006.95.122

Packing: 5000 pcs

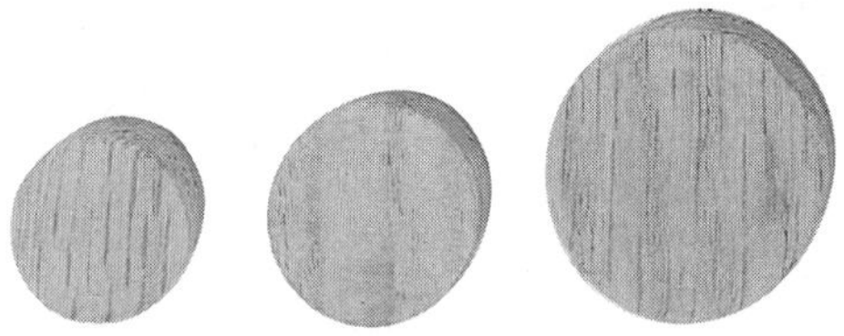

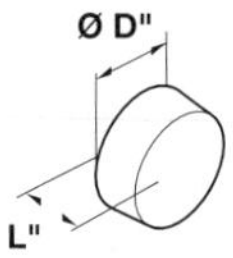

Flat Head Furniture Plugs
Tapered Side Grain
Red Oak

Size D	Size L	Cat. No.
3/8	1/4	006.95.111
1/2	1/4	006.95.112
5/8	1/4	006.95.113
3/4	1/4	006.95.114
1	1/4	006.95.115

Packing: 5000 pcs

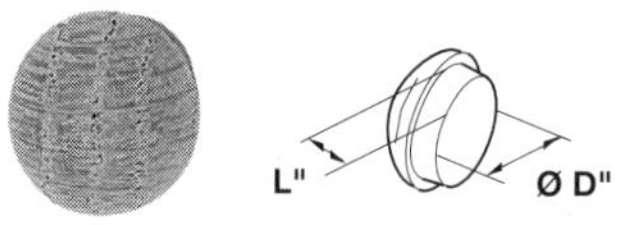

Button Plugs
Red Oak

Size D	Size L	Cat. No.
3/8	1/8	006.95.151
1/2	1/8	006.95.152
1/2	3/16	006.95.153

Packing: 5000 pcs

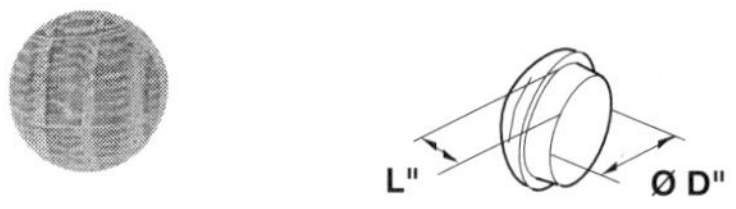

Mushroom
Head Button
Birch

Size D	Size L	Cat. No.
3/8	5/16	006.95.251
1/2	21/16	006.95.252
1/2	13/32	006.95.253
5/8	5/16	006.95.254

Packing: 5000 pcs

- **Pound into place and sand smooth.**

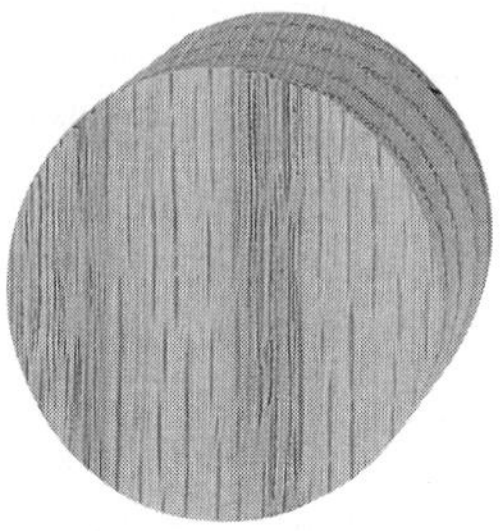

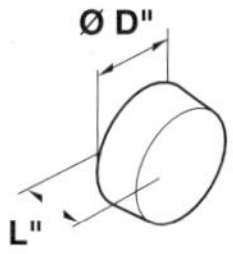

Hole Plugs
Red Oak

Size D	Size L	Packing	Cat. No.
35mm	9/16	10 pcs.	340.41.410
8mm	7/16	20 pcs.	340.41.400

Dimensional data not binding.
We reserve the right to alter specifications without notice.

Dimensions shown in inches

Wood Shaker Pegs

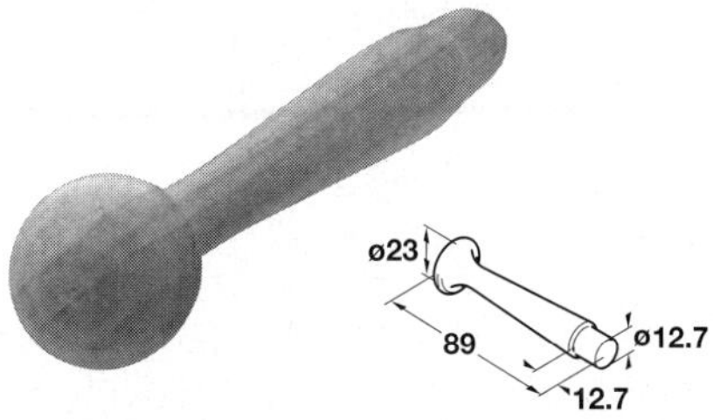

Poplar

Cat. No.	196.99.800

Packing: 500 pcs.

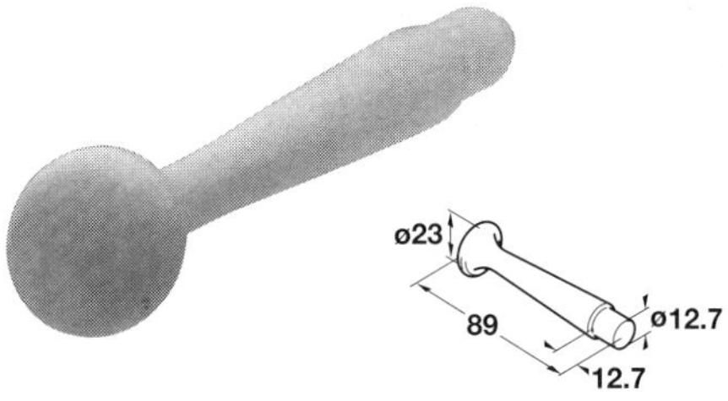

Maple

Cat. No.	196.99.100

Packing: 500 pcs

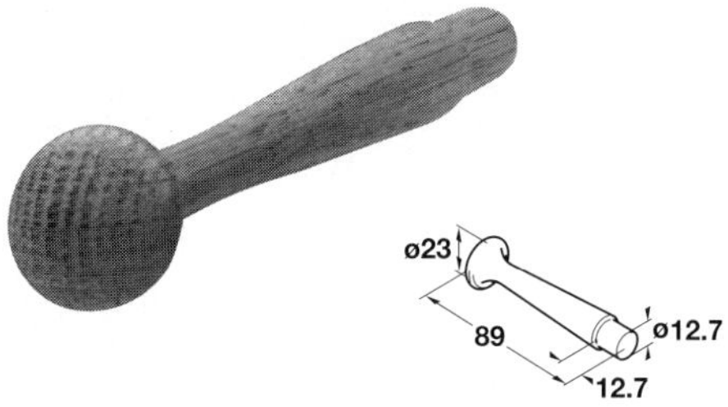

Red Oak

Cat. No.	196.99.400

Packing: 500 pcs

HÄFELE

Drilling Jig

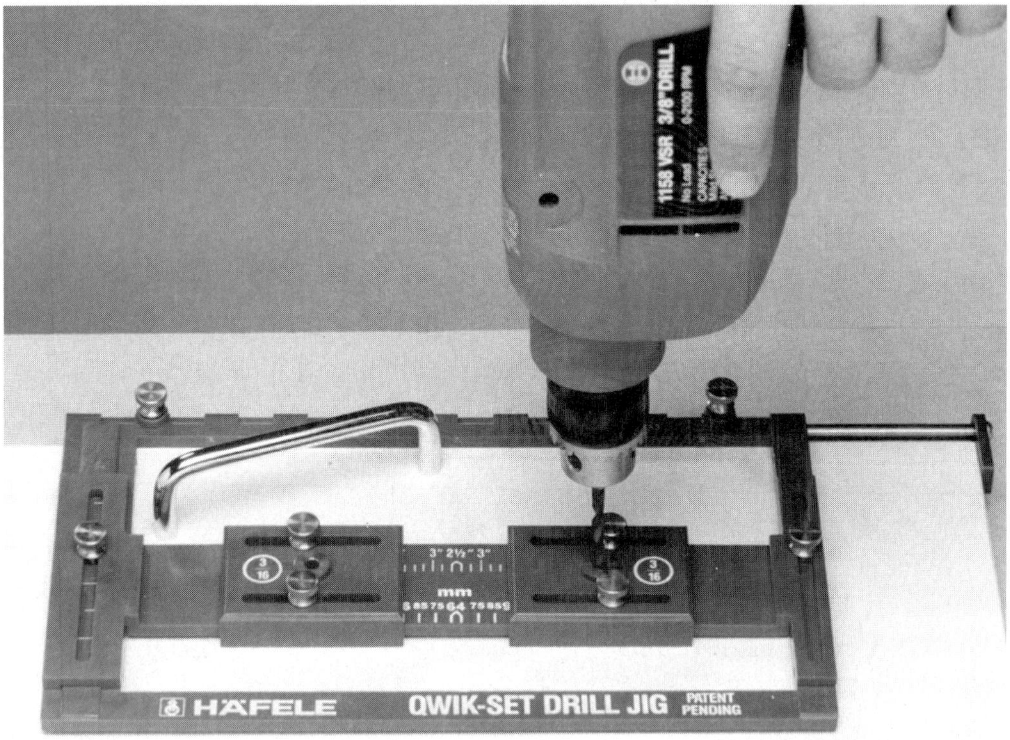

Qwik-Set Drill Jig for pulls on doors or drawer fronts. This very handy and practical drill jig is ideal for the small to medium size shop to drill the holes for decorative hardware.
With metric and inch scale.
Use a 4.5 mm or 3/16" drill.

Cat. No.	001.31.233

Packing: 1 pc.

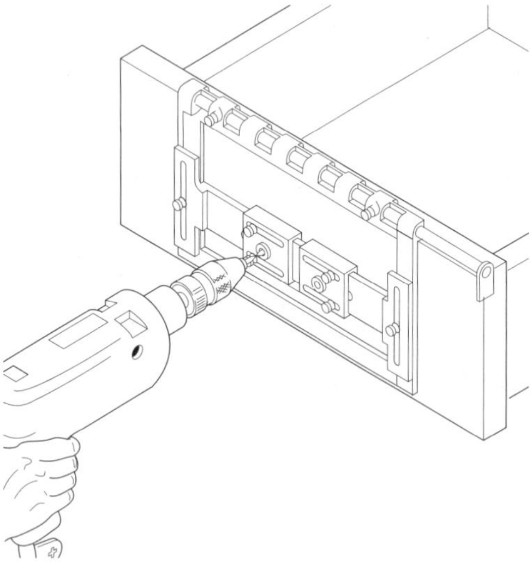

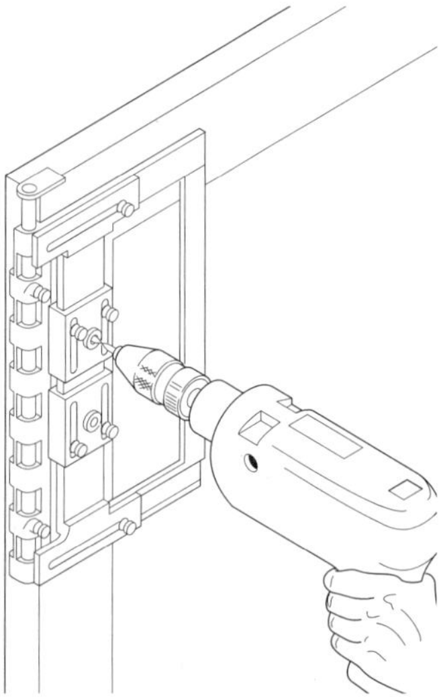

Product Guide: Locks

HÄFELE

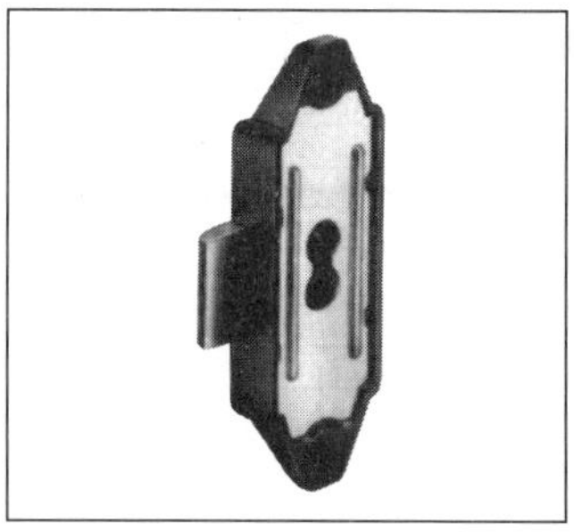

Rim Locks
Pages **2.3, 2.27, 2.35**

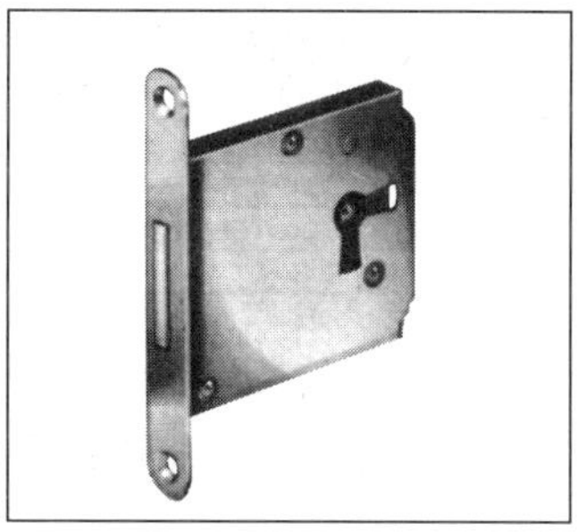

Mortise and Half Mortise Locks
Pages **2.5, 2.38**

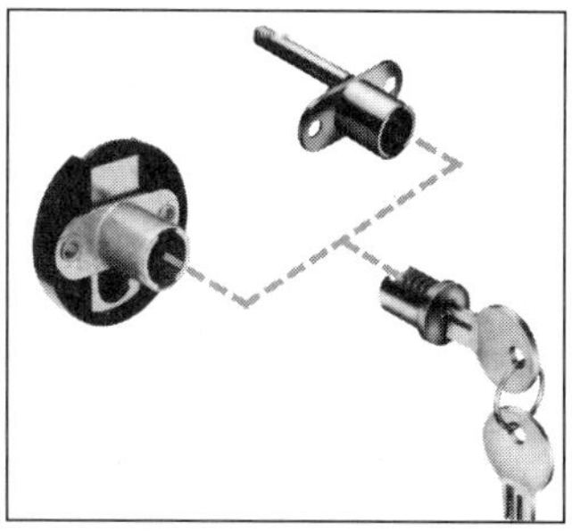

Cylinder Module Systems
Pages **2.13 – 2.26**

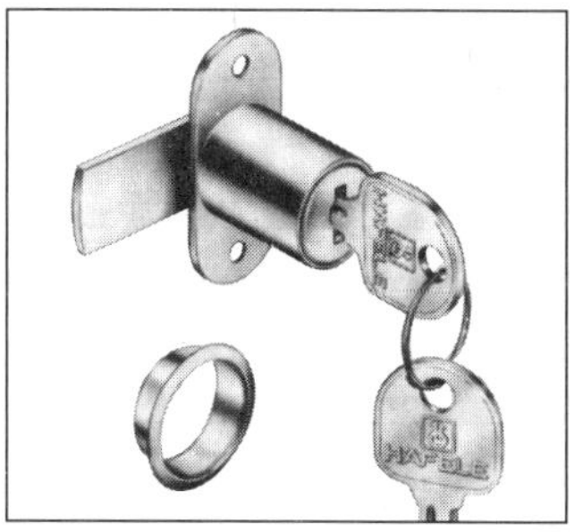

Cam Locks
Pages **2.15, 2.29, 2.36**

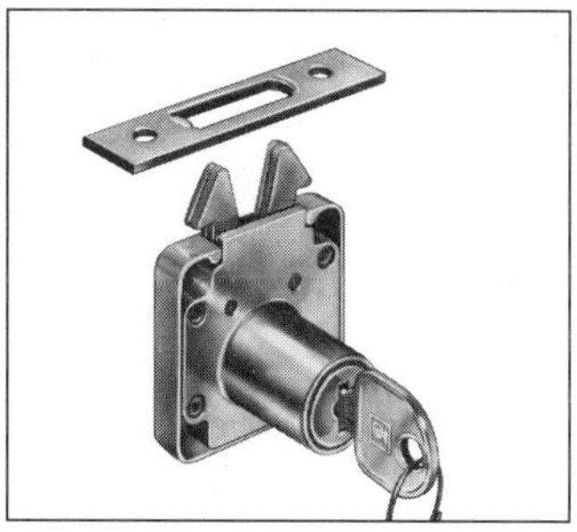

Tambour Door Locks
Pages **2.31, 2.38**

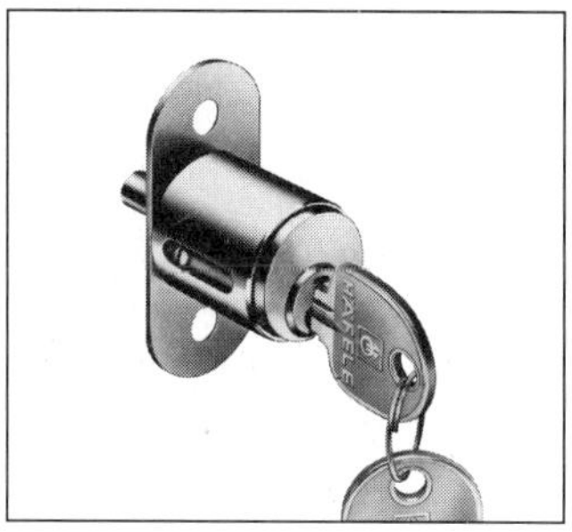

Pushbutton Locks
Pages **2.17, 2.32, 2.39**

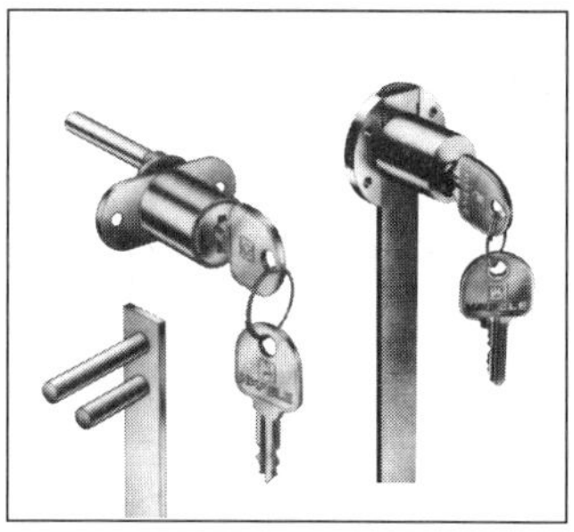

Central locking Systems
Pages **2.18 – 2.51**

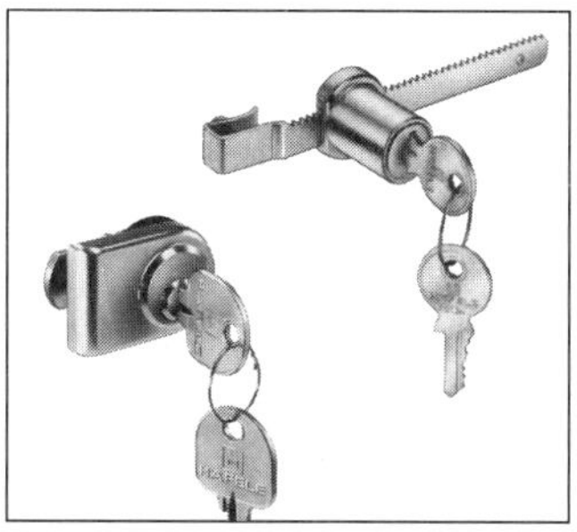

Glass Door Locks
Pages **2.52 – 2.54**

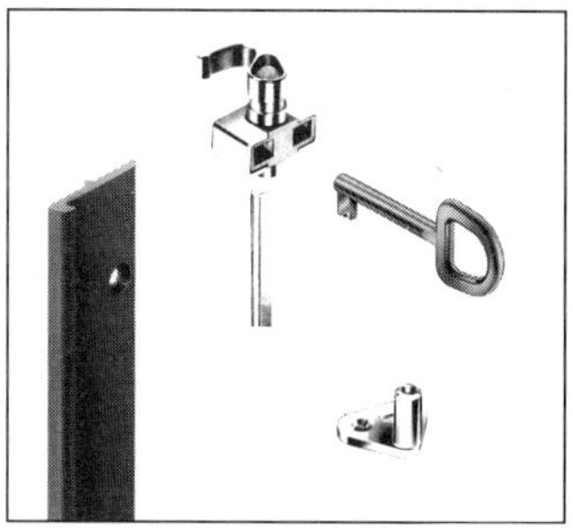

Wardrobe/Espagnolette Locks
Pages **2.17, 2.55**

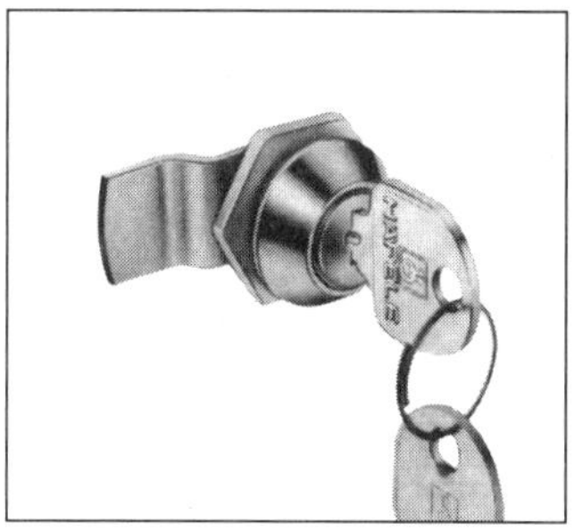

Locks For Metal Furniture
Pages **2.30**

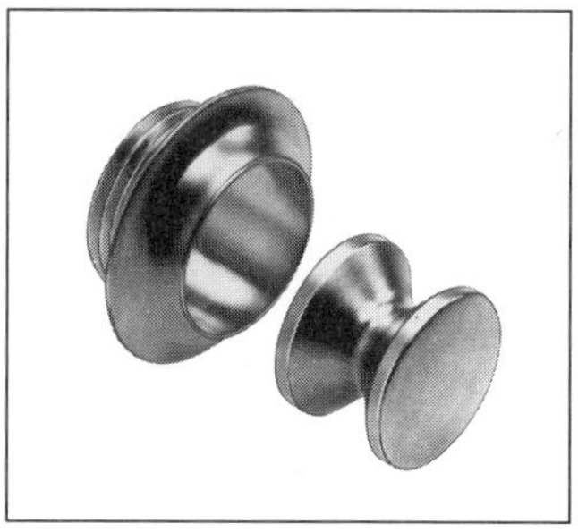

Push-Button Locks
Pages **2.61 – 2.62**

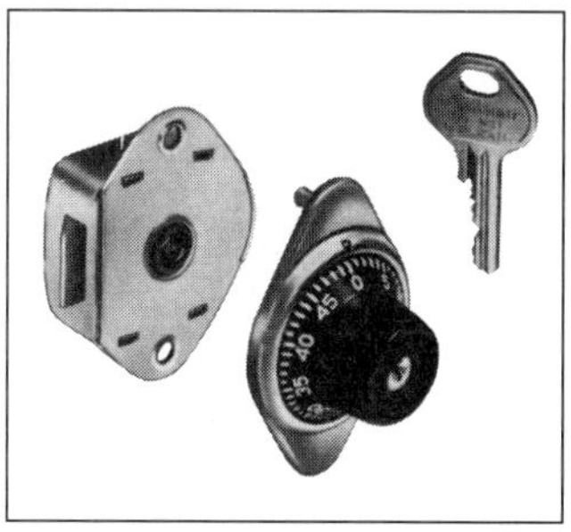

Locker Locks
Pages **2.65**

Product Guide For:

- Catches
- RTA and PAS® Connectors
- Shelf Supports and Folding Brackets
- Bed Fittings

See Pages 2.66 to 2.67

Locking Systems

Review of locking systems

Lever bit key
Key changes: 1

Three bit levers
Key changes: 1 to 6

Three bit levers, with grooved bit
Key changes: 1 to 48

Cylinder, with plate levers/single sided key
Key changes: 200

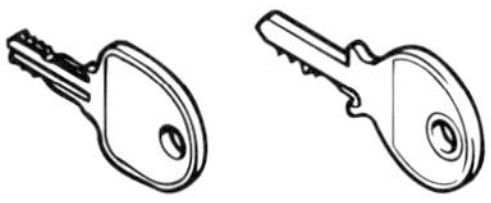

Cylinder, with plate levers/2-sided key
Key changes: 1000

Cylinder, with pin levers
Key changes: 10,000 (ø 18 mm)
to 20,000 (ø 22 mm)

Cylinder, with pin levers
Key changes: 60,000

Cylinder, with pin levers
KABA® system
Key changes: 100,000

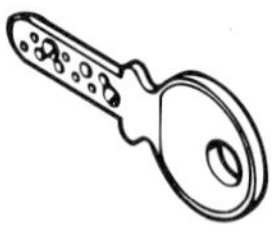

How to determine lock handing

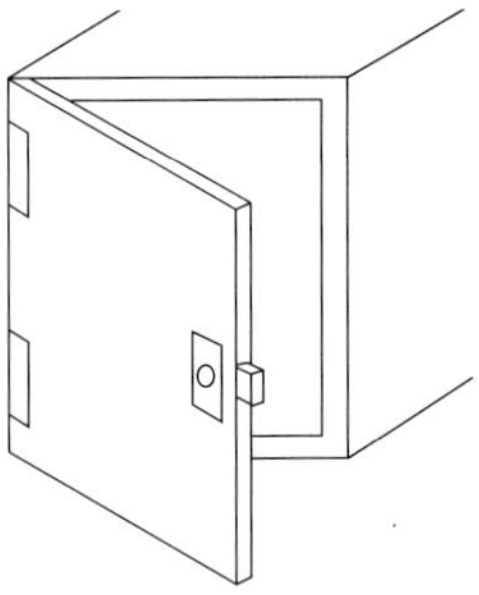

Door hinged on left = Left lock

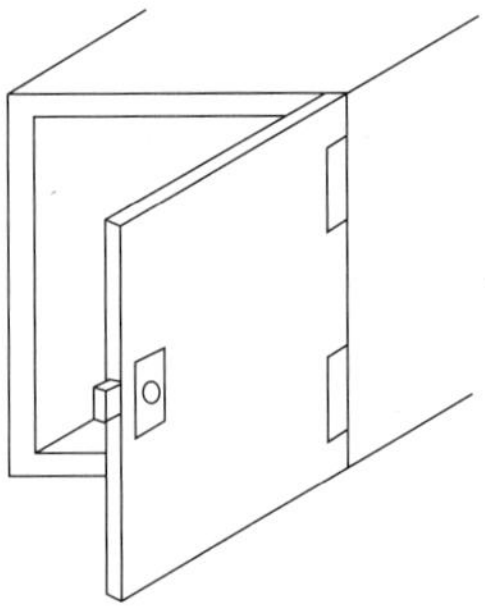

Door hinged on right = Right lock

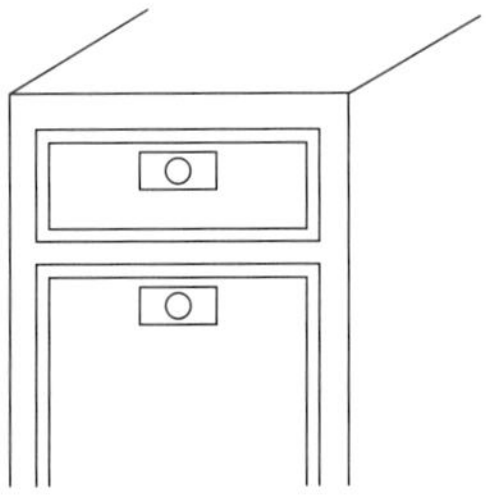

Drawer = Drawer lock

Review of Master Key Systems
Master key systems (MK systems)
Example: The keys to all desks and cabinets are different, but the master key fits all the locks in the entire system.

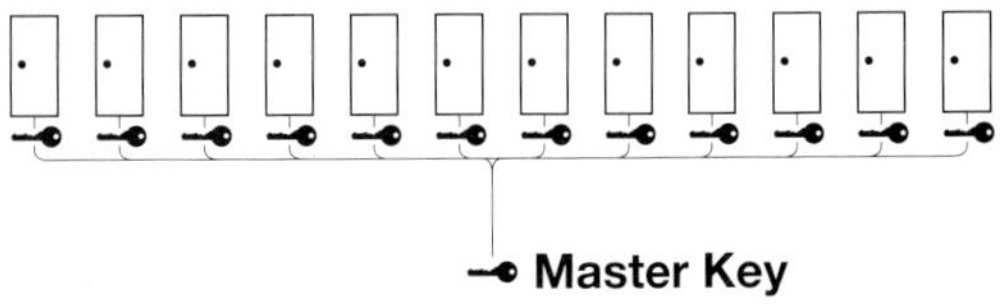

General master key systems (GMK systems)
Example: The keys to all desks and cabinets are different. All the locks in different departments can be locked with the respective group key (GK) but these are not interchangeable. It is possible for different groups (two in the example shown) to be fully controlled by a master group key (MGK) while excluding other departments (one in the example shown). Only the general master key (GMK) fits all the locks in the entire system.

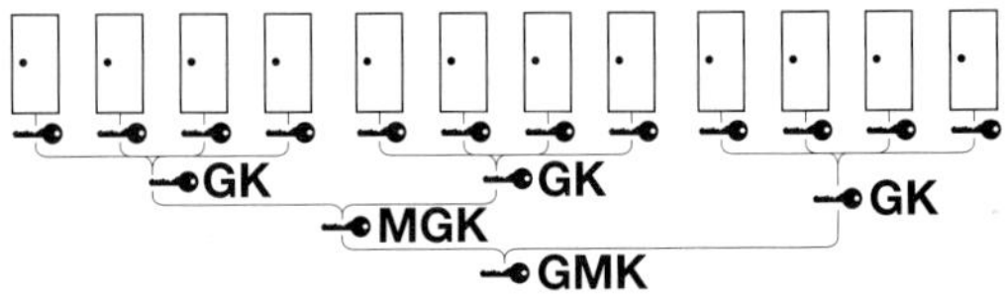

Rim Locks - Lever Bit

HÄFELE

Rim Locks, for lever bit keys
Backset 12.5 mm
Left or right hand.

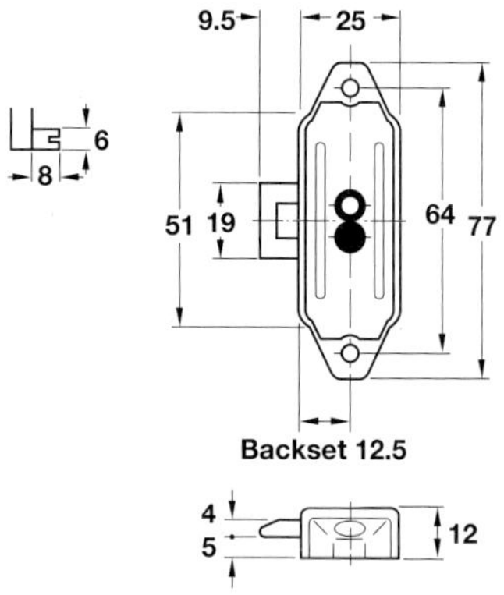

Finish: plastic case
Keyed alike

Application		left	right
Cat. No.	white	211.41.775	211.41.720
	brown	211.41.177	211.41.122

Packing: 10 pcs.

Rim Locks, for lever bit keys
Left or right hand.

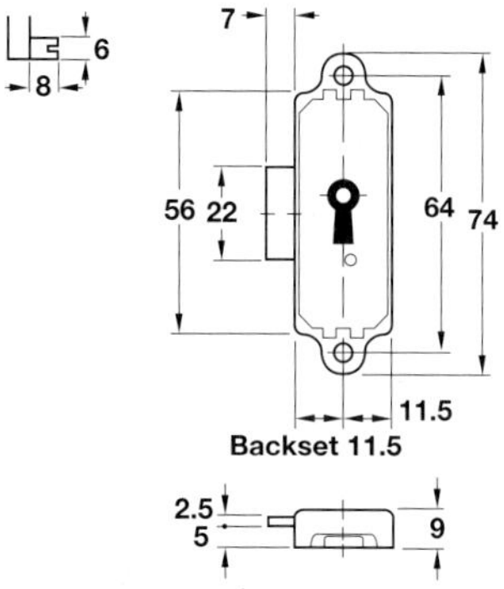

Finish: zinc die cast case
Keyed alike
Nickel-plated

Application		left	right
Cat. No.	Backset 11.5 mm	211.02.723	211.02.714
	Backset 15.0 mm	211.02.741	211.02.732

Bronzed

Application		left	right
Cat. No.	Backset 11.5 mm	211.02.120	211.02.110
	Backset 15.0 mm	211.02.140	211.02.130

Packing: 10 pcs.

Rim Locks, for lever bit keys
Backset 11.5 mm
Left or right hand.

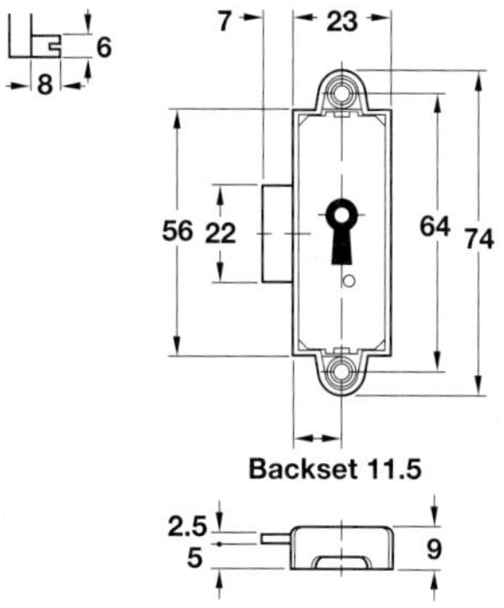

Finish: steel case, bronzed
Keyed alike

Application	left	right
Cat. No.	211.02.027	211.02.018

Packing: 10 pcs.

Dimensions in mm

The rim locks shown on this page have extra narrow lock cases, making them especially suitable for panel-type doors.

Decorative keys should be ordered separately.
See pages 2.10 – 2.12

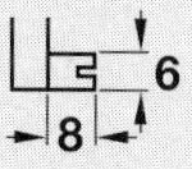

HÄFELE

Rim Locks - Lever Bit

Decorative keys should be ordered separately.
See pages 2.10 – 2.12

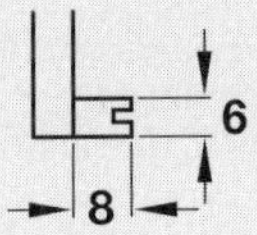

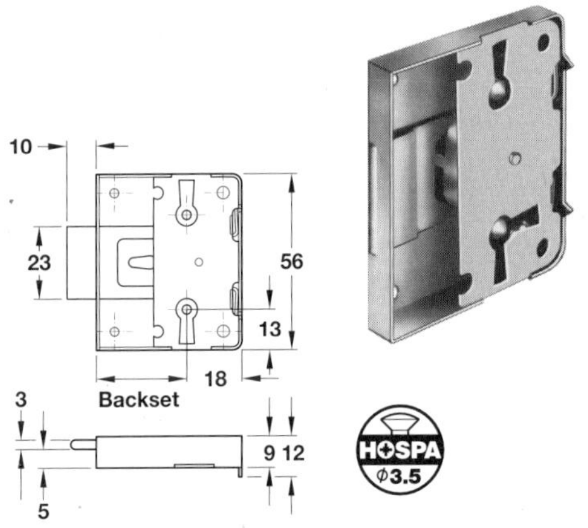

Rim Lock for lever bit keys
- for left, right or drawer use

Finish: steel, polished, nickel-plated

Cat. No.	**Backset 15 mm**	211.01.708
	Backset 20 mm	211.01.717
	Backset 25 mm	211.01.726
	Backset 30 mm	211.01.735
	Backset 35 mm	211.01.744
	Backset 40 mm	211.01.753

Packing: 10 pcs.

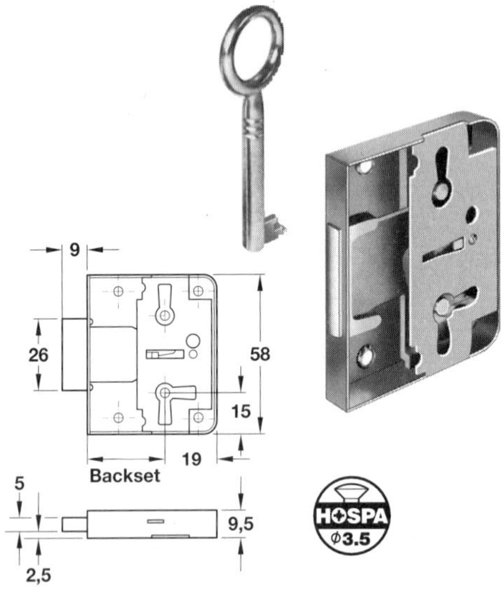

Rim Lock for lever bit keys
- left, right or drawer use
- with straight dead bolt
- **includes lever bit key** with **6 key changes**

Finish: steel case unfinished, nickel-plated
Accessories: 1 nickel-plated key

Cat. No.	**Backset 15 mm**	211.10.207
	Backset 30 mm	211.10.234

Packing: 10 pcs.

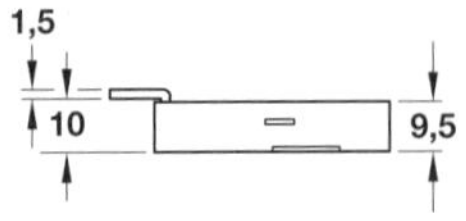

with cranked dead bolt

Cat. No.	**Backset 30 mm**	211.29.304

Packing: 10 pcs.

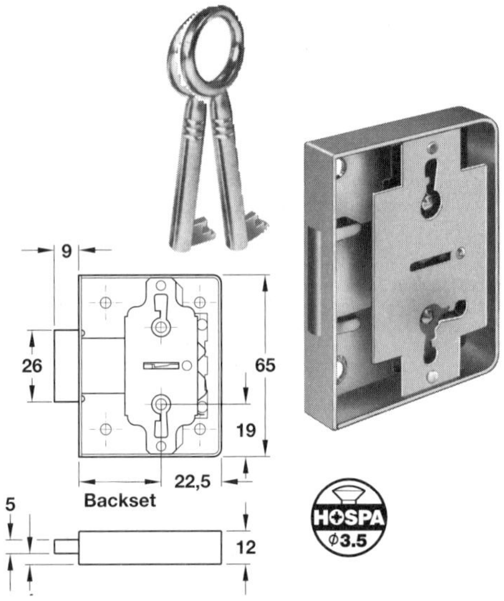

Rim Locks for lever bit keys
- for left, right and drawer use
- **2 nickel-plated keys included** with **3 levers and grooves =** 48 key changes

Finish: steel, case, unfinished nickel-plated
Accessories: 2 nickel-plated keys

Key changes: 1 - 12

Cat. No.	**Backset 20 mm**	215.01.217
	Backset 30 mm	215.01.315

Key changes: 13 - 24

Cat. No.	**Backset 20 mm**	215.01.226
	Backset 30 mm	215.01.324

Key changes: 25 - 36

Cat. No.	**Backset 20 mm**	215.01.235
	Backset 30 mm	215.01.333

Key changes: 37- 48

Cat. No.	**Backset 20 mm**	215.01.224
	Backset 30 mm	215.01.342

Packing: 12 pcs.

Dimensional data not binding. We reserve the right to alter specifications without notice.

Dimensions in mm

Mortise Locks - Lever Bit

Decorative keys should be ordered separately.
See pages 2.10 – 2.12

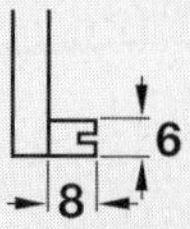

Mortise Locks, for lever bit keys

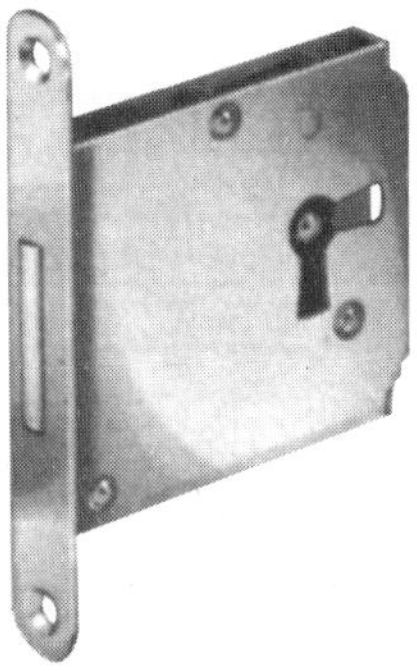

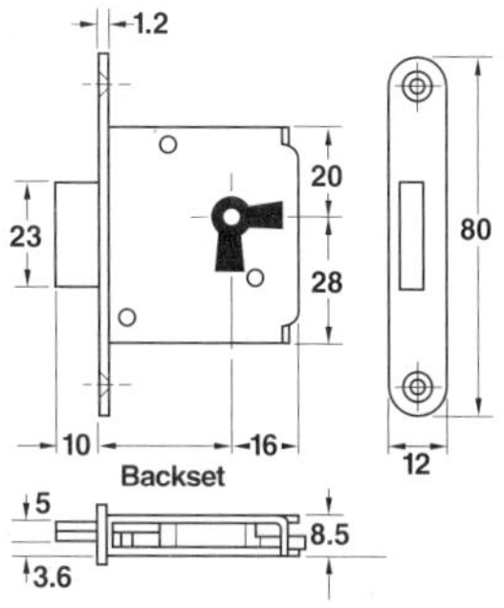

Finish: steel face plate, polished, brass-plated
Keyed alike

Application		Left/drawer	Right/drawer
Cat. No.	Backset 15 mm	213.21.308	213.21.200
	Backset 20 mm	213.21.317	213.21.219
	Backset 30 mm	213.21.335	213.21.237
	Backset 40 mm	213.21.353	213.21.255

Packing: 10 pcs.

Mortise Locks, for lever bit keys

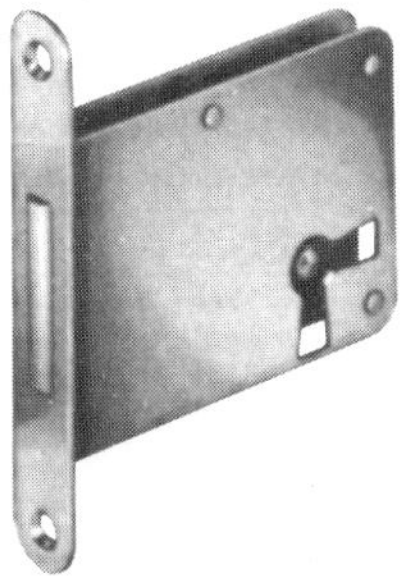

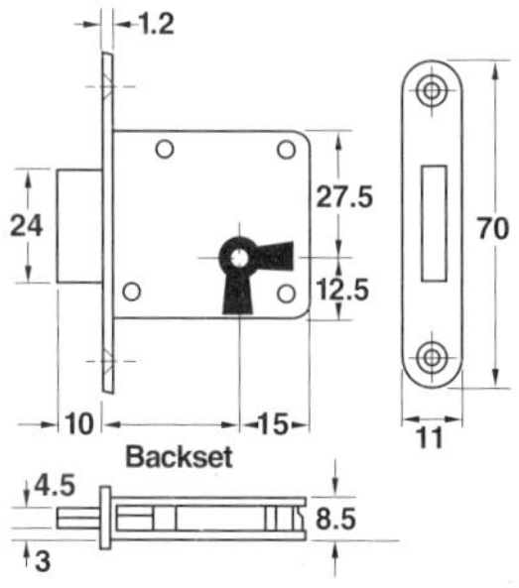

Finish: steel face plate, brass-plated
Keyed alike

Application		Left/drawer	Right/drawer
Cat. No.	Backset 15 mm	213.01.306	213.01.208
	Backset 20 mm	213.01.315	213.01.217
	Backset 25 mm	213.01.324	213.01.226
	Backset 30 mm	213.01.333	213.01.235
	Backset 35 mm	213.01.342	213.01.244
	Backset 40 mm	213.01.351	213.01.253

Packing: 10 pcs.

HÄFELE

English Type Locks - Lever Bit

- Half-Mortised - installs flush to back of panel.
- Solid brass construction.
- Keyed alike.

Half Mortise Lock for Lever Bit, Key included
Backset 17 mm.
Fits drawer and door
Accessories: 1 lever bit key

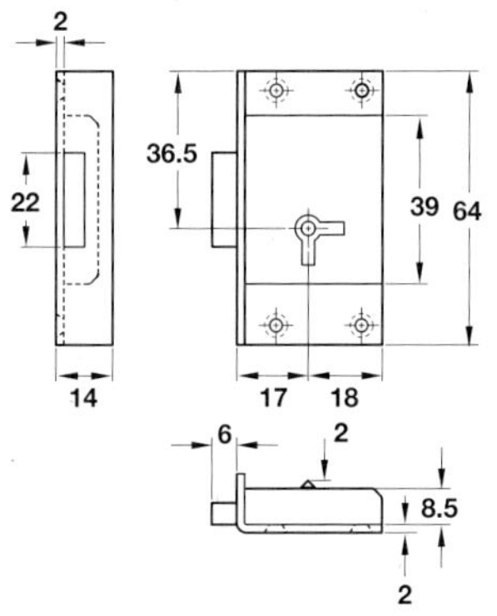

Finish: Lock: brass polished and lacquered,
Key: malleable iron, brass-plated

Application	Cat. No.
Right hand/drawer	212.07.821
Left hand/drawer	212.07.830

Packing: 1 pc.

Half Mortise Lock for Lever Bit, Key included
Backset 21 mm.
Fits drawer and right door
Accessories: 1 lever bit key

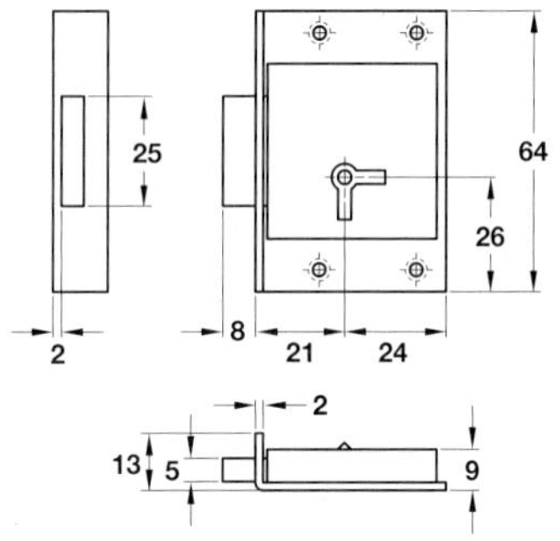

Finish: Lock: brass polished and lacquered,
Key: malleable iron, brass-plated

Application	Cat. No.
Right/drawer	212.09.825

Packing: 1 pc.

- For writing desks and reproduction furniture.
- Solid brass, keyed alike.

Sloping Face Desk Lock for Lever Bit, Key included

Backset 25 mm.
Fits drawer and right door
Accessories: 2 lever bit keys

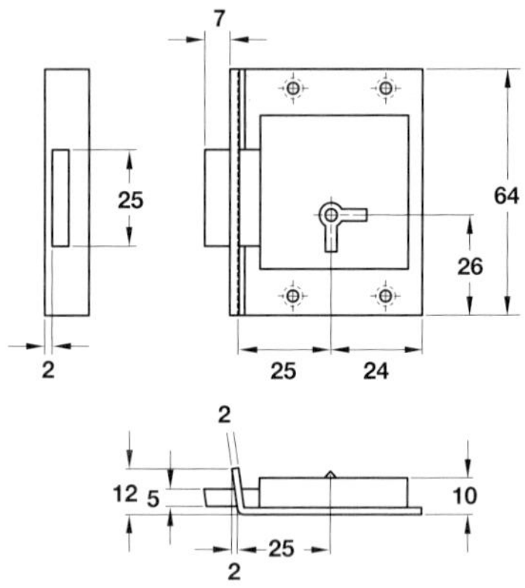

Finish: Lock: brass polished and lacquered,
Key: malleable iron, brass-plated

Cat. No.	212.08.837

Packing: 1 pc.

Rim Lock for Lever Bit, Key included
Backset 16 mm.
Left or right hand door.

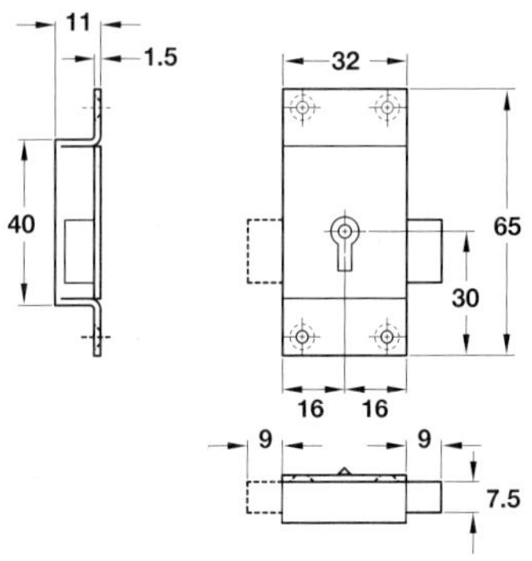

Finish: Lock: brass polished and lacquered
Key: malleable iron, brass-plated

Cat. No.	211.09.811

Packing: 1 pc.

English Type Locks - Lever Bit

Half-Mortise Lock for Lever Bit, Key included
Backset 11 mm.
Accessories: 1 lever bit key, 1 strike plate

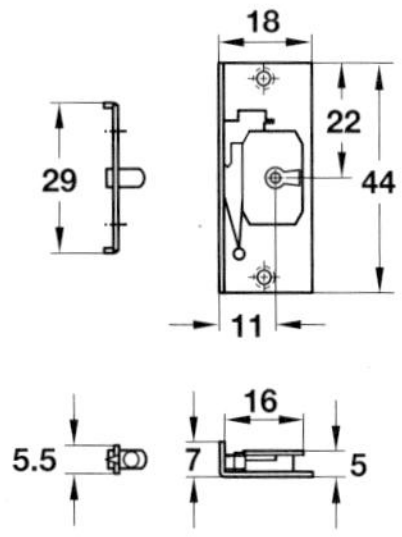

Finish: Lock: brass; key: malleable iron, brass-plated;
Strike plate: brass

Cat. No.	218.35.129

Packing: 20 pcs.

- Small size, ideal for jewelry boxes etc.
- With screw-mounted locking strike plate.

Half-Mortise Lock for Lever Bit, Key included
Backset 15 mm.
Accessories: 1 lever bit key, 1 strike plate

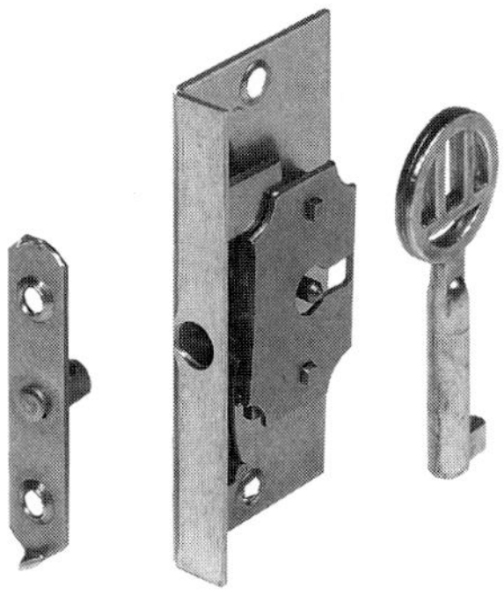

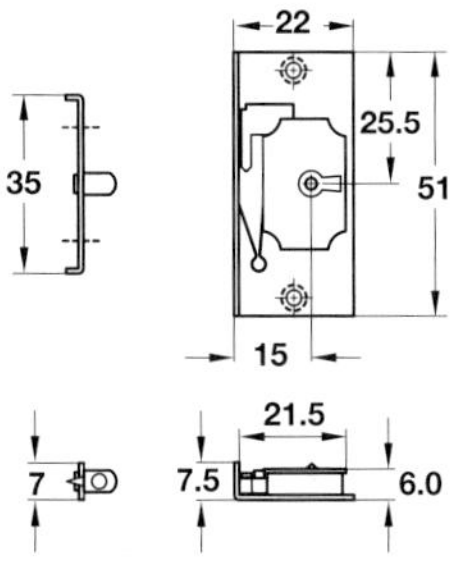

Finish: Lock: brass; key: malleable iron, brass-plated;
Strike plate: brass

Cat. No.	218.35.156

Packing: 20 pcs.

Half-Mortise Lock for Lever Bit, Key included
Backset 15 mm.
Accessories: 1 lever bit key, 1 strike plate

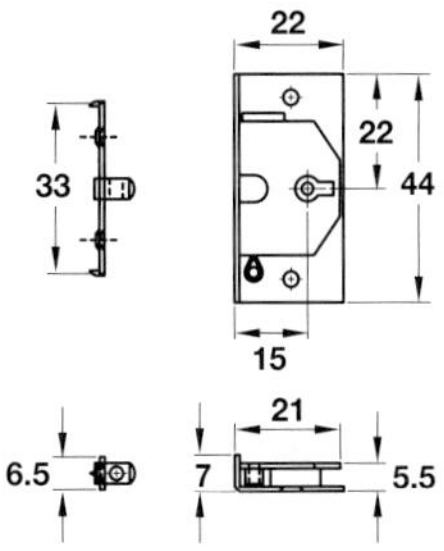

Finish: Lock: brass; key: malleable iron, brass-plated;
Strike plate: brass

Cat. No.	218.36.153

Packing: 20 pcs.

Dimensional data not binding.
We reserve the right to alter specifications without notice.

HÄFELE

English Type Locks - Lever Bit

- Full-mortise lock
- Keyed alike

Mortise Lock Brass for Lever Bit,
Key included
Backset 16.5 mm.
Accessories: Key, Strike plate

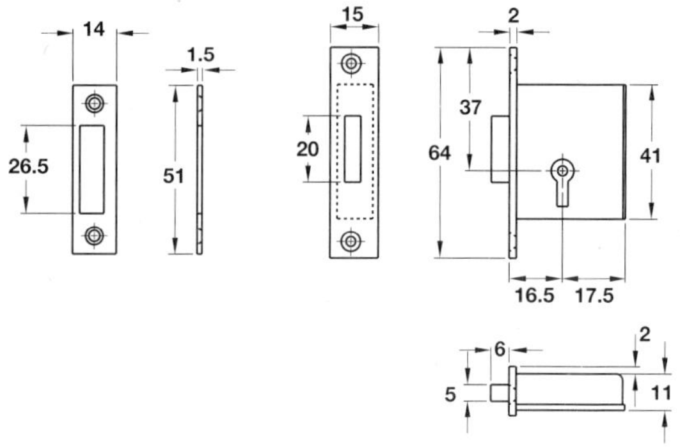

Finish: Lock: brass polished and lacquered,
Key: malleable iron, brass plated
Strike plate: brass, polished and lacquered

Cat. No.	Right hand	213.02.821
	Left hand	213.02.830

Packing: 1 piece

Roll Top Mortise Lock for Lever Bit,
Key included
Backset 25 mm.
Accessories: Key, Strike plate,
and escutcheon

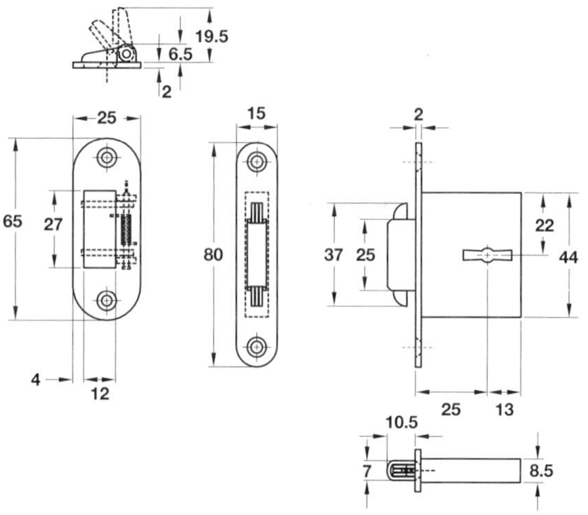

Finish: Steel case, brass polished,
face plate, strike plate and escutcheon,
brass polished

Cat. No.	217.60.805

Packing: 1 piece

Miscellaneous Locks - Lever Bit

Tambour Door Mortise Locks for bit lever, Key included
Accessories: 1 nickel-plated key and
1 strike plate

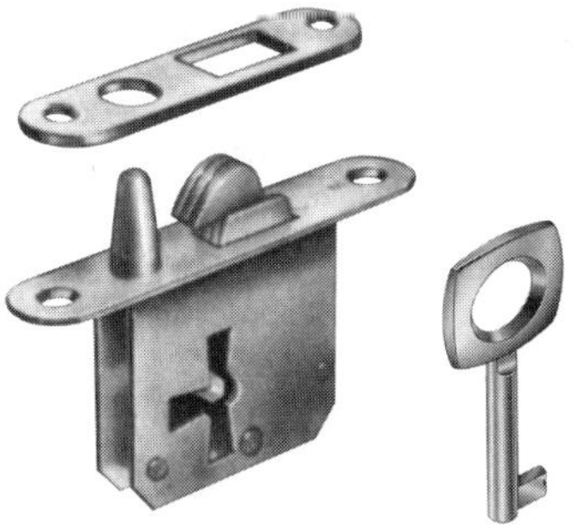

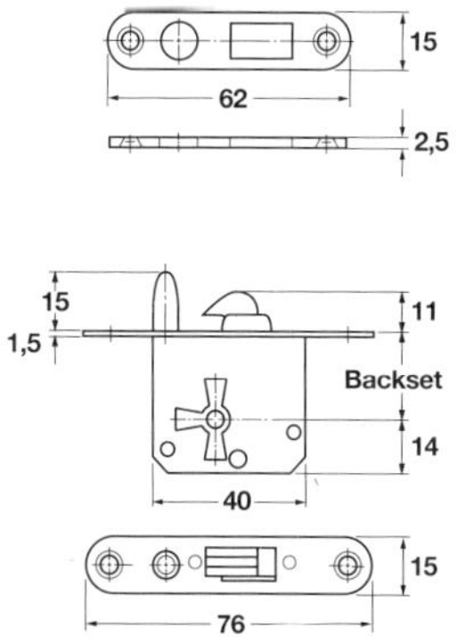

Finish: steel face plate and strike plate, brass-plated

Left/drawer

Cat. No.	backset 15 mm	217.10.109
	backset 22 mm	217.10.127

Right/drawer

Cat. No.	backset 15 mm	217.10.001
	backset 22 mm	217.10.029

Packing: 10 pcs.

HOSPA Φ3.0 HOSPA Φ3.0

Dimensions in mm

Hook Bolt Mortise Lock, with triangular follower and removable hook bolt.
For left, right or drawer use.
Accessories: 1 bitless key, 1 bushing and 1 strike plate

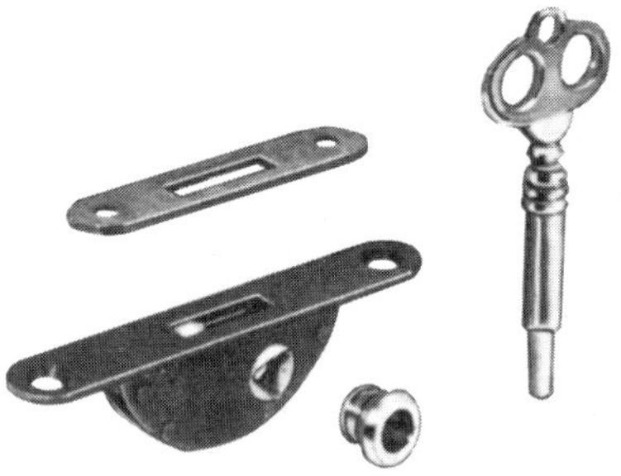

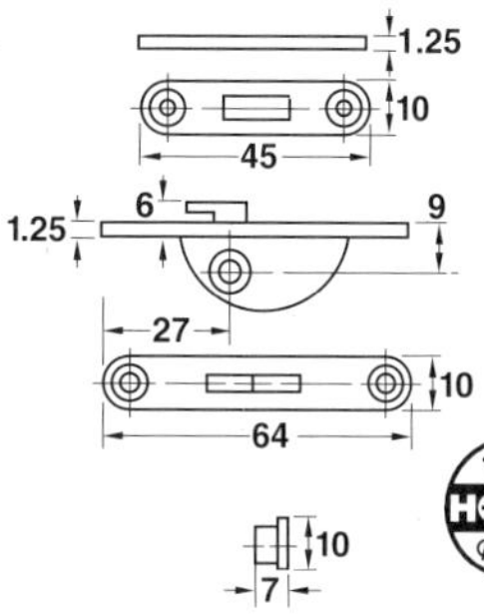

HOSPA Φ5.0

Finish: bronzed

Cat. No.	238.06.108

Packing: 50 pcs.

Inlaid Cashbox lock
Accessories: 1 nickel-plated key and
1 brass strike plate

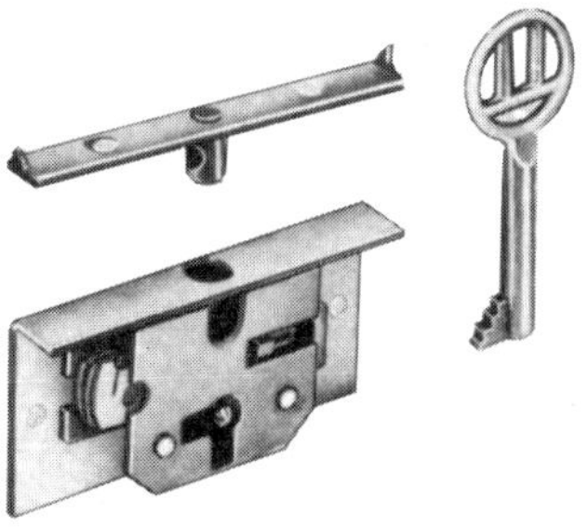

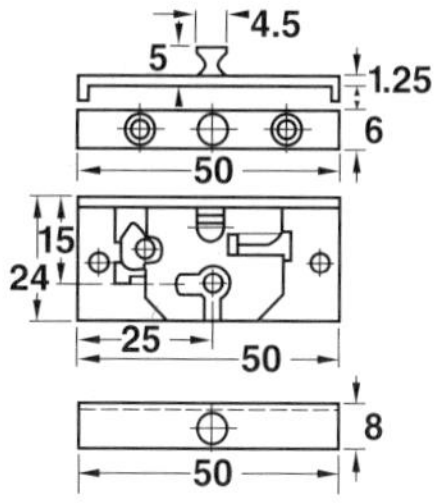

Finish: Case, steel: levers and backplate, brass

Application	Right/drawer
Cat. No.	218.40.157

Packing: 1 pc.

HÄFELE

Decorative Keys - Lever Bit

Decorative Keys
the desired key must match the type of lock selected in terms of:

a) bit size and shape 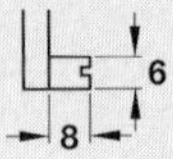

b) length of shank .

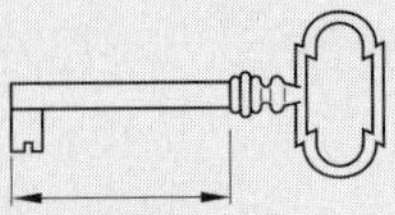

2 Locks, Catches, RTA and PAS® Fittings Shelf Supports Bed Fittings

Bit dimensions 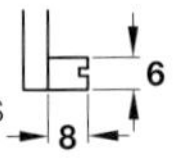

Finish: zinc, die cast

Effective shank length		30 mm
Cat. No.	nickel polished	204.11.787
	nickel matt	204.11.689
	brass polished	204.11.581

Packing: 10 pcs.

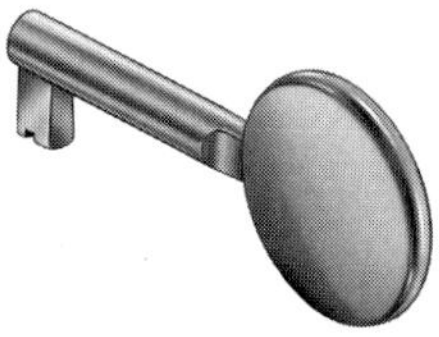

Bit dimensions 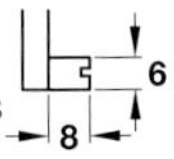

Finish: zinc, die cast

Effective shank length		35 mm
Cat. No.	nickel matt	204.58.682
	brass polished	204.58.584
	burnished brown	204.58.182

Packing: 10 pcs.

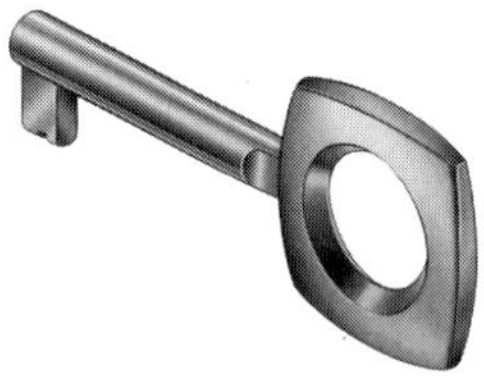

Bit dimensions 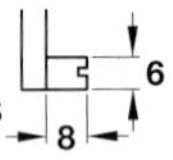

Finish: zinc, die cast

Effective shank length		35 mm
Cat. No.	nickel polished	203.88.783
	nickel matt	203.88.685
	brass polished	203.88.587

Packing: 10 pcs.

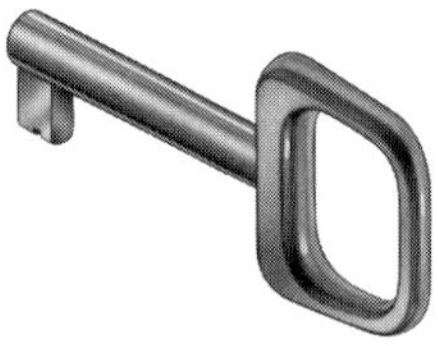

Bit dimensions 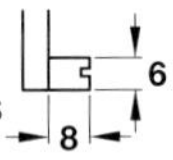

Finish: zinc, die cast

Effective shank length		35 mm
Cat. No.	nickel polished	204.13.781
	nickel matt	204.13.683
	brass polished	204.13.585

Packing: 10 pcs.

Bit dimensions 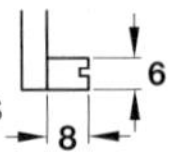

Finish: zinc, die cast

Effective shank length		35 mm
Cat. No.	nickel matt	203.78.689
	brass polished	203.78.581
	burnished brown	203.78.189

Packing: 10 pcs.

Bit dimensions 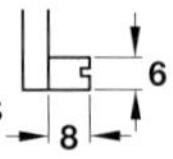

Finish: zinc, die cast

Effective shank length		35 mm	40 mm
Cat. No.	nickel polished	204.47.787	204.48.784
	nickel matt	204.47.689	204.48.686
	brass polished	204.47.581	204.48.588

Packing: 10 pcs.

Bit dimensions 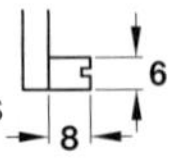

Finish: zinc, die cast

Effective shank length		38 mm
Cat. No.	nickel matt	204.57.685
	brass polished	204.57.587
	burnished brown	204.57.185

Packing: 10 pcs.

Bit dimensions 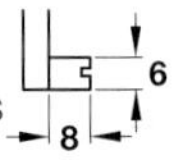

Finish: zinc, die cast

Effective shank length		38 mm
Cat. No.	nickel matt	204.59.689
	brass polished	204.59.581
	burnished brown	204.59.189

Packing: 10 pcs.

Decorative Keys - Lever Bit

HÄFELE

Decorative Keys
the desired key must match the type of lock selected in terms of:

a) bit size and shape

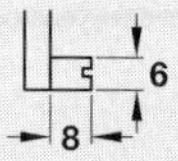

b) length of shank .

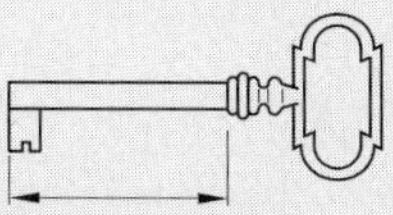

Effective shank length

Locks, Catches, RTA and PAS® Fittings
Shelf Supports
Bed Fittings
2

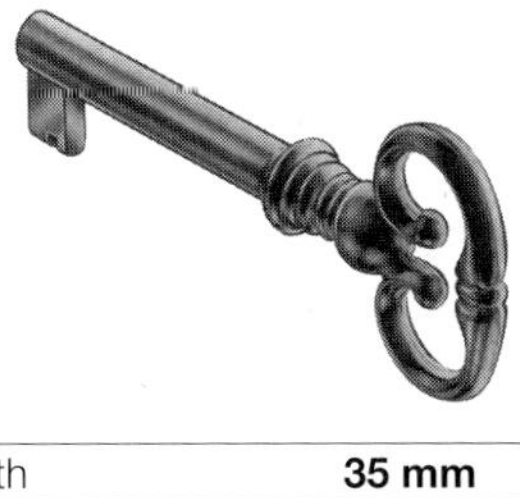

Bit dimensions

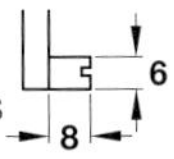

Finish: zinc, die cast

Effective shank length		**35 mm**
Cat. No.	brass polished	200.68.580
	burnished brown	200.68.188

Packing: 10 pcs.

Bit dimensions

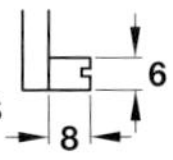

Finish: zinc, die cast

Effective shank length	**35 mm**
Cat. No. black antique	200.60.388

Packing: 10 pcs.

Bit dimensions

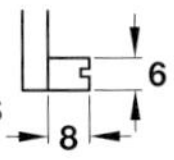

Finish: zinc, die cast

Effective shank length		**38 mm**
Cat. No.	brass polished	201.88.587
	burnished brown	201.88.185

Packing: 10 pcs.

Bit dimensions

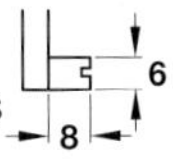

Finish: zinc, die cast

Effective shank length		**38 mm**
Cat. No.	brass polished	200.58.584
	burnished brown	200.58.182

Packing: 10 pcs.

Bit dimensions

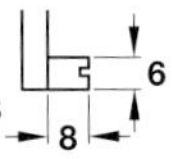

Finish: zinc, die cast

Effective shank length		**40 mm**
Cat. No.	nickel polished	204.17.789
	nickel matt	204.17.681
	brass polished	204.17.583

Packing: 10 pcs.

Bit dimensions

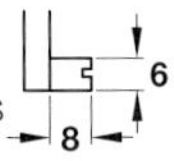

Finish: zinc, die cast

Effective shank length	**40 mm**
Cat. No. black antique	200.79.387

Packing: 10 pcs.

Bit dimensions

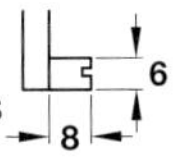

Finish: zinc, die cast

Effective shank length		**40 mm**
Cat. No.	nickel matt	204.18.688
	brass polished	204.18.580
	burnished brown	204.18.180

Packing: 10 pcs.

Bit dimensions

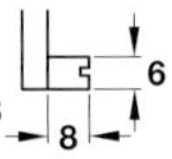

Finish: zinc, die cast

Effective shank length		**40 mm**	**50 mm**
Cat. No.	nickel matt	200.65.687	
	brass-plated polished	200.65.589	200.66.586
	burnished brown	200.65.187	200.66.184

Packing: 10 pcs.

Dimensional data not binding.
We reserve the right to alter specifications without notice.

HÄFELE

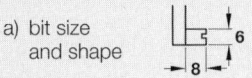

Solid Brass Decorative Keys - Lever Bit

Decorative Keys
the desired key must match the type of lock selected in terms of:

a) bit size and shape

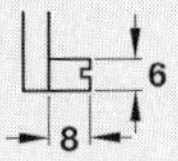

b) length of shank .

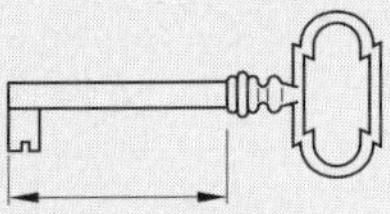

Effective shank length

Bit dimensions

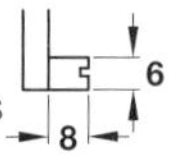

Finish: brass

Effective shank length		**35 mm**
Cat. No.	polished nickel-plated	206.47.787
	nickel matt	206.47.689
	polished	206.47.585

Packing: 10 pcs.

2 **Locks, Catches, RTA and PAS® Fittings Shelf Supports Bed Fittings**

Bit dimensions

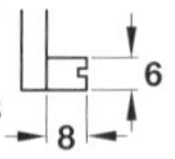

Finish: brass

Effective shank length		**33 mm**
Cat. No.	polished	200.59.885
	burnished brown	200.59.189

Packing: 10 pcs.

Bit dimensions

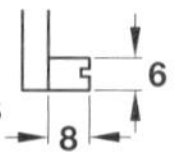

Finish: brass

Effective shank length		**35 mm**
Cat. No.	polished	200.57.881
	burnished brown	200.57.185

Packing: 10 pcs.

Decorative Escutcheons

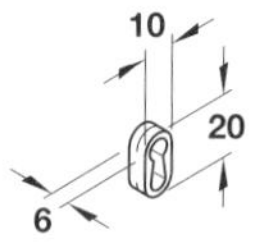

Finish: brass, brushed

Cat. No.	185.10.524

Packing: 100 pcs.

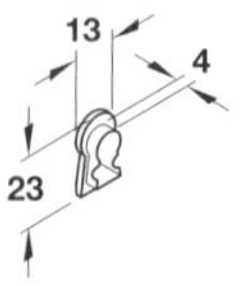

Finish: brass, polished

Cat. No.	185.30.839

Packing: 100 pcs.

Dimensional data not binding. We reserve the right to alter specifications without notice.

Timberlock - The Cylinder Module System

HÄFELE

The Timberlock - Cylinder Module System from Häfele is the most versatile locking system for your home or office furniture needs. It is based on separate lock modules that allow you to create many combinations of locking systems. Separate lock bodies and lock cores can be changed with only an installation key .

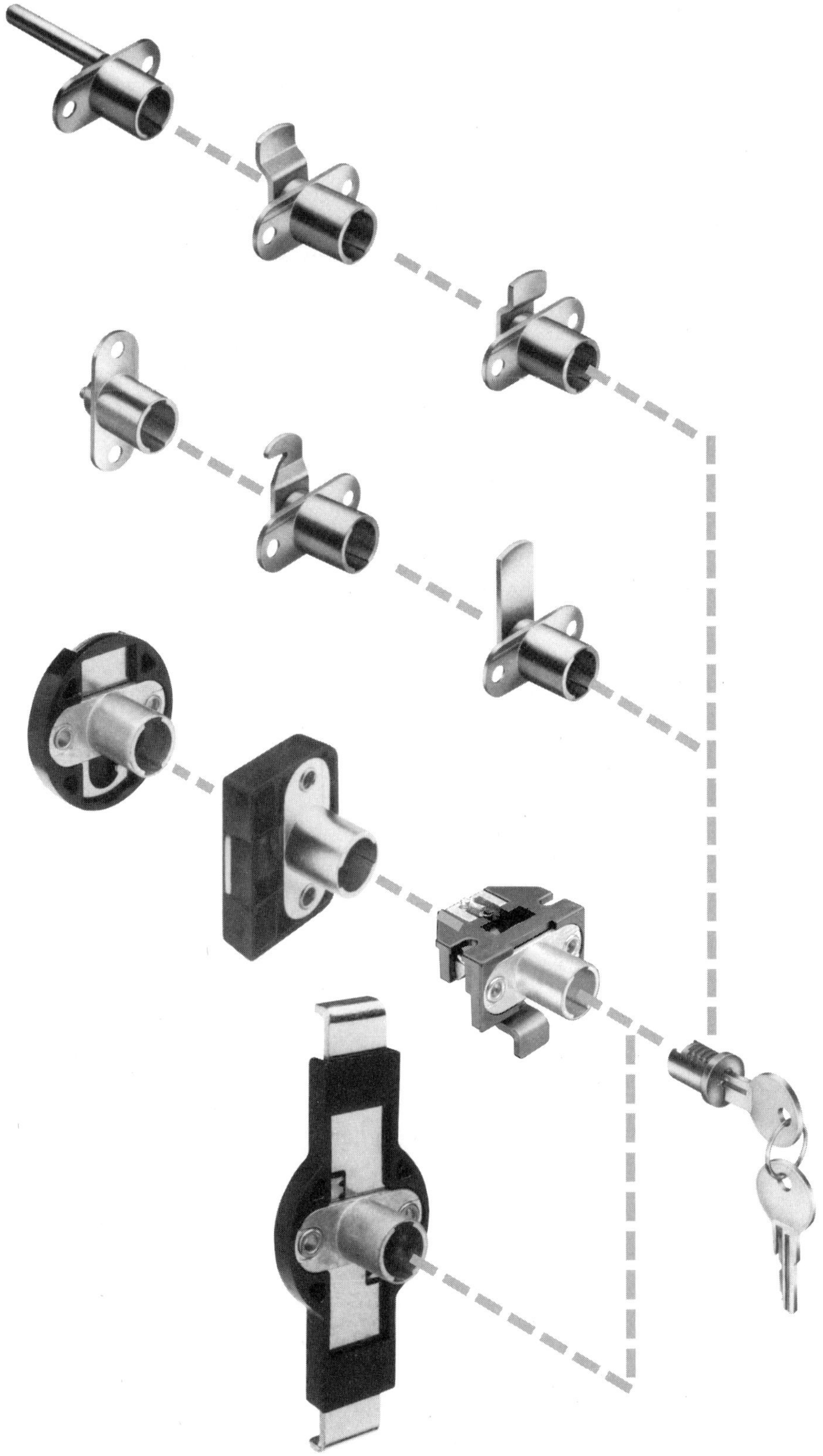

Dimensional data not binding.
We reserve the right to alter specifications without notice.

HÄFELE

Cylinder Module System

- Separates the lock core from cylinder housing. Any combination of locking systems can be obtained.
- Manufacturer can install fully functional locking systems.
- Operated by applying a combination tool to a square spindle. The lock core is only installed when the premises are occupied.
- Simplifies the planning of locking systems. Changes can be made, without difficulty. Lock cores can be installed or replaced with the aid of an installation key only.

Cylinder Rosette

For any **Cylinder Body**
Note: Requires 19mm diameter hole for installation with lock cylinders.

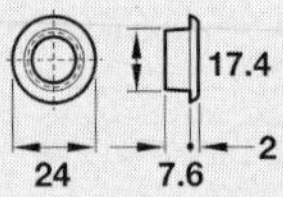

Finish: brass

nickel-plated	210.04.062
gold-plated	210.04.054
bronzed	210.04.017
black	210.04.035

Packing: 10 pcs.

Protective cap

Keeps interior of cylinder housing free of paint and dirt after lock is installed.

Finish: PVC

Cat. No.	210.02.095

Packing: 100 pcs.

The cylinder housings and lock cores are marked (see diagram, below). Thus, a series of furniture doors can all be locked with the same direction of turn, if the markings are positioned identically.

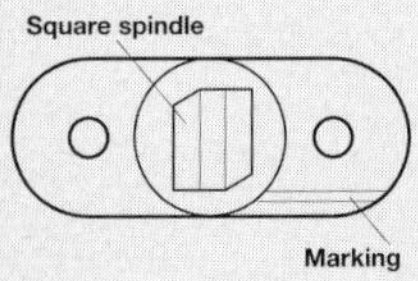

Dimensional data not binding. We reserve the right to alter specifications without notice.

Cylinder Module System

Lock Core

Suitable for any **Cylinder Body**
Finish: zinc die cast, unfinished; lock face: see table below; plate levers: brass
5 plate levers = 500 possible key changes
Accessories: 2 keys, nickel-plated brass

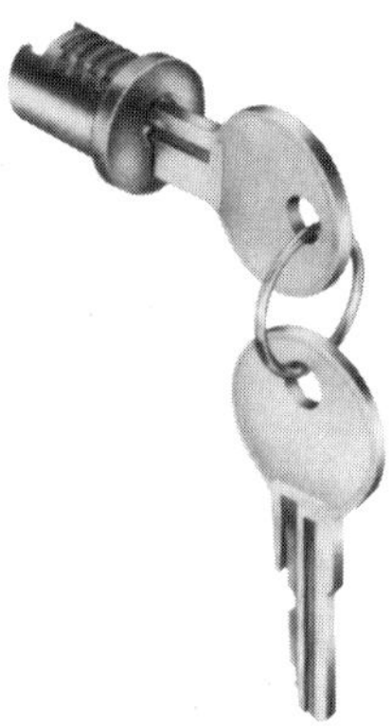

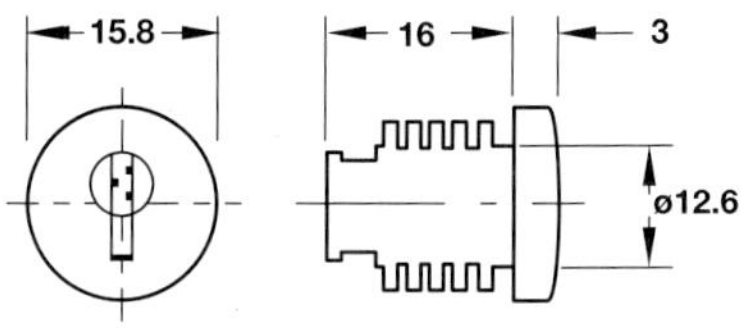

Keyed different

Finish:	nickel-plated	gold-plated	bronzed-epoxy	black-epoxy
Cat. No.	210.04.606	210.04.803	210.04.106	210.04.302

Packing: 500 pcs.

Keyed alike

Finish:	nickel-plated	gold-plated	bronzed-epoxy	black-epoxy
Keying		Cat. No.		
100 TA	210.04.615	210.04.812	210.04.115	210.04.311
101 TA	210.04.624	210.04.821	210.04.124	210.04.320
102 TA	210.04.633	210.04.830	210.04.133	210.04.339
103 TA	210.04.642	210.04.849	210.04.142	210.04.348
104 TA	210.04.651	210.04.858	210.04.151	210.04.357
105 TA	210.04.660	210.04.867	210.04.160	210.04.366
106 TA	210.04.679	210.04.876	210.04.179	210.04.375
107 TA	210.04.688	210.04.885	210.04.188	210.04.384
108 TA	210.04.697	210.04.894	210.04.197	210.04.393
109 TA	210.04.704	210.04.901	210.04.204	210.04.400

Packing 10 pcs.

Installation Key

To install or remove lock cores

Finish: brass

Cat. No.	210.02.004

Packing: 1 pc.

Master key, fits all TA lock cores (see table above)

Finish: brass

Cat. No.	210.02.059

Packing: 1 pc.

Key blanks

Can be cut to replace broken or lost keys.

Finish: brass

Cat. No.	210.02.00X

Packing: 1 pc.

Cylinder Module System
Cam Locks/Deadbolt Locks

Deadbolt Lock
Lift: 9.5mm

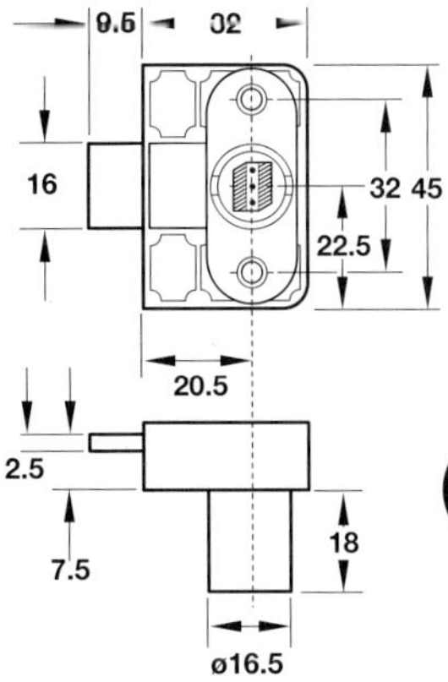

Finish: Lock case: black nylon
Cylinder housing: zinc die cast, unfinished
Bolt: steel, nickel plated

Can be used	Left/Right	Drawer
Cat. No.	232.12.302	232.12.311

Packing: 10 pcs.

Deadbolt Lock
Lift: 12mm

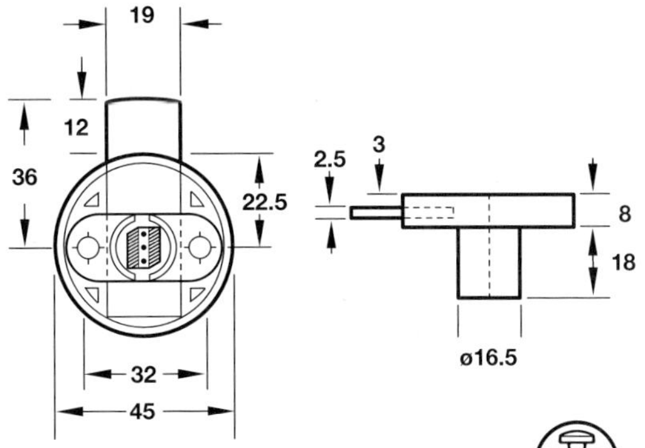

Finish: Lock case: black nylon
Cylinder housing: zinc die cast, unfinished
Bolt: steel, nickel plated

Can be used	Left/Right *	Drawer
Cat. No.	232.18.304	232.18.313

* Rotate cylinder core 180° to install.
Packing: 10 pcs.

Deadbolt Lock – Offset Bolt
For face-frame cabinets.
Lift: 12mm

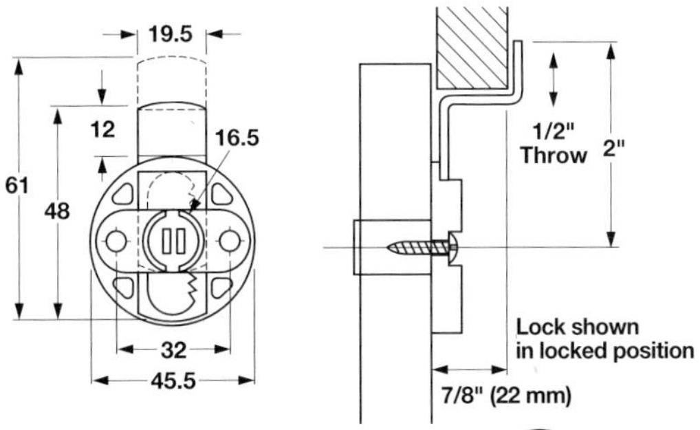

Finish: steel, zinc-plated; nylon, black

Cat. No.	232.18.360

Packing: 10 pcs.

Deadbolt Lock - double doors
Lift: 12mm
(Both bolts)
Must be mounted in lower left or upper right hand door.

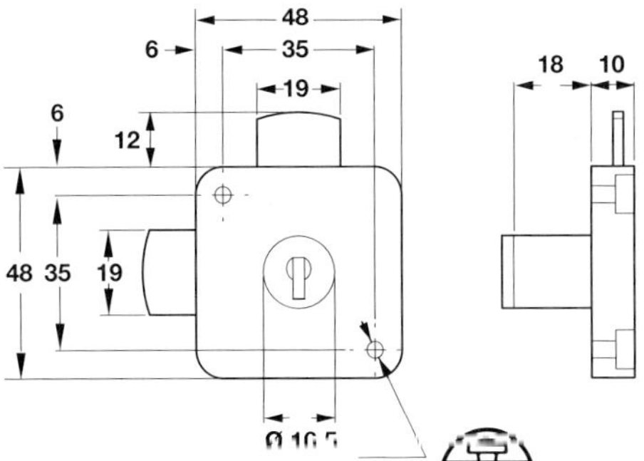

Finish: Lock case: black nylon;
Cylinder housing: zinc die cast

Cat. No.	232.35.300

Packing: 1 pc.

Locks, Catches, RTA and PAS® Fittings
Shelf Supports
Bed Fittings
2

Cylinder Rosette
For any **Cylinder Body**
Note: Requires 19mm (3/4") diameter hole for installation with lock cylinders.

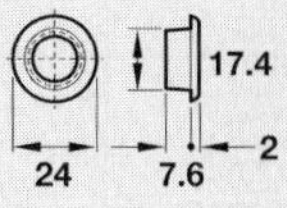

Finish: brass

nickel-plated	210.04.062
gold-plated	210.04.054
bronzed	210.04.017
black	210.04.035

Packing: 10 pcs.

- Offset cam eliminates need for strike plates on face frame application where door or drawer overlays face frame.

Protective cap
Keeps interior of cylinder housing free of paint and dirt after lock is installed.

Finish: PVC

Cat. No.	210.02.095

Packing: 10 pcs.

Dimensional data not binding.
We reserve the right to alter specifications without notice.

HÄFELE

Cylinder Module System Cam Locks

- Cams may be easily removed, changed and reoriented in the field.
- Only removal of 1/4" nut is required to change cam.

Cam Lock Body
With straight, extended lever.
Rotation: 180°.

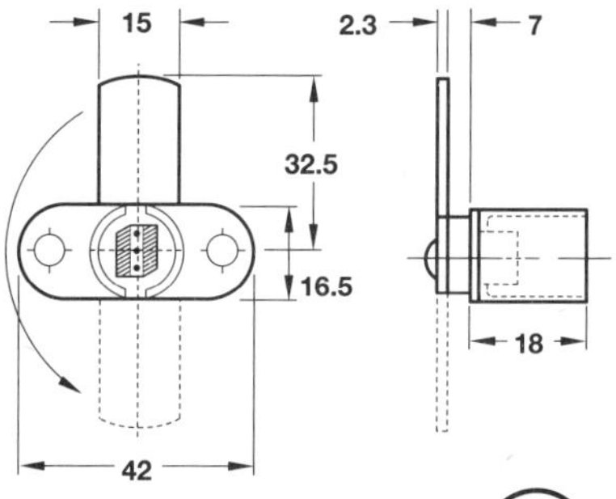

Finish: Cylinder housing: zinc die cast, unfinished
Lever: steel, nickel plated

Cat. No.		
	horizontal installation	235.08.303
	vertical installation	235.08.358

Packing: 10 pcs.

HOSPA Φ3,5

Cam Lock Body
With outward-cranked lever.
Rotation: 180°.

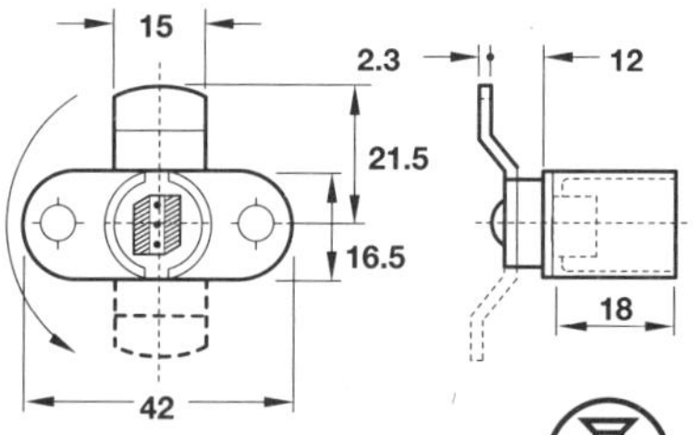

Finish: Cylinder housing: zinc die cast, unfinished
Lever: steel, nickel plated

Cat. No.		
	horizontal installation	235.08.009
	vertical installation	235.08.054

Packing: 10 pcs.

HOSPA Φ3,5

Cam Lock Body
With inward-cranked lever.
Rotation: 180°.

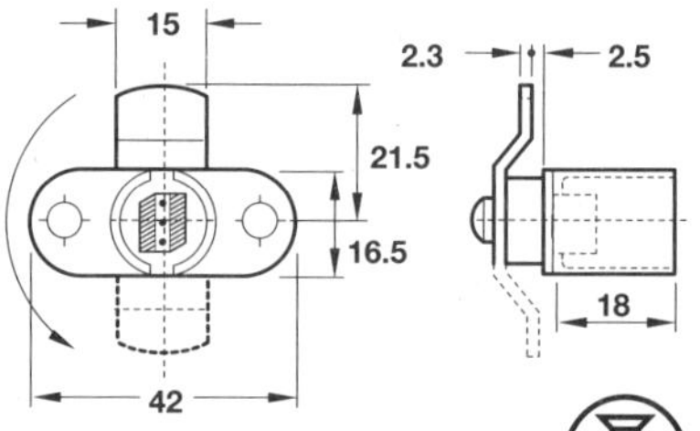

Finish: Cylinder housing: zinc die cast, unfinished
Lever: steel, nickel plated

Cat. No.		
	horizontal installation	235.08.107
	vertical installation	235.08.152

Packing: 10 pcs.

HOSPA Φ3,5

Cam Lock Body
With outward-cranked, hooked lever. Rotation: 180°.

Finish: Cylinder housing: zinc die cast, unfinished
Lever: steel, nickel plated

Cat. No.		
	horizontal installation	235.08.205
	vertical installation	235.08.250

Packing: 10 pcs.

HOSPA Φ3,5

Cylinder Rosette
For any **Cylinder Body**
Note: Requires 19mm (3/4") diameter hole for installation with lock cylinders.

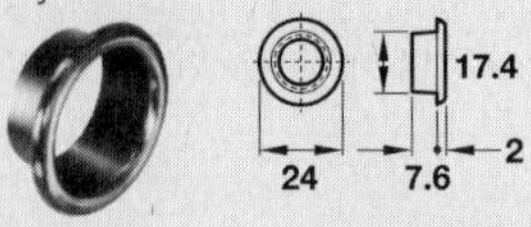

Finish: brass

nickel-plated	210.04.062
gold-plated	210.04.054
bronzed	210.04.017
black	210.04.035

Packing: 10 pcs.

Protective cap
Keeps interior of cylinder housing free of paint and dirt after lock is installed.

Finish: PVC

Cat. No.	210.02.095

Packing: 10 pcs.

Universal Cam Lock Body
Adjustable from 7/8" (22 mm) – 1 3/8" (35 mm) by merely turning the mounting flange. Barrel is conveniently marked with lines to facilitate setting depth. Rotation - 90°. Supplied with 2 different cams and can be oriented in any of the 3 positions shown.

- Packaged with two different cams, straight and offset.
- Can be assembled in any of three different orientations.

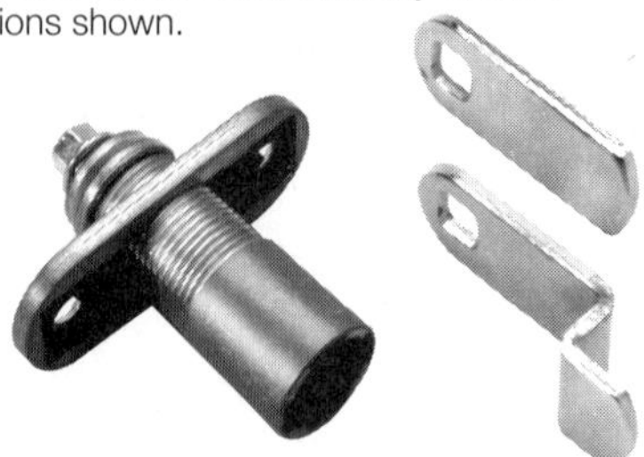

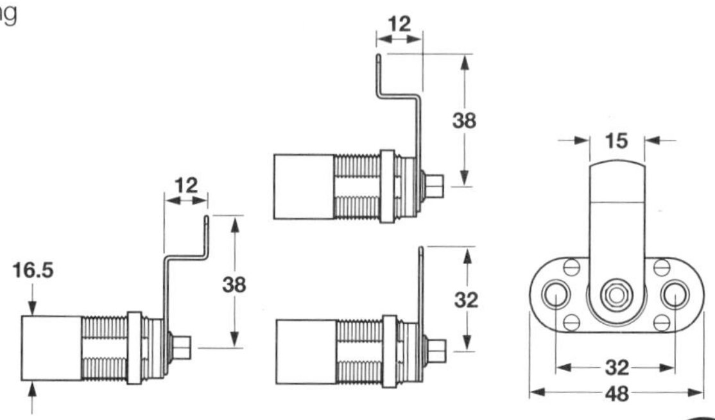

Finish: Zinc-unfinished, steel - nickel-plate

Cat. No.	235.09.000

Packing: 10 pcs.

HOSPA Φ3,5

Dimensions in mm

Dimensional data not binding.
We reserve the right to alter specifications without notice.

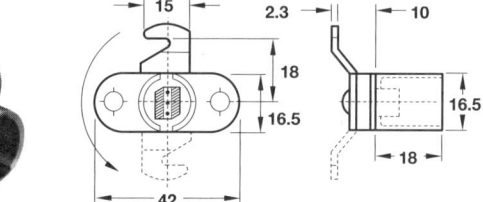

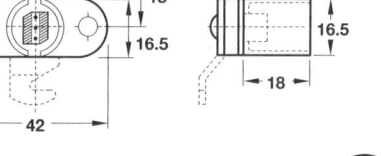

Cylinder Module System
Special Deadbolt Locks

The most economical arrangement for locking two drawers simultaneously is shown in the diagram on the right

Only a single hole must be drilled in the desk or cabinet side panel and the lock is then installed vertically. A stop wedge is now screwed to each drawer side panel. Once the cylinder core has been installed, the lock is ready for use.

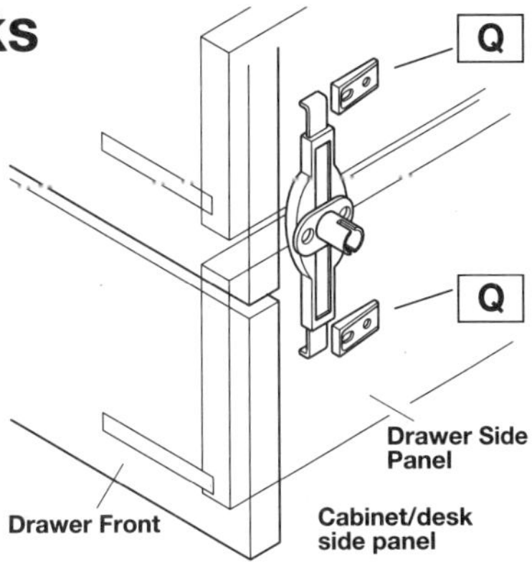

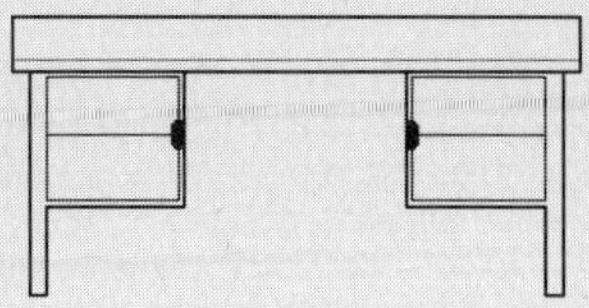

Central Locking System - 2 drawer
For two drawers with lockbar. Lift: 12mm.

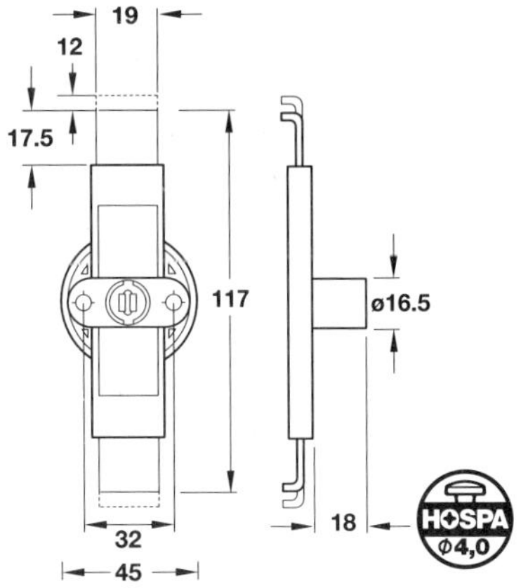

Finish: Lock case, black nylon
Cylinder housing: zinc die cast, unfinished
Bars: steel, nickel-plated

Cat. No.	234.92.300

Packing: 10 pcs.
Accessory Q can be found on page 2.25.

Wardrobe/Overhead Storage Lock
Lift: 12mm.

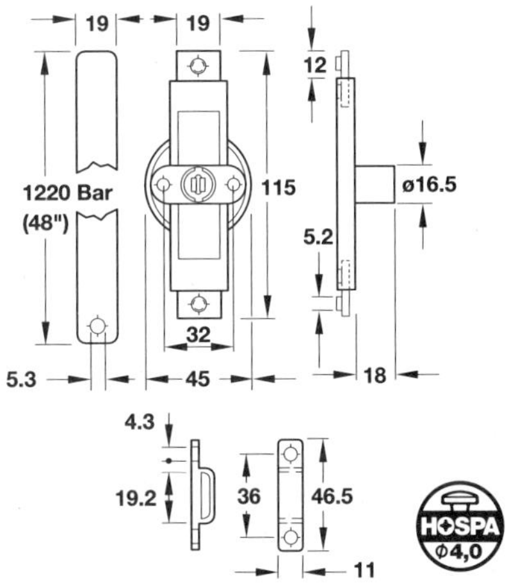

Finish: Lock case, black nylon
Cylinder housing: zinc die cast, unfinished
Bars: steel, black powder-coated
Bar retainers: black nylon

Cat. No.	horizontal installation	223.63.300
	vertical installation	223.63.355

Packing: 1 set, consists of: 1-lock body
2-bars, 1220mm (48") each
6-bar retainers

Suitable strike plates can be found on pages 2.26

Push-button Lock

- Compatible with all Timberlock Lock Cores.
- Small 3/4" diameter has better appearance than most other push locks.
- Black barrel looks attractive when lock is mounted in thinner panels
- Competitive price

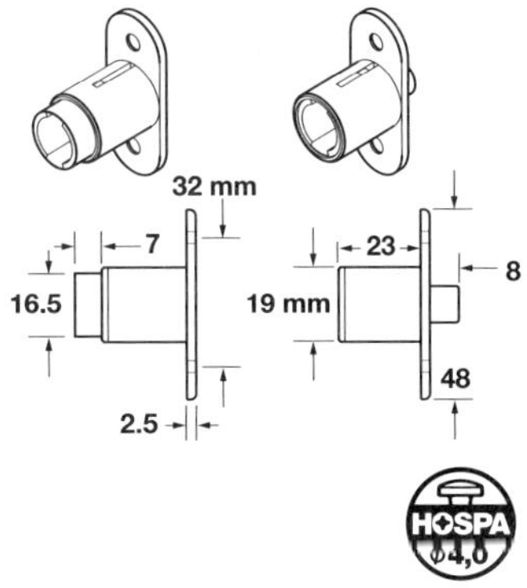

Finish: Lock case, black nylon
Cylinder housing: zinc die cast, unfinished

Cat. No.	234.65.000

Packing: 1pc.

Cylinder Rosette
For any **Cylinder Body**
Note: Requires 19 mm (3/4") diameter hole for installation with lock cylinders.

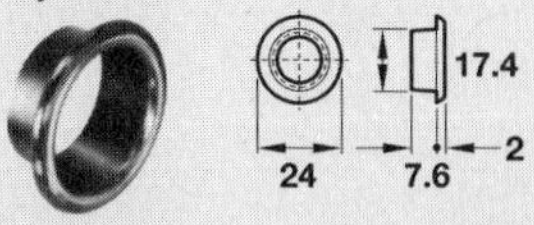

Finish: brass

nickel-plated	210.04.062
gold-plated	210.04.803
bronzed	210.04.017
black	210.04.035

Packing: 10 pcs.

Protective cap
Keeps interior of cylinder housing free of paint and dirt after lock is installed.

Finish: PVC

Cat. No.	210.02.095

Packing: 100 pcs.

Suitable strikes can be found on pages 2.26

Dimensional data not binding.
We reserve the right to alter specifications without notice.

HÄFELE

Cylinder Module System
Single Pedestal Front Mount

Permits locking from the front either in a fixed position in a lock strip or in a drawer front, in which case it travels with the drawer. Can be installed on the left or right side of the cabinet, as preferred.

2 Locks, Catches, RTA and PAS® Fittings Shelf Supports Bed Fittings

Cylinder Rosette

For any **Cylinder Body**
Note: Requires 19mm (3/4") diameter hole for installation with lock cylinders.

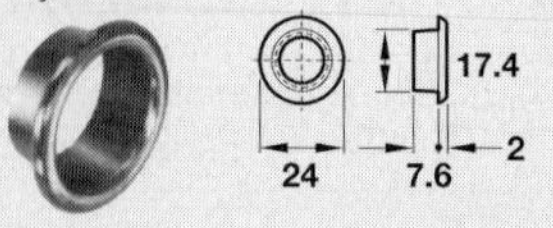

Finish: brass

nickel-plated	210.04.062
gold-plated	210.04.054
bronzed	210.04.017
black	210.04.035

Packing: 100 pcs.

Protective cap

Keeps interior of cylinder housing free of paint and dirt after lock is installed.

Finish: PVC

Cat. No.	210.02.095

Packing: 100 pcs.

***Note: Accessories can be found on page 2.24**

A **Lock body with lifting pin**
Rotation: 180º; lift: 12mm.

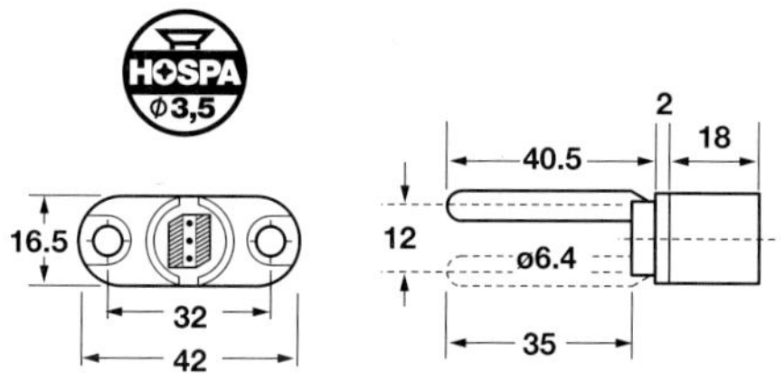

Finish: Zinc die cast, unfinished

Cat. No.	234.85.001

Packing: 10 pcs.

AA **Lockbar clip**
To fit lock body **A**. Mounts at any location along lockbar **L** with combination tool. (Page 2.24)

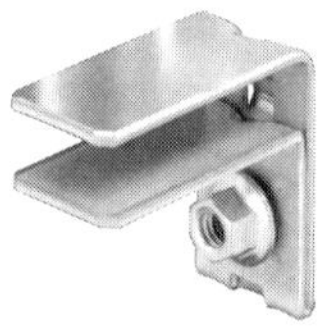

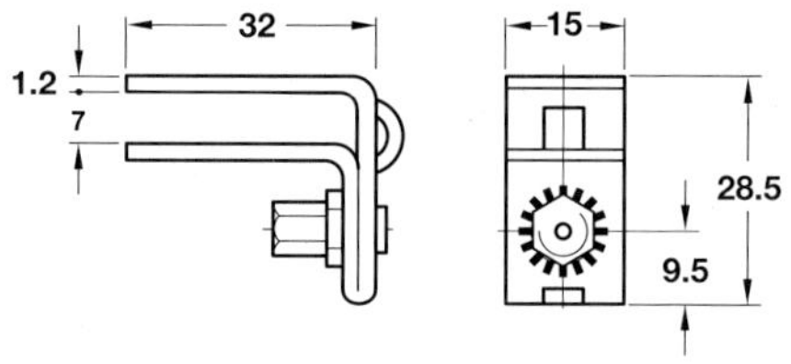

Finish: Steel, zinc-plated

Cat. No.	234.87.998

Packing: 10 pcs.

Typical Applications

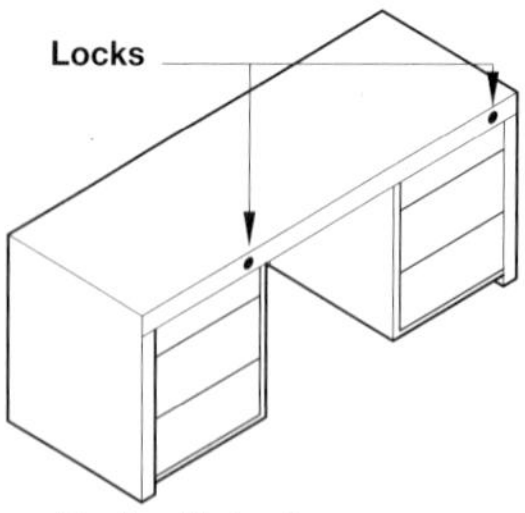

Desk with Lock
Mounted in Fixed Rail

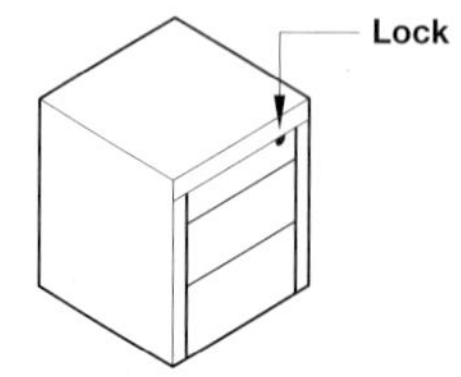

Mobile Pedestal with Lock
Mounted in Drawer Front

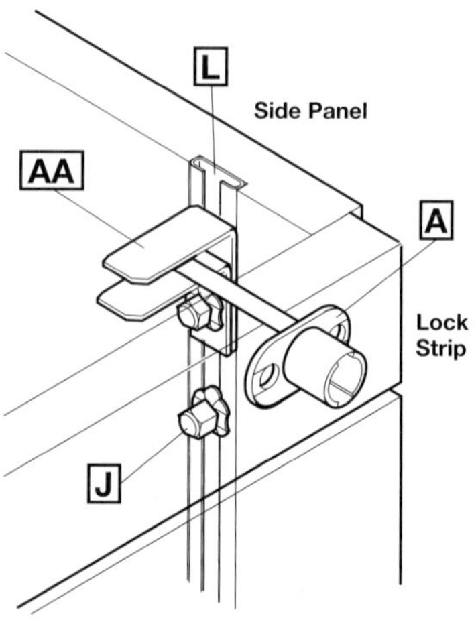

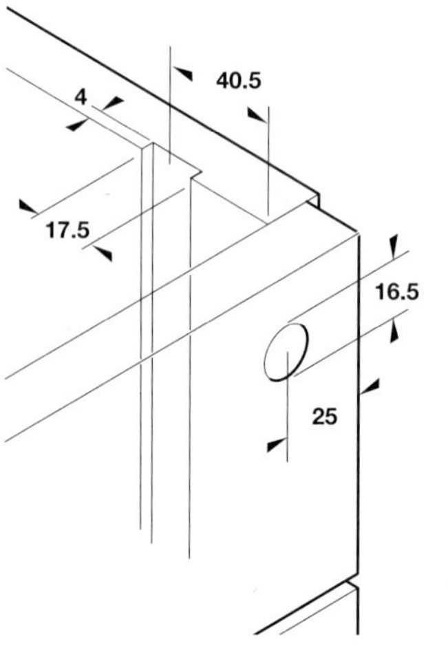

Drilling & routing diagram

Dimensions in mm

Dimensional data not binding. We reserve the right to alter specifications without notice.

Cylinder Module System Single Pedestal Side Mount

HÄFELE

An economical arrangement which allows installation of the lock body in the side panel at any position. Can be installed on the left or right side of cabinet as preferred.

B Side Mount Lock Body with locking lug

Rotation: 180°, lift: 12mm

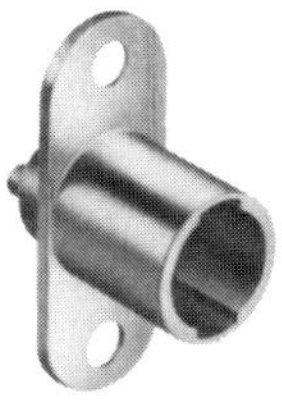

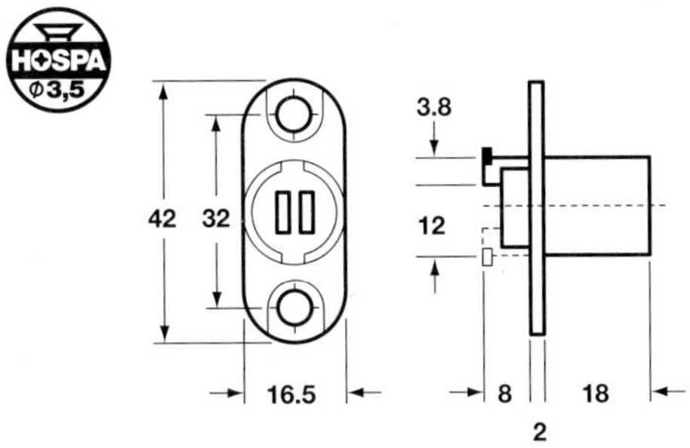

Finish: Zinc die cast, unfinished

Cat. No.	234.86.017

Packing: 10 pcs.

BB Lockbar clip

To fit lock body B. Mounts at any location along lockbar L with combination tool. (see page 2.24).

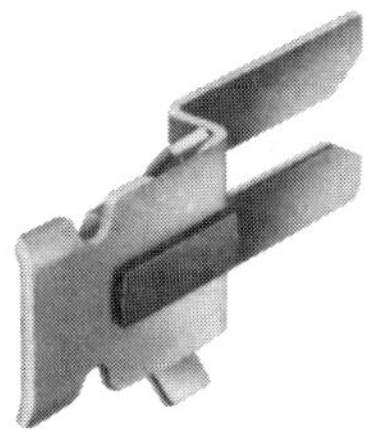

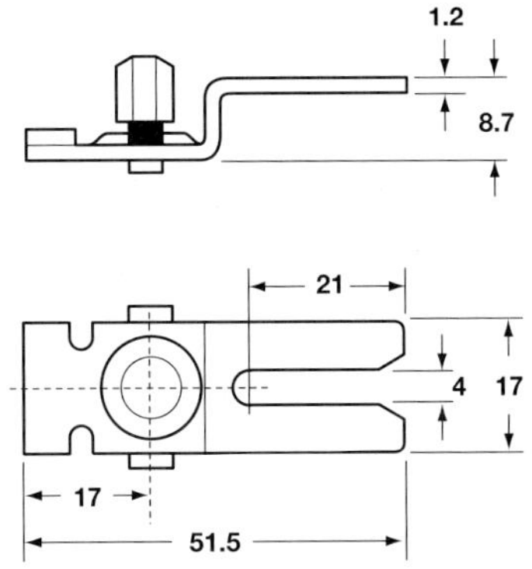

Finish: Steel, zinc die cast plate

Cat. No.	234.86.900

Packing: 10 pcs.

Cylinder Rosette

For any **Cylinder Body** Note: Requires 19mm (3/4") diameter hole for installation with lock cylinders.

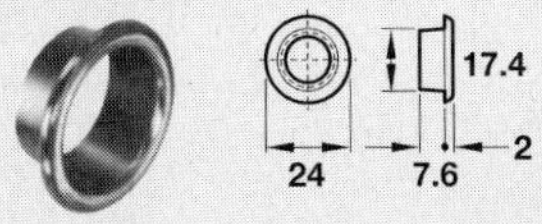

Finish: brass

nickel-plated	210.04.062
gold-plated	210.04.054
bronzed	210.04.017
black	210.04.035

Packing: 10 pcs.

Protective cap

Keeps interior of cylinder housing free of paint and dirt after lock is installed.

Finish: PVC

Cat. No.	210.02.095

Packing: 100 pcs.

Typical Applications

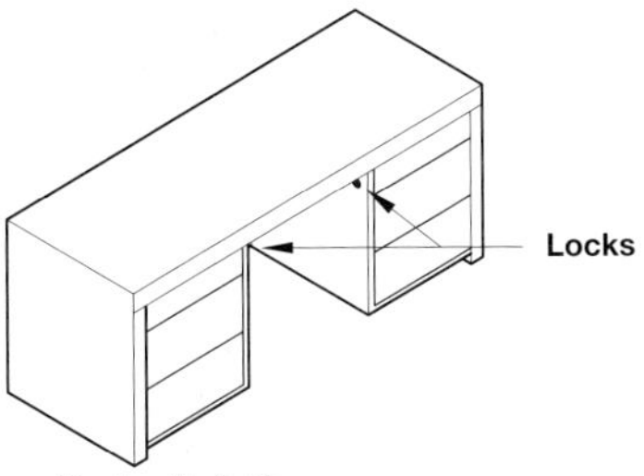

Desk with lock
Mounted in kneespace panel

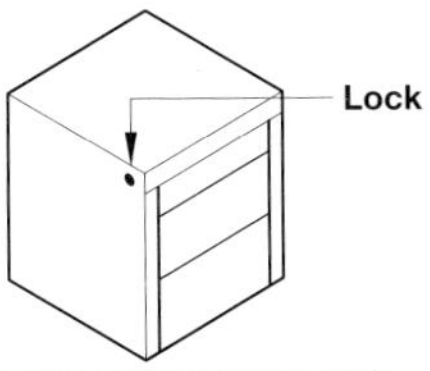

Mobile pedestal with lock
Mounted in side panel

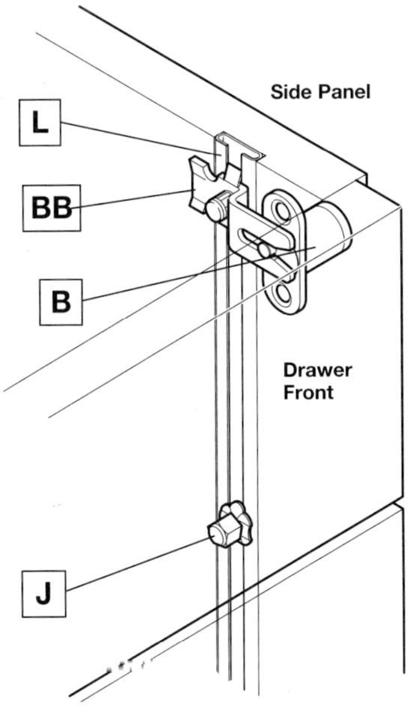

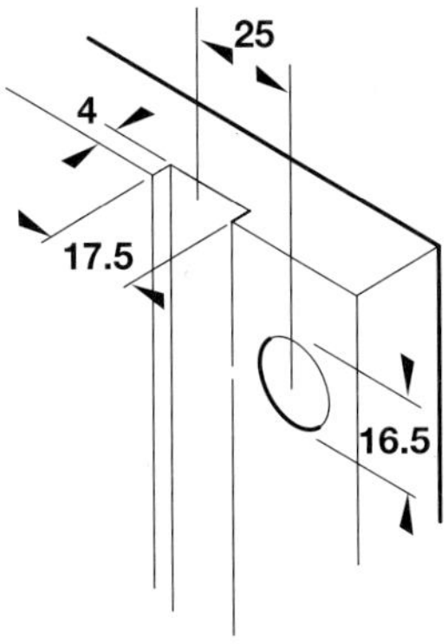

Drilling & routing diagram

Accessories L, J for single pedestal locks can be found on page 2.24.

Dimensions in mm

HÄFELE

Cylinder Module System
Central Locking Rail Mount Lock

Timberlock provides a complete system for central locking of desks and credenzas, with one lock mounted in a minimum 25mm front exposed rail.

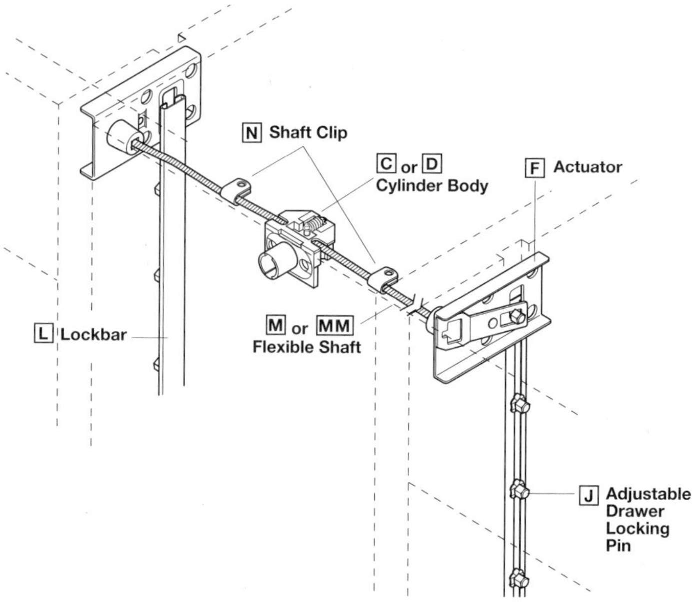

C Central Locking System Body - Center Drawer Application

With center drawer bolt.
Accommodates flexible shaft M or MM

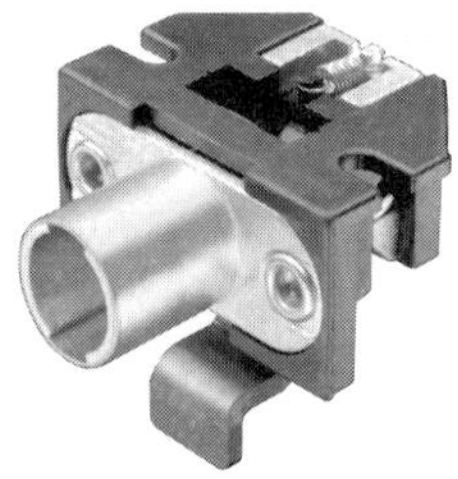

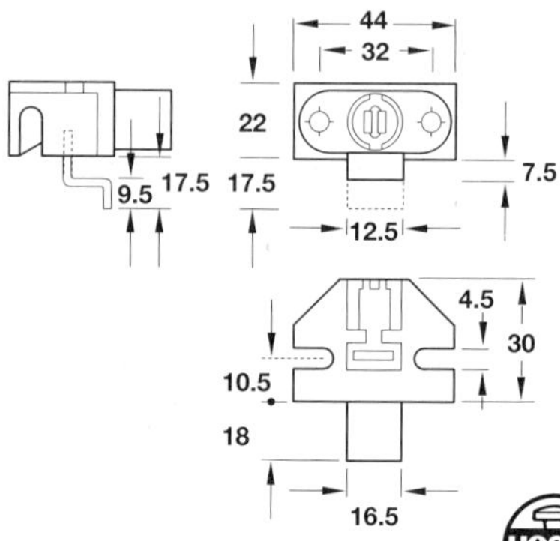

Finish: Lock case, black nylon
Cylinder housing: zinc die cast, unfinished

Cat. No.	237.46.054

Packing: 10 pcs.

D Central Locking System Body - without Center Drawer

Finish: Lock case, black nylon
Cylinder housing: zinc die cast, unfinished

Cat. No.	237.46.003

Packing: 10 pcs.

F Lockbar Actuator

Transmits horizontal rotation of flexible shaft M or MM vertical movement of lockbar L.

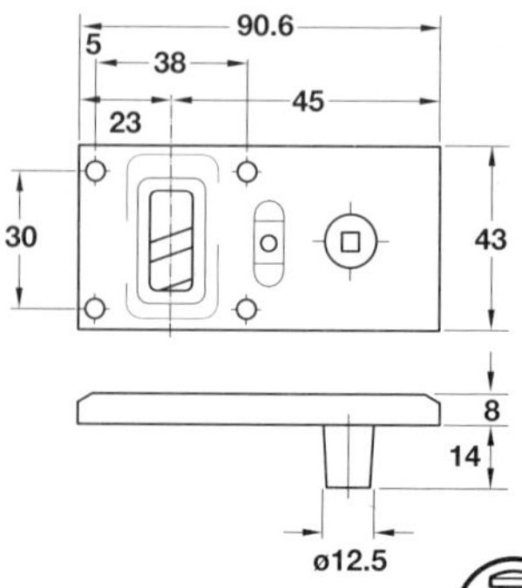

Finish: steel, galvanized; spindle guide: black plastic

Cat. No.	234.87.023

Packing: 10 pcs.

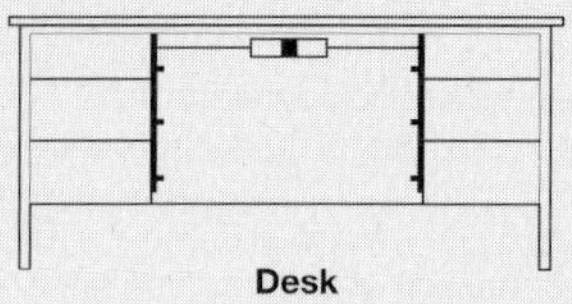

Desk

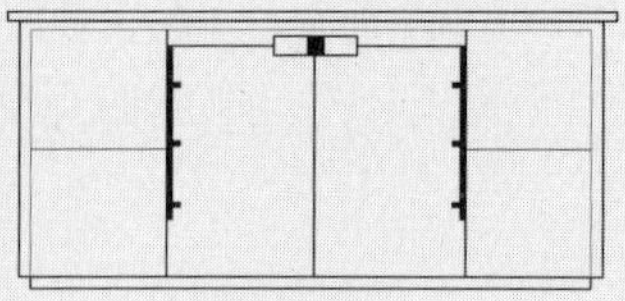

Credenza

Cylinder Rosette

For any **Cylinder Body** Note: Requires 19mm (3/4") diameter hole for installation with lock cylinders.

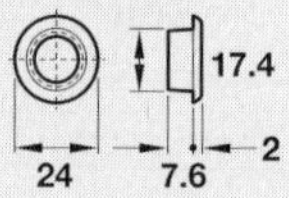

Finish: brass

nickel-plated	210.04.062
gold-plated	210.04.803
bronzed	210.04.017
black	210.04.035

Packing: 10 pcs.

Protective cap

Keeps interior of cylinder housing free of paint and dirt after lock is installed.

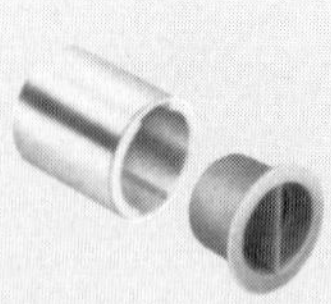

Finish: PVC

Cat. No.	210.02.095

Packing: 100 pcs.

Accessories for installation can be found on pages 2.25.

Cylinder Module System Lateral File/Anti-Tip

Timberlock provides a complete system for central locking of desks and credenzas, with one lock mounted in a minimum 25mm front exposed rail.

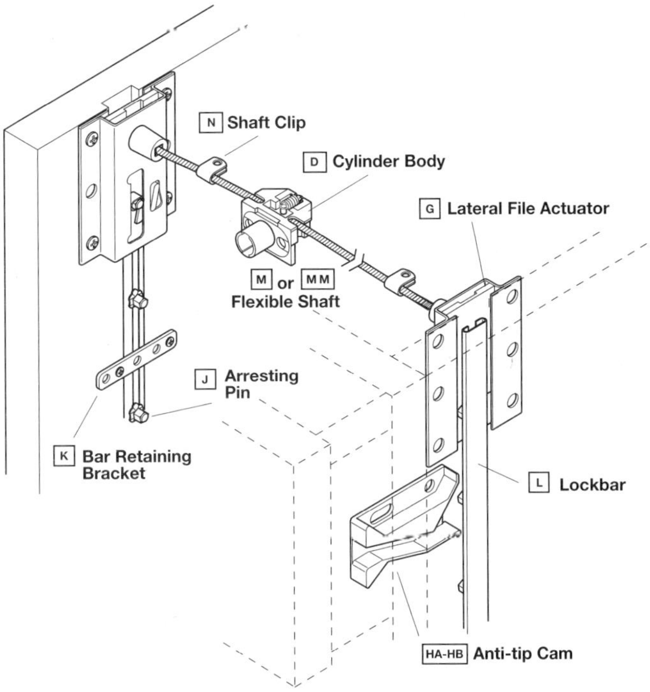

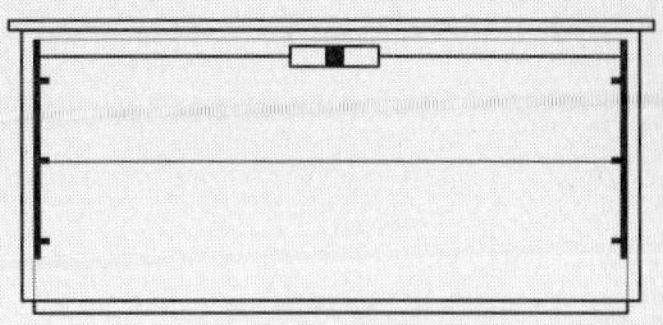

Lateral File Application

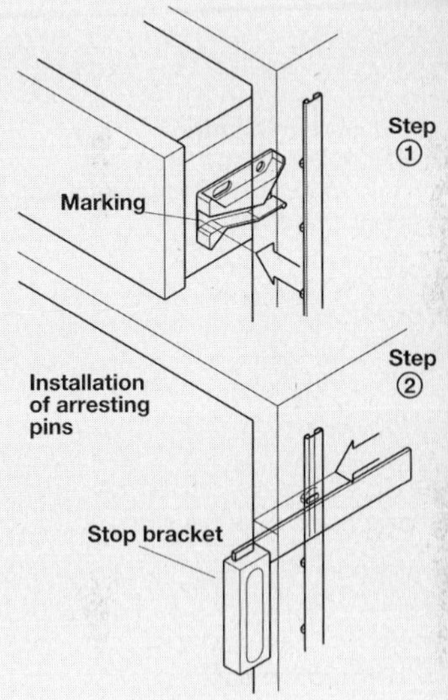

Installation of cam plates H must be used in this combination as anti-tip mechanism for up to 4 drawers.

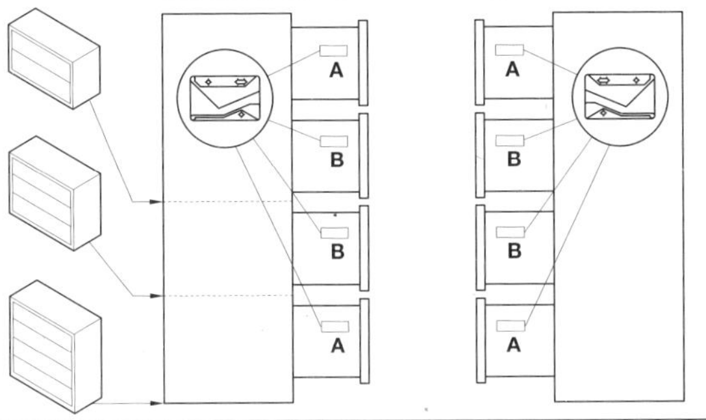

Space-saving locking system, installed directly behind doors or drawer front panels. The gear unit is secured to the cabinet top panel. The cylinder housing is mounted in the drawer front and is separated from the gear unit when the drawer is opened.

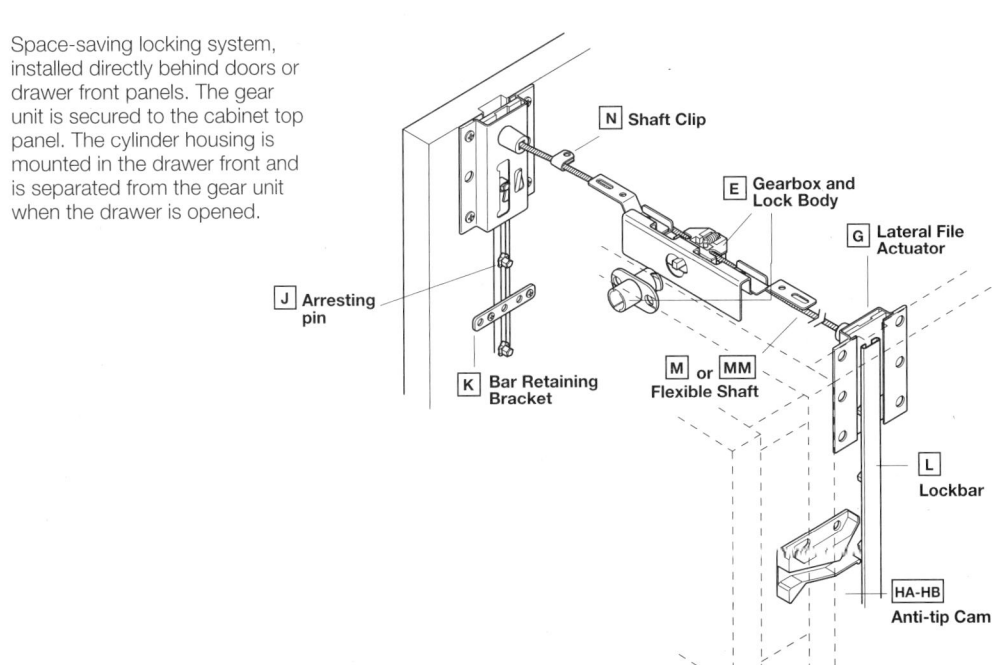

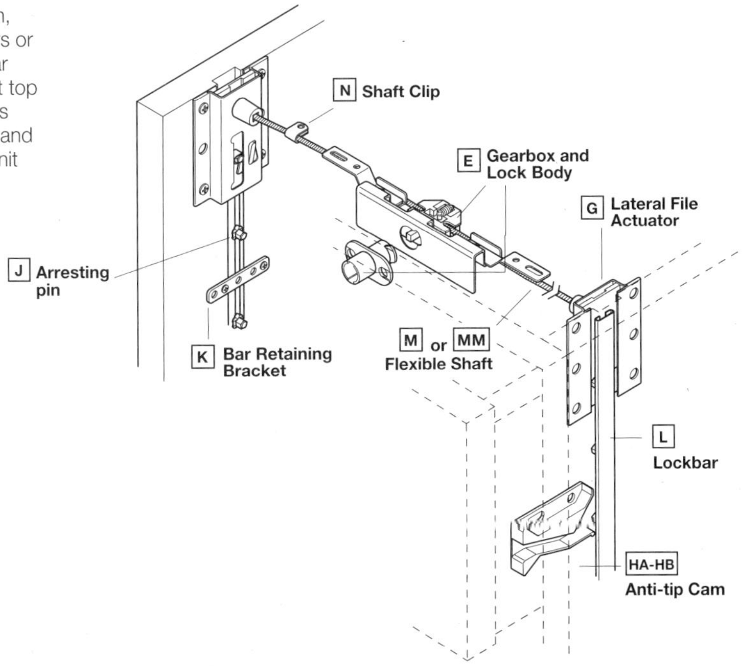

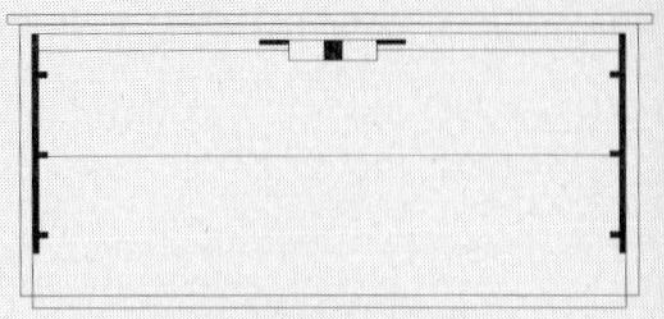

Lateral File Application

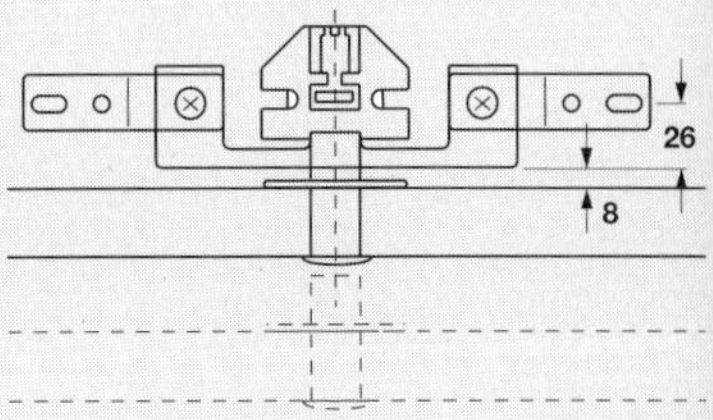

Dimensional data not binding. We reserve the right to alter specifications without notice.

HÄFELE

Cylinder Module System Lateral File/Anti-Tip

D Central Locking System Body

Accommodates flexible shaft M or MM.

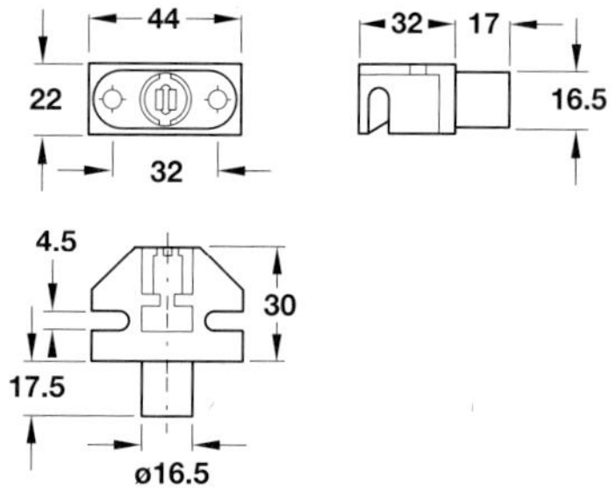

Finish: Lock case, black nylon
Cylinder housing: zinc die cast, unfinished

Cat. No.	237.46.003

Packing: 10 pcs.

E Gear & Lock Body

For installation in drawer front/door, accommodates flexible shaft M or MM.

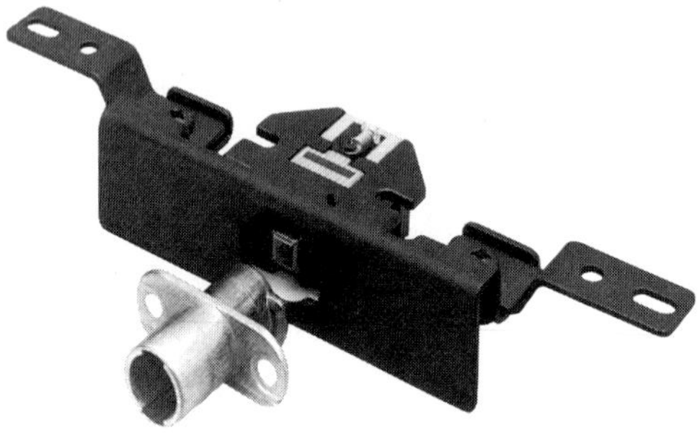

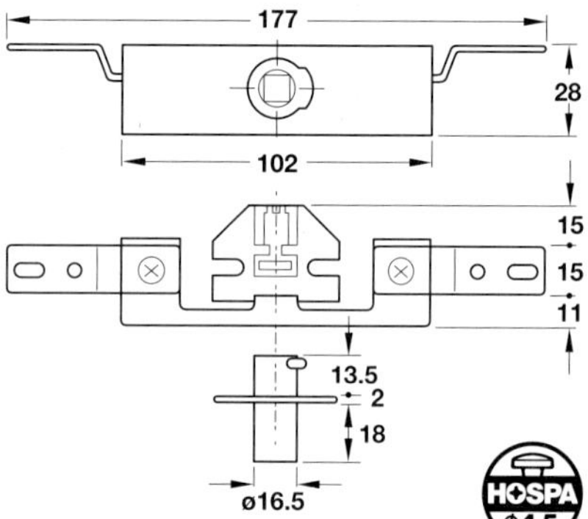

Finish: Gearbox, black plastic
Mounting plates and retaining brackets: steel, black
Lock body: zinc die cast, unfinished

Cat. No.	237.43.053

Packing: set includes: 1 lock body; 1 gearbox

G Actuator

Transmits movement of flexible shaft M or MM to lockbar L.

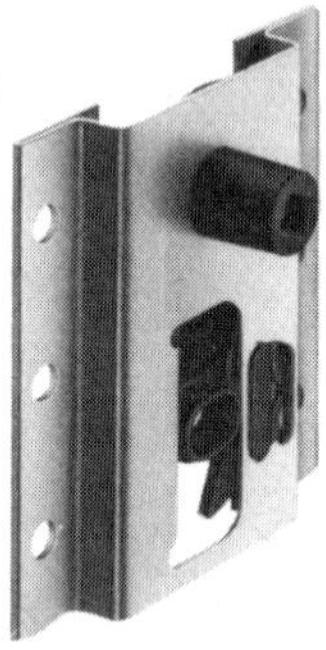

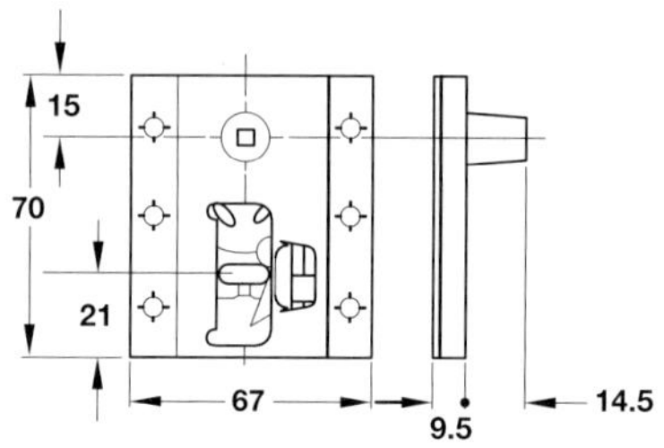

Finish: steel, zinc-plated; mechanism: black plastic

Cat. No.	237.44.023

Packing: 1 pc.

HA-HB Anti-tip Cams

The anti-tip mechanism prevents more than one drawer from being opened at a time, which in turn prevents the cabinet from tipping forward. Meets or exceeds BIFMA specifications.

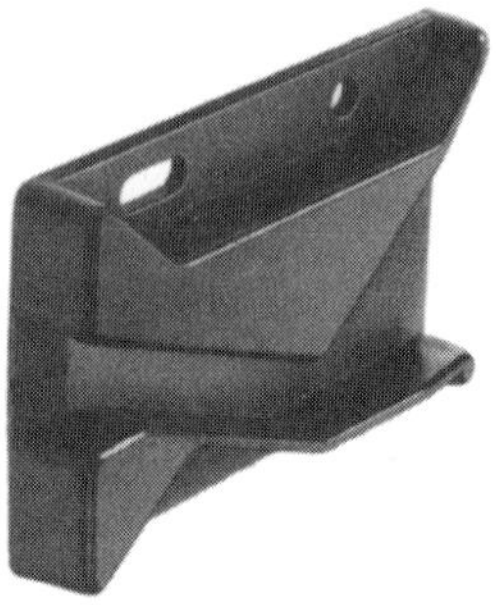

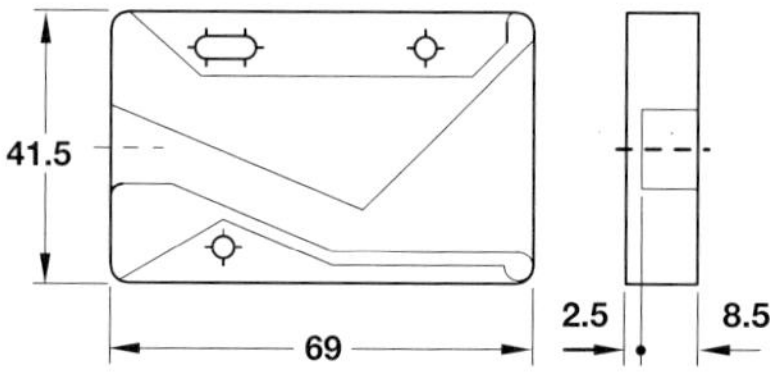

Finish: black nylon

Cat. No.		
	HA	237.44.372
	HB	237.44.363

Packing: 1 pc.

Cylinder Rosette

Note: Requires 19mm (3/4") diameter hole for installation with lock cylinders.

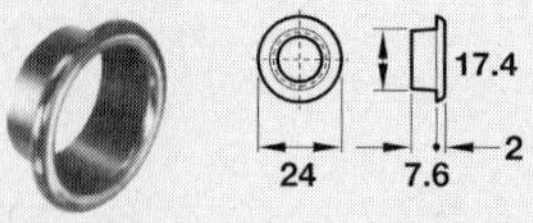

Finish: brass

nickel-plated	210.04.062
gold-plated	210.04.803
bronzed	210.04.017
black	210.04.035

Protective cap

Keeps interior of cylinder housing free of paint and dirt after lock is installed.

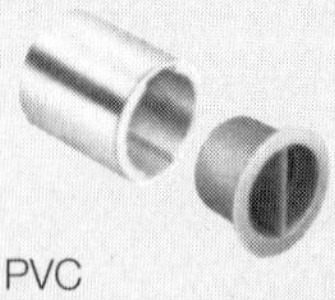

Finish: PVC

Cat. No.	210.02.095

Packing: 1 pc.

Cylinder Module System Accessories

Snapper
- Used for applications calling for an anti-tip system that does not require a lock.
- Does not require the use of D or E or M flexible shaft.
- Secure against jarring out of place during shipping. However, for added assurance, use wedge lock listed below.

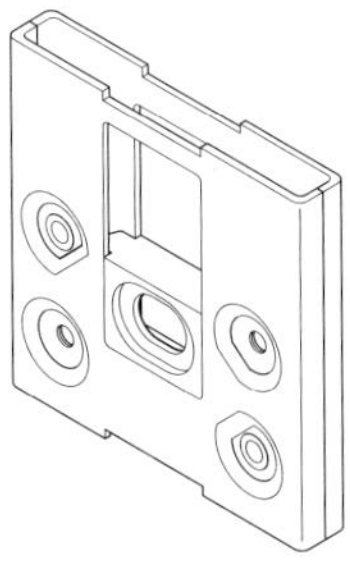

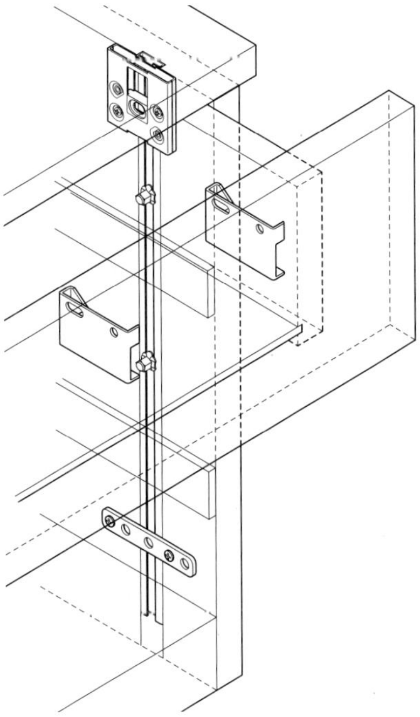

Finish: steel, zinc-plated

Cat. No.	237.44.113

Packing: 10 pcs.

Wedge Lock
- Used only with anti-tip system not using a lock.
- Must only be used with system incorporating lockbar snapper above.
- Prevents jamming due to lockbar bounce caused during shipping.
- The wedge lock is marked "remove after shipping" and usually drops off when the drawers are opened the first time.

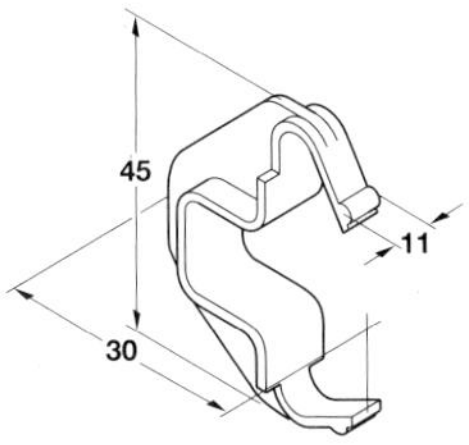

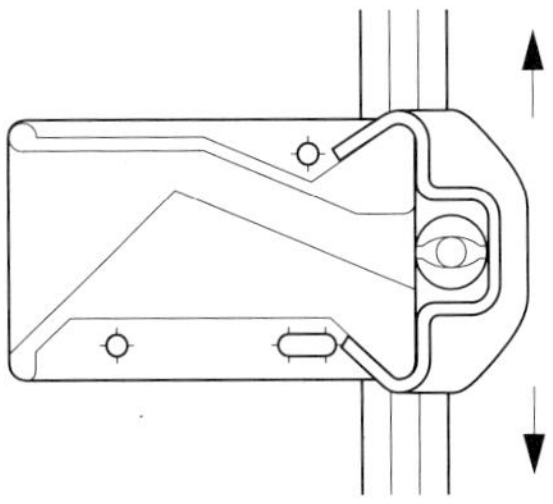

Finish: plastic, red

Cat. No.	237.44.990

Packing: 10 pcs.

Lockbar Marker
- For marking position of pins in file drawer with anti-tip mechanism.
- Pins are merely positioned between the two lines indicated by marker.
- Insures proper alignment of arresting pins.

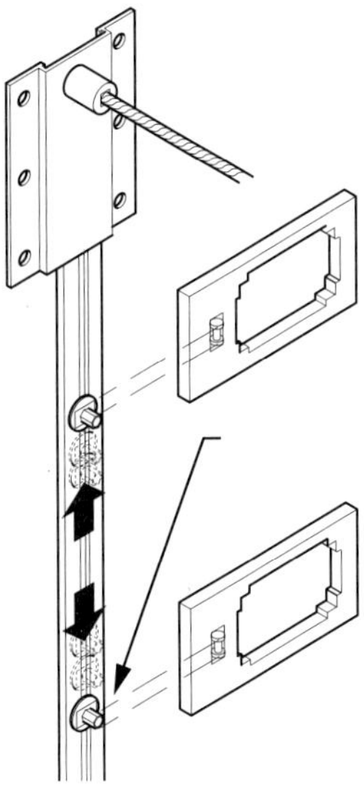

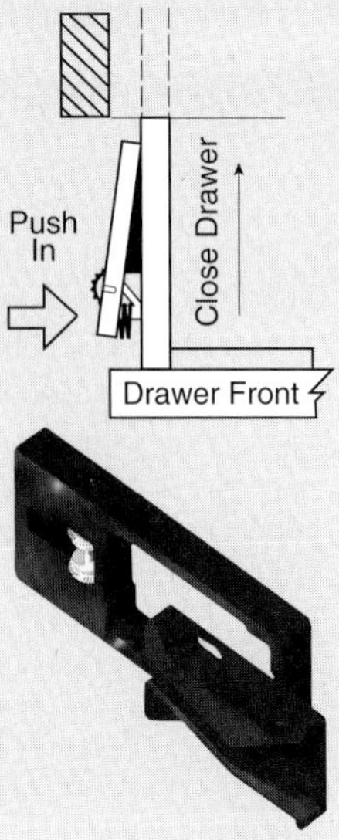

Finish: plastic, black

Cat. No.	001.32.025

Packing: 1 pc.

HÄFELE

Cylinder Module System Accessories

L Lockbar

For use with any central locking assembly from the cylinder module system.

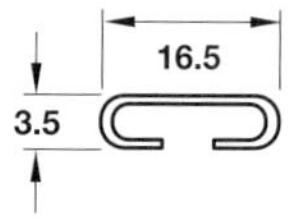

Finish: Steel, zinc-plated

Cat. No.	457	mm long	234.87.818
	609	mm long	234.87.827
	915	mm long	234.87.836
	1220	mm long	234.87.845

Packing: 1 pc.

J Arresting pins

Hexagonal section, for installation in lockbar L, using combination tool, at any desired position.

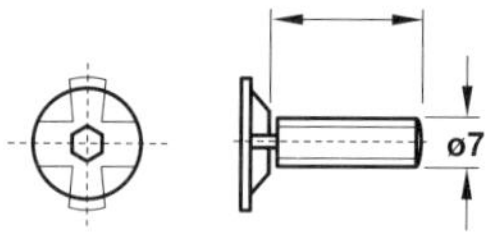

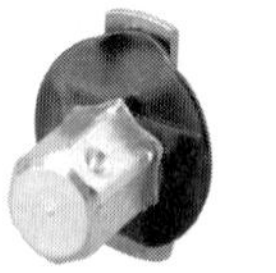

Finish: Pin: steel, nickel-plated
Wing screw and lock washer: steel, black

Cat. No.	9.5 mm long	237.22.714
	13 mm long	237.22.723
	16 mm long	237.22.732
	19 mm long	237.22.741
	22 mm long	237.22.750
	25 mm long	237.22.769
	32 mm long	237.22.778
	38 mm long	237.22.787
	51 mm long	237.22.796

Packing: 100 pcs.

K Bar Retaining Bracket

With guide lug.

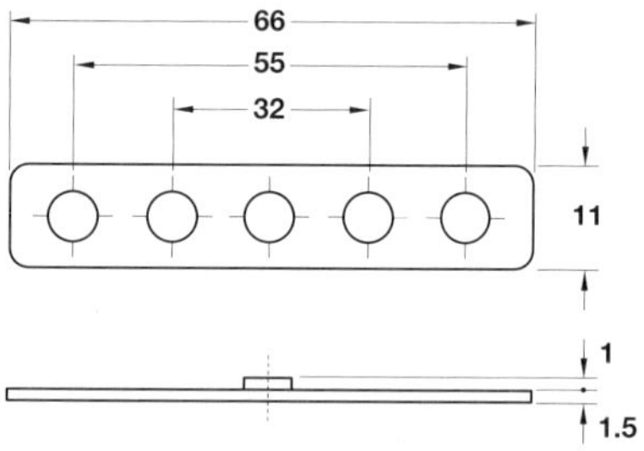

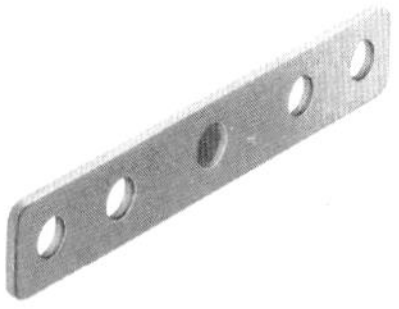

Finish: Steel, zinc-plated

Cat. No.	234.87.989

Packing: 100 pcs.

HOSPA Φ3,5

Combination Tool

To install arresting pins J in lockbar L.
In addition to the hexagon head, the tool incorporates a notched sleeve which engages the square lug in the cylinder housing, thus enabling any lock in the module system to be operated before the cylinder core is installed.

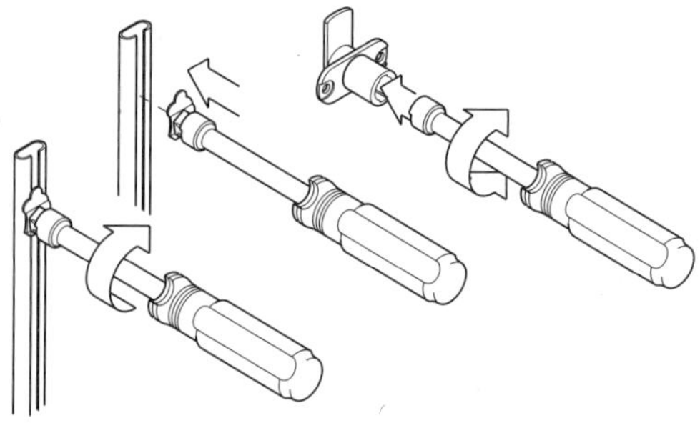

Finish: Hardened steel, nickel-plated
Handle: plastic, clear/red

Cat. No.	006.36.653

Packing: 1 pc.

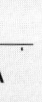

Special-purpose drill bit - Ø 16.5 mm

Suitable for any cylinder housing in the system. Can also be used in clockwise multi-spindle drilling machines with 10mm chuck.

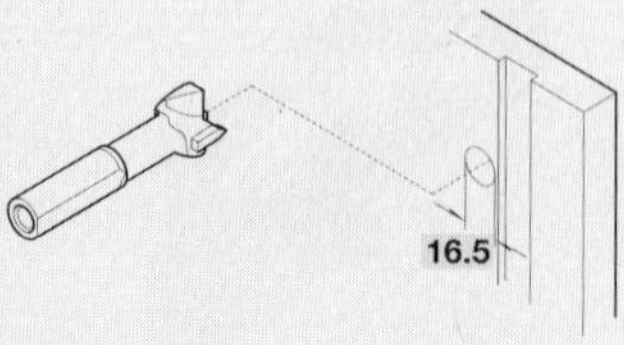

Finish: Shank made of special tool steel, carbide-tipped bit

Cat. No.	001.24.194

Packing: 1 pc.

Cylinder Module System Accessories

M Flexible Shaft

Fits central locking system locks C, D and E
When ordering specify dimensions A and B
(see box at right).

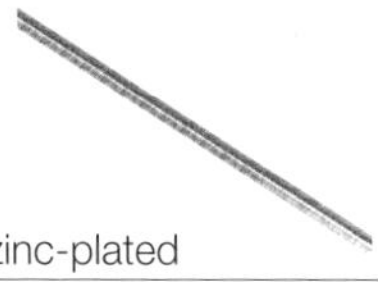

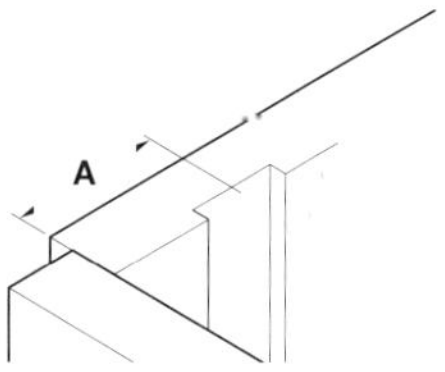

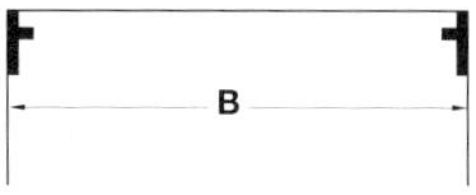

1. Specify lock body model.
C · D or E

2. Dimension A,
between 35mm (min.) and
100mm (max.)

3. Dimension B,
internal cabinet width

Finish: Shaft: steel, zinc-plated

Cat. No.	237.44.10X.77

Packing: 1 pc.

MM Adjustable Shaft Kit

- Can be used to fabricate any size shaft from 24" to 44" by simply cutting the square shaft to the desired length.
- Supplied with:
  2 - extended shaft clips
  2 - square shafts - 12" ea
  1 - flexible shaft - 20" ea.
  2 - shaft connectors
  1 - allen key for installation

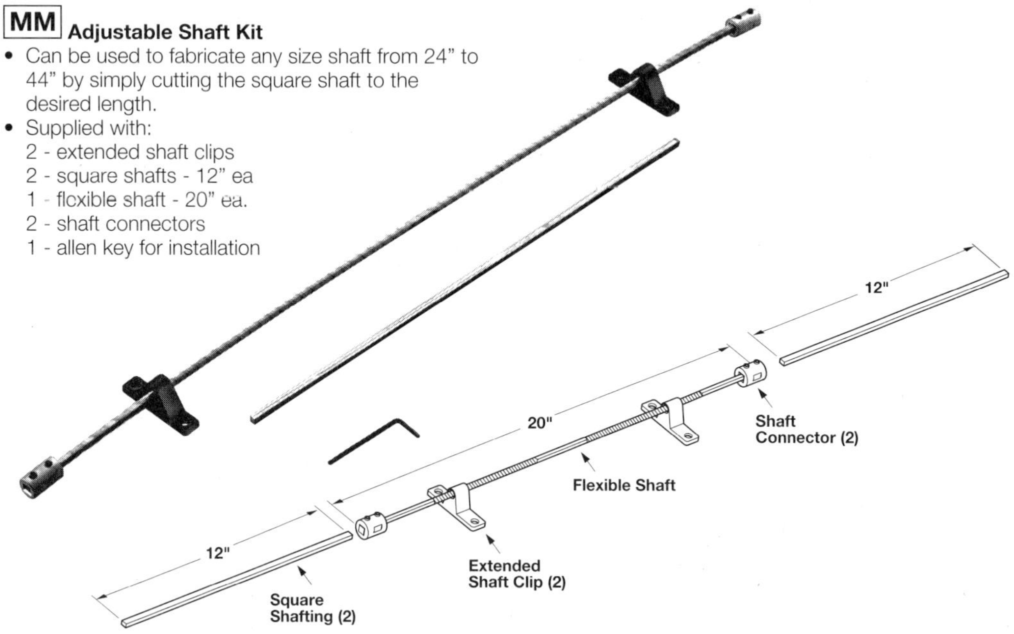

Finish: steel, zinc-plated; plastic, black

Cat. No.	237.60.010

Packing: 1 pc.

N Shaft Clip

Fits flexible shaft M above. Holds shaft to cabinet.

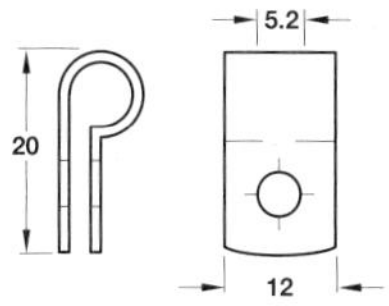

Finish: plastic, natural

Cat. No.	237.44.014

Packing: 100 pcs.

HOSPA Φ4,0

Q Drawer Locking Wedge

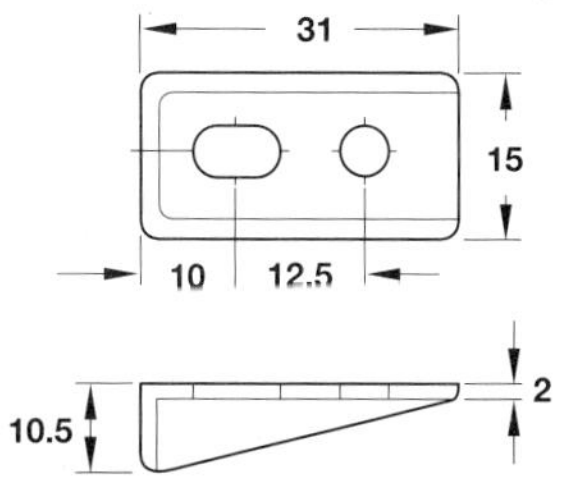

Finish: plastic, black

Cat. No.	234.91.090

Packing: 100 pcs.

HOSPA Φ4,0

Dimensional data not binding.
We reserve the right to alter
specifications without notice.

HÄFELE

Cylinder Module System Accessories

Strike Plate
Screw-mounted,
belt loop type.

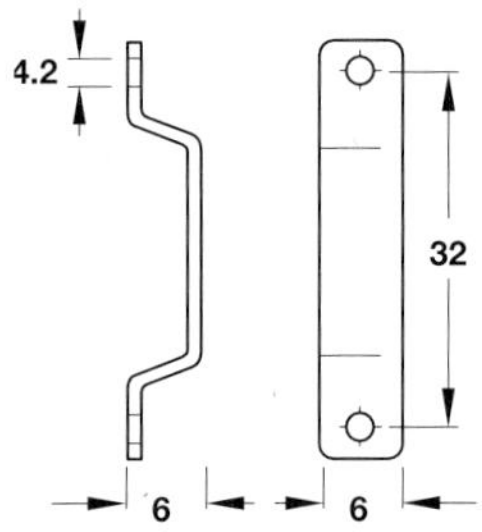

Finish: steel black

Cat. No.	239.61.319

Packing: 10 pcs.

2 Locks, Catches, RTA and PAS® Fittings
Shelf Supports
Bed Fittings

Strike Plate
5mm outwards projection. Screw-mounted.

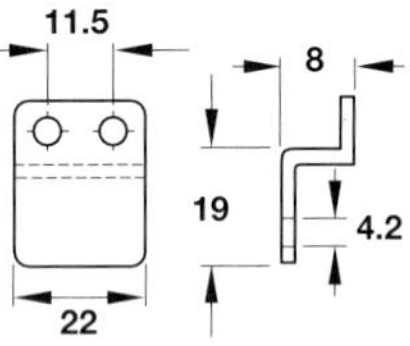

Finish: steel, black

Cat. No.	239.61.328

Packing: 10 pcs.

Angle Strike
90° angle
screw-mounted.

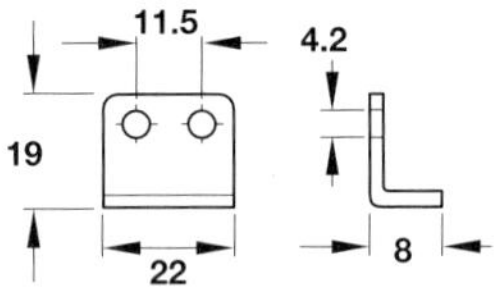

Finish: steel, black

Cat. No.	239.61.337

Packing: 10 pcs.

Strike Plate
For lever lock cylinders

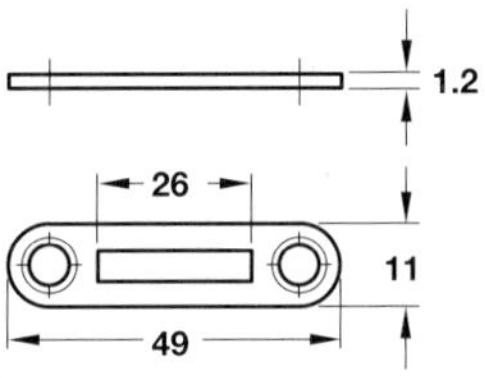

Finish: steel, black

Cat. No.	239.08.705

Packing: 10 pcs.

Strike Plate
For hook lever lock cylinder.

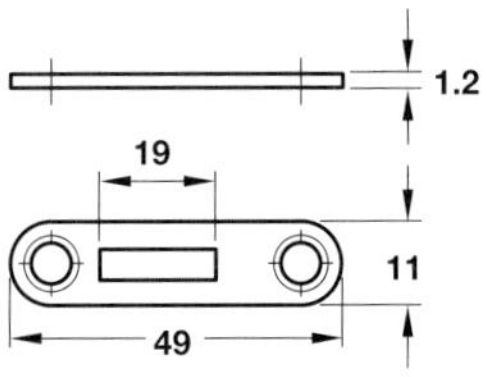

Finish: steel, black

Cat. No.	239.08.723

Packing: 10 pcs.

Rim Locks

Economical rim lock with cylinder, especially suitable for high volume mass-produced furniture.

Locks, Catches, RTA and PAS® Fittings
Shelf Supports
Bed Fittings
2

Rim Lock, with ø 18 mm cylinder.
For left hand use.
5 plate levers = 200 key changes.
Accessories: 2 keys

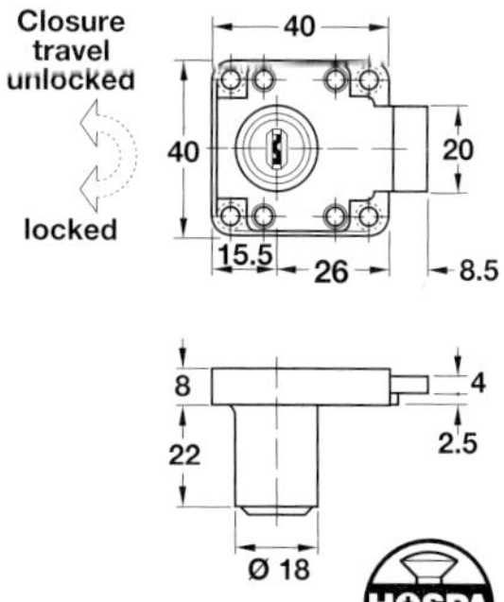

Finish: Case, zinc die cast
Cylinder: zinc die cast

		Keyed different	Keyed alike - FH1
Cat. No.	gold-colored	232.04.917	232.04.962
	matt nickel-plated	232.04.613	232.04.668
	chrome-plated	232.04.211	232.04.266

Packing: 10 pcs.

Rim Lock, with ø 18 mm cylinder.
For right hand use.
5 plate levers = 200 key changes.
Accessories: 2 keys

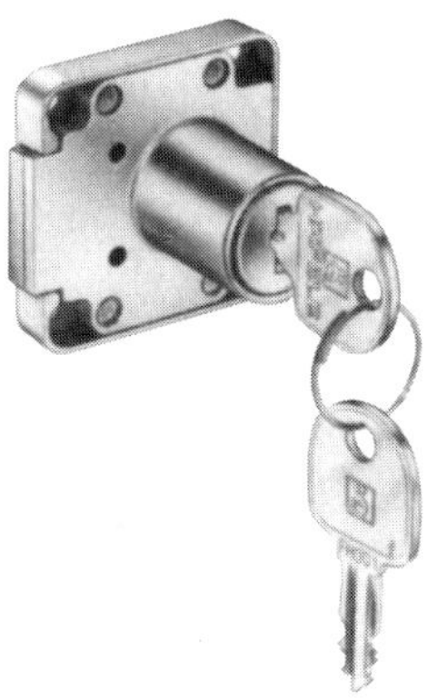

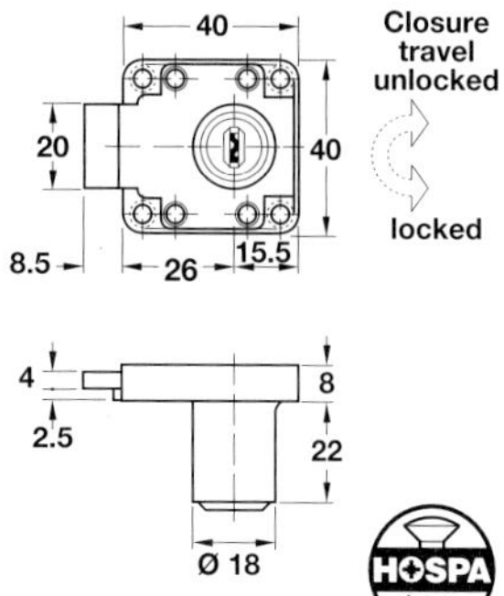

Finish: Case, zinc die cast
Cylinder: zinc die cast

		Keyed different	Keyed alike - FH1
Cat. No.	gold-colored	232.04.908	232.04.953
	matt nickel-plated	232.04.604	232.04.659
	chrome-plated	232.04.202	232.04.257

Packing: 10 pcs.

Rim Lock, with ø 18 mm cylinder.
For drawer use.
5 plate levers = 200 key changes.
Accessories: 2 keys

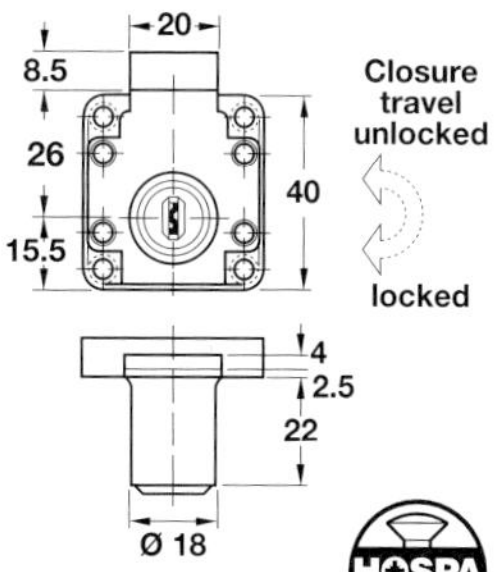

Finish: Case, zinc die cast
Cylinder: zinc die cast

		Keyed different	Keyed alike - FH1
Cat. No.	gold-colored	232.04.926	232.04.971
	matt nickel-plated	232.04.622	232.04.677
	chrome-plated	232.04.220	232.04.275

Packing: 10 pcs.

Spacer Plate
For doors of insufficient thickness, spacer plates can be installed between lock and door to prevent the cylinder from projecting excessively from the door.

Finish: plastic, light gray

Cat. No.	232.03.992

Packing: 10 pcs.

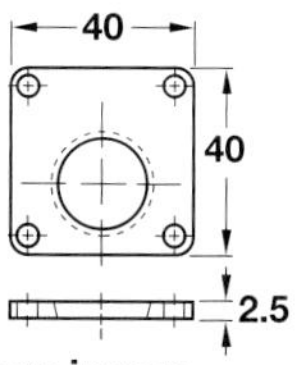

Dimensions in mm

Cylinder Rosettes, ordered separately.

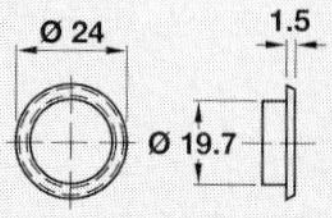

Finish: brass

Color	Cat. No.
polished	219.19.871
matt, nickel-plated	219.19.675
chrome-plated	219.19.273

Packing: 10 pcs.

Key blanks, for FH 1 series

Cat. No.	209.99.008

Packing: 1 pc.

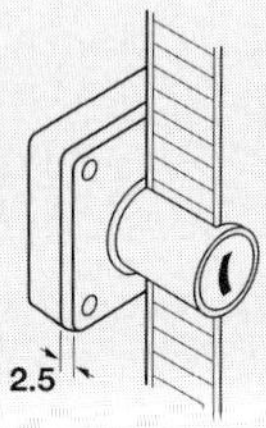

Dimensional data not binding. We reserve the right to alter specifications without notice.

HÄFELE

Mortise/Cam Locks

Mortise Lock Case

Finish: steel face plate, brass-plated

Left

Dimension A	Cat. No.
15 mm	230.23.172
30 mm	230.23.323
40 mm	230.23.421

Right/drawer

Dimension A	Cat. No.
15 mm	230.23.154
30 mm	230.23.305
40 mm	230.23.403

Packing: 1 pc.

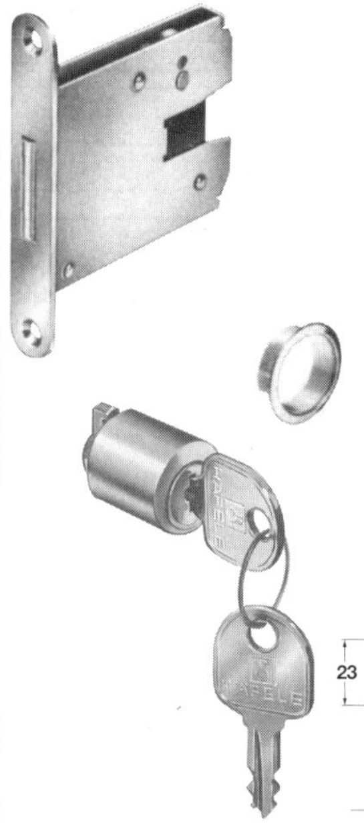

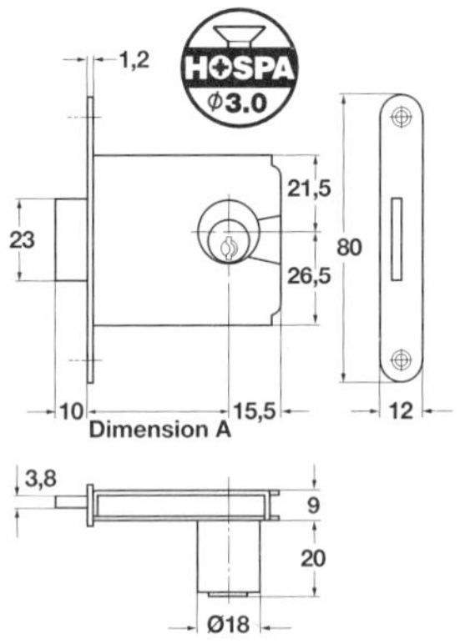

Cylinder For Mortise Lock Case
5 plate levers = 200 key changes.
Accessories: 2 keys

Finish: zinc die cast, matt nickel-plated

Keyed different:

Cat. No.	230.22.602

Keyed alike

Cat. No.	Key change FH 1	230.22.611
	Key change FH 2	230.22.620
	Key change FH 3	230.22.639
	Key change FH 4	230.22.648
	Key change FH 5	230.22.657

Packing: 1 pc.

Cylinder Rosettes, ordered separately.

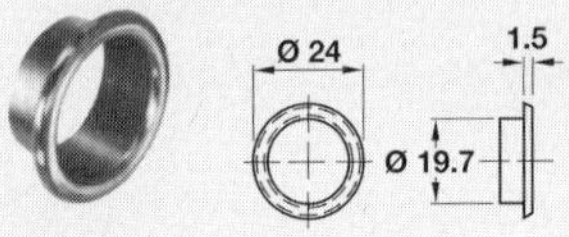

Finish: brass

Color	Cat. No.
polished	219.19.871
matt, nickel-plated	219.19.675
chrome-plated	219.19.273

Packing: 10 pcs.

Key blanks, for FH 1 series

Cat. No.	209.99.008

Packing: 10 pcs.

Cam Locks, with cylinders, for vertical mounting.
Closure travel 90°
5 plate levers = 200 key changes.
Accessories: 2 keys

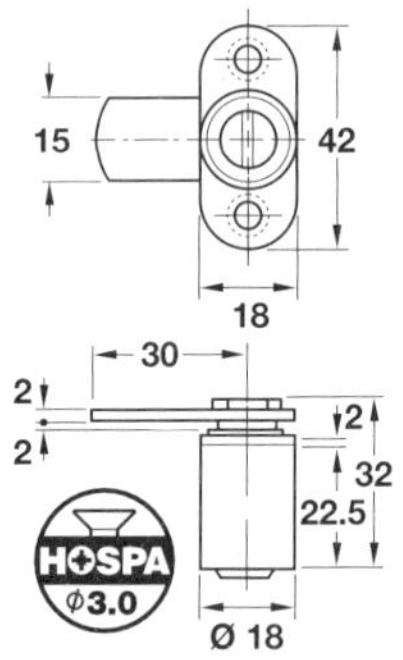

Finish: Mounting plate: zinc die cast, matt nickel-plated
Lever: steel, zinc-plated
Cylinder: zinc die cast, matt nickel-plated

Keyed different

Closure direction	90°	90°
Cat. No.	235.04.609	235.04.654

Keyed alike

Closure direction		90°	90°
Cat. No.	Key change FH 1	235.04.814	235.04.912
	Key change FH 2	235.04.823	235.04.921
	Key change FH 3	235.04.832	235.04.930
	Key change FH 4	235.04.841	235.04.949
	Key change FH 5	235.04.850	235.04.958

Packing: 10 pcs.

Dimensional data not binding.
We reserve the right to alter specifications without notice.

Cam Locks/Inlaid Locks

MINI-LOCK 40, inlaid locks with cylinder.
5 plate levers = 200 key changes.
Accessories: 2 keys

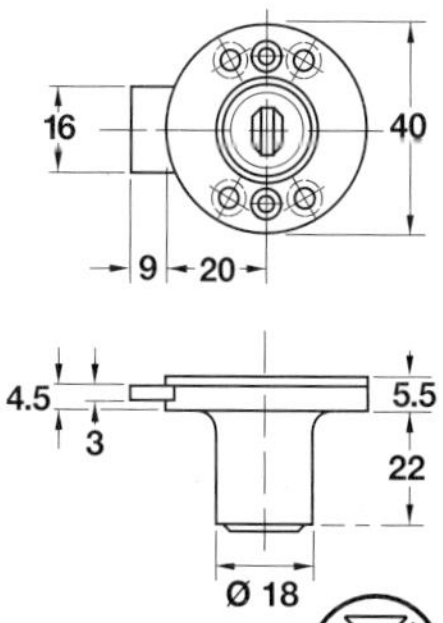

Finish: zinc die cast case and steel backplate: matt nickel-plated
Cylinder: zinc die cast, matt nickel-plated

Keyed different

Left

Cat. No.	230.12.704

Right

Cat. No.	230.12.606

Drawer

Cat. No.	230.12.802

Packing: 10 pcs.

Keyed alike

Application		Left	Right	Drawer
Cat. No.	Key change FH 1	230.12.713	230.12.615	230.12.811
	Key change FH 2	230.12.722	230.12.624	230.12.820
	Key change FH 3	230.12.731	230.12.633	230.12.839
	Key change FH 4	230.12.740	230.12.642	230.12.848
	Key change FH 5	230.12.759	230.12.651	230.12.857

Packing: 10 pcs.

RONDELL, inlaid flap locks with cylinder
With key trap (key removable only when locked).
5 plate levers = 200 key changes.
Accessories: 2 keys

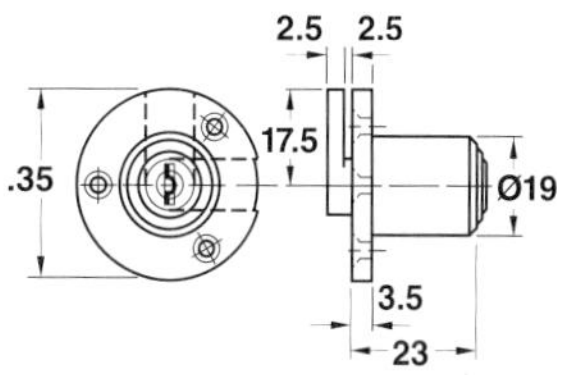

Finish: zinc die cast case

Keyed different

Cat. No.	matt nickel-plated	219.27.051
	gold-colored	219.27.551

Keyed alike: Key change FH1

Cat. No.	matt nickel-plated	219.27.006
	gold-colored	219.27.506

Packing: 10 pcs.

Cylinder Rosettes,
ordered separately.

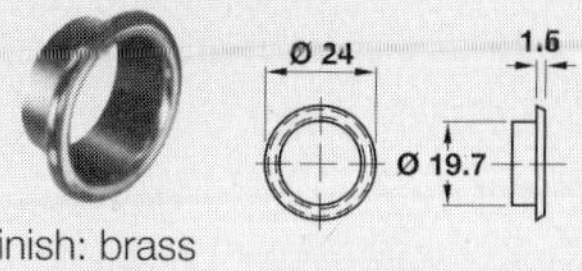

Finish: brass

Color	Cat. No.
polished	219.19.871
matt, nickel-plated	219.19.675
chrome-plated	219.19.273

Packing: 10 pcs.

Key blanks, for FH 1 series

Cat. No.	209.99.008

Packing: 1 pc.

If the door is sufficiently thick, spacers can be placed between the lock and inside of the door to prevent the lock projecting excessively from the door.

Spacers

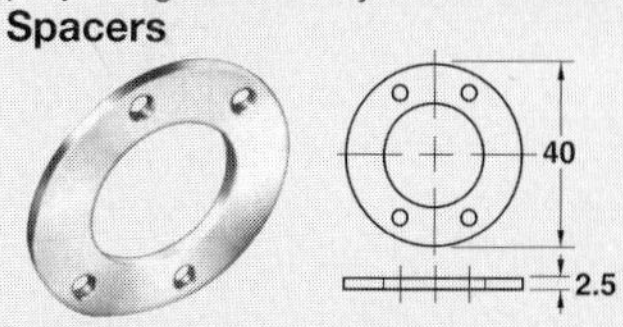

Finish: plastic, light gray

Cat. No.	230.07.990

Packing: 1 and 10 pcs.

Key blanks, for FH 1 series

Cat. No.	209.99.008

Packing: 1 pc.

Cylinder Rosettes,
ordered separately.

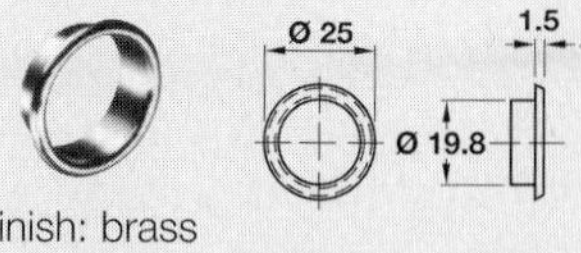

Finish: brass

Cat. No.	polished	219.27.882
	matt nickel-plated	219.27.686

Packing: 10 pcs.

Dimensional data not binding.
We reserve the right to alter specifications without notice.

Dimensions in mm

HÄFELE

Cam Locks For Metal Furniture

Cam Locks, with straight lever
Clip attachment
Closure travel: 180° or 90°
Suitable for 0.8-1.5 or 1.6-2.3 mm gauge sheet metal
5 plate levers = 200 key changes
Accessories: 2 keys, 1 locking cam, 1 spring washer and 1 clip

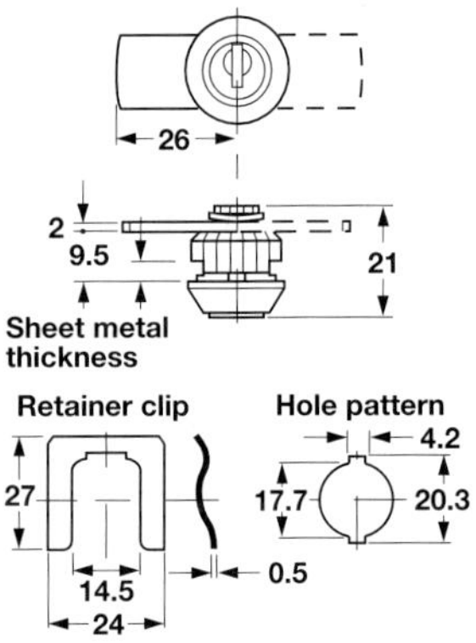

Finish: steel clip, hardened; steel lever, zinc-plated
Cylinder: zinc die cast, polished chrome-plated

Keyed different

Closure direction		180°	90°	90°
Cat. No.	0.8-1.5 mm sheet metal	235.70.201	235.70.210	235.70.229
	1.6-2.3 mm sheet metal	235.71.208		

Keyed alike: key change FH1

Closure direction		180°	90°	90°
Cat. No.	0.8-1.5 mm sheet metal	235.70.256	235.70.265	235.70.274
	1.6-2.3 mm sheet metal	235.71.253		

Packing: 10 pcs.

2 Locks, Catches, RTA and PAS® Fittings
Shelf Supports
Bed Fittings

Key blanks, for FH 1 series

Cat. No.	209.99.008

Packing: 1 pc.

Cam Locks, with straight lever
Nut attachment
Closure travel: 180° or 90°
5 plate levers = 200 key changes
Accessories: 2 keys, 1 locking cam, 1 spring washer and 1 nut

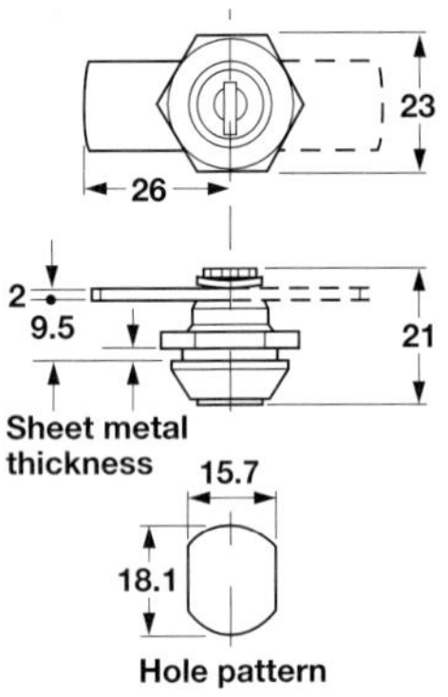

Finish: steel nut and lever, zinc-plated
Cylinder: zinc die cast, polished chrome-plated

Keyed different

Closure direction	180°	90°	90°
Cat. No. 0.8-1.5 mm sheet metal	235.72.205	235.72.214	235.72.223

Keyed alike: key change FH1

Closure direction	180°	90°	90°
Cat. No. 0.8-1.5 mm sheet metal	235.72.250	235.72.269	235.72.278

Packing: 10 pcs.

*Reposition lever as necessary to change closure direction.

Cam Locks, cranked lever
Closure travel: 180°
5 plate levers = 200 key changes
Accessories: 2 keys, 1 locking cam, 1 spring washer and 1 nut

Keyed different

Closure direction	180°
Cat. No. 0.8-2.5 mm sheet metal	234.64.208

Keyed alike: key change FH1

Closure direction	180°
Cat. No. 0.8-2.5 mm sheet metal	234.64.253

Packing: 10 pcs.

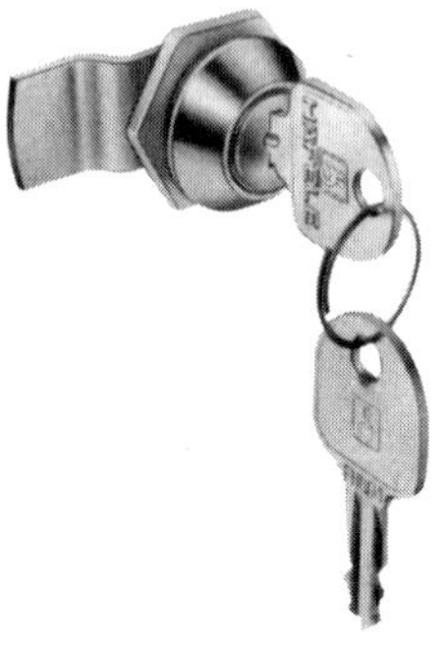

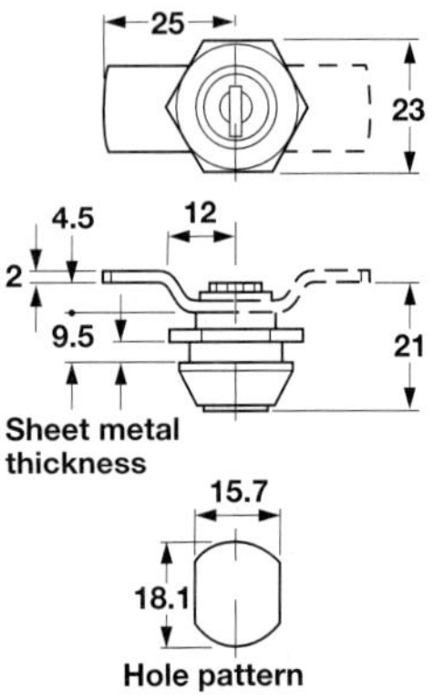

Dimensions in mm

Dimensional data not binding. We reserve the right to alter specifications without notice.

Tambour Door Locks

HÄFELE

Tambour Door Lock Case

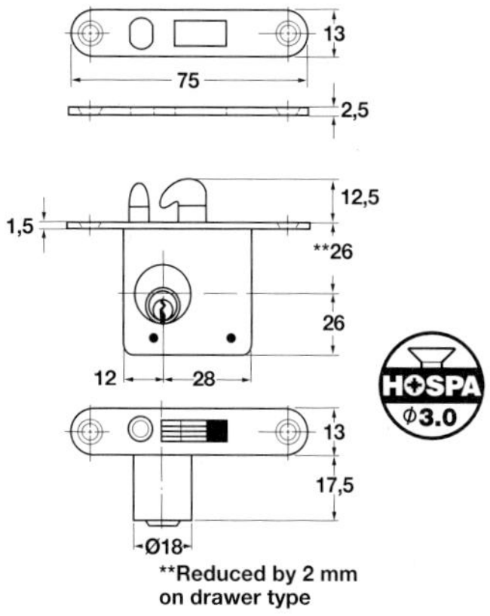

Finish: brass face plate, matt nickel-plated

Left

Cat. No.	230.37.256

Packing: 1 pc.

Right/Drawer

Cat. No.	230.37.201

Packing: 1 pc.

Cylinder For Tambour Door Lock Case
5 plate levers = 200 key changes.
Accessories: 2 keys

Keyed different

Cat. No.	230.22.602

Keyed alike

Cat. No.	Key change FH1	230.22.611
	Key change FH2	230.22.620
	Key change FH3	230.22.639
	Key change FH4	230.22.648
	Key change FH5	230.22.657

Packing: 1 pc.

Tambour Door Rim Lock, with cylinder
5 plate levers = 200 key changes.
Accessories: 2 keys and 1 strike plate

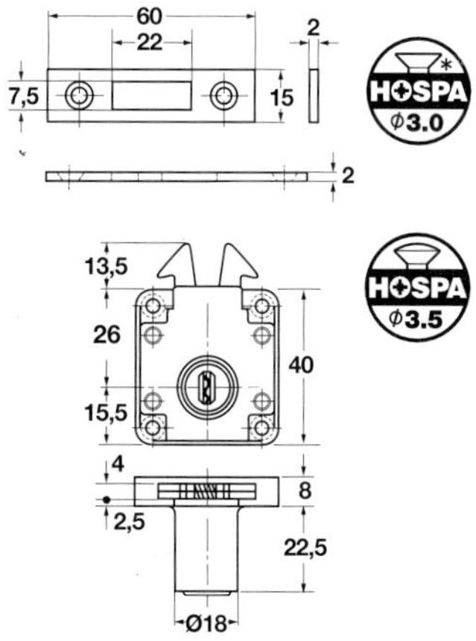

Finish: Zinc die cast case, matt nickel-plated
Strike plate: steel, zinc-plated
Cylinder: zinc die-cast, matt nickel-plated

Keyed different

Cat. No.	232.07.605

Keyed alike

Cat. No.	Key change FH1	232.02.614
	Key change FH2	232.02.623
	Key change FH3	232.02.632
	Key change FH4	232.02.641
	Key change FH5	232.02.650

Packing: 10 pcs.

Cylinder Rosettes,
ordered separately.

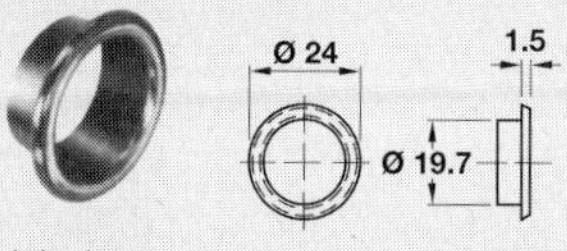

Finish: brass

Color	Cat. No.
polished	219.19.871
matt, nickel-plated	219.19.675
chrome-plated	219.19.273

Packing: 10 pcs.

Key blanks, for FH 1 series

Cat. No.	209.99.008

Packing: 1 pc.

Tambour door locks

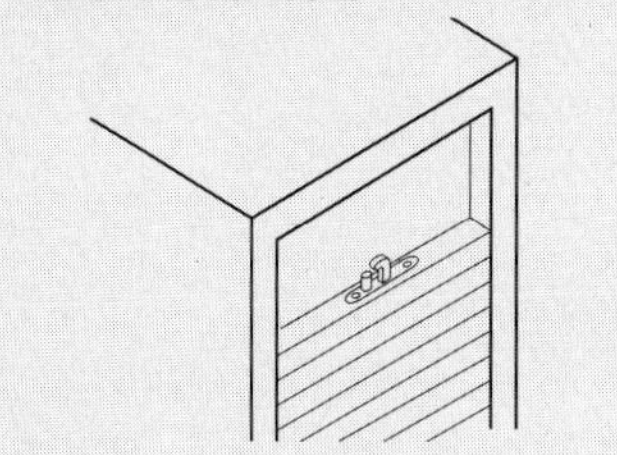

...can also be used for lightweight sliding doors.

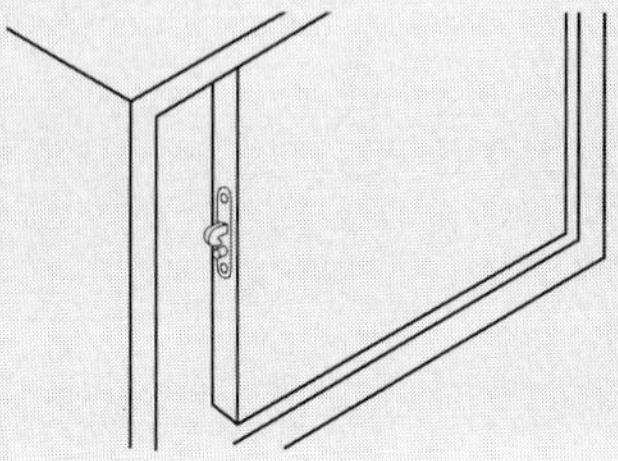

Dimensional data not binding.
We reserve the right to alter specifications without notice.

Dimensions in mm

HÄFELE

Pushbutton Lock/Central Locking System

Pushbutton Lock, 18 mm diameter
Function: Close, by pressing the cylinder
Open, only with key
Locking pin with M5 internal thread.
5 plate levers = 200 key changes.
Accessories: 2 keys

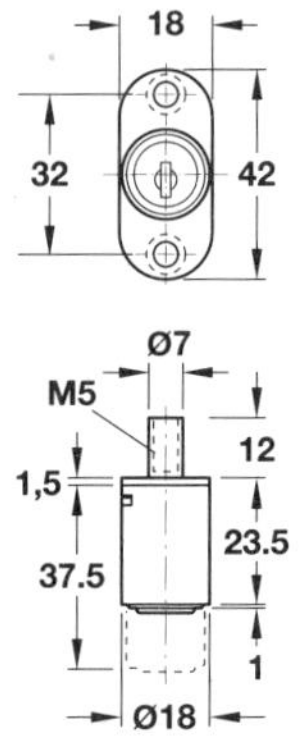

Finish: zinc die-cast case

Keyed different

Application	matt nickel-plated	gold-plated
Cat. No.	234.50.600	234.50.800

Packing: 10 pcs.

Keyed alike

Application		matt nickel-plated	gold-plated
Cat. No.	Key change FH1	234.50.601	234.50.801
	Key change FH2	234.50.602	234.50.802
	Key change FH3	234.50.603	234.50.803
	Key change FH4	234.50.604	234.50.804
	Key change FH5	234.50.605	234.50.805

Packing: 10 pcs.

Cylinder Rosettes,
ordered separately.

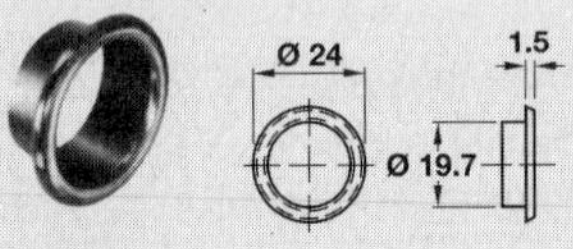

Finish: brass

Color	Cat. No.
polished	219.19.871
matt, nickel-plated	219.19.675
chrome-plated	219.19.273

Packing: 10 pcs.

Locking socket, to be ordered separately.

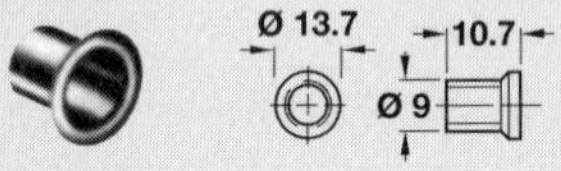

Finish: brass, nickel-plated

Cat. No.	234.59.994

Packing: 100 pcs.

Key blanks, for FH 1 series

Cat. No.	209.99.008

Packing: 1 pc.

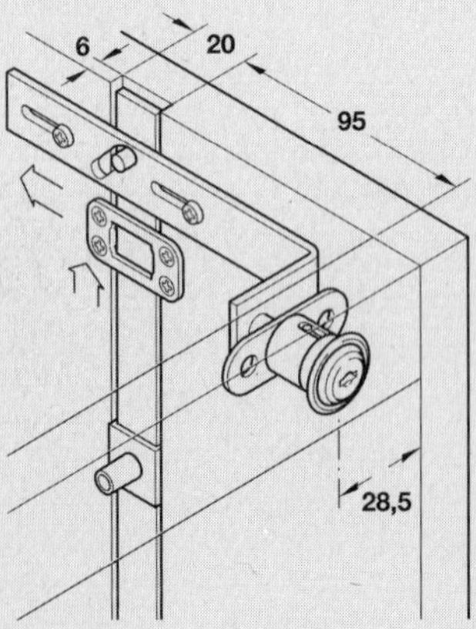

Accessories
for all central locking system pushbutton locks

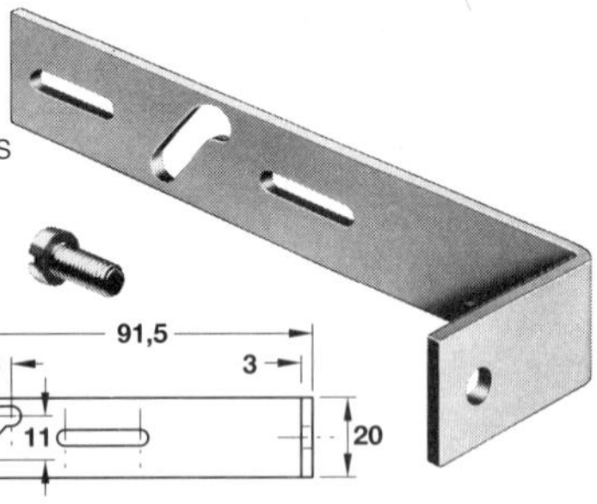

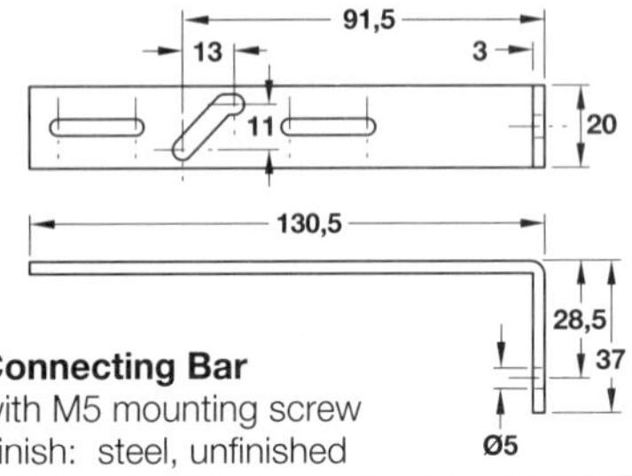

Connecting Bar
with M5 mounting screw
Finish: steel, unfinished

Application	left	right
Cat. No.	237.11.257	237.11.202

Packing: 1 pc.

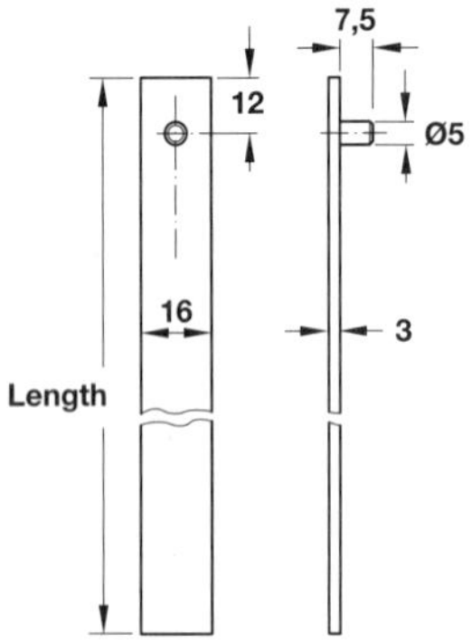

Lockbar
Finish: steel, unfinished

Cat. No.	500 mm length	237.21.217
	600 mm length	237.21.235
	800 mm length	237.21.271
	1000 mm length	237.21.315

Packing: 1 pc.

Dimensional data not binding. We reserve the right to alter specifications without notice.

Dimensions in mm

Central Locking Cylinders and Systems

Central Locking System With Lockbar, ø 18 mm
5 plate levers = 200 key changes.
Accessories: 2 keys

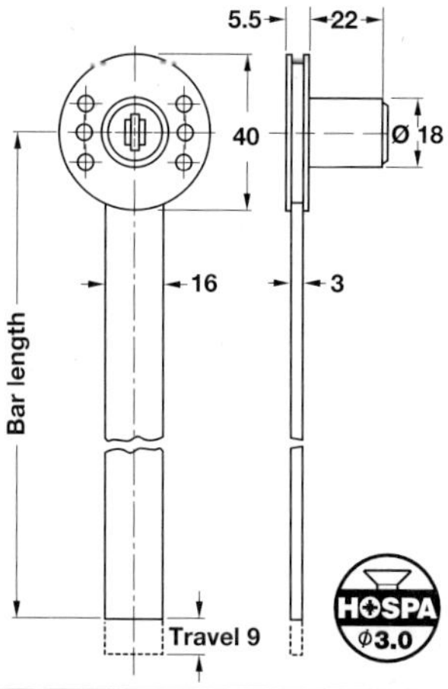

Finish: zinc die-cast case and steel backplate, matt nickel-plated
Bar: aluminum, unfinished
Cylinder: zinc die cast, matt nickel-plated

Keyed different

Bar length: (mm)	500	600
Cat. No.	237.30.609	237.30.707

Keyed alike

Bar length: (mm)		500	600
Cat. No.	Key change FH 1	237.30.618	237.30.716
	Key change FH 2	237.30.627	237.30.725
	Key change FH 3	237.30.636	237.30.734
	Key change FH 4	237.30.645	237.30.743
	Key change FH 5	237.30.654	237.30.752

Packing: 10 pcs.

Central Locking Cylinder, ø 18 mm, indirect action.
Key - 180°
Lifting pin travel - 180°
5 plate levers = 200 key changes.
Accessories: 2 keys

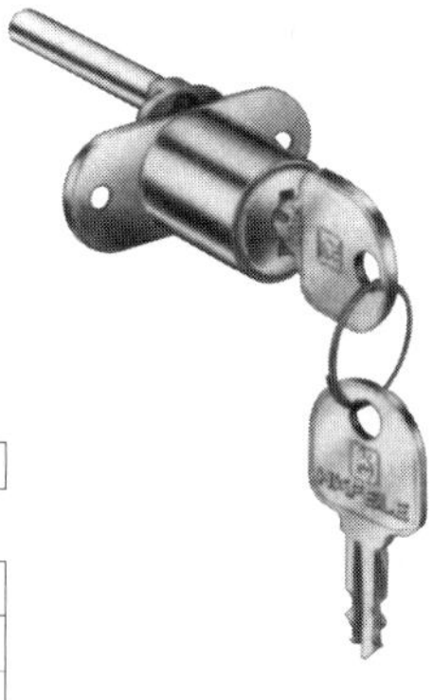

Front view

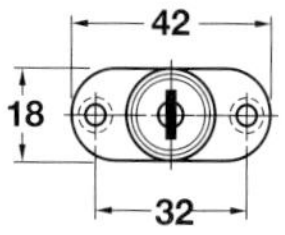

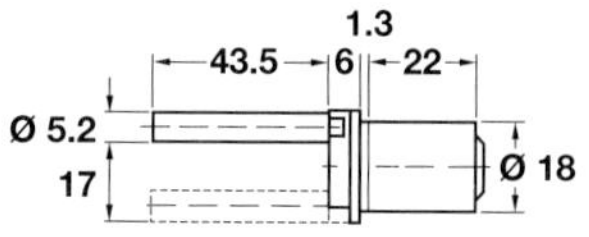

Side view

Finish: Mounting plate: zinc die cast, matt nickel-plated
Cylinder: zinc die cast, matt nickel-plated

Keyed different

Cat. No.	234.77.705

Keyed alike

Cat. No.	Key change FH1	234.77.714
	Key change FH2	234.77.723
	Key change FH3	234.77.732
	Key change FH4	234.77.741
	Key change FH5	234.77.750

Packing: 1 pc.

Dimensions in mm

Cylinder Rosettes,
ordered separately.

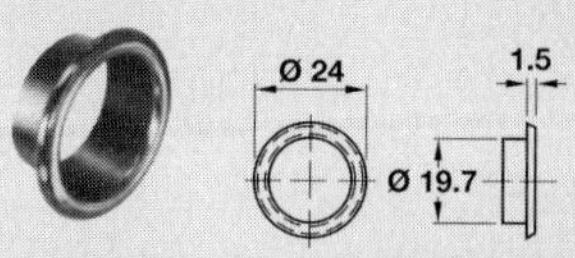

Finish: brass

Color	Cat. No.
polished	219.19.871
matt, nickel-plated	219.19.675
chrome-plated	219.19.273

Packing: 10 pcs.

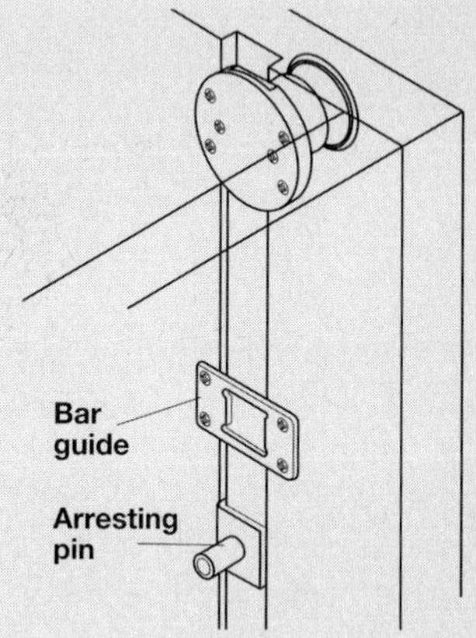

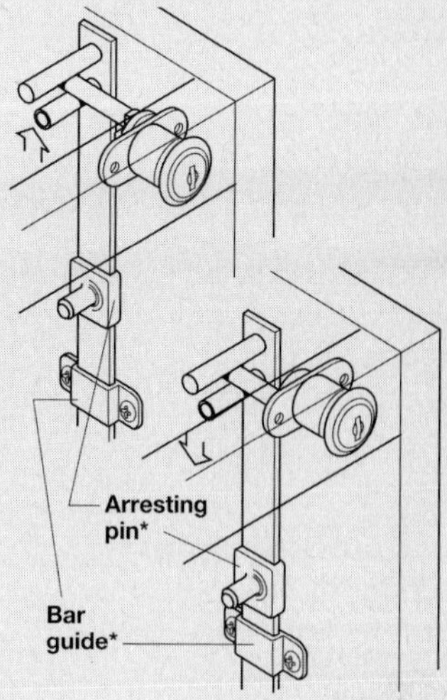

Key blanks, for FH 1 series

Cat. No.	209.99.008

Packing: 1 pc.

HÄFELE

Central Locking System Accessories

Guides can be used for surface-mounted (left) or recessed (right) bars by reversing their position.

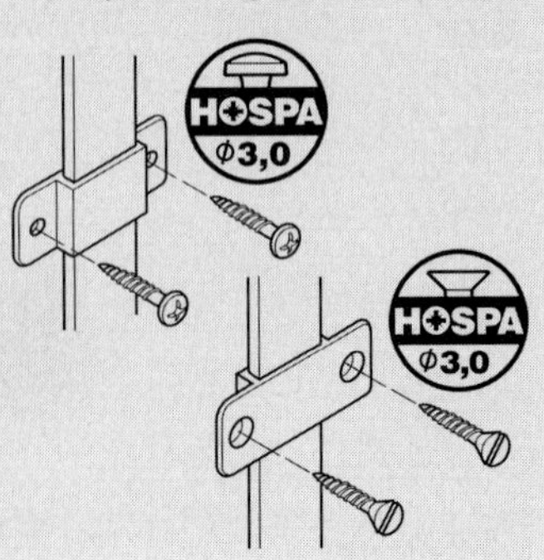

2 Locks, Catches, RTA and PAS® Fittings
Shelf Supports
Bed Fittings

The guides and arresting pins are designed for a bar section measuring 16 x 3 mm.
All the central locking systems illustrated on pages **2.32** to **2.33** use accessories with these dimensions.

Bar guide, open type
Finish: plastic, white

Cat No.	237.23.720

Packing: 200 pcs.

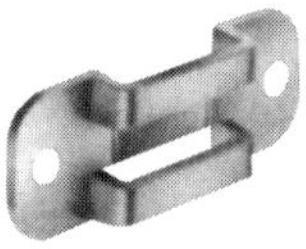

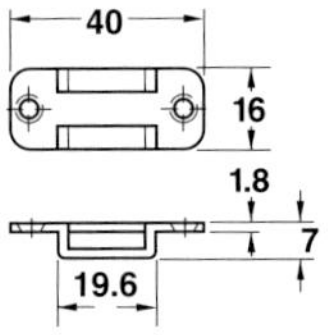

Bar guide, open type
Finish: steel, galvanized

Cat No.	237.23.006

Packing: 100 pcs.

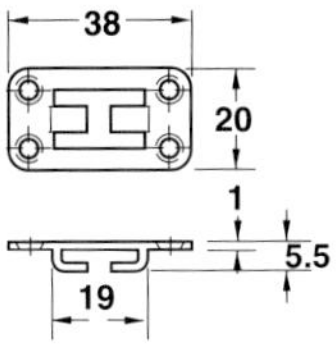

Arresting pin
Accessory: 1 threaded bolt
Finish: zinc die cast

Cat No.	237.22.027

Packing: 100 pcs.

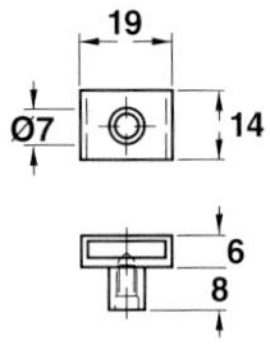

Arresting Pin
Finish: zinc die cast, nickel matt
Accessory: 1 slotted set screw

Cat. No.	237.22.107

Packing: 100 pcs.

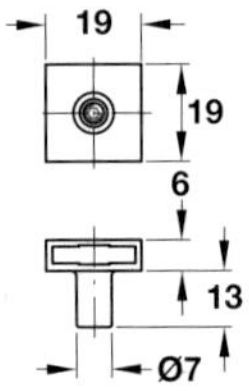

Mounting arrangement for a right-hand drawer...

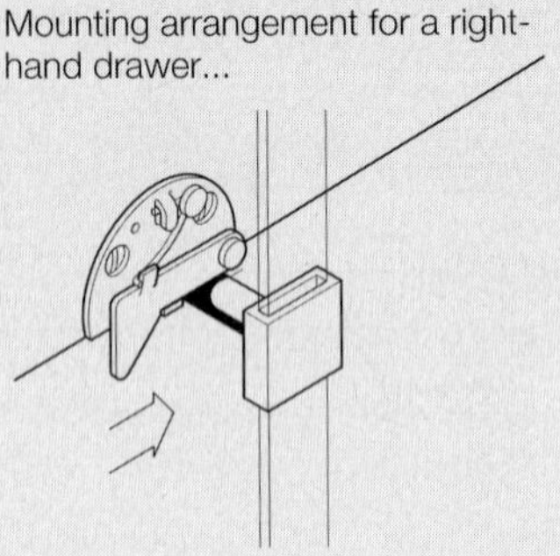

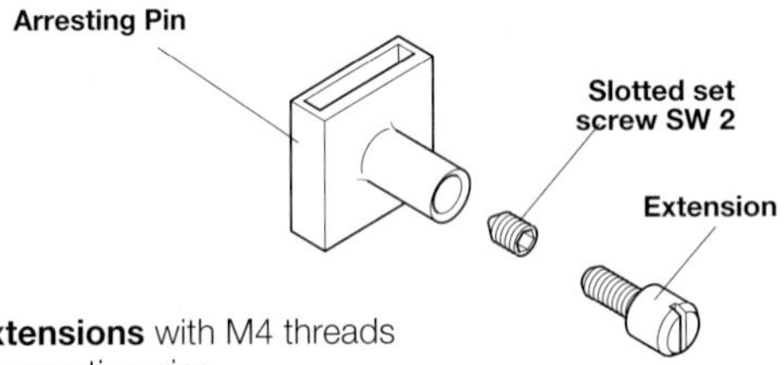

Extensions with M4 threads
for arresting pins
Finish: steel, zinc-plated

Cat. No.	for length **17 mm**	237.22.189
	for length **20 mm**	237.22.214
	for length **25 mm**	237.22.269
	for length **30 mm**	237.22.312

Packing: 100 pcs.

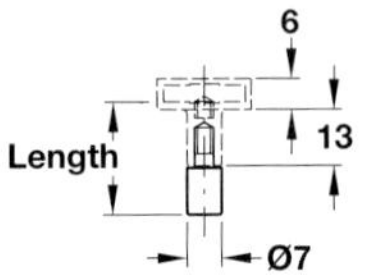

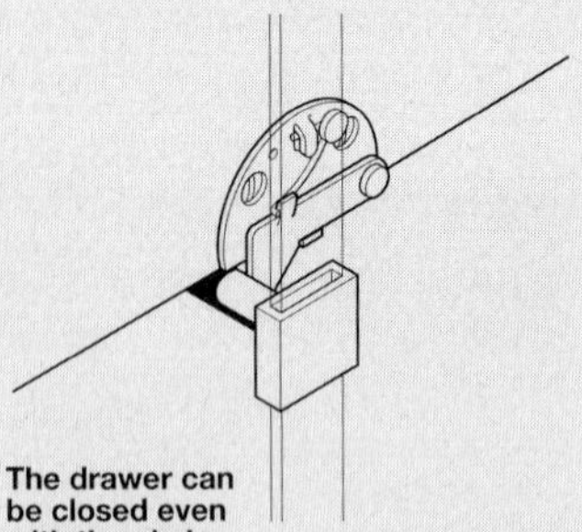

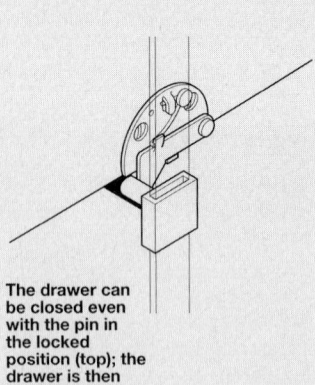

The drawer can be closed even with the pin in the locked position (top); the drawer is then locked in position (bottom).

Drawer catches, screw-mounted
Finish: steel, nickel-plated

Cat. No.	left	237.16.752
	right	237.16.707

Packing: 100 pcs.

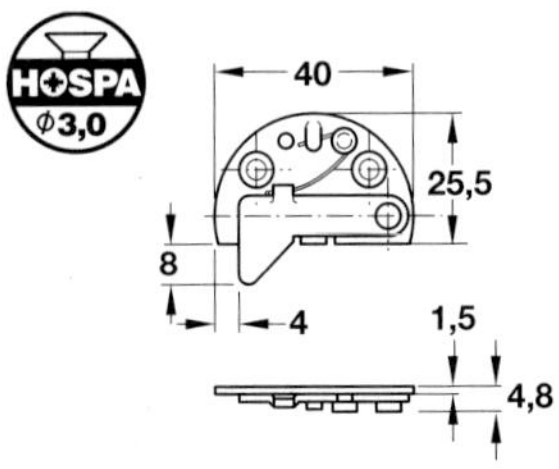

Bars for central locking systems
Finish: aluminum

Cat No.	Length 600 mm	234.78.033
	Length 820 mm	234.78.051

Packing: 50 pcs.

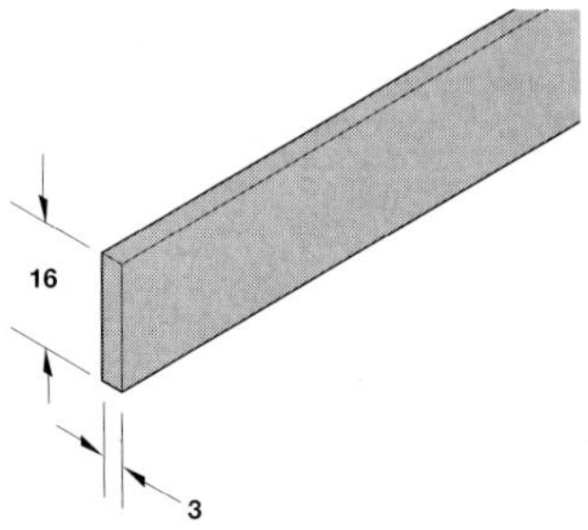

Dimensional data not binding.
We reserve the right to alter specifications without notice.

Dimensions in mm

Rim Locks

Spring Rim Lock, with 18 mm diameter cylinder.
5 pin levers = 20,000 key changes.
Accessories: 2 keys and 1 cylinder rosette

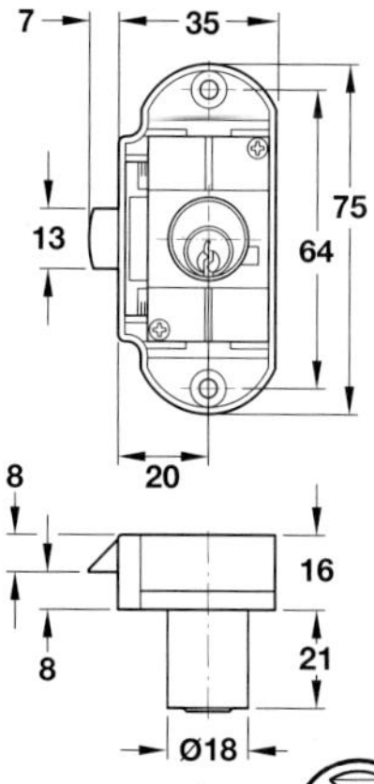

Keyed different

	Finish	left	right
Cat. No.	white	231.15.700	231.15.600
	brown	231.15.100	231.15.000

Keyed alike

	Finish: white	left	right
Cat. No.	H 1	231.15.701	231.15.601
	H 2	231.15.702	231.15.602
	H 3	231.15.703	231.15.603
	H 4	231.15.704	231.15.604
	H 5	231.15.705	231.15.605

Keyed alike

	Finish: brown	left	right
Cat. No.	H 1	231.15.101	231.15.001
	H 2	231.15.102	231.15.002
	H 3	231.15.103	231.15.003
	H 4	231.15.104	231.15.004
	H 5	231.15.105	231.15.005

Packing: 1 pc.

HOSPA Φ3.5

With master key system

Cat. No.	231.05.18X

Packing: pc. pcs.

With general master key system

Cat. No.	231.05.19X

Cat. No.	Key blank	*209.99.044

Packing: 1 pc.

Key blanks, for H series

Cat. No.	209.99.044

Packing: 10 pcs.

Locks, Catches, RTA and PAS® Fittings
Shelf Supports
Bed Fittings
2

Mini-bar Spring Rim Lock, with telltale and reset feature
5 pin levers = 20,000 key changes.
Accessories: 2 keys

Finish: Plastic case, brown
Cylinder: brass, matt nickel-plated

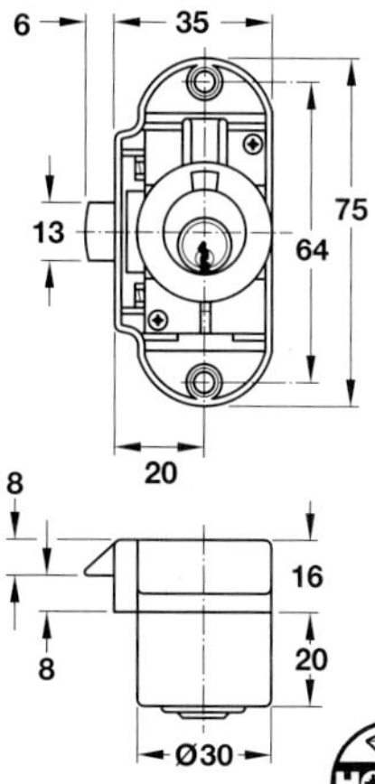

Keyed alike: Key change H1

application		left	right
Cat. No.	brown	231.10.101	231.10.001

Packing: 1 pc.

Telltale Reset Key

Cat. No.	231.10.095

Packing: 1 pc.

HOSPA Φ3.5

Minibar Spring Lock, as shown above **but featuring Master Key System***

Cat. No.	231.10.098

Packing: 1 pc.

Master Key, also doubles as **Telltale Reset Key**

Cat. No.	231.10.099

Packing: 1 pc.

The spring rim lock is also available as a mini-bar lock with a telltale window above the cylinder casing. As the description implies, this version is particularly suitable for use on mini-bars in hotel rooms. When the bar is initially unlocked by hotel guest, the red telltale appears above the cylinder, indicating to the room service staff that the guest has probably removed a drink or snack which must be replaced and billed.

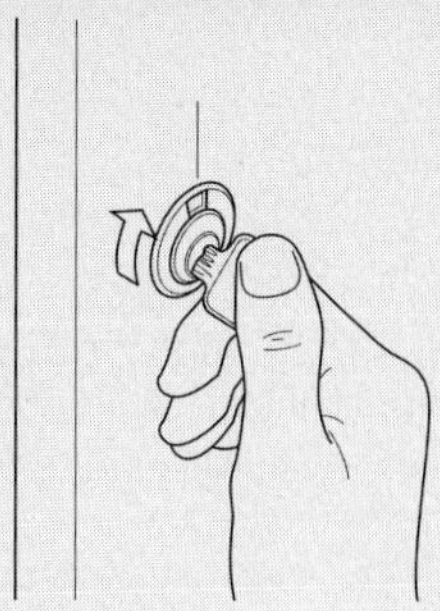

Dimensions in mm

Dimensional data not binding. We reserve the right to alter specifications without notice.

HÄFELE

Cam Locks

Key blanks, for H series

Cat. No.	209.99.044

Packing: 10 pcs.

Cam Lock, with cylinder, for vertical mounting.
Closure travel 90° (with key trap).
5 pin levers = 10,000 key changes.
Accessories: 2 keys, 1 cylinder rosette, 1 locking cam and 2 nuts

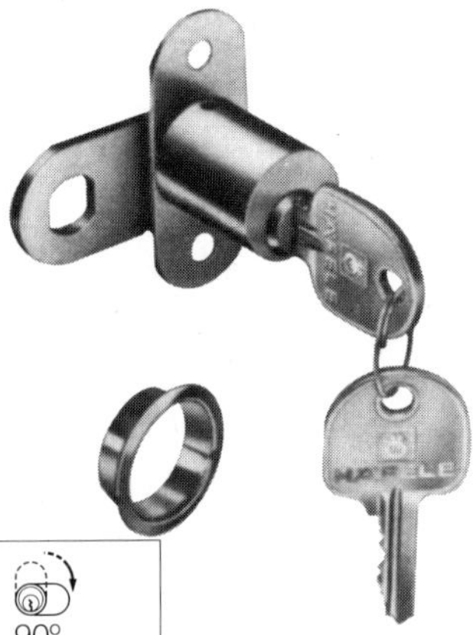

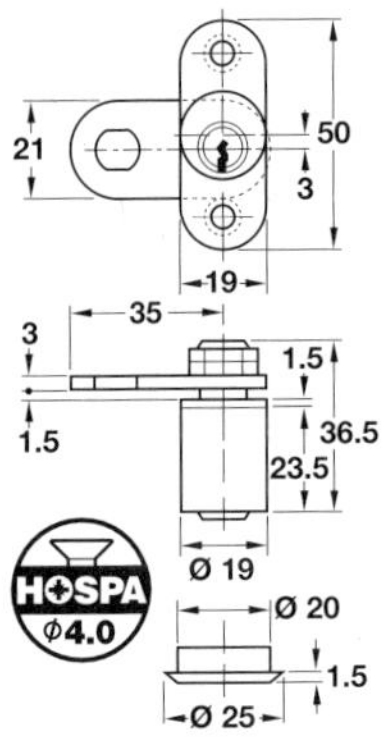

Finish: Mounting plate: steel, matt nickel-plated
Nuts and lever: steel, zinc-plated
Cylinder: brass, matt nickel-plated

Keyed different

Closure direction	90°	90°
Cat. No. white	235.03.602	235.03.657

2 Locks, Catches, RTA and PAS® Fittings Shelf Supports Bed Fittings

Keyed alike

Closure direction		90°	90°
Cat. No.	Key change H1	235.03.817	235.03.915
	Key change H2	235.03.826	235.03.924
	Key change H3	235.03.835	235.03.933
	Key change H4	235.03.844	235.03.942
	Key change H5	235.03.853	235.03.951

Packing: 1 pc.

With master key system

Cat. No.	235.03.68X

With general master key system

Cat. No.	235.03.69X

*Closure orientation is achieved by repositioning the bolt.

Cam lock with Cylinder, for horizontal mounting
Closure travel 90°, (with key trap)
5 pin levers-10,000 key changes
Accessories: 2 keys, 1 cylinder rosette, 1 locking lever and 2 nuts.

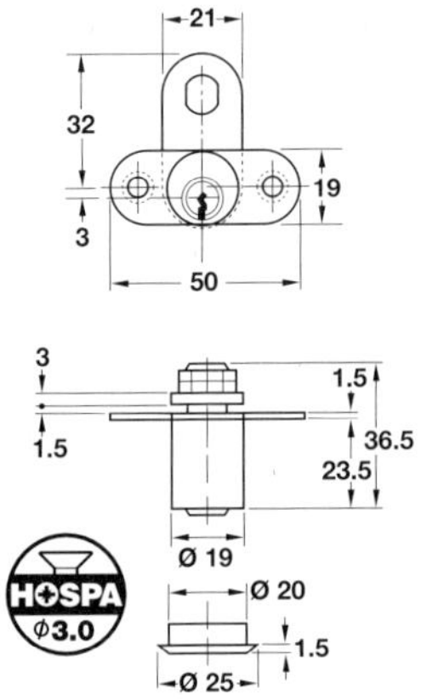

Finish: Mounting plate: steel, matt nickel-plated; Cam: steel, zinc-plated
Cylinder: brass, matt nickel-plated

Keyed different

Closure direction	90°	90°
Cat. No. white	235.03.700	235.03.755

Packing: 10 pcs.

*Closure orientation is achieved by repositioning the bolt.

With master key system

Cat. No.	235.03.78X

With general master key system

Cat. No.	235.03.79X

Dimensions in mm

Dimensional data not binding. We reserve the right to alter specifications without notice.

Flap Lock/Inlay Lock

HÄFELE

RONDELL, inlaid flap lock with cylinder
With key trap (key only removable when locked).
5 pin levers = 20,000 key changes.
Accessories: 2 keys and 1 cylinder rosette

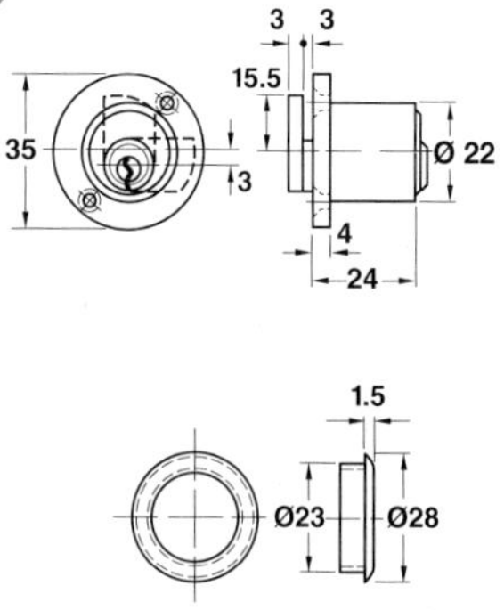

Finish: zinc die-cast case, matt nickel-plated
Cylinder: brass, matt nickel-plated

Keyed different:

Cat. No.	219.19.602

Packing: 1 pc.

With master key system

Cat. No.	219.19.78x

With general master key system

Cat. No.	219.19.79x

HOSPA Φ3.0

Inlay Lock with Cylinder
5 pin levers = 20,000 key changes.
Accessories: 2 keys and 1 cylinder rosette
Finish: zinc die-cast case, matt nickel-plated
Cylinder: brass, matt nickel-plated

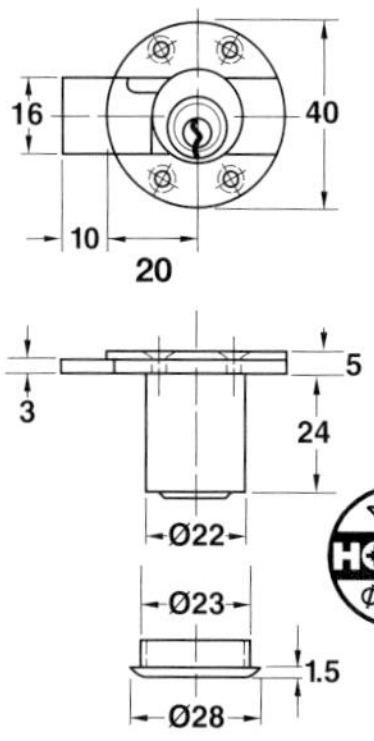

Keyed different

Left

Cat. No.	230.19.614

Right

Cat. No.	230.19.605

Drawer

Cat. No.	230.19.623

Packing: 10 pcs.

HOSPA Φ3.0

Keyed alike

Application		Left	Right	Drawer
Cat. No.	Key change H1	230.19.810	230.19.712	230.19.918
	Key change H2	230.19.829	230.19.721	230.19.927
	Key change H3	230.19.838	230.19.730	230.19.936
	Key change H4	230.19.847	230.19.749	230.19.945
	Key change H5	230.19.856	230.19.758	230.19.954

Packing: 1 pc.

With master key system

Cat. No.	230.19.68X

With general master key system

Cat. No.	230.19.69X

Key blanks, for H series

Cat. No.	209.99.044

Packing: 10 pcs.

Advantages of RONDELL locks:
The inside of the drop-leaf or door remains completely flat. With the flap open, the lock and catch lie within the panel, with no projecting parts. The key trap presents an additional advantage. Since the key can only be withdrawn when the flap is locked shut…

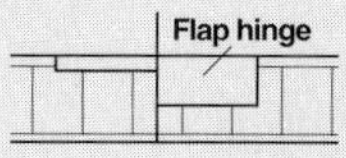

…it cannot fall out when the flap is lowered.

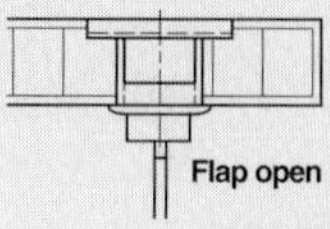

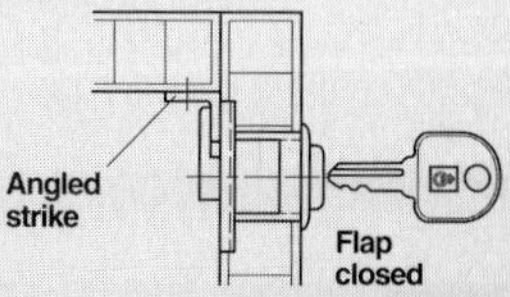

If the door is sufficiently thick, spacers can be placed between the lock and inside of the door to prevent the lock projecting excessively from the door.

Spacers

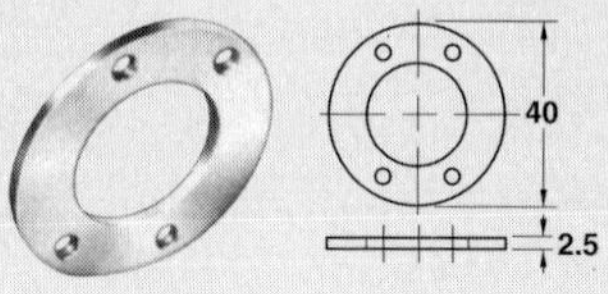

Finish: plastic, light gray

Cat. No.	230.13.998

Packing: 1 and 10 pcs.

Dimensional data not binding.
We reserve the right to alter specifications without notice.

HÄFELE

Mortise Locks - For Tambour Doors

Key blanks, for H series

Cat. No.	209.99.044

Packing: 10 pcs.

Mortise Lock For Tambour Door

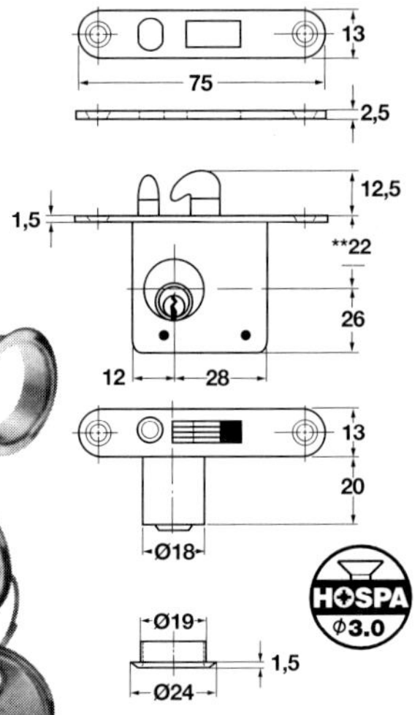

**Reduced by 3 mm on drawer type

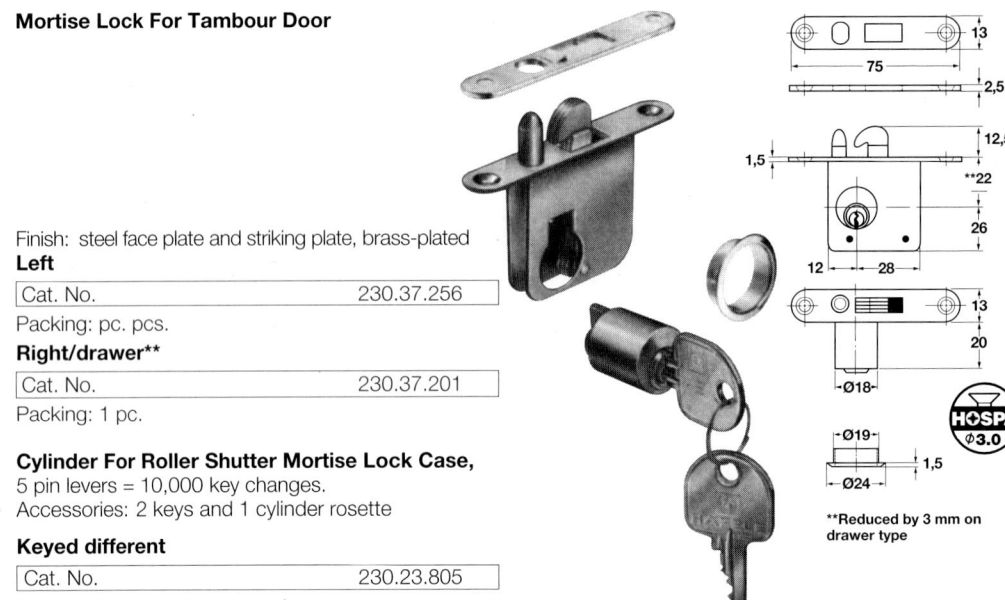

Finish: steel face plate and striking plate, brass-plated

Left

Cat. No.	230.37.256

Packing: pc. pcs.

Right/drawer**

Cat. No.	230.37.201

Packing: 1 pc.

Cylinder For Roller Shutter Mortise Lock Case,
5 pin levers = 10,000 key changes.
Accessories: 2 keys and 1 cylinder rosette

Keyed different

Cat. No.	230.23.805

Keyed alike

Cat. No.	Key change H1	230.23.814
	Key change H2	230.23.823
	Key change H3	230.23.832
	Key change H4	230.23.841
	Key change H5	230.23.850

Packing: 1 pc.

With master key system

Cat. No.	230.23.98X

With general master key system

Cat. No.	230.23.99X

Mortise Lock for Tambour Doors

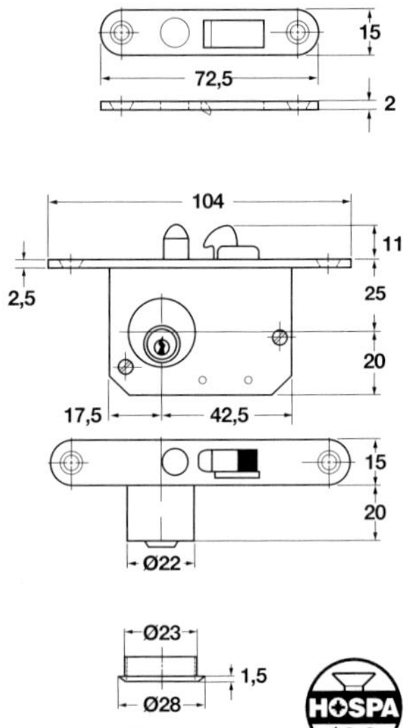

Finish: brass face plate and steel strike plate, matt nickel-plated

Application	Left, right, drawer
Cat. No.	230.30.202

Packing: 1 pc.

Cylinder For Lock Case
5 pin levers = 20,000 key changes.
Accessories: 2 keys and 1 cylinder rosette

Finish: Brass, matt nickel-plated

Keyed different

Cat. No.	230.20.804

Keyed alike

Cat. No.	Key change H1	230.20.813
	Key change H2	230.20.822
	Key change H3	230.20.831
	Key change H4	230.20.840
	Key change H5	230.20.859

Packing: 1 pc.

With master key system

Cat. No.	230.20.98X

With general master key system

Cat. No.	230.20.99X

Dimensions in mm

Pushbutton Lock

HÄFELE

Pushbutton Lock, ø 22 mm
Function: Closing, by pressing the cylinder
Opening, only with key
Locking pin with M5 inside thread.
5 pin levers = 10,000 key changes.
Accessories: 2 keys, 1 cylinder rosette and 1 socket

Finish: zinc die-cast case, nickel-plated
Cylinder: brass, matt nickel-plated

Keyed different

Cat. No.	234.58.602

Keyed alike

Cat. No.	Key change H1	234.58.611
	Key change H2	234.58.620
	Key change H3	234.58.639
	Key change H4	234.58.648
	Key change H5	234.58.657

Packing: 1 pc.

With master key system

Cat. No.	234.58.68X

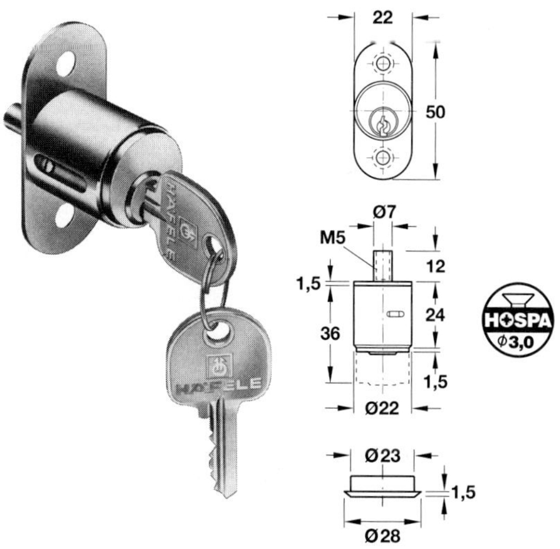

With general master key system

Cat. No.	234.58.69X

Locking Socket,
ordered separately.

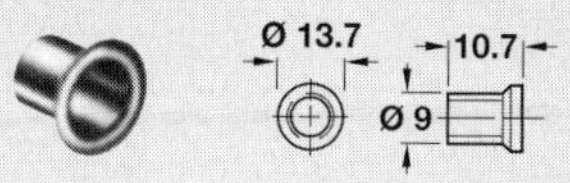

Finish: Brass, nickel-plated

Cat. No.	234.59.994

Packing: 10 pcs.

Key blanks, for H series

Cat. No.	209.99.044

Packing: 10 pcs.

Locks, Catches, RTA and PAS® Fittings
Shelf Supports
Bed Fittings
2

Accessories
for all central locking system pushbutton locks

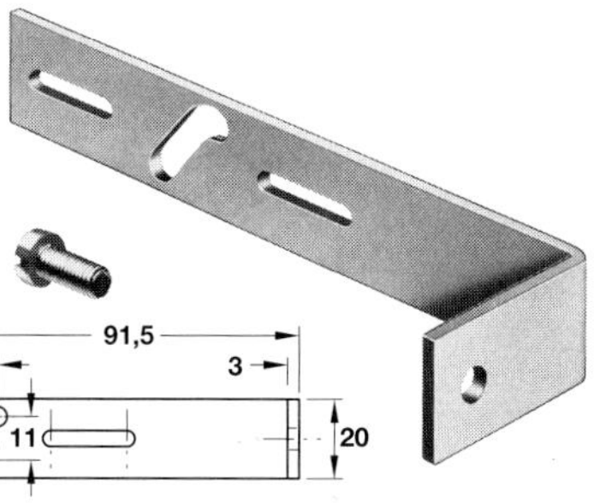

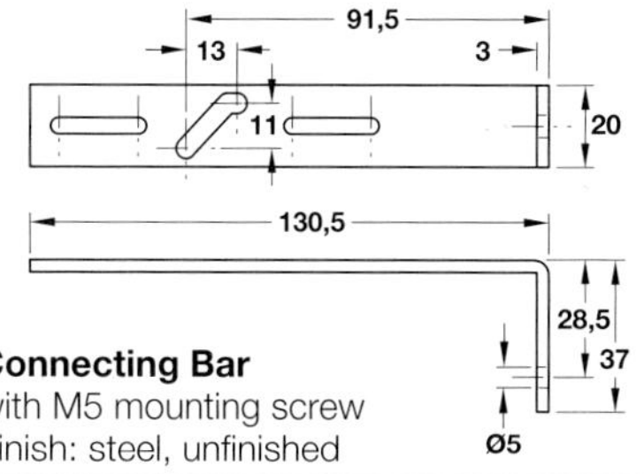

Connecting Bar
with M5 mounting screw
Finish: steel, unfinished

Application	left	right
Cat. No.	237.11.257	237.11.202

Packing: 1 pc.

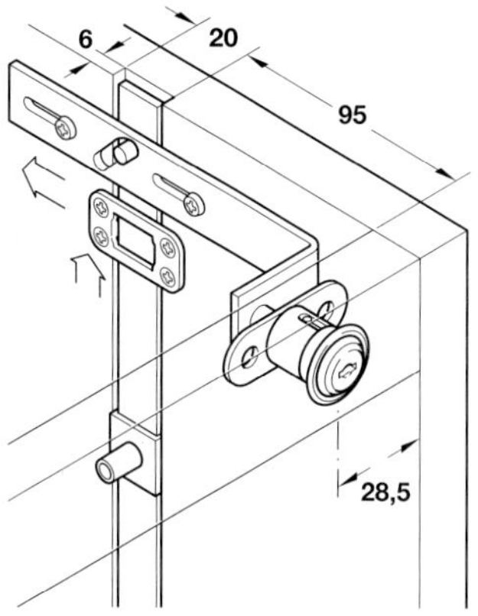

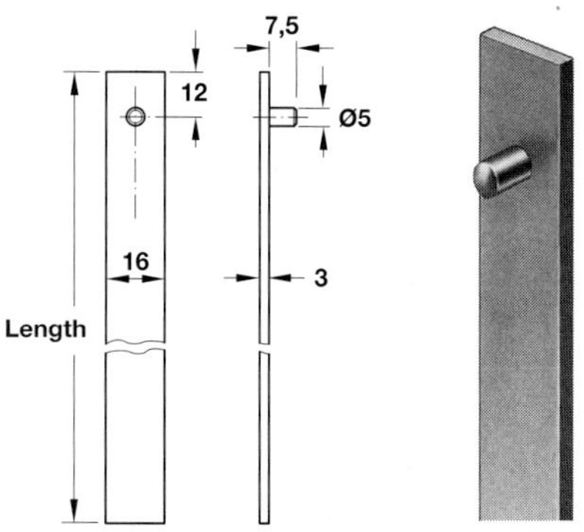

Lockbar
Finish: steel, unfinished

Cat. No.	500 mm long	237.21.217
	600 mm long	237.21.235
	800 mm long	237.21.271
	1000 mm long	237.21.315

Packing: 1 pc.

***Central Locking System accessories to complete the installation are shown on 2.42**

Dimensional data not binding.
We reserve the right to alter specifications without notice.

Dimensions in mm

HÄFELE

Central Locking Cylinders and Systems

Key blanks, for H series

Cat. No.	209.99.044

Packing: 10 pcs.

Locked

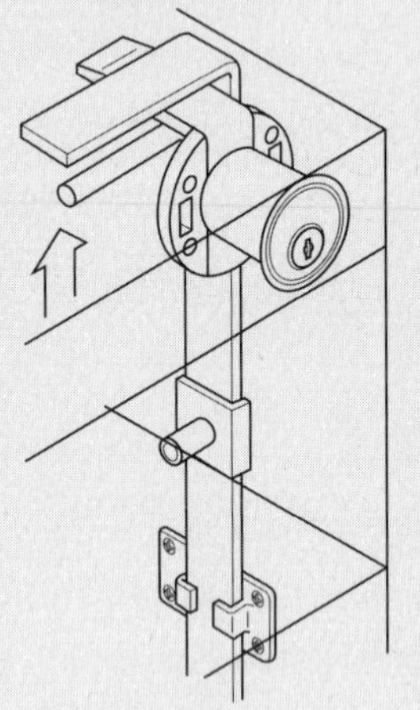

Unlocked

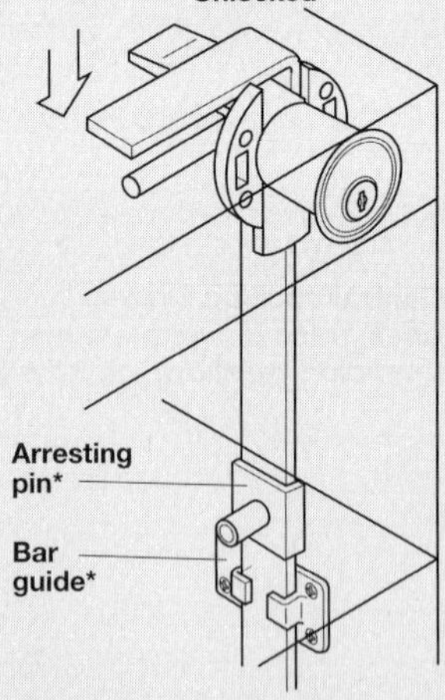

***Central Locking System accessories to complete the installation are shown on page 2.42**

Central Locking System, ø 22 mm cylinder,
5 pin levers = 20,000 key changes.
Accessories: 2 keys and 1 cylinder rosette
Bar length: 600 mm

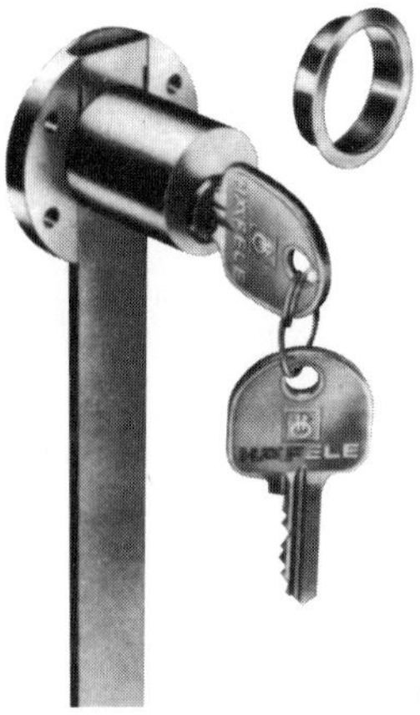

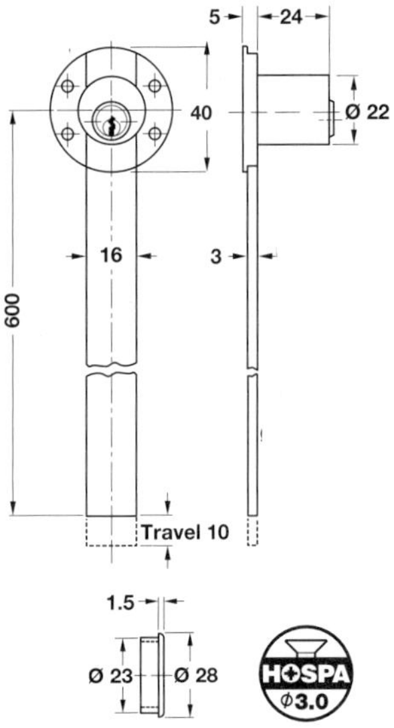

Finish: Zinc die-cast backplate, matt nickel-plated
Bar: steel, unfininished
Cylinder: brass, matt nickel-plated

Keyed different

Cat. No.	237.32.612

Keyed alike

Cat. No.	Key change H1	237.32.710
	Key change H2	237.32.729
	Key change H3	237.32.738
	Key change H4	237.32.747
	Key change H5	237.32.756

Packing: 1 pc.

With master key system

Cat. No.	237.32.68X

With general master key system

Cat. No.	237.32.69X

Central Locking Cylinder, ø 22 mm,
Key = closure travel 360°
Lifting = closure travel 180°
5 pin levers = 20,000 key changes.
Accessories: 2 keys and 1 cylinder rosette

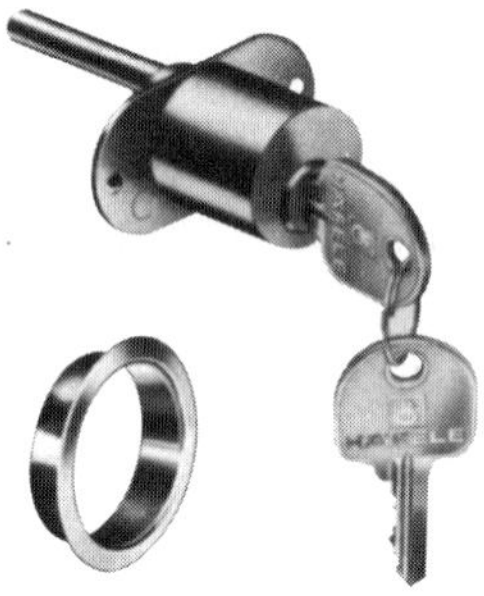

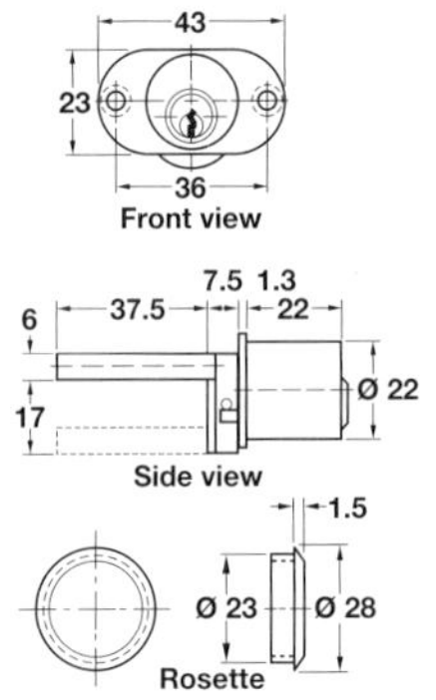

Finish: Mounting plate: steel, matt nickel-plated
Cylinder: brass, matt nickel-plated

Keyed different

Cat. No.	234.71.605

Keyed alike

Cat. No.	Key change H1	234.71.614
	Key change H2	234.71.623
	Key change H3	234.71.632
	Key change H4	234.71.641
	Key change H5	234.71.650

Packing: 1 pc.

With master key system

Cat. No.	234.71.68X

With general master key system

Cat. No.	234.71.69X

Central Locking Bars
Finish: steel, unfinished

Cat. No.	Length 500 mm	237.10.214
	Length 600 mm	237.10.232
	Length 800 mm	237.10.250
	Length 1000 mm	237.10.278
	Length 1500 mm	237.10.296

Packing: 1 pc.

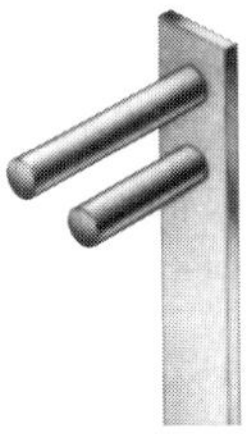

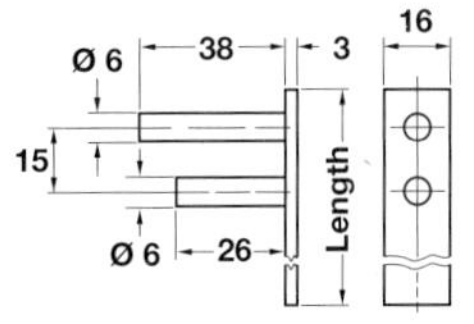

Dimensions in mm

Dimensional data not binding.
We reserve the right to alter specifications without notice.

Central Locking Cylinders and Systems

HÄFELE

Central Locking Cylinder, ø 22 mm
Key = closure travel 360°
Lifting pin = 10 mm
5 pin levers = 20,000 key changes.
Accessories: 2 keys and 1 cylinder rosette

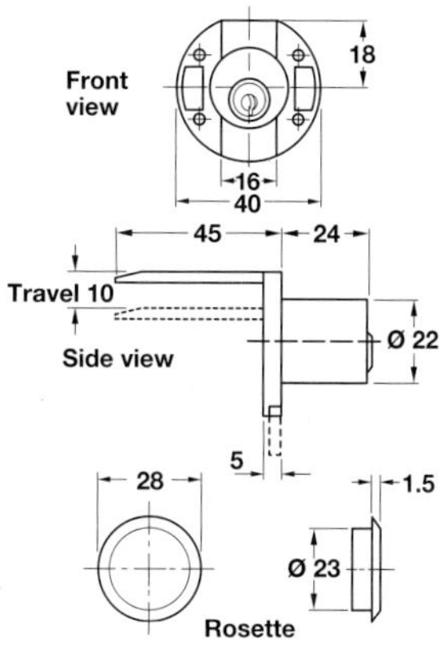

Finish: zinc die-cast backplate, matt nickel-plated
Cylinder: brass, matt nickel-plated

Keyed different

Cat. No.	234.74.606

Keyed alike

Cat. No.	Key change H1	234.74.615
	Key change H2	234.74.624
	Key change H3	234.74.633
	Key change H4	234.74.642
	Key change H5	234.74.651

Packing: 1 pc.

With master key system

Cat. No.	234.74.68X

With general master key system

Cat. No.	234.74.69X

Central Locking Bars

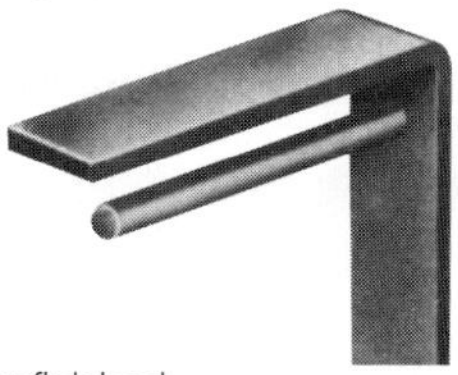

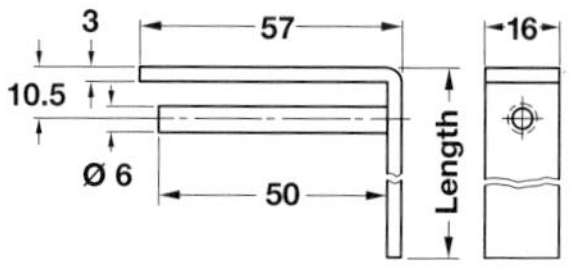

Finish: steel, unfinished

Cat. No.	Length 500 mm	237.09.417
	Length 600 mm	237.09.435
	Length 800 mm	237.09.453
	Length 1000 mm	237.09.471

Packing: 1 pc.

Dimensions in mm

The cylinders shown on this page incorporate a direct-action lifting pin which raises the locking bar by the necessary 10 mm as the key is turned. Unlocking occurs on the same basis. The cylinder can either be installed in the fixed trim panel (as in the example shown) or, if no such panel is provided, in the drawer front itself.

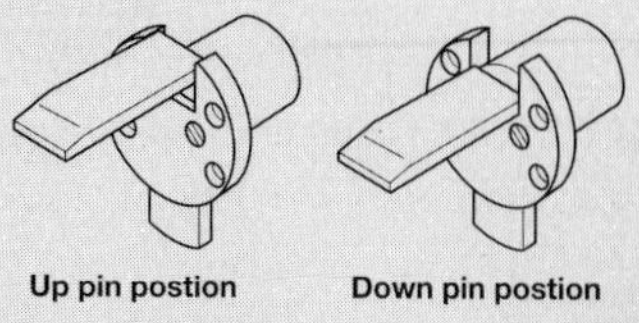

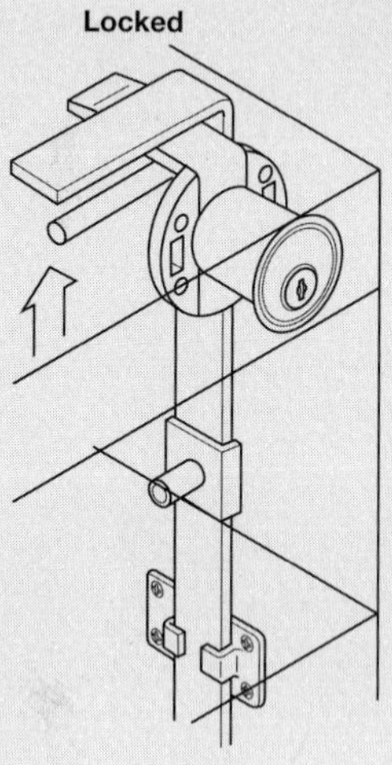

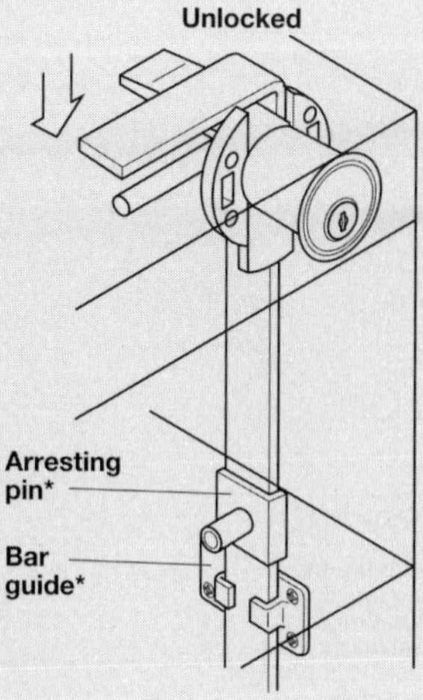

***Central Locking System accessories to complete the installation are shown on page 2.42**

Key blanks, for H series

Cat. No.	209.99.044

Packing: 10 pcs.

HÄFELE

Central Locking System Accessories

Guides can be used for surface-mounted (left) or recessed (right) bars by reversing their position.

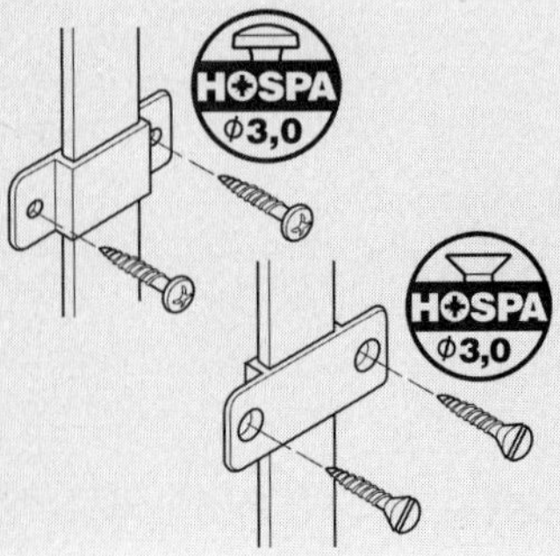

The guides and arresting pins are designed for a bar section measuring 16 x 3 mm.
All the central locking systems illustrated on pages **2.39** to **2.41** use accessories with these dimensions.

Bar guide, open type
Finish: plastic, white

Cat No.	237.23.720

Packing: 200 pcs.

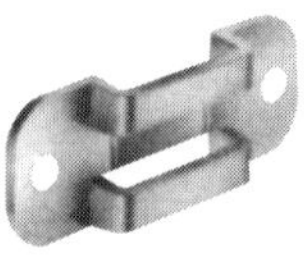

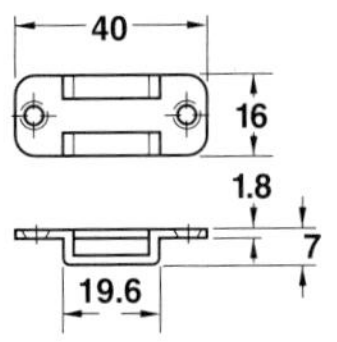

Bar guide, open type
Finish: steel, galvanized

Cat No.	237.23.006

Packing: 100 pcs.

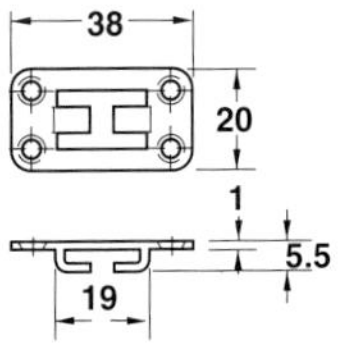

Arresting pin
Accessory: 1 threaded bolt
Finish: zinc-die cast

Cat No.	237.22.027

Packing: 100 pcs.

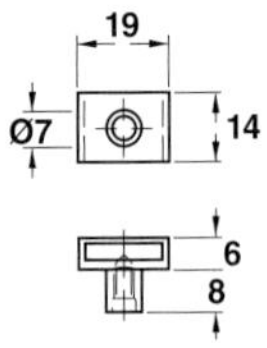

Mounting arrangement for a right-hand drawer...

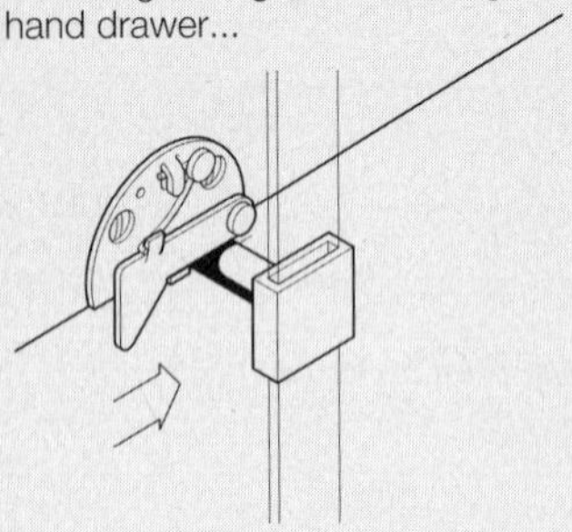

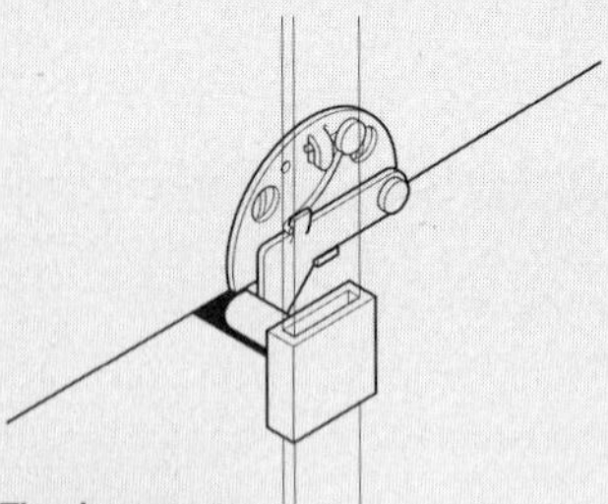

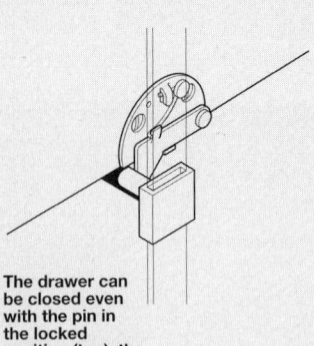

The drawer can be closed even with the pin in the locked position (top); the drawer is then locked in position (bottom).

Arresting Pin
Finish: zinc-die cast, nickel matt
Accessory: 1 slotted set screw

Cat. No.	237.22.107

Packing: 100 pcs.

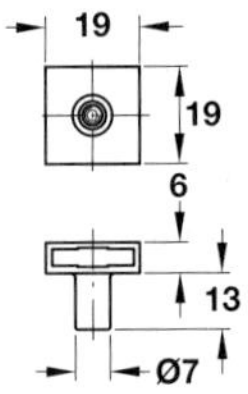

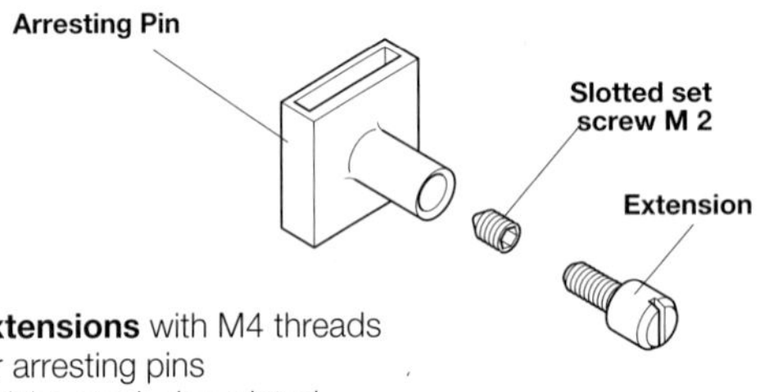

Extensions with M4 threads
for arresting pins
Finish: steel, zinc-plated

Cat. No.	for length **17 mm**	237.22.189
	for length **20 mm**	237.22.214
	for length **25 mm**	237.22.269
	for length **30 mm**	237.22.312

Packing: 100 pcs.

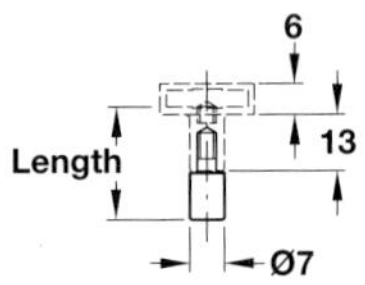

Drawer catches, screw-mounted
Finish: steel, nickel-plated

Cat. No.	left	237.16.752
	right	237.16.707

Packing: 100 pcs.

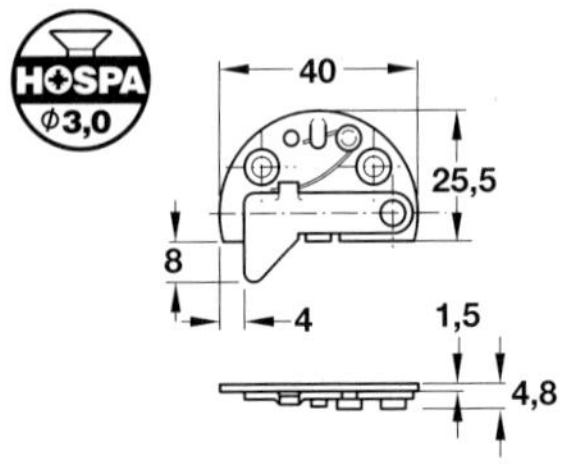

Bars for central locking systems
Finish: aluminum

Cat No.	Length 600 mm	234.78.033
	Length 820 mm	234.78.051

Packing: 50 pcs.

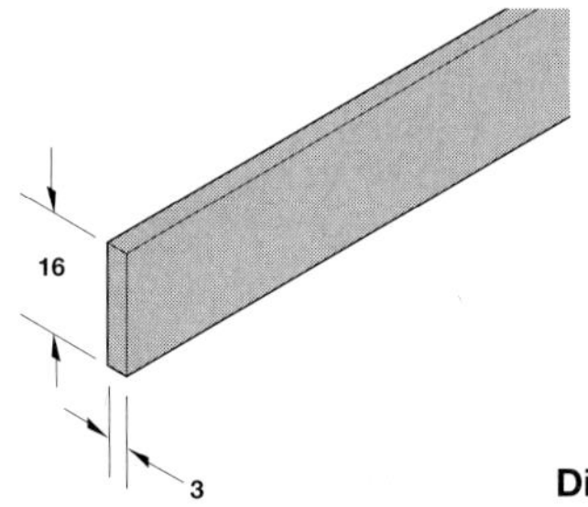

Dimensional data not binding.
We reserve the right to alter specifications without notice.

Dimensions in mm

KABA Locks

Mortise Lock Case

Finish: brass face plate, matt nickel-plated

Left

Cat. No.	230.24.455

Packing: 1 pc.

Right

Cat. No.	230.24.409

Drawer

Cat. No.	230.24.491

Packing: 1 pc.

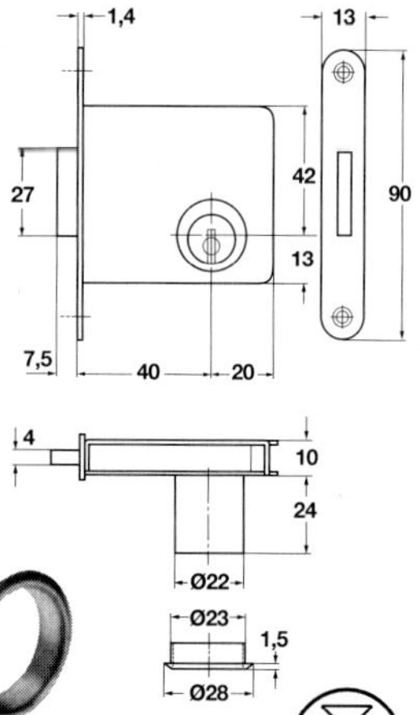

KABA Cylinder For Mortise Lock Case

8 pin levers = 10,000 key changes.
Accessories: 2 keys and 1 cylinder rosette
Can be combined with cylinders for building applications.
Finish: brass, matt nickel-plated

Keyed different

Cat. No.	230.24.802

Keyed alike

Cat. No.	Key change K1	230.24.811
	Key change K2	230.24.820
	Key change K3	230.24.839
	Key change K4	230.24.848
	Key change K5	230.24.857

Packing: 1 pc.

With master key system

Cat. No.	230.24.98X

With general master key system

Cat. No.	230.24.99X

Locks, Catches, RTA and PAS® Fittings
Shelf Supports
Bed Fittings

2

KABA Cylinder Mounting:

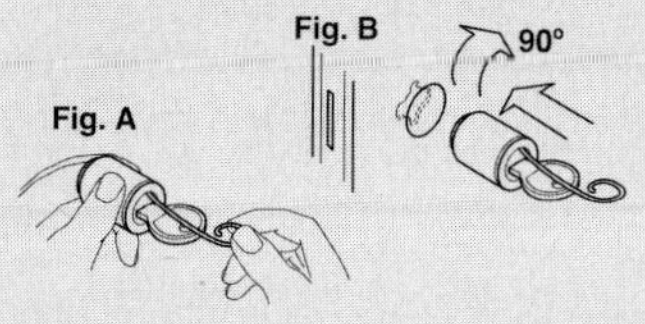

1. Determine the position for key removal.
2. Turn the key a few degrees clockwise until the mounting pin can be inserted (Fig. A)
3. Install the cylinder in the same attitude in the lock case hole and turn clockwise with the 90° to the stop. When the pin is withdrawn, the cylinder remains firmly secured in the lock case.

Cam locks with KABA Cylinders

Closure travel 360°, restricted to 100° approx. by locking pin on mounting plate (with key trap).
8 pin levers = 100,000 key changes.
Accessories: 2 keys, 1 cylinder rosette, 1 locking cam and 2 screws

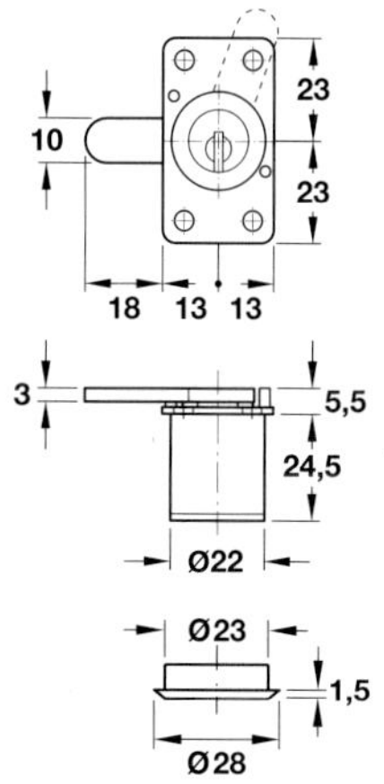

Finish: Mounting plate and cam: steel, zinc-plated
Cylinder: brass, matt nickel-plated

Keyed different

Closure direction	100° A	100° B	100° F
Cat. No.	235.00.601	235.00.656	235.00.692

Packing: 10 pcs.

With master key system

Cat. No.	235.00.78X

With general master key system

Cat. No.	235.00.79X

Dimensional data not binding.
We reserve the right to alter specifications without notice.

HÄFELE

The KABA system brings improvements over traditional serrated key locks by offering a greater number of levers and the transfer of the pin reading function from the edge of the key to the flat faces on each side. In spite of the resulting increase in security, duplicate keys can be made locally if required.

One glance at the key...
...is all you need to recognize a KABA lock. In this case, a KABA lock offering 100,000 key changes.

Rim Locks

Rim Lock, with ø 22 mm KABA cylinder.
Right hand (can be adapted for left/drawer use).
8 pin levers = 100,000 key changes.
Accessories: 2 keys, 1 cylinder rosette and 1 strike plate

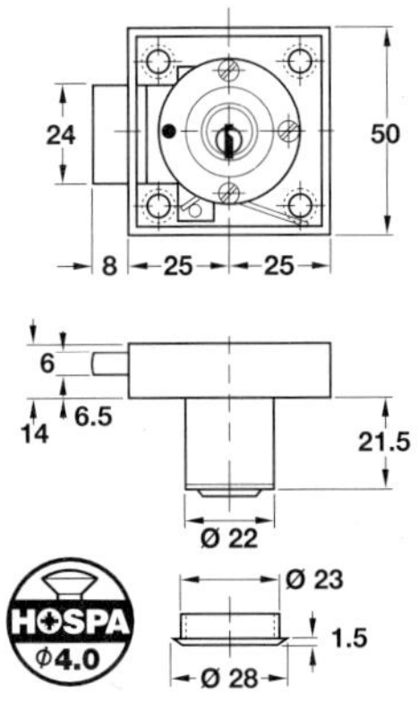

Finish: Case: steel, brass strike plate
Bolt: brass

Cat. No.	230.06.224

Packing: 1 pc.

With master key system

Cat. No.	230.06.28X

With general master key system

Cat. No.	230.06.29X

Strike Plate

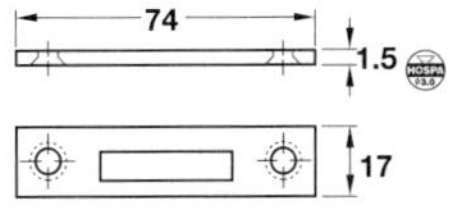

Spring Rim Lock, with ø 22 mm KABA cylinder.
Right-hand (can be adapted for left/drawer use).
8 pin levers = 100,000 key changes.
Accessories: 2 keys, 1 cylinder rosette and 1 angle strike

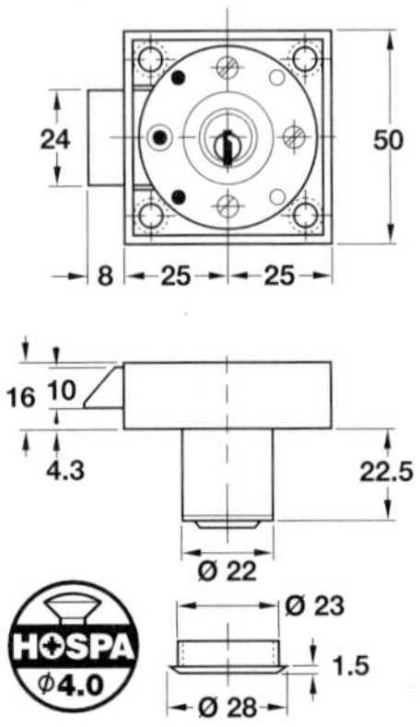

Finish: Case and strike: steel ; Bolt: brass

Cat. No.	231.06.229

Packing: 1 pc.

With master key system

Cat. No.	231.06.28X

With general master key system

Cat. No.	231.06.29X

Angle Strike

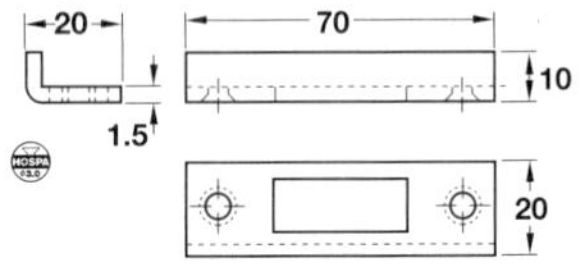

Spacers

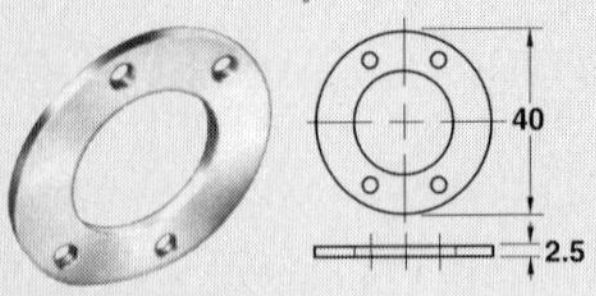

Finish: Plastic, light gray

Cat. No.	230.13.998

Packing: 1 and 10 pcs.

Inlay Lock, with ø 22 mm KABA cylinders.
8 pin levers = 100,000 key changes.
Accessories: 2 keys and 1 cylinder rosette

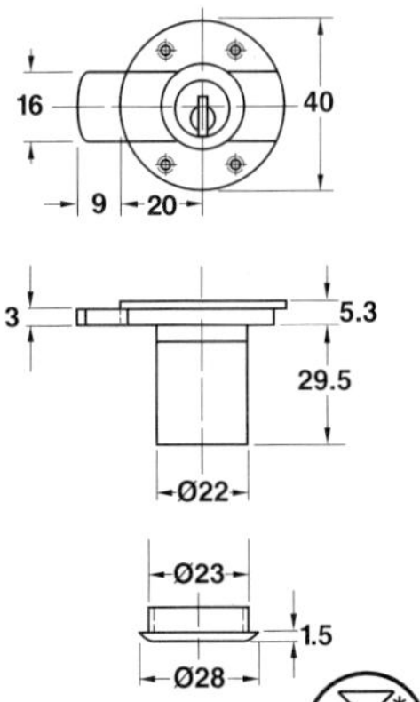

HOSPA Φ3.0

Finish: zinc die-cast case, matt nickel-plated
Cylinder: brass, matt nickel-plated

Keyed different
Left

Cat. No.	230.13.612

Right

Cat. No.	230.13.603

Drawer

Cat. No.	230.13.621

Packing: 1 pc.

With master key system

Cat. No.	230.13.18X

With general master key system

Cat. No.	230.13.19X

Dimensions in mm

Dimensional data not binding.
We reserve the right to alter specifications without notice.

Pushbutton Locks

HÄFELE

KABA Pushbutton Lock, ø 25 mm
Function: Closing, only with key
Opening, only with key
8 pin levers = 100,000 key changes.
Accessories: 2 keys, 1 cylinder rosette and 1 socket

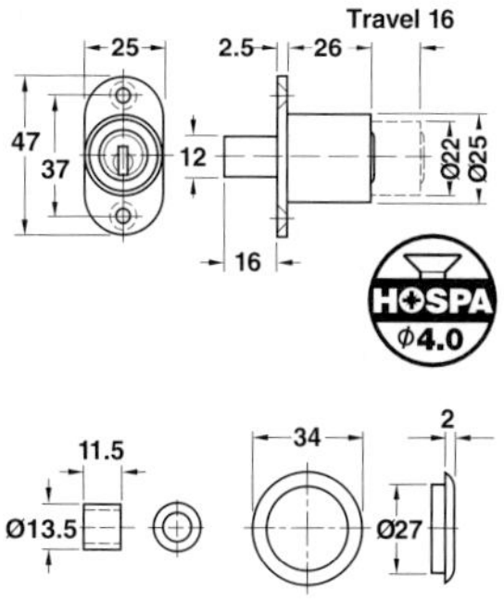

Finish: Case and mounting plate: steel, matt nickel-plated
Cylinder: brass, matt nickel-plated

Keyed different

Cat. No.	234.41.607

Keyed alike

Cat. No.	Key change K1	234.41.616
	Key change K2	234.41.625
	Key change K3	234.41.634
	Key change K4	234.41.643
	Key change K5	234.41.652

Packing: 1 pc.

With master key system

Cat. No.	234.41.68X

With general master key system

Cat. No.	234.41.69X

KABA Pushbutton Lock, ø 25 mm
Function: Closing, only with key
Opening, only with key
8 pin levers = 100,000 key changes.
Accessories: 2 keys, 1 cylinder rosette and 1 socket

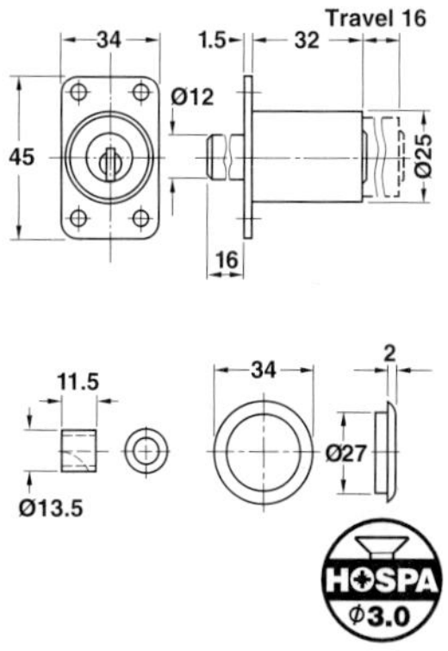

Finish: Case and mounting plate: steel, matt nickel-plated
Cylinder: brass, matt nickel-plated

Keyed different

Cat. No.	234.42.604

Keyed alike

Cat. No.	Key change K1	234.42.613
	Key change K2	234.42.622
	Key change K3	234.42.631
	Key change K4	234.42.640
	Key change K5	234.42.659

Packing: 1 pc.

With master key system

Cat. No.	234.42.68X

With general master key system

Cat. No.	234.42.69X

Dimensions in mm

HÄFELE

Central Locking Systems

The locks shown on this page incorporate a lifting pin which rotates upwards 180° on closing, raising the locking bar to the locked position. A typical installation is shown. The cylinder can either be installed in the fixed trim panel (as in the example shown) or, if no such panel is provided, in the drawer front itself.

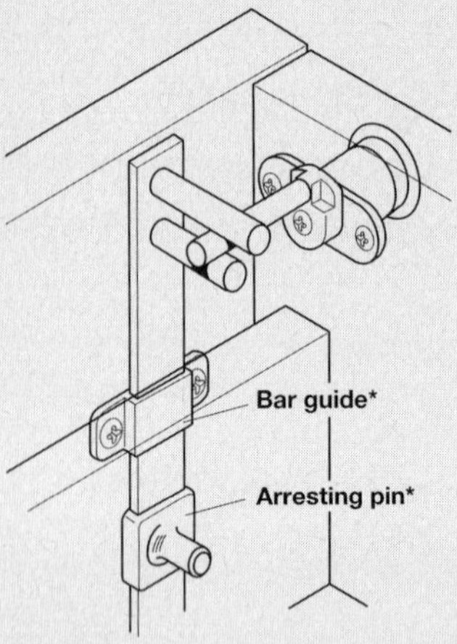

***Central Locking System accessories to complete the installation are shown on page 2.48**

KABA Central Locking Cylinder, ø 22 mm, indirect action.
Key = closure travel 360°
Lifting pin = closure travel 180°
8 pin levers = 100,000 key changes.
Accessories: 2 keys and 1 cylinder rosette

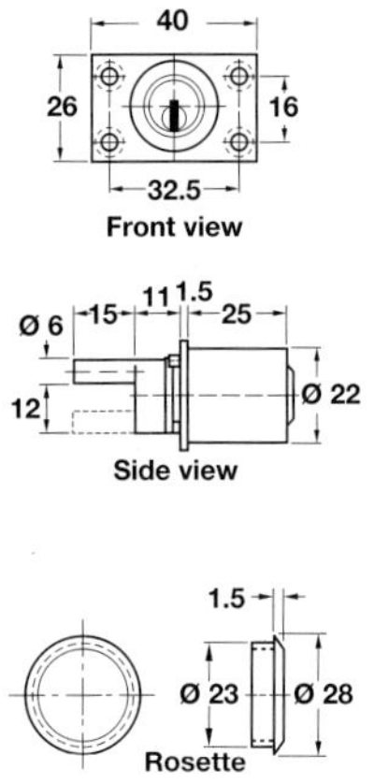

HOSPA ф3.0

Finish: Mounting plate, steel, zinc-plated
Cylinder: brass, matt nickel-plated

Keyed different

Cat. No.	234.72.602

Keyed alike

Cat. No.	Key change K1	234.72.611
	Key change K2	234.72.620
	Key change K3	234.72.639
	Key change K4	234.72.648
	Key change K5	234.72.657

Packing: 1 pc.

With master key system

Cat. No.	234.72.68X

With general master key system

Cat. No.	234.72.69X

KABA Central Locking Cylinder, ø 22 mm, indirect action.
Key = closure travel 360°
Lifting pin = closure travel 180°
8 pin levers = 100,000 key changes.
Accessories: 2 keys and 1 cylinder rosette
Can be combined with cylinders for building applications.

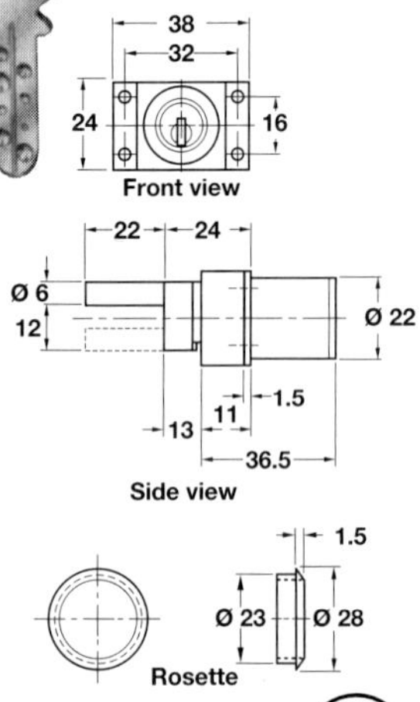

HOSPA ф3.0

Finish: Mounting bracket, steel, zinc-plated
Cylinder: brass, matt nickel-plated

Keyed different

Cat. No.	234.72.102

Keyed alike

Cat. No.	Key change K1	234.72.111
	Key change K2	234.72.120
	Key change K3	234.72.139
	Key change K4	234.72.148
	Key change K5	234.72.157

Packing: 1 pc.

With master key system

Cat. No.	234.72.18X

With general master key system

Cat. No.	234.72.19X

Central Locking Bars
Finish: steel, unfinished

Cat. No.	Length 500 mm	237.10.214
	Length 600 mm	237.10.232
	Length 800 mm	237.10.250
	Length 1000 mm	237.10.278
	Length 1500 mm	237.10.296

Packing: 1 pc.

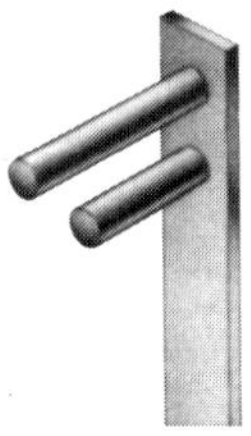

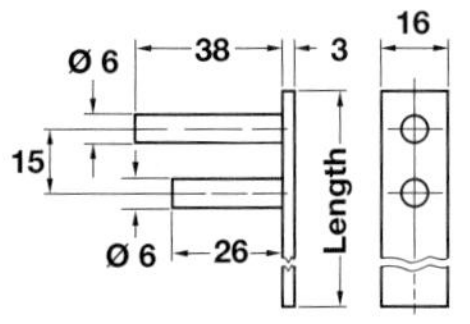

Dimensions in mm

Dimensional data not binding.
We reserve the right to alter specifications without notice.

Central Locking Systems

HÄFELE

KABA Central Locking Cylinder, ø 22 mm, direct action.
Key = closure travel 360°
Lifting pin = 10 mm
8 pin levers = 100,000 key changes.
Accessories: 2 keys and 1 cylinder rosette

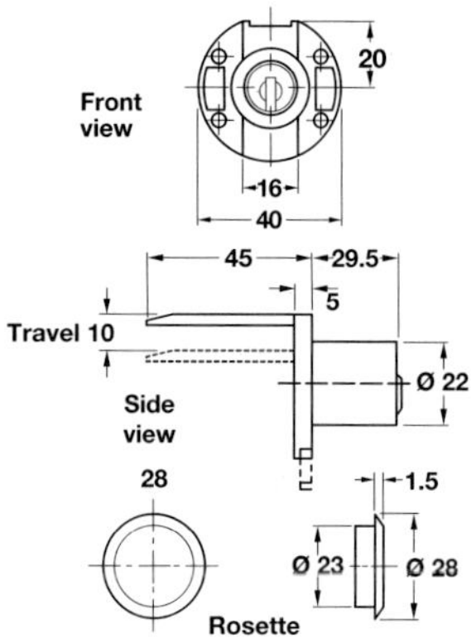

The cylinders shown on this page incorporate a direct-action lifting pin which raises the locking bar by the necessary 10 mm as the key is turned. Unlocking occurs on the same basis. The cylinder can either be installed in the fixed trim panel (as in the example shown) or, in the drawer front itself.

Locks, Catches, RTA and PAS® Fittings
Shelf Supports
Bed Fittings
2

Finish: Zinc die-cast backplate, matt nickel-plated
Cylinder: brass, matt nickel-plated

Keyed different

Cat. No.		234.75.603

Keyed alike

Cat. No.	Key change K1	234.75.612
	Key change K2	234.75.621
	Key change K3	234.75.630
	Key change K4	234.75.649
	Key change K5	234.75.658

Packing: 1 pc.

With master key system

Cat. No.		234.75.68X

With general master key system

Cat. No.		234.75.69X

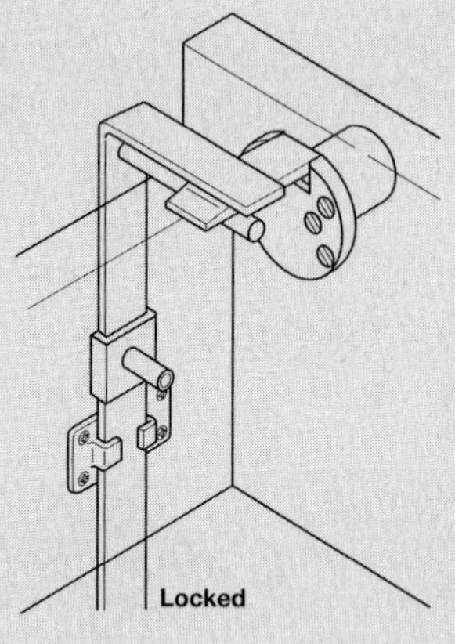

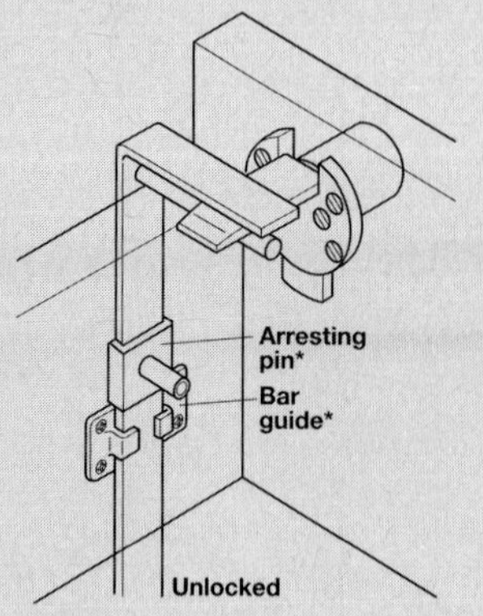

Central Locking Bars

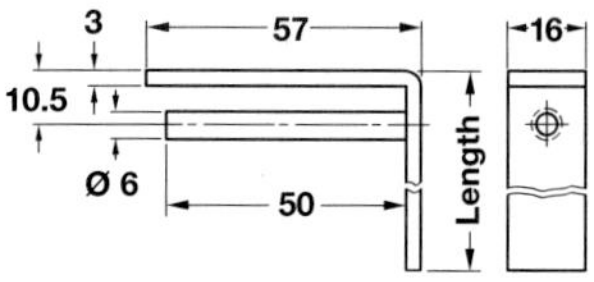

Dimensions in mm

Finish: steel, unfinished

Cat. No.	Length 500 mm	237.09.417
	Length 600 mm	237.09.435
	Length 800 mm	237.09.453
	Length 1000 mm	237.09.471

Packing: 1 pc.

***Central Locking System accessories to complete the installation are shown on page 2.48**

HÄFELE

Central Locking System Accessories

Guides can be used for surface-mounted (left) or recessed (right) bars by reversing their position.

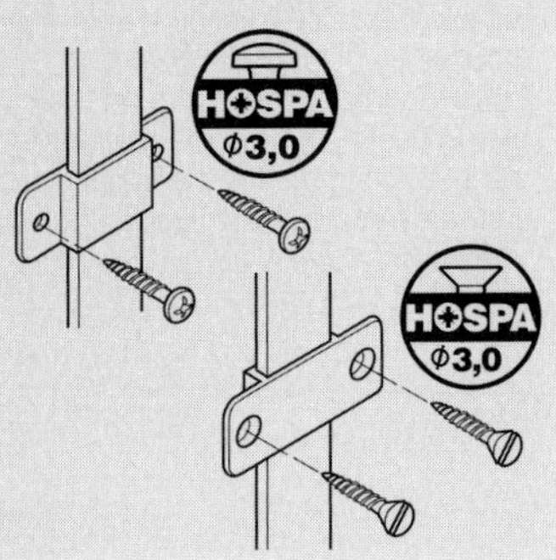

The guides and arresting pins are designed for a bar section measuring 16 x 3 mm.
All the central locking systems illustrated on pages **2.46** to **2.47** use accessories with these dimensions.

Bar guide, open type
Finish: plastic, white

Cat No.	237.23.720

Packing: 200 pcs.

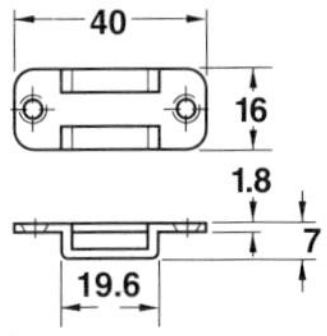

Bar guide, open type
Finish: steel, galvanized

Cat No.	237.23.006

Packing: 100 pcs.

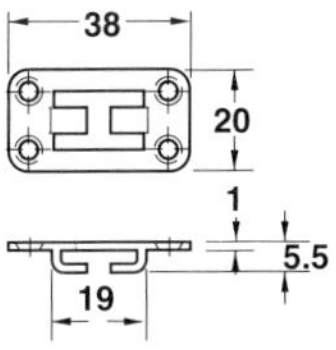

Arresting pin
Accessory: 1 threaded bolt
Finish: zinc die cast

Cat No.	237.22.027

Packing: 100 pcs.

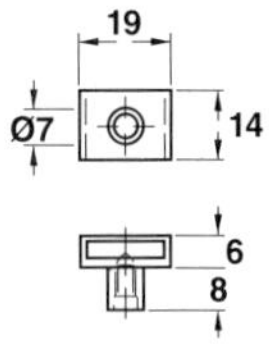

Arresting Pin
Finish: zinc die cast, nickel matt
Accessory: 1 slotted set screw

Cat. No.	237.22.107

Packing: 100 pcs.

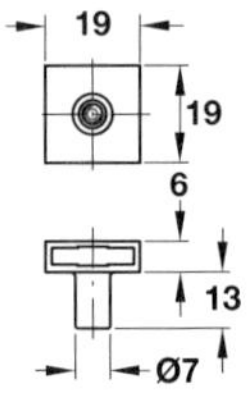

Mounting arrangement for a right-hand drawer...

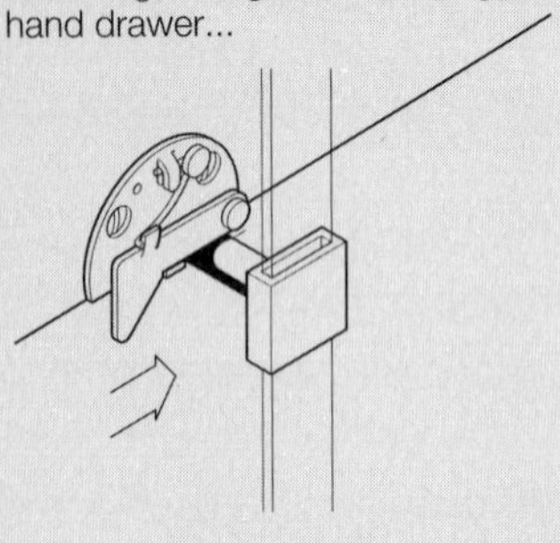

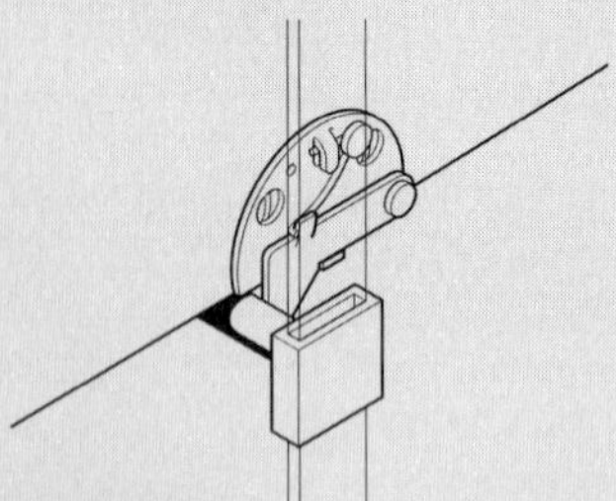

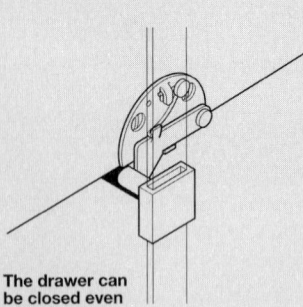

The drawer can be closed even with the pin in the locked position (top); the drawer is then locked in position (bottom).

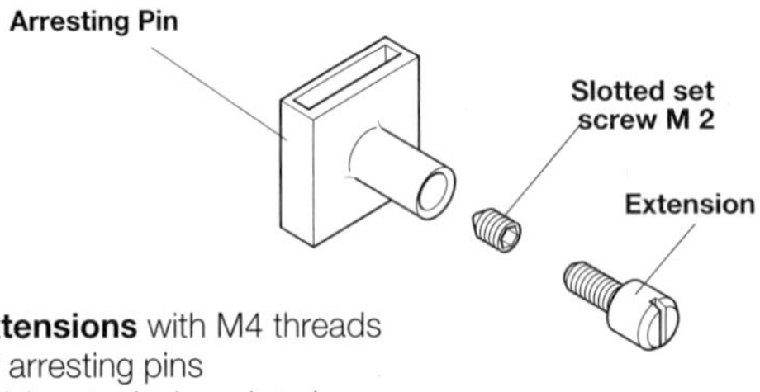

Extensions with M4 threads
for arresting pins
Finish: steel, zinc-plated

Cat. No.	for length **17 mm**	237.22.189
	for length **20 mm**	237.22.214
	for length **25 mm**	237.22.269
	for length **30 mm**	237.22.312

Packing: 100 pcs.

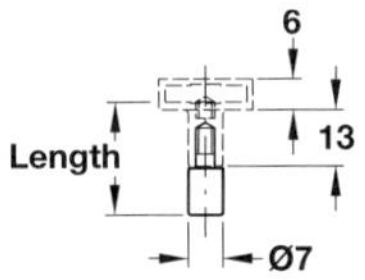

Drawer catches, screw-mounted
Finish: steel, nickel-plated

Cat. No.	left	237.16.752
	right	237.16.707

Packing: 100 pcs.

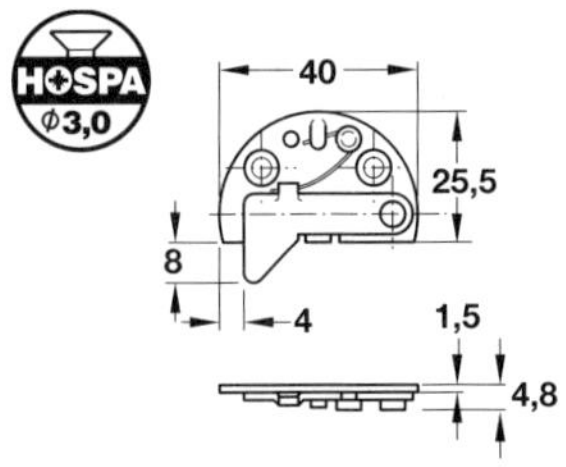

Bars for central locking systems
Finish: aluminum

Cat No.	Length 600 mm	234.78.033
	Length 820 mm	234.78.051

Packing: 50 pcs.

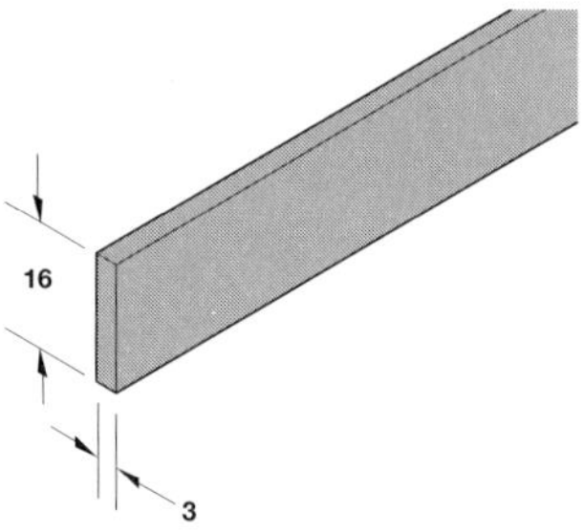

Dimensional data not binding.
We reserve the right to alter specifications without notice.

Dimensions in mm

Central Locking Systems

The lock shown on this page forms the basis of a central locking system which is recessed into case side panel for maximum space-savings. Loose backplates and bars leave the choice for individual selection of requested parts.

Central Locking System With Cylinder, ø 16 mm
5 plate levers = 200 key changes.
Accessories: 2 keys and 1 cylinder rosette

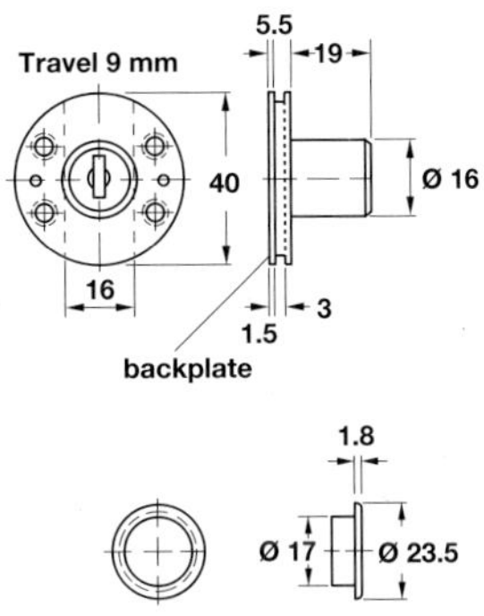

Finish: zinc die-cast case, with loose backplate, matt nickel-plated
Cylinder: Zinc die-cast, matt nickel-plated

Keyed different

Cat. No.	237.35.300

Keyed alike

Key No.	No.	No.
Cat. No.	1 - 237.35.319	7 - 237.35.373
	2 - 237.35.328	8 - 237.35.382
	3 - 237.35.337	9 - 237.35.391
	4 - 237.35.346	10 - 237.35.408
	5 - 237.35.355	
	6 - 237.35.364	

Packing: 20 pc.

Bars For Central Locking Systems

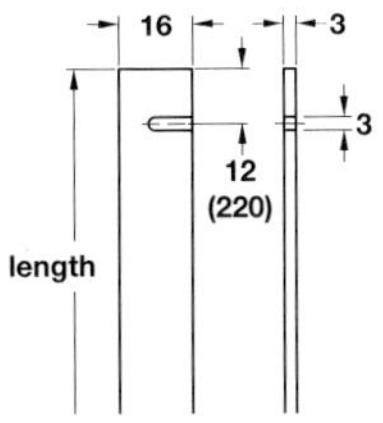

		Bar length	Notch from top end
Cat. No.	237.31.928	600 mm	12 mm
	237.35.917	820 mm	220 mm

Packing: 1 pc.

Dimensional data not binding.
We reserve the right to alter specifications without notice.

HÄFELE

Central Locking System Accessories

Guides can be used for surface-mounted (left) or recessed (right) bars by reversing their position.

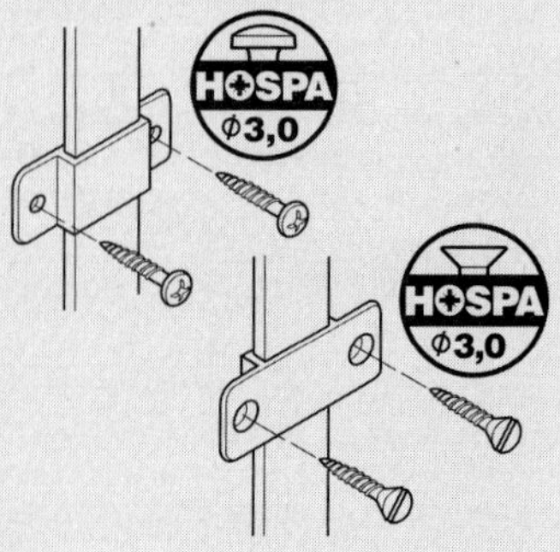

The guides and arresting pins are designed for a bar section measuring 16 x 3 mm.
All the central locking systems illustrated on page **2.49** use accessories with these dimensions.

Bar guide, open type
Finish: plastic, white

Cat No.	237.23.720

Packing: 200 pcs.

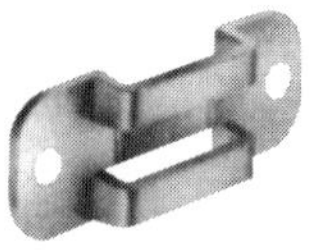

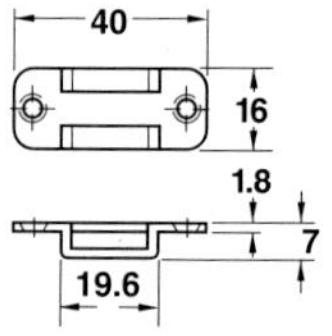

Bar guide, open type
Finish: steel, galvanized

Cat No.	237.23.006

Packing: 100 pcs.

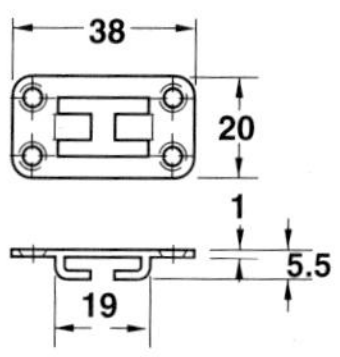

2 Locks, Catches, RTA and PAS® Fittings Shelf Supports Bed Fittings

Arresting pin
Accessory: 1 threaded bolt
Finish: zinc die cast

Cat No.	237.22.027

Packing: 100 pcs.

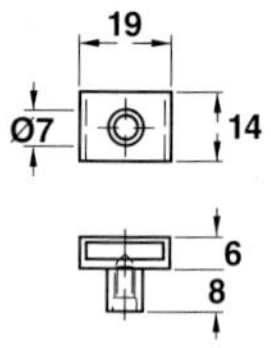

Arresting Pin
Finish: zinc die-cast, nickel matt
Accessory: 1 slotted set screw

Cat. No.	237.22.107

Packing: 100 pcs.

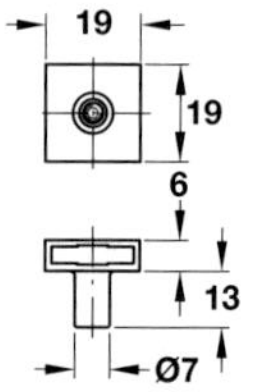

Mounting arrangement for a right-hand drawer...

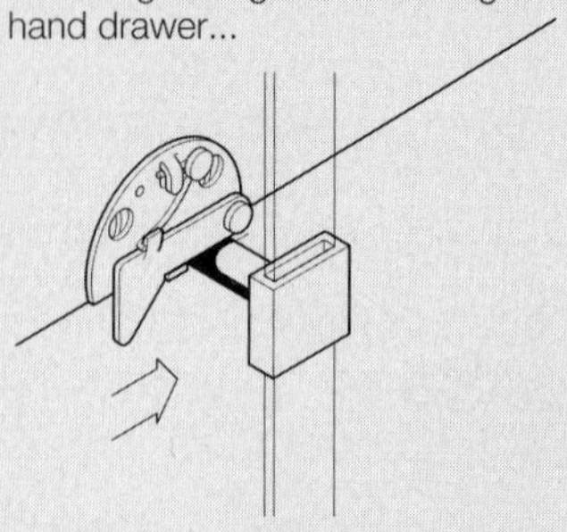

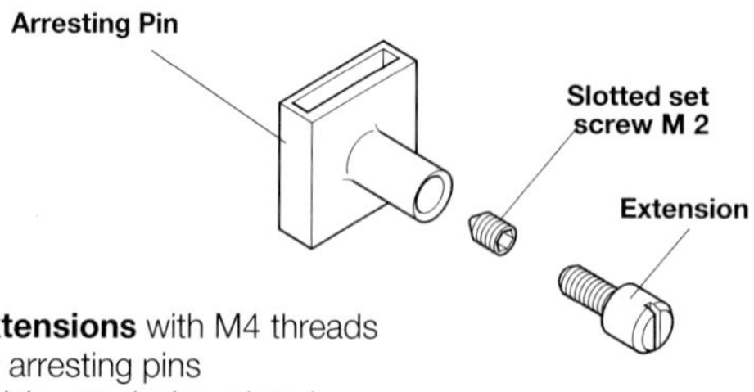

Extensions with M4 threads for arresting pins
Finish: steel, zinc-plated

Cat. No.	for length **17 mm**	237.22.189
	for length **20 mm**	237.22.214
	for length **25 mm**	237.22.269
	for length **30 mm**	237.22.312

Packing: 100 pcs.

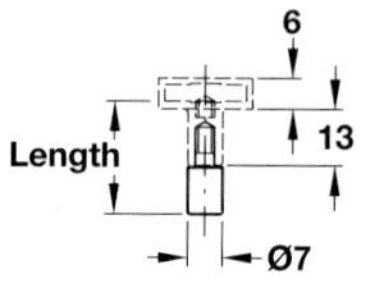

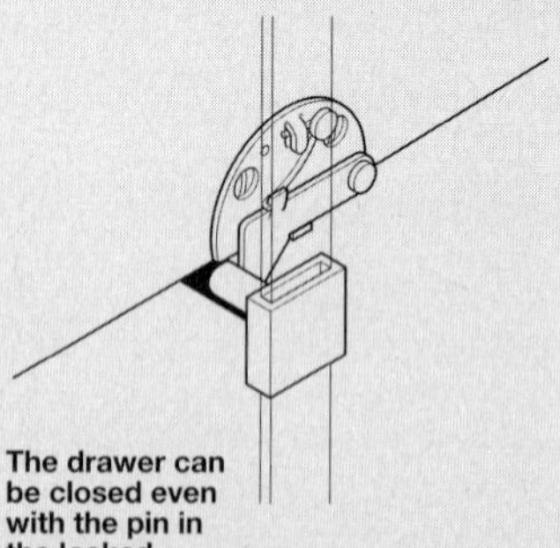

The drawer can be closed even with the pin in the locked position (top); the drawer is then locked in position (bottom).

Drawer catches, screw-mounted
Finish: steel, nickel-plated

Cat. No.	left	237.16.752
	right	237.16.707

Packing: 100 pcs.

HOSPA Φ3,0

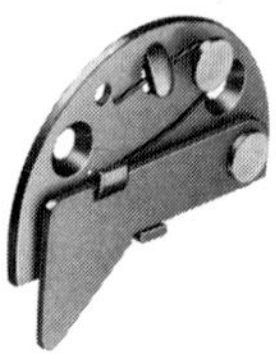

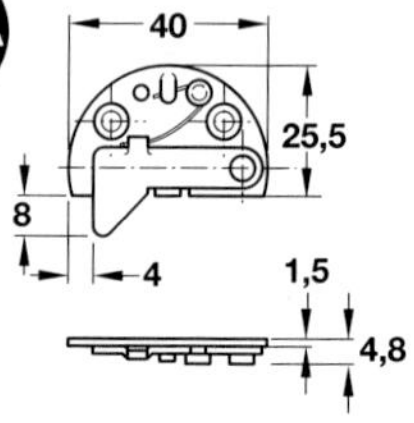

Bars for central locking systems
Finish: aluminum

Cat No.	Length 600 mm	234.78.033
	Length 820 mm	234.78.051

Packing: 50 pcs.

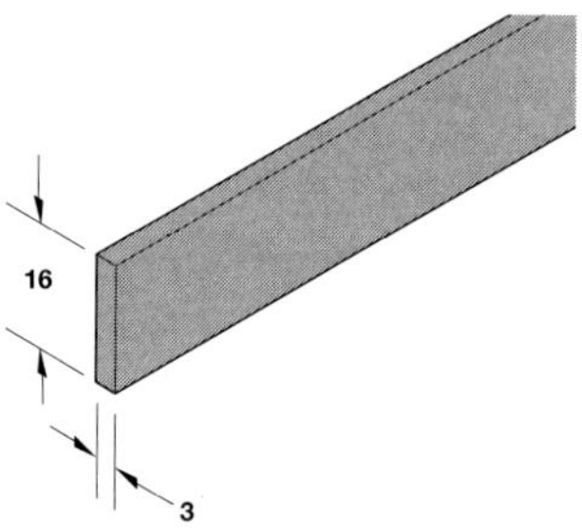

Dimensional data not binding. We reserve the right to alter specifications without notice.

Dimensions in mm

Built-In Central Locking Systems

HÄFELE

The central locking systems designed to be mounted on the rear panel of vertical multi-drawer cabinets. In the locking process, the hooks attached to the bar engage the loop catches on the drawers as they descend, locking the drawers in position.

- Hooks are spring-loaded, the drawer can be kept open as needed and shut later.
- Hooks are adjustable on the locking bar enabling them to be individually adapted to drawers of varying depths.
- Movement of the locking bar is effected by a roller, mounted at the upper end of the bar and actuated by a wedge-shaped driver

Horizontal Activator Bar, 600 mm length
Finish: steel, unfinished

Cat. No.	237.42.207

Packing: 1 pc.

Angled Activator
Finish: steel, zinc-plated

Cat. No.	237.42.047

Packing: 1 pc.

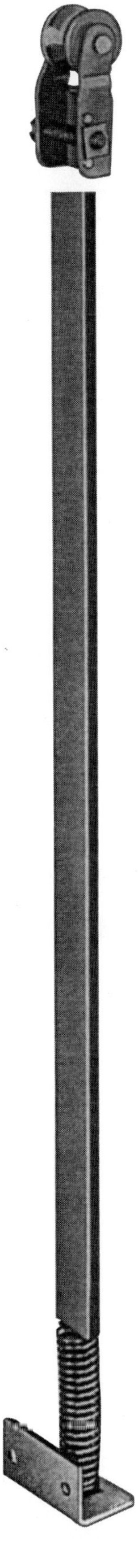

Roller For Vertical Lock Bar
Finish: steel, unfinished

Cat. No	237.42.010

Packing: 1 pc.

Bar Guide
Finish: steel, zinc-plated

Cat. No.	237.42.029

Packing: 1 pc.

Spring Hook
Finish: steel, zinc-plated

Cat. No.	237.42.001

Packing: 1 pc.

Strike
Finish: steel, zinc-plated

Cat. No.	237.42.038

Packing: 1 pc.

Vertical Lock Bar, 600 mm length
(with attached spring and bar guide)
Finish: steel, unfinished

Cat. No.	237.42.109

Packing: 1 pc.

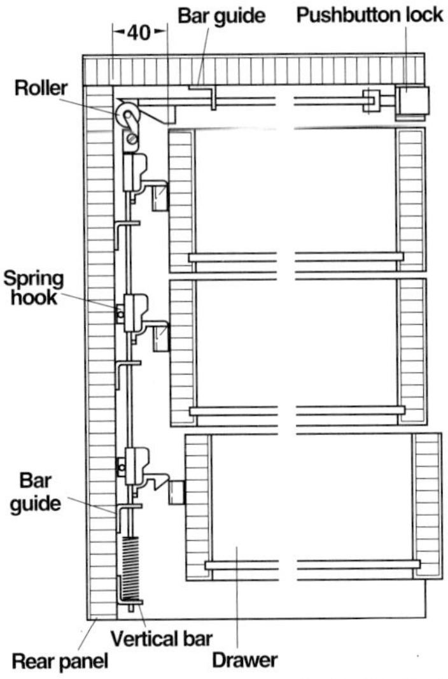

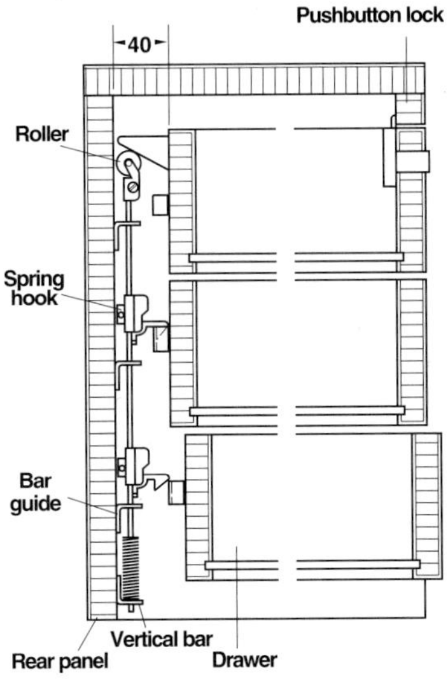

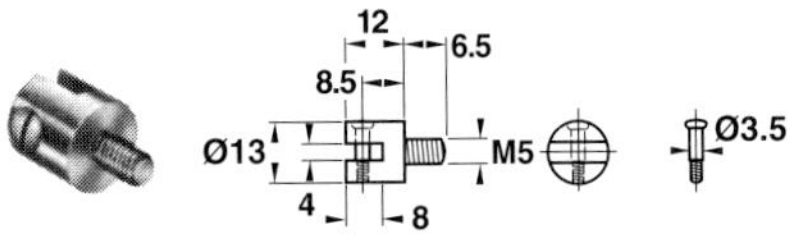

Connecting Piece For Push-button Cylinder
600 mm length
Accessories: 1 countersunk screw
Finish: brass

Cat. No.	234.58.997

Packing: 1 pc.

Dimensions in mm

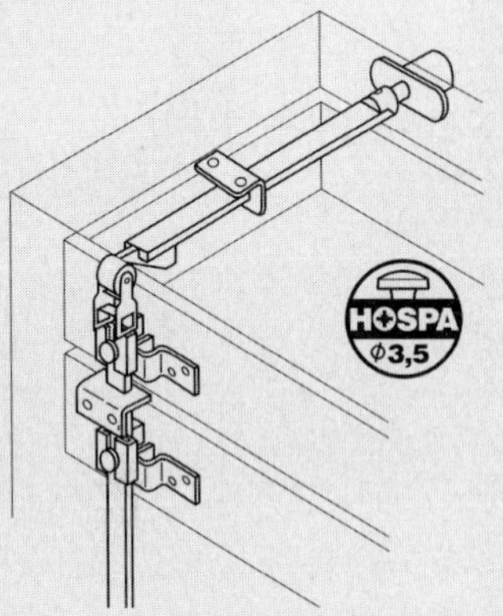

Push-button lock must be ordered separately. See page 2.39

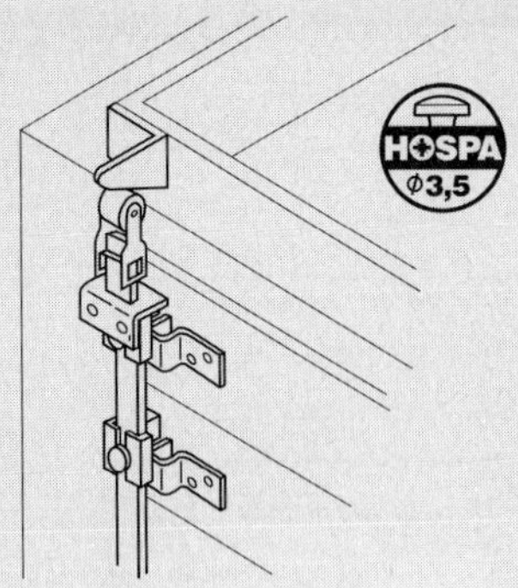

Rim lock must be ordered separately.

HÄFELE

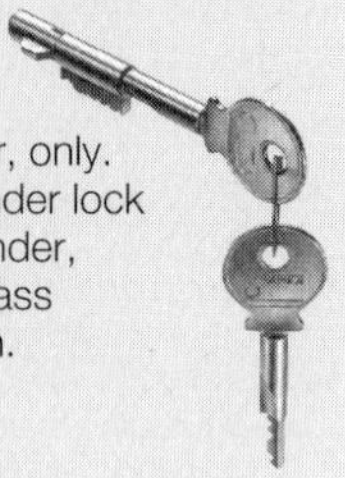

Key and cylinder, only.
Suitable for cylinder lock with plug-in cylinder, for wood and glass panel installation.

Key and cylinder, only key changes:

Cat. No.	233.22.009

Keyed alike:

	Cat. No.
key change 978	233.22.018
key change 901	233.22.027
key change 902	233.22.036
key change 903	233.22.045
key change 904	233.22.054
key change 906	233.22.063

Packing: 20 pcs.

Screws

Length	Cat. No.
M 3 x 5 mm	020.04.079
M 3 x 6 mm	020.04.088
M 3 x 8 mm	020.04.097
M 3 x 10 mm	020.04.006

Packing: 20 pcs. each

Dimensional data not binding.
We reserve the right to alter specifications without notice.

Sliding Door Locks

Cylinder Lock, with plug-in cylinder
For installation in wood panels from 16-19 mm
with key trap (key removable only when locked)
75 key changes
Accessories: 2 keys, 1 rosette

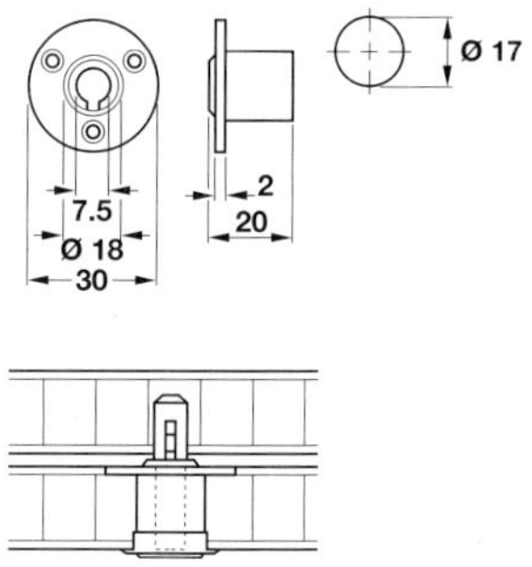

Finish: Housing: zinc die-cast, chrome-plated
Cylinder lock: steel, nickel-plated

Keyed different:

Cat. No.	234.55.209

Keyed alike:

Cat. No. key change 978	234.55.218
key change 901	234.55.227
key change 902	234.55.236
key change 903	234.55.245
key change 904	234.55.254
key change 906	234.55.263

Packing: 20 pcs.

Single parts:
Back- and front plates

Cat. No.	234.55.290

Packing: 20 pcs.

Wood applications

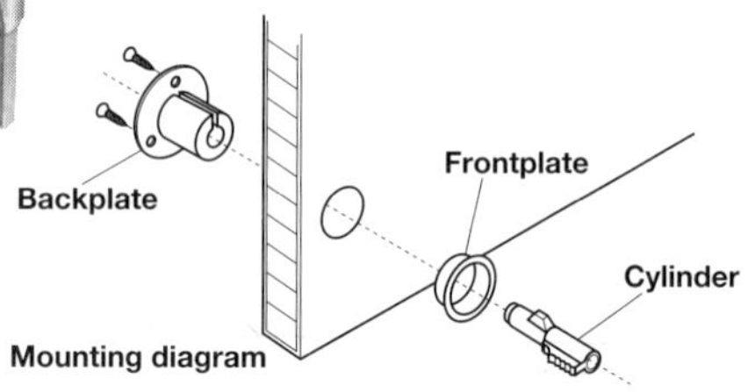

Cylinder Lock, with plug-in cylinder
For installation in glass panels from 6-8 mm
with key trap (key only removable when locked)
75 key changes
Accessories: 2 keys, 2 rubber washers and 2 mounting screws

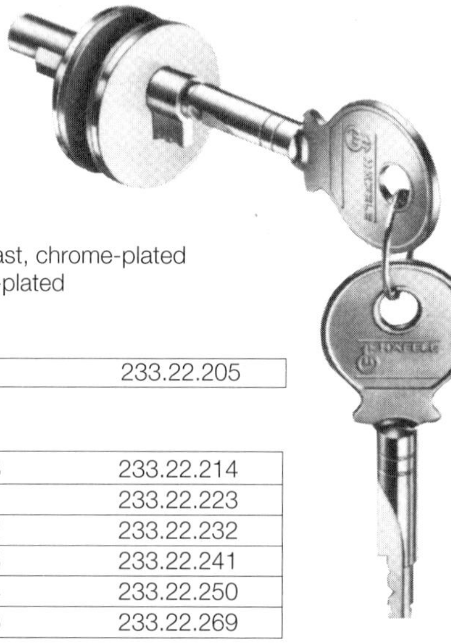

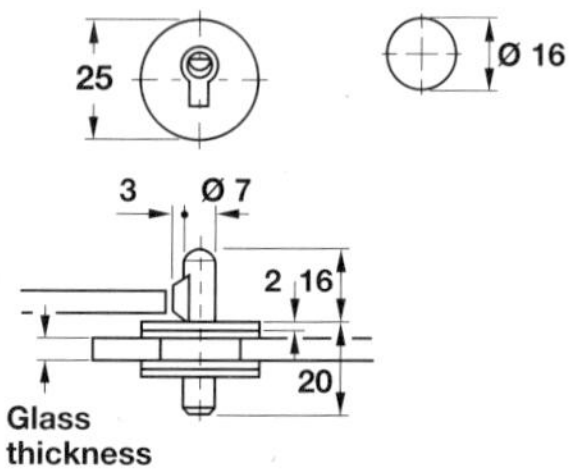

Finish: housing zinc die cast, chrome-plated
Cylinder lock: steel, nickel-plated

Keyed different:

Cat. No.	233.22.205

Keyed alike:

Cat. No. key change 978	233.22.214
key change 901	233.22.223
key change 902	233.22.232
key change 903	233.22.241
key change 904	233.22.250
key change 906	233.22.269

Packing: 20 pcs.

Single parts:
Back- and front plates

Cat. No.	233.22.296

Rubber washers

Cat. No.	233.22.983

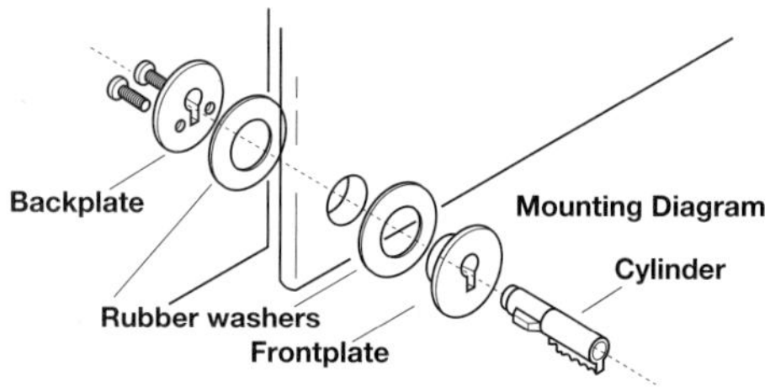

Dimensions in mm

Glass Door Locks

Cylinder Lock, with rack
Mounts on **4-8**** mm panels
6 plate levers = 1,000 key changes
Accessories: 2 keys

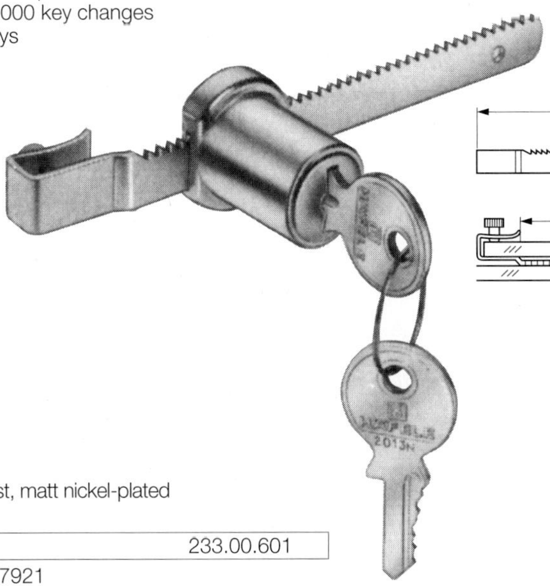

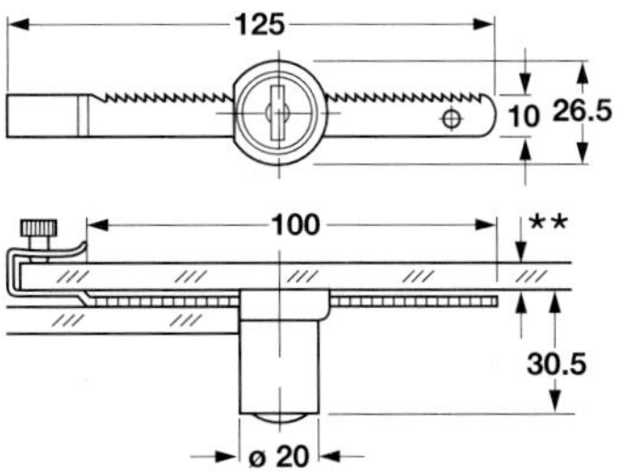

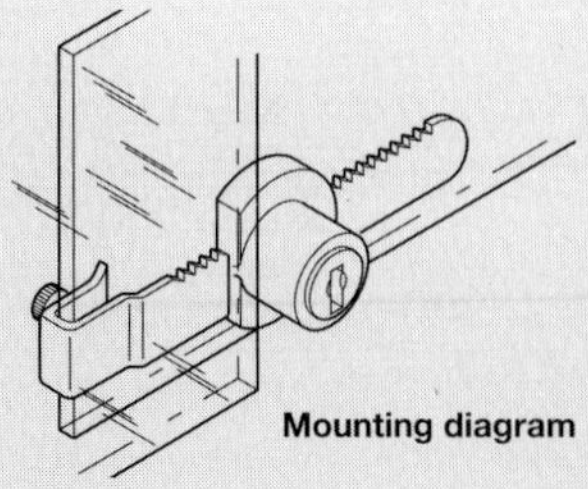
Mounting diagram

Finish: zinc die cast, matt nickel-plated
Keyed different

Cat. No.	233.00.601

Keyed alike: PL 7921

Cat. No.	233.00.610

Packing: 1 pc.

Glass Door Pin Lock
- backplate, screw-mounted
- for glass thickness **4** - **6** mm**
- with 6 plate levers = 1000 Key Changes

Finish: Housing and cylinder: zinc die-cast, nickel-plated matt
Accessories: 2 keys, 2 rubber spacers and 2 screws

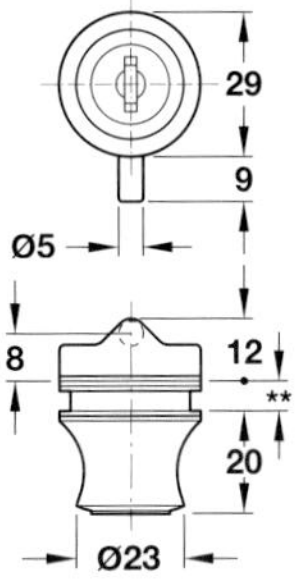

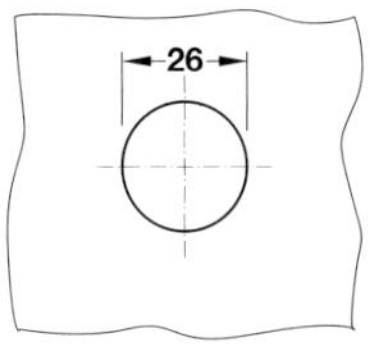

Glass drilling diagram

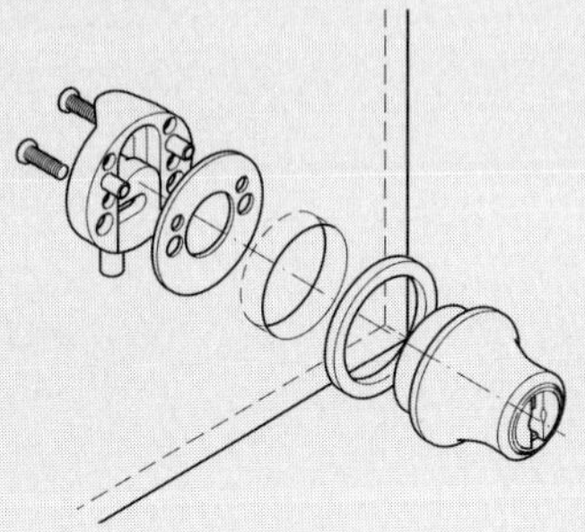

Keyed different: N 1000 PL

Cat. No.	233.05.600

Keyed alike:

Cat. No.	N 7921 PL	233.05.601
	N 7922 PL	233.05.602
	N 7923 PL	233.05.603
	N 7924 PL	233.05.604
	N 7925 PL	233.05.605

Packing: 1 pc.

Dimensions in mm

HÄFELE

Glass Door Locks for Hinged Doors

Overlay application

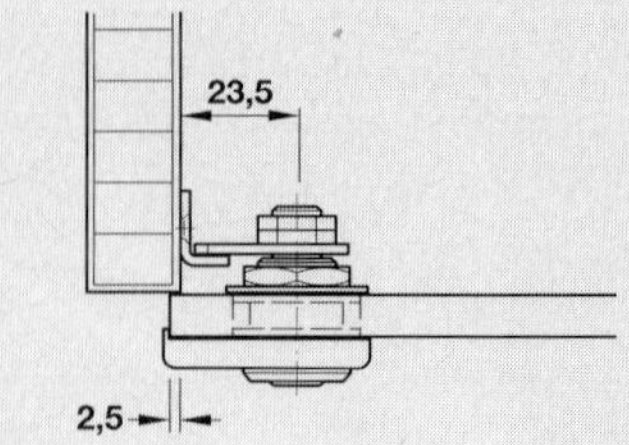

2
Locks, Catches, RTA and PAS® Fittings
Shelf Supports
Bed Fittings

Inset application

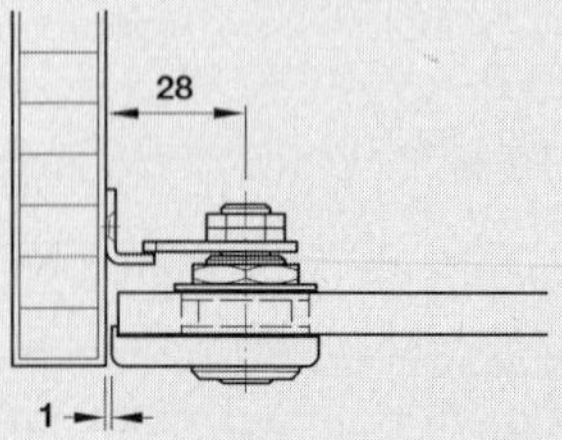

Key blanks, for H series

Cat. No.	209.99.044

Packing: 10 pcs.

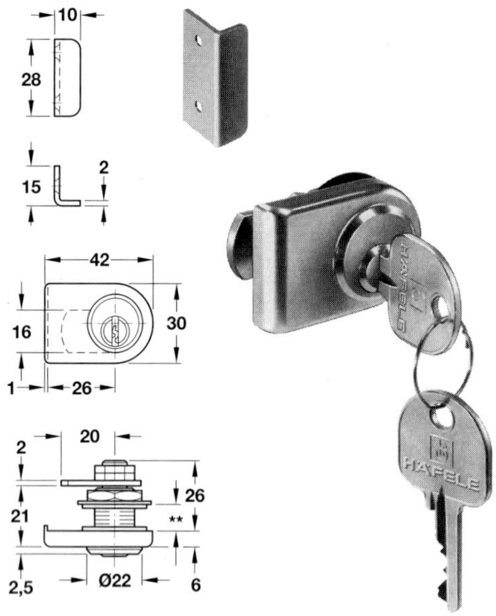

Glass Door Cylinder Cam Locks

- nut-mounted
- for glass thickness **4** to **10 mm****
- **Cam rotation 90°** (Key trap)
- with **5 pin levers=** 20,000 key changes

Finish: trim caps: zinc die-cast; cylinder: brass

Accessories: 2 keys, 1 cam, 3 nuts and 1 angle strike, steel
1 clamp plate and 1 washer, plastic

Keyed different

Cam rotation		90°	90°
Cat. No.	nickel-plated	233.33.600	233.33.655
	gold-colored	233.33.806	233.33.851

Keyed alike: key change H1

Cam rotation		90°	90°
Cat. No.	nickel-plated	233.33.619	233.33.664
	gold-plated	233.33.815	233.33.860

Packing: 1 pc.

Master Key System*

Cat. No.	233.33.698

General Master Key System*

Cat. No.	233.33.699

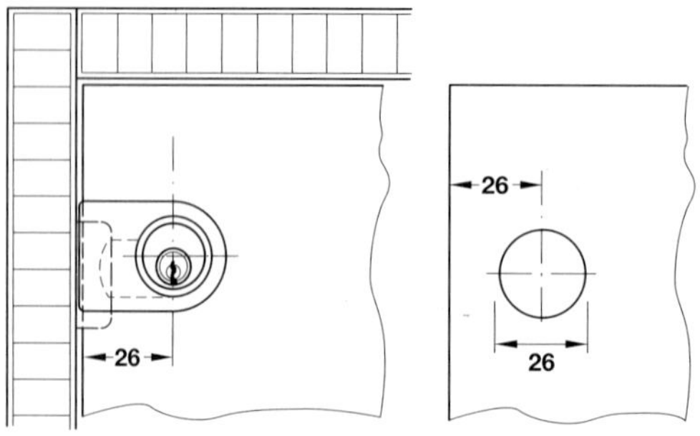

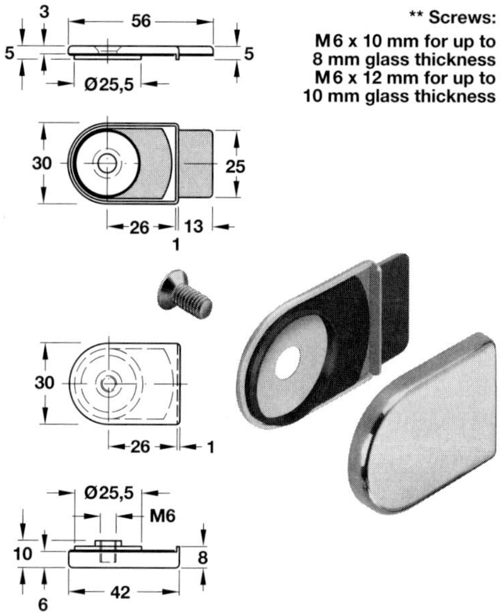

** Screws:
M6 x 10 mm for up to 8 mm glass thickness
M6 x 12 mm for up to 10 mm glass thickness

Strike plate to glass door cam lock

2 part, screw-mounted

- for glass thickness, **4** to **10 mm****
- allows two doors to be locked with one lock

Finish: zinc die-cast

Accessories: 2 M6 screws, 2 clamp plates and 1 washer, plastic

Cat. No.	nickel-plated	233.40.712
	gold-colored	233.40.810

Packing: 1 pcs.

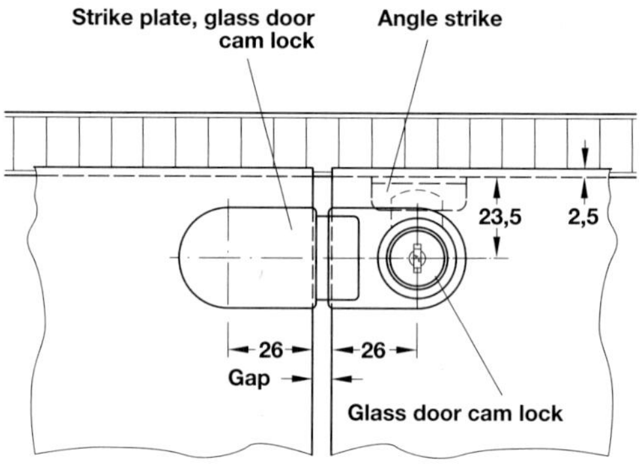

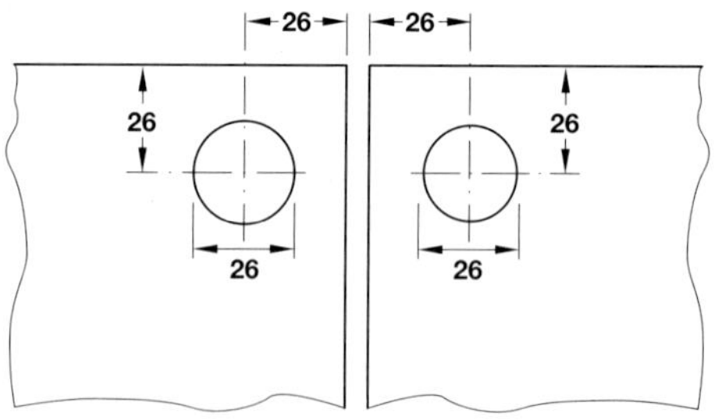

Glass drilling diagram

Dimensions in mm

Espagnolette Locks

HÄFELE

- Use with doors up to 2 m high
- The screw holes in the lock cases accept Varianta screws.

Lock cases for lever bit keys;
page 2.56

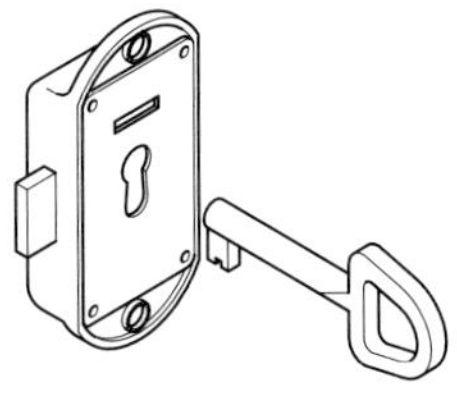

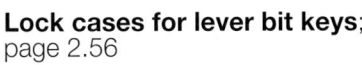

Lock cases with Ø 18 mm plate lever cylinder;
page 2.56

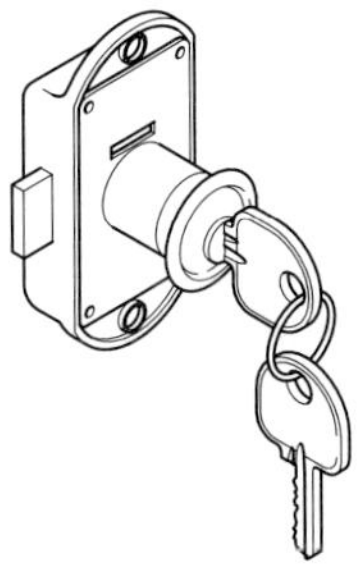

Lock cases with pin lever cylinder;
page 2.57

Lock cases with extended cylinder for knobs;
page 2.57

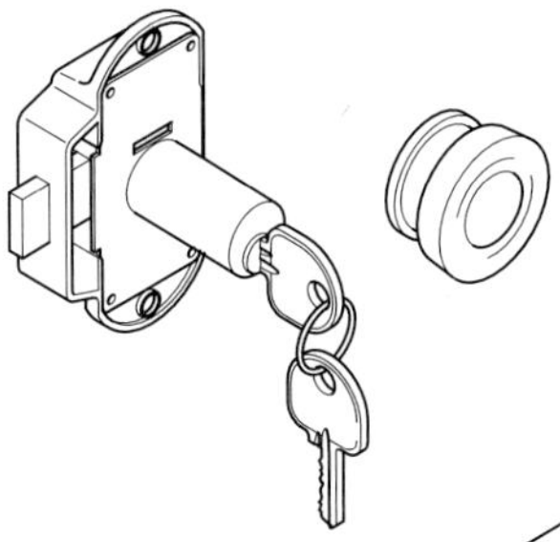

Lock cases with push button mechanism;
page 2.61

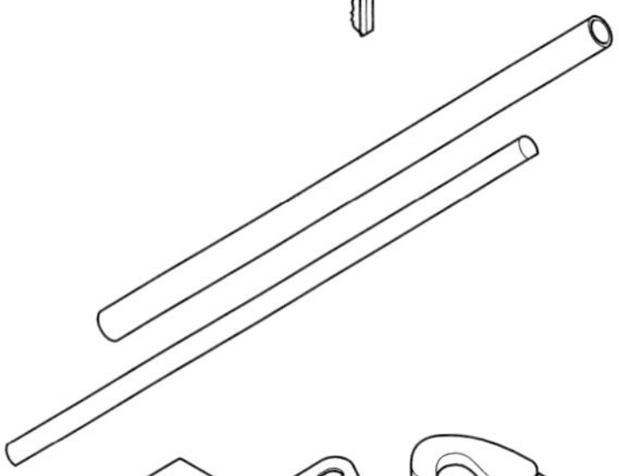

Espagnolette rod and rod cover;
page 2.58

Top and bottom catch hooks;
page 2.58

Rod guide;
page 2.58

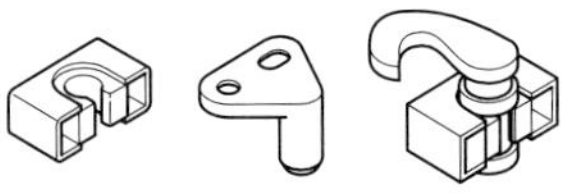

Locking bolt;
page 2.58

Strike plate for 1 door applications;
page 2.59

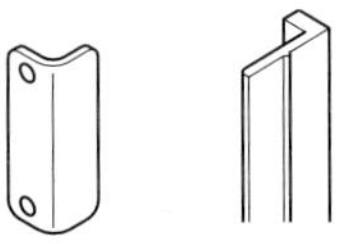

Closure strip for 2 door applications;
page 2.60

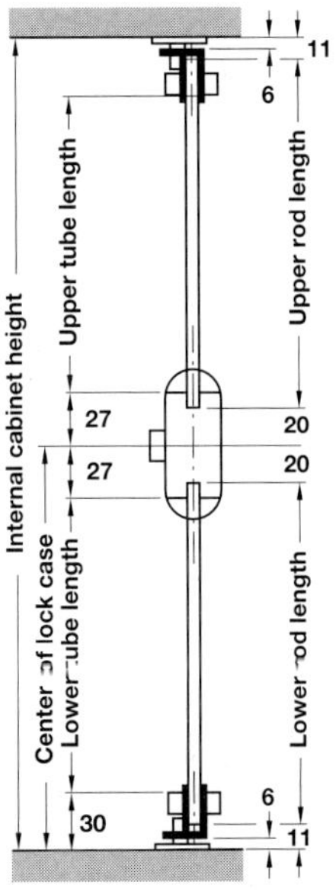

Cutting information

Rod dimensions:

Lower rod length = bottom to center of lock case **minus 31 mm**

Upper rod length = top to center of lock case **minus 31 mm**

Rod cover dimensions:

Lower tube length= bottom to center of lock case **minus 57 mm**

Upper tube length = top to center of lock case **minus 57 mm**

Locks, Catches, RTA and PAS® Fittings
Shelf Supports
Bed Fittings
2

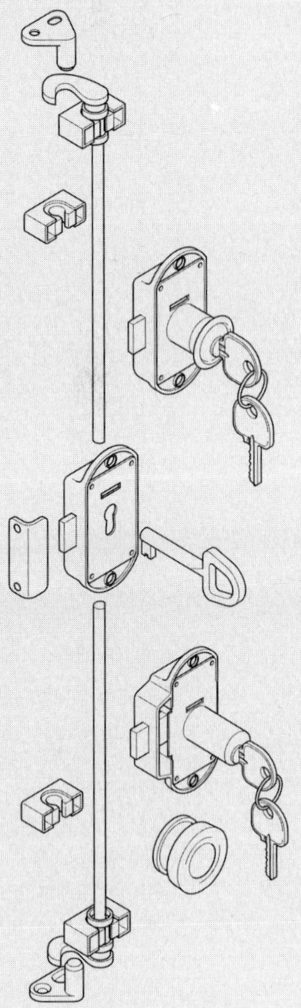

Dimensional data not binding.
We reserve the right to alter specifications without notice.

HÄFELE

Espagnolette Locks

- Decorative keys
- A choice is available on pages 2.10 to 2.12
- Choose a shank length of 35 to 40 mm
- Choose 8 x 6 mm bit configuration

Lock case for lever bit key,
backset 15 mm
Screw-mounted
Left or right handed

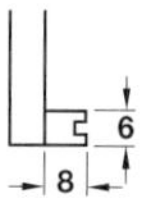

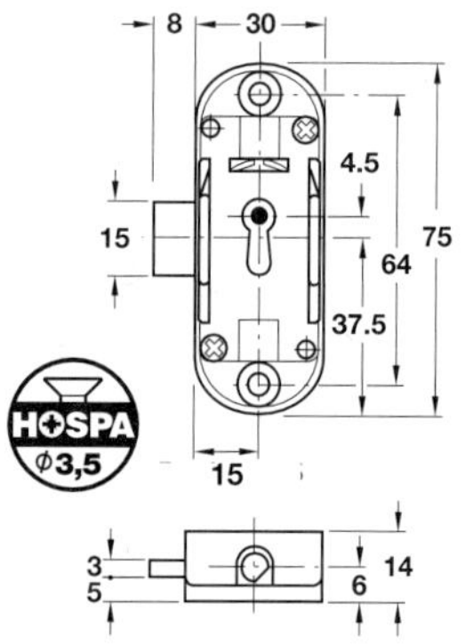

Finish: zinc die-cast

		left	right
Cat. No.	nickel-plated	225.56.654	225.56.609
	brass-plated	225.56.556	225.56.501
	brass antique	225.56.053	225.56.003

Packing: 10 pcs

Lock case with Ø 18 mm cylinder, backset 15 mm
- Left or right handed
- **5 plate levers** = 200 key changes
- Case: zinc die-cast, nickel-plated
- Cylinder: zinc die-cast, matt, nickel-plated
- Accessories: 2 keys and 1 cylinder rosette

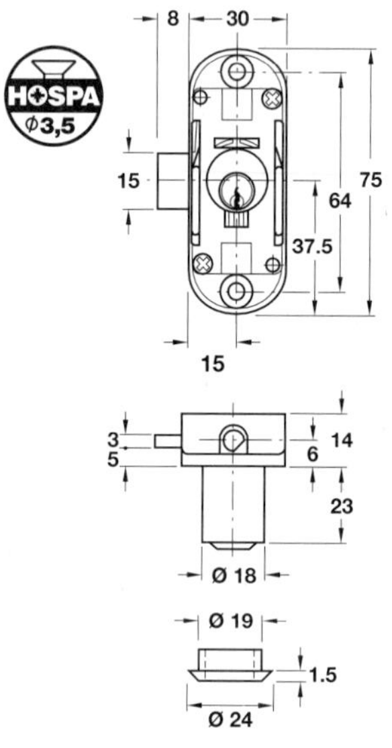

Rosette included

Keyed different	left	right
Cat. No.	225.53.653	225.53.608
Keyed alike	left	right
Key change FH1	225.53.911	225.53.813
Key change FH2	225.53.920	225.53.822
Key change FH3	225.53.939	225.53.831
Key change FH4	225.53.948	225.53.840
Key change FH5	225.53.957	225.53.859

Packing: 1 pc

Dimensions in mm

Espagnolette Locks

Lock case with Ø 18 mm cylinder, backset 15 mm
- Left or right handed
- **5 pin levers** = 10,000 key changes
- Case: zinc die cast, nickel-plated
- Cylinder: brass, matt, nickel-plated
- Accessories: 2 keys and 1 cylinder rosette

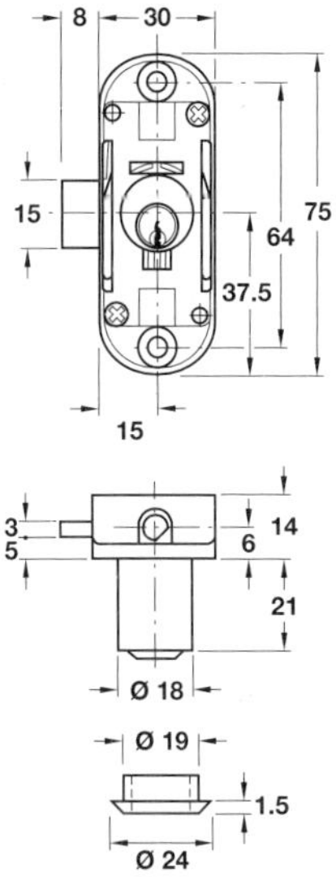

Keyed different	left	right
Cat. No.	225.58.658	225.58.603
Keyed alike	left	right
Key change H1	225.58.916	225.58.818
Key change H2	225.58.925	225.58.827
Key change H3	225.58.934	225.58.836
Key change H4	225.58.943	225.58.845
Key change H5	225.58.952	225.58.854

Packing: 1 pc

With master key system:

Cat. No.	225.58.68X*

With general master key system:

Cat. No.	225.58.69X*

Locks, Catches, RTA and PAS® Fittings
Shelf Supports
Bed Fittings
2

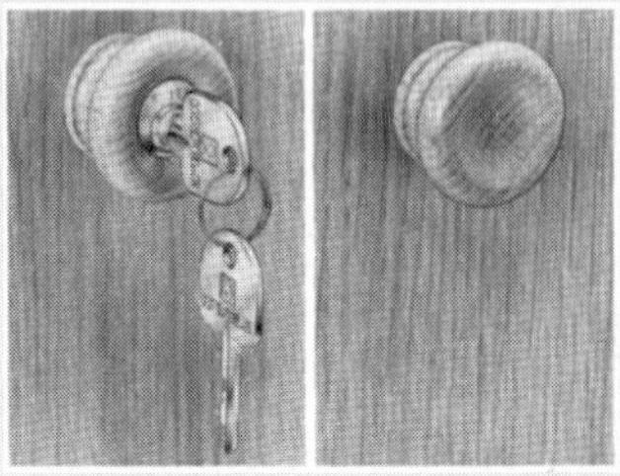

Lock case with extended Ø 18 mm cylinder, backset 25 mm
- To accommodate furniture knob-handle made to your own design.
- Left or right handed
- **5 pin levers** = 10,000 key changes
- Case: zinc die-cast, nickel-plated
- Cylinder: brass, matt, nickel-plated
- Accessories: 2 keys and 1 cylinder rosette

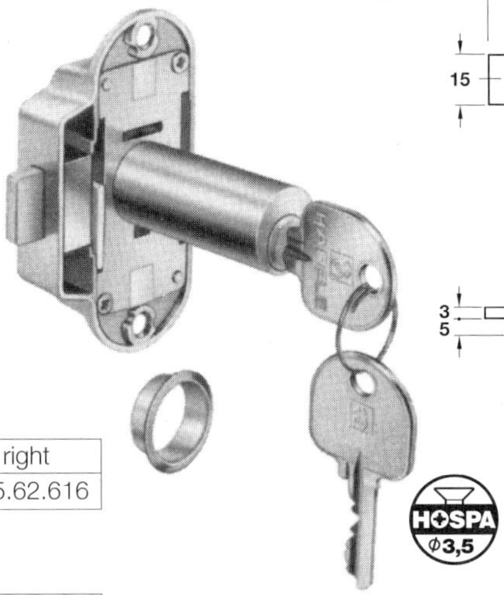

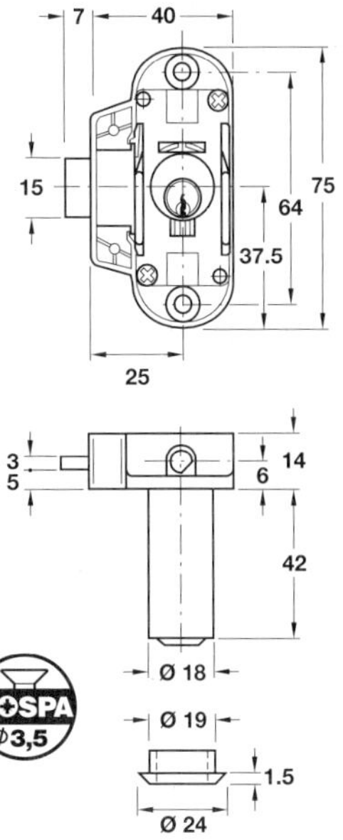

Finish: zinc die-cast, nickel-plated

Keyed different	left	right
Cat. No.	225.62.661	225.62.616

Packing: 1 pc

***With master key system:**

Cat. No.	225.62.68X

***With general master key system:**

Cat. No.	225.62.69X

Dimensions in mm

HÄFELE

Espagnolette Lock Accessories

Profile rod, drawn steel

Length	2000 mm	2500 mm
Finish	Cat. No.	
nickel-plated	226.07.209	226.07.254
bronzed	226.01.207	

Packing: 1 pc

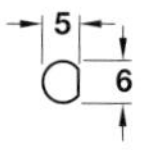

Rod cover, plastic

Length	2000 mm
Finish	Cat. No.
white	226.20.766
brown	226.20.168

Packing: 50 pcs

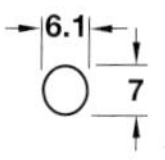

Top and bottom catch hooks, screw-mounted

Finish: zinc die-cast with plastic guides

	Cat. No.
nickel-plated	226.30.717
brass-plated	226.30.511
brass antique	226.30.113
bronzed	226.30.119

Packing: 10 pairs

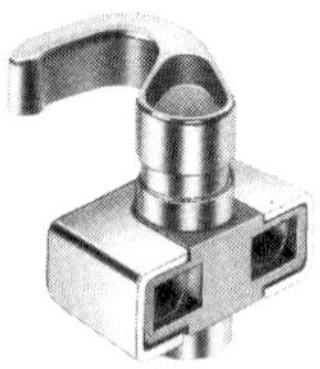

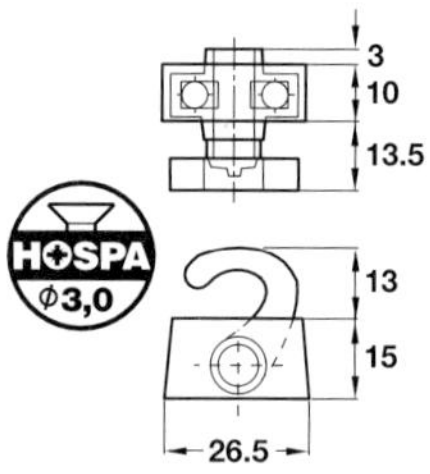

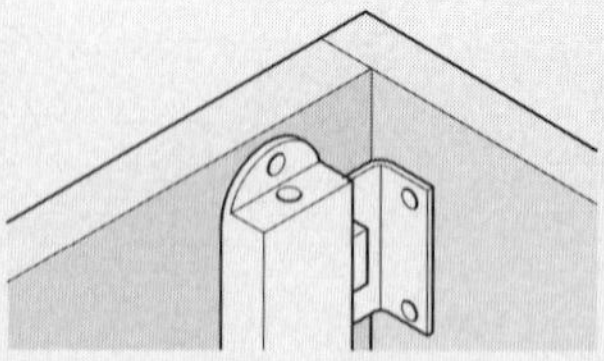

Rod guides, screw-mounted

Finish: zinc die-cast with plastic guides

	Cat. No.
nickel-plated	239.75.706
brass-plated	239.75.500
brass antique	239.75.103
bronzed	239.75.108

Packing: 20 pcs

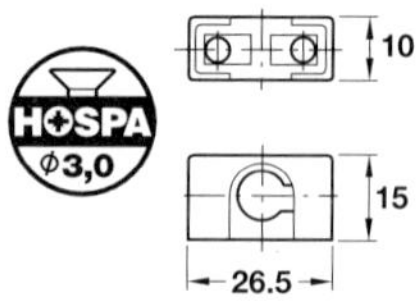

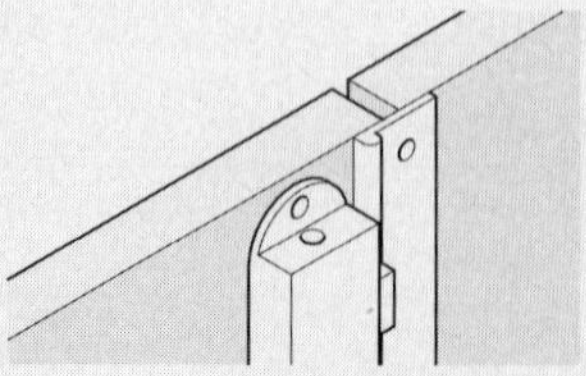

Locking bolt, screw-mounted plate, adjustable

Finish: zinc die-cast

	Cat. No.
nickel-plated	226.57.709
brass-plated	226.57.503
brass antique	226.57.101

Packing: 20 pcs

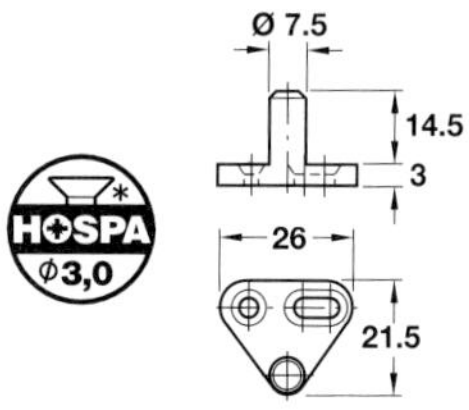

Dimensional data not binding. We reserve the right to alter specifications without notice.

Strike Plates

HÄFELE

Strike Plate
Screw-mounted,
belt loop type.

Finish: Steel black

Cat. No.	239.61.319

Packing: 10 pcs.

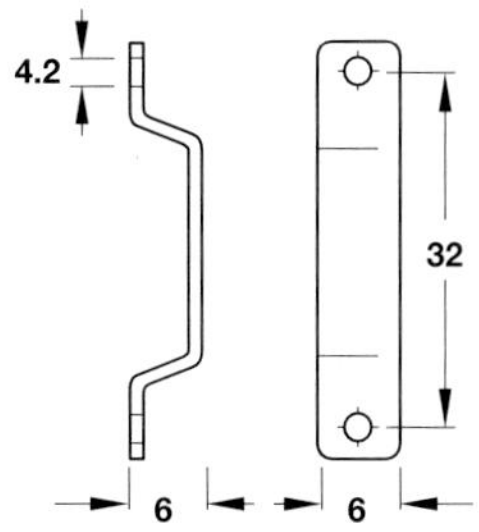

Strike Plate
5 mm outwards projection. Screw-mounted.

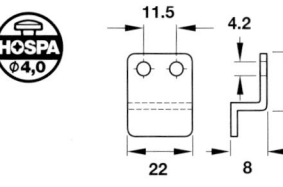

Finish: Steel, black

Cat. No.	239.61.328

Packing: 10 pcs.

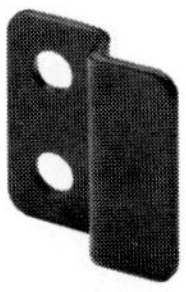
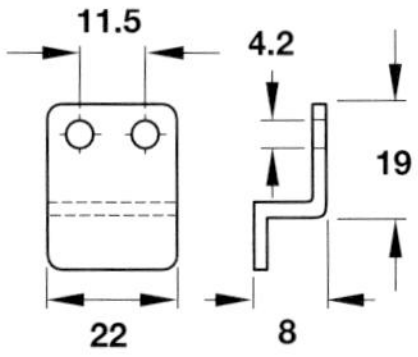

Angle Strike
90° angle
screw-mounted.

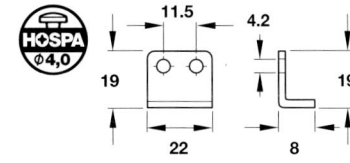

Finish: Steel, black

Cat. No.	239.61.337

Packing: 10 pcs.

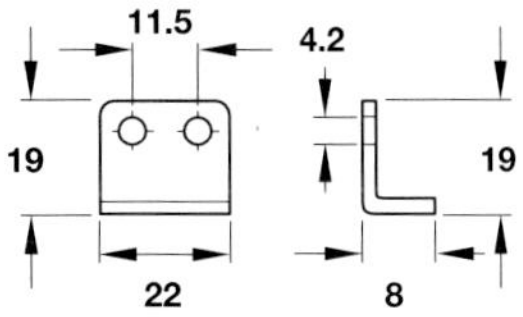

Strike Plate screw-mounted
Finish: steel

Cat. No.	nickel-plated	239.40.703
	black	239.40.301
brass-plated		239.40.507
	bronzed	239.40.105

Packing: 100 pcs.

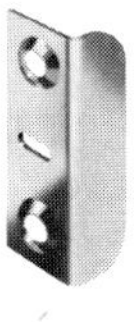
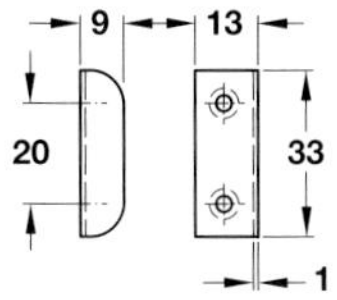

Strike Plate screw-mounted
Finish: steel

Cat. No.	nickel-plated	239.41.013
	brass-plated	239.41.513
	bronzed	239.41.111

Packing: 100 pcs.

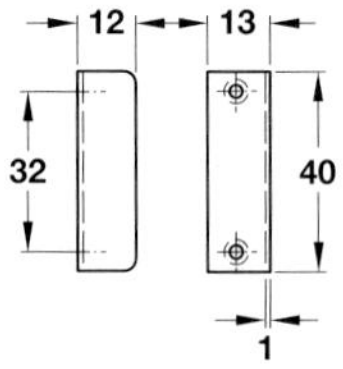

Strike Plate screw-mounted
Finish: steel

Cat. No.	nickel-plated	239.41.022

Packing: 100 pcs.

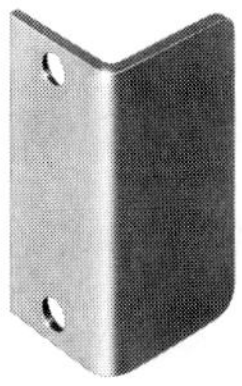
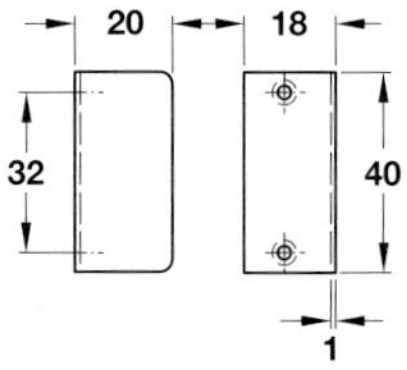

Strike Plate screw-mounted
Finish: steel

Cat. No.	nickel-plated	239.47.604

Packing: 100 pcs.

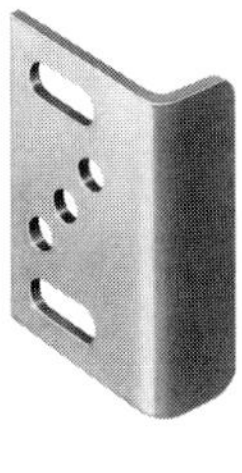
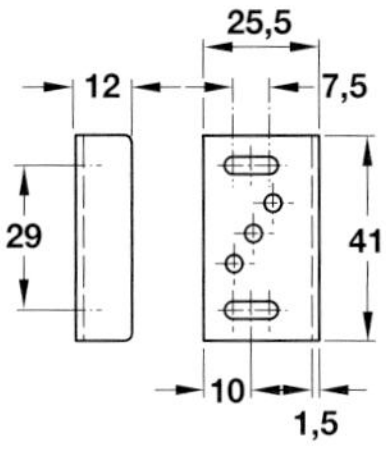

Strike Plate for series drilled holes with
adjustment slots.
Finish: plastic

Cat. No.	white	239.44.774
	brown	239.44.176

Packing: 10 and 100 pcs.

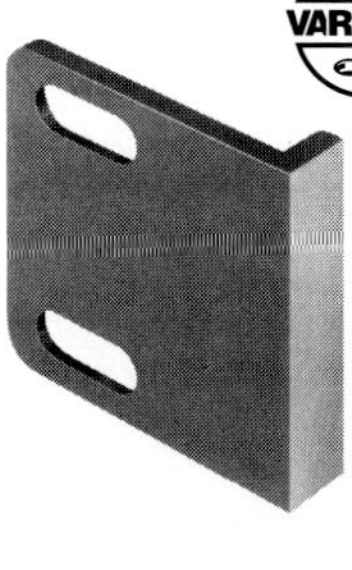
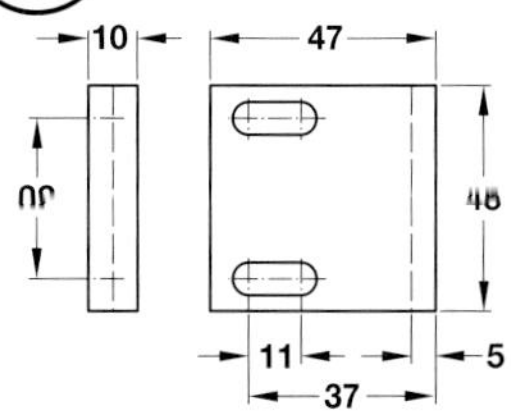

Dimensions in mm

Locks, Catches, RTA
and PAS® Fittings
Shelf Supports
Bed Fittings

2

Varianta Special Screw
Cylinder head with
Cross-slot PZ 2
Finish:
Steel, nickel-plated

Length (mm)	Cat. No. Ø3 mm	Ø5 mm
10.5	013.14.810	013.14.910
13.5	013.14.820	013.14.920
16.0	013.14.830	

Packing: 100 and 1000 pcs.

Dimensional data not binding.
We reserve the right to alter
specifications without notice.

Profile Strips

Door sealing profile with soft PVC lip; self adhesive.
Finish: plastic

Cat. No.	white	716.60.707
	brown	716.60.109
	beige	716.60.403

Packing: 2.5 meters

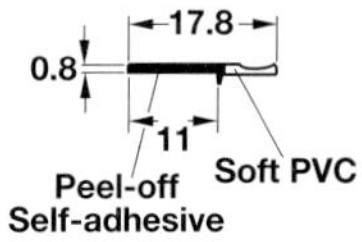

Door sealing profile with soft PVC lip; self adhesive.
Finish: plastic

Cat. No.	white	716.60.716
	brown	716.60.118
	beige	716.60.412

Packing: 2.5 meters

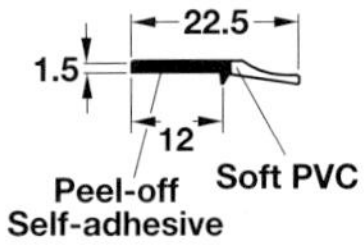

Closure strip
Finish: plastic

Cat. No.	white	716.57.488
	brown	716.51.486

Packing: 5 meters

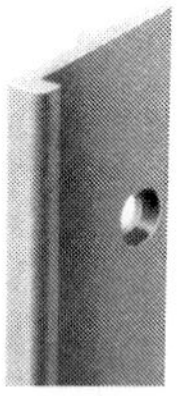

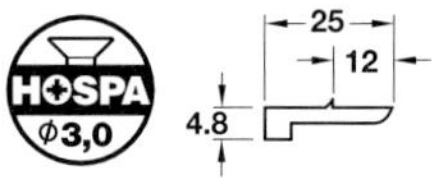

Ideal for:
- Wardrobe locks, Espagnolette locks…wherever a lock or sealing strip is needed.

Stop Strip screw-mounted
Finish: plastic

Cat. No.	white	239.92.750
	gray	239.92.550
	brown	239.92.150

Packing: 2.5 meters

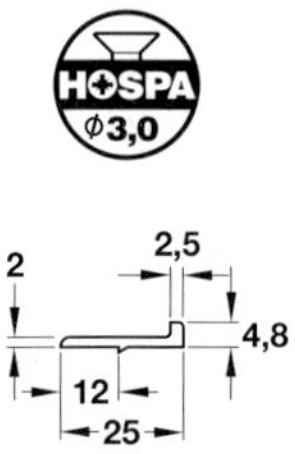

Stop Strips screw-mounted with self-hinged cover
Finish: plastic

Cat. No.	white	239.93.750
	gray	239.93.550
	brown	239.93.150
	black	239.93.350

Packing: 2.5 meters

Stop Strips screw-mounted with self-hinged cover
Finish: plastic

Cat. No.	white	239.93.780
	gray	239.93.580
	brown	239.93.180
	black	239.93.380

Packing: 2.5 meters

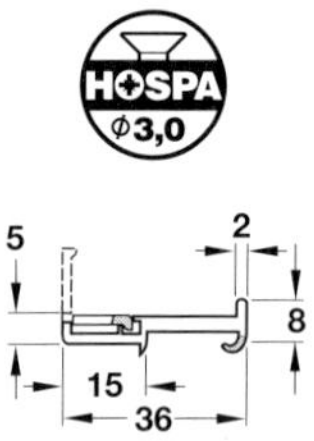

Stop Strips with pressure sensitive adhesive
Finish: plastic

Cat. No.	white	239.91.700
	gray	239.91.500
	brown	239.91.100
	black	239.91.300

Packing: 2.5 meters

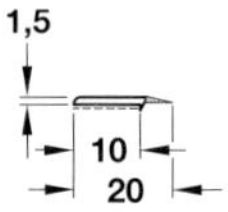

Stop Strips screw-mounted
Finish: plastic

Cat. No.	white	239.90.700
	brown	239.90.100

Packing: 2.5 meters

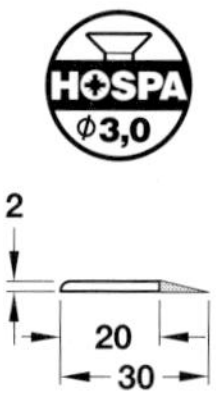

Dimensions in mm

Push-button Locks

Push-Lock featuring pushbutton locking mechanism

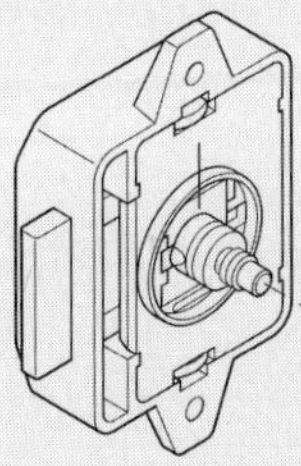

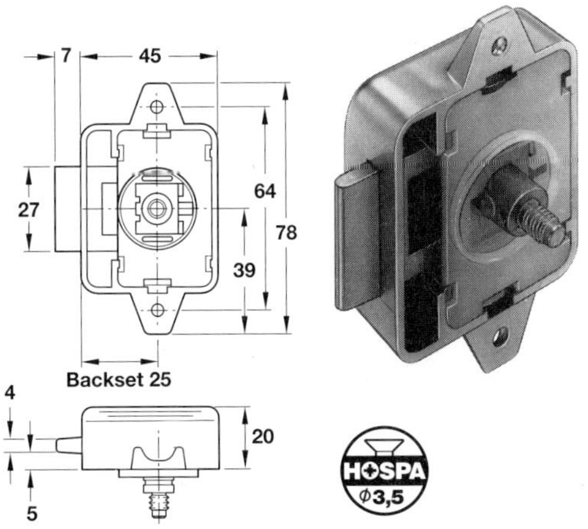

Push-Lock featuring push-button locking mechanism

- Screw-mounted
- One-sided operation

Finish: plastic housing

Cat. No.		
	nickel-plated, matt	211.60.609
	white	211.60.707
	brown	211.60.109

Packing: 100 pcs.

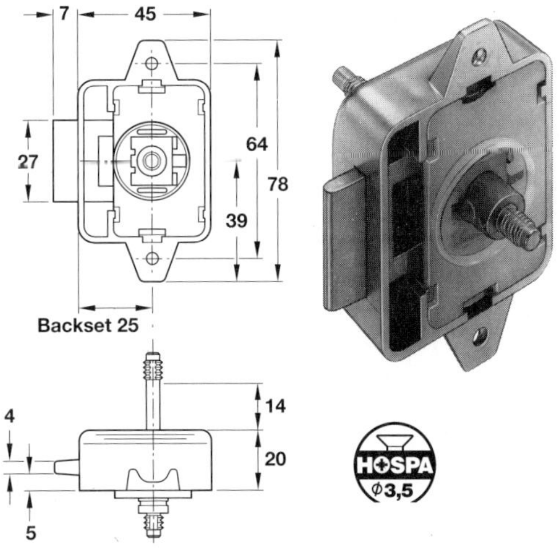

Push-Lock featuring push-button locking mechanism

- Screw-mounted
- Convenient two-sided operation

Finish: plastic housing

Cat. No.		
	white	211.60.752
	brown	211.60.190

Packing: 1 pc.

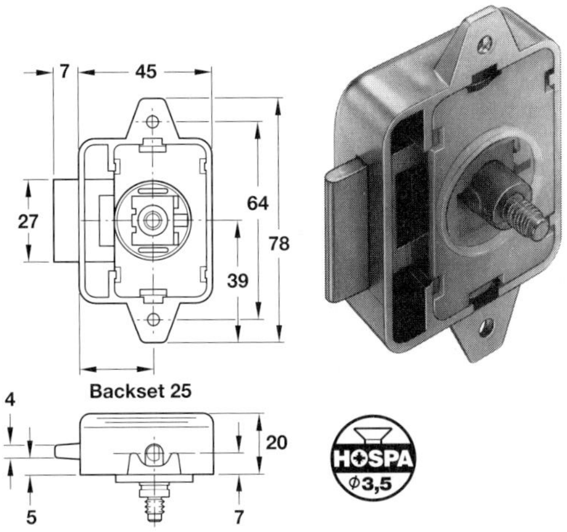

Push-Lock featuring pushbutton locking mechanism. Profile rod version

- for **6 mm Ø profile rod**
- for left or right-hand door application
- **one-side operatiion**
- **25 mm setback**

Finish: housing, plastic
Accessories: 1 pair of catch hooks

Cat. No.		
	nickel-plated, matt	225.22.603
	white	225.22.701
	brown	225.22.103

Packing: 100 pcs.

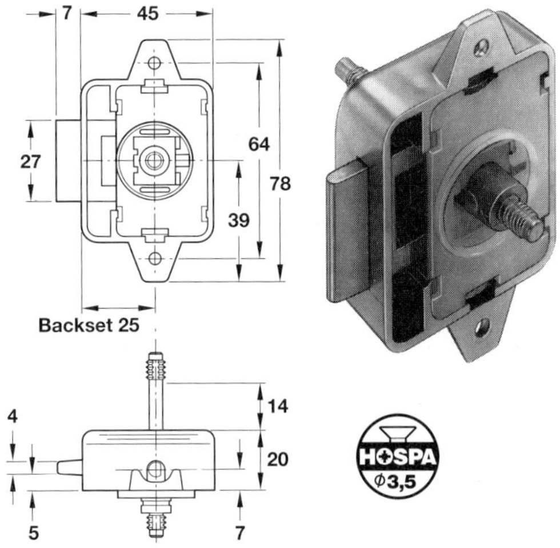

Push-Lock featuring pushbutton locking mechanism. Profile rod version

- for **6 mm Ø profile rod**
- for left or right-hand door application
- **convenient two-side operation**
- **25 mm setback**
- **Ideal for passage doors**

Finish: housing, plastic
Accessories: 1 pair of catch hooks

Cat. No.		
	white	225.22.756
	brown	225.22.185

Packing: 1 pc.

Push-Lock featuring pushbutton locking mechanism, profile rod version

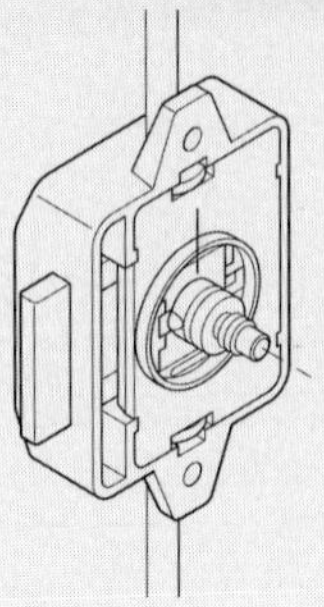

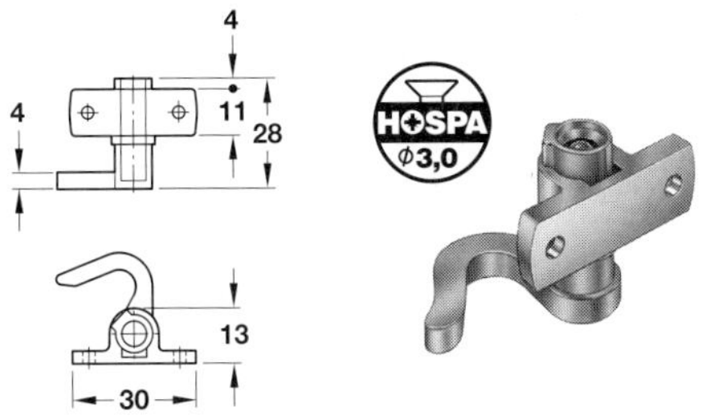

Profile rod locks come with color-coordinated **catch hooks:**

- Matt nickel-plated locks, zinc die-cast
- White or brown locks, plastic

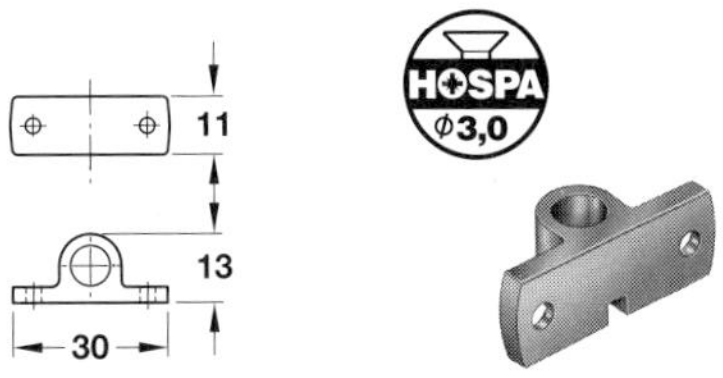

When using the profile lock in tall wardrobe applications, we recommend adding screw-mounted **profile rod guides.**

Finish:	Cat. No.
zinc die cast, matt nickel-plated	239.71.619
plastic, white	239.71.717
plastice, brown	239.71.119

Packing: 20 and 200 pcs.

Dimensions in mm

Dimensional data not binding. We reserve the right to alter specifications without notice.

HÄFELE

Push-Button Locks

For 13 mm
Door Thickness

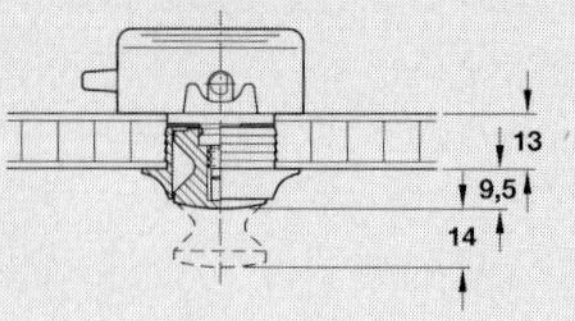

For 16 mm
Door Thickness

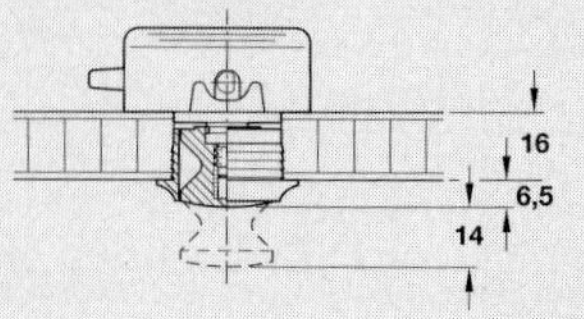

For 19 mm
Door Thickness

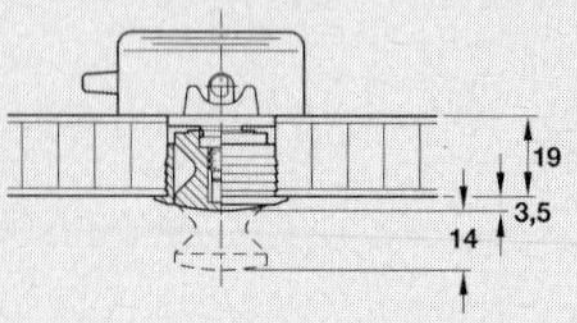

Push-button with Rosette

Finish: plastic

A variety of rosettes and buttons are available:

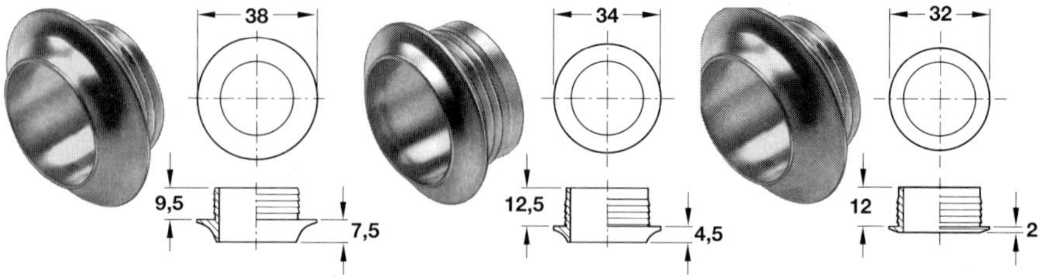

for door thickness		13 mm	16 mm	19 mm
Cat. No.	nickel-plated matt	229.01.604	229.01.613	229.01.622
	brass-plated polished	229.01.800	229.01.819	229.01.828
	antique brass	229.01.104	229.01.113	229.01.122
	white	229.00.705	229.00.714	229.00.723
	brown	229.00.107	229.00.116	229.00.125

Packing: 10 pcs. per type

Push-Button Only, for double-sided operation

Finish: plastic

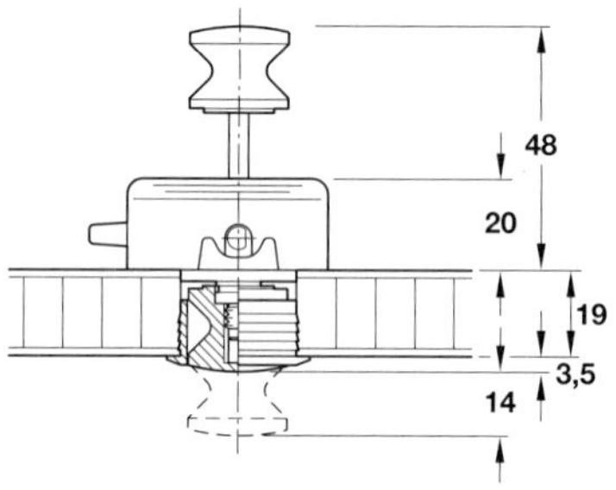

for door thickness		13 - 19 mm
Cat. No.	nickel-plated matt	229.01.677
	brass-plated polished	229.01.873
	antique brass	229.01.177
	white	229.00.796
	brown	229.00.198

Packing: 1 pc.

If application requires two-side Push-Lock operation, be sure to order 2 pushbuttons and 1 rosette to match wood thickness.
(See application example shown above.)

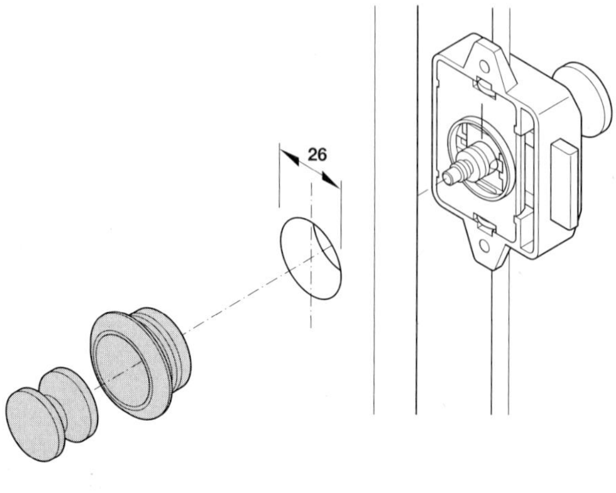

Lock Accessories

Strike Plate, screw-mounted
Finish: steel

Cat. No.	nickel-plated	239.05.704
	brass-plated	239.05.508

Packing: 10 and 100 pcs.

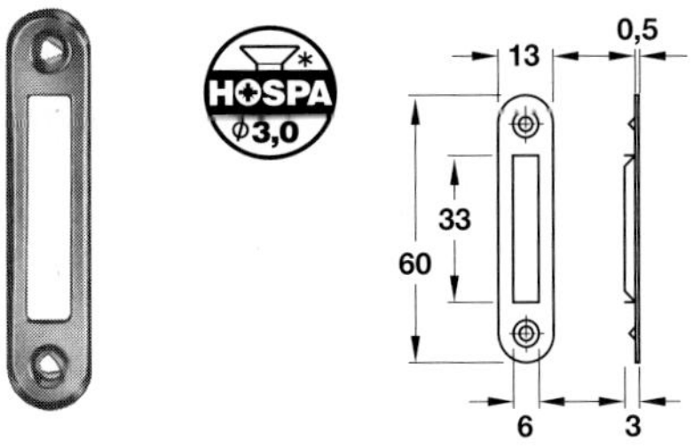

Strike Plate, flush screw-mounted
Finish: steel

Cat. No.	brass-plated	239.02.516

Packing: 10 and 100 pcs.

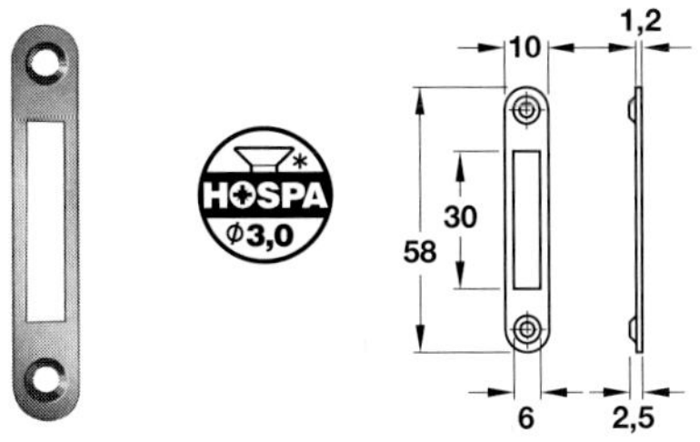

Strike Plate, screw-mounted
Finish: steel

Cat. No.	nickel-plated	239.26.703
	brass-plated	239.26.507

Packing: 10 and 100 pcs.

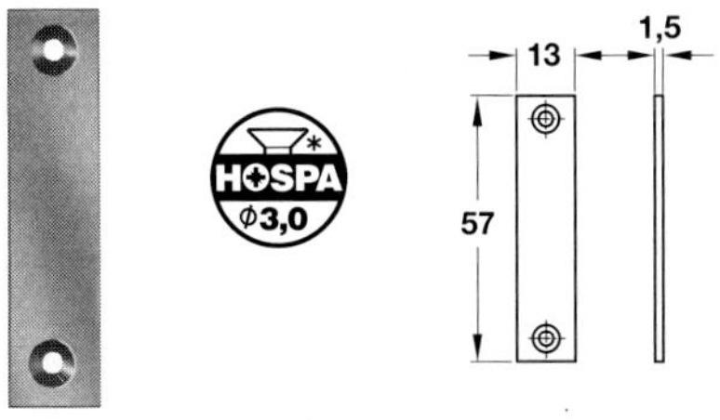

Dimensional data not binding.
We reserve the right to alter specifications without notice.

Dimensions in mm

HÄFELE

- Locks double doors without the necessity of an additional catch or bolt.
- Must be combined with either a cam lock or rim lock.

Door Bolt

Automatic Door Bolt

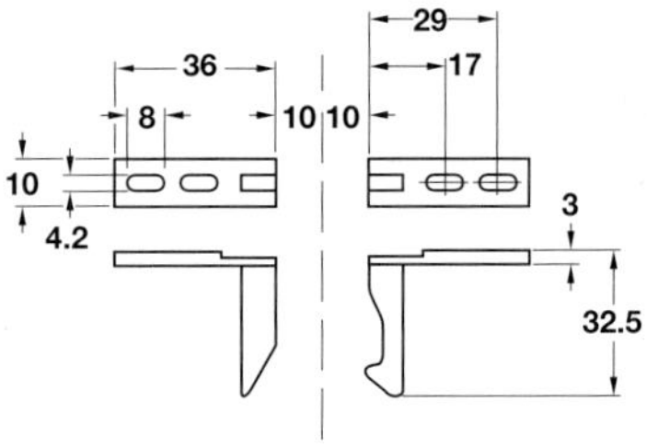

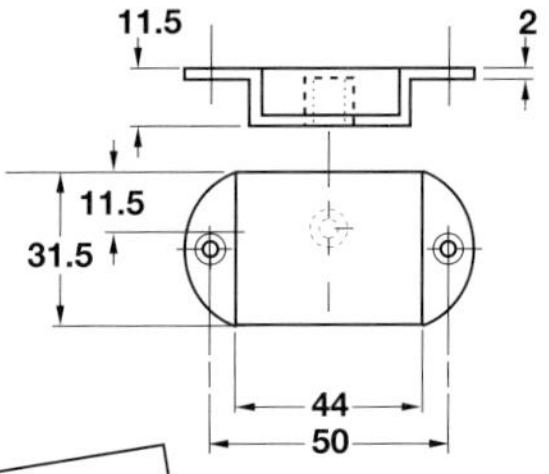

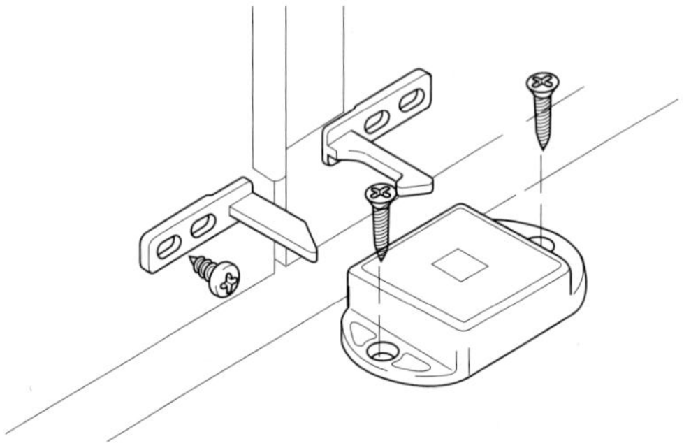

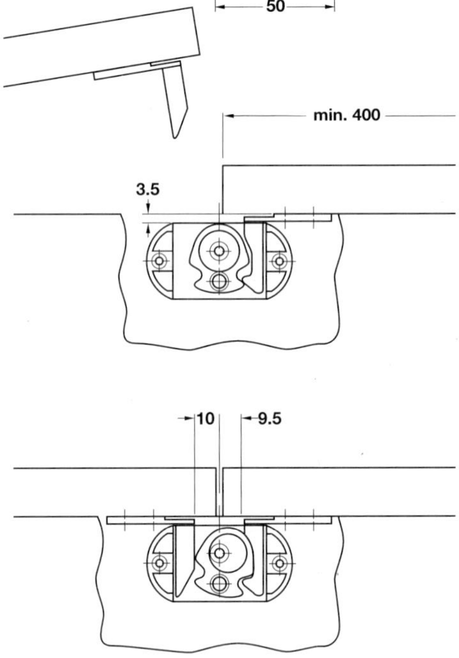

Finish: zinc die cast

Cat. No.	nickel-plated	245.58.754
	brass-plated	245.58.852
	bronzed	245.58.156

Packing: 20 pcs.

Dimensions in mm

Dimensional data not binding. We reserve the right to alter specifications without notice.

Locker Locks

HÄFELE

Mastercombi Rim Lock

With high-security combination and control key override facility
Accessories: 2 nuts with integral E clip

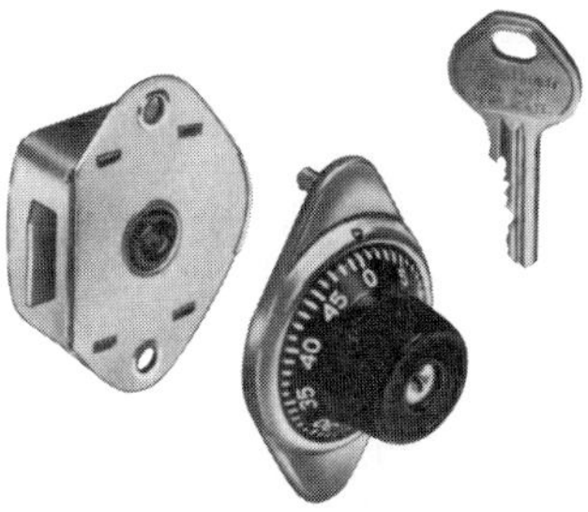

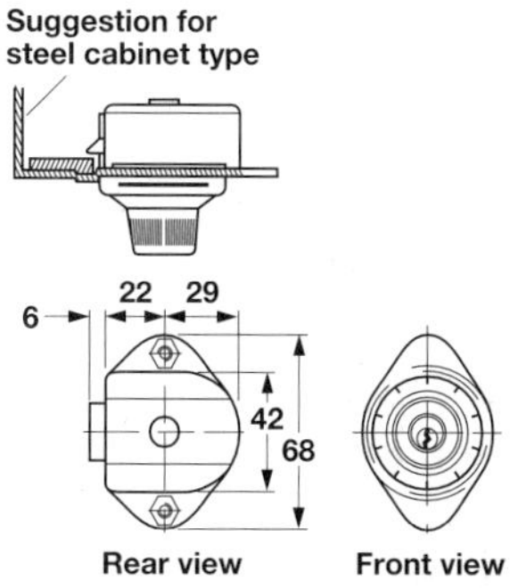

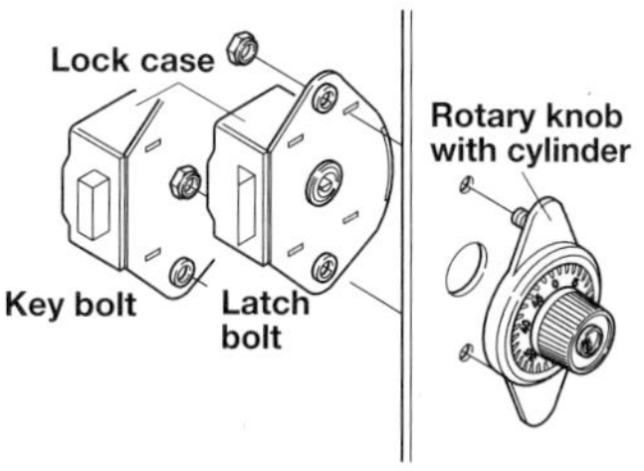

Finish: lock case steel, zinc-plated and chromatized;
Rosette: stainless steel; plastic rotary knob
Cylinder: brass

Installation of Mastercombi in steel doors

Mastercombi with latch bolt

Application	left	right
Cat. No.	231.13.055	231.13.000

Mastercombi with key bolt

Application	left	right
Cat. No.	0.231.12.058	0.231.12.003

Packing: 1 pc.

Control key, for Mastercombi

Cat. No.	230.12.606

Packing: 1 pc.

Special Flush Handle

Mastercombi installations in wood doors, 18.6 – 21.8 mm

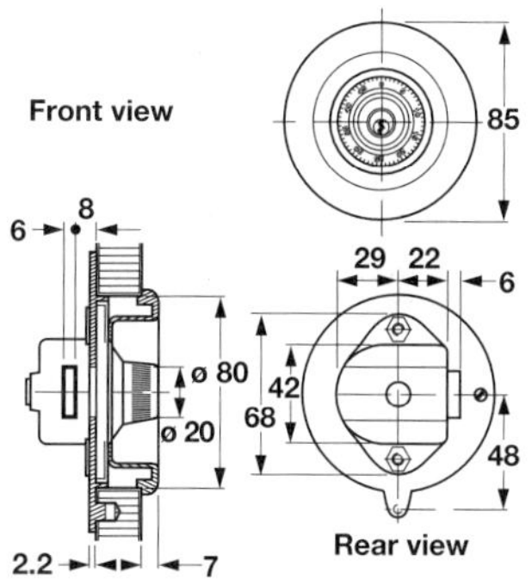

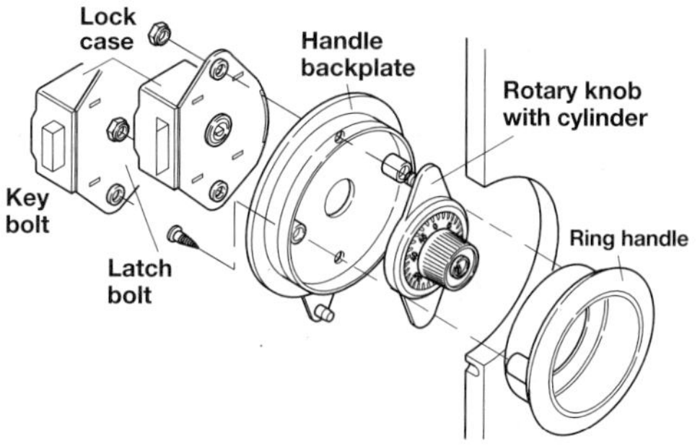

Finish: nylon, gray-white (RAL 9002)*

Door thickness (mm)	18.6-19.8	20.6-21.8
Cat. No.	231.14.507	231.14.516

Packing: 10 pcs.

Special Strike Plate

For Mastercombi installations in wood doors

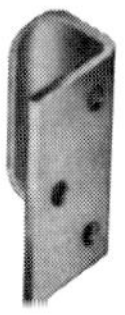

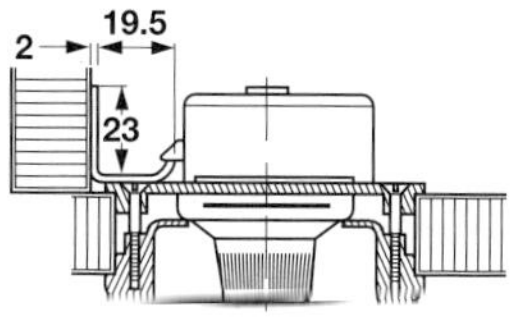

Dimensions in mm

For single doors

Cat. No.	231.13.706

Packing: 50 pcs.

Installation of Mastercombi in wood doors with flush handle

Mastercombi key controlled combination rim locks are suitable for general-purpose and cloakroom locks in all public and private sector buildings. The rustproof steel lock case is as equally resistant to forced entry as the strong (also rustproof) functional elements.
Features include:
High-security numerical combinations of three numbers in each lock, so that the combinations in thousands of locks are based on non-related series, making them mathematically incalculable.

Setting a new combination in the Mastercombi:
Turn the numerical scale ring at least one full turn to the right, then set it on the red"0" mark. Insert the control key and turn it 90° to the right, thus withdrawing the latch or key bolt and allowing the door to be opened. Next, depress the spring-loaded button on the back of the lock case and keep it applied while turning the numerical scale ring two turns to the right with the other hand to set it on the "48" mark. Now release the spring-loaded button. Turn the scale ring further to the right until the setting spring is heard to engage. The new combination is now set. Close door and remove the control key.

Important: Do not forget to make a note of the new combination.

Dimensional data not binding.
We reserve the right to alter specifications without notice.

HÄFELE

Product Guide - Connectors, RTA Fittings and Precision Assembly Systems®

1 Decorative Hardware

2 Locks, Catches, RTA and PAS® Fittings
Shelf Supports
Bed Fittings

3 Hinges
Flap and Lid Stays
Associated Fittings

4 Sliding Door Hardware
Drawer Slides
Television Supports

5 Kitchen Accessory Systems

6 Furniture Support Systems, Office and Computer Furniture Accessories

7 Store Fixtures
Profiles
Retainers

8 Interior Accessories
Wardrobe Accessories
Storage Systems
Furniture Lighting

0 Fastening Devices

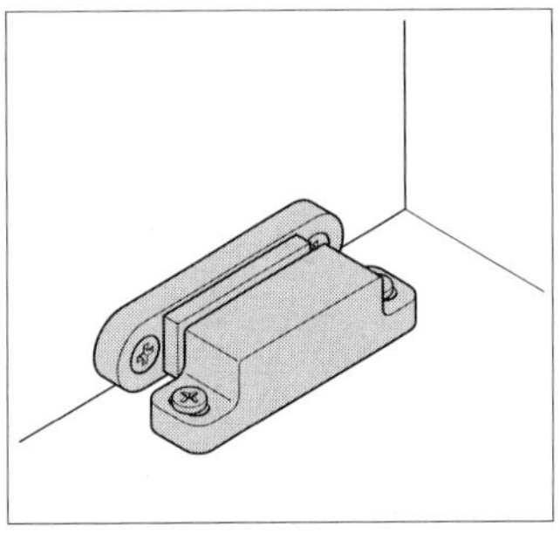

Magnetic Catches
Pages **2.68 - 2.74**

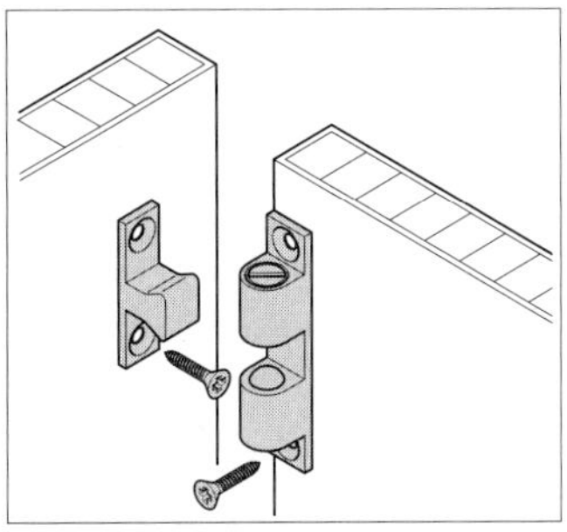

Ball Catches
Pages **2.75 - 2.78**

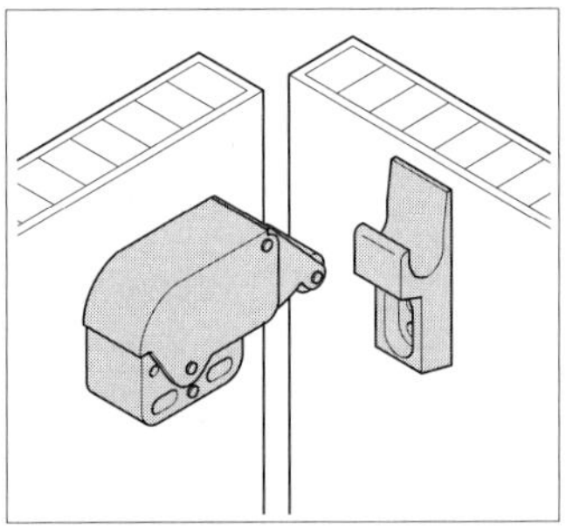

Spring Catches
Pages **2.79 - 2.86**

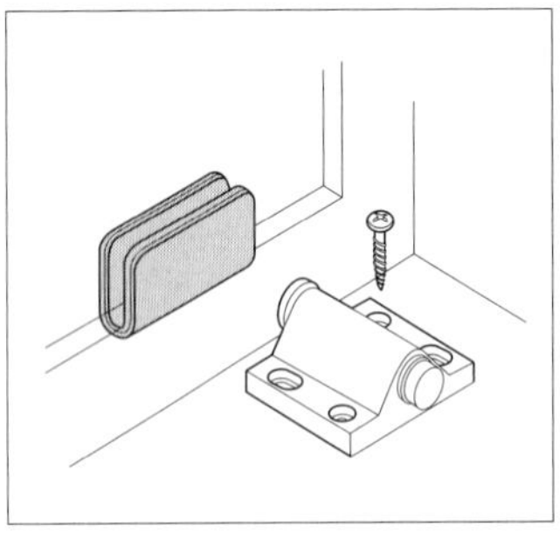

Strikes for Catches
Pages **2.87 - 2.88**

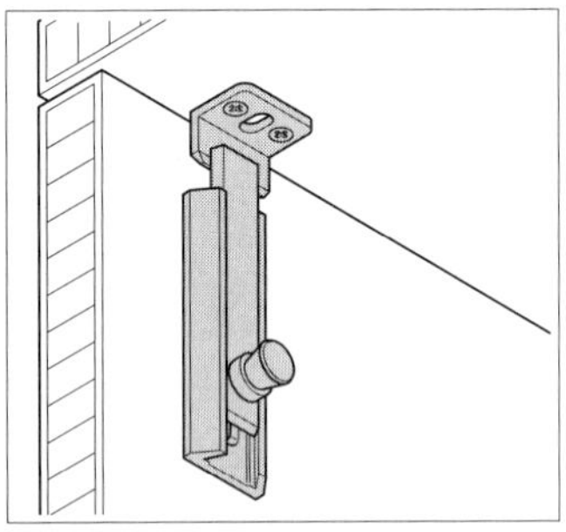

Door Bolts
Pages **2.89 - 2.91**

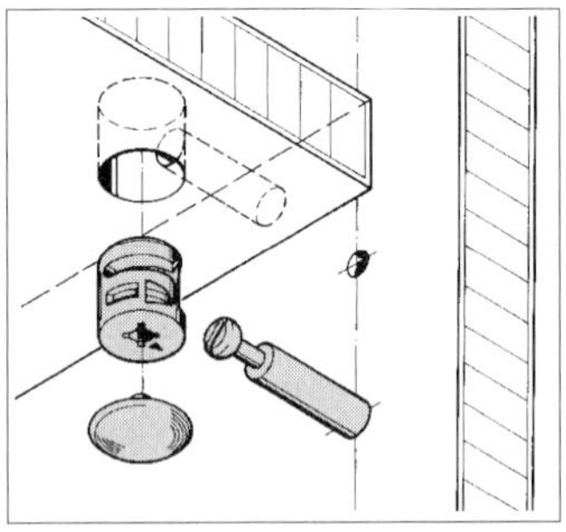

Minifix Precision Assembly Systems®
Pages **2.92 - 2.107**

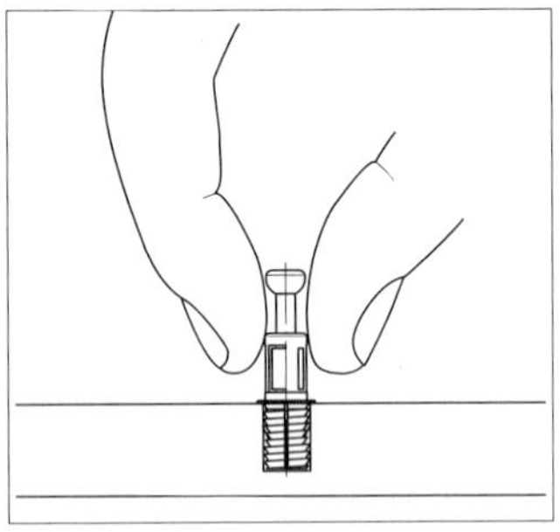

Toolless Minifix Bolts - PAS®
Pages **2.102**

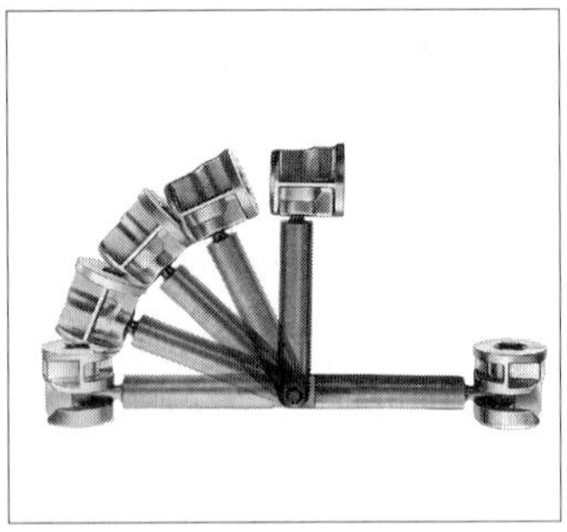

Minifix Miter Joint Connectors
Pages **2.104 - 2.105**

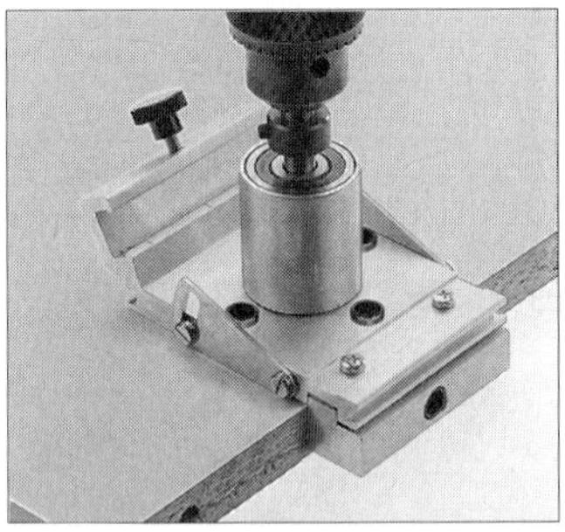

Unitool Jigs For RTA Connectors
Pages **2.108 - 2.109**

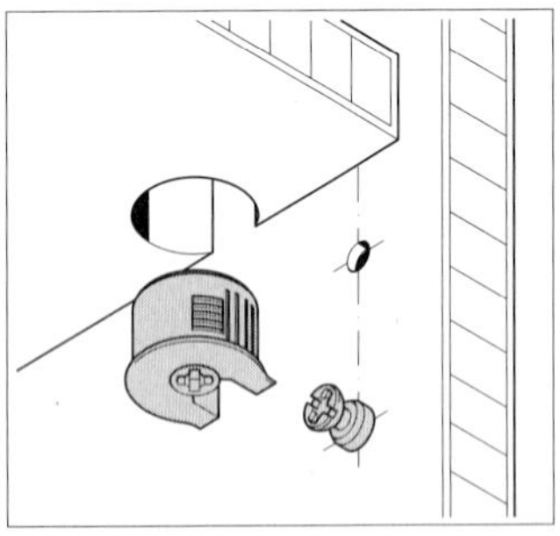

Rafix Precision Assembly Systems®
Pages **2.110 - 2.118**

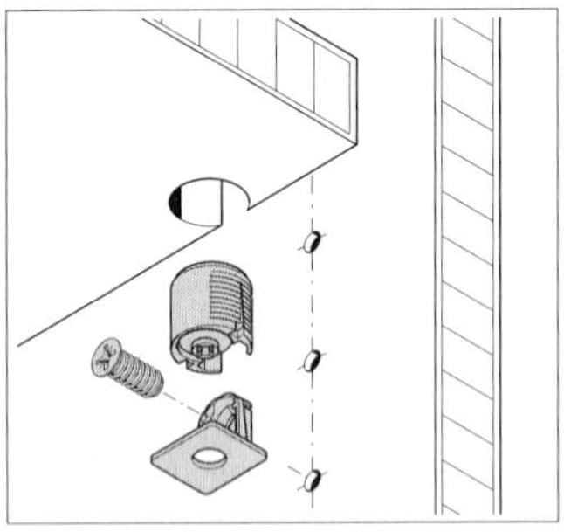

Tab-V Precision Assembly Systems®
Pages **2.121 - 2.123**

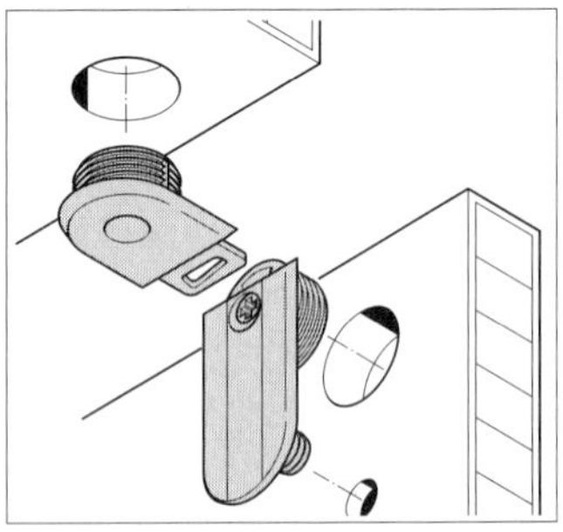

Solo 32 Presision Assembly Systems®
Pages **2.124**

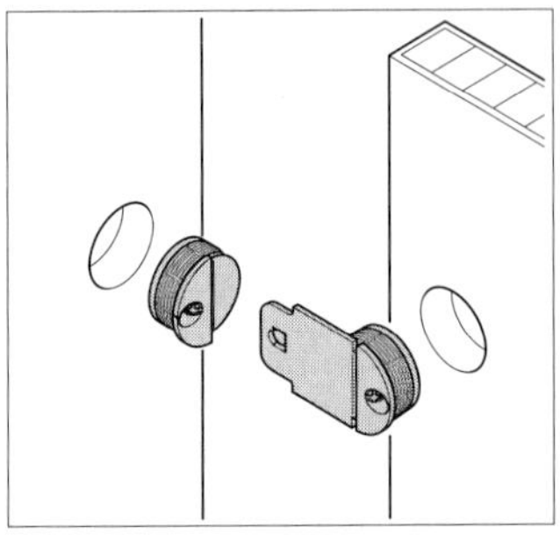

Universal Connectors
Pages **2.125 - 2.131**

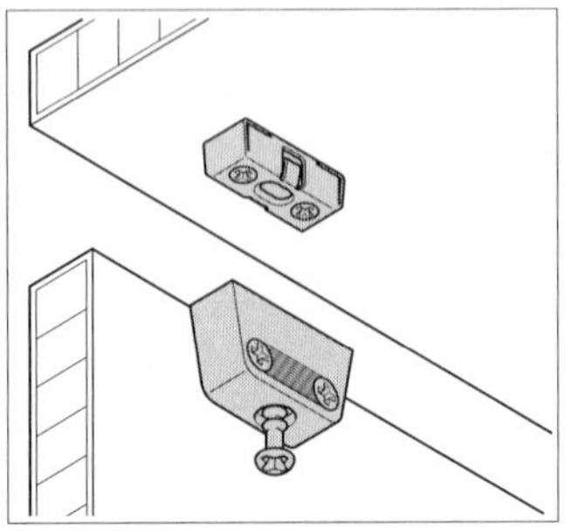

Surface Mounted RTA Fittings
Pages **2.132 - 2.134**

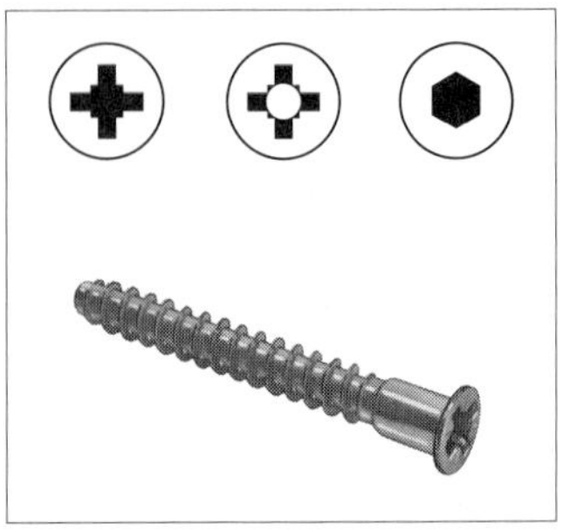

Confirmat Precision Assembly Systems®
Pages **2.135 - 2.138**

Shelf Supports, Folding Brackets, Bed Fittings

HÄFELE

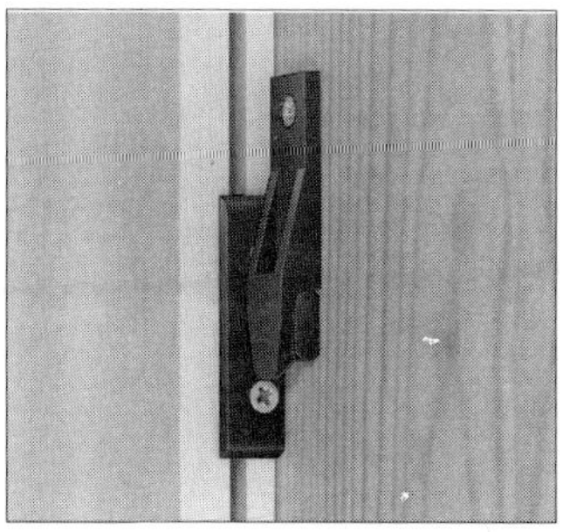

Keku Precision Assembly Systems®
Pages **2.139 - 2.142**

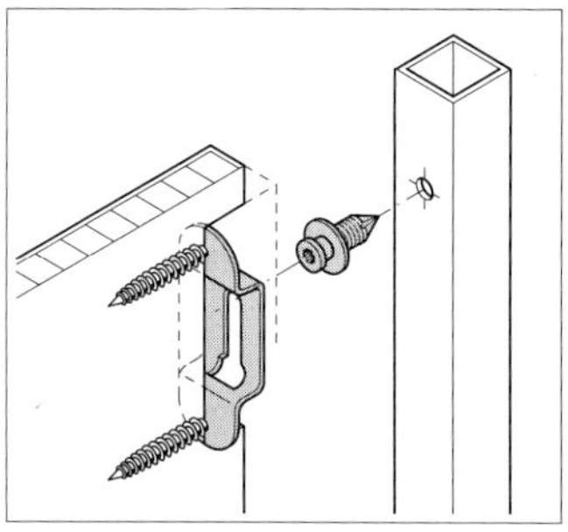

Modular Connectors
Pages **2.147 - 2.149**

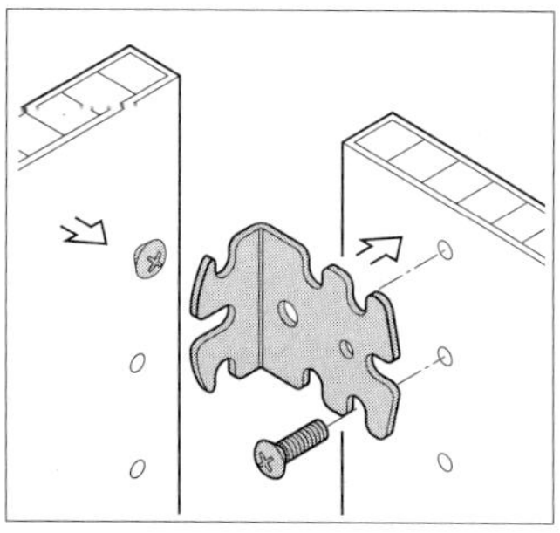

Connecting Brackets
Pages **2.150 - 2.153**

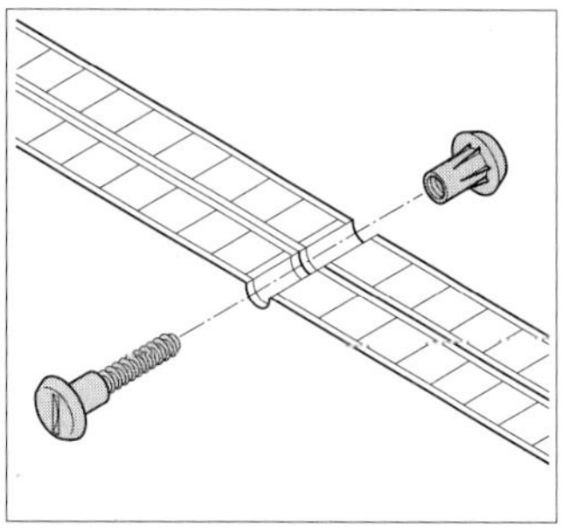

Threaded Sleeve Connectors
Pages **2..158 - 2.159**

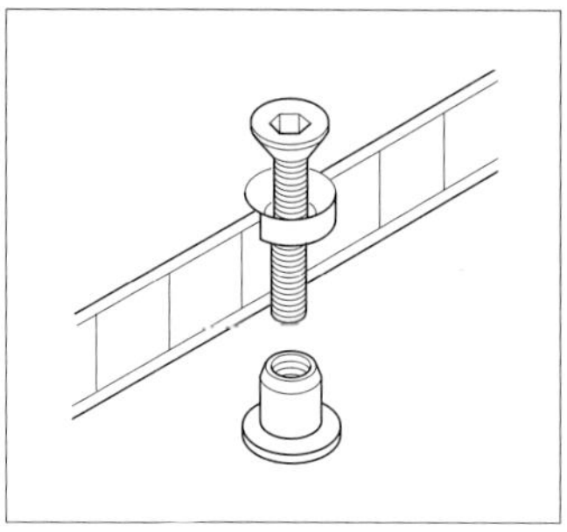

Multi-Purpose Connectors
Pages **2.161 - 2.168**

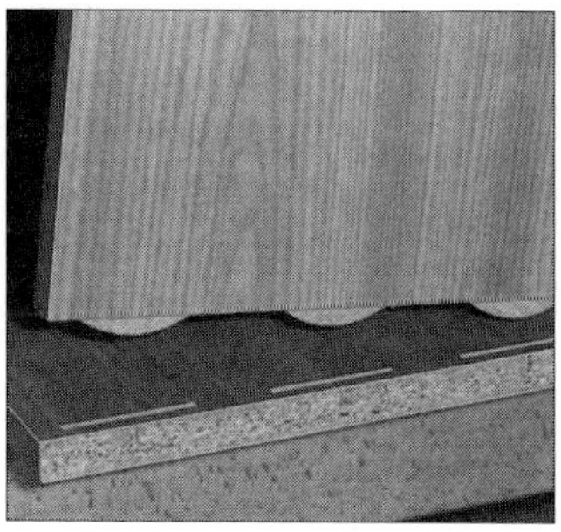

Wood Biscuits and Dowels
Pages **2.169**

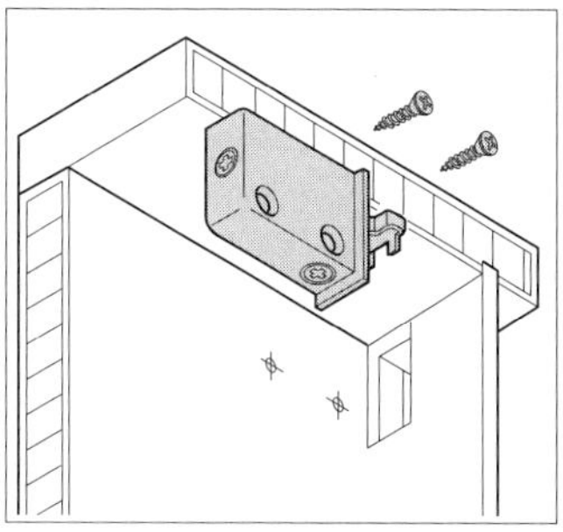

Cabinet Hanging Systems
Pages **2.171**

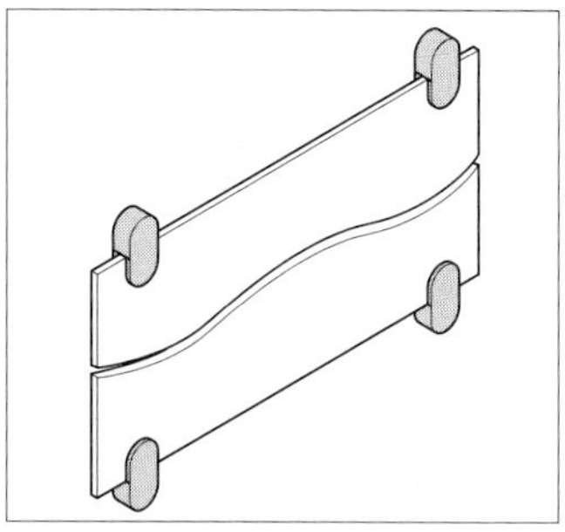

Glass Retaining Clips
Pages **2.173 - 2.174**

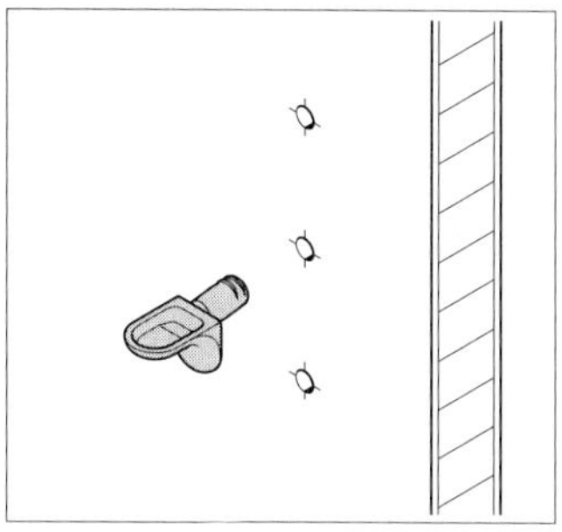

Shelf Supports
Pages **2.175 - 2.190**

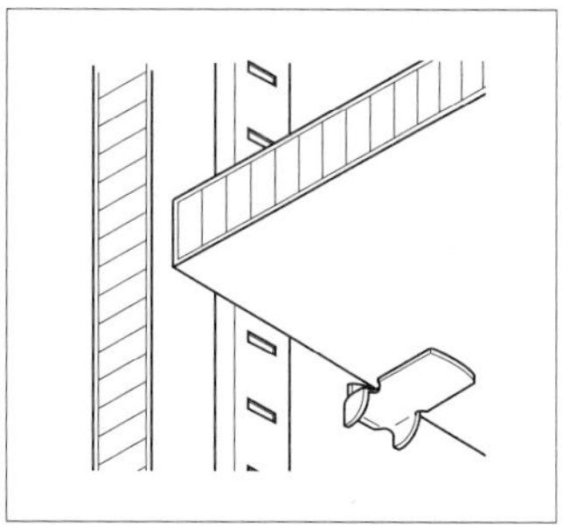

Shelf Support Systems
Pages **2.181**

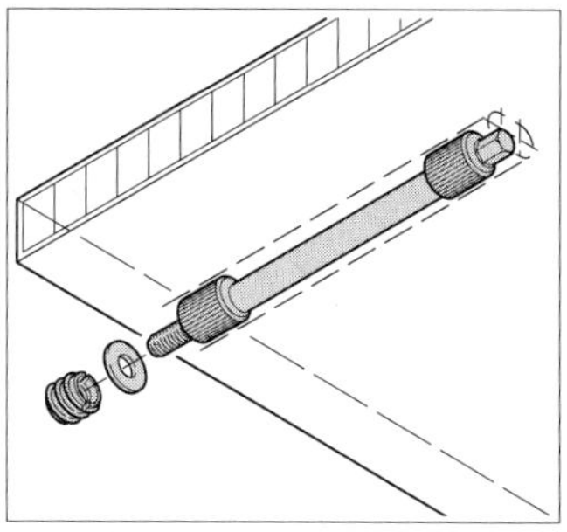

Adjustable Shelf Supports
Pages **2.191**

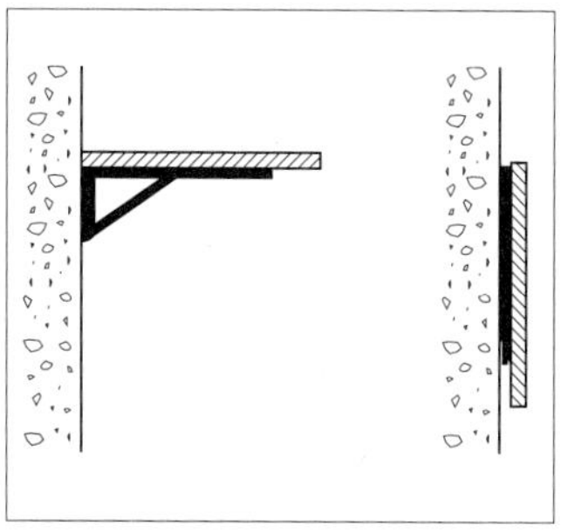

Folding Brackets
Pages **2.192 - 2.196**

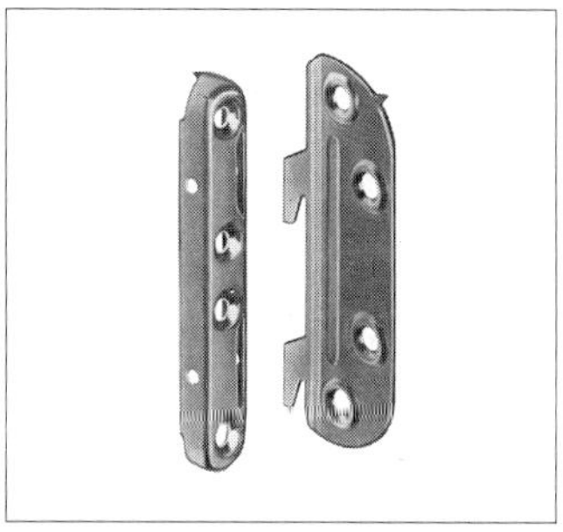

Bed Fittings
Pages **2.197 - 2.203**

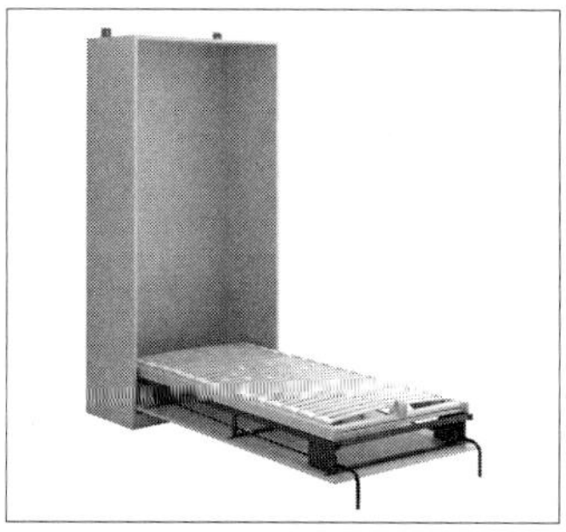

Folding Bed Mechanisms
Pages **2.204 - 2.206**

Mattresses For Folding Beds
Pages **2.207**

HÄFELE

Magnetic Catches

- This is the most economical magnetic catch
- Extremely flexible floating plates to compensate for alignment tolerances.
- Dimensions are rounded off.

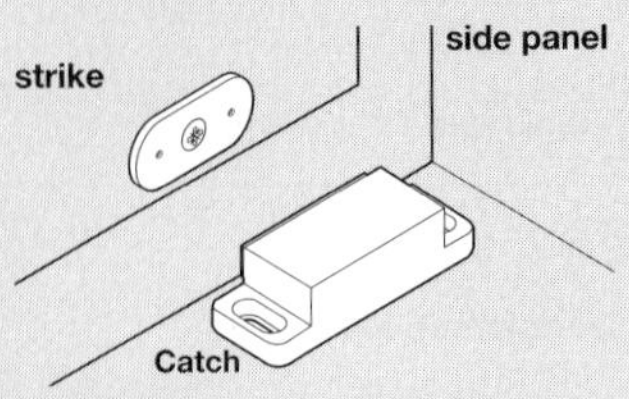

- Very flexible, floating upright magnets.
- Large strike
- Large oblong adjustment holes
- Metal base plate at catch.

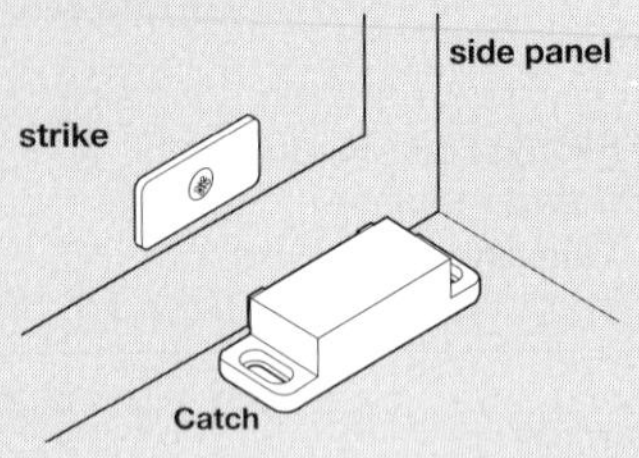

2.5 kg Pull With Strike

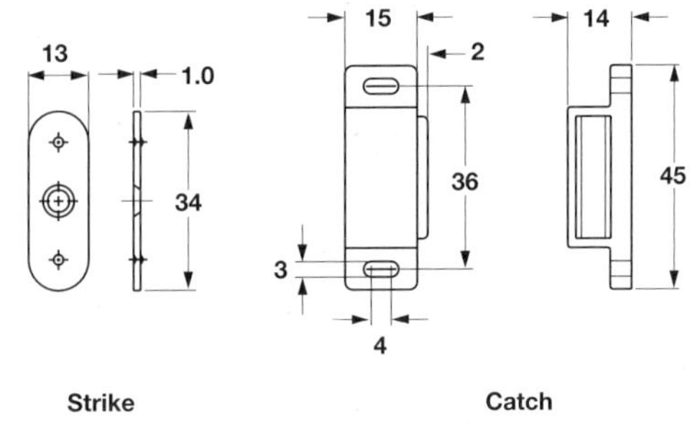

Finish: brown, plastic housing with metal, bronzed strike

Cat. No.	246.28.100

Packing: 100 pcs.

3.0 kg Pull With Strike

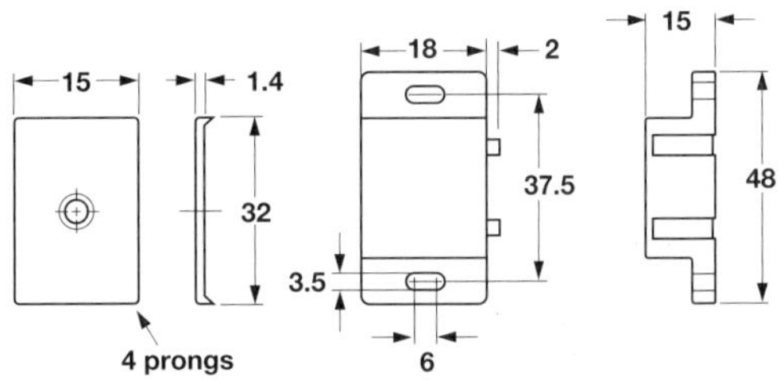

Finish: brown, plastic housing with metal, bronzed strike

Cat. No.	246.31.100

Packing: 1000 pcs.

Dimensions in mm

Magnetic Catches

HÄFELE

Floating permanent magnet poles catch adjust automatically to meet door-mounted strike.

Magnetic catch, screw-mounted

Catch: floating
Strike: fixed

Catch is plastic
Strike is steel

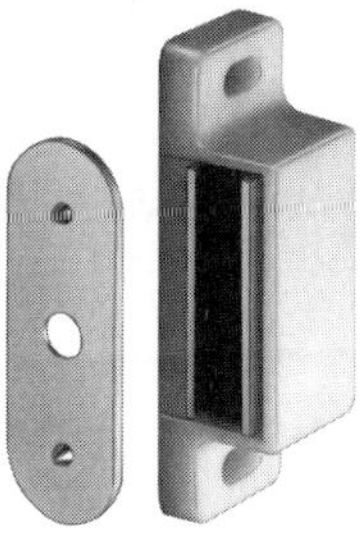

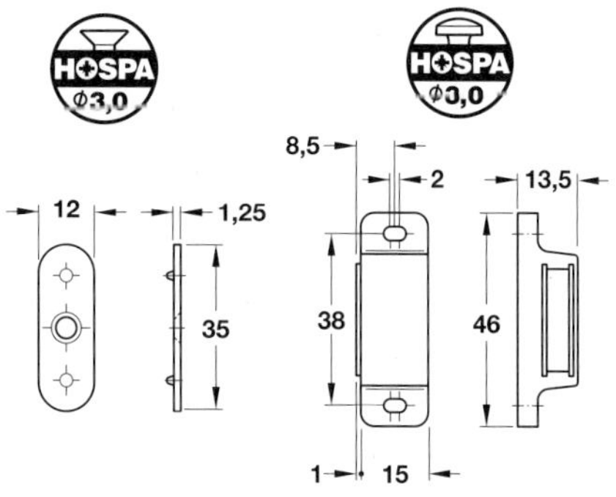

Strike
Catch

Holding power (approx.)		3-4 kg
Cat. No.	white	246.26.702
	brown	246.26.104
	black	246.26.300

Packing: 50 pcs.

Magnetic catch, screw-mounted

Catch: floating
Strikc: fixed

Catch is plastic
Strike is steel

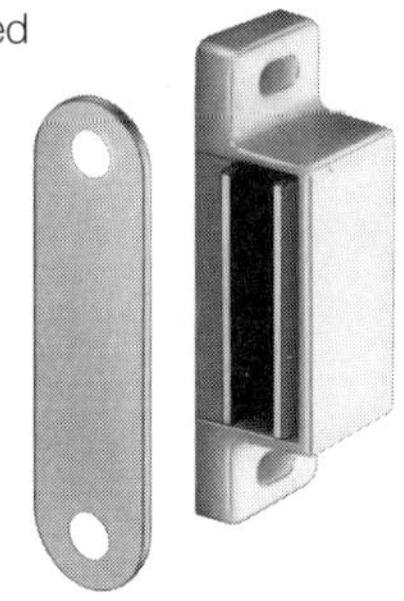

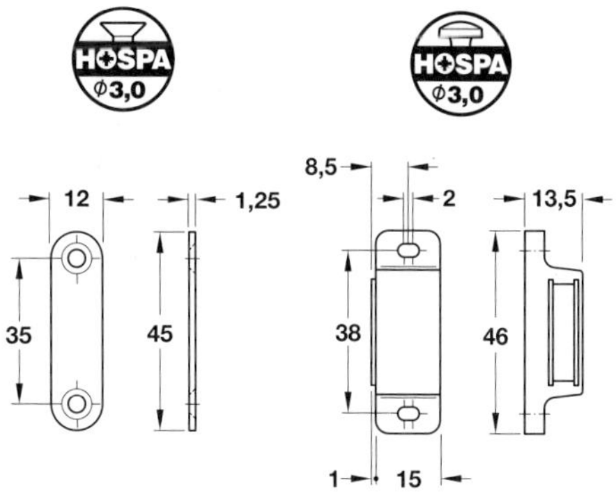

Strike
Catch

Holding power (approx.)		3-4 kg	4-5 kg
Cat. No.	white	246.26.720	246.29.703
	brown	246.26.122	246.29.105
	black		246.29.301

Packing: 50 pcs.

Magnetic catch, screw-mounted

Catch: floating
Strike: fixed

Catch and strike are plastic

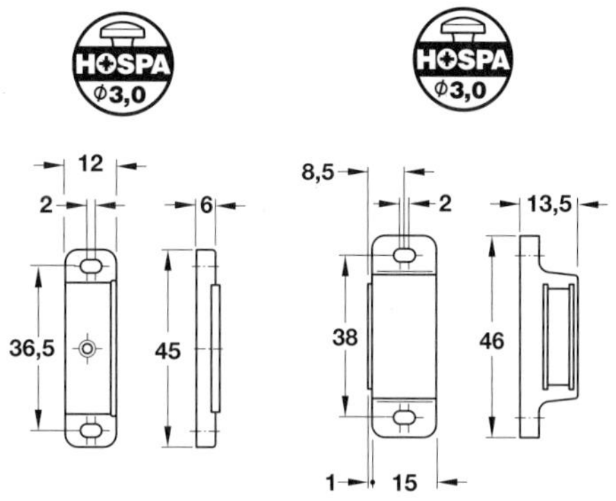

Strike
Catch

Holding power (approx.)		3-4 kg	4-5 kg
Cat. No.	white	246.26.711	246.29.712
	brown	246.26.113	246.29.114

Packing: 50 pcs.

Dimensions in mm

Lock, Catches, RTA and PAS® Fittings
Shelf Supports
Bed Fittings
2

Dimensional data not binding.
We reserve the right to alter specifications without notice.

HÄFELE

Magnetic Catches

The poles are fixed in the case, while the magnet core is adjustable.

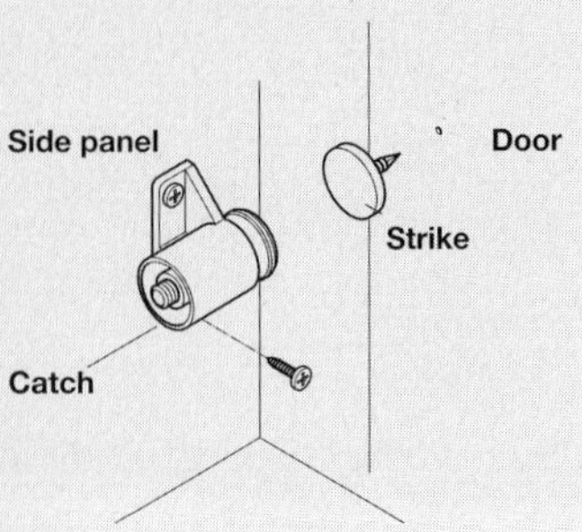

Magnetic catch, screw-mounted

Catch: fixed
Strike: floating
Catch is plastic
Strike is steel

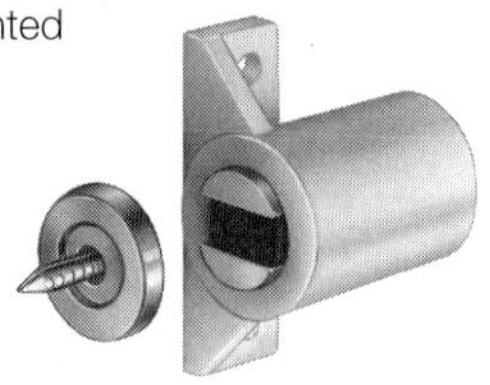

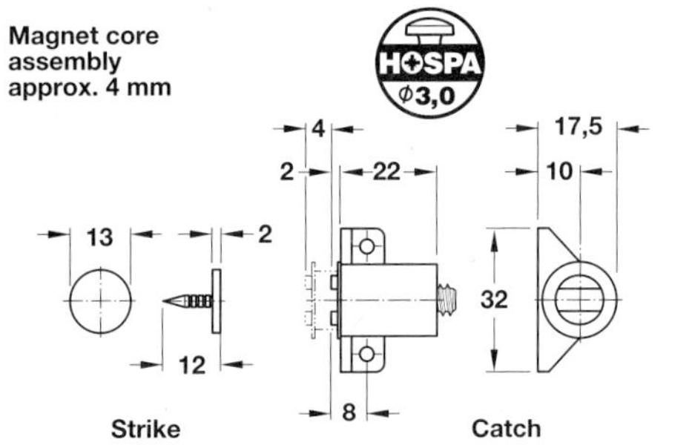

Holding power (approx.)		3-4 kg
Cat. No.	white	246.09.701
	brown	246.09.103

Packing: 50 pcs.

2 Lock, Catches, RTA and PAS® Fittings
Shelf Supports
Bed Fittings

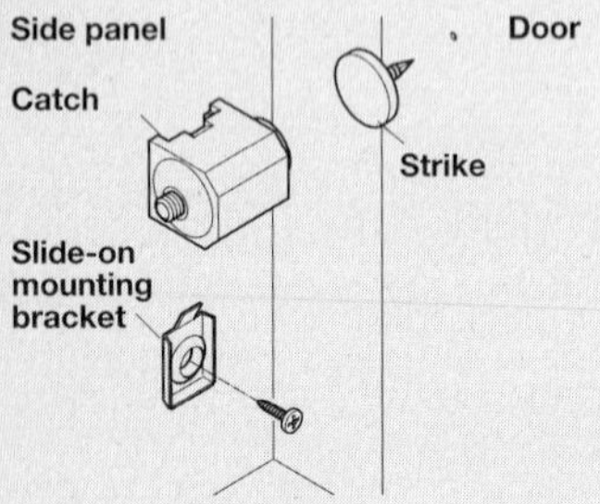

Magnetic catch, screw-mounted

Catch: fixed
Strike: floating
Catch is plastic
Strike is steel

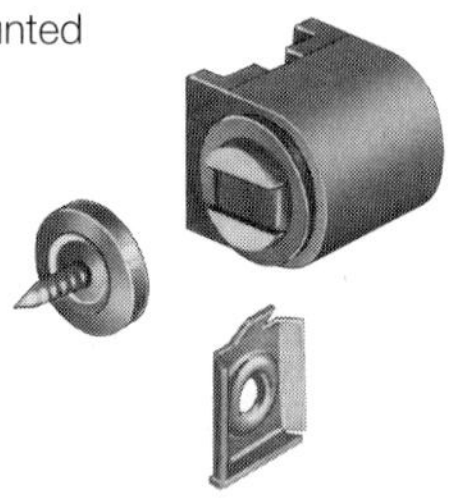

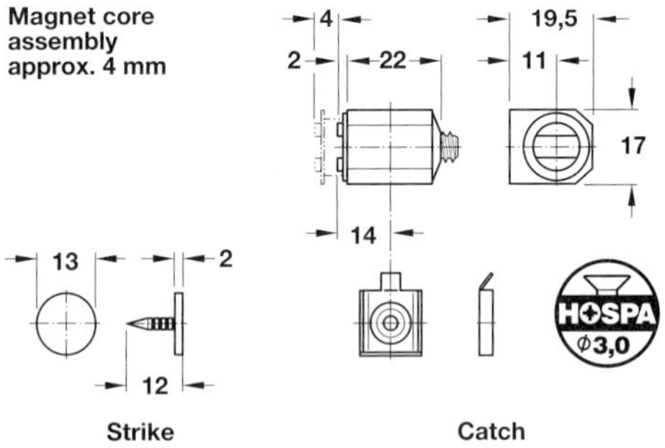

Holding power (approx.)		4 kg
Cat. No.	white	246.13.720
	brown	246.13.120

Packing: 50 pcs.

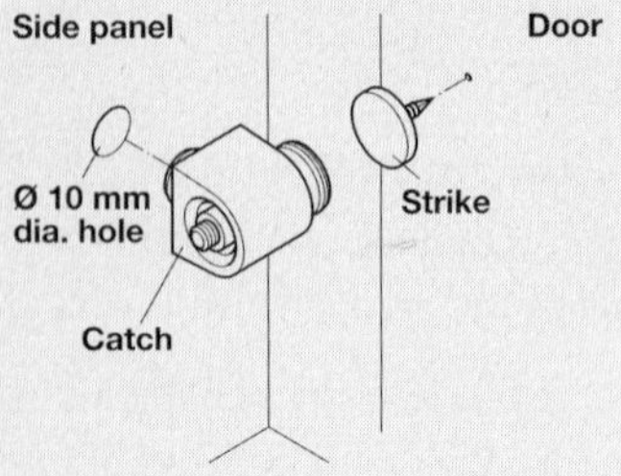

Magnetic catch, screw-mounted

Catch: fixed
Strike: floating
Catch is plastic
Strike is steel

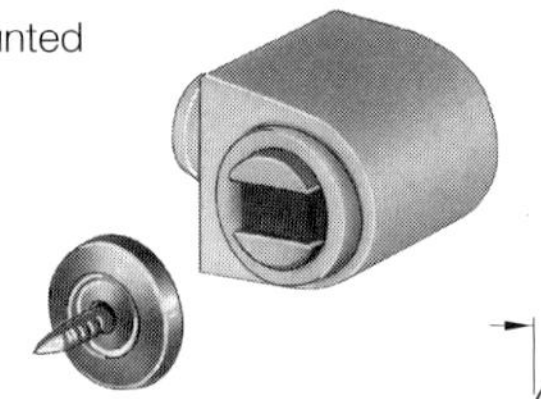

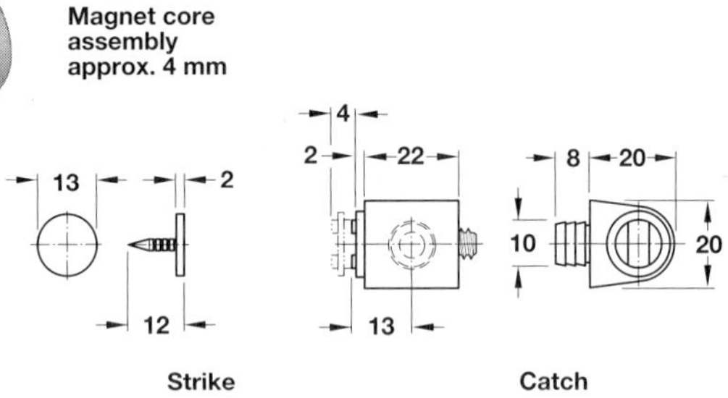

Holding power (approx.)		3-4 kg
Cat. No.	white	246.08.704
	brown	246.08.106
	black	246.07.300

Packing: 50 pcs.

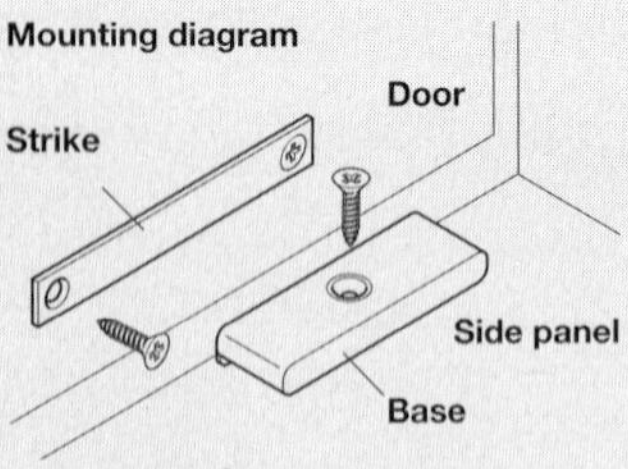

Strip magnet
- flat (only 6 mm high)
- adjustable
- floating poles

Magnetic catch, screw-mounted

Catch: fixed
Strike: floating
Catch is plastic
Strike is steel

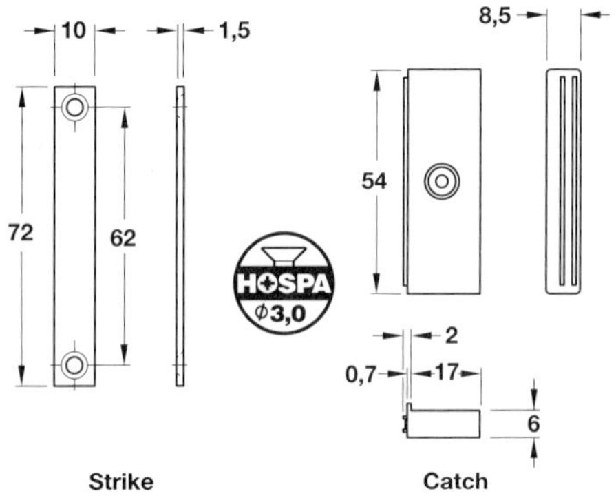

Holding power (approx.)		5 kg
Cat. No.	white	246.50.708
	brown	246.50.100

Packing: 20 pcs.

Metal case provides heat-resistance to 300° C.
Note: Holding power is diminished by **1%** per **5°** C (+). increase in temperature. Cooling restores the magnet's holding power to its original level.
No strike necessary with steel doors or lids.

Magnetic catch, screw-mounted

Catch: fixed
Strike: floating
Catch is metal
Strike is steel

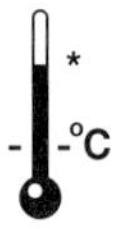

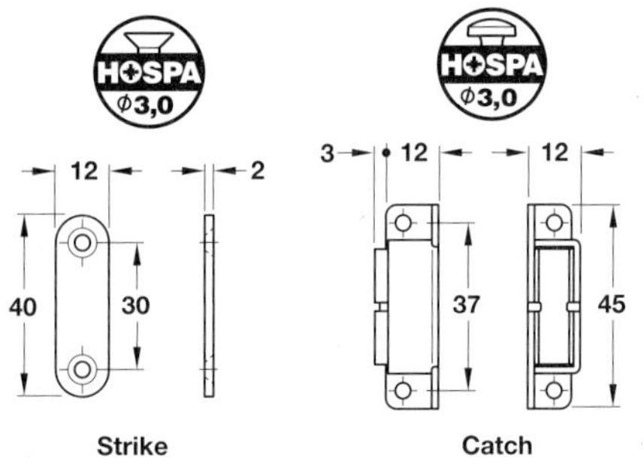

Holding power (approx.)	5 kg
Cat. No.	246.92.000

Packing: 12 pcs.

Dimensions in mm

Dimensional data not binding. We reserve the right to alter specifications without notice.

Magnetic Catches

Double magnetic catch, screw-mounted

Catch: floating
Strike: fixed

Catch is plastic
Strike is steel

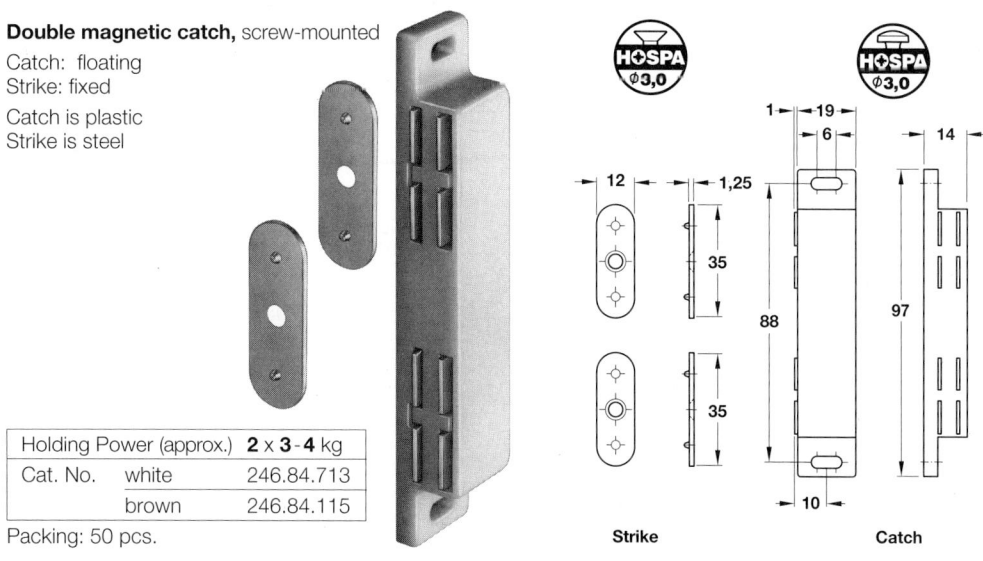

Holding Power (approx.)		**2** x **3**-**4** kg
Cat. No.	white	246.84.713
	brown	246.84.115

Packing: 50 pcs.

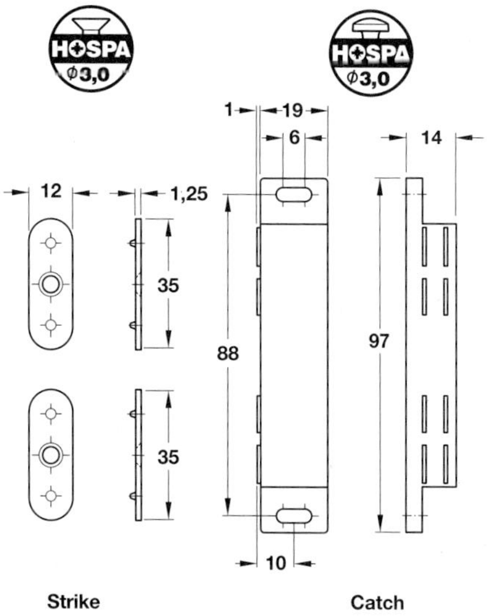

Double magnetic catch, screw-mounted

Catch: floating
Strike: fixed

Catch is plastic
Strike is steel

Holding Power (approx.)		**2** x **3**-**4** kg
Cat. No.	black	246.36.300

Packing: 50 pcs.

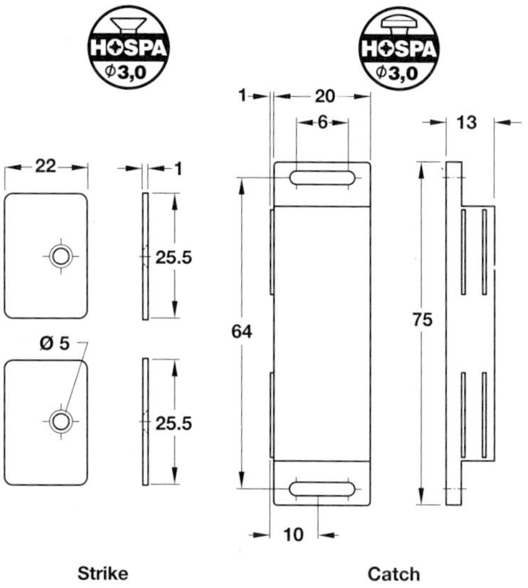

Dimensions in mm

HÄFELE

Floating permanent magnet poles in case adjust automatically to meet door-mounted strike,

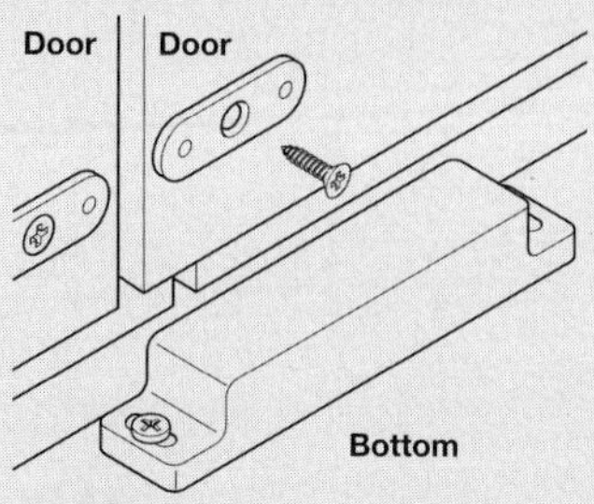

...to top or bottom panel of cabinet in two-door installations.

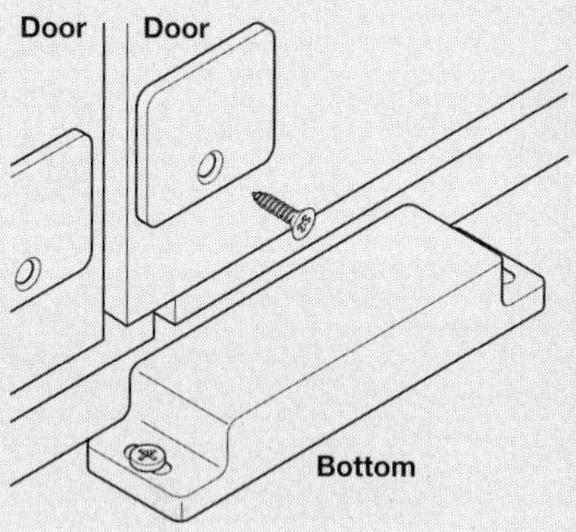

...to top or bottom panel of cabinet in two-door installations.

HÄFELE

Magnetic Catches, 32 mm System

Application

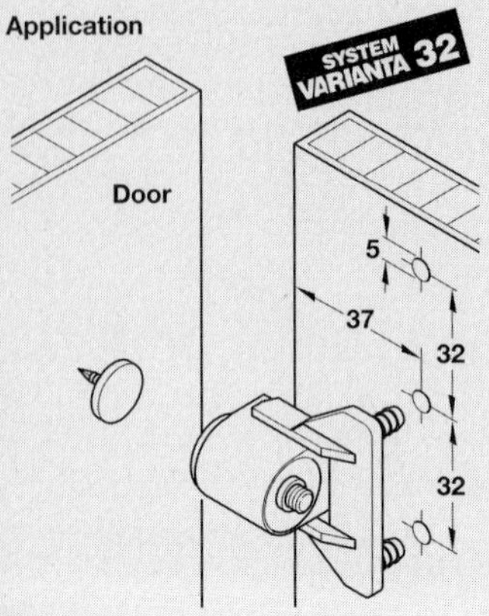

Press-fit Magnetic Catch

Catch: plastic
Strike: steel

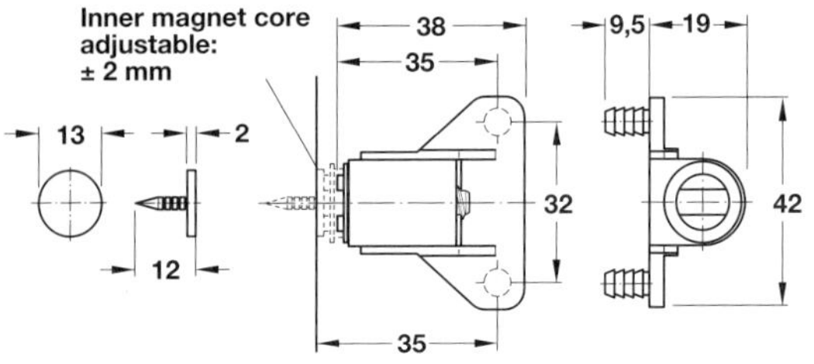

Holding force (approx.)		**4** kg
Cat. No.	white	246.13.740
	brown	246.13.140

Packing: 50 pcs.

Strike Catch

Application

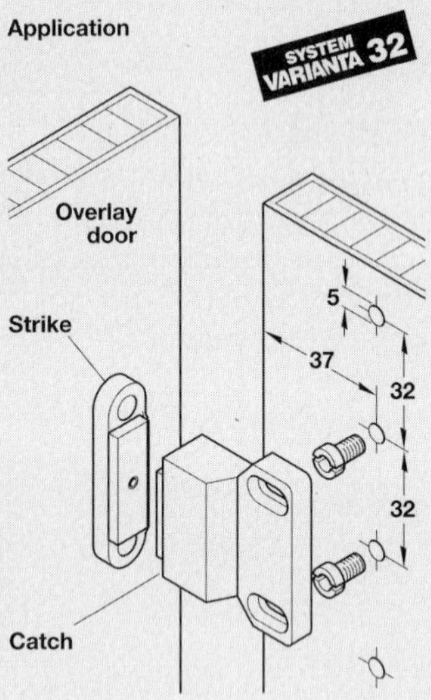

Screw-mounted Magnetic Catch

Catch: plastic
Strike: plastic

HOSPA ϕ3,0 HOSPA ϕ3,5

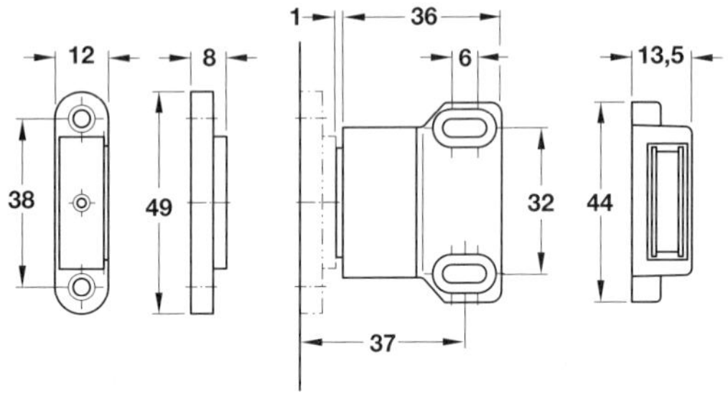

Holding force (approx.)		**3**-**4** kg	**4**-**5** kg
Cat. No.	white	246.11.701	246.17.703
	brown	246.11.103	246.17.105

Packing: 50 pcs.

Strike Catch

Spreading Insert with collar for **Ø 5 mm dia.** holes

Finish: nylon, natural

Length	7.5 mm	9.5 mm
Cat. No.	340.43.000	340.43.019

Packing: 1000 pcs.

For hole size-Ø 5 dia.

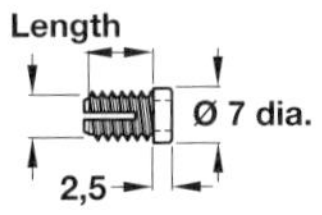

Dimensional data not binding. We reserve the right to alter specifications without notice.

Dimensions in mm

Magnetic Catches

HÄFELE

Low-profile Magnet
- For metal cabinets
- Inside mounting Ø 5 mm dia.
- No strike needed for metal doors

Screw-mount Magnet
with inside mounting hole
including M5 screw
Catch: steel, zinc-plated

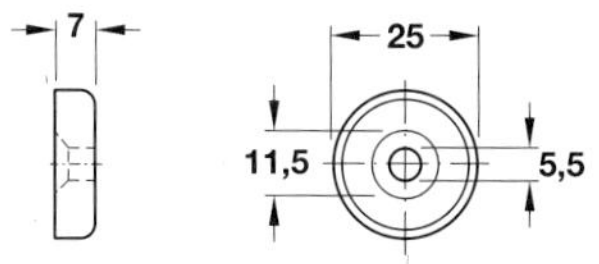

Catch

Holding force (approximately)	**3.6** kg
Cat. No.	246.86.025

Packing: 20 pcs.

Magnet for metal cabinets
Catch: all metal
Strike: steel

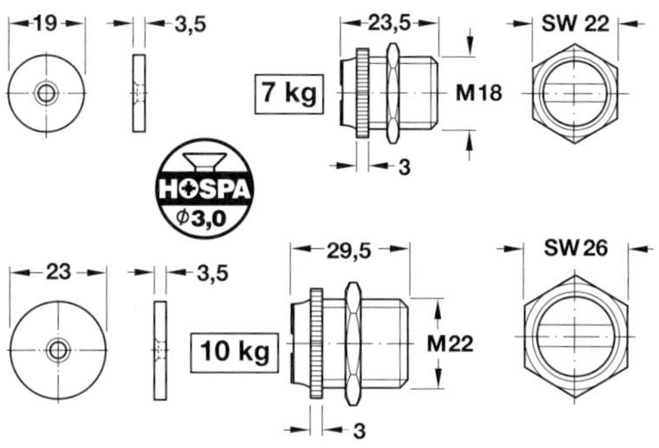

Strike

Catch

Holding force (appr.)	**7** kg	**10** kg
Cat. No.	246.95.010	246.95.020

Packing: 12 pcs.

Magnet for metal cabinets
Catch: all metal
Strike: steel

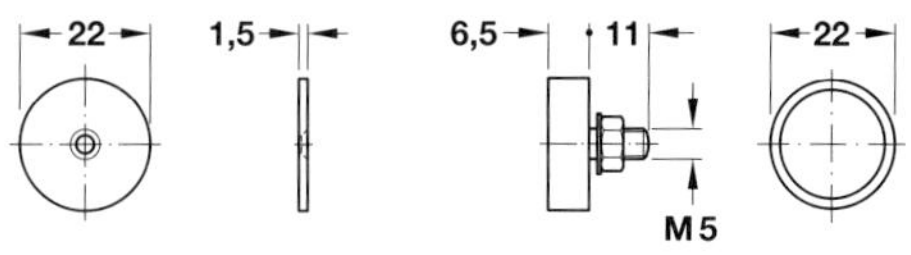

Strike

Catch

Holding force (approximately)	**3** kg
Cat. No.	246.96.008

Packing: 12 pcs.

Dimensional data not binding.
We reserve the right to alter specifications without notice.

HÄFELE

- **Magnetic catches,** for mortised installation in cabinet face edges
- Press-fit or glued.

These magnetic catches can be installed ...

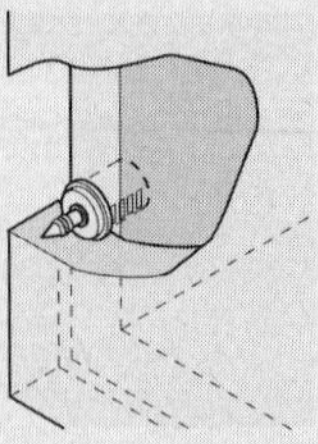

... in the face edge of the cabinet side panel ...

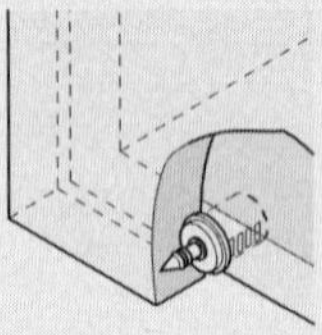

... or cabinet shelf

Recessed Magnetic Catches

Magnetic catch, approx. 2 kg pull
Catch: Press-fit, fixed plastic catch
Strike: Screw-mounted, fixed, chromed metal

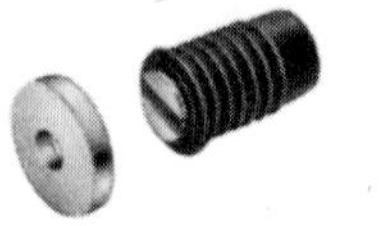

Finish: plastic catch, chromed metal strike

Color	black
Cat. No.	246.01.312

Packing: 100 pcs.

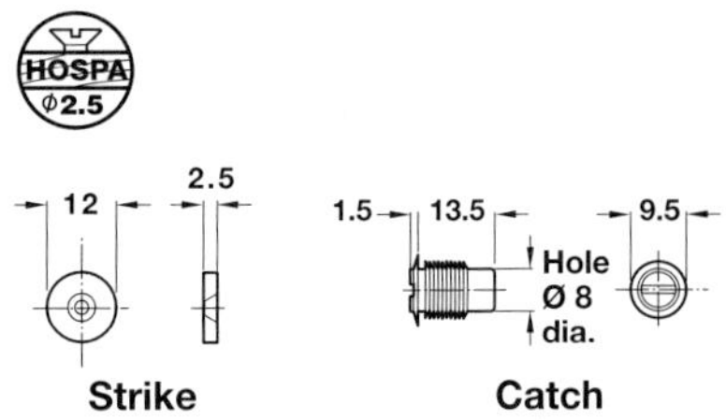

Magnetic catch, approx. 1.8 kg pull
Catch: Glued, fixed plastic catch
Strike: Screw-mounted, fixed, chromed metal

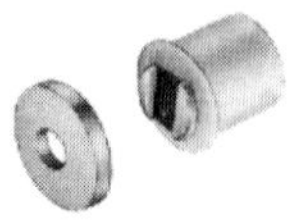

Finish: plastic catch, chromed metal strike

Color	brown	white
Cat. No.	246.00.100	246.00.708

Packing: 60 pcs.

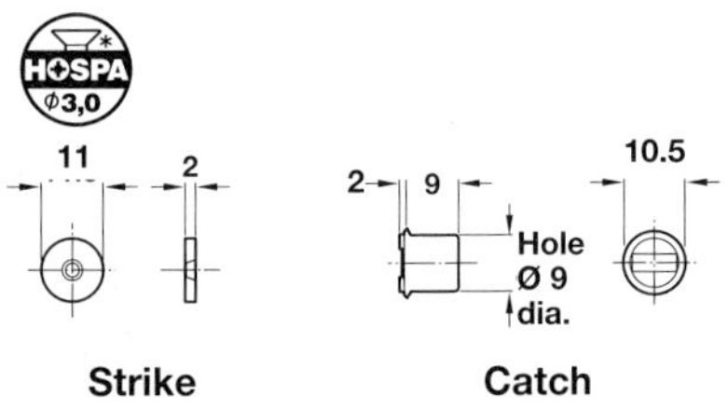

Magnetic catch, approx. 2.5-3.5 kg pull
Catch: Press-fit, fixed plastic catch
Strike: Screw-mounted, fixed, chromed metal

Finish: plastic catch, chromed metal strike

Color	brown	white
Cat. No.	246.03.101	246.03.709

Packing: 50 pcs.

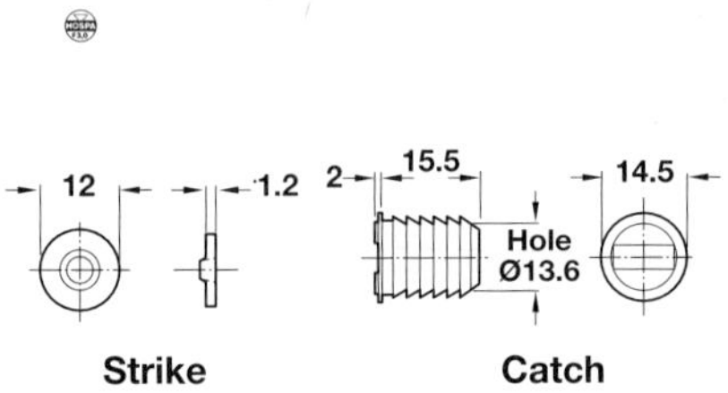

Magnetic catch, approx. 2-3 kg pull
Catch: Press-fit, fixed plastic catch
Strike: Knock-in, floating, chromed metal

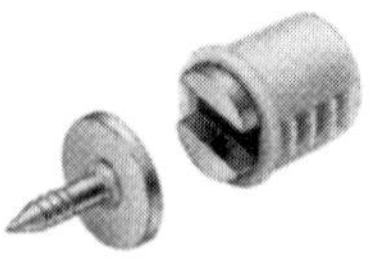

Finish: plastic catch, chromed metal strike

Color	white
Cat. No.	246.43.758

Packing: 200 pcs.

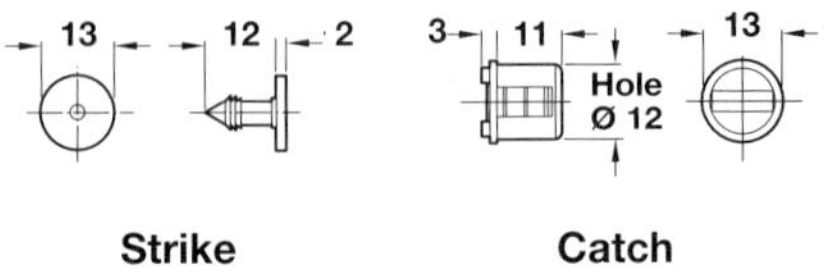

Magnetic catch, approx. 2 kg pull
Catch: Glued, fixed brass catch
Strike: Screw-mounted, fixed, chromed metal

Finish: brass catch, chromed metal strike

Color	nickel-plated
Cat. No.	246.12.002

Packing: 100 pcs.

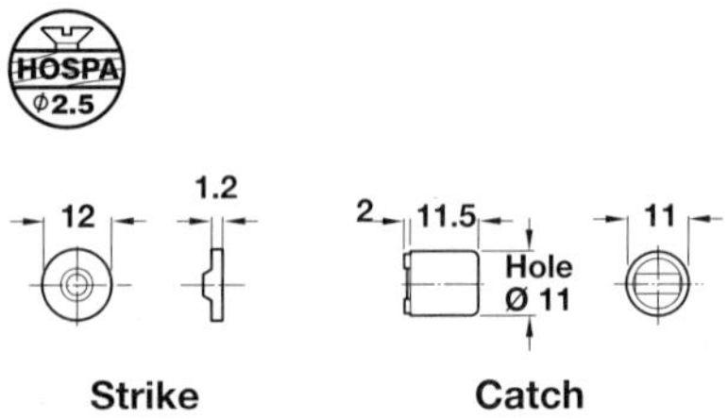

Magnetic catch, approx. 5 kg pull
Catch: Glued, brass catch, adjustable
Strike: Screw-mounted, fixed, chromed metal

Finish: brass catch, chromed metal strike

Color	nickel-plated
Cat. No.	246.02.211

Packing: 20 pcs.

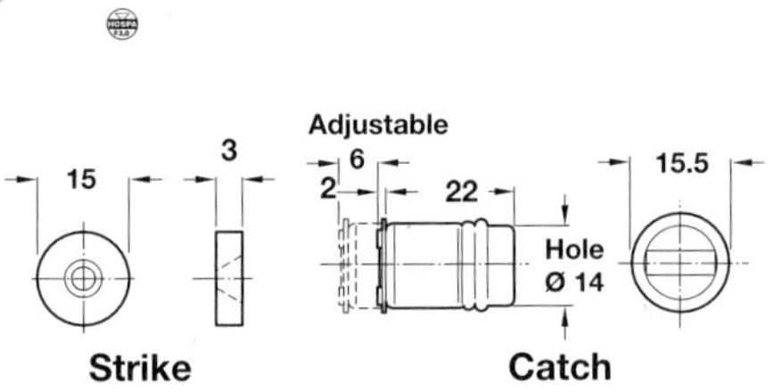

Dimensional data not binding. We reserve the right to alter specifications without notice.

Dimensions in mm

Elbow Catches

HÄFELE

Elbow Catch/Solid Brass

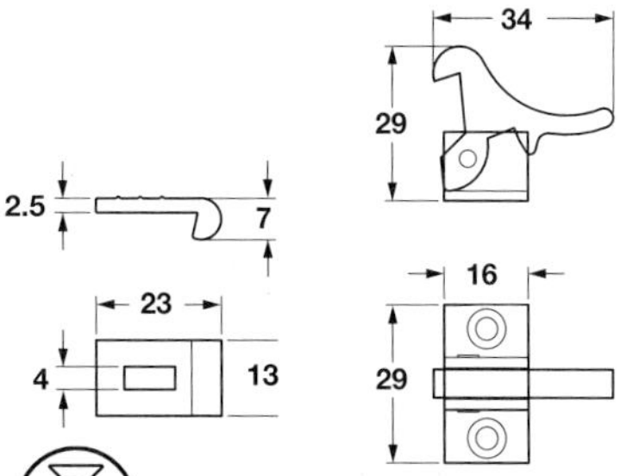

Cabinet doors
- Nonhanded: Can be used left or right
- Solid brass
- Rugged
- Spring-loaded
- Quiet secure engagement of strike
- Deluxe model

HOSPA Ø3.0

Finish: solid brass

Cat. No.	245.74.000

Packing: 100 per box

Elbow Catch/Steel

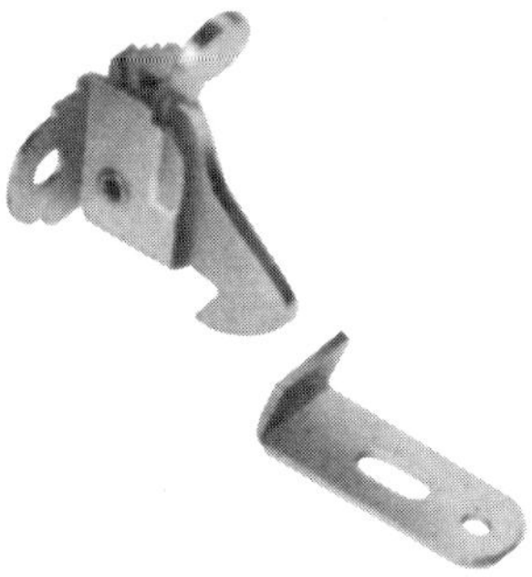

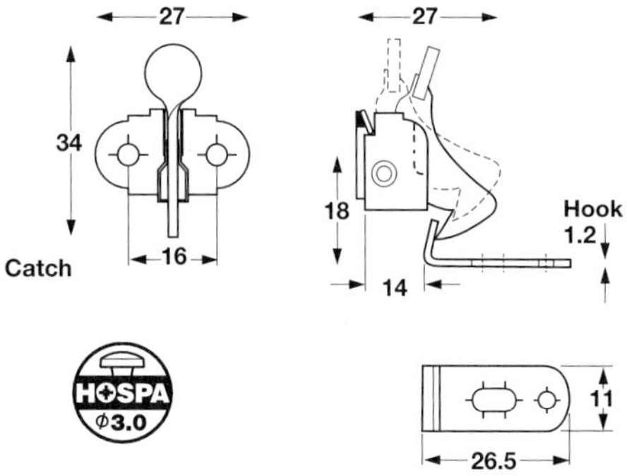

HOSPA Ø3.0

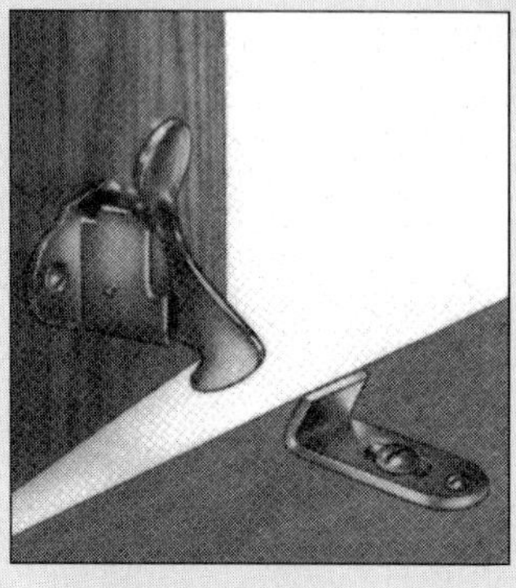

Finish: steel

Cat. No.	bronzed, screw-mounted	245.70.107
	brass-plated, screw-mounted	245.70.509

Packing: 100 pcs.

Dimensions in mm

- stamped steel
- oblong adjustment hole
- spring-loaded
- economy model

HÄFELE

Roller Catches

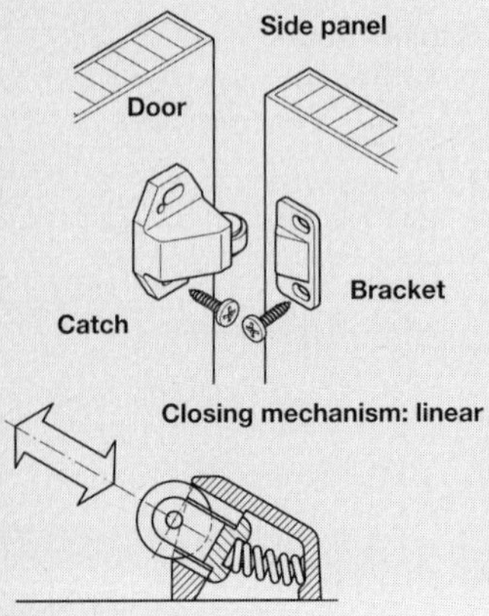

Roller Catch
Screw-mounted

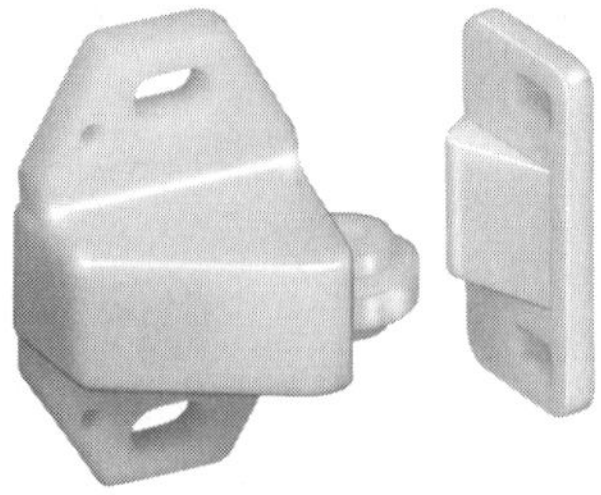

Finish: Roller, nylon
Base & stops, plastic

Cat. No.		
Cat. No.	white	243.15.704
	brown	243.15.106

Packing: 250 pcs.

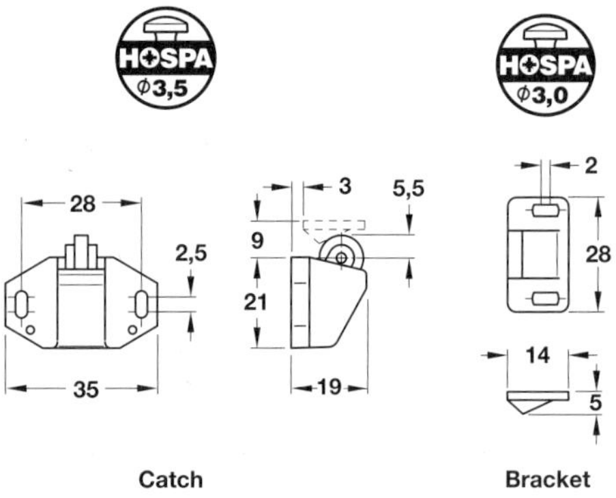

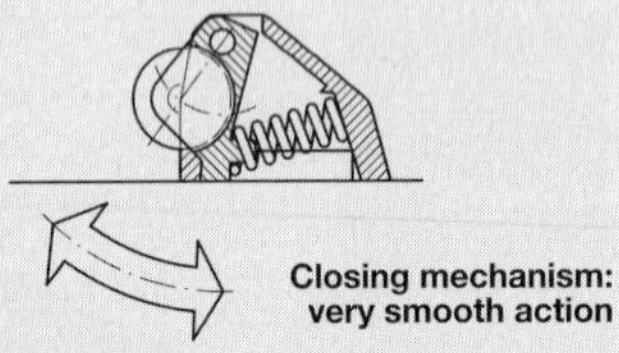

Roller Catch
Screw-mounted

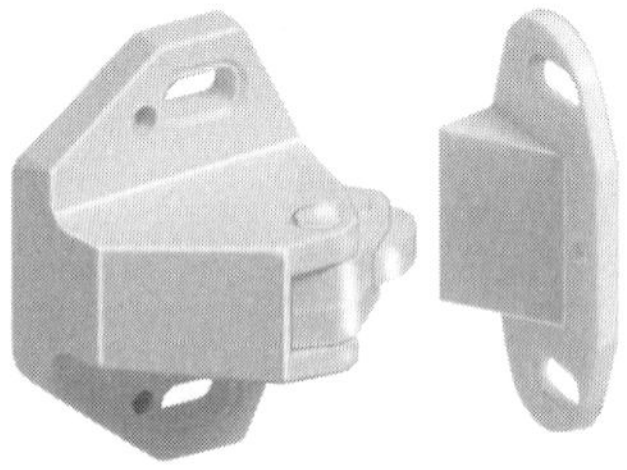

Finish: Roller, nylon
Base: plastic, white

Cat. No.	243.03.700

Packing: 100 pcs.

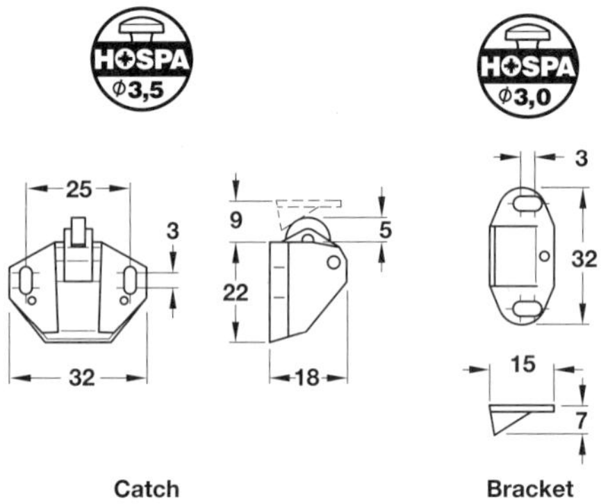

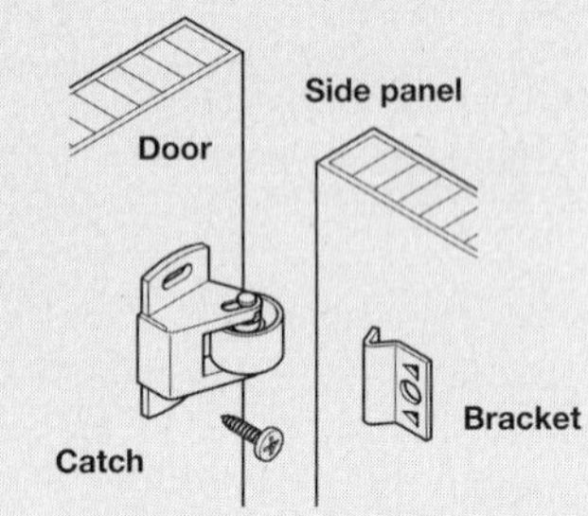

Roller Catch
Screw-mounted

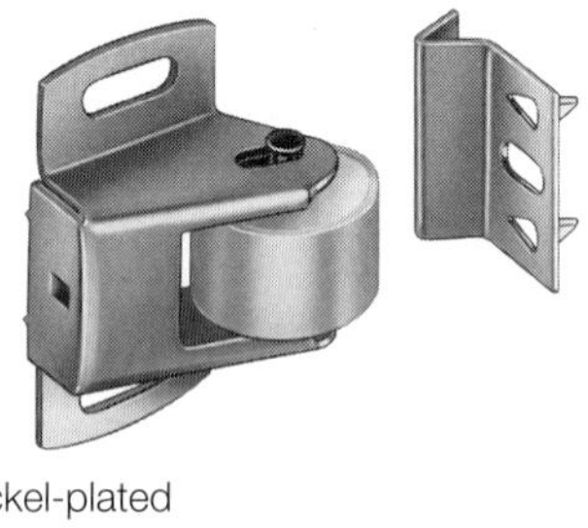

Finish: Roller, nylon
Stop: steel, nickel-plated
Catch: steel, nickel-plated

Cat. No.	241.01.719

Packing: 250 pcs.

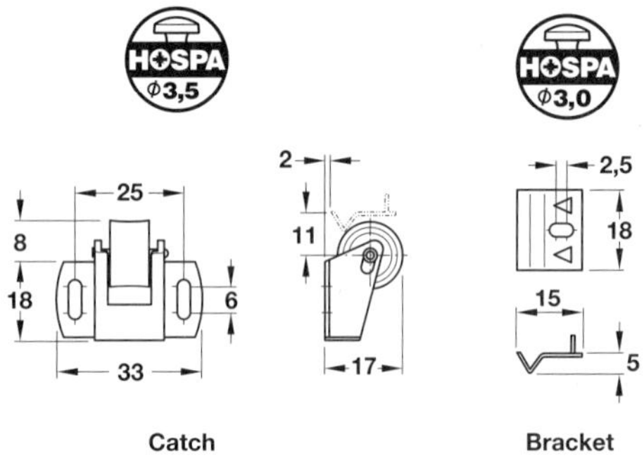

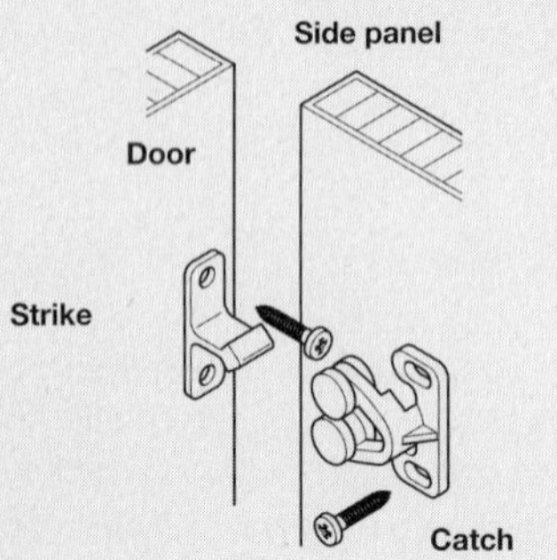

Twin Roller Catch
Screw-mounted

Finish: Roller, nylon
Strike: nylon
Catch: nylon

Cat. No.	natural	244.03.405
	brown	244.03.101

Packing: 100 pcs.

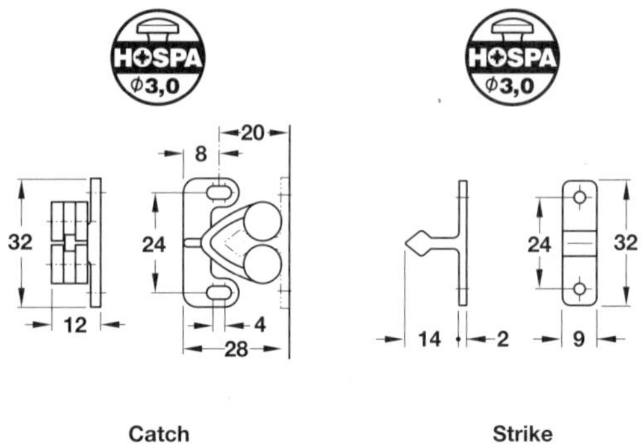

Dimensional data not binding.
We reserve the right to alter
specifications without notice.

Dimensions in mm

Ball Catches

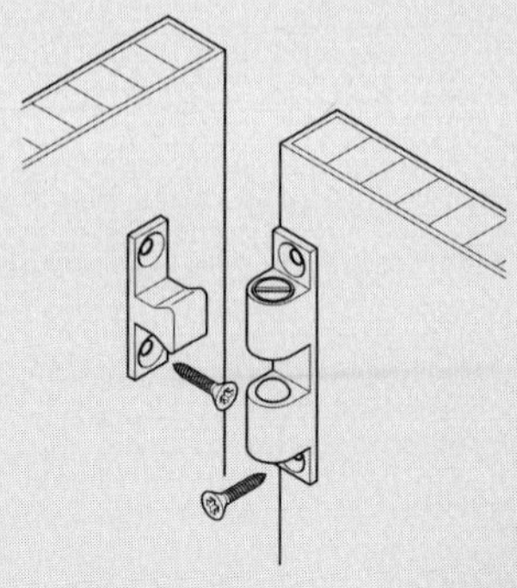

Lock, Catches, RTA and PAS® Fittings
Shelf Supports
Bed Fittings

2

Solid catches for heavy-duty applications

- Holding power is screwdriver-adjustable

Twin Ball Catch,

Screw-mounted

Finish: Ball: chrome steel
Other parts, brass, matt

HOSPA Φ3,0

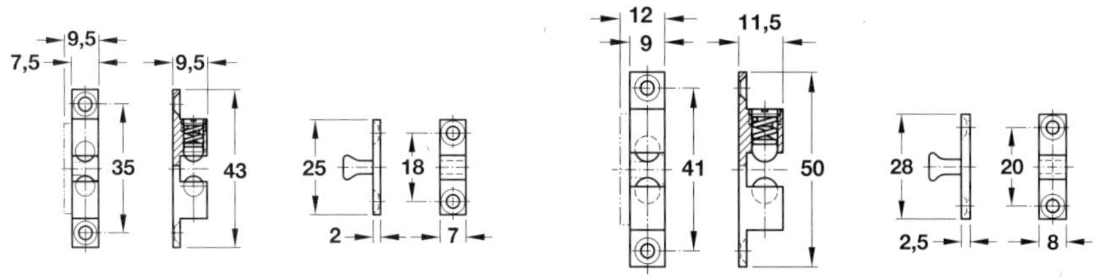

Catch | Strike | Catch | Strike

Cat. No.	244.20.102	244.20.111

Packing: 50 pcs.

HOSPA Φ3,5

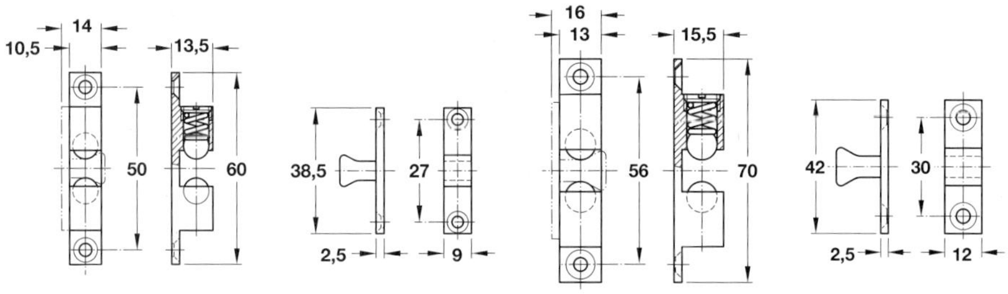

Catch | Strike | Catch | Strike

Cat. No.	244.20.120	244.20.139

Packing: 50 pcs.

Ball Catch With Strike

Press-fit

Finish: Balls: chrome steel
Catch & strike: steel, brass-plated

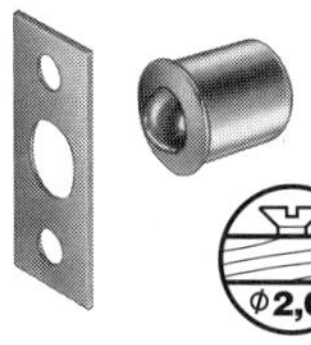

Φ2,0

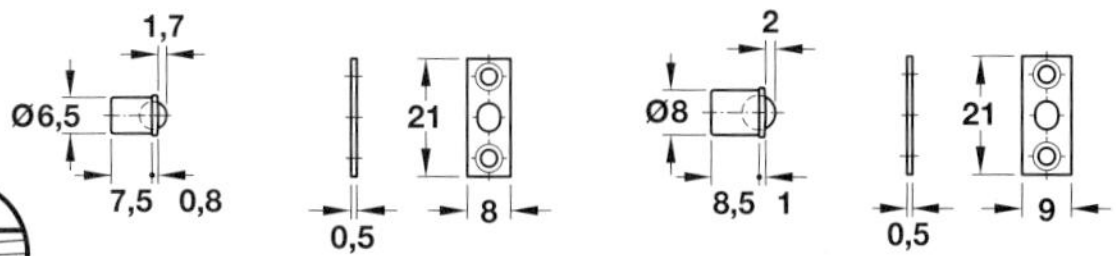

Catch | Strike | Catch | Strike

Cat. No.	241.80.505	241.80.514

Packing: 200 pcs.

HOSPA Φ2,5

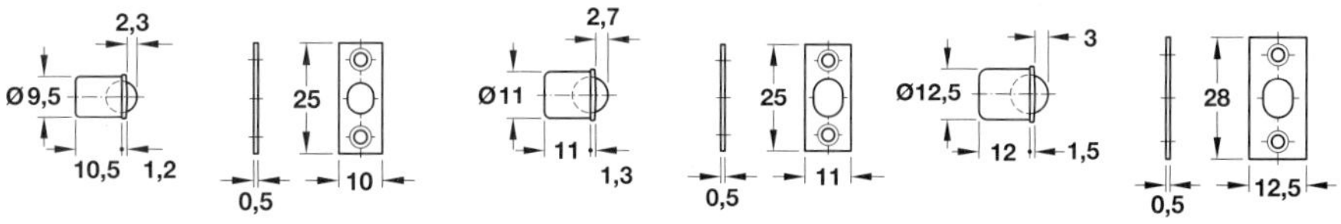

Catch | Strike | Catch | Strike | Catch | Strike

Cat. No.	241.80.523	241.80.532	241.80.541

Packing: 200 pcs. each

Ball Catch With Strike

Screw-mounted

Finish: Balls: chrome steel
Catch & strike: steel, brass-plated

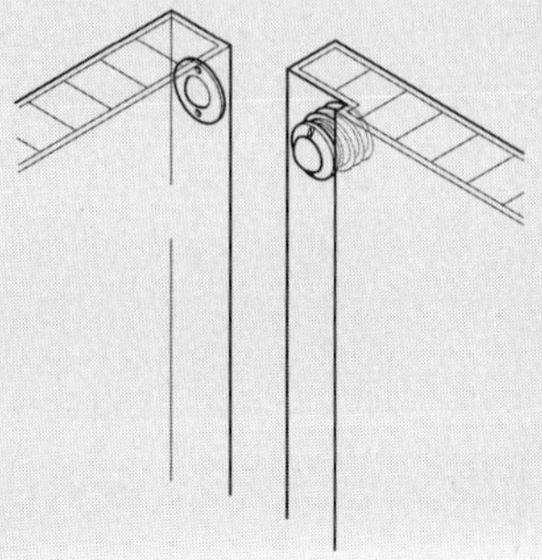

Φ 0,9 | Φ 1,6 | Φ 1,6

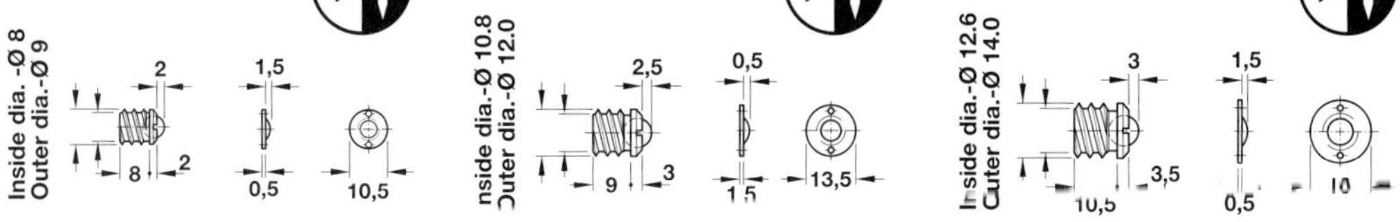

Catch | Strike | Catch | Strike | Catch | Strike

Cat. No.	241.86.105	241.86.114	241.86.123

Packing: 200 pcs. each

Dimensional data not binding.
We reserve the right to alter specifications without notice.

HÄFELE

Ball Catches

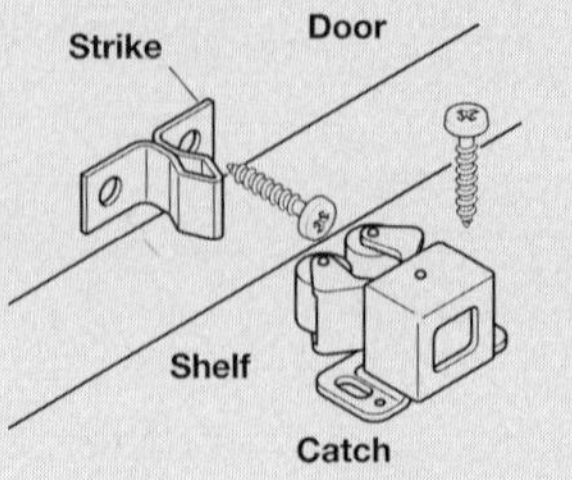

*Measurements are approximate.

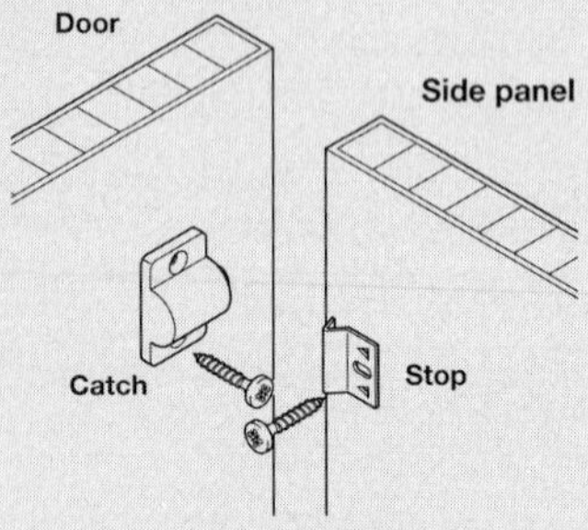

Elegant and dependable:

- Catch for 5-6.5 mm glass doors, which press-fits into a 15 mm hole in the cabinet and secured against twisting by longitudinal ribs.
- Practical complement to hinges for inset glass doors w/o an integral retaining spring.

Double Roller Catch, Low Back

Finish: Roller: nylon
Strike: steel
Catch: steel

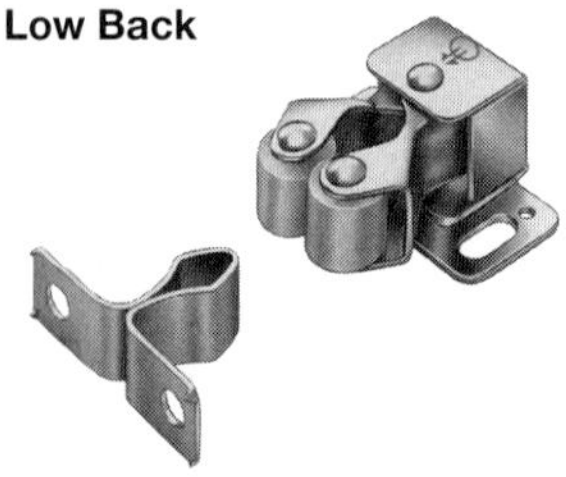

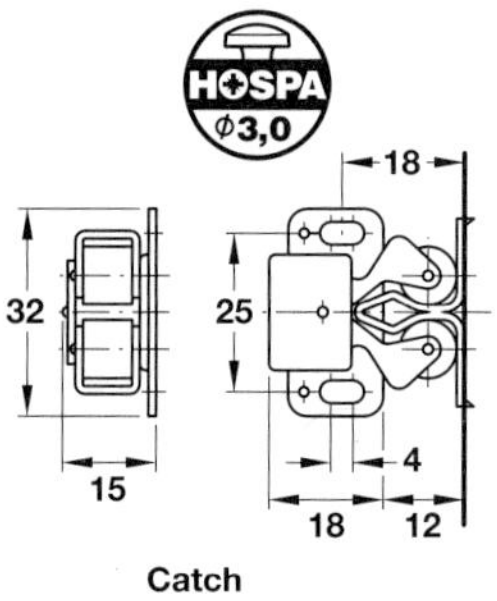

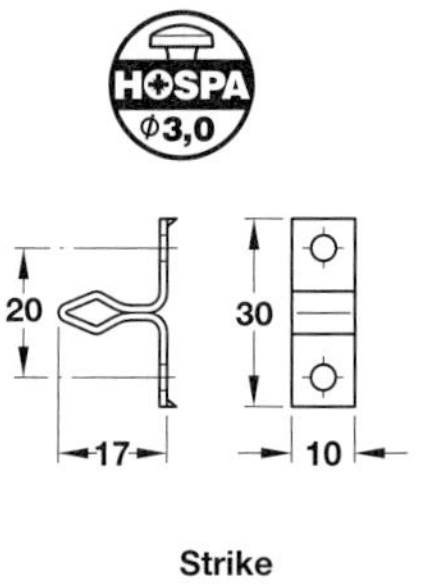

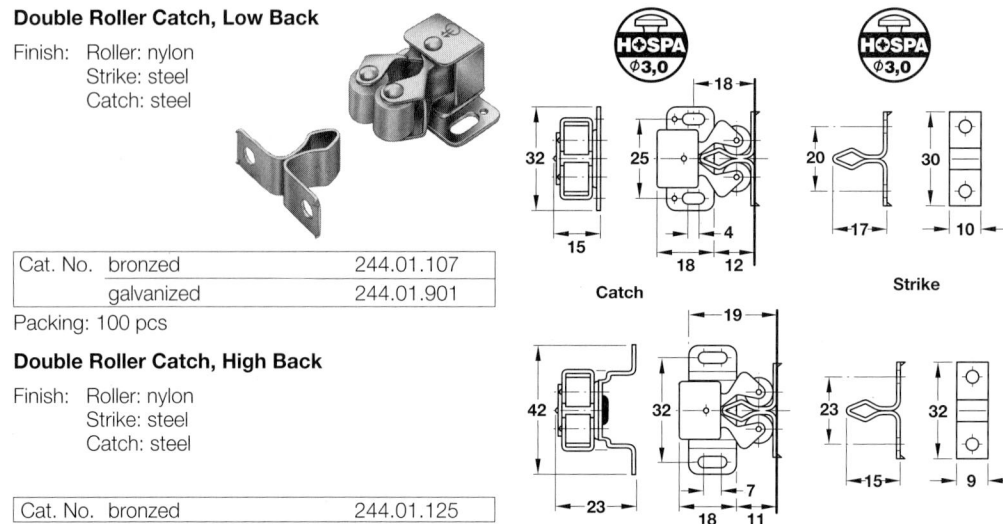

Cat. No.		
Cat. No.	bronzed	244.01.107
	galvanized	244.01.901

Packing: 100 pcs

Double Roller Catch, High Back

Finish: Roller: nylon
Strike: steel
Catch: steel

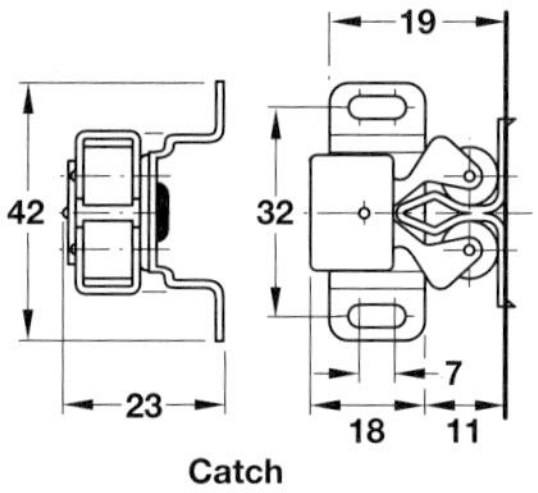

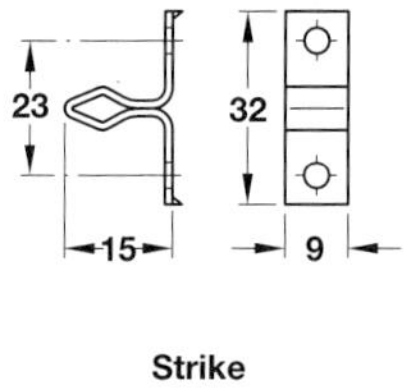

Cat. No.	bronzed	244.01.125

Packing: 100 pcs.

Ball, catch and stop

Screw-mounted

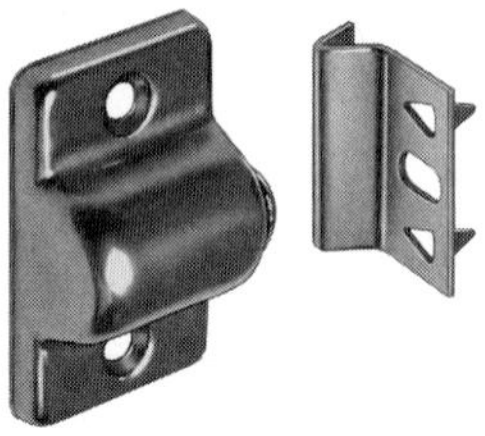

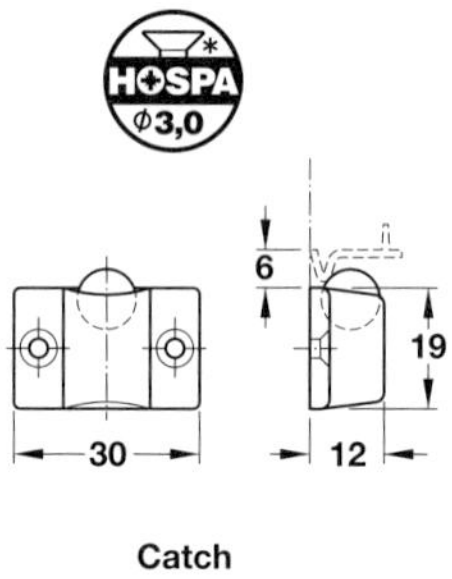

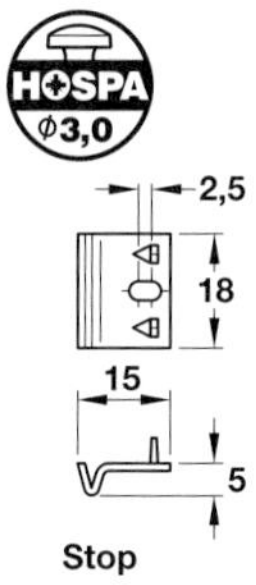

Cat. No.	241.10.718

Packing: 250 pcs.

Catch, for 5-6.5 mm glass doors

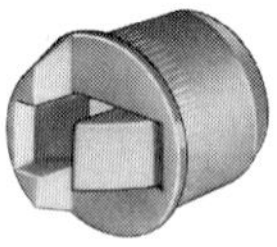

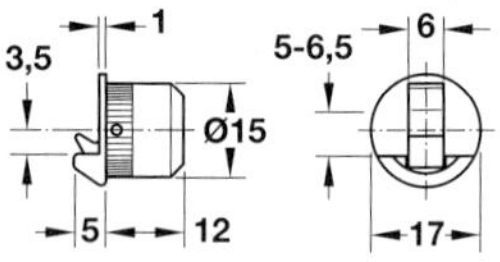

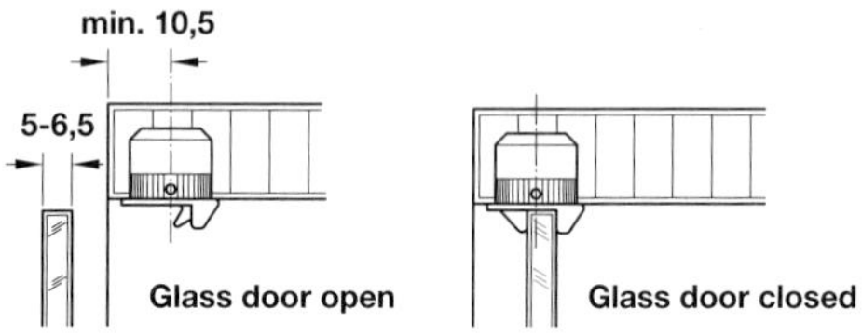

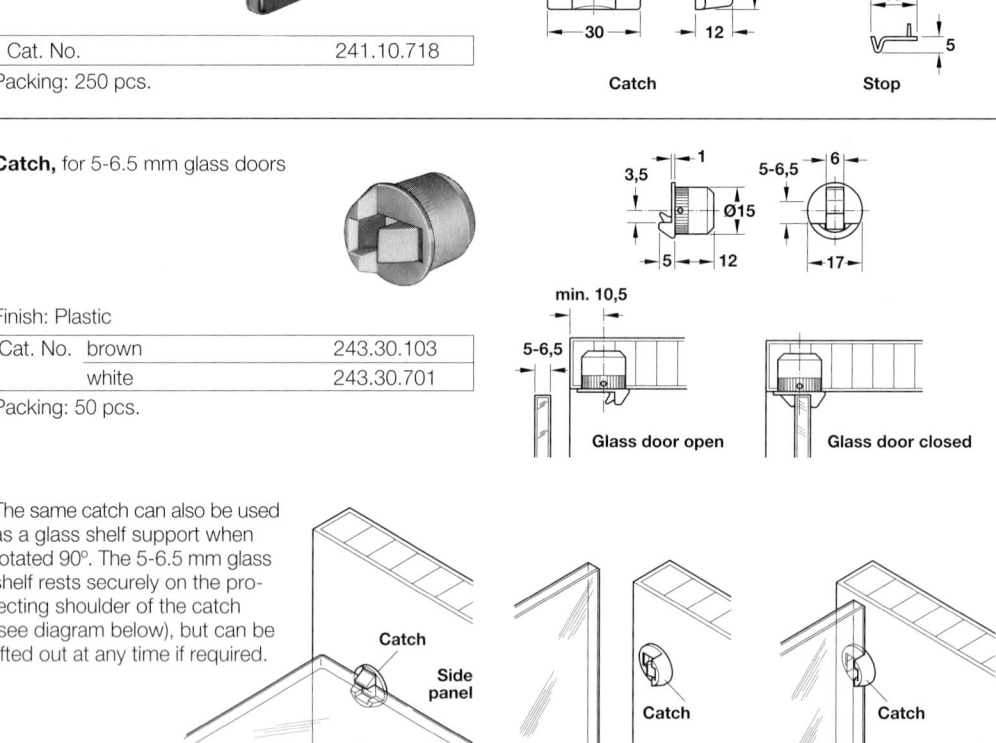

Finish: Plastic

Cat. No.		
Cat. No.	brown	243.30.103
	white	243.30.701

Packing: 50 pcs.

The same catch can also be used as a glass shelf support when rotated 90°. The 5-6.5 mm glass shelf rests securely on the projecting shoulder of the catch (see diagram below), but can be lifted out at any time if required.

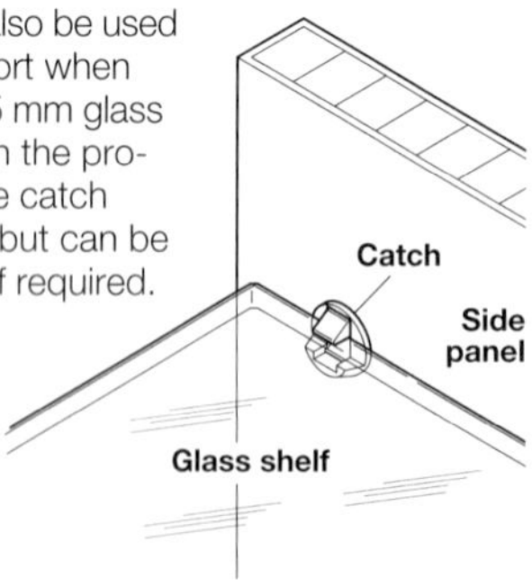

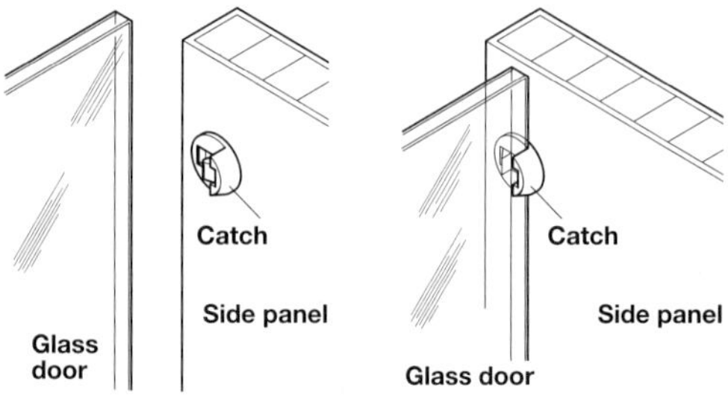

Dimensions in mm

Dimensional data not binding. We reserve the right to alter specifications without notice.

Toekick Spring Catches

Spring Catches, for butt or flush closing doors.

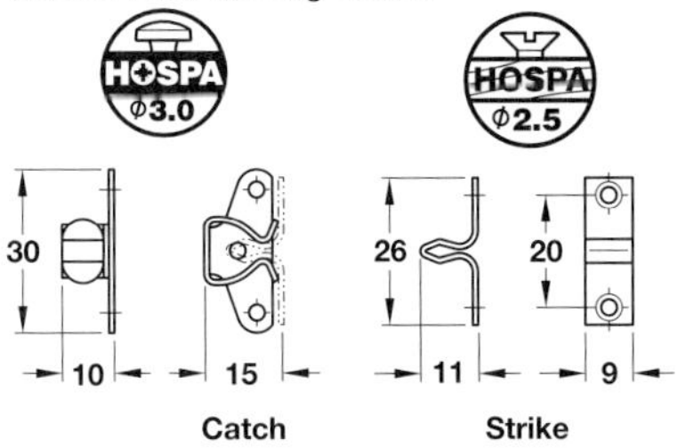

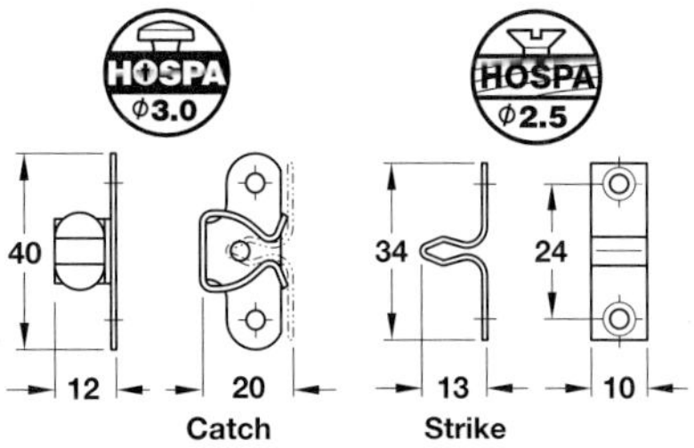

Finish: Spring catch, steel, blue tempered
Strike, steel, brass-plated

Cat. No.	245.05.502	245.06.509

Packing: 200 pcs.

Spring Catches, for butt or flush closing doors.

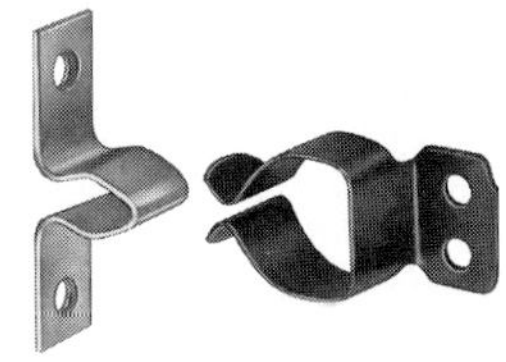

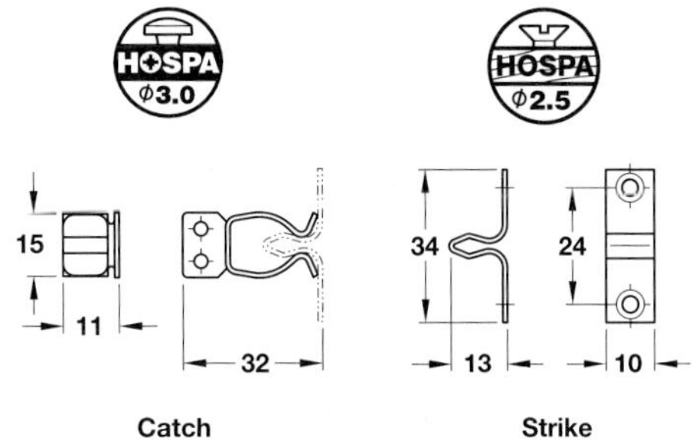

Finish: Spring catch, steel, blue tempered
Strike, steel, brass-plated

Cat. No.	245.02.501

Packing: 200 pcs.

32 mm Spring Catches, for butt or flush closing doors.

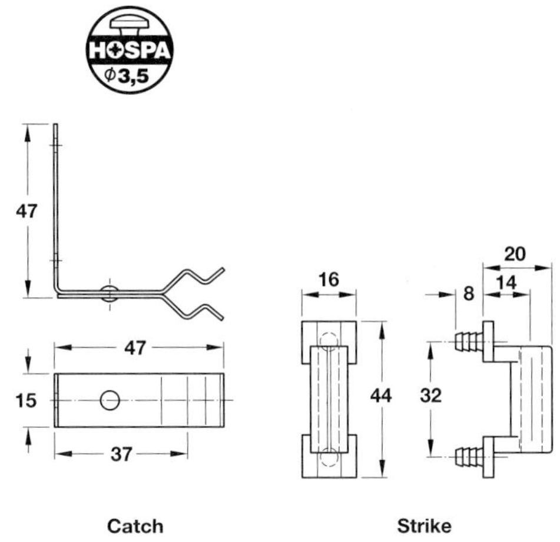

Finish: Spring catch, steel, blue tempered
Strike, press-in nylon

Cat. No.	245.07.757

Packing: 100 pcs.

32 mm Spring Catches, for butt or flush closing doors.

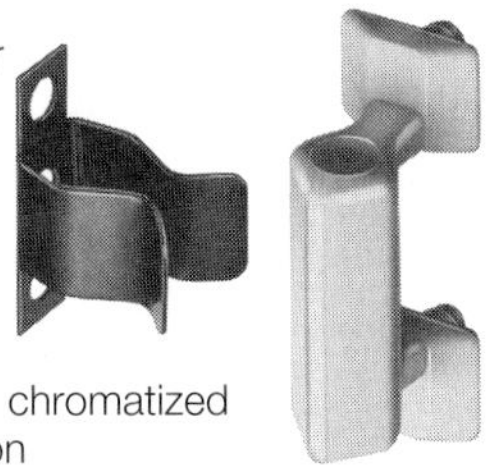

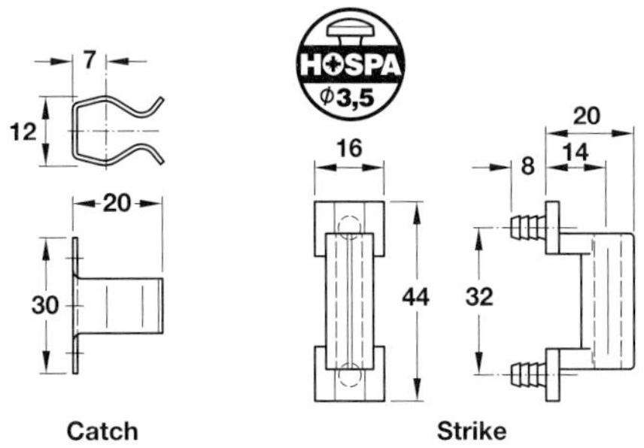

Finish: Spring catch, steel, chromatized
Strike, press-in nylon

Cat. No.	245.07.711

Packing: 100 pcs.

Spring Catches, for butt or flush closing doors.

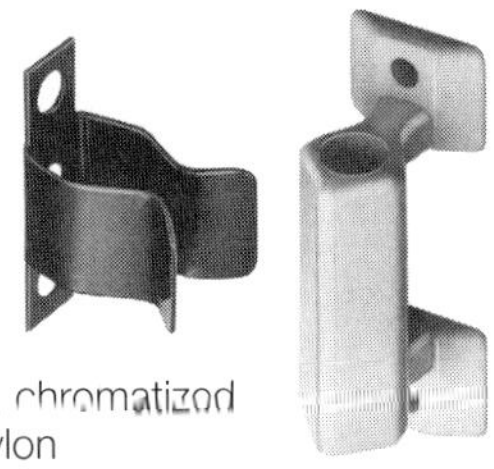

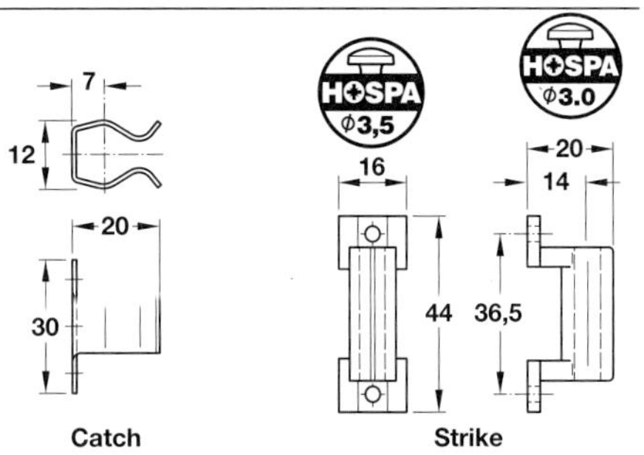

Finish: Spring catch, steel, chromatized
Strike, screw-on nylon

Cat. No.	245.07.702

Packing: 100 pcs.

Dimensions in mm

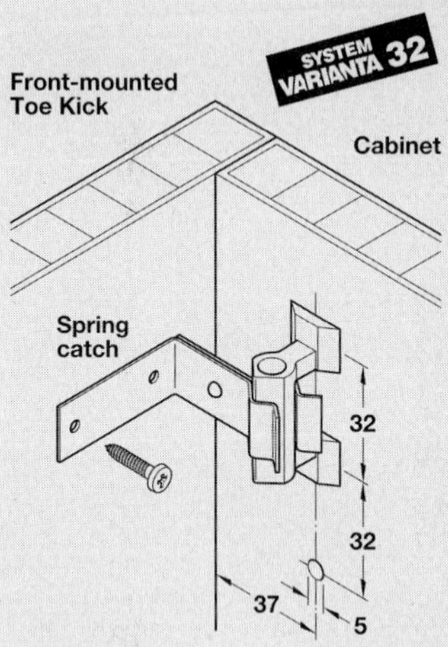

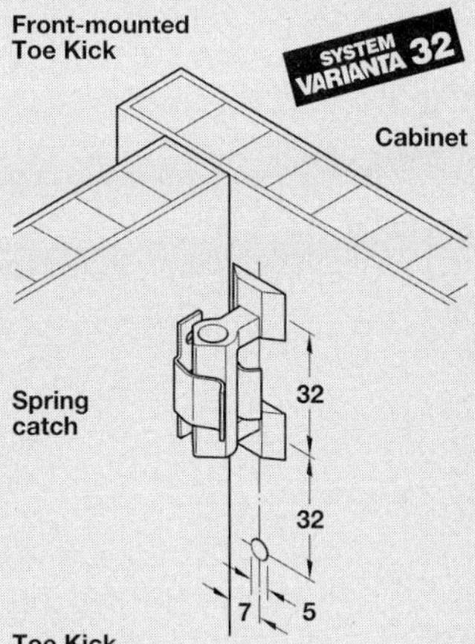

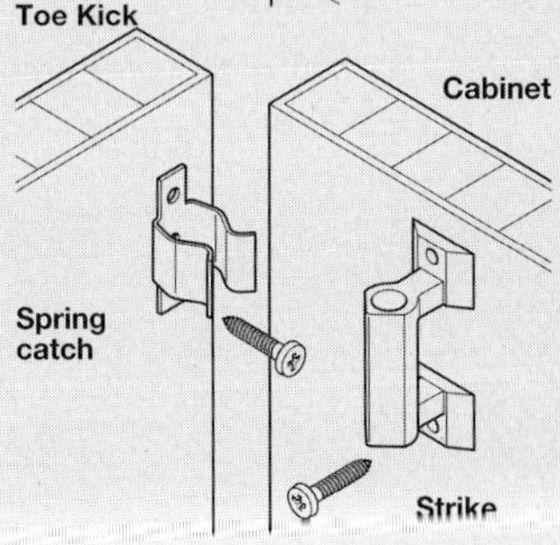

Dimensional data not binding.
We reserve the right to alter specifications without notice.

HÄFELE

Ball Catches

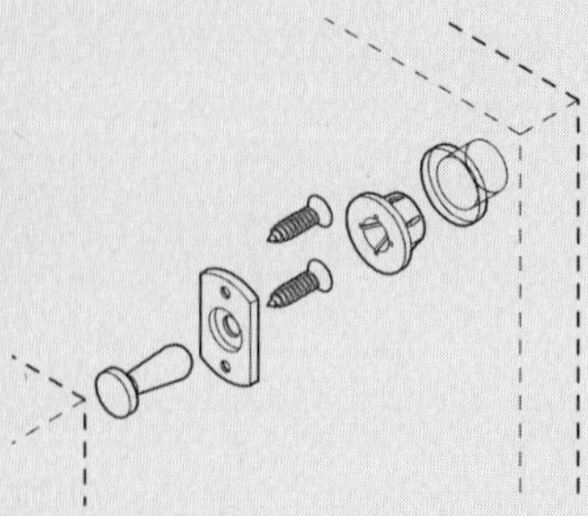

- To attach and remove, without tools, panels, frames etc.
- Pin floats in mounting plate - flexible drilling tolerances.

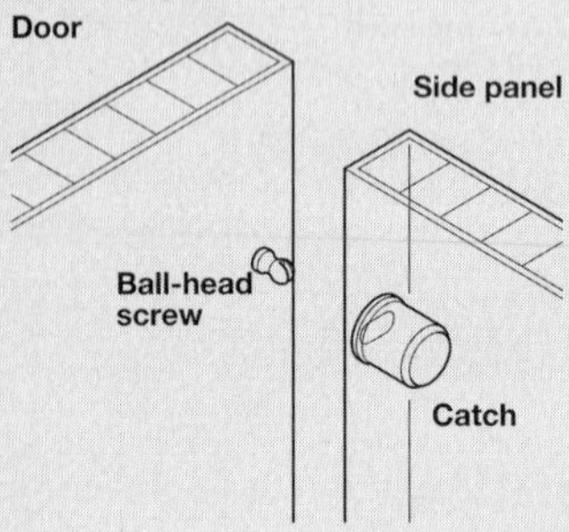

Speaker Panel Connector

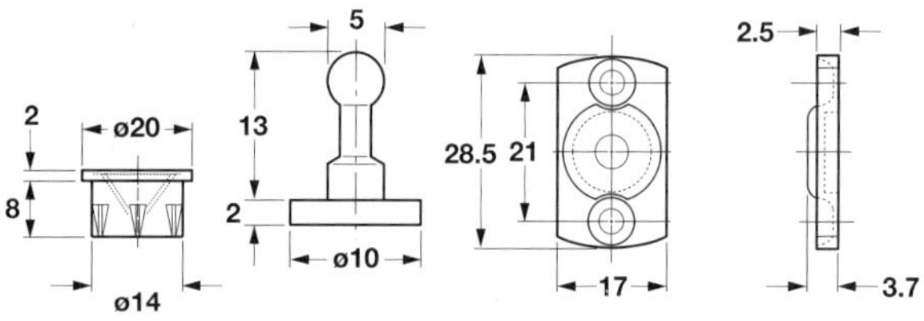

Finish: plastic, black

Cat. No.	260.71.303

Packing: 3000 sets (1 set = 3 pcs.)

Retaining Spring, ball-head screw and catch

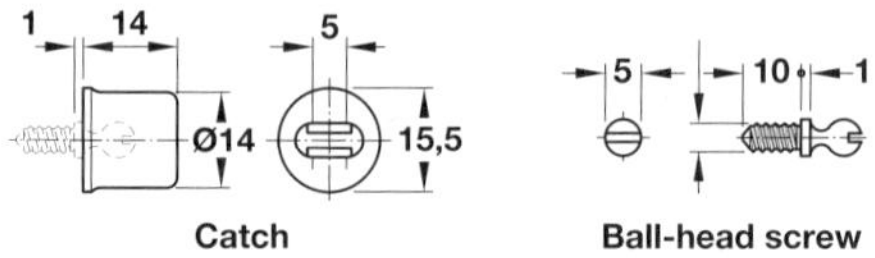

Finish: Ball-head screw: brass, bright; screw-mount
Catch: steel, brass-plated; press-fit

Cat. No.	241.90.501

Packing: 100 pcs.

Dimensions in mm

Dimensional data not binding.
We reserve the right to alter specifications without notice.

Pressure Catches

Mini-Latch Automatic Spring Catch
Screw-mounted

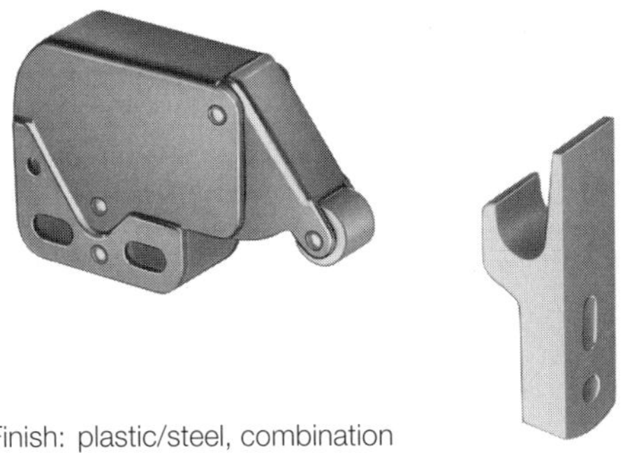

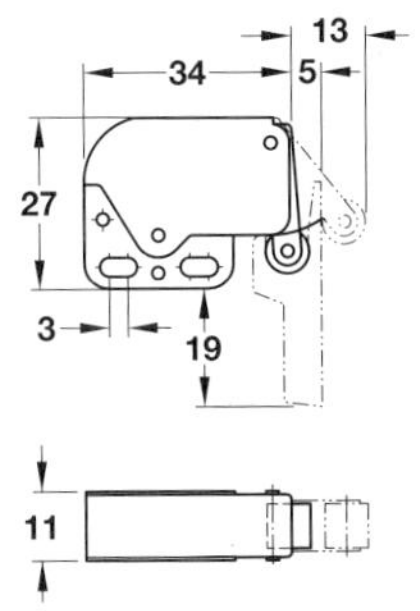

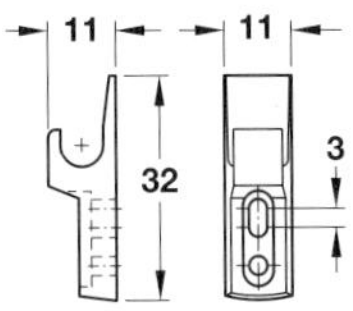

Finish: plastic/steel, combination
Strike: plastic

Cat. No.	white	245.54.710
	brown	245.54.514

Packing: 50 pcs.

Catch Strike

Quick-Latch Automatic Spring Catch
Screw-mounted

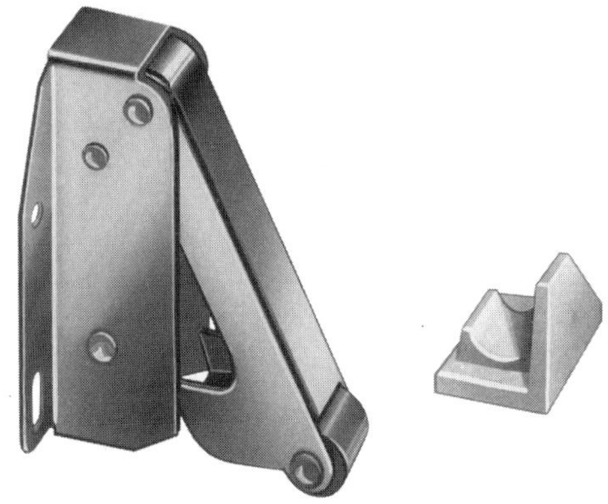

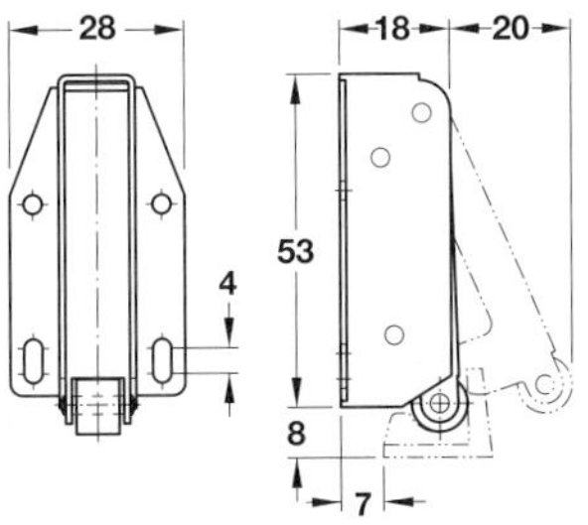

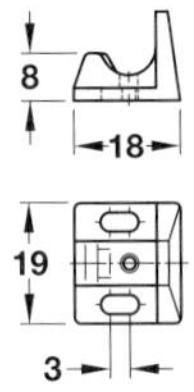

Finish: Strike: plastic, white, screw-mounted
Catch: steel

Cat. No.	bright-galvanized	245.55.913
	brass-plated	245.55.502
	bronzed	245.55.100

Packing: 50 pcs.

Catch Strike

Touch-Latch Automatic Spring Catch
Screw-mounted

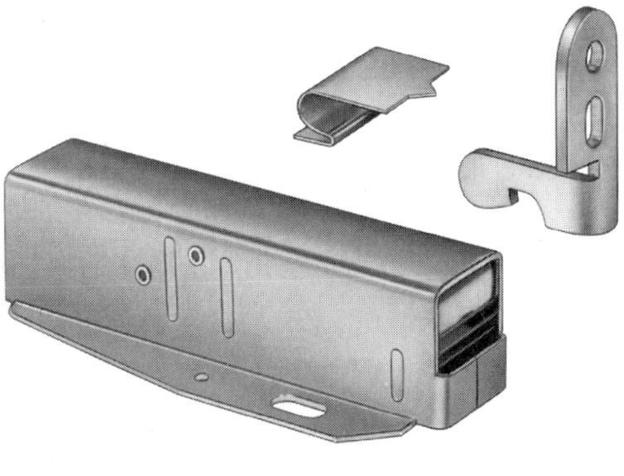

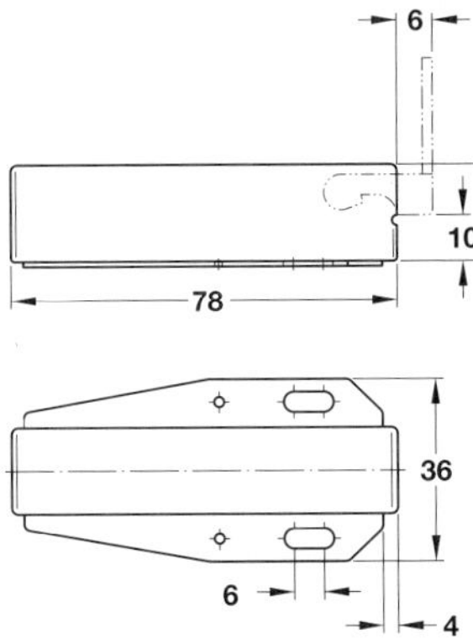

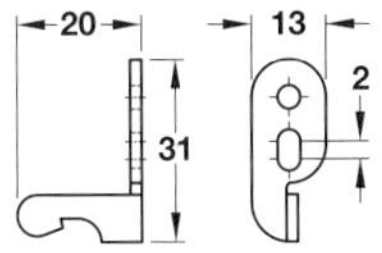

Finish: All parts: steel, zinc-plated,

Cat. No.	245.56.901

Packing: 50 pcs.

Catch Strike

- The release function can be activated with light pressure on the door.
- Door opens automatically
- To close door light pressure against door is required.

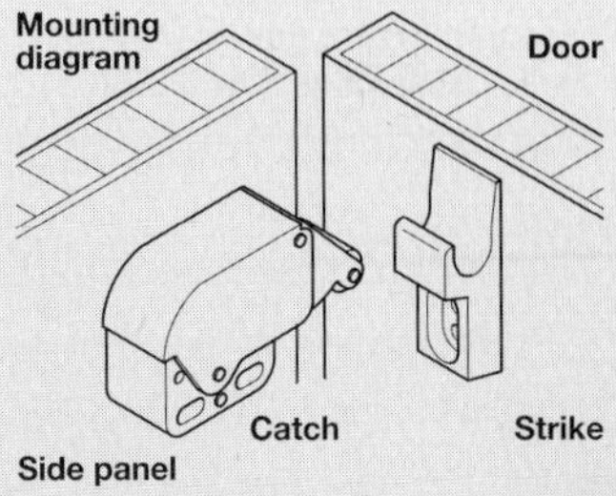

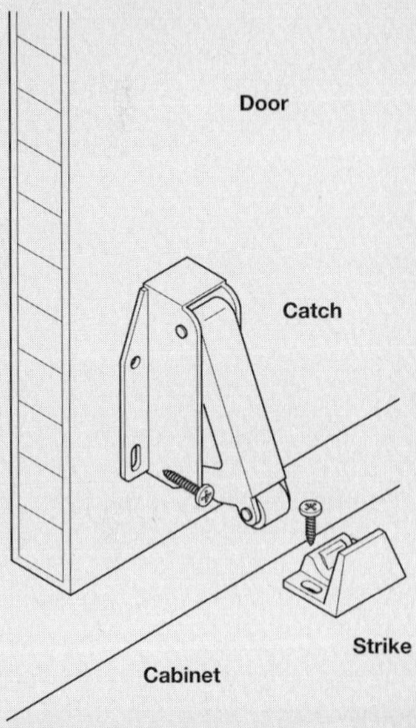

Position of strikeplate:
- A guide is supplied to center the hole for the slot in the strike.
- It is placed in the catch housing and will locate the hole center when the door is pressed against it.

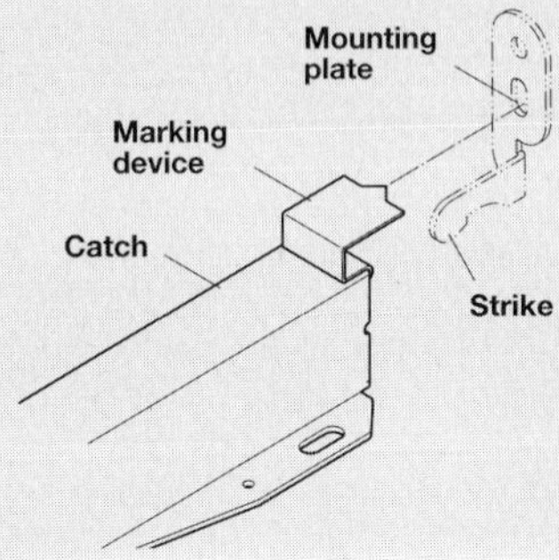

HÄFELE

Magnetic Pressure Catches

To make push latches suitable for specific use on modern entertainment centers with glass doors, special finger pulls have been developed for push-fit mounting on glass panels, which also serve as the strike for the magnetic catch. (See page **2.87-2.88**)

Push Latch is a type of automatic catch with a permanent magnet as the retaining element. The opening and closing functions, however, are similar to those of an automatic spring catch. Light pressure on the door is sufficient to close it securely or open it to the extent needed for any further magnetic holding power to be overcome manually.

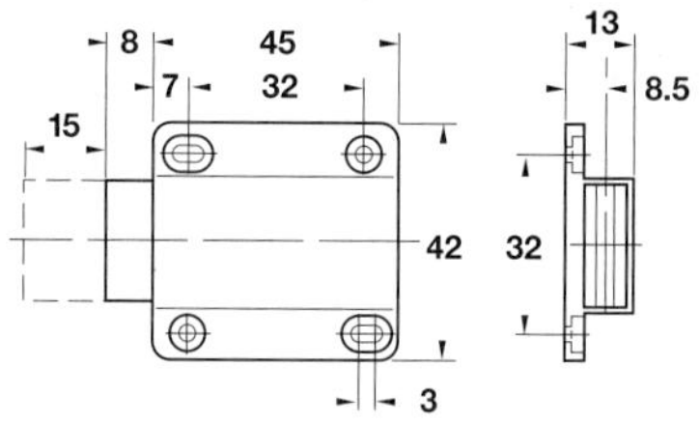

Magnetic Pressure Catch

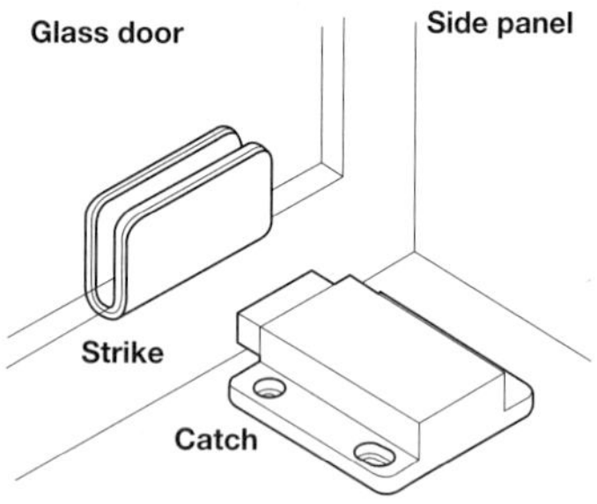

Finish: plastic, screw-mounted

Cat. No.		
	brown	245.61.126
	white	245.61.724
	black	245.61.322

Packing: 100 pcs. each

Matching strikes must be ordered separately

Magnetic Pressure Catch

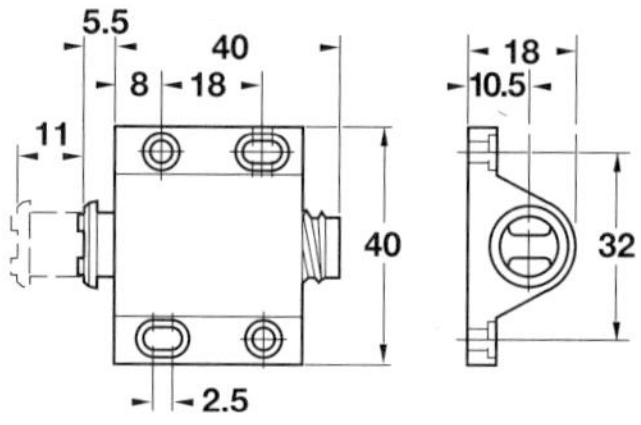

- Measurements are approx. ± 0.5 mm

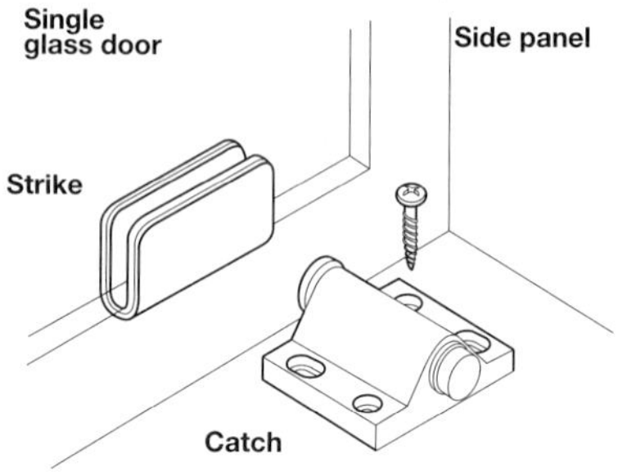

Finish: plastic, screw-mounted

Cat. No.		
	brown	245.60.183
	black	245.60.389

Packing: 100 pcs. each

Matching strikes must be ordered separately

Naturally, push latch magnetic catches are also suitable for wood doors (screw-mounted strikes for this purpose are featured on page 2.98 and all other types of furniture.

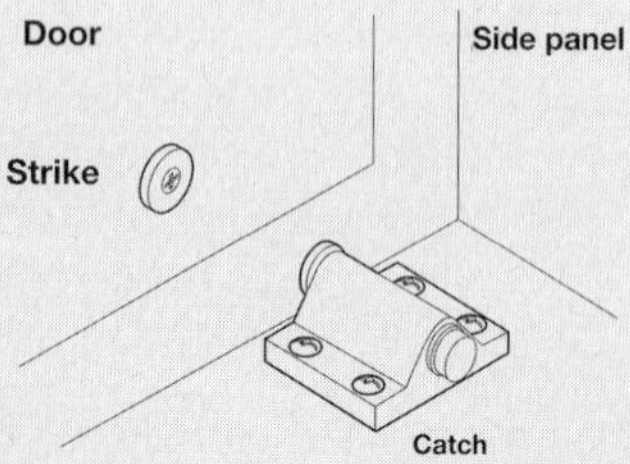

Magnetic Pressure Catch

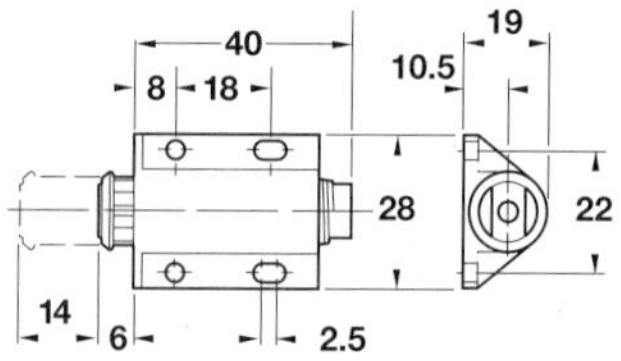

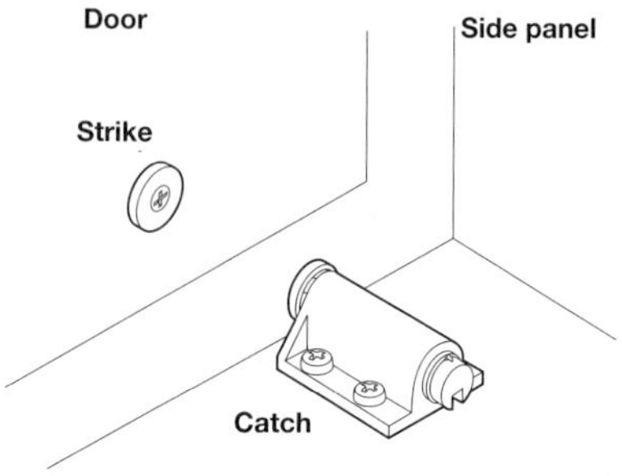

Finish: plastic, screw-mounted

Cat. No.		
	brown	245.80.110
	white	245.80.710
	black	245.80.310

Packing: 100 pcs. each

Matching strikes must be ordered separately

Dimensional data not binding. We reserve the right to alter specifications without notice.

Dimensions in mm

Magnetic Pressure Catches

HÄFELE

Magnetic Pressure Catch

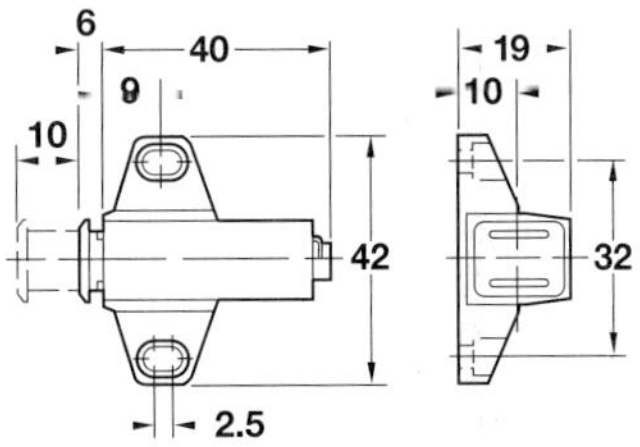

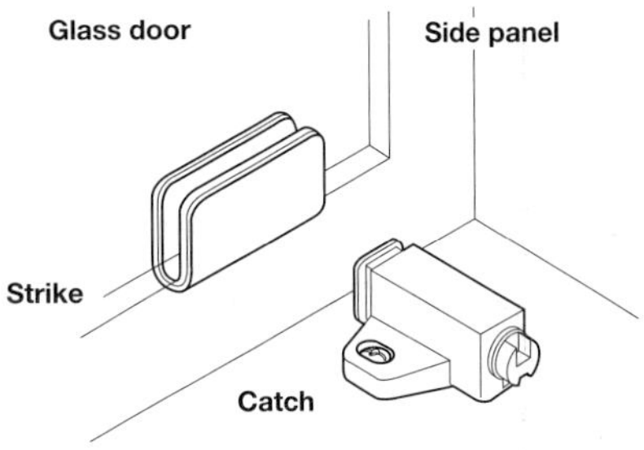

Finish: plastic, screw-mounted

Cat. No.	brown	245.81.110
	black	245.81.310

Packing: 100 pcs.

Matching strikes must be ordered separately

Magnetic Pressure Catch

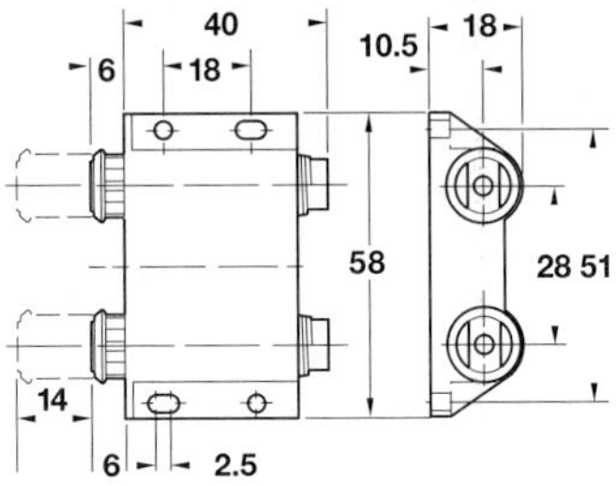

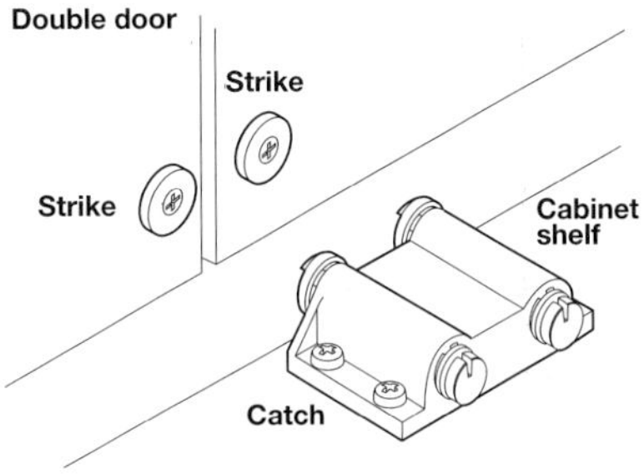

Finish: plastic, screw-mounted

Cat. No.	brown	245.80.120
	white	245.80.720
	black	245.80.320

Packing: 100 pcs.

Matching strikes must be ordered separately

Magnetic Pressure Catch

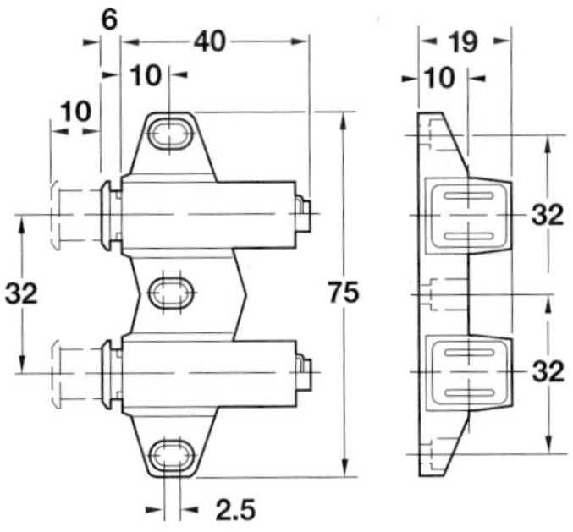

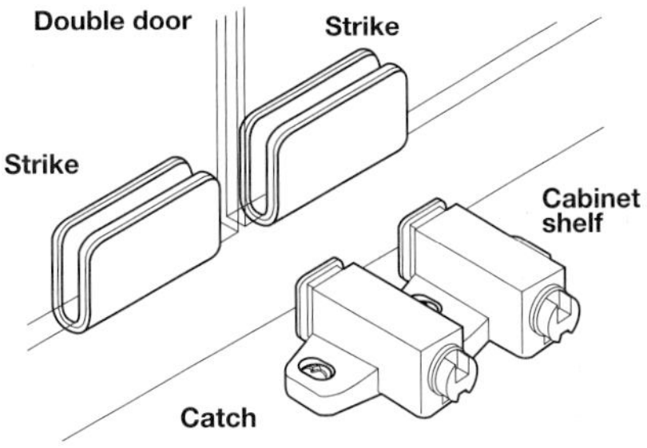

Finish: plastic, screw-mounted

Cat. No.	brown	245.81.120
	white	245.81.720
	black	245.81.320

Packing: 100 pcs.

Matching strikes must be ordered separately

Dimensions in mm

- Measurements are approx. ± 0.5 mm

- Strikes can be found on catalog page **2.87-2.88**.

HÄFELE

Magnetic Push Catches

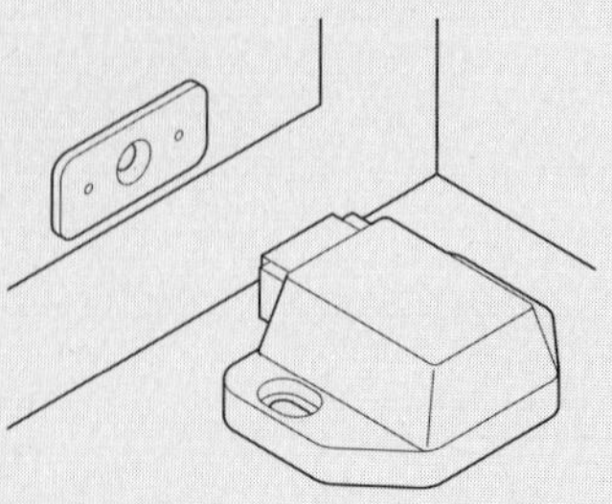

- All 32 mm compatible, screw-mount and knock-in application
- 8 mm throw
- For door overlay applications
- All parts black

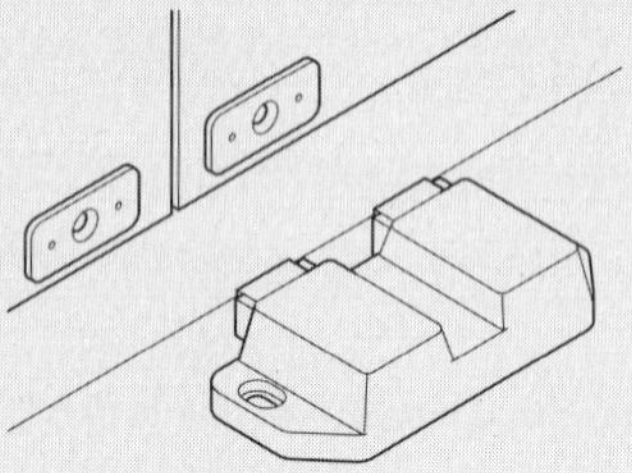

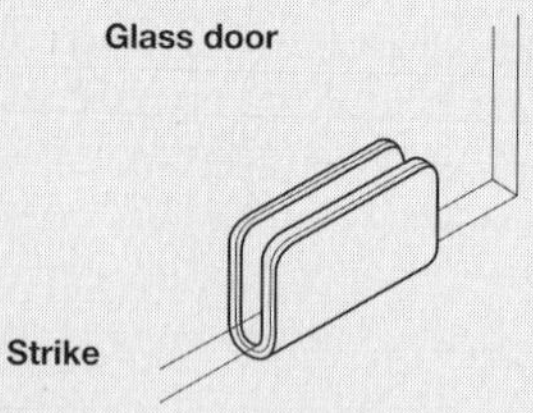

Strike can be found on catalog page **2.87-2.88**.

Magnetic push latch, screw-mounted

HOSPA Φ3,0

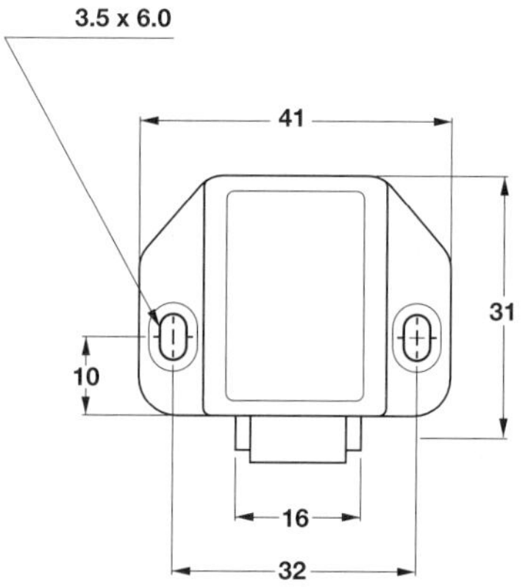

Material: plastic catch
Finish: black

Cat. No.	245.75.310

Packing: 100 pcs/no strikes

Magnetic push latch, with dowels, for 1/4" holes

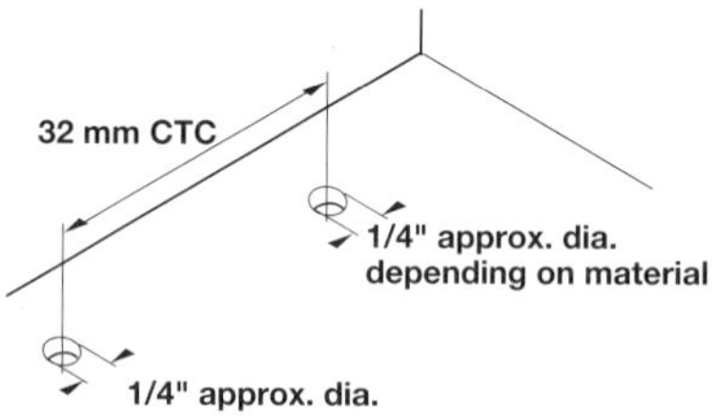

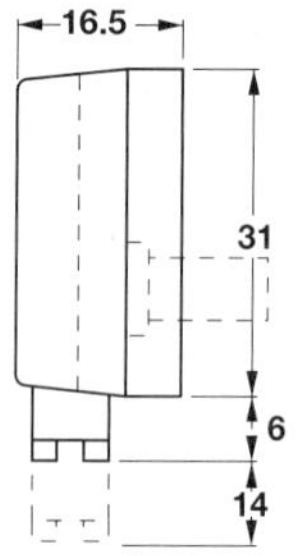

Material: plastic catch
Finish: black

Cat. No.	245.75.315

Packing: 100 pcs./no strikes

Magnetic push latch, without dowels, screw-mounted

HOSPA Φ3,0

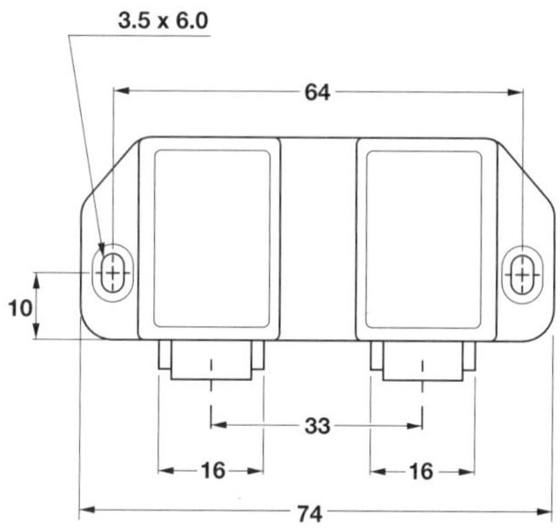

Material: plastic catch
Finish: black

Cat. No.	245.75.320

Packing: 50 pcs./no strikes

Magnetic push latch, with dowels, for 1/4" holes

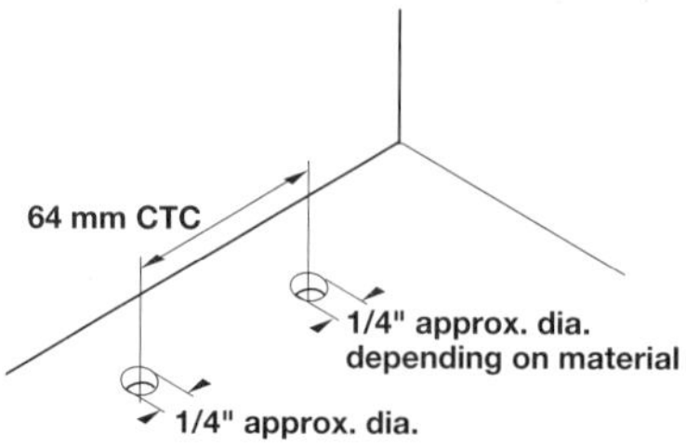

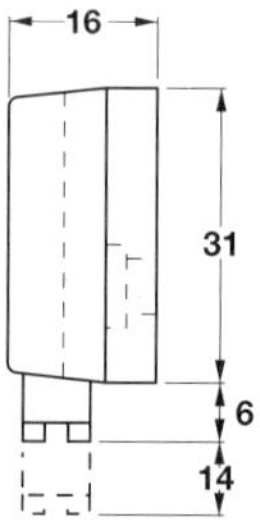

Material: plastic catch
Finish: black

Cat. No.	245.75.325

Packing: 50 pcs./no strikes

Dimensional data not binding.
We reserve the right to alter specifications without notice.

Magnetic Pressure Catches

Magnetic Pressure Catch

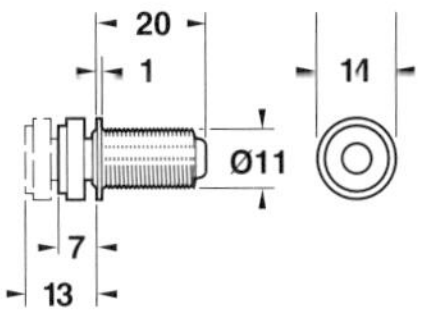

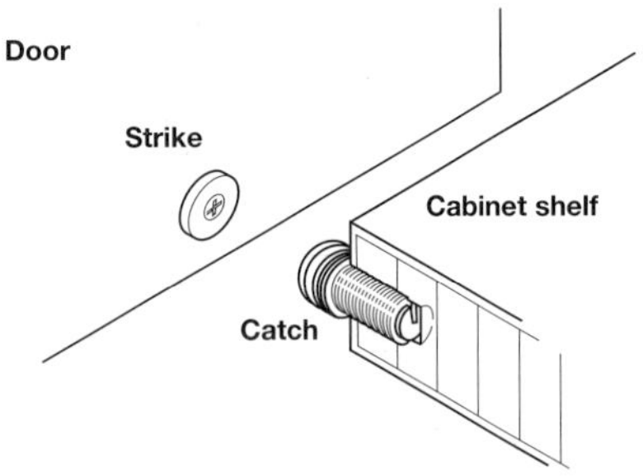

Finish: plastic, black press-fit

Cat. No.	245.62.301

Packing: 100 pcs.

Matching strikes must be ordered separately

- Measurements are approx. ± 0.5 mm

Magnetic Pressure Catch

HOSPA ⌀3,0

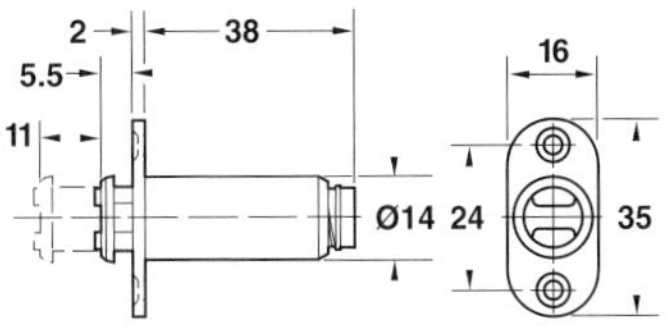

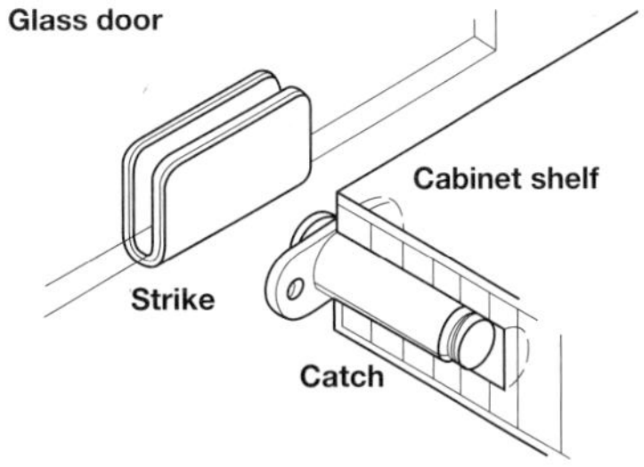

Finish: plastic, mortise/screw-mounted

Cat. No.	brown	245.62.114
	white	245.62.712
	black	245.62.310

Packing: 100 pcs.

Matching strikes must be ordered separately

- Strikes can be found on catalog page **2.87-2.88**.

Magnetic Touch Latch

with extra long throws.

For overlay door, give 3mm (1/8: gap between door and cabinet frame for pushing space. Comes with screws.

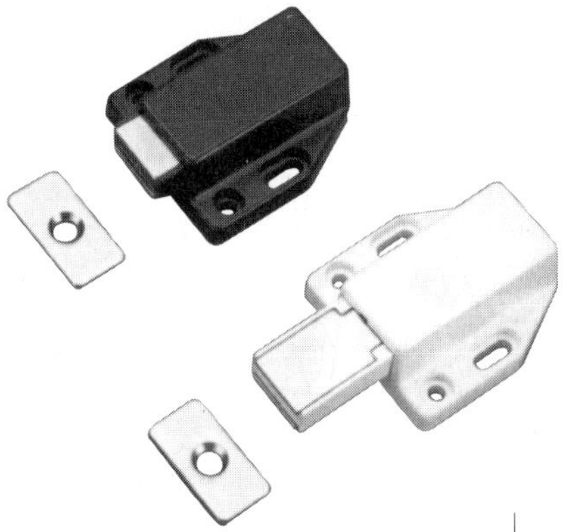

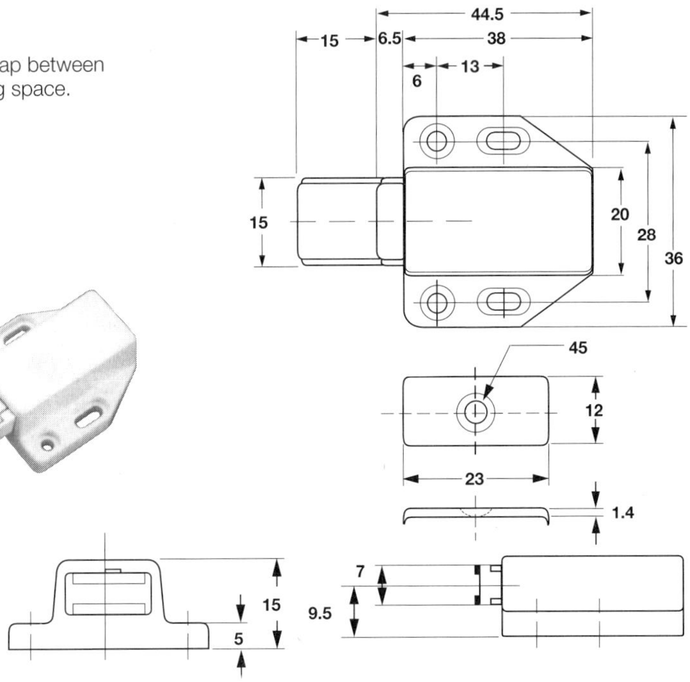

Magnetic pull: 1.4 kg
Material: Catch-ABS
Finish: Strike: metal, yellow galvanized

Cat. No.	white	245.61.730
	brown	245.61.330

Packing: 20 pcs./box

Dimensions in mm

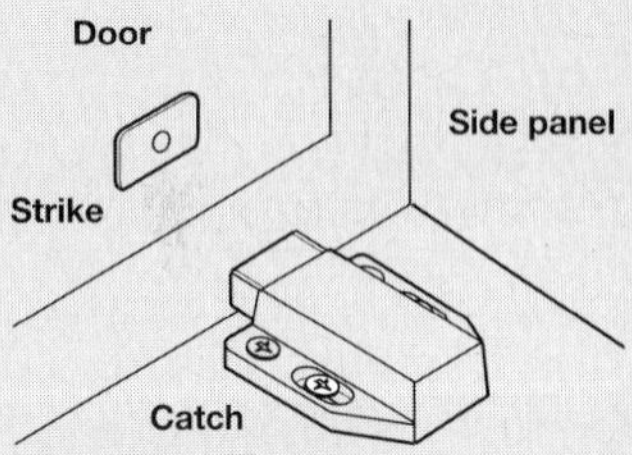

- Extremely reliable
- Longer throw (push) than other catches

- Inset application

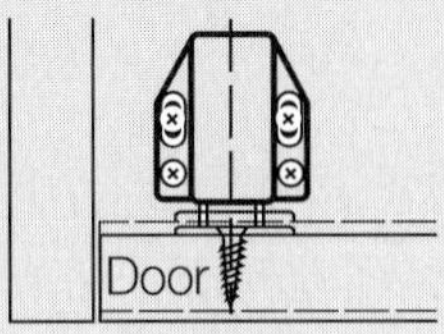

- Overlay application

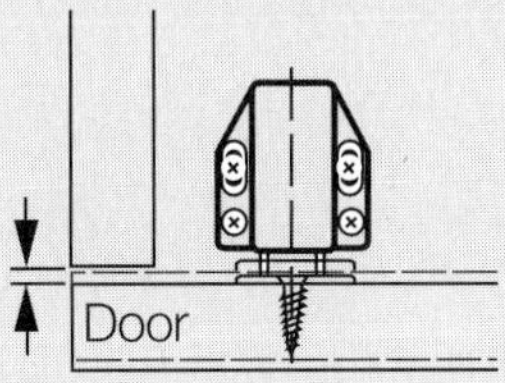

Gap = 3 mm (⅛")

Dimensional data not binding. We reserve the right to alter specifications without notice.

HÄFELE

Non-magnetic Pressure Catches

- Especially suited for use where magnets would be harmful such as near computer tapes and disk storage.
- Cannot be pulled open or pushed open from the inside by falling objects.

Non-magnetic pressure catch

This pressure catch was created based on same concept as that of a magnetic catch. A gentle push is all is takes to open or close door.

Holding power: 4 kg.

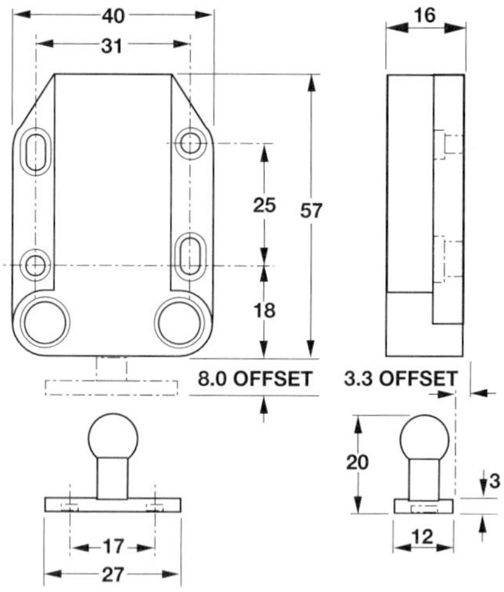

Finish: plastic, black

Cat. No.	245.50.301

Packing: 30 pcs., including 6 screws/each

Compact non-magnetic pressure catch

Holding power: 3 kg.

- Smaller version of above.
- Same basic features
- In addition, the strike consists of two parts allowing for easy adjustment even after the body is attached.
- Lower holding power.

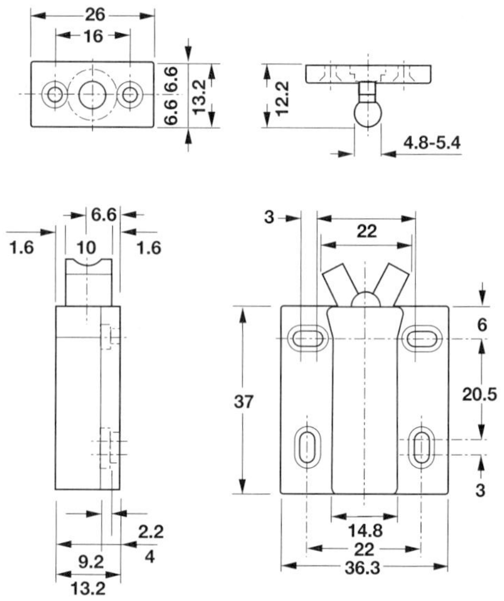

Finish: plastic, black

Cat. No.	245.50.310

Packing: 40 pcs., including 6 screws/each

Mounted **through** back of drawer

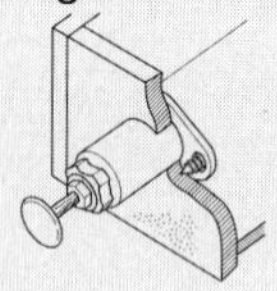

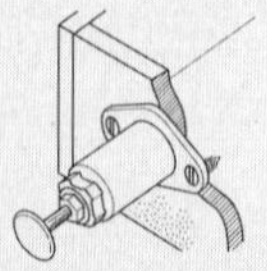

Mounted **on** back of drawer

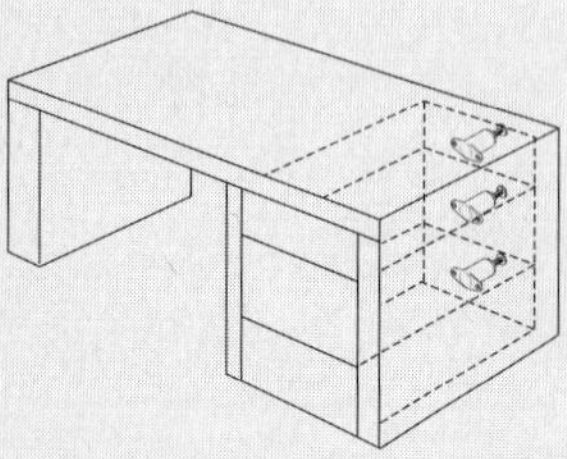

Flexi-touch Drawer Latch

Spring latch releases drawer with the touch of a finger.Attachable from back or through back of drawer. Not for overlay drawer fronts.

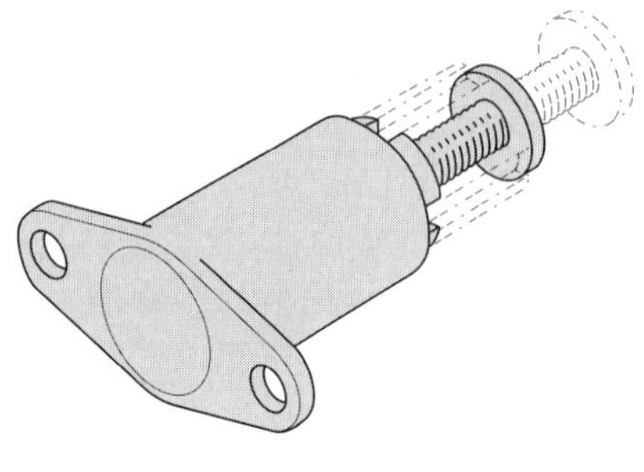

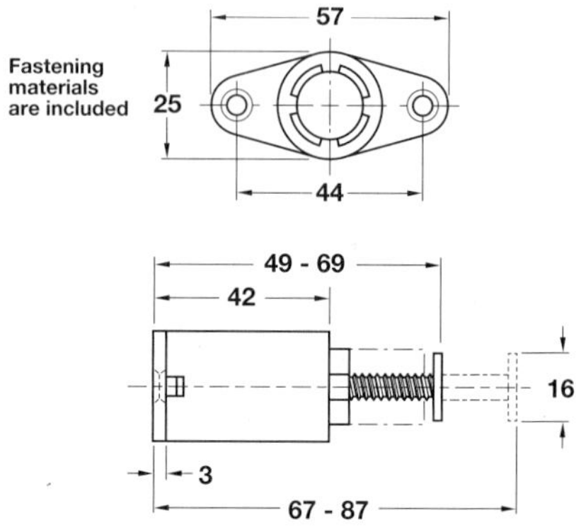

Finish: plastic, beige

Cat. No.	245.52.403

Packing: 50 pcs., including screws

Dimensions in mm

Dimensional data not binding. We reserve the right to alter specifications without notice.

Finger Pulls and Strikes, for Magnetic Pressure Catches

Strike with and without finger pulls for glass doors and plain strike for wood doors. These strikes are for use in combination with automatic spring or magnetic catches on glass or wood doors. Slight pressure with finger is sufficient to open the door in the case of automatic magnetic catches.
Application for strikes and finger pulls are shown below.

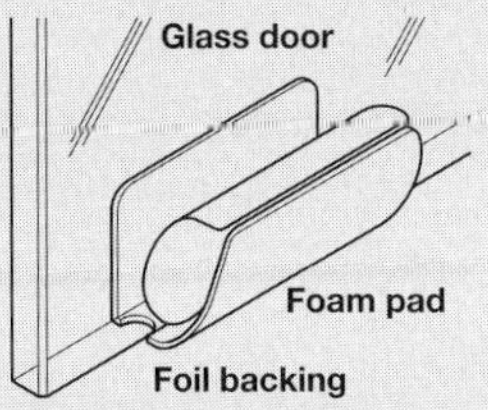

Remove protective backing and attach foam liner to the glass door, then push the strike or finger pull into the pad.

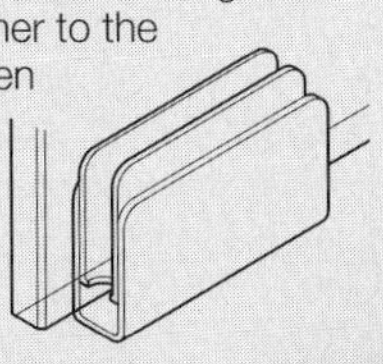

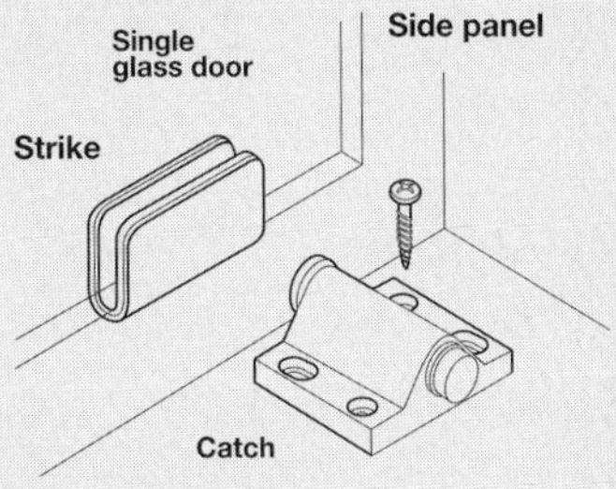

Strike, for glass doors, 5–6 mm thick in combination with automatic spring catches.

Finish: steel, bonded to self-adhesive foam pad

	black	brass-plated
Cat. No.	245.66.309	245.66.809

Packing: 100 pcs. each

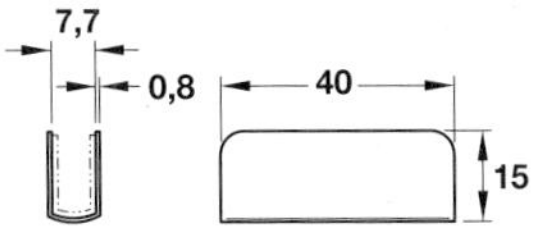

Strike, for glass doors, 5–6 mm thick in combination with automatic spring catches.

Finish: steel, bonded to self-adhesive foam pad

	black	brass-plated	chrome-plated
Cat. No.	245.71.300	245.71.800	245.71.202

Packing: 100 pcs. each

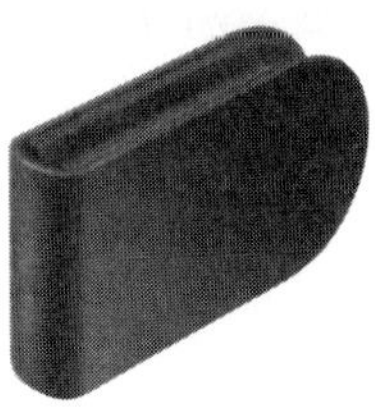

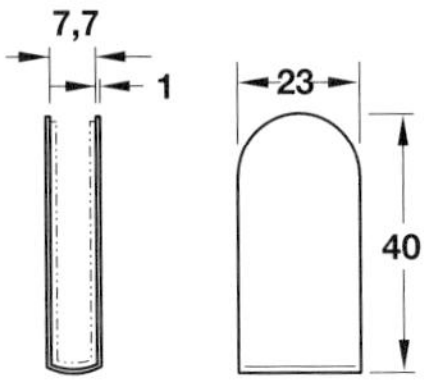

Strike, for glass doors, 5–6 mm thick in combination with automatic spring catches.

Finish: steel, bonded to self-adhesive foam pad

	black	brass-plated	chrome-plated
Cat. No.	245.63.326	245.63.826	245.63.228

Packing: 100 pcs. each

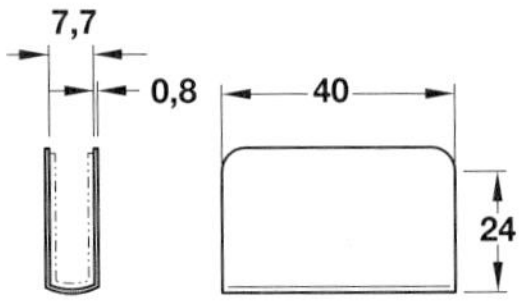

Strike, for glass doors, 5–6 mm thick in combination with automatic spring catches.

Finish: steel, bonded to self-adhesive foam pad

	black	brass-plated	chrome-plated
Cat. No.	245.63.335	245.63.835	245.63.237

Packing: 100 pcs. each

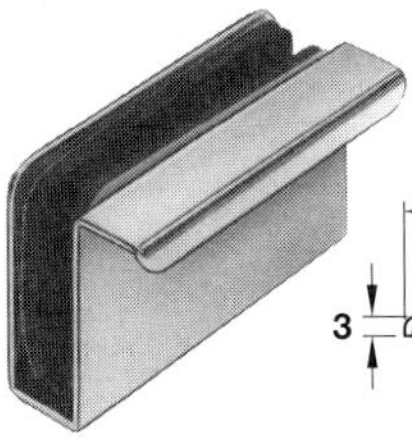

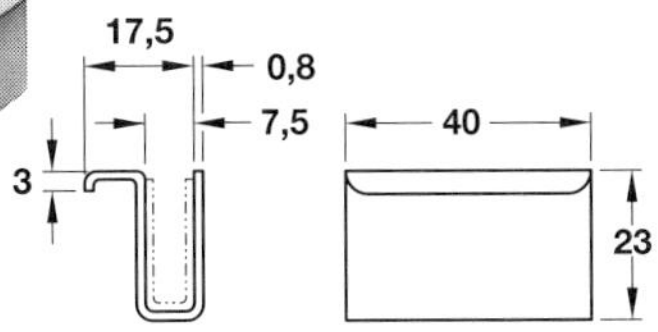

Finger pull, for glass doors, up to 6 mm with fixing screw

Finish: zinc, die-cast

	nickel-plated, matt	black, matt
Cat. No.	154.22.607	154.22.303

Packing: 100 pcs.

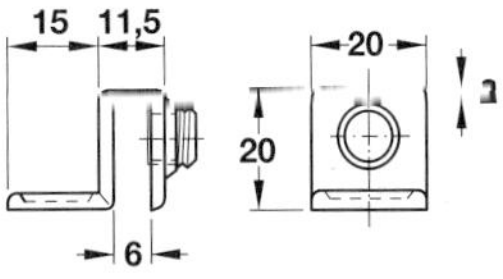

Dimensions in mm

*** Cannot be used with magnetic catches**

Dimensional data not binding. We reserve the right to alter specifications without notice.

HÄFELE

Finger Pulls and Strikes, for Magnetic Pressure Catches

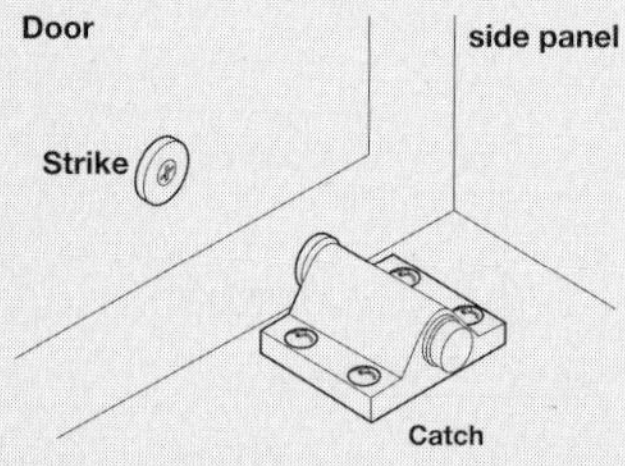

Strike, for wood doors, in combination with automatic spring or magnetic catches.

Finish: steel, screw-mounted

	galvanized	bronzed
Cat. No.	245.63.997	245.63.291

Packing: 100 pcs. each

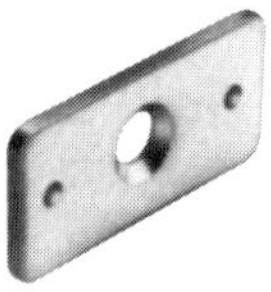

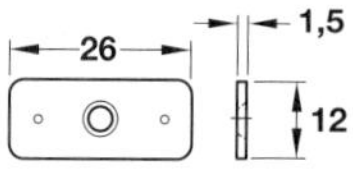

HOSPA Φ3.0

Strike, for wood doors,
in combination with magnetic catches.

Finish: steel, screw-mounted

	galvanized	bronzed
Cat. No.	245.63.988	245.63.282

Packing: 100 pcs. each

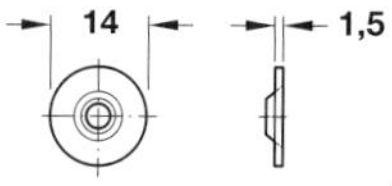

HOSPA Φ3.0

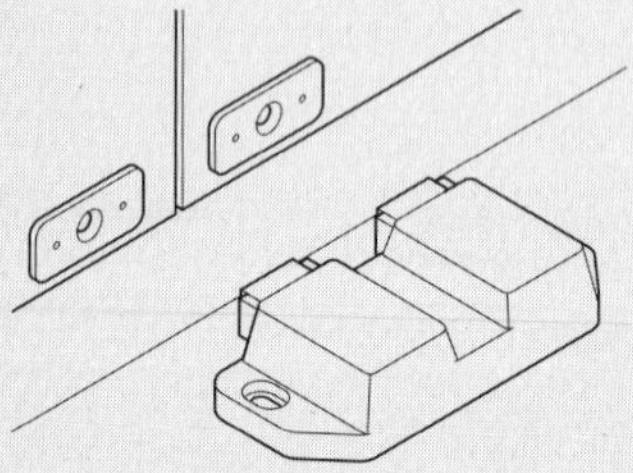

Strike, for wood doors, in combination with automatic spring or magnetic catches.

Finish: steel, zinc-plated

Cat. No.	246.26.793

Packing: 100 pcs. each

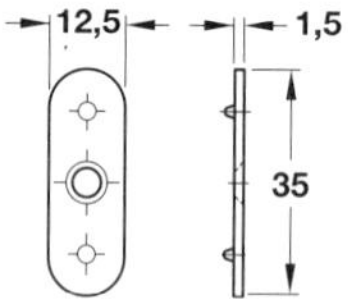

HOSPA Φ3.0

Strike, for wood doors, in combination with automatic spring or magnetic catches.

Finish: steel, screw-mounted

	black
Cat. No.	246.36.390

Packing: 500 pcs. each

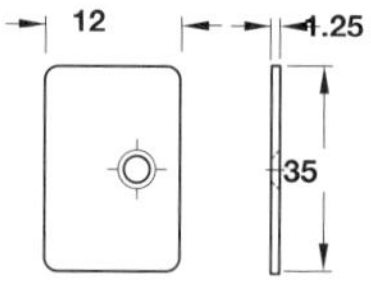

HOSPA Φ3.0

Dimensions in mm

Dimensional data not binding.
We reserve the right to alter specifications without notice.

Brass Furniture Bolts

HÄFELE

Furniture Bolts, with concealed screw holes, solid brass with straight slide.

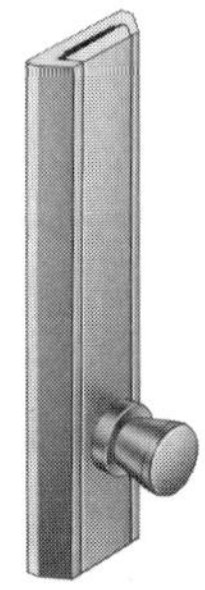

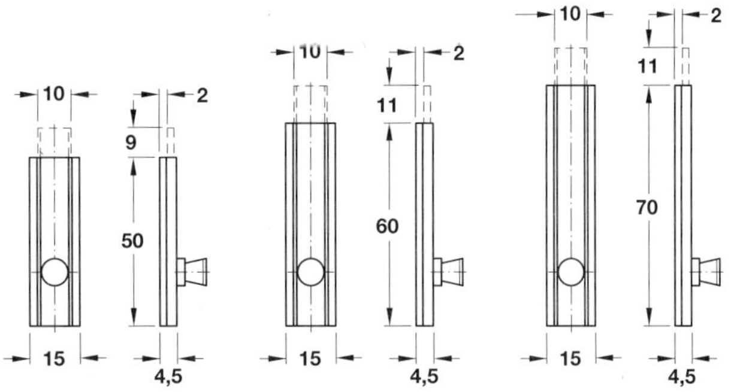

Finish: brass

Cat. No.				
	chrome, matt	252.01.629	252.01.638	252.01.647
	brass sanded	252.01.227	252.01.236	252.01.245

Packing: 20 pcs.

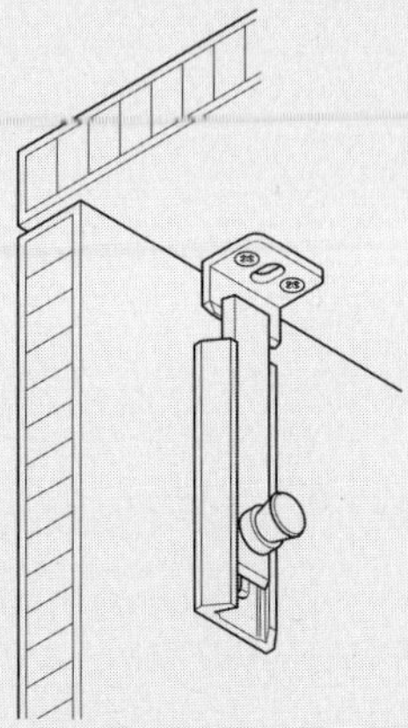

Furniture Bolts, with concealed screw holes, brass with cranked slide.

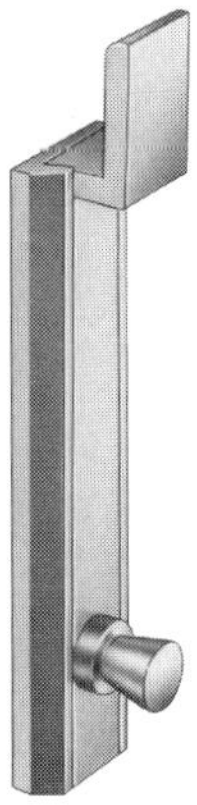

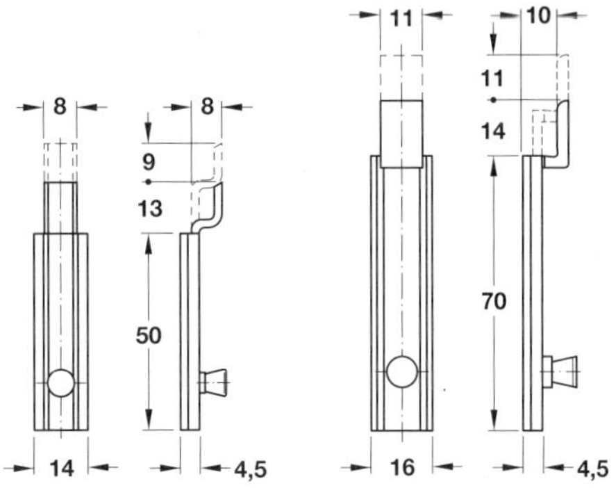

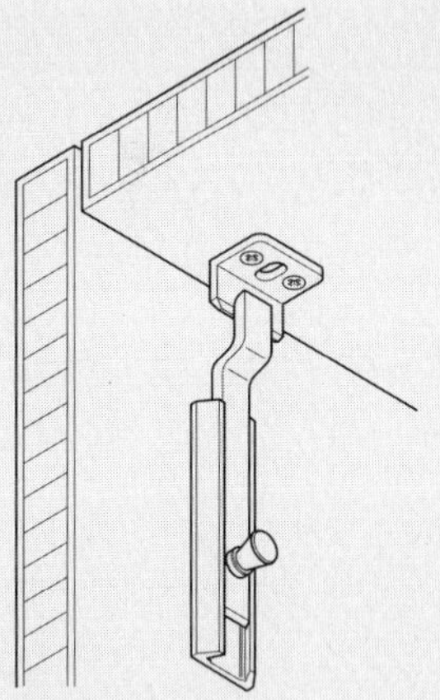

Finish: brass

Cat. No.			
	chrome, polished	252.02.626	252.02.644
	polished	252.02.224	252.02.242

Packing: 10 pcs.

Mounting directions
for furniture bolt

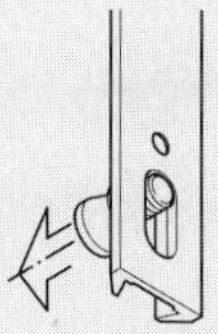

Unscrew the threaded knob so that...

...the screw holes are exposed.

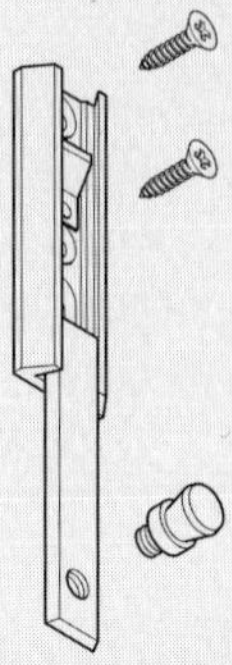

The guide can now be installed.

Return the slide and screw into place.

Strike, 2 prongs and 1 screw hole

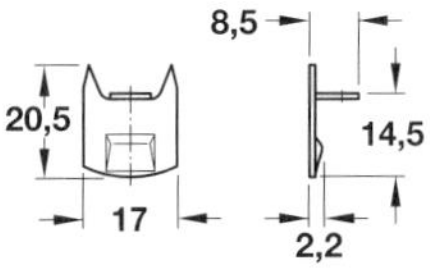

Finish: steel

Cat. No.		
	nickel-plated	251.70.709
	brass-plated	251.70.503

Packing: 100 pcs.

Strike, 2 screw holes

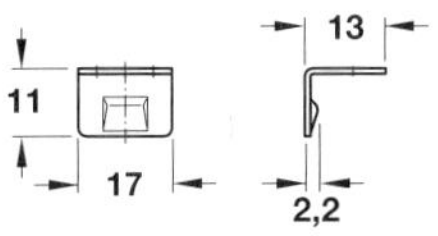

Finish: steel

Cat. No.		
	nickel-plated	251.74.707
	brass-plated	251.74.501

Packing: 100 pcs.

Strike, plain bracket and 3 screw holes

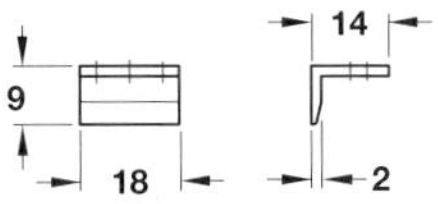

Finish: brass

Cat. No.		
	nickel-plated	251.60.703
	polished	251.60.007

Packing: 100 pcs.

Dimensional data not binding. We reserve the right to alter specifications without notice.

HÄFELE

Furniture Bolts

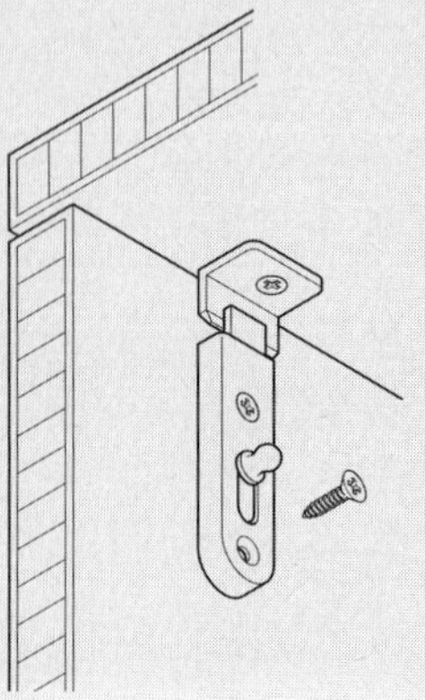

2 Locks, Catches, RTA and PAS® Fittings
Shelf Supports
Bed Fittings

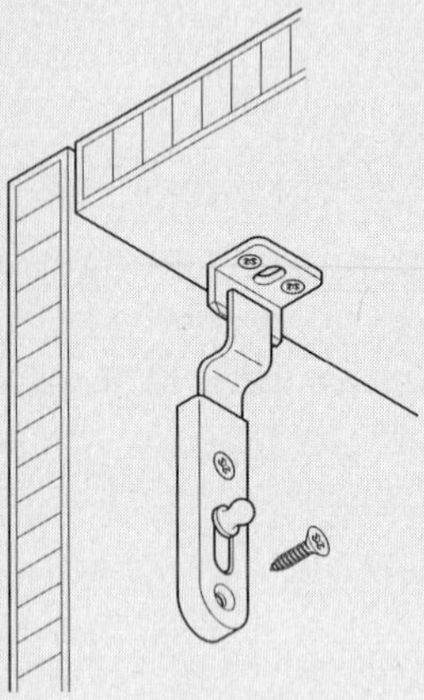

Mounting screws:
Hospa screws
Countersunk
Cross-slot PZ 1
Finish: steel, yellow chromatized

Length	Cat. No.
16 mm	015.35.253

Finish: steel, yellow chromatized

Length	Cat. No.
16 mm	015.33.259

Packing: 1000 Pcs.

- Strikes can be found on catalog page **2.89**.

Dimensional data not binding. We reserve the right to alter specifications without notice.

Furniture Bolt With Straight Slide
Screw-mounted

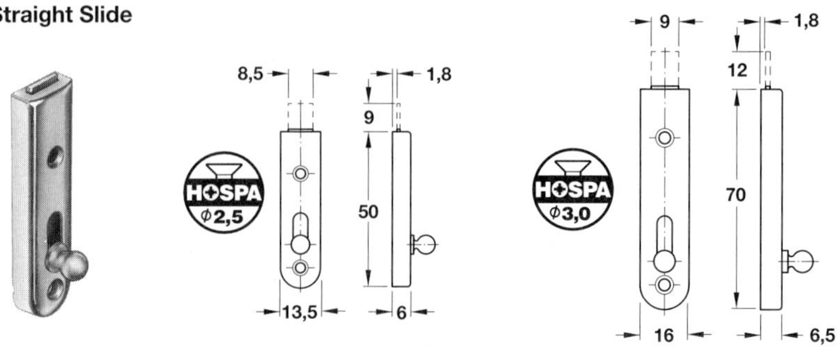

Finish: steel

Cat. No.	nickel-plated	251.01.106	251.01.124
	brass-plated	251.01.008	251.01.026

Packing: 250 pcs.

Furniture Bolt With Straight Slide
Screw-mounted

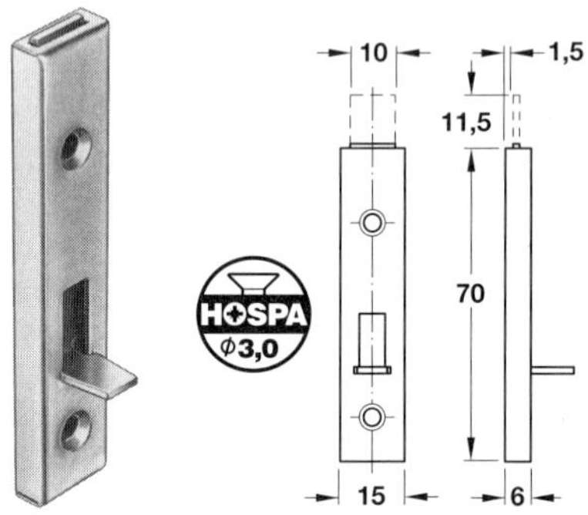

Finish: steel

Cat. No.	nickel-plated	251.10.703
	brass-plated	251.10.507

Packing: 100 pcs.

Straight, Press-fit

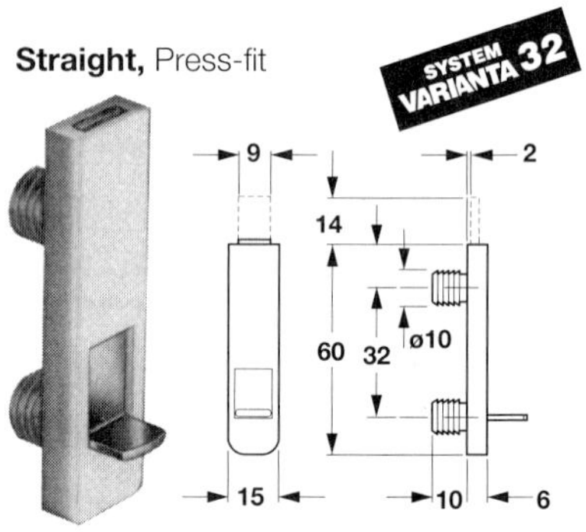

Finish: plastic, spring and slide metal

white	251.53.119
brown	251.53.717

Furniture Bolt With Cranked Slide
Screw-mounted

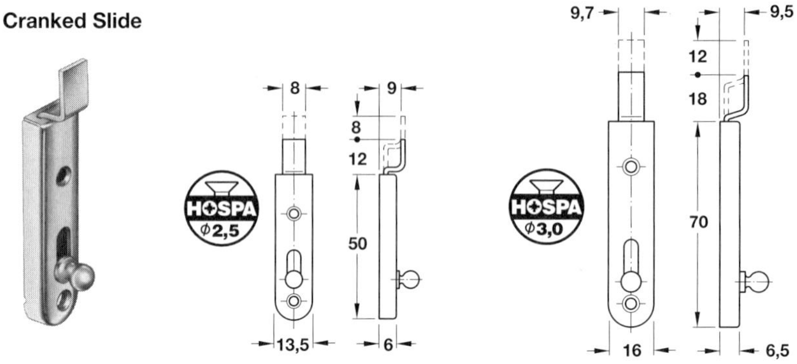

Finish: steel

Cat. No.	nickel-plated	251.02.103	251.02.121
	brass-plated	251.02.005	251.02.023

Packing: 250 pcs.

Furniture Bolt,
screw-mounted, plastic,

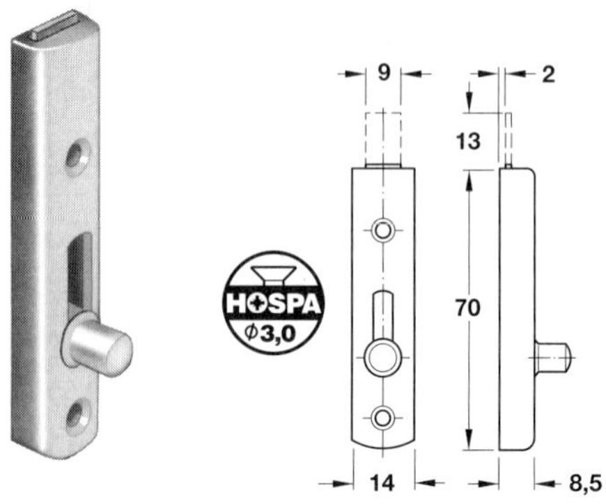

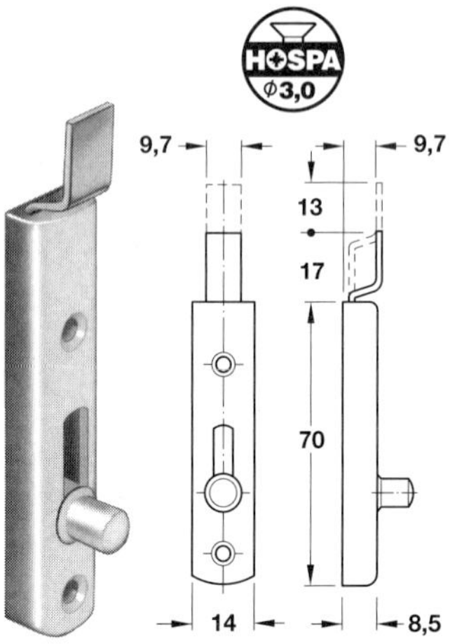

Finish: plastic base
metal slide and spring

Sliding Bar		straight	cranked
Cat. No.	white	251.50.207	251.51.204
	brown	251.50.109	251.51.106

Packing: 250 pcs.

Dimensions in mm

Flush, Barrel and Tower Bolts

Furniture Bolt
for flush mounting in door edge.
Straight.

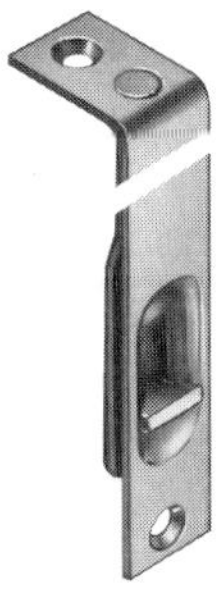

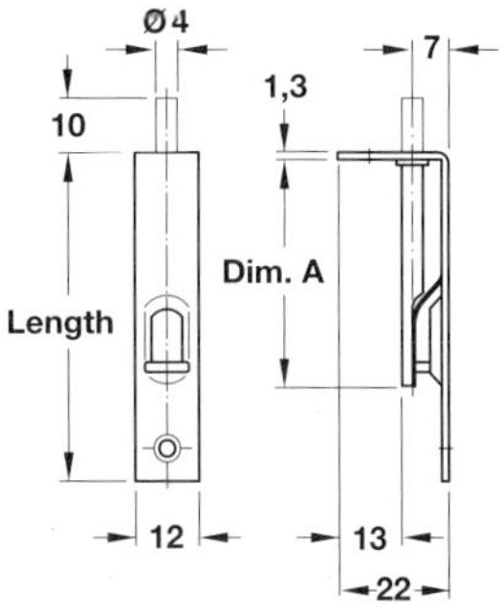

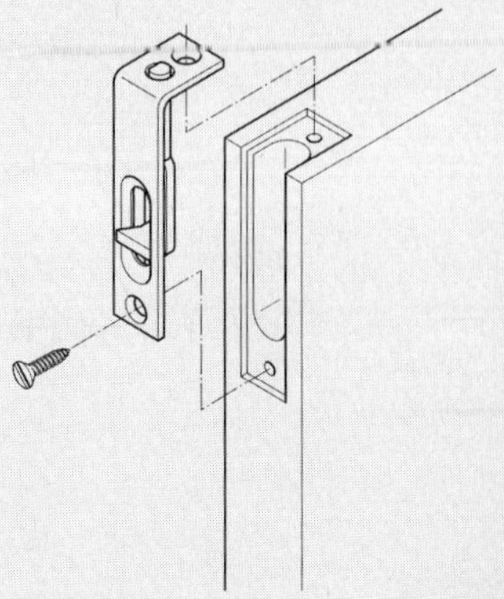

Finish: steel, yellow chromated

Length (mm)	**60**	**80**
Dimension A (mm)	41 (31)	61 (51)
Cat. No.	253.00.314	253.00.332

Packing: 20 pcs.

Barrel bolt, screw-mounted
Brass.
Straight.

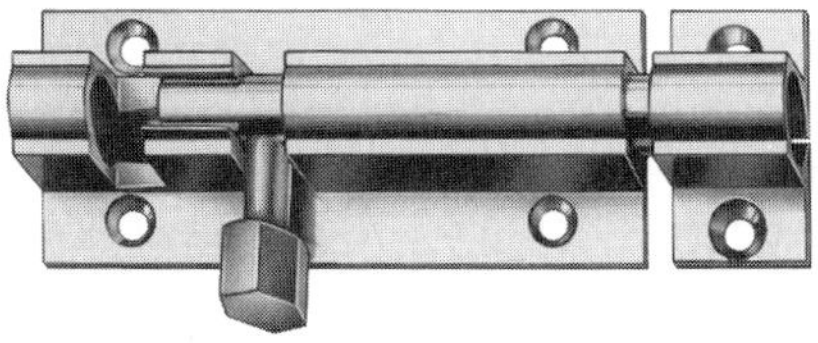

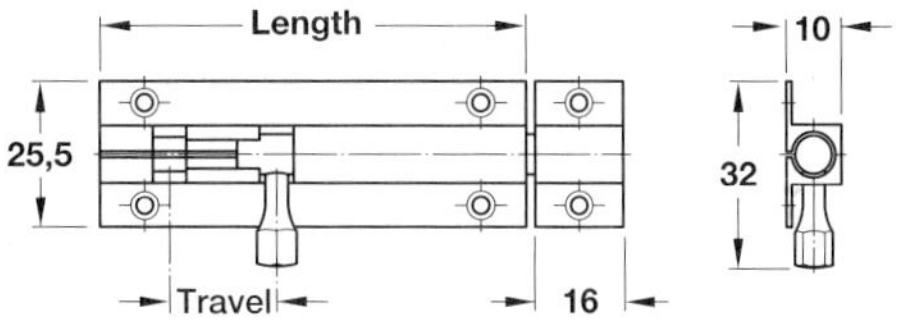

Finish: profiled brass, chrome-plated

Travel (mm)	10	14	22
Length (mm)	**40**	**60**	**80**
Cat. No.	252.70.713	252.70.722	252.70.731

Packing: 10 pcs.

Tower bolt, screw-mounted
spring-loaded.
Straight.

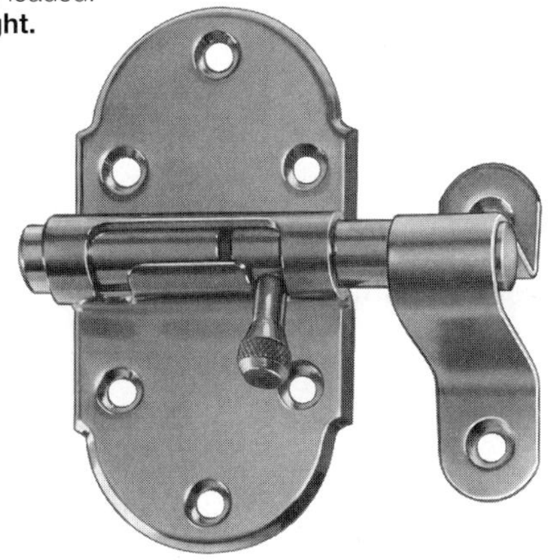

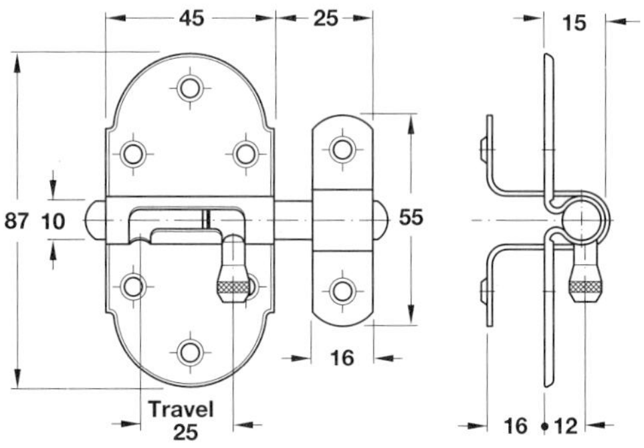

Finish: steel, nickel-plated polished

Cat. No.	252.72.708

Packing: 10 pcs.

Flush door bolt,
screw-mounted

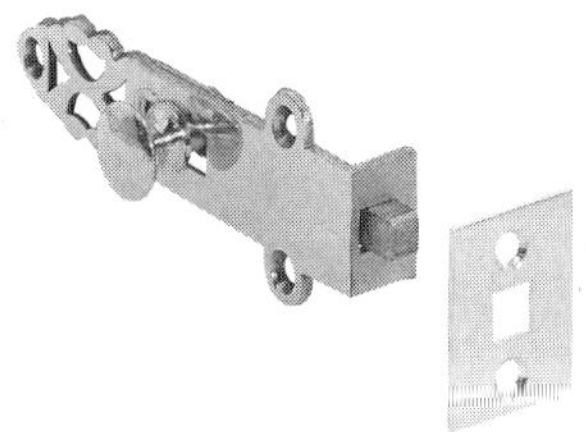

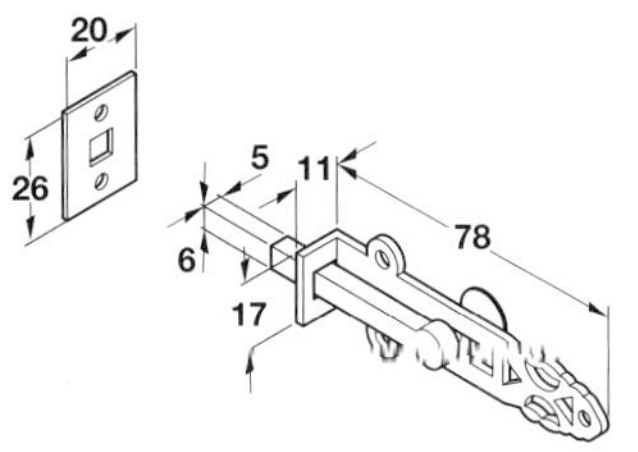

Finish: brass

Cat. No.	polished and lacquered	252.75.816
	antique	252.75.110

Packing: 10 pcs.

Mounting screws:
Hospa particle board screws with **countersunk head** and cross-slot PZ 1
Finish:
yellow chromatized

HOSPA Φ2,5

Length	Cat. No.
16 mm	015.33.259

Packing: 1000 pcs.

Mounting screws:
Hospa particle board screws with **countersunk* head** and cross-slot PZ 1
Finish:
steel, nickel-plated

HOSPA Φ3,0

Length	Cat. No.
15 mm	015.35.333

Packing: 1000 pcs.
*Small head: Ø 5 mm

Mounting screws:
Hospa particle board screws **raised head screw** with cross-slot head PZ 2
Finish:
steel, nickel-plated

HOSPA Φ3,5

Length	Cat. No.
15 mm	015.55.639
17 mm	015.55.648
20 mm	015.55.657

Packing: 1000 pcs.

Dimensions in mm

HÄFELE

Minifix Precision Assembly System®

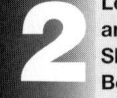

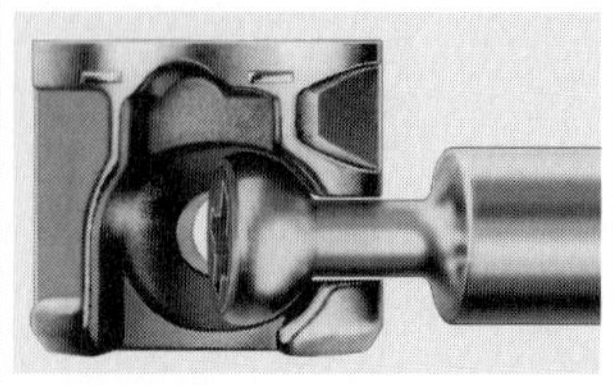

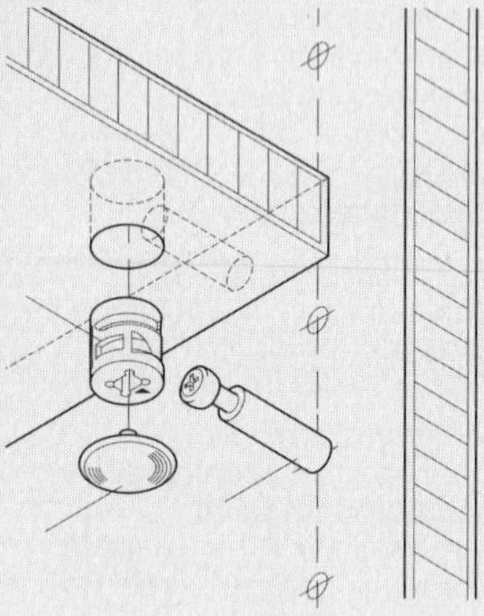

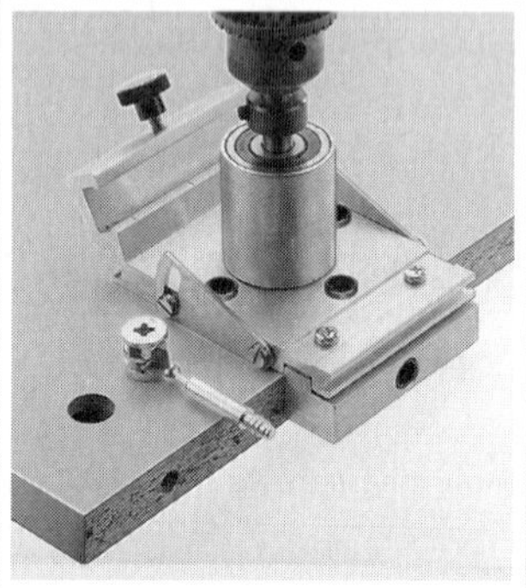

Contents

Minifix Precision Assembly Systems

»Minifix« centric sphere furniture connectors

Minifix fittings offer definite advantages:

The half round connecting bolt head locates centrally in the cup-shaped cam recess from any angle and is then positively secured. See sectional drawings in left-hand column.

- automatic centering of the bolt means that shelves are no longer subject to lateral displacement relative to the side panel;
- long tightening distance of more than 5 mm by only half a turn of cam;
- long tightening distance for increased tolerances compensation;
- secure tightening is guaranteed even in case of repeated disassembly and re-assembly;
- tight joint secure against loosening
- delicate and elegant shape.

Minifix 15 cams in **zinc die-cast**, for wood thicknesses from **16 mm,** incorporating the necessary tightening element, can be locked with any of the following:

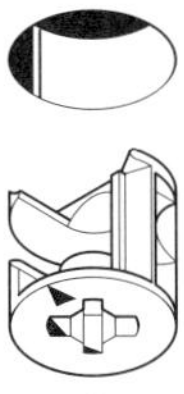

The cam must be installed with the arrow pointing directly towards the bolt.

Cross-slot screwdriver, size 2 or 3

Flat-blade screwdriver, size 6 x 1,5

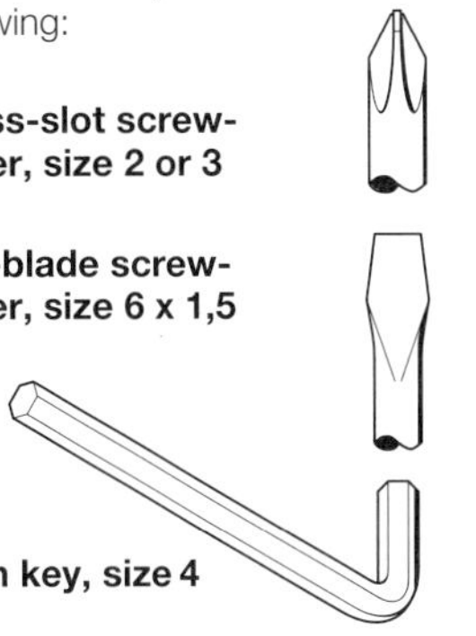

Allen key, size 4

For wood thicknesses from **12 mm** use cross-slot screwdriver size 2 only, for wood thicknesses **13 and 15 mm,** flat-blade screwdriver can be used.

Plastic Minifix 15 cams feature a single slot and can be locked with a large-blade screwdriver, a key or a coin.

The »Minifix clockface« below demonstrates correct tightening:

The long tightening distance **A** of appr. **5,7 mm** produced by only one half turn of the cam offers the following benefits:

- Variations in hole size of +1 mm to appr -0,5 mm are compensated for without loss of efficiency.
- Tension is rapidly achieved as the cam is tightened, before the arrow reaches the 195° stop (12:30).

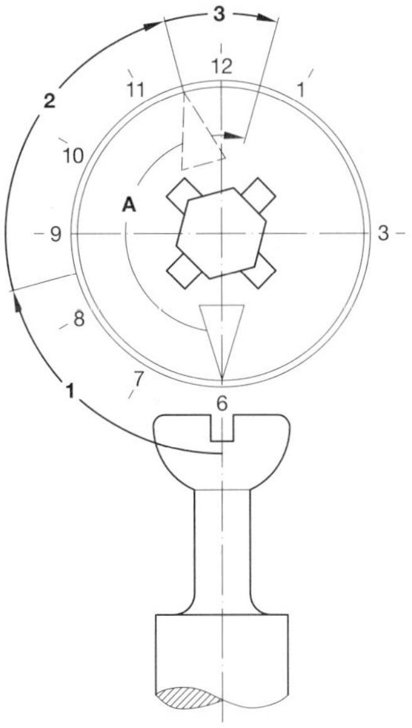

The tightening distance **A** can be separated into **3 travel segments** with different functions namely:

1. Closing distance:
0° - 75° (6 to 8:30) = **3,2 mm** pull.
This turn is necessary to draw the bolt head into the center of the cam (no tightening occurs within this segment).

2. Tightening distance:
75° - 165° (8:30 to 11:30) = **2 mm** pull.
This segment is sufficient to ensure rigid tensioning. Provided the specified drill-hole size has been met, tightening will be initiated as early as 120°C (10 o'clock). Optimum security will be reached at 165° (11.30).

3. Retightening distance:
165° - 195° (11:30 to 12:30) = **0,5 mm** pull is required:
• To accommodate variations in drill-hole size or if the furniture is assembled and disassembled repeatedly or requires retightening due to severe loading conditions.

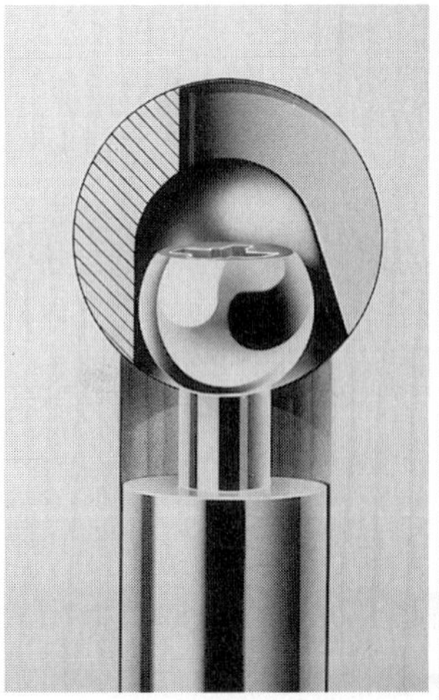

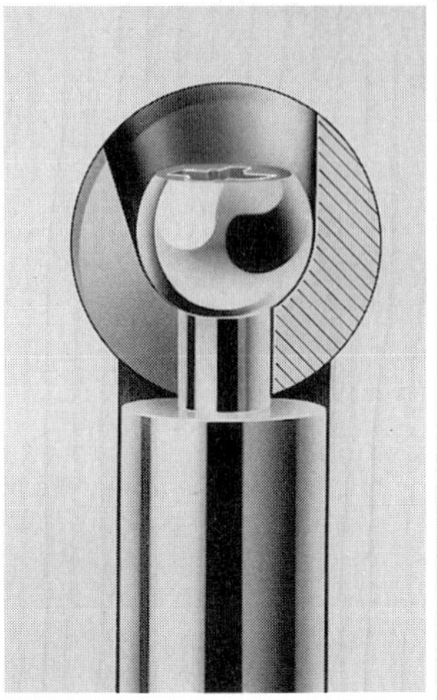

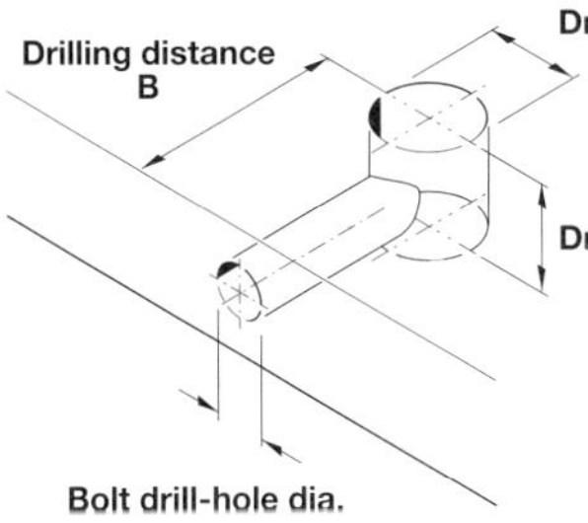

Important:

Drill-hole dia. = depend. on cam type (**dia. 15, 12 and 10 mm**), see the following Minifix cam pages

Drilling depth = depend. on cam type and wood thickness **12, 13, 16, 19, 23** and **29 mm** (see details in ordering tables of the Minifix cam pages)

Drilling distance B = choice between **B 24** (24 mm), **B 34** (34 mm) and **B 16** (16 mm), distance between drill-hole center to panel front edge

Bolt drill-hole dia. = drill-hole in panel edge for the connecting bolt **dia. 5 mm, 7 mm** or **8 mm**

Dimensional data not binding.
We reserve the right to alter specifications without notice.

Dimensions in mm

HÄFELE

Minifix P.A.S.®

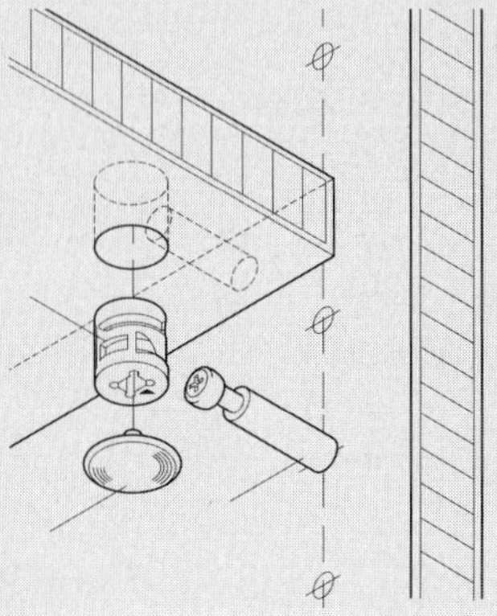

There is a wide range of cams to choose from, including **zinc die-cast** in unfinished, chromated, nickel-plated and black finishes, with or without flanged rims. Or in **plastic** with or without flanged rims in white, beige, brown and black finishes.

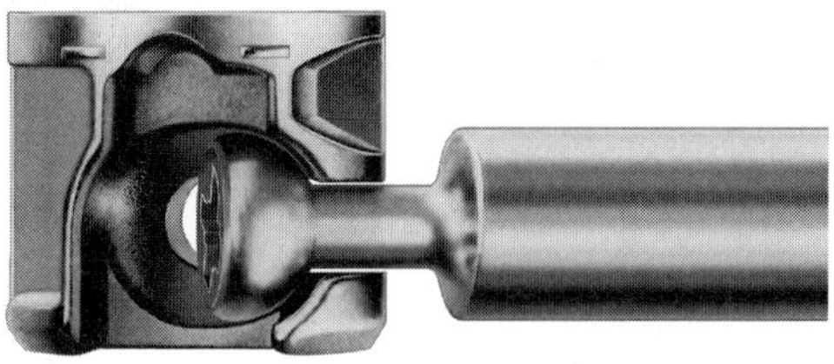

For every application, there is a suitable Minifix cam. Choose between **dia. 15** and **dia. 12 mm**.

Cams are available for wood thicknesses of **12, 13, 16, 19, 23 and 29 mm** ensuring that the connecting bolt is centered in the shelf in any application.

The cams are complemented by a complete line of connecting bolts, sleeves and dowels to solve any fastening problem.

Even complicated miter-joints can be constructed using specially developed miter-joint connectors.

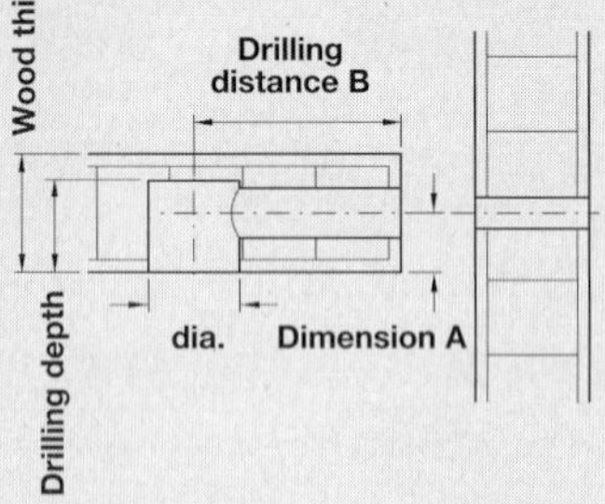

Some typical Minifix 15 and 12 mounting examples for single and double-sided installations:

Direct installation of connecting bolt for dia. 3 or dia. 5 mm holes

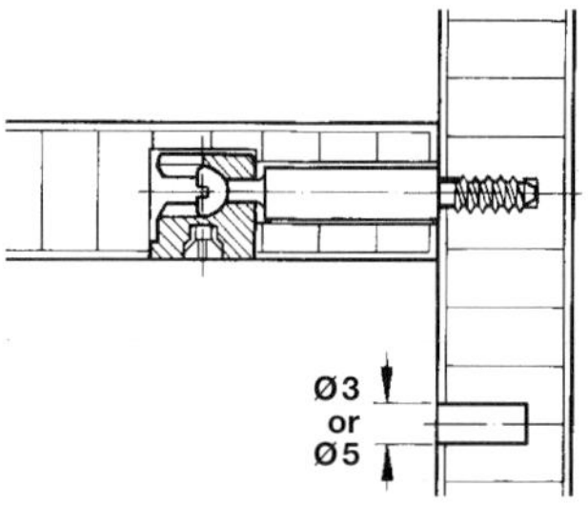

Connecting bolt with M4 thread for screw-mounting into sleeves or dowels, for dia. 5 mm holes

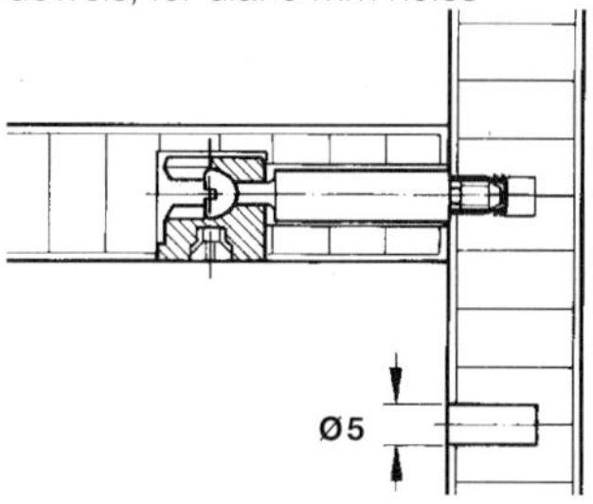

Connecting bolt with M6 thread for screw-mounting into sleeves or dowels for dia. 8 or 10 mm holes

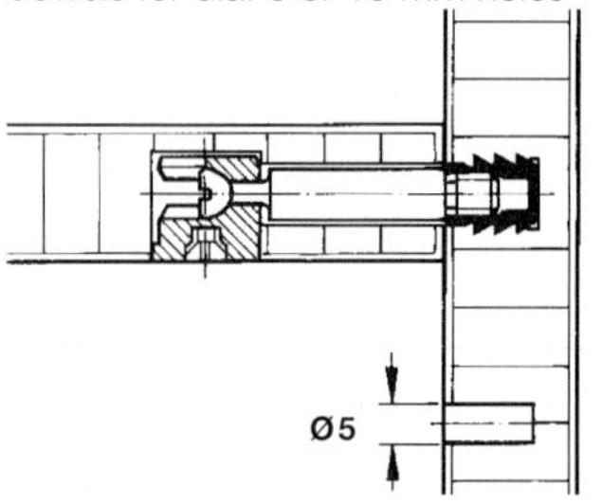

Press-fitting of connecting bolt with plastic-coated sleeve for dia. 5 or dia. 8 mm holes

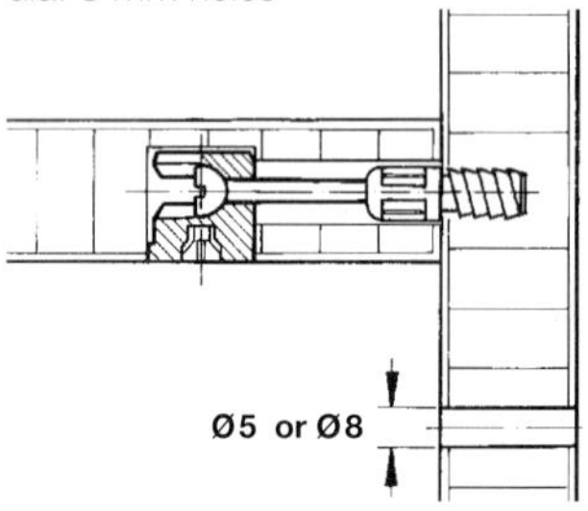

Installation of connecting bolt with M4 thread in sleeve with end screw for dia. 5 mm holes . . .

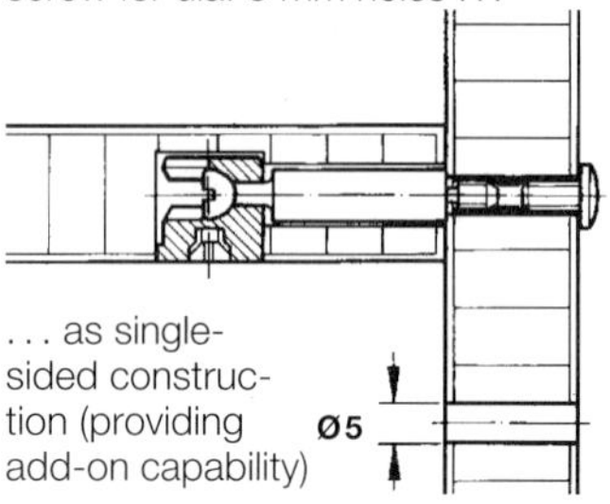

. . . as single-sided construction (providing add-on capability)

Insertion of capped bolt for dia. 8 mm holes as single-sided construction

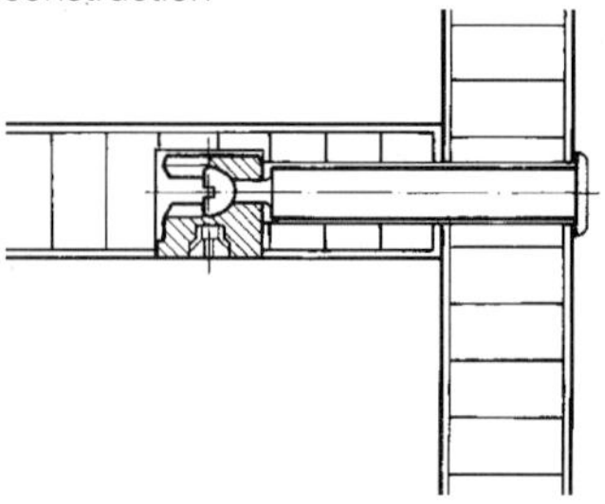

Double-sided construction by installation of connecting bolt through dia. 5 mm holes (shelf and side panel)

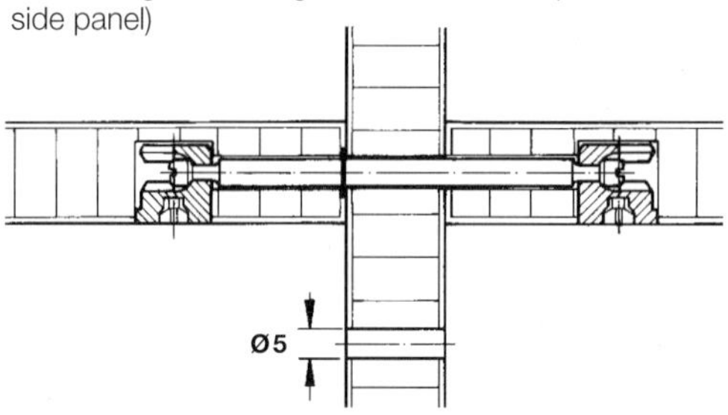

Double-sided construction by installation of 2 connecting bolts with M4 thread in sleeves in dia. 5 mm hole

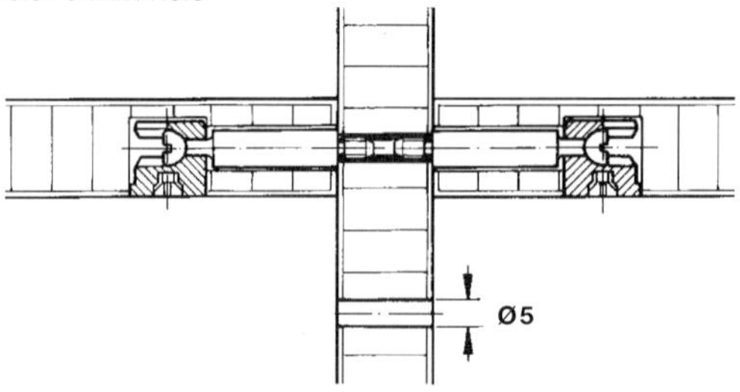

Now there is a fitting for mitered joints - the new Minifix GV mitered joint connector, for any angle from 30° to 180° - see page **2.104**.

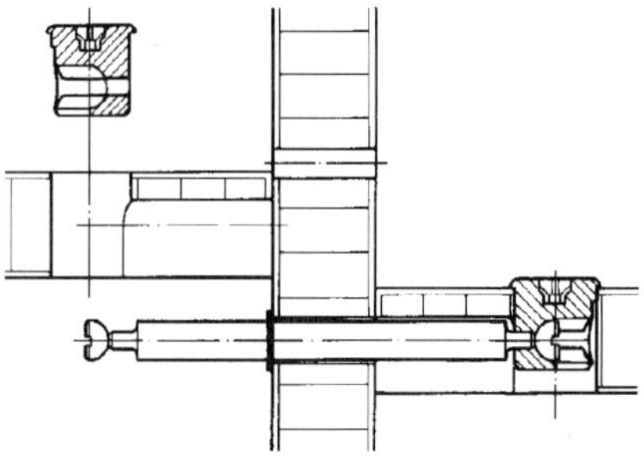

With their recessed bases, Minifix 15 cams (with or without rim flange) can be used in a variety of ways and are easy to install. Thus the lower shelf can be mounted with the cam inverted, if the cam hole and bolt recess are made as shown in the adjoining example.

Dimensional data not binding. We reserve the right to alter specifications without notice.

Dimensions in mm

Minifix 12 Cams

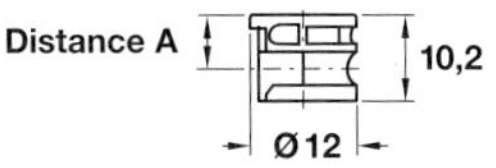

Minifix 12 cam
in zinc die-cast without flanged

Wood thickness from:	Distance A Center locking pos.	Drilling depth	Cat. No. unfinished	nickel-plated	black
12 mm	6,0 mm	10,2 $^{+0,2}$ mm	262.17.014	262.17.710	262.17.318

Packing: 1000 pcs.

All the connecting bolts illustrated on pages **2.98 to 2.104** and **2.107** can be used with these zinc die-cast cams.

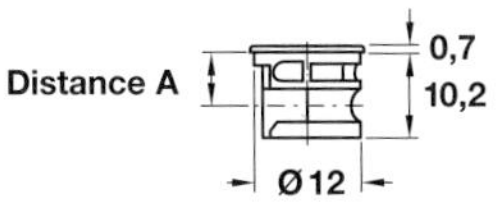

Minifix 12 cam
in zinc die-cast with flanged rim

Wood thickness from:	Distance A Center locking pos.	Drilling depth	Cat. No. unfinished	nickel-plated	black
12 mm	6,0 mm	10,2 $^{+0,2}$ mm	262.18.011	262.18.717	262.18.315

Packing: 1000 pcs.

These zinc die-cast Minifix cams can only be locked with the **cross-slot screwdriver size 2**

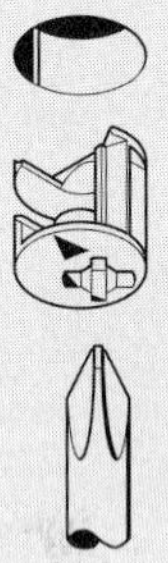

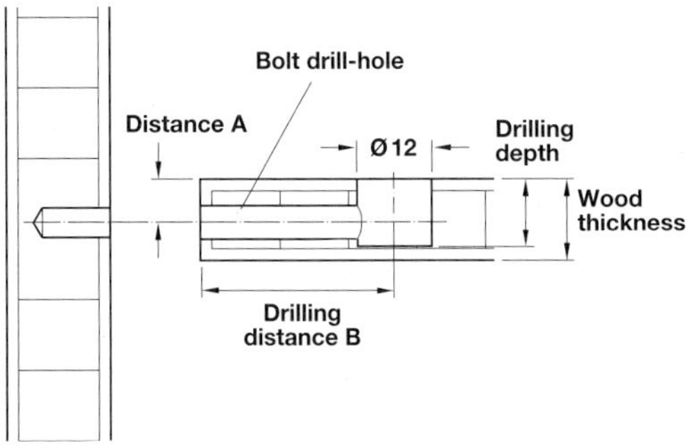

Bolt drill-hole = **dia. 5** or **8 mm** depending on choice of connecting bolt

Drill-hole dia. = **12 mm**

Drilling depth = 10,2 mm for both cams

Distance A = 1/2 wood thickness (6 mm)

Drill. distance B = choice between **B 24** (24 mm) or **B 34** (34 mm), distance between drill-hole center and front panel

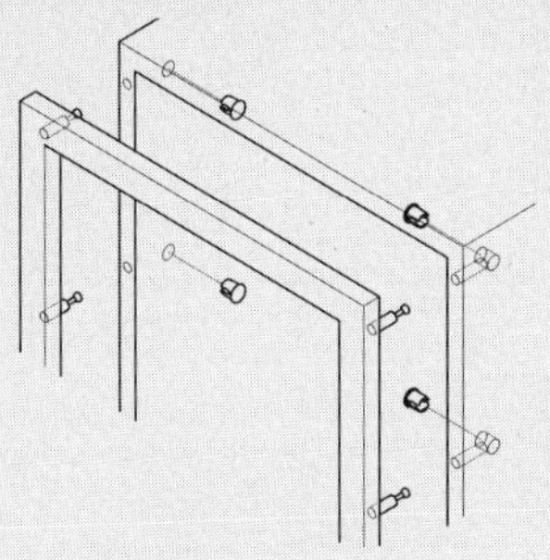

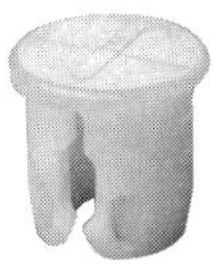

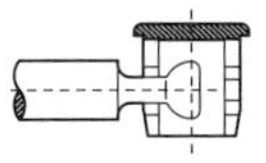

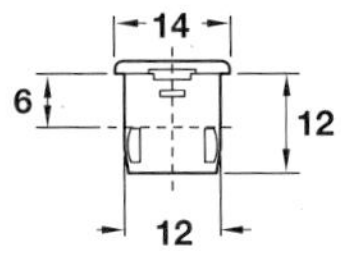

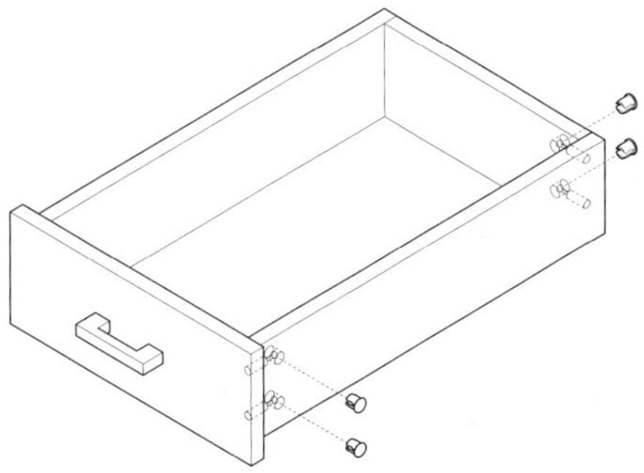

Minifix 12 plastic with "snap" feature

For 12mm diameter holes.

Wood thickness from:	Distance A Center locking pos.	Drilling depth	Cat. No. white	beige	brown	black
12 mm	6,0 mm	12.0 $^{+0,2}$ mm	262.14.700	262.14.400	262.14.100	262.14.300

Packing: 5000 pcs.

- Snaps over the bolt with the push of a finger
- No tools needed to engage cam to bolt
- For light-duty connections
- Releasable cam with flat-blade screwdriver
- For multiple use

Dimensional data not binding. We reserve the right to alter specifications without notice.

Dimensions in mm

HÄFELE

Minifix 15 Cams

All the connecting bolts illustrated on pages **2.98 to 2.104** and **2.107** can be used with these zinc die-cast cams.

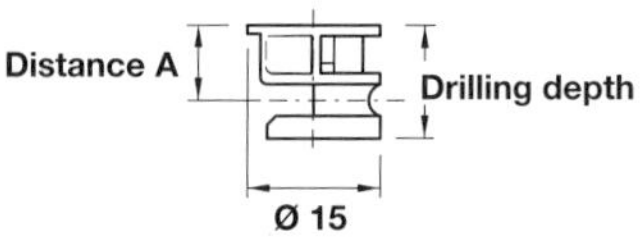

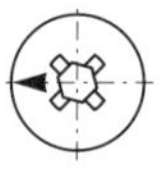

Minifix 15 cam
in **zinc die-cast** without flanged rim

Wood thickness from:	Distance A Center locking pos.	Drilling depth	Cat. No. unfinished	nickel-plated	black
13 mm	6.5 mm	11.0 +0.2 mm	262.26.237	262.26.639	262.26.835
16 mm	8.0 mm	12.5 +0.5 mm	262.26.219	262.26.611	262.26.817
19 mm	9.5 mm	14.5 +0.5 mm	262.26.228	262.26.620	262.26.826
23 mm	11.5 mm	16.5 +0.5 mm	262.26.264	262.26.666	262.26.862
29 mm	14.5 mm	19.5 +0.5 mm	262.26.291	262.26.693	262.26.899

Packing: 1000 pcs.

2 Locks, Catches, RTA and PAS® Fittings Shelf Supports Bed Fittings

For *allen key size 4 mm
For cross-slot screw-driver no. 2 and 3
For flat-blade screwdrivers 6 x 1.5

* Except **12 mm** and **13 mm** cams, do not accept allen key.

For Minifix cams without flanged rims and wood thicknesses **13 and 15 mm**

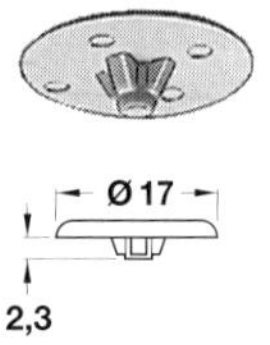

Trim cap, plastic

Cat. No.		
	white	262.24.760
	pine	262.24.064
	brown	262.24.162
	black	262.24.368

Packing: 500

Non-standard colors available minimum order 100,000

For Minifix cams without flanged rims and wood thicknesses **16, 18, 19, 23 and 29 mm**

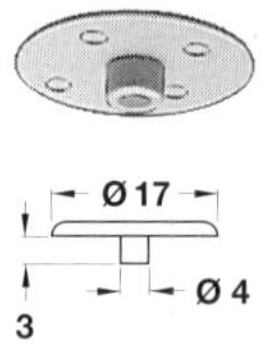

Trim cap, plastic

Cat. No.		
	white	262.24.751
	pine	262.24.055
	brown	262.24.153
	black	262.24.359
	gray	262.24.525

Packing: 500

Non-standard colors available minimum order 100,000

All three corners can be used for tightening.

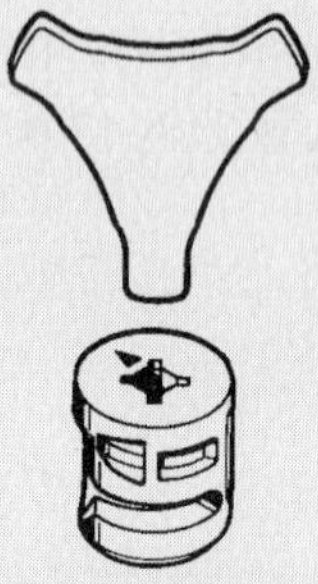

Tightening key. Finish: steel, for Minifix cams in zinc die-cast

Cat. No.	006.36.911

Packing: 100

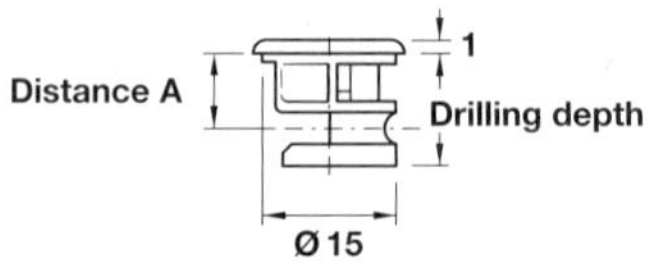

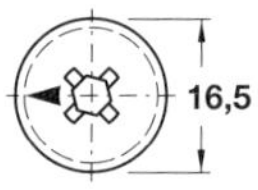

Minifix 15 cam
in **zinc die-cast** with flanged

Wood thickness from:	Distance A Center locking pos.	Drilling depth	Cat. No. unfinished	nickel-plated	black
16 mm	8.0 mm	12.5 +0.5 mm	262.25.212	262.25.614	262.25.810
19 mm	9.5 mm	14.5 +0.5 mm	262.25.221	262.25.623	262.25.829
23 mm	11.5 mm	16.5 +0.5 mm	262.25.267	262.25.669	262.25.865
29 mm	14.5 mm	19.5 +0.5 mm	262.25.294	262.25.696	262.25.892

Packing: 1000 pcs.

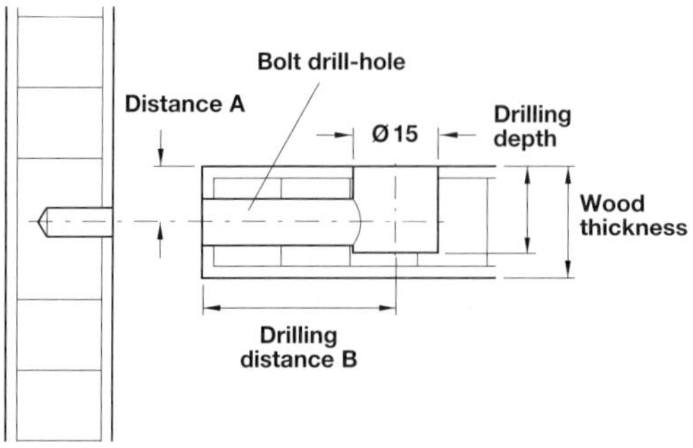

Bolt drill-hole = **dia. 5** or **8 mm** depending on choice of connecting bolt

Drill-hole dia. = depending on cam type and wood thickness (see ordering table)

Distance A = 1/2 wood thickness (see ordering table)

Drill. distance B = choice between **B 24** (24 mm) or **B 34** (34 mm), distance between hole center and front panel

Dimensional data not binding. We reserve the right to alter specifications without notice.

Minifix 15 Cams

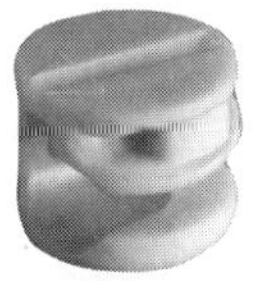

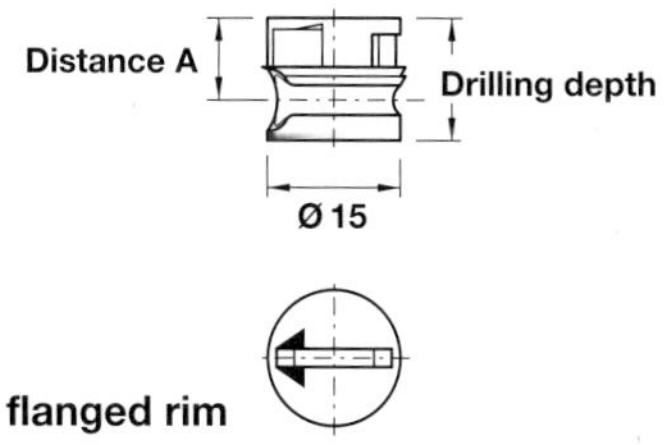

Minifix 15 cam
in plastic without flanged rim

Wood thickness from:	Distance A Center locking pos.	Drilling depth	Cat. No. white	beige	dark brown	light brown	black
16 mm	8,0 mm	12,5 +0,2 mm	262.16.704	262.16.419	262.16.106	262.16.115	262.16.302

Packing: 1000 pcs.

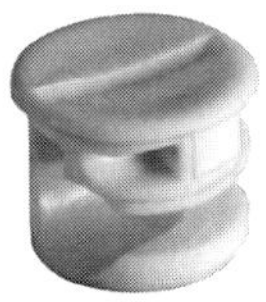

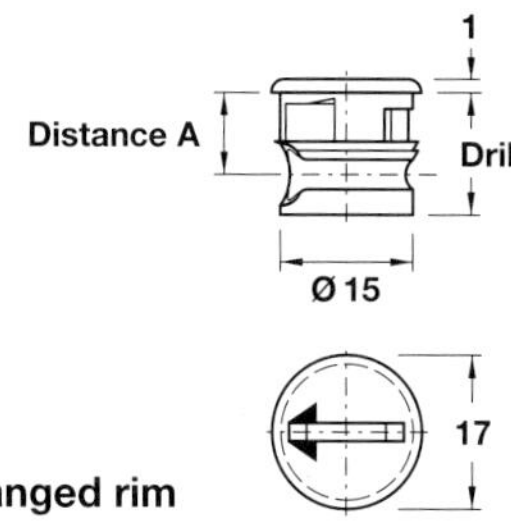

Minifix 15 cam
in plastic with flanged rim

Wood thickness from:	Distance A Center locking pos.	Drilling depth	Cat. No. white	beige	brown	black
16 mm	8,0 mm	12,5 +0,2 mm	262.16.759	262.16.464	262.16.151	262.16.357

Packing: 1000 pcs.

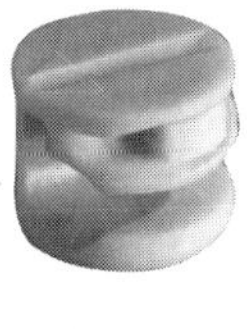

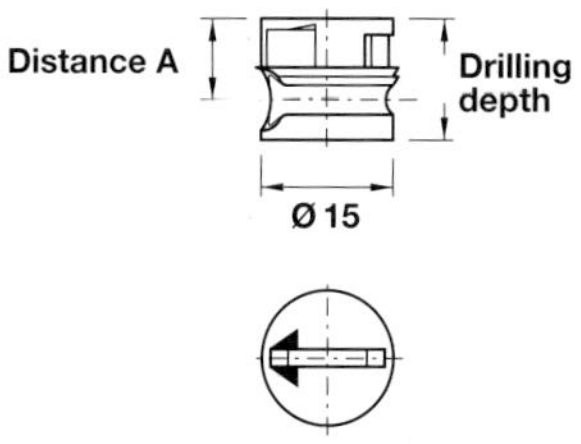

Minifix 15 cam
Plastic Clip
without flanged rim

When inserted, the bolt head **clips** into the cam. This holds the furniture sections in place until the fitting has been tightened.

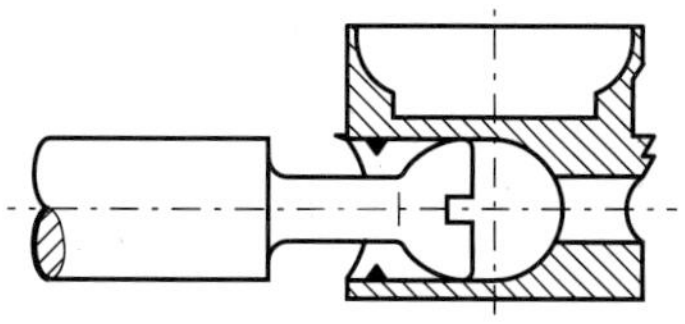

Wood thickness from:	Distance A Center locking pos.	Drilling depth	Cat. No. white	beige	brown	black
16 mm	8,0 mm	12,5 +0,2 mm	262.16.731	262.16.437	262.16.133	262.16.339

Packing: 1000 pcs.

All the connecting bolts illustrated on pages **2.98 - 2.104** can be used with these zinc die-cast cams.

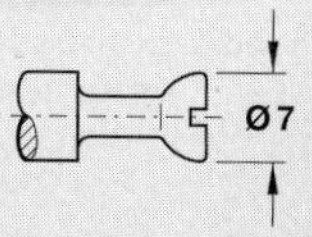

Locks, Catches, RTA and PAS® Fittings
Shelf Supports
Bed Fittings
2

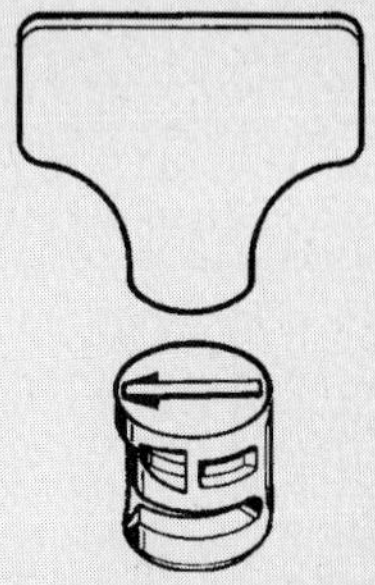

Tightening key. Finish: steel, for Minifix cams in plastic

Cat. No.	006.36.902

Packing: 100 pcs.

Variantool-N series drilling jig is an ideal addition to the Unitool drilling jig. For drilling hole lines or groups of holes; see page **0.12**

Unitool drilling jig for precision drilling for the **Minifix-12** and **Minifix-15** ranges of RTA fittings in the most common wood thicknesses of **16, 19** and **23** mm and drilling distance B24 or B34 mm for drilling bolt-holes; see page **2.108**.

Dimensional data not binding.
We reserve the right to alter specifications without notice.

Dimensions in mm

HÄFELE

Minifix Connecting Bolts

Connecting bolts with

= **cross-slot**
- tightening with cross-slot screwdriver size 2 only

= **combination slot**
- tightening with cross-slot screwdriver size 2 and flat-blade screwdriver

Connecting bolts for **direct screw-mounting** and **press-fitting** in single and doubled-sided installations **in holes dia. 3 mm** (with dowels **in holes dia. 5 mm**)

Connecting bolt
Finish: steel, plastic-coated with special thread

B = Drilling distance	24 mm	34 mm
Cat. No. chromated yellow	262.27.430	262.28.437
Packing:	3000 pcs.	2000 pcs.

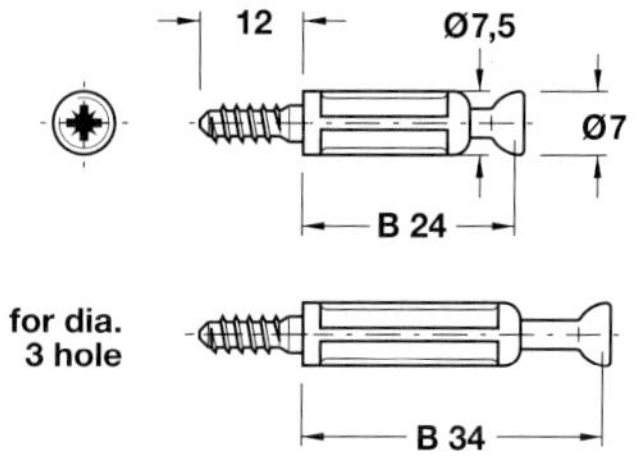

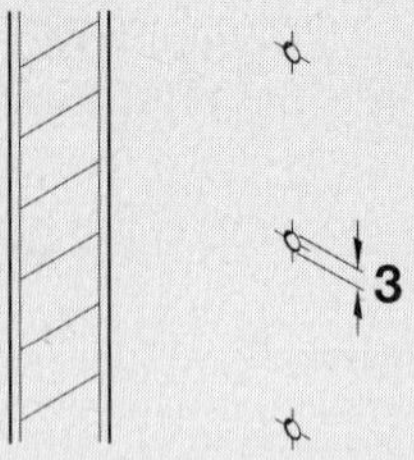

Connecting bolt
Finish: steel, with special thread

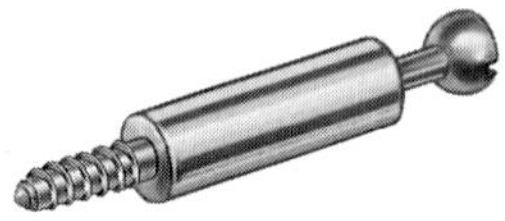

B = Drilling distance	**24 mm**	**34 mm**
Cat. No. galvanized	262.27.912	262.28.919
Packing:	2500 pcs.	2000 pcs.

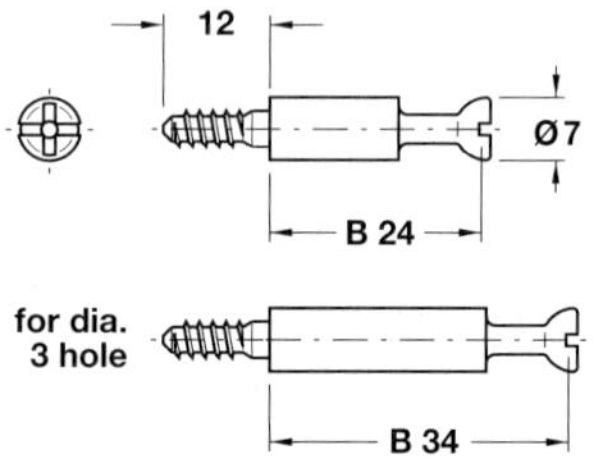

The connecting bolt illustrated above can be used together with the following . . .

Spreading dowel
Finish: Nylon, natural-colored, in **dia. 5 mm holes**

Cat. No.	042.98.051

Packing: 5000 pcs.

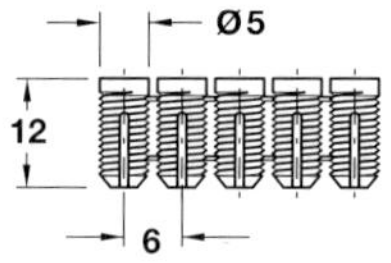

injection-moulded in sets of 20 pieces

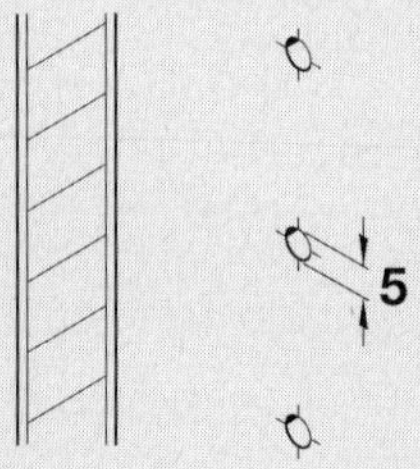

Connecting bolts for **press-fitting into dia. 5 mm holes**

Connecting bolt
Finish: steel, plastic-coated with harpoon-type thread

B = Drilling distance	**24 mm**	**34 mm**
Cat. No. unfinished	262.08.202	262.10.202
Packing:	3000 pcs.	2000 pcs.

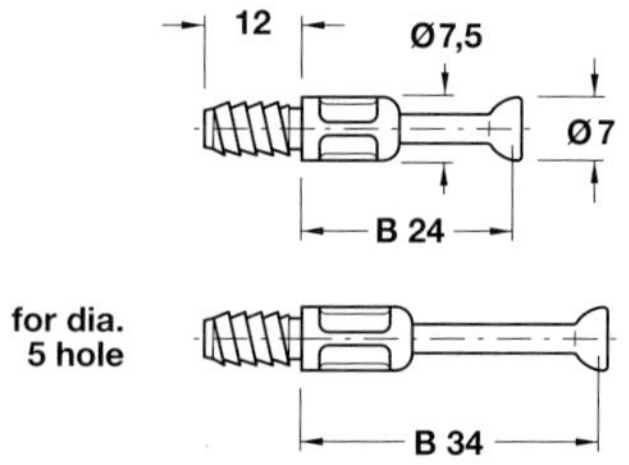

Dimensional data not binding. We reserve the right to alter specifications without notice.

Dimensions in mm

Minifix Connecting bolts

Connecting bolts, for **direct screw-mounting** in single and doubled-sided installations **in holes dia. 5 mm** (with glued dowels **in holes dia. 10 mm**)

Connecting bolt/composite

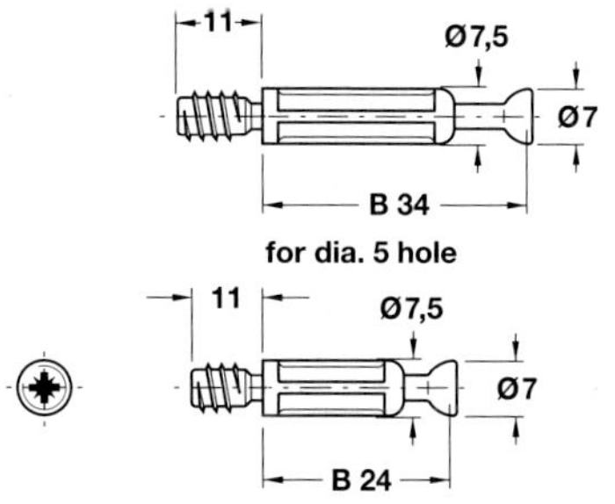

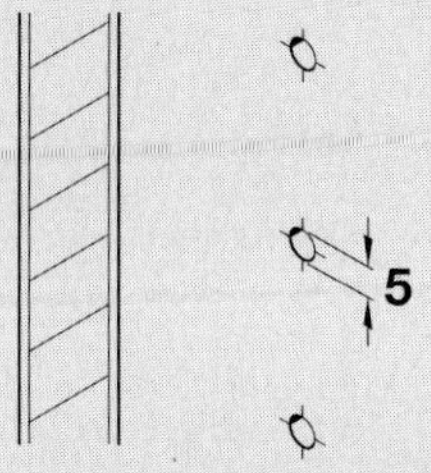

Thread length 11 mm standard
Finish: Steel, plastic-coated with special thread

B = Drilling distance	24 mm	34 mm
Cat. No. chromated yellow	262.27.449	262.28.446
Packing:	3000 pcs.	2000 pcs.

Glued dowel
The connecting bolt illustrated above can be used with the following . . .

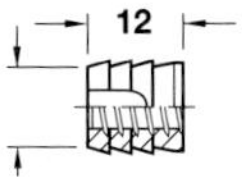

Thread length 8 mm
Finish: Plastic, with special internal speed thread in dia. 10 mm holes.

Cat. No.	039.32.050
Packing: 5000 pcs.	

Locks, Catches, RTA and PAS® Fittings
Shelf Supports
Bed Fittings
2

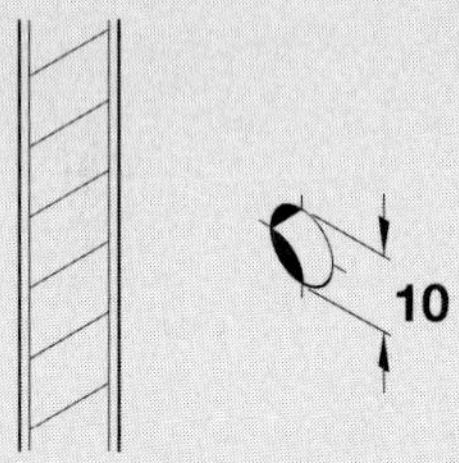

Connecting bolt/cold-formed

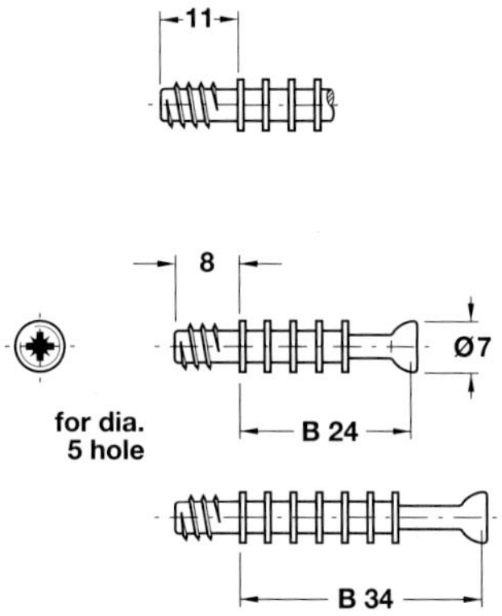

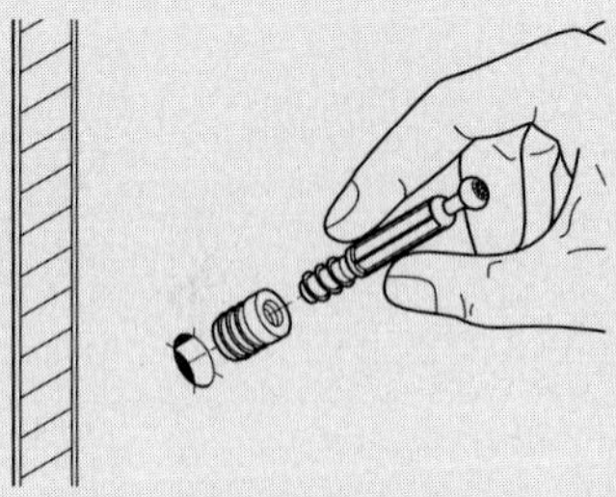

Thread length 11 mm standard

B = Drilling distance	24 mm	34 mm
Cat. No. galvanized	262.27.627	262.28.624
Packing:	2500 pcs.	2000 pcs.

Thread length 8 mm
Finish: steel, with special thread

B = Drilling distance	24 mm	34 mm
Cat. No. galvanized	0.262.27.620	0.262.28.620
Packing:	2500 pcs.	2000 pcs.

Connecting bolt/turned

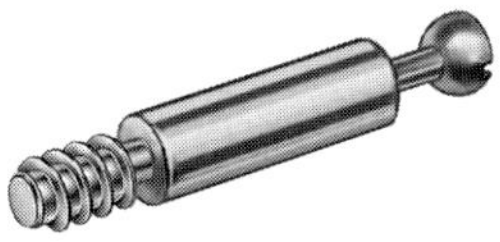

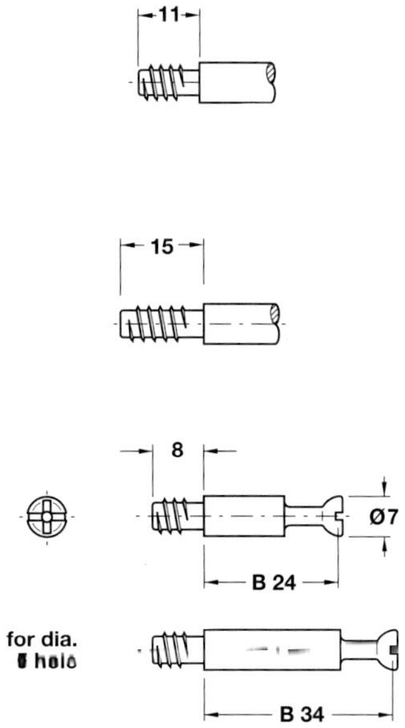

Thread length 11 mm standard
Finish: steel, with special thread

B = Drilling distance	24 mm	34 mm
Cat. No. unfinished	262.27.029	262.28.026
galvanized	262.27.921	262.28.928
Packing:	2500 pcs.	2000 pcs.

Thread length 15 mm

B = Drilling distance	24 mm	34 mm
Cat. No. galvanized	262.27.832	262.28.839
Packing:	2000 pcs.	2000 pcs.

Thread length 8 mm

B = Drilling distance	24 mm	34 mm
Cat. No. galvanized	262.27.920	262.28.920
Packing:	2500 pcs.	2000 pcs.

Connecting bolts with

- **= cross-slot**
  - tightening with cross-slot screwdriver size 2 only
- **= combination slot**
  - tightening with cross-slot screwdriver size 2 and flat-blade screwdriver

Dimensional data not binding. We reserve the right to alter specifications without notice.

Dimensions in mm

HÄFELE

Minifix Connecting Bolts

Connecting bolts with

- = **cross-slot**
  - tightening with cross-slot screwdriver size 2 only
- = **combination slot**
  - tightening with cross-slot screwdriver size 2 and flat-blade screwdriver

Connecting bolts with **M4 thread** for screw-attachment into dowels or sleeves for single or double-sided installations. Sleeves or dowels can be selected for **holes between dia. 5, dia. 8** or **dia. 10 mm**

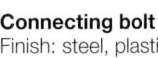

Connecting bolt
Finish: steel, plastic-coated with M4 thread

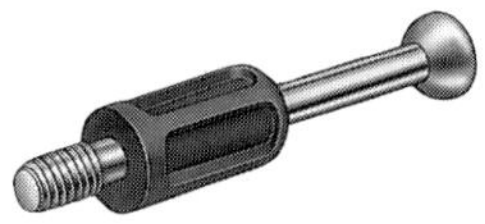

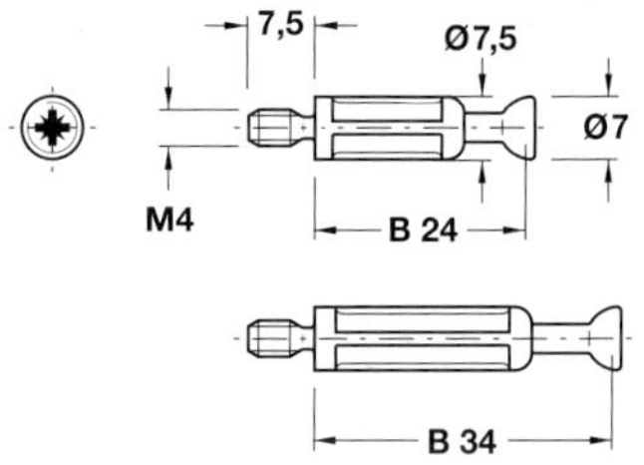

B = Drilling distance	24 mm	34 mm
Cat. No. chromated yellow	262.27.458	262.28.455

Packing: 3000 pcs. 2000 pcs.

Connecting bolt
Finish: steel, with M4 thread

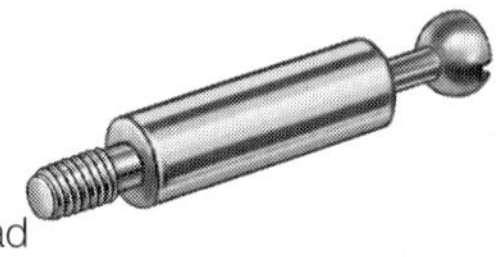

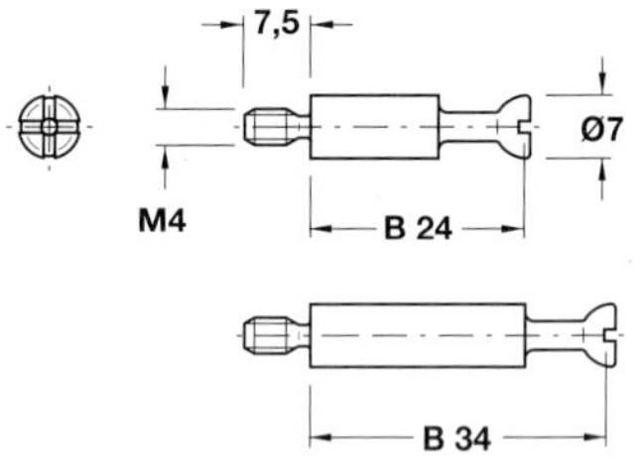

B = Drilling distance	24 mm	34 mm
Cat. No. galvanized	262.27.930	262.28.937

Packing: 1000 pcs. 2000 pcs.

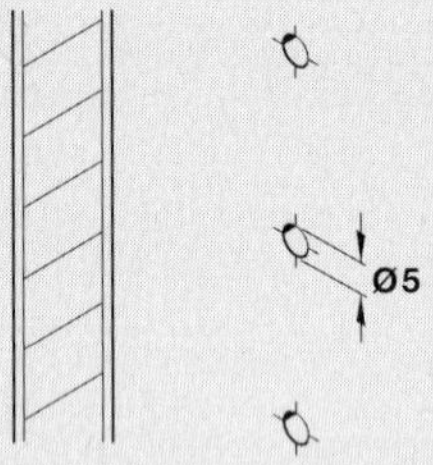

The connecting bolt illustrated above can be used with the following elements:

Spreading dowel with M4 internal thread. Finish: brass, bright

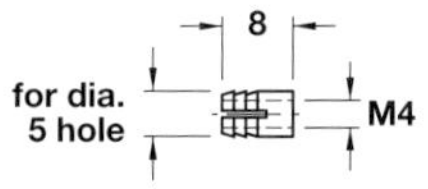

Cat. No.	051.45.004

Packing: 3000 pcs.

Sleeve, smooth, with M4 internal thread. Finish: steel, suitable for **double-sided installations**

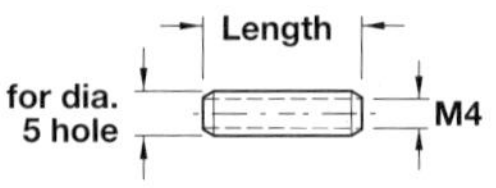

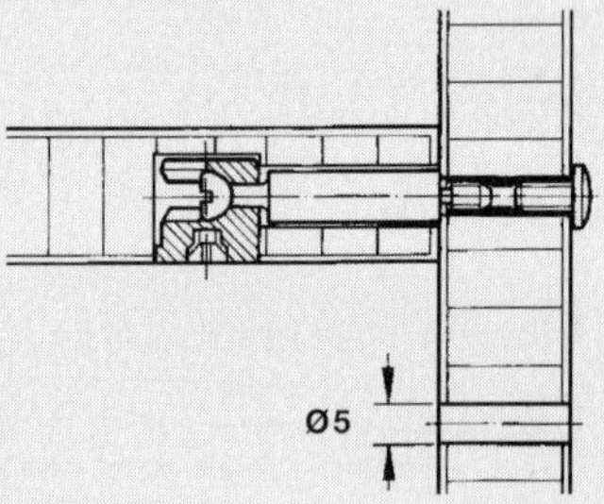

Length	15 mm	18 mm	22 mm
galvanized	267.00.911	267.00.912	267.00.913

Packing: 1000 pcs.

End screw with M4 thread
Finish: steel, can be used as **end bolt**

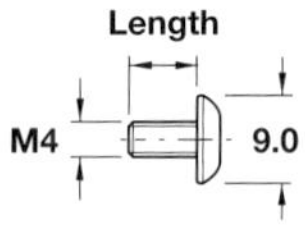

Length	8 mm	10 mm
nickel-plated	020.92.711	020.92.720
bronzed	020.92.113	020.92.122

Packing: 2000 pcs.

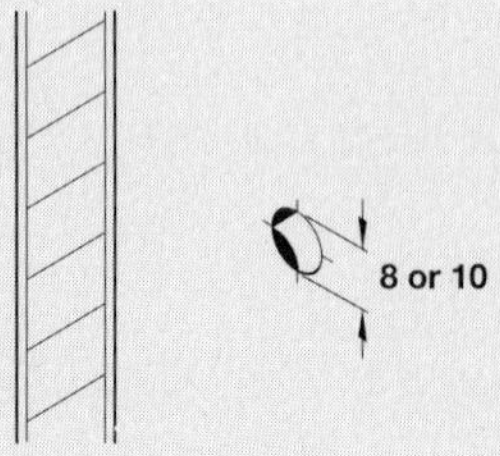

Glued dowel with M4 internal thread
Finish: nylon, natural-colored

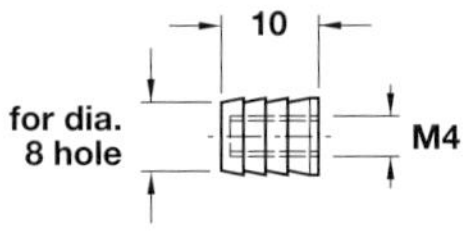

Cat. No.	039.33.042

Packing: 1000 pcs.

Minifix Connecting Bolts

HÄFELE

Connecting bolts with **M6 thread** for screw-attachment into dowels for single-sided installations.
Dowels can be selected for **holes dia. 8** or **dia. 10 mm.**

Connecting bolt, turned
Finish: steel, with M6 thread

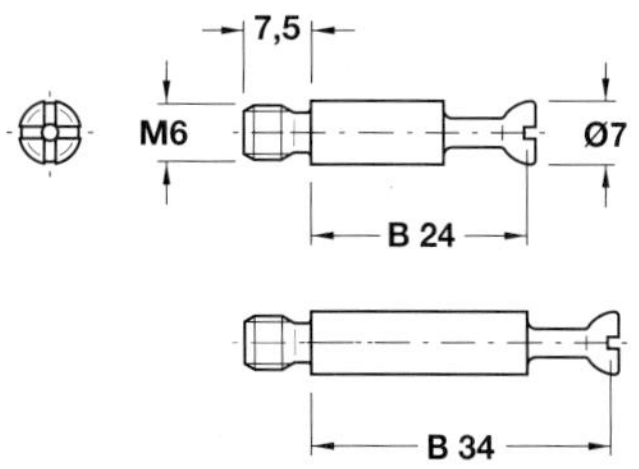

B = Drilling distance		**24 mm**	**34 mm**
Cat. No.	galvanized	262.27.949	262.28.946

Packing: 2500 pcs. 2000 pcs.

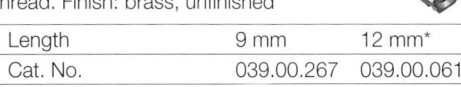

Connecting bolt, cold-formed
Finish: steel, with M6 thread

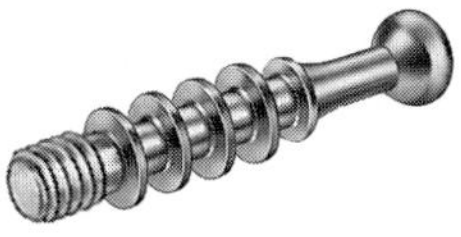

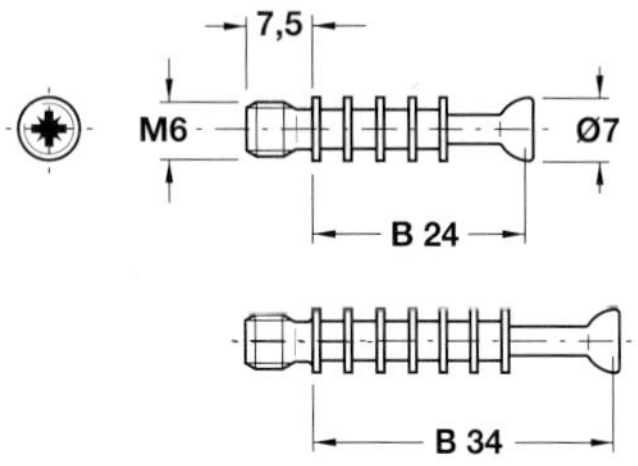

B = Drilling distance		**24 mm**	**34 mm**
Cat. No.	galvanized	262.27.645	262.28.642

Packing: 2500 pcs. 2000 pcs.

The connecting bolts illustrated above can be used with the following elements:

Spreading dowel with M6 internal thread. Finish: brass, unfinished

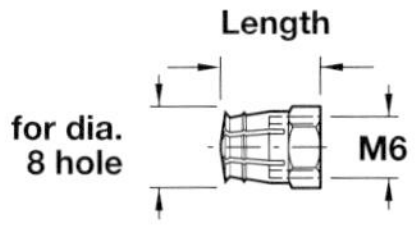

* with nylon pellet
Minimum drilling depth = 15 mm

Length	9 mm	12 mm*
Cat. No.	039.00.267	039.00.061

Packing: 2000 pcs. 1000 pcs.

Glued dowel with M6 internal thread
Finish: nylon, natural-colored

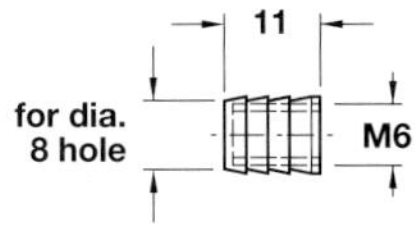

Cat. No.	039.33.462

Packing: 5000 pcs.

Glued dowel with M6 internal thread
Finish: nylon, natural-colored

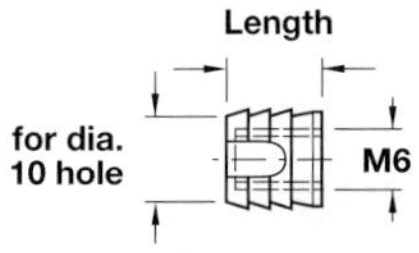

Length	9 mm	11 mm	13 mm
Cat. No.	039.33.364	039.33.266	039.33.060

Packing: 1000 pcs. 5000 pcs. 5000 pcs.

Dowel string
with M6 internal thread
Finish: nylon, natural-colored

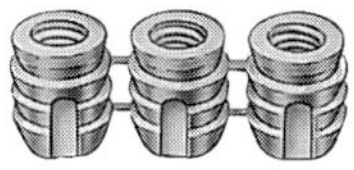

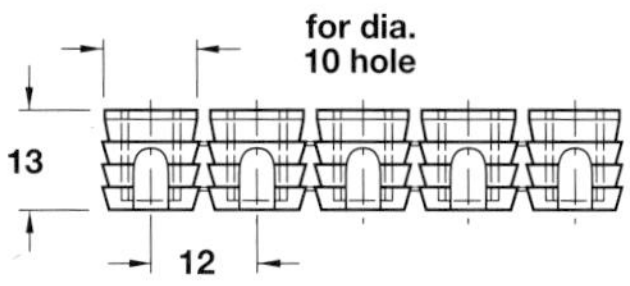

Cat. No.	039.34.067

Packing: 1000 pcs.

Connection bolts for **press-fitting** into **dia. 8 mm holes**

Connecting bolt
Finish: steel, plastic-coated,
with harpoon-type thread

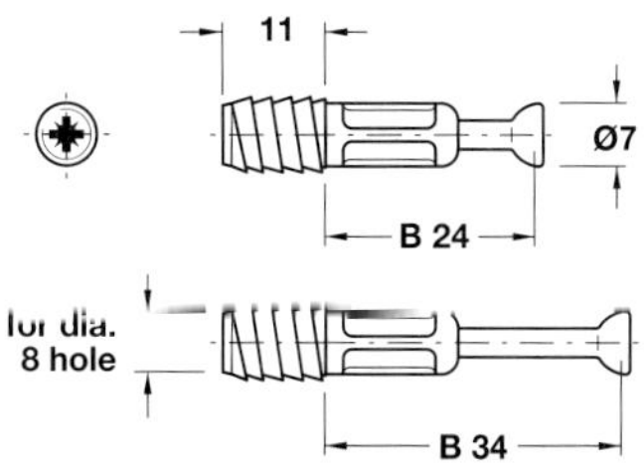

B = Drilling distance		**24 mm**	**34 mm**
Cat. No.	unfinished	262.08.300	262.10.300

Packing: 2000 pcs.

Dimensions in mm

Connecting bolts with

= **cross-slot**
- tightening with cross-slot screwdriver size 2 only

= **combination slot**
- tightening with cross-slot screwdriver size 2 and flat-blade screwdriver

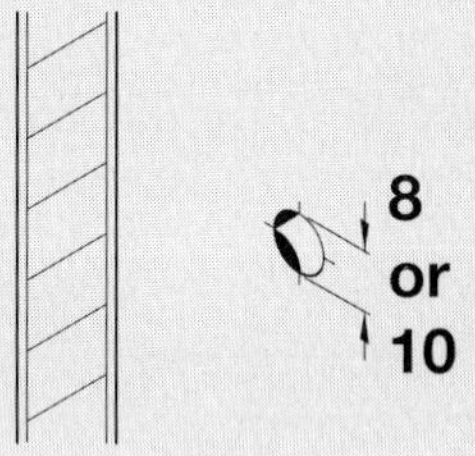

More **multi-purpose connectors** with M6 internal threads suitable for M6 connecting bolts can be found in the Complete Häfele catalog.

HÄFELE

Minifix Spreading bolts for RTA Furniture

Tool-less connection system
- for craftsmen and industry
- for easy-to-assemble RTA furniture

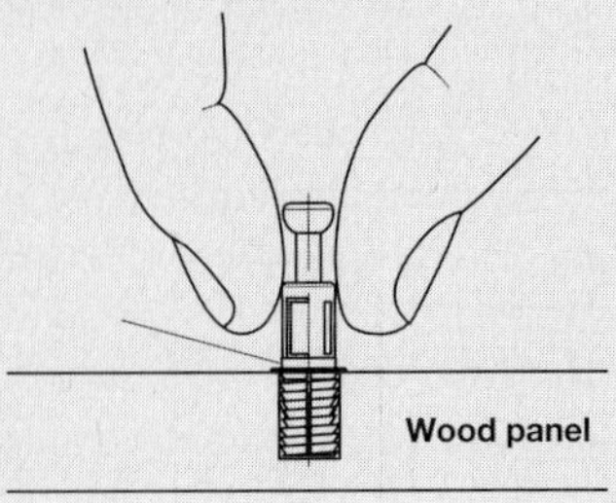

- No tools required for insertion
- No tools required for disassembly

When the bolt is tightened, the taper spreads the dowel, which presses the screw threads into the wood. The greater the effect of the tightening forces, the more durable the connection. When dismantling the furniture, the bolt can be unscrewed by hand again.

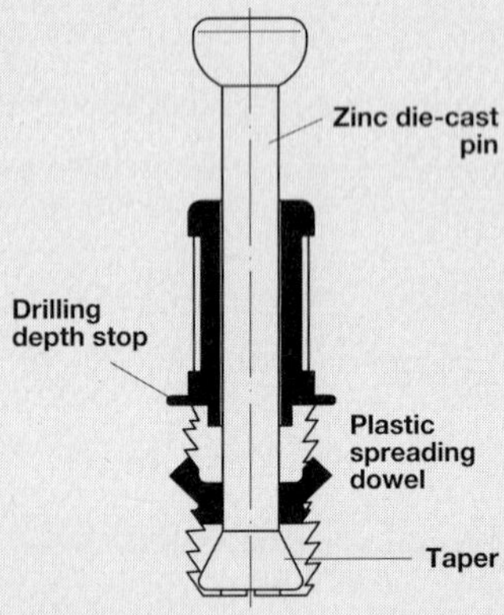

- Depth stop ensures ideal bolt position
- No damage to surface due to insertion and unscrewing of spreading bolt
- Can be used from panel thickness 15 mm

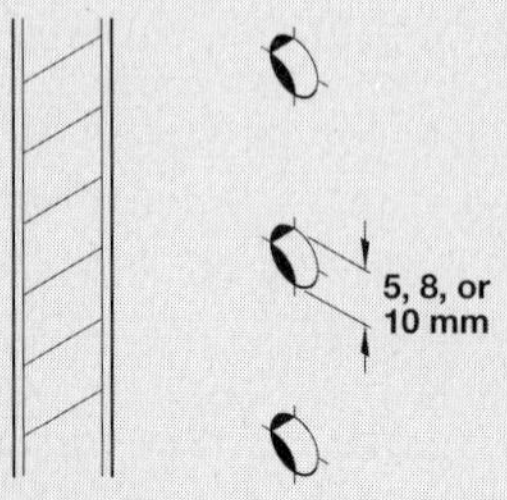

Dimensional data not binding.
We reserve the right to alter specifications without notice.

Spreading bolt, two parts
Bolt made of zinc die-cast
Spreading dowel with harpoon thread made of plastic, black

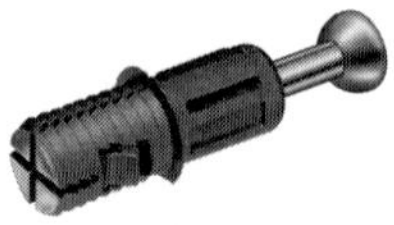

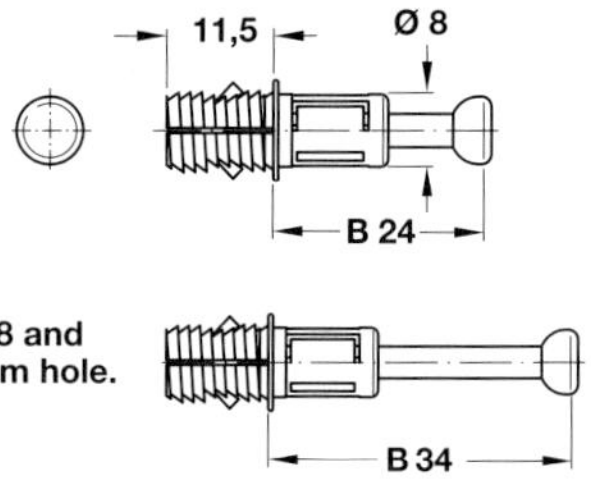

for hole Ø 5 mm

B = drilling distance	24 mm	34 mm
Cat. No.	262.09.220	262.09.320

Packing: 1000 pcs.

for hole Ø 8 mm

B = drilling distance	24 mm	34 mm
Cat. No.	262.09.200	262.09.300

Packing: 1000 pcs.

for hole Ø 10 mm

B = drilling distance	24 mm	34 mm
Cat. No.	262.09.210	262.09.310

Packing: 1000 pcs.

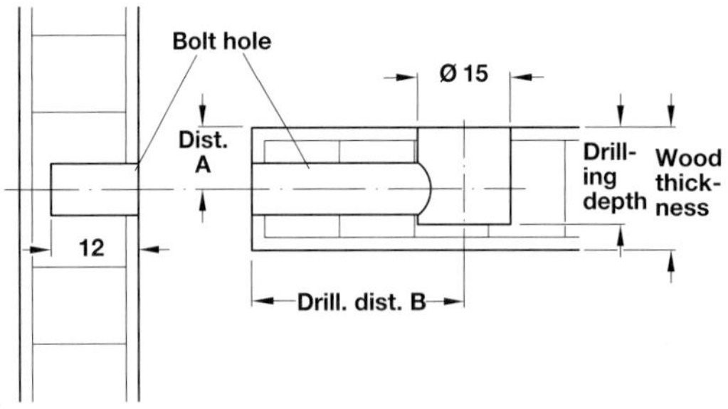

Bolt hole = **Ø 5, 8 mm and 10 mm**

Drilling depth = depending on cam type and wood thickness (see table)

Distance A = 1/2 wood thickness (see table)

Drilling dist. B = optional between **B 24** (24 mm) or **B 34** (34 mm), drilling distance from cam center to front edge

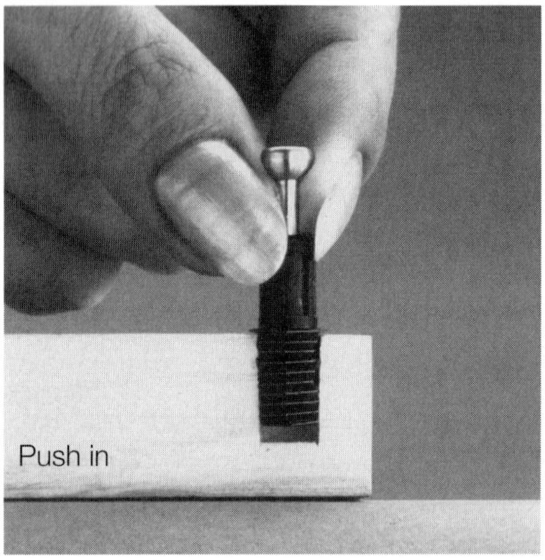

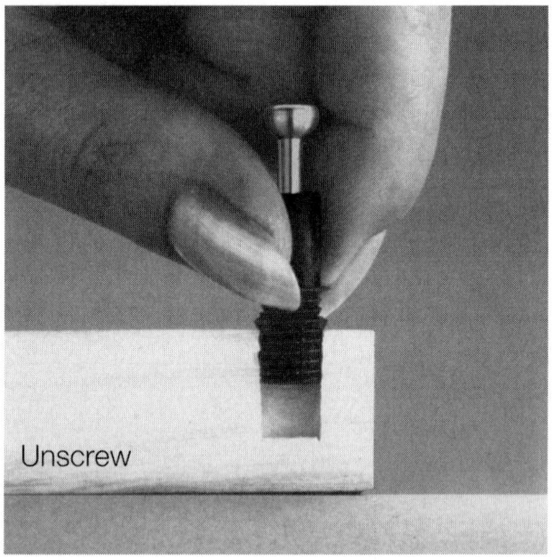

The new spreading bolt designed for use with the Minifix connector system from Häfele addresses the demands of today's RTA furniture styling.
No tools are required for assembly. The ingenious spreading bolt is simply pushed by hand into the 5, 8 or 10 mm holes in the side panel and produces an immediate and firm locking connection when tightened. The Minifix spreading bolt rounds off the comprehensive Minifix connector range from Häfele for efficient RTA furniture assembly. The simple and uncomplicated use of this range of fittings is particularly welcomed by laypersons faced with the often daunting task of putting together RTA furniture purchases.

The bolt comprises a tapered metal pin with the typical Minifix spherical head. This is embedded into a plastic spreading dowel. The top of the dowel is fitted with a stop and an easy-grip sheathing which makes manual insertion simplicity itself. The furniture components are drawn together ideally with a firm locking connection, as the stop ensures a uniform tensioned length of 34 mm. Use a No. 3 cross-slot bit. When the bolt is tightened, the taper spreads the dowel, so pressing the screw threads into the wood. The greater the effect of the tightening forces, the more durable the connection.
When dismantling the furniture, the bolt can be unscrew again by hand.

Dimensions in mm

Minifix Connecting Bolts

HÄFELE

Connecting bolts for through-installation for single or double-sided installation using **holes dia. 8 mm**

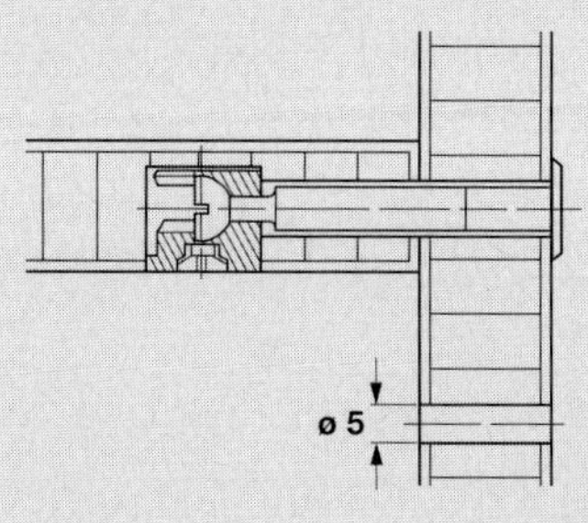

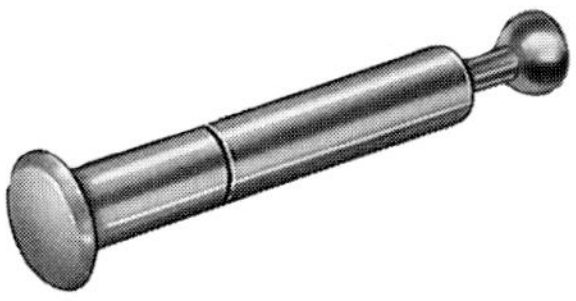

Capped bolt
Finish: steel

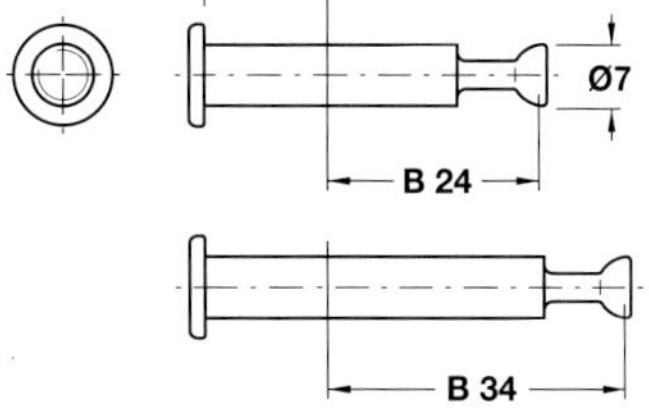

panel thickness 16 mm

B = Drilling distance		**24 mm**	**34 mm**
Cat. No.	nickel-plated	262.27.752	262.28.759
	bronzed	262.27.154	262.28.151

panel thickness 19 mm

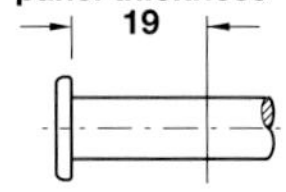

B = Drilling distance		**24 mm**	**34 mm**
Cat. No.	nickel-plated	262.27.761	262.28.768
	bronzed	262.27.163	262.28.160

Packing: 1000 pcs.

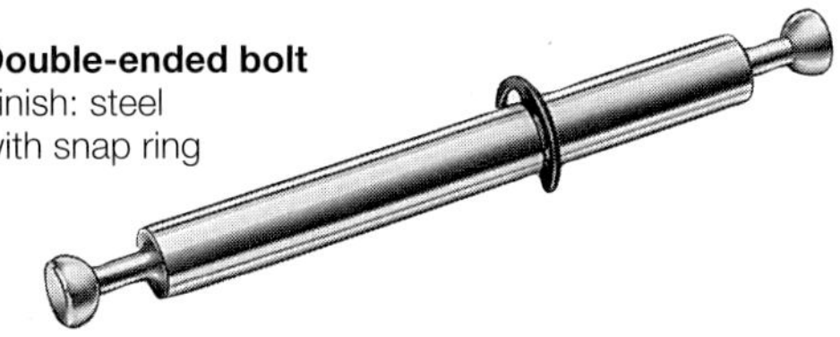

Double-ended bolt
Finish: steel
with snap ring

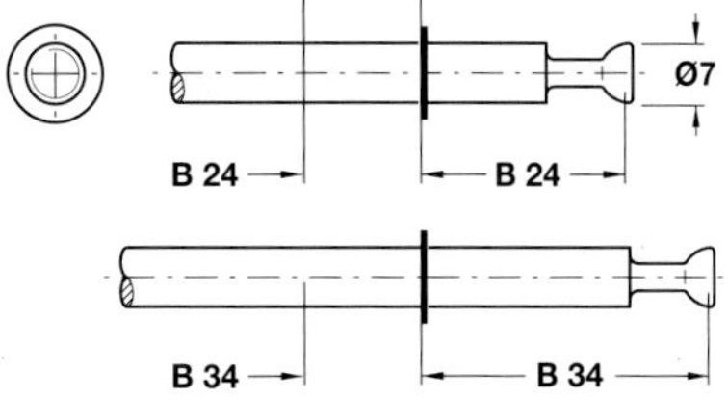

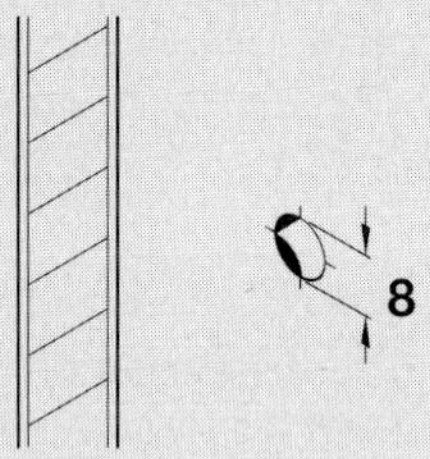

panel thickness 16 mm

B = Drilling distance		**24 mm**	**34 mm**
Cat. No.	galvanized	262.27.805	262.28.802

Packing: 1000 pcs.

panel thickness 19 mm

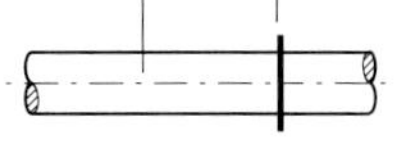

B = Drilling distance		**24 mm**	**34 mm**
Cat. No.	galvanized	262.27.814	262.28.811

Packing: 100 pcs.

Double-ended bolt with center ridge for panel joints using **holes dia. 7 mm** (to eliminate up and down movements, 7 mm pilot holes are recommended).

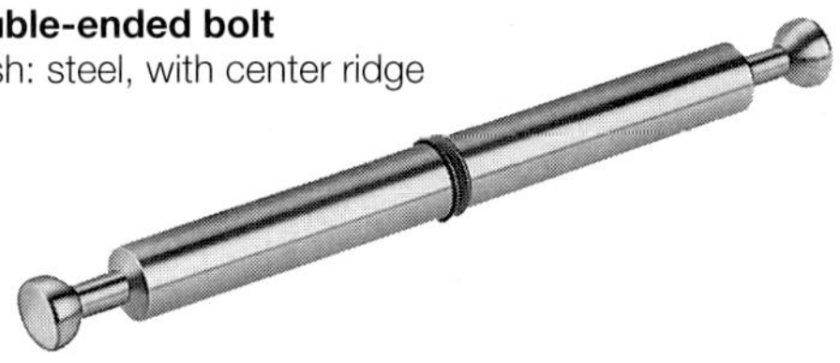

Double-ended bolt
Finish: steel, with center ridge

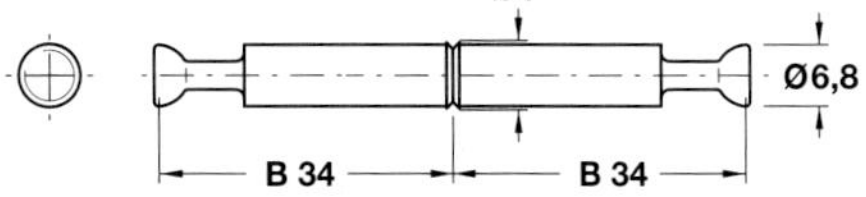

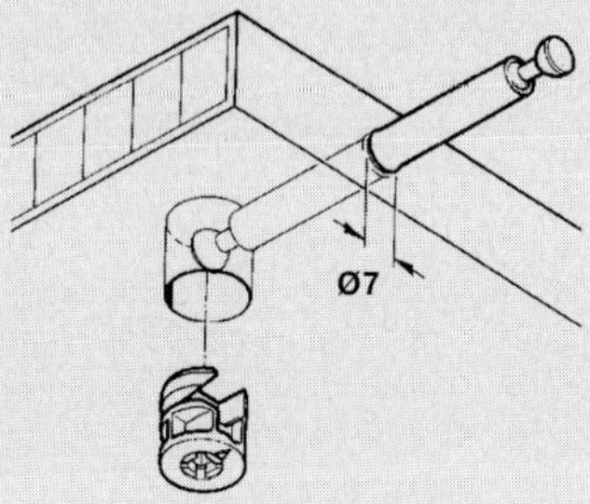

B = Drilling distance		**34 mm**
Cat. No.	galvanized	262.28.786

Packing: 500 pcs.

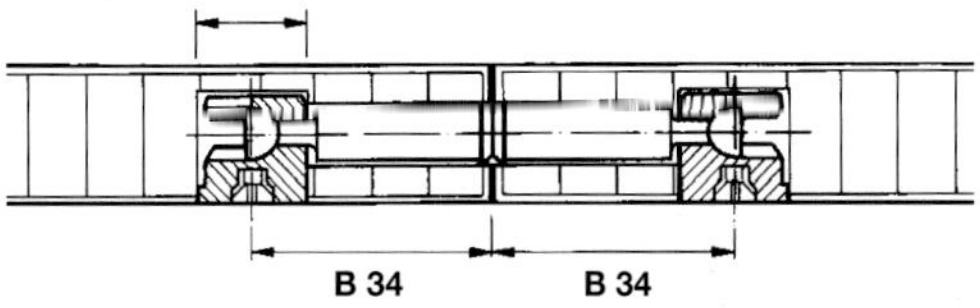

Dimensional data not binding.
We reserve the right to alter specifications without notice.

Dimensions in mm

HÄFELE

Minifix Miter Joint Connectors

A practical method of joining miter-jointed cabinets and profiles without costly gluing, and of making large panels of furniture with miter joints which combine RTA convenience with extreme stability on assembly.

Minifix GV miter joint connectors, with or without nylon sleeves, are hinged connecting bolts, capable of securing miter joints at any angle from 30° to 180°.

These connectors should preferably be used only with dia. 15 mm Minifix cams made of zinc die-cast.

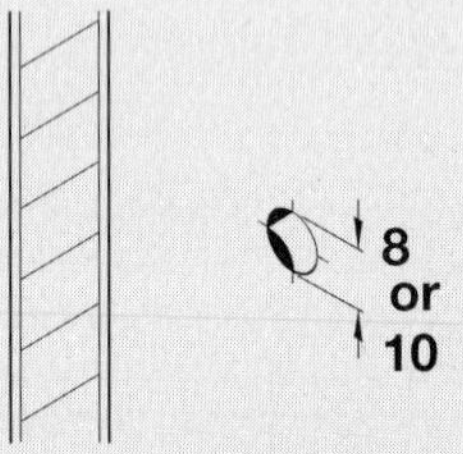

Multi-purpose fasteners with M6 internal thread, suitable for use with the Minifix GV M6 connector, are featured in The Complete Häfele catalog.

The tensioning distance can be adjusted to the optimum amount by tightening or loosening the connector as needed.

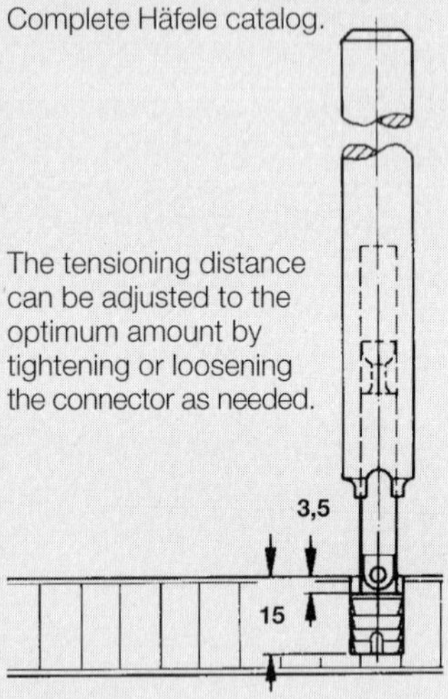

The Minifix GV miter joint connector takes the form of a double-ended hinged bolt. It can be used for any joint angle from **90°** to **180°**.

Dimensional data not binding. We reserve the right to alter specifications without notice.

Miter joint connectors **with or without sleeves** for single sided installation using **holes dia. 8 and 10 mm**

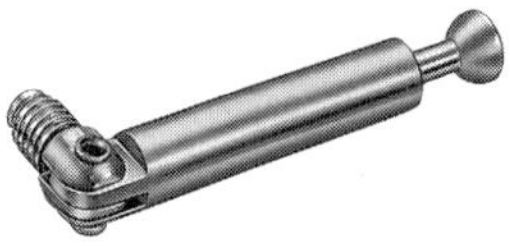

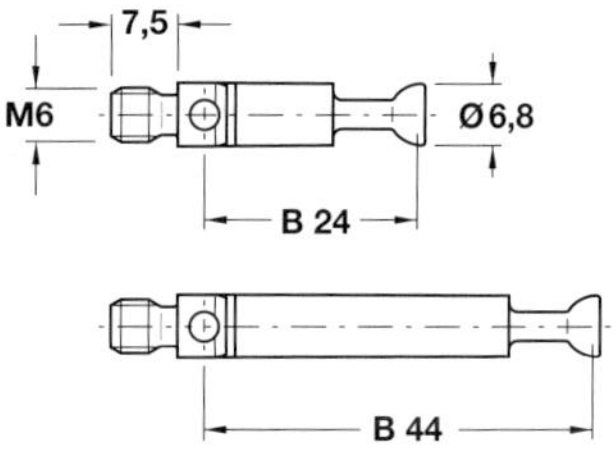

Miter joint connector
Minifix GV M6. Finish: steel

B = Drilling distance	**44 mm**
Cat. No. galvanized	262.12.984

Packing: 1000 pcs.

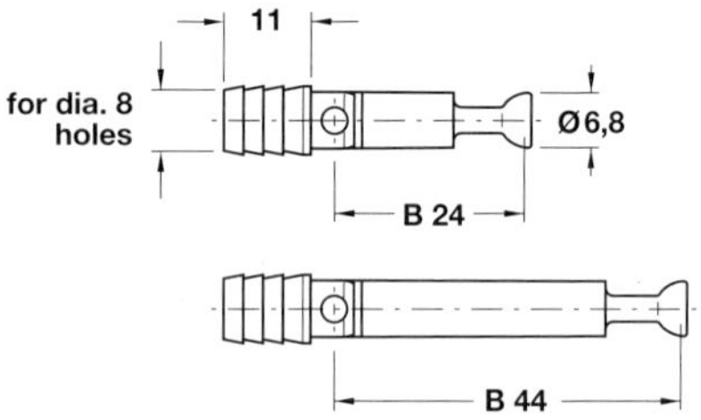

Miter joint connector
Minifix GV. Finish: steel, with nylon sleeve

B = Drilling distance	**44 mm**
Cat. No. galvanized	262.12.804

Packing: 100 pcs.

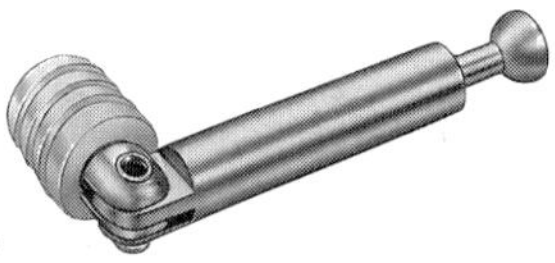

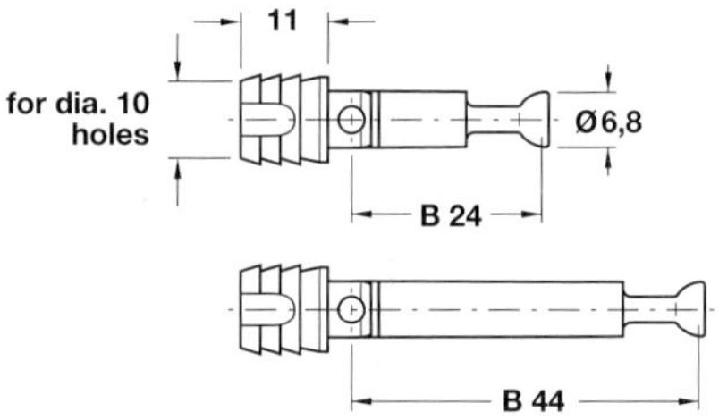

Miter joint connector
Minifix GV. Finish: steel, with nylon sleeve

B = Drilling distance	**44 mm**
Cat. No. galvanized	262.12.813

Packing: 100 pcs.

When knocking in Minifix GV connectors with nylon sleeves, we recommend using this **punch tool** made of hardened steel.

Cat. No.	001.32.614

Packing: 1 pc.

Minifix GV hinged miter joint connector for double-sided installation using **holes dia. 7 mm**

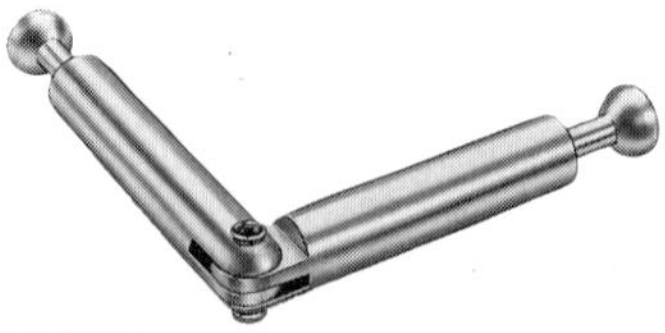

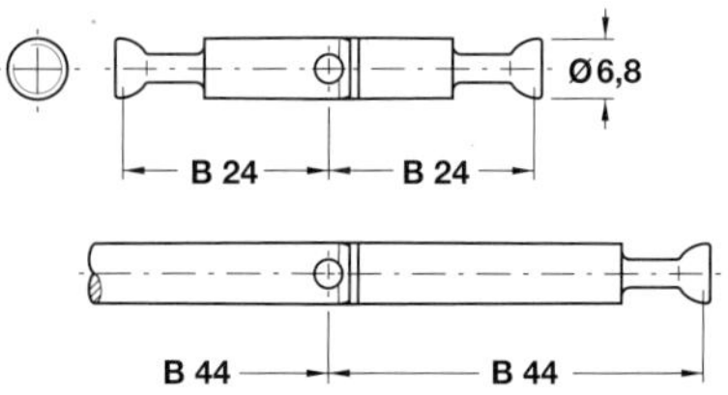

Miter joint connector
Minifix GV with steel hinge

B = Drilling distance	**24 mm**	**44 mm**
Cat. No. galvanized	262.12.859	262.12.939

Packing: 500 pcs.

Dimensions in mm

Tools for Minifix Miter Joint Connectors

A **precision drilling jig** and a **marking gauge** have been developed to ensure accurate installation of Minifix GV miter joint connectors.

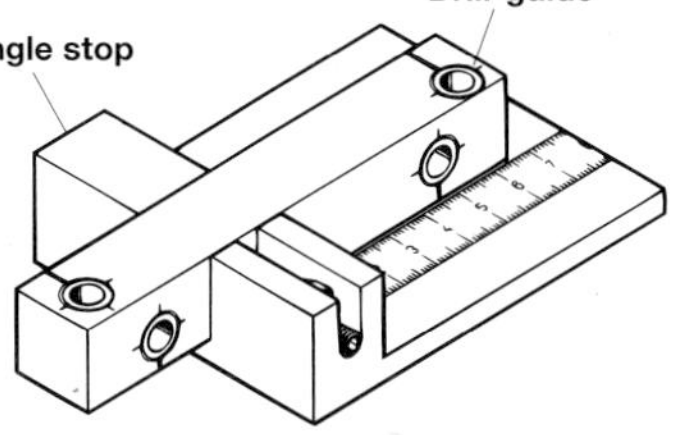

Precision drilling jig for the required **dia. 7 mm** hole, comprising:
angle stop with 0 to 8 mm scale for inset interval adjustment, and socket head screw to secure the drill-guide, for wood thicknesses of **16, 19, 23** and **29 mm**.
Material: zinc die-cast with hardened drilling bushes

Cat. No.	001.27.202

Packing: 1 set

HSS twist drill
for bolt holes **dia. 7 mm**

Cat. No. 001.41.220

Packing: 1 pcs.

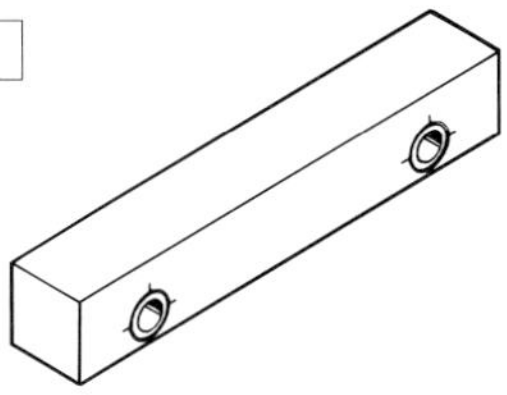

Additional drill-guide for **13** and **15 mm** wood thickness;
for mounting on the angle stop
Material: zinc die-cast with hardened drilling bushes

Cat. No.	001.27.239

Packing: 1 pc.

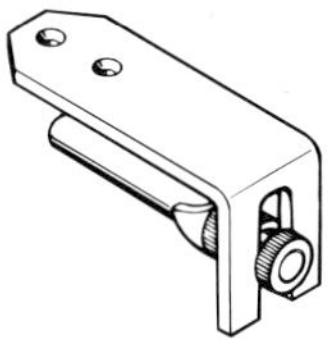

Precision marking gauge
for **dia. 15 mm** cam holes
comprising:
guide pin with two pointed stops, and marking jig with locating hole to center the drill-hole for the cam.
Material: hardened steel

Cat. No.	001.27.211

Packing: 1 set

The **precision marking gauge** can only be used for miter cut angles up to **45° maximum.**

Cut panels for assembly at miter angle.

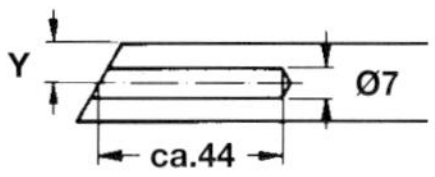

Drill **dia. 7 mm hole at drilling center Y** appropriate to thickness of wood.

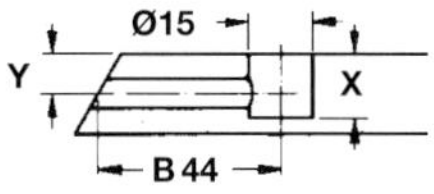

Drill **dia. 15 mm** hole for housing to appropriate **drilling depth X**.

Dimensions in mm

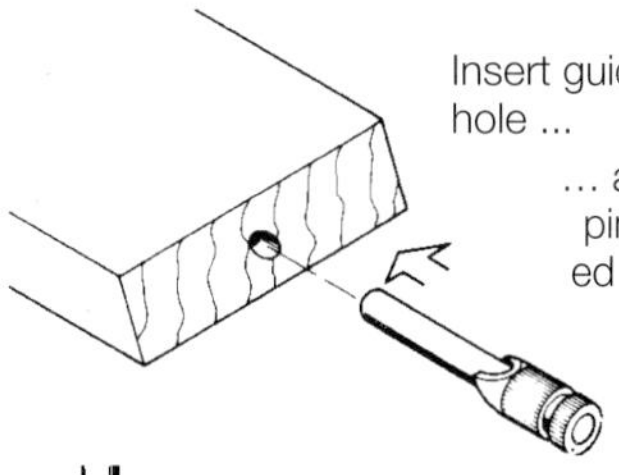

Insert guide pin into drill hole ...

... and keep turning the pin until the two pointed stops are in contact with the cut face.

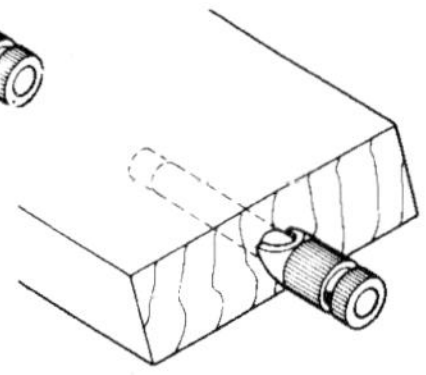

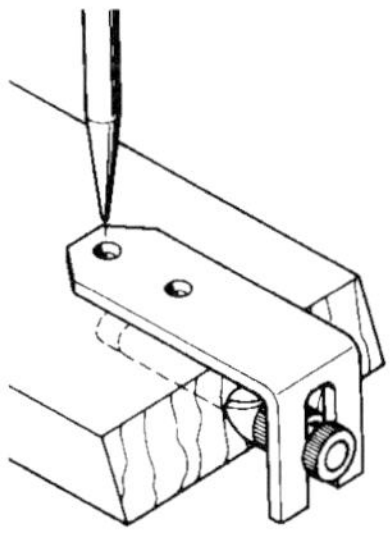

Install marking jig over groove in guide pin and mark center of cam.

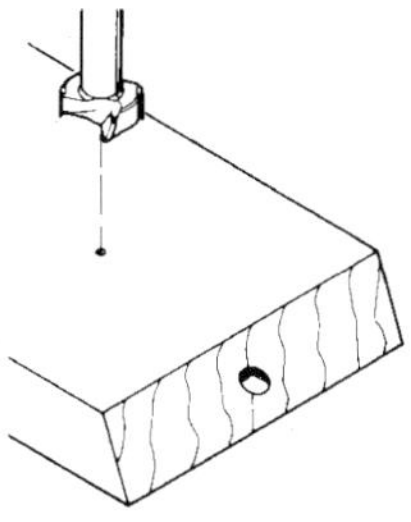

Drill dia.15 mm hole in accordance with drilling depth X.

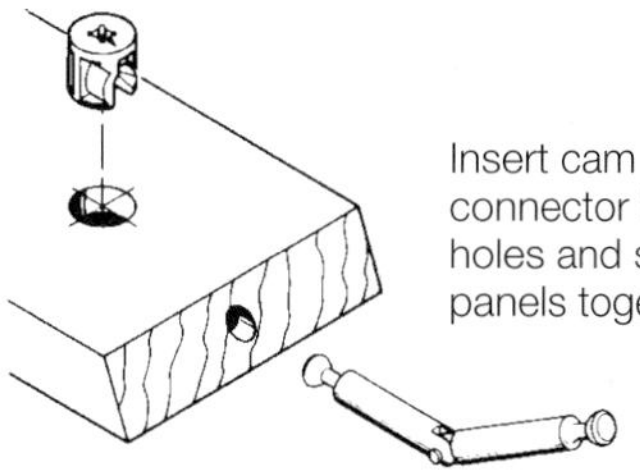

Insert cam and Minifix GV connector in respective drill-holes and secure the two panels together.

Inset distance table

To determine the center point for Minifix cam drill holes; e.g. wood thickness **19 mm** and miter joint angle **60°** = inset distance **49,5 mm**

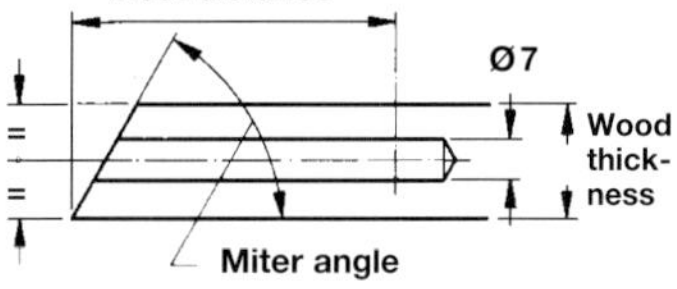

Wood thickness / Miter angle / Inset distances (mm)

Miter angle	12	13	15	16	17	18	19	20	21	22°	23	29	32
20°	60,5	61,9	64,6	66	67,4	68,7	70,1	71,5	72,8	74,2	75,6	83,9	88
22,5°	58,5	59,7	62,1	63,3	64,5	65,7	66,9	68,1	69,3	70,6	71,8	79	82,6
25°	56,9	57,9	60,1	61,2	62,2	63,3	64,4	65,4	66,5	67,6	68,7	75,1	78,3
30°	54,4	55,3	57	57,9	58,7	59,6	60,5	61,3	62,2	63,1	63,9	69,1	71,7
35°	52,6	53,5	54,7	55,4	56,1	56,9	57,6	58,3	59	59,7	60,4	64,7	66,9
40°	51,2	51,7	52,9	53,5	54,1	54,7	55,3	55,9	56,5	57,1	57,7	61,3	63,1
45°	50	50,5	51,5	52	52,5	53	53,5	54	54,5	55	55,5	58,5	60
50°	49	49,5	50,3	50,7	51,1	51,6	52	52,4	52,8	53,2	53,6	56,2	57,4
55°	48,2	48,6	49,3	49,6	50	50,3	50,7	51	51,4	51,7	52,1	54,2	55,2
60°	47,5	47,8	48,3	48,6	48,9	49,2	49,5	49,8	50,1	50,4	50,6	52,4	53,2
65°	46,8	47	47,5	47,7	48	48,2	48,4	48,7	48,9	49,1	49,4	50,8	51,5
67,5°	46,5	46,7	47,1	47,3	47,5	47,7	47,9	48,1	48,3	48,6	48,8	50	50,6
70°	46,2	46,4	46,7	46,9	47,1	47,3	47,5	47,6	47,8	48	48,2	49,3	49,8
75°	45,6	45,7	46	46,1	46,2	46,4	46,5	46,7	46,8	46,9	47,1	47,9	48,3
80°	45	45,1	45,3	45,4	45,5	45,6	45,7	45,8	45,9	45,9	46	46,6	46,8
85°	44,5	44,6	44,7	44,7	44,7	44,8	44,8	44,9	44,9	45	45	45,3	45,4
90°	44	44	44	44	44	44	44	44	44	44	44	44	44

Important

This table contains the distances for miter joint connectors with drilling distance **B 44**.

For drilling distance **B 24**, **20 mm** must be **deducted** from the given dimensions.

Formula for calculating inset distance: **tan x 1/2 wood thickness + 44 mm.**

The type of connector selected will depend on the intended application, e.g. connectors with nylon sleeves should be used for joint angles from 30° to 180°...

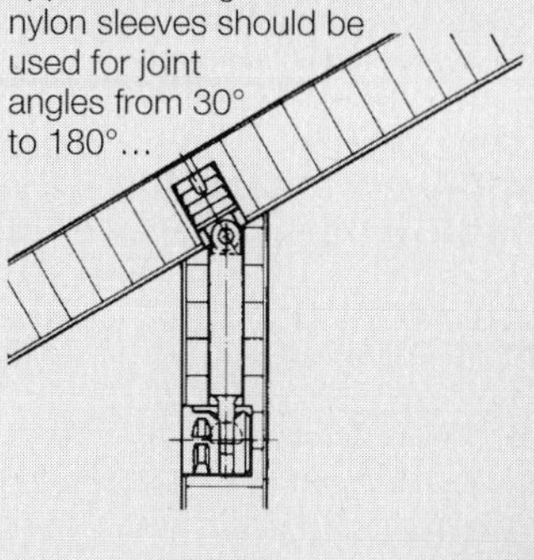

...or GV connectors for angles from 20° to 90°.

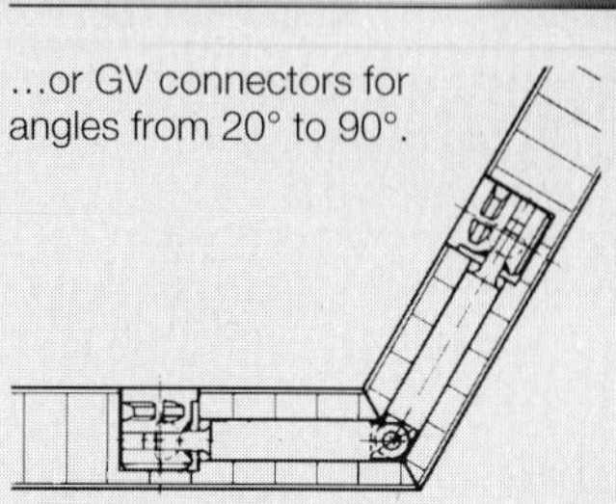

Using the
Precision drilling jig

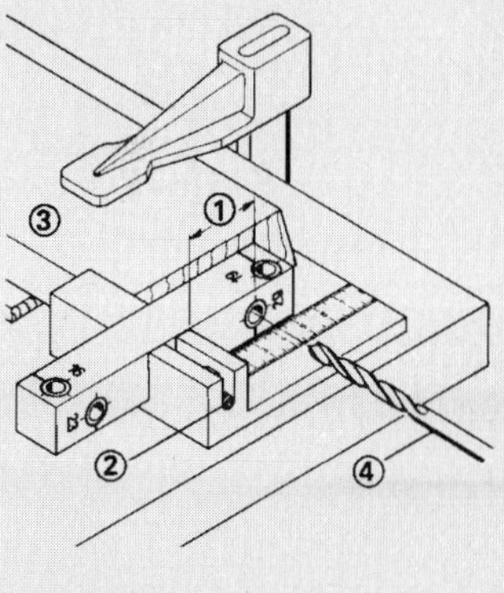

① Measure inset distance from edge of panel and transfer to drilling jig.

② Fix inset distance on drilling jig with the Allen screw.

③ Secure panel and jig with a screw-clamp.

④ With dia. 7 mm twist bit, drill hole approx. 44 mm deep.

For miter cuts of less than 45° (feasible with Minifix GV connectors with sleeves), the drill-hole center - B 44 - for the cam must be marked out by hand (see inset distance table left).

HÄFELE

Minifix 12 and 15 Cams

Only the connecting bolts illustrated on facing page showing 5 mm bolts may be used with these zinc die-cast cams.

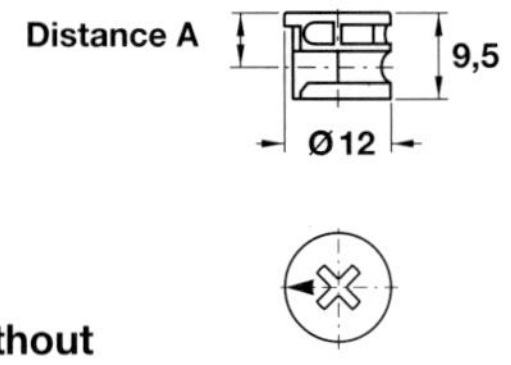

Minifix 12 cam
in zinc die-cast without

Wood thickness from:	Distance A Center locking pos.	Drilling depth	Cat. No. unfinished	nickel-plated	black
12 mm	6,0 mm	9,5 $^{+0,2}$ mm	262.07.054	262.07.750	262.07.358

Packing: 1000 pcs.

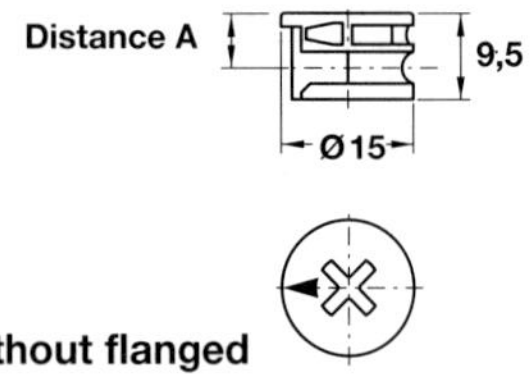

Minifix 15 cam
in zinc die-cast without flanged

Wood thickness from:	Distance A Center locking pos.	Drilling depth	Cat. No. unfinished	nickel-plated	black
12 mm	6,0 mm	9,5 $^{+0,2}$ mm	262.26.059	262.26.755	262.26.853

Packing: 1000 pcs.

All three ends can be used for tightening.

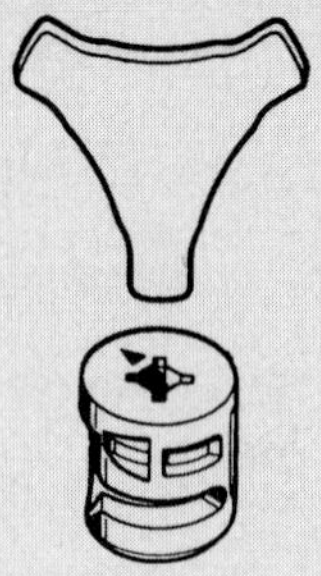

Tightening key. Finish: steel, for Minifix cams in zinc die-cast

Cat. No.	006.36.911

Packing: 100 pcs.

For **Minifix 15** cam without flanged rims and for wood thickness **12 mm**

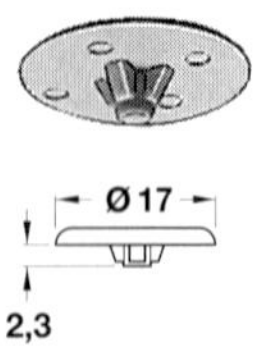

Trim cap, plastic

Cat. No.	white	262.24.760
	pine	262.24.064
	brown	262.24.162
	black	262.24.368

Packing: 500 pcs.

Non-standard colors available 100,000 minimum order

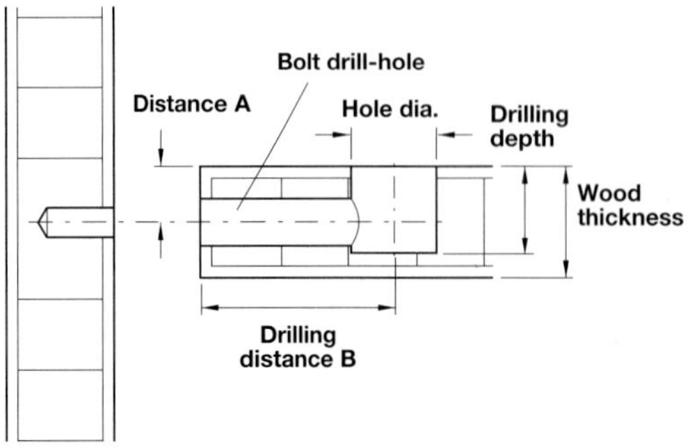

Bolt drill-hole = **dia. 5** or **8 mm** depending on choice of connecting bolt

Drill-hole dia. = **12** or **15 mm** depending on choice of cam

Drilling depth = 9.5 mm for both cams

Distance A = 1/2 wood thickness (6 mm)

Drill. distance B = choice between **B 24** (24 mm) or **B 34** (34 mm), distance between drill-hole center and front panel

Dimensions in mm

Dimensional data not binding. We reserve the right to alter specifications without notice.

HÄFELE

Minifix Connecting bolts

Connecting bolts for screw-mounting or through-mounting in single or double-sided installations in **dia. 5 mm drill holes**

Connecting bolt
Finish: steel with special thread

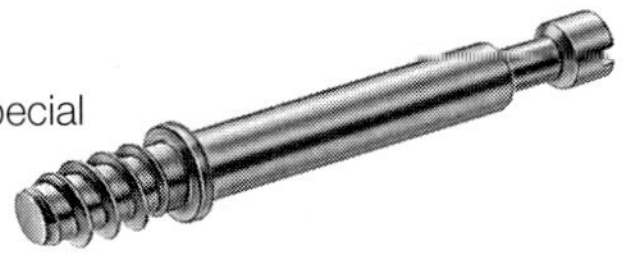

B= Drilling distance		**34 mm**
Cat. No.	unfinished	262.28.188

Packing: 1000 pcs.

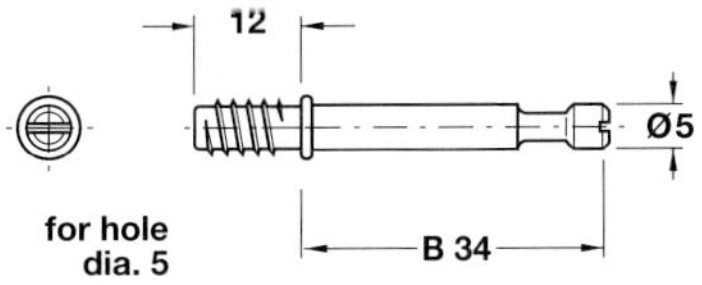

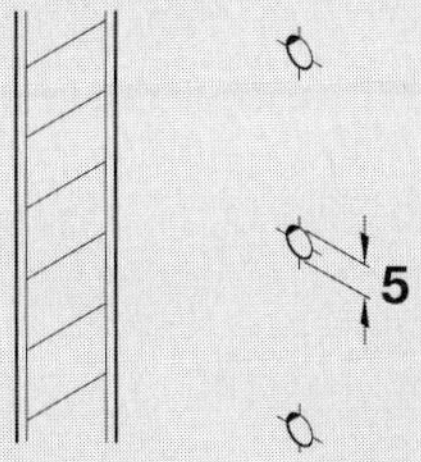

Capped bolt
Finish: steel, with countersunk head

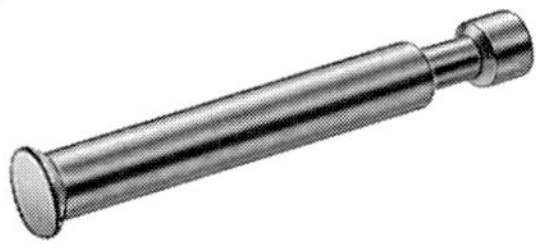

panel thickness 19 mm

B= Drilling distance		**24 mm**
Cat. No.	nickel-plated	262.27.789

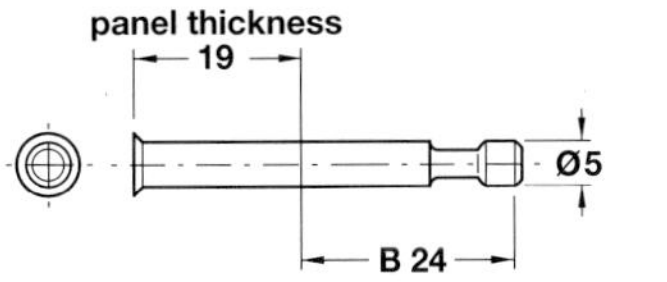

panel thickness 16 mm

B= Drilling distance		**34 mm**
Cat. No.	nickel-plated	262.28.704
	brass-plated	262.28.508

Packing: 1000 pcs.

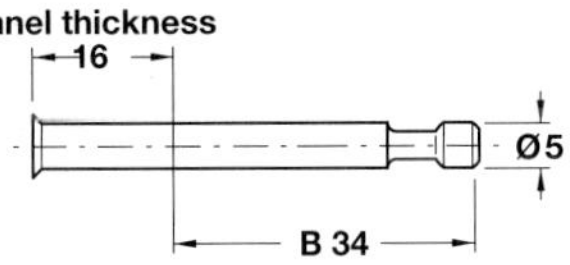

Locks, Catches, RTA and PAS® Fittings
Shelf Supports
Bed Fittings
2

- These special 5 mm bolts should only be used with cams shown on page 308.

Double-ended bolt
Finish: steel, with snap ring

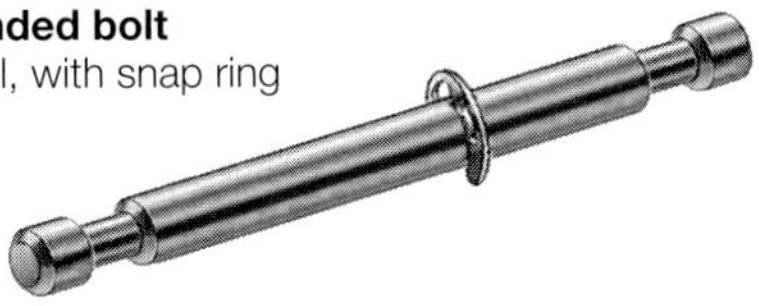

panel thickness 19 mm

B= Drilling distance		**24 mm**
Cat. No.	unfinished	262.27.243

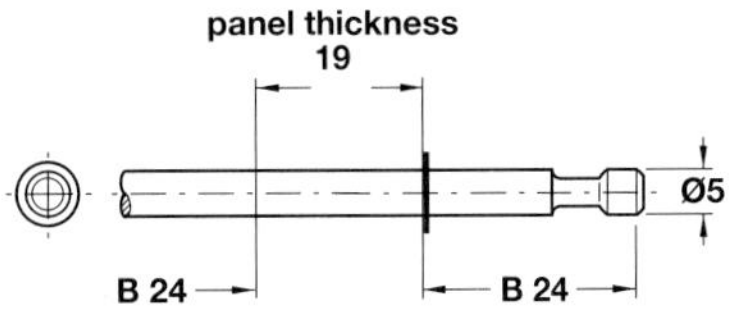

panel thickness 16 mm

B= Drilling distance		**34 mm**
Cat. No.	galvanized	262.28.875

Packing: 1000 pcs.

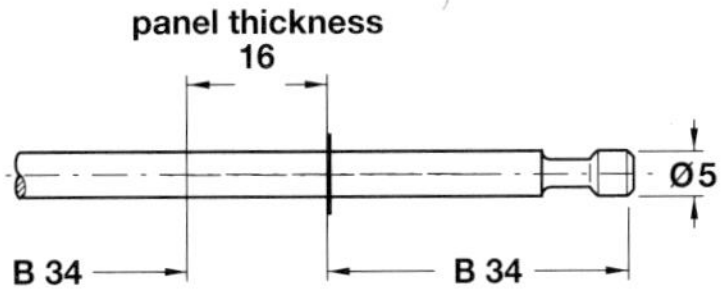

Special double-ended bolts for **miter joint connections** such as for rim profiles, picture frames etc.

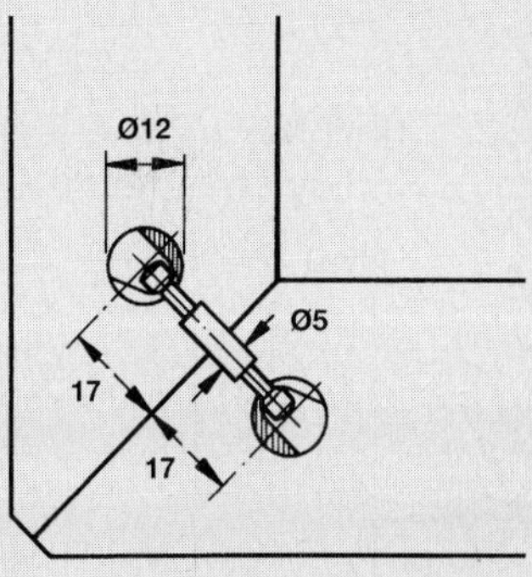

Double-ended bolt
for miter joint connections
Finish: steel

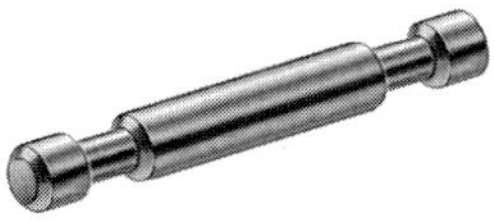

Cat. No.	unfinished	262.29.023

Packing: 500 pcs.

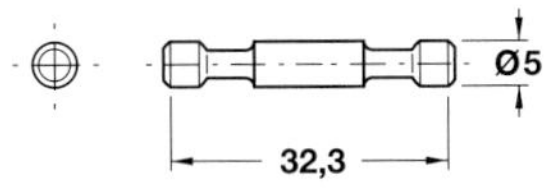

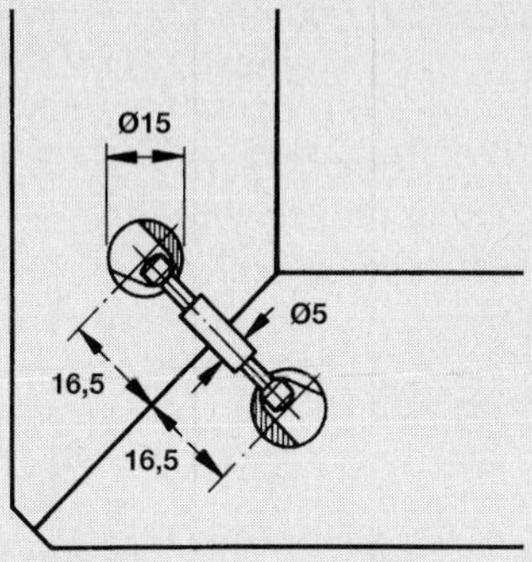

This connecting bolt requires a **dia. 8 mm bolt hole**

Connecting bolt
Finish: steel with special thread

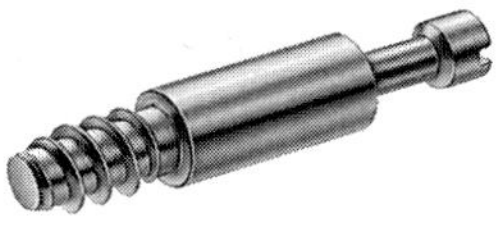

Thread length 9 mm

B= Drilling distance		**24 mm**
Cat. No.	galvanized	262.06.913

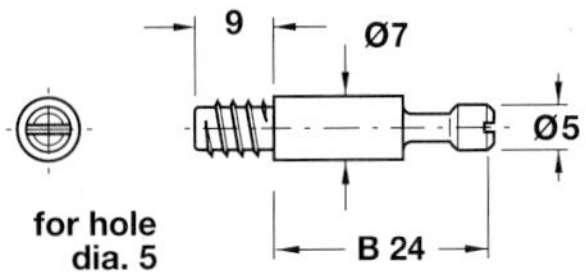

Thread length 10,5 mm

B= Drilling distance		**24 mm**
Cat. No.	galvanized	262.06.922

Packing: 2500 pcs.

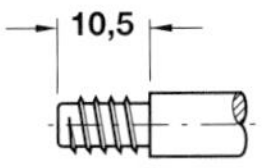

Dimensions in mm

Dimensional data not binding. We reserve the right to alter specifications without notice.

HÄFELE

Unitool Drilling Jig for Minifix 12 and 15

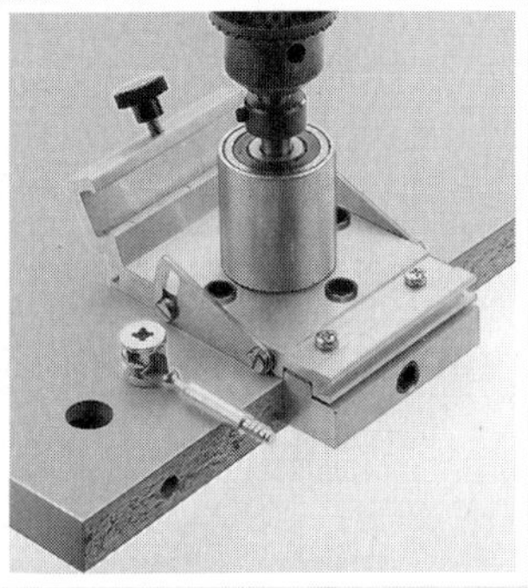

*** Necessary for a complete system.**

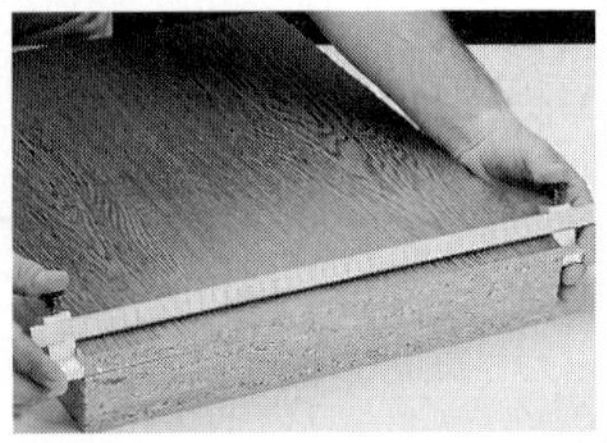

Locating rule with 2 end stops for checking wood components up to 800 mm wide

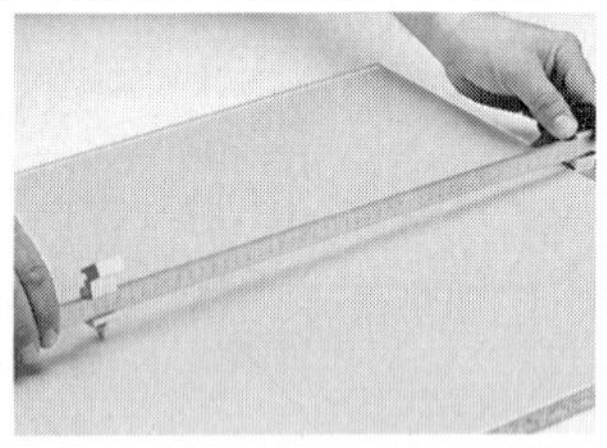

Transfer of measurements using rule, scribing pin and end stop for similar types of wood components

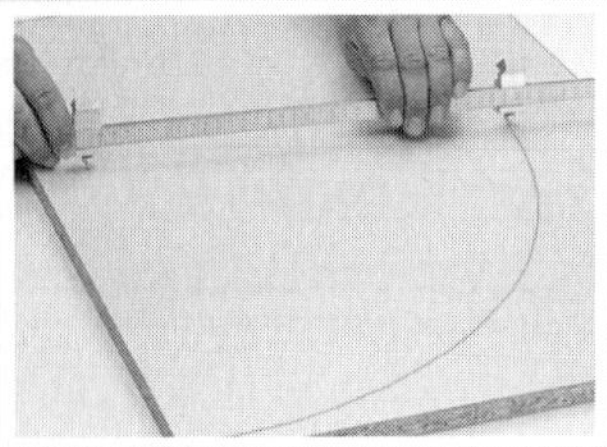

Using the locating rule and two scribing pins, circles can be marked up to 1600 mm in diameter

Dimensional data not binding. We reserve the right to alter specifications without notice.

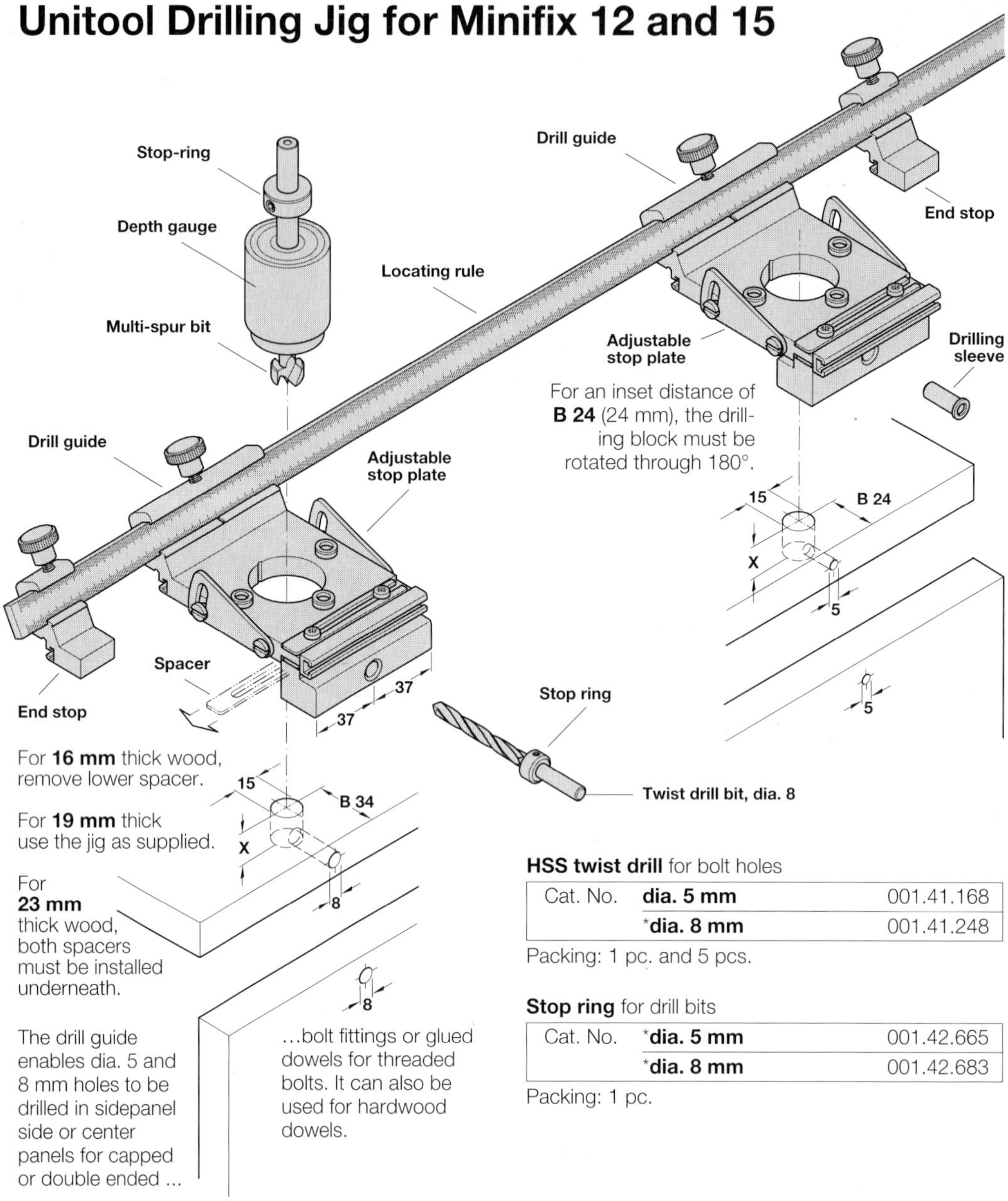
Stop-ring
Depth gauge
Multi-spur bit
Locating rule
Drill guide
End stop
Adjustable stop plate
Drilling sleeve
For an inset distance of B 24 (24 mm), the drilling block must be rotated through 180°.
15
B 24
X
5
Drill guide
Adjustable stop plate
Spacer
End stop
37
37
Stop ring
Twist drill bit, dia. 8
For 16 mm thick wood, remove lower spacer.
For 19 mm thick use the jig as supplied.
For 23 mm thick wood, both spacers must be installed underneath.
15
B 34
X
8
8
The drill guide enables dia. 5 and 8 mm holes to be drilled in sidepanel side or center panels for capped or double ended ...
...bolt fittings or glued dowels for threaded bolts. It can also be used for hardwood dowels.

HSS twist drill for bolt holes

Cat. No.	**dia. 5 mm**	001.41.168
	***dia. 8 mm**	001.41.248

Packing: 1 pc. and 5 pcs.

Stop ring for drill bits

Cat. No.	***dia. 5 mm**	001.42.665
	***dia. 8 mm**	001.42.683

Packing: 1 pc.

With this drilling jig, holes can be drilled efficiently for Minifix fittings in wood thicknesses of **16, 19 and 23 mm**. Adaptation to the required thickness is achieved by repositioning the spacers. An inset drilling distance of **37 mm** from each end can be obtained with the aid of the adjustable stop-plates.
The drill guide has been designed in such a way that it can be used as an aid to single unit installation or, by mounting two guides to the locating rule, as a complete production jig.

Unitool drilling jig for precision drilling for the **Minifix 15 and 12** range of RTA fittings**.**
Comprising:
1 locating rule with double-ended scale 800 x 15 x 6 mm, 2 drill-guides with adjustable stop-plates, 1 drilling sleeve for bolt holes **dia. 5 mm** and 2 end stops

*Cat. No.	001.25.404

Packing: 1 set

Depth gauge, material: plastic with 2 ball-bearings, stop-ring and Allen key, for bits with shank dia. 10 mm and max. hole diameter of up to 20 mm

*Cat. No.	001.28.740

Packing: 1 pc.

Carbide multi-spur bit with centering tip
Shank dia. 10 mm, length 139 mm

Cat. No.	**dia. 12 mm**	001.24.489
	dia. 15 mm	001.24.443

Packing: 1 pc.

Locating rule with 800 mm double-ended scale

Cat. No.	001.27.793

Packing: 1 pc.

End stop with adjusting screw

Cat. No.	001.27.757

Packing: 1 pc.

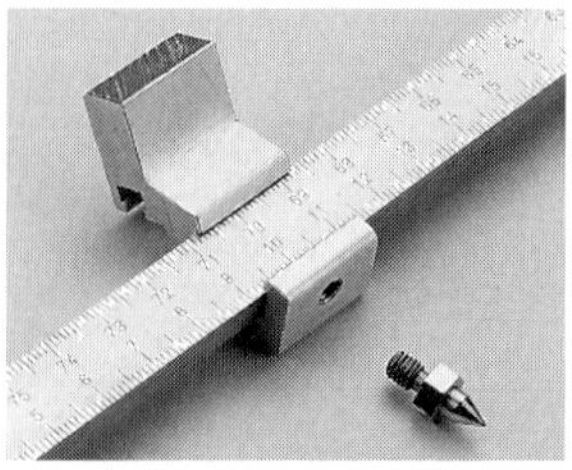

Marking device: Simply unscrew the adjusting screw from the end stop and screw in the scribing pin.

Scribing pin for screwing into end stops

Cat. No.	001.27.775

Packing: 1 pc.

Drill guide with adjustable stop plates

Cat. No.	001.25.413

Packing: 1 pc.

Drilling bushing for bolt hole **dia. 5 mm** for insertion into dia. 8 mm drilling sleeve

Cat. No.	001.25.806

Packing: 1 pc.

Unitool Drilling Jig for Rafix

HÄFELE

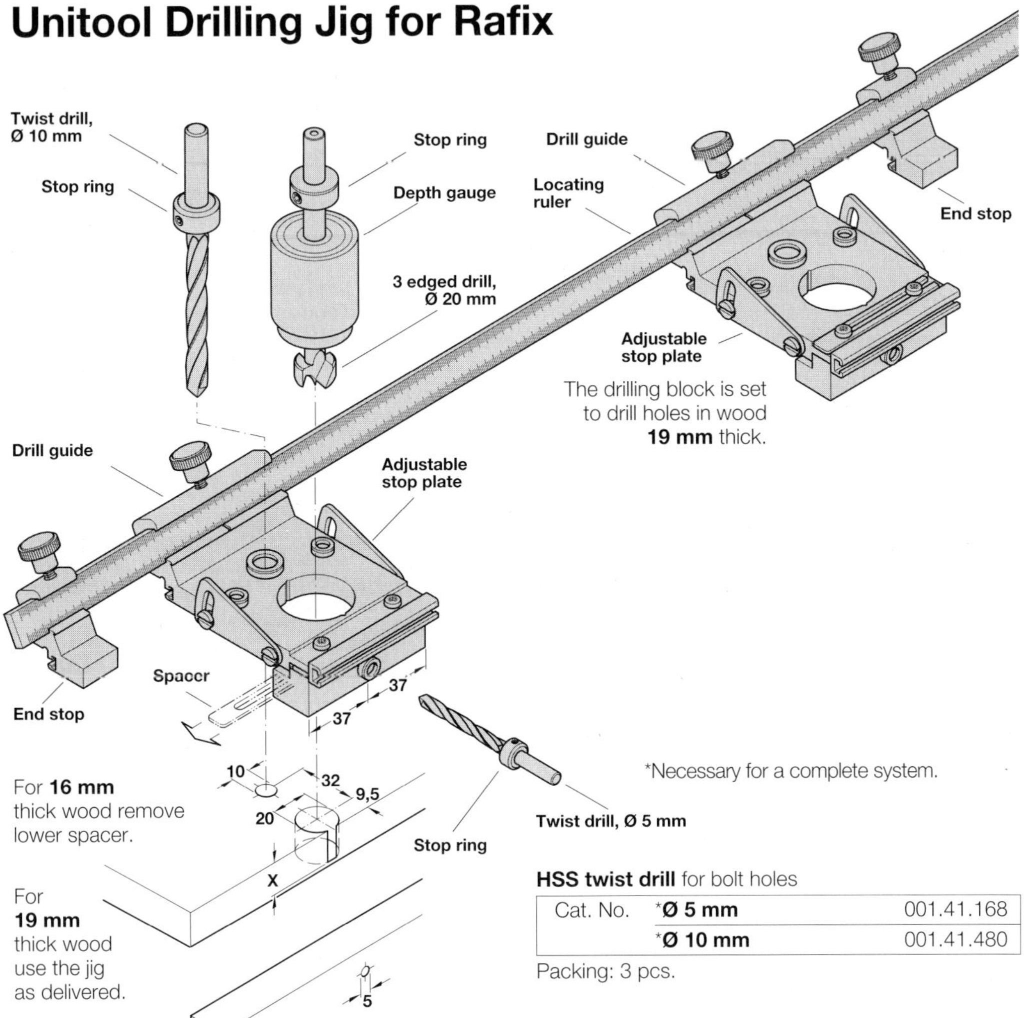

*Necessary for a complete system.

To ensure that the Ø 5 mm holes are correctly located in the sidepanel side or middle panel according to the wood ... thickness of **16 and 19 mm**, the drilling block is appropriately adjusted for the wood thickness by means of the spacers.

With this drill jig, holes can be economically drilled for Rafix connectors in wood thicknesses of **16 and 19 mm**. The corresponding wood thicknesses are achieved by remounting the spacers accordingly. The adjustable stop plates on the drill guides make an inset drilling distance for the series of holes of **37 mm** from both sides possible. The drill guide is so designed that it can be used as a single drill jig or, when two drill guides are mounted on the locating ruler, as a complete drilling jig.

Unitool drilling jig for precise drilling for the **Rafix** RTA fittings program.
Consisting of:
1 locating ruler with double scale 800 x 15 x 6 mm
2 drill guides with adjustable stop plates
2 end stops.

*Cat. No.	001.25.208

Packing: 1 set

Depth gauge of steel, galvanized with 2 ball bearings, stop ring and hexagon key, for drill with Ø 10 mm shank and max. drill Ø to 20 mm

*Cat. No.	001.28.740

Packing: 1 pc.

Carbide tipped 3 edged drill with centering tip for **Rafix** and **Rafix 32 cams**
drill Ø 20 mm, shank Ø 10 mm, length 139 mm

Cat. No.	001.24.425

Packing: 1 pc.

HSS twist drill for bolt holes

Cat. No.	***Ø 5 mm**	001.41.168
	***Ø 10 mm**	001.41.480

Packing: 3 pcs.

Stop ring for drill

Cat. No.	***Ø 5 mm**	001.42.665
	***Ø 10 mm**	001.42.692

Packing: 1 pc.

Also available separately:

Locating ruler with 800 mm double scale

Cat. No.	001.27.793

Packing: 1 pc.

End stop with clamping screw

Cat. No.	001.27.757

Packing: 1 pc.

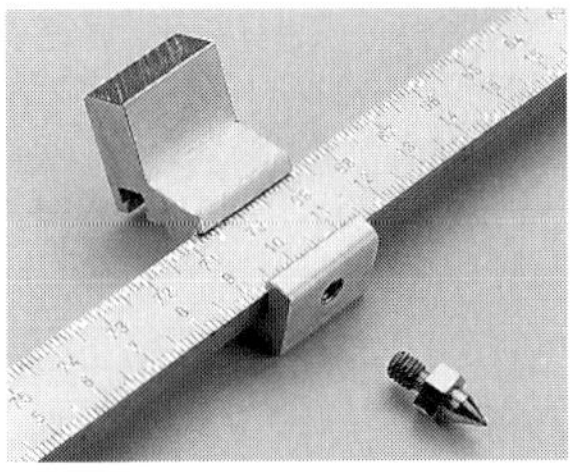

Compass device:
Simply remove the clamping screw from the end stop and screw in the scriber pin.

Scriber pin screws into the end stops

Cat. No.	001.27.775

Packing: 1 pc.

Drill guide with adjustable stop plates

Cat. No.	001.25.217

Packing: 1 pc.

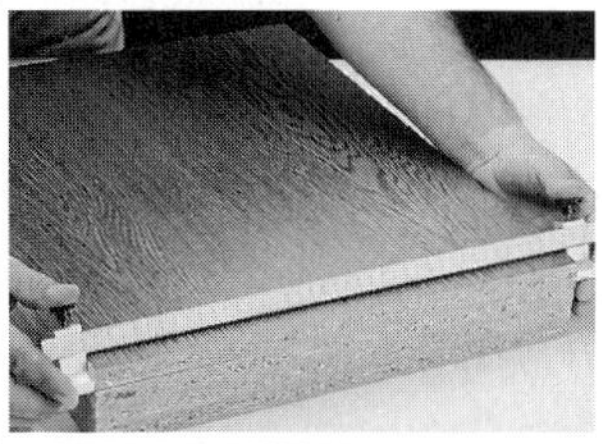

Ruler with 2 end stops for checking wooden components up to max. 800 mm in width

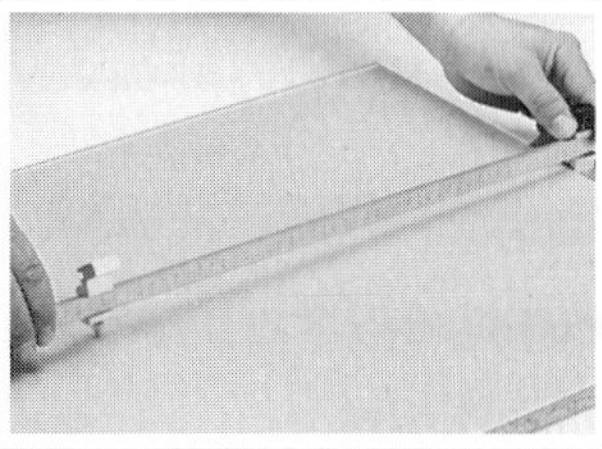

Transferring of measurements on similar wooden parts with ruler, scribing pin and end stop.

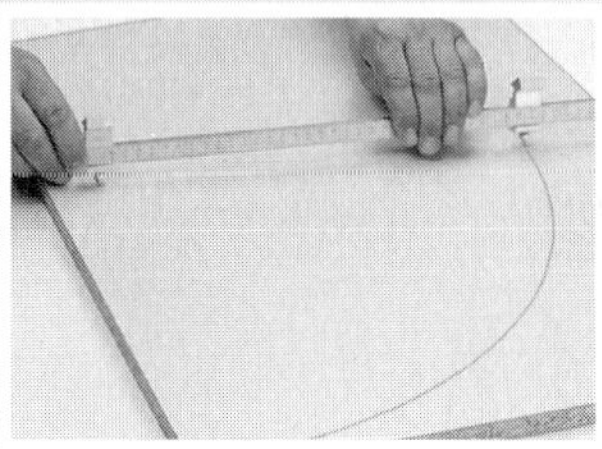

Circles up to 1600 mm in diameter can be drawn using the ruler and two scribing pins.

HÄFELE

Rafix - Precision Assembly System®

Flush-fit Rafix mounting

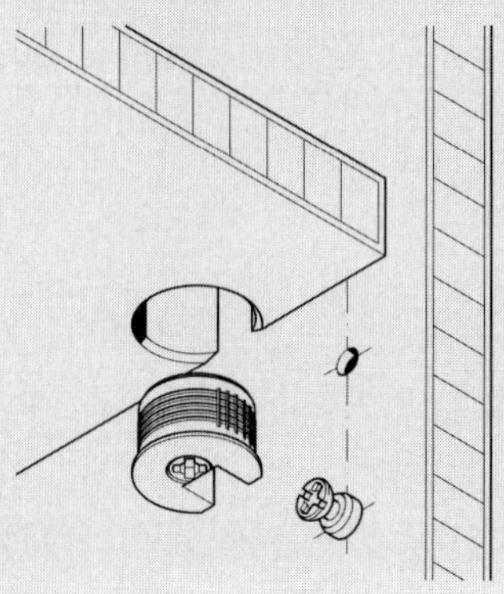

Rafix mounting example

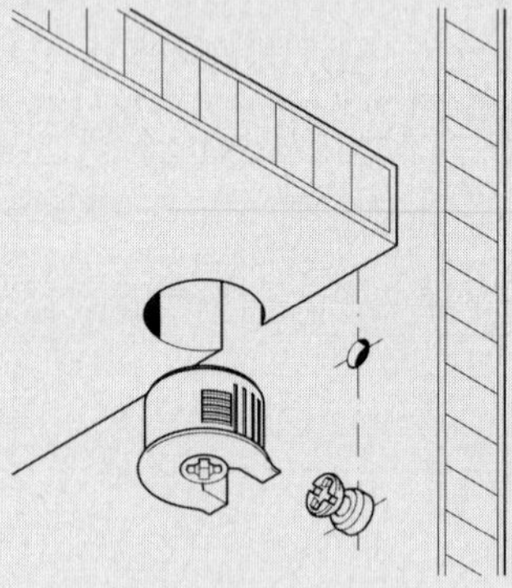

Rafix 32 mounting example

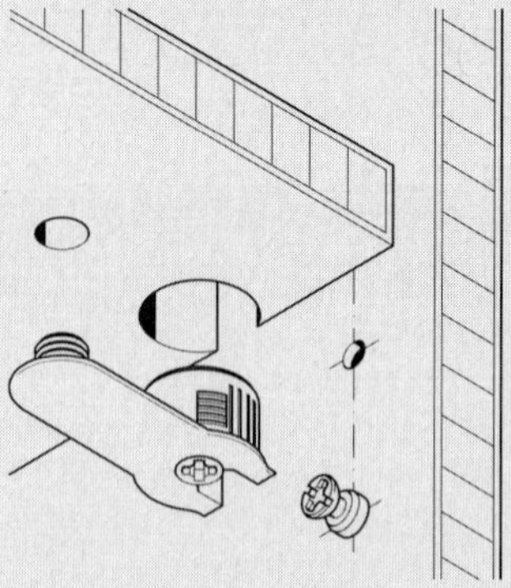

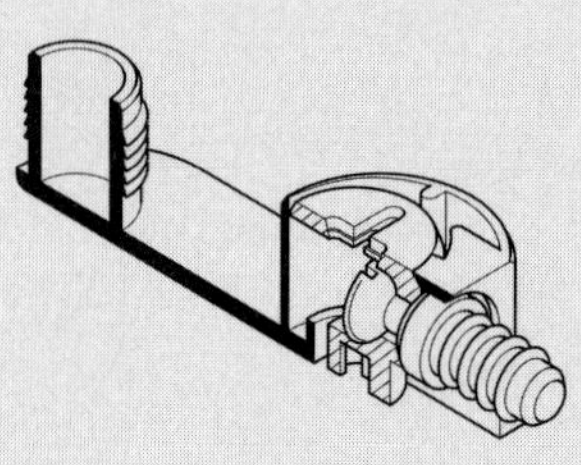

Precision Assembly System »Rafix« with the principle of the self-centering ball

The Rafix housings have tightening elements with a self-centering ball principle and offer the following advantages:

- No displacement of side panels because bolts are centrally guided
- Tolerances are compensated for by long tightening distance
- Secure fastening is ensured, even after repeated loosening and tightening
- All drilling operations are made on flat surfaces

A choice can be made from housings with rim **of zinc, die-cast**, in the finishes nickel-plated and burnished, - **of plastic**, in the colors white, beige, brown, gray and black

Rafix »flush fittings« no projecting fitting parts due to countersunk rim on the housing.

Suitable for wood thicknesses of **16 and 19 mm.**

For many assembly problems a complete program of

Without ridge

enabling the cross member to be assembled **end-on** or **from above**.

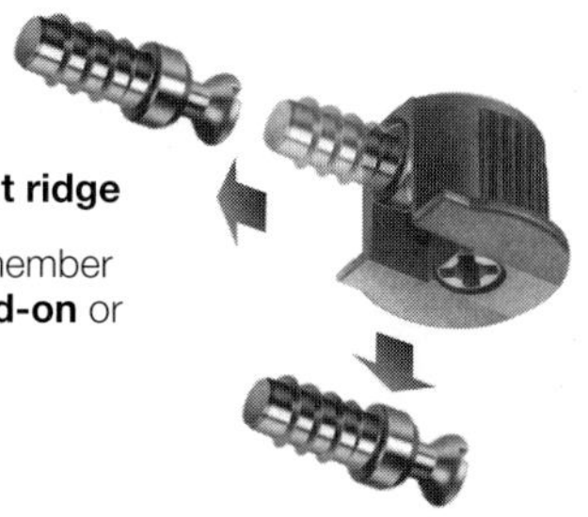

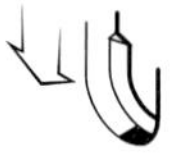

With ridge

the cross member can only be installed **from above** and the cabinet elements are pre-assembled.

Rafix mounting examples, for single- and double-sided assembly through:

Direct installation of bolt in Ø 3 resp. Ø 5 mm holes

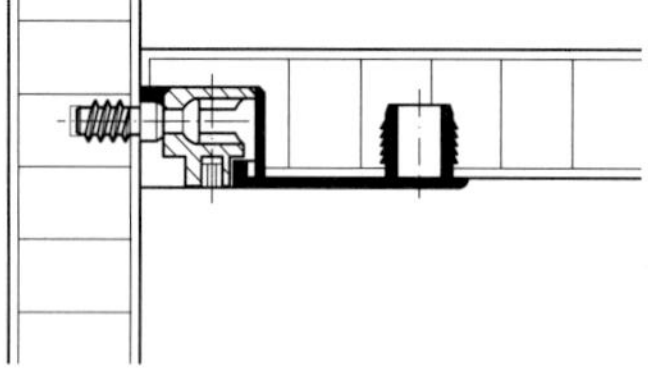

Connecting bolt with M4 or M6 thread screwed into a dowel or sleeve for Ø 8 resp. Ø 10 mm holes

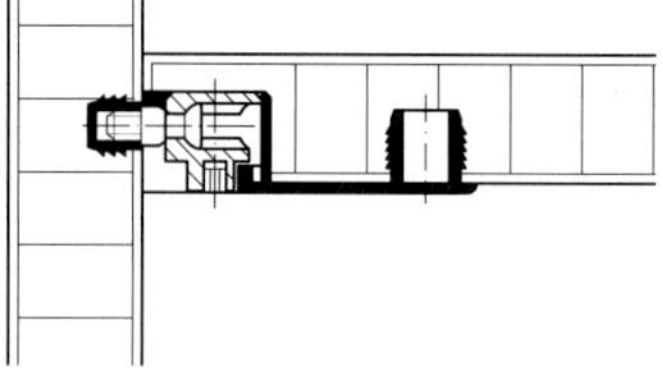

For single sided assembly, capped bolt for insertion from outside in Ø 8 mm holes

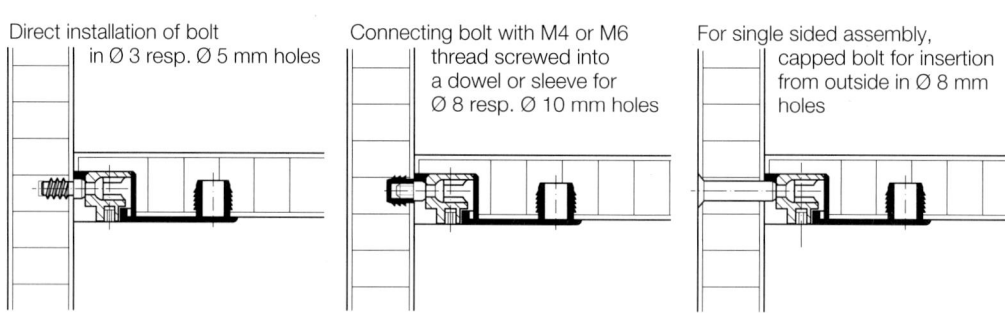

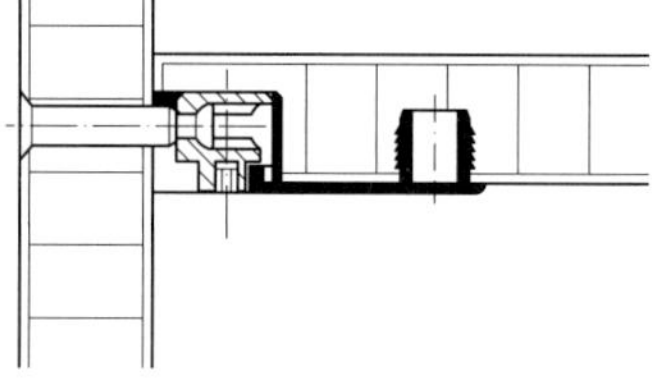

Double-ended bolt for double-sided assembly to be inserted in Ø 5 mm holes

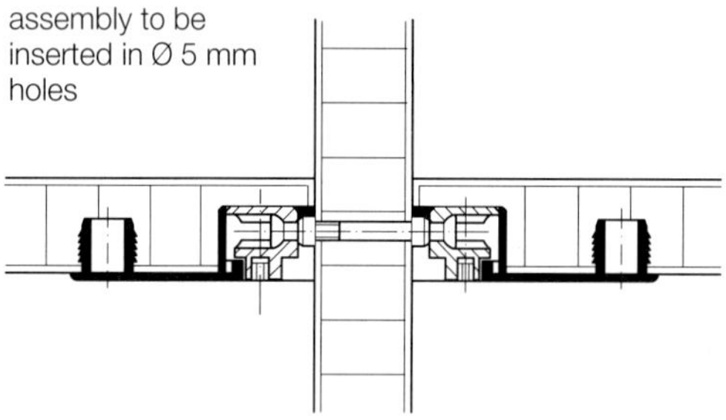

Double-ended bolt for double-sided assembly to be inserted in Ø 8 mm holes

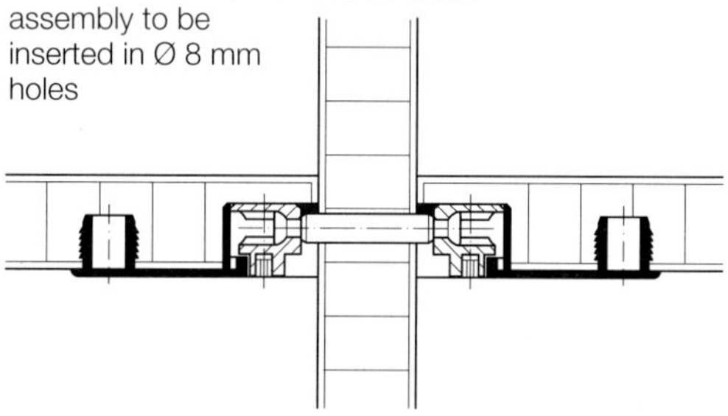

Due to the specially designed tightening element in the housing a concealed mounting is possible.
A Ø 10 mm through-hole must be drilled to permit tightening of the fitting.

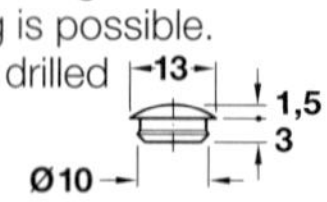

Trim cap of plastic

Cat. No.	white	045.13.704
	beige	045.13.400
	brown	045.13.106
	black	045.13.300

Packing: 100 pcs.

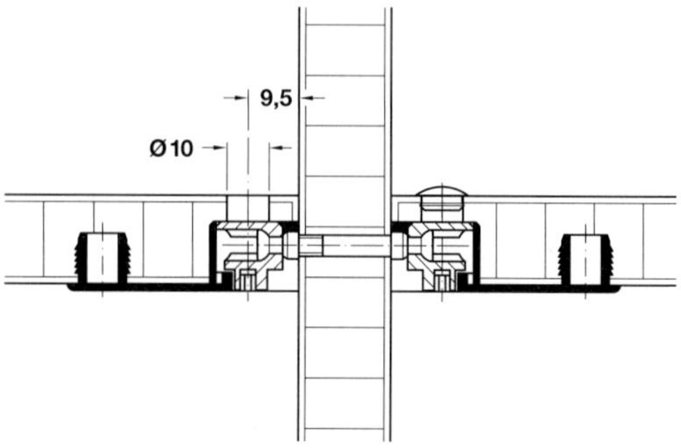

Rafix Housing for Ø 7 mm Connecting Bolt

HÄFELE

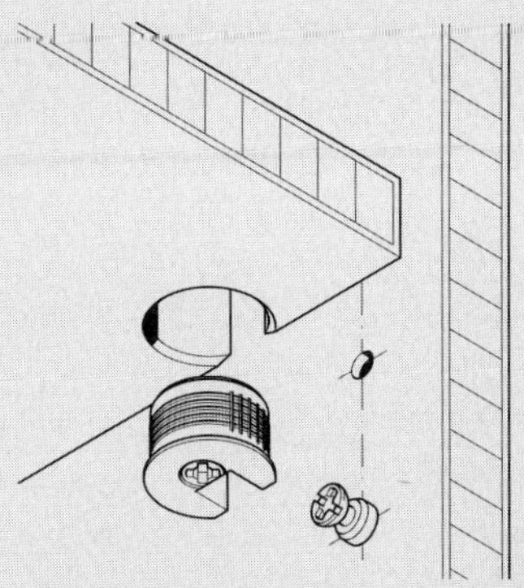

Rafix housing «flush fitting» of
plastic, **without ridge**
with zinc die-cast
tightening element

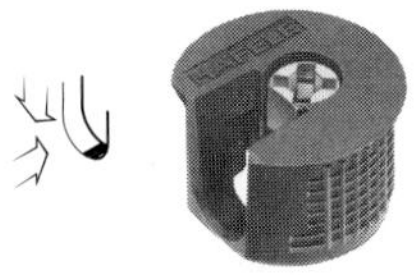

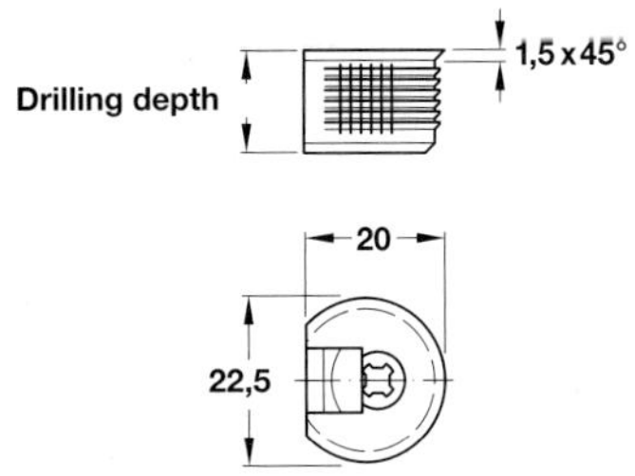

For wood thicknesses from:	Dimension A mounting center	Drilling depth	Cat. No. white	beige	brown	black
16 mm	8,0 mm	12,7 $^{+0,2}$ mm	263.50.738	263.50.434	263.50.130	263.50.330
19 mm	9,5 mm	14,2 $^{+0,2}$ mm	263.50.756	263.50.452	263.50.158	263.50.350

Packing: 1000 pcs.

Locks, Catches, RTA and PAS® Fittings
Shelf Supports
Bed Fittings

2

«Flush fitting» Rafix

- No projecting parts due to the countersunk rim on the housing
- Housing is mounted flush to shelf
- Shelves can be stacked without spacers

For Rafix housing «flush fitting» suitable only for **19 mm** wood thicknesses

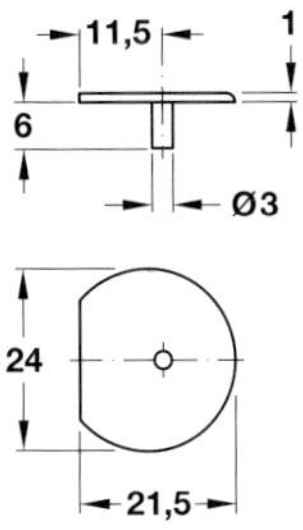

Trim cap, plastic

Cat. No.	white	263.59.704
	beige	263.59.400
	brown	263.59.106
	black	263..59.302

Packing: 1000 pcs.

Other colors available. Minimum order100,000 pcs.

Countersunk drill-bit suitable for «flush fitting» Rafix housing with three carbide tipped cutters, 10 mm shank, flattened on one side and with M5 x 8 mm adjusting screw

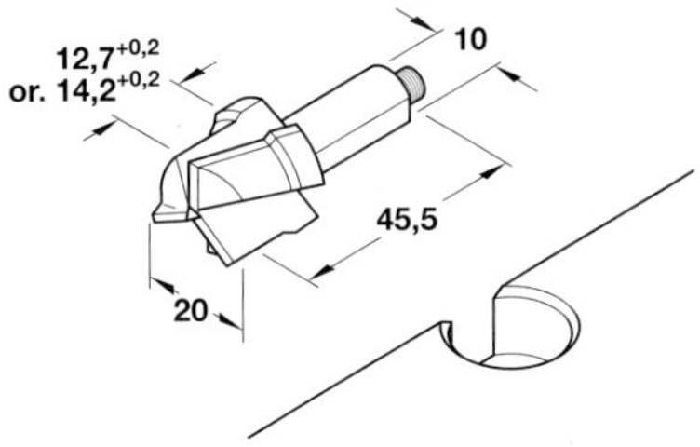

Suitable for wood thickness		16 mm	19 mm
Cat. No.	left-hand	001.24.318	001.24.336
	right-hand	001.24.309	001.24.327

Packing: 1 pc.

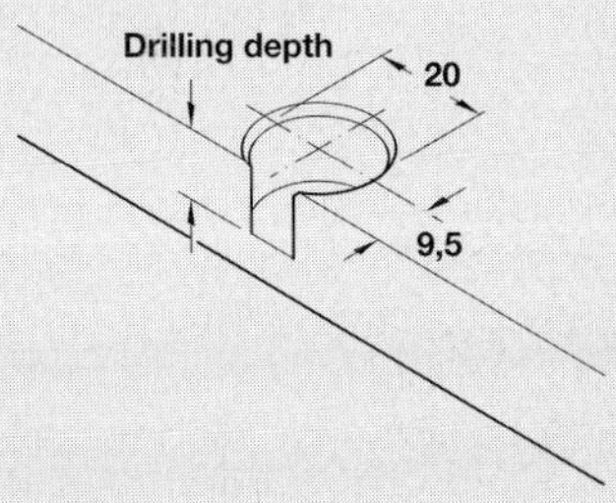

Drill-bit mount with M10 internal thread
for the drill above

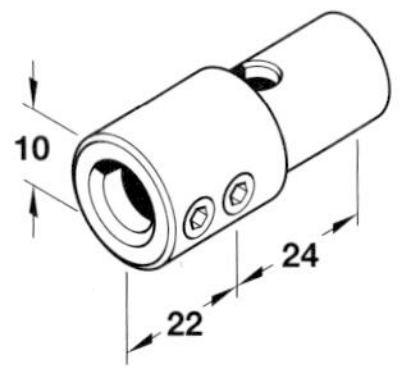

Cat. No.	left-hand	001.91.097
	right-hand	001.91.088

Packing: 1 pc.

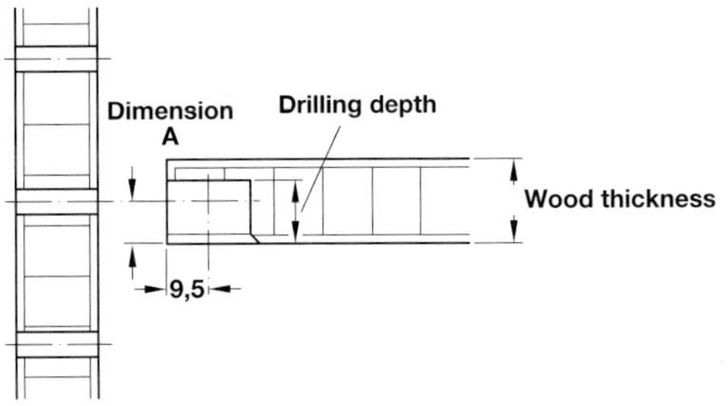

Drilling depth = depending on housing type and wood thickness (see ordering table)

Dimension A = 1/2 wood thickness (see ordering table)

Dimensional data not binding. We reserve the right to alter specifications without notice.

HÄFELE

Rafix Housing for Ø 7 mm Connecting Bolt

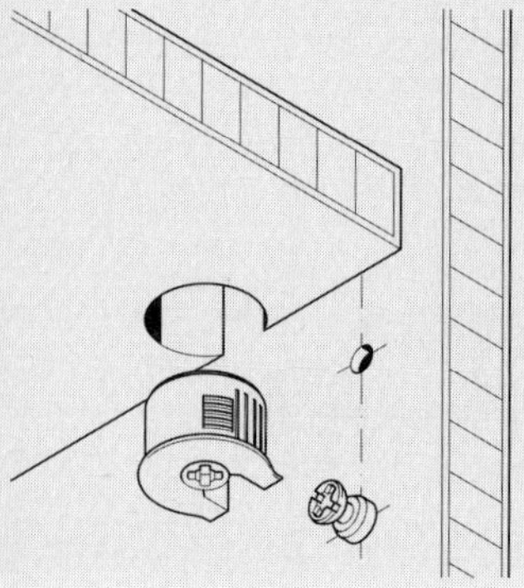

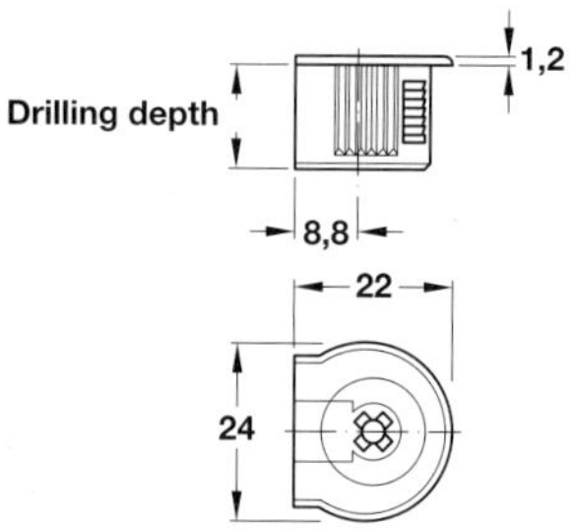

Rafix housing of zinc die-cast, without ridge
with zinc die-cast tightening element

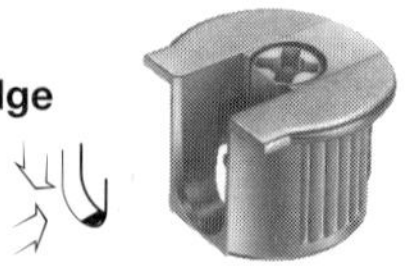

For wood thicknesses from:	Dimension A mounting center	Drilling depth	Cat. No. nickel plated	bronzed
16 mm	8,0 mm	12,7 +0,2 mm	263.11.731	263.11.133
19 mm	9,5 mm	14,2 +0,2 mm	263.11.759	263.11.151

Packing: 500 pieces

As above, **with ridge**

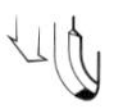

Wood thicknesses from:	Dimension A mounting center	Drilling depth	Cat. No. nickel plated	bronzed
16 mm	8,0 mm	12,7 +0,2 mm	263.15.739	263.15.131
19 mm	9,5 mm	14,2 +0,2 mm	263.15.757	263.15.159

Packing: 500 pieces

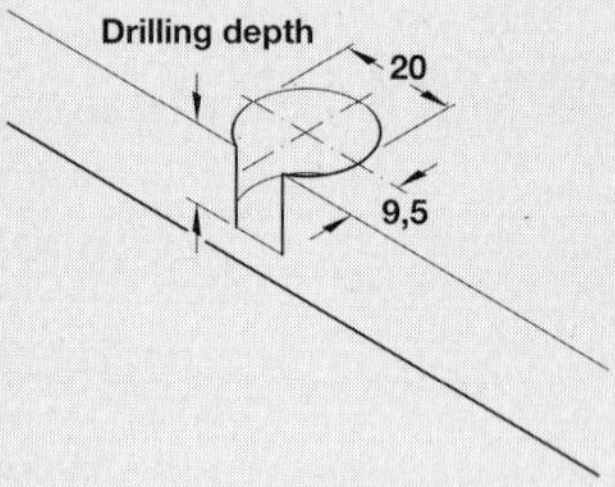

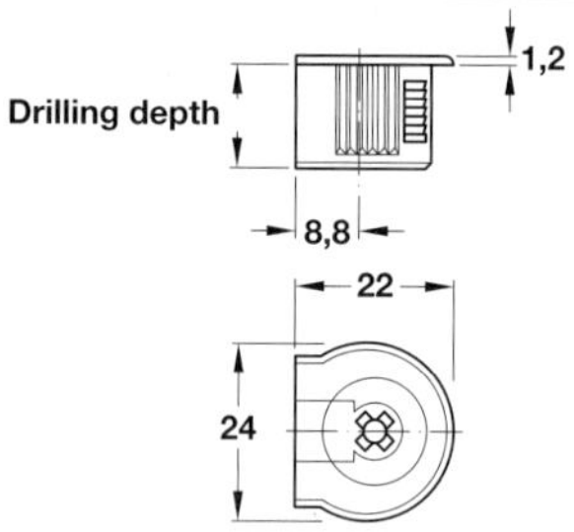

Rafix housing of plastic, without ridge
with zinc die-cast tightening element

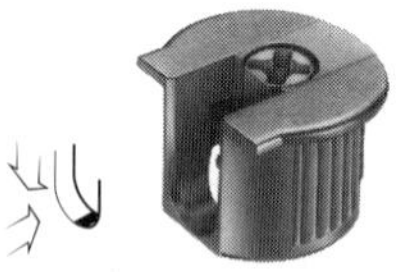

Ideal for:
Closets, wardrobes, store fixtures
- only vertical boring required

Wood thicknesses from:	Dimension A mounting center	Drilling depth	Cat. No. white	beige	brown	black	gray
16 mm	8,0 mm	12,7 +0,2 mm	263.10.734	263.10.430	263.10.136	263.10.332	263.10.538
19 mm	9,5 mm	14,2 +0,2 mm	263.10.752	263.10.458	263.10.154	263.10.350	263.10.556

Packing: 1000 pieces

As above, **with ridge**

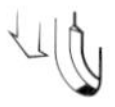

Wood thicknesses from:	Dimension A mounting center	Drilling depth	Cat. No. white	beige	brown
16 mm	8,0 mm	12,7 +0,2 mm	263.14.732	263.14.438	263.14.134
19 mm	9,5 mm	14,2 +0,2 mm	263.14.750	263.14.456	263.14.152

Packing: 1000 pieces

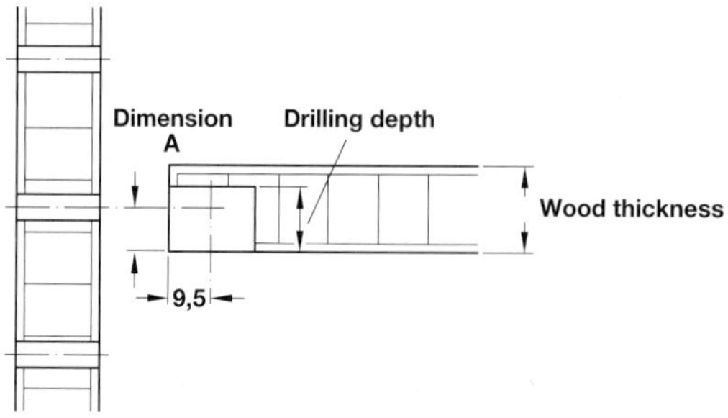

Drilling depth = depending on housing type and wood thickness (see ordering table)

Dimension A = 1/2 wood thickness (see ordering table)

Rafix Housing for Ø 7 mm Connecting Bolt

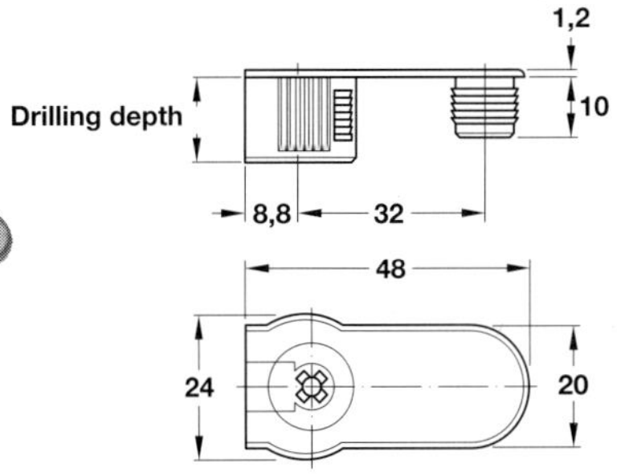

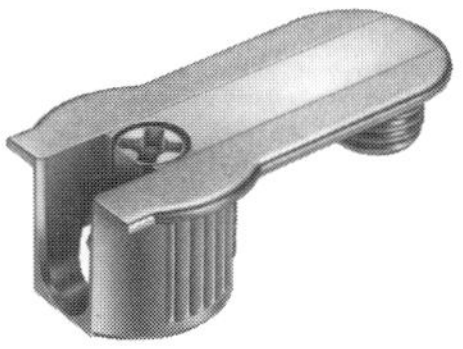

Rafix 32 housing
of zinc die-cast without ridge
with zinc die-cast
tightening element

For wood thicknesses from:	Dimension A mounting center	Drilling depth	Cat. No. nickel plated	bronzed
16 mm	8,0 mm	12,7 +0,3 mm	263.13.735	263.13.137
19 mm	9,5 mm	14,2 +0,3 mm	263.13.753	263.13.155

Packing: 500 pcs.

As above, **with ridge**

Wood thicknesses from:	Dimension A mounting center	Drilling depth	Cat. No. nickel plated	bronzed
16 mm	8,0 mm	12,7 +0,3 mm	263.17.733	263.17.135
19 mm	9,5 mm	14,2 +0,3 mm	263.17.751	263.17.153

Packing: 500 pcs.

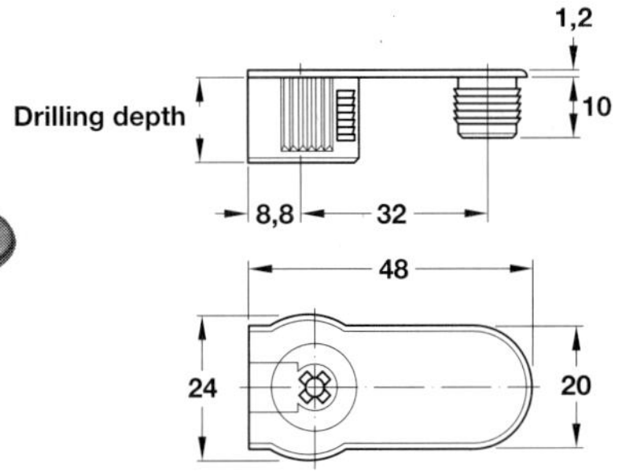

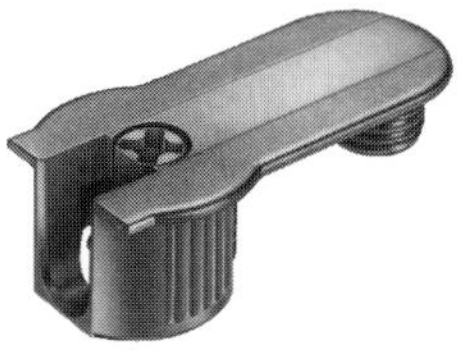

Rafix 32 housing
of plastic, without ridge
with zinc die-cast
tightening element

Wood thicknesses from:	Dimension A mounting center	Drilling depth	Cat. No. white	beige	brown	black	gray
16 mm	8,0 mm	12,7 +0,3 mm	263.12.738	263.12.434	263.12.130	263.12.336	263.12.532
19 mm	9,5 mm	14,2 +0,3 mm	263.12.756	263.12.452	263.12.158	263.12.354	263.12.550

Packing: 1000 pcs.

As above, **with ridge**

Wood thicknesses from:	Dimension A mounting center	Drilling depth	Cat. No. white	beige	brown
16 mm	8,0 mm	12,7 +0,3 mm	263.16.736	263.16.432	263.16.138
19 mm	9,5 mm	14,2 +0,3 mm	263.16.754	263.16.450	263.16.156

Packing: 1000 pcs.

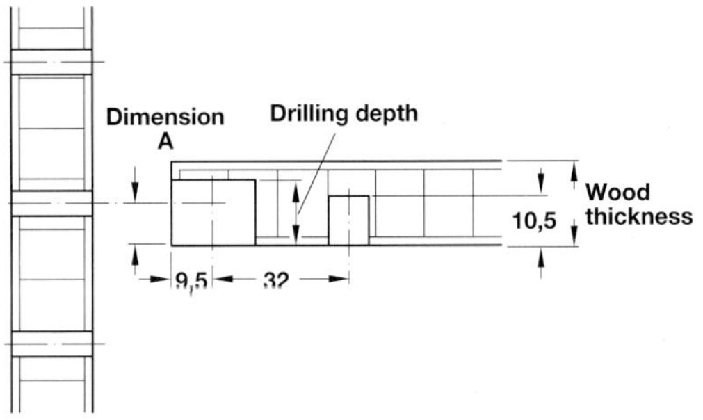

Drilling depth = depending on housing type and wood thickness (see ordering table)

Dimension A = 1/2 wood thickness (see ordering table)

Dimensions in mm

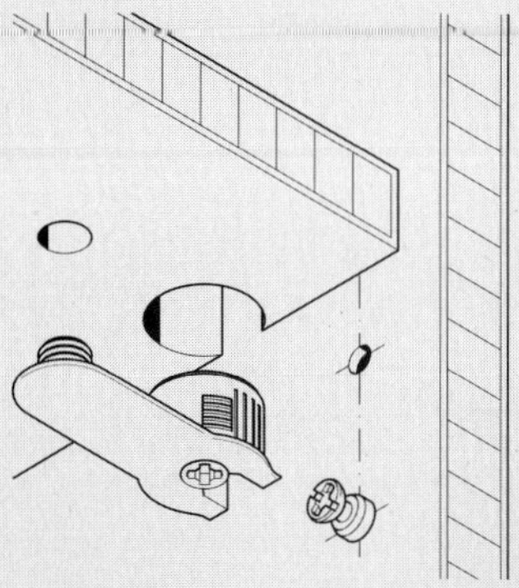

Locks, Catches, RTA and PAS® Fittings
Shelf Supports
Bed Fittings
2

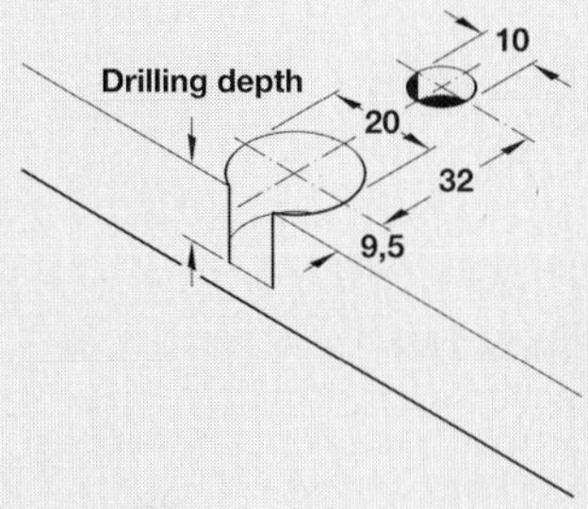

Ideal for:
Closets, wardrobes, store fixtures
- only vertical boring required
- with addtional dowel for additional strength and aligns the connector

Dimensional data not binding.
We reserve the right to alter specifications without notice.

HÄFELE

Rafix TAB housing for Ø 7 mm connecting bolts

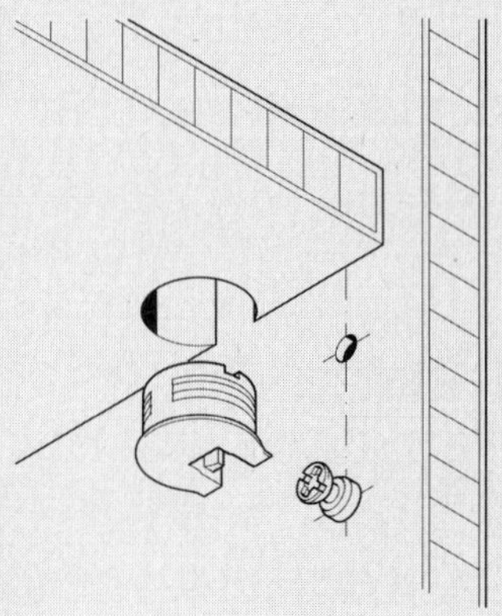

Rafix TAB is a continuation of the Rafix design line for shelf connections:

- The housing is pressed into the shelf and pushed onto a Rafix connecting bolt of Ø 7 mm
- The tapered surfaces of Rafix TAB ensure an exceptionally tight connection
- Rafix TAB features a catch which prevents the shelf from moving upwards away from the Rafix connecting bolt
- For shelf and support panels, drop-down shelves can be fastened using Rafix TAB alone
- For tall cabinets, Rafix connectors may also be inserted in the shelves, to prevent the side panels from bulging

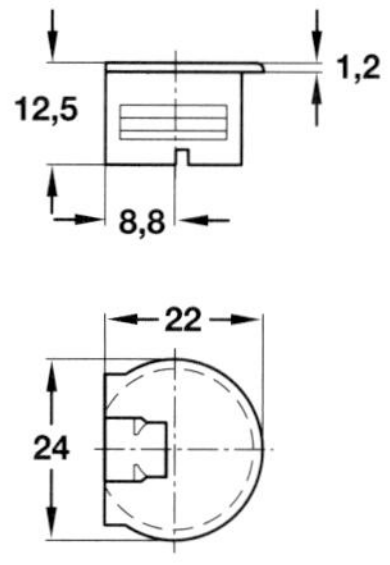

Rafix TAB housing
plastic

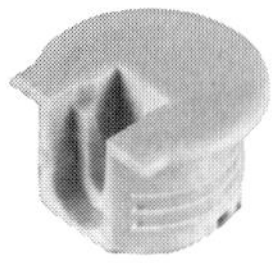

For wood thicknesses from:	Dimension A Central fastening	Drilling depth	Cat. No. white	beige	brown	black
16 mm	8,0 mm	12,7 $^{+0,3}$ mm	263.09.731	263.09.437	263.09.133	263.09.339

Packing: 100, 1000 and 5000 pcs.

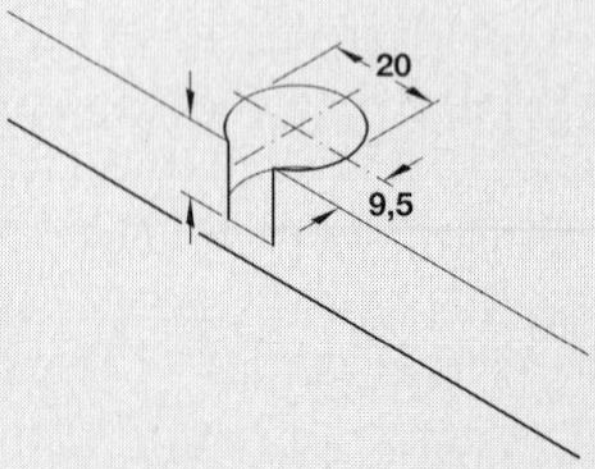

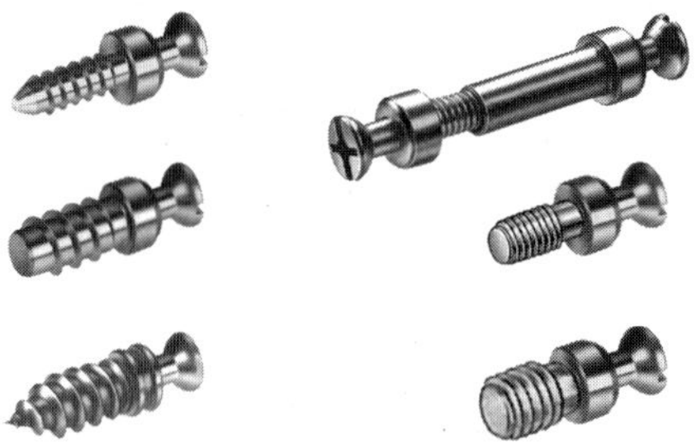

Important note:

For Rafix TAB, find connecting bolts and accessories on pages **2.115** to **2.118**.

Rafix TAB rounds off the Rafix connector system by making various interesting combinations possible.

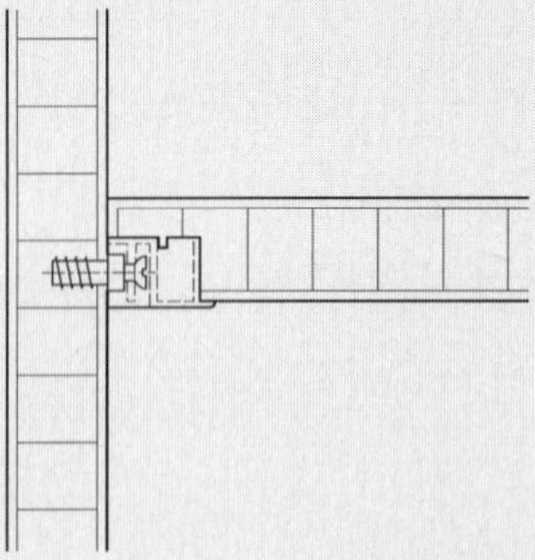

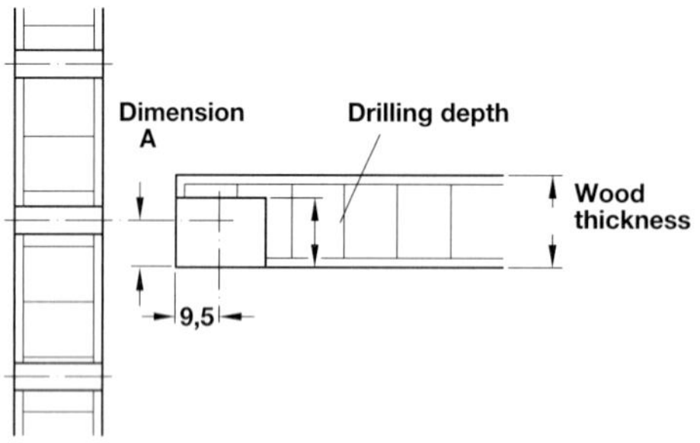

Drilling depth = depending on type of housing and thickness of wood (see Ordering Table)

Dimension A = 1/2 wood thickness (see Ordering Table)

Dimensions in mm

Dimensional data not binding. We reserve the right to alter specifications without notice.

Rafix Connecting Bolts, Ø 7 mm

HÄFELE

Connecting bolts for direct **screw fastening** on single-sided assemblies in **Ø 3** or **Ø 5 mm holes** or for through insertion on double-sided assemblies in **Ø 5 mm holes**

Connecting bolt
steel with special thread

Cat. No. galvanized	263.20.810

Packing: 1000 pcs.

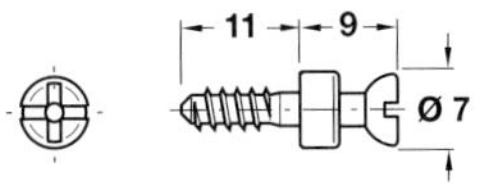

for Ø 3 mm hole

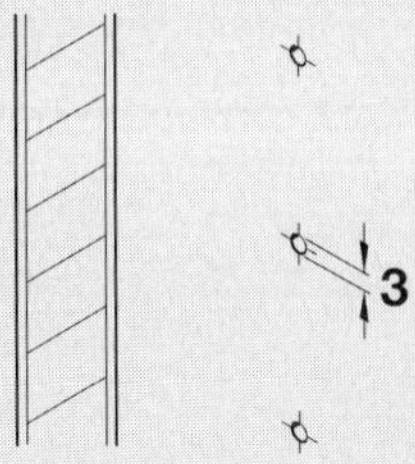

The connecting bolts above can be used with the following . . .

Spreading dowel of nylon, natural-colored, for use in **Ø 5 mm holes**

Cat. No.	042.98.051

Packing: 5000 pcs.

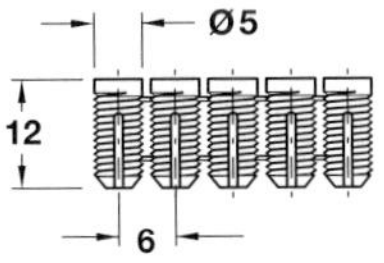

20 piece mould

Connecting bolts with

 = **Cross-slot**
- suitable for PZ 2 cross-slot only

 = **Combination slot**
- suitable for PZ 2 cross-slot and flat blade

Connecting bolt
steel with special thread

Thread length	8 mm	11 mm	15 mm
Cat. No. galvanized	263.20.838	263.20.847	263.20.856

Packing: 2000 pcs.

Thread length

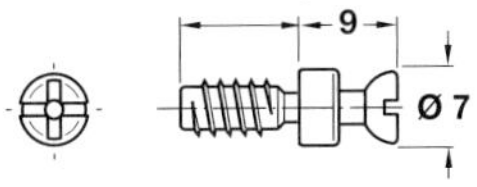

for Ø 5 mm hole

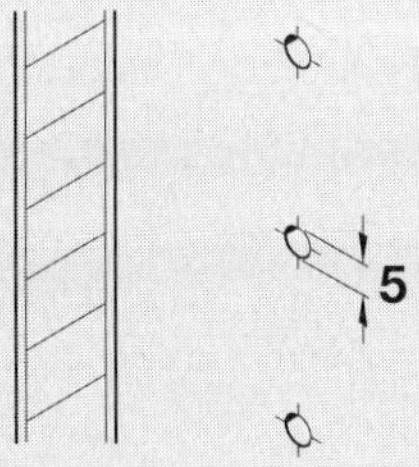

Connecting bolt
steel with special thread

Cat. No. galvanized	263.20.981

Packing: 5000 pcs.

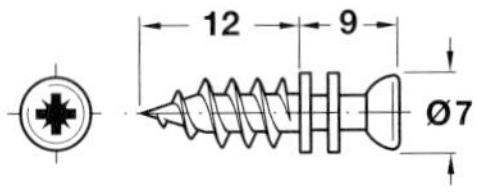

for Ø 5 mm hole

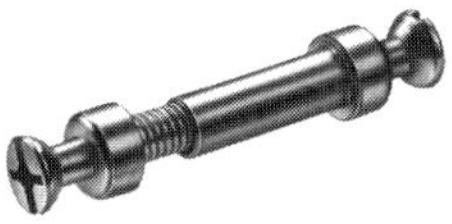

Double-ended bolt of steel
for double-sided assemblies

for side panel thickness	16 - 22 mm
Cat. No. galvanized	263.24.943

Packing: 2000 pcs.

Panel thickness

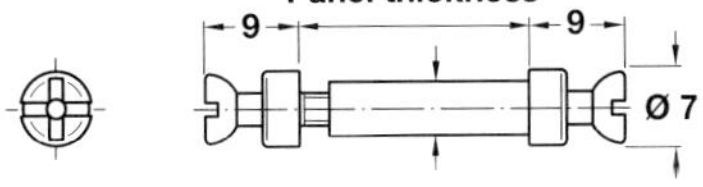

for Ø 5 mm hole

Dimensions in mm

Dimensional data not binding. We reserve the right to alter specifications without notice.

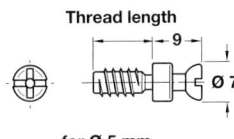

HÄFELE

Rafix Connecting Bolts, Ø 7 mm

Connecting bolts with **M4 thread** to be screwed into dowels or sleeves for single- or double-sided assemblies. Dowels or sleeves can be selected for **holes of Ø 5, Ø 8** or **Ø 10 mm.**

Connecting bolts with

= Combination slot
- suitable for PZ 2 cross-slot and flat blade

Connecting bolt
steel with M4 thread

Cat. No.	galvanized	263.21.817

Packing: 1000 pcs.

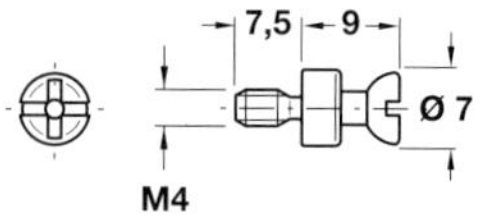

The above connecting bolts above can be used with the following parts.

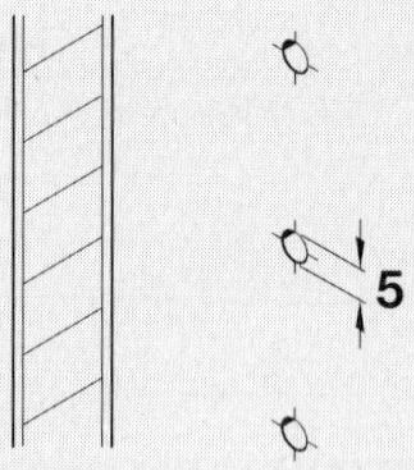

Spreading dowel with M4 internal thread
Finish: brass, unfinished

Cat. No.	051.45.004

Packing: 3000 pcs.

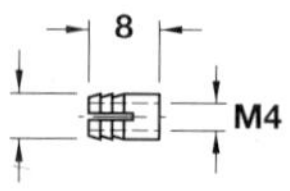

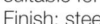

Sleeve, smooth with M4 internal thread
suitable for **double-sided assemblies**
Finish: steel

Length	15 mm	18 mm	22 mm
unfinished	267.00.011	267.00.012	267.00.013
galvanized	267.00.911	267.00.912	267.00.913

Packing: 1000 pcs.

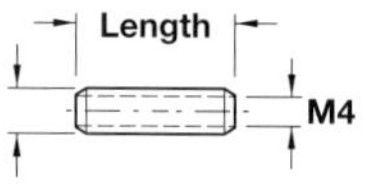

End screw with M4 thread of steel, usable as **end cap bolt**
(extension possibilities)

Length		8 mm	10 mm
Cat. No.	nickel-plated	020.92.711	020.92.720
	burnished	020.92.113	020.92.122

Packing: 2000 pcs.

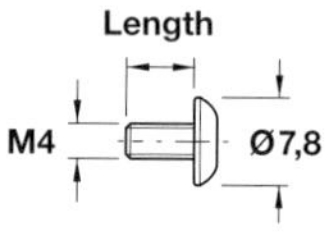

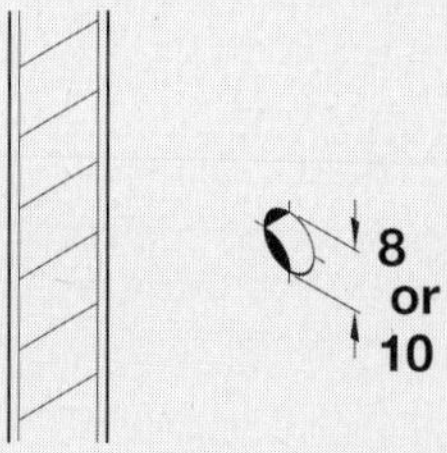

Glue-in dowel with M4 internal thread
Finish: nylon, natural-colored

Length	8 mm	10 mm
Cat. No.	039.33.140	039.33.042

Packing: 1000 pcs.

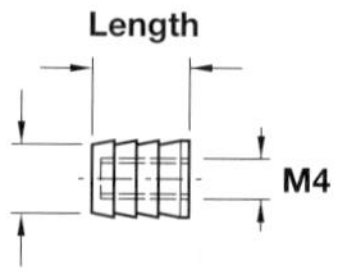

Glue-in dowel with M4 internal thread
Finish: nylon, natural-colored

Length	11 mm
Cat. No.	039.33.239

Packing: 5000 pcs.

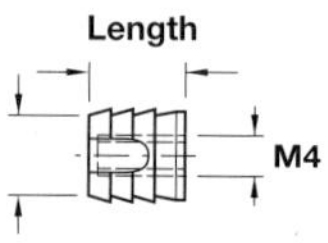

Dimensional data not binding.
We reserve the right to alter specifications without notice.

Dimensions in mm

Rafix Connecting Bolts, Ø 7 mm

HÄFELE

Connecting bolts with **M6 thread** to be screwed into dowels for single-sided assemblies. Dowels can be selected for **holes of Ø 8** or **Ø 10 mm.**

Connecting bolts with

= **Combination slot**
- suitable for PZ 2 cross-slot and flat blade

Connecting bolt
steel with M6 thread

Cat. No.	galvanized	263.21.826

Packing: 1000 pcs.

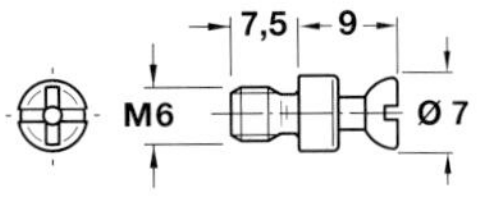

The above connecting bolts above can be used with the following dowels.

Locks, Catches, RTA and PAS® Fittings
Shelf Supports
Bed Fittings
2

Spreading dowel with M6 internal thread
Finish: brass, unfinished

Length	9 mm	12 mm*
Cat. No.	039.00.267	039.00.061
Packing:	2000 pcs.	1000 pcs.

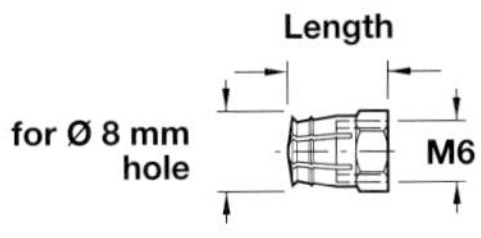

* **With nylon ball**
Minimum drilling depth = 15 mm

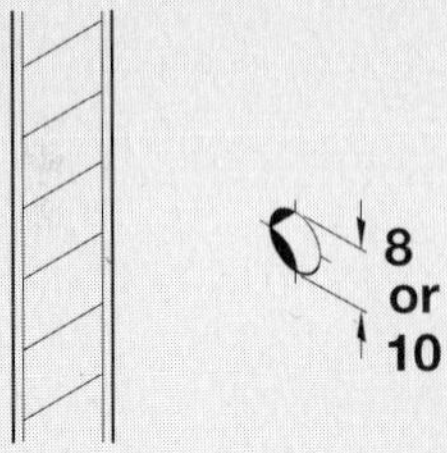

Glue-in dowel with M6 internal thread
Finish: nylon, natural-colored

Cat. No.	039.33.462

Packing: 5000 pcs.

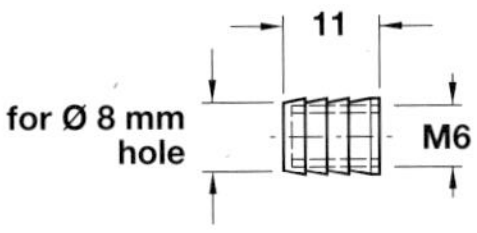

Glue-in dowel with M6 internal thread
Finish: nylon, natural-colored

Length	9 mm	11 mm	13 mm
Cat. No.	039.33.364	039.33.266	039.33.060
Packing:	1000 pcs.	5000 pcs.	5000 pcs.

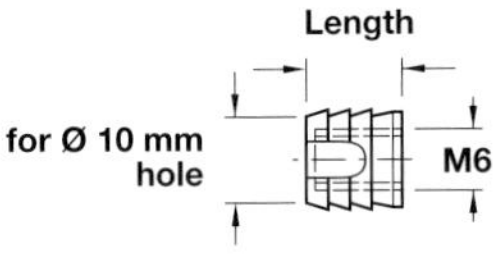

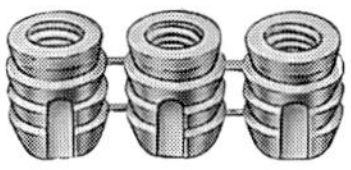

Strip of glue-in dowels
with M6 internal thread
Finish: nylon, natural-colored

Cat. No.	039.34.067

Packing: 1000 pcs.

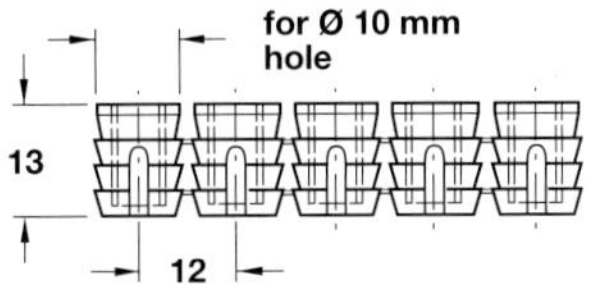

20 pieces molded together

Strip of spreading dowels
with M6 internal thread of nylon, natural-colored

Cat. No.	039.35.064

Packing: 1000 pcs.

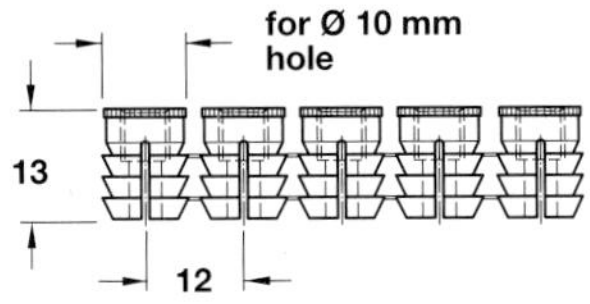

20 pieces molded together

Dimensional data not binding. We reserve the right to alter specifications without notice.

Dimensions in mm

HÄFELE

Rafix Connecting Bolts, Ø 7 mm and Ø 5 mm

Connecting bolts for insertion through **Ø 8 mm holes** in side panels on single- or double-sided assemblies.

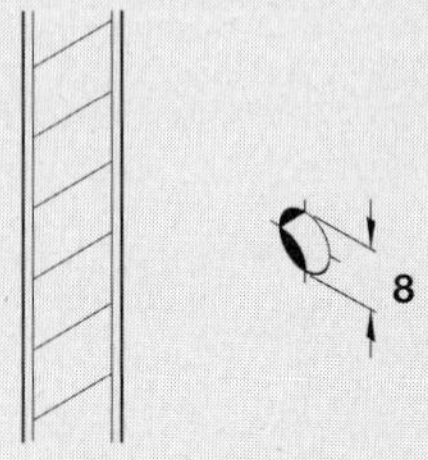

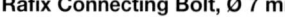

Rafix Connecting Bolt, Ø 7 mm

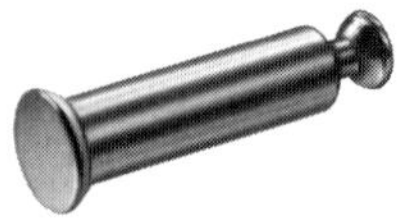

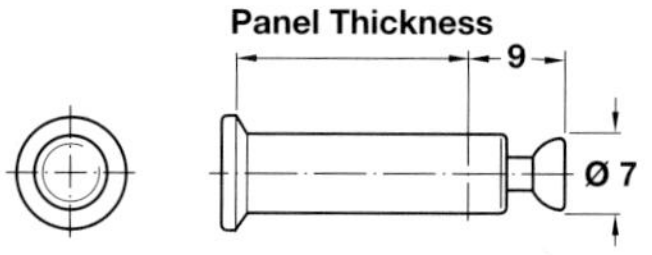

Capped bolt
Finish: steel

side panel thickness		16 mm	19 mm
Cat. No.	nickel-plated	263.25.726	263.25.735
	bronzed	263.25.128	263.25.137

Packing: 1000 pcs.

Rafix Connecting Bolt, Ø 7 mm

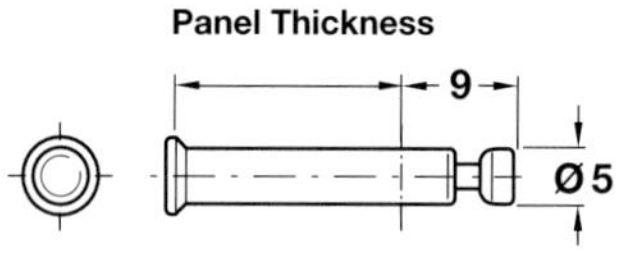

Double-ended bolt of steel
for double-sided assemblies

side panel thickness		16 mm	19 mm
Cat. No.	galvanized	263.24.925	263.24.934

Packing: 1000 pcs.

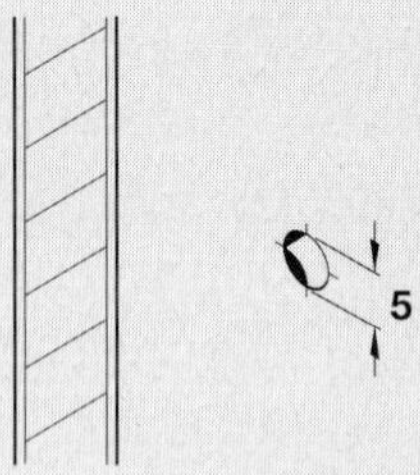

Rafix Connecting Bolt, Ø 5 mm

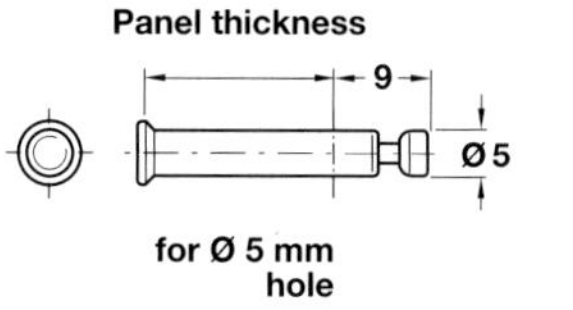

Capped bolt of steel,
for installation into Ø 5 mm hole

side panel thickness		16 mm	19 mm
Cat. No.	nickel-plated	263.45.728	263.45.737

Packing: 1000 pcs.

Dimensional data not binding.
We reserve the right to alter specifications without notice.

Dimensions in mm

Screw-mounted and Plug-In Rasant-Tab Housings

The Rafix system of housings and bolts are ideal for use in combination with **Rasant-Tab**. Rafix uses the same drilling pattern and has an identical appearance when installed.

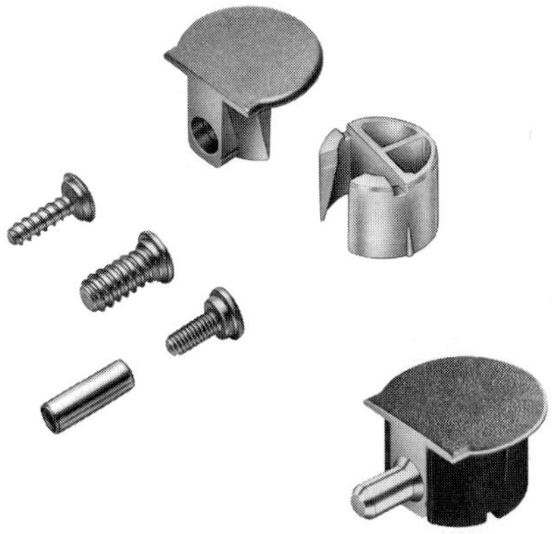

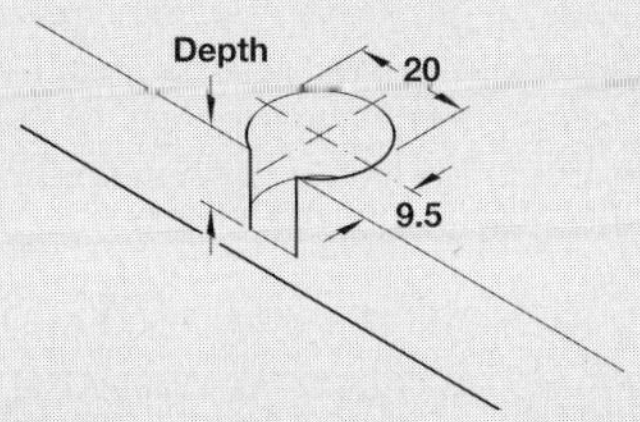

Some typical Rasant-Tab mountings for single and double side installations:

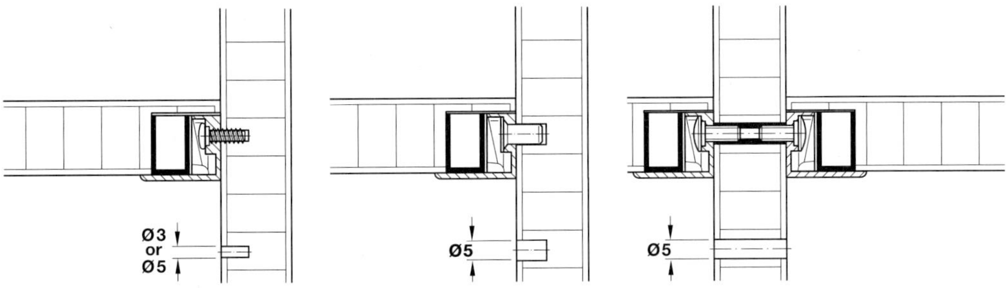

Screw-mounted support using Varianta special screw in ø 3 mm holes.

Plug-in support in series-drilled, ø 5 mm holes.

Double-sided construction using screw-mounted supports with Varianta-thread M4 screws and internally-threaded sleeves in ø 5 mm holes.

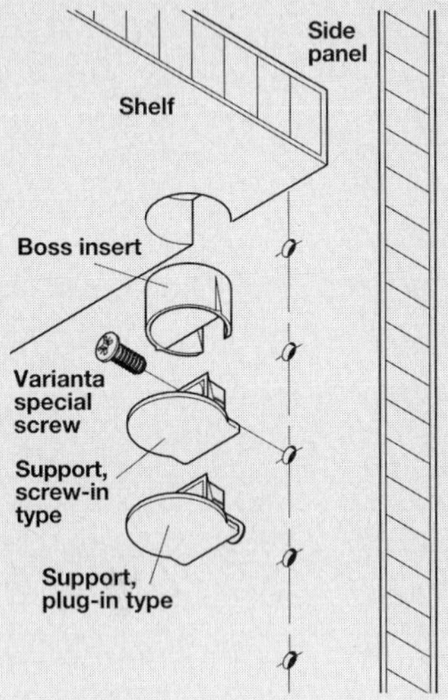

- Rasant-Tab shelf support system Range consists of:
- Cup with a plug-in support for ø 5 mm pre-drilled holes
- Cup with screw fix support for pre-drilled ø3 mm or ø5 mm holes
- Screw-in Rasant-Tab gives added stability to structural cross-members
- Plug-in Rasant-Tab prevents the shelf being dislodged or falling out
- Generous supporting surface ensures a high load capacity
- Lateral pull of connector provides added stability to side panels
- Particularly suitable for heavy wood shelves, tall cabinets, wardrobes
- The cup insert is flush with surface, therefore shelves can be stacked on top of each other

Dimensions in mm

HÄFELE

Screw-mounted and Plug-in Rasant-Tab Housing

Varianta special screw:
to secure supporting element and requiring ø 3 mm hole.
Finish:
Steel, nickel-plated

Length	Ø 3 mm	Ø 5 mm
10.5	013.20.814	013.20.912
13.5	013.20.832	013.20.930
16.0	013.20.841	013.20.949

Packing: 500 Pcs.

Rasant-Tab, screw-on
Includes:
Male: zinc, die-cast
Insert: plastic, natural

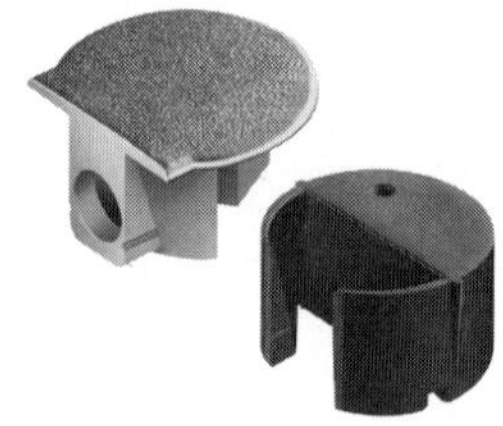

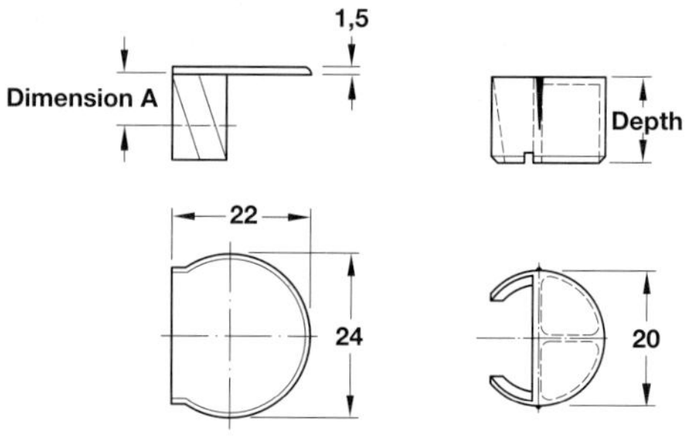

Wood thicknesses:	Dimension A	Depth	Cat. No. nickel-plated	black
16 mm	7.5 mm	12.5 mm	262.36.510	262.36.410
19 mm	9.5 mm	14.5 mm	262.36.520	262.36.420

Packing: 1000 Pcs.

Varianta-Screw M4, for two sided installation with M4 sleeve in ø 5 mm holes.
Finish: steel, nickel-plated

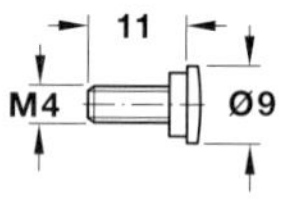

Cat. No.	020.91.901

Packing: 500 Pcs.

Sleeve, with internal M4 thread, for use on center panel.
Finish: steel

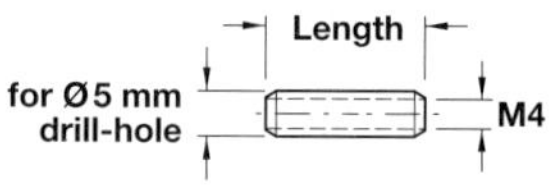

Length	15 mm	18 mm	22 mm
unfinished	267.00.011	267.00.012	267.00.013
zinc-plated	267.00.911	267.00.912	267.00.913

Packing: 1000 Pcs.

Rasant-Tab, plug-in
Includes:
Male: zinc, die-cast
Insert: plastic, natural

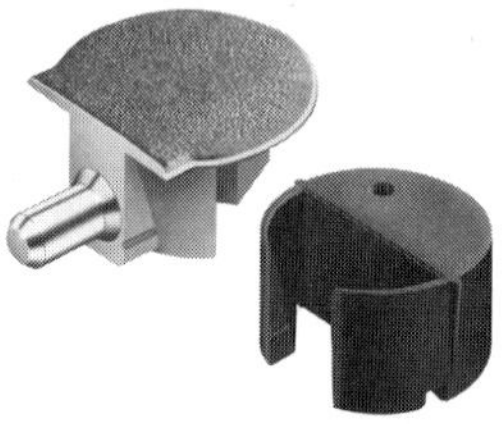

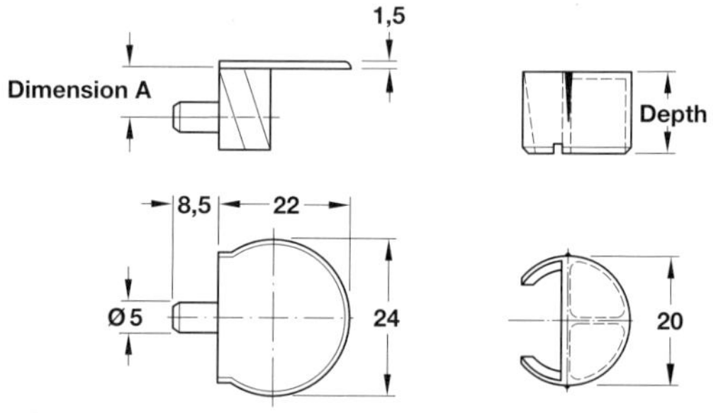

Wood thicknesses:	Dimension A	Depth	Cat. No. nickel-plated	black
16 mm	7.5 mm	12.5 mm	262.35.510	262.35.410
19 mm	9.5 mm	14.5 mm	262.35.520	262.35.420

Packing: 1000 Pcs.

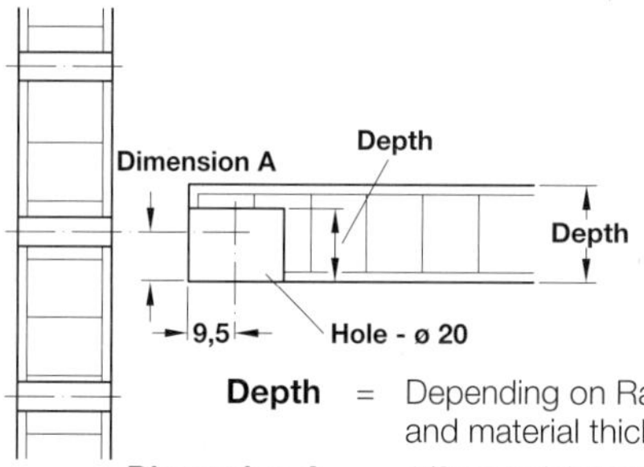

Depth = Depending on Rasant-Type and material thickness
Dimension A = 1/2 material thickness

Example: Center panel application.

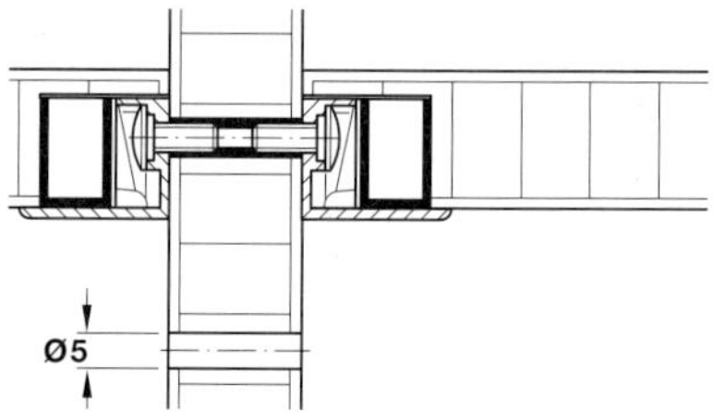

Dimensions in mm

Dimensional data not binding.
We reserve the right to alter specifications without notice.

TAB V and TAB Shelf Fasteners

HÄFELE

The ideal fasteners for shelves

They are used where conventional shelf supports are no longer adequate and genuine structural fastening elements are required.

Two types are available
- **TAB V** to lock and secure shelves
- **TAB** for securing shelves to side panels

The fitting consists of two parts:
- A support element (screw-mounted or plug-fit)
- A cup insert

The cup insert is pressed flush into a Ø 18 mm hole. The angular connecting surfaces of the cup insert and the support element pull the shelf securely onto the side panel. After assembly, only the small base plate of the support element can be seen.

TAB V shelf fastener, consisting of: supporting element and cup insert **with** tensioning element
- Excellent angular rigidity and pull-out resistance
- Pulls the shelf onto side panel
- Locks shelf to side panel and prevents tipping

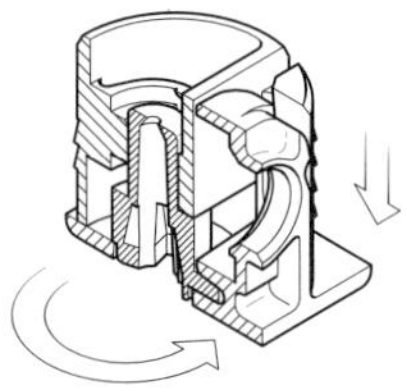

TAB shelf fastener, consisting of: supporting element and cup insert **without** tensioning element
- Excellent angular rigidity
- Pulls the shelf onto side panel

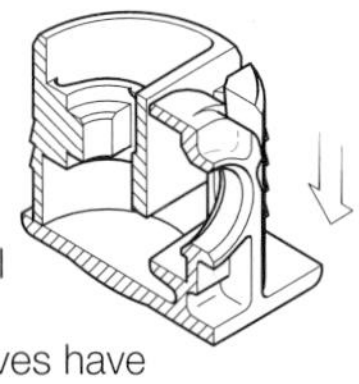

This fitting can used when shelves have to be rapidly removed and reinstalled at a different height.

The cup inserts are flush. Preassembled shelves can be stacked without spacers.

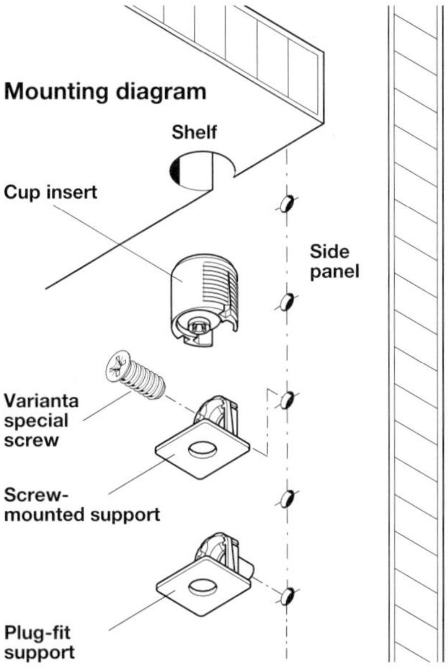

Shelf locking fitting for wood thicknesses from:
16, 19 and **26 mm**

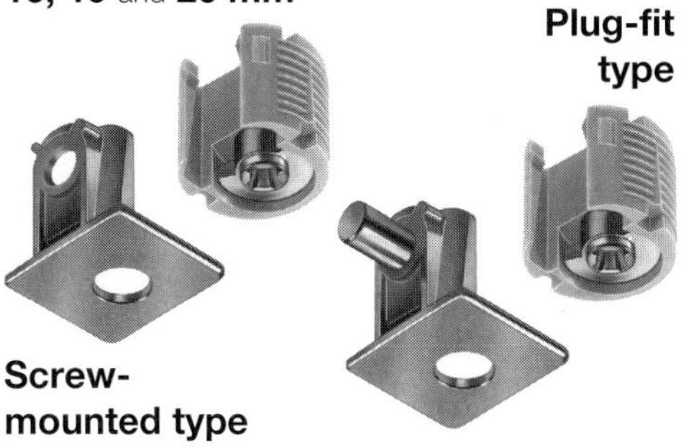

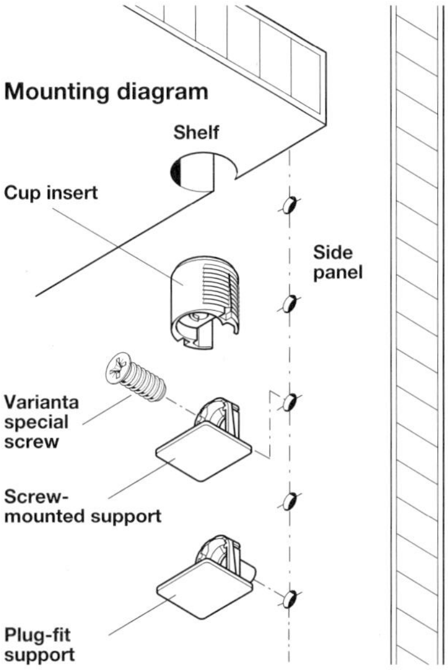

Shelf locking fitting for wood thicknesses from:
16, 19 and **26 mm**

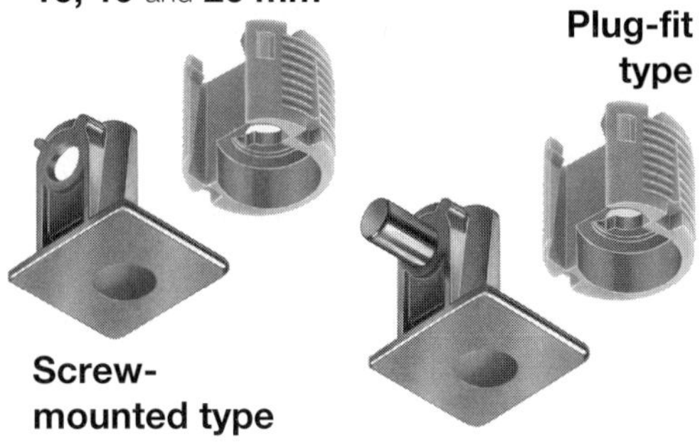

Mounting examples for single and double sided installations

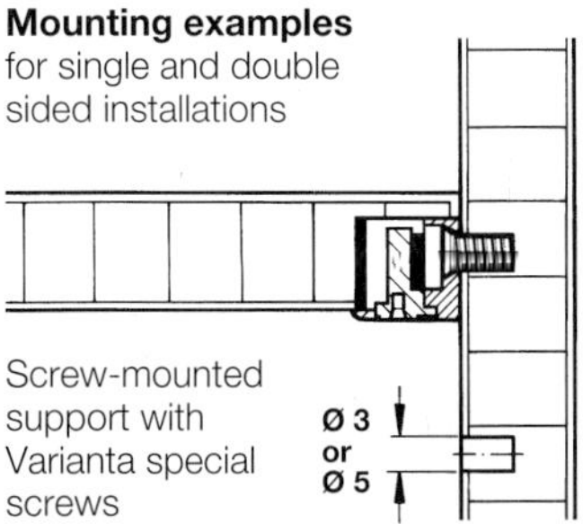

Screw-mounted support with Varianta special screws

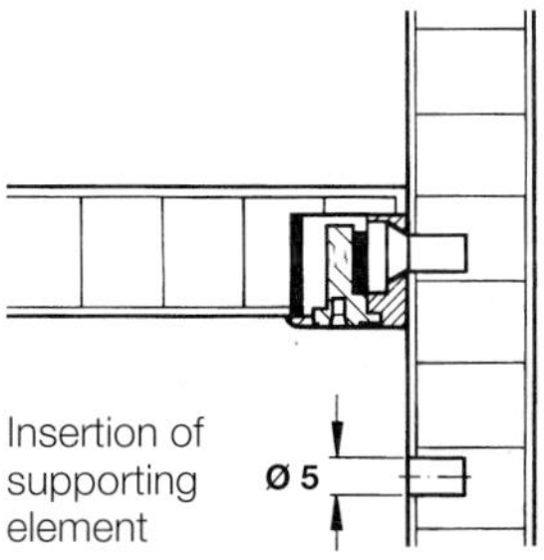

Insertion of supporting element

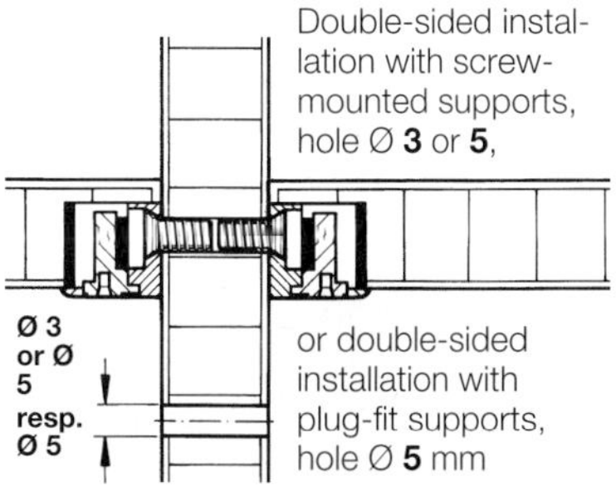

Double-sided installation with screw-mounted supports, hole Ø **3** or **5**,

or double-sided installation with plug-fit supports, hole Ø **5** mm

TAB V

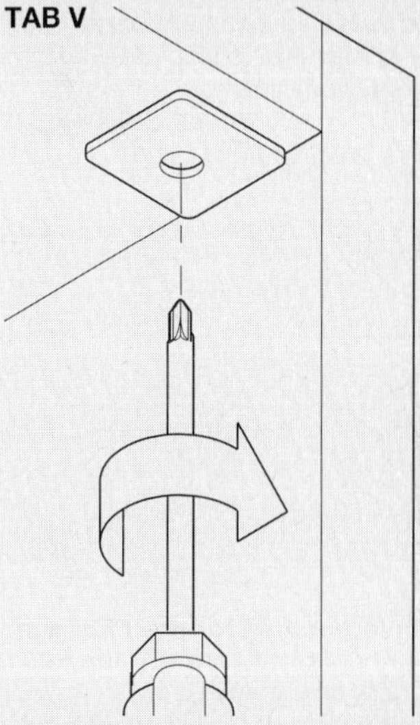

With clip and positive locking device.

TAB

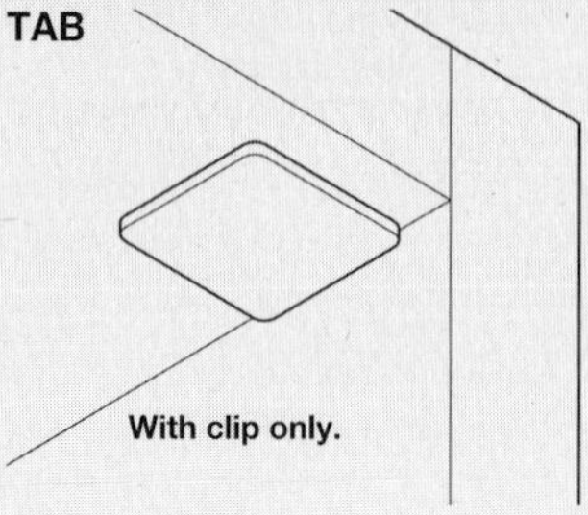

HÄFELE

TAB V Precision Assembly System®

with clip and locking cam

TAB V shelf fasteners consisting of: support and cup insert **with** tensioning element

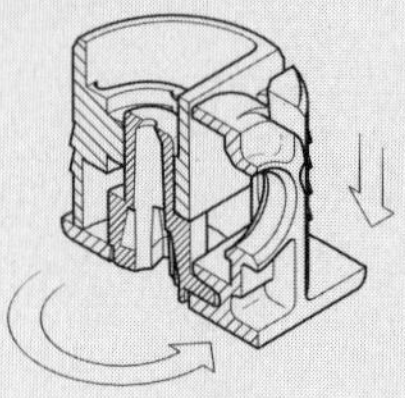

- Excellent angular rigidity and pull-out resistance
- Pulls shelf onto side panel
- Locks shelf to side panel and prevents tipping
- Cup inserts lie flush, allowing shelves to be stacked.

to lock and secure shelves in place

Shelf fastener

screw-mounted

consisting of:
zinc die-cast support and natural colored plastic cup insert with zinc die-cast cam

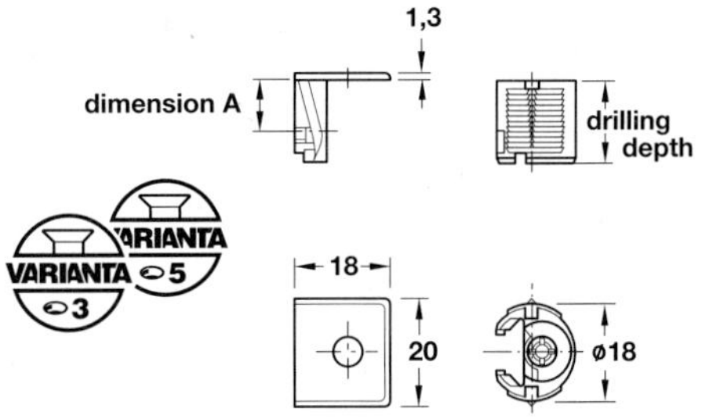

For wood thicknesses from:	Dimension A fastening center	Drilling depth	Cat. No. nickel-plated	black
16 mm	8.0 mm	13.0 mm	263.66.530	263.66.334
19 mm	9.5 mm	15.0 mm	263.66.558	263.66.352
26 mm	13.0 mm	18.5 mm	263.66.585	263.66.389

Packing: 100 pcs.

Mounting screws:
Varianta special screws,
flat headed
with PZ 2 cross-slot
Material: steel, nickel-plated

Length	Hole **Ø 3** mm	Hole **Ø 5** mm
10.5 mm	013.15.617	013.15.715
13.5 mm	013.15.626	013.15.724
16.0 mm	013.15.635	013.15.733

Packing: 500 pcs.

Insertion tool for shelf fastener

- For easy and precise insertion of the cup inserts.
- The tool incorporates a special recess to accommodate the cup insert.
- Once the tool has been aligned parallel to the edge of the cabinet, the cup insert is installed with light hammer taps.

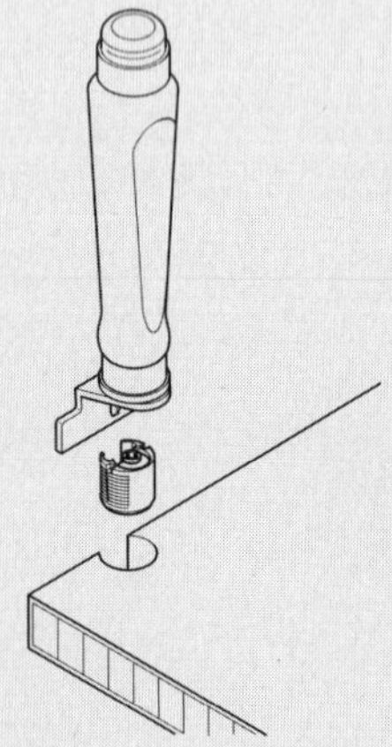

Shelf fastener

plug-fit

into Ø 5 mm holes,
consisting of:
zinc die-cast support and natural colored plastic cup insert with zinc die-cast cam

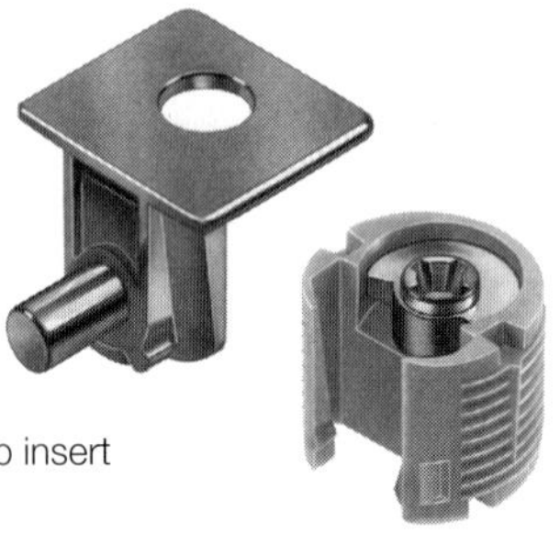

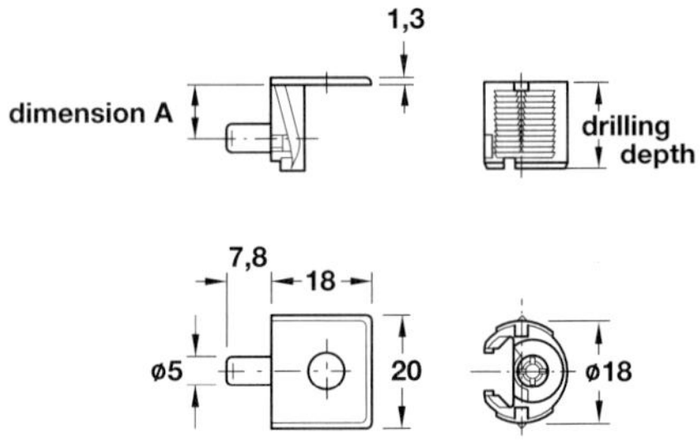

For wood thicknesses from:	Dimension A fastening center	Drilling depth	Cat. No. nickel-plated	black
16 mm	8.0 mm	13.0 mm	263.67.537	263.67.331
19 mm	9.5 mm	15.0 mm	263.67.555	263.67.359
26 mm	13.0 mm	18.5 mm	263.67.582	263.67.386

Packing: 100 pcs.

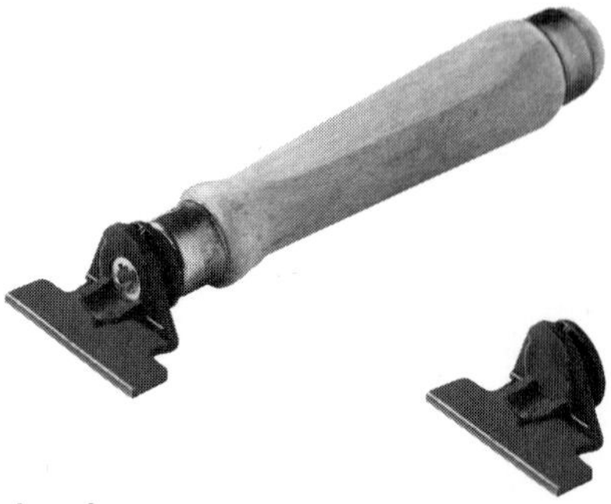

Insertion tool for shelf fastener
Materials: hardwood handle with steel ring reinforcements, plastic mount to accommodate cup insert.

Cat. No.	001.32.749

Packing: 1 pc.

One-way insertion tool for shelf fastener
Finish: plastic, black

Cat. No.	001.32.758

Packing: 1 pc.

Dimensions in mm

Dimensional data not binding. We reserve the right to alter specifications without notice.

TAB Shelf Precision Assembly System®
with clip only

to connect shelves
to side panels

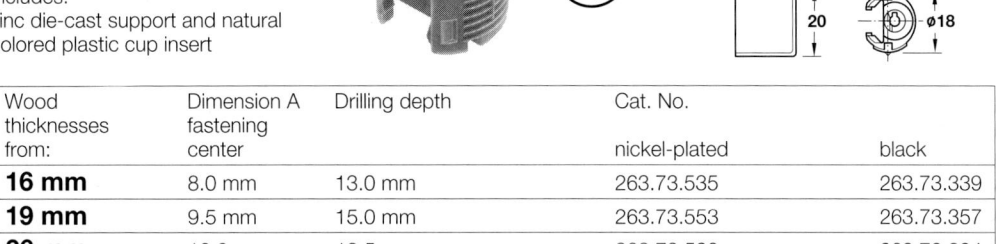

Shelf fastener
screw-mounted
Includes:
zinc die-cast support and natural colored plastic cup insert

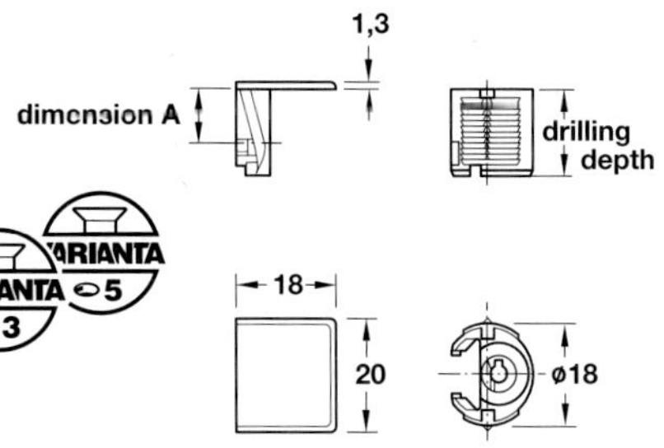

Wood thicknesses from:	Dimension A fastening center	Drilling depth	Cat. No. nickel-plated	black
16 mm	8.0 mm	13.0 mm	263.73.535	263.73.339
19 mm	9.5 mm	15.0 mm	263.73.553	263.73.357
26 mm	13.0 mm	18.5 mm	263.73.580	263.73.384

Packing: 100 and 1000 pcs. each

Mounting screws:
Varianta special screws,
flat headed
with PZ 2 cross-slot
Material: steel, nickel-plated

Length	hole **Ø 3** mm	hole **Ø 5** mm
10.5 mm	013.15.617	013.15.715
13.5 mm	013.15.626	013.15.724
16.0 mm	013.15.635	013.15.733

Packing: 500 pcs.

Shelf fastener
plug-fit
into Ø 5 mm holes,
Includes:
zinc die-cast support and natural colored plastic cup insert

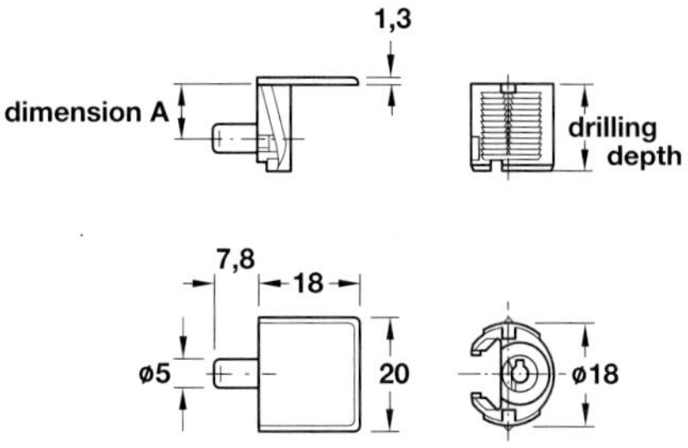

For wood thicknesses from:	Dimension A fastening center	Drilling depth	Cat. No. nickel-plated	black
16 mm	8.0 mm	13.0 mm	263.74.532	263.74.336
19 mm	9.5 mm	15.0 mm	263.74.550	263.74.354
26 mm	13.0 mm	18.5 mm	263.74.587	263.74.381

Packing: 100 pcs.

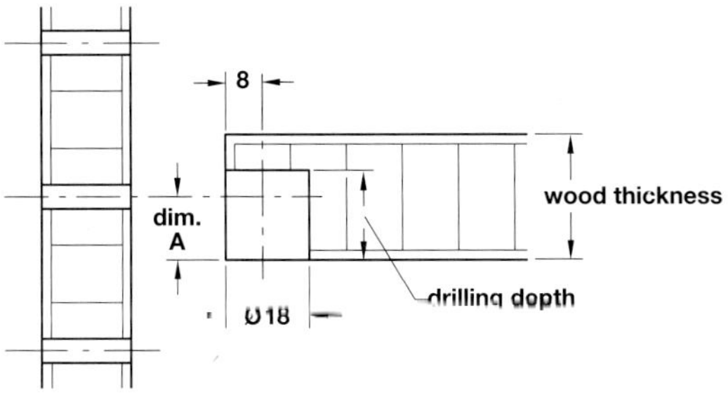

Drilling depth
depending on type and wood thickness (see ordering table)

Dimensions in mm

HÄFELE

TAB V shelf fasteners consisting of:
support and cup insert
without tensioning element

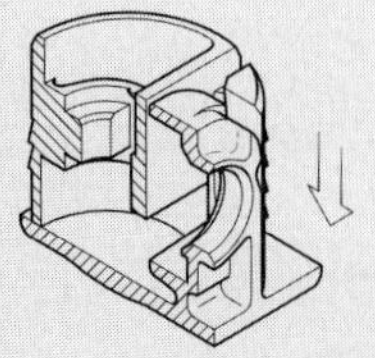

Locks, Catches, RTA and PAS® Fittings
Shelf Supports
Bed Fittings
2

This fitting should be used in situations where shelves are to be rapidly removed, and if required installed at a different level.
- Excellent rigidity at joints
- Pulls shelf onto side panel
- Cup inserts lie flush, allowing shelves to be stacked.

Dimensional data not binding.
We reserve the right to alter specifications without notice.

HÄFELE

Solo 32 Fitting
- Snap-in feature
- Extremely high corner stability

Mounting diagram

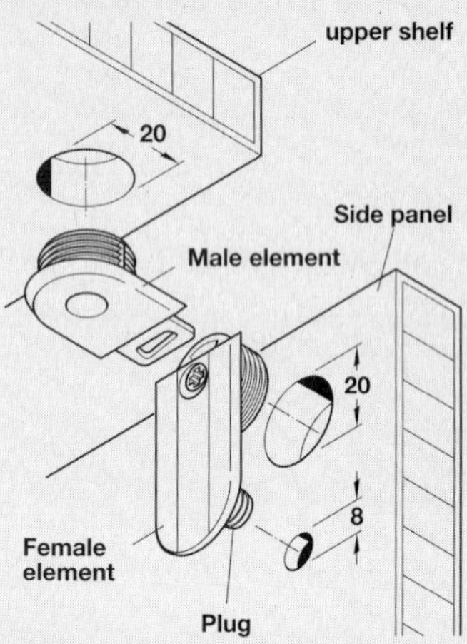

Mounting screws:
Varianta special screws, with **countersunk head** and cross-slot PZ 2

Finish: steel, nickel-plated

Length (mm)	Cat. No. Ø 3 mm	Ø 5 mm
10,5	013.15.617	013.15.715
13,5	013.15.626	013.15.724
16,0	013.15.635	013.15.733

Packing: 500 pcs.

Dimensional data not binding. We reserve the right to alter specifications without notice.

Solo 32 Clip Connector

Solo 32
With dowels
2 parts:
- clip-part with tightening device
- male part

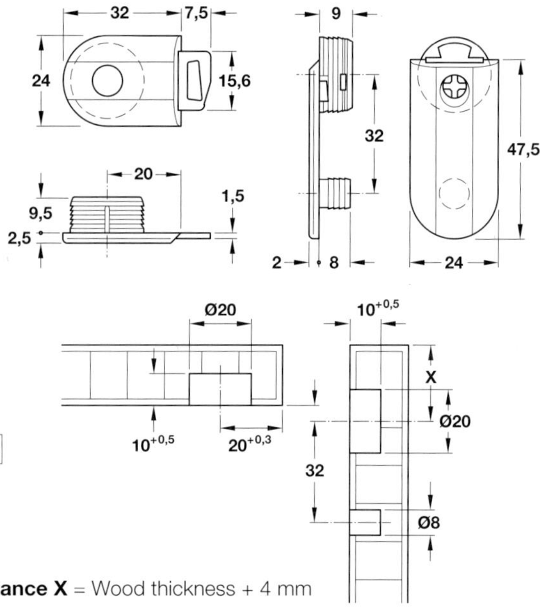

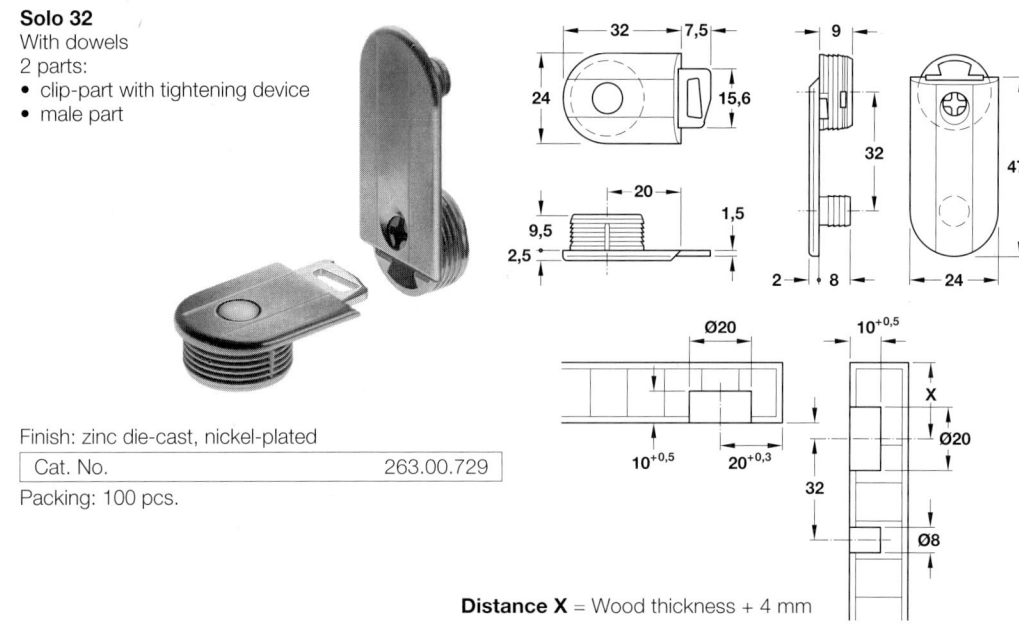

Finish: zinc die-cast, nickel-plated

Cat. No.	263.00.729

Packing: 100 pcs.

Distance X = Wood thickness + 4 mm

Typical Installations

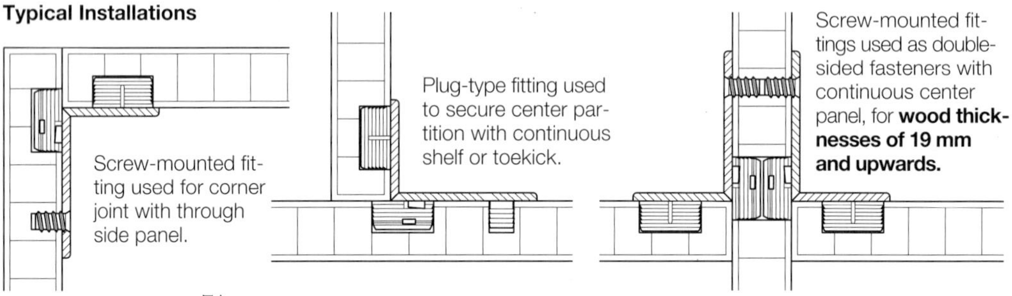

Screw-mounted fitting used for corner joint with through side panel.
Plug-type fitting used to secure center partition with continuous shelf or toekick.
Screw-mounted fittings used as double-sided fasteners with continuous center panel, for wood thicknesses of 19 mm and upwards.

Function diagram

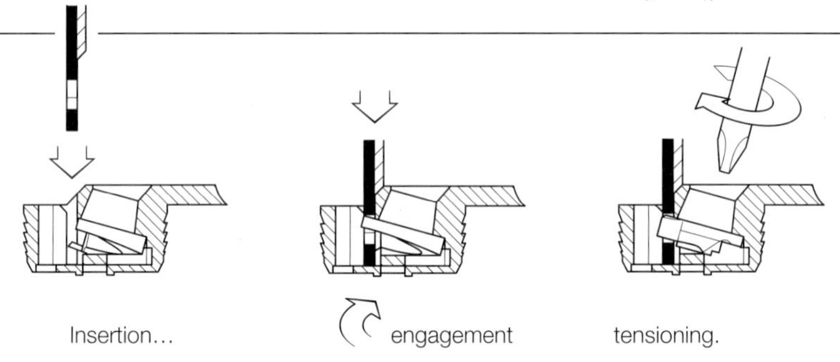

Dimensions in mm

Dimensions in mm

Universal Connector

HÄFELE

BV-Mini cabinet connector

Includes:
Plastic casing with pre inserted locking screw for recessed installation.
Connecting bracket: hardened steel, nickel-plated.

Color	Cat. No.
white	263.80.709
beige	263.80.405
brown	263.80.101
black	263.80.307

Packing: 100 pcs.

Mounting diagram

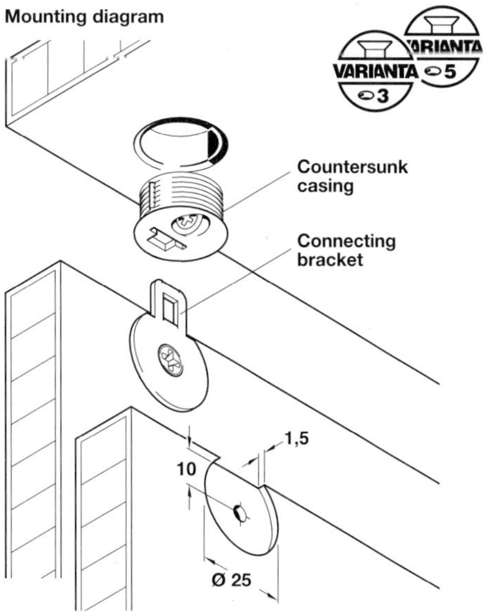

Connecting bracket **screw mounted:**

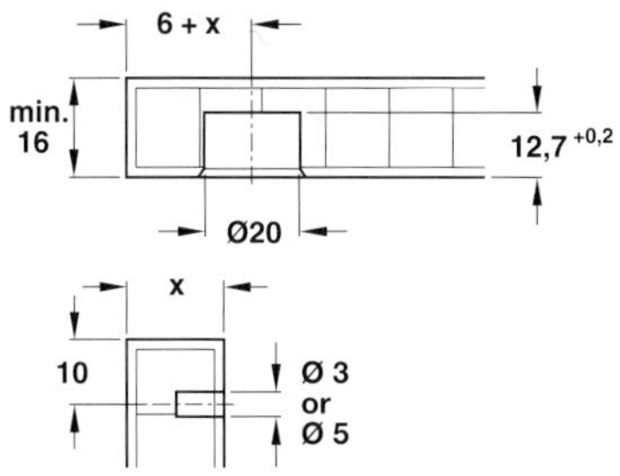

Connecting bracket **screw recessed:**

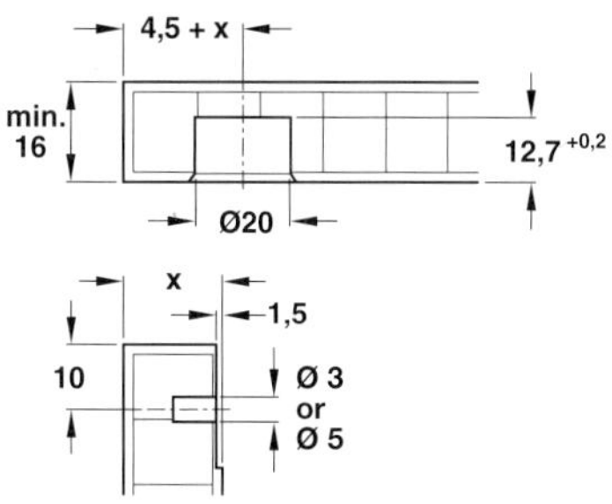

Countersunk drill-bit

suitable for BV-Mini
Three carbide-tipped cutters; Ø 10 mm shank, flattened on one side, with M 5 x 8 mm adjusting screw.

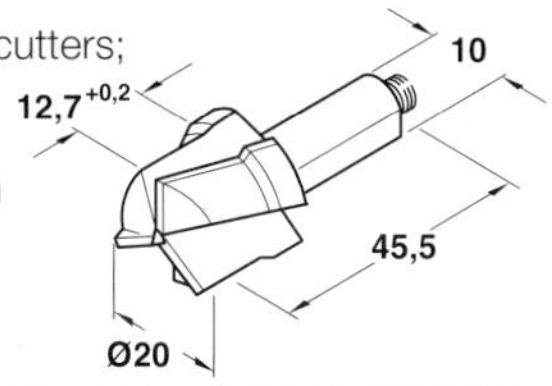

Drilling direction	Cat. No.
Left-hand	001.24.318
Right-hand	001.24.309

Packing: 1 pc.

Drill-bit mount with M 10 internal thread, accepts bit with Ø 10 mm shank. Also available with M10 external thread if required.

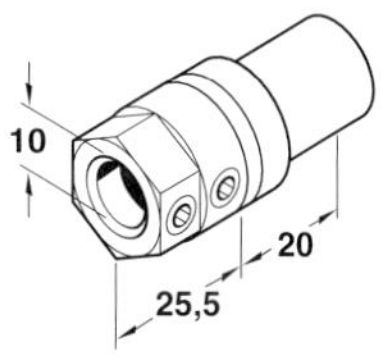

Drilling direction	Cat. No.
Left-hand	001.91.097
Right-hand	001.91.088

Packing: 1 pc.

Bed connector BV Mini
Countersunk connector for recessed installation in cabinets, furniture and bed frames

Locks, Catches, RTA and PAS® Fittings
Shelf Supports
Bed Fittings
2

Advantages:
- When assembling the furniture parts, the connecting bracket snaps into the plastic casing and is prefixed, before the connecting screw is tightened
- Fitting does not project
- Easy assembly
- Excellent angular rigidity
- The connecting screw is secured in the casing with a PZ 2 cross-slot screwdriver
- The casing can be inserted manually or automatically

Dimensional data not binding.
We reserve the right to alter specifications without notice.

Dimensions in mm

HÄFELE

Lever Connector

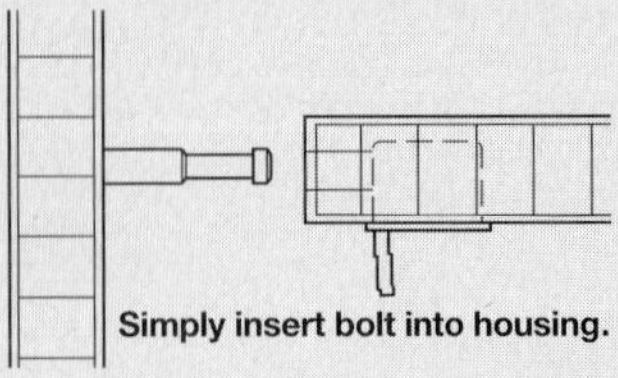

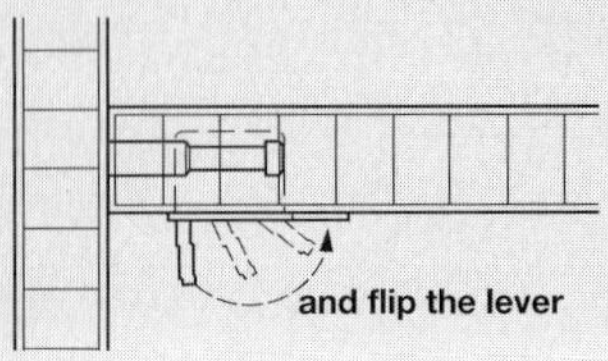

Lever Connector with Bolt

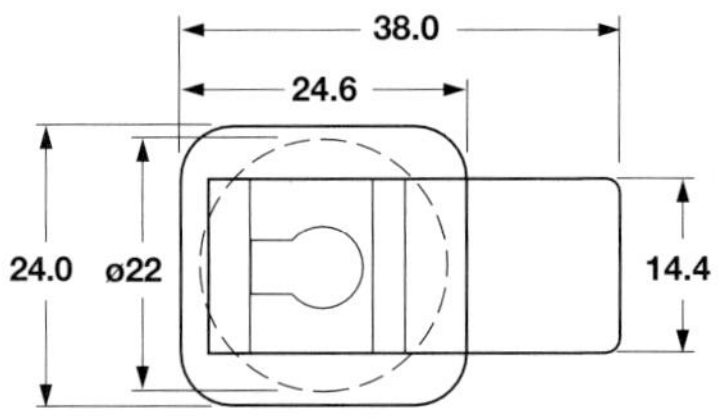

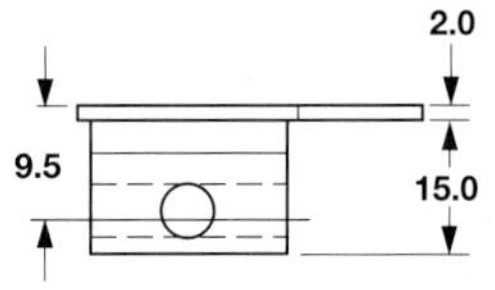

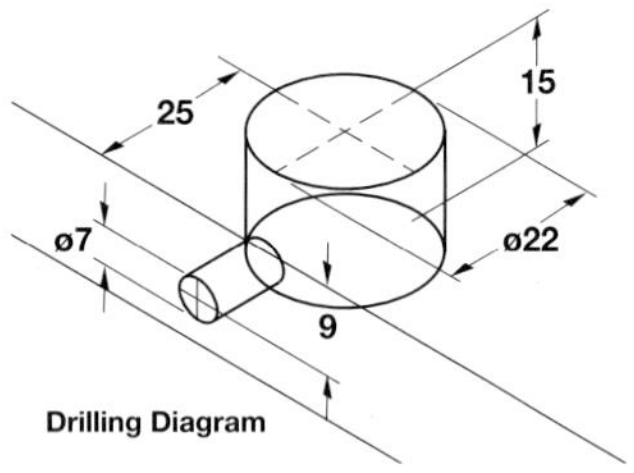

Finish: Plastic

Cat. No.	brown	262.39.118
	white	262.39.716
	black	262.39.314

Packing: 1000 pcs.

M6 Bolt

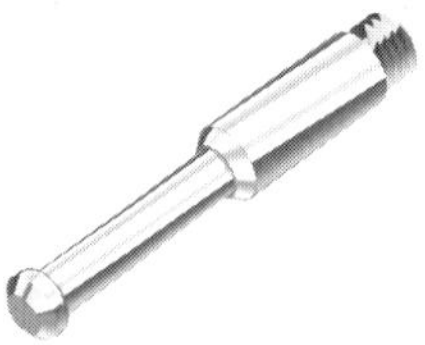

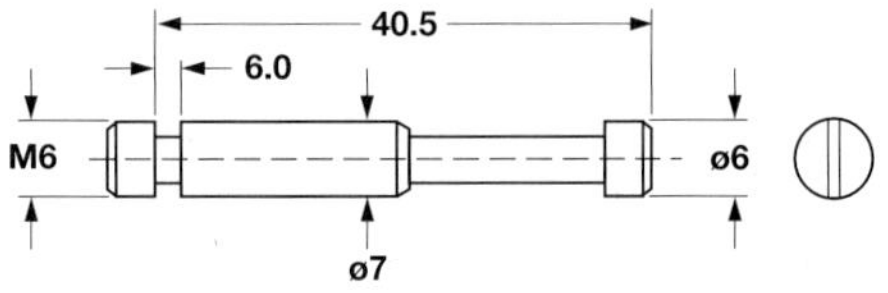

Finish: Steel, galvanized

Cat. No.	262.39.903

Packing: 1000 pcs.

Spreading Dowel

Spreading dowel, extremely high pull-out strength, with **M6** internal thread for press-fit installation in ø 8 mm holes

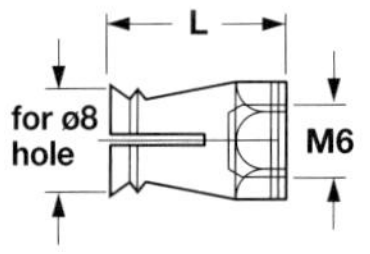

Finish: Brass

Min. drill Depth	Length	Cat. No.	Qty.
9.5 mm	9 mm	039.00.267	2000
15 mm	12 mm	039.00.061	1000
18 mm	15 mm	039.00.169	1000

Dimensional data not binding.
We reserve the right to alter specifications without notice.

Dimensions in mm

Confa 30 Universal Connector

HÄFELE

Recessed universal connector for very sturdy and heavily loaded connections

- long travel distance
- quickly tightened
- can be tightened with 6 mm Allen key
- even a cordless drill can be used for quick assembly

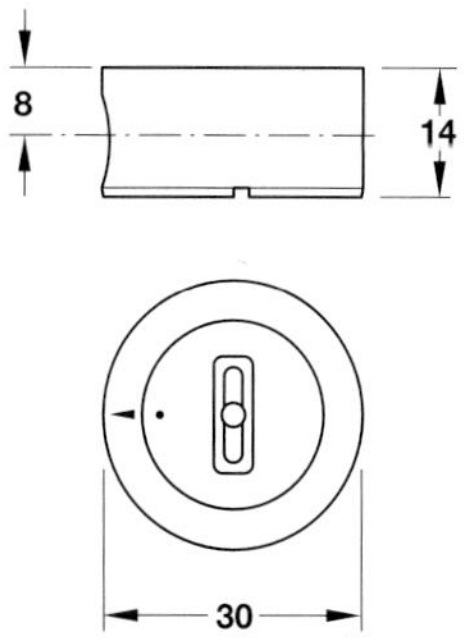

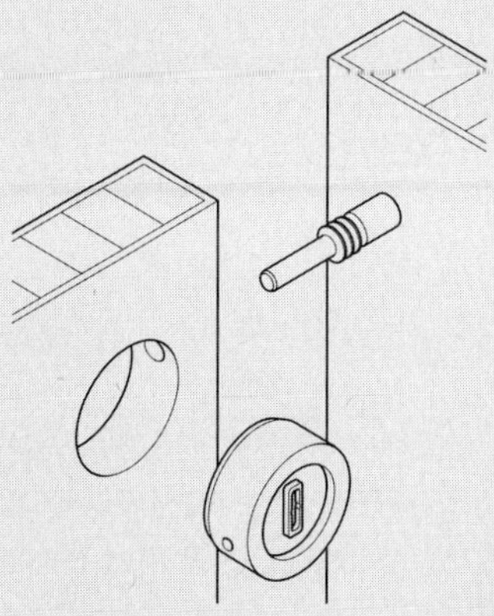

Finish:
Zinc die-cast housing,
with tightening element, unfinished steel

Wood thicknesses from:	Dimension A mounting center	Drilling Depth	Cat. No.
16 mm	1/2 wood thickness	1/2 wood thickness + 6 mm	262.55.300

Packing: 100 pcs.

Locks, Catches, RTA and PAS® Fittings Shelf Supports Bed Fittings **2**

Trim cap, plastic, cam needs to be recessed 3 mm to accept cover cap

Cat. No.		
	white	262.65.790
	brown	262.65.190
	black	262.65.390

Packing: 100 pcs.

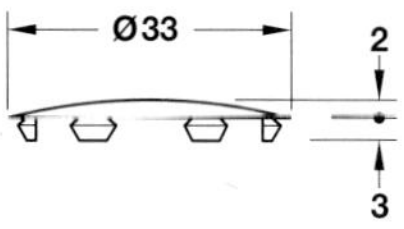

Connecting bolt,
Finish: steel with M6 thread

B= Drilling Dim.	**27 mm**
Cat. No. zinc-plated	262.85.900

Packing: 100 pcs.

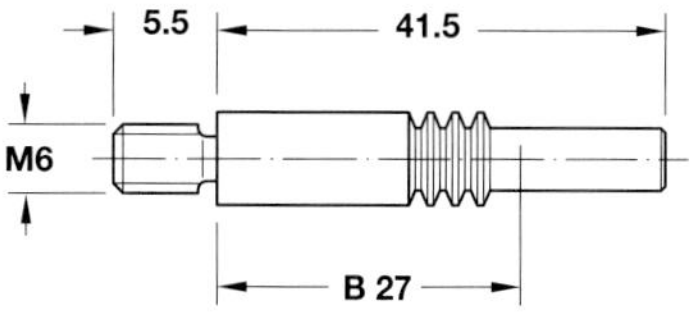

The **Confa 30** can be used with the following parts.

M8 screw socket
Finish: unfinished steel with screw-slot

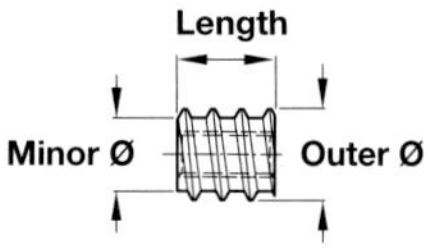

Inner thread	**M 6**	**M 6**	**M 6**	**M 6**
Outer Ø	10	12	12	12
Inner Ø	7	9	9	9
length	12	11	13	15
Cat. No.	030.00.351	030.00.306	030.00.315	030.00.324
Packing:	1000 pcs.	1000 pcs.	100 pcs.	1000 pcs.

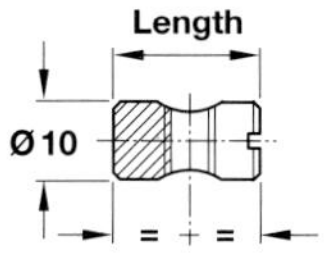

M6 cross dowel
Finish: galvanized steel with screw-slot

Length	Cat. No.
14 mm	264.82.014
20 mm	264.82.020

Packing: 1000 pcs.

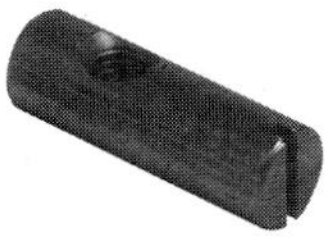

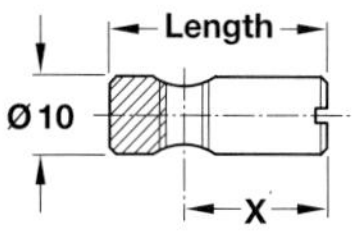

M6 cross dowel
Finish: galvanized steel with screw-slot

Length	Dim. X	Cat. No.
14 mm	8 mm	264.81.014
30 mm	20 mm	264.81.030

Packing: 1000 pcs.

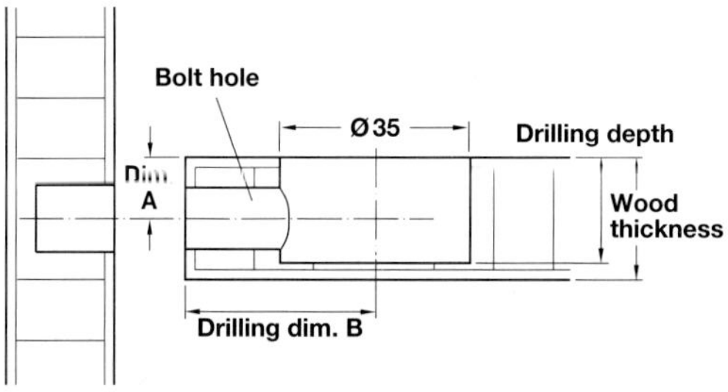

Bolt hole = Ø 8 mm
Drilling depth = 1/2 wood thickness + 6 mm
Dimension A = 1/2 wood thickness
Drilling dimension B = optional between **B 27**, drilling distance from cam center to front edge

Dimensions in mm

Dimensional data not binding. We reserve the right to alter specifications without notice.

HÄFELE

Confa 35 Universal Connector

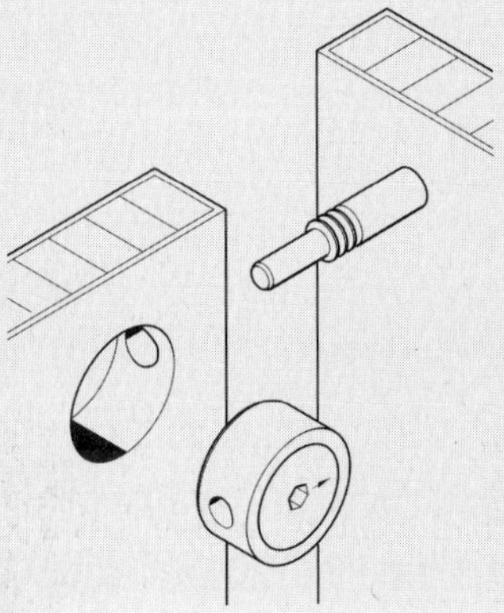

Recessed universal connector for very sturdy and heavily loaded joints

- long travel distance
- quickly tightened
- can be tightened with 6 mm Allen key
- even a cordless drill can be used for quick assembly

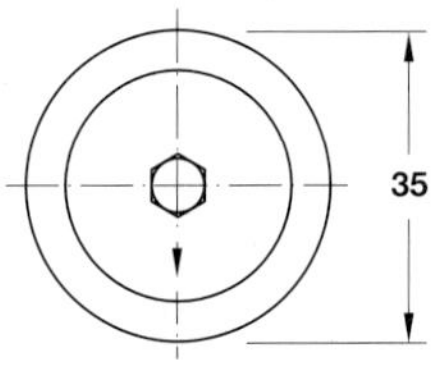

Finish:
Zinc die-cast housing,
with tightening element, unfinished steel

Wood thicknesses from:	Dimension A mounting center	Drilling Depth	Cat. No.
24 mm	1/2 wood thickness	1/2 wood thickness + 8 mm	262.69.009

Packing: 100 pcs.

Trim cap, plastic, cam needs to be recessed 3 mm to accept covercap

Cat. No.	white	262.69.798
	brown	262.69.198
	black	262.69.398

Packing: 100 pcs.

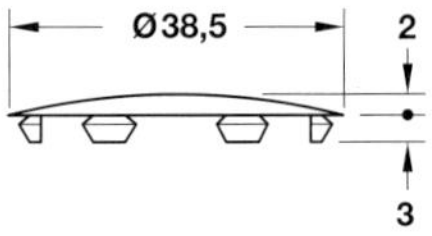

2
Locks, Catches, RTA and PAS® Fittings
Shelf Supports
Bed Fittings

Connecting bolt,
Finish: steel with M8 thread

B= Drilling Dim.	**35 mm**	**55 mm**
Cat. No. zinc-plated	262.69.036	262.69.045

Packing: 100 pcs.

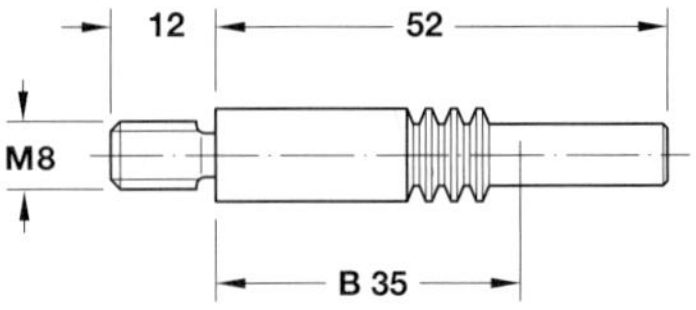

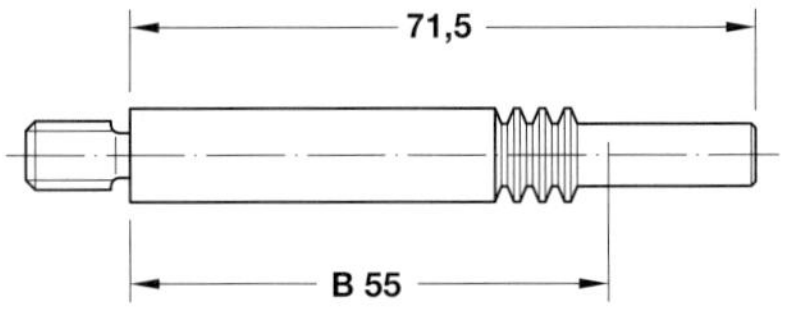

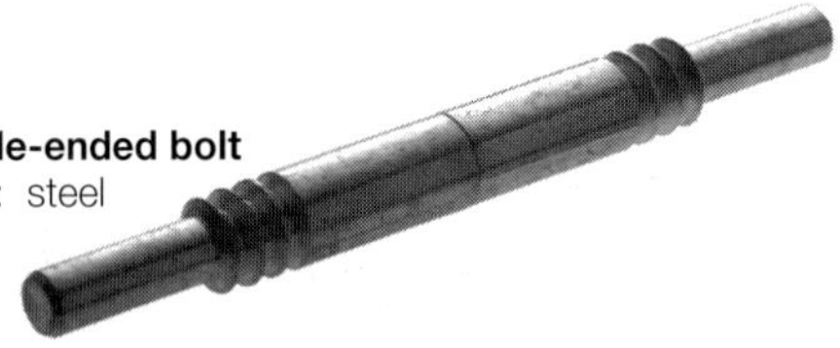

Double-ended bolt
Finish: steel

B= Drilling dim.	**35 mm**
Cat. No. zinc-plated	262.69.950

Packing: 100 pcs.

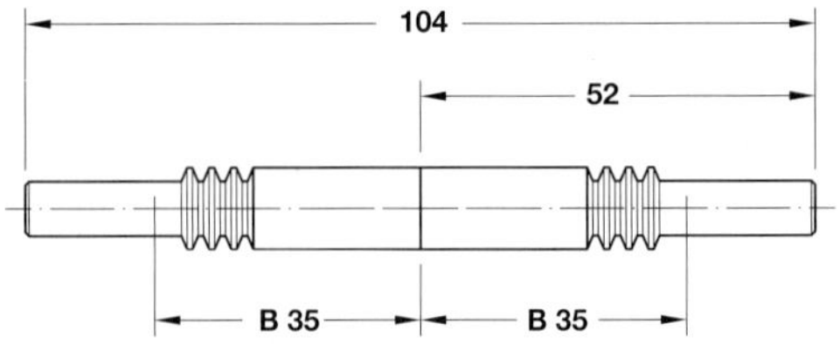

The above connecting bolts can be used with the following parts.

M 6 Allen key

Cat. No.	008.28.268

Packing: 1 pc.

M8 screw socket
Finish: unfinished steel with screw-slot

Outer Ø	14 mm	16 mm
Inner Ø	11,5 mm	12 mm
Length	15 mm	18 mm
Cat. No.	030.00.404	030.00.422

Packing: 100 pcs.

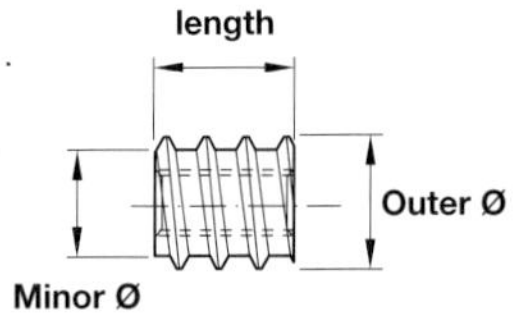

M8 cross dowel
Finish: galvanized steel with screw-slot

Cat. No.	264.83.920

Packing: 100 pcs.

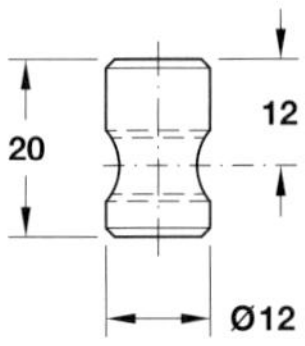

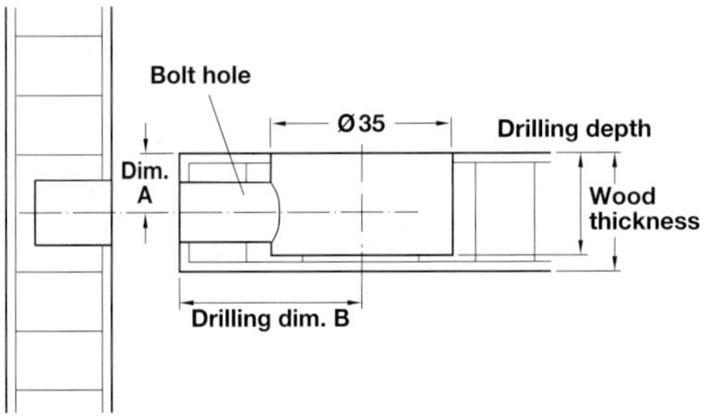

Bolt hole = Ø 11 mm
Drilling depth = 1/2 wood thickness + 8 mm
Dimension A = 1/2 wood thickness
Drilling dimension B = optional between **B 35** (35 mm) or **B 55** (55 mm), drilling distance from housing center to front edge

Dimensions in mm

HÄFELE

Universal Furniture Connectors

Confir-Plan® Universal Fitting

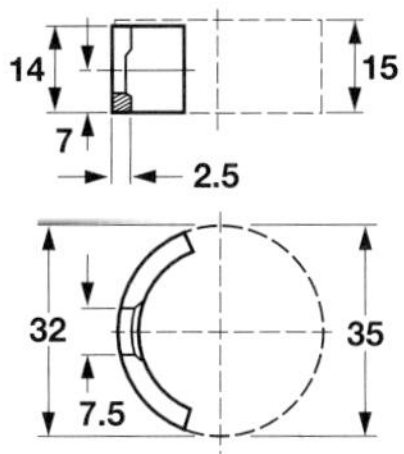

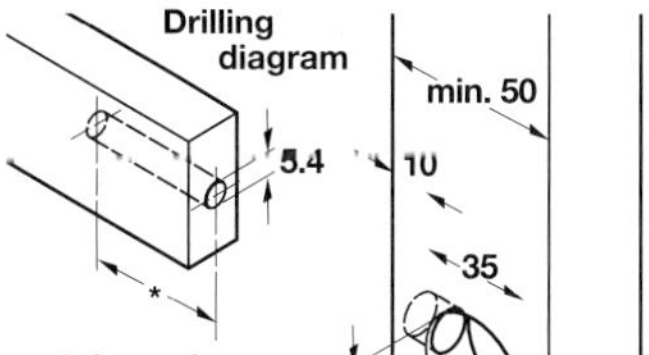

Distance* depends on length of Confirmat one-piece connecting screw employed.

Finish: steel, yellow chromatized

Cat. No.	260.51.909

Packing: 500 pcs.

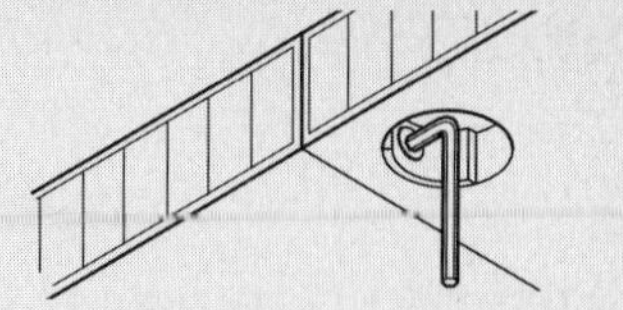

- High degree of angular rigidity.
- Above-average pull resistance and inconspicuous appearance.
- Especially suitable for upholstered furniture bases, for solid wood table and chair frames.
- Has the advantage over conventional bolt fastenings of being completely invisible from the exterior.

One-Piece Connector

The universal fitting is designed around the Confirmat one-piece connector, featuring deep threads which cut into the wood.

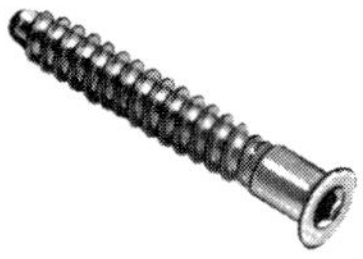

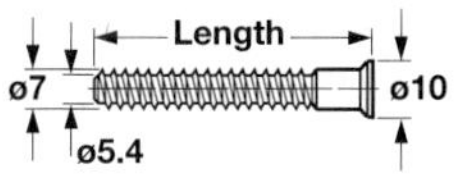

Finish: steel, galvanized

Cat. No.	38 mm long	264.43.096
	50 mm long	264.43.194
	70 mm long	264.43.292

Packing: 1000 pcs.

Allen Key, 4 mm

For tightening Confirmat one-piece connector

Cat. No.	008.28.044

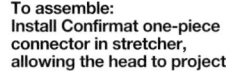

Packing: 500 pcs.

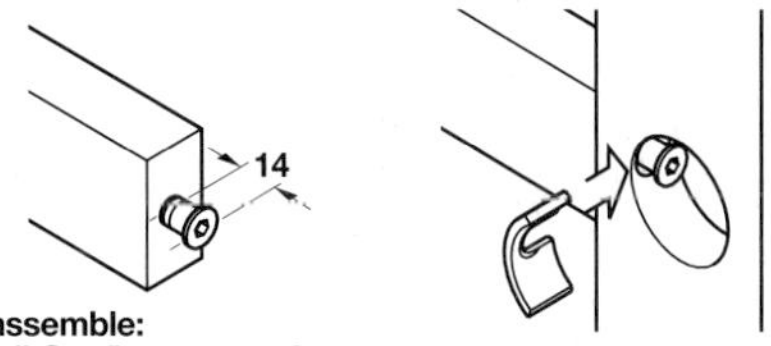

To assemble:
Install Confirmat one-piece connector in stretcher, allowing the head to project enough to install the pressure plate over the screw head. Then tighten to secure.

Lock, Catches, RTA and PAS® Fittings
Shelf Supports
Bed Fittings
2

Trim Cap

For recess.

Finish: plastic, brown

Cat. No.	260.51.196

Packing: 500 pcs.

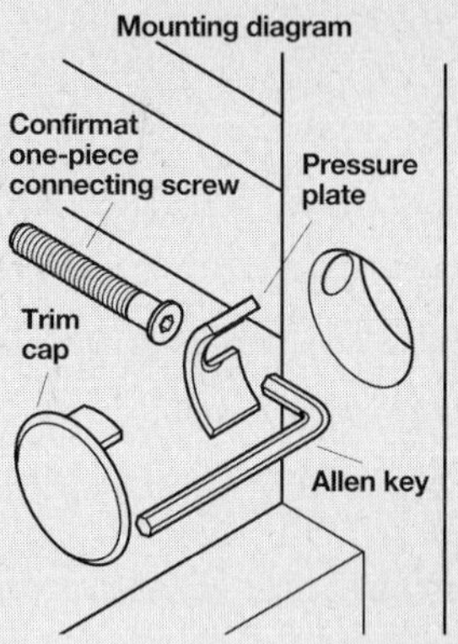

Connector for Chairs and Frames.

This connector is ideally suited for joining chair frames, sofa frames and other furniture frames. During tightening, the nylon pressure plate is forced against the threads of the stud bolt. This provides a very strong joint which never needs tightening.

Cross-Nut
M6, center thread

Stud Bolt, M6

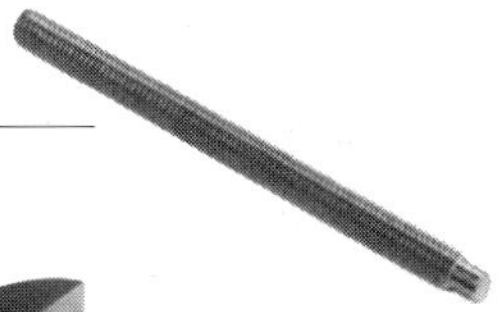

Pressure Plate

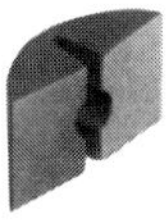

Washer

Hexagon Nut, M6

Frame Mounting-Fitting

Includes:
1 M6 Cross-nut bolt, center thread; steel galvanized
1 M6 Stud bolt; steel galvanized
1 Pressure plate, nylon white
1 Washer; steel galvanized
1 M6 Hexagon nut; steel galvanized

Cat. No.	260.52.906

Packing: 100 sets

Trim Cap

For recess
(to be ordered separately)

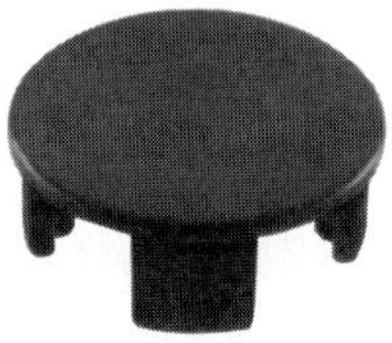

Finish: plastic

Cat. No.	brown	260.52.193
	white	260.52.791

Packing: 500 pcs.

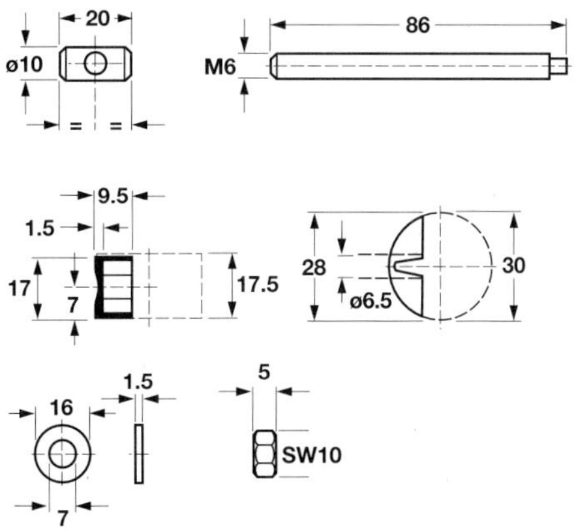

Box-end wrench, 10 mm

For tightening connector for chairs and frames
(to be ordered separately)

Cat. No.	008.22.640

Packing: 100 pcs.

Dimensions in mm

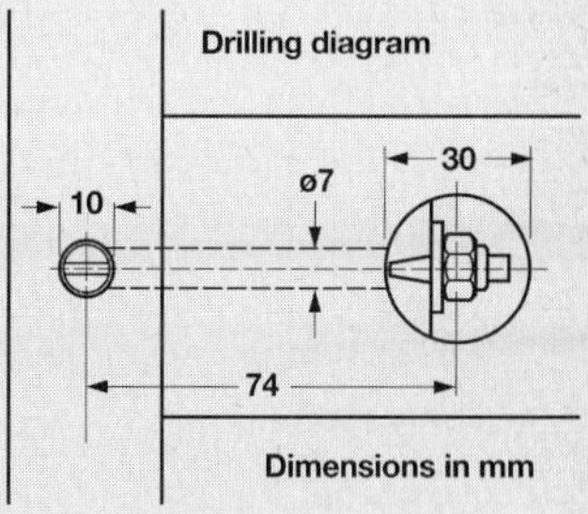

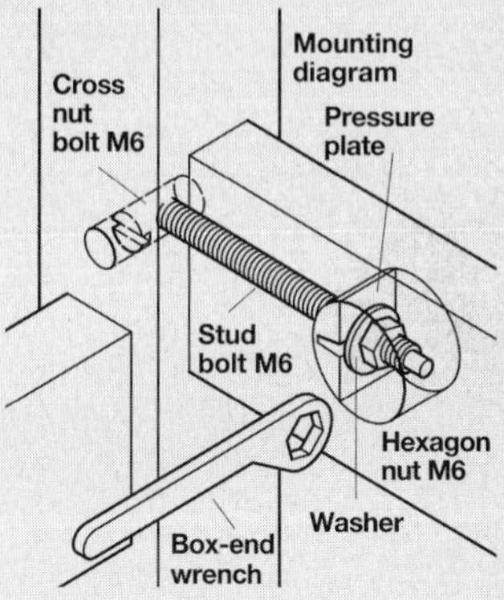

Dimensional data not binding. We reserve the right to alter specifications without notice.

HÄFELE

Special Connectors

- **Giro-bolt lock** provides quick yet exceptionally strong joints.
- Giro-bolt locks have unlimited applications for any situation requiring a strong, yet easily releasable joint.

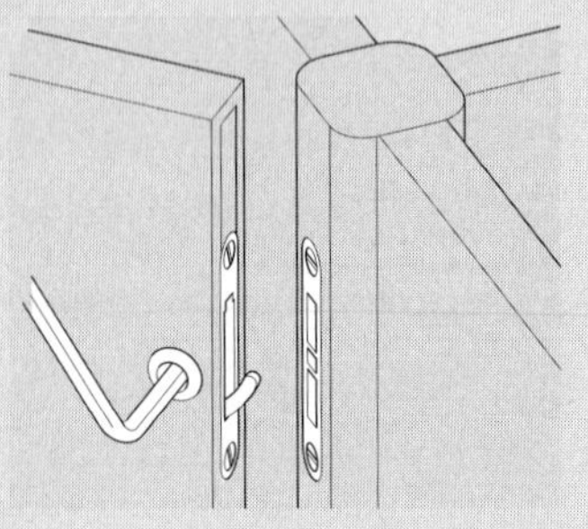

Allen key, to secure and release the Giro-bolt lock

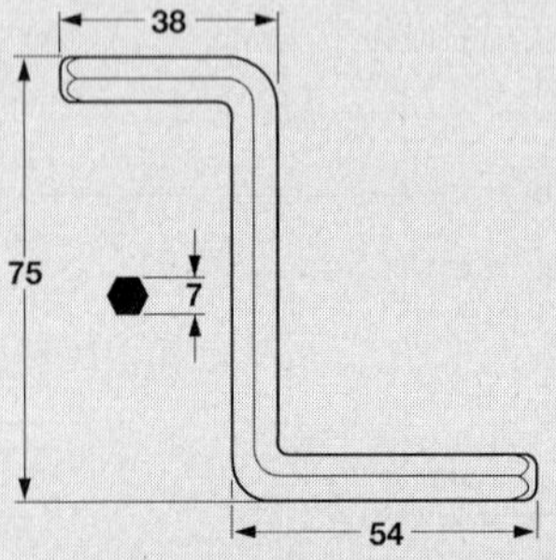

Cat. No.	008.28.670

Packing: 1 pc

Giro-bolt lock
with stop

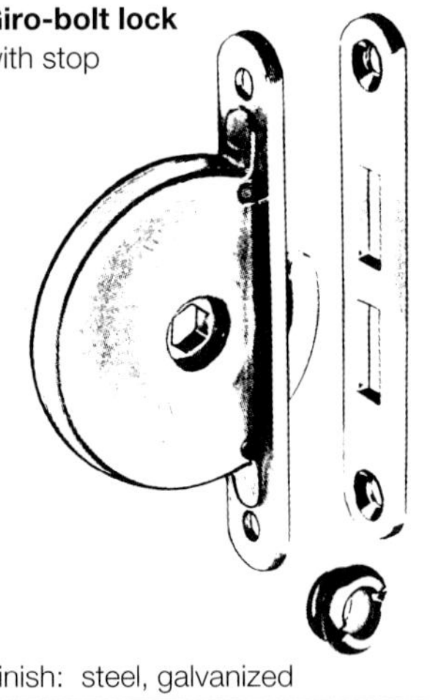

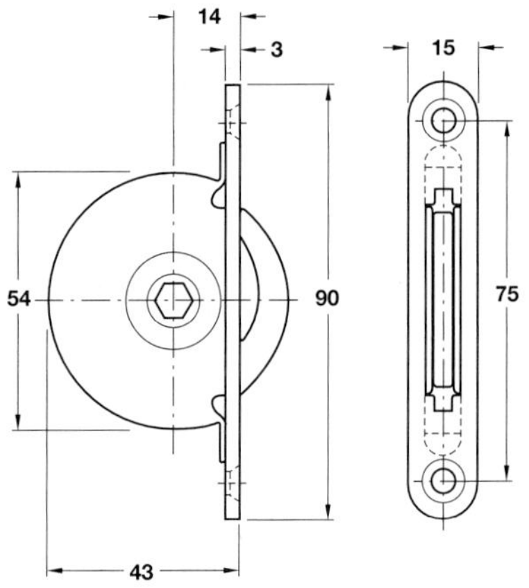

Finish: steel, galvanized

Cat. No.	261.05.902

Packing: 150 pcs.

Strike plate for Giro-bolt lock

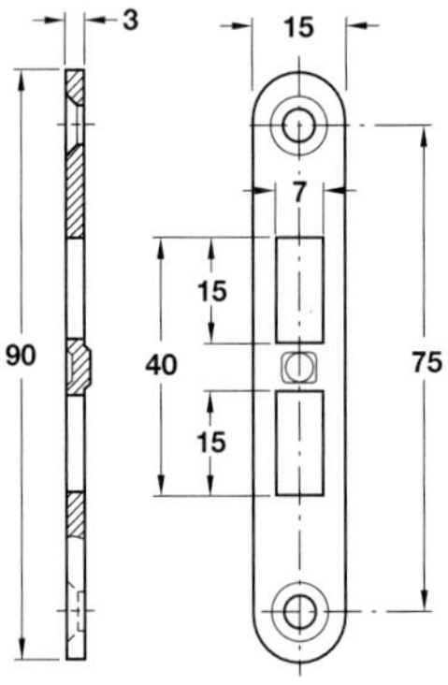

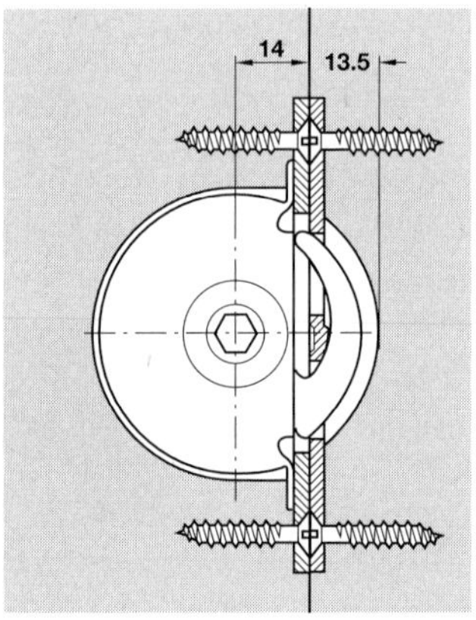

Finish: steel, galvanized

Cat. No.	261.05.993

Packing: 100 pcs.

Sleeve, with thread, for Giro-bolt lock

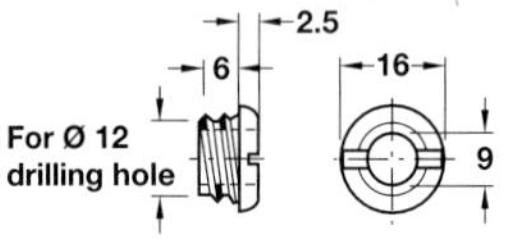

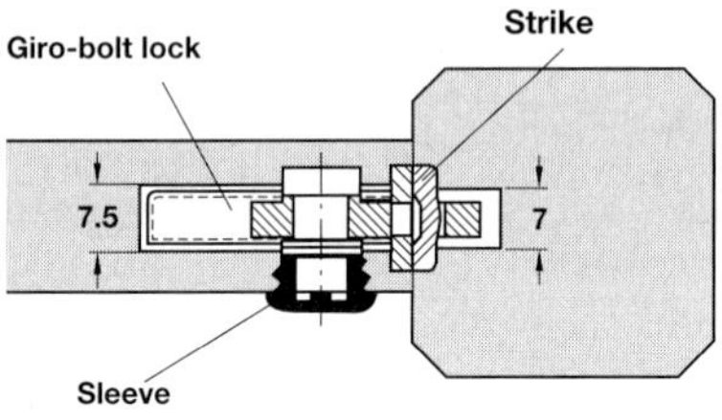

Finish: brass, unfinished

Cat. No.	261.05.984

Packing: 50 pcs.

Hamburg-style connector, heavy-duty fitting
Includes two Ø 35 mm mounting plates, surface mounted or recessed which are pulled together with a capstan screw to form a permanent, tight-fitting joint.

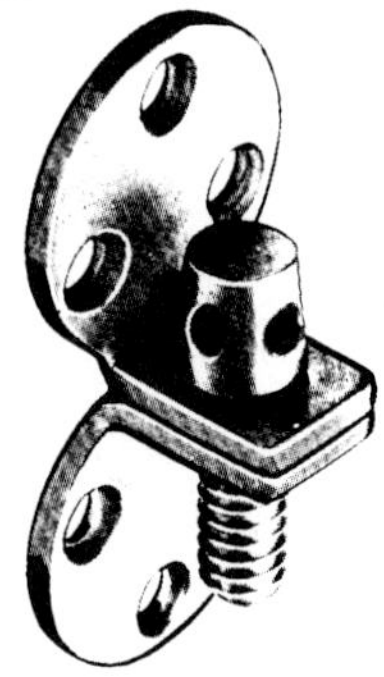

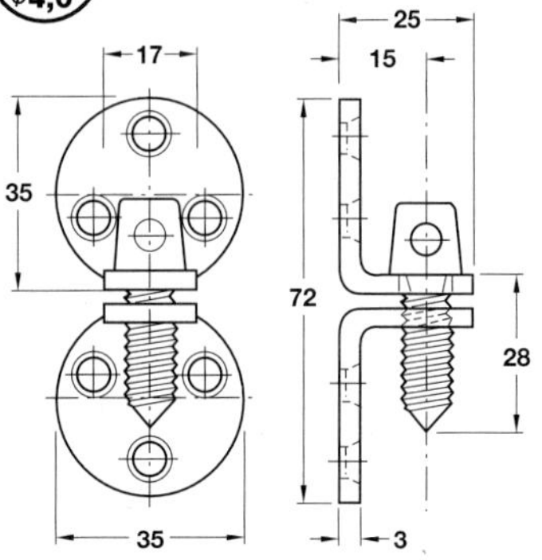

Finish: steel, brass-plated

Cat. No.	262.54.500

Packing: 20 pcs.

Dimensions in mm

Arret Fastener and RTA Fittings

HÄFELE

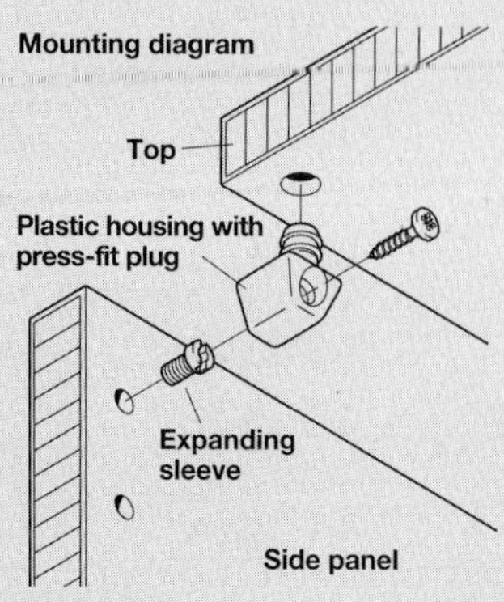

Arret Fastener 15 mm

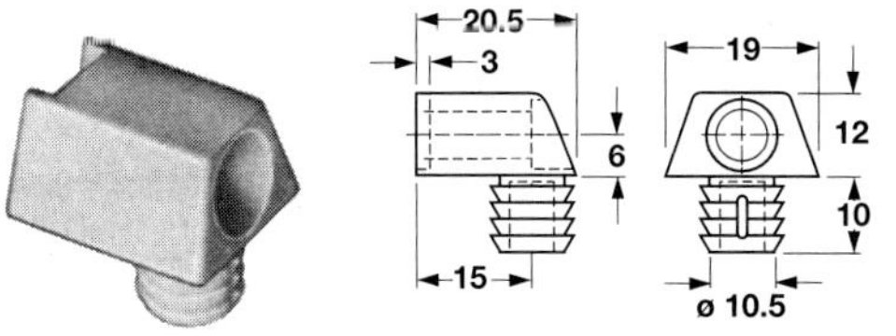

Finish: plastic

Cat. No.	brown	273.93.166
	white	273.93.764

Packing: 1000 pcs.

Arret Fastener 11.5 mm

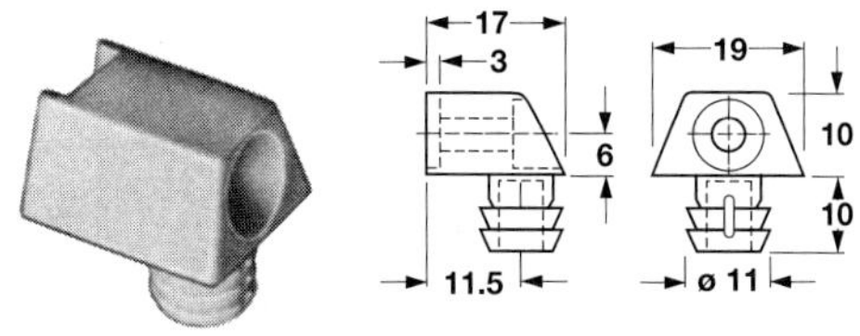

Finish: plastic

Cat. No.	brown	262.40.139
	white	262.40.737

Packing: 500 pcs.

Hospa Pan Head Screw

Finish: steel, galvanized

Cat. No.	015.71.679

Packing: 1000 pcs.

Expanding Sleeve, With Collar

Finish: nylon, natural-colored

Cat. No.	340.43.019

Packing: 1000 pcs.

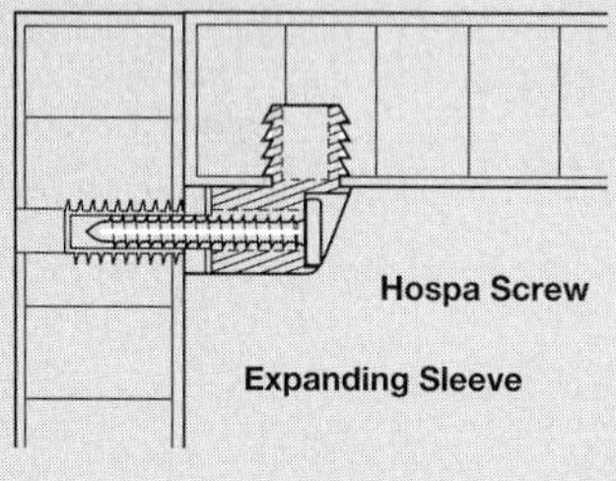

M4 Screw, With Combination Slot

Finish: steel, galvanized

Cat. No.	022.35.234

Packing: 1000 pcs.

Sleeve, With M4 Internal Thread

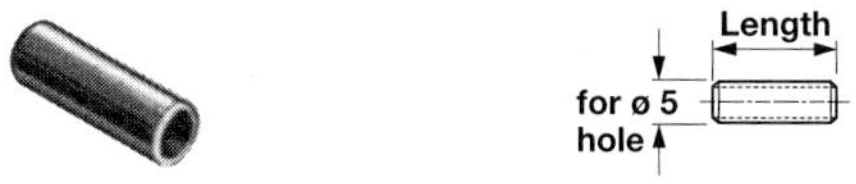

Finish: steel, galvanized

Cat. No.	15 mm long	267.00.911
	18 mm long	267.00.912
	22 mm long	267.00.913

Packing: 1000 pcs.

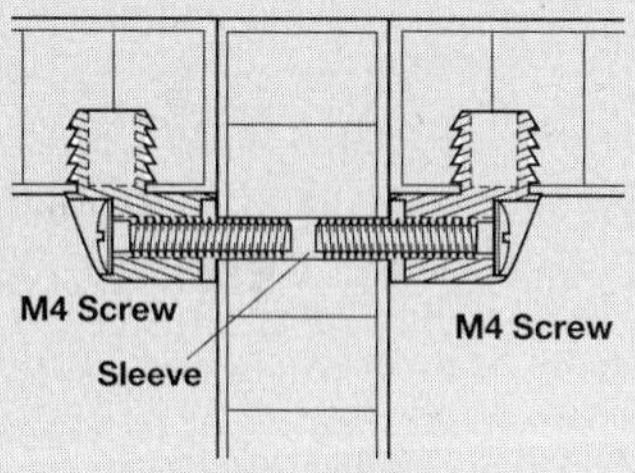

One-Piece RTA Connector

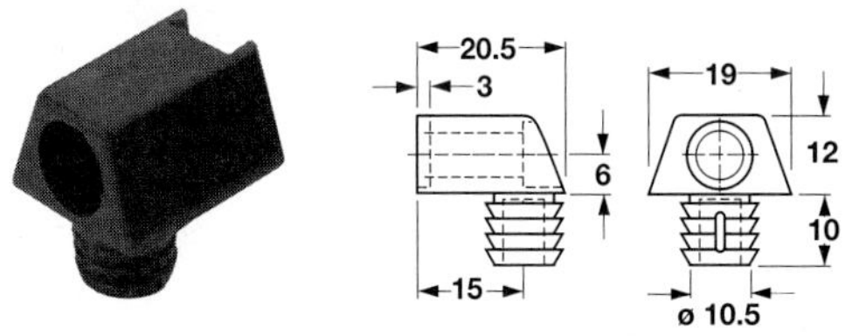

Finish: nylon, brown

Cat. No.	273.93.184

Packing: 500 pcs.

Two-Piece RTA Connector

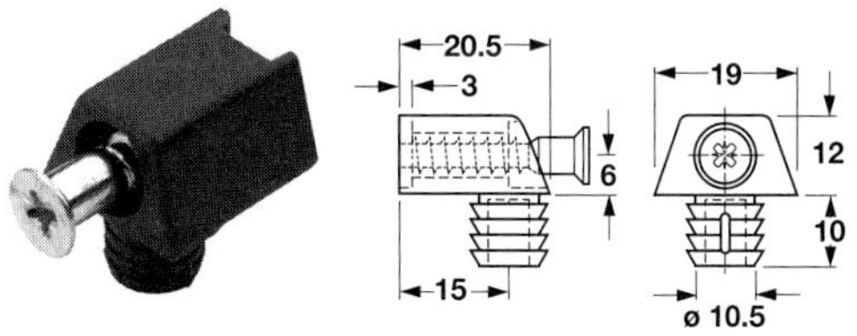

Finish: nylon, brown

Cat. No.	262.32.100

Packing: 500 pcs.

Confirmat Screw, 6.0 x 26 mm

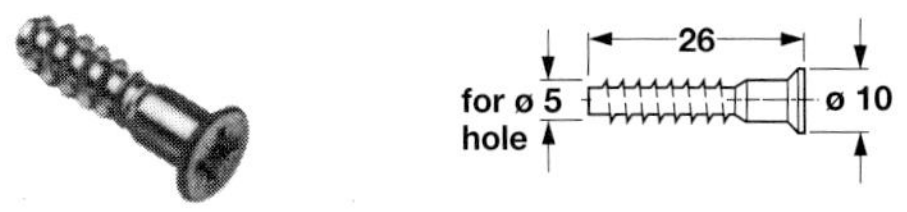

Finish: steel, galvanized

Cat. No.	264.51.392

Packing: 5000 pcs.

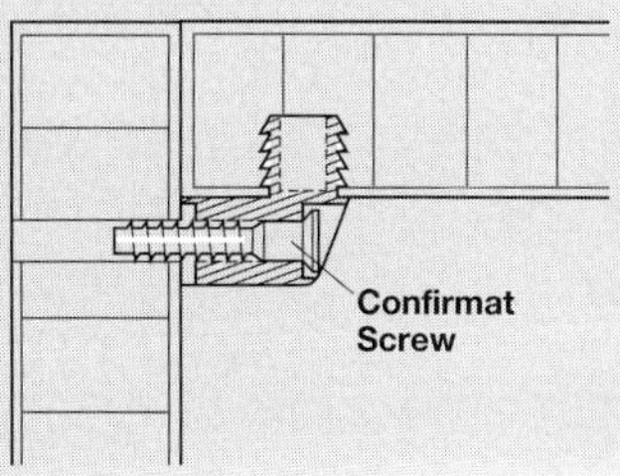

Dimensional data not binding. We reserve the right to alter specifications without notice.

Dimensions in mm

HÄFELE

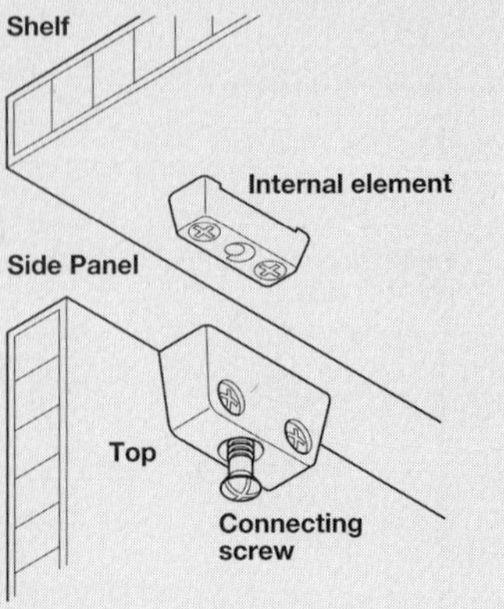

Screw Mounted RTA Fitting

Trapez RTA Fitting, with fastening screw

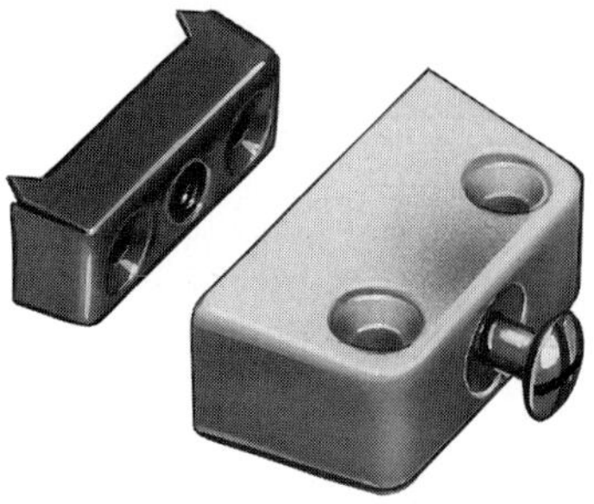

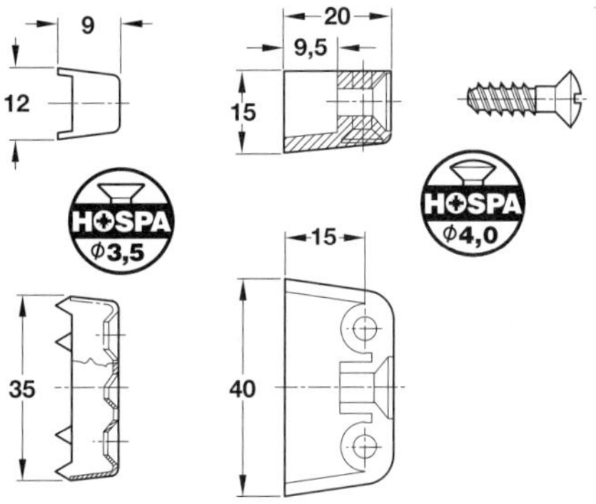

Finish: brown or white plastic outer housing, plug element in steel, brass-plated and fastening screw in galvanized steel.

Cat. No.	white	262.61.709
	brown	262.61.101

Packing: 100 pcs.

Connector RV with Tolerance Compensation

Clip Connector top element is made of **Zinc alloy** (internal element to be ordered separately)

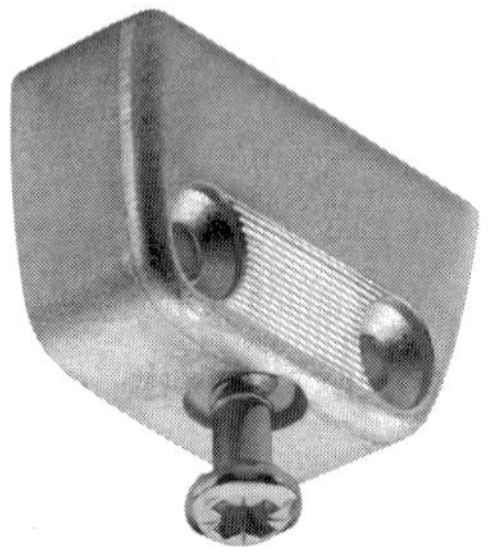

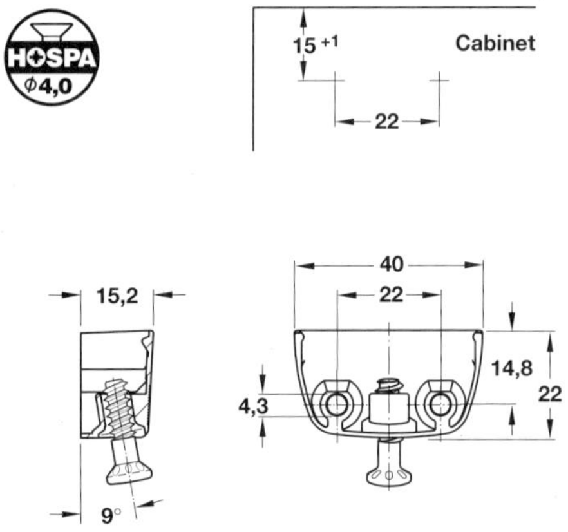

Connecting screw made of steel, pre-mounted
Finish: zinc-alloy

Cat. No.	chromated	262.72.901
	black	262.72.301

Packing: 500 pcs.

RV/U-T3 Clip Connector bottom element with tolerance compensation **± 1.5 mm**

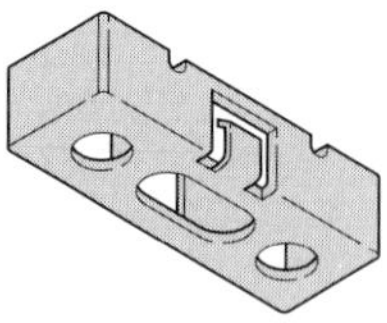

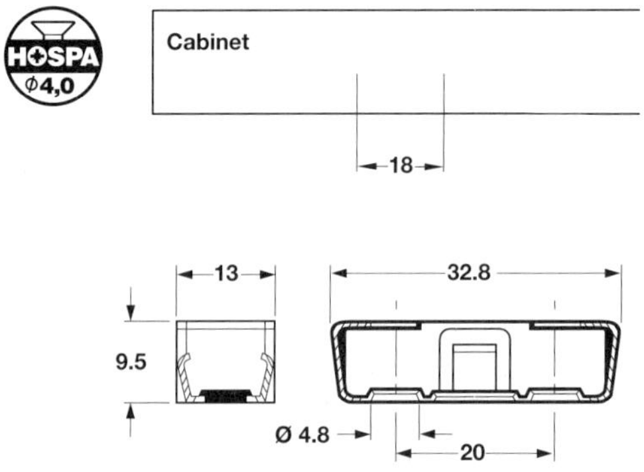

Finish: steel, nickel-plated

Cat. No.	262.72.953

Packing: 500 pcs.

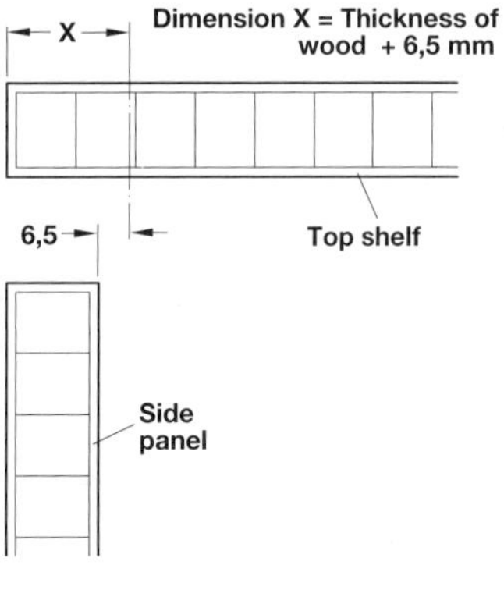

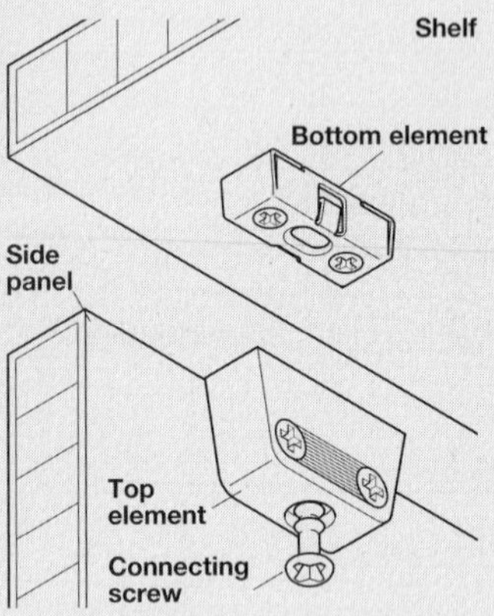

Clip cabinet connector with bottom element
Especially suitable for solid wood furniture. An additional clip panel in the bottom element compensates tolerances of up to ± 2 mm.

- The bottom element locks into the top element thus pre-fixing the panels
- Installation and dismantling is facilitated by this pre-fixing function
- The connector can be processed manually or automatically -streamlined series assembly
- High angular stability
- 9° position of connecting screw facilitates assembly

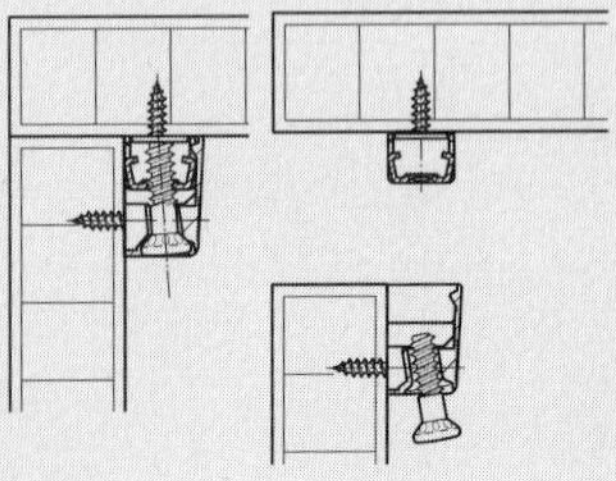

Dimensional data not binding. We reserve the right to alter specifications without notice.

Dimensions in mm

Press-fit, Clip-Connector RV

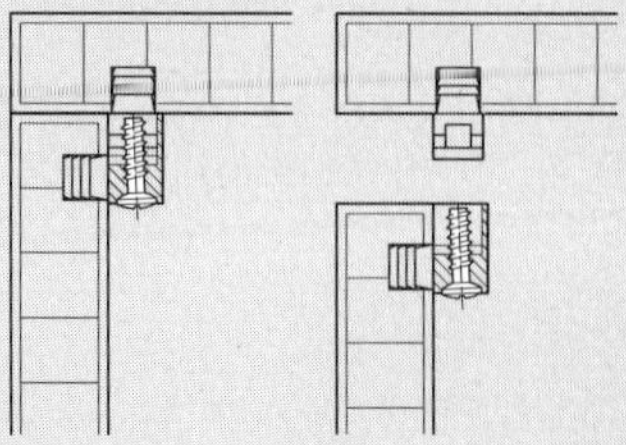

The ideal clip connector which is simple to install, for straightforward assembly operations. The particular advantage of this connector is the straightforward fastening by press-fitting the two elements together. The internal element locks into the top element thus pre-fixing the panels before finally adjusted with the pre-mounted screw.

Top Element

Clip connector with pre-mounted screw.
10 mm plugs

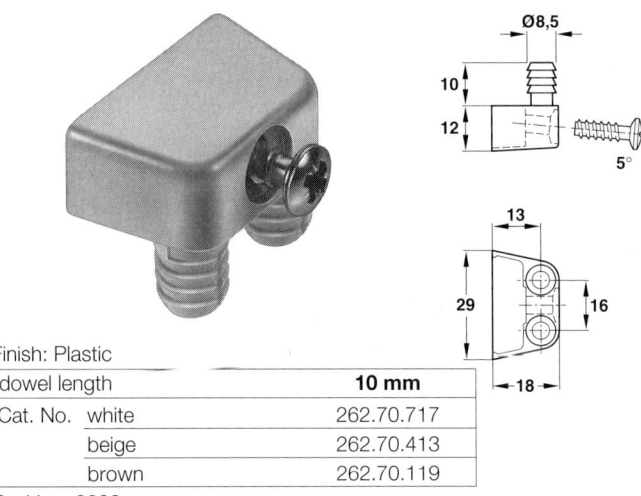

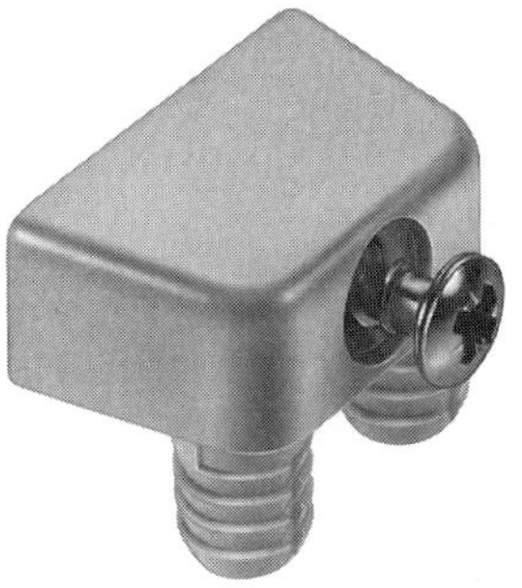

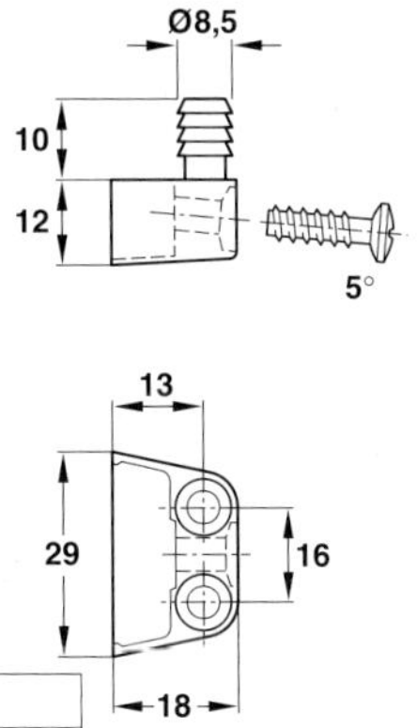

Drilling diagram

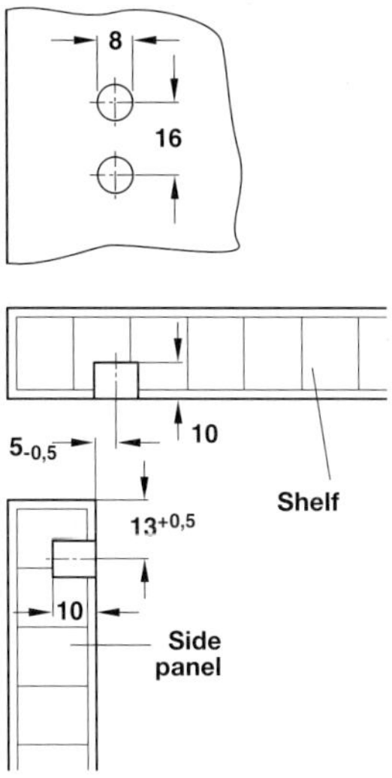

Finish: Plastic

dowel length		10 mm
Cat. No.	white	262.70.717
	beige	262.70.413
	brown	262.70.119

Packing: 2000 pcs.

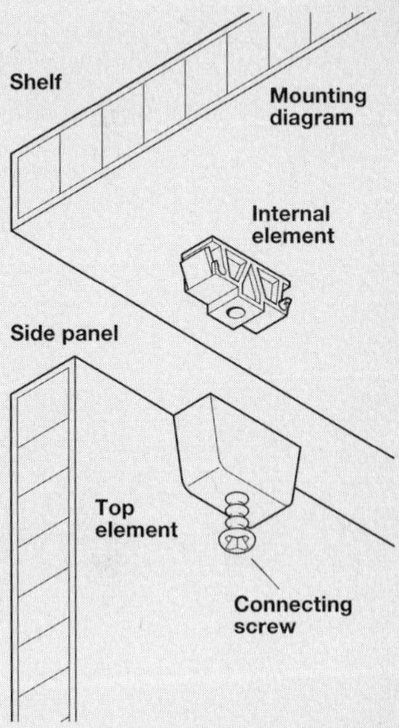

Internal Element

Clip side panel connector (to be ordered seperately). With plugs.

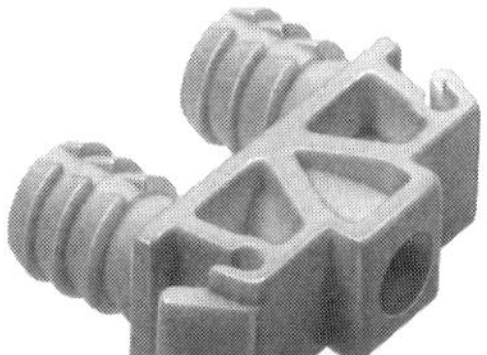

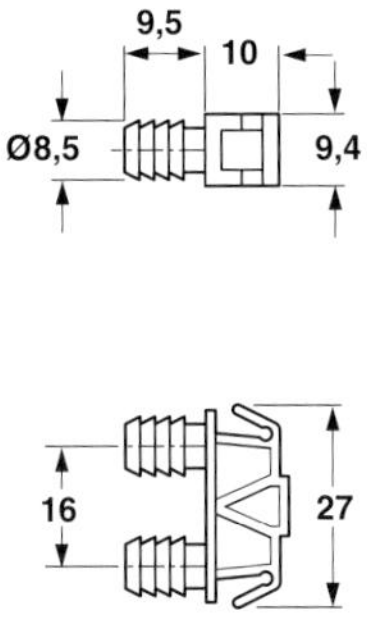

Drilling diagram

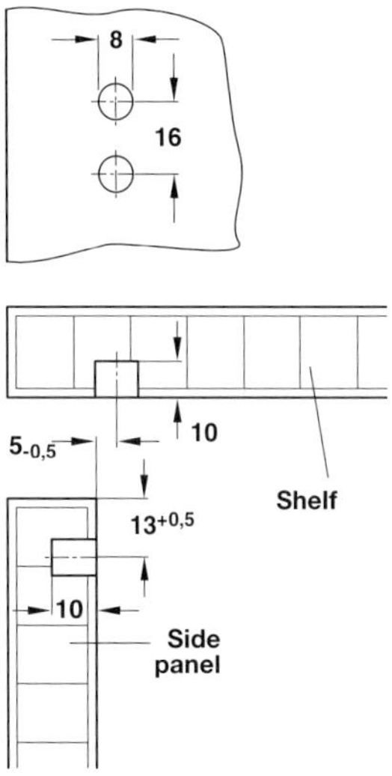

Finish: Plastic

dowel length	9.5 mm
Cat. No. beige	262.70.431

Packing: 2000 pcs.

Dimensional data not binding.
We reserve the right to alter specifications without notice.

Dimensions in mm

HÄFELE

Surface Mounted Connectors

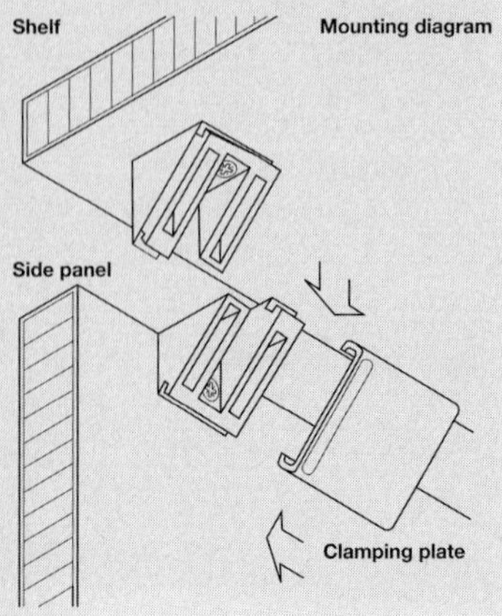

Quickfix fitting includes two identical blocks which are screw-mounted to the shelf and side panel respectively and held securely together by a clamping plate.
Exceptional rigidity is assured by the extensive interlocking area of the two screw-mounted components.

HOSPA Ø3.5

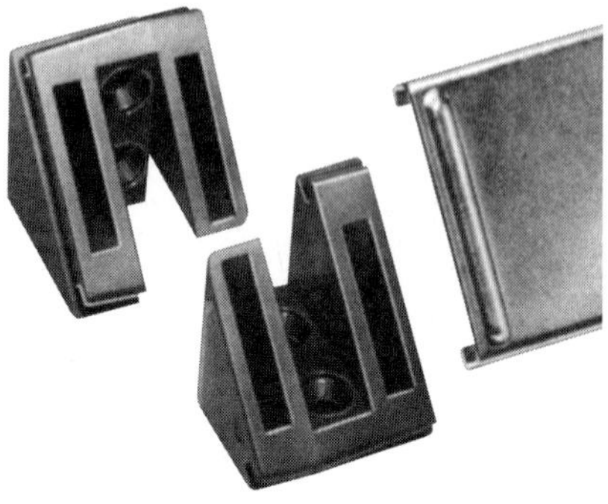

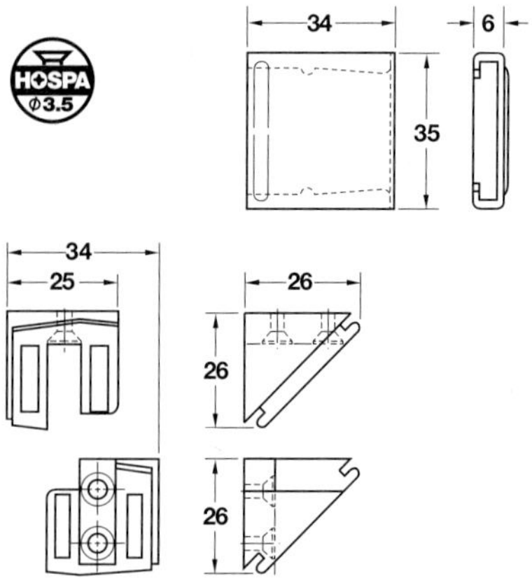

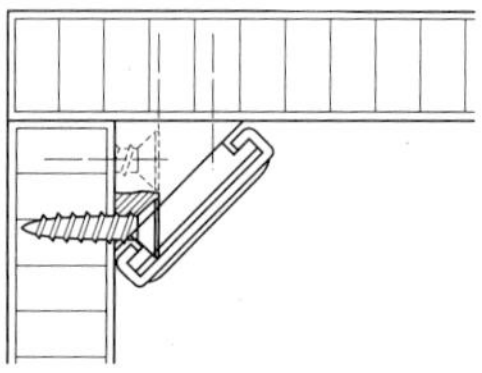

Finish: plastic/steel

Cat. No.	brown	262.68.708
	white	262.68.100

Packing: 50 pcs.

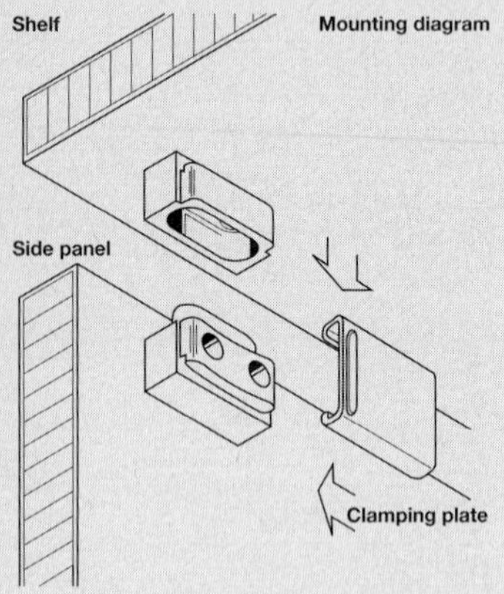

Quickfast fitting includes two rectangular, screw-mounted elements (male and female, with taper effect), providing a secure interlocking grip, locked together by a steel clamping plate.

HOSPA Ø3.5

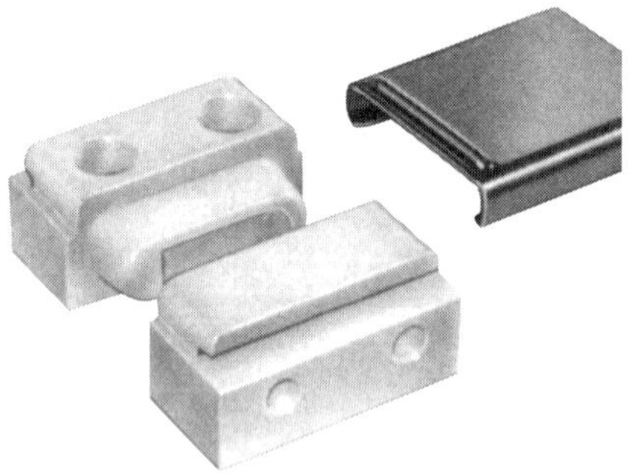

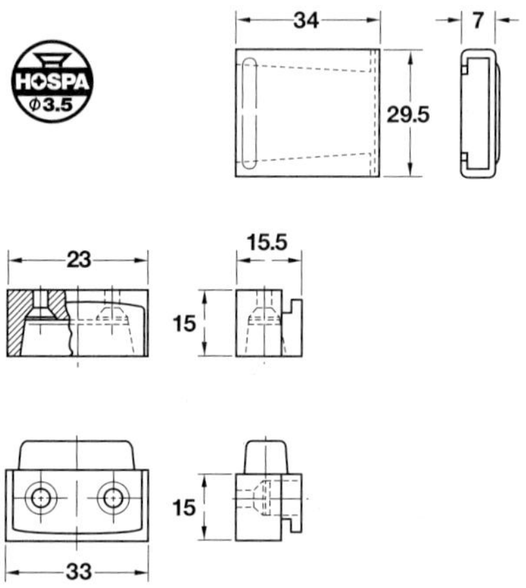

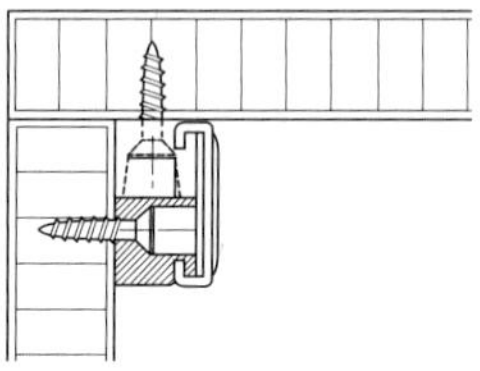

Finish: plastic

Cat. No.	brown	262.67.103
	white	262.67.701

Packing: 100 pcs.

Lockfix is a sturdy fitting for casegoods with exceptional tensioning strength through its eccentric cam. Offering extensive travel and ease of installation.

HOSPA Ø4,0

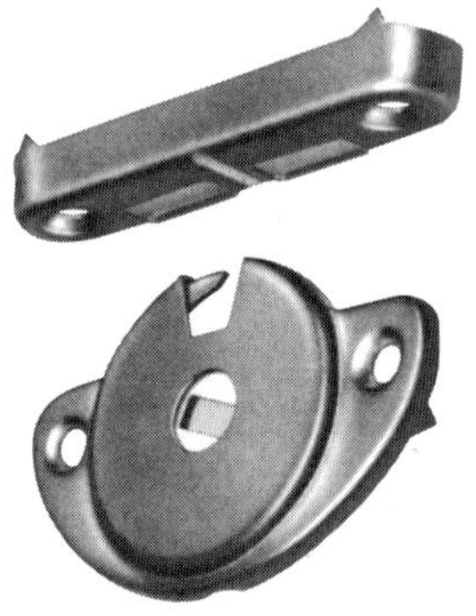

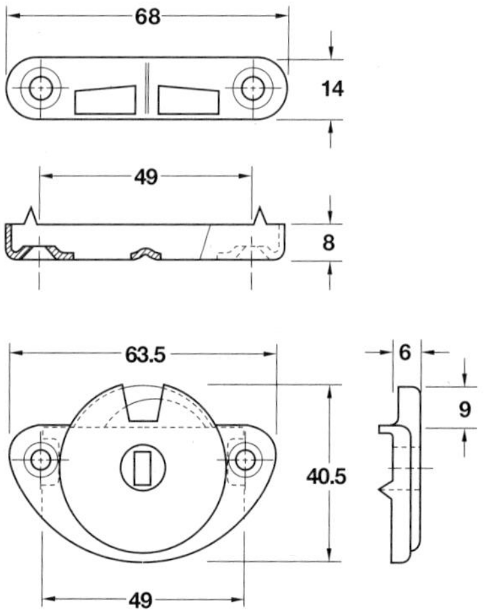

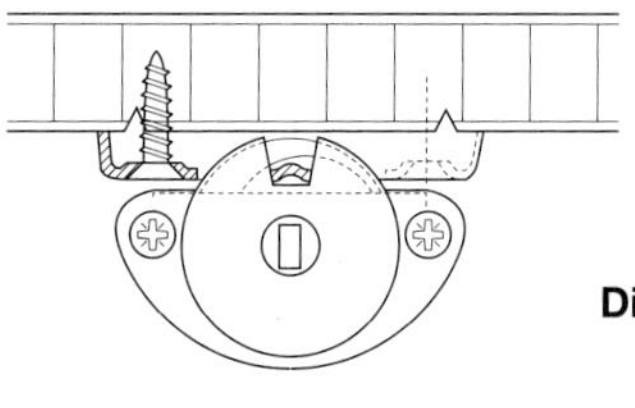

Finish: steel

Cat. No.	brass-plated	261.04.503

Packing: 100 pcs.

Dimensional data not binding.
We reserve the right to alter specifications without notice.

Dimensions in mm

Confirmat® Drilling Systems and Corner Clamps

Confirmat Tools

With the Zentrix drilling system and special drill, the required holes for the Confirmat one-piece connector can be drilled in a single operation. The drilling system incorporates a stop which ensures correctly angled, located and centered drilling to guarantee perfect joints. The drilling system also provides for the shortest possible drilling times. With a few manual operations, it can be adjusted to the appropriate panel thickness of 16mm (5/8"); 19 mm (3/4") or 22 mm (7/8"), while drilling for center panel installations can be accomplished by visual reference to a mark. The Zentrix drill attachment, with two telescopic cylinders connected by a spring, fits any power drill with a 43 mm diameter neck.

Electric Drill, 3/8" variable speed 110 V, 60 HZ, 2.8 A for Zentrix drilling system

Cat. No.	001.61.446

Packing: 1 pc.

Zentrix drilling system for Confirmat® connectors with depth stop and two Allen Keys for installation of 50 mm connectors.

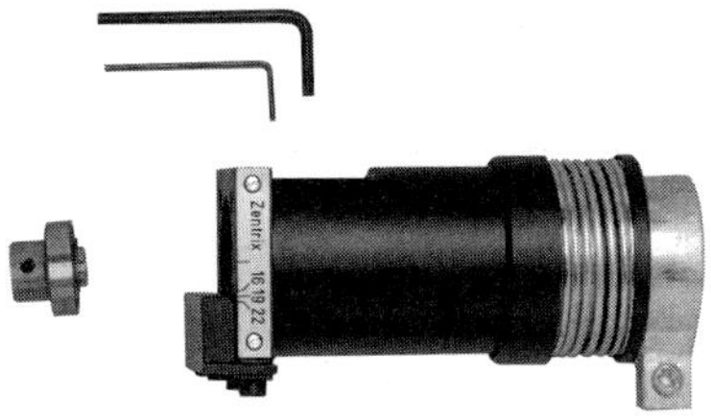

Cat. No.	001.22.510

Packing: 1 set

The Firmus clamp is ideal for assembling short runs, individual items or samples. The rapid-action clamp can be used in any situation where cabinet elements or panels must be joined at right angles.

For panel thickness of 15-27 mm.

Cat. No.	003.73.268

Packing: 1 set

The Corner Clamp WS-3 is designed to fit, align and hold material at a 90° angle.

Cat. No.	003.73.286

Packing: 1 unit pack

Special drill for Confirmat installation, for use with Zentrix drilling system.

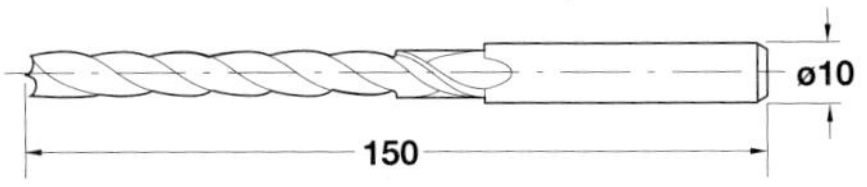

1st step ø dia. **5.4mm**
2nd step ø dia. **7mm**
countersunk ø dia. **10mm**

Cat. No.	Length		Box Qty.
001.22.672	150	HSS	1
001.24.970	150	HM-tipped	1

1st step ø dia. **4mm**
2nd step ø dia. **5mm**
countersunk ø dia. **8mm**

Cat. No.	Length		Box Qty.
001.22.663	150	HSS	1

Locks, Catches, RTA and PAS® Fittings
Shelf Supports
Bed Fittings
2

Dimensional data not binding. We reserve the right to alter specifications without notice.

HÄFELE

Confirmat® P.A.S.® One-piece Connector

Confirmat®
- Ideal furniture fastener.
- Long shank, deep-cut thread ensure accurate, close-fitting joints between panels
- High pull-out resistance and strength at the corners.
- Cost-effective.
- Only a single drilling operation for side panels and shelves.
- Consistently secure joints are assured even with repeated assembly/disassembly operations.

***Note: Confirmat® one-piece connectors can be supplied in non-standard lengths and/or finishes in minimum quantities.**

2 **Locks, Catches, RTA and PAS® Fittings Shelf Supports Bed Fittings**

Screwdriver Bit, for Confirmat connector with cross-slot Z

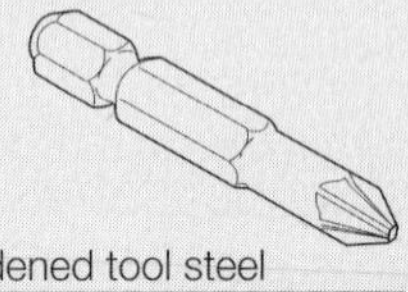

Finish: hardened tool steel

Cat. No.	Size 1	006.37.276.PM
	Size 2	006.37.285.PM
	Size 3	006.37.294.PM

Packing: 25 pcs.

Allen Socket Bit, for Confirmat connetor with 4 mm hexagon socket head.

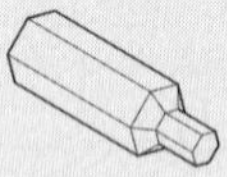

Finish: hardened tool steel

Cat. No.	006.37.945

Packing: 1 pc.

Allen Keys, with M4 hexagon shank and flat blade.

Finish: hardened tool steel, black

Cat. No.	008.28.642

Packing: 1 pc.

Allen Keys, for Confirmat connector with hexagon socket head.

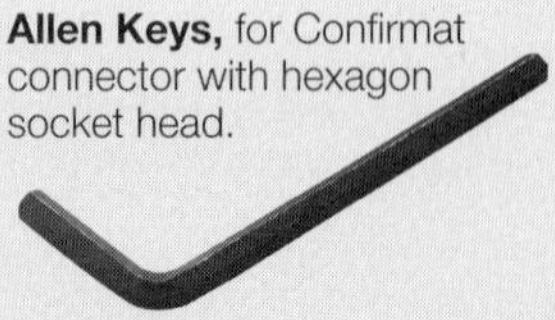

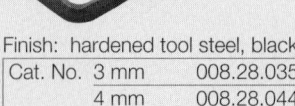

Finish: hardened tool steel, black

Cat. No.	3 mm	008.28.035
	4 mm	008.28.044

Packing: 1 pc.

Dimensional data not binding. We reserve the right to alter specifications without notice.

Confirmat® Precision Assembly System®

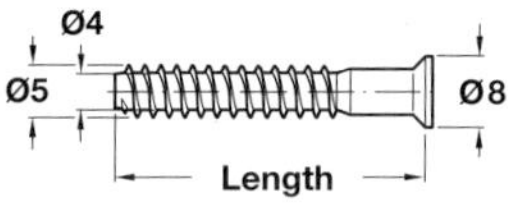

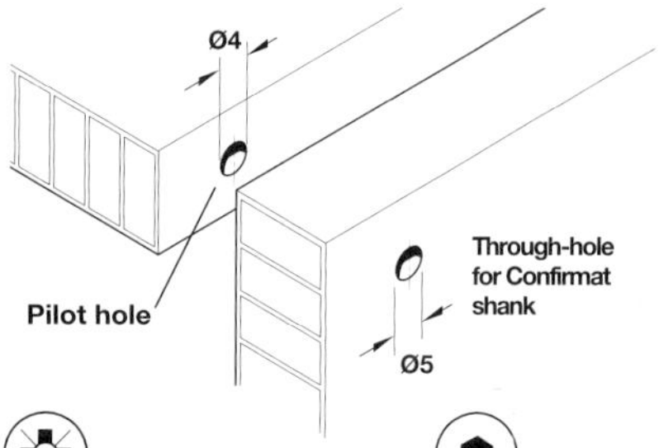

Drill hole Ø **4 mm**
Shank Ø **5 mm**
Head Ø **8 mm**

	Finish: steel	length	Cross-slot size 2 drilled head, Ø 2.4 mm	Hex socket head 3 mm
Cat. No.	zinc-plated	40 mm	264.37.098	264.39.092
	bronzed	40 mm	264.37.034	264.39.038
	zinc-plated	50 mm	264.37.196	264.39.190
	bronzed	50 mm	264.37.132	264.39.136

Packing: 1000 pcs.

Trim cap
press-fit in Confirmat head

	Finish: plastic	**Ø 12 mm**	**Ø 12 mm**
Cat. No.	light brown		045.01.124
	dark brown	045.18.101	045.01.222
	black	045.18.307	
	white	045.18.709	045.01.722
	pine	045.18.209	
	beige		045.01.428
	almond	045.18.450	

Packing: 1000 pcs.

Confirmat® one-piece connector

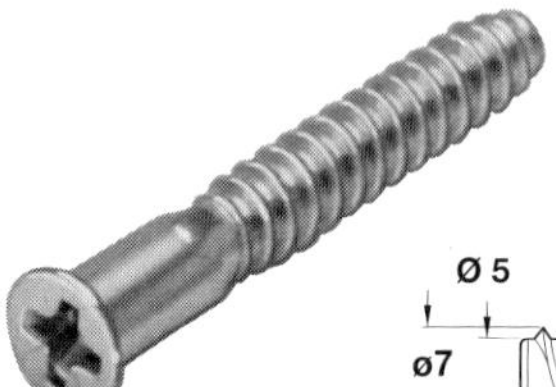

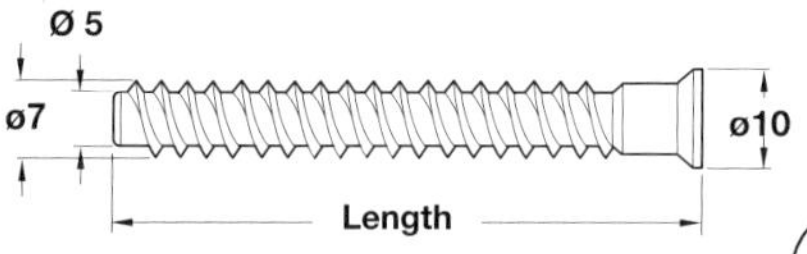

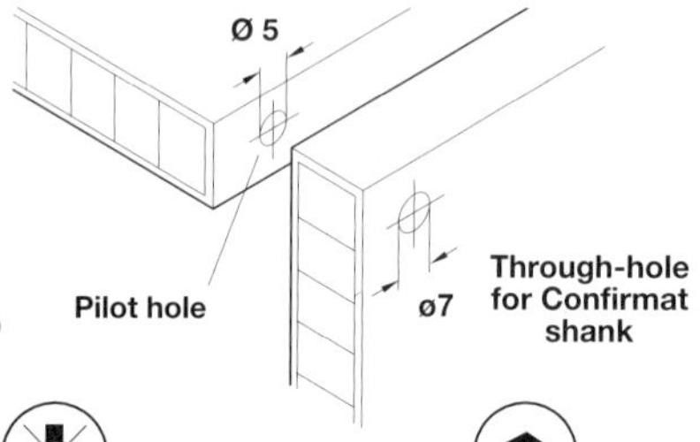

Drill hole Ø **5 mm**
Shank Ø **7 mm**
Head Ø **10 mm**

	Finish: steel	length	Cross-slot size 2 drilled head, Ø 3 mm	Hex socket head 3 mm
Cat. No.	zinc-plated	40 mm	264.52.095	264.53.092
	bronzed	40 mm	264.52.031	264.53.038
	zinc-plated	50 mm	264.52.193	264.53.190
	bronzed	50 mm	264.52.139	264.53.136

Packing: 1000 pcs.

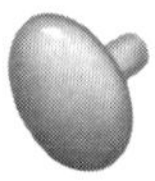

Trim cap
press-fit in Confirmat head

	Finish: plastic	**Ø 12 mm**	**Ø 15 mm**	**Ø 12 mm**
Cat. No.	light brown	045.01.106	045.01.115	045.01.133
	dark brown	045.01.204		045.01.231
	black	045.01.302	045.01.311	045.01.339
	white	045.01.704	045.01.713	045.01.731
	pine	045.01.008		045.01.035
	beige	045.01.400		
	almond	045.01.455	045.01.473	045.01.464

Packing: 1000 pcs.

Dimensions in mm

Confirmat® P.A.S.® One-piece Connector

HÄFELE

Confirmat® Precision Assembly Systems®

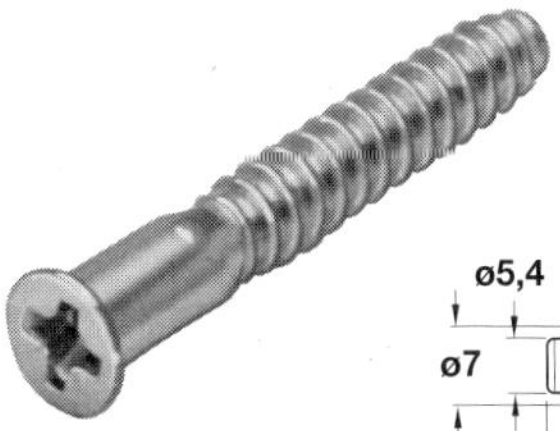

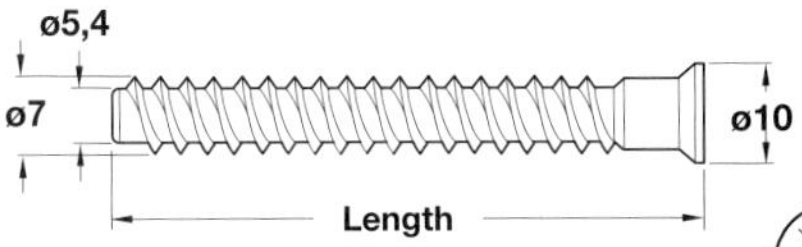

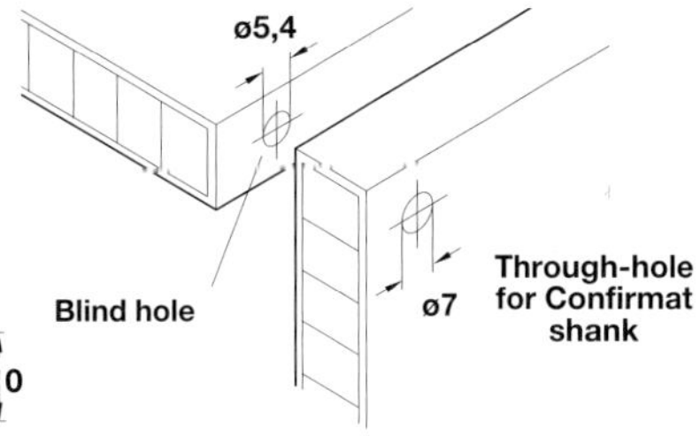

Drill hole Ø **5.4 mm**
Shank Ø **7 mm**
Head Ø **10 mm**

	Finish: steel	length	Cross-slot size 3 drilled head, Ø 3 mm	Hex socket head 4 mm
Cat. No.	zinc-plated	40 mm	264.52.099	264.39.096
	bronzed	40 mm	264.52.035	264.39.032
	zinc-plated	50 mm	264.52.197	264.39.194
	bronzed	50 mm	264.52.133	264.39.130
	zinc-plated	70 mm	264.42.295	264.43.292
	bronzed	70 mm	264.42.231	264.43.238

Packing: 1000 pcs.

Trim cap
press-fit in Confirmat head

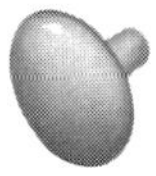

	Finish: plastic		Ø 12 mm	Ø 15 mm	Ø 12 mm
Cat. No.	light brown		045.01.106	045.01.115	045.01.133
	dark brown		045.01.204		045.01.231
	black		045.01.302	045.01.311	045.01.339
	white		045.01.704	045.01.713	045.01.731
	pine		045.01.008		045.01.035
	beige		045.01.400		
	almond		045.01.455	045.01.473	045.01.464

Packing: 1000 pcs.

Lock, Catches, RTA and PAS® Fittings
Shelf Supports
Bed Fittings

2

Confirmat® Self-countersinking 7 x 50
with cross-slot drive head and nibs.

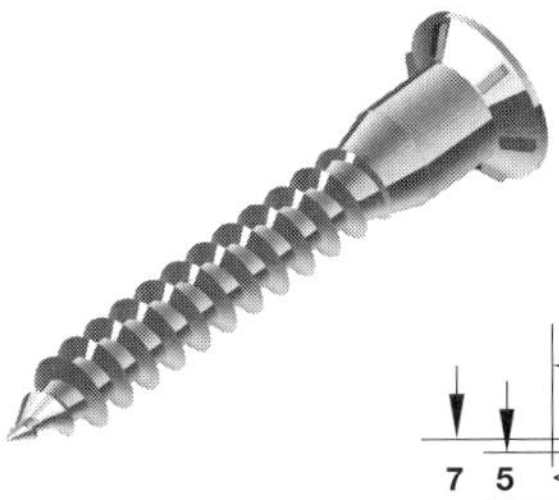

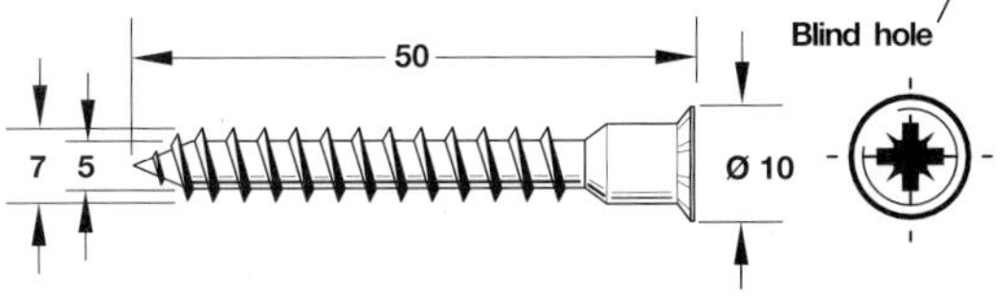

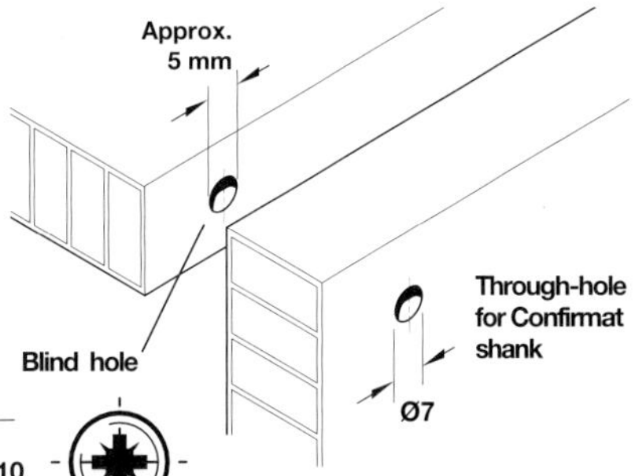

- One piece connector
- Extremely strong
- With tip, easy insertion into blind hole.
- **No countersink necessary.** Nibs countersink hole.
- See jigs on page **2.135**.
- See drill bits - 5mm and 7mm on page **2.135**.

Finish: steel, zinc-plated

Cat. No.	264.44.190

Packing: 1000 pcs.

Cross-slot Size 3 with headbore 3mm for covercaps.

Confirmat® with Cylinder Head

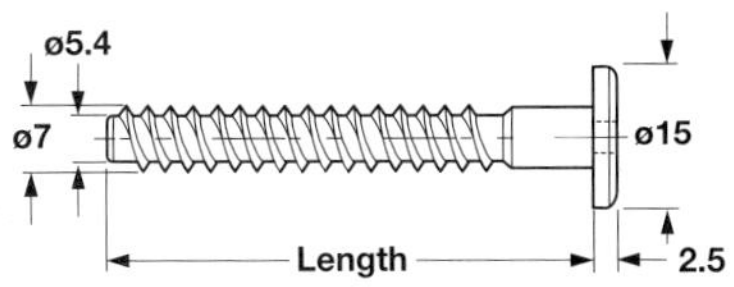

Drill hole Ø **5.4 mm**
Shank Ø **7 mm**
Head Ø **15 mm**

	Finish: steel	length		Hex socket head 4 mm
Cat. No.	nickel-plated	50 mm		264.47.174
	bronzed	50 mm		264.47.138
	nickel-plated	70 mm		264.47.272
	bronzed	70 mm		264.47.236

Packing: 500 pcs.

Dimensions in mm

Dimensional data not binding.
We reserve the right to alter specifications without notice.

HÄFELE

- One piece connector
- Extremely strong
- With tip, easy insertion into blind hole.
- No countersink necessary. Nibs countersink hole.
- See jigs on page **2.135**.
- See drill bits – 5mm and 7mm on page **2.135**.

Confirmat® P.A.S.® One-piece Connector

Confirmat® Self-countersinking
7 x 50 Steel zinc-plated
with cross-slot drive head and nibs.

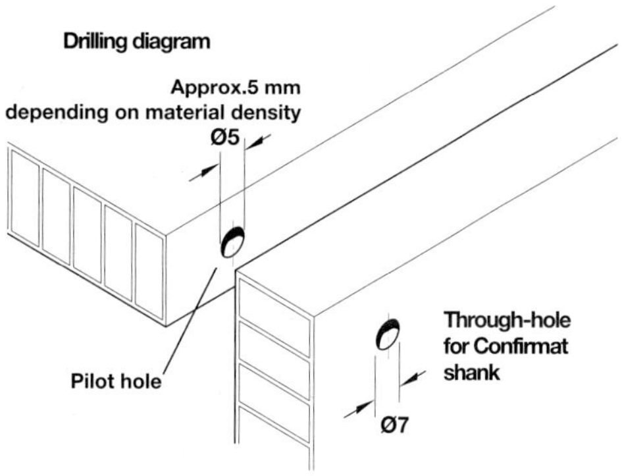

Finish: steel, zinc-plated

Cat. No.	264.44.190

Packing: 100 and 1000 pcs.

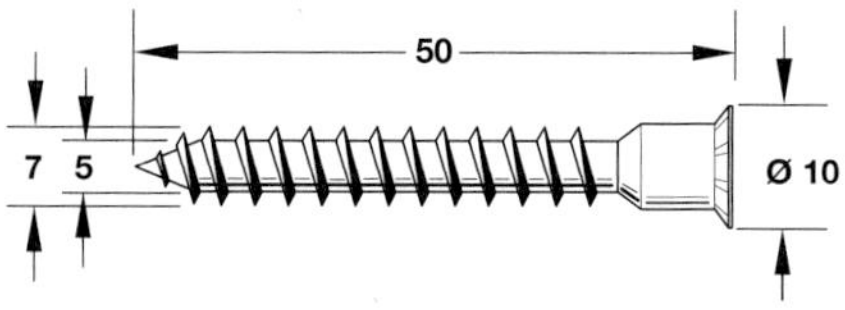

Cross-slot Size 3
with headbore 3mm for
cover caps.

Rapid Dowel

Rapid dowel can be pressed in by hand, no special tool required.
Requires only 5mm holes, same drill bit.

1 through hole – vertical
1 blind hole – horizontal

Primarily used to connect 1/2 inch drawer backs without tools, but can also be used to connect rear panels in a user-friendly way.

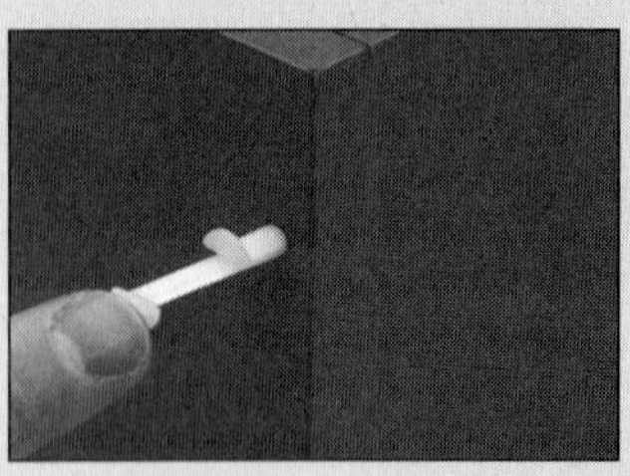

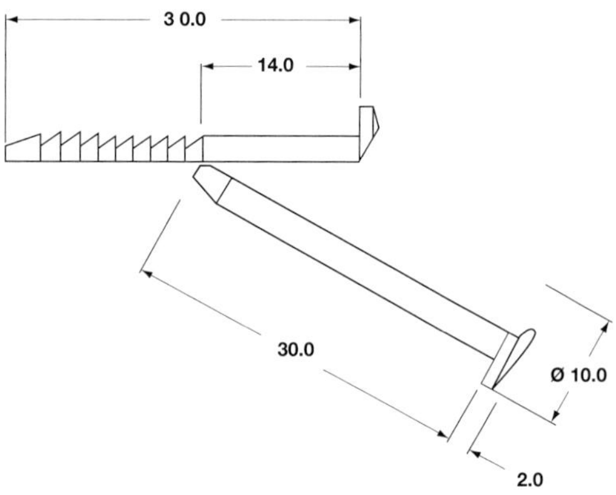

- No tools required–press in by hand
- User friendly
- Only one 5mm hole required
- Can be used with or without glue
- If dowel breaks apart before insertion, place ribbed anchor first, then insert the wedge.
- For additional strength add a drop of glue

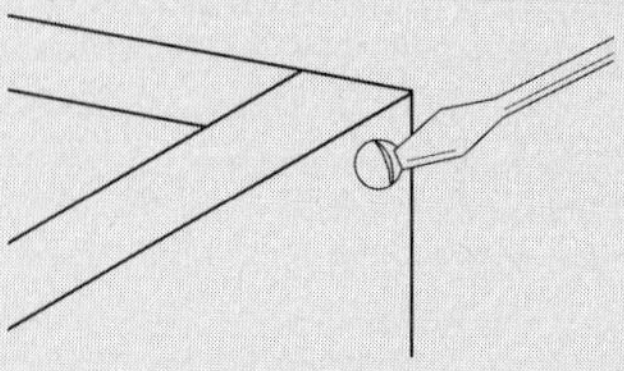

- Releasable with a screwdriver

Finish: plastic

	white	brown
Cat. No.	260.32.708	260.32.100

Packing: 5000 pcs.

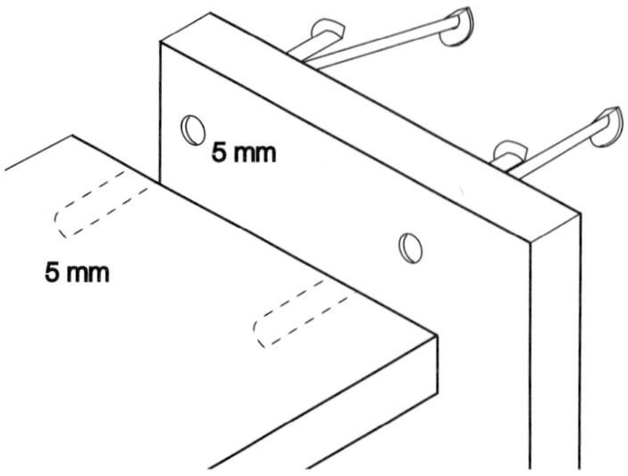

Dimensional data not binding.
We reserve the right to alter specifications without notice.

Dimensions in mm

Keku Suspension Fitting

HÄFELE

- **Keku suspension fittings** frame can be pre-assembled.
- Panels are hung on site.
- Made of tough Macrolon with a temperature resistance of -100° C to +135° C.
- Can also be used for ceiling cladding or heavy wood panels.
- Releases without tools

Keku suspension fitting

Includes: frame component, screw-mounted;
panel component, screw-mounted;
both elements mounted with Hospa particle board screws.

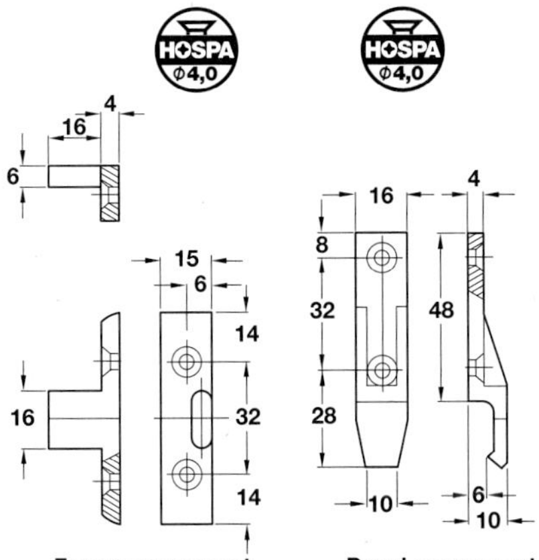

Frame component Panel component

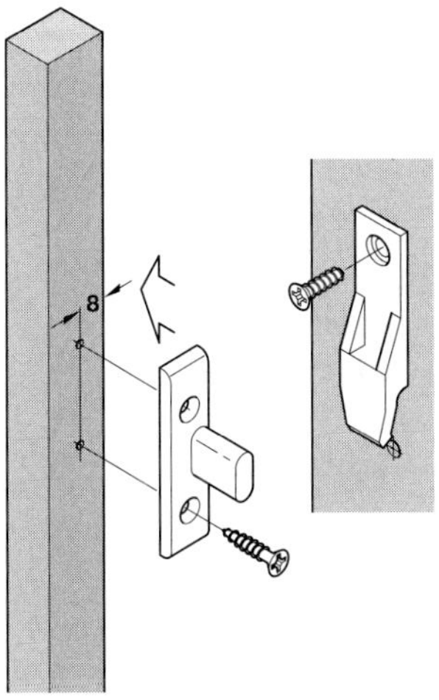

Finish: plastic, black

Cat. No.	262.49.310

Packing: 250 pairs

Keku suspension fitting

Includes: frame component, groove-mounted and screwed; panel component, screw-mounted using Hospa particle board screws, or Varianta screws.

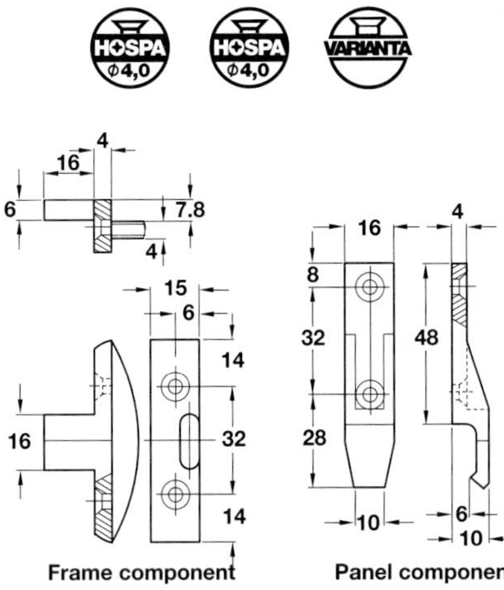

Frame component Panel component

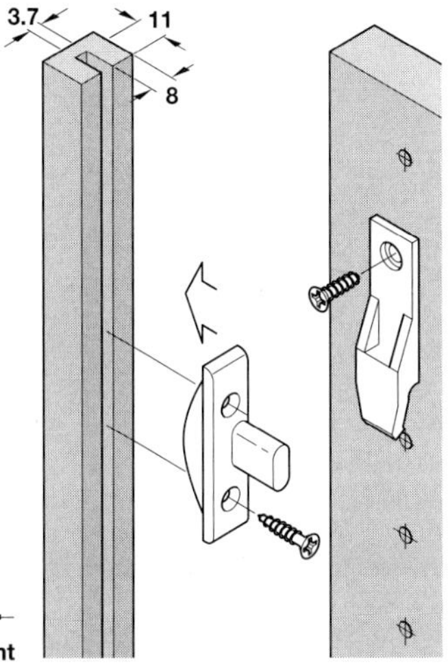

Finish: plastic, black, for wood screws

Cat. No.	262.49.338

Packing: 250 pairs

For mounting with Varianta screws

Cat. No.	262.49.329

Packing: 250 pairs

Varianta special screw, used to mount the panel component in system holes

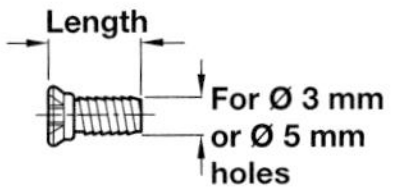

Flat head

Finish: steel, nickel-plated

Drill-hole		Ø3 mm	Ø5 mm
Cat. No.	10.5 mm long	013.15.617	013.15.715
	13.5 mm long	013.15.626	013.15.724
	16.0 mm long	013.15.635	013.15.733

Packing: 500 pcs.

Dimensions in mm

HÄFELE

- **Keku push-fit fasteners**
- Trim panels can be mounted from the front
- Heavy panels are securely clamped together
- Releases without tools

- **Keku fasteners**
- A real problem-solver
- For quick, easy use during in-house assembly or on construction site
- Not visible from outside
- No tool required to attach or unattach.
- Use for false drawer fronts, spacer panels, toekicks, wall/sealing paneling, cover panels, modesty panels, etc.

Keku Press-Fit Fasteners

Keku push-fit fastener
Includes:
frame element, screw-mounted;
panel element, screw-mounted

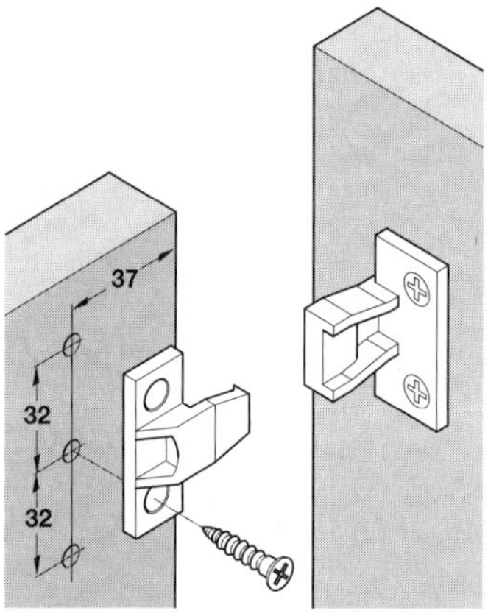

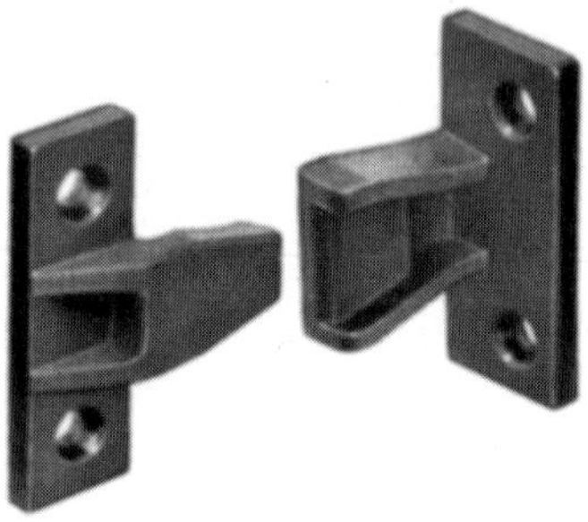

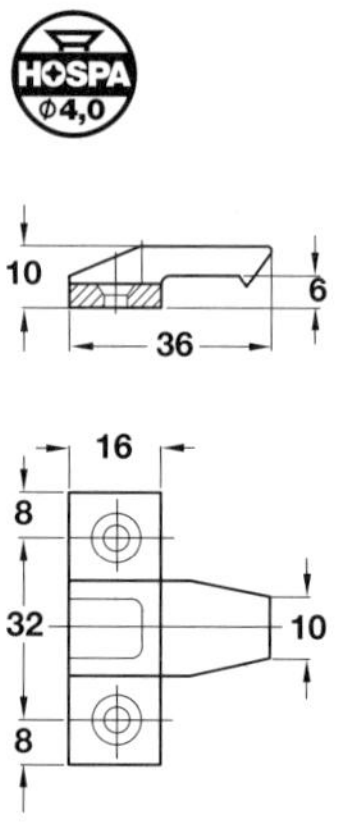

Frame component

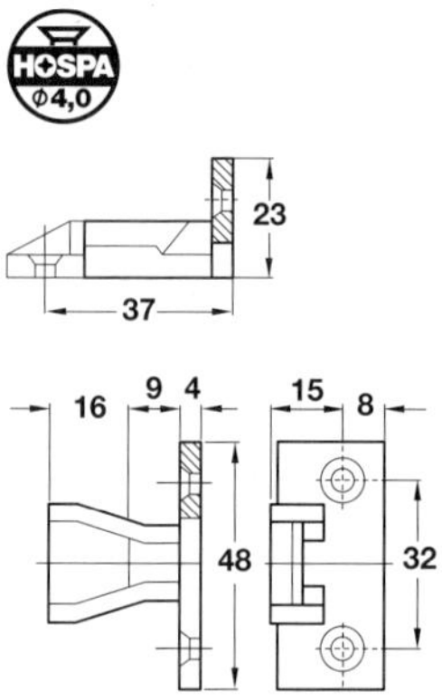

Panel component

Finish: plastic Hospa/Hospa

Cat. No.	black	262.50.313
	white	262.50.715

Packing: 200 pairs

Keku press-fit fastener
Includes: frame element, screw-mounted in, Ø 3 mm or Ø 5 mm holes with Varianta special screws; panel element, screw-mounted with Hospa particle board screws.

Finish: plastic, black Varianta/Hospa

Cat. No.	262.50.322

Packing: 200 pairs

Finish: plastic Varianta/Varianta

Cat. No.	262.50.340

Packing: 200 pairs

Dimensional data not binding.
We reserve the right to alter specifications without notice.

Dimensions in mm

Keku AD Double Partition Fasteners

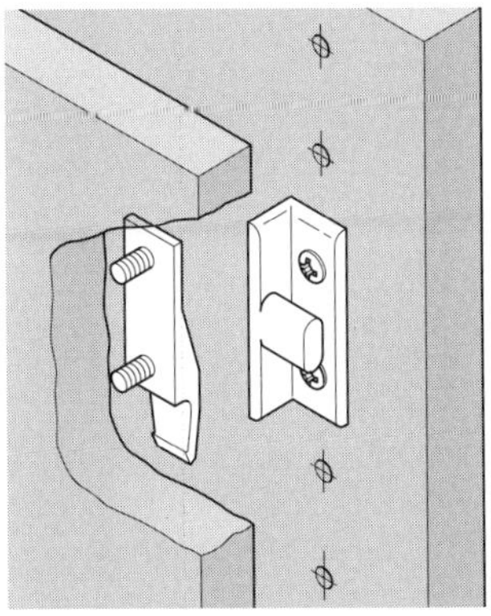

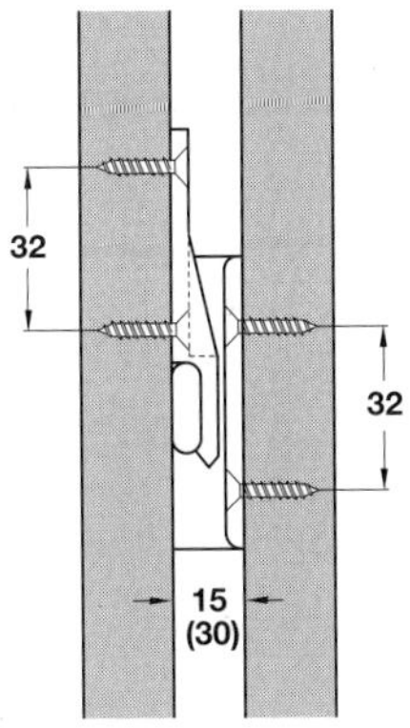

- **Keku AD double partition fasteners** secure trims and cladding panels directly to walls with no wood subframe.
- Permits cavity-type doors, sides etc, for sound insulating material or cable ducting.
- Made of tough Macralon with a temperature resistance of 100°C to +135°C.
- Can be used for ceiling cladding as well as walls.
- Releases without tools.
- The Keku double partition fastener can be secured with Varianta screws in Ø 3 mm or Ø 5 mm system holes, or with Hospa screws.

Keku AD double partition fastener
Screw-mounted
For 15 mm cavity between panels
Black Macralon

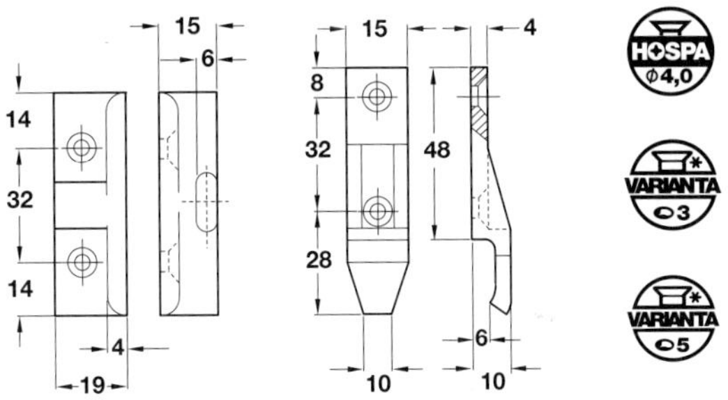

Finish: plastic, black for Hospa screws

Cat. No.	262.51.310

Packing: 200 pairs

Mounted with Varianta screws

Cat. No.	262.51.365

Packing: 200 pairs

Keku AD double partition fastener
Screw-mounted
For 30 mm cavity between panels
Black Macralon

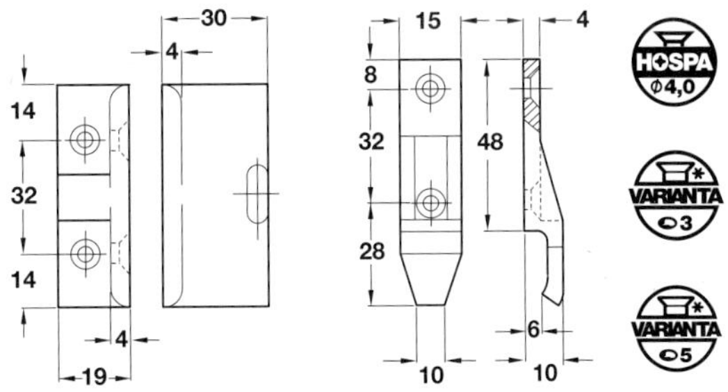

Finish: plastic, black for Hospa screws

Cat. No.	262.51.329

Packing: 150 pairs

Mounted with Varianta screws

Cat. No.	262.51.374

Packing: 150 pairs

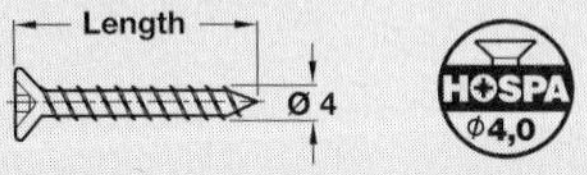

Hospa particle board screws

Length	Cat. No
15 mm	015.31.826
17 mm	015.31.835
20 mm	015.31.844

Packing: 1000 pcs.

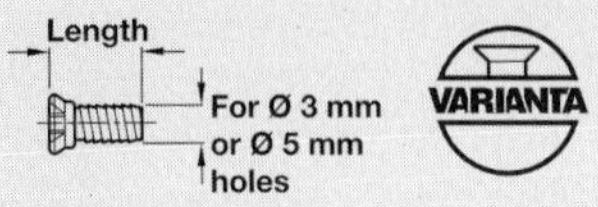

Varianta special screws

Length	Hole Ø3 mm	Hole Ø5 mm
10.5 mm	013.15.617	013.15.715
13.5 mm	013.15.626	013.15.724
16.0 mm	013.15.635	013.15.733

Packing: 500 pcs.

Dimensional data not binding.
We reserve the right to alter specifications without notice.

Dimensions in mm

HÄFELE

Press-fit Fastener

Macrolon is temperature resistant, -100° C to +135° C

Locks, Catches, RTA and PAS® Fittings Shelf Supports Bed Fittings (2)

Attachment screws:
Varianta-flat head screws with PZ 2 cross-slot.
Finish:
Steel, nickel-plated

length (mm)	Cat. No. Ø 3 mm	Ø 5 mm
10.5	013.15.617	013.15.715
13.5	013.15.626	013.15.724
16.0	013.15.635	013.15.733

Packing: 100 and 1000 pcs.

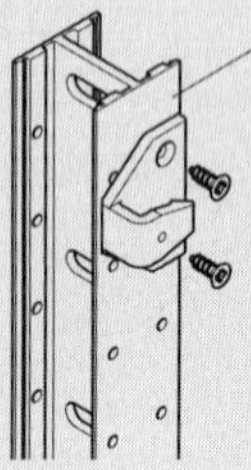

Description and ordering data, see Product Group **7** "Keku Interior Finishing System" **7.7 - 7.13**

Note:
Do not use chemical solutions and aggressive lubricants on load-bearing plastic fittings.

Keku fittings are also available in white, minimum order 5,000 pcs. (by Cat. No.)

AS Panel Component

Screw-mounted to panels.
(Order frame component separately)

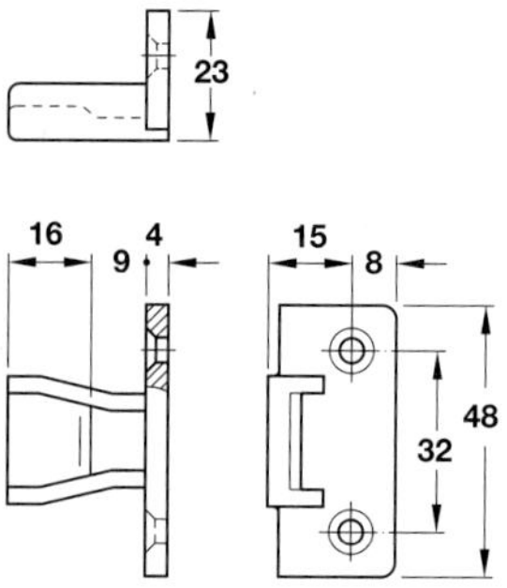

Finish: macrolon, black

Mounted with:	Cat. No.
Hospa-screws	262.50.359
Varianta-screws	262.50.358

Packing: 200 pcs.

ASR Frame Component

Screw-mounted to frame

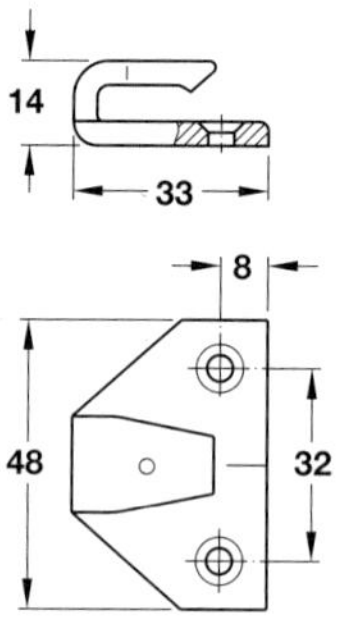

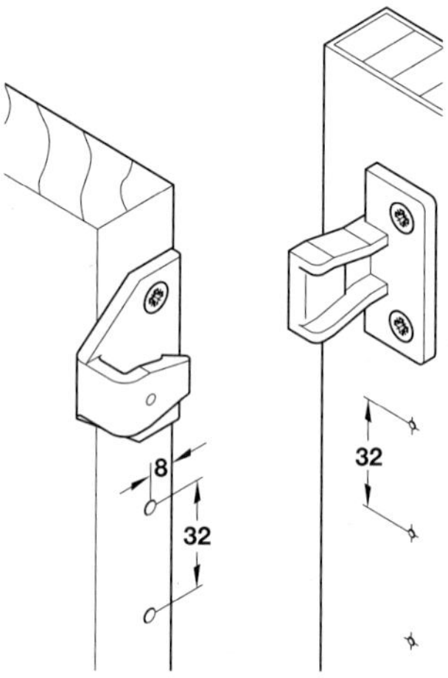

Finish: macrolon, black

Mounted with:	Cat. No.
Hospa-screws	262.50.390
Varianta-screws	262.50.391

Packing: 200 pcs.

Dimensions in mm

Uni - Connector

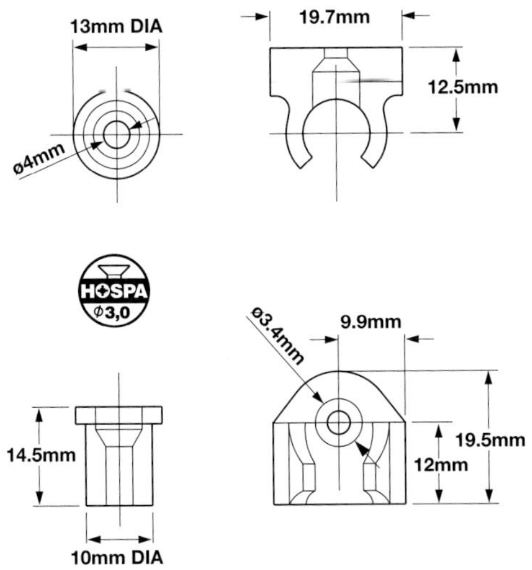

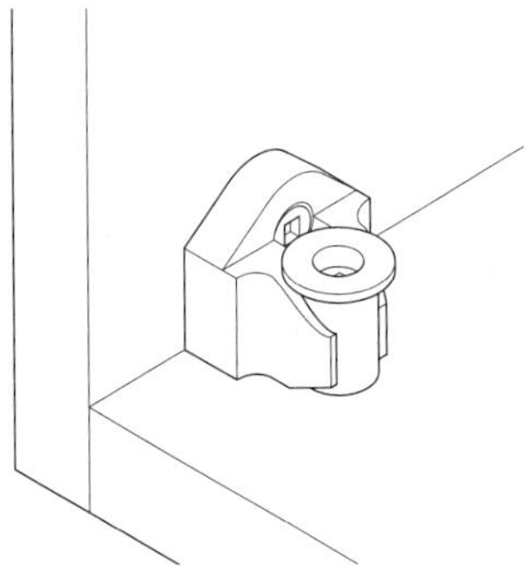

Finish: plastic, black

Cat. No.	260.15.300

Packing: 1000 sets/1 male, 1 female.

Can be screwed directly into the wood or into a pre-drilled 5mm hole if sleeves 042.98.051 are used.

Spreading Dowel, for use in Ø 5 mm holes.

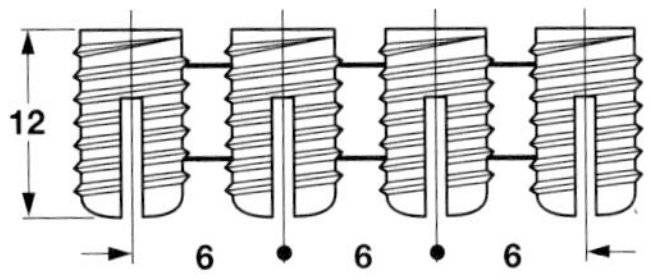

Finish: nylon, natural

Cat. No.	042.98.051

Packing: 5000 pcs.

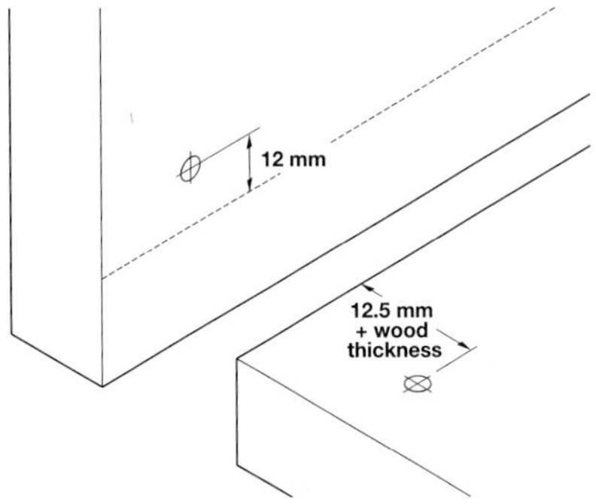

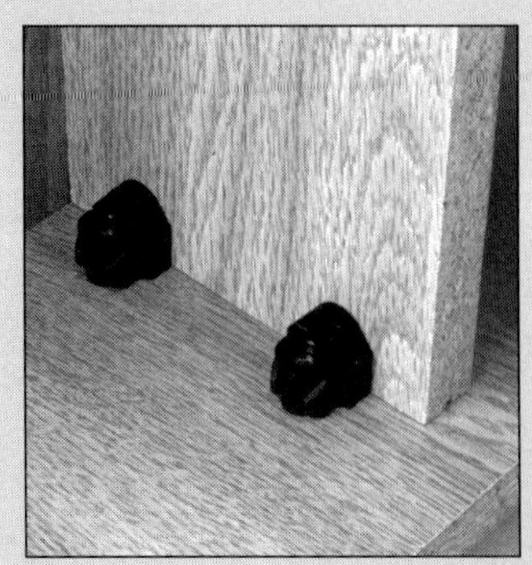

Locks, Catches, RTA and PAS® Fittings Shelf Supports Bed Fittings **2**

- The Uni - Connector is an all-purpose connector. Applications include...
- Spacers/fillers
- Access panels
- False drawer fronts...

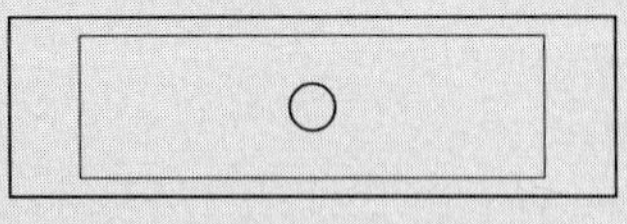

- And can be used for entire pieces of furniture.

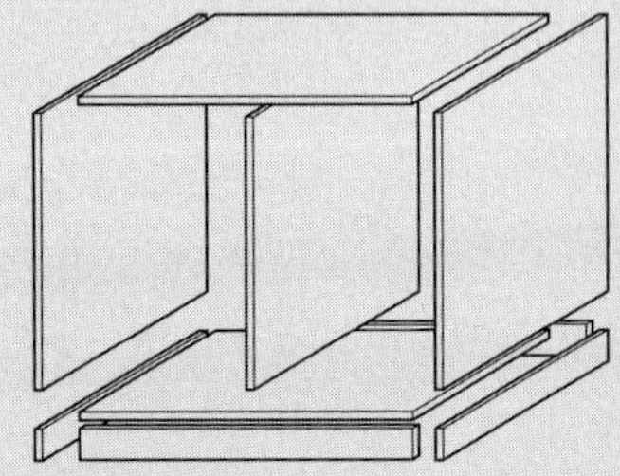

- Only vertical drilling necessary.
- Extremely durable plastic material.
- Easy to assemble and dissassemble.
- No tools needed.
- Can also be used as a pivot.

Dimensions in mm.

Dimensional data not binding. We reserve the right to alter specifications without notice.

HÄFELE

Troxi - Precision Assembly System®

Because of the simple mounting and the easy adjustment of the Troxi fastener, you will save precious installation time at the shop and at the building site:

- Attachment of elements for exterior doors, heavy interior doors, sound resistant doors, etc...
- The mounting of veneered or layered panel elements.
- Also for mounting of blinds, railing units, wall paneling, mirrors, etc...
- Exact centering, no extensive measuring.

- No glue, no clamps. (no wasted time waiting for it to dry)
- Minimal cavity depth.
- Space requirements of only 10 mm (3/8") for attachment.
- For invisible face to face mounting - no tools needed.

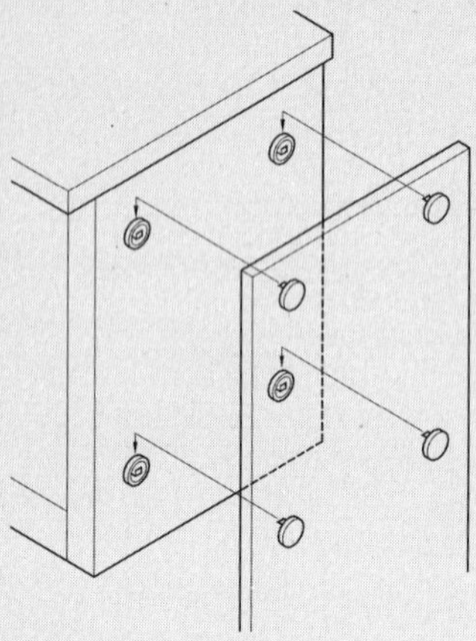

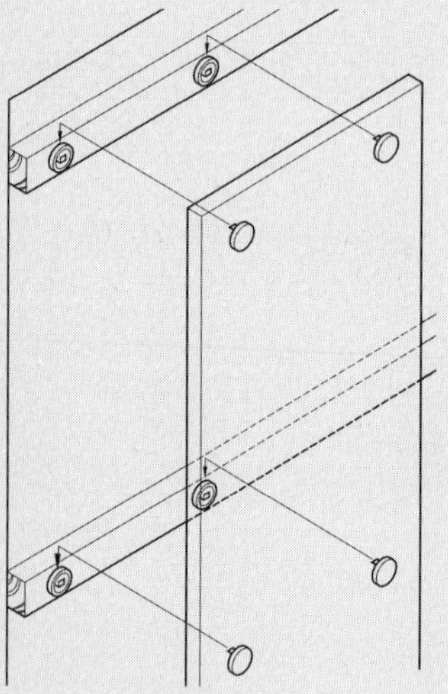

Metal Fasteners, tensile strength 140 kg. (308 lbs.) per piece

Blue
Side adjustment

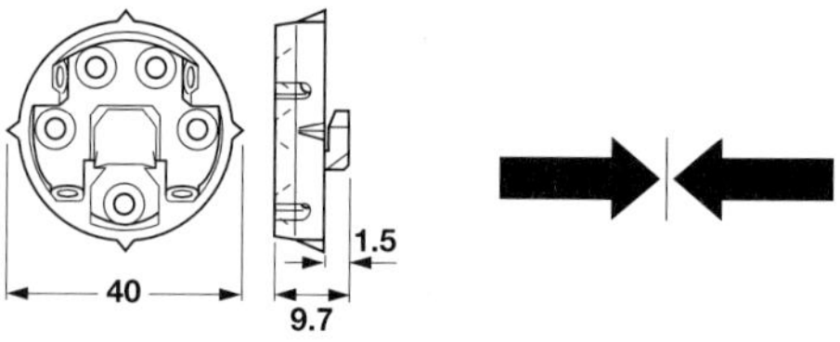

Finish: zinc, die-cast

Cat. No.	262.52.013

Packing: 50 pcs.

Yellow
max. 6 mm (1/4")
adjustable to both sides

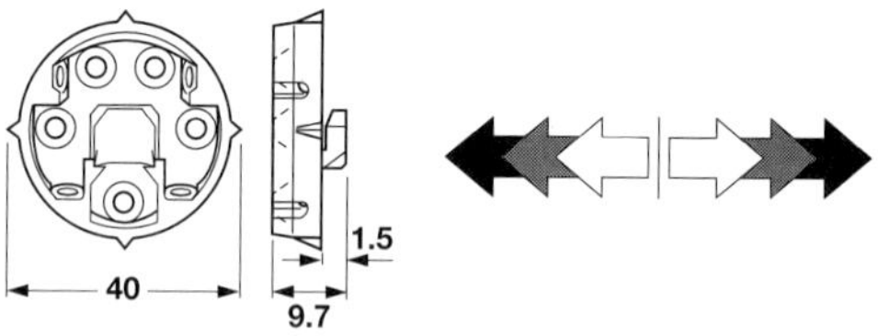

Finish: zinc, die-cast

Cat. No.	262.52.022

Packing: 50 pcs.

Plastic Fasteners, tensile strength 50 kg. (110 lbs.) per piece

Red
Side adjustment

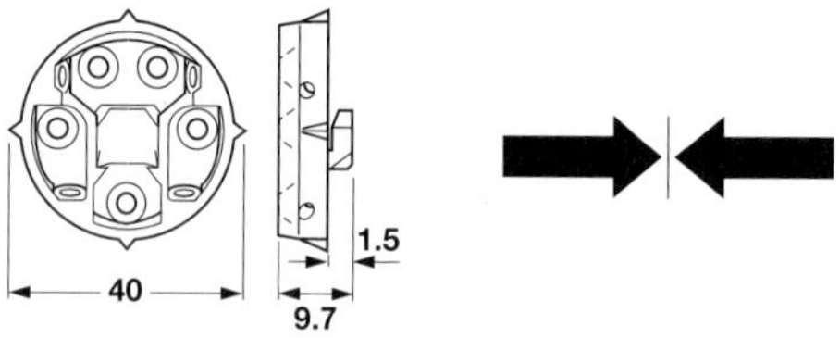

Finish: plastic

Cat. No.	262.52.111

Packing: 50 pcs.

Green
max. 6 mm (1/4")
adjustable to both sides

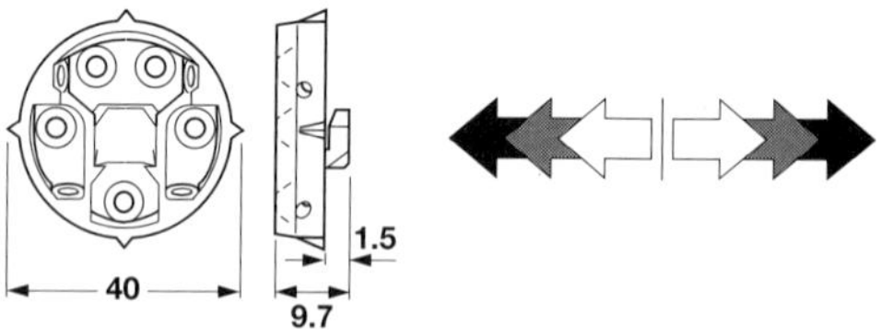

Finish: plastic

Cat. No.	262.52.120

Packing: 50 pcs.

Dimensions in mm

***Please note: Troxi fasteners were not designed to mount ceiling panels.**

Mounting screws: 

into bottom

into side

Dimensional data not binding. We reserve the right to alter specifications without notice.

Tools

Markers
Centering tip adjustable in height
(worn points can be replaced)

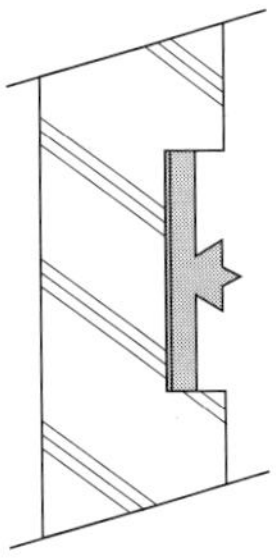

Cat. No.	262.52.906

Packing: 20 pcs.

Special Marker
With the additional flange, the pressure on the marker is not transmitted to the bottom of the hole, eliminating possible panel break through or bulging.
Designed especially for thin panels.
Centering tip is height adjustable
(worn points can be replaced)

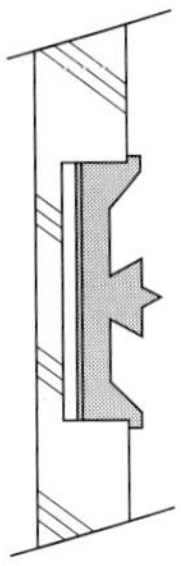

Cat. No.	262.52.942

Packing: 50 pcs.

Position Marker
By installing position markers in existing hole, the element can be brought back to its original position. An indispensable help with the later use of TROXI® fasteners.

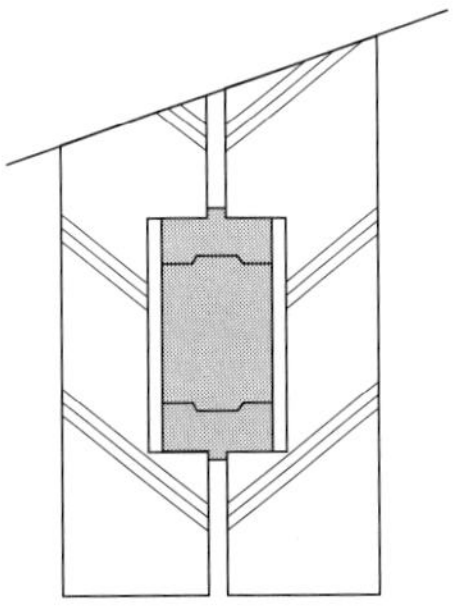

Cat. No.	262.52.960

Packing: 50 pcs.

Impression Jigs
Impression jigs should be installed in the pre-drilled hole, horizontally aligned and lightly tapped on the red button, creating four indentations in the side wall of the drilled hole.
The fasteners will self-align when firmly pressed into the drilled hole, eliminating misalignment.

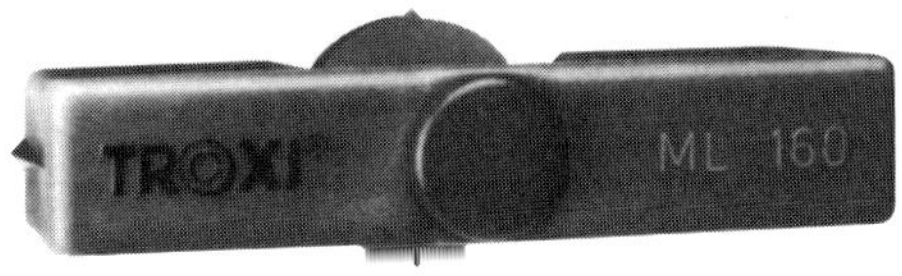

Cat. No.	262.52.951

Packing: 1 pc.

Replacement Points
For markers (Cat. No. 262.52.906) and (Cat. No. 262.52.942) above

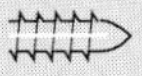

Cat. No.	262.52.915

Packing: 25 pcs.

Replacement Marker Plate for Impression Jig
Worn plates can be easily replaced.

Cat. No.	262.52.979

Packing: 1 pc.

HÄFELE

Drills

HSS-Drill 40 mm
Special steel, adjustable drill tip.

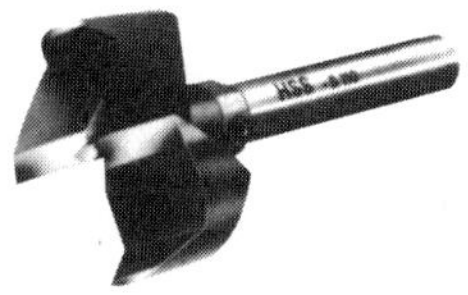

Cat. No.	262.52.808

Packing: 1 pc.

Carbide Tipped-Drill 40 mm
Carbide tipped pieces, adjustable drill tip.

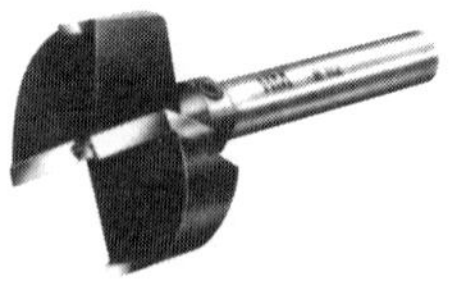

Cat. No.	262.52.817

Packing: 1 pc.

Depth Adjuster, with return spring
The drill bit rests in the ring of the depth adjuster.
The bit is guided perpendicular to the work.
Exact and quick adjustment with allen key.

Cat. No.	262.52.933

Packing: 1 pc.

HÄFELE

Modular Connectors

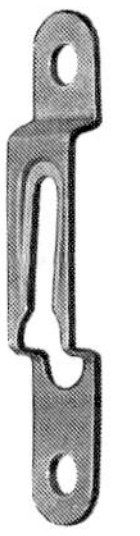

For panels from
16 mm **19 mm** **22 mm**

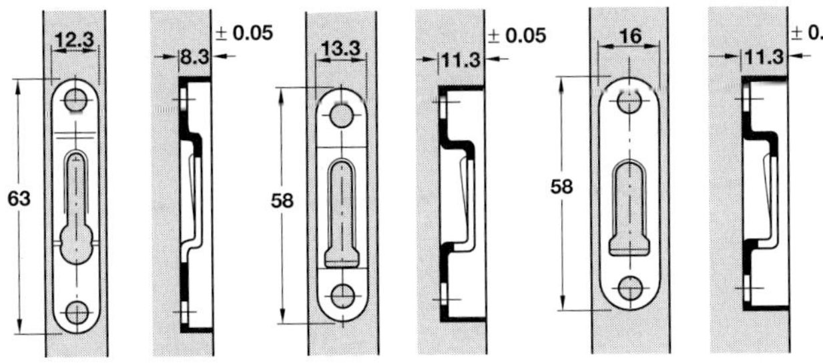

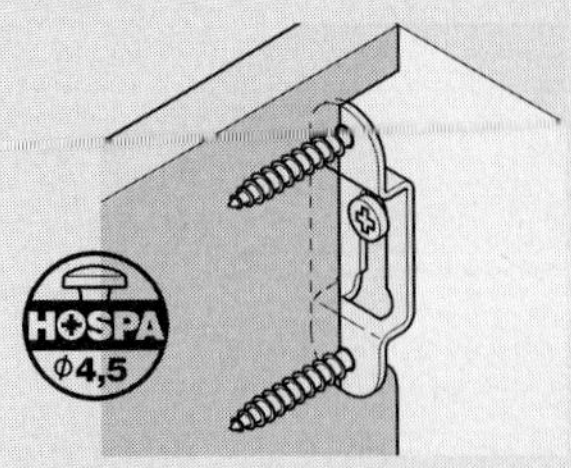

Standard Modular

Panel thickness	Cat. No.
16 mm	262.47.049
19 mm	262.47.021
22 mm	262.47.076

Packing: 1000 pcs.

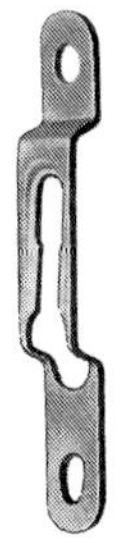

For panels from
13 mm **16 mm**

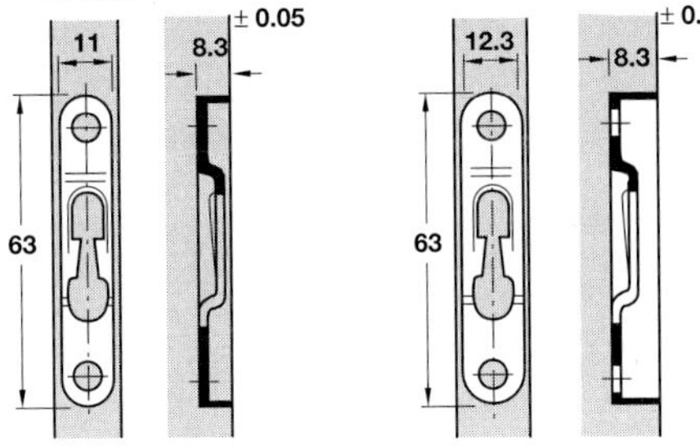

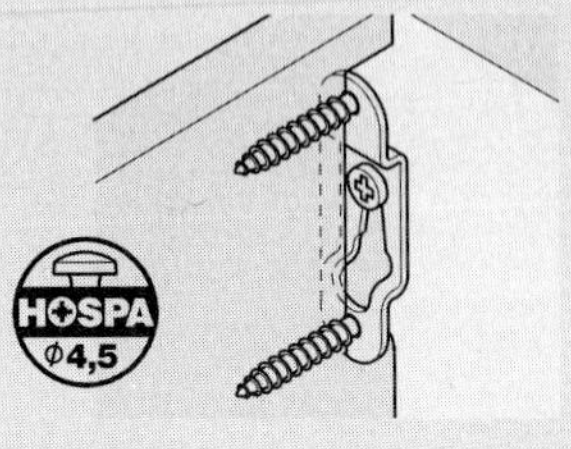

Semi-permanent Modular

Panel thickness	Cat. No.
16 mm	262.47.094
19 mm	262.47.058

Packing: 1000 pcs.

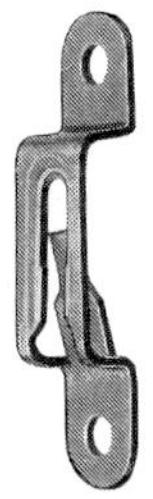

For panels from
19 mm **22 mm**

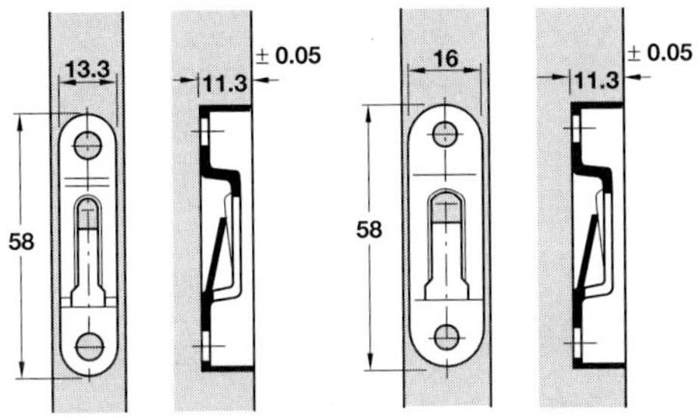

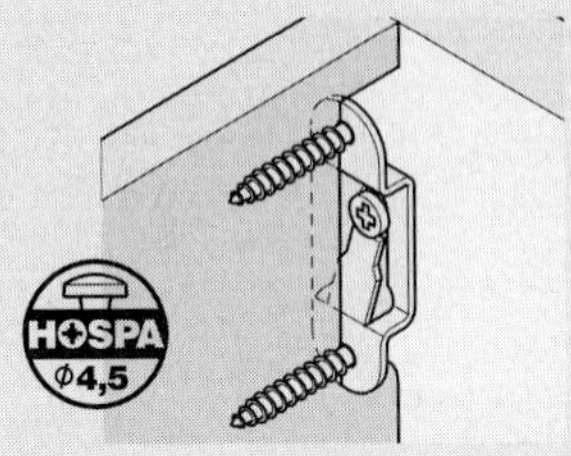

Permanent Modular

Panel thickness	Cat. No.
19 mm	262.47.012
22 mm	262.47.067

Packing: 1000 pcs.

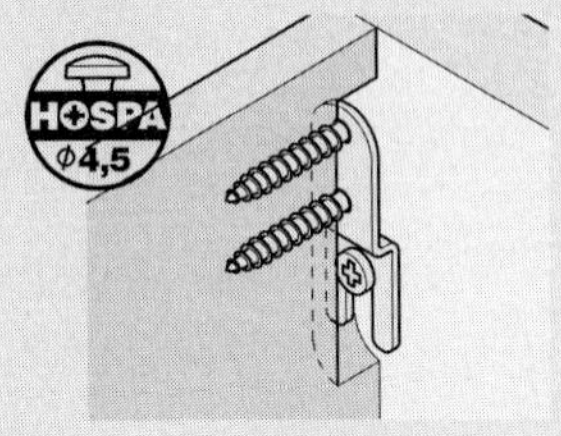

For panels from
19 mm

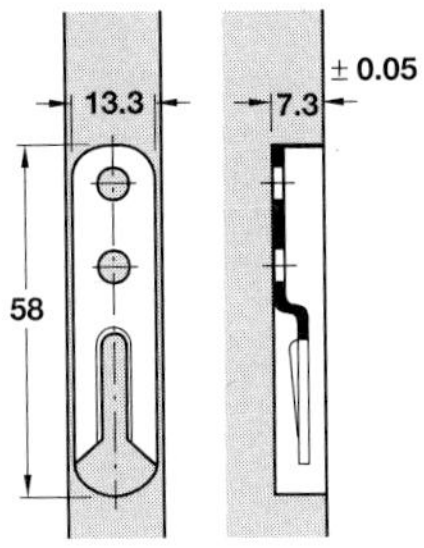

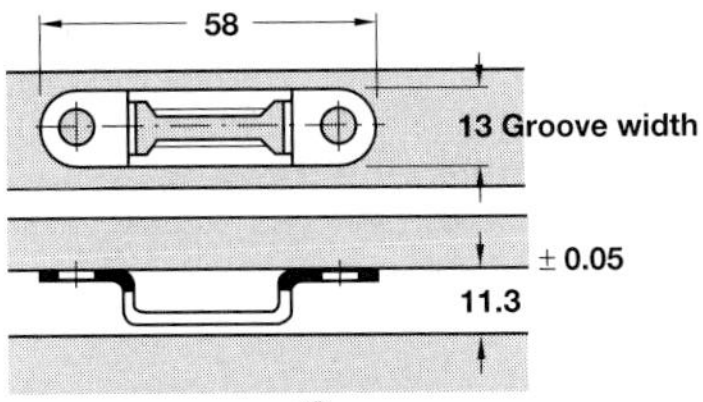

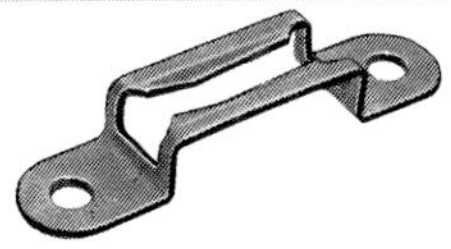

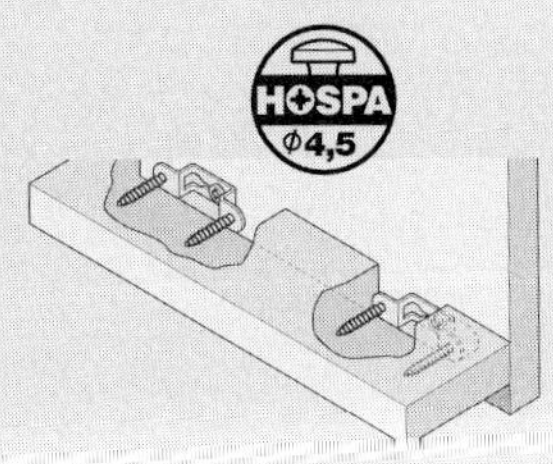

Open Modular

Panel thickness	Cat. No.
19 mm	262.47.030

Packing: 1000 pcs.

Press-fit Modular

Panel thickness	Cat. No.
17 mm	262.47.003

Packing: 1000 pcs.

Dimensional data not binding.
We reserve the right to alter specifications without notice.

HÄFELE

Modular Connectors 32 mm-Compatible

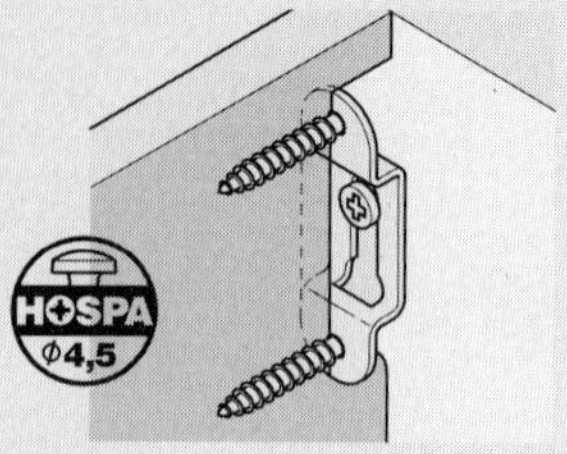

For panels from

16 mm 19 mm

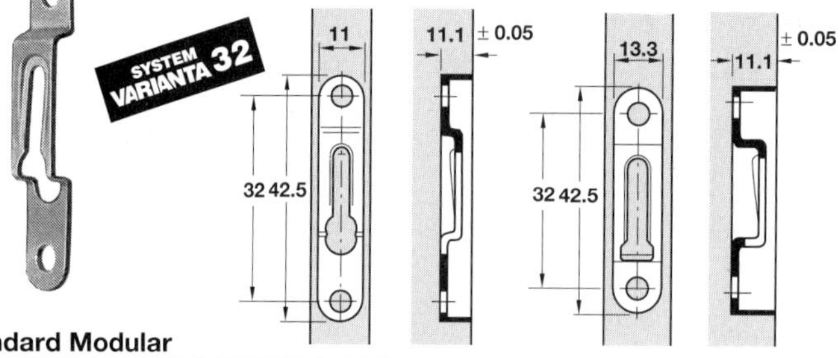

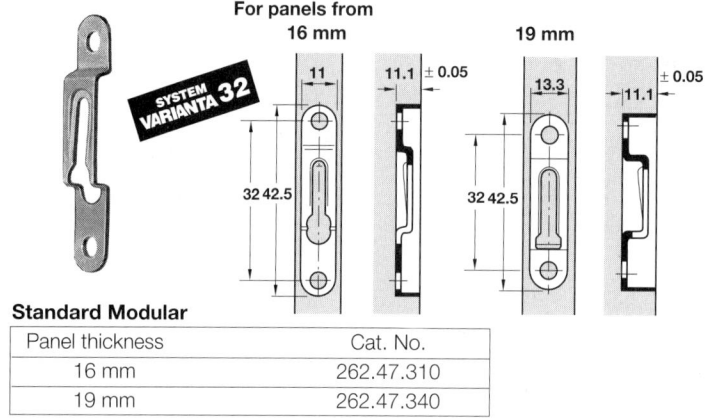

Standard Modular

Panel thickness	Cat. No.
16 mm	262.47.310
19 mm	262.47.340

Packing: 1000 pcs.

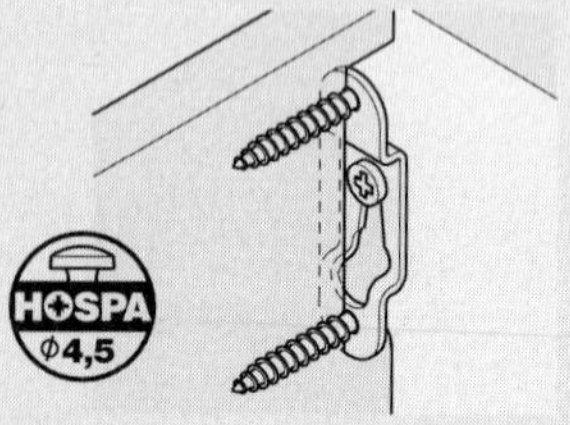

For panels from

16 mm 19 mm

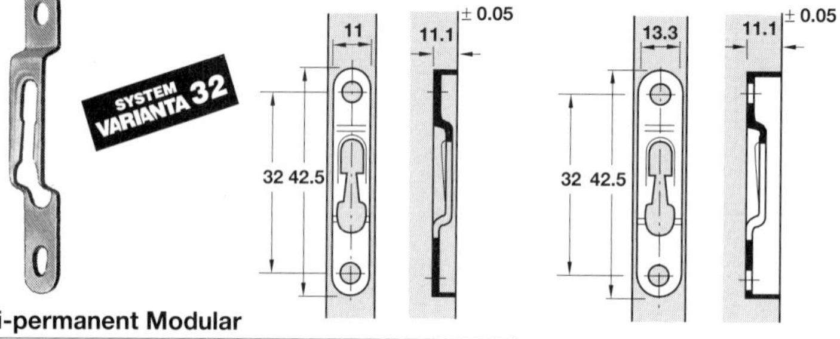

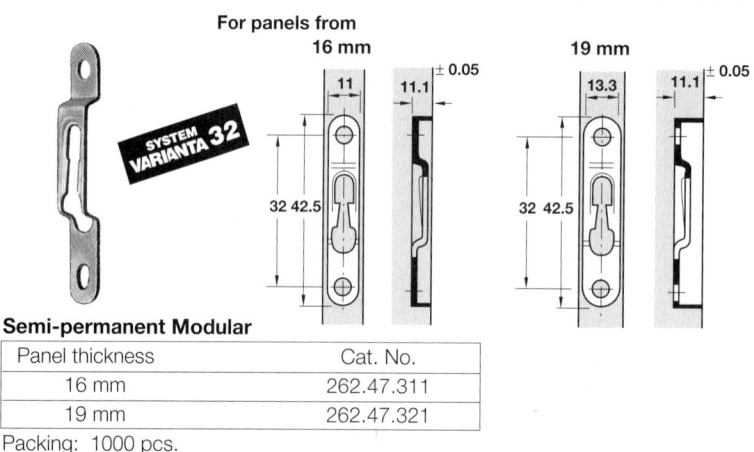

Semi-permanent Modular

Panel thickness	Cat. No.
16 mm	262.47.311
19 mm	262.47.321

Packing: 1000 pcs.

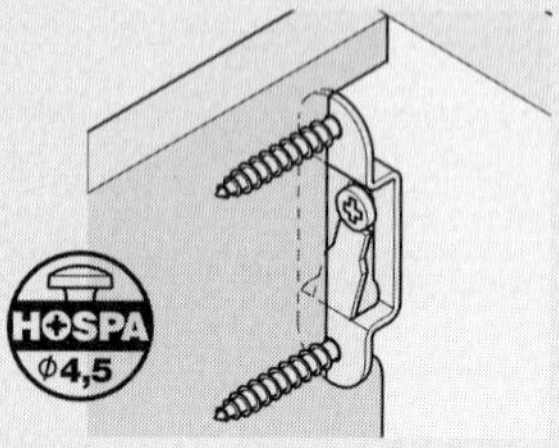

For panels from

16 mm 19 mm

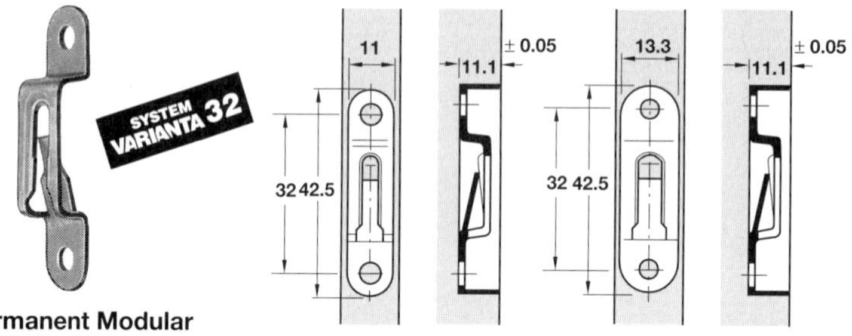

Permanent Modular

Panel thickness	Cat. No.
16 mm	262.47.312
19 mm	262.47.342

Packing: 1000 pcs.

Dimensional data not binding.
We reserve the right to alter specifications without notice.

Modular Connecting Fittings

Modular Screw, with wood screw thread
for installation in Ø 4 and Ø 5 mm hole.
Finish: steel, galvanized

for use with **10-13 mm wide** modular housings

Length	12.5	262.47.978
	16.0	262.47.987
	25.0	262.47.996
	32.0	262.47.870

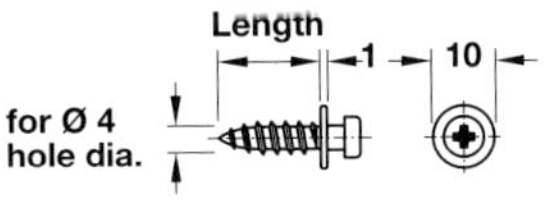

for use with **16 mm wide** modular housings

Length	16.0	262.47.889
	32.0	262.47.898

Packing: 100 pcs.

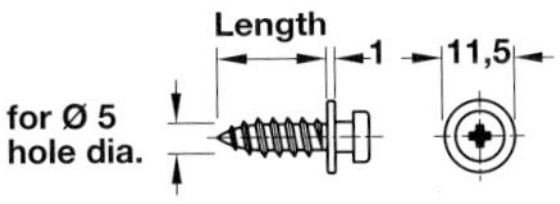

Modular screws
for single-sided
installation in wood.

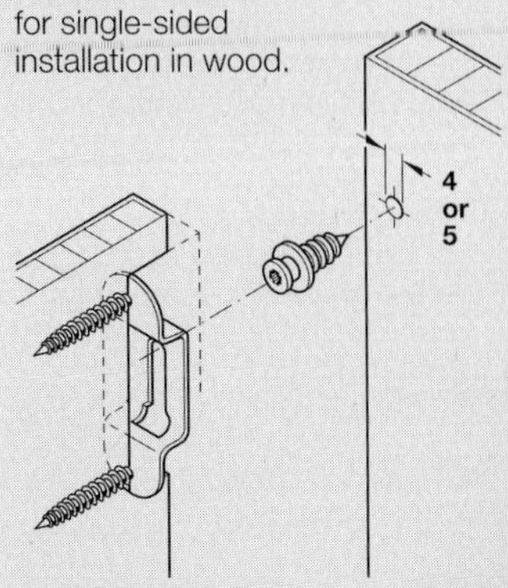

Modular Screw, with special thread
for installation in Ø 5 mm
series-drilled hole
Finish: steel, galvanized

for use with **10-13 mm wide** modular housings

Cat. No.	262.47.807

Packing: 100 pcs.

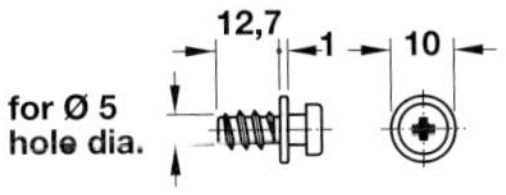

Locks, Catches, RTA and PAS® Fittings Shelf Supports Bed Fittings **2**

Modular screws
for installation in wood,
in series-drilled holes to

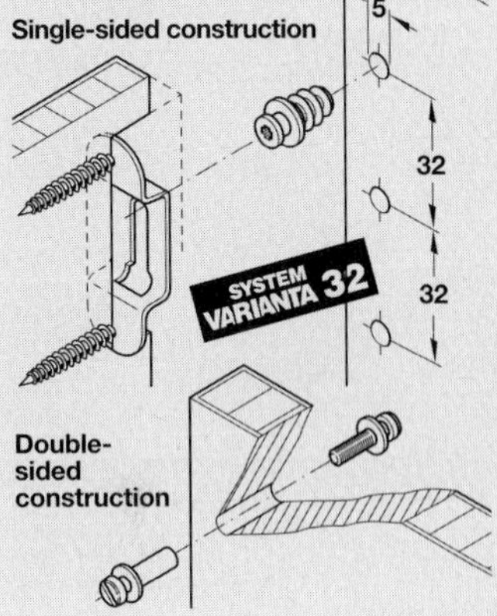

Modular Screw, with M4 thread
for insertion through Ø 5 mm
series-drilled holes.
Finish: steel, galvanized

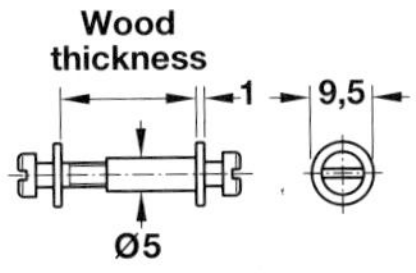

for use with **10-13 mm wide** modular housings

Wood thickness	Cat. No.
16 - 24	262.47.923

Packing: 100 pcs.

Modular Screw, with self-tapping thread
for installation in metal structures,
in Ø 4 mm hole.
Finish: steel, galvanized

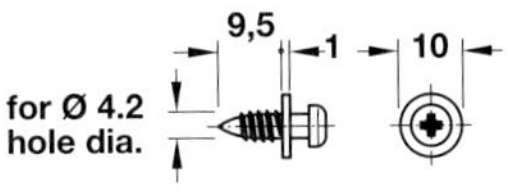

for use with **10-13 mm wide** modular housings

Cat. No.	Ø 3/16"	262.47.969

for use with **16 mm wide** modular housings

Cat. No.	Ø 7/32"	262.47.861

Packing: 100 Pcs.

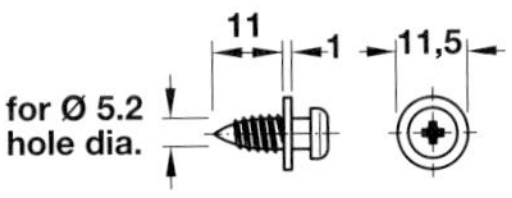

Modular screws
for installation in
metal.

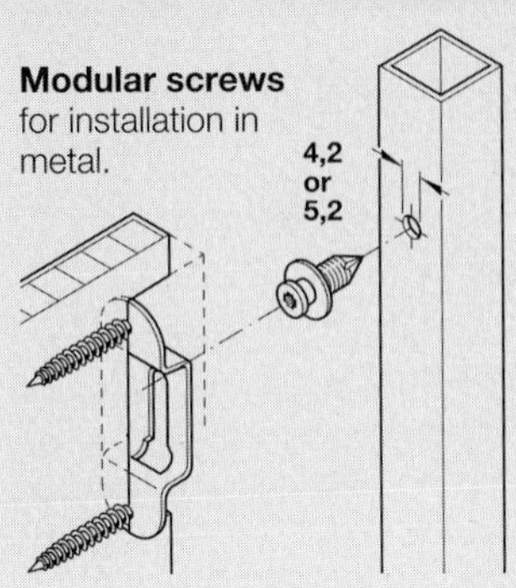

Modular Screw, with special thread
for installation in Ø 5 mm
series-drilled holes.
Finish: steel, galvanized

for **all size** clips

Cat. No.	262.47.902

Packing: 100 pcs.

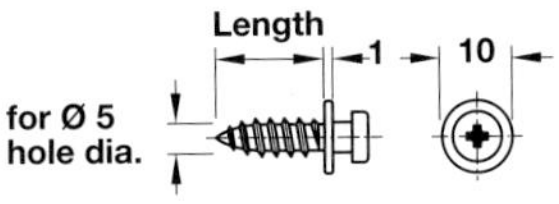

Dimensional data not binding.
We reserve the right to alter
specifications without notice.

HÄFELE

Conaxi Joint Connector Fitting

- **Conaxi joint connector** is an exceptionally strong fastener made of zinc die-cast.
- Ideal for use by interior decorating firms, exhibition stand contractors, shopfitters, etc.
- For single-sided and double-sided constructions.
- For right-angled, acute and obtuse angled joints, curved or complex arrangements (range variable between 45° and 270°).
- If mounted on one side only, the Conaxi joint connector can function as a hinge.

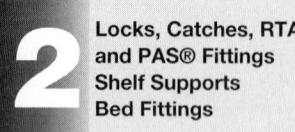

- Includes:
  2 nickel-plated zinc die-cast joint connector housings
  4 plastic trim caps in black, gray or polished nickel-plated

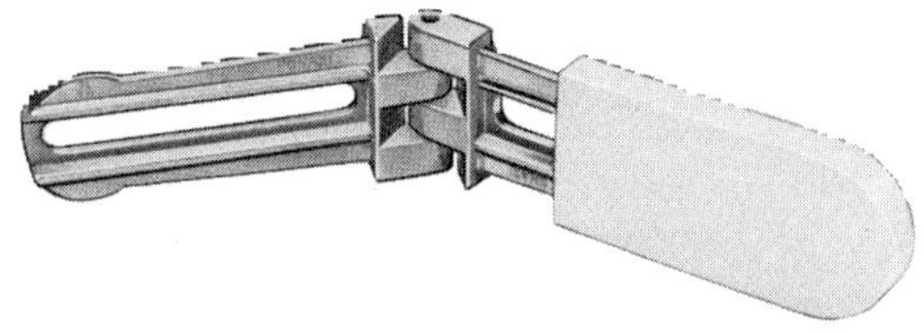

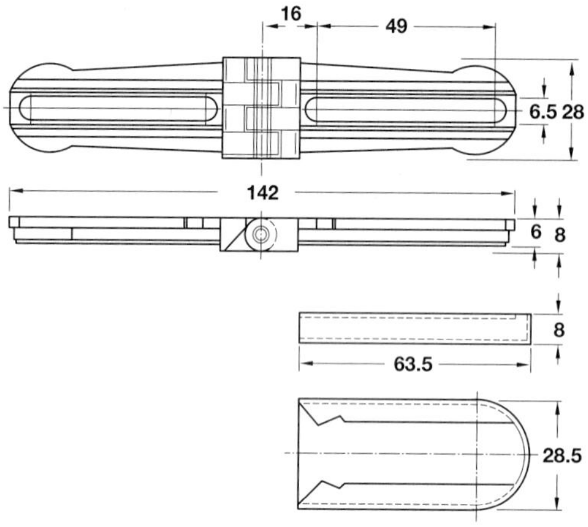

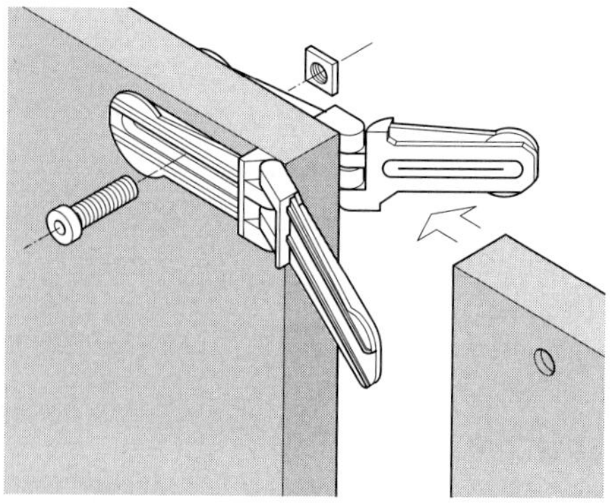

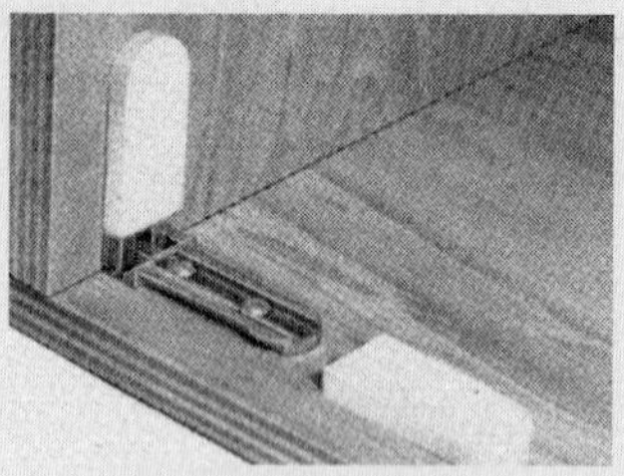

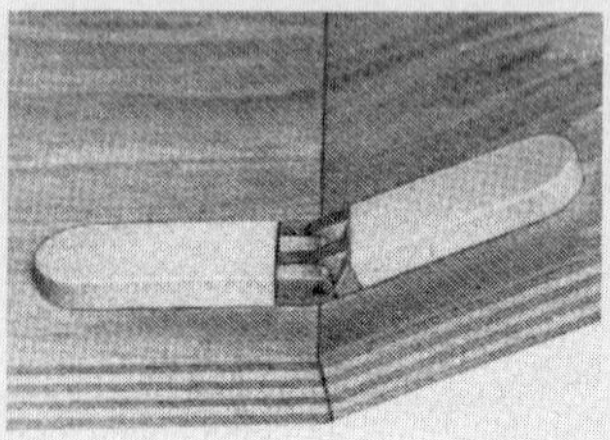

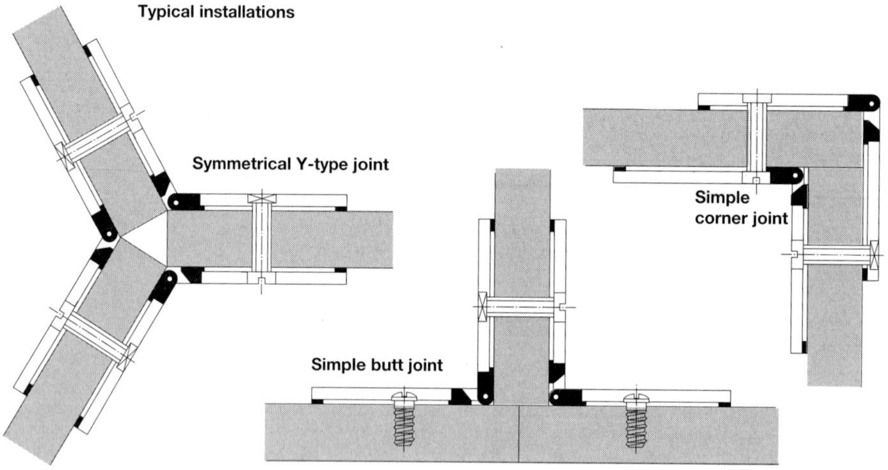

Finish: plastic catch, chromed metal strike

Finish:		zinc die-cast, nickel-plated
Cat. No.	with black trim caps	264.00.304
	with gray trim caps	264.00.500
with polished nickel-plated trim caps		264.00.706

Packing: 10 sets

Mounting hardware must be ordered separately:

For single-side installation:
- **Varianta** with Pozidriv cross-slot, size 2
- Galvanized steel

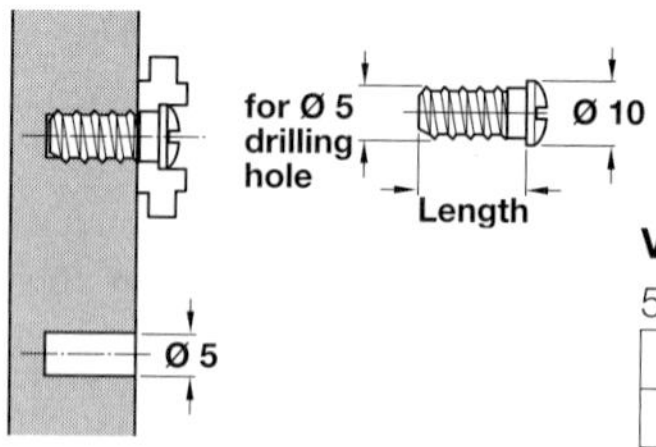

Varianta screw, zinc-plated, 5 mm hole

Length	Cat. No.
10.5 mm	013.20.912
13.5 mm	013.20.930
16.0 mm	013.20.949

Packing: 500 pcs

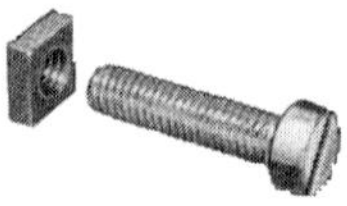

For double-side through-hole installation:
- **M6 cheese head screw**, single slot
- Galvanized steel

- **M6 square nut**, flat
- Galvanized steel

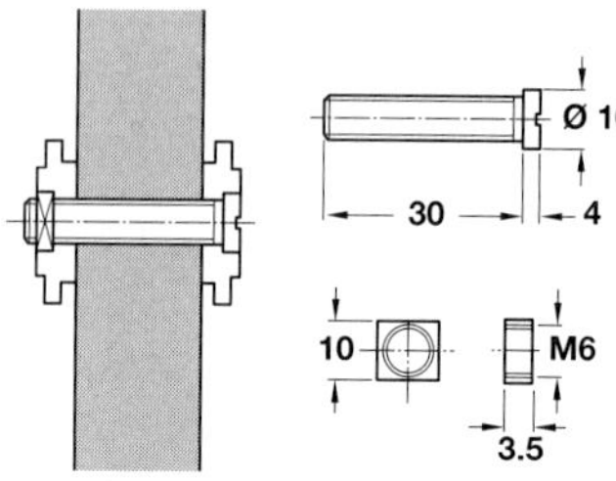

M6 cheese head screw

Length	Cat. No.
30 mm	020.46.362

Packing: 100 pcs

M6 square nut

Cat. No.	034.00.066

Packing: 100 pcs

Dimensions in mm

Angle Brackets and Supports

Topfix Angle Bracket

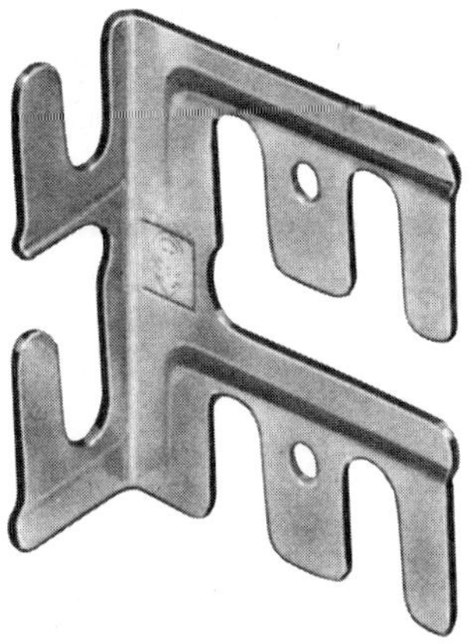

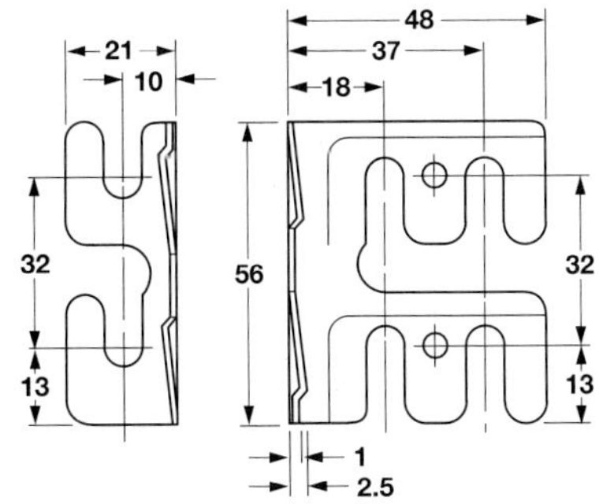

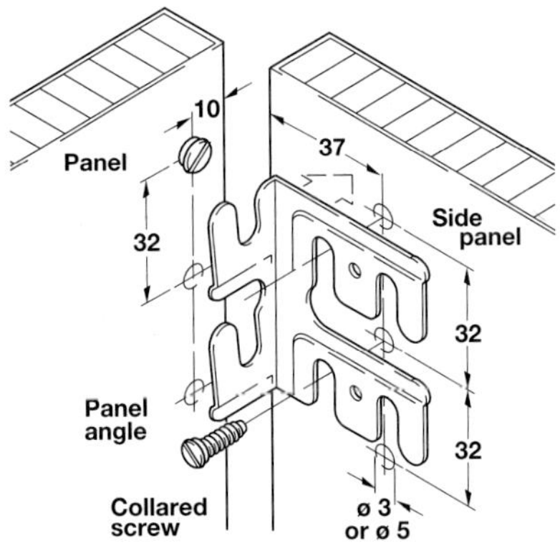

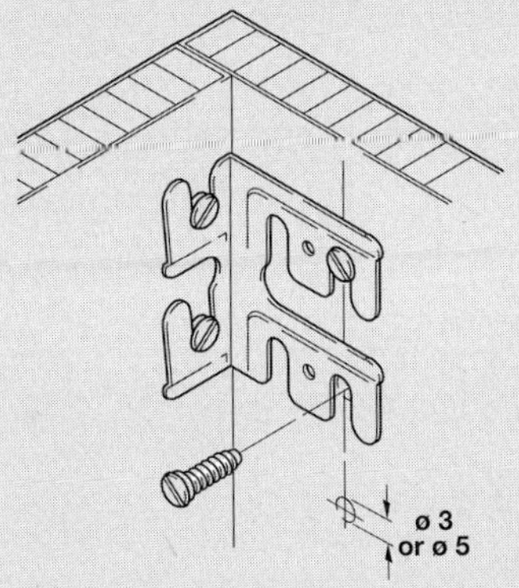

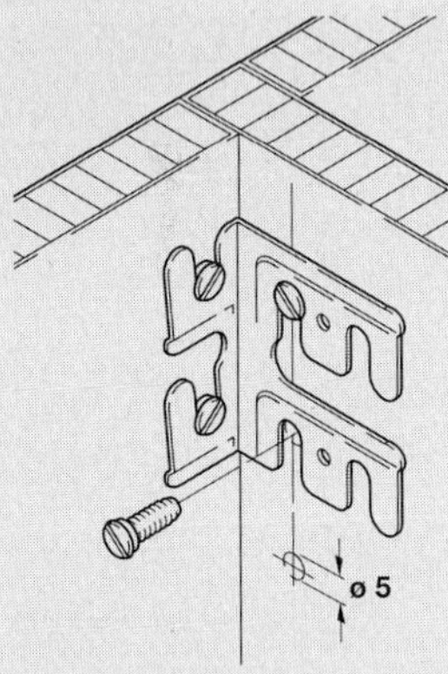

Finish: steel, galvanized

Cat. No.	264.27.912

Packing: 50 pairs (50 right-hand, 50 left-hand)

Collared Screw, with M4 thread (2-part).
For double-sided constructions with wood thicknesses of 16–22 mm.

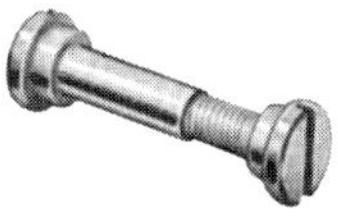

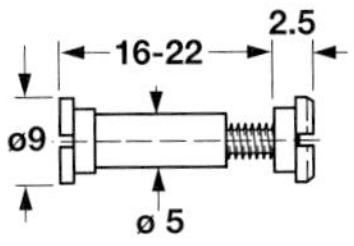

Finish: steel, galvanized

Cat. No.	264.27.994

Packing: 200 pcs.

Collared Screw, with special thread (2-part).
For single-sided and panel installations.

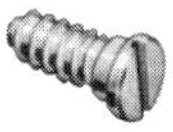

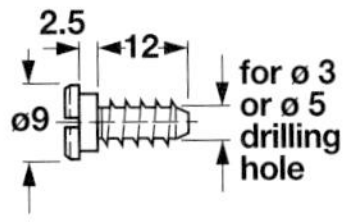

Finish: steel, galvanized

Cat. No.	264.27.985

Packing: 200 pcs.

Two-Part Panel Support

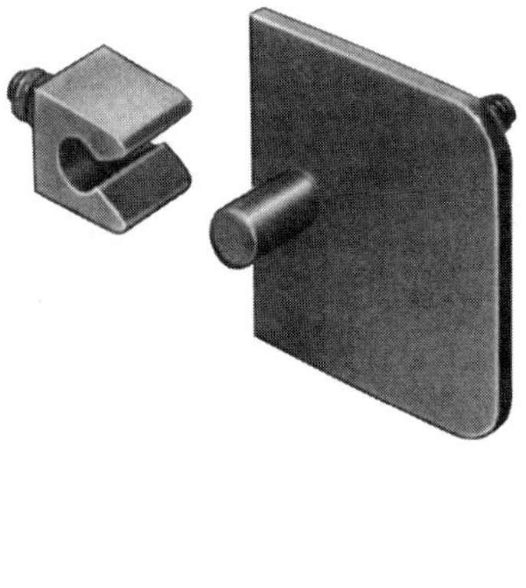

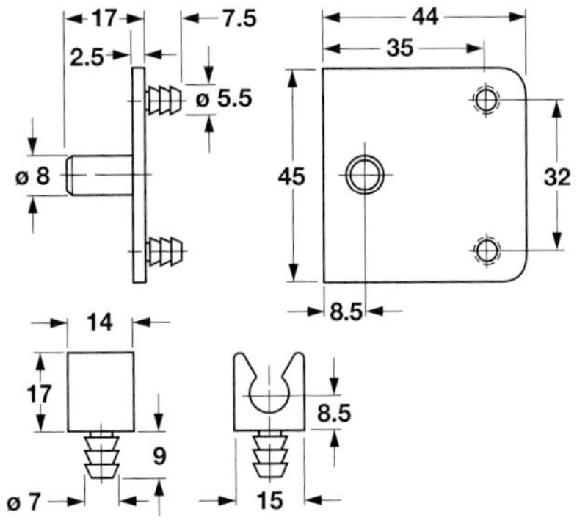

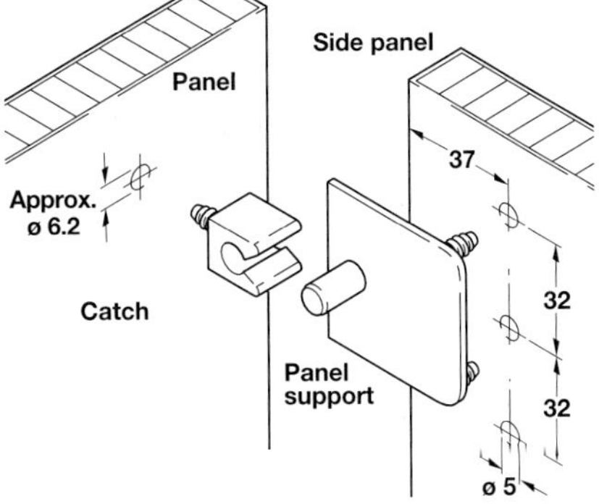

Finish: plastic, brown

Cat. No.	245.08.101

Packing: 100 pcs.

Dimensions in mm

Dimensional data not binding.
We reserve the right to alter specifications without notice.

HÄFELE

Connecting Brackets

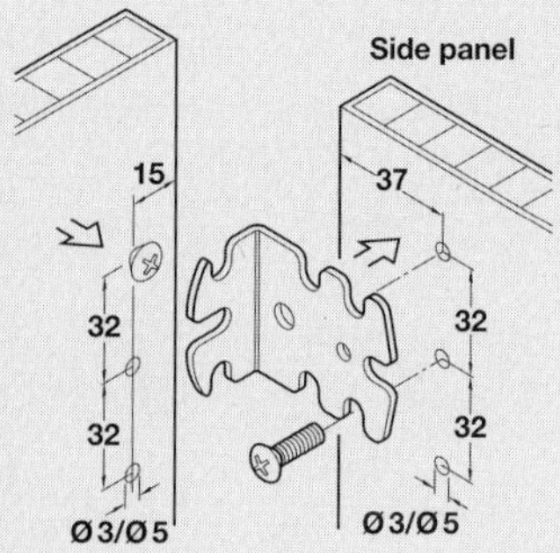

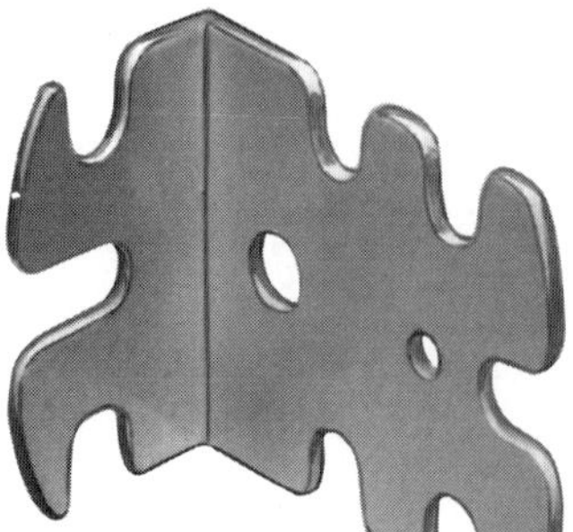

Universal Bracket

Finish: steel

Cat. No.	galvanized	264.25.909
	white, plastic-coated	264.25.703

Packing: 200 pcs.

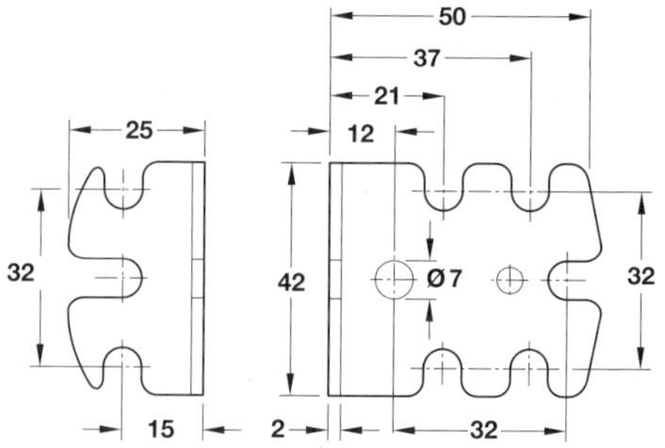

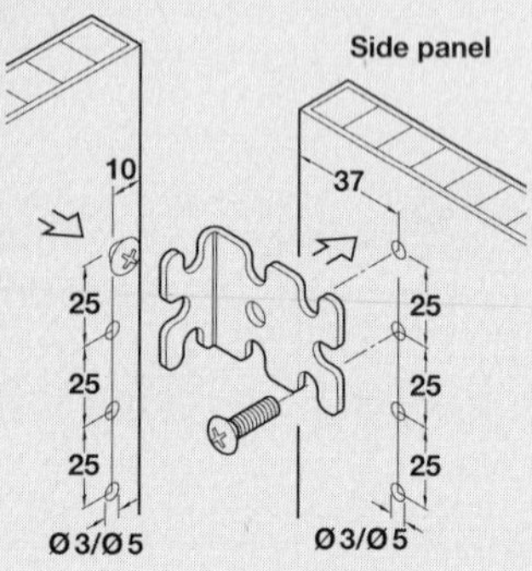

Universal Bracket

Finish: steel, galvanized

Cat. No.	264.28.955

Packing: 100 pcs.

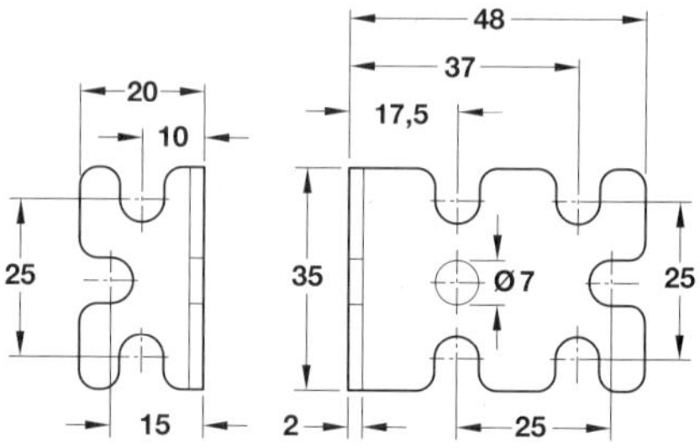

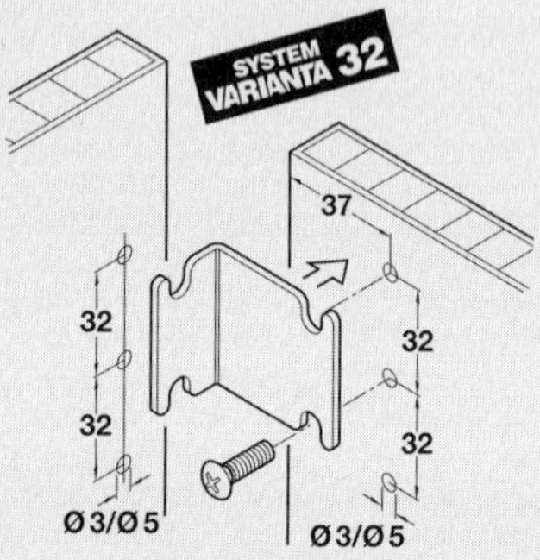

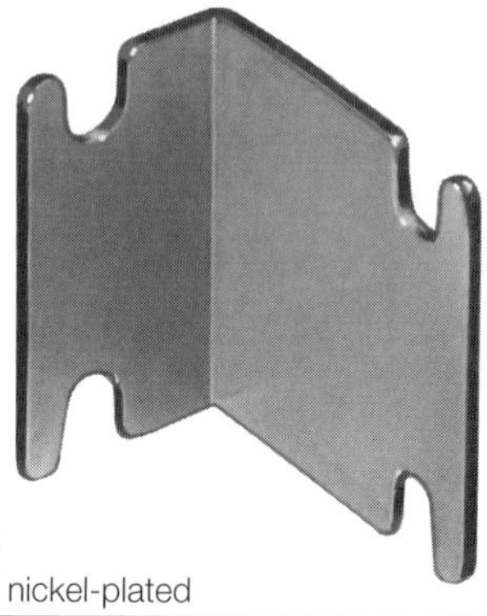

Rear Panel Bracket

Finish: steel, polished nickel-plated

Cat. No.	264.24.206

Packing: 100 pcs.

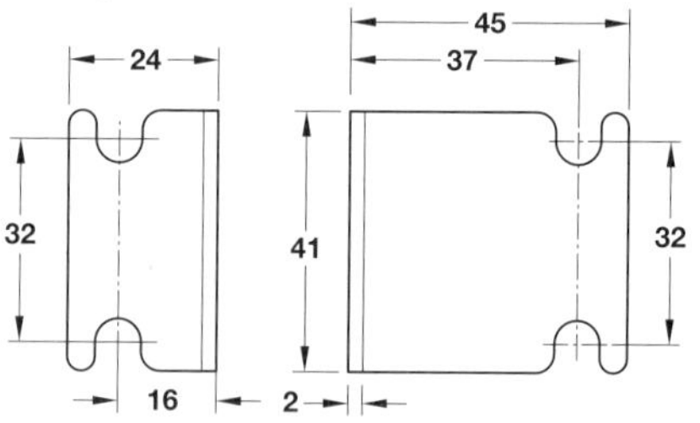

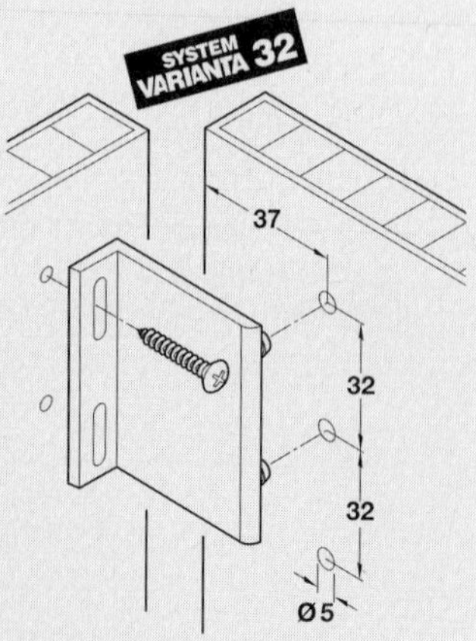

Rear Panel Bracket

Finish: plastic, white

Cat. No.	260.12.706

Packing: 250 pcs.

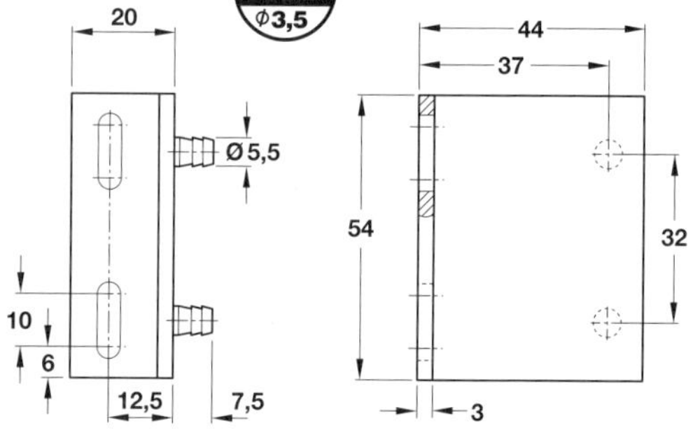

Dimensional data not binding. We reserve the right to alter specifications without notice.

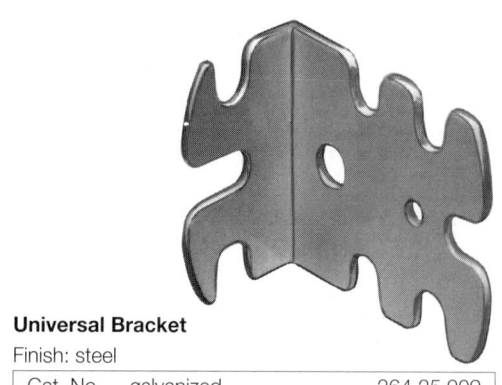

Dimensions in mm

Plates and Brackets

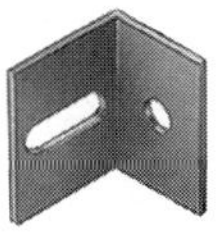
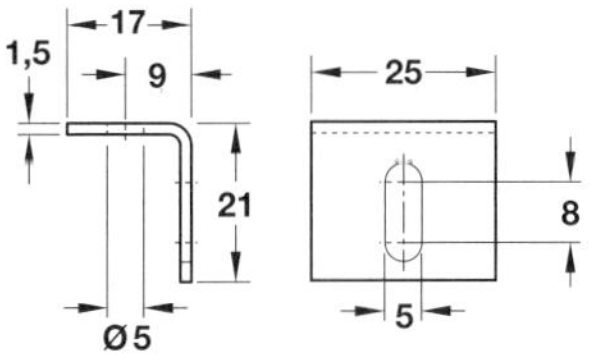

Table Plate
with screw-hole and slot
Finish: steel, nickel-plated

Cat. No.	260.25.703

Packing: 250 pcs.

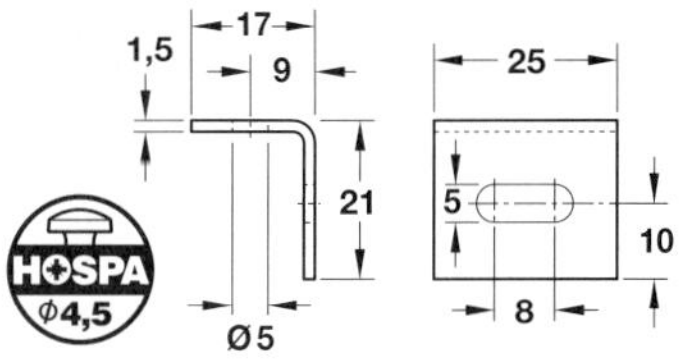

Table Plate
with screw-hole and slot
Finish: steel, nickel-plated

Cat. No.	260.26.700

Packing: 250 pcs.

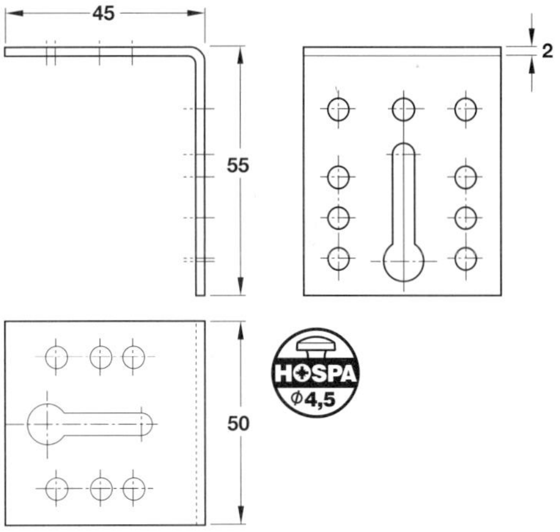

Fastening bracket,
with harpoon bolt
Finish: steel, nickel-plated

Cat. No.	558.12.943

Packing: 50 pcs.

Corner Braces,
with screw-holes
Material gauge: 2 mm

A x B	C	Screw size	steel, yellow galvanized
25 x 25	15	3.0	260.28.502
40 x 40	15	3.0	260.28.504
50 x 50	15	3.0	260.28.505
60 x 60	18	3.5	260.28.506
80 x 80*	18	3.5	260.28.508

Packing: 100 pcs.

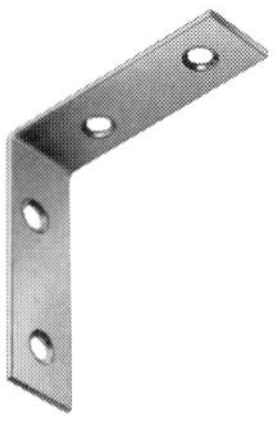
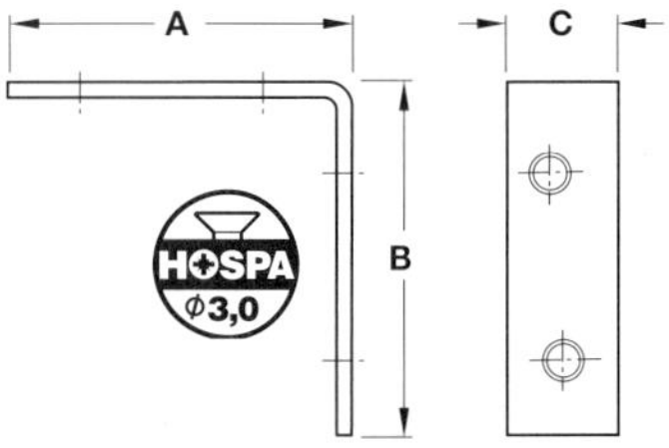

Corner Brace,
with screw-holes
Material gauge: 2 mm

A x B	C	Screw size	steel, yellow galvanized
100 x 100	18	3.5	260.28.510

Packing: 50 pcs.

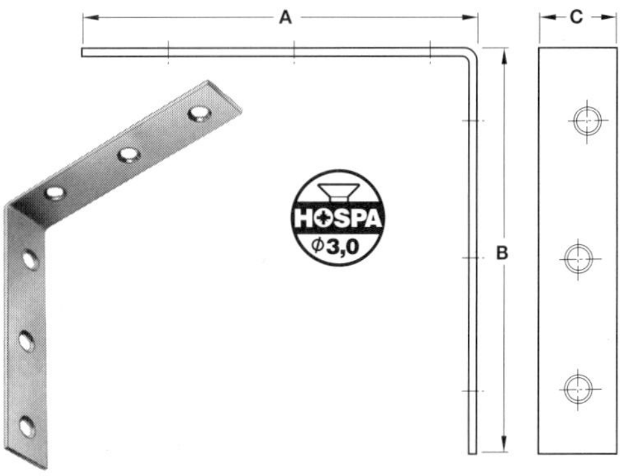

Angle Bracket, screw-mounted.
For furniture assembly.

Finish: plastic

Cat. No.	black	260.24.304
	brown	260.24.108
	white	260.24.706

Packing: 100 pcs.

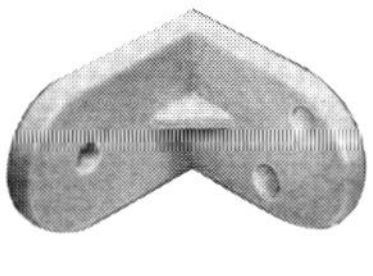
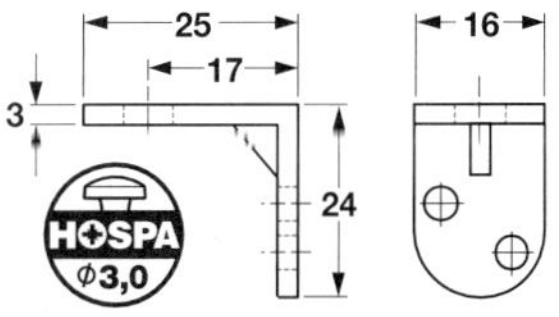

Dimensions in mm

Locks, Catches, RTA and PAS® Fittings
Shelf Supports
Bed Fittings
2

Dimensional data not binding.
We reserve the right to alter specifications without notice.

HÄFELE

Joint Connectors

Recessed worktop connectors

These concealed connectors allow work surfaces to be connected rapidly and securely. The semi-circular fastening elements are pressed against the recess walls as tension is applied.

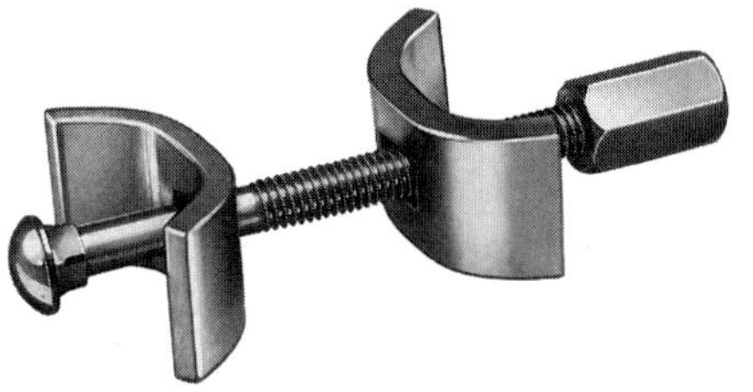

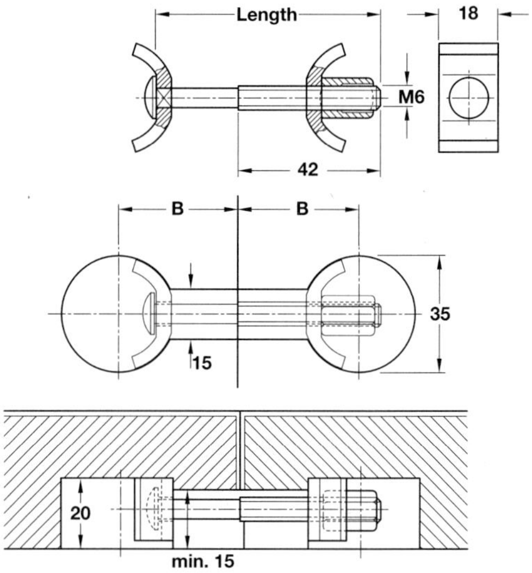

Finish: steel, zinc-plated

Length	Drilling Distance B	Cat. No.
65 mm	from 32 to 41 mm	262.96.211
150 mm	from 75 to 84 mm	262.96.220

Packing: 50 pcs.

Work Surface Fastener

The work surface fastener is easily installed and quickly assembled for material from 16 mm (5/8"). By providing even pressure between the surface joint pieces, this fastener holds without glue. The joint can be disassembled if necessary.

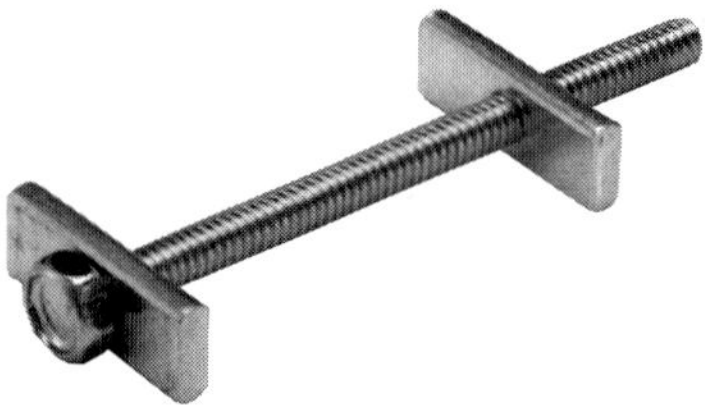

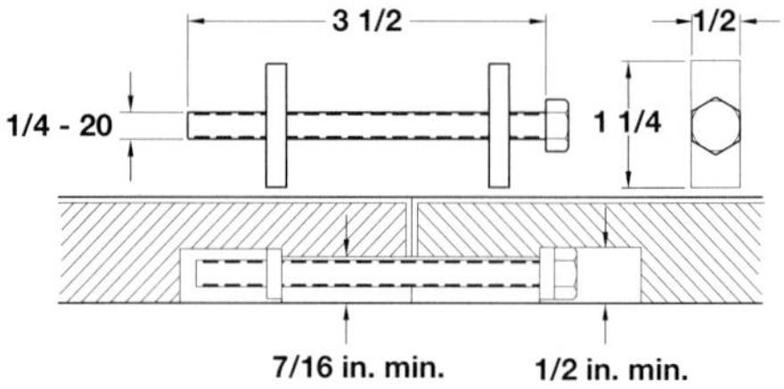

Screw length	Cat. No.
89 mm (3 1/2")	262.93.952

Packing: 500 pcs.

Dimensional data not binding. We reserve the right to alter specifications without notice.

Dimensions in mm

Miter Joint Connectors

HÄFELE

Picture frames, raised panel door, decorative profiles, miter joints, or wherever a miter joint has to be pulled together tightly.

- Only vertical drilling
- No routers needed
- Easy to install with hammer
- No screwdrivers, no glue
- Can be installed on construction site
- Can eliminate clamps, which are difficult to place on miters.
- Any angle, 180° to 90°

Miter Joint Connector, 15 x 25 mm

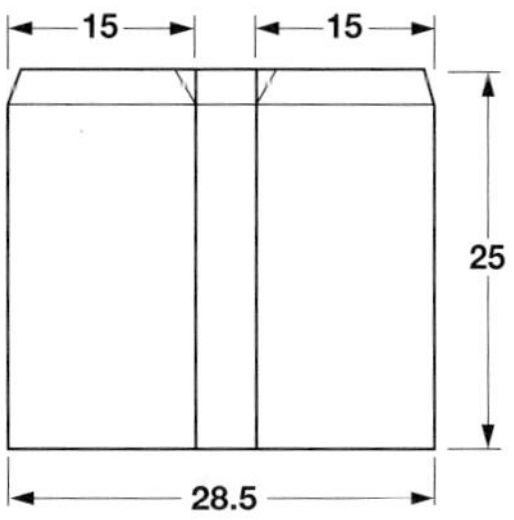

Finish: plastic, white

Cat. No.	261.98.730

Packing: 1800 pcs.

Miter Joint Connector, 15 x 12.5 mm

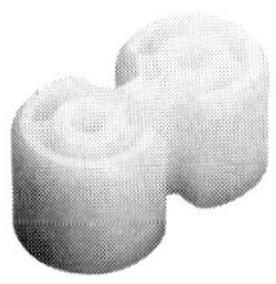

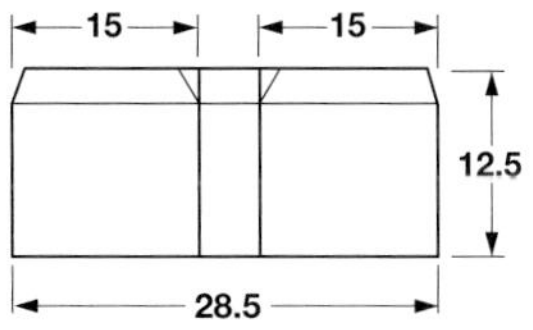

Finish: plastic, white

Cat. No.	261.98.720

Packing: 3500 pcs.

Miter Joint Connector, 8 x 7 mm

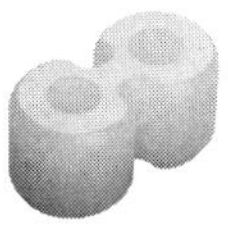

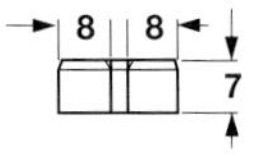

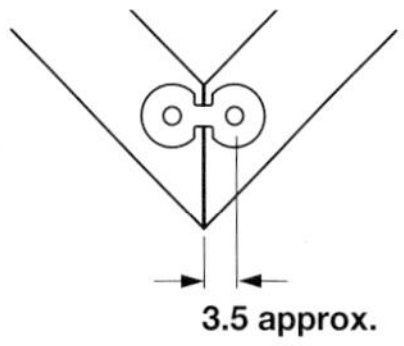

Finish: plastic, white

Cat. No.	261.98.710

Packing: 5000 pcs.

Locks, Catches, RTA and PAS® Fittings
Shelf Supports
Bed Fittings
2

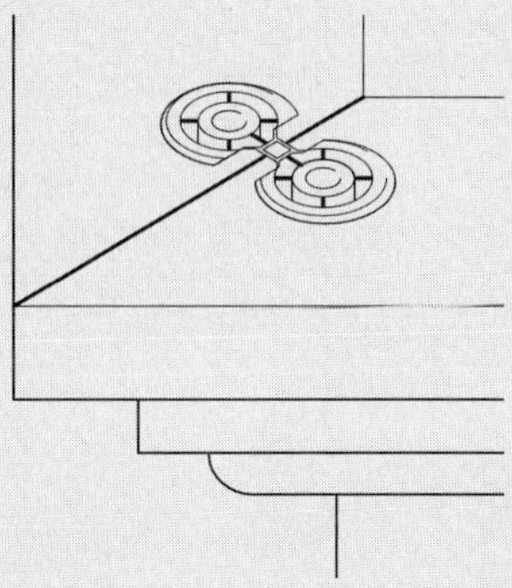

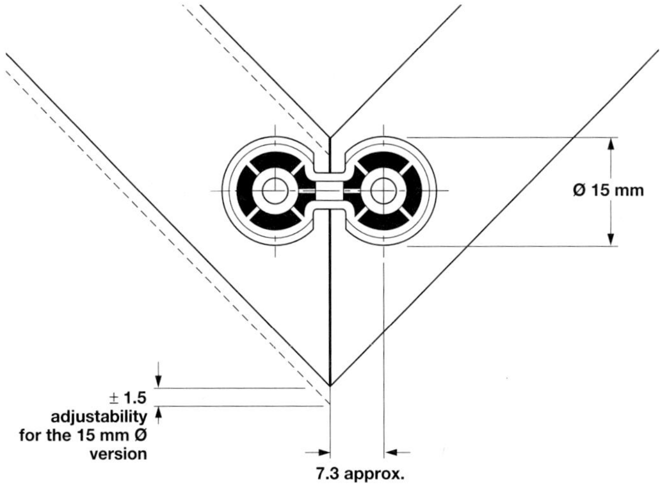

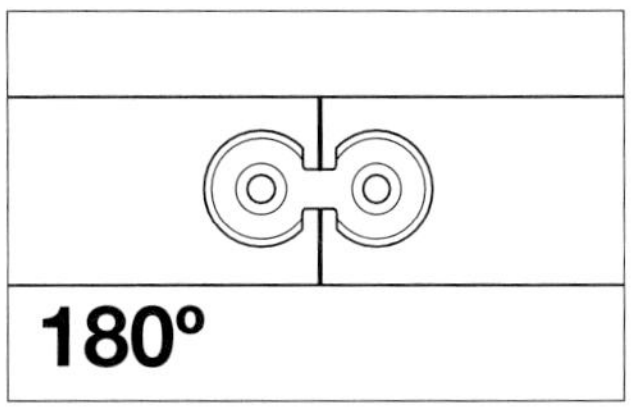

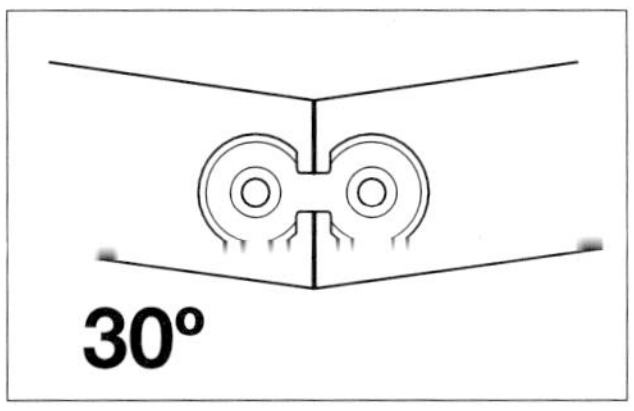

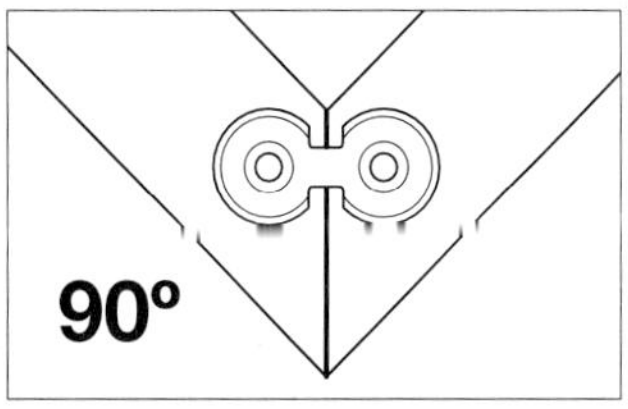

Dimensions in mm

Dimensional data not binding. We reserve the right to alter specifications without notice.

HÄFELE

Miter Joint Connectors

Minifix cams must be ordered separately.

2 **Locks, Catches, RTA and PAS® Fittings Shelf Supports Bed Fittings**

- For a wide variety of Minifix cams see page **2.95 - 2.97**.

Miter joint connecting fitting for crown moldings. The basic component for the miter joint connectors shown below is the Minifix 15 cam. Application of the centric sphere principle means that the mitered joint faces are not misaligned on tightening. There is a choice of three types of connecting bolt, depending on the profile design and joint configuration.

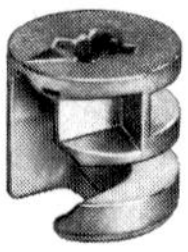

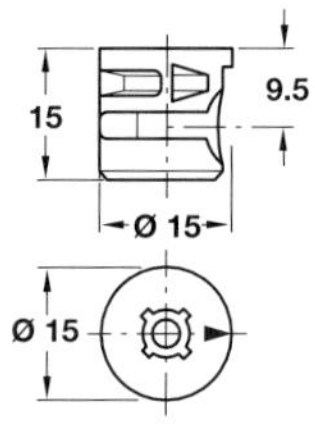

Miter joint cam
Finish: zinc die-cast, unfinished

Cat. No.	262.26.228

Packing: 1000 pcs.

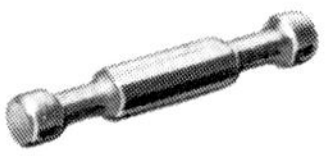

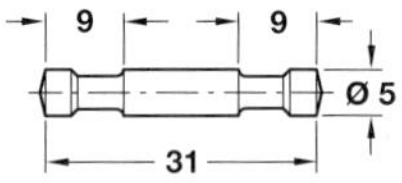

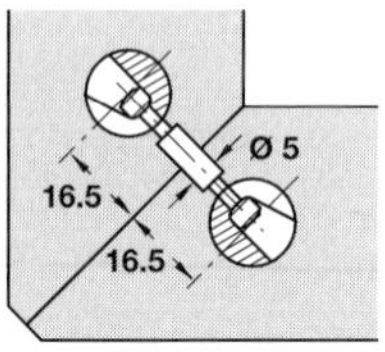

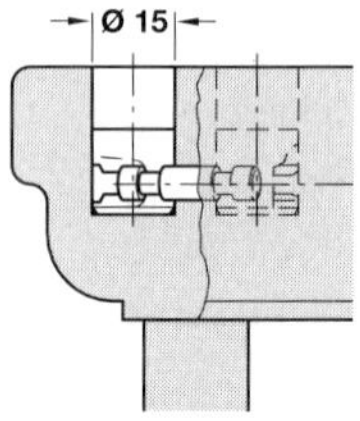

Miter joint connecting bolt
Finish: steel, galvanized

Cat. No.	262.29.920

Packing: 500 pcs.

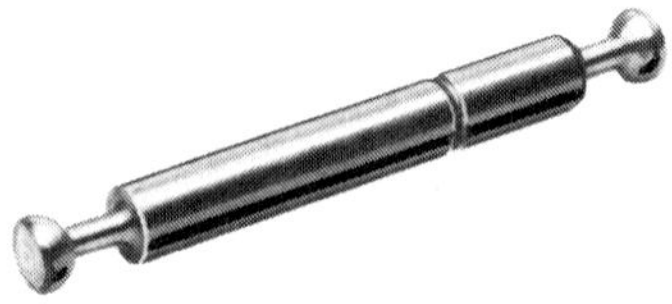

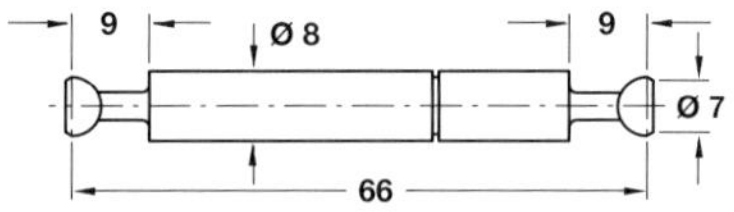

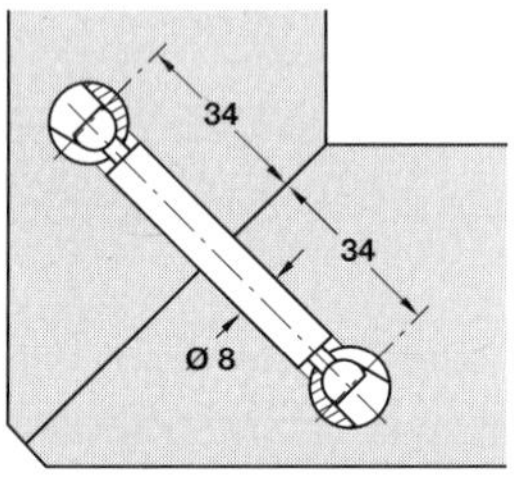

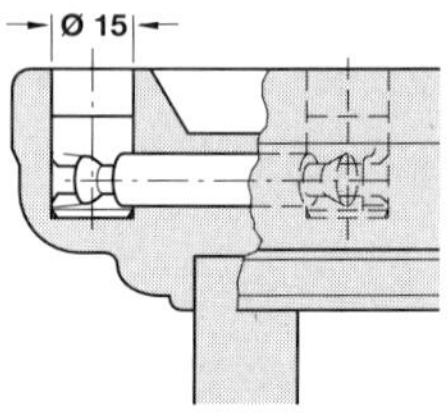

Miter joint connecting bolt
Finish: steel, unfinished

Cat. No.	262.27.216

Packing: 500 pcs.

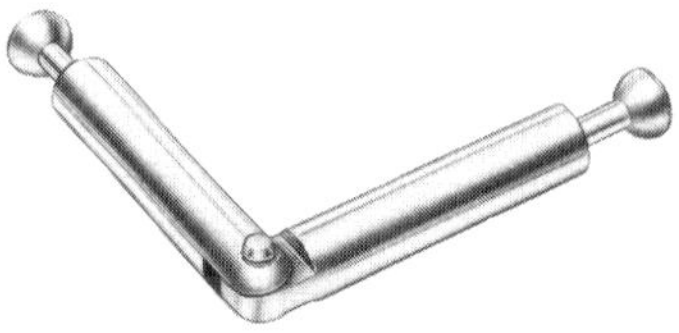

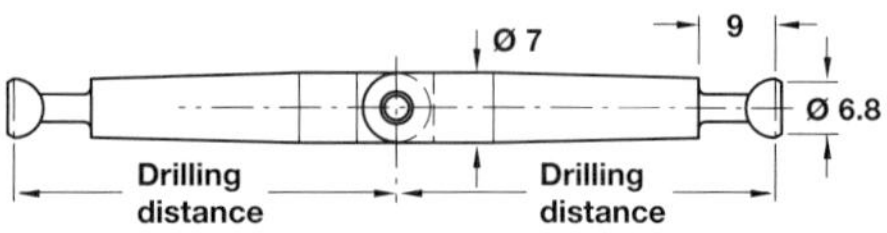

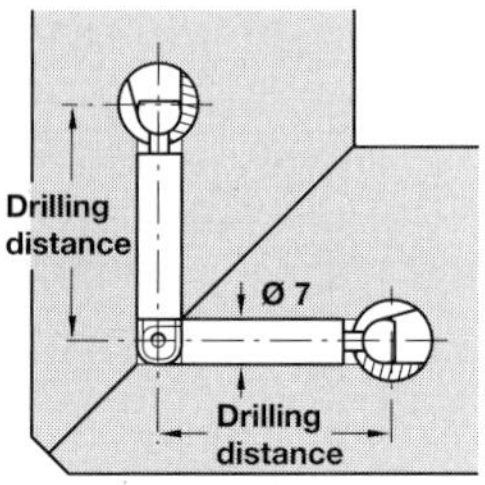

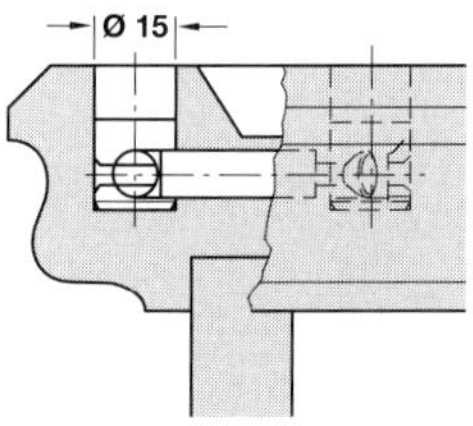

Miter joint connecting bolt
Finish: steel, galvanized

Cat. No.	262.12.939

Packing: 500 pcs.

Dimensional data not binding. We reserve the right to alter specifications without notice.

Dimensions in mm

Dowel Connectors

HÄFELE

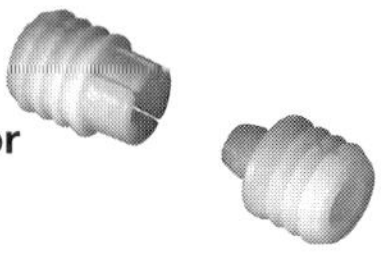

Press-fit Two-Piece Connector
two-piece detatchable

Finish: nylon, natural-colored

Cat. No.	267.20.700

Packing: 1000 pcs.

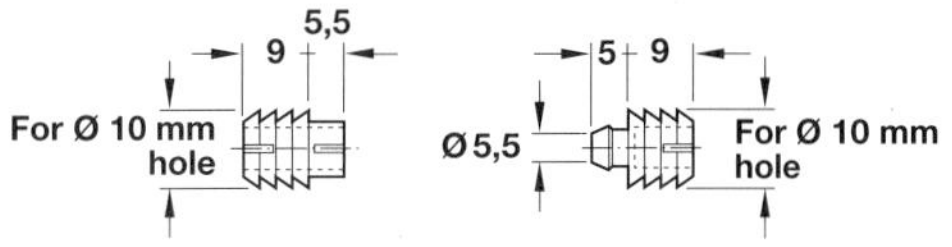

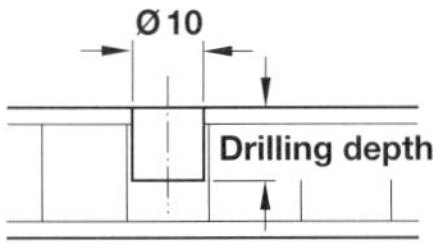

Drilling depth

for female	10 mm
for male	15 mm

Special tools (to be ordered separately)

Tool set,
Includes:
1 handle
1 lifting bit for central pin
1 punch (male)
1 punch (female)

Cat. No.	006.47.003

Packing: 1 set

Special bit
for press-fit connector

Finish	Cat. No.
HSS	006.47.012
HM-tipped	006.47.076

Packing: 1 pc.

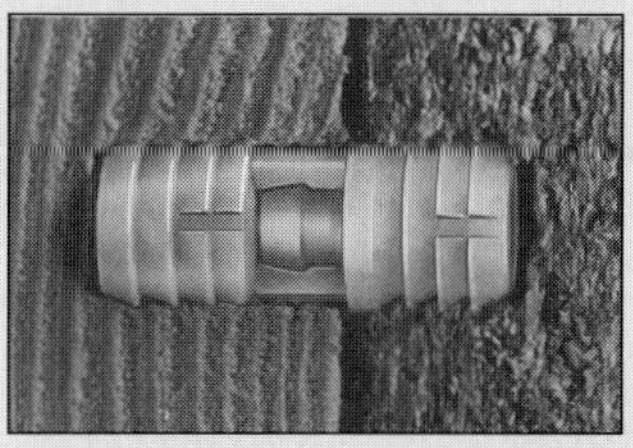

- Capable of disassembly at any time and with parting resistance of up to 15 kg.

Centring Pin

Cat. No.	006.47.067

Packing: 10 pcs.

Locks, Catches, RTA and PAS® Fittings
Shelf Supports
Bed Fittings

2

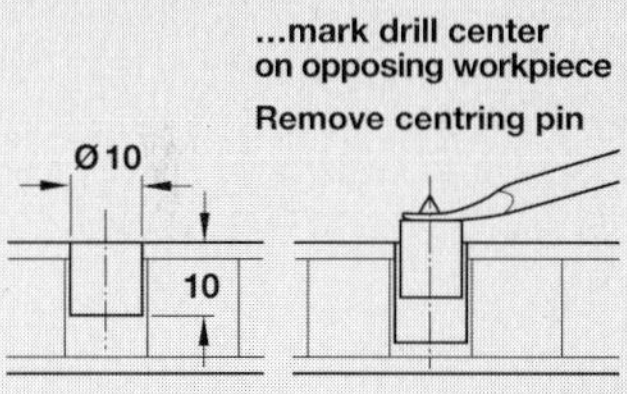

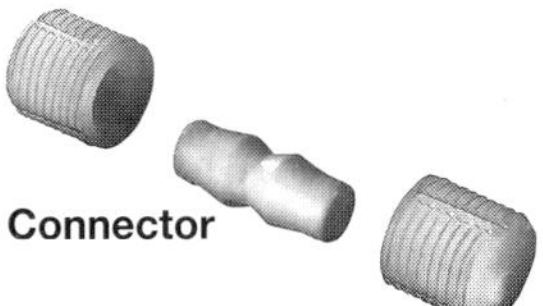

Press-fit Three-Piece Connector
two-piece detatchable

Finish: nylon, natural-colored

Cat. No.	267.21.730

Packing: 1000 pcs.

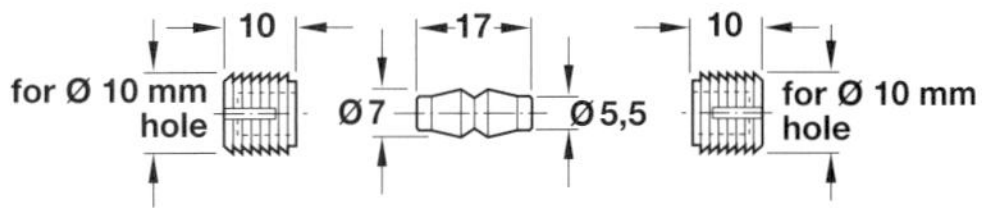

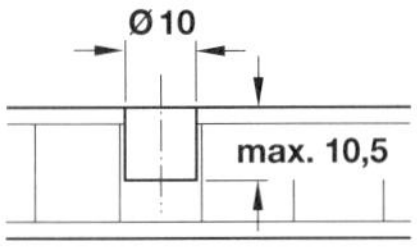

- Concealed connector which includes a nylon plug and sleeve offering non-release fastening of furniture components. This fitting is particularly suitable for assembling individual pieces of furniture in the workshop.

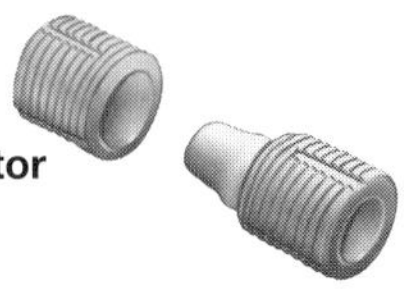

Press-fit Two-Piece Connector
permanent

Finish: nylon, natural-colored

Cat. No.	267.21.720

Packing: 100 pcs.

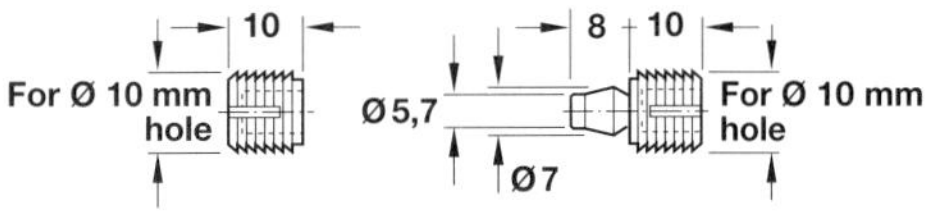

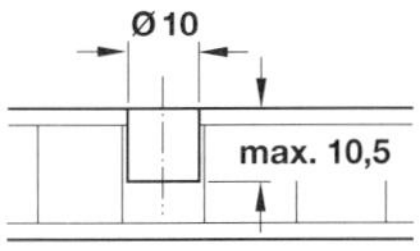

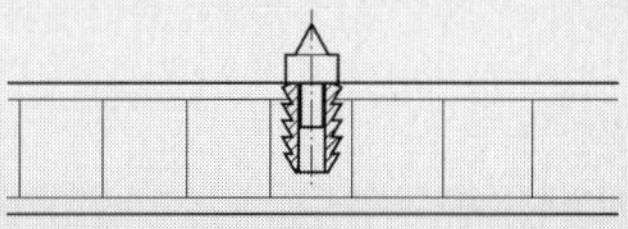

Insert centering pin

Press-fit Two-Piece Connector
permanent

Finish: Dowel-head screw: steel, galvanized
Sleeve: nylon, natural-colored

Cat. No.	267.22.900

Packing: 100 pcs. each screw and sleeve and 10 centering pins

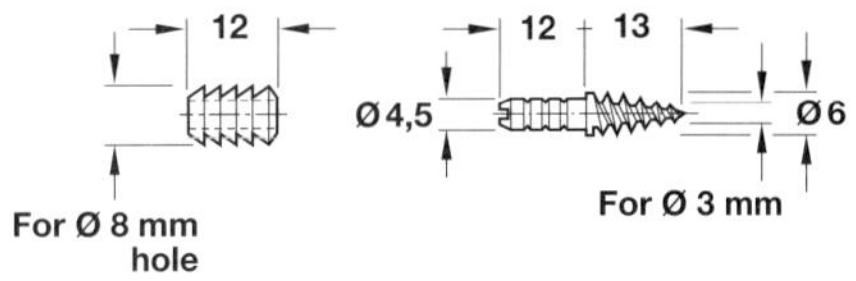

Dimensions in mm

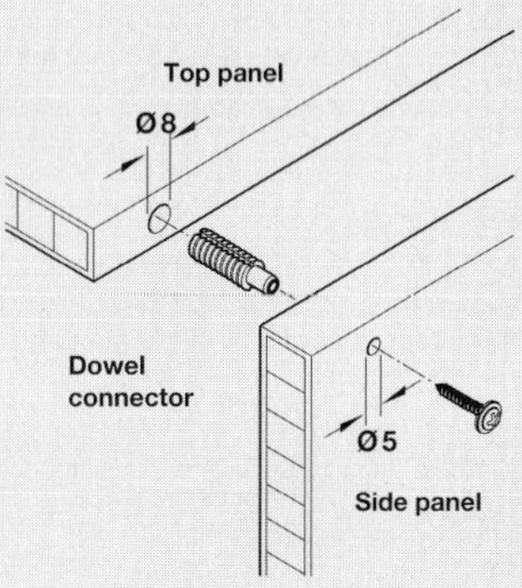

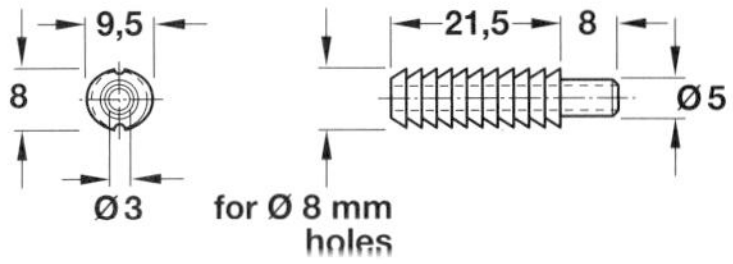

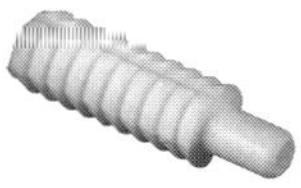

Oval Dowel Connector

Finish: plastic

Cat. No.	264.90.700

Packing: 100 pcs.

The dowel is tapped into the edge of the top panel with the oval spreading sideways (see above).
This will prevent splitting or warping of the material even when using thin panels. Attachment to the sidewall is done with panhead screws (see installation drawing).

Dimensional data not binding.
We reserve the right to alter specifications without notice.

Tapped Sleeve Connectors

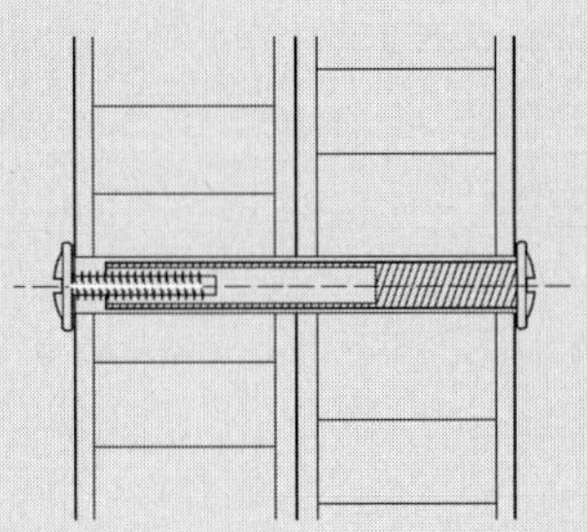

M4 Sleeve with M4 internal thread and universal head for flat-blade, Phillips and cross-slot screw-drivers.

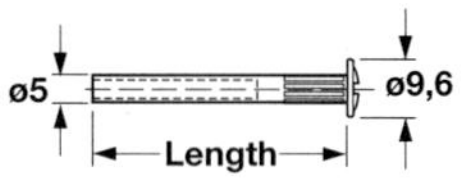

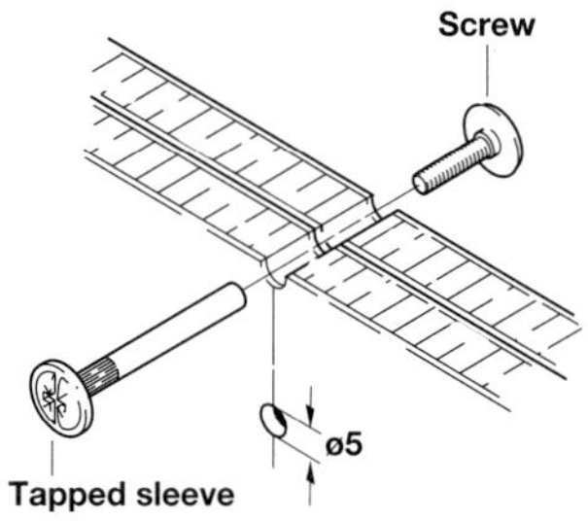

Dimensions in mm

Finish: steel, nickel-plated — Cat. No.

wood thickness	
28-36 mm 27mm long	267.01.715
37-45 mm 35mm long	267.01.717

Packing: 1000 pcs.

M4 Screw with universal head for flat-bladed, Phillips and cross-slot screwdrivers

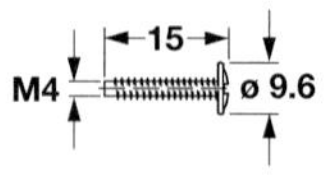

Finish: Steel, nickel-plated	
Cat. No.	022.34.157

Packing: 1000 pcs.

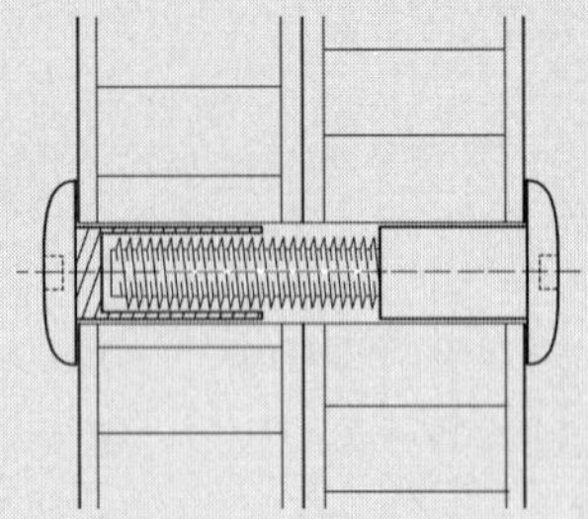

M6 Fastening Screw (complete fitting)

Featuring plastic socket and screw head with galvanized steel threaded bolt and screwdriver slot.

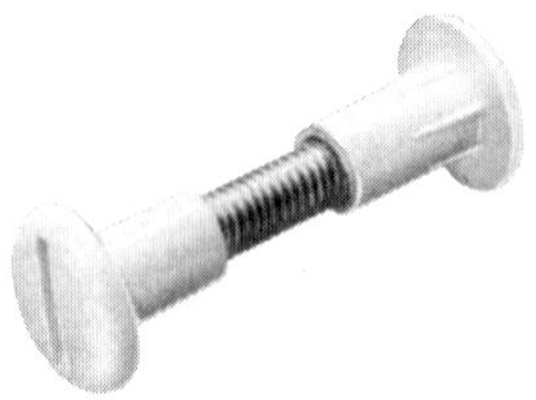

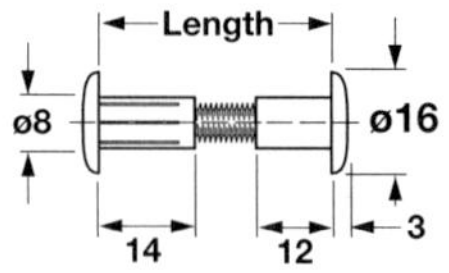

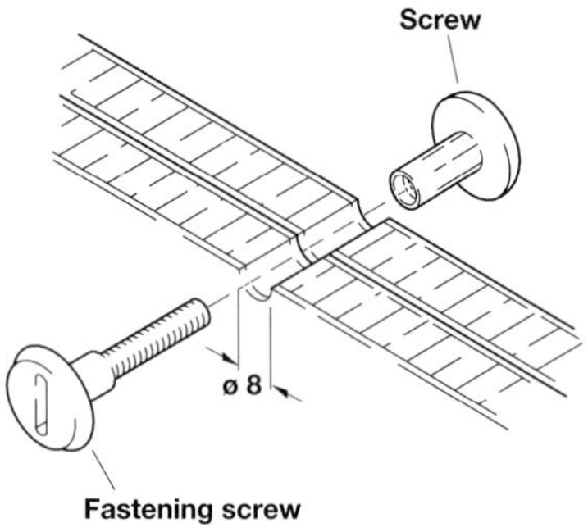

Finish: plastic

		white	brown
Cat. No.	length 30-36 mm	267.06.702	267.06.102
	length 35-41 mm	267.06.703	267.06.103
	length 39-45 mm	267.06.704	267.06.104

Packing: 1000 pcs. each

M6 Fastening Screw (complete fitting)

All-metal version featuring screw with steel thread and screwdriver slot, sleeve with milled finish.

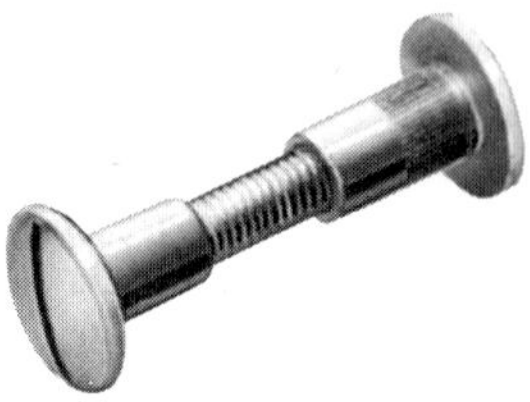

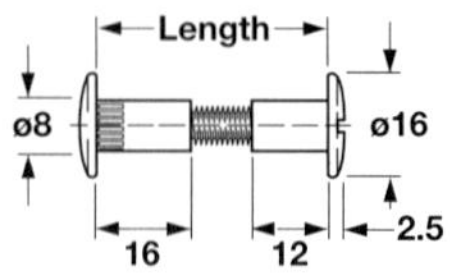

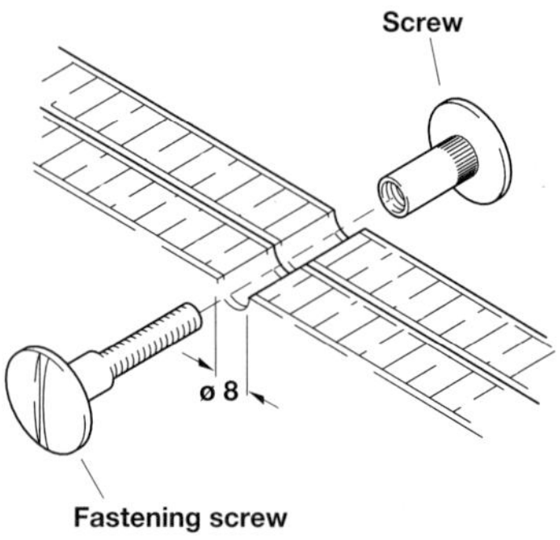

Finish: steel, galvanized

Cat. No.	length 32-38 mm	267.07.902
	length 36-42 mm	267.07.903
	length 39-46 mm	267.07.904

Packing: 100 pcs.

Dimensions in mm

Fastening Screws

Fastening Screw and Sleeve

With special thread and cross-slot Z, size 2.

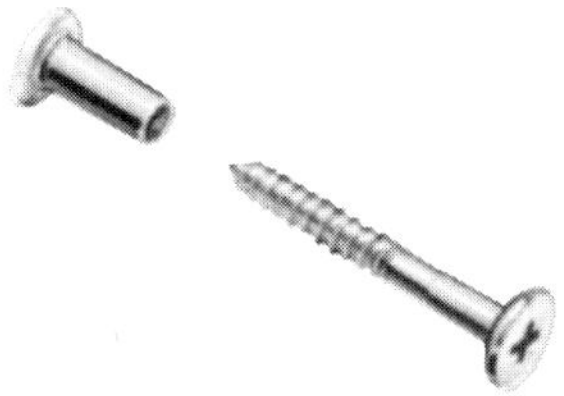

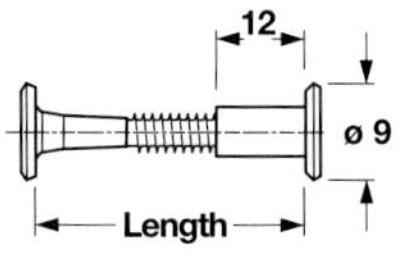

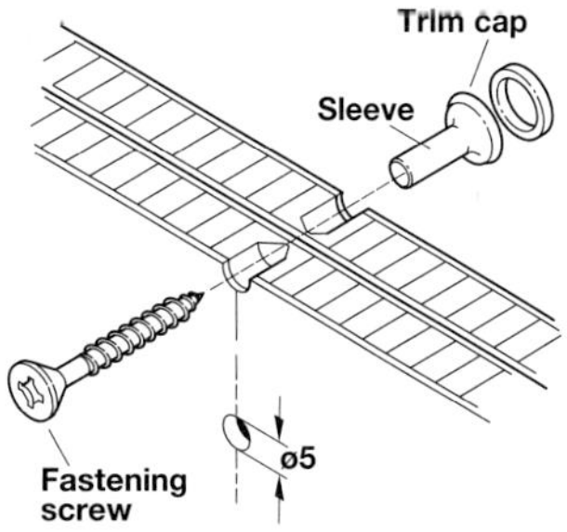

Finish: steel, galvanized

Cat. No.	length 31-34 mm	267.02.903
	length 37-40 mm	267.02.904
	length 47-50 mm	267.02.905

Packing: 1000 pcs.

Fastening Screw

M4 screw with raised head and cross-slot Z, size 2

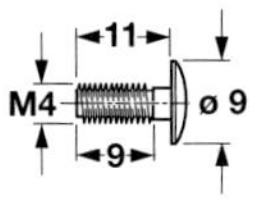

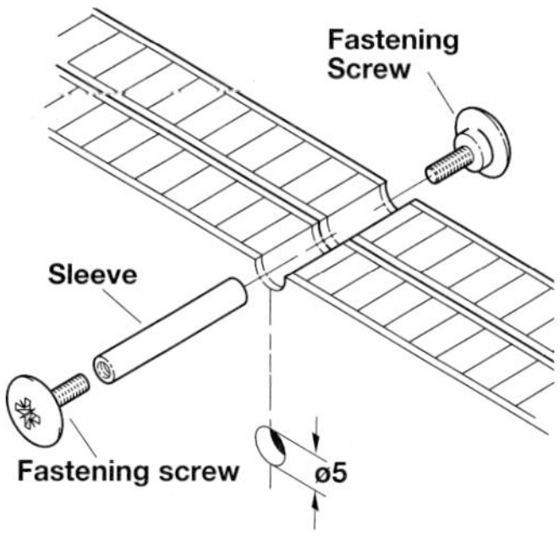

Finish: steel, nickel-plated

Cat. No.	11 mm long	267.00.720

Packing: 10,000 pcs.

Sleeves with M4 Internal Thread

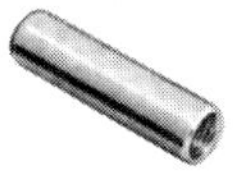

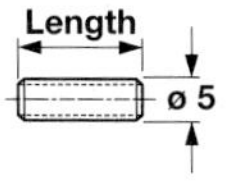

Finish: steel	length	unfinished	galvanized
Cat. No.	15 mm long	267.00.011	267.00.911
	18 mm long	267.00.012	267.00.912
	22 mm long	267.00.013	267.00.913
	30 mm long		267.00.916

Packing: 1000 pcs.

Milled Sleeve with M4 Internal Thread

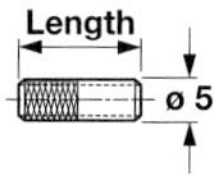

Finish: brass, unfinished

Cat. No.	14 mm long	267.12.014
	22 mm long	267.12.022

Packing: 1000 pcs.

M4 Fastening Screw with ø 2.4 mm recess in head for trim cap.

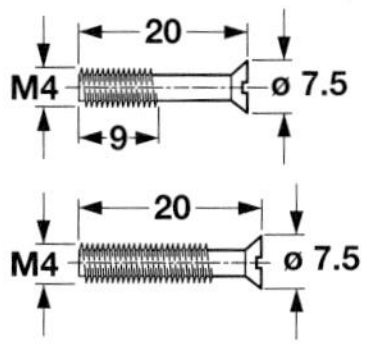

Finish: steel, unfinished

Cat. No.	20 mm long	267.10.020
	23 mm long	267.10.023

Packing: 5,000 pcs.

Threaded Sleeve with M4 internal thread and ø 2.4 mm recess in head for trim cap.

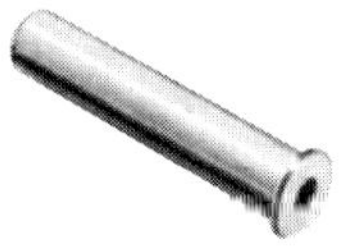

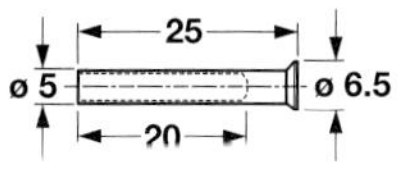

Finish: brass, unfinished

Cat. No.	267.11.025

Packing: 1000 pcs.

Trim Cap

For screw and sleeve heads.

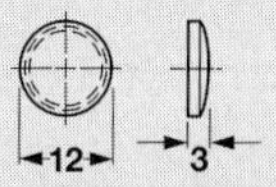

Finish: plastic

Cat. No.	white	267.02.790
	beige	267.02.490
	brown	267.02.190

Packing: 1000 pcs.

Trim Caps

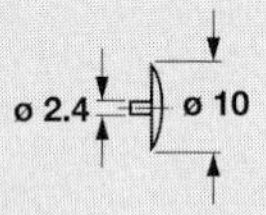

Finish: plastic

Cat. No.	white	024.02.708
	brown	024.02.100
	black	024.02.306

Packing: 1000 pcs.

Dimensional data not binding. We reserve the right to alter specifications without notice.

Dimensions in mm

HÄFELE

Mending Plates

Mending Plate

Finish: steel, galvanized

Length	50 mm	260.21.509
	70 mm	260.21.705

Packing: 200 pcs.

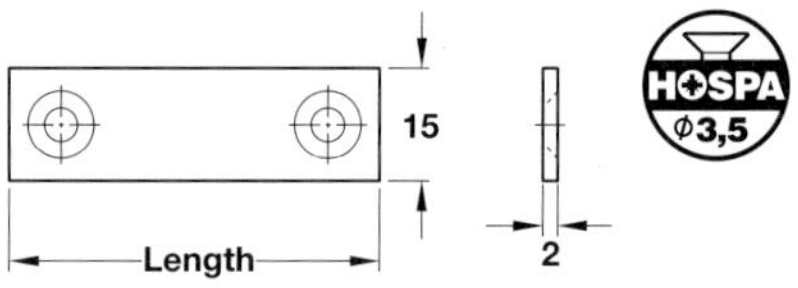

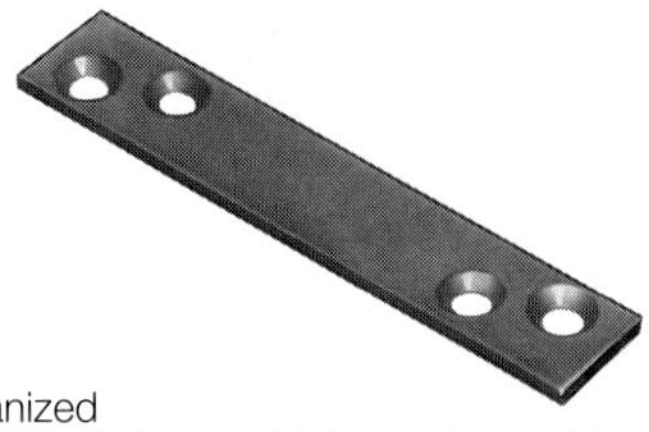

Mending Plate

Finish: steel, galvanized

Length	60 mm	260.20.011
	80 mm	260.20.020
	100 mm	260.20.039

Packing: 150 pcs.

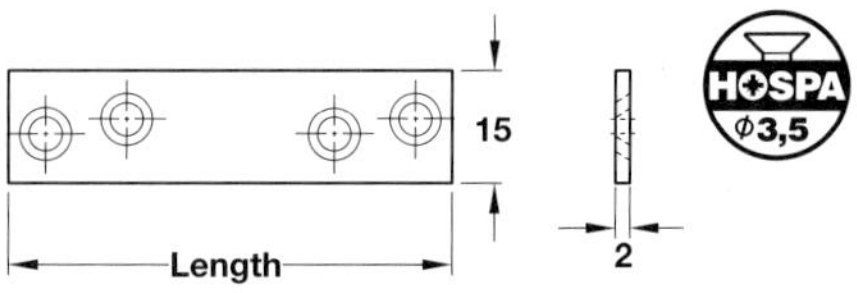

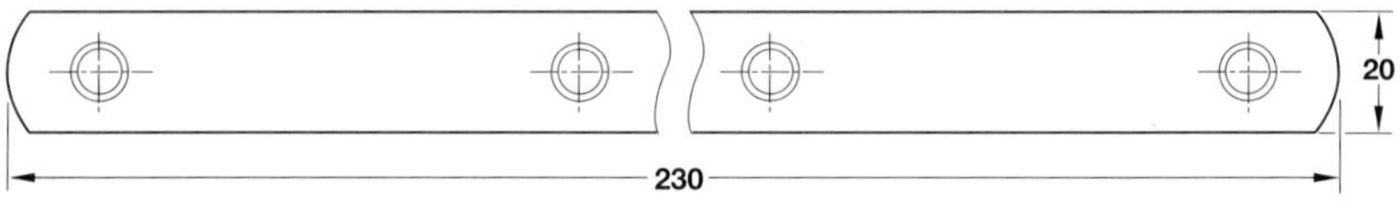

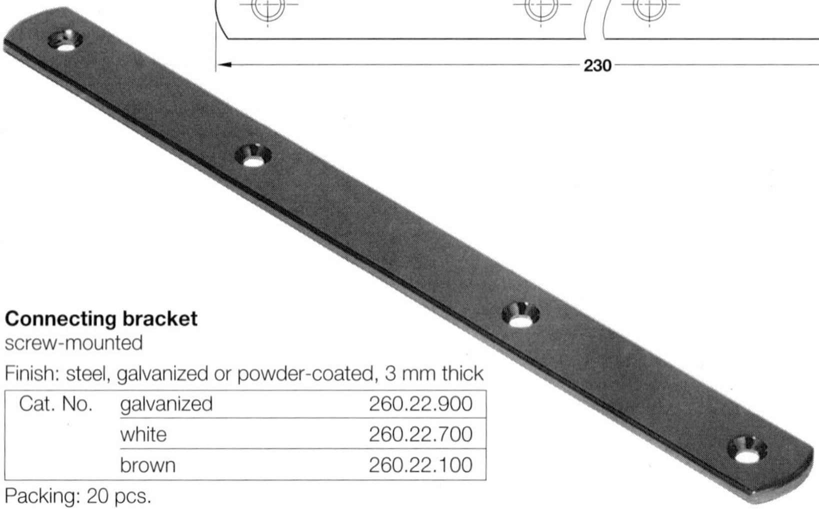

Connecting bracket

screw-mounted

Finish: steel, galvanized or powder-coated, 3 mm thick

Cat. No.	galvanized	260.22.900
	white	260.22.700
	brown	260.22.100

Packing: 20 pcs.

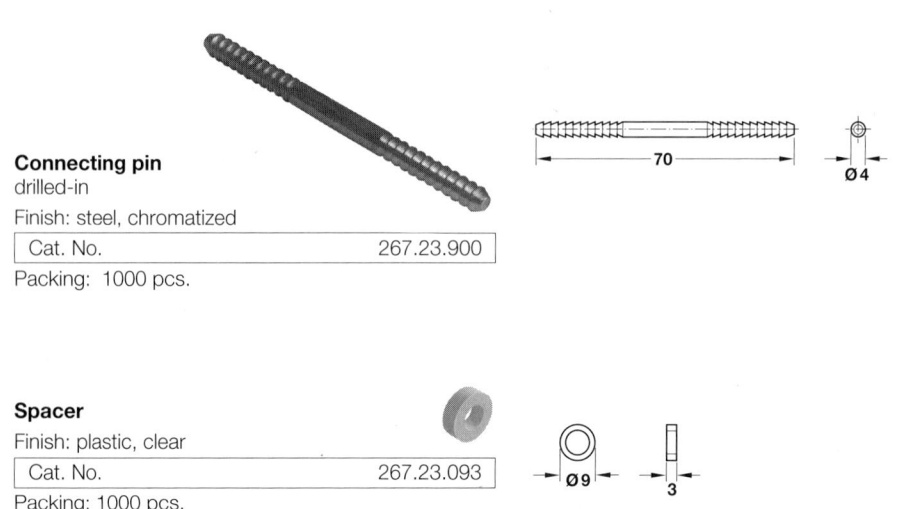

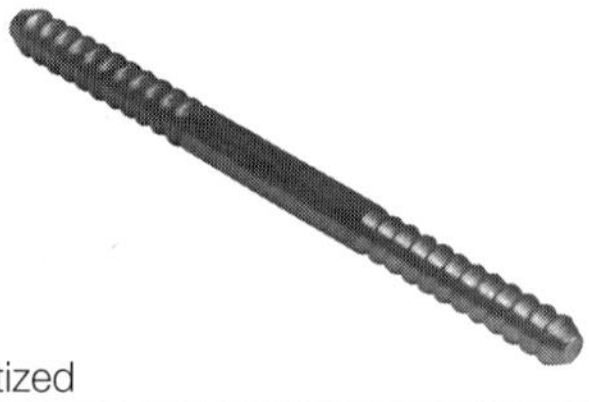

Connecting pin

drilled-in

Finish: steel, chromatized

Cat. No.	267.23.900

Packing: 1000 pcs.

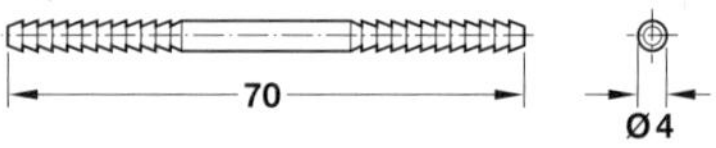

Spacer

Finish: plastic, clear

Cat. No.	267.23.093

Packing: 1000 pcs.

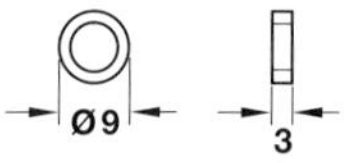

2 Locks, Catches, RTA and PAS® Fittings
Shelf Supports
Bed Fittings

Door panel connector
Uniform front view, e.g. in base cabinets without drawer door, in stacked panel installations.

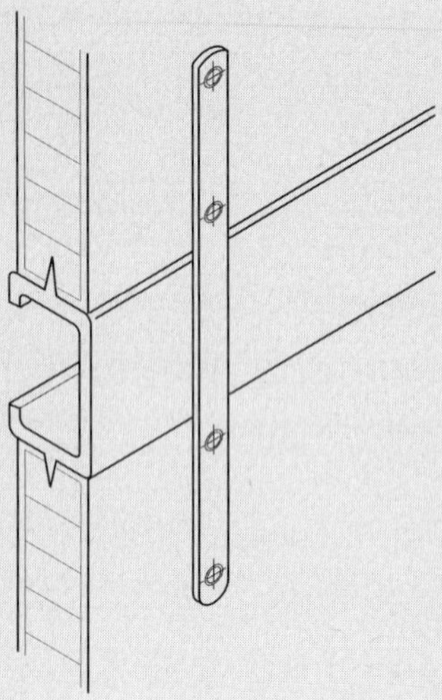

Spacer
To achieve desired gap between door and stacked panel.

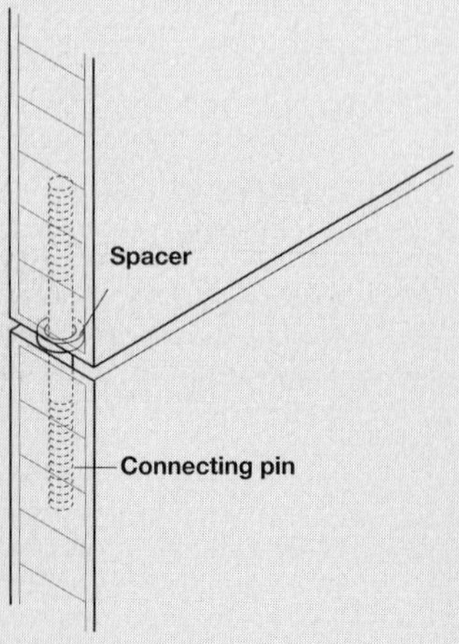

Dimensional data not binding. We reserve the right to alter specifications without notice.

Dimensions in mm

Multi-purpose Connectors

M6 Joint connector bolt, Type JCB-B
flat-headed with M4 hexagon socket.
Finish: steel, bronzed

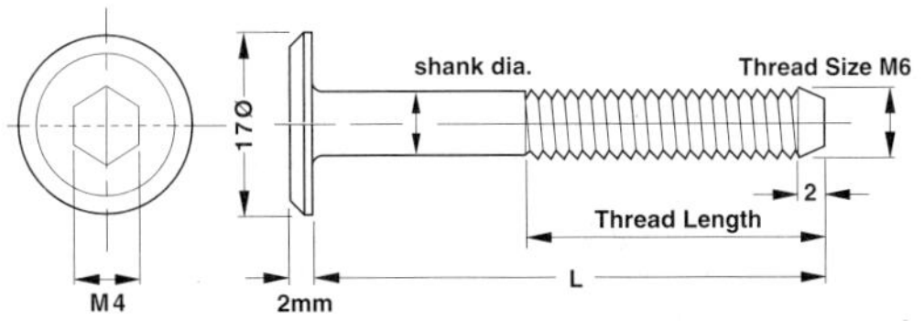

Cat. No.	Overall Length	Thread Length	Packing
264.77.130	30 mm	20 mm	2000 pcs.
264.77.135	35 mm	25 mm	1000 pcs.
264.77.140	40 mm	30 mm	1600 pcs.
264.77.145	45 mm	35 mm	1500 pcs.
264.77.150	50 mm	40 mm	1400 pcs.
264.77.155	55 mm	40 mm	1300 pcs.
264.77.160	60 mm	40 mm	1200 pcs.
264.77.170	70 mm	40 mm	900 pcs.
264.77.180	80 mm	40 mm	800 pcs.
264.77.200	100 mm	40 mm	500 pcs.
264.77.210	110 mm	40 mm	400 pcs.
264.77.220	120 mm	40 mm	300 pcs.

Hexagonal keys

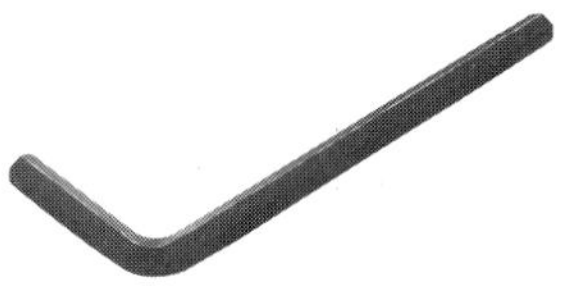

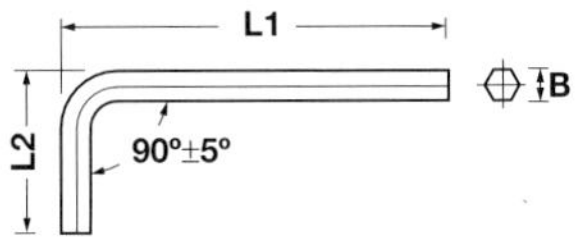

Finish: steel

Cat. No.	Size= B	L_1	L_2	color	Packing
008.28.044	M4	65	25	black	2000 pcs.
008.28.062	M5	65	25	zinc	1000 pcs.
008.28.268	M6	70	30	zinc	500 pcs.

Allen Key "Z" shape

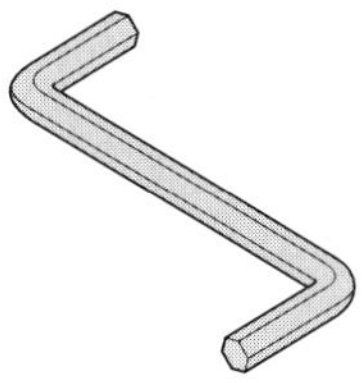

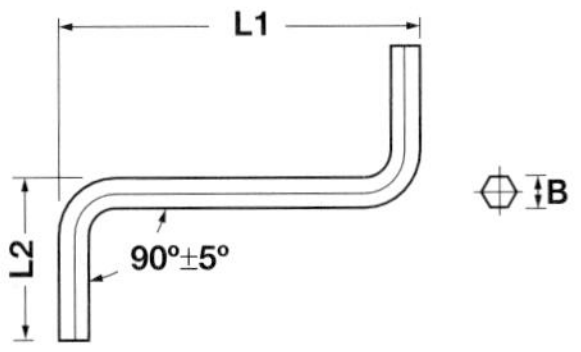

Finish: zinc plated

Cat. No.	Size= B	L_1	L_2	Packing
008.28.530	M4	46	19	2000 pcs.
008.28.540	M6	46	19	3000 pcs.

HÄFELE

Multi-Purpose Connectors

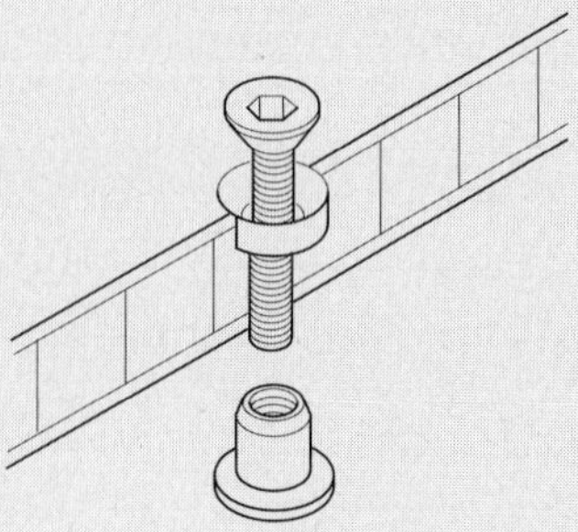

M4 Allen Key
Finish: steel, unfinished

Cat. No.	008.28.044

Packing: 2000 pcs.

M6 Countersunk Screw, to DIN 7991
with M4 hexagon socket

Length	Cat. No. nickel-plated	bronzed	Packing
50 mm	264.70.750	264.70.150	2500 pcs.
60 mm	264.70.760	264.70.160	1000 pcs.
70 mm	264.70.770	264.70.170	1000 pcs.

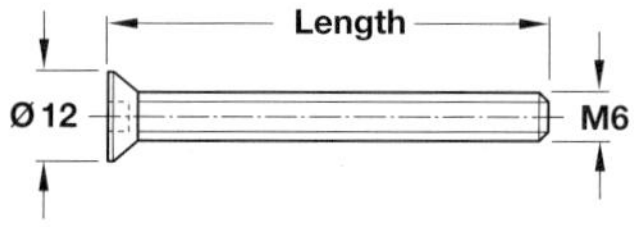

M 6 Threaded Pin
Finish: steel, unfinished

Cat. No.	264.72.060

Packing: 3000 pcs.

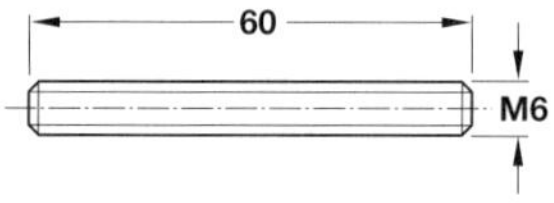

Countersunk Collar
suitable for M6 countersunk screw
Finish: steel

	Cat. No.
nickel-plated	264.73.760
bronzed	264.73.160

Packing: 1000 pcs.

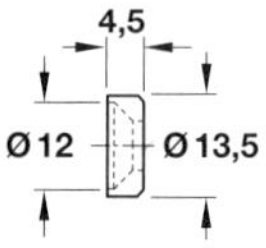

M 6 Sleeve Nut
with M4 hexagon socket
Finish: steel, bronzed

Cat. No.	264.74.160

Packing: 1000 pcs.

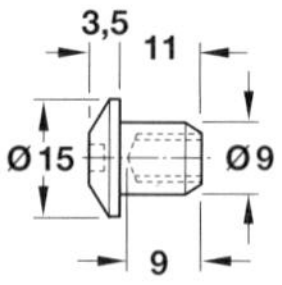

M 6 Sleeve Nut
with M4 hexagon socket
Finish: steel, bronzed

Cat. No.	264.75.160

Packing: 1000 pcs.

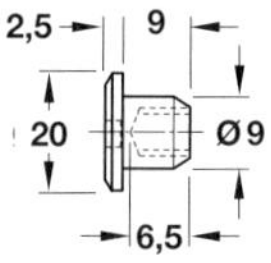

M 6 Cross Dowel
with off-center thread

Cat. No.	264.80.713

Packing: 2000 pcs.

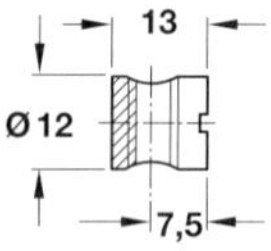

M6 Cross Dowel
Finish: steel, unfinished

Length	Dimension X	Cat. No.
14 mm	8 mm	264.81.014
30 mm	20 mm	264.81.030

Packing: 1000 pcs.

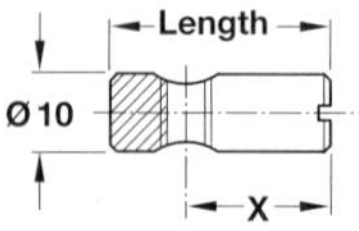

M 6 Cross Dowel
Finish: steel, unfinished

Length	Cat. No.
14 mm	264.82.014
20 mm	264.82.020

Packing: 1000 pcs.

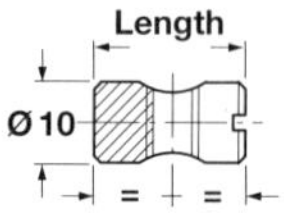

Dimensions in mm

Dimensional data not binding.
We reserve the right to alter specifications without notice.

Multi-Purpose Connectors-M6

M6 Insert nut, Type E

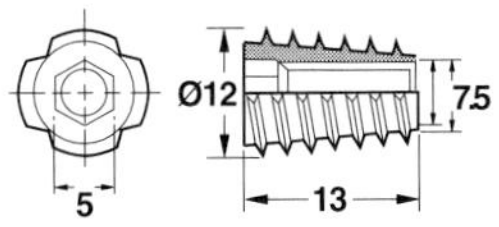

Finish: die-cast, zinc-plated

Cat. No.	13 mm	032.06.237

Packing: 5000 pcs.

M6 Cross Dowel
center thread

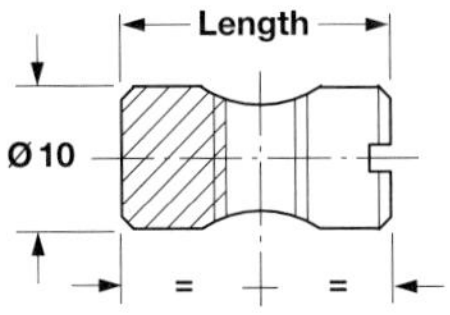

Finish: steel, unfinished

Cat. No.	14 mm long	264.82.014
	20 mm long	264.82.020

Packing: 1000 pcs.

M6 Cross dowel, Type JRN
with off-center thread, phillips

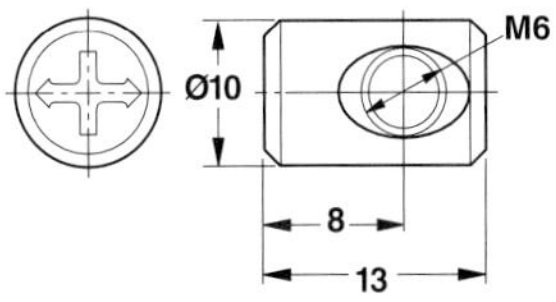

Finish: steel

Cat. No.	13 mm	264.87.913

Packing: 4000 pcs.

Dimensions in mm

HÄFELE

Multi-Purpose Connectors 1/4-20

1/4-20 Joint Connector Bolt, Type JCB-B

flat-head with M4 hexagon socket.

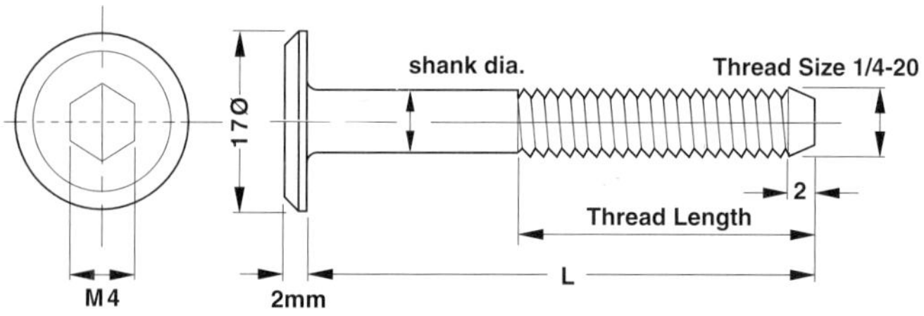

	antique bronze	black oxide	length	thread length	Packing
Cat. No.	264.76.130	264.76.330	30 mm	20 mm	2000 pcs.
	264.76.135	264.76.335	35 mm	25 mm	1800 pcs.
	264.76.140	264.76.340	40 mm	30 mm	1600 pcs.
	264.76.145	264.76.345	45 mm	35 mm	1500 pcs.
	264.76.150	264.76.350	50 mm	40 mm	1400 pcs.
	264.76.155	264.76.355	55 mm	40 mm	1300 pcs.
	264.76.160	264.76.360	60 mm	40 mm	1200 pcs.
	264.76.170	264.76.370	70 mm	40 mm	900 pcs.
	264.76.180	264.76.380	80 mm	40 mm	800 pcs.
	264.76.200		100 mm	40 mm	500 pcs.
	264.76.210		110 mm	40 mm	400 pcs.
	264.76.220		120 mm	40 mm	300 pcs.

1/4-20 JCN Nut Screw-mounted

5 mm hexagonal socket.

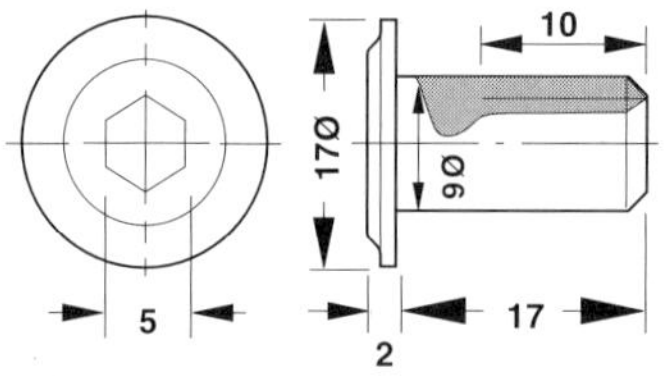

Finish:	nickel-plated	brass-plated	antique bronze-plated	black oxide
Cat. No.	267.10.617	267.10.517	267.10.117	267.10.317
Packing in pcs:	3000	3000	4000	4000

1/4-20 Type B Insert Knock-in

Blind Hole Size 9.0

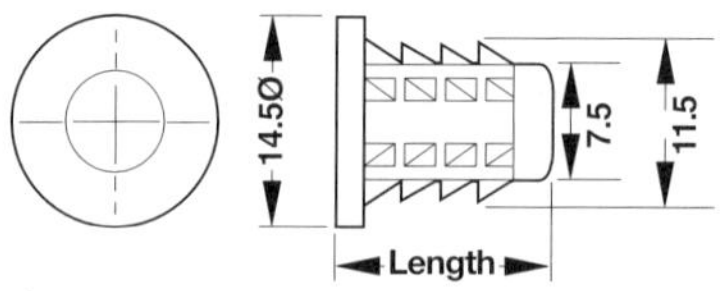

Finish	Cat. No.	length	Packing
zinc, die-cast	039.03.065	11 mm	6000 pcs.
zinc, die-cast	039.02.062	15 mm	6000 pcs.
black oxide	039.03.366	15 mm	6000 pcs.

1/4-20 Type D Insert Screw-mounted

6 mm hexagonal socket.
Blind Hole Size 9.0

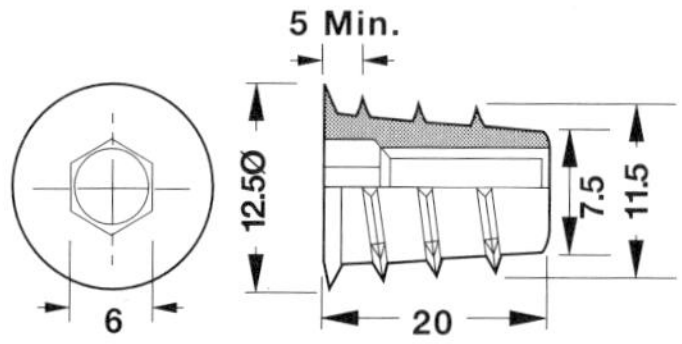

Cat. No.	zinc, die-cast	030.02.266
	black oxide	030.02.364

Packing: 6000 pcs.

Dimensions in mm

Dimensional data not binding.
We reserve the right to alter specifications without notice.

Multi-Purpose Connectors 1/4-20

1/4-20 Type E Insert Screw-mounted
with 6 mm hexagonal socket.

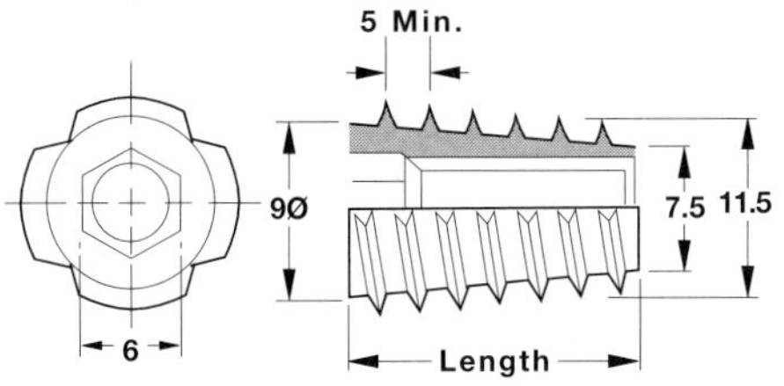

Finish:	nickel-plated	brass-plated	antique bronze-plated	black oxide
Length	13 mm	20 mm	13 mm	20 mm
Cat. No.	030.06.166	030.06.269	030.06.362	030.06.460
Packing in pcs:	6000	6000	5000	3000

1/4-20 Cross Dowel-slotted
off-center thread.

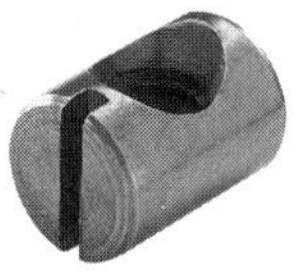

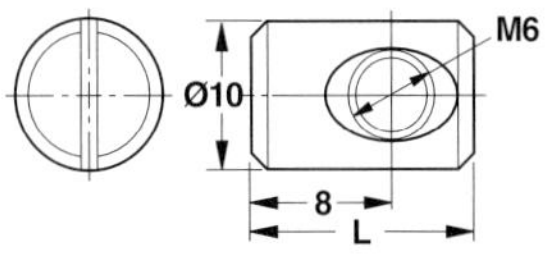

Finish: steel

Cat. No.	length	Packing
264.85.014	14 mm	5000
264.85.030	30 mm	2000

1/4-20 Cross Dowel-Phillips
center thread.

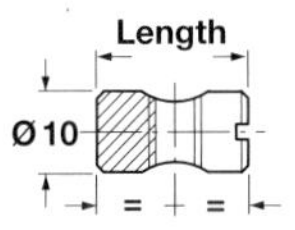

Finish: steel

Cat. No.	length	Packing
264.86.913	13 mm	5000
264.86.014	14 mm	5000
264.86.020	30 mm	4000

1/4-20 Cross Dowel, Type JRN
off-center thread, phillips

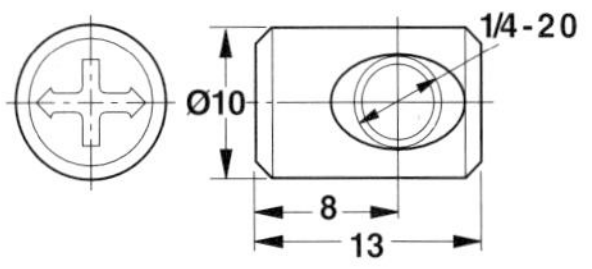

Finish: steel

Cat. No.	length	Packing
264.85.913	13 mm	5000

Dimensions in mm

HÄFELE

Multi-Purpose Connectors

T-nuts
pronged
Finish: steel

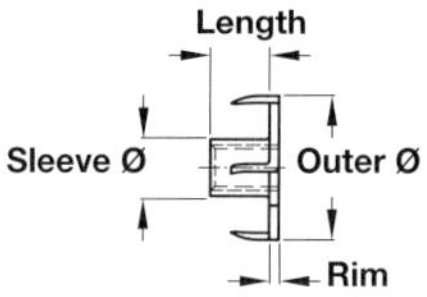

Internal thread	**M 4**	**M 5**	**M 6**	**M 8**	**M 10**
Outer Ø	15	18	19	22,5	26
Sleeve Ø	5.5	6.5	7.5	10	11.5
Length	7.5	8	8	9.5	11
Rim	1	1	1.3	1.5	2
Cat. No unfinished	031.00.249	031.00.258	031.00.267	031.00.285	031.00.301
Packing in pcs.	1000	1000	1000	500	500

Screw-in sockets
screwdriver slot
Finish: steel, unfinished

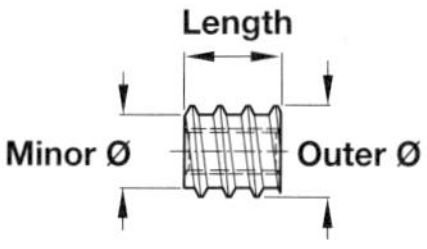

Internal thread	**M 4**	**M 4**	**M 5**
Outer Ø	8	8	10
Minor Ø	5.5	5.5	7
Length	8	10	10
Cat. No.	030.00.100	030.00.119	030.00.208
Packing in pcs.	1000	100	100

Internal thread	**M 6**	**M 6**	**M 6**	**M 6**
Outer Ø	10	12	12	12
Minor Ø	7	9	9	9
Length	12	11	13	15
Cat. No.	030.00.351	030.00.306	030.00.315	030.00.324
Packing in pcs.	1000	1000	100	1000

Internal thread	**M 8**	**M 8**	**M 10**
Outer Ø	14	16	18.5
Minor Ø	11.5	12	15
Length	15	18	15
Cat. No.	030.00.404	030.00.422	030.00.502
Packing in pcs.	100	100	100

Glue-in sockets
glue grooves
Finish: nylon, natural-colored

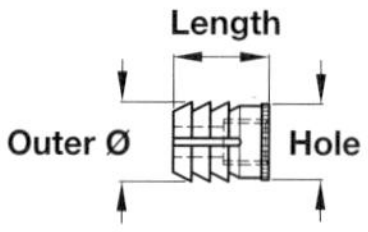

Internal thread	**M 4**	**M 4**	**M 4**	**M 5**
Outer Ø	8.5	8.5	11	11
Hole Ø	8	8	10	10
Length	8	10	10	13
Cat. No.	039.33.140	039.33.042	039.33.239	039.33.051
Packing in pcs.	1000	1000	1000	100

Internal thread	**M 6**	**M 6**	**M 6**	**M 6**
Outer Ø	8.5	11	11	11
Hole Ø	8	10	10	10
Length	11	9	11	13
Cat. No.	039.33.462	039.33.364	039.33.266	039.33.060
Packing in pcs.	5000	1000	5000	5000

Internal thread	**M 8**
Outer Ø	11.2
Hole Ø	9,5
Length	12
Cat. No.	039.33.186

Packing: 100 pcs.

Dimensions in mm

Multi-Purpose Connectors

Spreading dowel
with M4 internal thread, milled surface.
Finish: brass

Cat. No.	051.45.004

Packing: 3000 pcs.

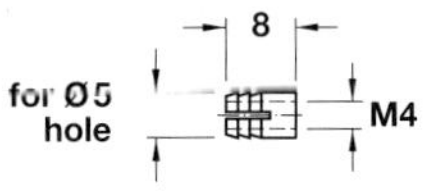

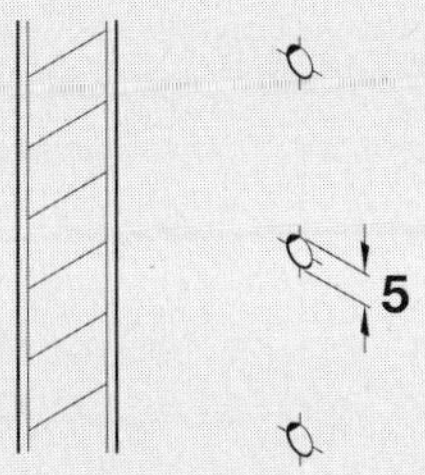

Spreading dowel with collar
Finish: nylon, natural-colored

Cat. No. 7.5 mm long	340.43.000

Packing: 500 pcs.

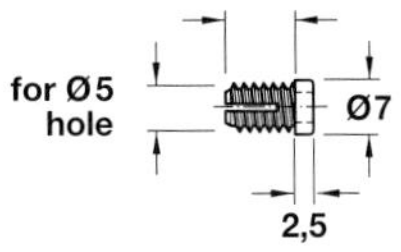

Locks, Catches, RTA and PAS® Fittings
Shelf Supports
Bed Fittings

2

Spreading dowel without collar
Finish: nylon, natural-colored

Cat. No. 9 mm long	042.98.033

Packing: 1000 pcs.

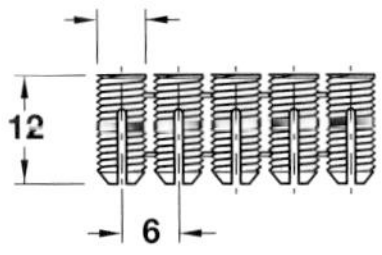

Strip of 20 injection moulded spreading dowels

The SYSTEM VARIANTA 32 offers many advantages as a design principle for RTA furniture.

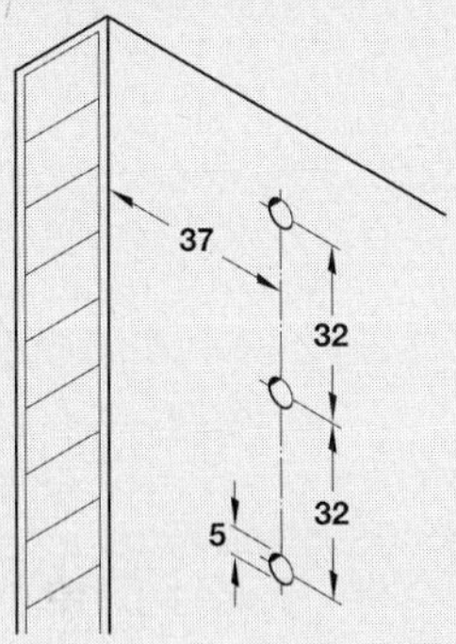

Spreading dowel
with M6 internal thread
Finish: nylon, natural-colored

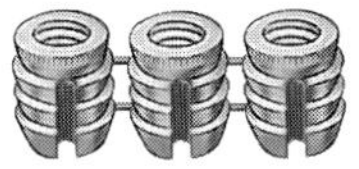

Cat. No.	039.35.064

Packing: 1000 pcs.

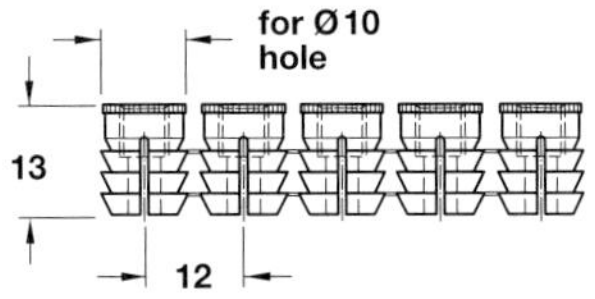

Knock in sleeve

Sleeve, with M6 internal thread
and milled surface, for press-fit installation.
Finish: plastic, white

Cat. No.	262.76.700

Packing: 1000 pcs.

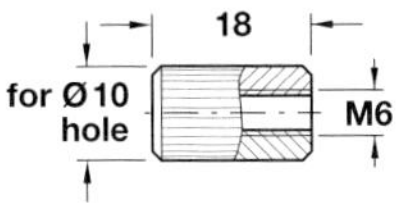

Dimensions in mm

Many types of RTA fittings can be installed using system holes drilled at 32 mm intervals on a line 37 mm from the panel face edge.

HÄFELE

Dowel Connectors

Application for brass insert

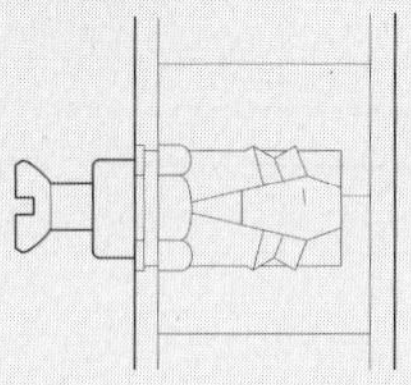

Spreading dowel

Extremely high pull-out strength, with M6 internal thread for press-fit installation in Ø 8 mm holes.

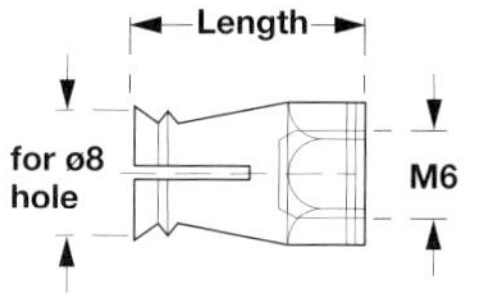

Finish: brass

Cat. No.		Min. drill depth	Packing
039.00.267	w/o pellet	9.5 mm	2000 pcs.
039.00.061	w/pellet	15 mm	1000 pcs.
039.00.169	w/pellet	18 mm	1000 pcs.

Spreading dowel

Extremely high pull-out strength, with 1/4-20" internal thread for press-fit installation in Ø 8 mm holes.

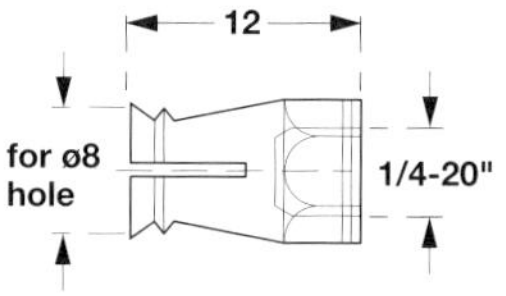

Finish: brass

Cat. No.		Min. drill depth	Packing
039.01.068	w/pellet	15 mm	2000 pcs.
039.01.160	w/o pellet	9.5 mm	1000 pcs.

- For solid and detachable connections.
- This dowel is made of high-grade, high-impact plastic for invisible and corrosion proof connections.
- The tooth-like grooves of the dowels guarantee a tight fit even without glue.
- EXACT dowels save labor on ceiling, door and wall paneling as they can also be driven into brick and concrete.

"EXACT" connector

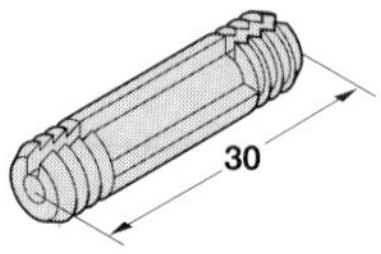

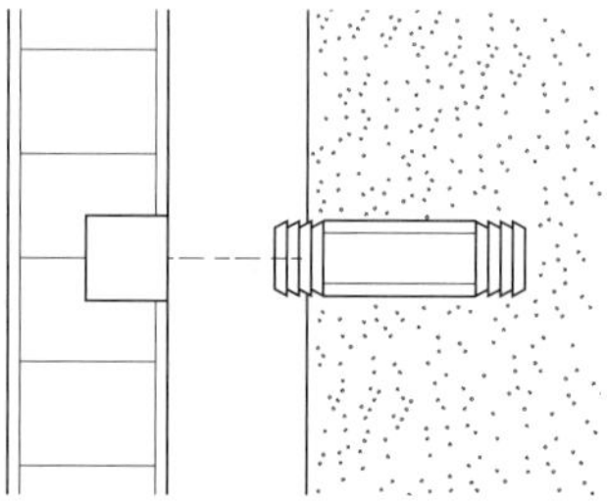

Finish: plastic, white

Cat. No.	5 x 30 mm long	267.72.700
	8 x 30 mm long	267.70.700

Packing: 1000 pcs.

- To reinforce a 90° connection the miter dowel is ideal aid.
- Made of nylon with the mounting flexibility and strength for a rigid connection.

Miter dowel

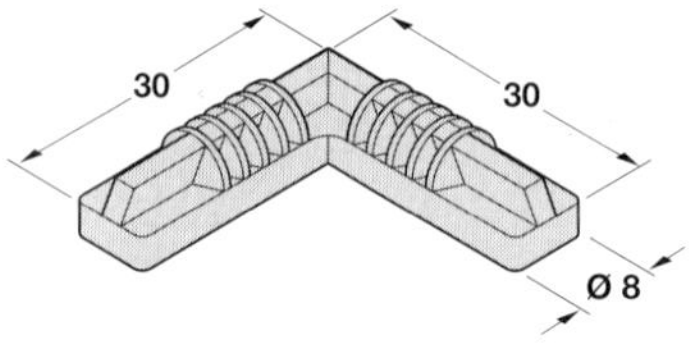

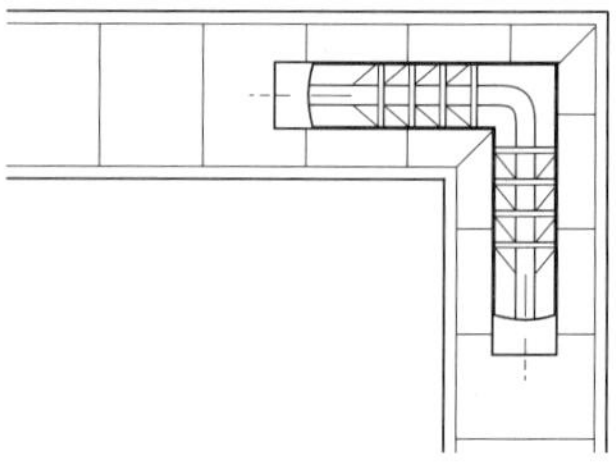

Finish: nylon

Cat. No.	267.71.700

Packing: 1000 pcs.

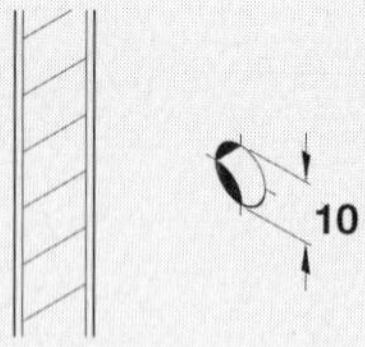

Glued dowel, with special internal thread in Ø 10 mm holes.

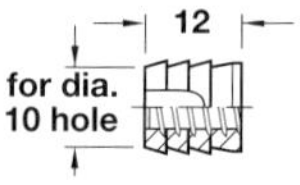

Finish: plastic

Cat. No.	039.32.050

Packing: 5000 pcs.

- Furniture doors only function correctly when the furniture is perfectly level, the Cuni wedge strips ensure that it does.
- Furniture can be leveled effortlessly and precisely to the millimeter with plastic Cuni wedge strips:
- Place the strip under furniture to level. Once level, simply snap off the Cuni sections
- Plastic sections can be broken off from 1 mm to 8 mm.

Cuni furniture wedges

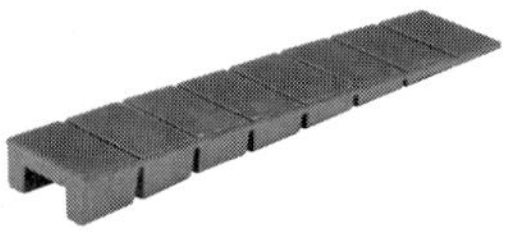

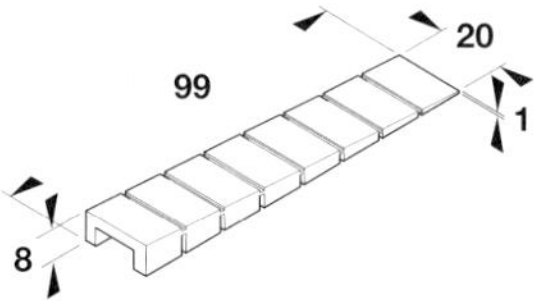

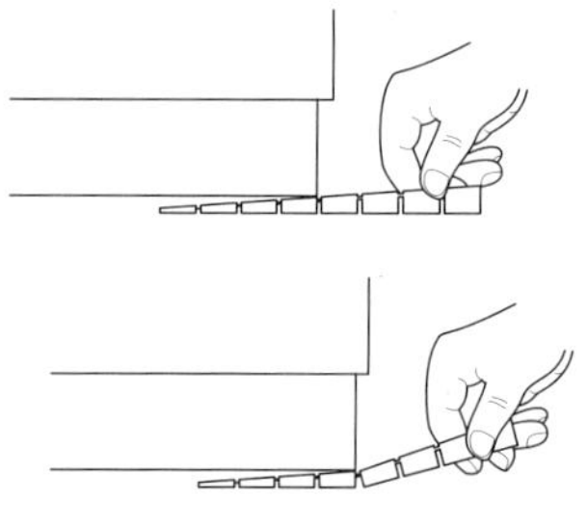

Finish: plastic

Cat. No.	brown	006.90.900
	white	006.90.920

Packing: 250 pcs.

Dimensions in mm

Dimensional data not binding. We reserve the right to alter specifications without notice.

Wood Dowels

Made of kiln-dried beechwood, these dowel pins feature a fluted design for better gluing and a stronger connection.

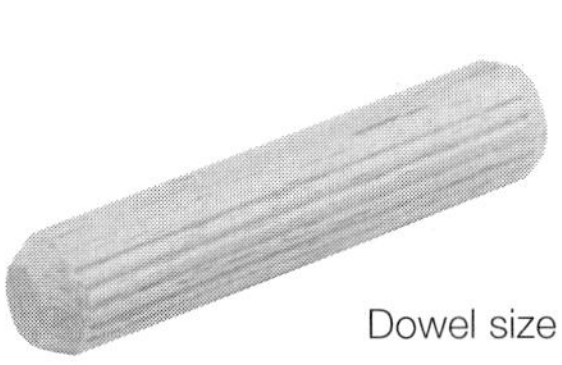

Dowel size

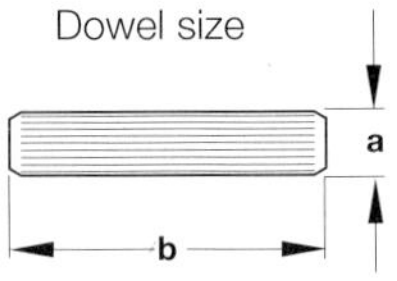

Application
- Glued case connections
- Non glued connections in combination with mechanical fastener

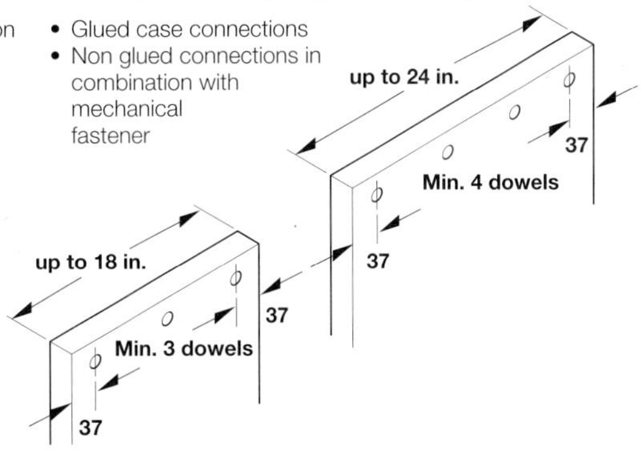

Cat. No.	Material/size a x b		Packing
267.83.025	Wood	5x25 mm	10,000 pcs.
267.83.027	Wood	5x27 mm	10,000 pcs.
267.83.030	Wood	5x30 mm	10,000 pcs.
267.83.035	Wood	5x35 mm	10,000 pcs.
267.83.040	Wood	5x40 mm	10,000 pcs.
267.83.125	Wood	6x25 mm	10,000 pcs.
267.83.127	Wood	6x27 mm	10,000 pcs.
267.83.130	Wood	6x30 mm	10,000 pcs.
267.83.135	Wood	6x35 mm	10,000 pcs.
267.83.140	Wood	6x40 mm	10,000 pcs.
267.83.225	Wood	8x25 mm	5000 pcs.
267.83.230	Wood	8x30 mm	5000 pcs.
267.83.232	Wood	8x32 mm	5000 pcs.
267.83.235	Wood	8x35 mm	5000 pcs.
267.83.238	Wood	8x38 mm	5000 pcs.
267.83.240	Wood	8x40 mm	5000 pcs.
267.83.250	Wood	8x50 mm	5000 pcs.
267.83.330	Wood	10x30 mm	2500 pcs.
267.83.335	Wood	10x35 mm	2500 pcs.
267.83.340	Wood	10x40 mm	2500 pcs.
267.83.345	Wood	10x45 mm	2500 pcs.
267.83.350	Wood	10x50 mm	2500 pcs.

Cat. No.	Material/size a x b		Packing
267.80.102	Wood	1/4" x 1"	5000 pcs.
267.80.105	Wood	1/4" x 1 1/4"	5000 pcs.
267.80.107	Wood	1/4" x 1 1/2"	5000 pcs.
267.80.110	Wood	1/4" x 1 3/4"	5000 pcs.
267.80.112	Wood	1/4" x 2"	5000 pcs.
267.80.113	Wood	1/4" x 2 1/4"	5000 pcs.
267.80.115	Wood	1/4" x 2 1/2"	5000 pcs.
267.80.202	Wood	5/16" x 1"	5000 pcs.
267.80.205	Wood	5/16" x 1 1/4"	5000 pcs.
267.80.207	Wood	5/16" x 1 1/2"	5000 pcs.
267.80.212	Wood	5/16" x 2"	5000 pcs.
267.80.302	Wood	3/8" x 1"	5000 pcs.
267.80.305	Wood	3/8" x 1 1/4"	5000 pcs.
267.80.307	Wood	3/8" x 1 1/2"	5000 pcs.
267.80.312	Wood	3/8" x 2"	5000 pcs.
267.80.507	Wood	7/16" x 1 1/2"	5000 pcs.
267.80.512	Wood	7/16" x 2"	5000 pcs.
267.80.519	Wood	7/16" x 3"	5000 pcs.
267.80.707	Wood	1/2" x 1 1/2"	5000 pcs.
267.80.712	Wood	1/2" x 2"	5000 pcs.
267.80.719	Wood	1/2" x 3"	5000 pcs.
267.80.812	Wood	5/8" x 2"	5000 pcs.

Locks, Catches, RTA and PAS® Fittings
Shelf Supports
Bed Fittings

2

Wood Biscuits
Die-cut from beechwood blanks, these biscuit assemblers (or wood joining plates) are compressed for strength and cross-hatched to improve glue bonding. When used with any water-based glue, the biscuit swells within the joint providing excellent holding power.

Application
- For all types of butt or miter joints

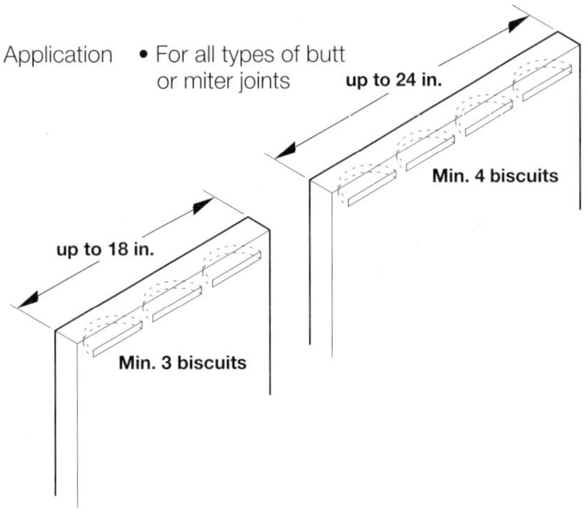

Cat. No.	H x L	Groove Depth	Groove Thickness	Size	Packing
267.90.000	15x47 mm	8 mm	4 mm	0	[illegible]000 pcs.
267.90.010	19x53 mm	10 mm	4 mm	10	6500 pcs.
267.90.020	23x56 mm	12 mm	4 mm	20	5000 pcs.

Dimensional data not binding. We reserve the right to alter specifications without notice.

Dimensions in mm

HÄFELE

Multi-Purpose Hangers

Recessed Hanger, sawtooth

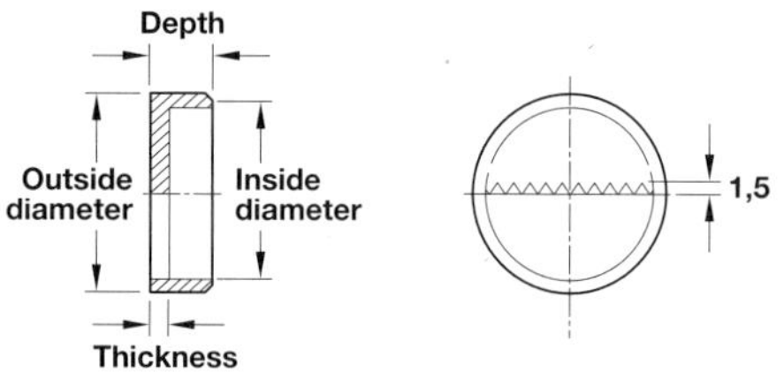

Finish: plastic, white

Outer diameter	20	30
Inner diameter	16	27
Depth	8.5	11.5
Thickness	2	2.5
Cat. No.	290.50.720	290.50.730
Packing:	100 pcs.	100 pcs.

Recessed Hanger,
key hole

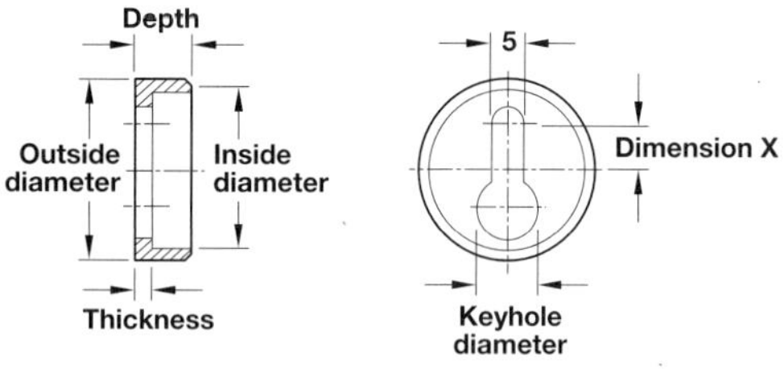

Finish: plastic, white

Outer diameter	20	30
Inner diameter	16	27
Depth	10	11.5
Thickness	2	2.5
Keyhole diameter	9	10
Dimension X	5	7.5
Cat. No.	290.51.720	290.51.730
Packing:	100 pcs.	100 pcs.

Dimensions in mm

Cabinet Suspension Fittings

HÄFELE

Wall Rail

Length 2.5 m (98")
screw-hole increments of 50 mm (= 2")
Finish: extruded aluminum mill

Cat. No.	290.12.000

Packing: 1 pc. 2.5 m long

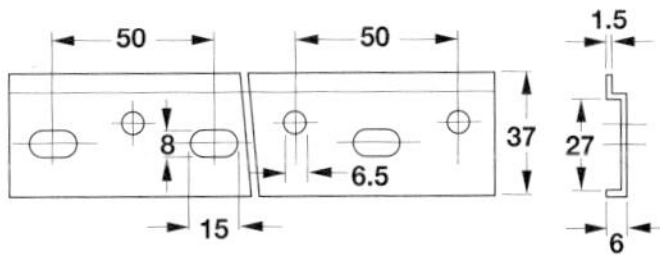

Wall Rail

Length 2.5 mm (98")
screw-hole increments of 50 mm (= 2")
Finish: steel, mill

Cat. No.	290.11.900

Packing: 1 pc. 2.5 m long

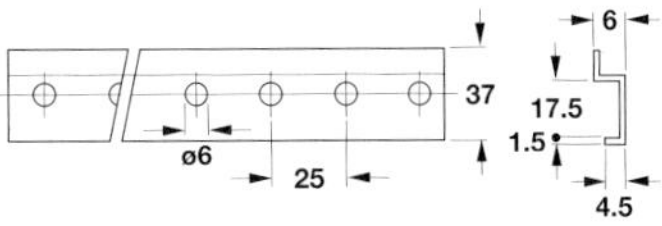

Covering strip

Gives clean appearance to the part(s) of the rail not covered by cabinets or other closet-components.
Finish: plastic, white

Cat. No.	290.12.780

Packing: 1 pc. 2.5 m long (18")

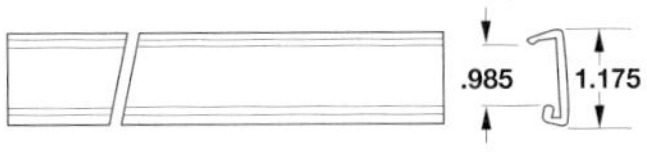

- The strong aluminum and steel rails shown here mount to the wall studs to provide a bracing support for cabinets, shelves and other closet components
- The wall rail makes installation quick and easy
- Components attach precisely and securely using Häfele cabinet hangers
- By attachment of the white covering strip the rail blends into the wall giving a clean appearance in the closet

Locks, Catches, RTA and PAS® Fittings
Shelf Supports
Bed Fittings
2

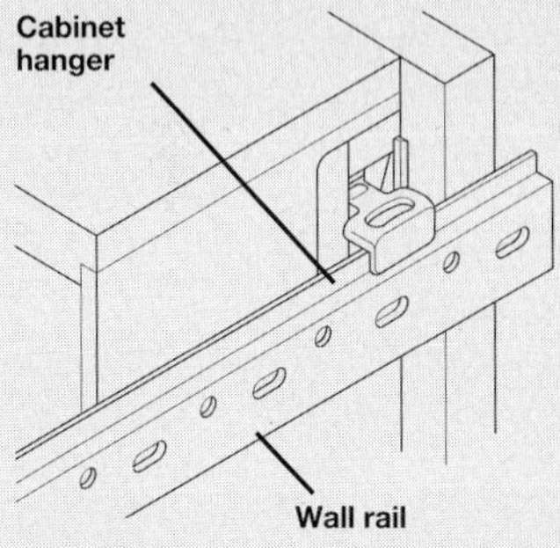

We recommend to attach wall rail to wall studs only with dry wall screws. Do not attach to sheetrock only.

Screw-mounted Cabinet Hanger

Wall rail suspension

- Vertical adjustment: 16 mm
  Depth adjustment: 15 mm
- Lateral adjustment: 10 mm
- Load carrying capacity per pair: 200 kg

Finish: steel, nickel-plated

Cat. No.	left	290.02.701
	right	290.02.700

Packing: 100 pcs.

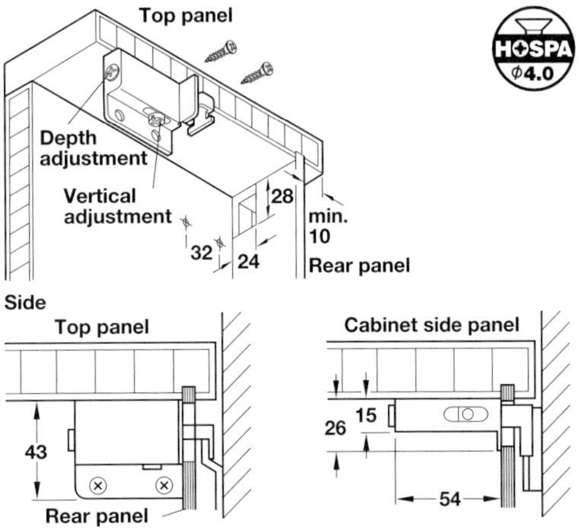

Screw-mounted Cabinet Hanger

Wall rail suspension

- Vertical adjustment: 16 mm
  Depth adjustment: 15 mm
- Lateral adjustment: 10 mm
- Load carrying capacity per pair: 240 kg

Finish: steel, beige nickel-plated

Cat. No.	left	290.07.401
	right	290.01.400

Finish: steel, white epoxy-coated

Cat. No.	left	290.07.701
	right	290.07.700

Packing: 100 pcs.

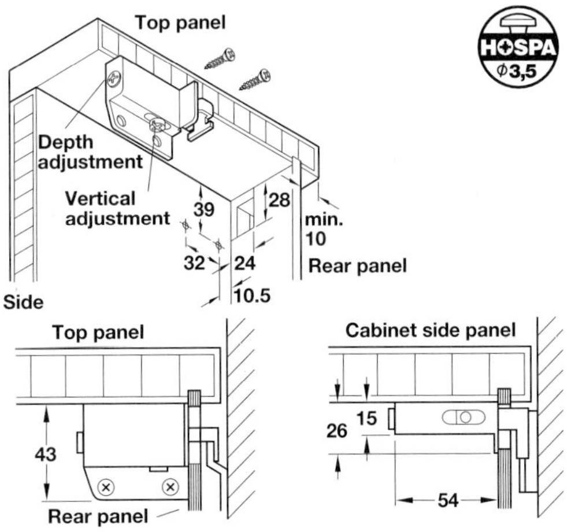

- With the hangers pre-attached the cabinets can be instantly and securely hooked into place.
- The cabinet hangers can be readily adjusted for depth and height to assure a precise fit.
- This attachment flexibility means cabinets can be quickly removed and rearranged in a variety of configurations.

Cabinet Hanger with Dowels Ø 1(

Wall rail suspension

- Vertical adjustment: 12 mm
  Depth adjustment: 14 mm
- Lateral adjustment: 12 mm
- Load carrying capacity per pair: 150 kg

Finish: plastic, white

Cat. No.	left	290.00.711
	right	290.00.710

Packing: 250 pcs.

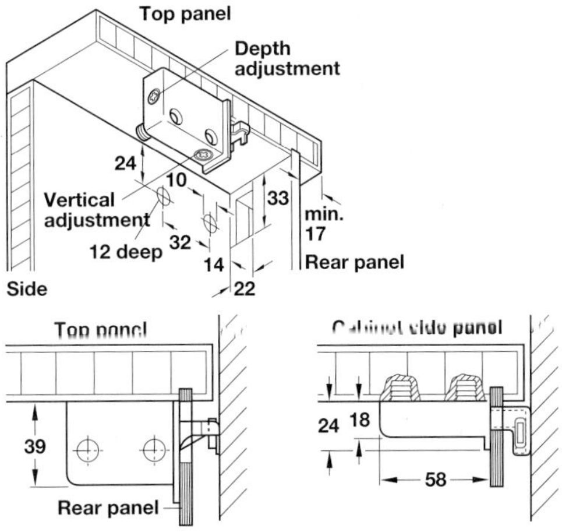

Dimensions in mm

Dimensional data not binding. We reserve the right to alter specifications without notice.

HÄFELE

Drawer Front Adjustment Fittings

Front Panel Adjustment Fittings

Consisting of: 1 insert, 15 mm dia.
1 adjusting element

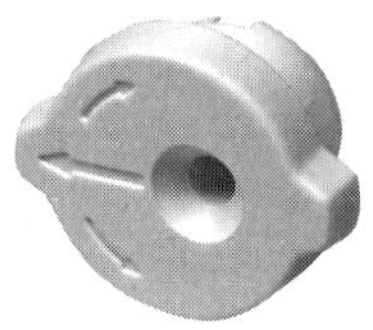

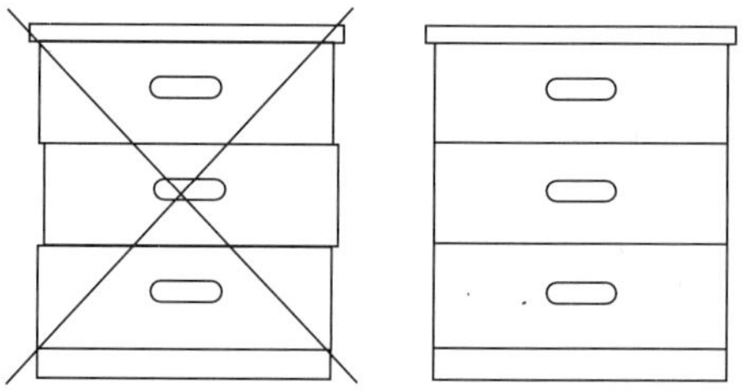

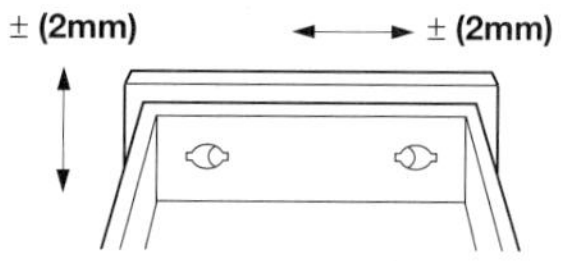
± (2mm)
± (2mm)

Pressed or glued into a 15 mm dia. hole in drawer front panel. (Minimum thickness of drawer front panel = 8 mm).
Insert and adjusting element are placed according to drawing below.
Drawer front panel at right fastened with 3.5 (#6) Hospa - Screws.
Front panel can be adjusted ± 2 mm in the horizontal or vertical direction.
Loosen the Hospa-Screws before adjusting.

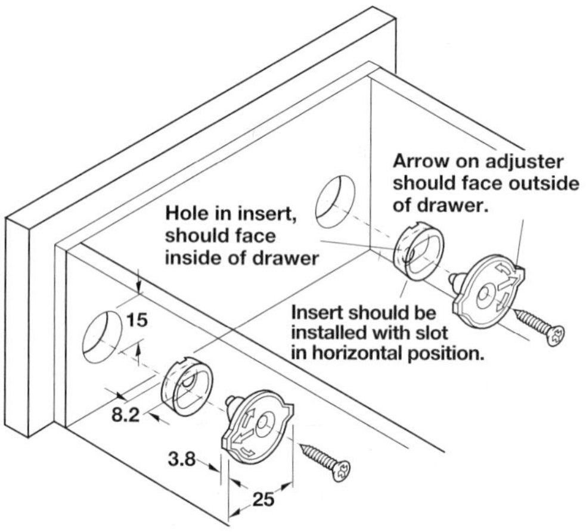
Arrow on adjuster should face outside of drawer.
Hole in insert, should face inside of drawer
Insert should be installed with slot in horizontal position.
15
8.2
3.8
25

Finish: plastic, white

Cat. No.	039.60.709

Packing: 200 pcs.

Drawer-Front Connector

Pressed in a 20 mm hole in drawer front.
Allows for ± 2 mm horizontal or vertical adjustment.

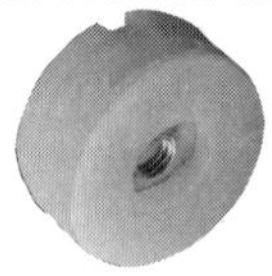

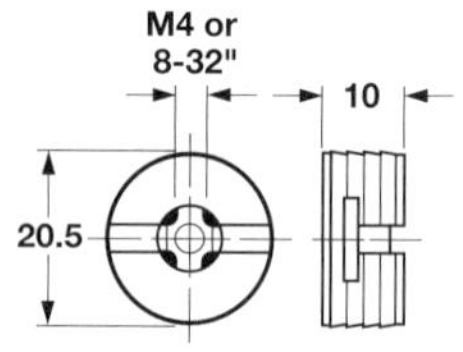
M4 or 8-32"
10
20.5

Finish: plastic, white

Cat. No.		
Cat. No.	M4	430.90.704
	8-32	430.90.713

Packing: 1000 pcs.

Dimensional data not binding.
We reserve the right to alter specifications without notice.

Glass Retainer Clips

HÄFELE

Glass Retainer Clip

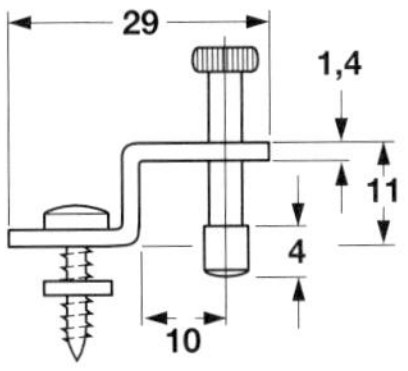

Finish: steel, bronzed

Cat. No.	291.02.109

Packing: 1000 pcs.

Glass Retainer Clip

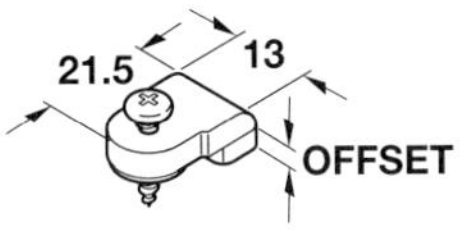

Finish: plastic with soft plastic tip

offset	color	Cat. No.
4.8 mm	clear	291.03.420
4.8 mm	oak	291.03.124
3.2 mm	clear	291.03.440
3.2 mm	oak	291.03.144
6.35 mm	clear	291.03.430
6.35 mm	oak	291.03.134

Packing: 5000 pcs.

Complete assembly for easy installation

- Wood screw is held in place by a small washer for ease of assembly
- Pressure screw has a soft vinyl tip.

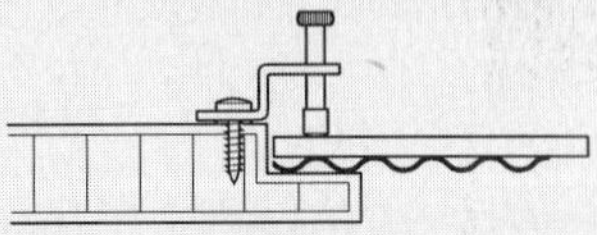

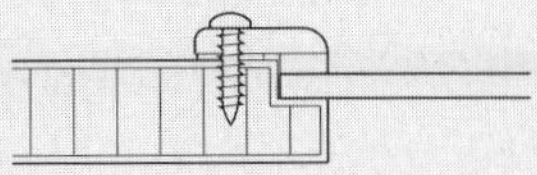

HÄFELE

Mirror Fittings

HEWI-Mirror Holder

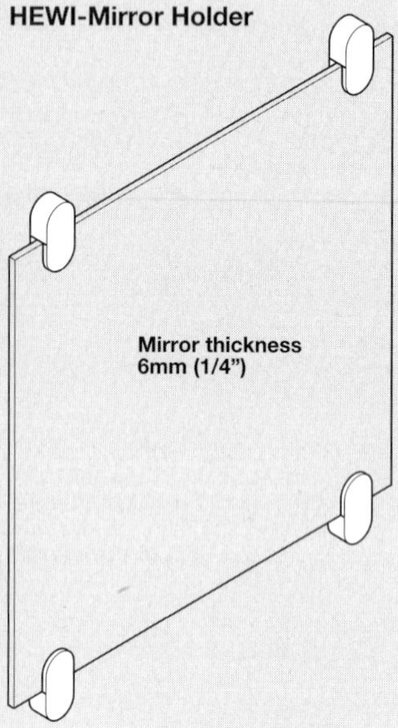

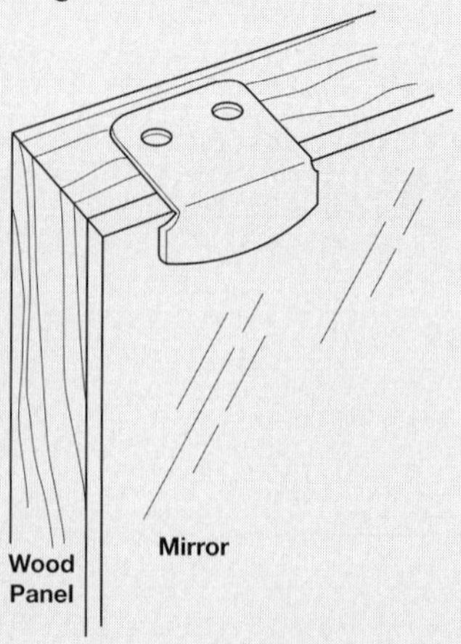

Mirror Holder
for frameless mirrors

Includes:
- 2 brackets, fixed
- 2 brackets with spring
- 4 wood screws ø 3.5 mm
- 4 plastic dowels for ø 6 mm holes

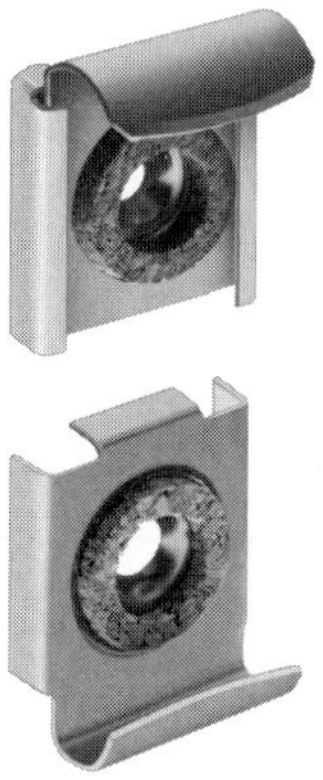

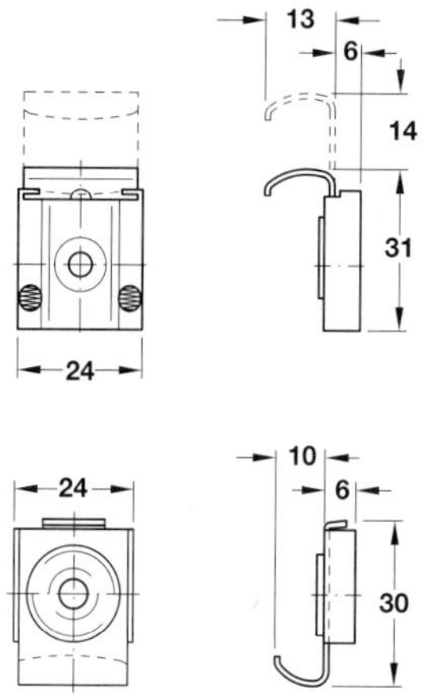

Finish: Brass, chrome-polished

Cat. No.	293.50.025

Packing: 25 sets

HEWI-Mirror Holder,
for 6 mm (1/4") thick mirrors

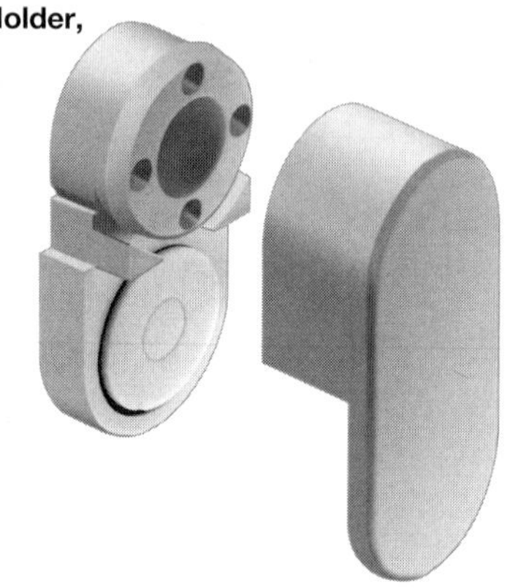

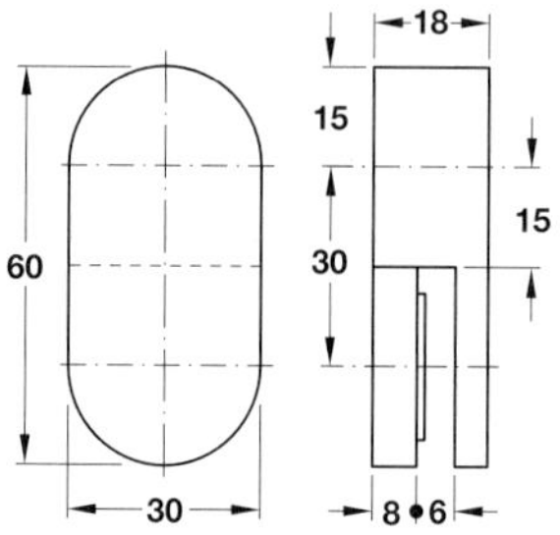

Finish: Nylon,

Cat. No.	white	988.32.101
	brown	988.32.109

Packing: 1 pc. (includes mounting hardware)

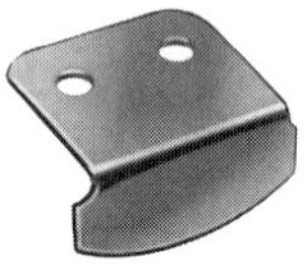

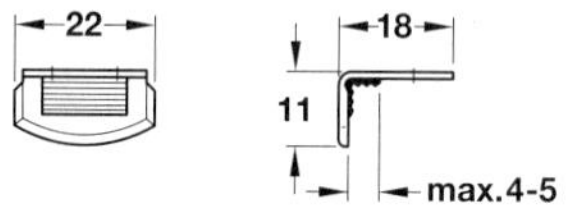

Mirror Holder, with rubber pad
Finish: Steel, nickel-plated

Cat. No.	291.01.013

Packing: 500 pcs.

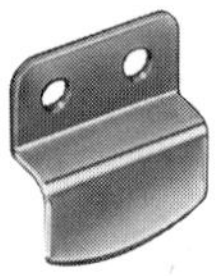

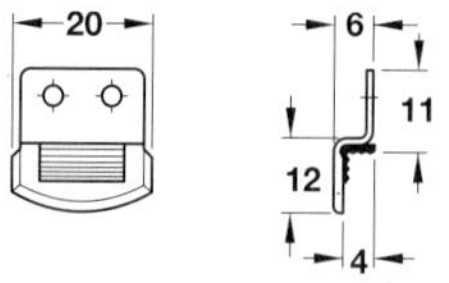

Mirror Holder, cranked with rubber pad
Finish: Steel, nickel-plated

Cat. No.	291.21.015

Packing: 500 pcs.

Mirror Holder, round with rubber pad
Finish: brass, nickel-plated

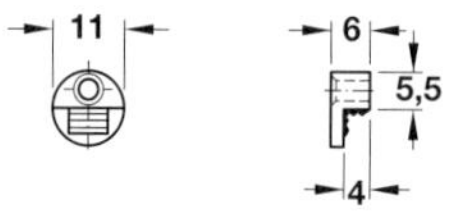

Cat. No.	292.01.705

Packing: 100 pcs.

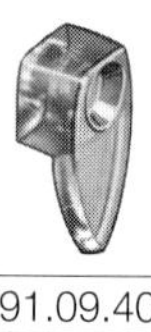

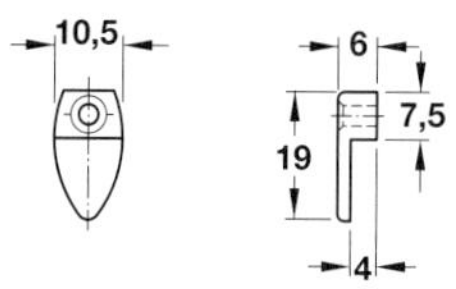

Mirror Holder, oval shaped
Finish: Plastic, clear

Cat. No.	291.09.402

Packing: 1000 pcs.

Dimensional data not binding. We reserve the right to alter specifications without notice.

Dimensions in mm

Recessed Shelf Fastener

HÄFELE

Shelf fastener for economical installation in holes in shelves. Includes plug for mounting in a ø 5 mm and ø 3 mm hole in the cabinet side panel.

Shelf Support

With one-piece moulded plug, ø 5 mm; for wood thicknesses from **16 mm upwards.**

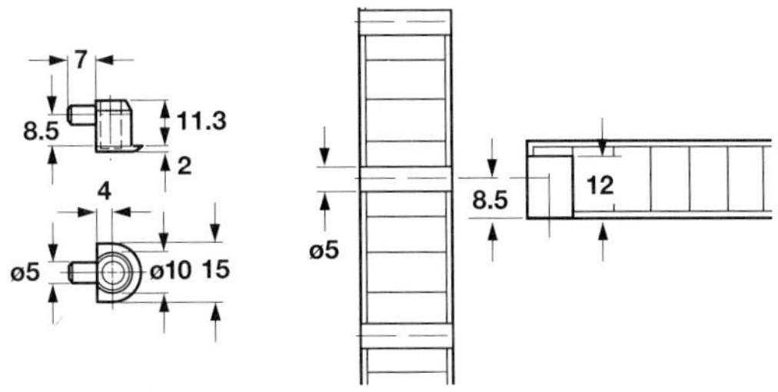

Finish: Plastic

Cat. No.		
	brown	282.81.110
	beige	282.81.414
	white	282.81.718

Packing: 3000 pcs.

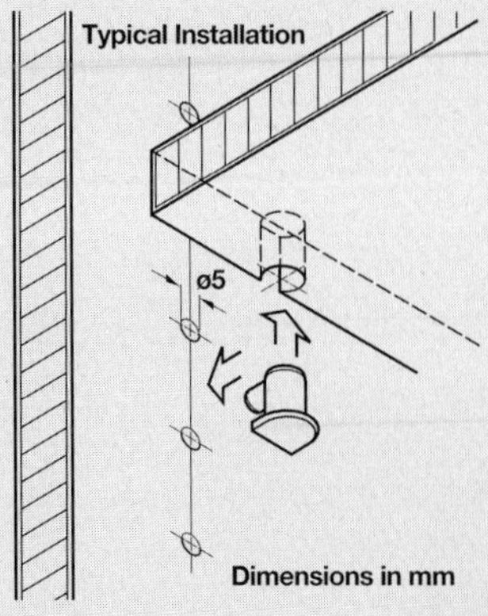

Locks, Catches, RTA and PAS® Fittings
Shelf Supports
Bed Fittings

2

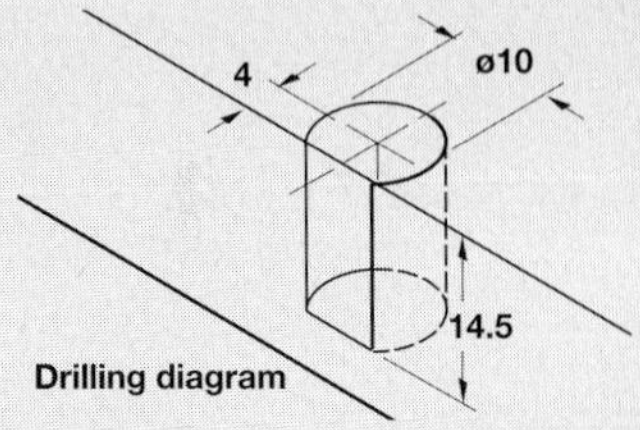

Shelf Support

With galvanized steel pin insert, ø 5 mm; for wood thicknesses from **18 mm upwards.**

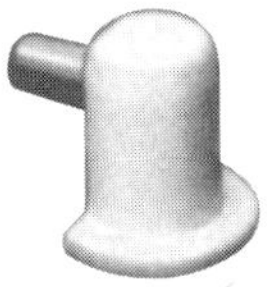

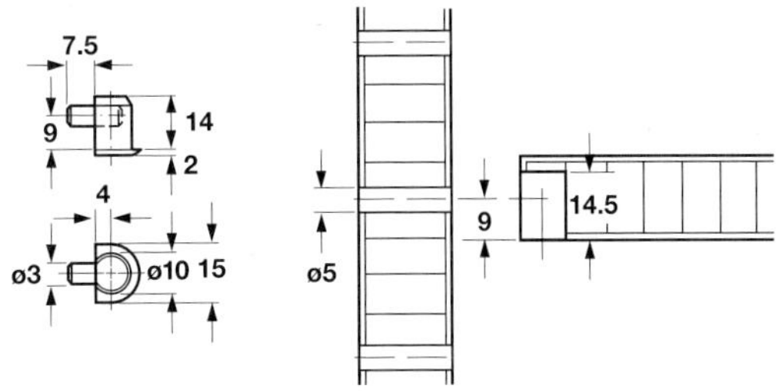

Finish: Plastic

Cat. No.		
	brown	282.81.129
	beige	282.81.423
	white	282.81.727

Packing: 2500 pcs.

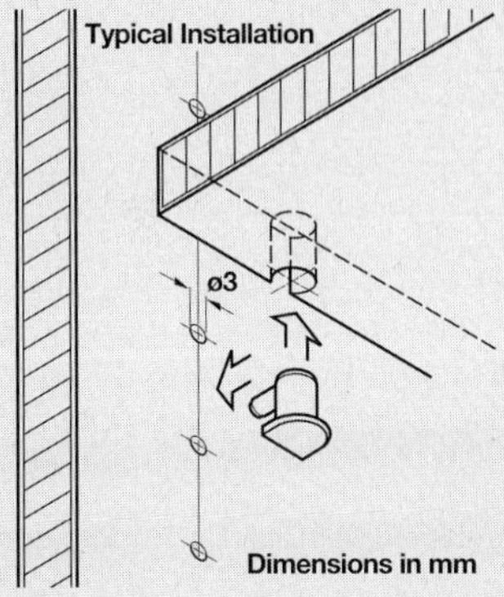

Shelf Support

With galvanized steel pin insert, ø 3 mm; for wood thicknesses from **24 mm upwards.**

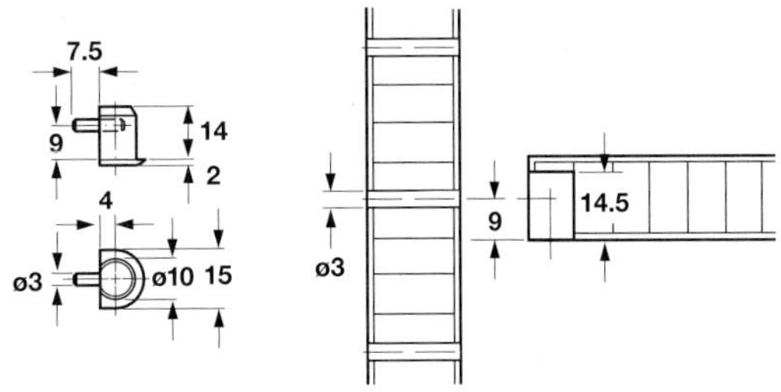

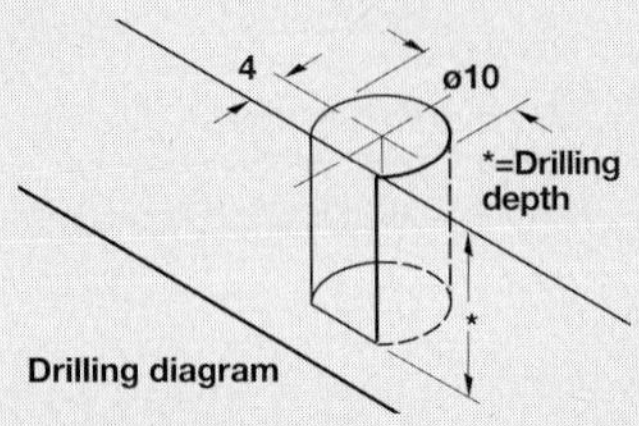

Finish: Plastic

Cat. No.		
	brown	282.81.174
	beige	282.81.478
	white	282.81.772

Packing: 1000 pcs.

Dimensional data not binding. We reserve the right to alter specifications without notice.

Dimensions in mm

HÄFELE

Metal Shelf Supports

For inserting in drilled holes:

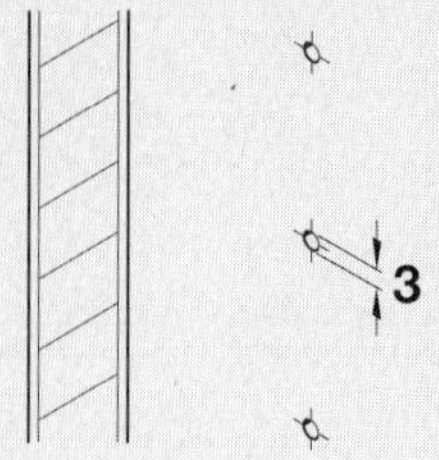

Shelf Support Ø 3 mm

Finish: steel, galvanized

Cat. No.	282.43.914

Packing: 500 pcs.

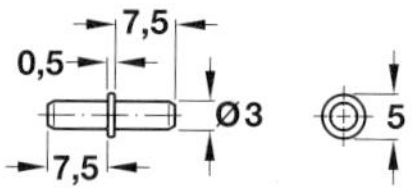

Shelf Support Ø 3 mm

Finish: steel, nickel-plated

Cat. No.	282.43.727

Packing: 5000 pcs.

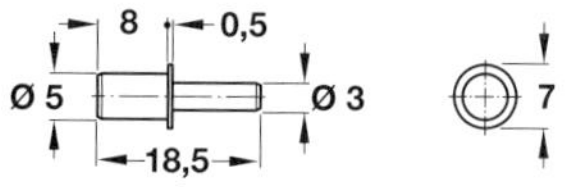

Shelf support Ø 3 mm

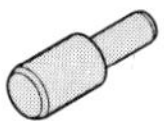

Finish: steel

Cat. No.	nickel-plated	282.06.706
	brass-plated	282.06.500

Packing: 2000 pcs.

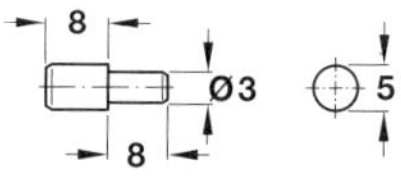

Shelf support Ø 3 mm

Finish: steel

Cat. No.	nickel-plated	282.04.720
	brass-plated	282.04.524

Packing: 5000 pcs.

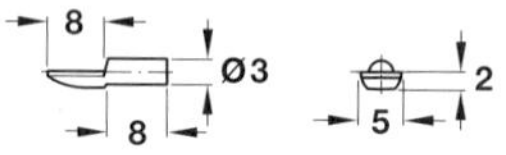

Shelf support Ø 3 mm

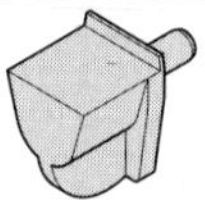

with steel pin
Finish: plastic;
steel pin, galvanized

Cat. No.	clear	282.27.438
	white	282.27.732
	brown	282.27.134
	beige	282.27.536
	clear w/6.9mm pin for 3/8 side panels	282.28.430

Packing: 3000 pcs.

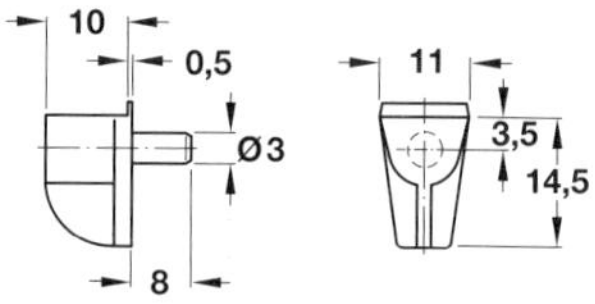

For inserting in drilled holes

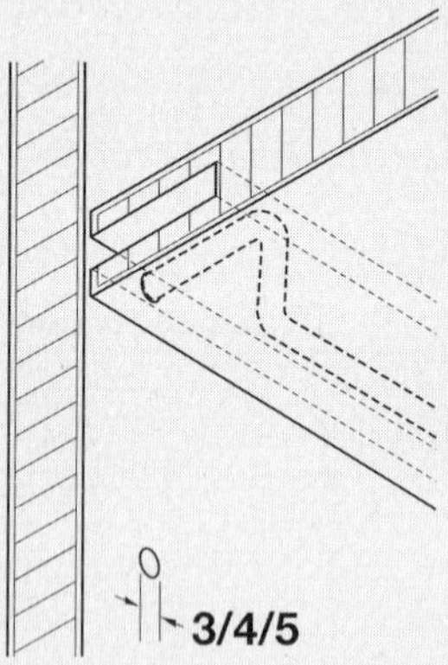

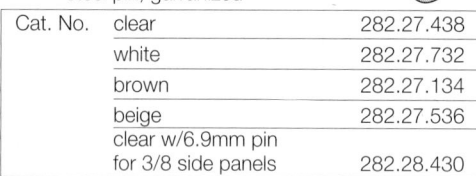

Swedish-type shelf support

Plugs-into two drill-holes to provide invisible mounting for grooved shelf

Finish: **Ø 3 mm** steel wire, nickel-plated

Cat. No.	160 mm length	282.71.703
	224 mm length	282.71.712
	320 mm length	282.71.721

Finish: **Ø 4 mm** steel wire, nickel-plated

Cat. No.	160 mm length	282.72.700
	224 mm length	282.72.719
	320 mm length	282.72.728

Finish: **Ø 5 mm** steel wire, nickel-plated

Cat. No.	160 mm length	282.73.707
	224 mm length	282.73.716
	320 mm length	282.73.725

Packing: 100 pcs.

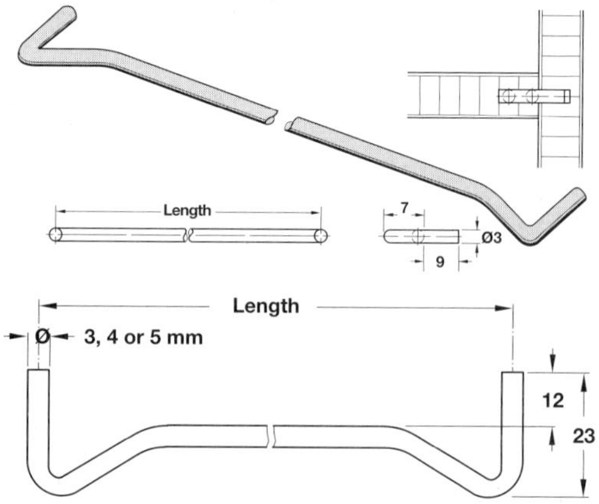

For inserting in drilled holes

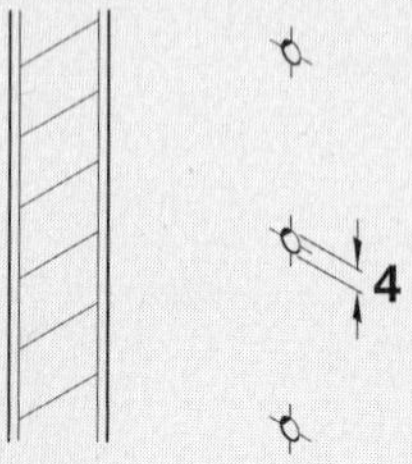

Shelf Support Ø 4 mm

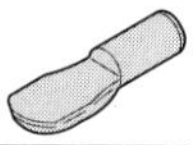

Finish: steel

Cat. No.	nickel-plated	282.04.702
	brass plated	282.04.506

Packing: 500 pcs.

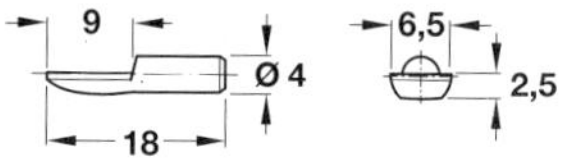

Dimensional data not binding. We reserve the right to alter specifications without notice.

Dimensions in mm

Metal Shelf Supports

HÄFELE

Shelf Support Ø 5 mm
angular, with riveted pin.

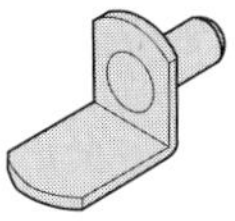

Finish: steel

Cat. No.	brass-plated	282.11.501
	nickel-plated	282.11.707

Packing: 1000 pcs.

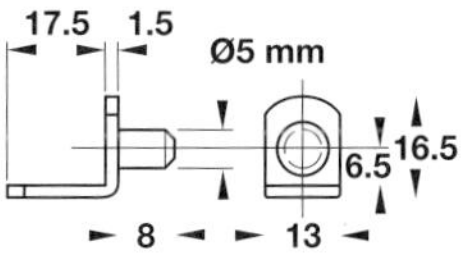

Shelf Support Ø 5 mm
angular, with riveted pin and securing screw hole.
Finish: steel

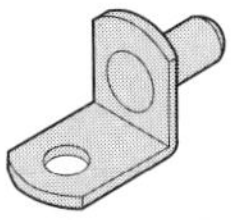

Cat. No.	brass-plated	282.11.510
	nickel-plated	282.11.710
	bronzed	282.11.110

Packing: 1000 pcs.

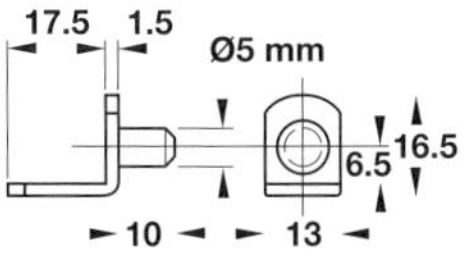

Shelf support Ø 5 mm
Finish: steel

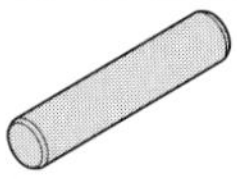

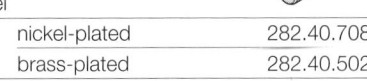

Cat. No.	nickel-plated	282.40.708
	brass-plated	282.40.502

Packing: 5000 pcs.

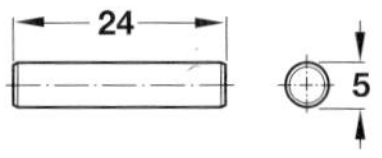

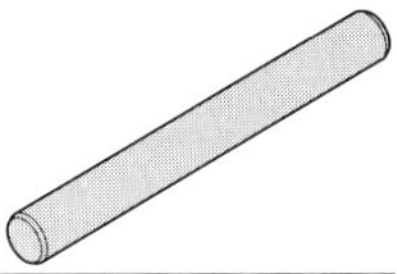

Shelf support Ø 5 mm
Finish: steel, nickel-plated

Cat. No.	282.41.705

Packing: 1000 pcs.

Shelf support with M4 thread
screw-mounts in expanding sleeve
Finish: steel, nickel-plated

Cat. No.	282.39.705

Packing: 500 pcs.

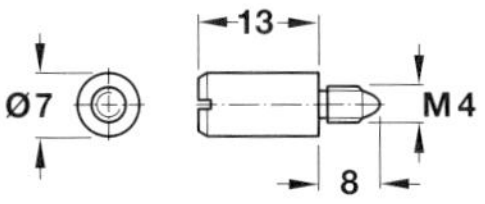

Expanding sleeve with M4 thread
for knocking into Ø 5 mm drilled holes
Finish: brass

Cat. No.	051.45.004

Packing: 3000 pcs.

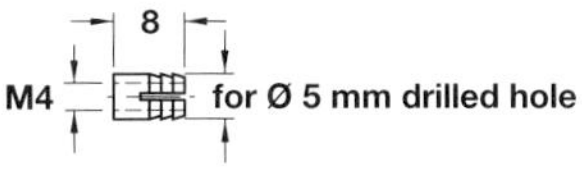

Shelf cap retainer Ø 5 mm
For installation in Ø 5 mm system holes. For shelf thickness of 16 mm.

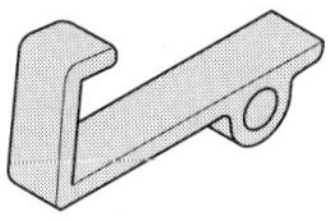

Finish: plastic

Cat. No.	white	282.16.766

Packing: 500 pcs.

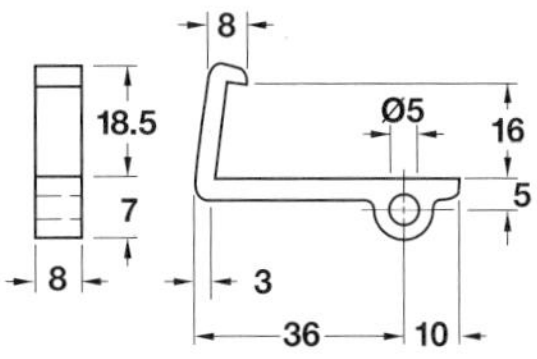

Shelf retainer Ø 5 mm
For installation in Ø 5 mm system holes. For shelf thickness of 19 mm.

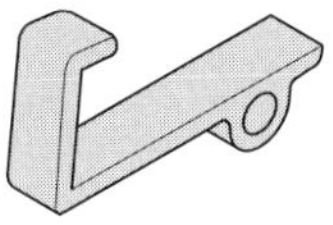

Finish: plastic

Cat. No.	beige	282.16.471
	white	282.16.775

Packing: 500 pcs.

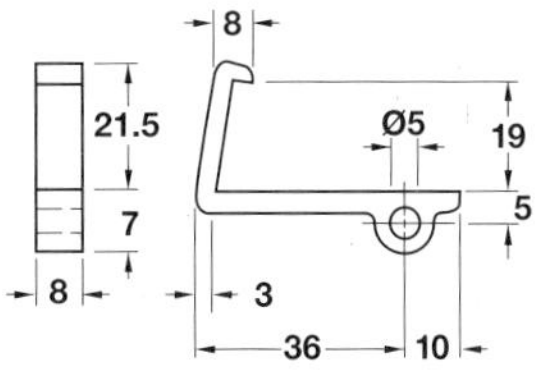

Shelf support Ø 5 mm
Finish: steel

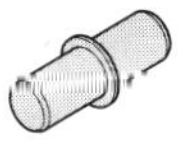

Cat. No.	bronzed	282.43.101
	galvanized	282.43.905

Packing: 1000 pcs.

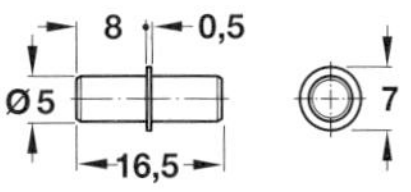

Dimensions in mm

For inserting in drilled holes:

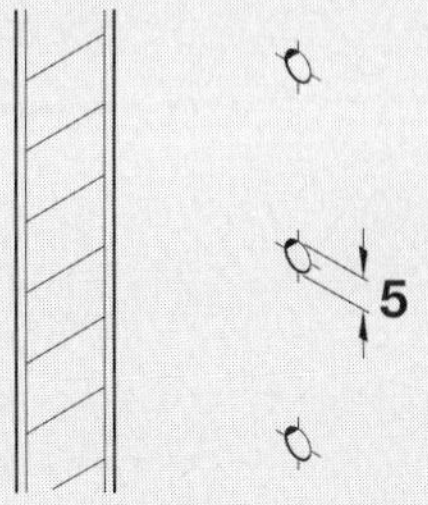

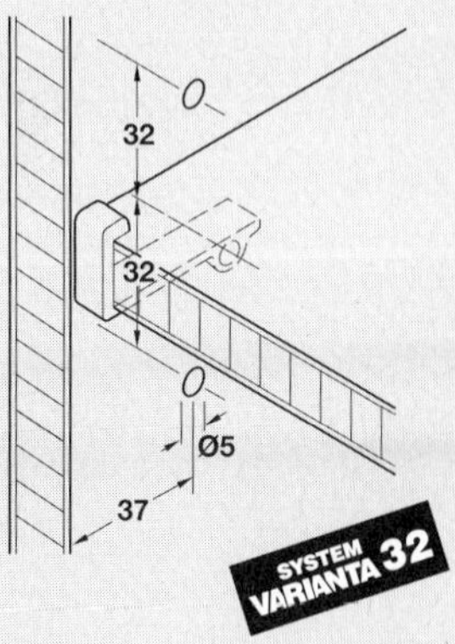

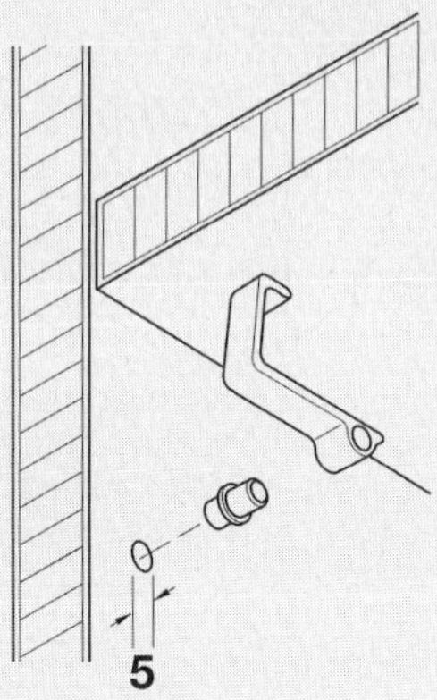

Dimensional data not binding. We reserve the right to alter specifications without notice.

HÄFELE

Metal Shelf Supports

For inserting in drilled holes:

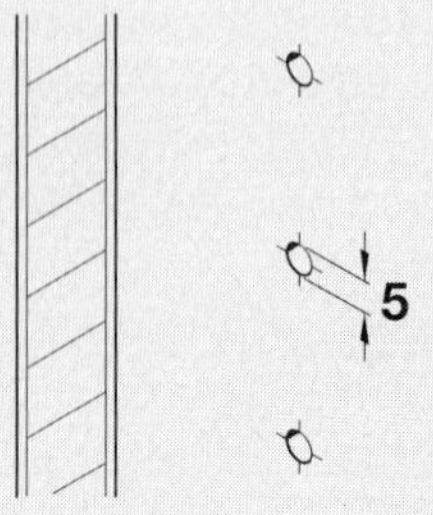

Shelf support Ø 5 mm
Finish: steel, nickel-plated

Cat. No.	282.43.727

Packing: 5000 pcs.

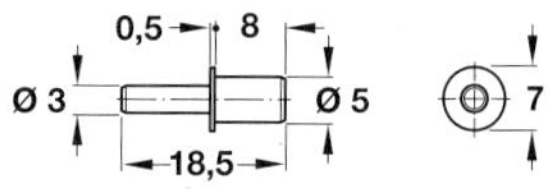

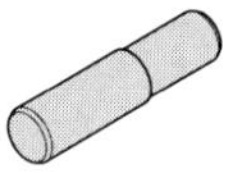

Shelf support Ø 5 mm
Finish: steel, nickel-plated

Catalog No.	282.42.702

Packing: 1000 pcs.

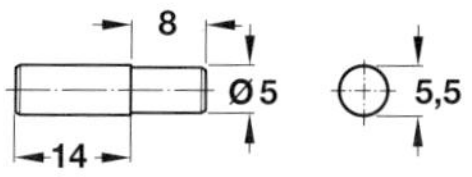

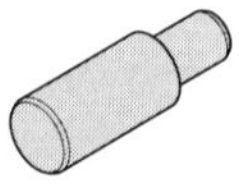

Shelf support Ø 5 mm
Finish: steel

Cat. No.	nickel-plated	282.38.708
	brass-plated	282.38.502

Packing: 500 pcs.

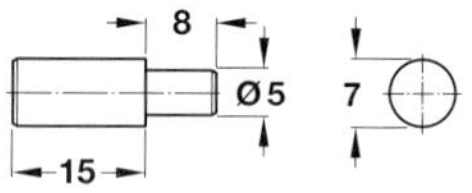

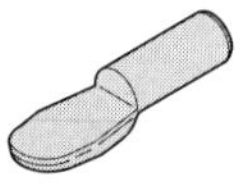

Shelf support Ø 5 mm
Finish: steel

Cat. No.	nickel-plated	282.04.711
	brass-plated	282.04.515
	burnished	282.04.113

Packing: 2000 pcs.

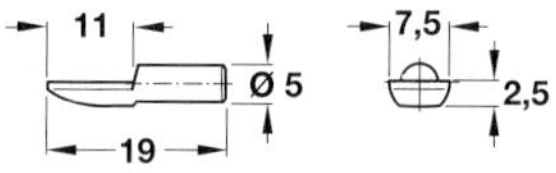

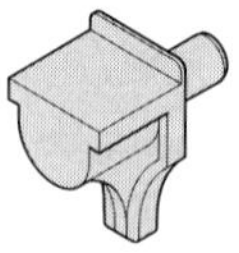

Shelf support Ø 5 mm
with steel pin
Finish: plastic;
steel pin, galvanized

Cat. No.	clear	282.27.401
	white	282.27.705
	brown	282.27.107
	beige	282.27.509
	black	282.27.303

Packing: 3000 pcs.

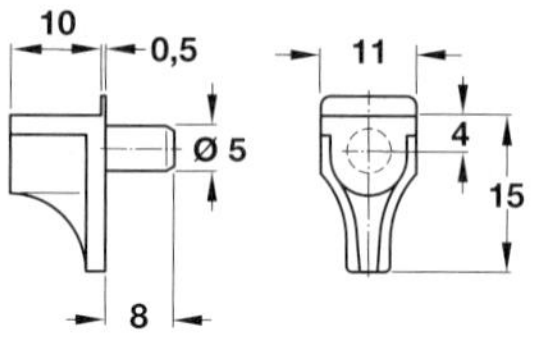

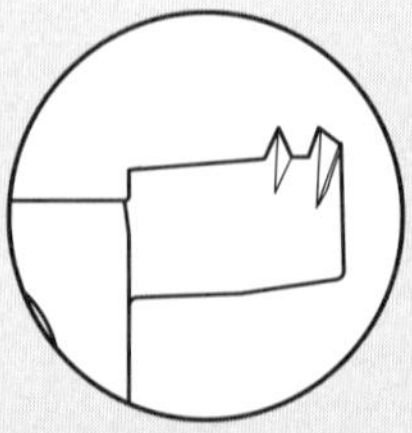

These ribs anchor themselves in the system holes due to pressure from the shelf. This is an important feature for areas prone to earthquakes.

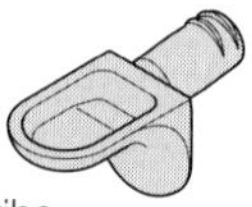

Shelf support Ø 5 mm with 2 wedged ribs
Finish: zinc die-cast

Cat. No.	nickel-plated	282.24.710
	black	282.24.310

Packing: 500 pcs.

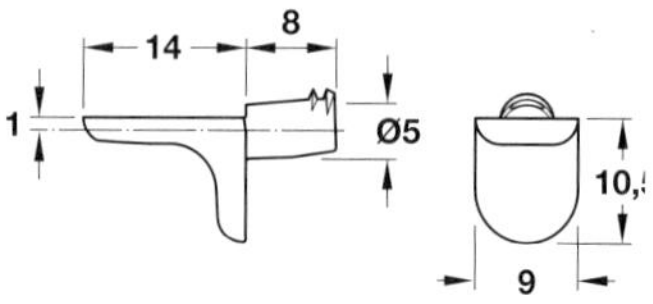

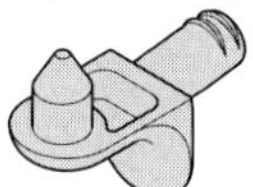

Shelf support Ø 5 mm with 2 wedged ribs and shelf-fixing lug
Finish: zinc die-cast

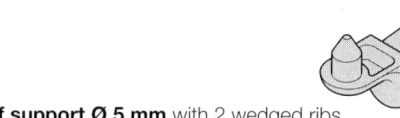

Cat. No.	nickel-plated	282.24.720
	black	282.24.320

Packing: 500 pcs.

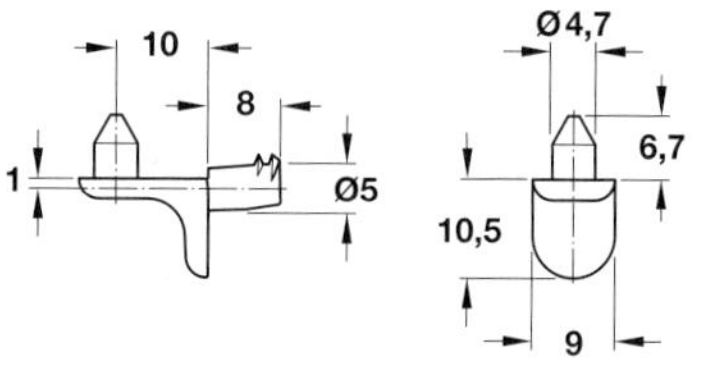

Dimensional data not binding. We reserve the right to alter specifications without notice.

Dimensions in mm

Metal Shelf Supports

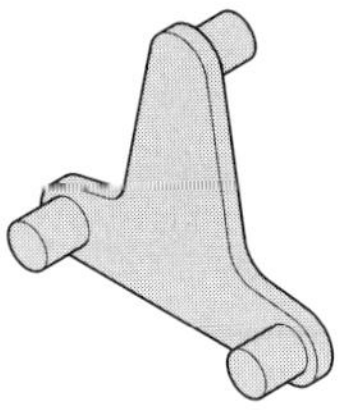

Ex-Cellent H® Ø 5 mm
shelf clamp support for
wood shelves from **16 - 22** mm
Finish: zinc die-cast, nickel-plated

Cat. No.	282.23.725

Packing: 500 pcs.

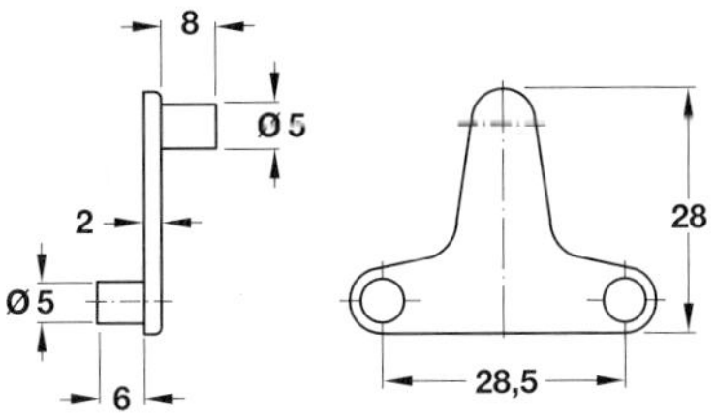

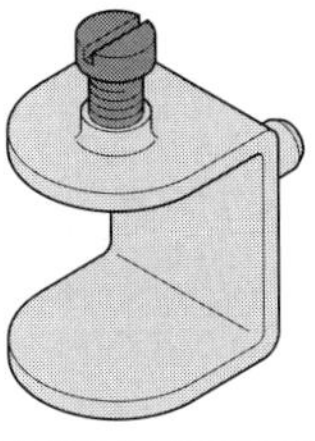

Shelf support Ø 5 mm
with set screw
for **20 mm** wood thickness
Finish: steel, nickel-plated
set screw: plastic

Cat. No.	282.20.751

Packing: 100 pcs.

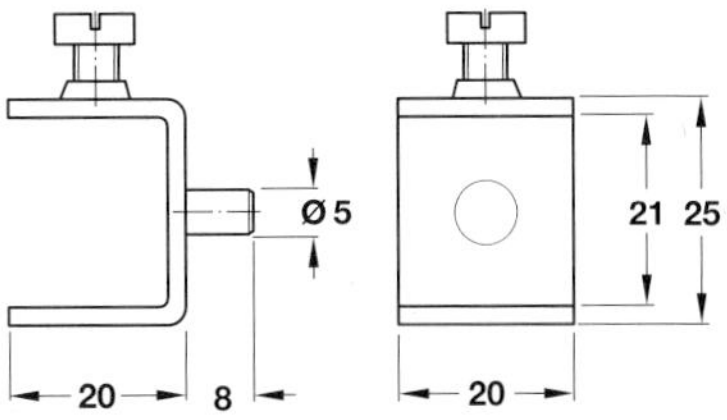

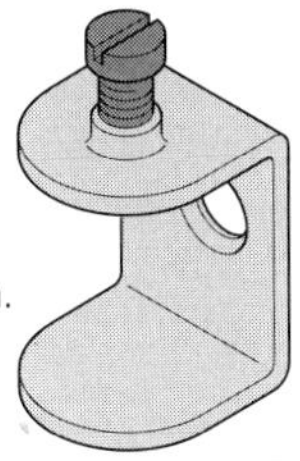

Shelf support for screw-mounting
with set screw, in system holes
for **20 mm** wood thickness, 3 + 5 mm.
mounting with Varianta screw
Finish: steel, nickel-plated
set screw: plastic

Cat. No.	282.19.758

Packing: 100 pcs.

VARIANTA 3 / VARIANTA 5

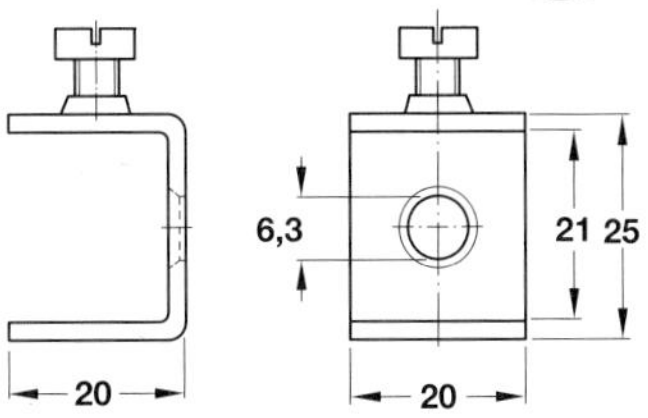

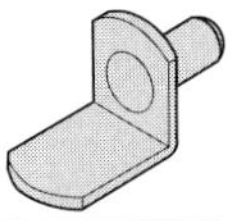

Shelf Support Ø 1/4"
angular, with riveted pin

Finish: steel

Cat. No.		
	brass-plated	282.11.565
	nickel-plated	282.11.761
	bronzed	282.11.163

Packing: 1000 pcs.

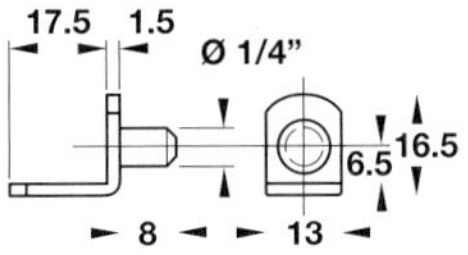

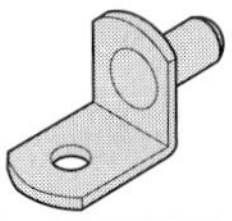

Shelf Support Ø 1/4"
angular, with riveted pin and
securing screw hole

Finish: steel

Cat. No.		
	brass-plated	282.11.556
	nickel-plated	282.11.752
	bronzed	282.11.154

Packing: 1000 pcs.

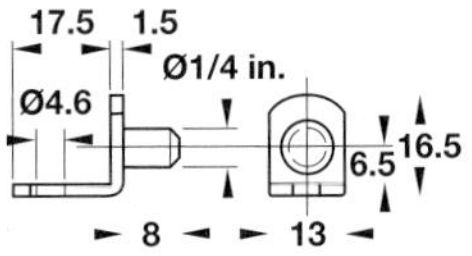

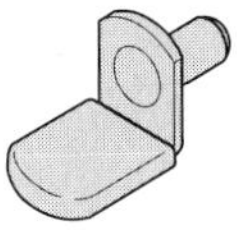

Shelf Support Ø 1/4"
for glass shelves, angular with
riveted pin and protective cover

Finish: steel

Cat. No.	brass-plated	282.11.574

Packing: 1000 pcs.

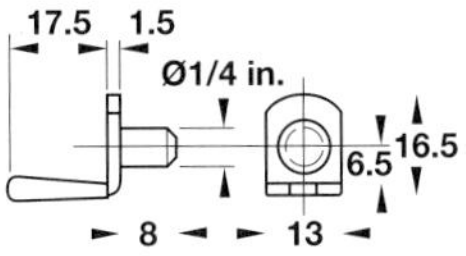

Shelf Support Ø 1/4"
spoon-shaped

Finish: steel

Cat. No.		
	black	282.04.337
	brass-plated	282.04.533
	nickel-plated	282.04.739

Packing: 1000 pcs.

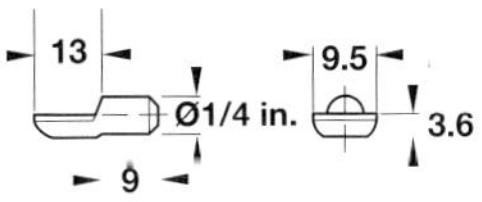

Dimensions in mm

HÄFELE

For inserting in drilled holes:

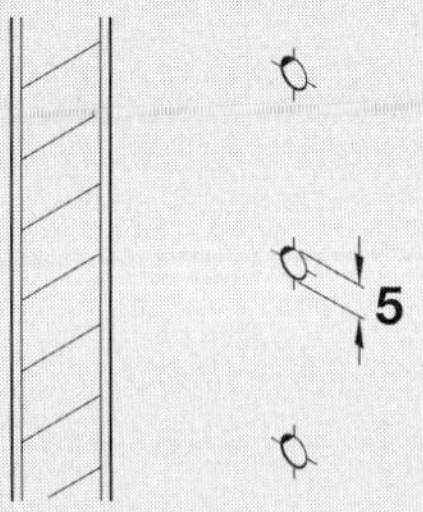

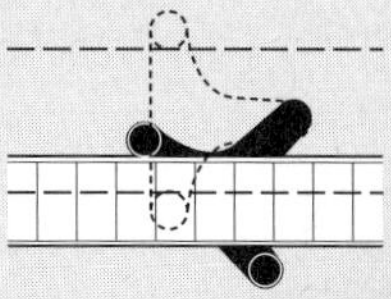

Locks, Catches, RTA and PAS® Fittings
Shelf Supports
Bed Fittings

2

Screw-mounted

Important assembly note
Must be mounted with the **set screw on the top** otherwise the shelf will rest on screw and not on metal bracket as intended.

Mounting screws:
Special Varianta screws
flat head with
PZ 2 cross slots
Finish:
steel, nickel-plated

Length	Cat. No.	
(mm)	Ø 3 mm	Ø 5 mm
10.5	013.15.617	013.15.715
13.5	013.15.626	013.15.724
16.5	013.15.635	013.15.733

Packing: 500 pcs.

Mounting screws:
Special Varianta screws
flat head with
PZ 2 cross slots
Finish:
steel, nickel-plated

Length	Cat. No.
(mm)	Ø 5 mm
10.5	013.14.718
13.5	013.14.727
16.0	013.14.736

Packing: 500 pcs.

For inserting in drilled holes:

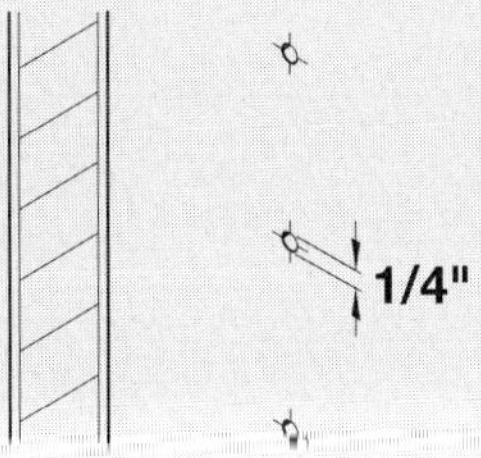

Dimensional data not binding.
We reserve the right to alter specifications without notice.

HÄFELE

Metal Shelf Supports

For inserting in drilled holes:

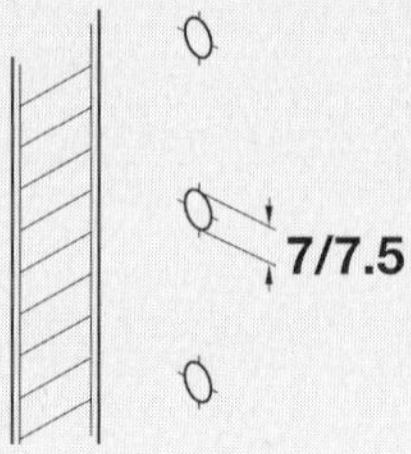

Mounting screws:
Special Varianta screws
flat head with
PZ 2 cross slots
Finish:
steel, nickel-plated

Length (mm)	Cat. No. Ø 3 mm	Cat. No. Ø 5 mm
10.5	013.15.617	013.15.715
13.5	013.15.626	013.15.724
16.5	013.15.635	013.15.733

Packing: 500 pcs.

Mounting screws:
Special Varianta screws
flat head with
PZ 2 cross slots
Finish:
steel, nickel-plated

Length (mm)	Cat. No. Ø 5 mm
10.5	013.14.718
13.5	013.14.727
16.0	013.14.736

Packing: 500 pcs.

Please order separately:

mounting screws:
Hospa particle board screws
countersunk head with
PZ 2 cross slots
Finish:
steel

length	nickel-plated
17 mm	015.35.646
20 mm	015.35.655

Packing: 1000 pcs.

Shelf support Ø 7 mm
inserted to grommet shown
Finish: steel

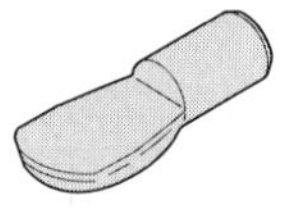

Cat. No.		
Cat. No.	nickel-plated	282.01.701
	brass-plated	282.01.505

Packing: 500 pcs.

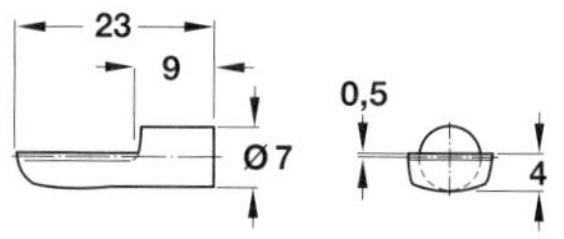

Grommet for shelf support shown above
Ø 7.5 mm drilled hole
Finish: steel

Cat. No.	nickel-plated	282.50.704
	brass-plated	282.50.508

Packing: 500 pcs.

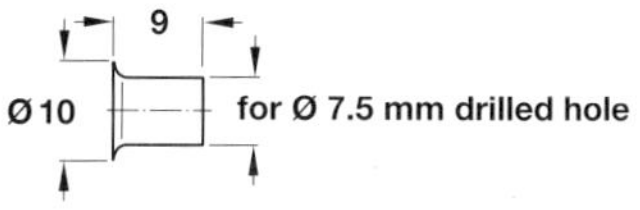

Shelf support Ø 7 mm
inserted to grommet shown
Finish: steel, nickel-plated

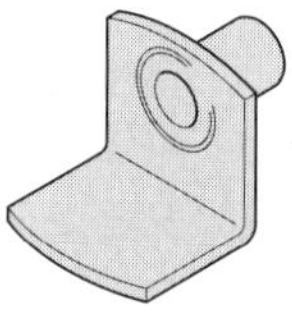

Cat. No.	282.10.700

Packing: 1000 pcs.

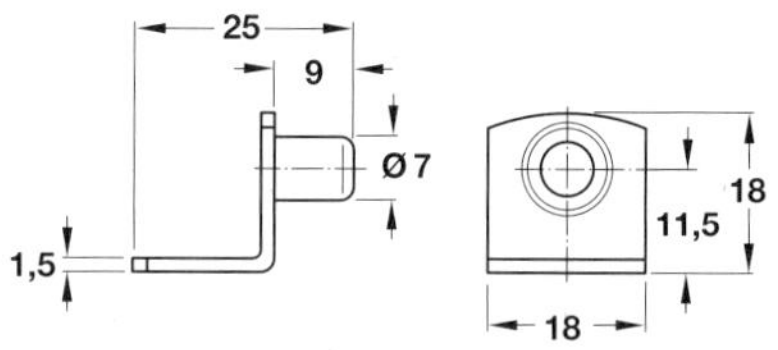

Grommet for shelf support shown above
Ø 7.5 mm drilled hole
Finish: steel, nickel-plated

Cat. No.	282.50.704

Packing: 1000 pcs.

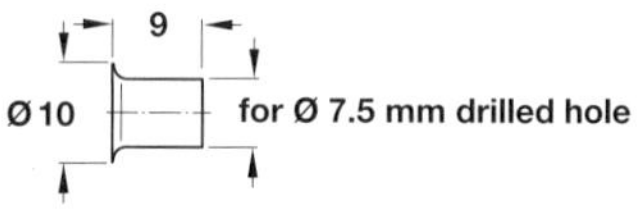

Twist drill bit
for Ø 7.5 mm sleeve

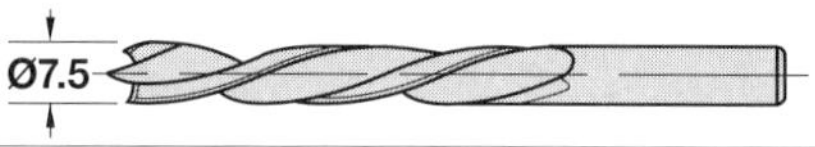

Cat. No.	001.20.061

Packing: 1 pc.

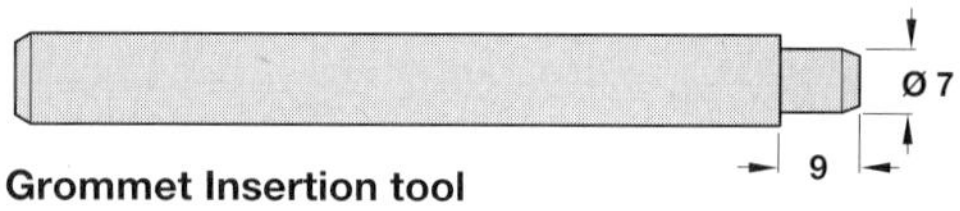

Grommet Insertion tool
Ø 7,5 mm

Cat. No.	006.36.751

Packing: 1 pc.

Shelf support screw-mounted
in Ø 5 mm series holes. 3 + 5 mm.
Features shelf-fixing lug
Finish: zinc die-cast

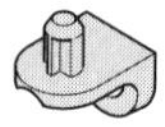

Cat. No.	nickel-plated	282.24.704
	burnished	282.24.106

Packing: 500 pcs.

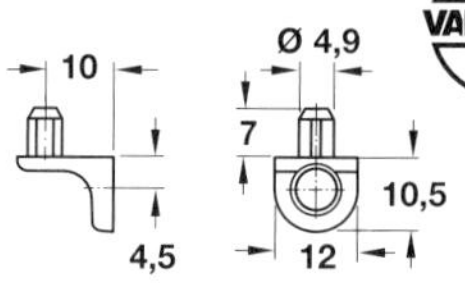

Shelf support for screw-mounting
with cap, also suitable for glass shelves
Finish: zinc die-cast, plastic cap

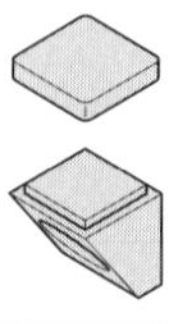

Cat. No.	nickel-plated	282.18.706
	burnished	282.18.108

Packing: 1000 pcs.

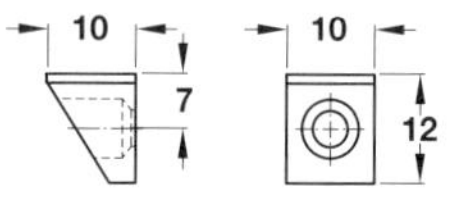

Dimensional data not binding.
We reserve the right to alter
specifications without notice.

Metal Shelf Supports

Standard 10 x 5 mm
for shelf support 14 x 10 mm
Finish: steel, nickel-plated

Cat. No.	283.05.017

Packing: 3.5 m

Shelf support 14 x 10 mm
for standard 10 x 5 mm, standard
Finish: steel, galvanized

Cat. No.	283.51.920

Packing: 1000 pcs.

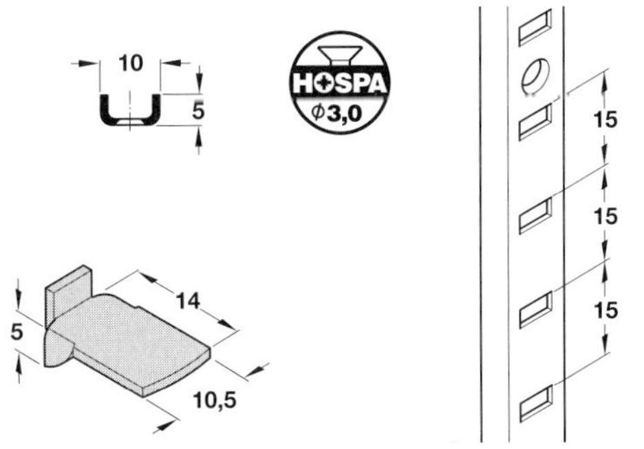

Standard 16 x 6 mm
for shelf support 28 x 16 mm
Finish: steel, nickel-plated

Cat. No.	283.07.011

Packing: 3.5 m

Shelf support 28 x 16 mm
for 16 x 6 mm, standard
Finish: steel, galvanized

Cat. No.	283.61.926

Packing: 200 pcs.

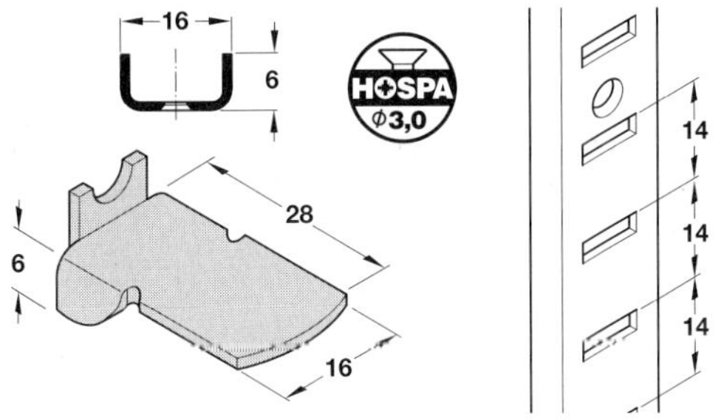

Standard 20 x 8 mm
for shelf support 34 x 15 mm
Finish: aluminum, silver colored anodized

Cat. No.	283.13.911

Packing: 5 m

Shelf support 34 x 15 mm
for 20 x 8 mm, standard
Finish: aluminum, silver colored anodized

Cat. No.	283.64.918

Packing: 100 pcs.

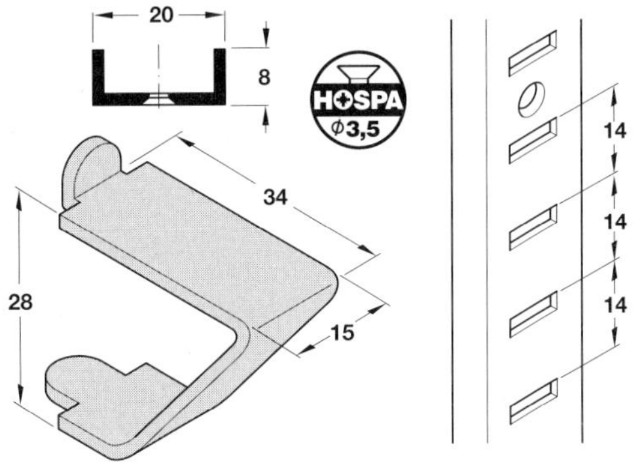

Standard*
25 mm intervals, for shelf supports
Finish: aluminum

Cat. No.	silver anodized	283.12.905
	gold anodized	283.12.807

Packing: 3.5 m

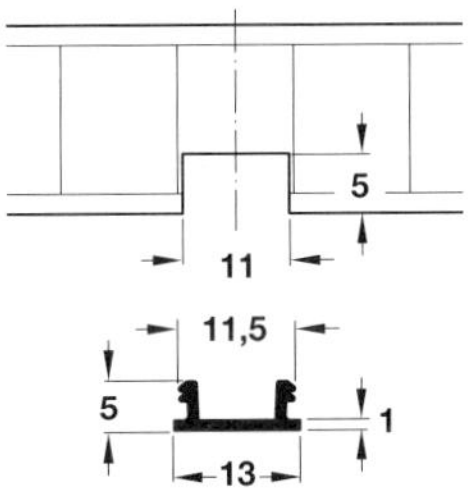

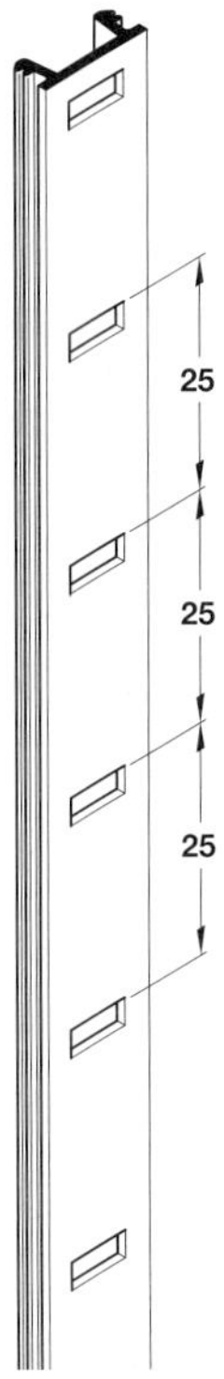

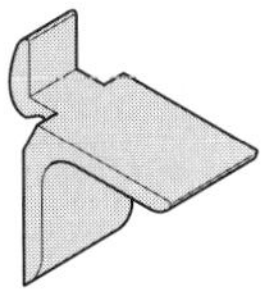

Shelf support
for the above standards at 25 mm intervals
Finish: aluminum

Cat. No.	silver anodized	283.68.907
	gold anodized	283.68.809

Packing: 200 pcs.

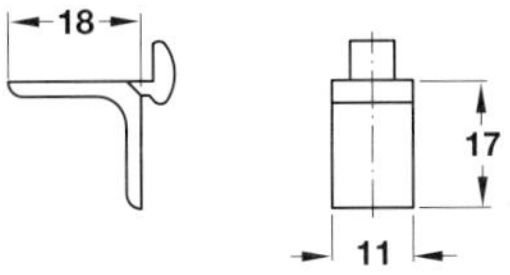

Dimensions in mm

Shelf support systems
For screw-mounted

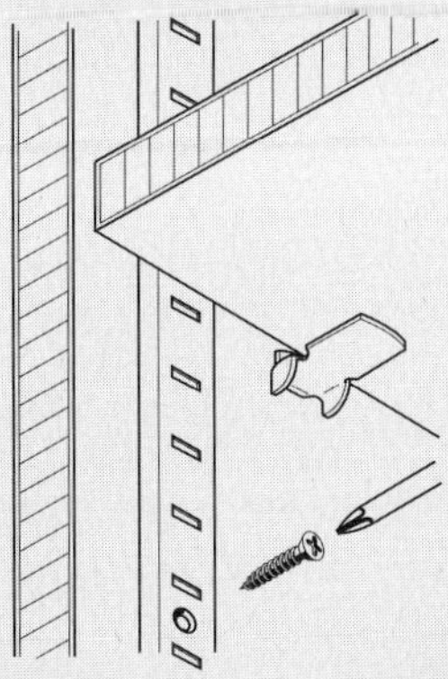

Mounting screws:
Hospa particle board screws
countersunk head with
PZ 2 cross slots
Finish:
steel, galvanized
HOSPA Φ3,0

length	Cat. No.
13 mm	015.31.522
15 mm	015.31.531
17 mm	015.31.540

Packing: 1000 pcs.

Mounting screws:
Hospa particle board screws
countersunk head with
PZ 2 cross slots
Finish:
steel, galvanized
HOSPA Φ3,5

length	Cat. No.
13 mm	015.31.620
15 mm	015.31.639
17 mm	015.31.648

Packing: 1000 pcs.

*For knocking into groove

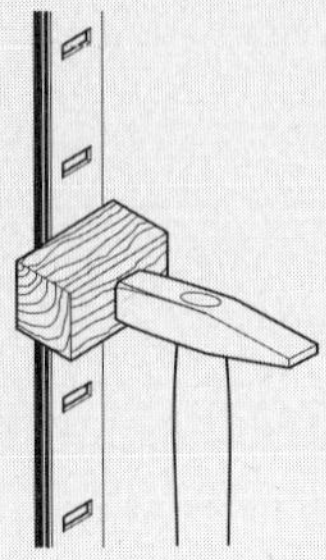

Dimensional data not binding.
We reserve the right to alter
specifications without notice.

HÄFELE

Plastic Shelf Supports

For inserting in drilled holes:

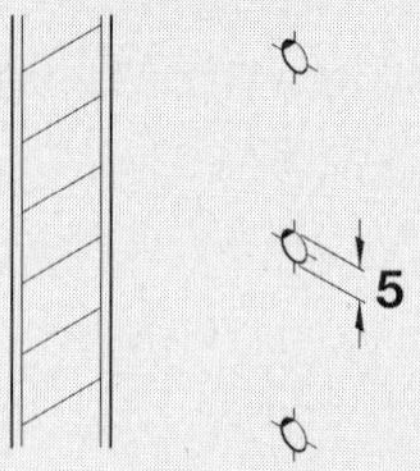

Shelf support Ø 5 mm
Finish: plastic

Cat. No.	white	282.36.704
	brown	282.36.106

Packing: 5000 pcs.

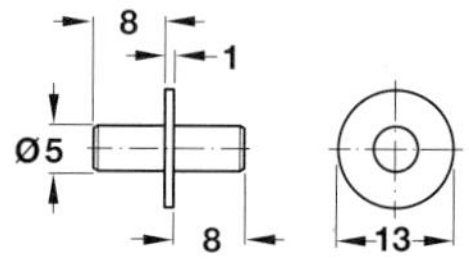

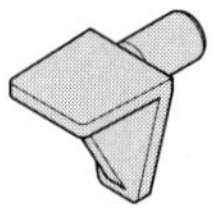

Shelf support Ø 5 mm
Finish: plastic

Cat. No.	white	283.63.715
	brown	283.63.117

Packing: 5000 pcs.

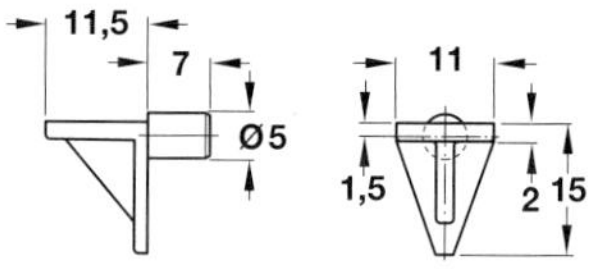

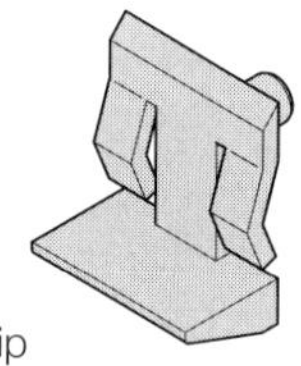

Shelf support Ø 5 mm with spring clip
Finish: plastic

Cat. No.	white	282.33.703
	brown	282.33.105
	black	282.33.301
	beige	282.33.409

Packing: 500 pcs.

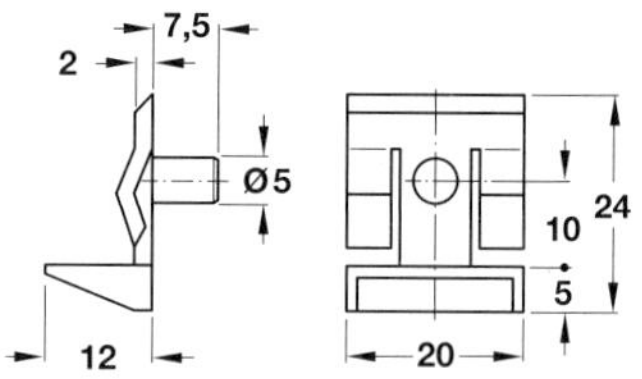

Shelf Support Ø 5 mm
angular, with collar

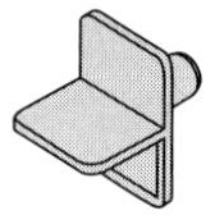

Finish: plastic

Cat. No.	brown	282.22.111
	beige	282.22.415
	white	282.22.719
	clear	282.22.013

Packing: 1000 pcs.

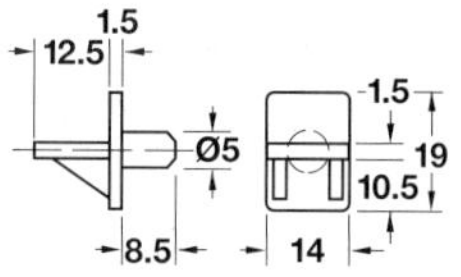

Shelf Support Ø 5 mm
angular form

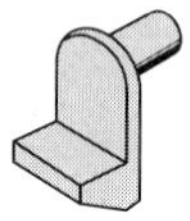

Finish: plastic

Cat. No.	white	282.37.701

Packing: 500 pcs.

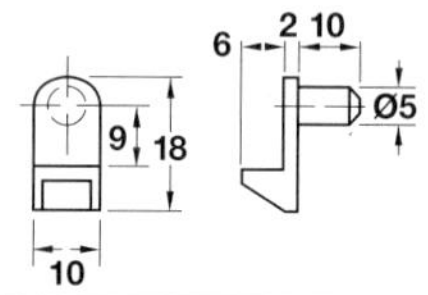

Shelf Support Ø 5 mm
to provide invisible mounting for grooved shelf
Finish: plastic

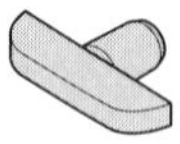

Cat. No.	brown	282.21.105
	white	282.21.703

Packing: 1000 pcs.

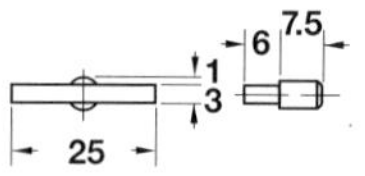

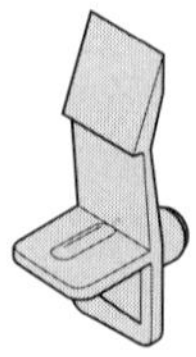

Shelf Support Ø 5 mm
with grooved plug and spring clip,
for wood shelves **16 mm (5/8") thick**

Finish: plastic

Cat. No.	beige	282.17.423
	white	282.17.727

Packing: 5000 pcs.

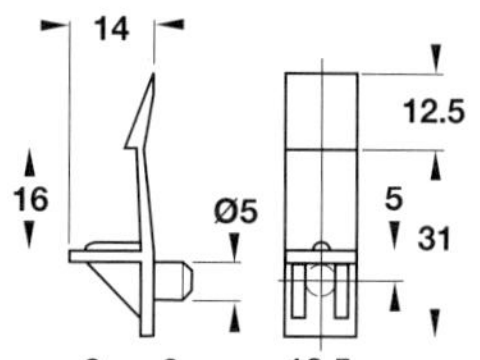

Plastic Shelf Supports

Shelf Support Ø 5 mm
with grooved plug and spring clip, for wood shelves **19 mm (3/4")** thick

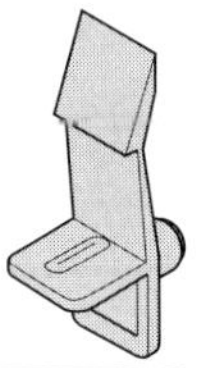

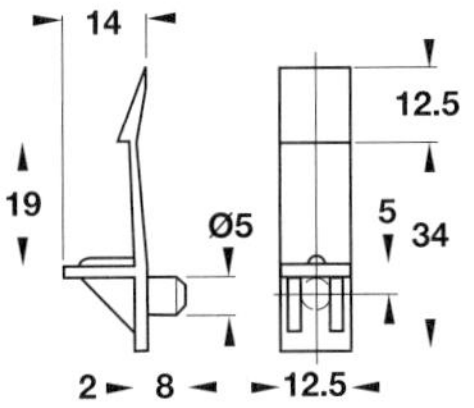

Finish: plastic

Cat. No.	beige	282.17.432
	white	282.17.736

Packing: 500 pcs.

Shelf support Ø 5 mm
with additional screw-mounting possibility on shelf and side panel
Finish: plastic

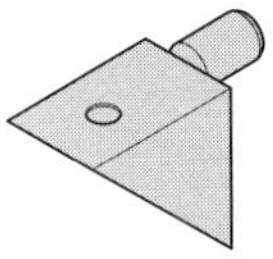

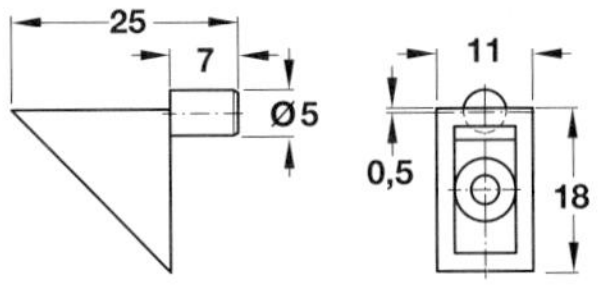

Cat. No.	white	283.50.709
	brown	283.50.101

Packing: 1000 pcs.

HOSPA Ø3,0

Shelf support Ø 5 mm
with expanding sleeve and premounted screw
Finish: plastic

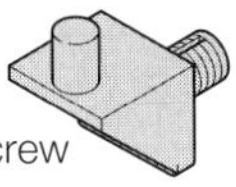

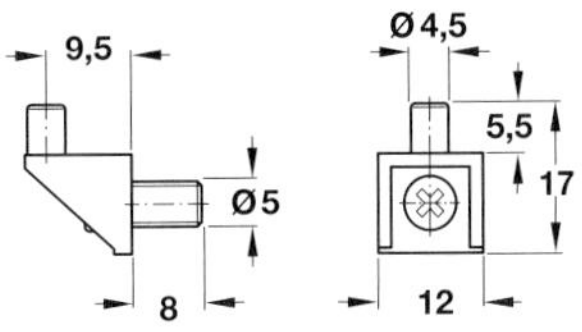

Cat. No.	white	282.25.710
	brown	282.25.112

Packing: 1000 pcs.

Shelf support Ø 6 mm
Finish: plastic

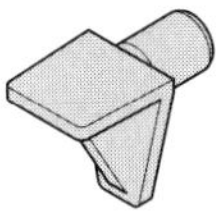

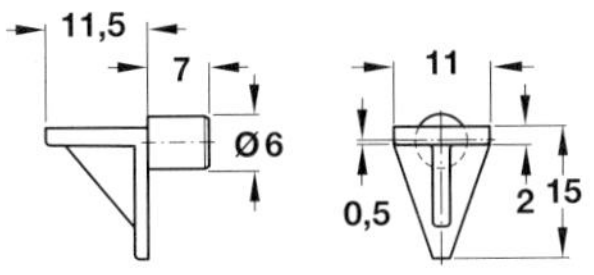

Cat. No.	white	283.63.706
	brown	283.63.108

Packing: 5000 pcs.

Shelf support Ø 6 mm
for standards with system holes

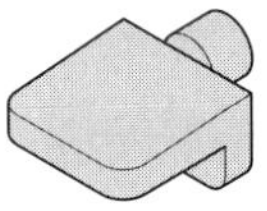

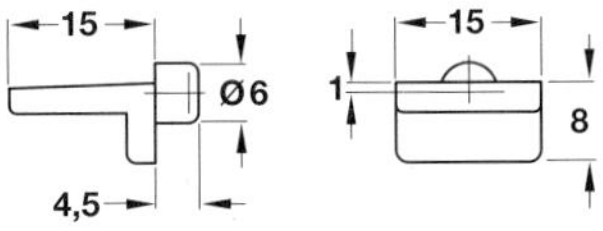

Finish: plastic

Cat. No.	283.48.718

Packing: 100 pcs.

For inserting in system holes:

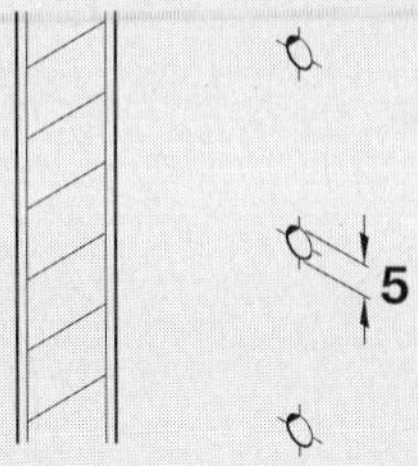

Mounting screws:
Hospa particle board screws **countersunk head** with PZ 2 cross slots
Finish:
steel, galvanized

HOSPA Ø3,0

length	Cat. No.
13 mm	015.31.522
15 mm	015.31.531
17 mm	015.31.540

Packing: 1000 pcs.

Screw-mounted with additional shelf attachment.

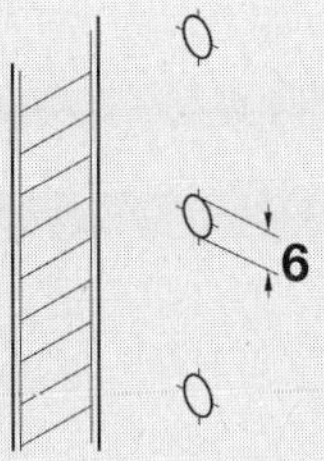

Dimensional data not binding. We reserve the right to alter specifications without notice.

Dimensions in mm

HÄFELE

Plastic Shelf Supports

For inserting in drilled holes:

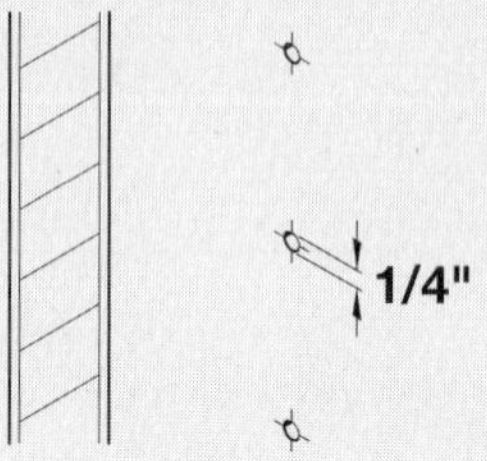

2
Locks, Catches, RTA
and PAS® Fittings
Shelf Supports
Bed Fittings

Shelf Support Ø 1/4"
angular, with collar and grooved plug

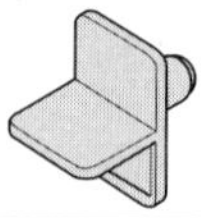

Finish: plastic

Cat. No.		
	brown	282.22.120
	beige	282.22.424
	white	282.22.728
	clear	282.22.022

Packing: 1000 pcs.

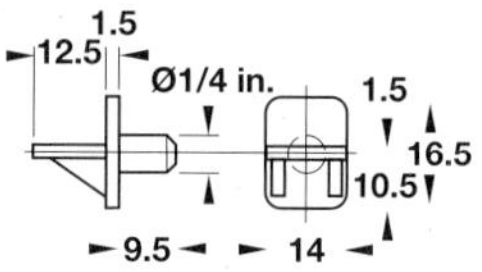

Shelf Support Ø 1/4"
with grooved plug and spring clip, for wood shelves **12 mm (1/2") thick**

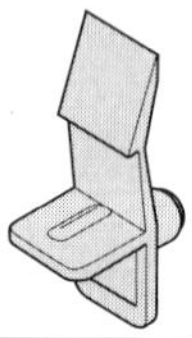

Finish: plastic

Cat. No.		
	beige	282.17.469
	white	282.17.763

Packing: 500 pcs.

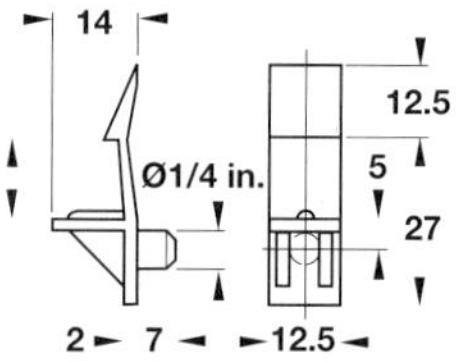

Shelf Support Ø 1/4"
with grooved plug and spring clip, for wood shelves **16 mm (5/8") thick**

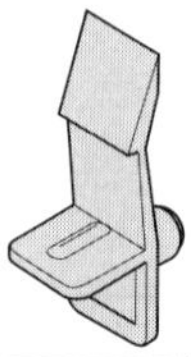

Finish: plastic

Cat. No.		
	beige	282.17.478
	white	282.17.772

Packing: 500 pcs.

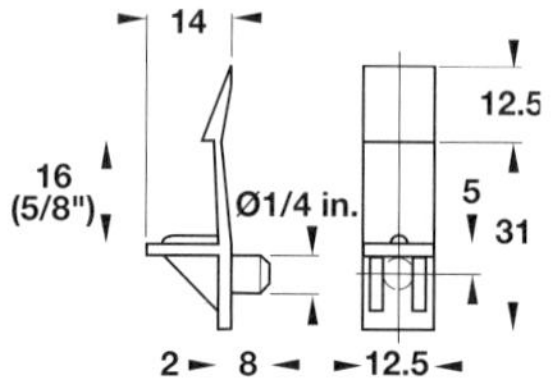

Shelf Support Ø 1/4"
with grooved plug and spring clip, for wood shelves **19 mm (3/4") thick**

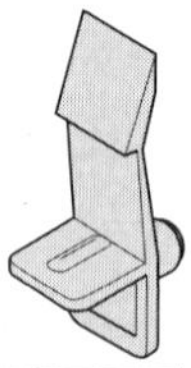

Finish: plastic

Cat. No.		
	beige	282.17.487
	white	282.17.781

Packing: 500 pcs.

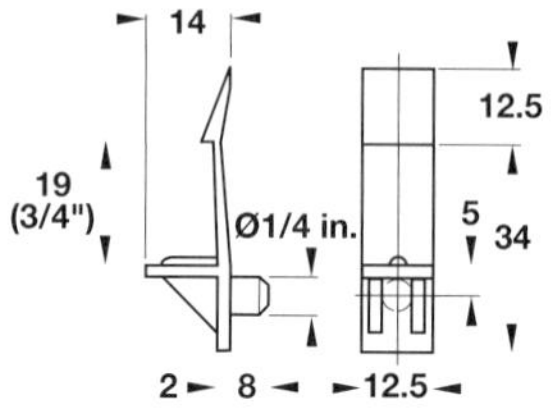

Shelf support
Finish: steel

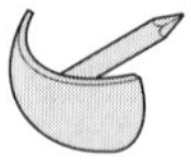

Cat. No.		
	nickel-plated	281.10.705
	brass-plated	281.10.509

Packing: 500 pcs.

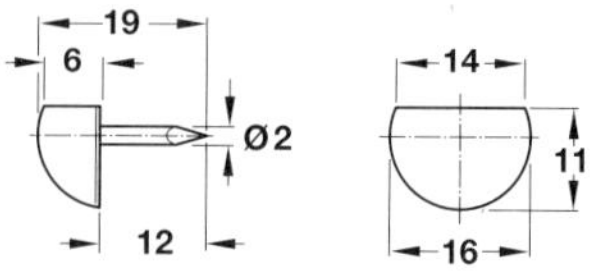

Shelf support
with inserted nail
Finish: steel nail, galvanized
plastic support

Cat. No.		
	white	281.23.702
	brown	281.23.104

Packing: 1000 pcs.

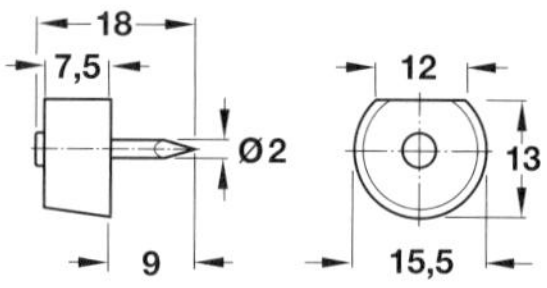

Dimensional data not binding.
We reserve the right to alter specifications without notice.

Dimensions in mm

Plastic Shelf Supports

HÄFELE

For inserting in drilled holes:

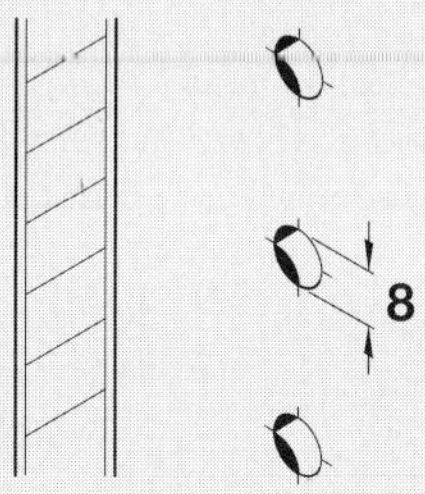

Shelf support with stop
for inserting in grommet shown below
Finish: plastic, white

Cat. No.	282.32.706

Packing: 500 pcs.

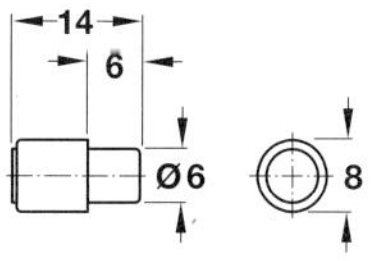

Sleeve for shelf support shown above
Ø 8 mm drilled hole
Finish: plastic, white

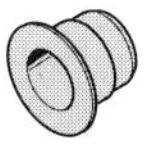

Cat. No.	282.62.704

Packing: 500 pcs.

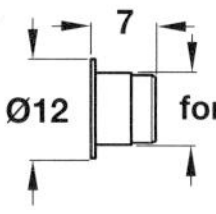

Shelf support
for inserting in grommet shown below
Finish: plastic

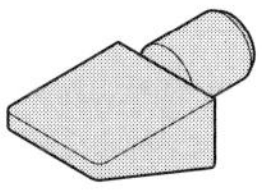

Cat. No.	white	282.34.700
	brown	282.34.102

Packing: 500 pcs.

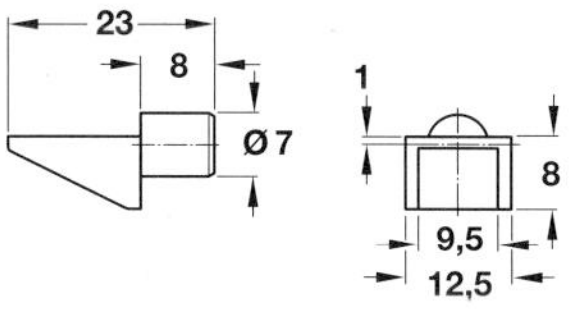

Grommet for shelf support shown above
Ø 10 mm drilled hole
Finish: plastic

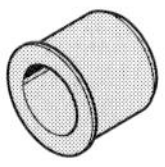

Cat. No.	white	282.64.708
	brown	282.64.100

Packing: 500 pcs.

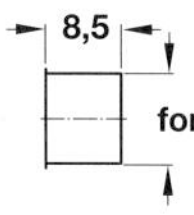

Locks, Catches, RTA and PAS® Fittings
Shelf Supports
Bed Fittings
2

For inserting in drilled holes:

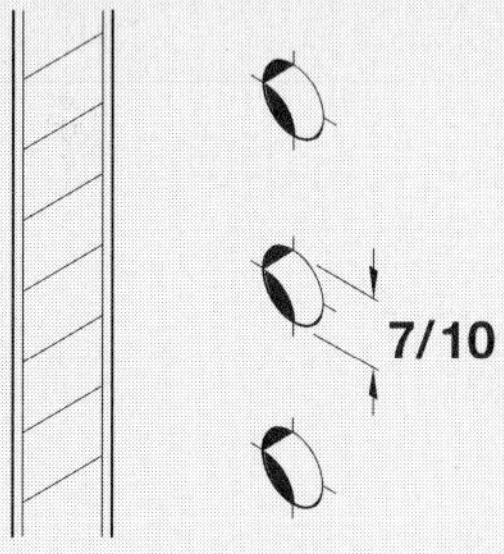

Drill bit (sleeve wood drill) for Ø 8 mm sleeves

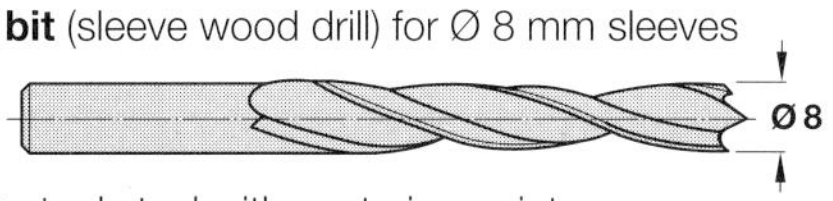

Finish: tool steel with centering point

Cat. No.	001.20.123

Packing: 1 piece

Drill bit (sleeve wood drill) for Ø 10 mm sleeves

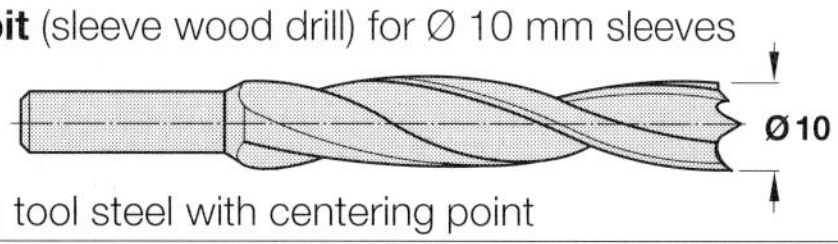

Finish: tool steel with centering point

Cat. No.	001.20.141

Packing: 1 piece

Dimensional data not binding.
We reserve the right to alter specifications without notice.

Dimensions in mm

HÄFELE

Shelf support systems

For knocking into groove

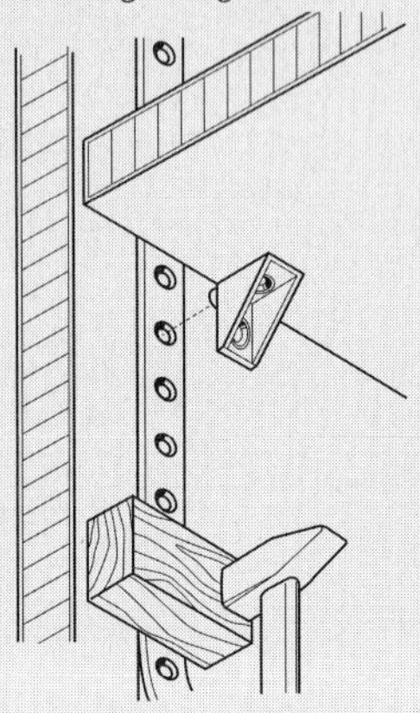

2 **Locks, Catches, RTA and PAS® Fittings**
Shelf Supports
Bed Fittings

Plastic Shelf Supports

Shelf support strip

Finish: plastic

Cat. No.	brown	283.44.112
	beige	283.44.710

Packing: 40 lengths of 2.5 m (98")

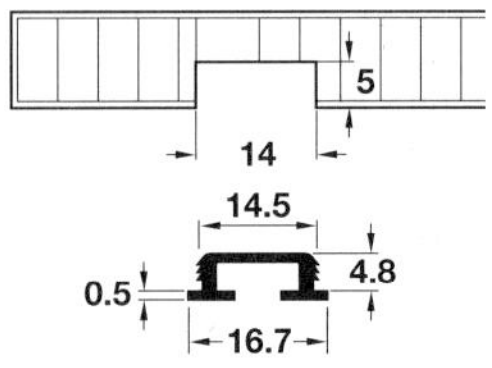

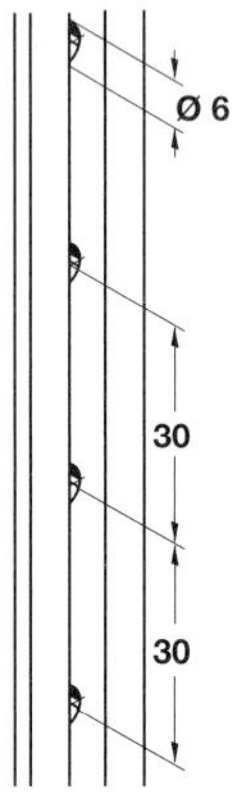

Shelf support

Finish: plastic

Cat. No.	brown	283.52.114
	beige	283.52.712

Packing: 1000 pcs.

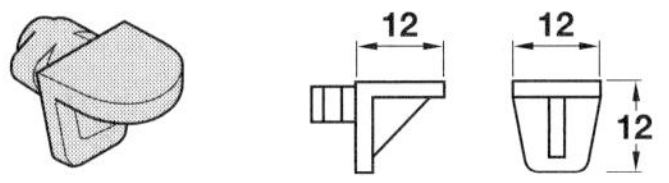

Standard
15 mm intervals, for shelf supports
Finish: plastic

Cat. No.	white	283.45.708
	brown	283.45.100

Packing: 2.5 m (98")

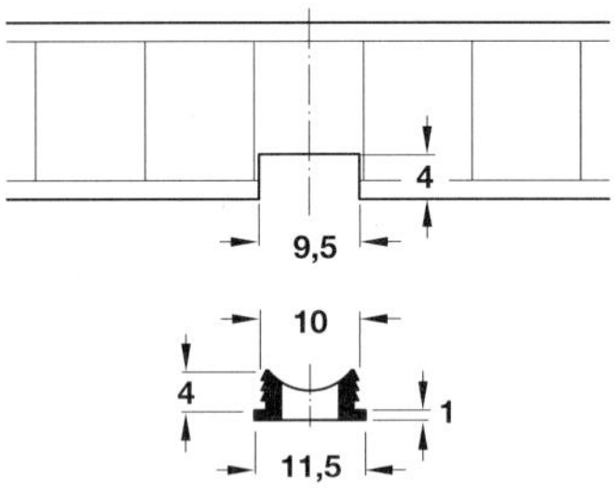

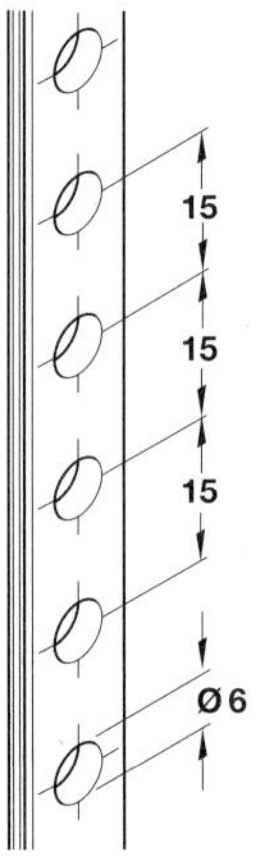

Shelf support
for standard shown above
Finish: plastic

Cat. No.	white	283.49.706
	brown	283.49.108

Packing: 1000 pcs.

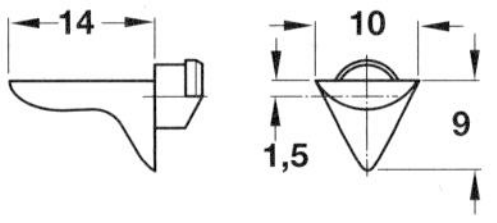

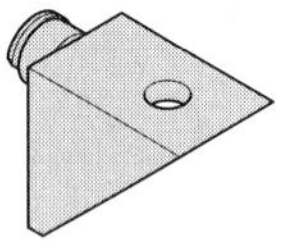

Shelf support
for standard shown above
Finish: plastic

Cat. No.	white	283.47.702
	brown	283.47.104

Packing: 1000 pcs.

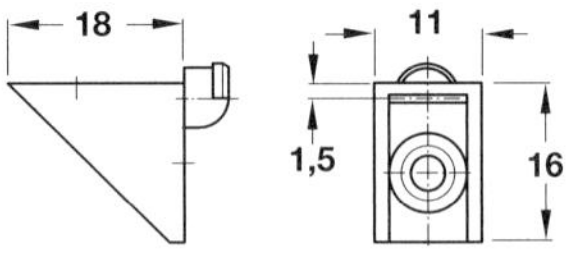

Standard
30 mm intervals, for shelf supports
Finish: plastic (PVC)

Cat. No.	white	283.54.707
	brown	283.54.109

Packing: 2.5 m (98")

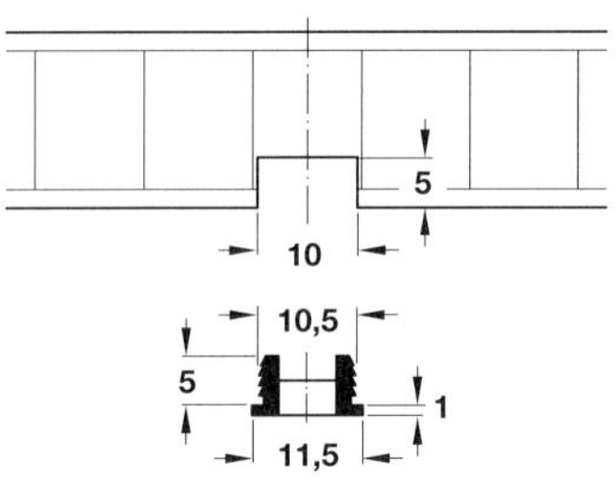

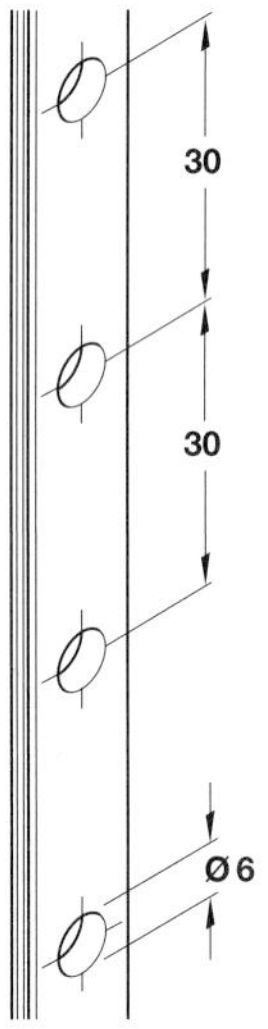

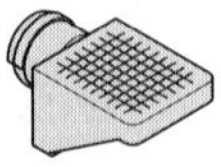

Shelf support
for standard shown above with 30 mm intervals
Finish: plastic (nylon)

Cat. No.	white	283.55.704
	brown	283.55.106

Packing: 1000 pcs.

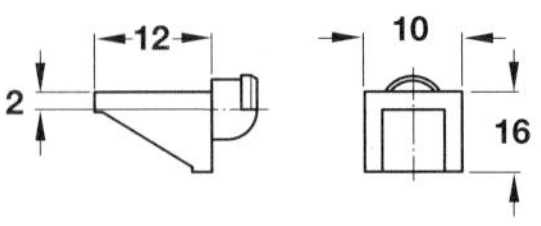

Dimensions in mm

Metal Shelf Supports

Glass shelf support Ø 3 mm with cap
Finish: steel, galvanized
cap: plastic, clear

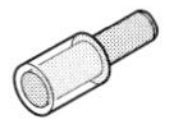

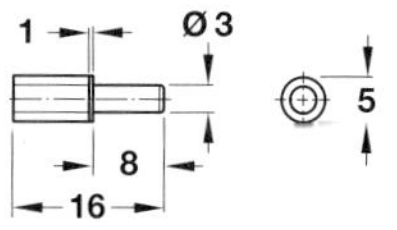

Cat. No	281.40.712

Packing: 500 pcs.

Glass shelf support Ø 3 mm with cap
Finish: steel, nickel-plated
cap: plastic, clear

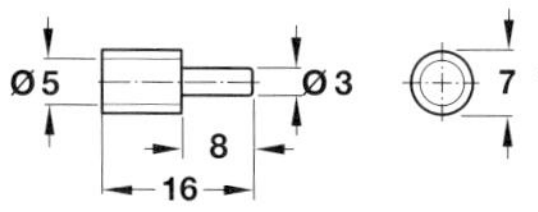

Cat. No.	281.40.703

Packing: 500 pcs.

Glass shelf support Ø 5 mm with cap
Finish: steel, galvanized
cap: plastic,
clear

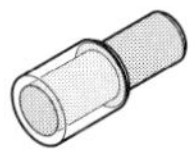

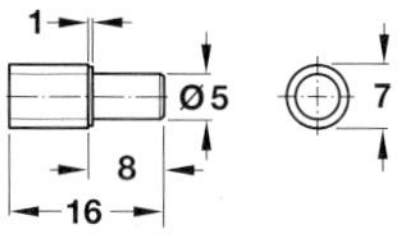

Cat. No.	281.41.906

Packing: 500 pcs.

Glass shelf support Ø 5 mm
with 2 wedged ribs
Finish: zinc die-cast
glass support: plastic, clear

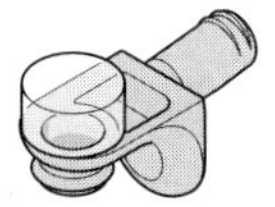

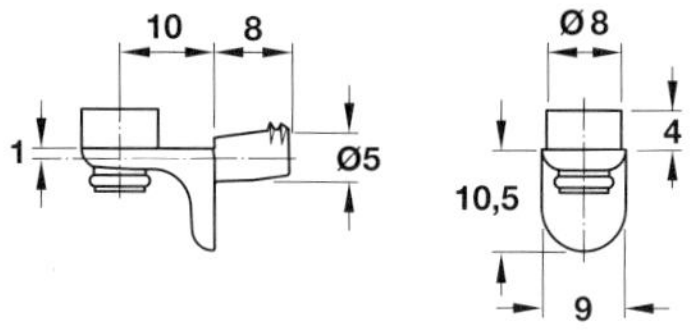

Cat. No.	nickel-plated	282.24.730
	black	282.24.330

Packing: 500 pcs.

Ex-Cellent H® Ø 5 mm
shelf clamp support for
glass shelves from **6 - 10** mm
plastic-coated clamping pins
Finish: zinc die-cast

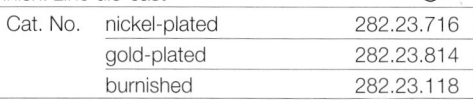

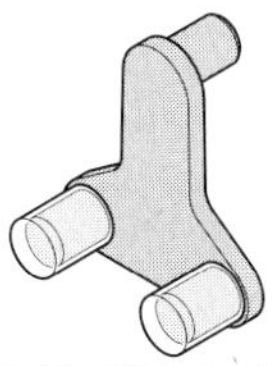

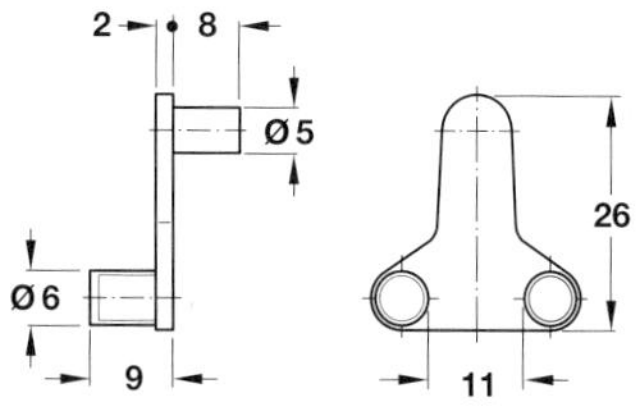

Cat. No.	nickel-plated	282.23.716
	gold-plated	282.23.814
	burnished	282.23.118

Packing: 500 pcs.

Glass shelf support Ø 5 mm
with set screw
for **9 mm** glass thickness
Finish: steel, nickel-plated
set screw: plastic

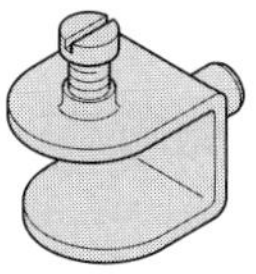

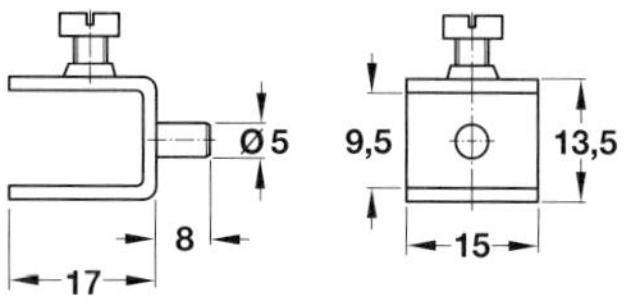

Cat. No.	282.20.715

Packing: 100 pcs.

Glass shelf support Ø 5 mm
with set screw
for **13 mm** glass thickness
Finish: steel, nickel-plated
set screw: plastic

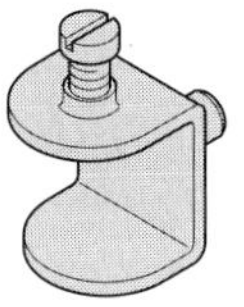

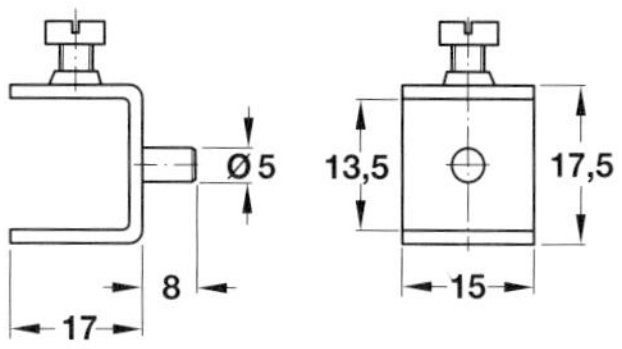

Cat. No.	282.20.724

Packing: 100 pcs.

HÄFELE

For inserting in drilled holes:

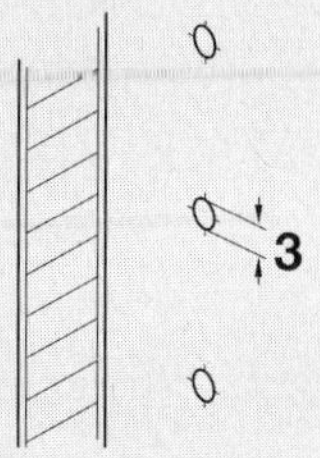

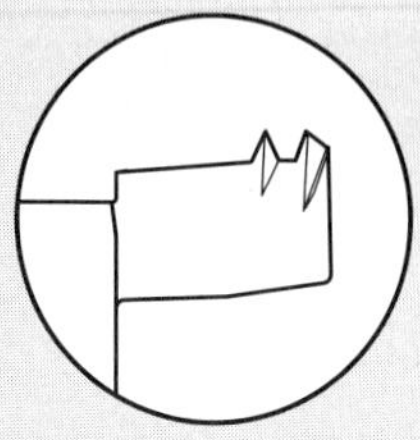

These ribs anchor themselves in the system holes due to pressure from the shelf. This is an important feature for areas prone to earthquakes.

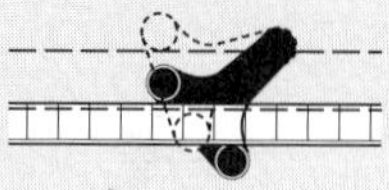

Important assembly note
(for the glass shelf supports with set screws)

To ensure that the set screw functions correctly, the shelf supports must be mounted with **the set screw on the top**.
If the locking screw is on the bottom, the shelf will load it and could cause it to loosen.

For inserting in drilled holes:

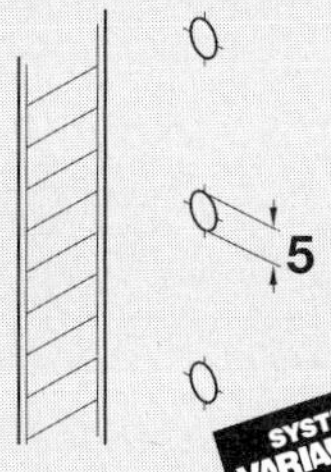

SYSTEM VARIANTA 32

Dimensional data not binding.
We reserve the right to alter specifications without notice.

Dimensions in mm

HÄFELE

Metal Shelf Supports

For inserting in drilled holes:

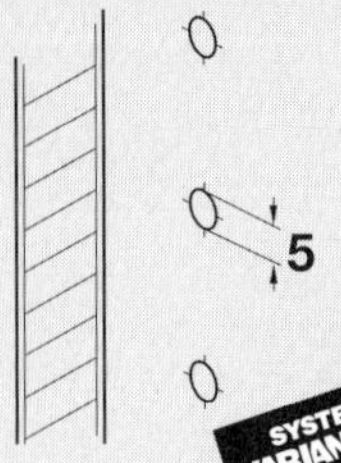

SYSTEM VARIANTA 32

Mounting screws:
Hospa particle board screws **countersunk head** with PZ 2 cross slots
Finish:
steel

HOSPA Φ3,5

length	burnished	nickel-plated
15 mm	015.39.635	015.35.637
17 mm	015.39.644	015.35.646
20 mm	015.39.653	015.35.655

Packing: 1000 pcs.

Glass shelf support Ø 5 mm
with steel pin
for **4 mm** glass thickness
Finish: plastic, clear
pin: steel, nickel-plated

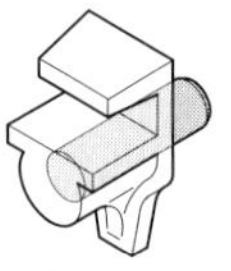

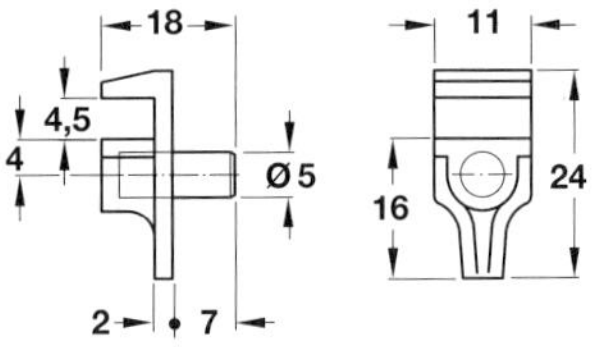

Cat. No.	287.26.445

Packing: 2000 pcs.

Glass shelf support Ø 5 mm
with steel pin
for **5 mm** glass thickness
Finish: plastic, clear
pin: steel, nickel-plated

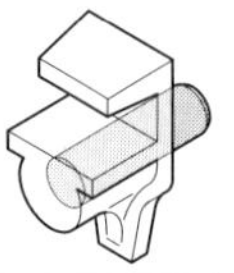

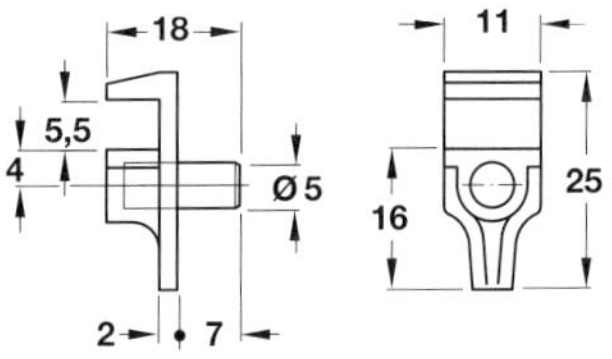

Cat. No.	287.26.454

Packing: 2000 pcs.

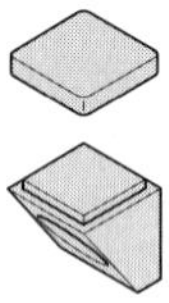

HOSPA Φ3,5

Glass shelf support
for screw-mounted with cap
Finish: zinc die-cast, plastic cap

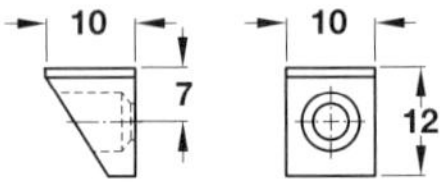

Cat. No.		
	nickel-plated	282.18.706
	burnished	282.18.108

Packing: 1000 pcs.

Dimensional data not binding.
We reserve the right to alter specifications without notice.

Dimensions in mm

Plastic Shelf Supports

For inserting in drilled holes:

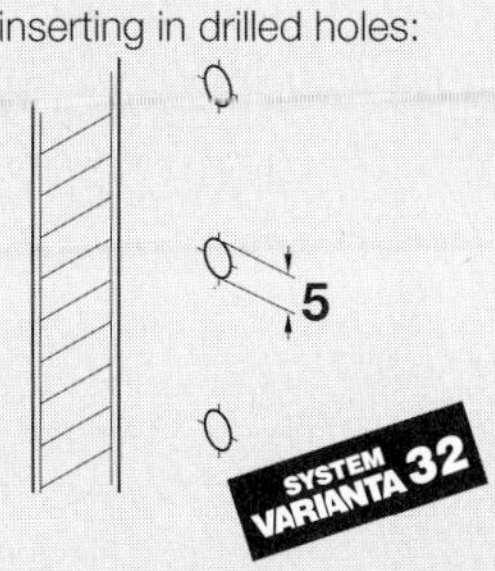

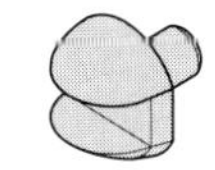

Glass shelf support Ø 5 mm
For glass shelf thickness of 4 mm, 5 mm, and 6 mm
Finish: plastic, white and clear

Cat. No.	white	**4** mm	287.28.743
	white	**5** mm	287.28.752
	white	**6** mm	287.28.770
	clear	**4** mm	287.28.440
	clear	**5** mm	287.28.450
	clear	**6** mm	287.28.470

Packing: 2500 pcs.

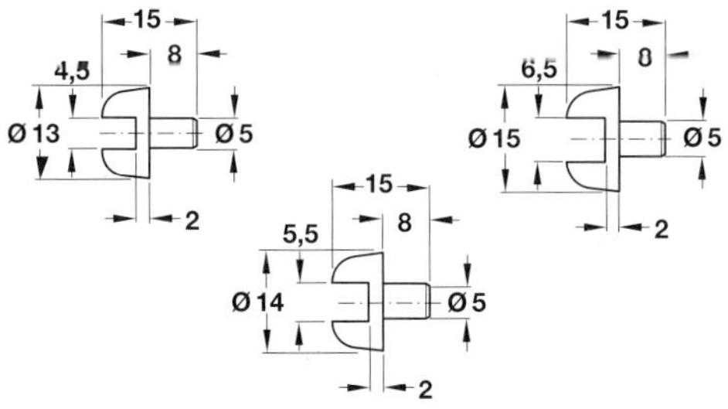

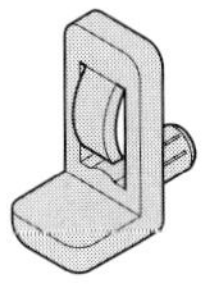

Glass shelf support Ø 5 mm
with safety catch
for glass thicknesses up to max. **6** mm
Finish: plastic

Cat. No.	clear	281.42.403
	white	281.42.707
	brown	281.42.109

Packing: 500 pcs.

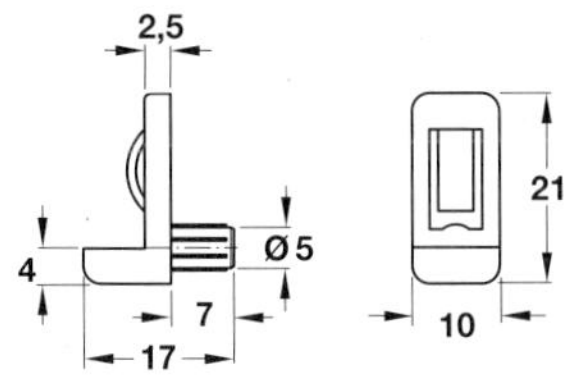

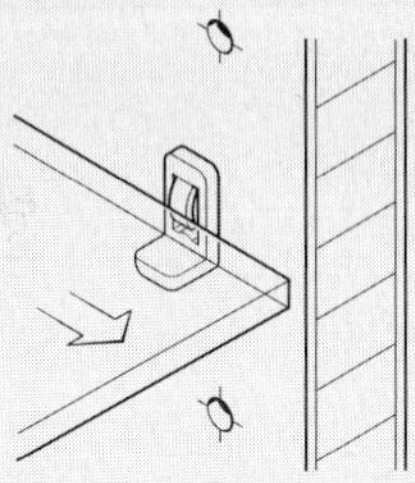

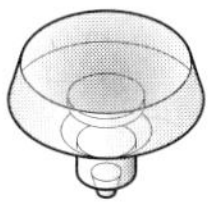

Glass shelf support with suction effect
Finish: soft PVC

Cat. No.	297.34.003

Packing: 500 pcs.

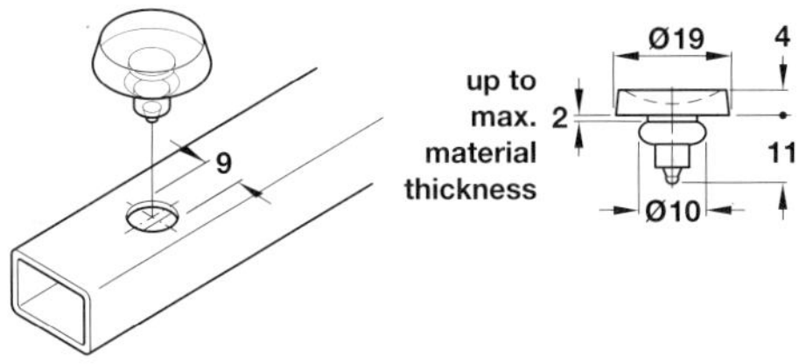

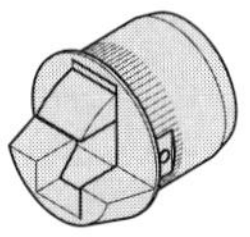

Glass shelf support for press-fitting into a Ø 15 mm hole, for glass shelves from **5 - 6,5** mm thick
Finish: plastic

Cat. No.	white	243.30.701
	brown	243.30.103

Packing: 50 pcs.

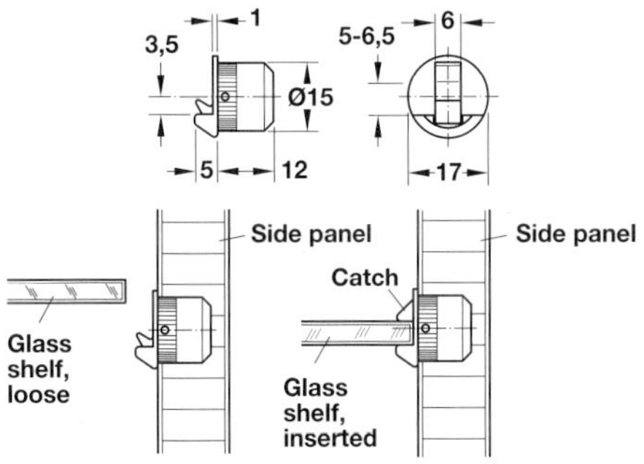

Splined to prevent turning in hole.

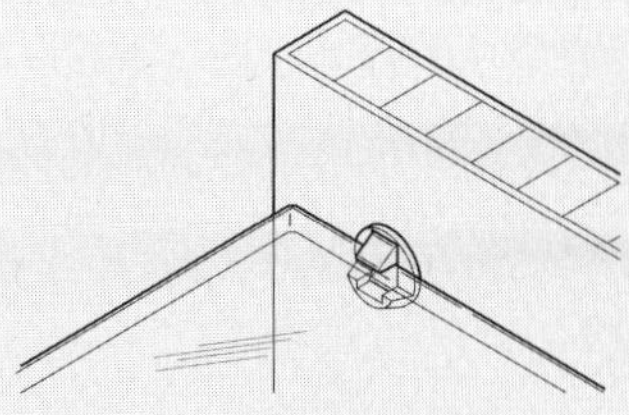

The **safety catch** prevents unintentional lifting or tilting of glass shelves.
Nevertheless the glass shelf can be withdrawn to the front without difficulty.

Dimensional data not binding.
We reserve the right to alter specifications without notice.

Dimensions in mm

HÄFELE

Shelf Hold-downs

Shelf hold-down

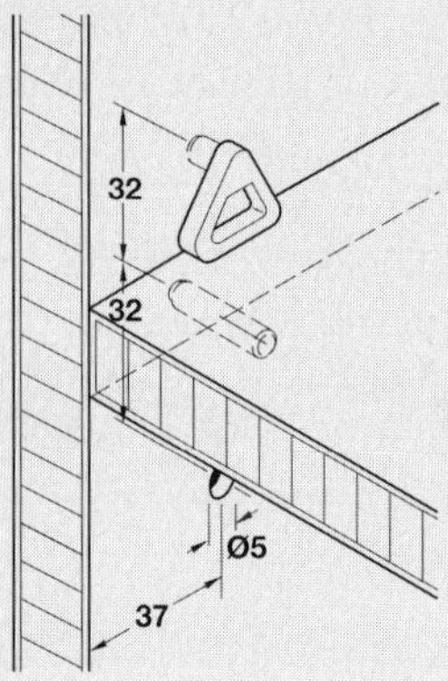

2 **Locks, Catches, RTA and PAS® Fittings Shelf Supports Bed Fittings**

For inserting in drilled holes:

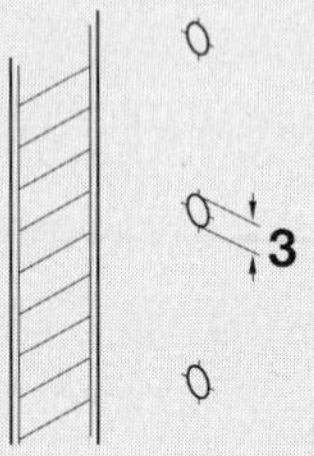

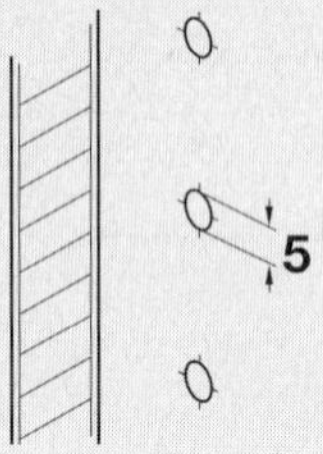

Shelf hold-down Ø 3 mm
32 mm intervals
Shelf thickness: **variable**

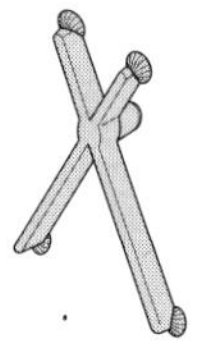

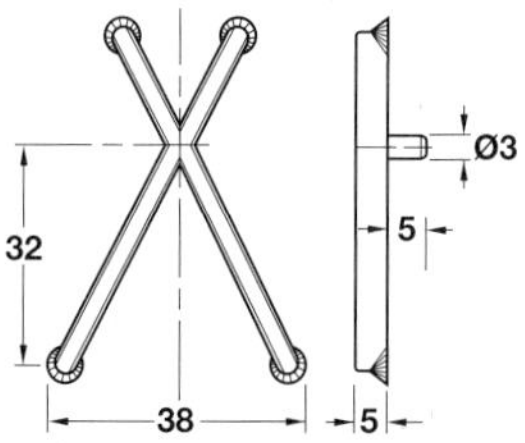

Finish: plastic, white

Cat. No.	282.28.711

Packing: 5000 pcs.

Shelf hold-down Ø 5 mm
32 mm intervals
Shelf thickness: **variable**

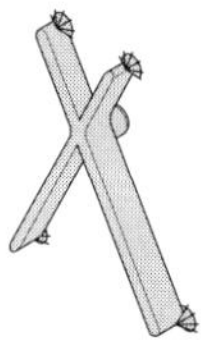

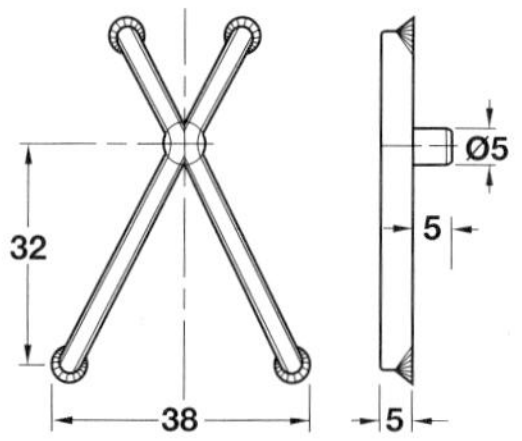

Finish: plastic, white

Cat. No.	282.28.702

Packing: 5000 pcs.

Shelf hold-down for insertion in Ø 5mm system holes at 32 mm intervals
Shelf thickness: **16 mm**
Finish: plastic, white

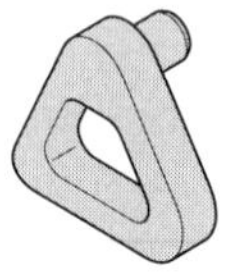

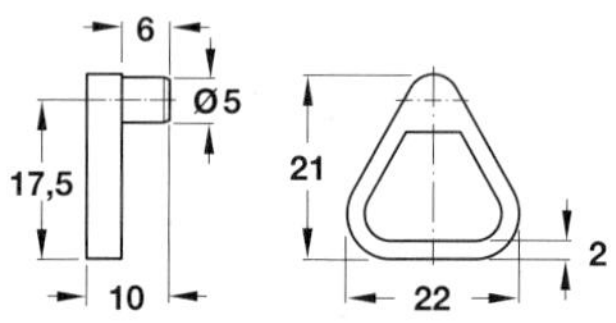

Cat. No.	282.28.720

Packing: 3000 pcs.

Shelf hold-down Ø 5 mm
32 mm intervals
Shelf thickness: **19 mm**
Finish: plastic

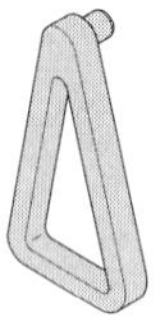

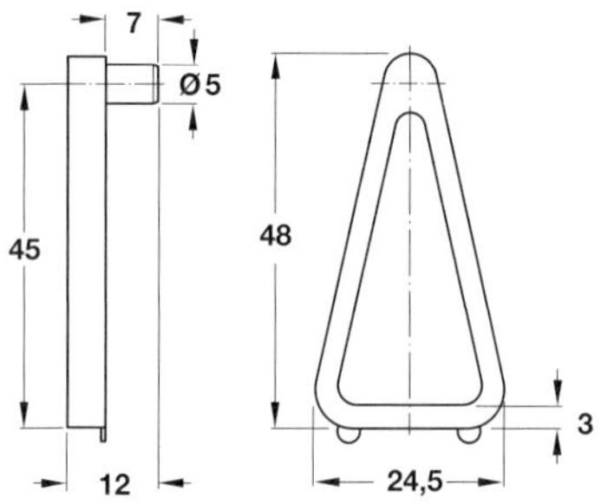

Cat. No.	beige	282.28.739
	white	282.28.730

Packing: 2800 pcs.

Dimensional data not binding.
We reserve the right to alter specifications without notice.

Dimensions in mm

12 mm Shelf Supports

HÄFELE

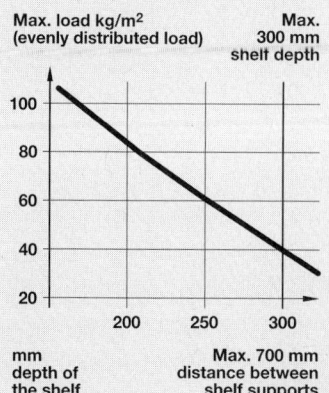

Shelf supports, for invisible fastening of shelves **from 19 mm wood thickness on** in living room, kitchen, bath and bedroom areas.

Advantages:
- Adjustment without tools by turning the plastic sleeve
- The hexagonal end on the shelf support permits installation with 1/4" using a cordless drill or with a 6 mm open end wrench or box-end wrench.

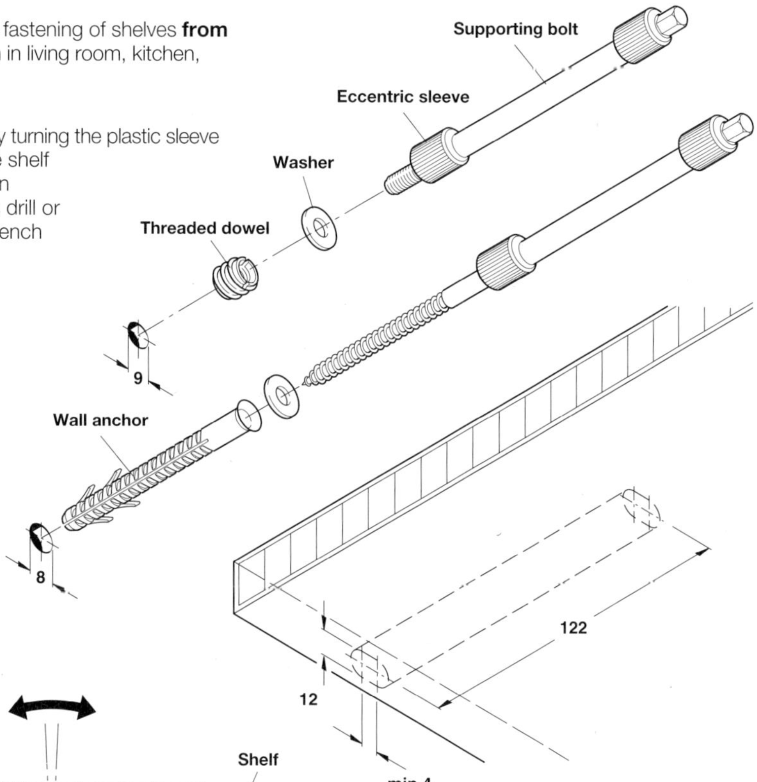

Dimensions in mm

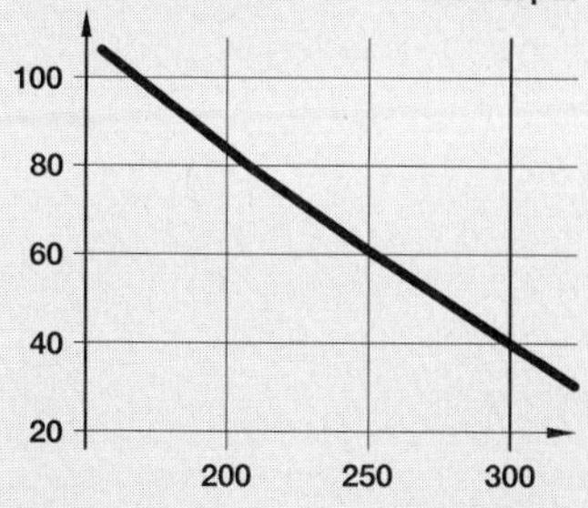

Height and level adjustment possible as shown on the right

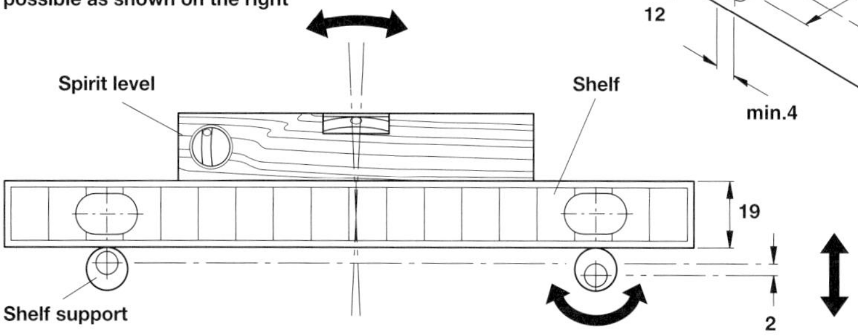

Locks, Catches, RTA and PAS® Fittings
Shelf Supports
Bed Fittings

2

These shelf supports can be installed directly into masonry walls or woodwork.

To make adjustments possible, the insertion hole must be laterally elongated. This can be done with a slot drilling machine or a chain mill.

Adjust height and level, set the shelf on the shelf supports mounted in the wall and then adjust by turning the plastic sleeves.

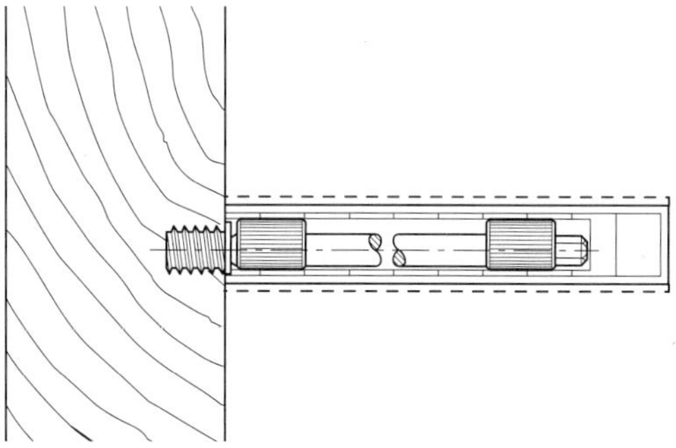

Shelf support, 12 mm, for screw-mounted
Includes:
1 support bolt with M6 thread, steel, galvanized
2 plastic sleeves, pre-mounted, polyamide
1 washer, steel, galvanized
1 threaded sleeve M6 x 15 mm, steel, galvanized

Cat. No.	283.32.032

Packing: 20 pcs. (20 support bolts, washers, and threaded dowels each, as well as 40 eccentric sleeves)

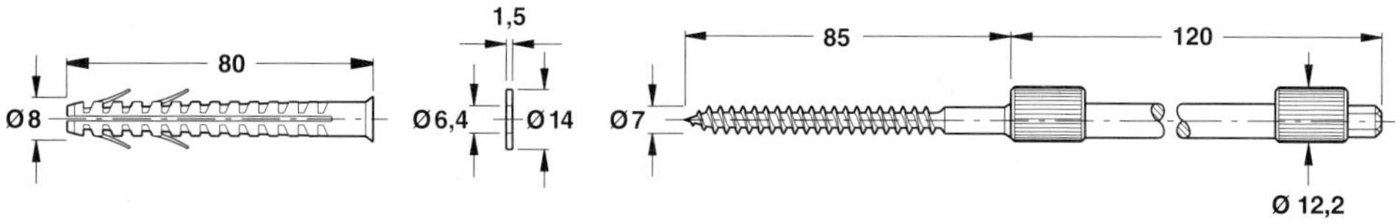

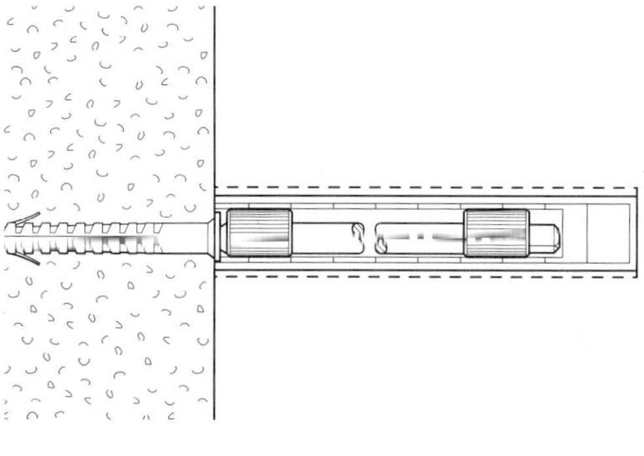

Shelf support, 12 mm, press-fit type
Includes:
1 support bolt with M6 thread, steel, galvanized
2 plastic sleeves, pre-mounted, polyamide
1 washer, steel, galvanized
1 Fischer structural wall anchor S 8H 80 R, nylon, gray

Cat. No.	283.32.014

Packing: 20 pcs. (20 support bolts, washers, and threaded dowels each, as well as 40 eccentric sleeves)

HÄFELE

Brackets

Load capacities are approximate figures and can change depending on application. These figures were determined by static testing–distributing the weight evenly over the surface, but not extending the length of the bracket.

Bracket

Finish: steel, lacquered

Dimensions A	C	B	Screw hole	Load capacity kg/pair	Cat. No. brown	white
100	125	33	4,1	40 (88 lbs)	287.30.216	287.30.118
125	150	34	4,1	40 (88 lbs)	287.30.225	287.30.127
150	200	36	5,0	50 (110 lbs)	287.30.243	287.30.145
200	250	39	5,0	50 (110 lbs)	287.30.261	287.30.163
250	300	44	5,2	60 (132 lbs)	287.30.270	287.30.172
300	350	47	5,2	70 (154 lbs)	287.30.289	287.30.181

Packing: 20 pcs.

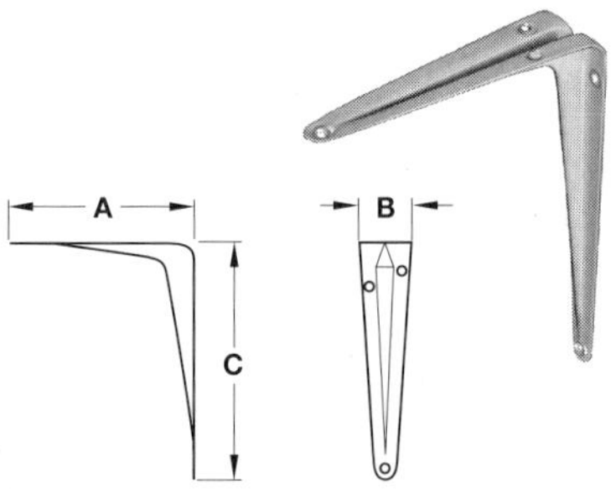

Bracket

Finish: aluminium, lacquered

Dimensions A	C	B	Screw hole	Load capacity kg/pair	Cat. No. brown	white
100	150	20	3,5	80 (175 lbs)	287.35.122	287.35.720
150	200	20	5,0	120 (265 lbs)	287.35.131	287.35.739
200	250	24	5,0	130 (285 lbs)	287.35.140	287.35.748
200	300	26	6,0	150 (330 lbs)	287.35.159	287.35.757

Packing: 10 pcs.

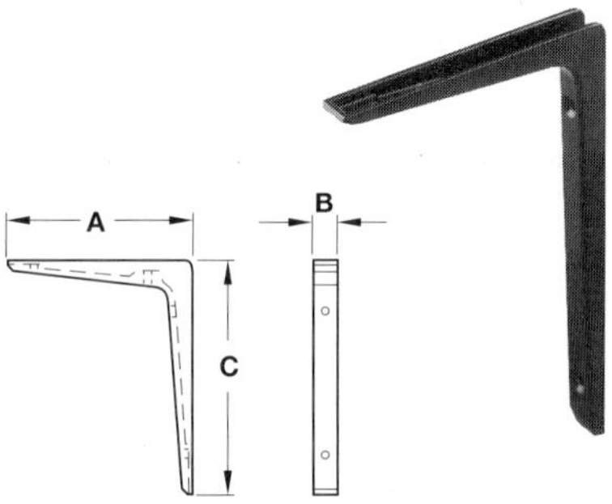

Hebgo bracket

load capacity to 150 kg (330 lbs) per pair

Finish: steel, gray primed

Dimensions A	C	B	Cat. No.
200	80	46	287.44.416
240	80	46	287.44.425
280	100	53	287.44.434
330	100	53	287.44.443
380	130	65	287.44.452
480	130	65	287.44.461
580	170	82	287.44.470
680	170	82	287.44.489

Packing: 1 pc.

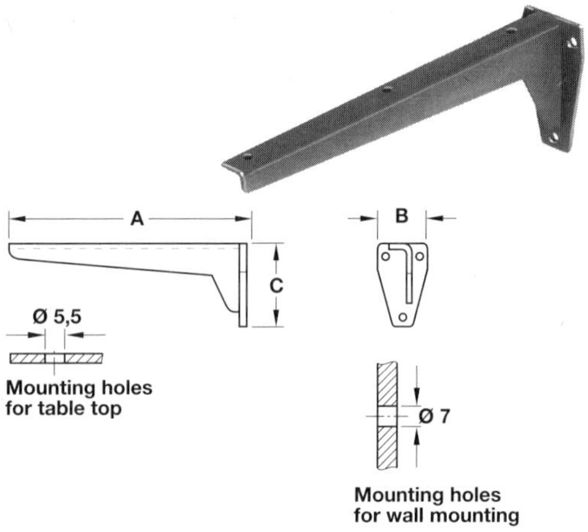

Hebgo bracket

load capacity to 500 kg (1100 lbs) per pair

Finish: steel, gray primed

Dimensions A	C	B	Cat. No.
380	180	80	287.45.459
480	180	80	287.45.468
580	220	100	287.45.477
680	220	100	287.45.486
780	220	100	287.45.495

Packing: 1 pc.

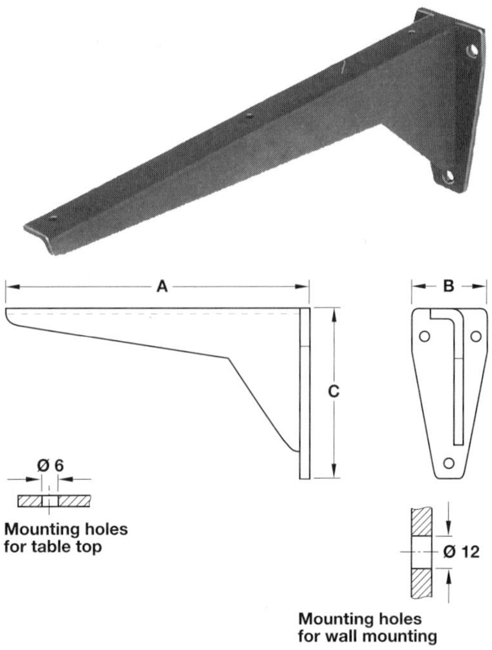

Dimensional data not binding. We reserve the right to alter specifications without notice.

Dimensions in mm

Brackets

HÄFELE

Load capacities are approximate figures and can change depending on application. These figures were determined by static testing–distributing the weight evenly over the surface, but not extending the length of the bracket.

Bracket, folding with locking device

Finish: steel, enameled

Dimensions A	C	D	B	Screw hole	Load capacity kg/pair	Cat. No. brown	white
200	210	35	25	3,5	50 (110 lbs)	287.40.203	287.40.105
310	310	40	27	4,0	70 (154 lbs)	287.40.212	287.40.114
400	425	40	27	4,0	85 (187 lbs)	287.40.221	287.40.123

Packing: 10 pcs.

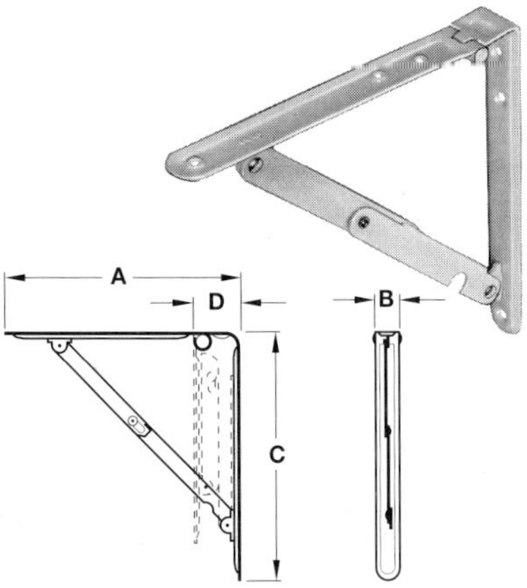

Locks, Catches, RTA and PAS® Fittings
Shelf Supports
Bed Fittings
2

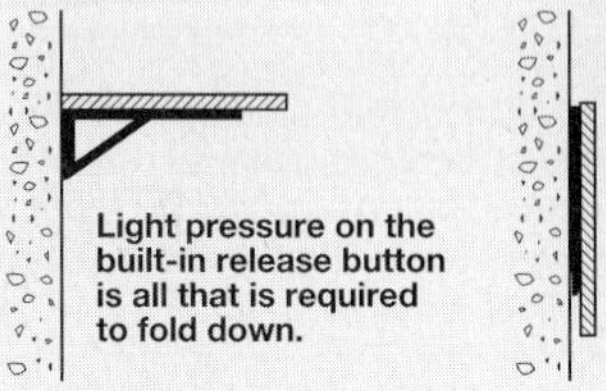

Light pressure on the built-in release button is all that is required to fold down.

Hinged spring bracket

screw-mounted, for vertical installation
load capacity to 40 kg (88 lbs) per pair

Finish: steel, yellow chromated

Dimensions A	C	B	Cat. No.
250	85	30	287.41.906
380	120	30	287.41.915

Packing: 10 pcs.

Finish: stainless steel

Dimensions A	C	B	Cat. No.
250	85	30	287.41.600
380	120	30	287.41.610

Packing: 10 pcs.

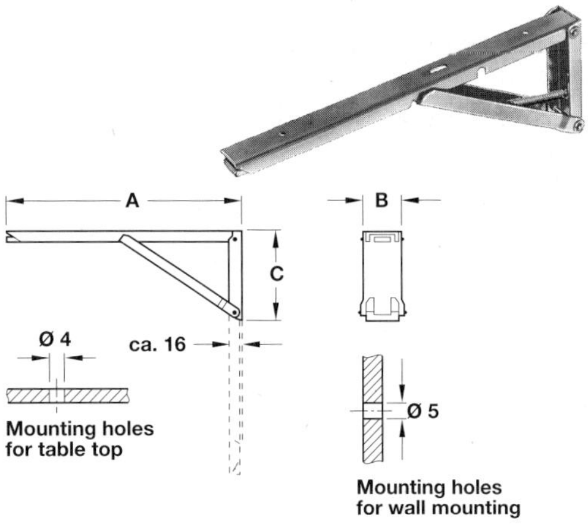

Hinged spring bracket

screw-mounted, for horizontal installation
load capacity to 30 kg (66 lbs) per pair

Finish: steel, yellow chromated

Dimensions A	C	B	Cat. No.
280	130	30	287.41.951

Packing: 10 pcs.

Finish: stainless steel

Dimensions A	C	B	Cat. No.
280	130	30	287.41.650

Packing: 10 pcs.

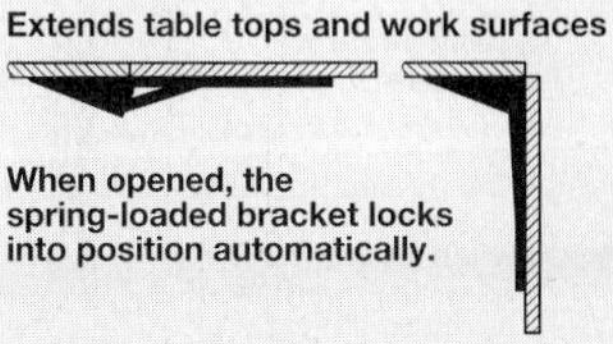

Extends table tops and work surfaces
When opened, the spring-loaded bracket locks into position automatically.

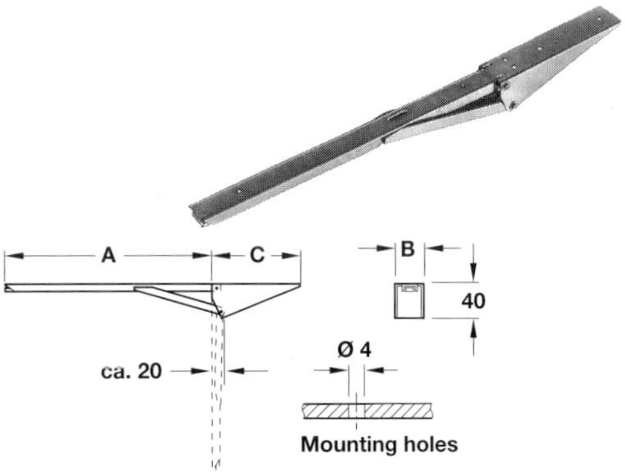

Bracket, folding with locking device

load capacity to 100 kg (220 lbs) per pair

Finish: steel, white lacquer; support, galvanized

Dimensions A	C	B	Cat. No.
200	105	60	287.54.720
250	105	60	287.54.725
300	105	60	287.54.730

Packing: 2 pcs.

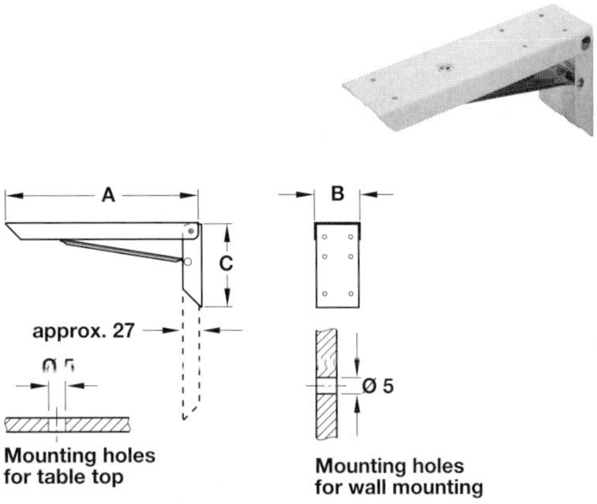

Dimensional data not binding. We reserve the right to alter specifications without notice.

Dimensions in mm

HÄFELE

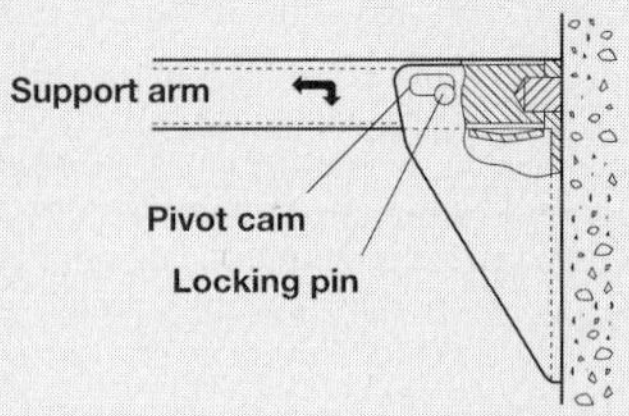

To fold down: lift and pull out the supporting arm.

To raise: lift and press the supporting arm down on the locking pin.

Load capacities are approximate figures and can change depending on application. These figures were determined by static testing–distributing the weight evenly over the surface, but not extending the length of the bracket.

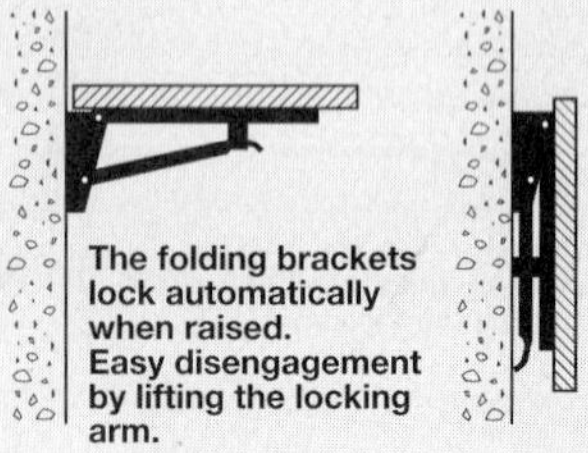

The folding brackets lock automatically when raised.
Easy disengagement by lifting the locking arm.

Brackets

Tikla folding table bracket

medium-duty model

load capacity to 300 kg (660 lbs) per pair

Finish: steel, brown lacquer

Dimensions A	C	D	B	Cat. No.
360	120	66	140	287.48.110
460	120	66	140	287.48.129
560	120	66	140	287.48.138
660	120	66	140	287.48.147

Packing: 2 pcs.

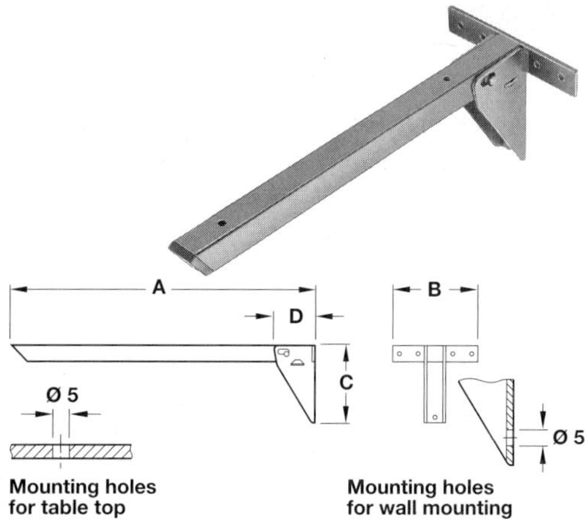

Hebgo folding table bracket

light-duty model

load capacity to 150 kg (330 lbs) per pair

Finish: steel, gray primed

Dimensions A	C	D	B	Cat. No.
330	134	50	82	287.42.403
380	134	50	82	287.42.412
480	152	50	82	287.42.421
580	178	50	82	287.42.430
680	178	50	82	287.42.449

Packing: 1 pc.

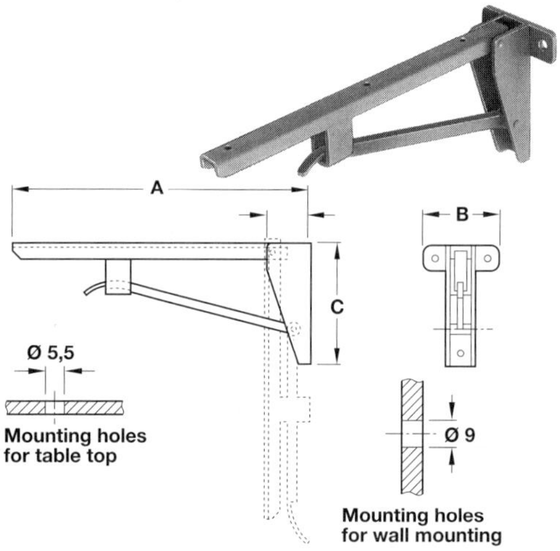

Hebgo folding table bracket

heavy-duty model

load capacity to 500 kg (1100 lbs) per pair

Finish: steel, gray primed

Dimensions A	C	D	B	Cat. No.
420	180	60	115	287.43.400
480	180	60	115	287.43.419
580	220	60	115	287.43.428
680	220	60	115	287.43.437
780	220	60	115	287.43.446

Packing: 1 pc.

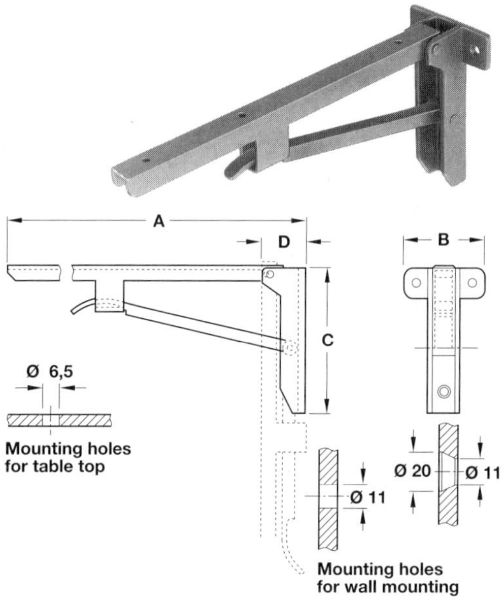

Dimensional data not binding. We reserve the right to alter specifications without notice.

Dimensions in mm

Brackets

HÄFELE

Hebgo bench bracket
heavy-duty model
load capacity to 500 kg (1100 lbs.) per pair

Finish: steel, galvanized

Dimensions A	C	B	Cat. No.
410	460	48	287.47.971

Packing: 1 pc.

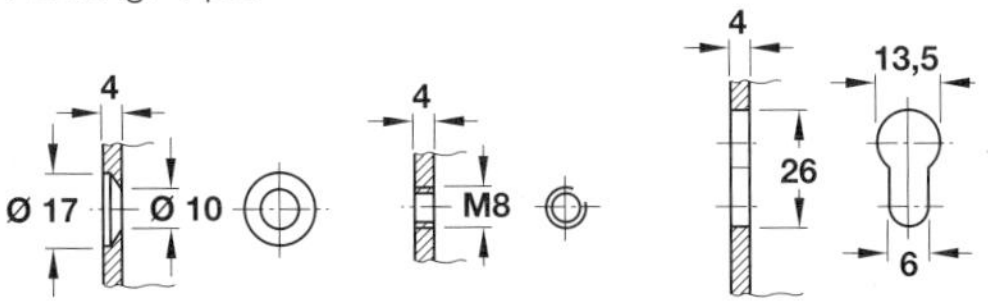

Mounting holes for wall mounting | **Mounting holes for visible backrest mounting** | **...for concealed backrest mounting**

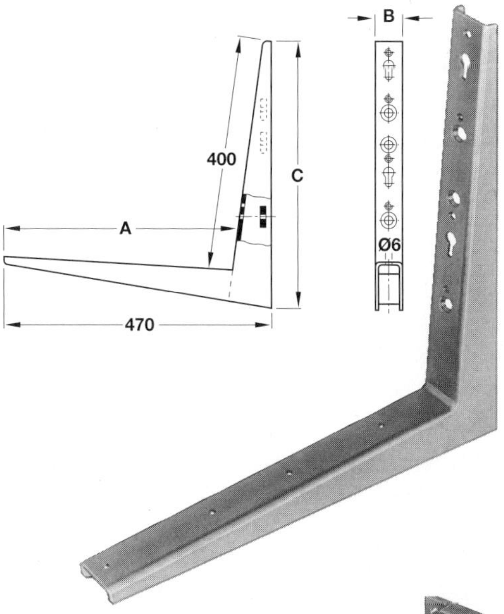

The drilling centers for the backrest can be accurately marked with the enclosed center punch. Mounting instructions are enclosed.

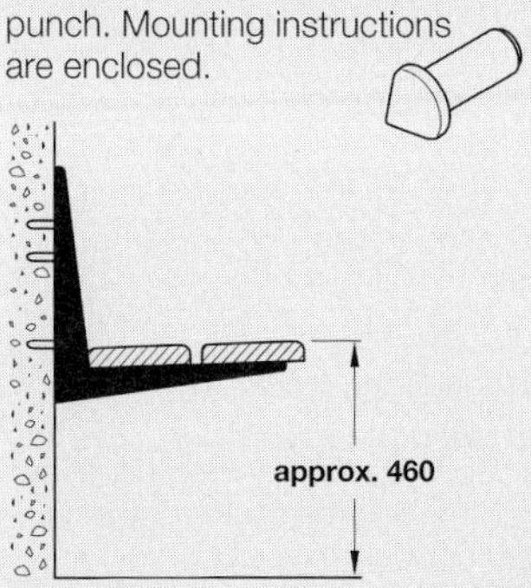

Locks, Catches, RTA and PAS® Fittings
Shelf Supports
Bed Fittings
2

Hebgo folding bench bracket
heavy-duty model for outdoor use
load capacity to 500 kg (1100 lbs.) per pair

Finish: steel, galvanized

Dimensions A	C	D	B	Cat. No.
380	208	114	90	287.47.917

Packing: 1 pc.

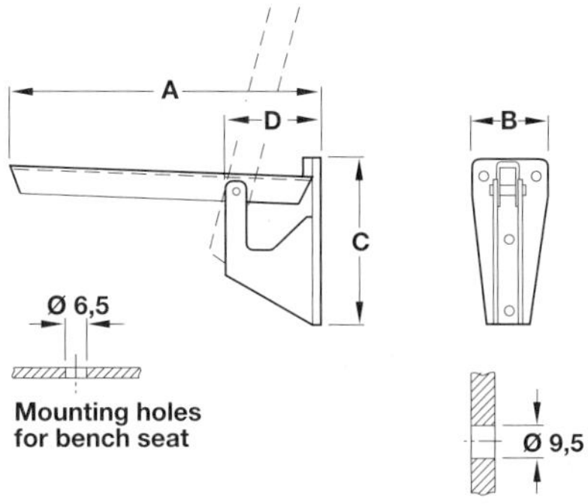

Mounting holes for bench seat

Mounting holes for wall mounting

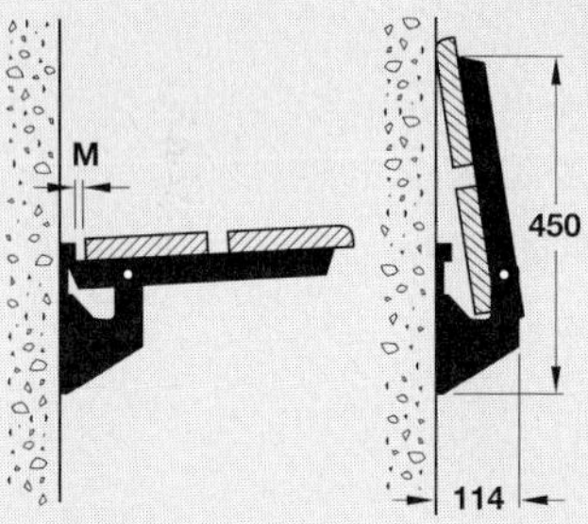

When folded up the bracket requires the space specified above. It is pre-drilled for the seat, which can be up to 40 mm thick.

Seat thickness	Minimum gap M
25 mm	17 mm
30 mm	17 mm
35 mm	22 mm
40 mm	28 mm

Bracket folding to the side
intended for use in RV's
and mobile homes.
Attached to the sink unit, is serves to support the sink.

Finish: plastic, brown

Cat. No.	287.50.147

Packing: 2 pcs.

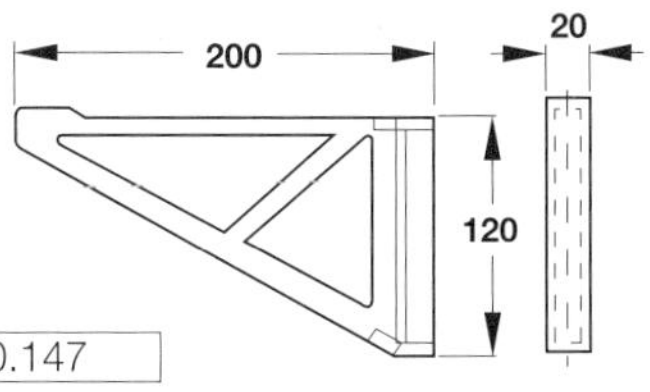

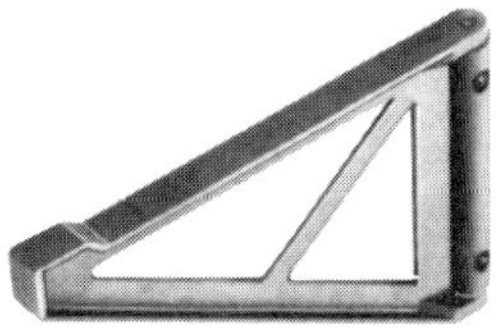

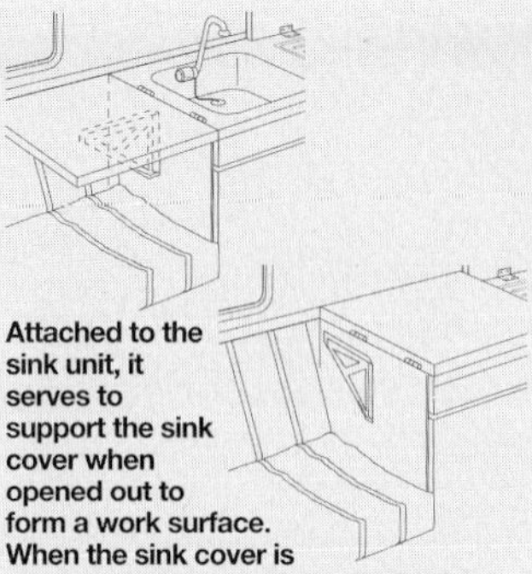

Attached to the sink unit, it serves to support the sink cover when opened out to form a work surface. When the sink cover is closed, the bracket can be folded back in either direction against the sink unit, where it locks into place.

Folding bracket
with locking device in supporting arm.
Load capacity to 50 kg. per pair

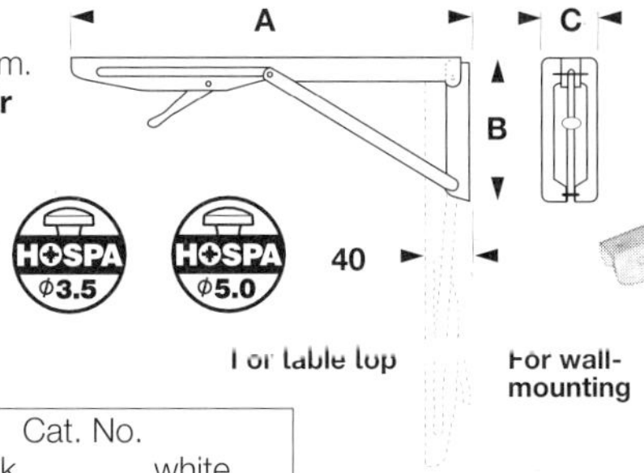

For table top | **For wall-mounting**

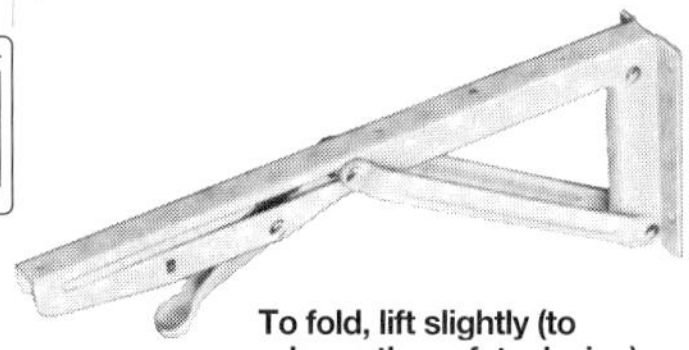

To fold, lift slightly (to release the safety device) Press the release lever and the bracket will fold down.

Finish: steel, bright galvanized

Dimensions A	B	C	Cat. No. black	white
300	115	42	287.49.322	287.49.724

Packing: 1 pc.

***Note: Load capacities are approximate figures and can change depending on application. These figures were determined by static test-distributing the weight evenly over the surface, but not extending the length of the bracket.**

Dimensional data not binding.
We reserve the right to alter specifications without notice.

Dimensions in mm

HÄFELE

Decorative Brackets

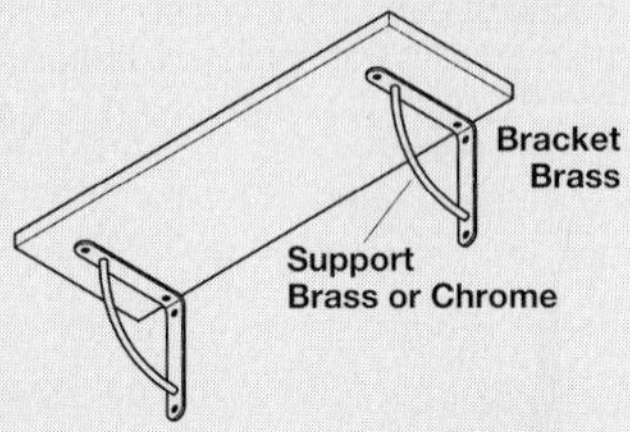

- Highly attractive and decorative
- Heavy duty steel
- For exposed use in kitchen and living room environment
- For book shelves

Bracket

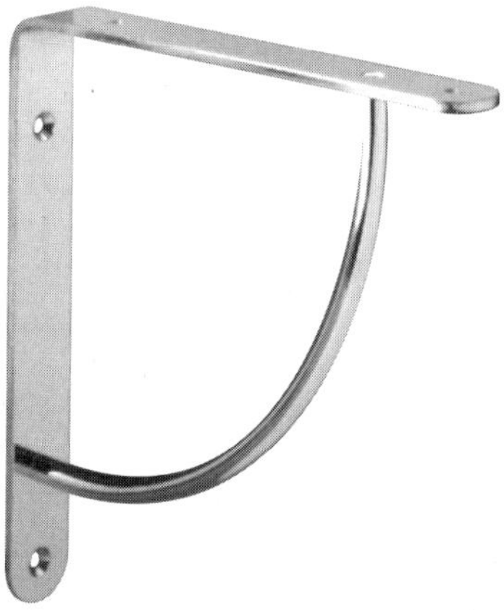

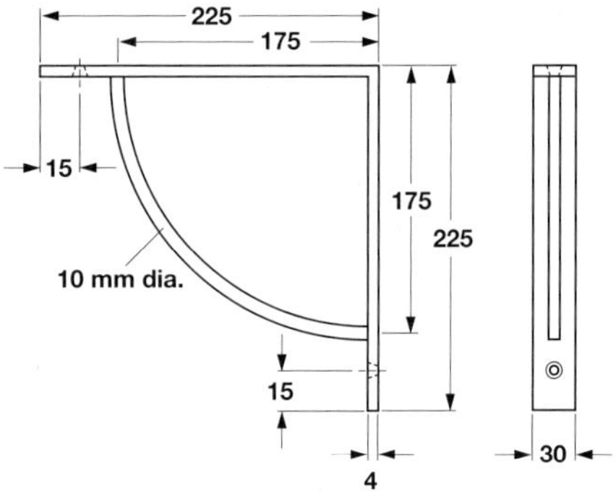

Finish: steel

	bracket	support	
Cat. No.	brass-plated	chrome-plated	287.70.200
	brass-plated	brass-plated	287.70.800

Packing: 1 pc w/mounting screws

Dimensions in mm

Bed Fittings/Concealed Hanger Plates

Profiled plates, for machined-recess installation. For use as RTA fittings for beds or uppholstered furniture.

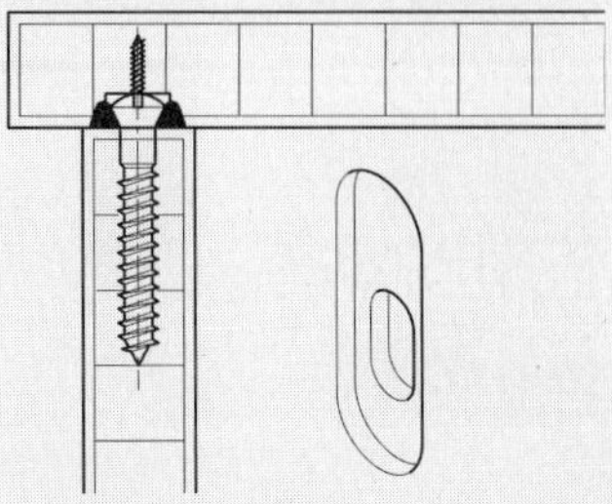

Dimensions of recesses should be taken directly from the fittings.

- Invisible
- Extremely strong
- Components can be assembled and disassembled w/o tools.
- Straight plates can also be inserted into a groove.

Keyhole Plates
for recessing

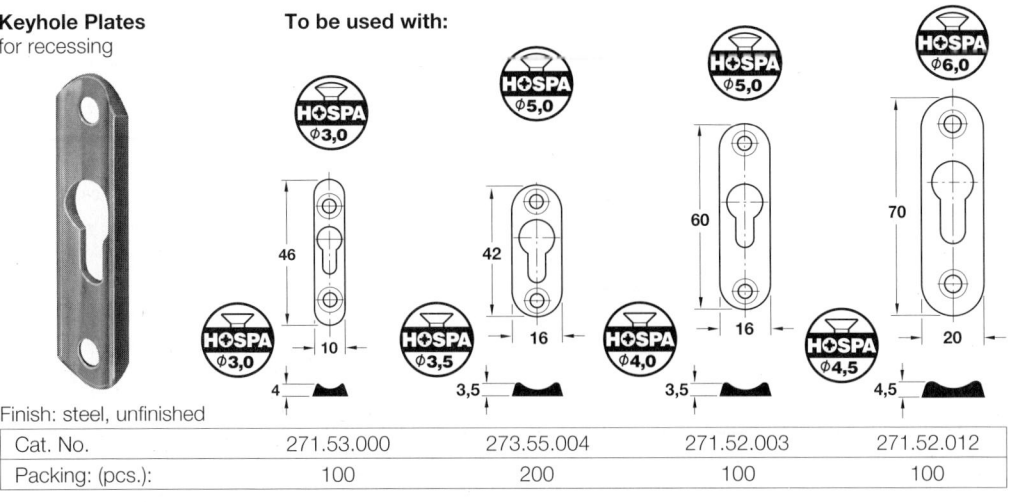

To be used with:

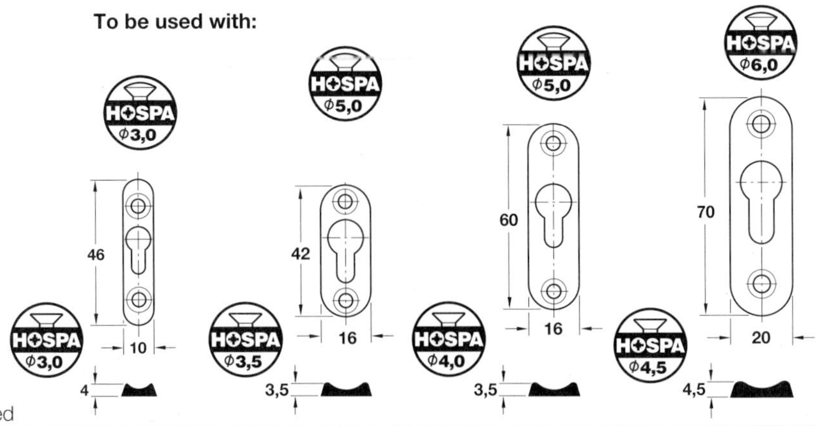

Finish: steel, unfinished

Cat. No.	271.53.000	273.55.004	271.52.003	271.52.012
Packing: (pcs.):	100	200	100	100

Keyhole Plate
for recessing

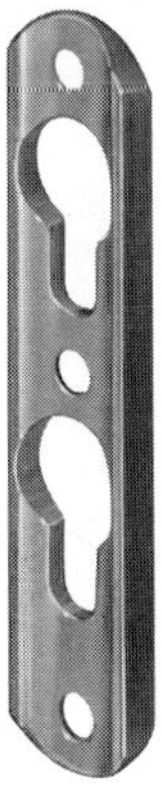

To be used with:

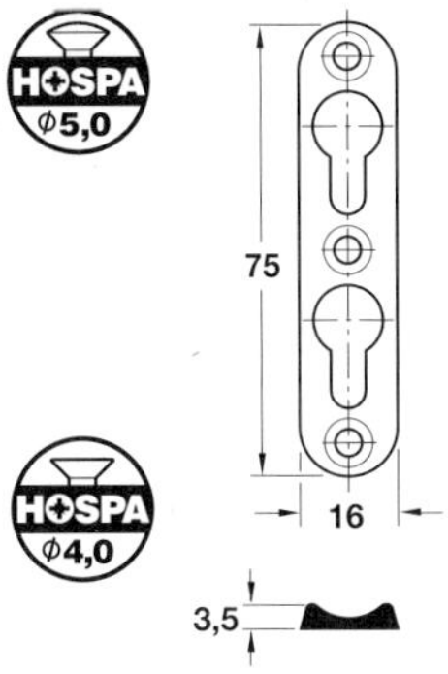

Finish: steel, unfinished

Cat. No.	273.56.010

Packing: 100 pcs.

Keyhole Fitting,
for drilled holes

To be used with:

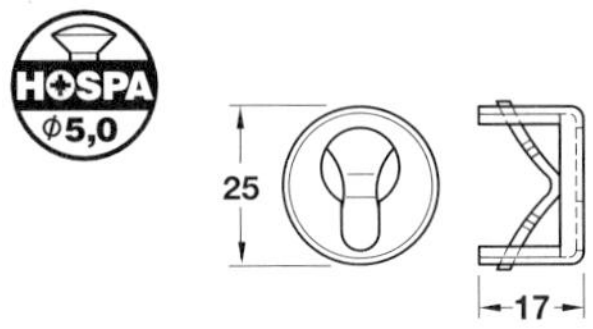

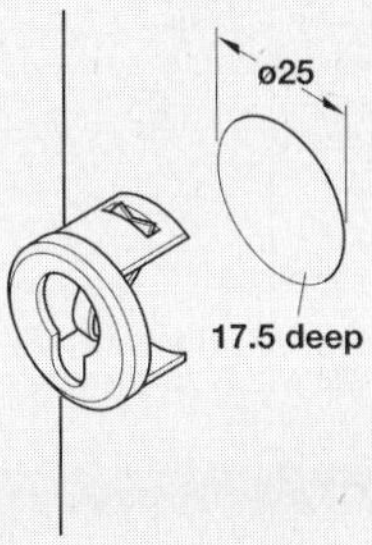

Finish: steel, unfinished

Cat. No.	271.60.023

Packing: 100 pcs.

Keyhole Fitting,
for drilled holes

To be used with:

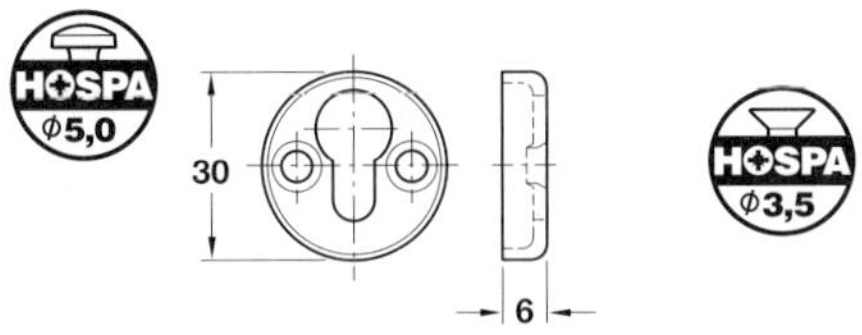

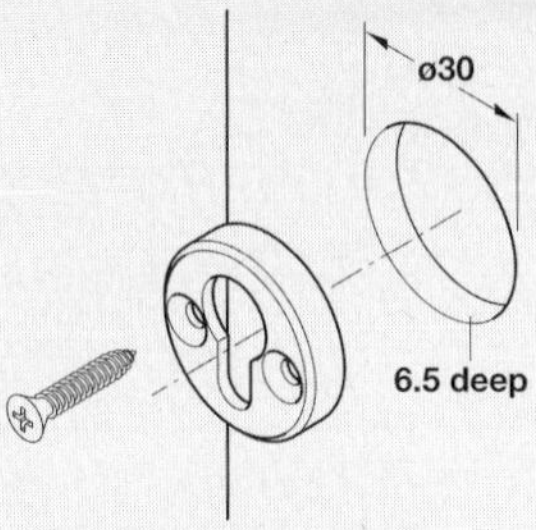

Finish: steel, unfinished

Cat. No.	271.61.306

Packing: 100 pcs.

Mounting Plate, screw-mounted with 2 slots and additional screw-holes

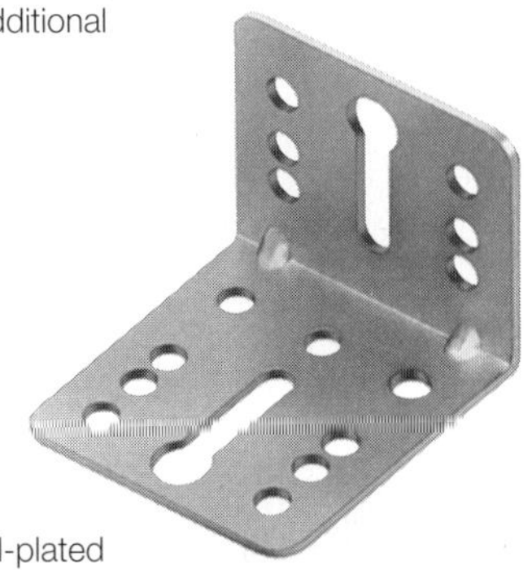

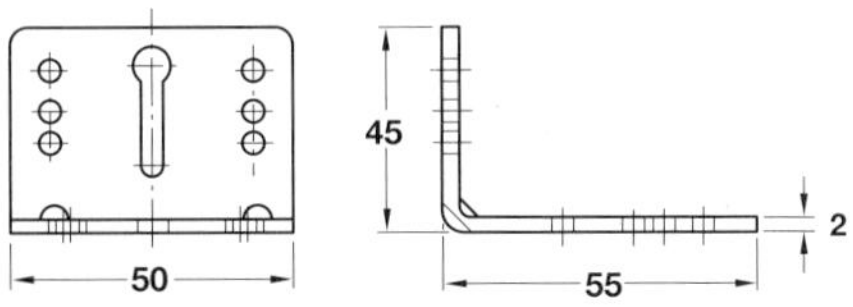

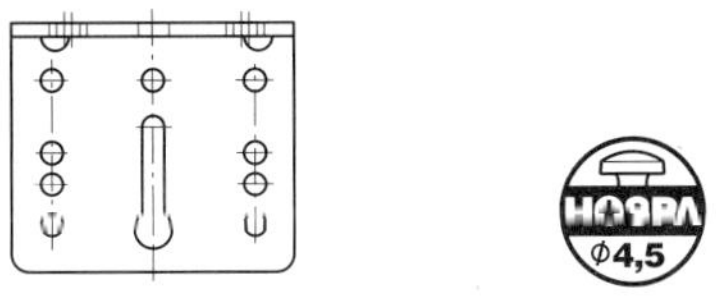

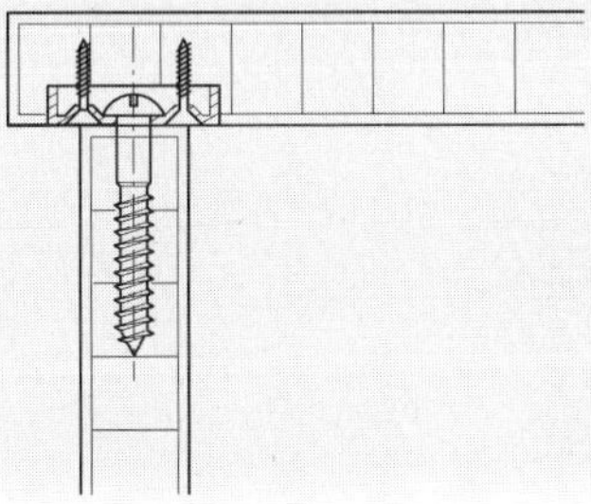

Finish: steel, nickel-plated

Cat. No.	558.12.943

Packing: 50 pcs.

Dimensional data not binding.
We reserve the right to alter specifications without notice.

HÄFELE

Universal BV Connector

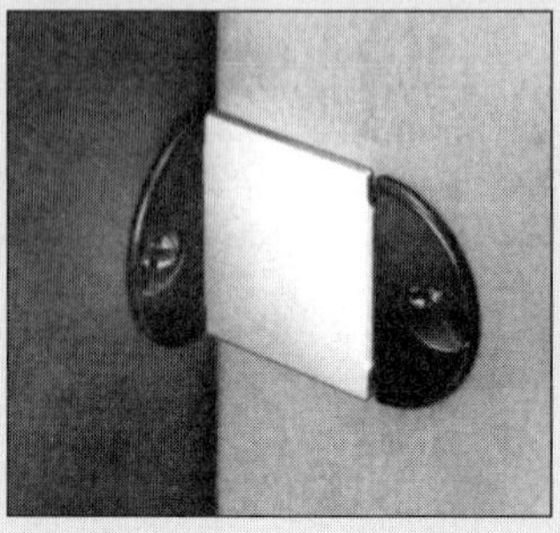

- Capability for automated installation of the two casings in mass production.
- The same casing is suitable for left-hand or right-hand installation.
- Eliminates projecting parts, simplifying shipping and storage.
- Simple assembly. The connecting bracket is secured in the casings with a screwdriver.
- Retensioning can be applied if necessary.

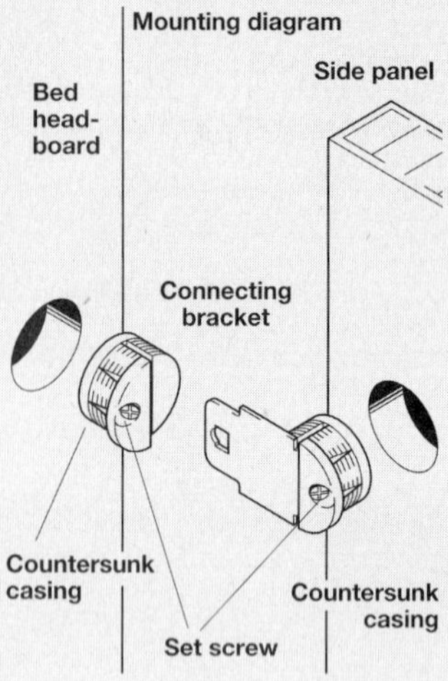

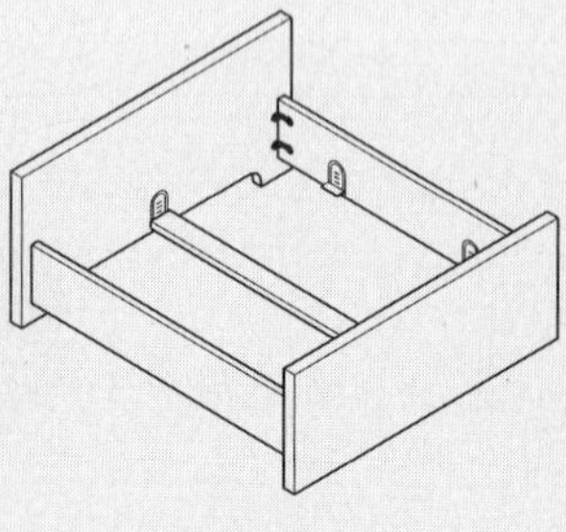

Universal BV Connector

For bedframes and other applications which require a heavy-duty connector.

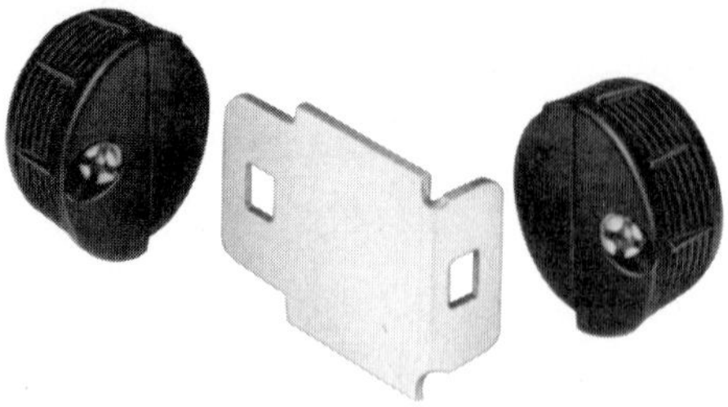

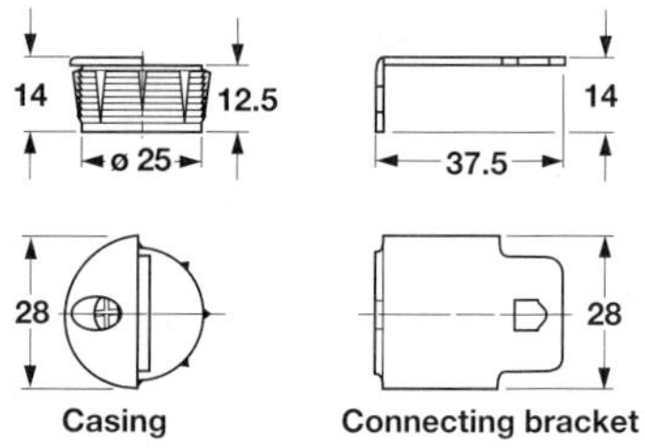

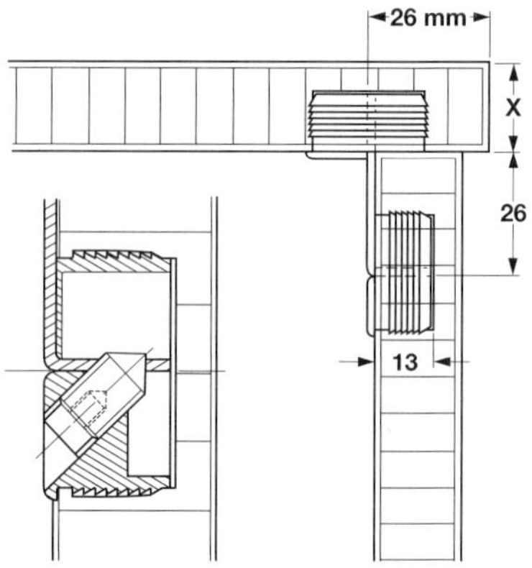

Finish: Connecitng bracket, hardened spring-steel
Housing: plastic w/pre-inserted locking screws

Cat. No.		
	white	273.60.112
	brown	273.60.710

Packing: 100 pcs.

Punch Tool For Universal BV Connector

Facilitating accurate installation of the casings, the punch tool features a profiled head to match the casing. After the locating flange has been aligned with the edge of the panel, the casing is lightly tapped into place.

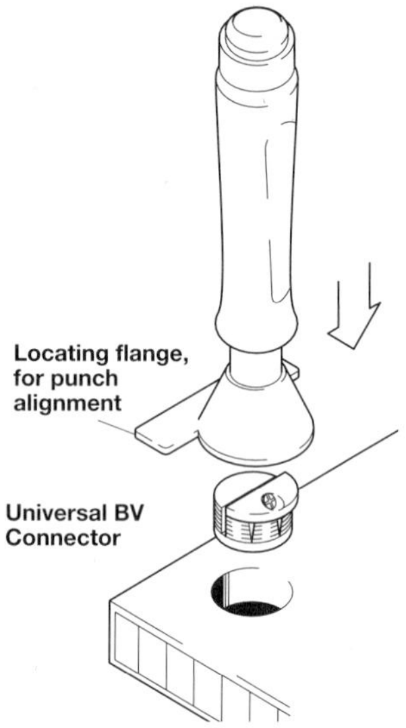

Finish: Handle, hardwood with metal loops
Head, plastic

Cat. No.	
	001.32.703

Packing: 1 pc.

Dimensional data not binding.
We reserve the right to alter specifications without notice.

Bed Fittings

Bed Fitting, screw-mounted

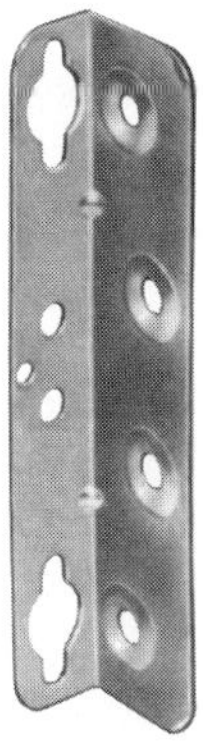

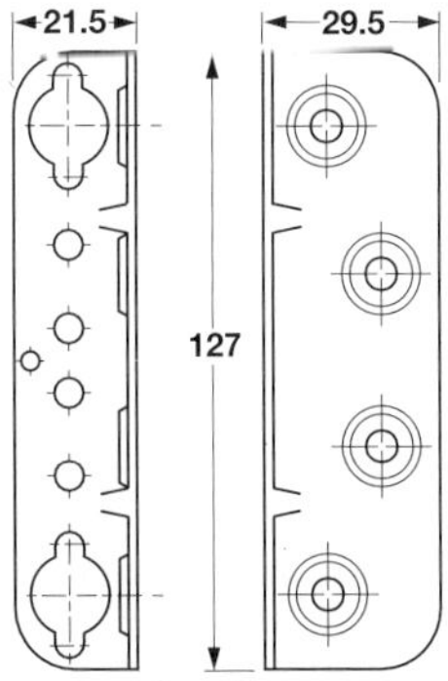

- Keyholes and safety holes.
- Can be used left or right.

Finish: steel, zinc-plated

Cat. No.	271.19.946

Packing: 100 pcs.

Cheese Head Screw M6 x 10mm

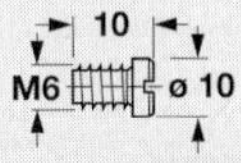

Finish: Steel, galvanized

Cat. No.	020.90.904

Packing: 200 pcs.

Connecting Fitting for various purposes, in particular for bed sides and heads.

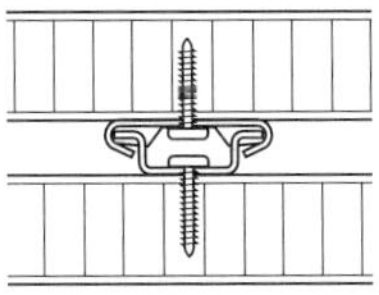

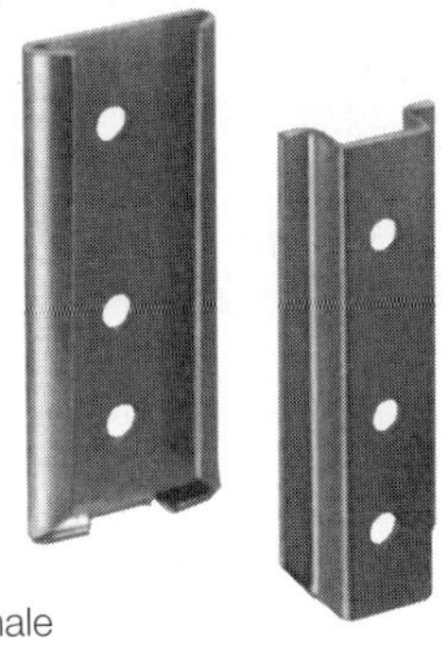

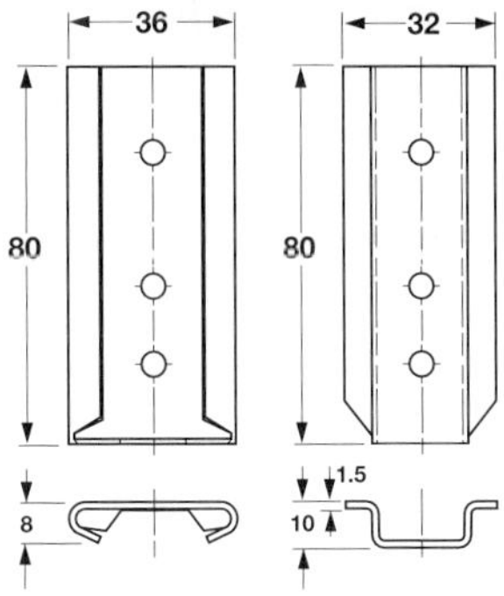

Finish: steel, galvanized 1 set = 1 male/1 female

Cat. No.	273.42.918

Packing: 25 sets each

Locks, Catches, RTA and PAS® Fittings
Shelf Supports
Bed Fittings
2

Ribbed Sleeve M6, Drive-in

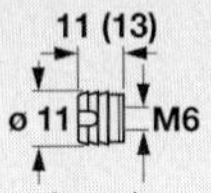

Finish: nylon, natural-colored

Cat. No. ø11x11mm	039.33.266
ø11x13mm	039.33.060

Packing: 5000 pcs.

"Berliner" Bed Fitting, for machined-recess installation.

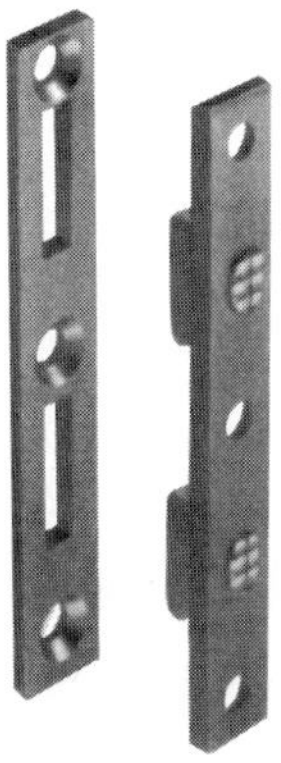

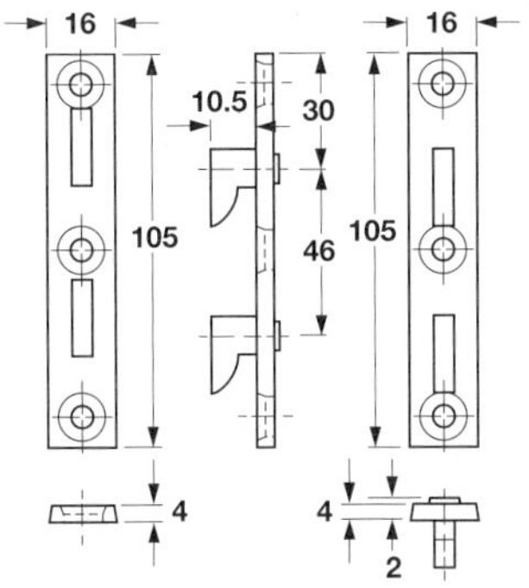

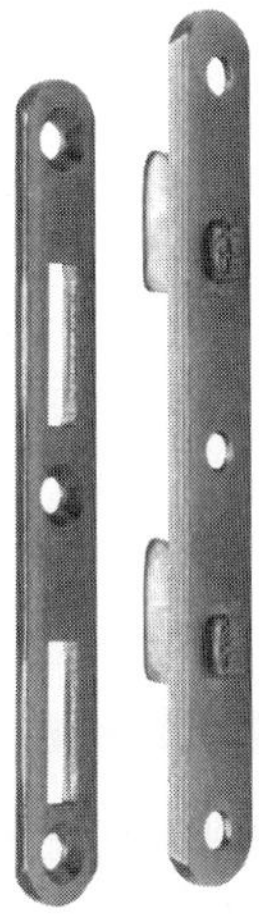

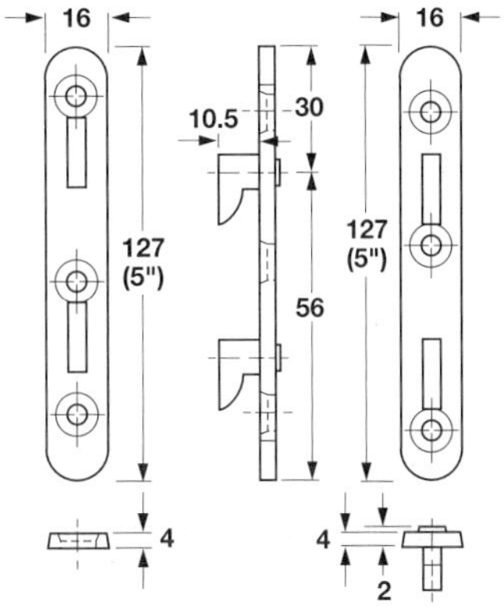

Finish: steel, unfinished 1 set = 4 male/4 female

Cat. No.	271.33.008

Packing: 6 sets each

Finish: steel, unfinished 1 set = 4 male/4 female

Cat. No.	271.33.090

Packing: 6 sets each

Threaded Sleeve M6, Screw-in

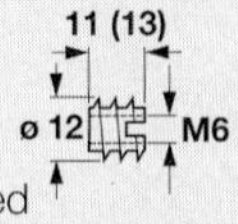

Finish: steel, unfinished

Cat. No.	ø12x11mm	ø12x13mm
	030.00.306	030.00.315

Packing: 1000 pcs. 100 pcs.

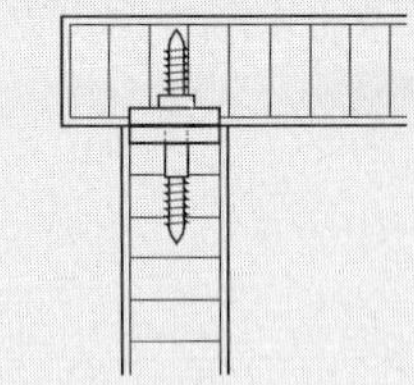

Connecting Fitting, Screw-mounted

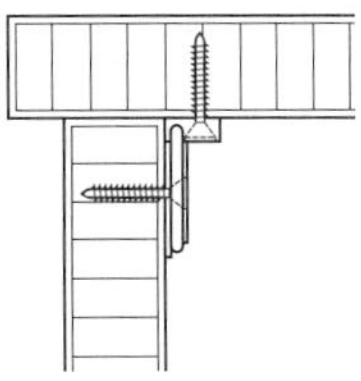

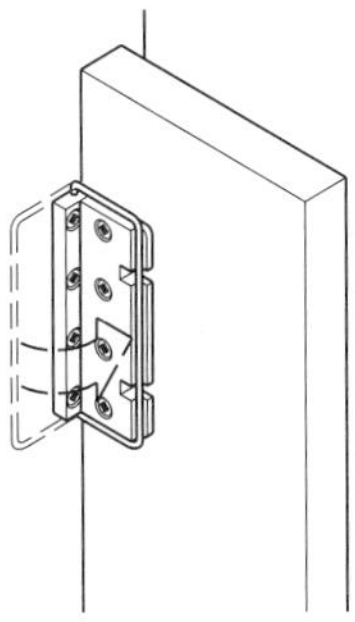

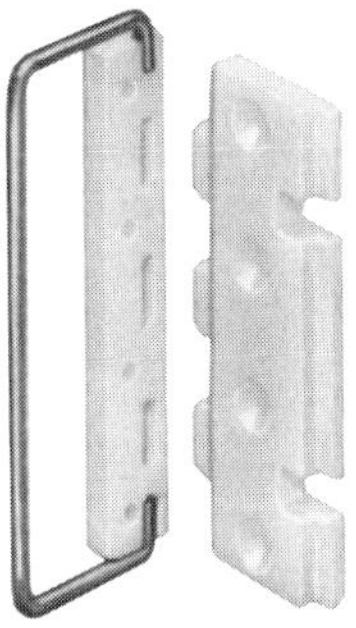

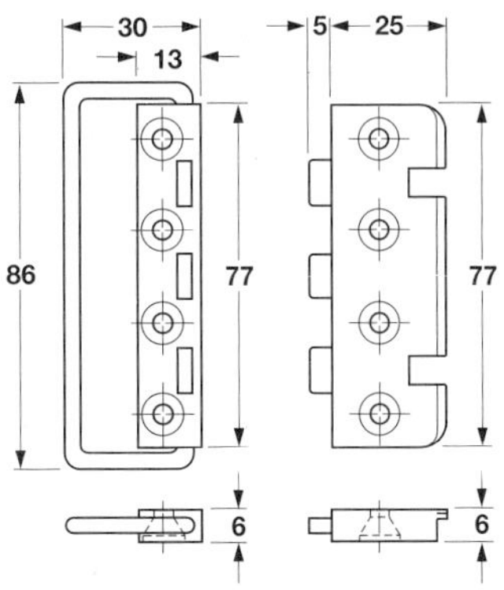

- Polyamide, with galvanized steel.
- Left or right use
- Fastening by press-fitting the two elements together & snapping the bail in place.
- Equally simple release by opening the bail.

Finish: plastic, natural-colored

Cat. No.	262.59.003

Packing: 100 pcs.

Dimensional data not binding.
We reserve the right to alter specifications without notice.

Dimensions in mm

HÄFELE

Bed Fittings

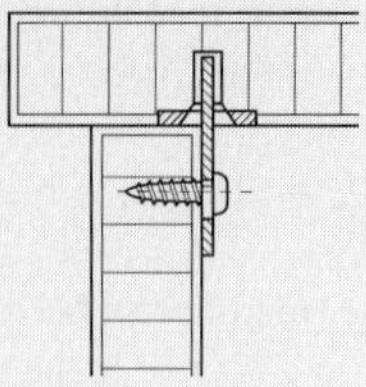

"Hagenia" hook-type bed connector, screw-mounted.
Tapered slots in the striking plate ensure safe, secure fastening.

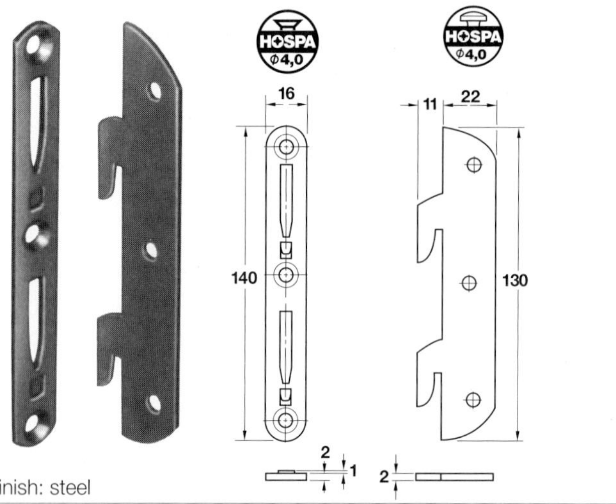

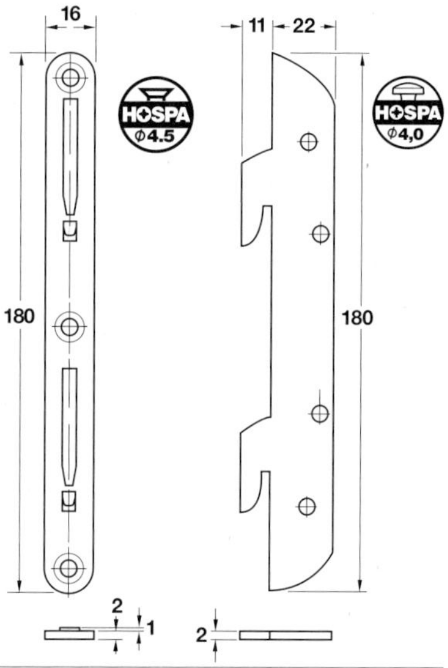

Finish: steel

Cat. No.	unfinished	271.32.001	271.32.029

Packing: 10 sets (40 each hook-in parts and striking plates)

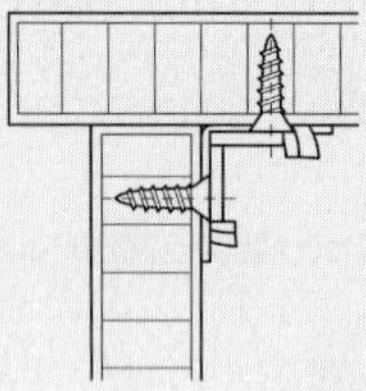

Bed connecting bracket, screw-mounted; can be used left or right; hook-type fastening. Sturdy design.

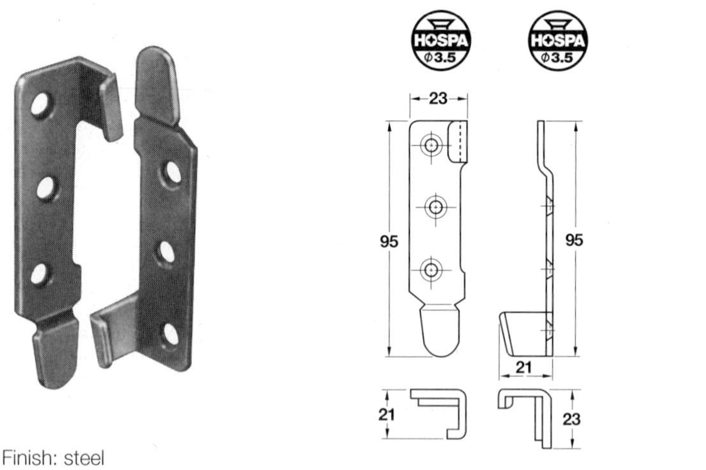

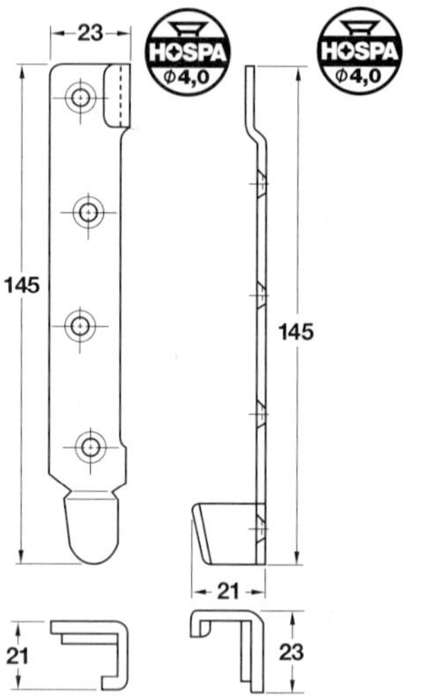

Finish: steel

Cat. No.	unfinished	271.05.004	271.05.013

Packing: 10 sets (40 each hook-in parts and striking plates)

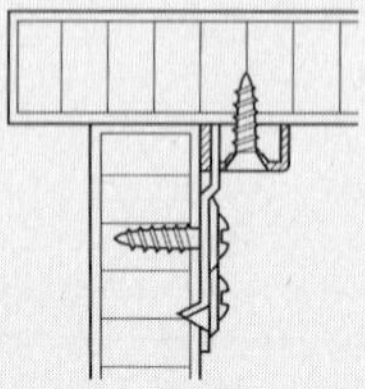

"Noval K" bed fitting, screw-mounted. With pointed teeth and cranked hook component.

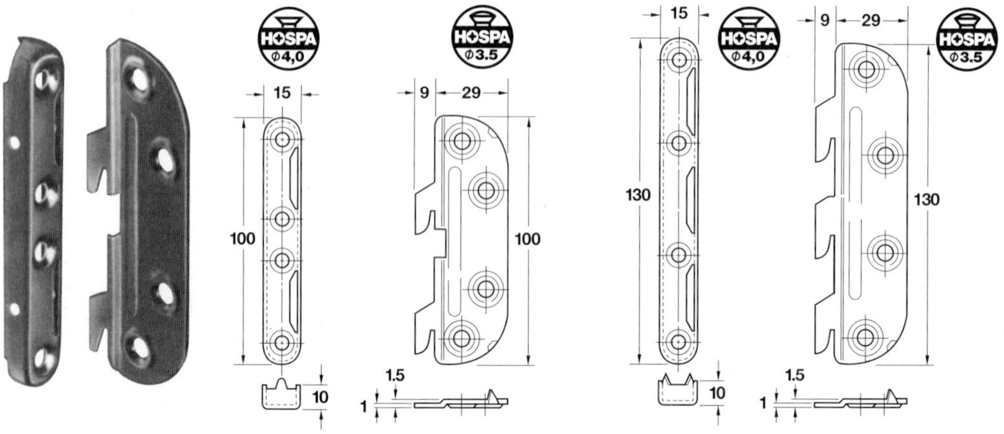

Finish: steel

Cat. No.			
	yellow, chromated	271.03.510	271.03.530
	silver, chromated	271.03.910	271.03.930

Packing: 10 sets (1 set is required to connect 4 corners. In this case 4 female parts, 2 left hooks, 2 right hooks.)

Dimensions in mm

Bed Fittings

Bed toekick fastener, screw-mounted.
For single or double beds, toekick thickness 19 mm (3/4"), usable left or right.
High strength fitting with non-twist design. The toekick is secured with a fastening screw and wing nut.

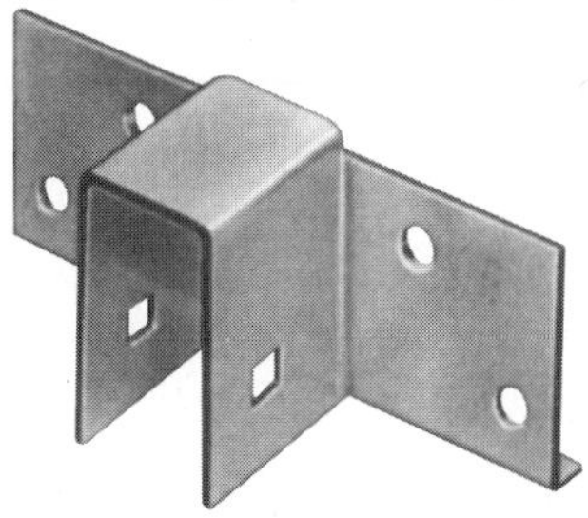

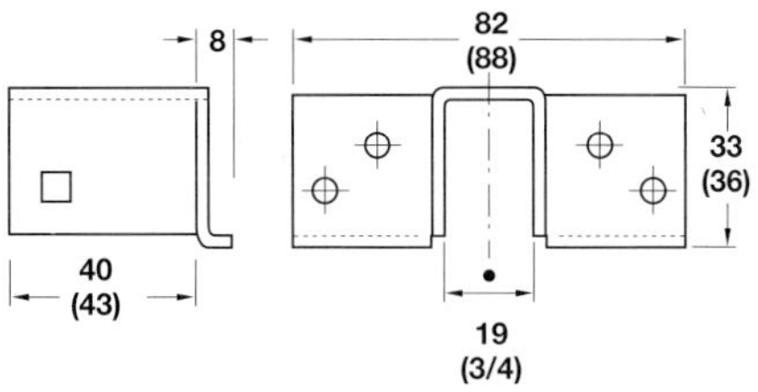

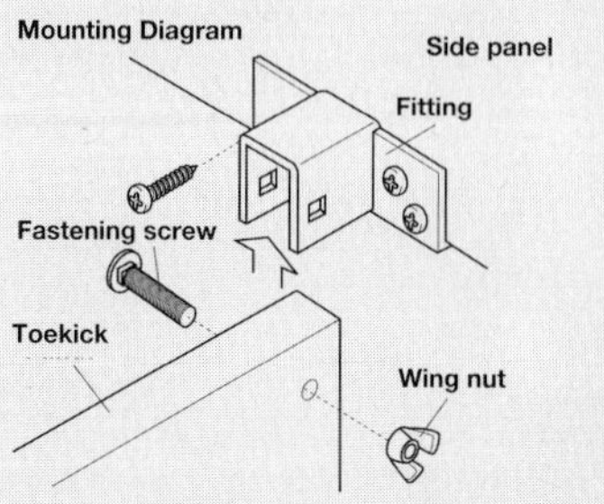

Finish: steel, zinc

Cat. No.	19 mm	273.07.937

Packing: 40 pcs.

Order separately:

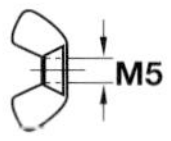

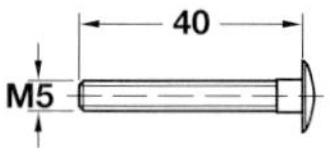

Wing Nut

Cat. No.	033.01.059

Packing: 100 pcs.

Fastening Screw

Cat. No.	025.01.644

Packing: 100 pcs.

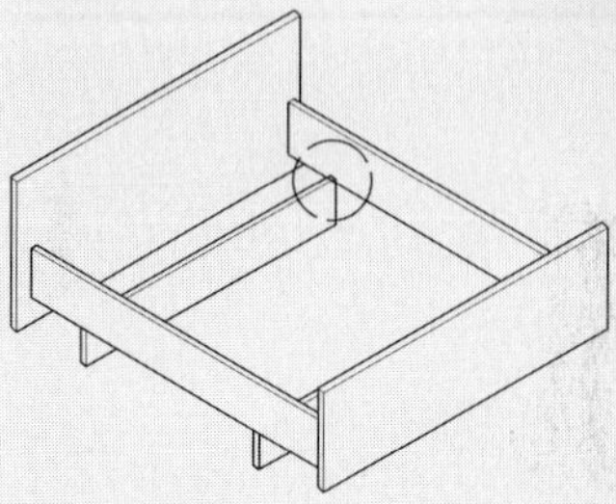

Bed toekick fastener, screw-mounted.
For single or double beds, toekick thickness 19 mm (3/4"). Capable of separation and for use left or right.
A sturdy connecting fitting comprising two parts, i.e. mounting plate for head or foot, U-bracket for toekick.

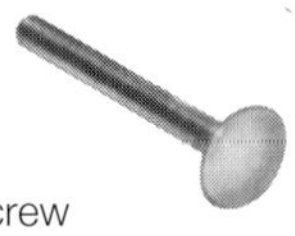

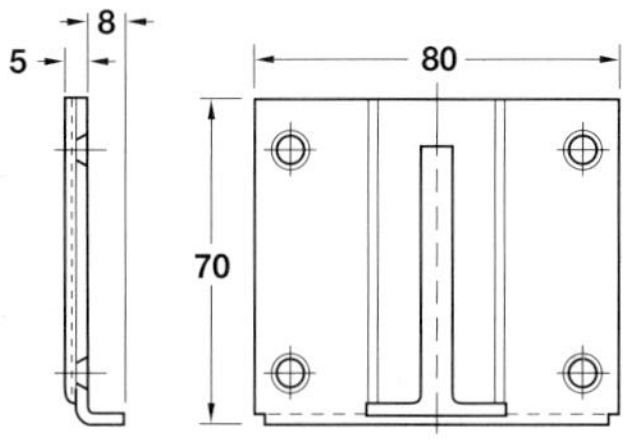

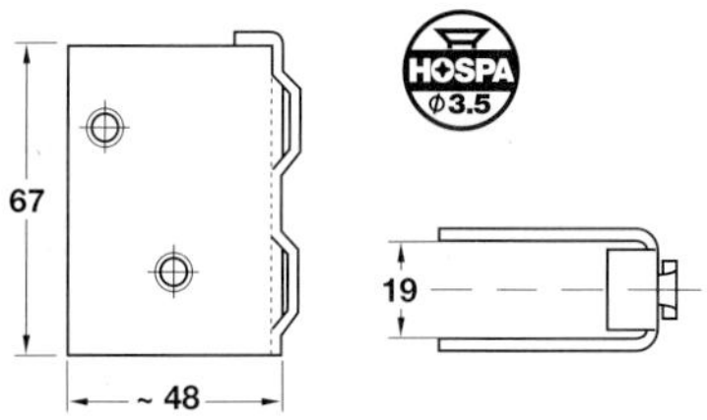

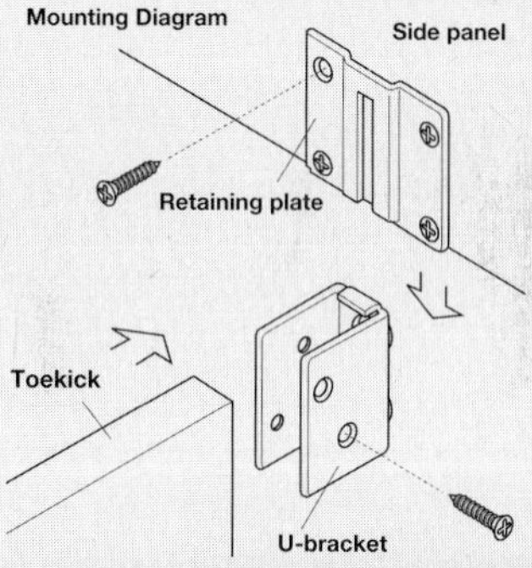

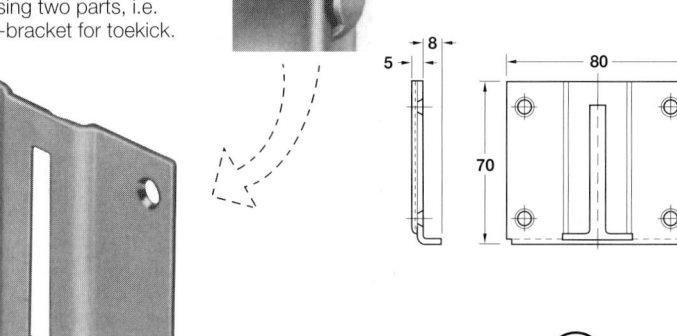

Finish: steel, zinc

Cat. No.	19 mm	273.08.907

Packing: 40 pcs. (1 pc = 1 male + 1 female)

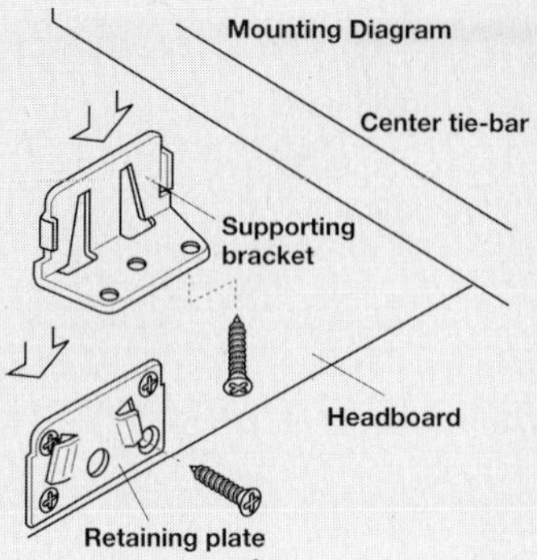

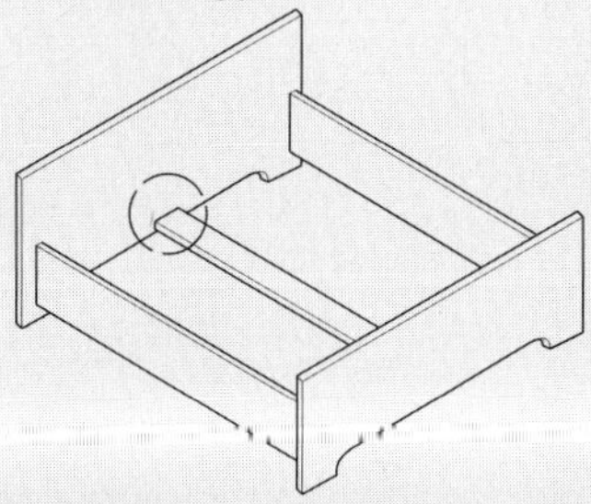

Double bed fitting, screw-mounted.
For beds with a central tie-bar. Fitting capable of separation. The supporting bracket is screwed to the tie-bar, the retaining plate to the head or foot.
The bed elements are securely held by the angled retaining flanges.

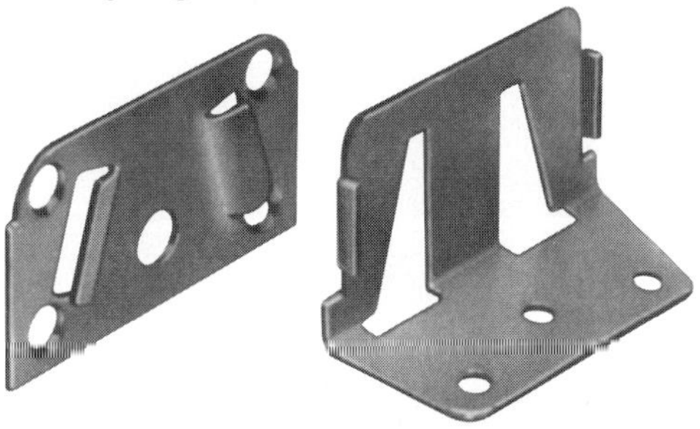

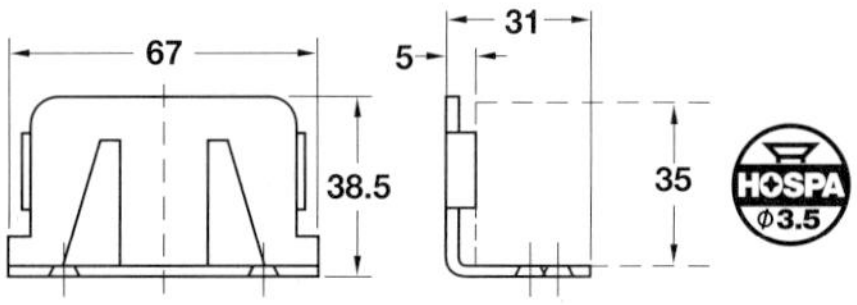

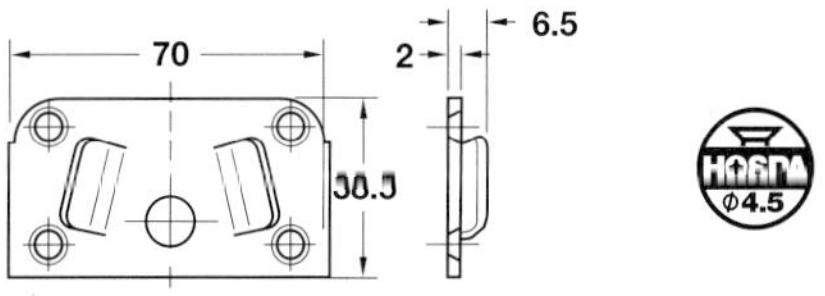

Finish: steel, yellow chromated

Cat. No.	273.03.510

Packing: 100 pcs. (1 pc = 1 male + 1 female)

Dimensions in mm

Dimensional data not binding.
We reserve the right to alter specifications without notice.

HÄFELE

Bed Fittings

Mounting diagram for slatted base, adjustable in three positions.

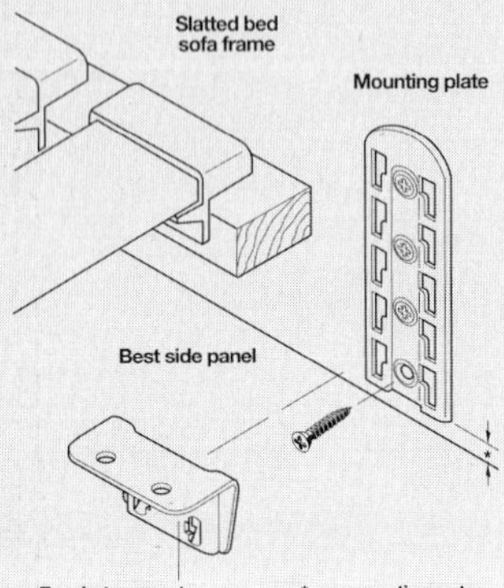

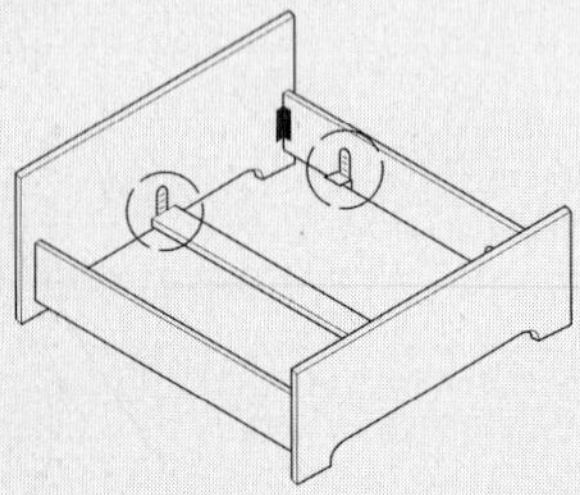

Mounting diagram for central tie-bar, adjustable in three positions.

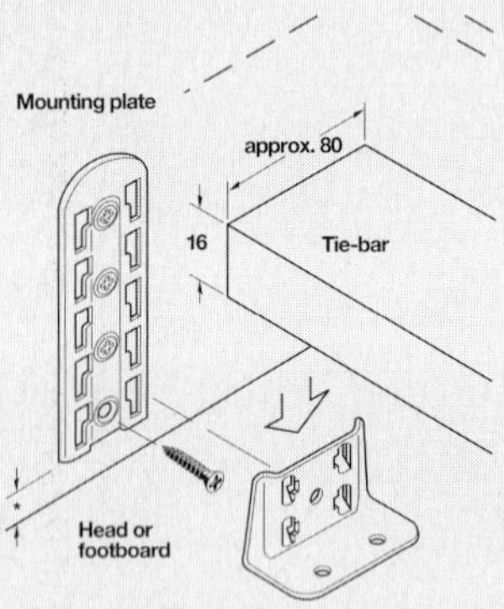

Screw-mounted bed fitting
allowing the adjustment of slatted bases for mattresses and upholstered furniture.
Suitable for single or double beds. This fitting can also be used to secure central tie-bars by reversing the support bracket (see mounting instructions).

HOSPA ⌀4,0

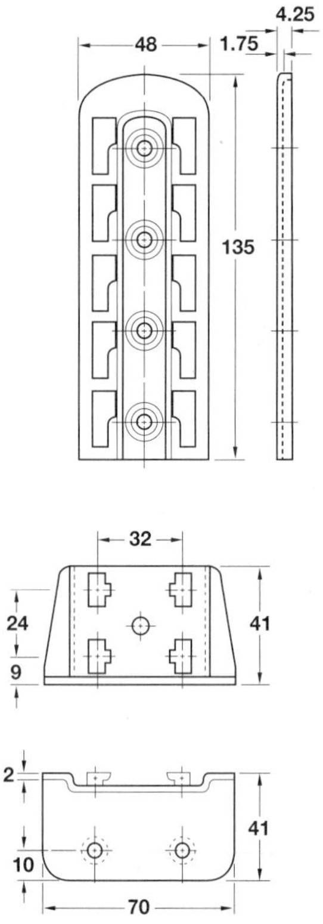

Finish: steel, galvanized

Catalog No.	273.41.939

Packing: 40 pcs. (40 each mounting plates and bracket support)

***Mounting notes**
When used on double beds with a 35 mm thick tie-bar, the slotted retaining plates at the head and foot must be mounted **5 mm** higher than those on the side panels, so that the support surfaces will all be at the same level.

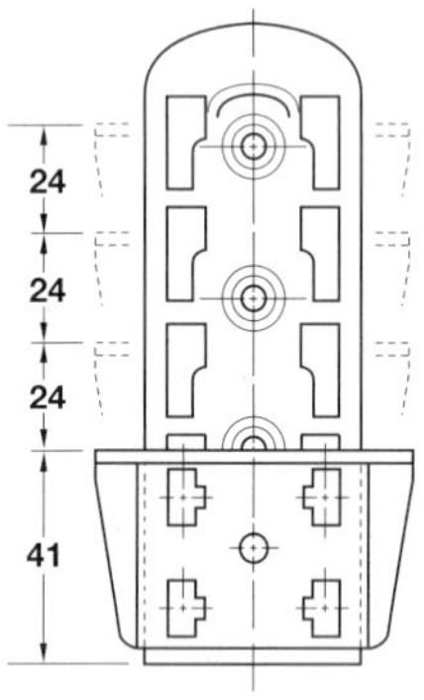

Three-stage vertical adjustment of tie-bar on double bed.

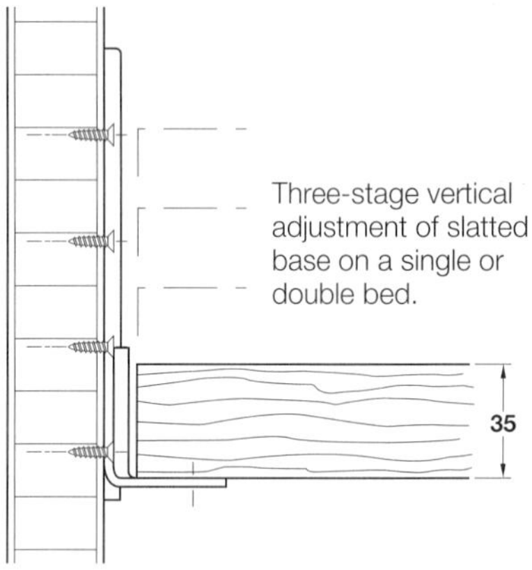

Three-stage vertical adjustment of slatted base on a single or double bed.

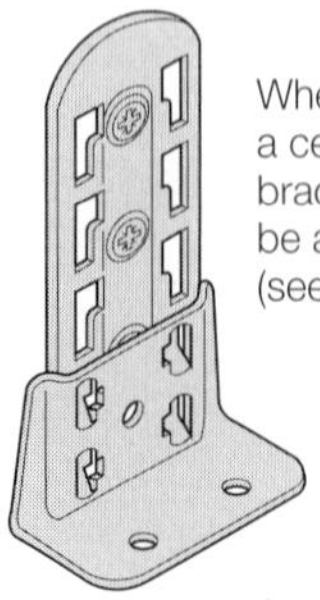

When used to secure a central tie-bar, the bracket support must be at the very bottom (see sketch).

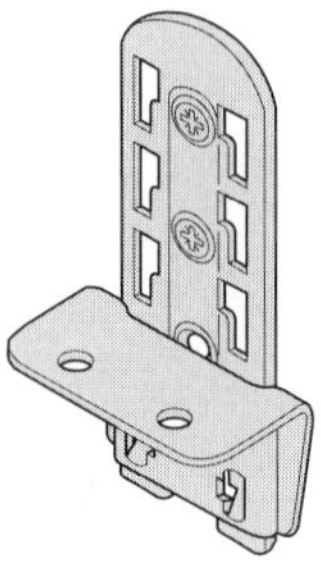

When used as a supporting fitting, the bracket support must be at the very top (see sketch).

Dimensional data not binding. We reserve the right to alter specifications without notice.

Dimensions in mm

Bed Fittings

Head section scissor jack
complete with mounting plates
raising height: max. 375 mm in 19 steps

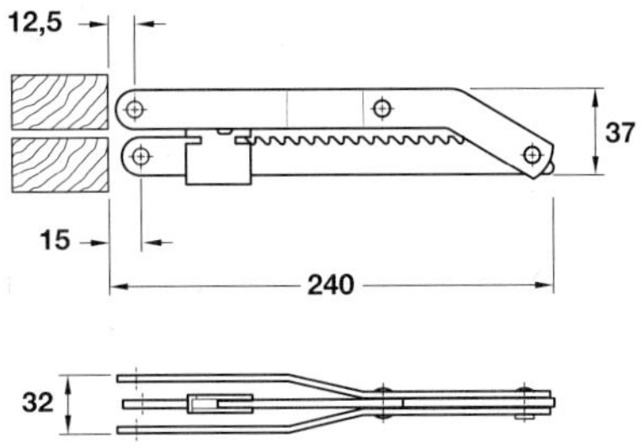

Finish: steel, yellow chromatized

Cat. No.	274.01.930

Packing: 20 pcs.

Upper mounting plate
with quick-action catch

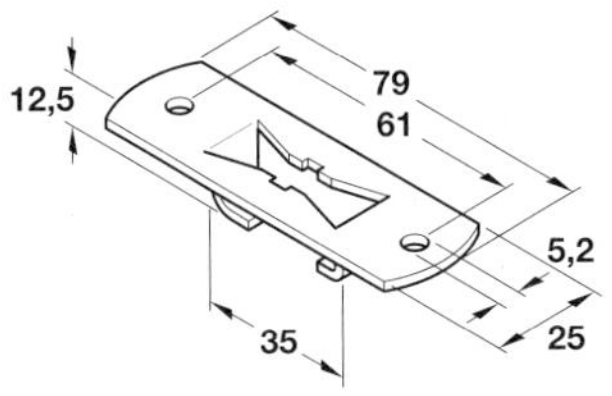

Lower mounting plate
(riveted)

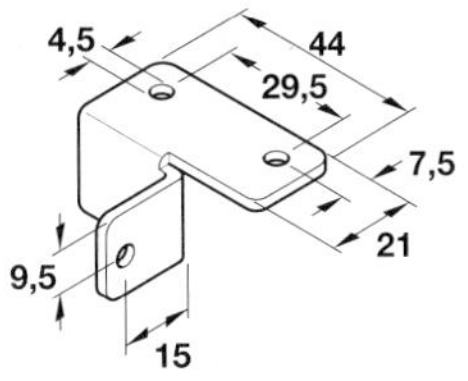

Foot section scissor jack
complete with mounting plates
raising height: max. 300 mm in 18 steps

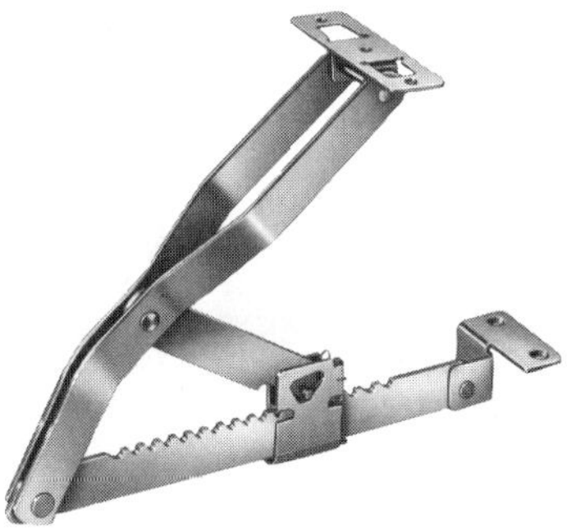

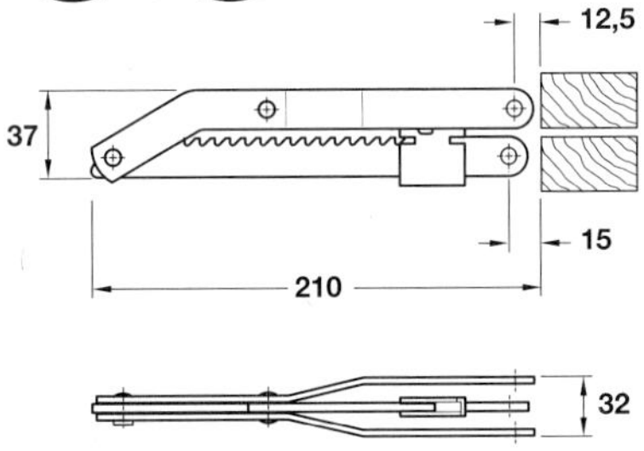

Finish: steel, yellow chromatized

Cat. No.	274.00.933

Packing: 20 pcs.

Upper mounting plate
with quick-action catch

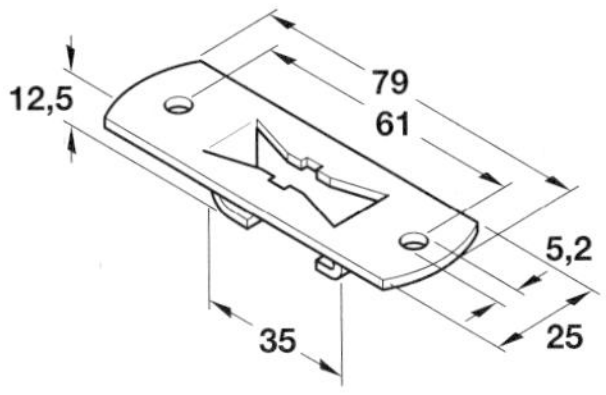

Lower mounting plate
(riveted)

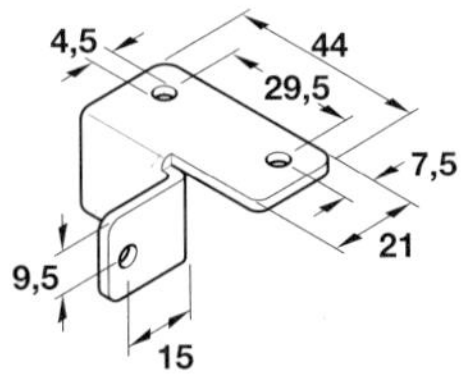

Dimensions in mm

Head section scissor jack

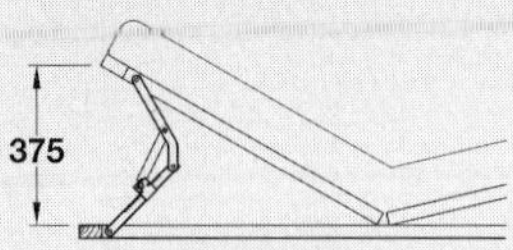

Foot section scissor jack

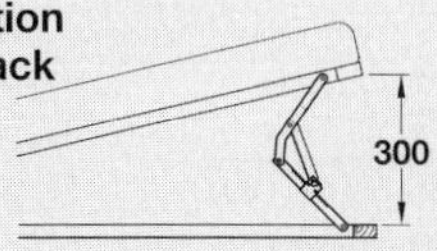

Lowering is achieved by lifting over the upper end position.

Applications for head section scissor jacks include...

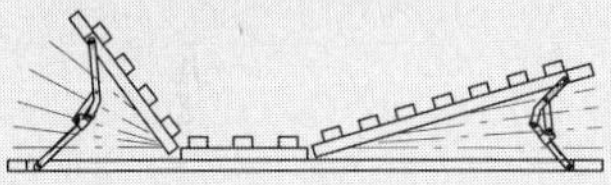

... adjustable head and foot sections of mattress frames ...

... or couches and French beds ...

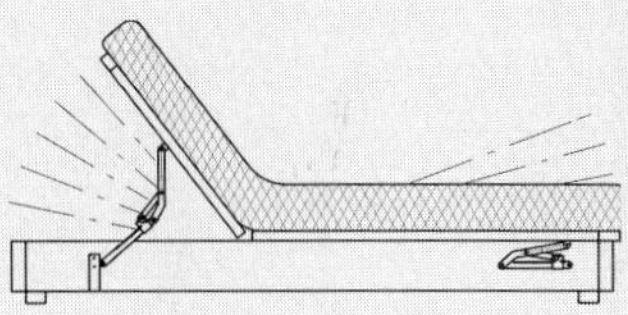

... just to mention a few.

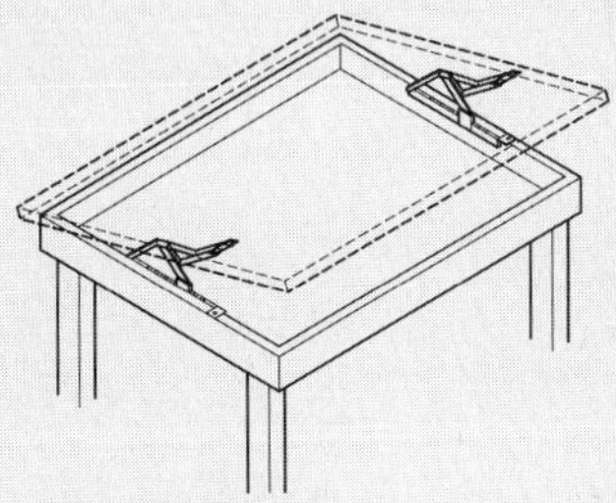

HÄFELE

Bed-lift Components

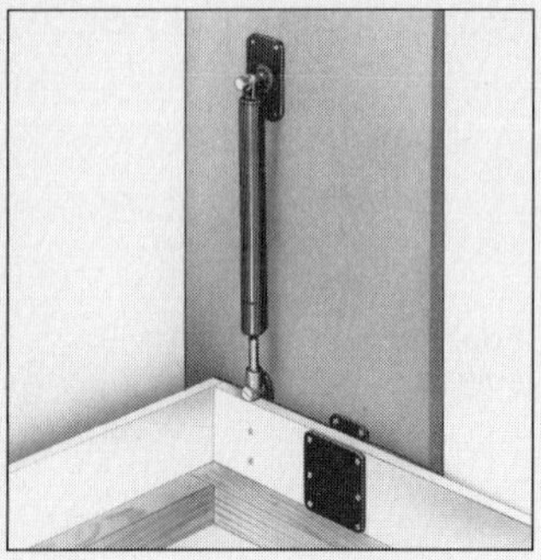

- Is recommended for twin-sized mattress 39" x 75"
- Mounting diagrams can be seen on following page
- Do not exceed recommended weight limits.
- Make sure bed is supported in down-position. (legs, etc...)
- Use throughbolts to install hardware.
- Use safety bracket against tipping.
- Install gas pistons with strap on pistons. Remove straps after pistons secured at pivots.

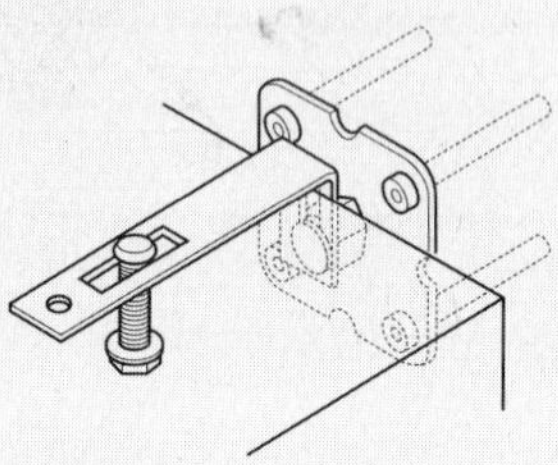

Safety stop
Finish: steel, powder-coated in an gray color

Cat. No.	271.98.100

Packing: 2 pcs.

Bed-lift for Vertical Mounting

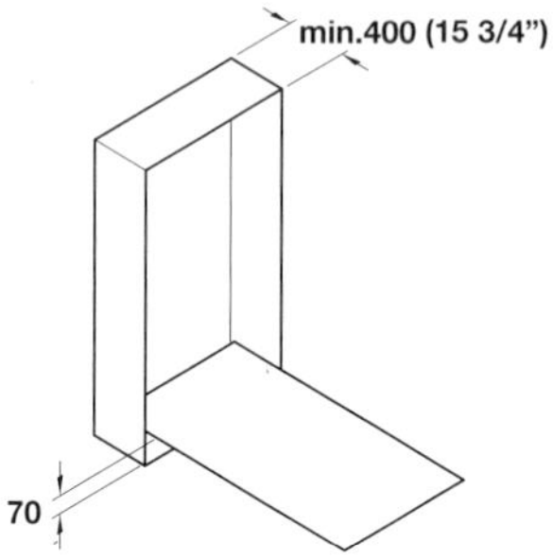

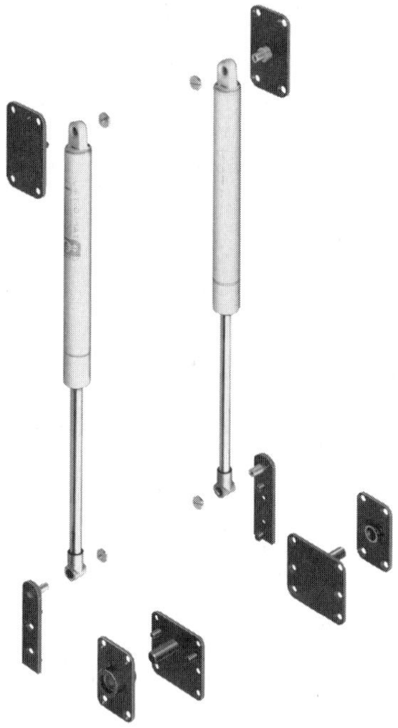

Includes:
- 2 pivot plates
- 2 upper and lower gas piston pivots
- 2 gas pistons 1100 Newtons
- 2 straps for mattress

Finish: steel, gray-brown

Cat. No.	271.95.955

Packing: 1 set

Bed-lift for Horizontal Mounting

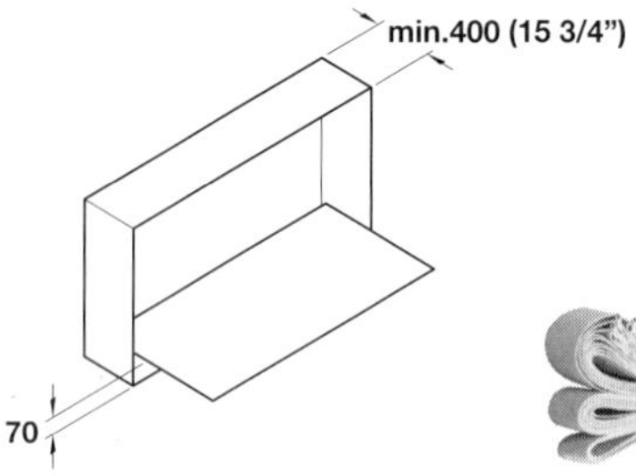

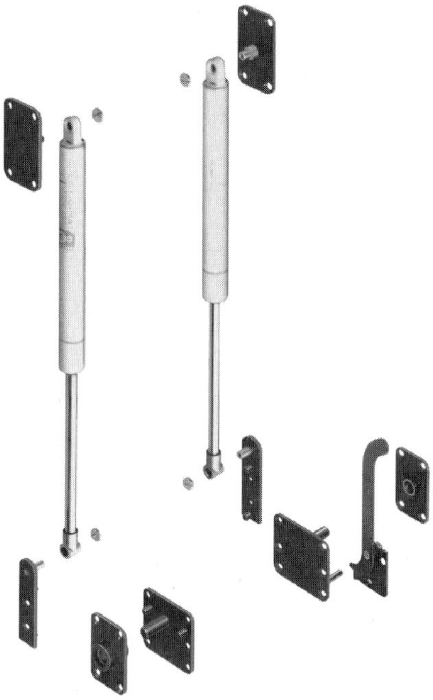

Includes:
- 2 pivot plates
- 2 upper and lower gas piston pivots
- 2 gas pistons 600 Newtons
- 1 safety lever
- 2 straps for mattress

Finish: steel, gray-brown

Cat. No.	271.95.946

Packing: 1 set

Folding Legs

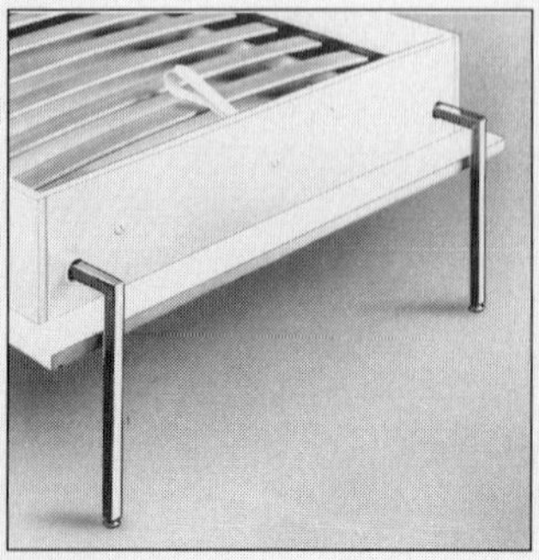

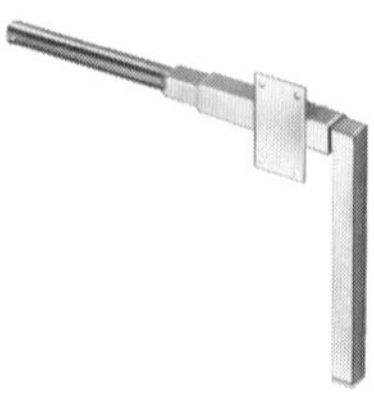

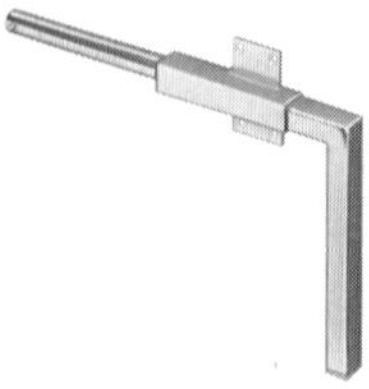

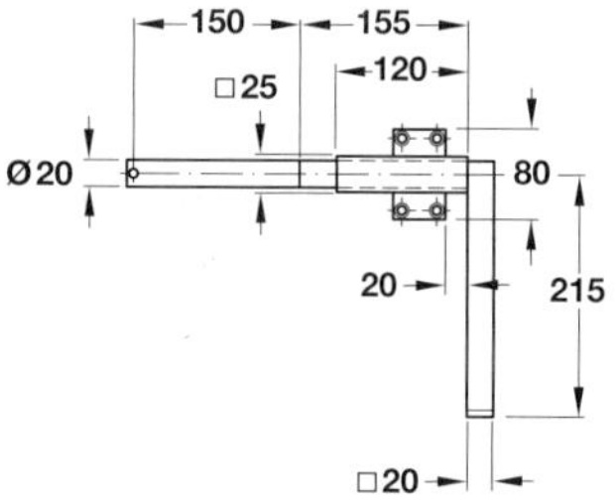

Dimensions in mm

Finish: steel

Cat. No.	271.95.964

Packing: 1 set

Legs need to be pulled out when bed is in an almost down position. Turn 90°.
The guide tube of the legs are mounted at the inside of the front plate, but behind bed frame.

Dimensions in mm

HÄFELE

Bed-lift Components

Foldaway bed fittings
This fitting is suitable for a foldaway bed to your own design. Weight rating must be adhered to. Is generally not recommeded for double or Queen-sized beds. Gas-filled struts control the opening and closing functions. Installation details are given in the mounting diagram.
The complete fitting comprises: 2 pivot bearing mounts and 2 counterplates with pivot pins, 2 upper brackets, 2 strut bearing mounts and 2 gas-filled struts.

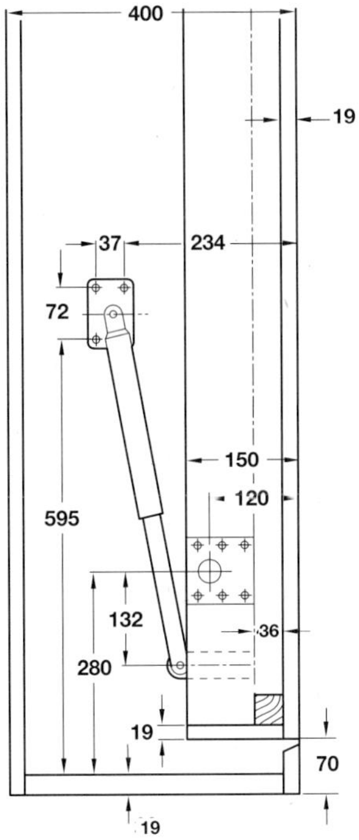

A precise **installation diagram**, with mounting instructions, is included with each pack.

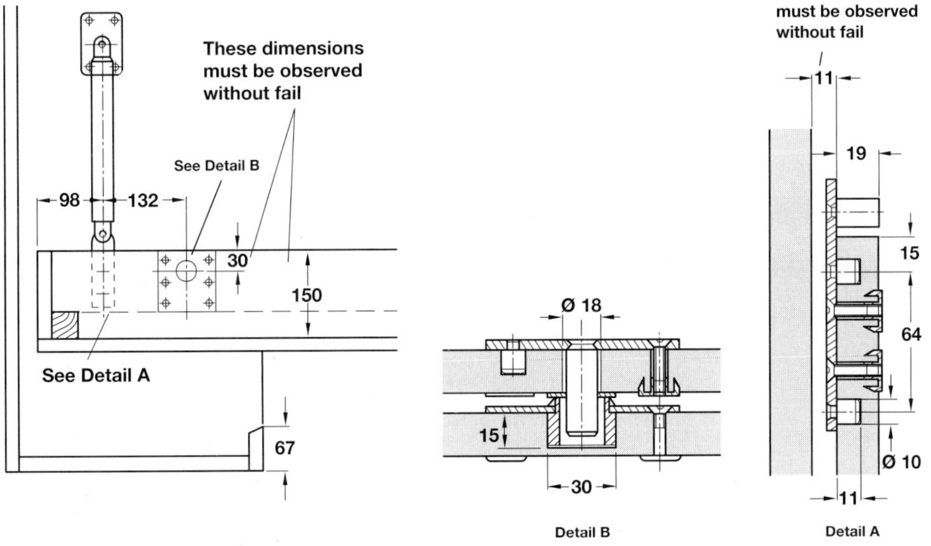

These bed fittings are an economical solution to build your own individually designed foldaway bed.

The gas pistons support a weight of approx. 55–65 kg (110–143 lbs) which equals the weight of a
- front plate 3/4 inch particle board and a
- mattress with bed linens (See twin size mattress pg. **2.207**)

Caution:
Bed must be secured to wall securely to guard against tipping.
The horizontal version must have the safety latch installed.
Gas pistons normally do not support double or queen beds.

Dimensions in mm

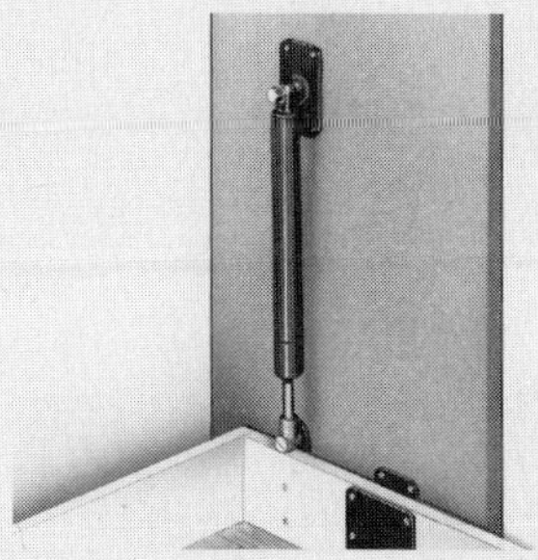

Locks, Catches, RTA and PAS® Fittings
Shelf Supports
Bed Fittings
2

Struts and folding feet for individual foldaway beds

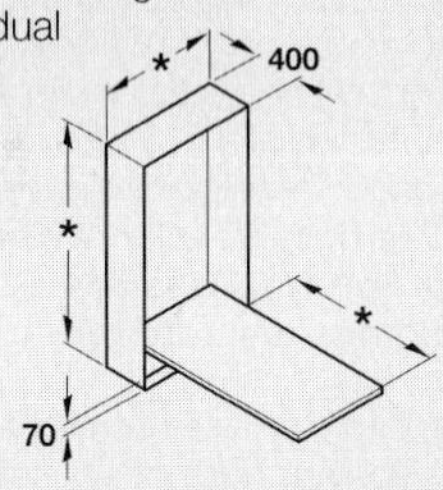

The folding legs must be in the out and down position when bed is lowered. Without leg support (due to leverage effect) the pivot points could break.

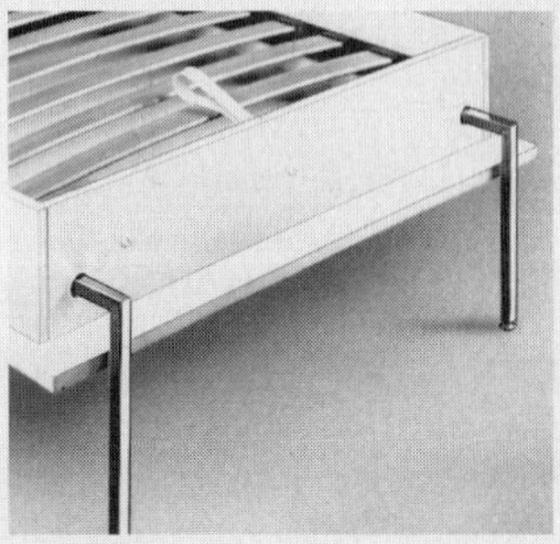

Instead of legs, large handles can be mounted which serve as supports when the bed is in the down position.

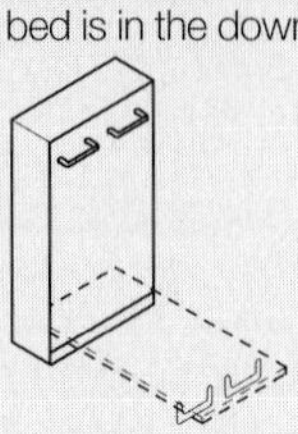

Another possibility is an overhead shelf.

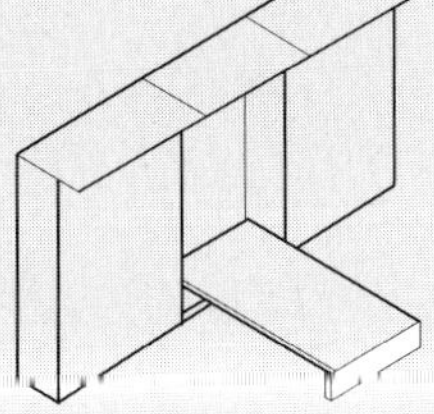

Dimensional data not binding.
We reserve the right to alter specifications without notice.

HÄFELE

Bed-lift, Complete System for Queen-size

Bed dimensions 2032 x 1524 mm, (80" x 60"); inset, adjustable front

- Sturdy, torsion-free, tubular steel frame, brown lacquer
- Integral automatic foot folding mechanism (i.e. the feet extend automatically when the bed is opened out for use and vice versa).
- Choice of toekick panel height from 75–95 mm.
- Laminated wooden slats, with elm finish,
- Mounted in articulated plastic seats, as mattress base.
- Concealed gas-filled struts.

Accessories: 3 bedding straps, safety brackets

2

Locks, Catches, RTA and PAS® Fittings
Shelf Supports
Bed Fittings

The gas filled pistons are designed to accompany a 19 mm (3/4") particle board front with a weight of approximately 100 lbs. and a mattress weighing up to 30 lbs. **The bed-lift will not operate properly unless these two ratings are adhered to.**

- Bed must be secured against tipping. Additional safety brackets on page **2.207**.
- See mattress on page **2.207**.

Queen-size with slatted mattress frame,
for inset front
Finish: steel, brown lacquer; slats: wood, elm

Cat. No.	271.92.130

Packing: 1 set, includes mounting instructions

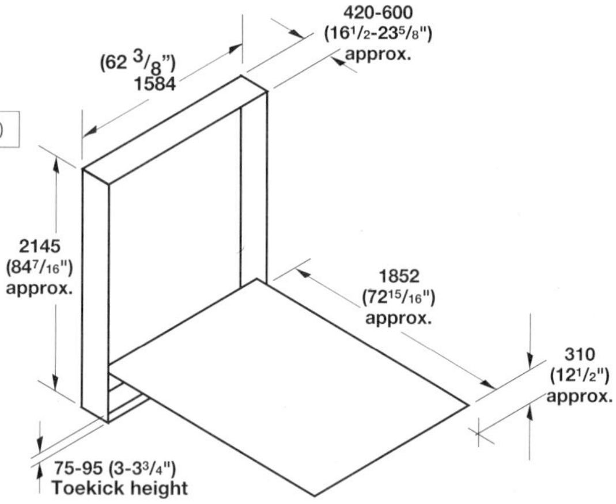

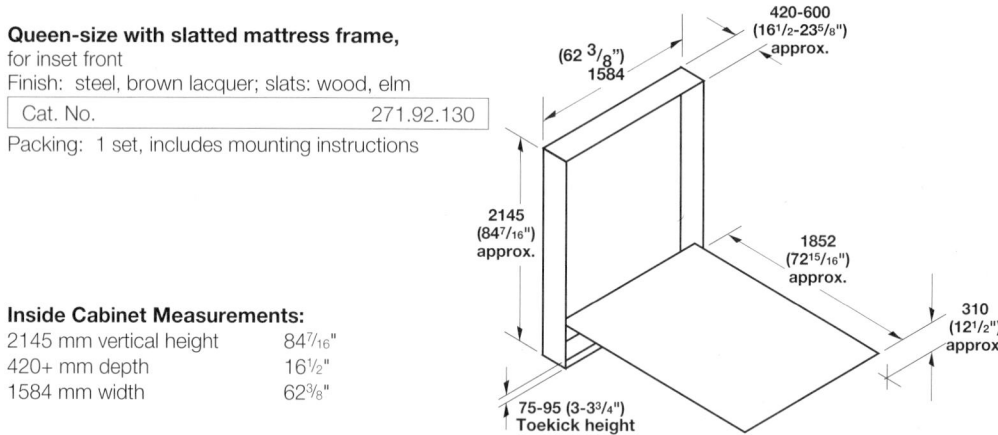

Inside Cabinet Measurements:

2145 mm vertical height	84 7/16"
420+ mm depth	16 1/2"
1584 mm width	62 3/8"

Bed-lift installation has never been so easy and safe. Hafele's bed-lift system comes complete with pre-mounted fittings and can be installed in 4 easy steps.

Now with quick installation...after the cabinet is built, it's a simple 4-step process to install the bed frame.

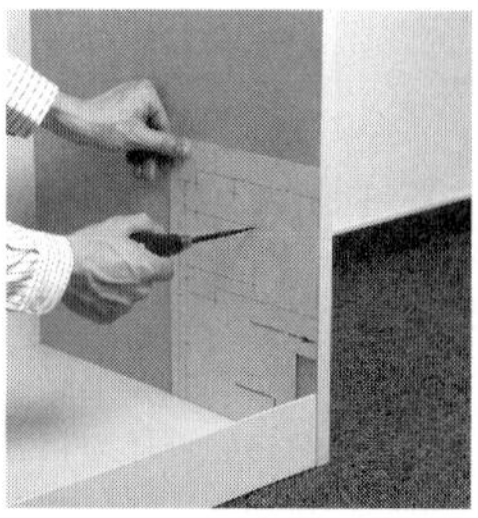

1. Mark drilling position on both panels with the aid of the included drilling pattern.

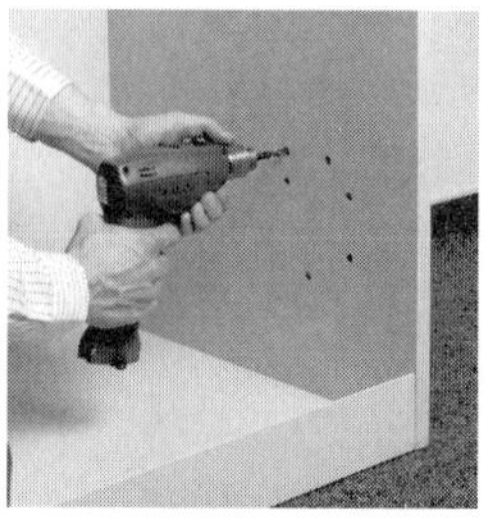

2. Drill 7 holes in each side panel.

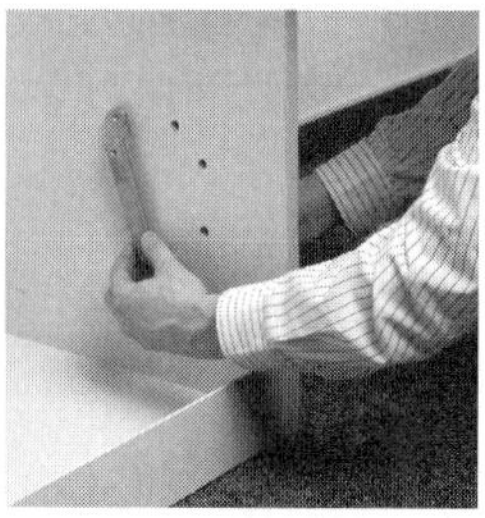

3. Fasten the two support brackets with the screws provided.

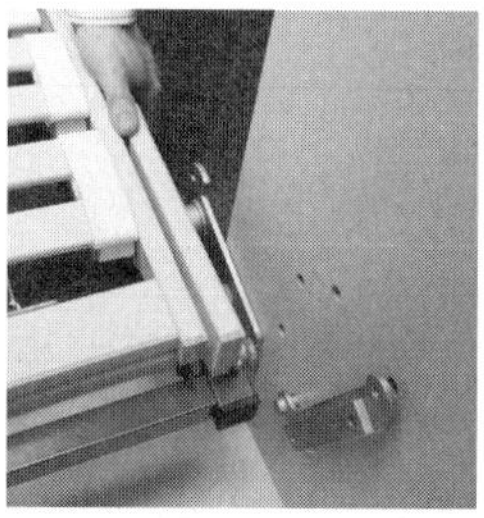

4. Slide bed frame onto support brackets, tighten screws, and attach the front panel.

Dimensional data not binding. We reserve the right to alter specifications without notice.

Dimensions in mm
Inches are approximate

Bed-lifts for Mattresses, Queen-size, Twin size

HÄFELE

- For folding bed on page 000 Hafele Cat. No. 271.2.130 and Häfele bed-fittings on page 000.

Locks, Catches, RTA and PAS® Fittings
Shelf Supports
Bed Fittings

2

Material: foam
Size: Queen-size and twin-size, height 5½ inches
Color: blue, welted white
Density: 45 lbs/cubic foot

Cat. No.	60 x 80 x 5.5" (25lbs) Queen	271.65.530
	39 x 75 x 5.5" (17lbs) Twin	271.65.510

Packing: 1 pc.
Fiber content: 100% Polyester
Finish: Fire retardant, Teflon coated

- Vertical bump test #701
- Motor vehicle safety #302
- Smoke density test #258
- More test data available upon request

"Safe" safety stop
Secures folding beds to wall.
The special design of this fitting ensures that force is distributed evenly over all the mounting bolts even offers adjustability for alignment.
The swiveling wall plate permits straightforward mounting in any position.

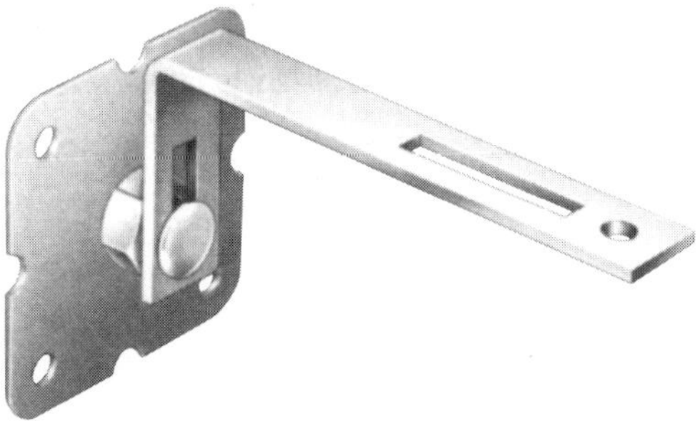

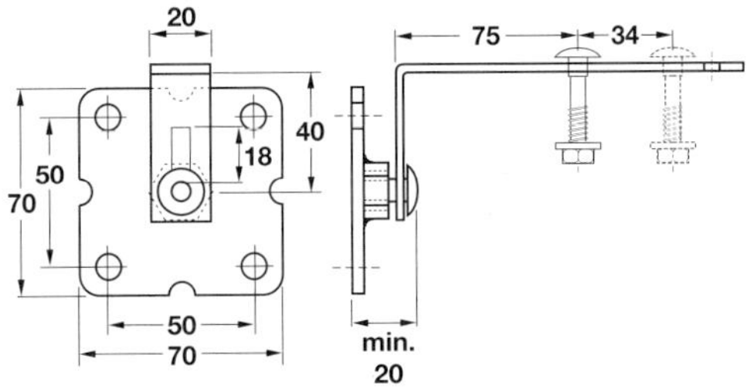

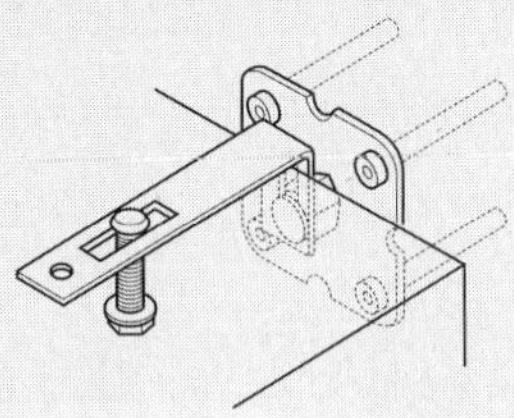

Finish: steel, galvanized

Cat. No.	271.98.100

Packing: 2 complete fittings (including all mounting bolts and Fisher S6R-60 wall anchors)

To comply with DIN 68 873, foldaway beds must be installed with a minimum of two safety fittings.

Dimensional data not binding.
We reserve the right to alter specifications without notice.

HÄFELE

Metric Conversion Chart

Length

For our purposes, the basic metric units of *length* are the **millimeter and the meter.**

To convert inches to millimeters, multiply inches x 25.4

Inches	To	Millimeters
1/16"		1.59 mm
1/8"		3.18 mm
3/16"		4.76 mm
1/4"		6.35 mm
3/8"		9.53 mm
1/2"		12.70 mm
5/8"		15.88 mm
3/4"		19.05 mm
7/8"		22.23 mm
1"		25.40 mm
2"		50.80 mm
4"		101.60 mm
6"		152.40 mm
8"		203.20 mm
10"		254.00 mm
12"		304.80 mm
16"		406.40 mm
18"		457.20 mm
21"		533.40 mm
24"		609.60 mm
27"		685.80 mm
30"		762.00 mm
33"		838.20 mm
36"		914.40 mm
39"		990.60 mm
48"		1219.20 mm

To convert millimeters to inches, divide millimeters by 25.4

Millimeters	To	Inches
1 mm		1/16"
3 mm		1/8"
6 mm		1/4"
8 mm		5/16"
10 mm		3/8"
12 mm		1/2"
16 mm		5/8"
19 mm		3/4"
22 mm		7/8"
25.4 mm		1"
32 mm		1 1/4"
100 mm		4"
305 mm		12"
500 mm		19 3/4"
1000 mm		39 3/8"

*Inches are expressed to the nearest 16th.

To convert meters to feet, multiply meters by 3.3

Meters	To	Feet
1 meter		3' 3 3/8"
2 meters		6' 6 3/4"
2.5 meters		8' 2 1/2"
4 meters		13' 1 1/2"
6 meters		19' 8 1/4"

Weight

The basic metric unit of *weight* is the **kilogram.**

To convert kilograms to pounds, multiply kilograms x 2.2

Kilograms	To	Pounds
1 kg		2.2 lbs.
10 kg		22 lbs.
50 kg		110 lbs.

Volume

The basic metric unit of *volume* is the **liter.**

To convert liters to gallons, multiply liters x 0.26

Liters	To	Gallons
1 liter		0.26 gallons
4 liter		1 gallon
15 liter		4 gallons

Product Guide - Hinges and Associated Fittings

Concealed Adjustable Hinges
Pages **3.2 - 3.43**

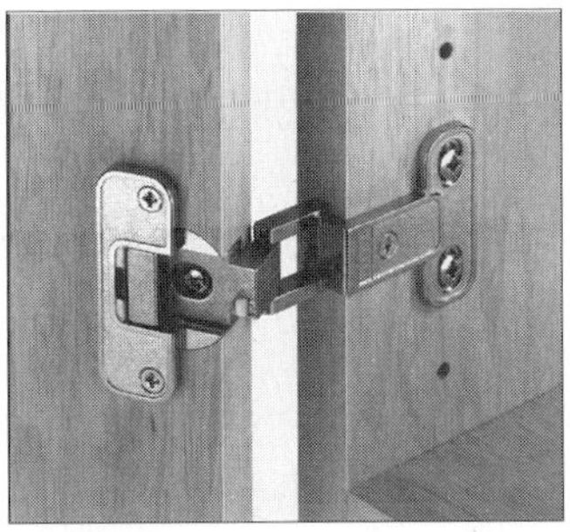

AXIMAT® Hinges
Pages **3.44 - 3.56**

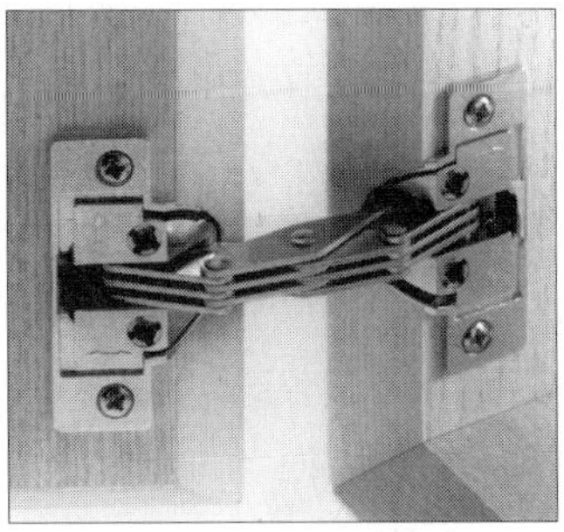

Miter Hinges / SpecialApplication
Pages **3.60**

Concealed Hinges
Pages **3.62 - 3.64**

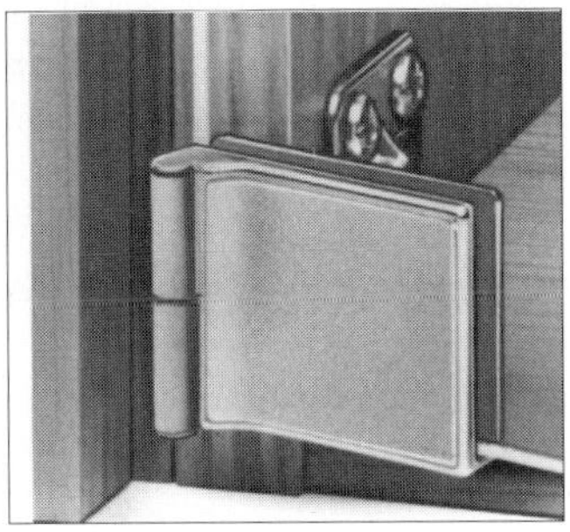

Glass Door Hinges
Pages **3.65 - 3.71**

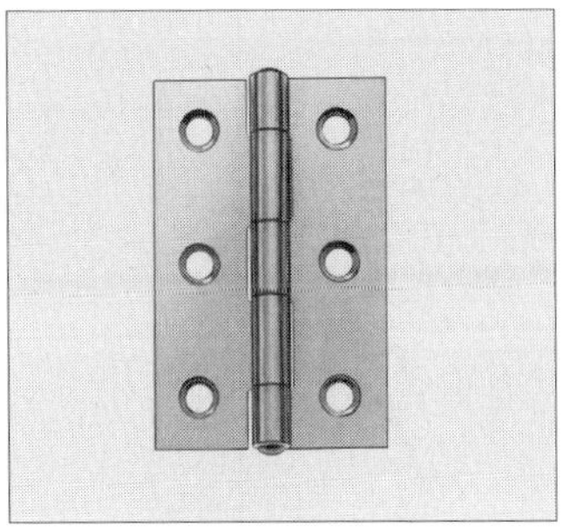

Knuckle Hinges
Pages **3.73 - 3.76**

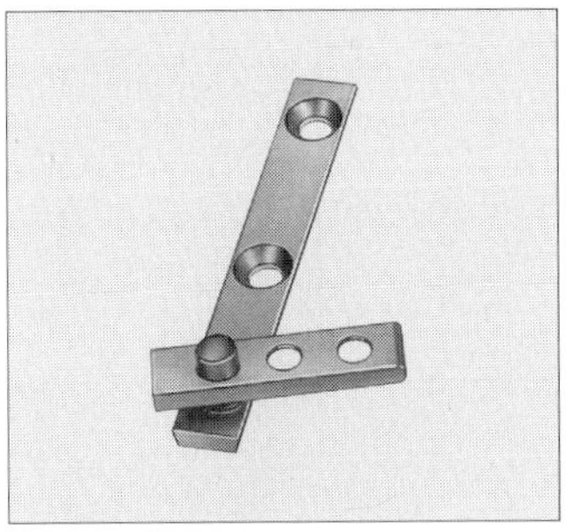

Pivot Hinges
Pages **3.77 - 3.78**

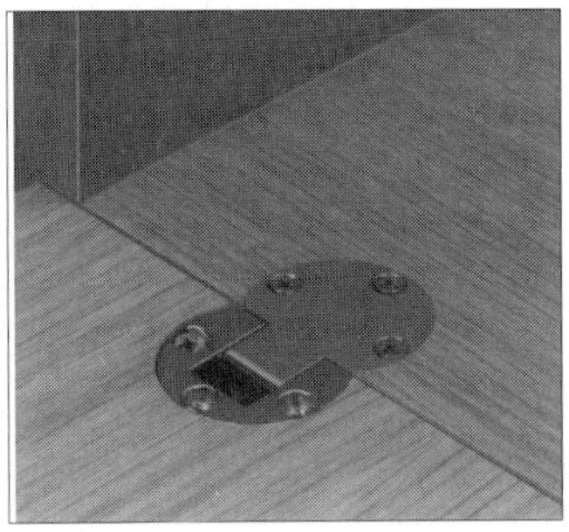

Flap Hinges
Pages **3.80 - 3.82**

Flap Stays
Pages **3.83 - 3.92**

Lid Stays
Pages **3.93 - 3.104**

Synchronizing Door Mechanism
Page **3.106**

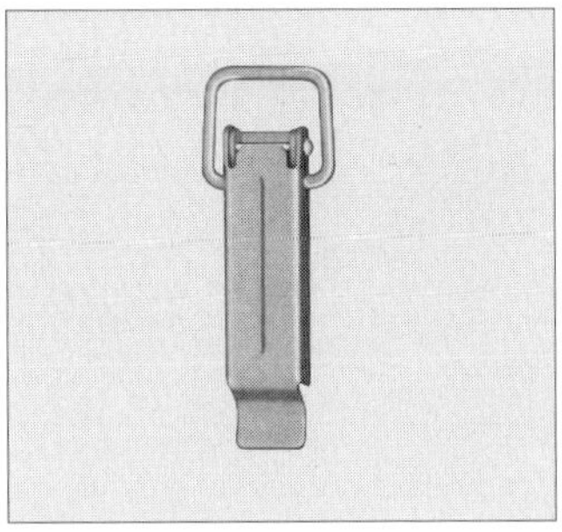

Chest Fittings
Page **3.107**

HÄFELE

Duomatic Hinges

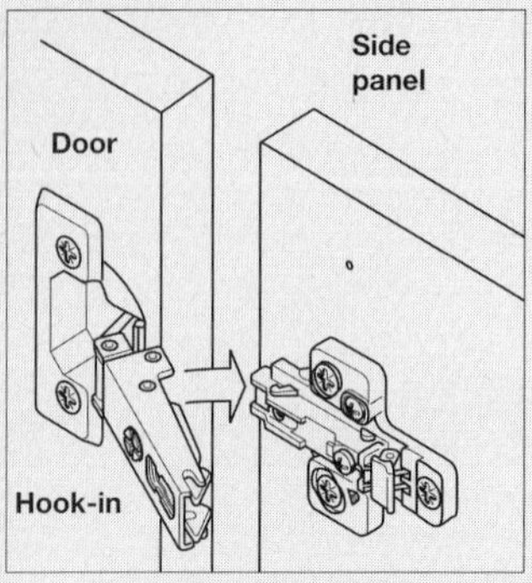

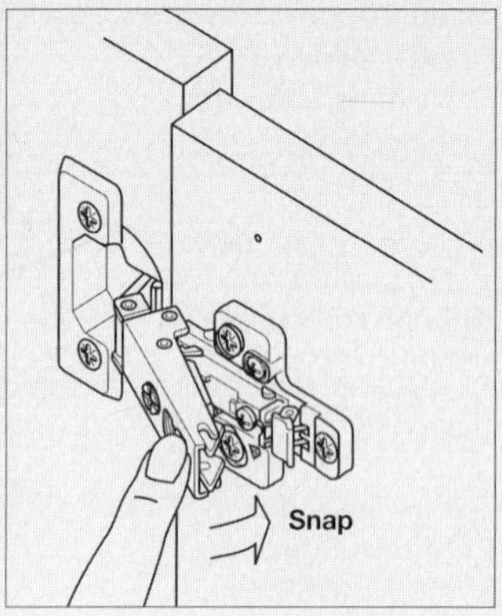

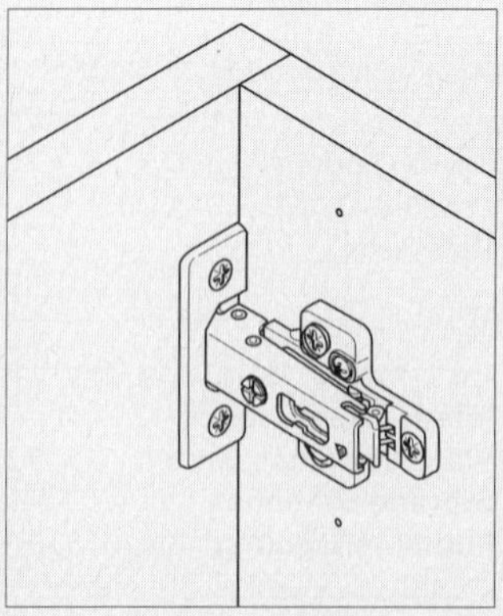

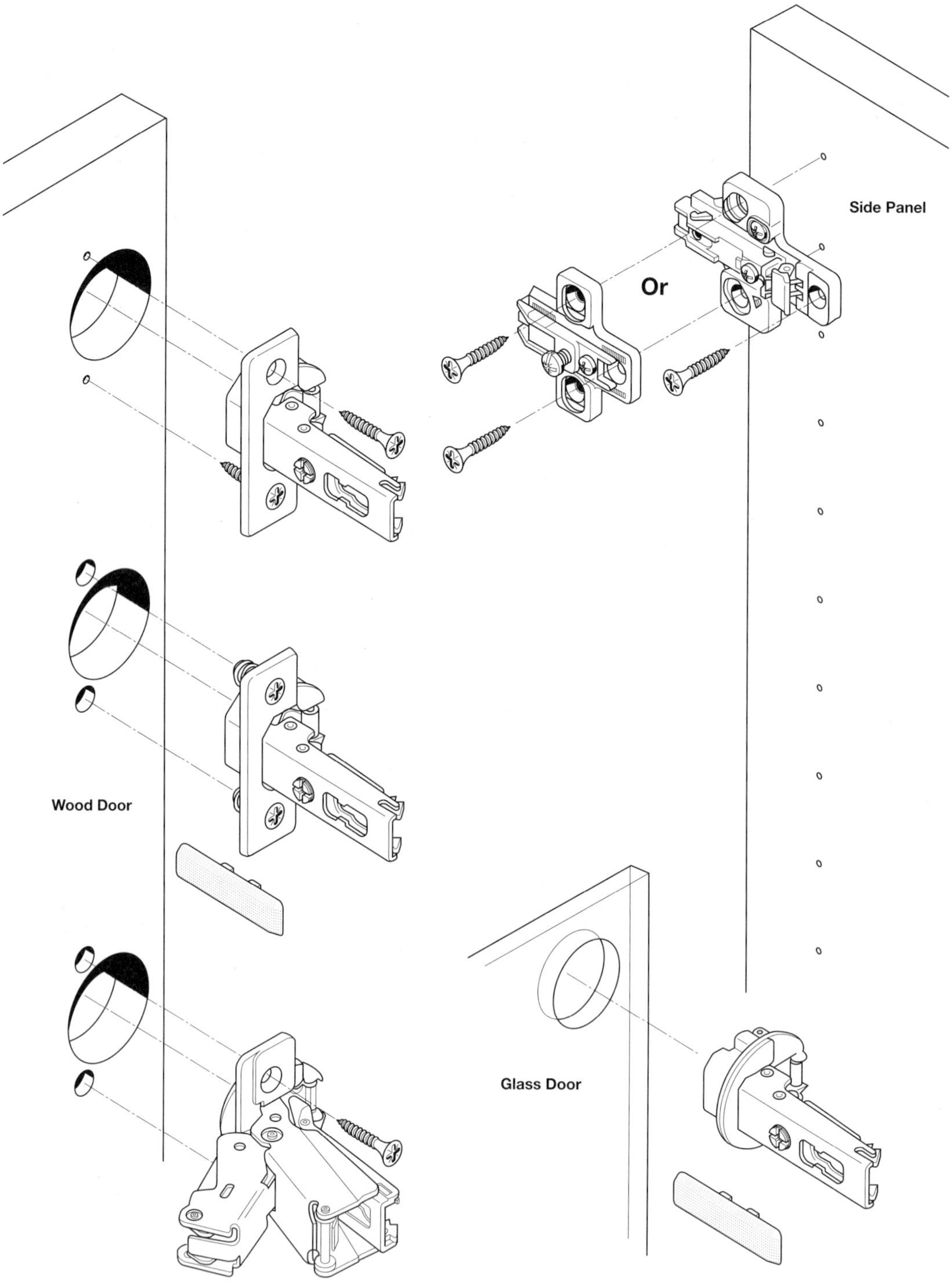

Adjustments

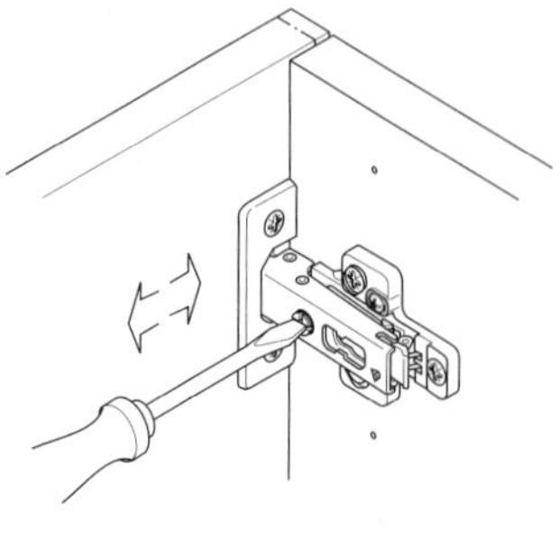

Horizontal
by screw adjustment

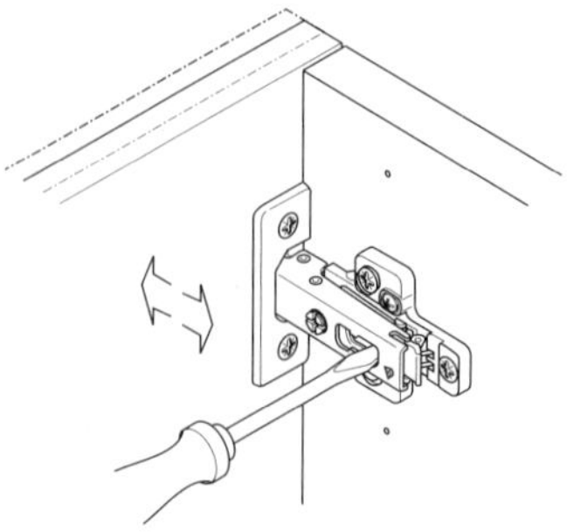

In and out
by loosening the hing-arm mounting screw

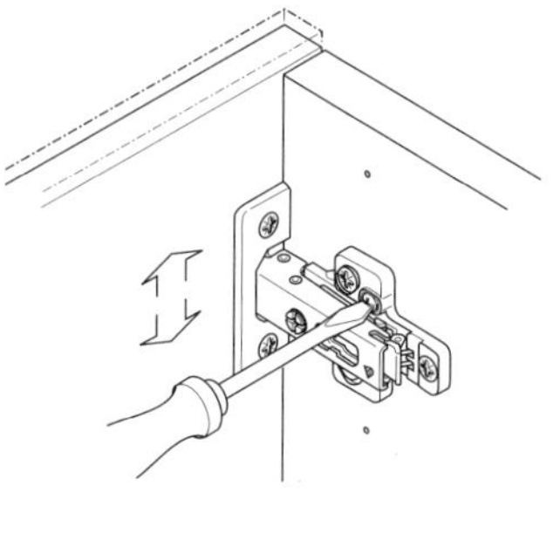

Vertical
via slots in the mounting plate

Duomatic Hinges

HÄFELE

Guide to Duomatic Hinges

Hinge type	Hinge cup material	Max. door opening angle	Cup mounting method	Type ❍ non self-closing ● self-closing 21	17	10	8	0	-1	Featured on page
	Steel	95°	Screw-mount or Press-fit		●		●	●		3.6
	Steel	110°	Screw-mount or Press-fit		●		●			3.7
	Steel	120°	Screw-mount or Press-fit		●		●			3.8
	Zinc die-cast 40mm dia.	95°	Screw-mount	●		●			●	3.9
	Plastic 26mm dia.	90°	Screw-mount		●		●	●		3.10
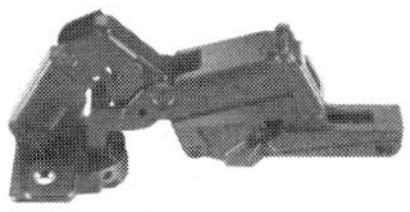	Zinc die-cast	165°	Screw-mount or Press-fit		●		●			3.11
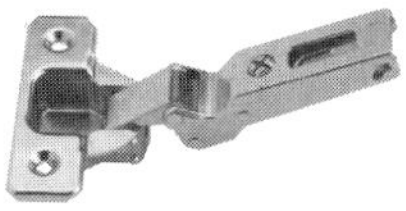	steel	95°	Screw-mount				●			3.15
	Steel	95°	Screw-mount or Press-fit				●			3.13
	Steel	95°	Screw-mount or Press-fit				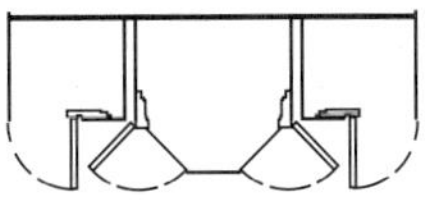 ●			3.14
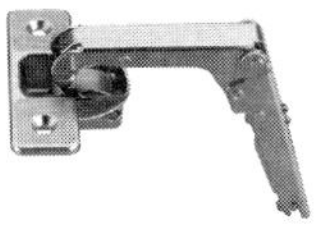	Steel Zinc die-cast	70°	Screw-mount or Press-fit				●			3.12

Hinges, Flap and Lid Stays Associated Fittings

3

Dimensional data not binding. We reserve the right to alter specifications without notice.

HÄFELE

Duomatic Hinges

Guide to Duomatic Clip Mounting plates

Mounting plate type	Wing plate	Mounting method	Material	System hole mounting	Reinforcement Type With vertical adjustment 2	3	5	6	8	11
	yes	screw	Zinc die-cast + steel		•		•			
	yes	screw	Zinc die-cast + steel	SYSTEM VARIANTA 32	•		•			
	yes	screw	Zinc die-cast + steel		•		•		•	•
	yes	screw	Zinc die-cast + steel	SYSTEM VARIANTA 32	•		•		•	•
	yes	screw	Zinc die-cast + steel			•		•		

Guide to Duomatic Mounting plates

Mounting plate type	Wing plate	Mounting method	Material	System hole mounting	Reinforcement Type With vertical adjustment 2	3	5	6	8	11
	yes	screw	Zinc alloy			•				
	yes	screw	Zinc die-cast		•		•			
	yes	screw	Zinc die-cast	SYSTEM VARIANTA 32	•		•			
	yes	screw	Steel		•		•		•	•
	yes	screw	Steel	SYSTEM VARIANTA 32	•		•		•	•

Duomatic Hinges

HÄFELE

Which hinge type?

Given the factors:
- Opening angle
- Hinge arm type
- Side panel thickness
- Door thickness
- Screw-mount or press-fit
- Mounting plate thickness
- Tab

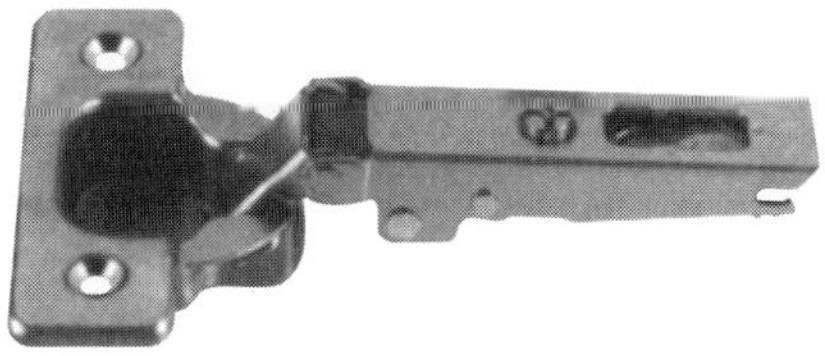

Use the following formula to determine overlay:

Hinge type *minus* mounting plate type *plus* tab = overlay

Sample Calculations

Hinge Type 17
Side panel mounting
for overlay doors

Hinge Type 8
Center panel/twin mounting
overlay doors

Hinge Type 0
Side panel mounting
for inset doors

(A) Full Overlay

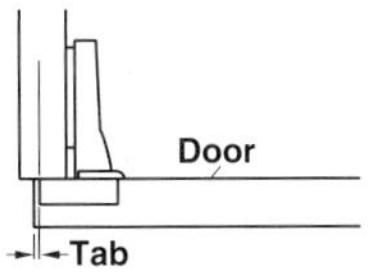

(B) Half Overlay or Twin Mounting

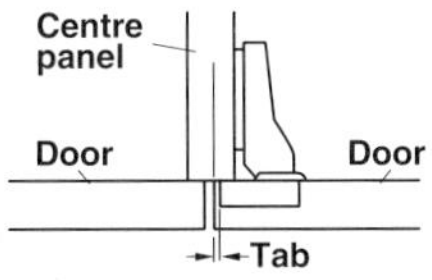

(C) Inset

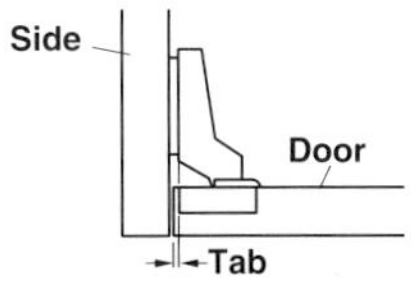

16 mm (5/8") Material	Hinge Type		Mounting Plate		Tab		Total Overlay
Full overlay (A)	17	-	5	+	3	=	15
Half overlay (B)	8	-	5	+	4	=	7
Inset (C)	0	-	2	+	3	=	*1

19 mm (3/4") Material	Hinge Type		Mounting Plate		Tab		Total Overlay
Full overlay (A)	17	-	2	+	3	=	18
Half overlay (B)	8	-	2	+	3	=	9
Inset (C)	0	-	2	+	3	=	*1

*Adjust to 0 overlay using side adjustment.

If there is no mounting plate with the required reinforcement, then the tab or gap must be altered.

How many hinges per door?

There is no hard and fast rule which applies. When determining the number of hinges needed, the main factors to consider are door size and weight. A trial mounting is advisable in case of any doubt, such as with doors supporting mirrors, or unusually wide doors. Avoid dispro-portionate door width/height ratios. Use this table for standard, conventional-material doors. When in doubt, always allow for an extra hinge.

- Commercial and heavy duty applications, see Häfele's Aximat hinge.

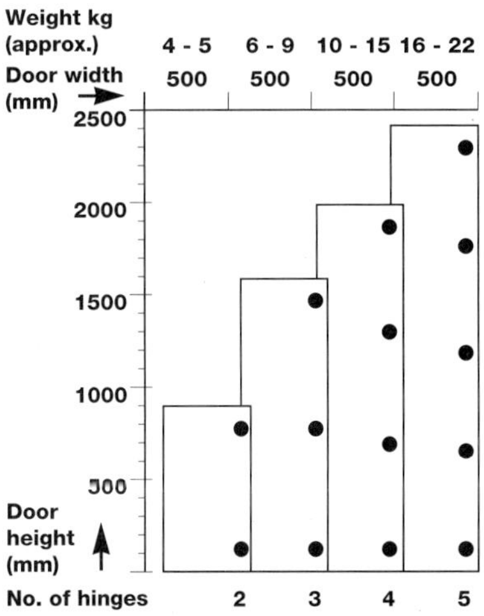

Hinges,
Flap and Lid Stays
Associated Fittings
3

Dimensional data not binding. We reserve the right to alter specifications without notice.

HÄFELE

Duomatic Hinges

Opening angle: 95°

- Door thickness 16 to 32 mm (5/8" - 1 1/4")
- Side panel thickness from 16 mm (5/8")
- Self-closing
- All-metal:
  Cup: steel, nickel-plated
  Hinge arm: steel, nickel-plated
- Tab = 3 - 8 mm

Corresponding mounting plates can be found on pages **3.16-3.19**

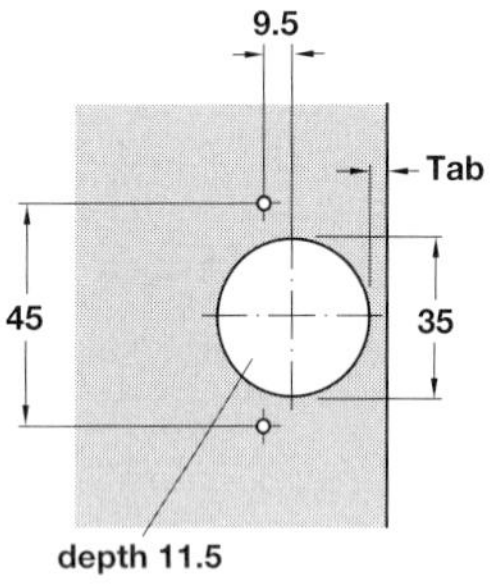

HOSPA ⌀3,5

Screw-mount

Mounting	Hinge arm		Hinge type	Cat. No.
Full overlay		straight	**17**	329.01.509
Half overlay		9 mm crank	**8**	329.01.518
Inset mounting		17 mm crank	**0**	329.01.536

Packing: 300 pcs.

Mounting screws:
Hospa particle board screws **raised head** with PZ 2 cross slot
Finish:
steel, nickel-plated

HOSPA ⌀3,5

Length	Cat. No.
15 mm	015.55.639
20 mm	015.55.657
25 mm	015.55.675

Packing: 1000 pcs.

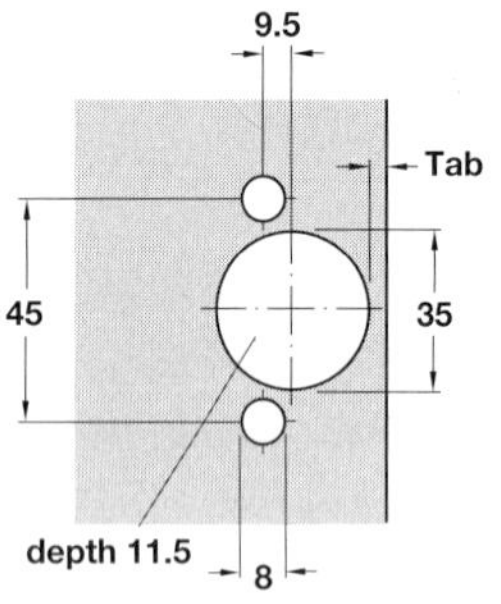

Press-fit, 45/9.5 hole pattern

Mounting	Hinge arm		Hinge type	Cat. No.
Full overlay		straight	**17**	329.01.554
Half overlay		9 mm crank	**8**	329.01.563
Inset mounting		17 mm crank	**0**	329.01.581

Packing: 300 pcs.

Max. door offset at 95º

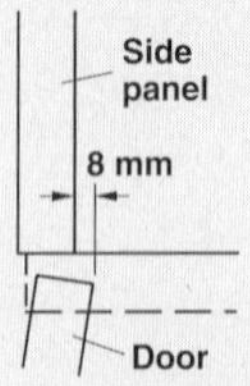

Protrusion shown is based on straight arm and smallest available mounting plate.

Trim caps for hinge arm, finish: plastic, black

Hinge arm	Catalog No.		
Straight		white	329.18.700
		black	329.18.308

Packing: 5000 pcs.

Dimensional data not binding. We reserve the right to alter specifications without notice.

Dimensions in mm

Duomatic Hinges

HÄFELE

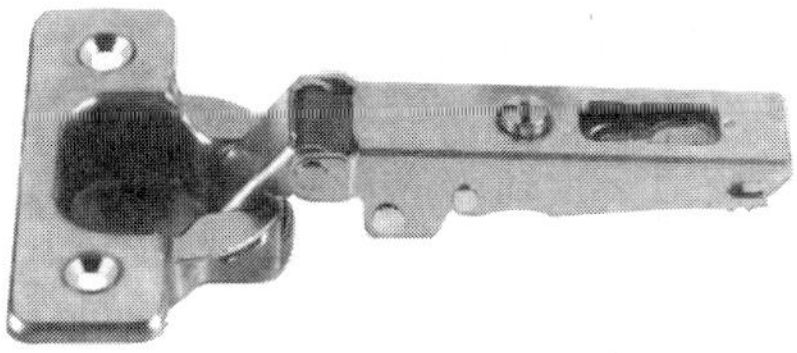

Opening angle: 110°

- Door thickness 16 to 26 mm (5/8" - 1")
- Side panel thickness from 16 mm (5/8")
- Self-closing
- All-metal:
  Cup: steel, nickel-plated
  Hinge arm: steel, nickel-plated
- Tab = 3 - 8 mm

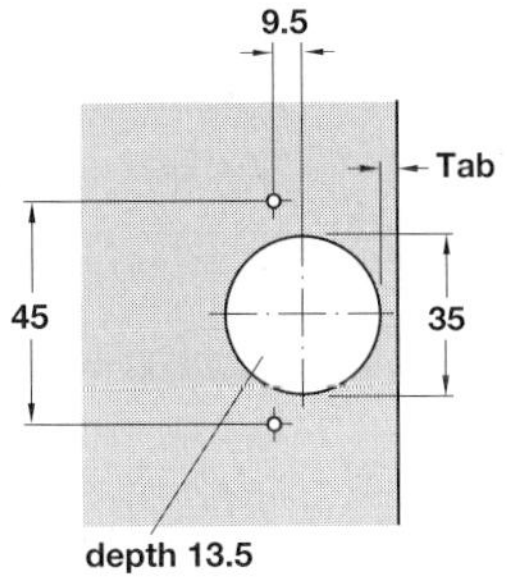

HOSPA ⌀3.5

Screw-mount

Mounting	Hinge arm		Hinge type	Cat. No.
Full overlay		straight	**17**	329.17.507
Half overlay		9 mm crank	**8**	329.17.516

Packing: 300 pcs.

Hinges, Flap and Lid Stays Associated Fittings **3**

Corresponding mounting plates can be found on pages **3.16-3.19**

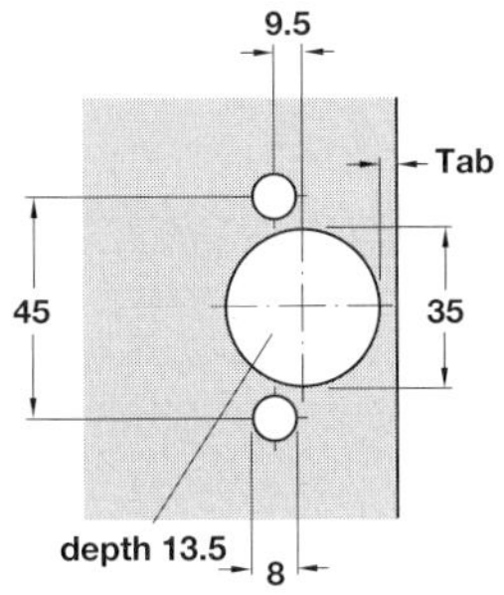

Press-fit 45/9.5 hole pattern

Mounting	Hinge arm		Hinge type	Cat. No.
Full overlay		straight	**17**	329.17.552
Half overlay		9 mm crank	**8**	329.17.561

Packing: 300 pcs.

Mounting screws:
Hospa particle board screws **raised head** with PZ 2 cross slot
Finish:
steel, nickel-plated

HOSPA ⌀3.5

Length	Cat. No.
15 mm	015.55.639
20 mm	015.55.657
25 mm	015.55.675

Packing: 1000 pcs.

Trim caps for hinge arm, finish: plastic, black

Hinge arm	Catalog No.		
Straight		white	329.18.700
		black	329.18.308

Packing: 5000 pcs.

Max. door offset at 110º

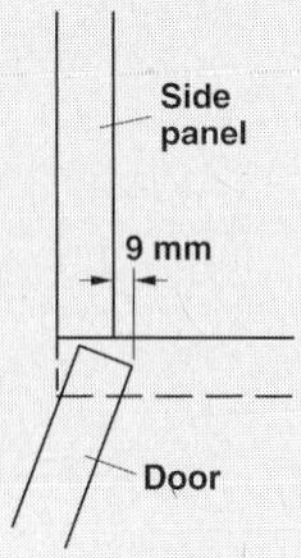

Protrusion shown is based on straight arm and smallest available mounting plate.

Dimensional data not binding. We reserve the right to alter specifications without notice.

HÄFELE

Duomatic Hinges

Opening angle: 120°

- Door thickness 16 to 26 mm (5/8" to 1")
- Side panel thickness from 16 mm (5/8")
- Self-closing
- All-metal:
  Cup: steel, nickel-plated
  Hinge arm: steel, nickel-plated
- Tab 3 – 8 mm

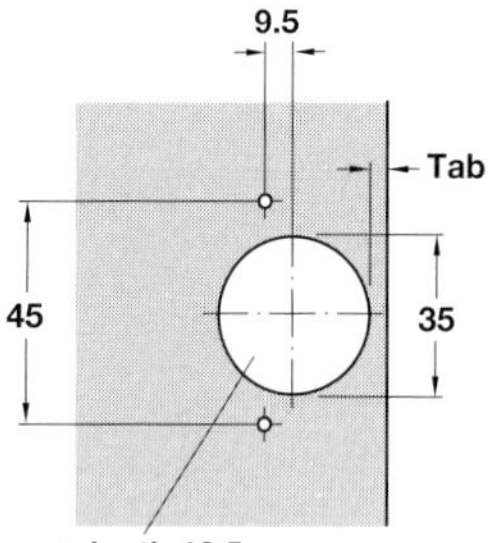

HOSPA Φ3.5

Screw-mount

Mounting	Hinge arm		Hinge type	Cat. No.
Full overlay		straight	**17**	329.03.503
Half overlay		9 mm crank	**8**	329.03.512

Packing: 300 pcs.

3 Hinges, Flap and Lid Stays Associated Fittings

Corresponding mounting plates can be found on pages **3.16-3.19**

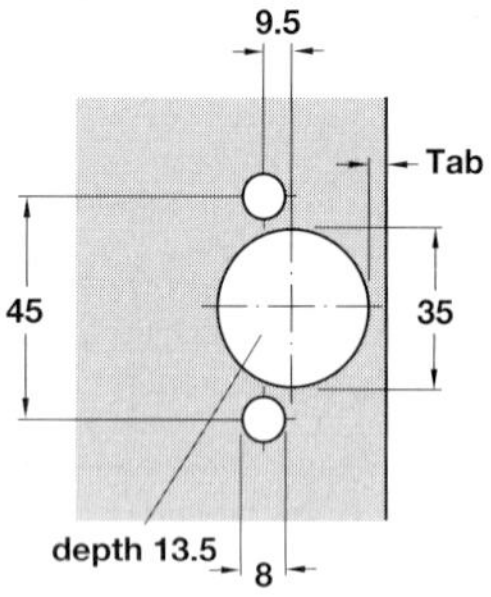

Press-fit 45/9.5 hole pattern

Mounting	Hinge arm		Hinge type	Cat. No.
Full overlay		straight	**17**	329.03.558
Half overlay		9 mm crank	**8**	329.03.567

Packing: 300 pcs.

Mounting screws:
Hospa particle board screws
raised head with
PZ 2 cross slot
Finish:
steel, nickel-plated

HOSPA Φ3.5

Length	Cat. No.
15 mm	015.55.639
20 mm	015.55.657
25 mm	015.55.675

Packing: 1000 pcs.

Trim caps for hinge arm, finish: plastic, black

Hinge arm	Catalog No.		
		white	329.18.700
Straight		black	329.18.308

Packing: 5000 pcs.

Max. door offset at 120º

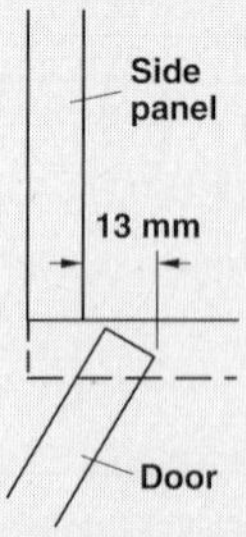

Protrusion shown is based on straight arm and smallest available mounting plate.

Dimensional data not binding. We reserve the right to alter specifications without notice.

Dimensions in mm

Duomatic Hinges For Thick Doors

HÄFELE

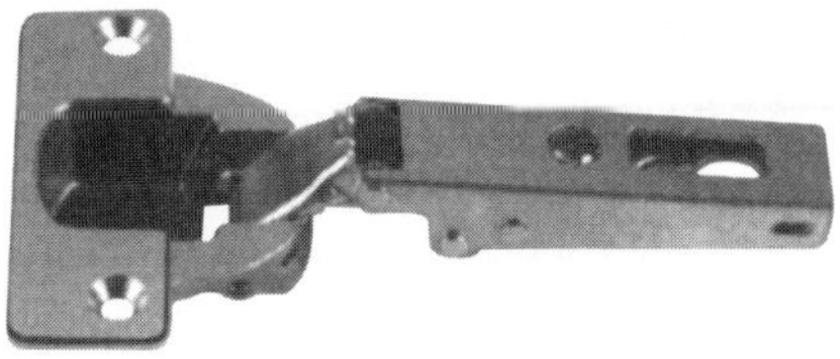

Opening angle: 95°

- Door thickness 18 to 43 mm (3/4" to 1 3/4")
- Side panel thickness from 16 mm (5/8")
- Self-closing
- All-metal:
  Cup: zinc die-cast, nickel-plated
  Hinge arm: steel, nickel-plated
- Tab 3 – 14 mm

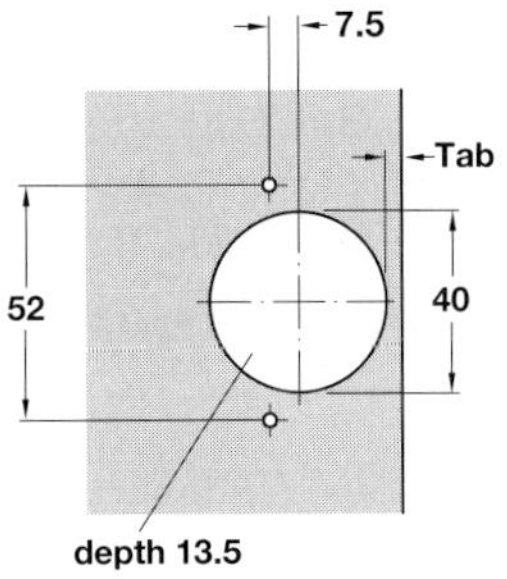

Screw-mount

Mounting	Hinge arm	Hinge type	Cat. No.
Full overlay	straight	**21**	329.05.605
Half overlay	11 mm crank	**10**	329.05.614
Inset mounting	22 mm crank	**-1**	329.05.632

Packing: 300 pcs.

For thick or built up doors

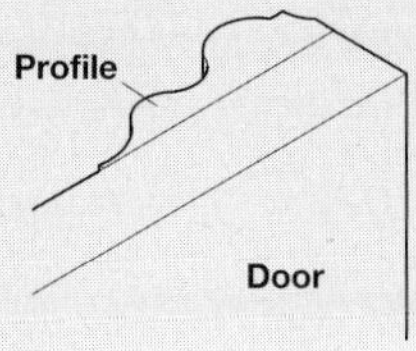

Hinges, Flap and Lid Stays Associated Fittings 3

Corresponding mounting plates can be found on pages **3.16-3.19**

Mounting screws:
Hospa particle board screws **raised head** with PZ 2 cross slot
Finish:
steel, nickel-plated

Length	Cat. No.
15 mm	015.55.639
20 mm	015.55.657
25 mm	015.55.675

Packing: 1000 pcs.

Trim caps for hinge arm, finish: plastic, black

Hinge arm	Catalog No.		
		white	329.18.700
Straight		black	329.18.308

Packing: 5000 pcs.

HÄFELE

Duomatic Hinges for Glass Doors

Opening angle:

Glass door hinges **screw mounted**
- Door thickness 4 to 6 mm (3/16" to 1/4")
- Side panel thickness from 16 mm (5/8")
- Self-closing
  Cup: plastic
  Hinge arm: steel, nickel-plated
- Tab 4 – 6 mm

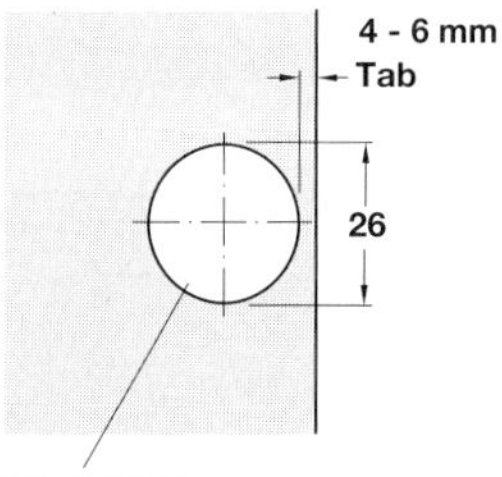

Hole pattern

Screw-mount

Mounting	Hinge arm		Hinge type	Cat. No.
Full overlay		straight	**17**	329.21.500
Half overlay		9 mm crank	**8**	329.21.511
Inset mounting		17 mm crank	**0**	329.21.532

Packing: 100 pcs.

3 **Hinges, Flap and Lid Stays Associated Fittings**

Corresponding mounting plates can be found on pages **3.16-3.19**

Round and D-shaped trim caps come complete with mounting screws and shims.

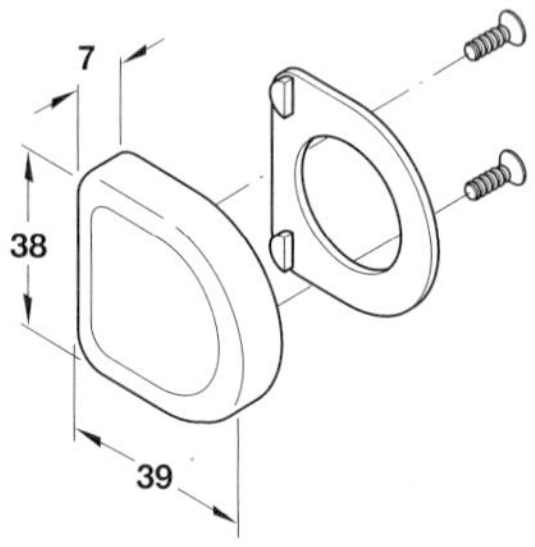

Trim caps, D-shaped
Material: plastic, metallized

Finish	Cat. No.
chrome-plated polished	329.22.220
gold-colored polished	329.22.820
black	329.22.320

Packing: 300 pcs.

Max. door offset at 90º

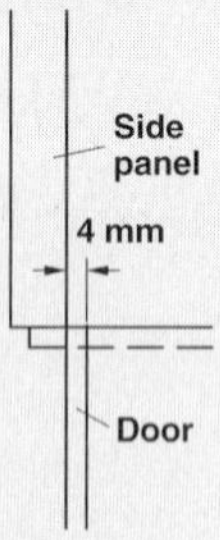

Protrusion shown is based on straight arm and smallest available mounting plate.

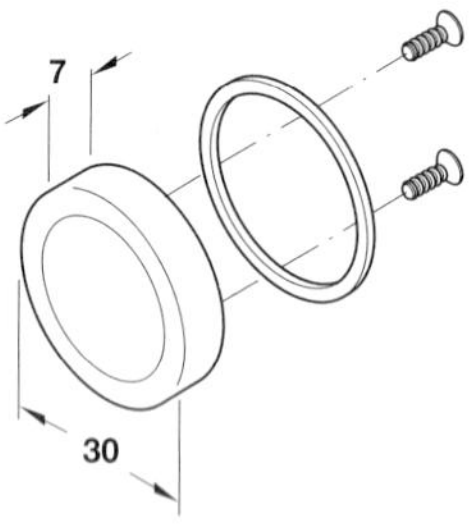

trim-caps, round
Material: plastic, metallized

Finish	Cat. No.
chrome-plated polished	329.22.210
gold-colored polished	329.22.810
black	329.22.310

Packing: 300 pcs.

To determine the correct tab distance for your application, please make a trial mounting using 1/4" wood material.

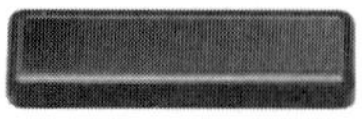

Trim caps for hinge arm, finish: plastic, black

Hinge arm	Catalog No.		
Straight		white	329.18.700
		black	329.18.308

Packing: 5000 pcs.

Dimensions in mm

Duomatic Hinges

Opening angle: 165°

- Door thickness 16 to 26 mm (5/8" to 1")
- Side panel thickness from 16 mm (5/8")
- Self-closing
- All-metal:
  Cup: zinc die-cast, nickel-plated
  Hinge arm: steel, nickel-plated
- Tab 3 – 8 mm

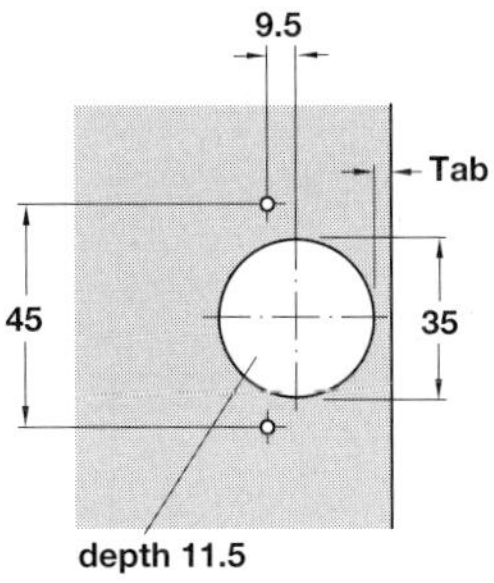

Screw-mounted

Mounting	Hinge arm	Hinge type	Cat. No.
Full overlay	straight	**17**	329.07.609
Half overlay	9 mm crank	**8**	329.07.618

Packing: 100 pcs.

Corresponding mounting plates can be found on pages **3.16-3.19**

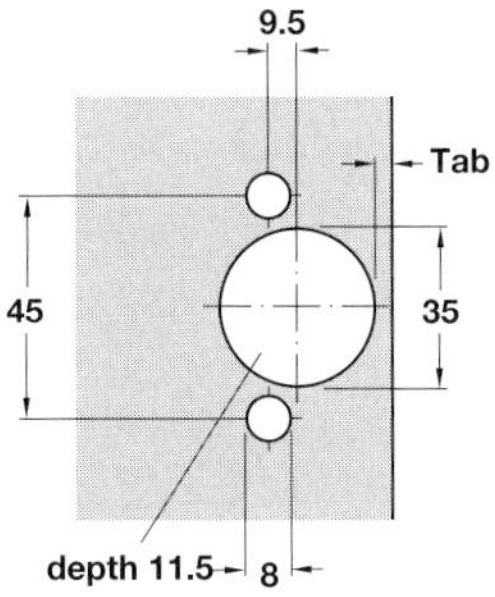

Press-fit in drilling diagram 45/9.5

Mounting	Hinge arm	Hinge type	Cat. No.
Full overlay	straight	**17**	329.07.654
Half overlay	9 mm crank	**8**	329.07.663

Packing: 100 pcs.

Mounting screws:
Hospa particle board screws **raised head** with PZ 2 cross slot
Finish:
steel, nickel-plated

Length	Cat. No.
15 mm	015.55.639
20 mm	015.55.657
25 mm	015.55.675

Packing: 1000 pcs.

Trim caps for hinge arm, finish: plastic, black

Hinge arm	Catalog No.		
		white	329.18.700
Straight		black	329.18.308

Packing: 5000 pcs.

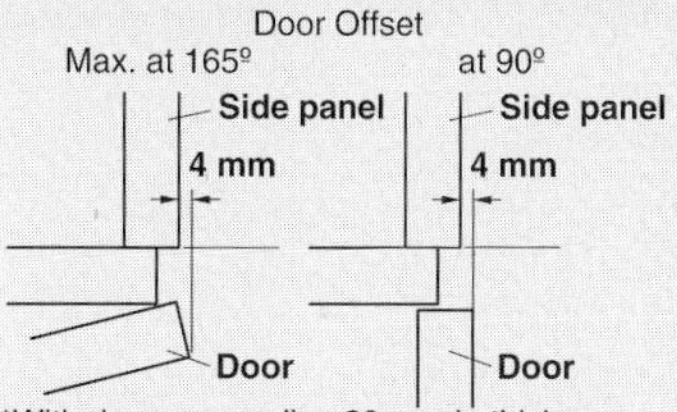

*With doors exceeding 20 mm in thickness, the opening angle is reduced if two doors are mounted in each side of the same panel.

Protrusion shown is based on straight arm and smallest available mounting plate.

Dimensional data not binding.
We reserve the right to alter specifications without notice.

Dimensions in mm

HÄFELE

Duomatic Pie-cut Corner Hinge

- Self-closing
- Maximum door thickness 23 mm
- For pie-cut applications

For thick door or doors with mouldings or with large radius edges, please refer to chart below.

Compatible with all standard Duomatic mounting plates.

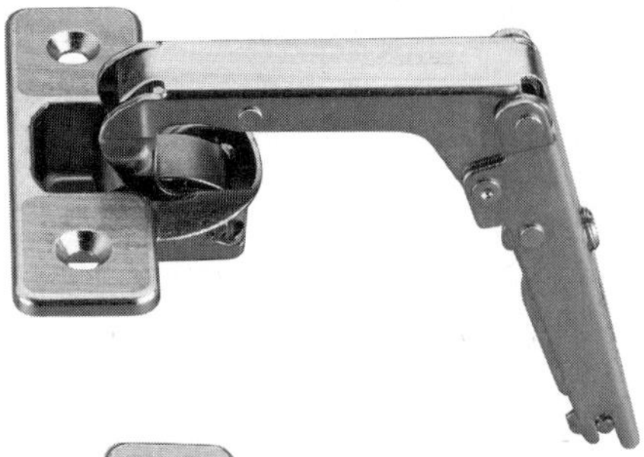

Opening angle: 70°

- 11 mm deep zinc die-cast cup
- Cup diameter 35 mm
- Opening angle of first door 70°
- Screw-mounted cup

Hole pattern

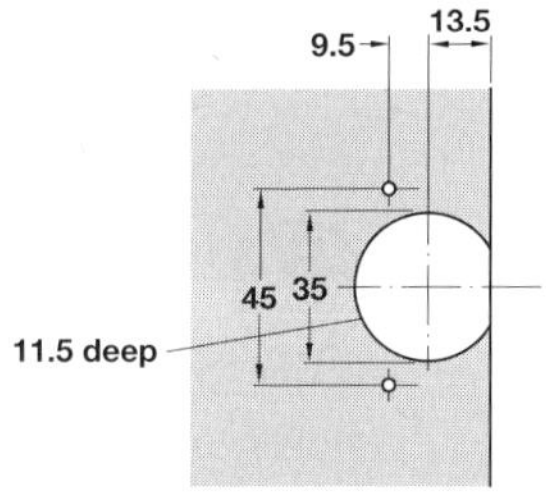

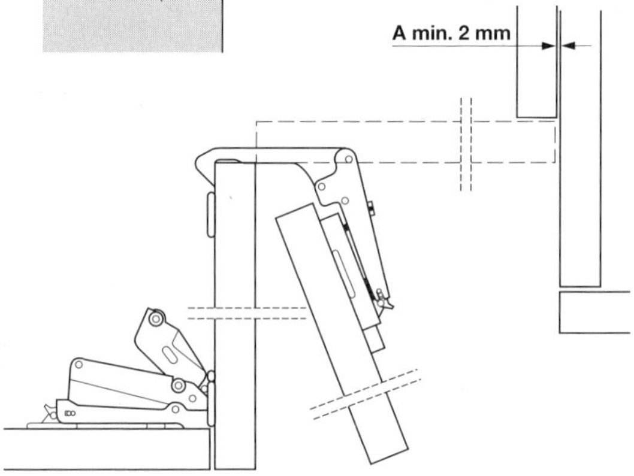

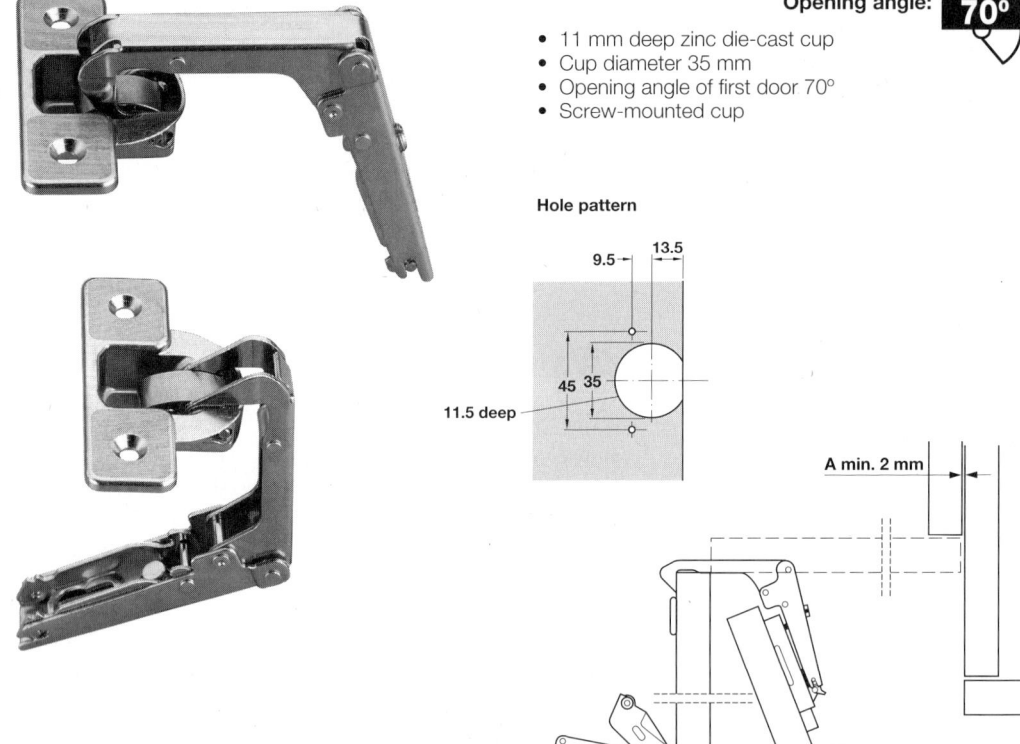

Finish: steel, nickel-plated

Cat. No.	329.19.600

Packing: 100 pcs.

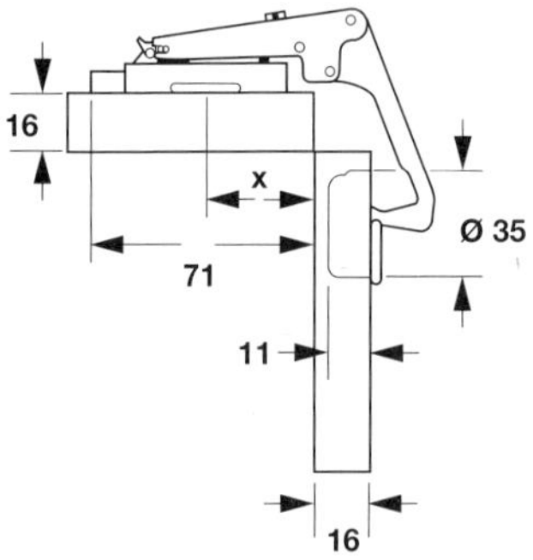

The maximum space required to accommodate the hinge is 71 mm with 16 mm thick doors. With thicker doors the amount of space required is reduced.

Mounting plate backset distance (X) varies according to door thickness.

door thickness in mm	16	19	22
backset distance for mounting plates	31	28	25

Mounting plate height varies according to door thickness.

door thickness in mm	16	19	22
mounting plate type	8	5	2
side adjustment	1 mm		1 mm

3 Hinges, Flap and Lid Stays Associated Fittings

Dimensions in mm

Duomatic Face Frame Hinges

HÄFELE

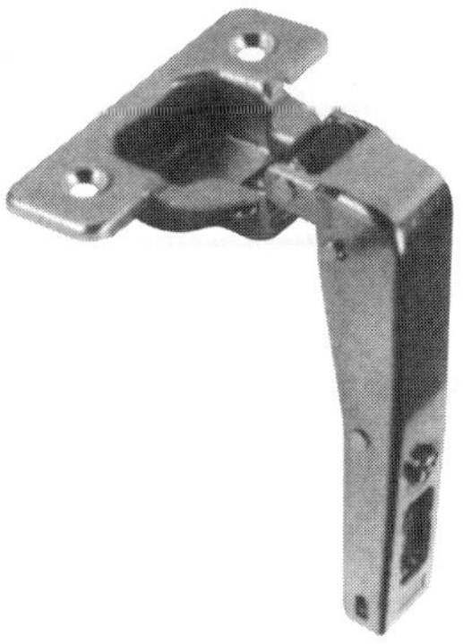

Opening angle: 95°

- Door thickness 16 to 26 mm (5/8" to 1")
- Self-closing
- All-metal:
  Cup: steel, nickel-plated
  Hinge arm: steel, nickel-plated
- Tab 3 – 8 mm

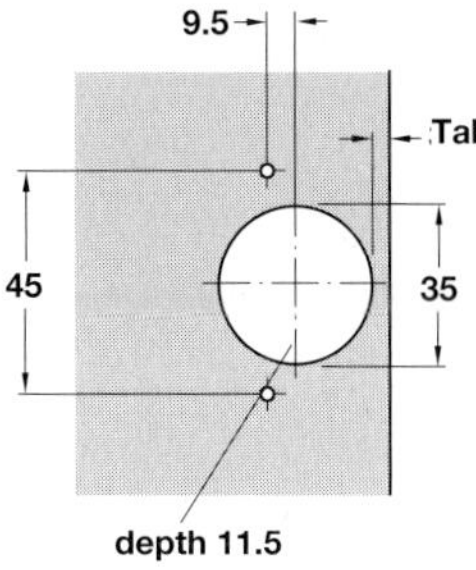

HOSPA Φ3.5

Screw-mount

Mounting	Hinge arm	Cat. No.
Inset mounting		329.11.505

Packing: 100 pcs.

Hinges, Flap and Lid Stays Associated Fittings 3

Corresponding mounting plates can be found on page **3.16-3.19**

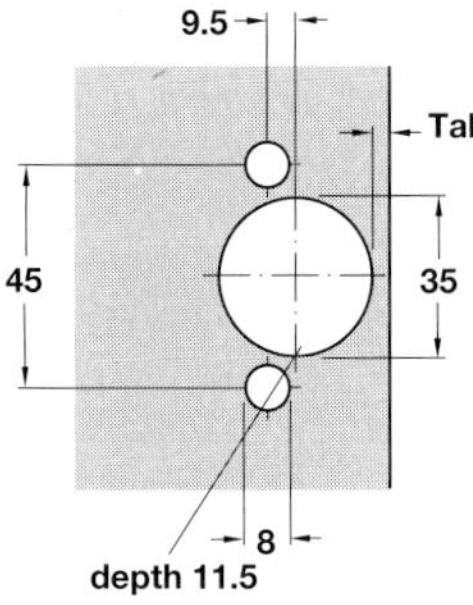

Press-fit 45/9.5 hole pattern

Mounting	Hinge arm	Cat. No.
Inset mounting		329.11.550

Packing: 100 pcs.

Mounting screws:
Hospa particle board screws
raised head with
PZ 2 cross slot
Finish:
steel, nickel-plated

Length	Cat. No.
15 mm	015.55.639
20 mm	015.55.657
25 mm	015.55.675

Packing: 1000 pcs.

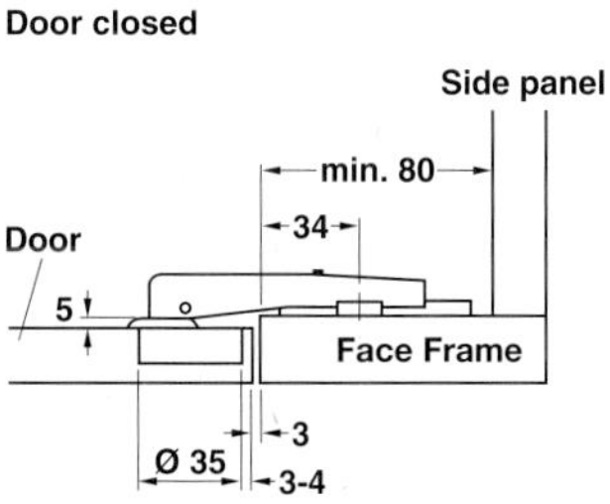

Single-side mounting (corner or center panel frame) installation diagrams with mounting plate models **2**, **5**, **8**

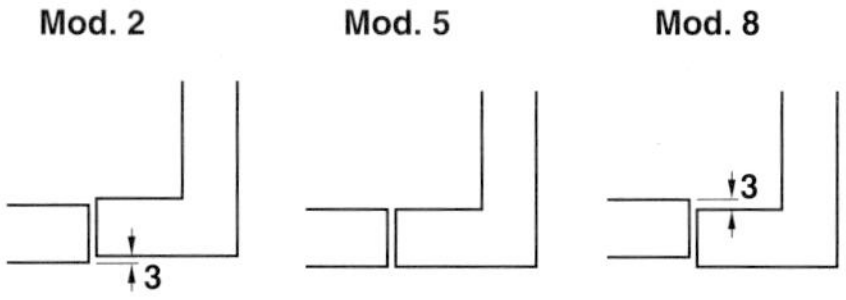

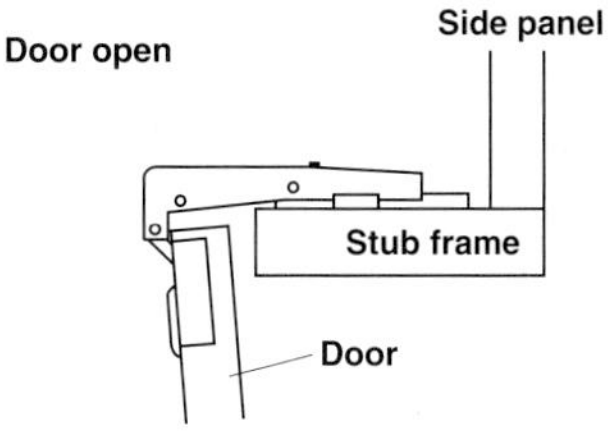

Typical mounting

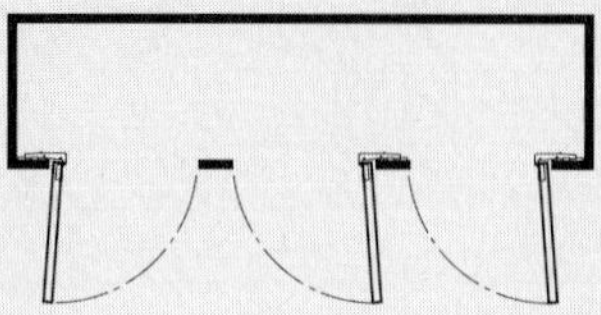

Trim caps for hinge arm, finish: plastic, black

Hinge arm	Catalog No.		
		white	329.18.700
Straight		black	329.18.308

Packing: 5000 pcs.

Dimensional data not binding. We reserve the right to alter specifications without notice.

Dimensions in mm

Duomatic Corner Hinges

Opening angle:

- Door thickness 16 to 26 mm (5/8" to 1")
- Self-closing
- All-metal:
  Cup: steel, nickel-plated
  Hinge arm: steel, nickel-plated
- For 45° corner application
- Tab 3 – 8 mm

Corresponding mounting plates can be found on page **3.16-3.19**

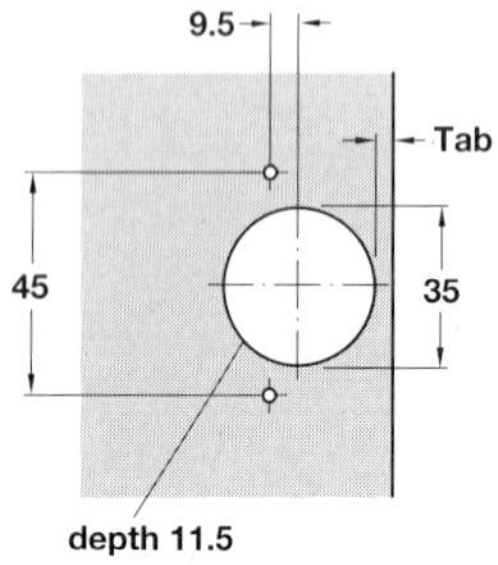

Screw-mounted

Mounting	Hinge arm	Cat. No.
Inset/ overlay		329.09.505

Packing: 100 pcs.

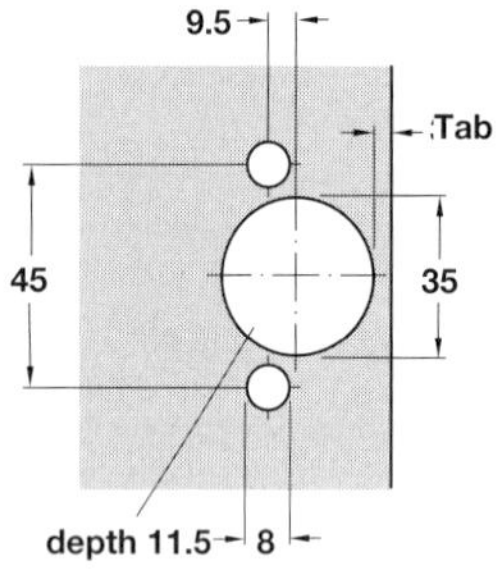

Press-fit 45/9.5 hole pattern

Mounting	Hinge arm	Cat. No.
Inset/ overlay		329.09.550

Packing: 100 pcs.

Mounting screws:
Hospa particle board screws **raised head** with PZ 2 cross slot
Finish:
steel, nickel-plated

Length	Cat. No.
15 mm	015.55.639
20 mm	015.55.657
25 mm	015.55.675

Packing: 1000 pcs.

Typical mounting

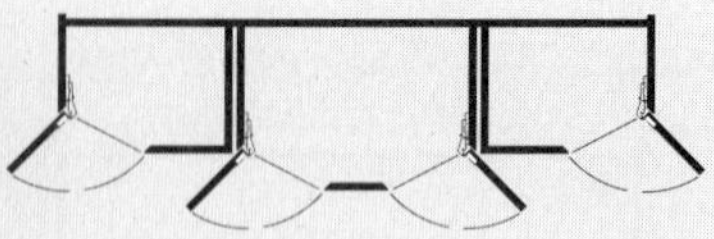

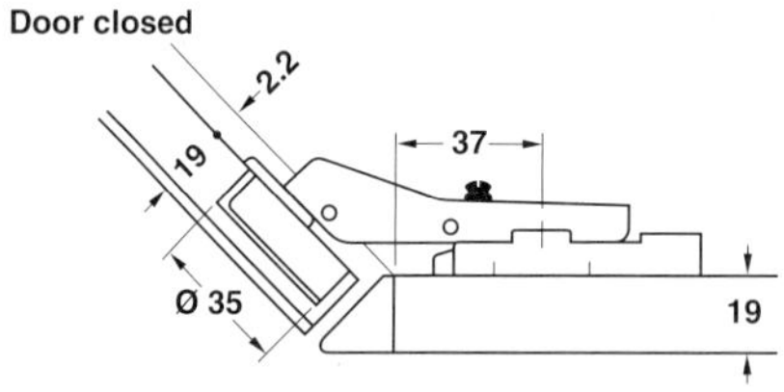

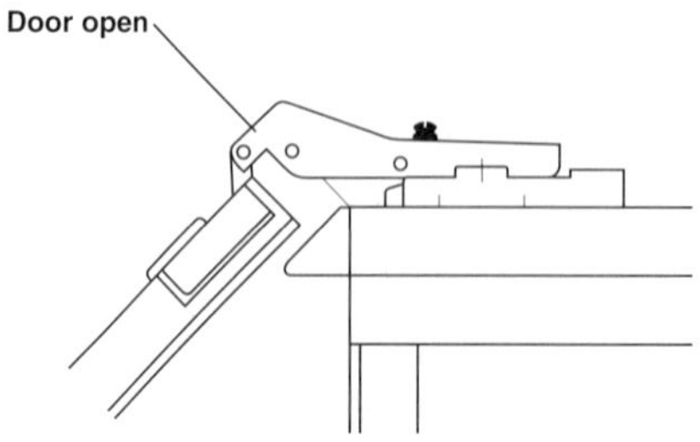

Trim caps for hinge arm, finish: plastic, black

Hinge arm	Catalog No.		
Straight		white	329.18.700
		black	329.18.308

Packing: 5000 pcs.

Dimensions in mm

Duomatic Negative Angle Hinge

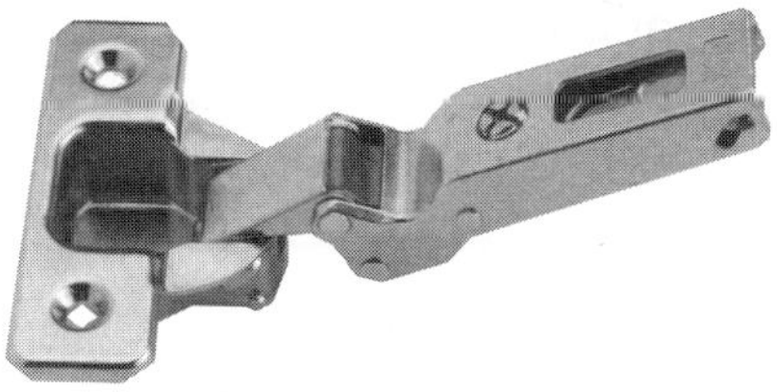

Opening angle: 45°

- Door thickness 16 to 26 mm (5/8" to 1")
- Side panel thickness from 16 mm (5/8")
- Self-closing
- All-metal:
  Cup: steel
  Hinge arm: steel, nickel-plated
- Tab = 3 - 6 mm

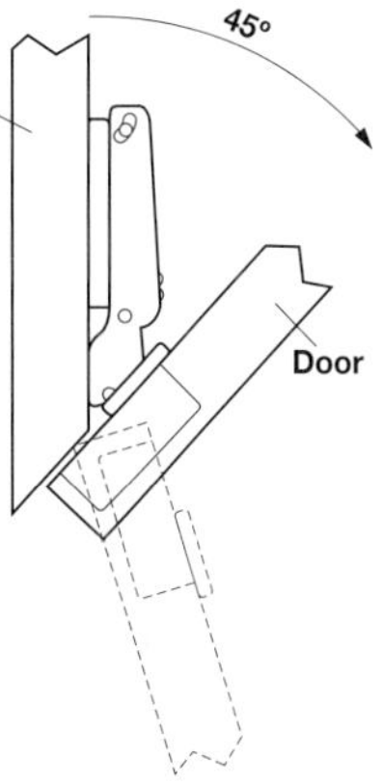

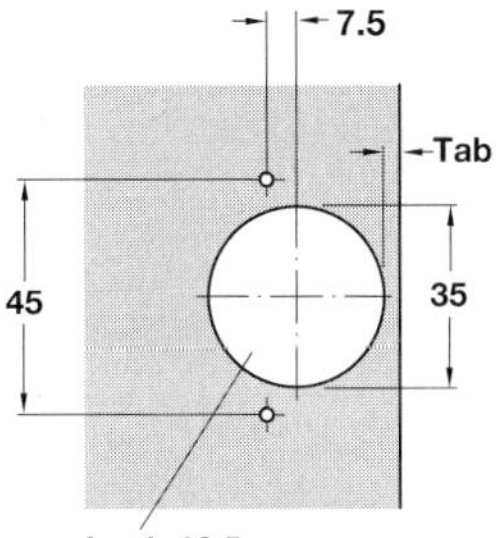

Screw-mount

Mounting	Hinge arm		Cat. No.
Full overlay		straight	329.09.514

Packing: 100 pcs.

Trim caps for hinge arm, finish: plastic

Hinge arm	Catalog No.		
		white	329.18.700
Straight		black	329.18.308

Packing: 5000 pcs.

Corresponding mounting plates can be found on page **3.16-3.19**

Mounting screws:
Hospa particle board screws **raised head** with PZ 2 cross slot
Finish:
steel, nickel-plated

Length	Cat. No.
15 mm	015.55.639
20 mm	015.55.657
25 mm	015.55.675

Packing: 1000 pcs.

Dimensions in mm

HÄFELE

Duomatic Clip Mounting Plates

Flanged mounting plates, **screw-mounted**
- Spring lever
- All metal

Independent vertical adjustment

Hole pattern

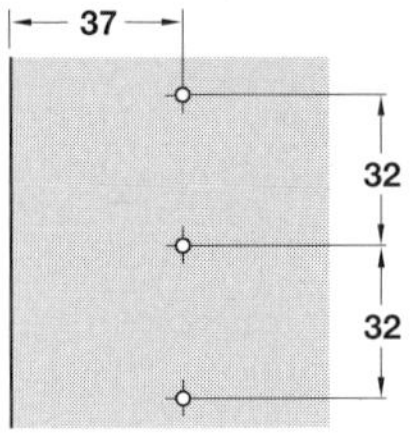

Reinforcement	type	Cat. No.
none	**2**	329.60.624
3 mm	**5**	329.60.651

Packing: 300 pcs.

Mounting screws:
Hospa particle board screws
countersunk head
with PZ 2
cross slot
Finish:
steel, nickel-plated

Length	Cat. No.
15 mm	015.35.824
17 mm	015.35.833

Packing: 1000 pcs.

Wing mounting plates,
screw-mounted in system holes
- Spring lever
- All-metal
- Pre-installed 11 mm Euro screws

Independent vertical adjustment

Hole pattern

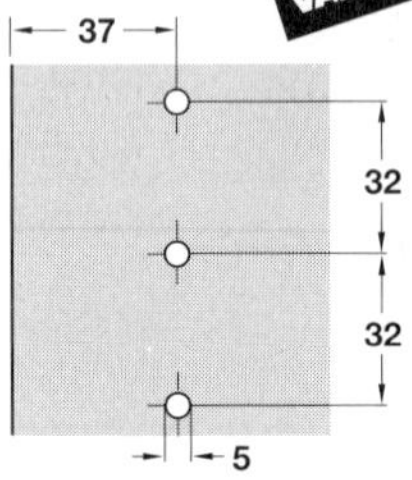

Reinforcement	type	Cat. No.
none	**2**	329.61.729
3 mm	**5**	329.61.756

Packing: 300 pcs.

3 Hinges, Flap and Lid Stays Associated Fittings

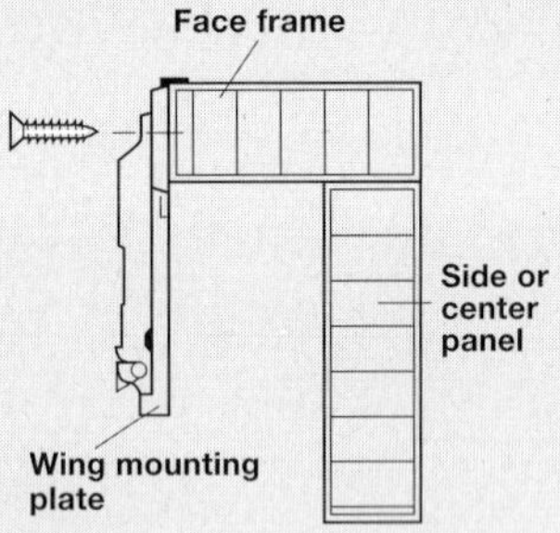

Face frame wing mounting plates, **screw-mounted**
- Spring lever
- All-metal

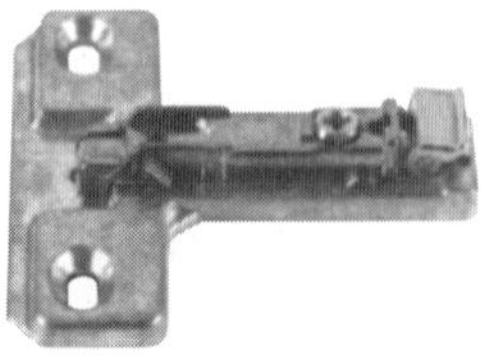

Vertical adjustment
(oblong holes)

Hole pattern

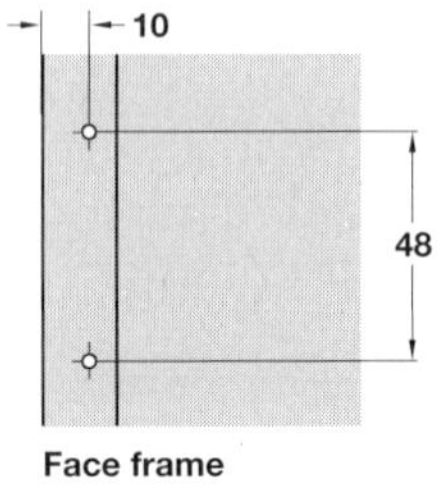

Reinforcement	type	Cat. No.
1 mm	**3**	329.64.631
4 mm	**6**	329.64.640

Packing: 300 pcs.

Mounting screws:
Hospa particle board screws
raised head
with PZ 2
cross slot
Finish:
steel, galvanized

Length	Cat. No.
15 mm	015.31.826
17 mm	015.31.835
20 mm	015.31.844

Packing: 1000 pcs.

Dimensional data not binding.
We reserve the right to alter specifications without notice.

Dimensions in mm

Duomatic Clip Mounting Plates

Wing mounting plates, **screw-mounted**
• Spring lever

Vertical adjustment
(oblong holes)

Hole pattern

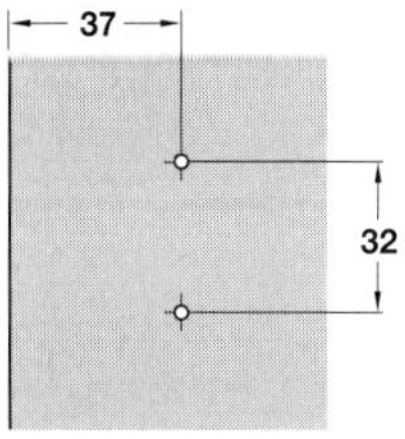

Reinforcement	type	Cat. No. Zinc	Cat. No. Steel
none	**2**		329.62.520
3 mm	**5**	329.62.557	
6 mm	**8**		329.62.682
9 mm	**11**	329.62.691	

Packing: 300 pcs.

Mounting screws:
Hospa particle board screws
countersunk head
with PZ 2
cross slot
Finish:
steel, nickel-plated

Length	Cat. No.
15 mm	015.35.824
17 mm	015.35.833

Packing: 1000 pcs.

Wing mounting plates,
screw-mounted in system holes
• 11 mm length for **single**-side mounting
• Pre-installed mounting screws
• Spring lever

Vertical adjustment
(oblong holes)

Hole pattern

SYSTEM VARIANTA 32

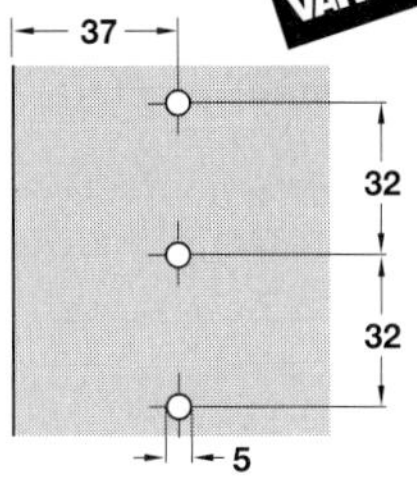

Reinforcement	type	Cat. No. Zinc	Cat. No. Steel
none	**2**		329.63.527
3 mm	**5**	329.63.750	
6 mm	**8**	329.63.787	
9 mm	**11**	329.63.796	

Packing: 300 pcs.

Dimensional data not binding.
We reserve the right to alter
specifications without notice.

Dimensions in mm

Duomatic-Slide On Mounting Plates

Wing mounting plates, **screw-mounted**
• Pre-installed hinge-arm retaining screws
• All-metal: steel, nickel-plated

Vertical adjustment
(oblong holes)

Reinforcement	type	Cat. No.
none	**2**	329.80.528
3 mm	**5**	329.80.555
6 mm	**8**	329.80.582
9 mm	**11**	329.80.699

Packing: 600 pcs.

Hole pattern

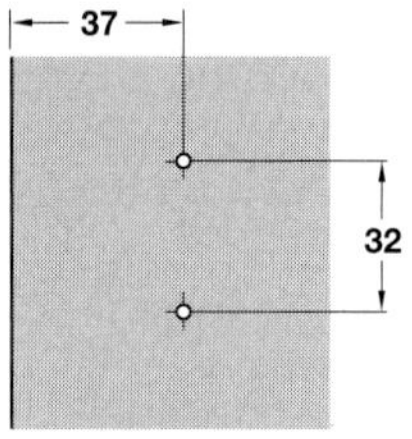

Mounting screws:
Hospa particle board screws
countersunk head
with PZ 2
cross slot
Finish:
steel, nickel-plated

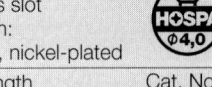

Length	Cat. No.
15 mm	015.35.824
17 mm	015.35.833

Packing: 1000 pcs.

Wing mounting plates, **screw-mounted in system holes**
• Pre-installed hinge-arm retaining screws
• 11 mm length for **single**-side mounting
• Vertical adjustment via oblong holes

Pre-installed mounting screws

Vertical adjustment
(oblong holes)

Reinforcement	type	Cat. No.
none	**2**	329.81.525
3 mm	**5**	329.81.552
6 mm	**8**	329.81.589
9 mm	**11**	329.81.794

Packing: 600 pcs.

Hole pattern

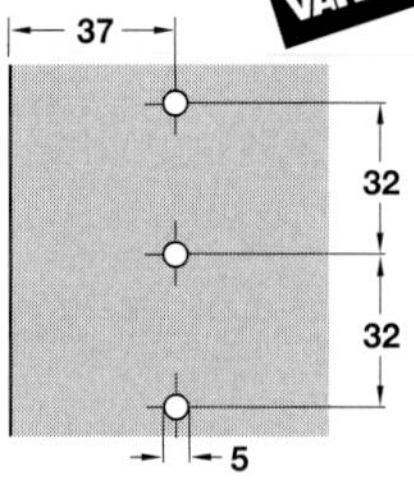

Duomatic-Slide On Mounting Plates

HÄFELE

Wing mounting plates, **screw-mounted**
• Pre-installed hinge-arm retaining screws

HOSPA Φ4,0

Independent vertical adjustment

Hole pattern

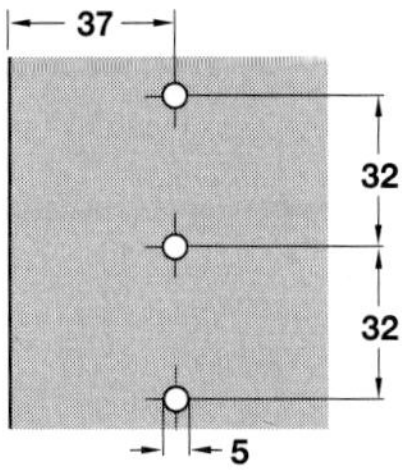

Reinforcement	type	Cat. No.
none	**2**	329.80.626
3 mm	**5**	329.80.653
9 mm	**11**	329.80.680

Packing: 600 pcs.

Mounting screws:
Hospa particle board screws
countersunk head
with PZ 2
cross slot
Finish:
steel, nickel-plated

HOSPA Φ4,0

Length	Cat. No.
15 mm	015.35.824
17 mm	015.35.833

Packing: 1000 pcs.

Wing mounting plates, **screw-mounted in system holes**
• Pre-installed hinge-arm retaining screws
• All-metal: zinc die-cast, nickel-plated
• Pre-installed fastening screws
• 11 mm length for single-side mounting.

Independent vertical adjustment

Hole pattern

SYSTEM VARIANTA 32

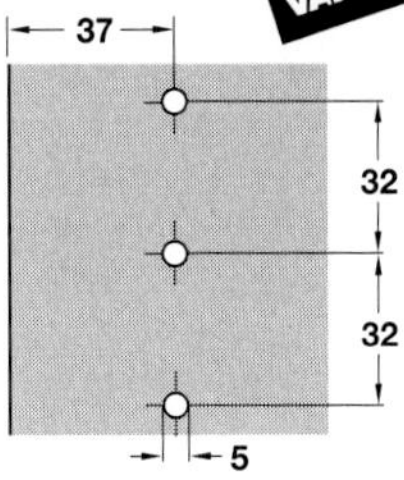

Reinforcement	type	Cat. No.
none	**2**	329.81.721
3 mm	**5**	329.81.758
9 mm	**11**	329.81.785

Packing: 600 pcs.

Hinges, Flap and Lid Stays Associated Fittings

3

Face frame mounting plates, **screw-mounted**
• Pre-installed hinge-arm retaining screws
• All-metal: zinc die-cast, nickel-plated

HOSPA Φ4,0

Vertical adjustment
(oblong holes)

Hole pattern

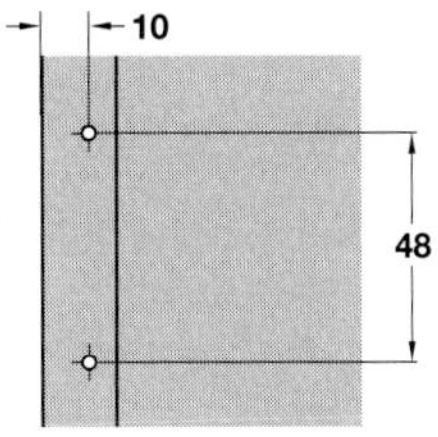

Face frame

Reinforcement	type	Cat. No.
3 mm	**3**	329.82.639

Packing: 600 pcs.

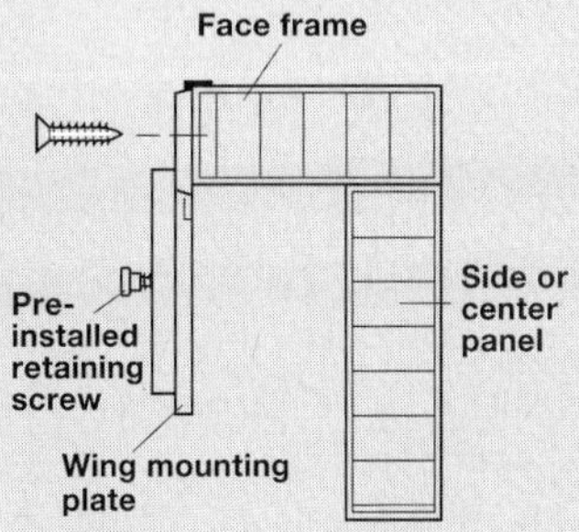

Mounting screws:
Hospa particle board screws
countersunk head
with PZ 2
cross slot
Finish:
steel, nickel-plated

HOSPA Φ4,0

Length	Cat. No.
15 mm	015.35.824
17 mm	015.35.833

Packing: 1000 pcs.

Dimensions in mm

HÄFELE

H-Series Hinges

Push-fit mounting diagram

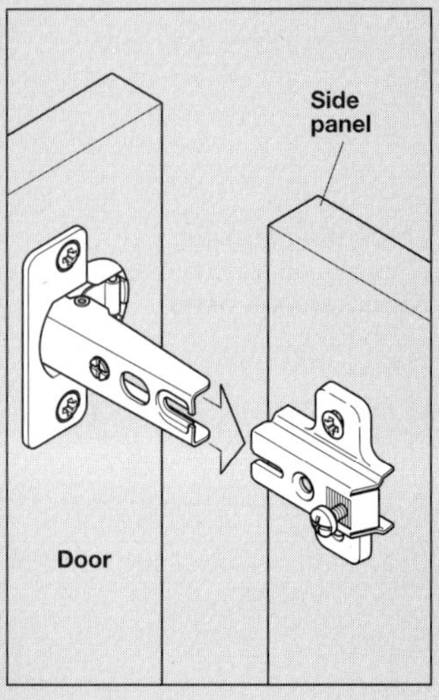

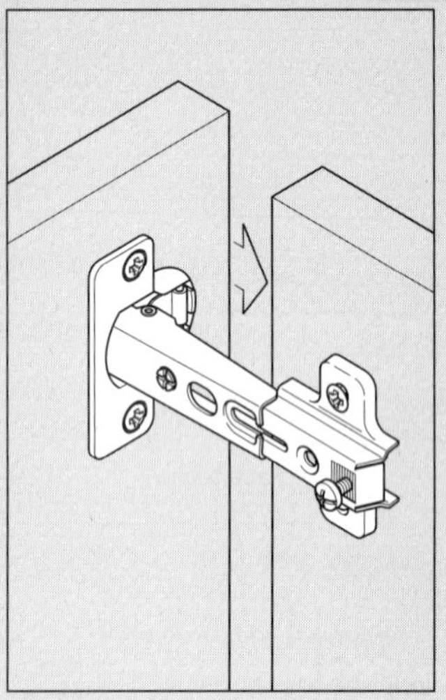

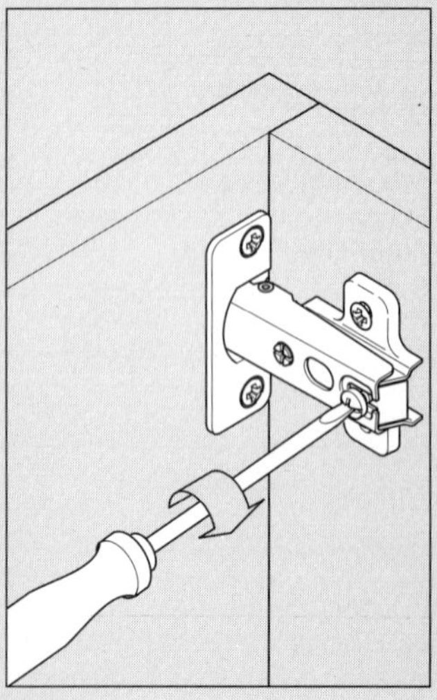

Slide-on hinges

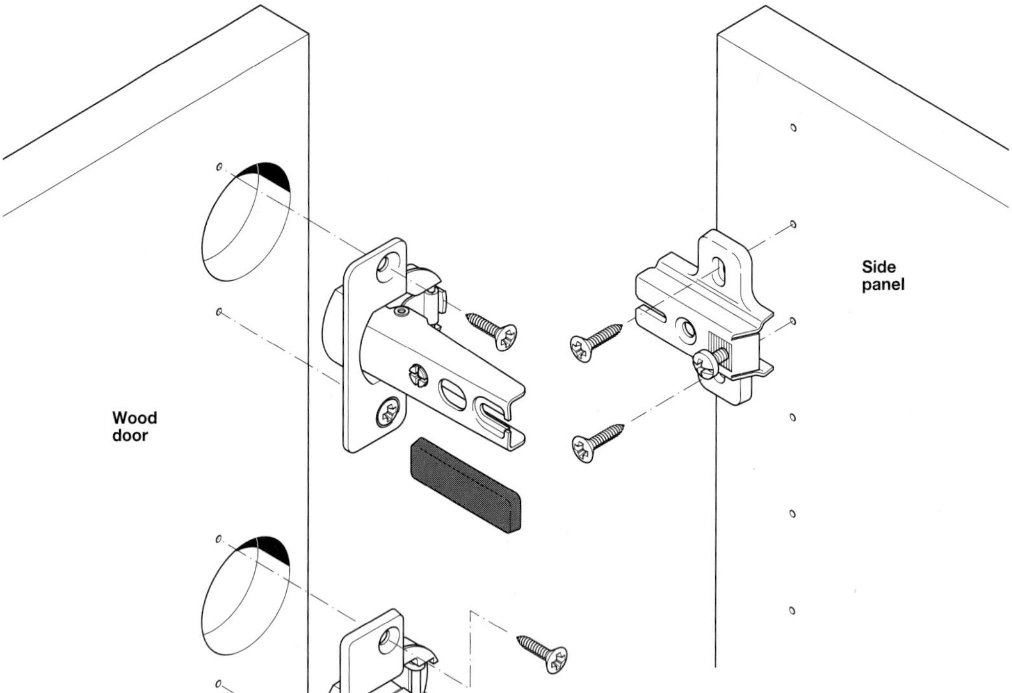

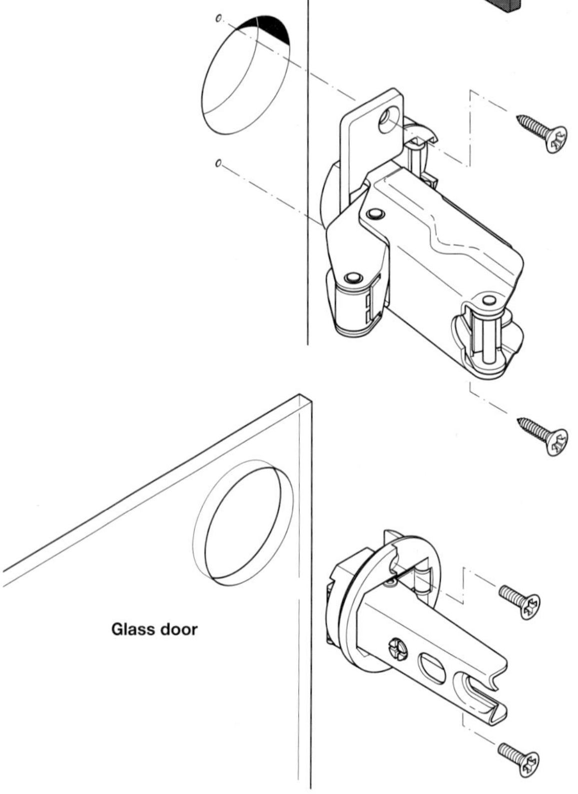

- All-metal
- Durable pivot bearing
- Steel moving parts
- Cup designed for automated insertion
- Self-closing
- Three-way adjustable
- Optional trim caps available

Adjustments

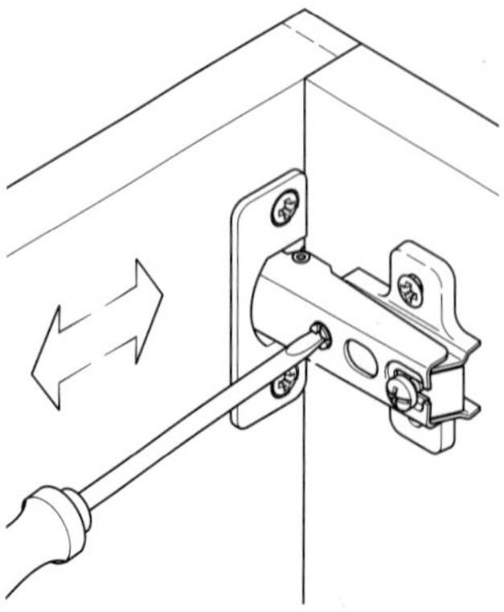

Horizontal
by screw adjustment

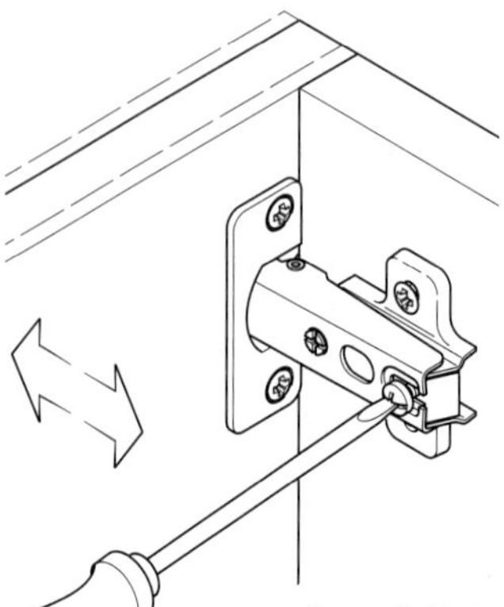

In-and-Out
by loosening the hinge-arm mounting screw

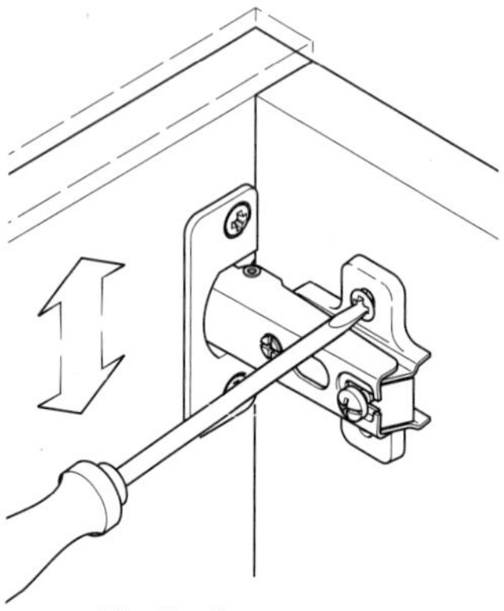

Vertical
via slots in the mounting plate

H-Series Hinges

HÄFELE

Guide to Hinges

Hinge type	Hinge cup material	Hinge arm	Opening angle	Type 18	Type 9	Type 1
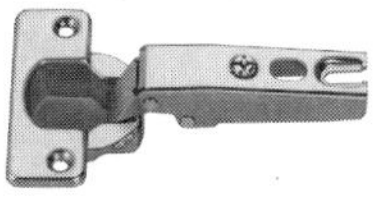	Steel	Steel	110°	•	•	•
 Profiled door hinge	Zinc die-cast	Steel	92°	22	•	2
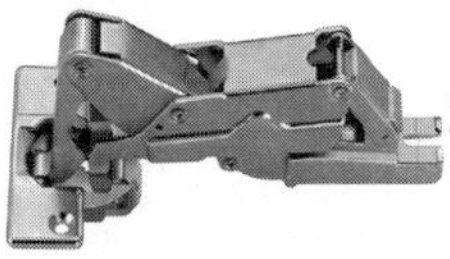	Zinc die-cast	Steel	175°	•	•	
 Glass door hinge	Plastic	Steel	92°	•	•	•
 Corner hinge	Steel	Steel	95°		 30° and 45°	
 Frame-mounting hinge	Steel	Steel	95°		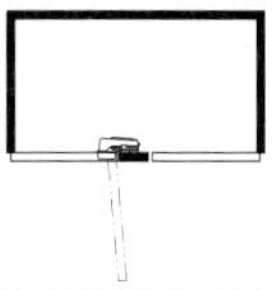	

Guide to Mounting Plates

Mounting plate type	Material	System hole installation	Reinforcement Type (vertical adjustment with oblong holes) 2	4	6	8
	Steel		•	•	•	•
	Steel	SYSTEM VARIANTA 32	•	•	•	•

Hinges,
Flap and Lid Stays
Associated Fittings

3

Dimensional data not binding.
We reserve the right to alter
specifications without notice.

HÄFELE

H-Series Hinges

Which hinge type?

Given the factors:

- Opening angle
- Hinge arm type
- Side panel thickness
- Door thickness
- Screw-mount or press-fit
- Mounting plate thickness
- Tab

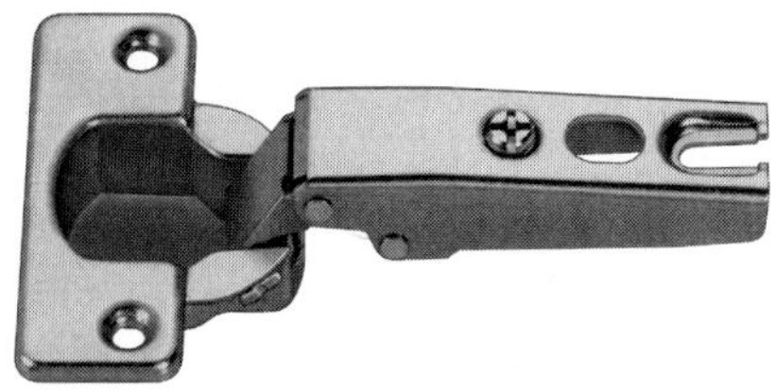

Use the following formula to determine overlay:

Hinge type *minus* mounting plate type *plus* tab = overlay

Sample Calculations

Hinge type **18** **Side panel mounting for overlay doors.**

(A) Full Overlay

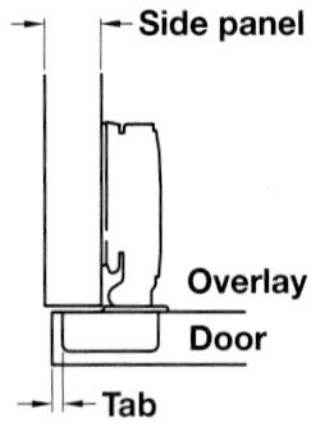

Hinge type **9** **Center panel**/twin mounting for overlay doors.

(B) Half Overlay or Twin Mounting

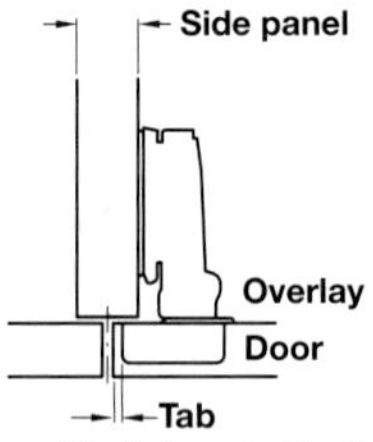

Hinge type **1** **Side panel mounting for inset doors.**

(C) Inset

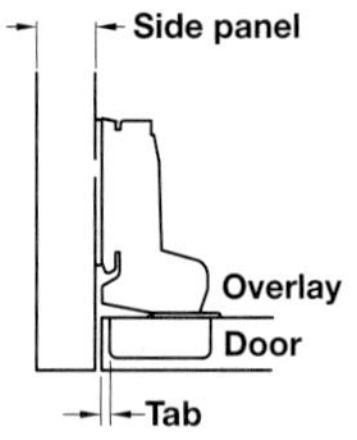

16 mm (5/8") Material	Hinge Type		Mounting Plate		Tab		Total Overlay
Full overlay (A)	18	-	6	+	3	=	15
Half overlay (B)	9	-	4	+	3	=	8
Inset (C)	1	-	4	+	3	=	0

19 mm (3/4") Material	Hinge Type		Mounting Plate		Tab		Total Overlay
Full overlay (A)	18	-	2	+	3	=	19
Half overlay (B)	9	-	2	+	3	=	10
Inset (C)	1	-	4	+	3	=	0

If there is no mounting plate with the required reinforcement, then the tab or side adjustment must be altered.

How many hinges per door?

There is no hard and fast rule which applies. When determining the number of hinges needed, the main factors to consider are door size and weight. A trial mounting is advisable in case of any doubt, such as with doors supporting mirrors, or unusually wide doors. Avoid disproportionate door width/weight ratios. Use this table for standard, conventional-material doors. When in doubt, always allow for an extra hinge.

- Commercial and heavy-duty applications, see Häfele's Aximat Hinge.

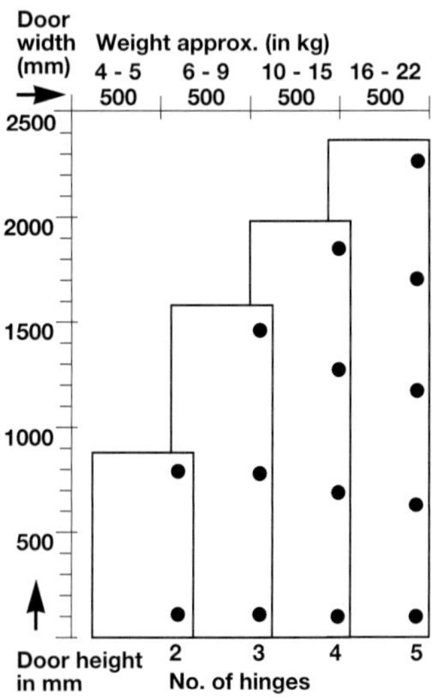

H-Series Hinges

HÄFELE

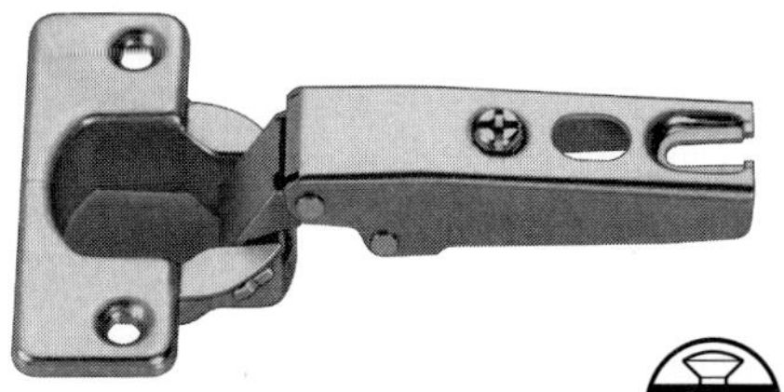

Opening angle: 110°

- Door thickness 15 to 26 mm (5/8"-1")
- Side panel thickness from 15 mm (5/8")
- Self-closing
- All-metal:
  Cup: steel, nickel-plated
  Hinge arm: steel, nickel-plated
- Tab = 3-6 mm

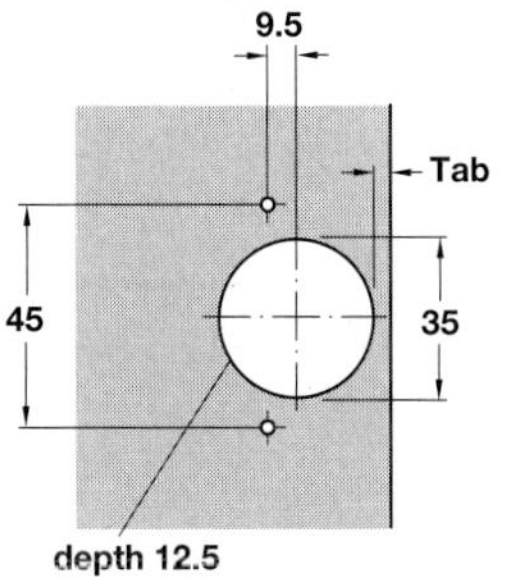

Screw-mount

Mounting	Hinge arm		Hinge type	Cat. No.
Full overlay		straight	**18**	316.03.602
Half overlay		9 mm crank	**9**	316.03.611
Inset mounting		17 mm crank	**1**	316.03.620

Packing: 250 pcs.

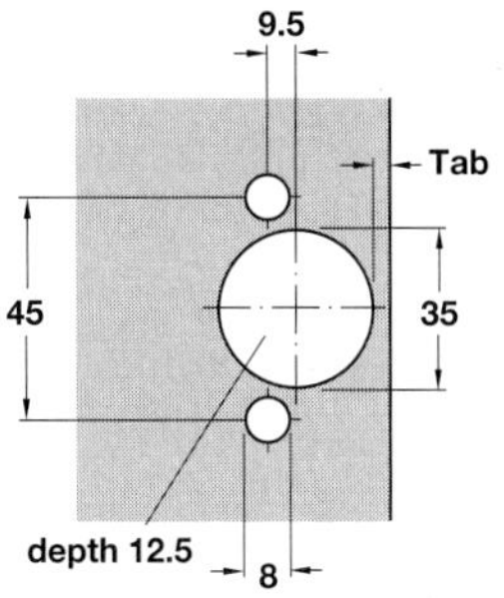

Press-fit, 45/9.5 hole pattern

Mounting	Hinge arm		Hinge type	Cat. No.
Full overlay		straight	**18**	316.03.657
Half overlay		9 mm crank	**9**	316.03.666
Inset mounting		17 mm crank	**1**	316.03.675

Packing: 250 pcs.

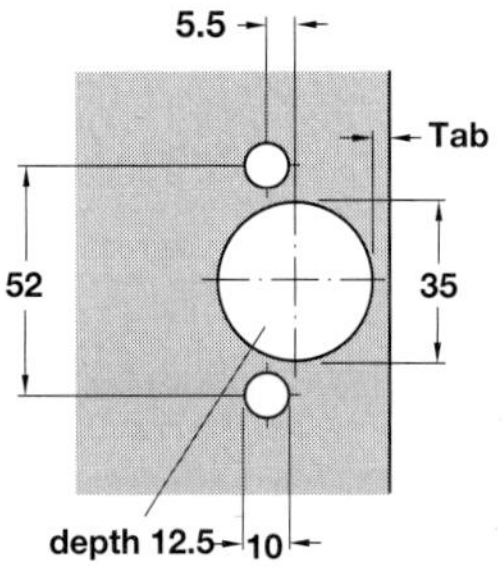

Press-fit, 52/5.5 hole pattern

Mounting	Hinge arm		Hinge type	Cat. No.
Full overlay		straight	**18**	316.01.750
Half overlay		9 mm crank	**9**	316.01.760
Inset mounting		17 mm crank	**1**	316.01.770

Packing: 250 pcs.

Trim caps for hinge arm, finish: plastic

Hinge arm		Cat. No.
Straight	also 9 and 17 mm crank	316.10.390

Packing: 250 pcs.

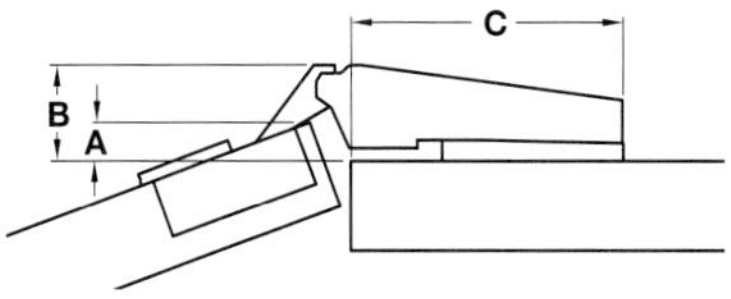

Hinge arm crank	Dim. **A**	Dim. **B**	Dim. **C**
Straight	2	14	58
9 mm crank	11	22	58
17 mm crank	19	30	58

Dim. **A** and **B** each + mounting plate thickness

Dimensions in mm

Hinges, Flap and Lid Stays Associated Fittings **3**

Corresponding mounting plates can be found on page **3.29**

Mounting screws:
Hospa particle board screws **raised head** with PZ 2 cross slot
Finish:
steel, nickel-plated

Length	Cat. No.
15 mm	015.55.639
20 mm	015.55.657
25 mm	015.55.675

Packing: 1000 pcs.

HÄFELE

H-Series Hinges for Profiled Doors

Corresponding mounting plates can be found on page **3.29**

Mounting screws:
Hospa particle board screws
raised head with
PZ 2 cross slot
Finish:
steel, nickel-plated

Length	Cat. No.
15 mm	015.55.639
20 mm	015.55.657
25 mm	015.55.675

Packing: 1000 pcs.

Door contour

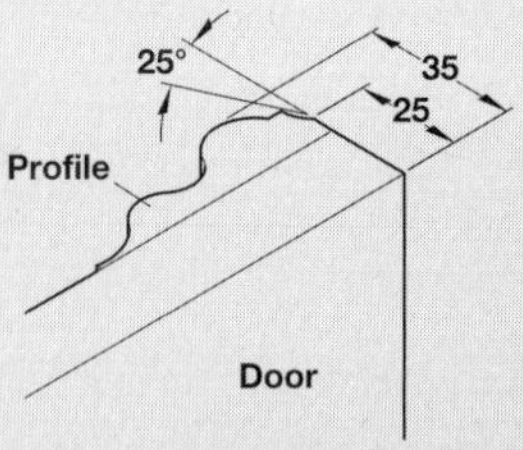

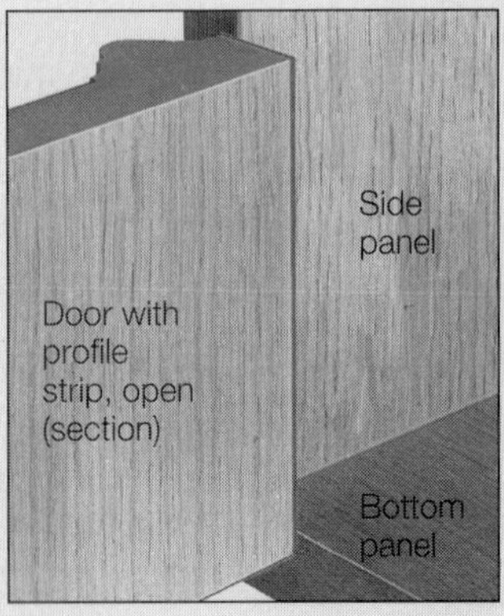

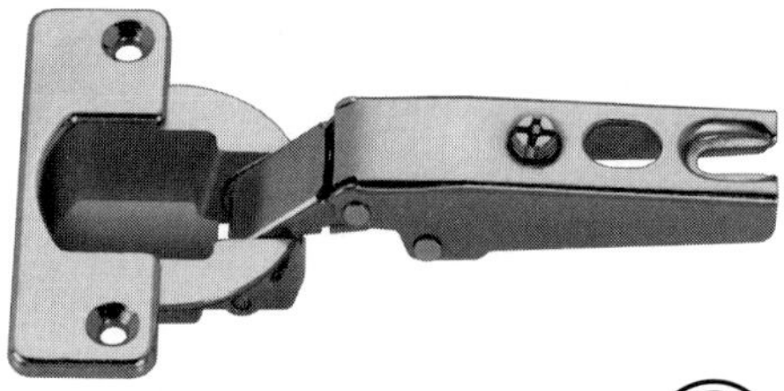

Opening angle: 92°

- Door thickness 24 to 35 mm (1" - 1 3/8")
- Side panel thickness from 16 mm (5/8")
- Self-closing
- All-metal:
  Cap: zinc die-cast, nickel-plated
  Hinge arm: steel, nickel-plated
- Tab = 3 - 14 mm

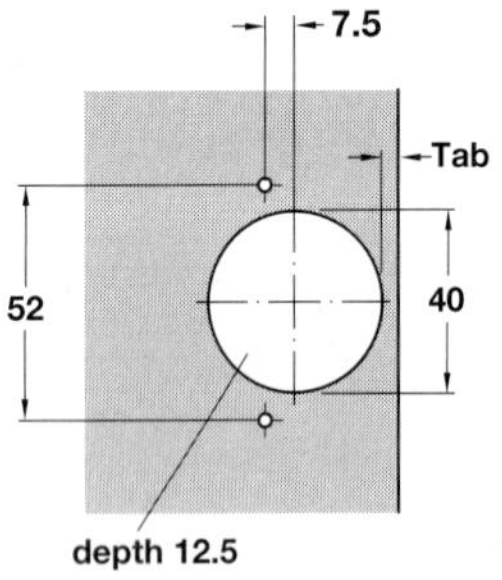

Screw-mount

Mounting	Hinge arm		Hinge type	Cat. No.
Full overlay		straight	**22**	316.06.600
Half overlay		9 mm crank	**10**	316.06.610
Inset mounting		17 mm crank	**2**	316.06.620

Packing: 250 pcs.

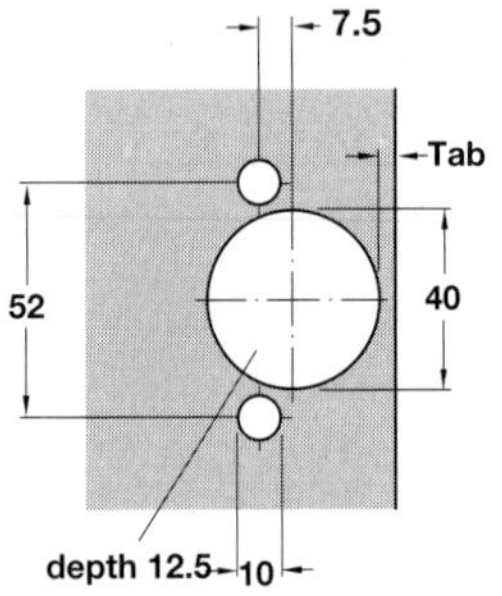

Press-fit, 52/7.5 hole pattern

Mounting	Hinge arm		Hinge type	Cat. No.
Full overlay		straight	**22**	316.06.650
Half overlay		9 mm crank	**10**	316.06.660
Inset mounting		17 mm crank	**2**	316.06.670

Packing: 250 pcs.

Trim caps for hinge arm, finish: plastic

Hinge arm			Cat. No.
Straight		also 9 and 17 mm crank	316.10.390

Packing: 250 pcs.

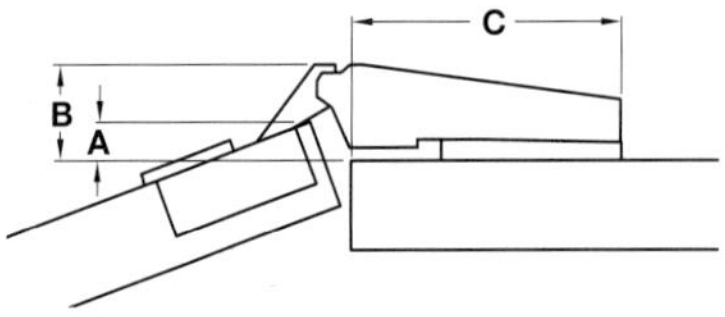

Hinge arm crank	Dim. **A**	Dim. **B**	Dim. **C**
Straight	2	14	58
10 mm crank	11	22	58
22 mm crank	26.5	37.5	58

Dim. **A** and **B** each + mounting plate thickness

Dimensions in mm

H-Series Hinges

HÄFELE

Opening angle: 175°

- Door thickness 20 to 26 mm (3/4" - 1")
- Side panel thickness from 16 mm (5/8")
- Self-closing
- All-metal:
  Cap zinc die-cast, nickel-plated
  Hinge arm: steel, nickel-plated
- Tab 3-6 mm

HOSPA Φ3,5

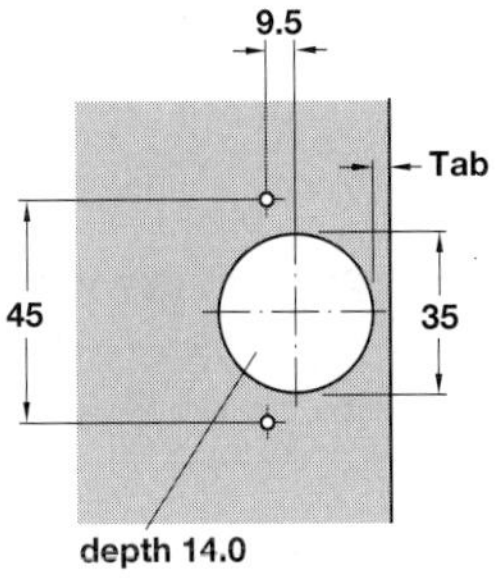

Screw-mounted

Mounting	Hinge arm	Hinge type	Cat. No.
Full overlay	straight	**18**	316.05.800
Half overlay	9 mm crank	**9**	316.05.810

Packing: 125 pcs.

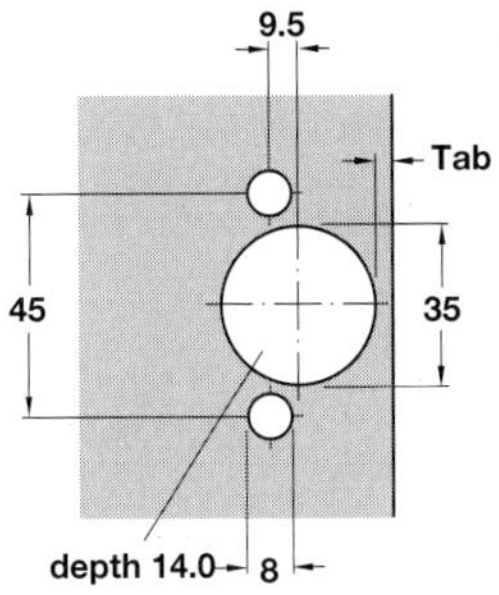

Press-fit, 45/9.5 hole pattern

Mounting	Hinge arm	Hinge type	Cat. No.
Full overlay	straight	**18**	316.05.850
Half overlay	9 mm crank	**9**	316.05.860

Packing: 125 pcs.

Hinges,
Flap and Lid Stays
Associated Fittings

3

Corresponding mounting plates can be found on page **3.29**

Mounting screws:
Hospa particle board screws **raised head** with PZ 2 cross slot
Finish:
steel, nickel-plated

HOSPA Φ3,5

Length	Cat. No.
15 mm	015.55.639
20 mm	015.55.657
25 mm	015.55.675

Packing: 1000 pcs.

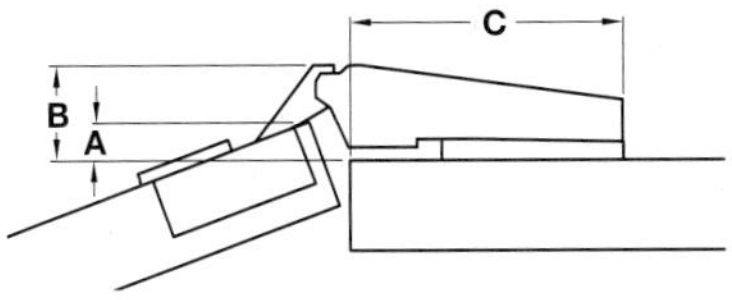

Hinge arm crank	Dim. **A**	Dim. **B**	Dim. **C**
Straight	– 0.5	24	58
9 mm crank	– 11.5	36	58

Dim. **A** and **B** each + mounting plate thickness
Dimensions in mm

HÄFELE

H-Series Hinges for Glass Doors

Corresponding mounting plates can be found on page **3.29**

Round and D-shaped trim caps come complete with mounting screws and shims.

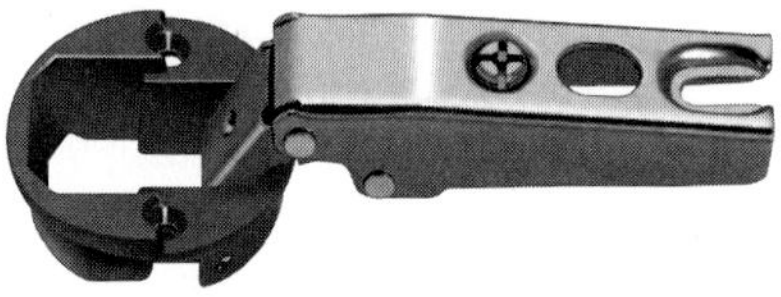

Opening angle: 92°

Glass door hinges
- Door thickness 4 to 7 mm (3/16" - 1/4")
- Side panel thickness from 16 mm (5/8")
- Self-closing
  Cap: plastic
  Hinge arm: steel, nickel-plated
- Tab 4 - 7 mm

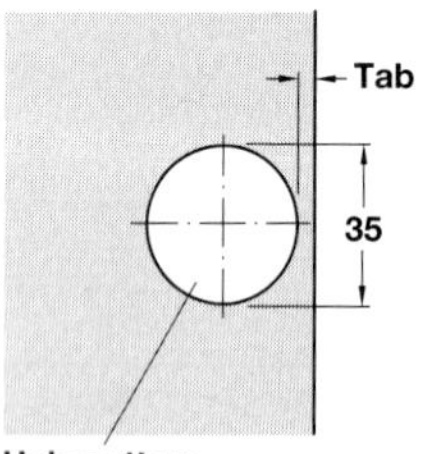

Hole pattern

Screw-mount

Mounting	Hinge arm	Hinge type	Cat. No.
Full overlay	straight	**18**	316.09.300
Half overlay	9 mm crank	**9**	316.09.310
Inset mounting	17 mm crank	**1**	316.09.320

Packing: 250 pcs.

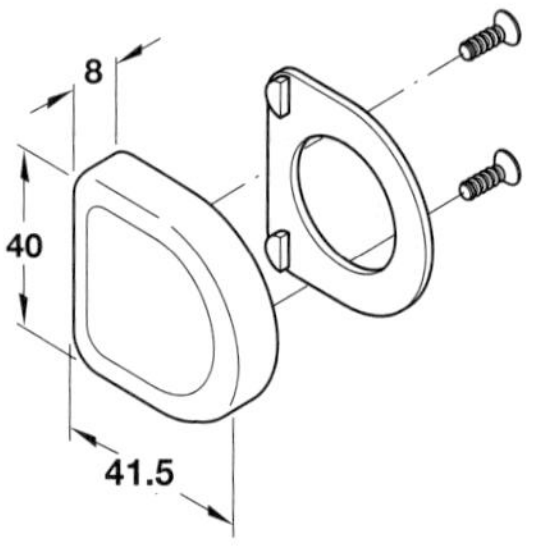

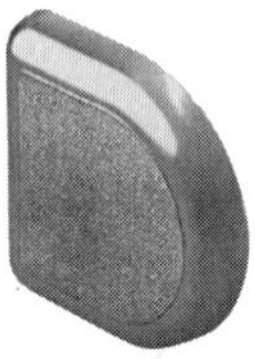

Trim caps, D-shaped
Material: zinc die-cast

Finish	Cat. No.
chrome-plated matt	316.10.410
gold matt	316.10.510
black	316.10.110

Packing: 200 pcs.

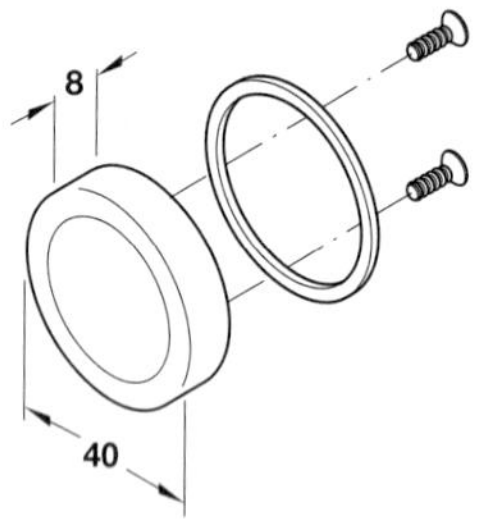

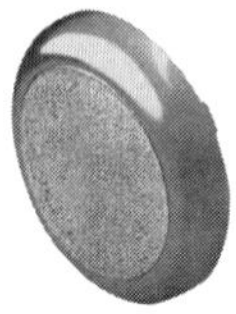

Trim caps, round
Material: zinc die-cast

Finish	Cat. No.
chrome-plated matt	316.10.420
gold matt	316.10.520
black	316.10.120

Packing: 200 pcs.

Trim caps for hinge arm, finish: plastic

Hinge arm		Cat. No.
Straight	also 9 and 17 mm crank	316.10.390

Packing: 250 pcs.

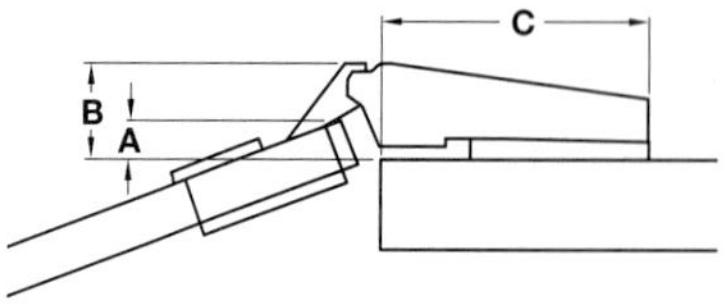

Hinge arm crank	Dim. **A**	Dim. **B**	Dim. **C**
Straight	5	14	58
9 mm crank	14	22	58
17 mm crank	21	30	58

Dim. **A** and **B** each + mounting plate thickness

Dimensions in mm

Dimensional data not binding. We reserve the right to alter specifications without notice.

H-Series Hinges For Corners

HÄFELE

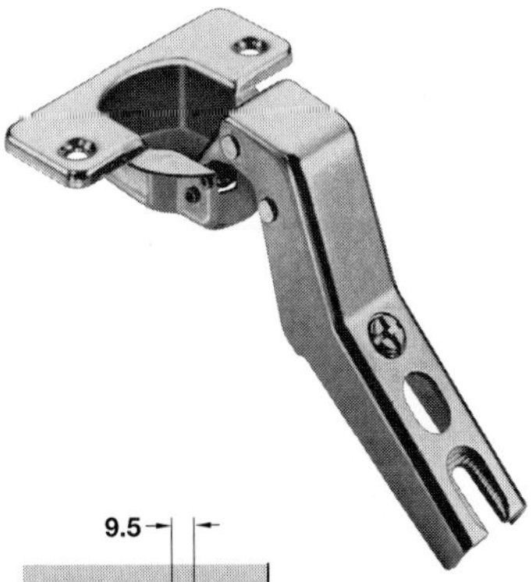

Opening angle: 95°

Corner hinges
- Door thickness 16 to 25 mm (5/8"-1")
- Self-closing
- All-metal:
  Cap: steel, nickel-plated
  Hinge arm: steel, nickel-plated
- Tab 3 - 8 mm

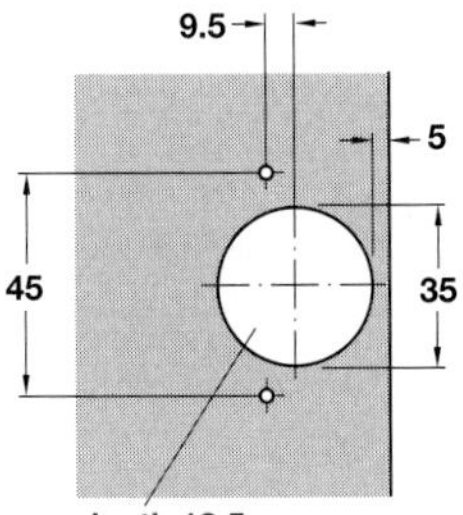

Screw-mount

Mounting	Hinge arm	Cat. No.
Overlay	**30°** angle	316.07.800
Overlay	**45°** angle	316.07.810

Packing: 250 pcs.

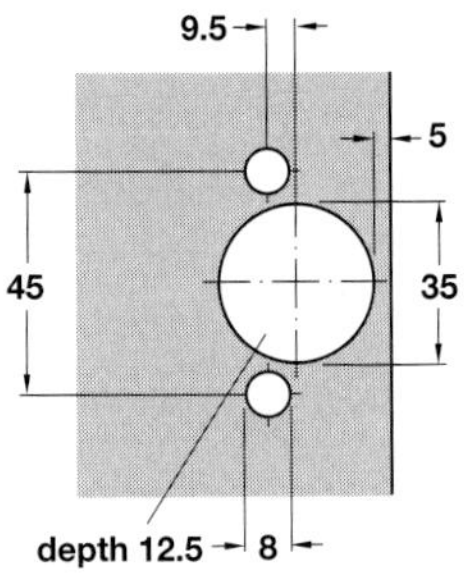

Press-fit, 45/9.5 hole pattern

Mounting	Hinge arm	Cat. No.
Overlay	**30°** angle	316.07.850
Overlay	**45°** angle	316.07.860

Packing: 250 pcs.

Corresponding mounting plates can be found on page **3.29**

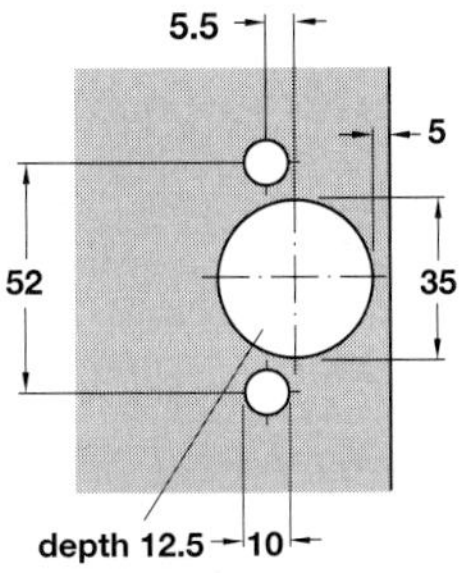

Press-fit, 52/5.5 hole pattern

Mounting	Hinge arm	Cat. No.
Overlay	**30°** angle	316.07.750
Overlay	**45°** angle	316.07.760

Packing: 50 pcs.

Mounting screws:
Hospa particle board screws
raised head with
PZ 2 cross slot
Finish:
steel, nickel-plated

Length	Cat. No.
15 mm	015.55.639
20 mm	015.55.657
25 mm	015.55.675

Packing: 1000 pcs.

Trim caps for hinge arm, finish: plastic, black

Hinge arm		Cat. No.
angle	for 30° and 45°	316.10.390

Packing: 5000 pcs.

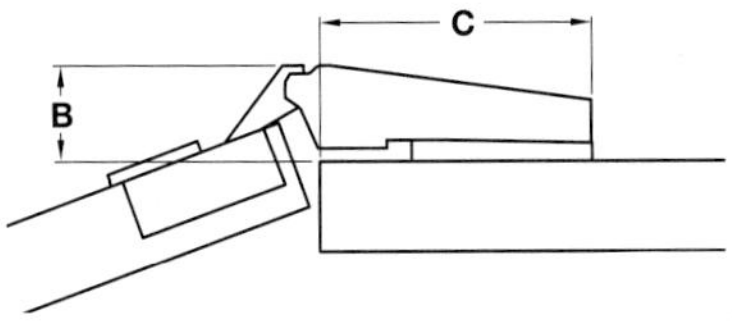

Hinge arm	Dim. **B**	Dim. **C**
30° angle	27	58
45° angle	26.5	58

Dim. **B**
+ mounting
plate thickness

Dimensions in mm

Mounting examples

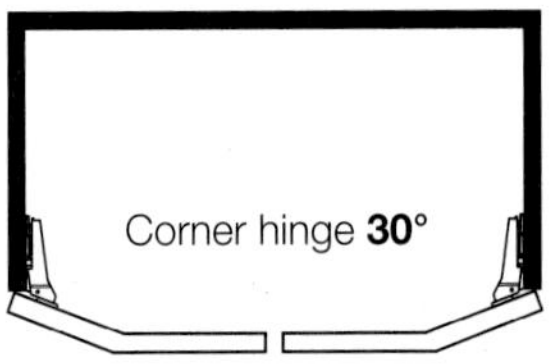

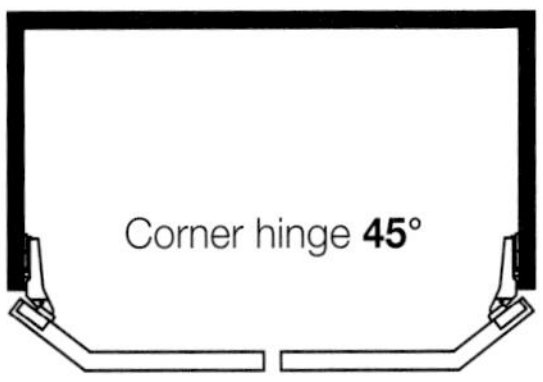

Dimensional data not binding.
We reserve the right to alter specifications without notice.

HÄFELE

H-Series Frame-Mounting Hinges

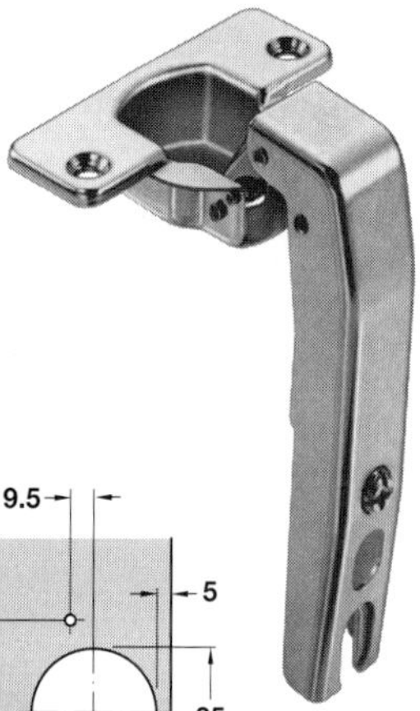

Opening angle: 95°

Frame-mounting hinges
- Door thickness 16 to 25 mm (5/8" - 1")
- Self-closing
- All-metal:
  Cap: steel, nickel-plated
  Hinge arm: steel, nickel-plated

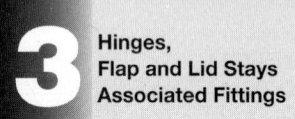

3 Hinges, Flap and Lid Stays Associated Fittings

Corresponding mounting plates can be found on page **3.29**

Mounting screws:
Hospa particle board screws **raised head** with PZ 2 cross slot
Finish:
steel, nickel-plated

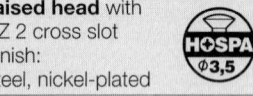

Length	Cat. No.
15 mm	015.55.639
20 mm	015.55.657
25 mm	015.55.675

Packing: 1000 pcs.

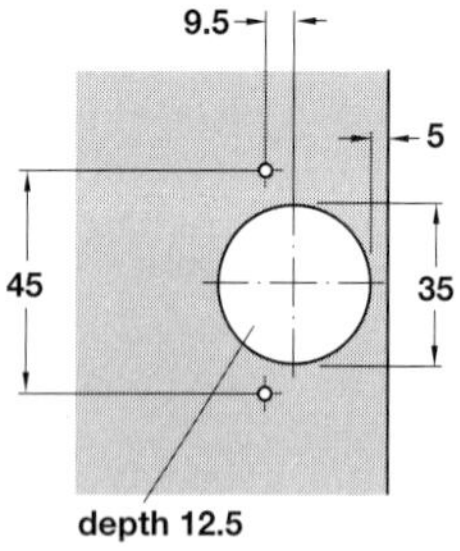

Screw-mount

Mounting	Hinge arm	Cat. No.
Inset mounting	**90°** angle	316.08.800

Packing: 25 pcs.

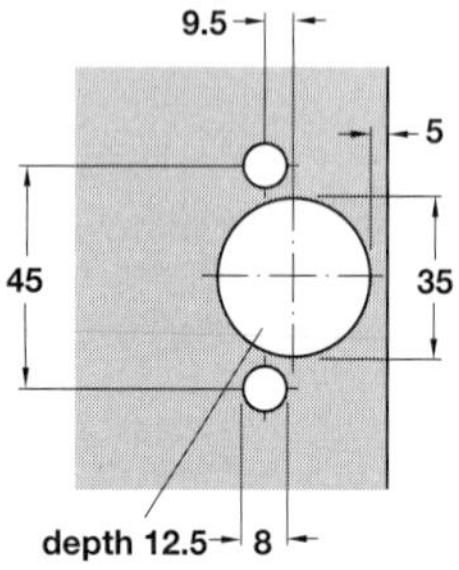

Press-fit, 45/9.5 hole pattern

Mounting	Hinge arm	Cat. No.
Inset mounting	**90°** angle	316.08.850

Packing: 25 pcs.

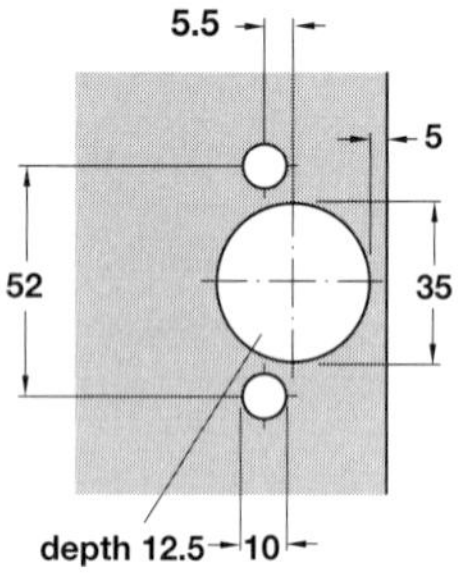

Press-fit, 52/5.5 hole pattern

Mounting	Hinge arm	Cat. No.
Inset Mounting	**90°** angle	316.08.750

Packing: 25 pcs.

Face frame cabinet

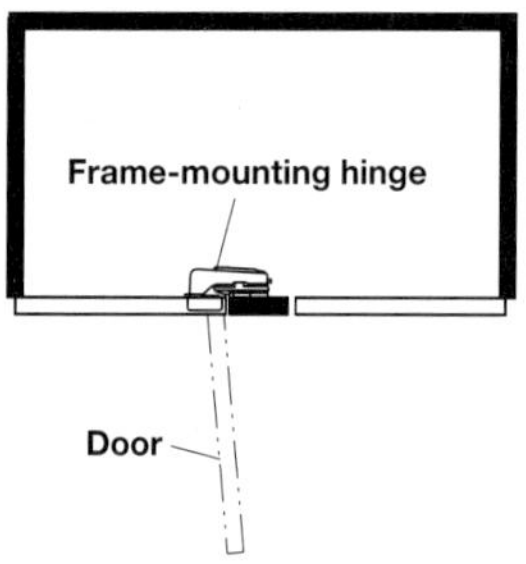

Door closed

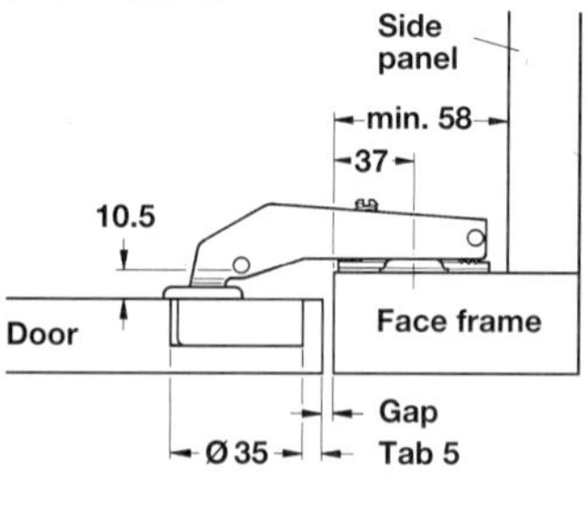

Door open

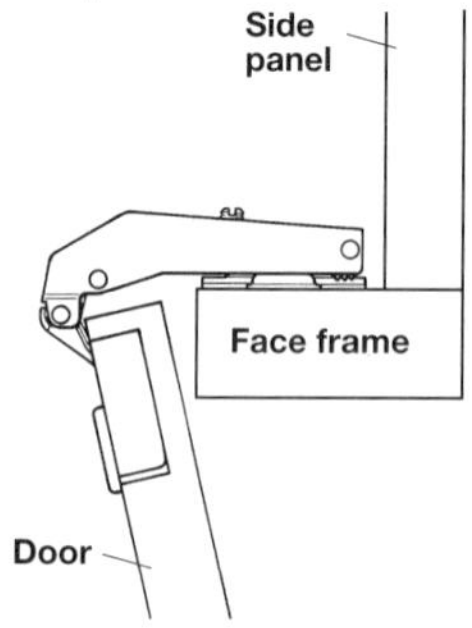

Trim caps for hinge arm, finish: plastic, black

Hinge arm	Cat. No.
angle 90°	316.10.390

Packing: 5000 pcs.

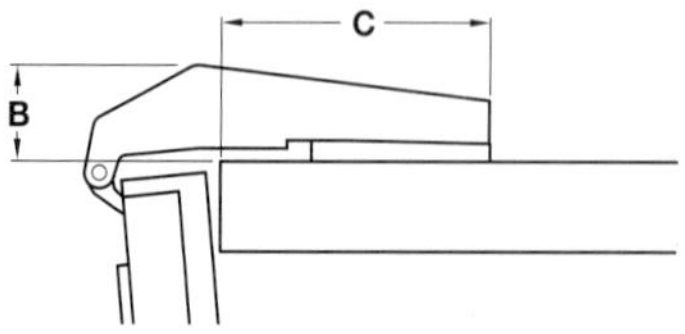

Hinge arm	Dim. **B**	Dim. **C**
with **90°** angle	14	58

Dim. **B** + mounting plate thickness

Dimensions in mm

Mounting Plates for H-Series Hinges-Slide On

HÄFELE

Wing mounting plates, **screw-mounted**
- Pre-installed hinge-arm retaining screw
- All-metal: steel, nickel-plated

HOSPA Φ4,0

Hole pattern

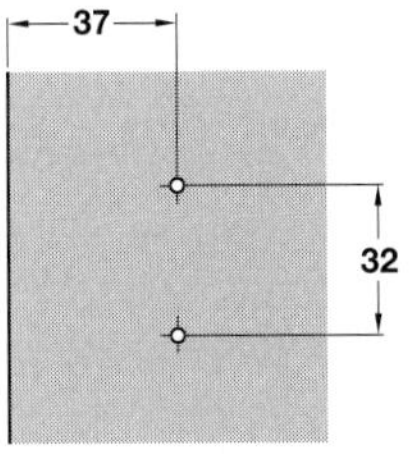

Vertical adjustment
(oblong holes)

Reinforcement	Type	Cat. No.
2 mm	**2**	316.91.620
4 mm	**4**	316.91.648
6 mm	**6**	316.91.666
8 mm	**8**	316.91.684

Packing: 500 pcs.

Wing mounting plates,
screw-mounted in system holes
- Pre-installed hinge-arm retaining screw
- Pre-installed mounting screws, 11 mm
- All-metal: steel, nickel-plated

Hole pattern

SYSTEM VARIANTA 32

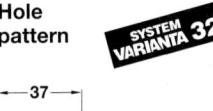

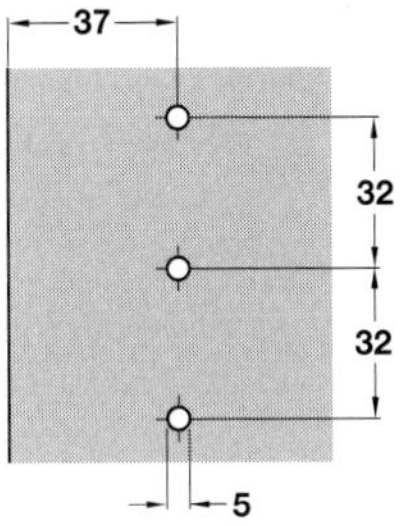

With vertical adjustment
(oblong holes)

Reinforcement	Type	Cat. No.
2 mm	**2**	316.91.627
4 mm	**4**	316.91.645
6 mm	**6**	316.91.663
8 mm	**8**	316.91.681

Packing: 500 pcs.

Mounting screws:
Hospa particle board screws
countersunk head
with PZ 2
cross slot
Finish:
steel, nickel-plated

HOSPA Φ4,0

Length	Cat. No.
15 mm	015.35.824
17 mm	015.35.833

Packing: 1000 pcs.

HÄFELE

H-Series SM

Speed mount application diagram

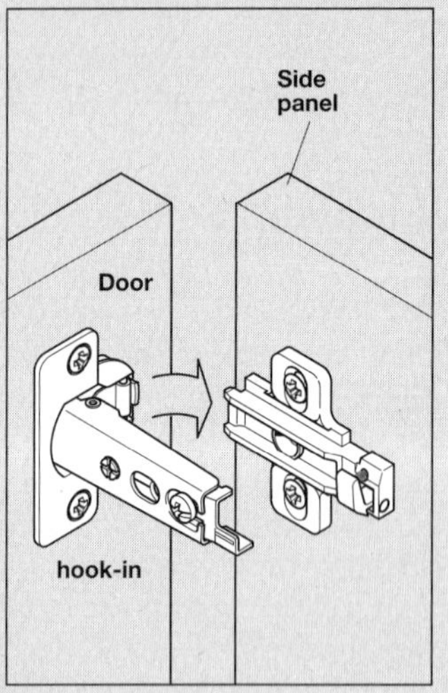

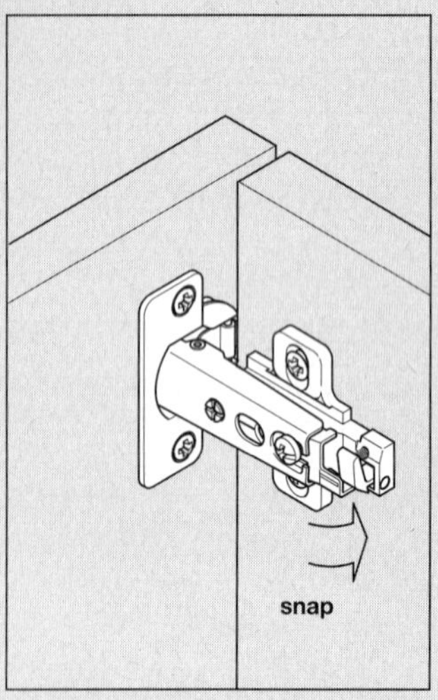

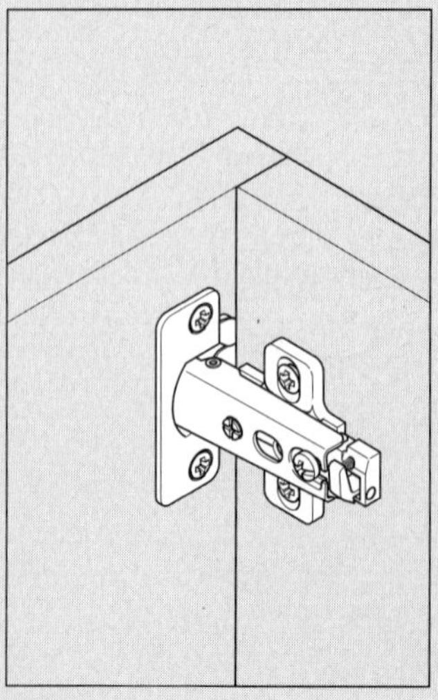

With speed mount feature on mounting plate

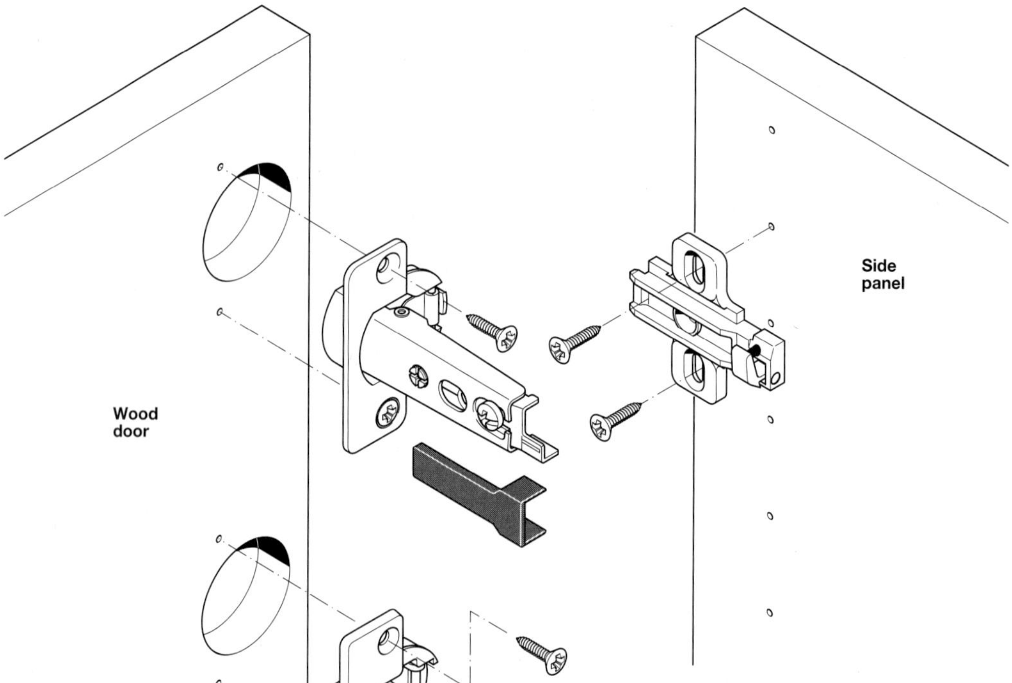

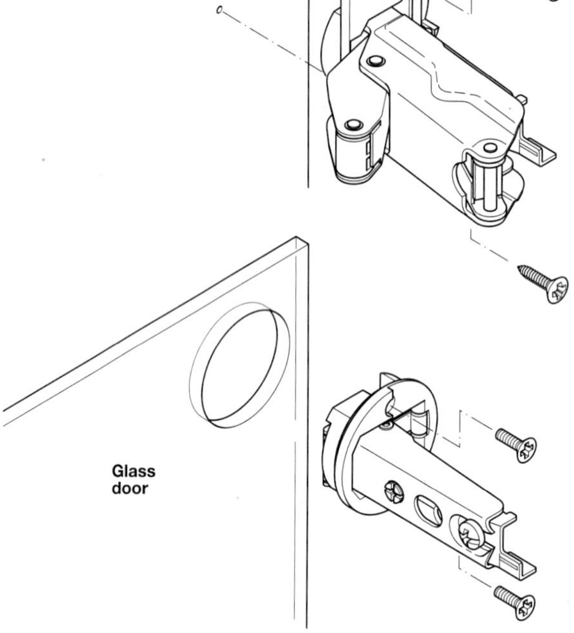

- All-metal
- Durable pivot bearing
- Steel moving parts
- Cup designed for automated insertion
- Self-closing
- Three-way adjustable
- Optional trim caps available with company logo imprint

Adjustments

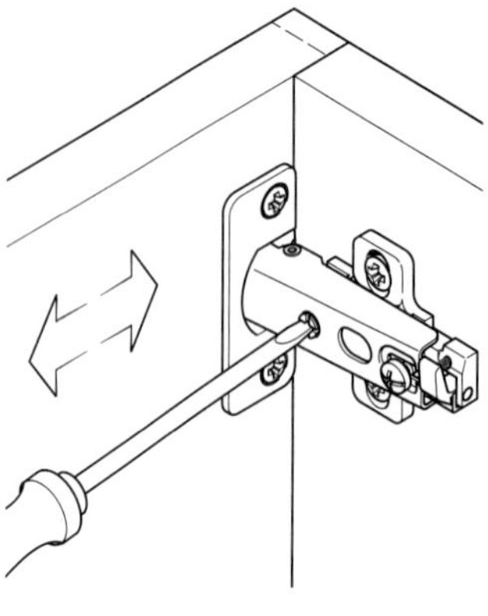

Horizontal
by screw adjustment

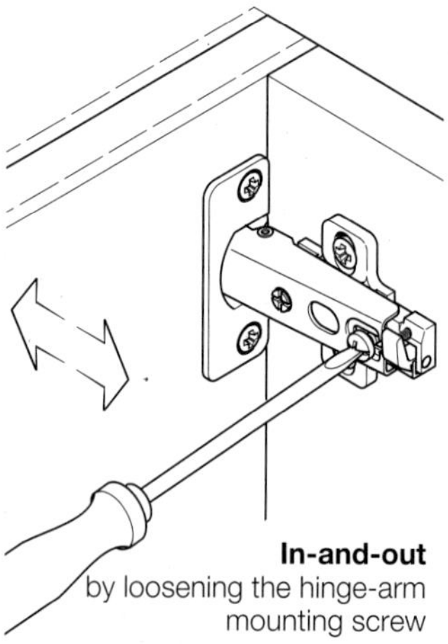

In-and-out
by loosening the hinge-arm mounting screw

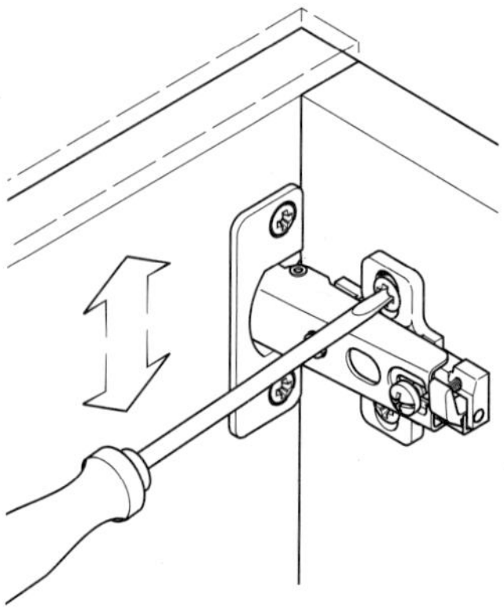

Vertical
via slots in the mounting plate

Dimensional data not binding. We reserve the right to alter specifications without notice.

H-Series SM Hinges

HÄFELE

Guide to Hinges

Hinge type	Hinge cup material	Hinge arm	Opening angle	Type 18	9	1
	Steel	Steel	110°	•	•	•
Profiled door hinge 	Zinc die-cast	Steel	92°	22	•	2
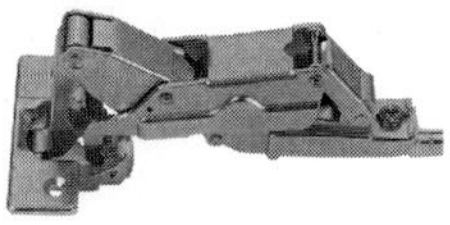	Zinc die-cast	Steel	175°	•	•	
Glass door hinge 	Plastic	Steel	92°	•	•	•
Corner hinge 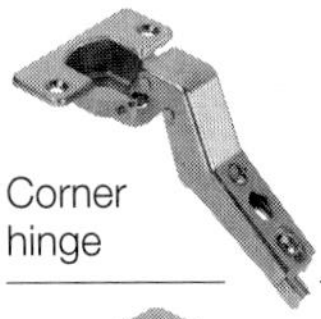	Steel	Steel	95°			
Face Frame Hinge 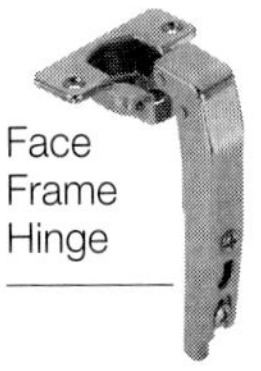	Steel	Steel	95°			

Guide to Mounting Plates

Mounting plate type	Material	System hole installation	Reinforcement Type (vertical adjustment with oblong holes) 2	4	6	8
	Steel		•	•	•	•
	Steel	SYSTEM VARIANTA 32	•	•	•	•

HÄFELE

H-Series SM Hinges

Which hinge type?

Given the factors:

- Opening angle
- Hinge arm type
- Side panel thickness
- Door thickness
- Screw-mount or press-fit
- Mounting plate thickness
- Tab

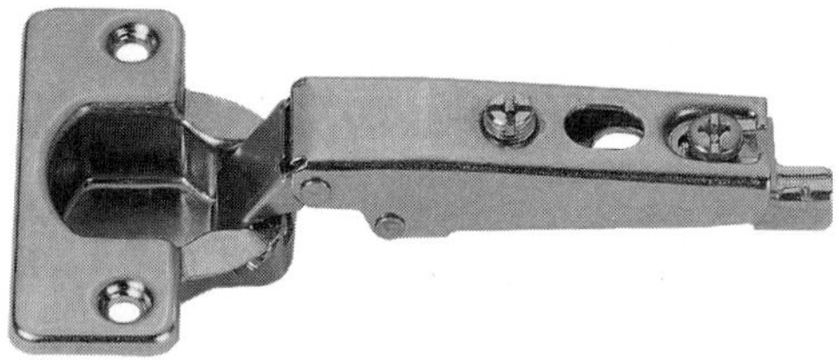

Use the following formula to determine overlay:

Hinge type *minus* mounting plate type *plus* tab = overlay

Sample Calculations

Hinge type **18** **Side panel mounting for overlay doors.**

(A) Full Overlay

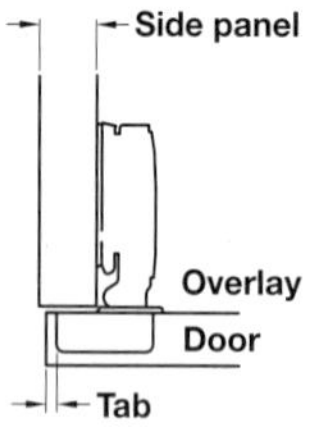

Hinge type **9** **Center panel**/twin mounting for overlay doors.

(B) Half Overlay or Twin Mounting

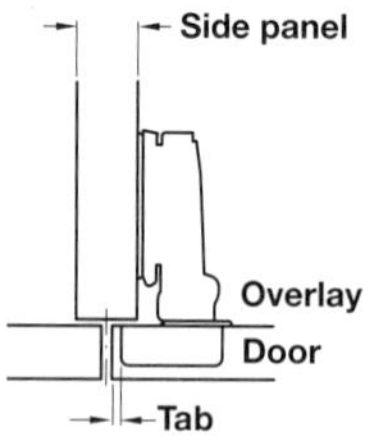

(in the case of twin mounting)

Hinge type **1** **Side panel mounting for inset doors.**

(C) Inset

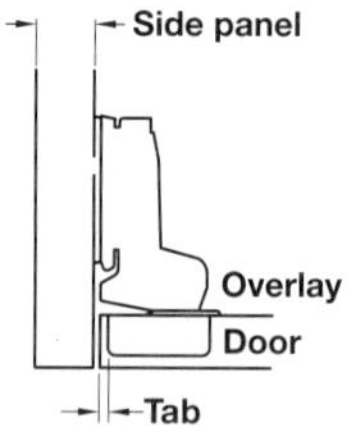

16 mm (5/8") Material	Hinge Type		Mounting Plate		Tab		Total Overlay
Full overlay (A)	18	-	6	+	3	=	15
Half overlay (B)	9	-	4	+	3	=	8
Inset (C)	1	-	4	+	3	=	0

19 mm (3/4") Material	Hinge Type		Mounting Plate		Tab		Total Overlay
Full overlay (A)	18	-	2	+	3	=	19
Half overlay (B)	9	-	2	+	3	=	10
Inset (C)	1	-	4	+	3	=	0

If there is no mounting plate with the required reinforcement, then the tab or side adjustment must be altered.

How many hinges per door?

There is no hard and fast rule which applies. When determining the number of hinges needed, the main factors to consider are door size and weight. A trial mounting is advisable in case of any doubt, such as with doors supporting mirrors, or unusually wide doors. Avoid disproportionate door width/height ratios. Use this table for standard, conventional-material doors. When in doubt, always allow for an extra hinge.

- Commercial and heavy-duty applications, see Häfele's Aximat Hinge.

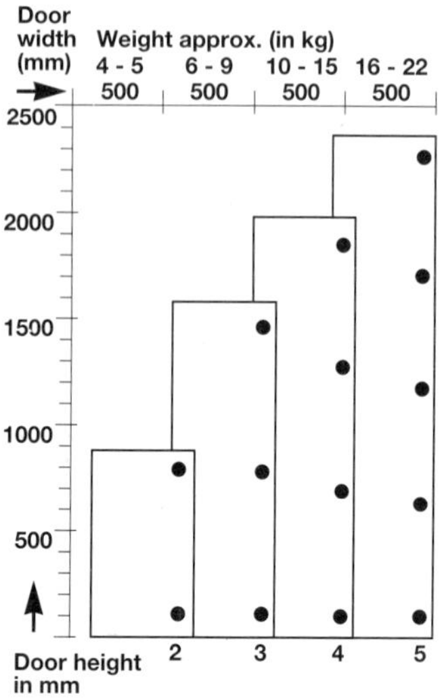

Dimensional data not binding. We reserve the right to alter specifications without notice.

H-Series SM Hinges

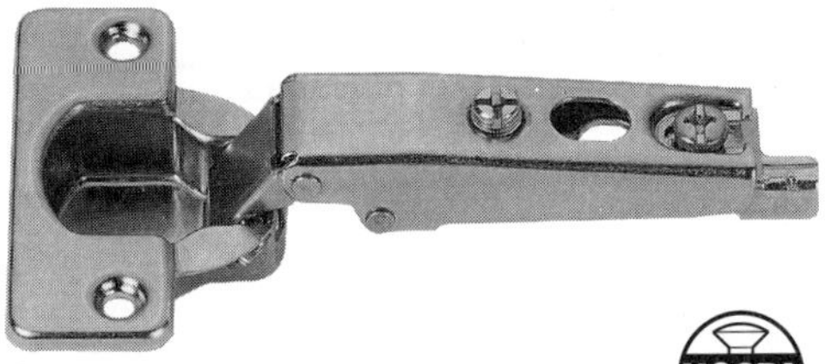

Opening angle: 110°

Hinges with **speed mount feature**
- Door thickness 15 to 26 mm (5/8" - 1")
- Side panel thickness from 15 mm (5/8")
- Self-closing
- All-metal:
  Cup: steel, nickel-plated
  Hinge arm: steel, nickel-plated
- Tab 3 - 6 mm

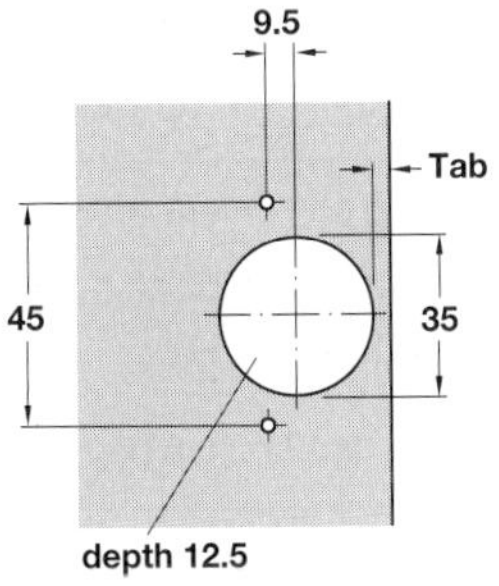

Screw-mount

Mounting	Hinge arm		Hinge type	Cat. No.
Full overlay		straight	**18**	318.01.530
Half overlay		9 mm crank	**9**	318.01.531
Inset mounting		17 mm crank	**1**	318.01.532

Packing: 250 pcs.

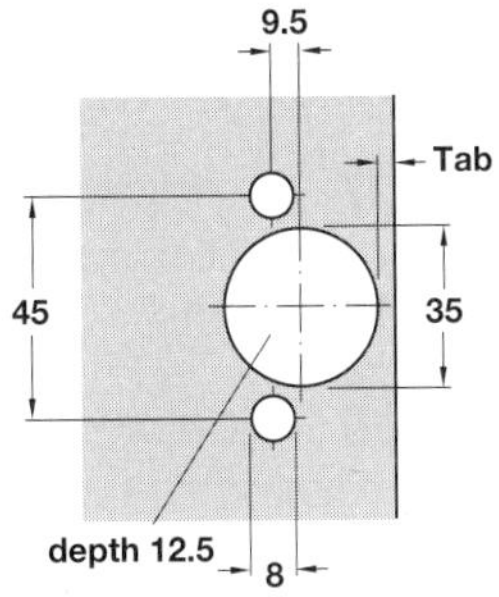

Press-fit, 45/9.5 hole pattern

Mounting	Hinge arm		Hinge type	Cat. No.
Full overlay		straight	**18**	318.01.540
Half overlay		9 mm crank	**9**	318.01.541
Inset mounting		17 mm crank	**1**	318.01.542

Packing: 250 pcs.

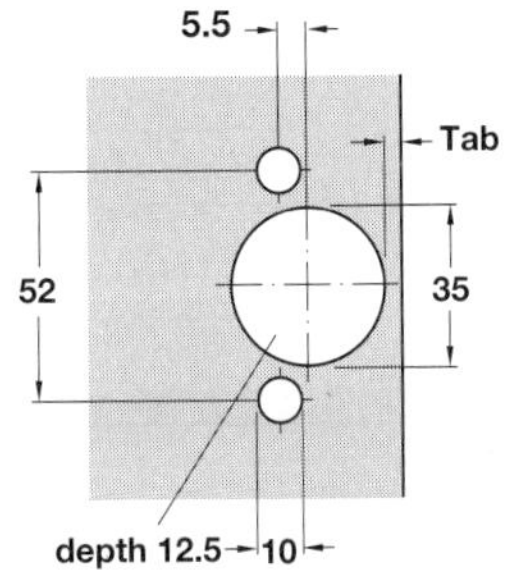

Press-fit, 52/5.5 hole pattern

Mounting	Hinge arm		Hinge type	Cat. No.
Full overlay		straight	**18**	318.01.520
Half overlay		9 mm crank	**9**	318.01.521
Inset mounting		17 mm crank	**1**	318.01.522

Packing: 250 pcs.

Trim caps for hinge arm, finish: plastic

Hinge arm		Cat. No.
Straight	Also 9 and 17 mm crank	318.10.390

Packing: 250 pcs.

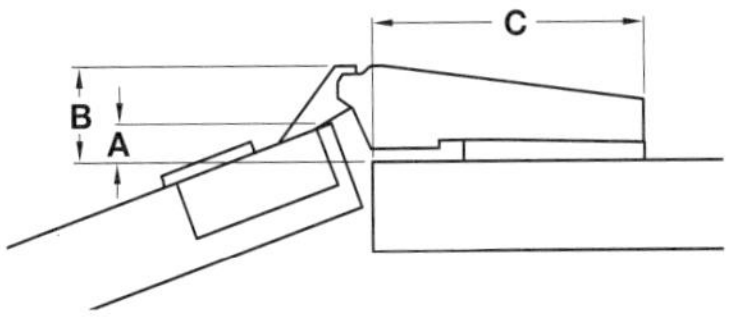

Hinge arm crank	Dim. **A**	Dim. **B**	Dim. **C**
Straight	2	14	68
9 mm crank	11	22	68
17 mm crank	19	30	68

Dim. **A** and **B** each + mounting plate thickness

Dimensions in mm

Hinges, Flap and Lid Stays Associated Fittings **3**

Corresponding mounting plates can be found on page. **3.39**

Mounting screws:
Hospa particle board screws **raised head** with PZ 2 cross slot
Finish:
steel, nickel-plated

Length	Cat. No.
15 mm	015.55.639
20 mm	015.55.657
25 mm	015.55.675

Packing: 1000 pcs.

HÄFELE

H-Series SM Hinges for Profiled Doors

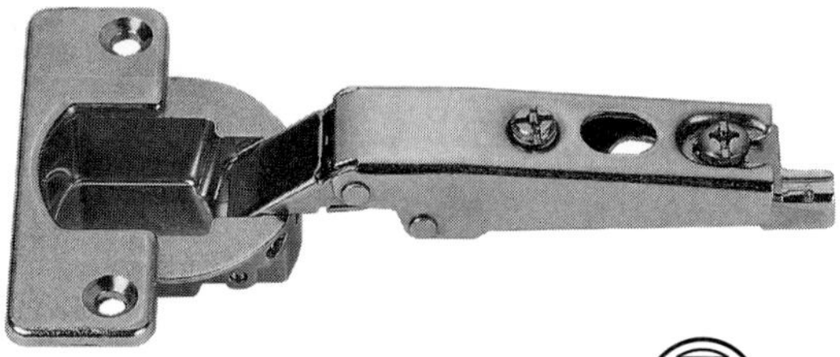

Opening angle: 92°

Hinges with **speed mount feature**
- Door thickness 24 to 35 mm (1" - 1 3/8")
- Side panel thickness from 16 mm (5/8")
- Self-closing
- All-metal:
  Cup: zinc die-cast, nickel-plated
  Hinge arm: steel, nickel-plated
- Tab 3 - 14 mm

HOSPA Φ3,5

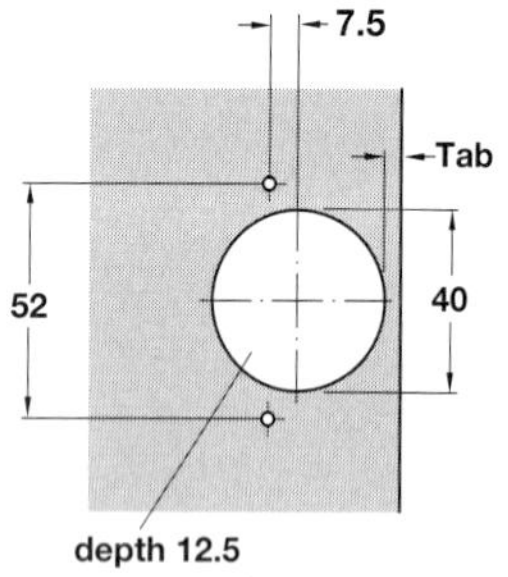

Screw-mount

Mounting	Hinge arm		Hinge type	Cat. No.
Full overlay		straight	**22**	318.06.600
Half overlay		9 mm crank	**10**	318.06.601
Inset mounting		17 mm crank	**2**	318.06.602

Packing: 250 pcs.

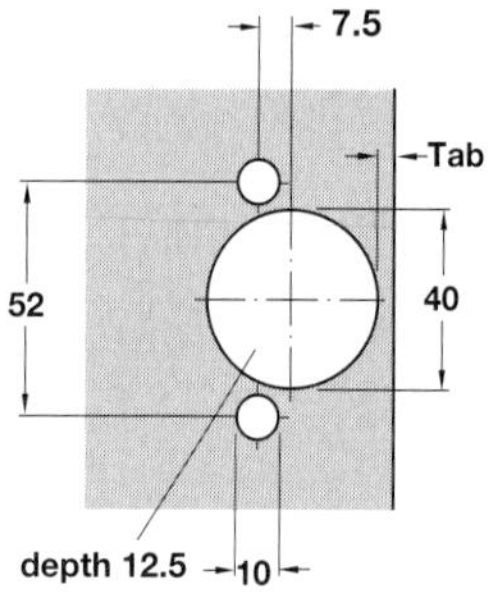

Press-fit, 52/7.5 hole pattern

Mounting	Hinge arm		Hinge type	Cat. No.
Full overlay		straight	**22**	318.06.630
Half overlay		9 mm crank	**10**	318.06.631
Inset mounting		17 mm crank	**2**	318.06.632

Packing: 250 pcs.

Corresponding mounting plates can be found on page **3.39**

Mounting screws:
Hospa particle board screws
raised head with
PZ 2 cross slot
Finish:
steel, nickel-plated

HOSPA Φ3,5

Length	Cat. No.
15 mm	015.55.639
20 mm	015.55.657
25 mm	015.55.675

Packing: 1000 pcs.

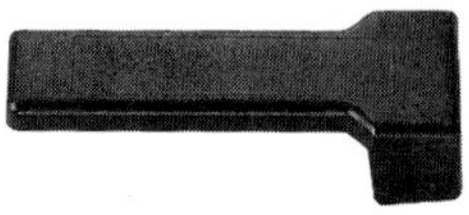

Trim caps for hinge arm, finish: plastic

Hinge arm			Cat. No.
Straight		also 9 and 17 mm crank	318.10.390

Packing: 250 pcs.

Door contour

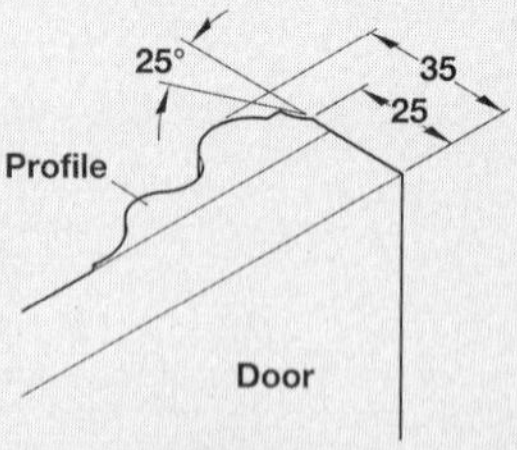

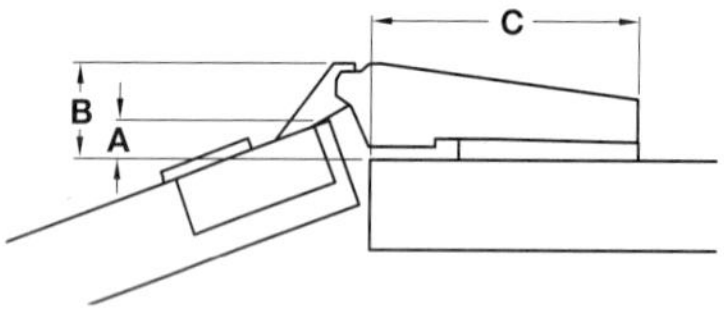

Hinge arm crank	Dim. **A**	Dim. **B**	Dim. **C**
Straight	2	14	68
9 mm crank	11	22	68
17 mm crank	26.5	37.5	68

Dim. **A** and **B** each + mounting plate thickness

Dimensions in mm

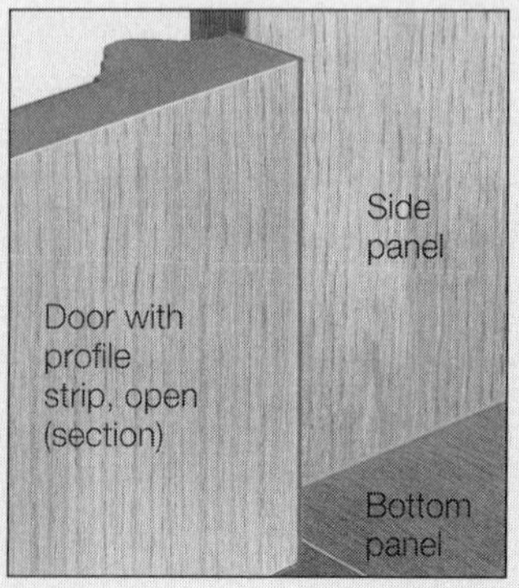

HÄFELE

H-Series SM Hinges

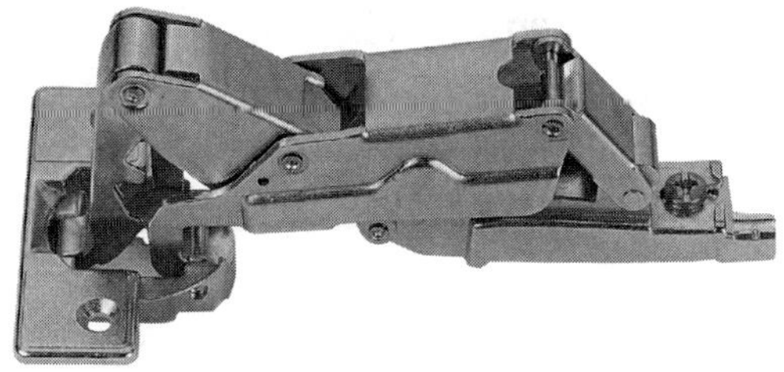

Opening angle:

Hinges with **speed mount feature**
- Door thickness 20 to 26 mm (3/4" - 1")
- Side panel thickness from 16 mm (5/8")
- Self-closing
- All-metal:
  Cup: zinc die-cast, nickel-plated
  Hinge arm: steel, nickel-plated
- Tab 3-6 mm

HOSPA Φ3,5

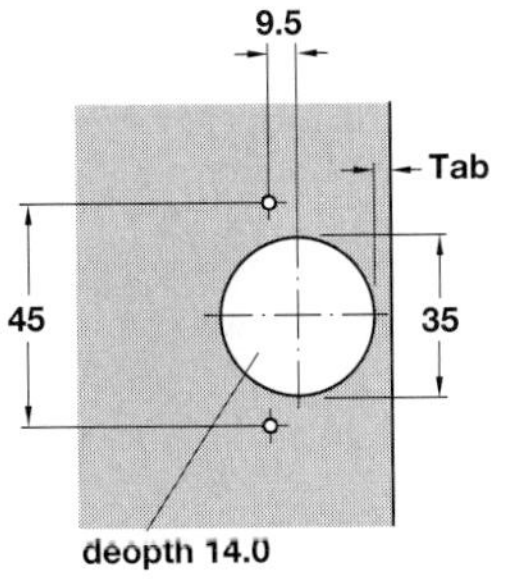

Screw-mount

Mounting	Hinge arm	Hinge type	Cat. No.
Full overlay	straight	**18**	318.05.630
Half overlay	9 mm crank	**9**	318.05.631

Packing: 125 pcs.

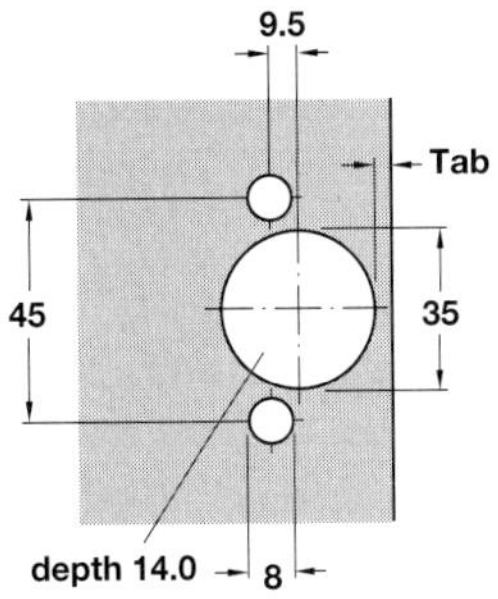

Press-fit, 45/9.5 hole pattern

Mounting	Hinge arm	Hinge type	Cat. No.
Full overlay	straight	**18**	318.05.640
Half overlay	9 mm crank	**9**	318.05.641

Packing: 125 pcs.

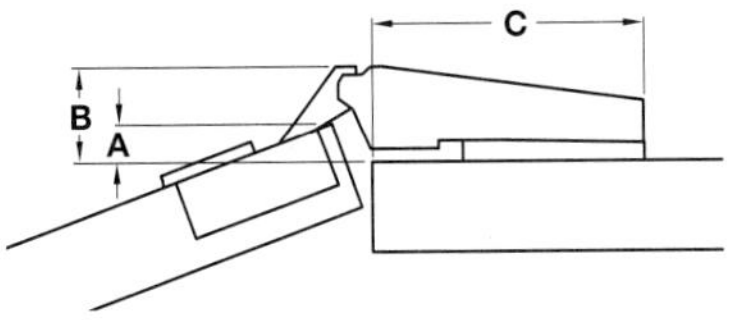

Hinge arm crank	Dim. **A**	Dim. **B**	Dim. **C**
Straight	– 0.5	24	68
12 mm	– 11.5	36	68

Dim. **A** and **B** each + mounting plate thickness
Dimensions in mm

Hinges, Flap and Lid Stays Associated Fittings **3**

Corresponding mounting plates can be found on page **3.39**

Mounting screws:
Hospa particle board screws **raised head** with PZ 2 cross slot
Finish:
steel, nickel-plated

HOSPA Φ3,5

Length	Cat. No.
15 mm	015.55.639
20 mm	015.55.657
25 mm	015.55.675

Packing: 1000 pcs.

HÄFELE

H-Series SM Hinges for Glass Doors

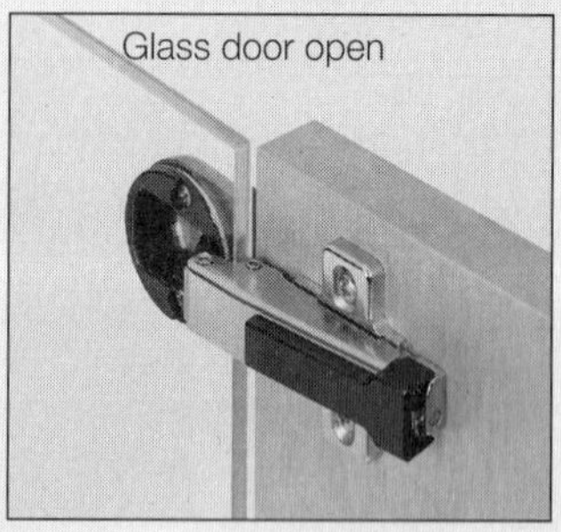

Opening angle: 92°

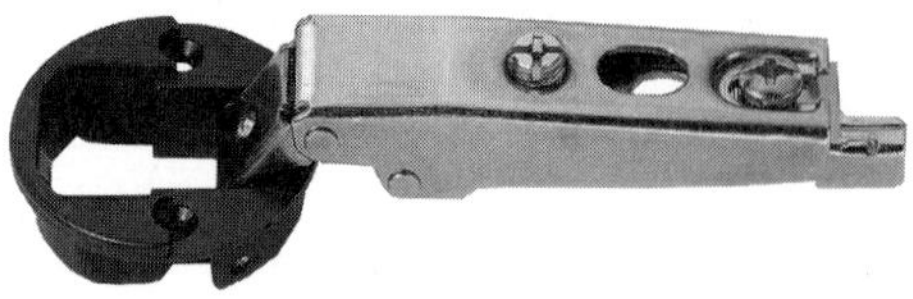

Glass door hinges with **speed mount feature**
- Door thickness 4 to 7 mm (3/16" to 1/4")
- Side panel thickness from 16 mm (5/8")
- Self-closing
  Cup: plastic
  Hinge arm: steel, nickel-plated
- Tab 4 - 9 mm

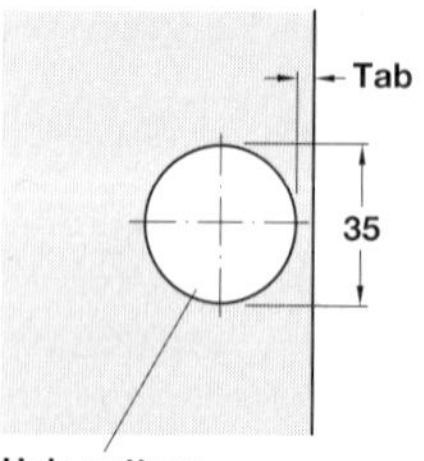

Hole pattern

Screw-mounted

Mounting	Hinge arm	Hinge type	Cat. No.
Full overlay	straight	**18**	318.09.300
Half overlay	9 mm crank	**9**	318.09.301
Inset mounting	17 mm crank	**1**	318.09.302

Packing: 1 and 100 pcs.

3 Hinges, Flap and Lid Stays Associated Fittings

Corresponding mounting plates can be found on page **3.39**

Round and D-shaped trim caps come complete with mounting screws and shims.

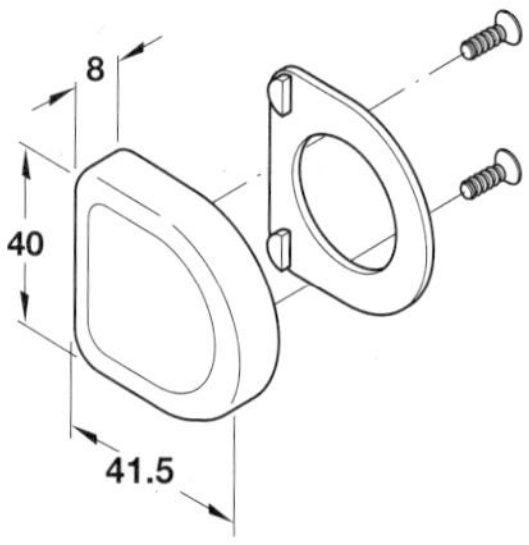

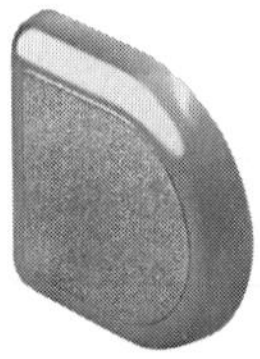

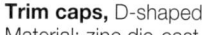

Trim caps, D-shaped
Material: zinc die-cast

Finish	Cat. No.
chrome-plated matt	316.10.410
gold matt	316.10.510
black	316.10.110

Packing: 1 and 100 pcs.

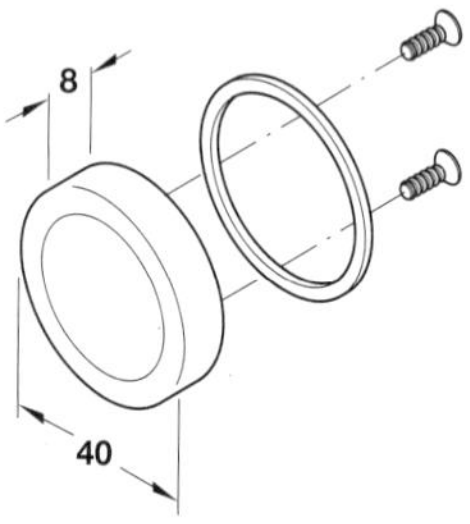

Trim caps, round
Material: zinc die-cast

Finish	Cat. No.
chrome-plated matt	316.10.420
gold matt	316.10.520
black	316.10.120

Packing: 1 and 100 pcs.

Trim caps for hinge arm, finish: plastic

Hinge arm		Cat. No.
Straight	Also 9 and 17 mm crank	318.10.390

Packing: 250 pcs.

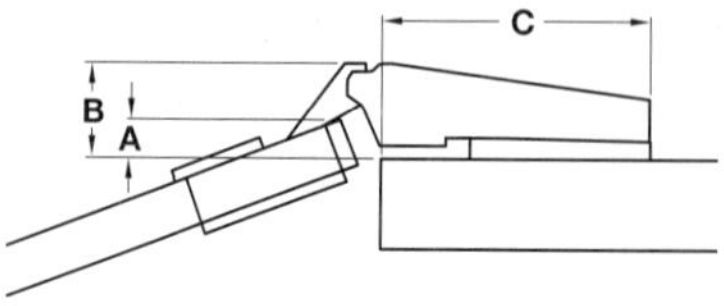

Hinge arm crank	Dim. **A**	Dim. **B**	Dim. **C**
Straight	5	14	68
9 mm	14	22	68
17 mm	21	30	68

Dim. **A** and **B** each + mounting plate thickness

Dimensions in mm

H-Series SM Hinges Corner Hinge

HÄFELE

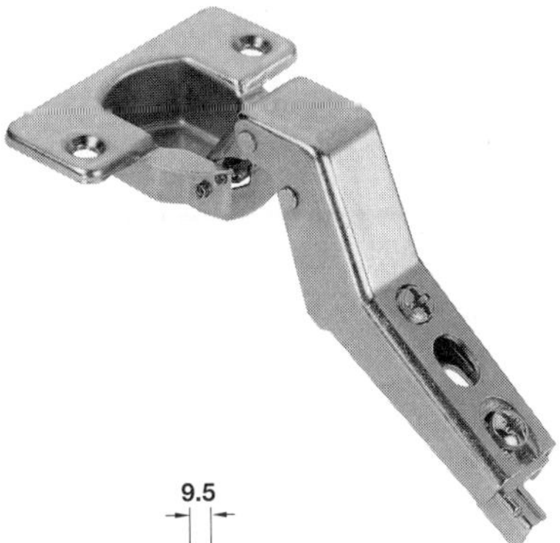

Opening angle: **95°**

Corner hinges with **speed mount feature**
- Door thickness 16 to 25 mm (5/8" to 1")
- Self-closing
- All-metal:
  Cup: steel, nickel-plated
  Hinge arm: steel, nickel-plated
- Tab 3 - 5 mm with smallest mounting plate

HOSPA Φ3,5

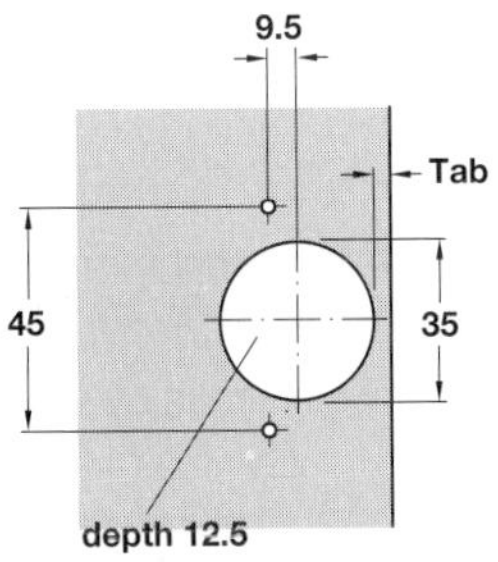

Screw-mount

Mounting	Hinge arm	Cat. No.
Overlay	**30°** angle	318.07.530
Overlay	**45°** angle	318.07.531

Packing: 1 and 50 pcs.

Hinges, Flap and Lid Stays Associated Fittings **3**

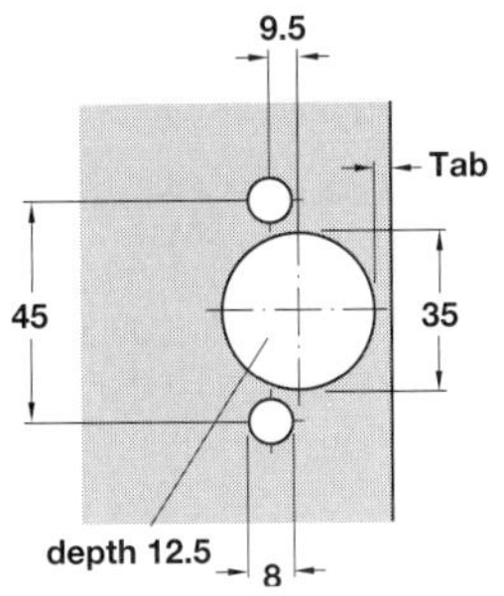

Press-fit, 45/9.5 hole pattern

Mounting	Hinge arm	Cat. No.
Overlay	**30°** angle	318.07.540
Overlay	**45°** angle	318.07.541

Packing: 1 and 50 pcs.

Corresponding mounting plates can be found on page **3.39.**

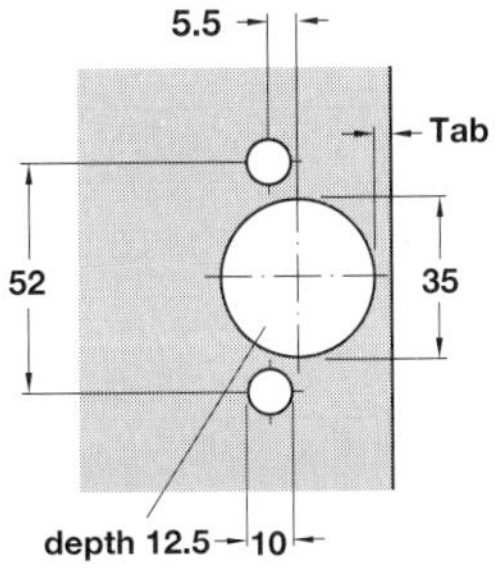

Press-fit, 52/5.5 hole pattern

Mounting	Hinge arm	Cat. No.
Overlay	**30°** angle	318.07.520
Overlay	**45°** angle	318.07.521

Packing: 1 and 50 pcs.

Mounting screws:
Hospa particle board screws **raised head** with PZ 2 cross slot
Finish:
steel, nickel-plated

HOSPA Φ3,5

Length	Cat. No.
15 mm	015.55.639
20 mm	015.55.657
25 mm	015.55.675

Packing: 1000 pcs.

- Trial mounting is recommended for different overlays on miter applications.

Trim caps for hinge arm, finish: plastic, black

Hinge arm	Cat. No.
for 30° and 45°	318.10.390

Packing: 250 pcs.

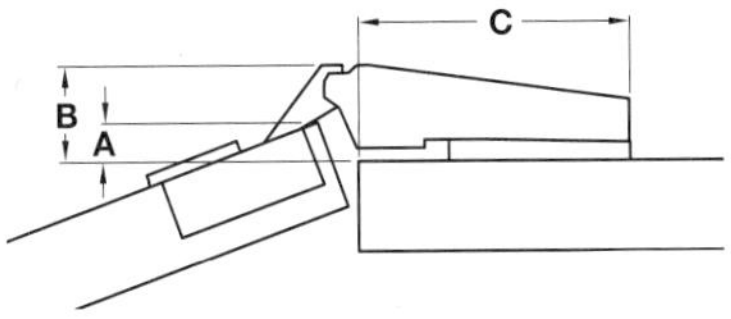

Hinge arm	Dim. **B**	Dim. **C**
30° angle	27	68
45° angle	26.5	68

Dim. **B** + mounting plate thickness

Dimensions in mm

Sample installations

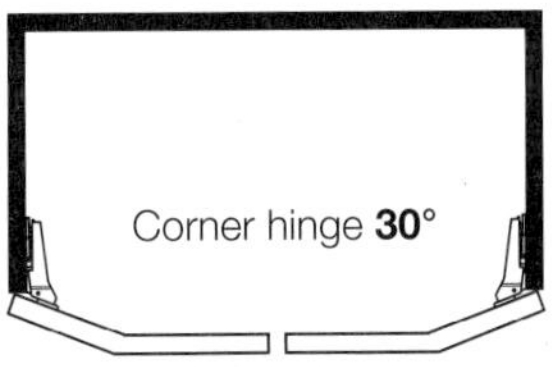

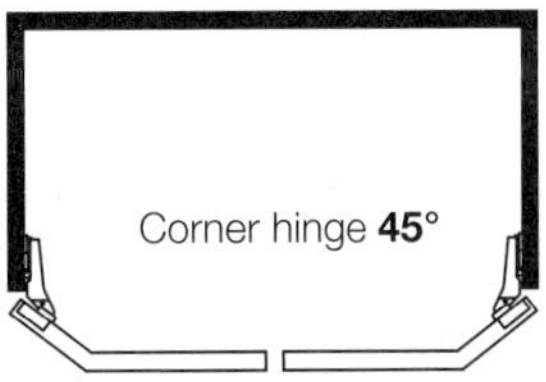

Dimensional data not binding. We reserve the right to alter specifications without notice.

HÄFELE

H-Series SM Face Mount Hinges

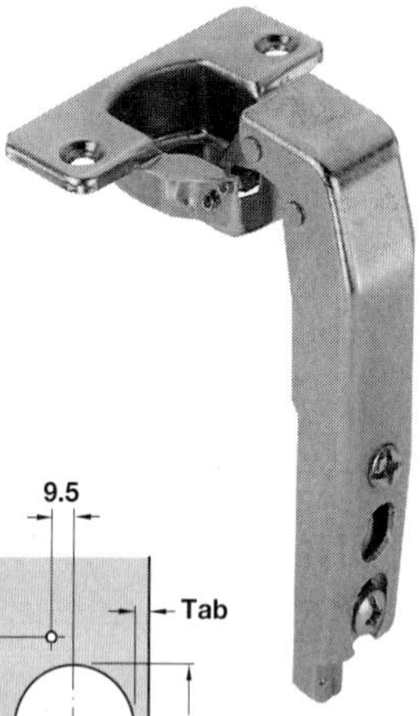

Opening angle: 95°

Frame-mounting hinges with **speed mount feature**
- Door thickness 16 to 25 mm (5/8" to 1")
- Self-closing
- All-metal:
  Cup: steel, nickel-plated
  Hinge arm: steel, nickel-plated

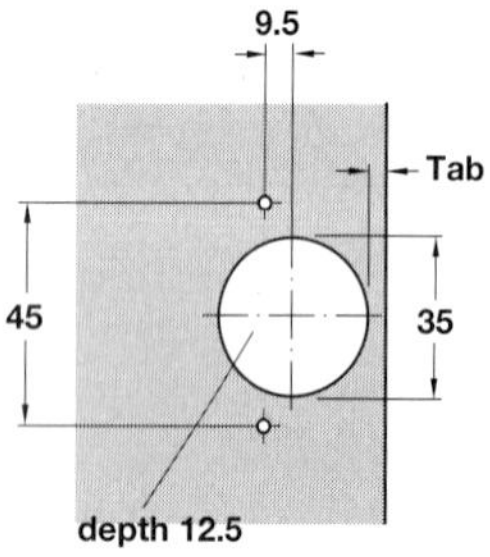

HOSPA Φ3,5

Screw-mount

Mounting	Hinge arm	Cat. No.
Inset mounting	**90°** angle	318.08.530

Packing: 1 and 25 pcs.

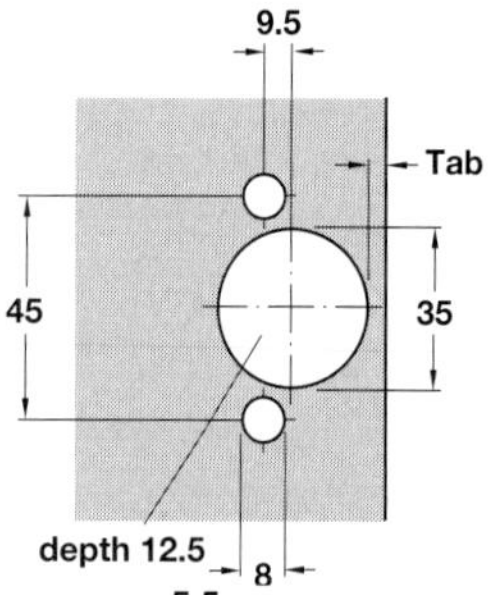

Press-fit, 45/9.5 hole pattern

Mounting	Hinge arm	Cat. No.
Inset mounting	**90°** angle	318.08.540

Packing: 1 and 25 pcs.

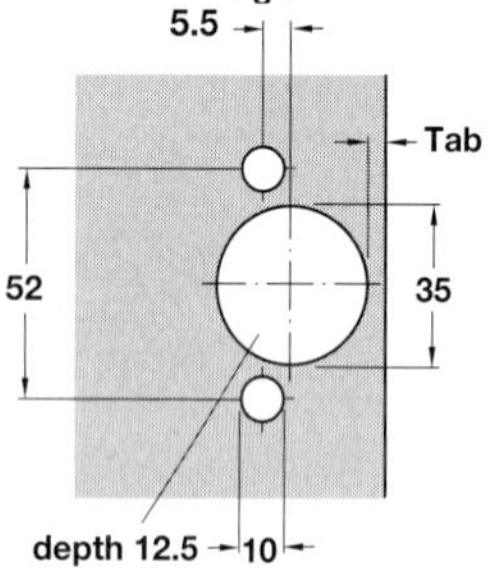

Press-fit, 52/5.5 hole pattern

Mounting	Hinge arm	Cat. No.
Inset mounting	**90°** angle	318.08.520

Packing: 1 and 25 pcs.

3 Hinges, Flap and Lid Stays Associated Fittings

Corresponding mounting plates can be found on page. **3.39**

Mounting screws:
Hospa particle board screws **raised head** with PZ 2 cross slot
Finish:
steel, nickel-plated

HOSPA Φ3,5

Length	Cat. No.
15 mm	015.55.639
20 mm	015.55.657
25 mm	015.55.675

Packing: 1000 pcs.

Face frame cabinet

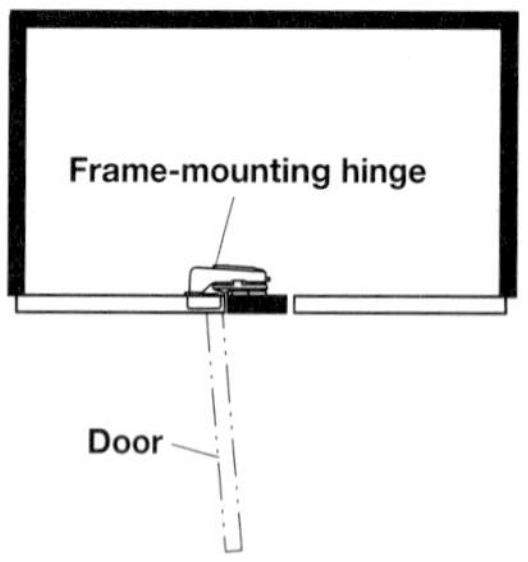

Door closed

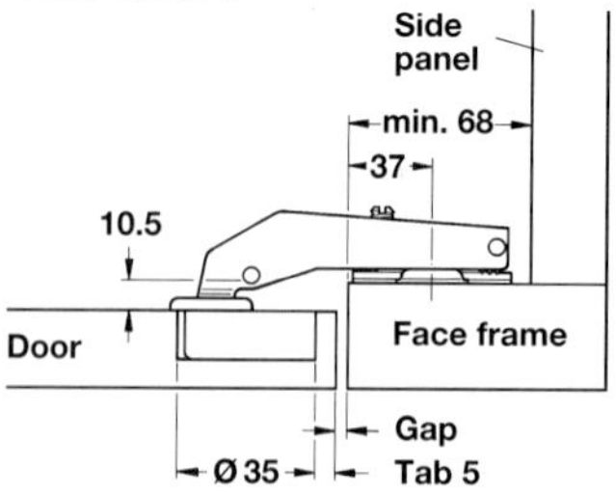

Door open

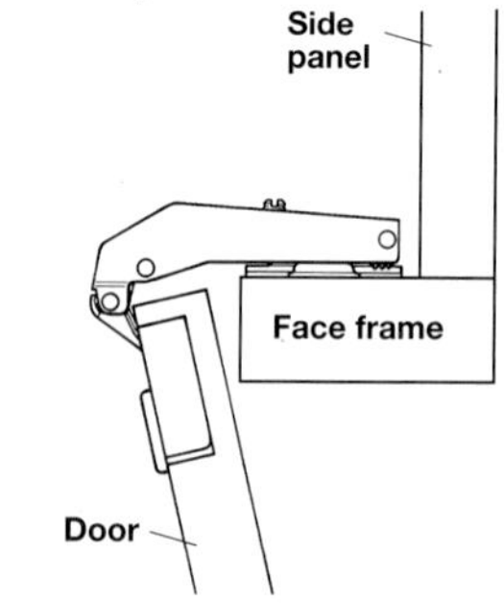

Trim caps for hinge arm, finish: plastic, black

Hinge arm	Cat. No.
90°	316.10.390

Packing: 250 pcs.

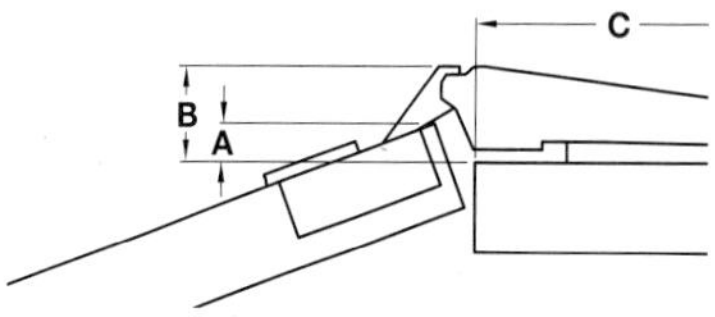

Hinge arm	Dim. **B**	Dim. **C**
with **90°** angle	14	58

Dim. **B** + mounting plate thickness

Dimensions in mm

Mounting Plates for H-Series SM Hinges

HÄFELE

Wing mounting plates, **screw-mounted**
- Pre-installed hinge-arm retaining screws
- Zinc die-cast, nickel-plated

HOSPA Φ4,0

Hole Pattern

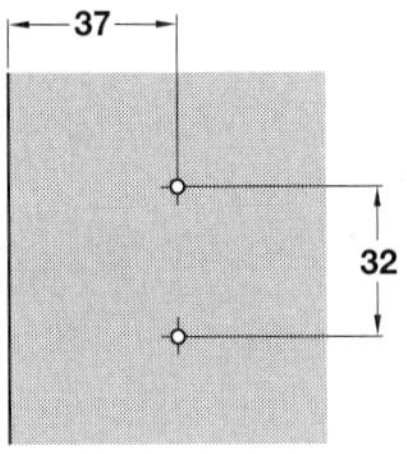

Vertical adjustment
(oblong holes)

Reinforcement	Type	Cat. No.
2 mm	**2**	318.20.603
4 mm	**4**	318.20.604
6 mm	**6**	318.20.606
8 mm	**8**	318.20.608

Packing: 250 pcs.

Mounting screws:
Hospa particle board screws
countersunk head
with PZ 2
crpss slot
Finish:
steel, nickel-plated

HOSPA Φ4,0

Length	Cat. No.
15 mm	015.35.824
17 mm	015.35.833

Packing: 1000 pcs.

Hinges,
Flap and Lid Stays
Associated Fittings
3

Wing mounting plates,
screw-mounted in system holes
- Pre-installed hinge-arm retaining screws
- Pre-installed mounting screws, 11 mm
- Zinc die-cast, nickel-plated

Hole Pattern

SYSTEM VARIANTA 32

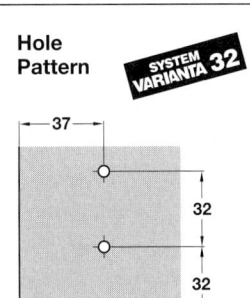

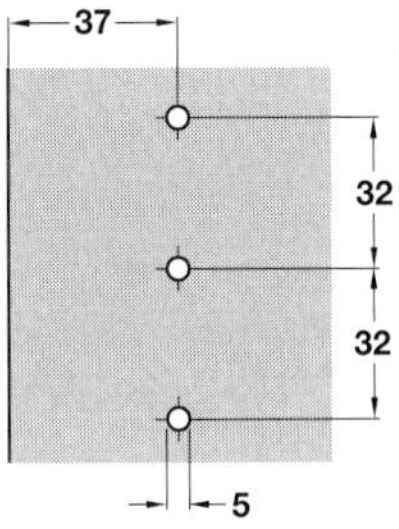

Vertical adjustment
(oblong holes)

Reinforcement	Type	Cat. No.
2 mm	**2**	318.20.613
4 mm	**4**	318.20.614
6 mm	**6**	318.20.616
8 mm	**8**	318.20.618

Packing: 250 pcs.

Dimensions in mm

HÄFELE

Door Bumpers, Trim Caps

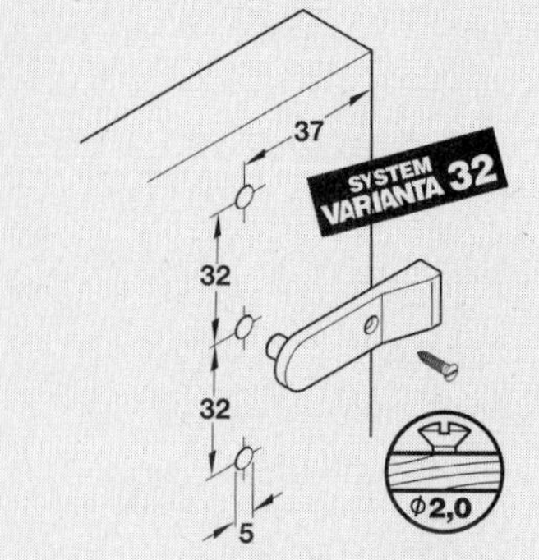

Door stop

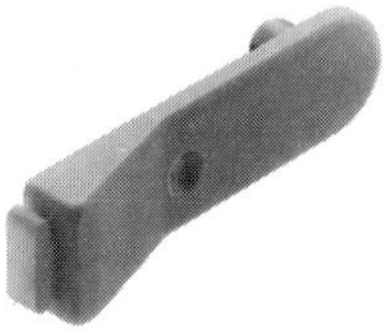
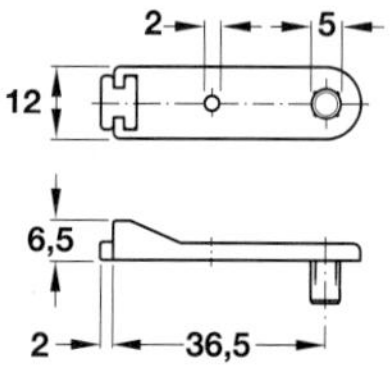

Finish: plastic

Cat. No.		
	white	356.29.746
	beige	356.29.442

Packing: 500 pcs.

Door Bumpers

Durable polyurethane, Self-adhesive, acrylate adhesive.

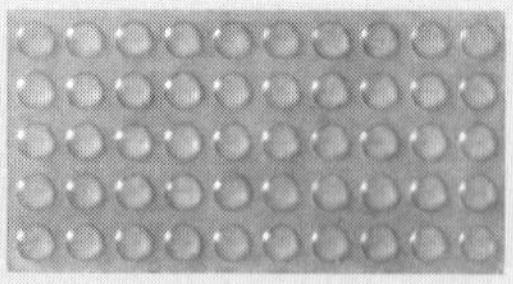

Finish: plastic, clear

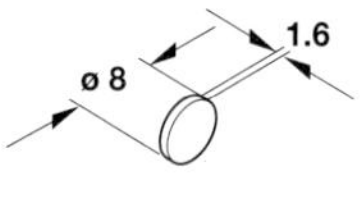

Cat. No.	356.21.428

Packing: 5040 pcs. (1 sheet = 144 pcs.)

Finish: plastic

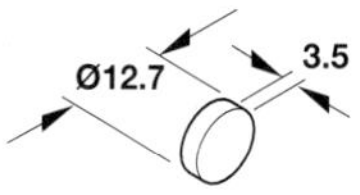

Cat. No.		
	clear	356.25.400
	brown	356.25.100

Packing: 5000 pcs. (1 sheet = 200 pcs.)

Finish: plastic

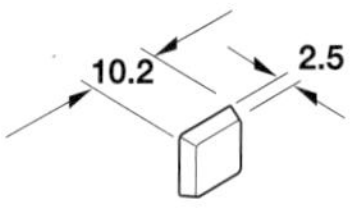

Cat. No.		
	clear	356.25.410
	brown	356.25.110

Packing: 5082 pcs. (1 sheet = 242 pcs.)

3 Hinges, Flap and Lid Stays Associated Fittings

Finish: plastic

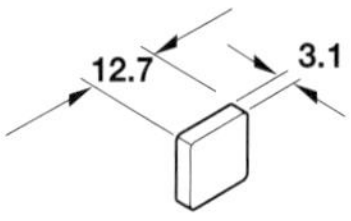

Cat. No.		
	clear	356.25.411
	brown	356.25.111

Packing: 5000 pcs. (1 sheet = 200 pcs.)

Finish: plastic

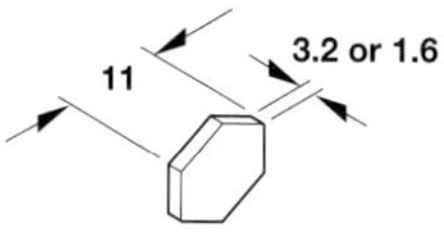

Cat. No.		
	brown 3.2 mm	356.25.121
	brown 1.6 mm	356.25.120

Packing: 3036 pcs. (1 sheet = 132 pcs.)

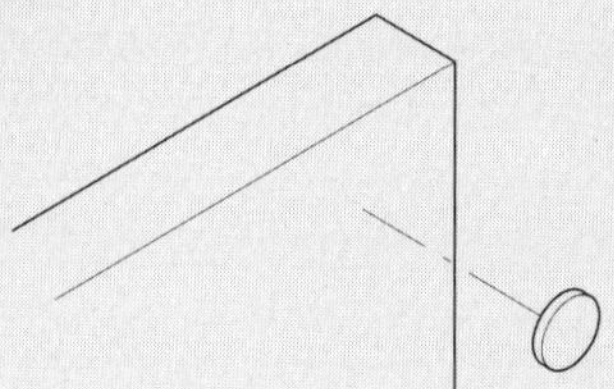

Door Bumper, press-fit

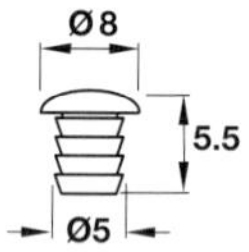

Finish: plastic, clear

Cat. No.		
	head height 1.5 mm	356.16.015
	head height 2 mm	356.16.020
	head height 2.5 mm	356.16.025

Packing: 5000 pcs.

Door Bumper, press-fit

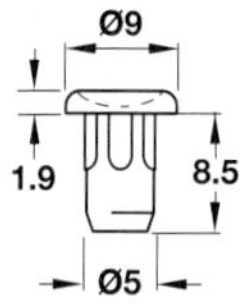

Finish: plastic, clear

Cat. No.	356.18.010

Packing: 5000 pcs.

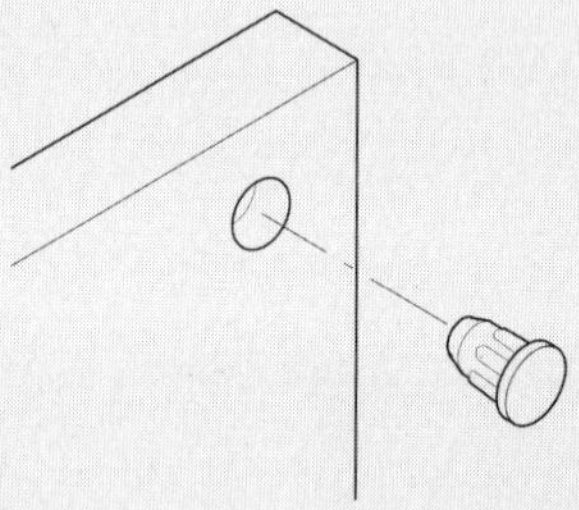

Door Bumper, press-fit

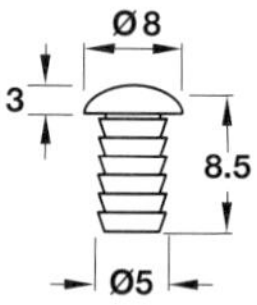

Finish: plastic, clear

Cat. No.	356.17.010

Packing: 5000 pcs.

Door Bumper, press-fit

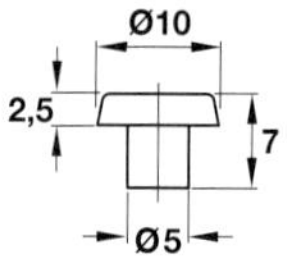

Finish: plastic, white

Cat. No.	356.20.707

Packing: 5000 pcs.

Door Bumper, knock-in

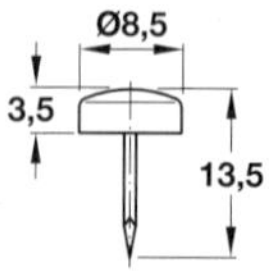

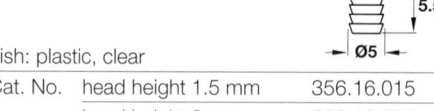

Finish: steel/plastic, white

Cat. No.	356.39.706

Packing: 500 pcs.

Door Bumper, clear press-fit

4 1/2" wide, 1296" length roll

Finish: plastic, clear

Cat. No.	356.25.105

Packing: 35,500 pcs. per roll

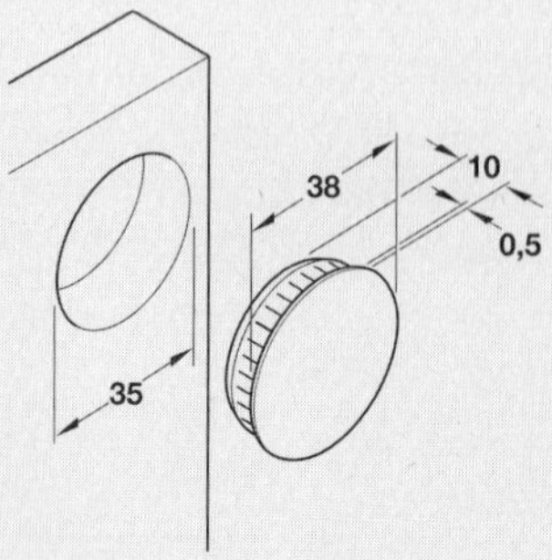

Door Bumper, press-fit, 6 mm dia.

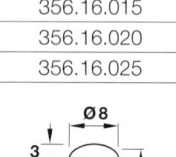

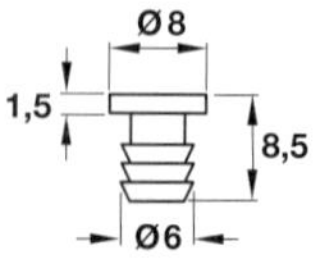

Finish: plastic

Cat. No.		
	clear	356.20.421
	white	356.20.725
	brown	356.20.127

Packing: 500 pcs.

Trim cap for cup holes, 35 mm dia.

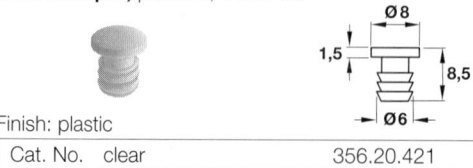

Finish: plastic

Cat. No.		
	white	340.41.702
	brown	340.41.104

Packing: 100 pcs.

Dimensions in mm

Dimensional data not binding. We reserve the right to alter specifications without notice.

Face-Frame Hinges and Mounting Plates

HÄFELE

Opening angle: 95°

- Self-closing
- All-metal:
  Cup: steel, nickel-plated
  Hinge arm: zinc die-cast; nickel-plated
- Tab 2.5 mm – 6.0 mm
- Recommended door thickness 16 - 20 mm (5/8" to 3/4")
- 3-way adjustable

HOSPA Φ3,5

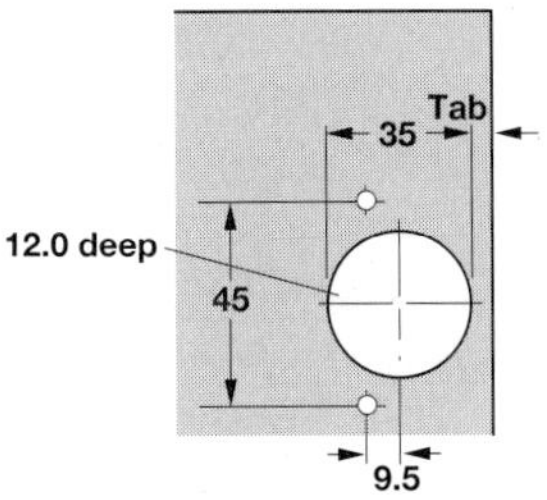

Screw-mount

Mounting	Hinge arm	Cat. No.
Full overlay		343.85.601

Packing: 250 pcs.

Hinges,
Flap and Lid Stays
Associated Fittings

3

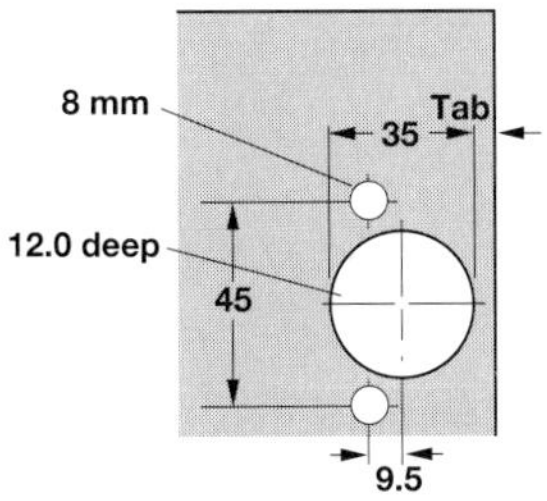

Press-fit, 45/9.5 hole pattern

Mounting	Hinge arm	Cat. No.
Full overlay		343.85.656

Packing: 250 pcs.

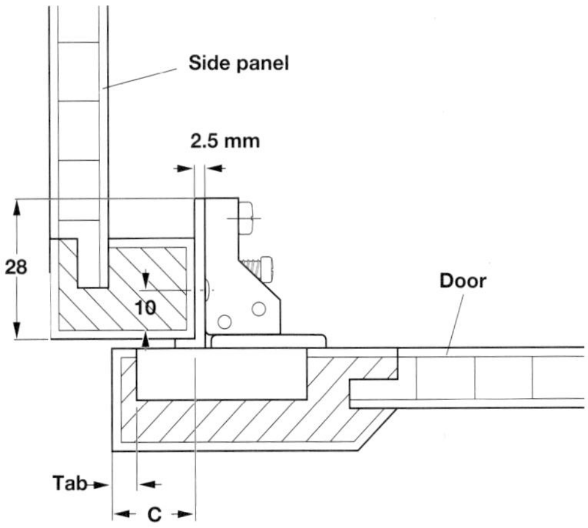

C = approximately 1/2" overlay, depending on Tab.

Mounting screws:
Hospa particle board screws
raised head with
PZ 2 cross slot
Finish:
steel, nickel-plated

HOSPA Φ3.5

Length	Cat. No.
15 mm	015.55.639
20 mm	015.55.657
25 mm	015.55.675

Packing: 1000 pcs.

Wing mounting plates, screw-mounted with pre-installed hinge arm mounting screw

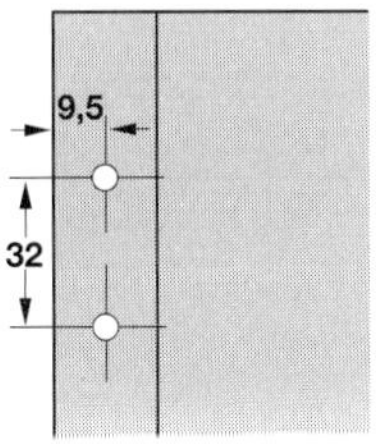

Finish: steel, nickel-plated

Cat. No.	343.86.528

Packing: 1200 pcs.

Dimensions in mm

Dimensional data not binding.
We reserve the right to alter specifications without notice.

HÄFELE

Face Frame Hinges

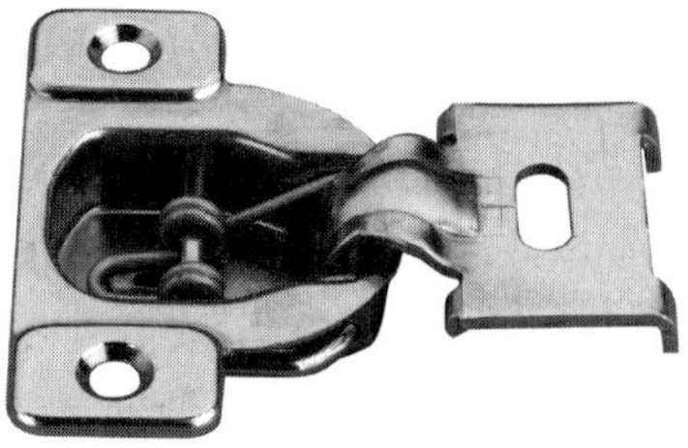

3 Hinges, Flap and Lid Stays Associated Fittings

For Hinge Cup:

Mounting screws:
Hospa particle board screws **raised head** with PZ 2 cross slot
Finish:
steel, nickel-plated

Length	Cat. No.
15 mm	015.55.639
20 mm	015.55.657
25 mm	015.55.675

Packing: 1000 pcs.

For Hinge Arm

Truss/washer-head screw
Finish:
zinc-plated

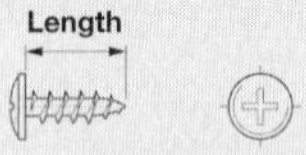

Dimension	Cat. No.
#8 x 9/16	013.13.917
#8 x 1	013.13.935
#8 x 1 1/4	013.13.944
#8 x 1 7/8	013.13.971

Packing: 1000 pcs.

Dimensional data not binding. We reserve the right to alter specifications without notice.

Opening angle:
Cup depth: 10 mm

Hole Pattern

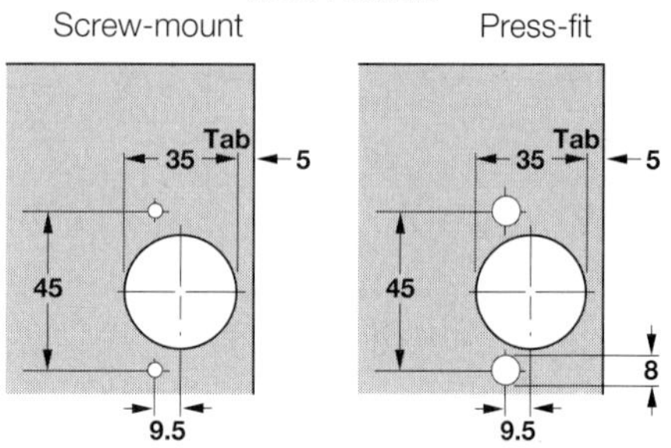

Door overlay: 1/2"

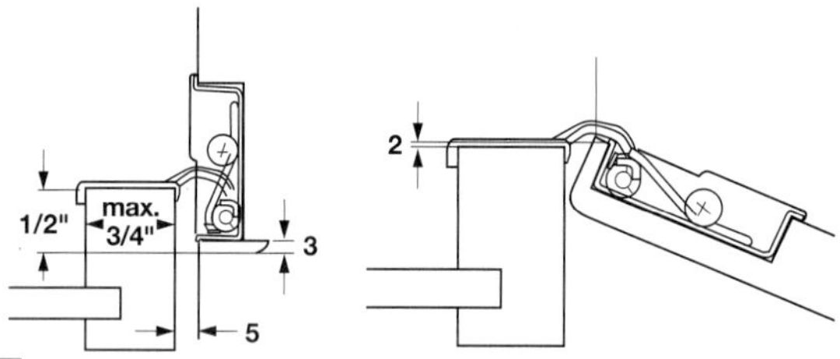

3.1 mm Door protrusion

Finish: steel, nickel-plated

Mounting	Cat. No.
Screw-mount	343.93.502
Press-fit with 8mm dowels	343.93.512

Packing: 200 pcs.

Door overlay: 9/16"

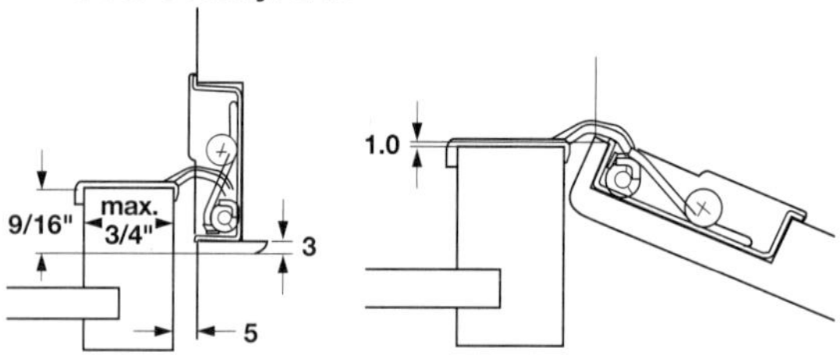

1.2 mm Door protrusion

Finish: steel, nickel-plated

Mounting	Cat. No.
Screw-mount	343.93.501
Press-fit with 8mm dowels	343.93.511

Packing: 200 pcs.

Door overlay: 5/8"

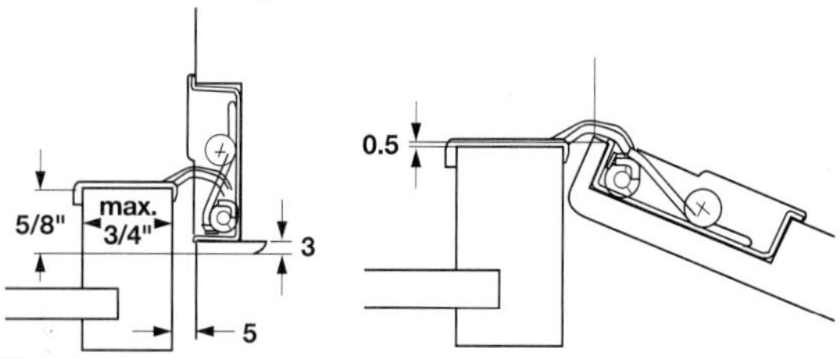

0 mm Door protrusion

Finish: steel, nickel-plated

Mounting	Cat. No.
Screw-mount	343.93.503
Press-fit with 8mm dowels	343.93.513

Packing: 200 pcs.

Face-Frame Hinges 110º Opening Angle

HÄFELE

Face-Frame Hinge Without Mounting Plate
Attaches directly to Face-Frame

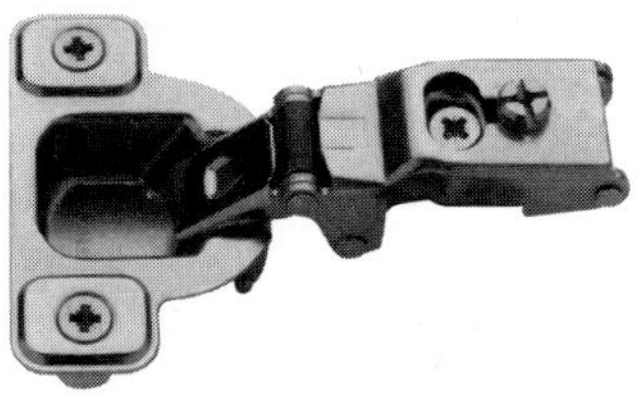

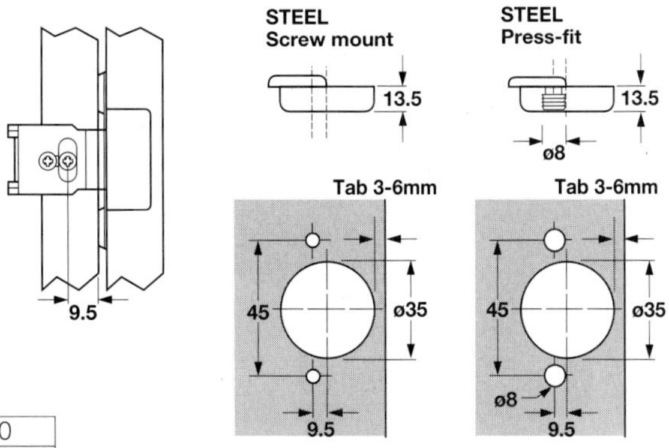

Finish: steel, nickel plated

Cat. No.	screw mount	343.92.610
	press-fit with 8 mm dowels	343.92.615

Packing: 300 pcs.

Face-Frame Hinge With Mounting Plate
Attaches directly to Face-Frame

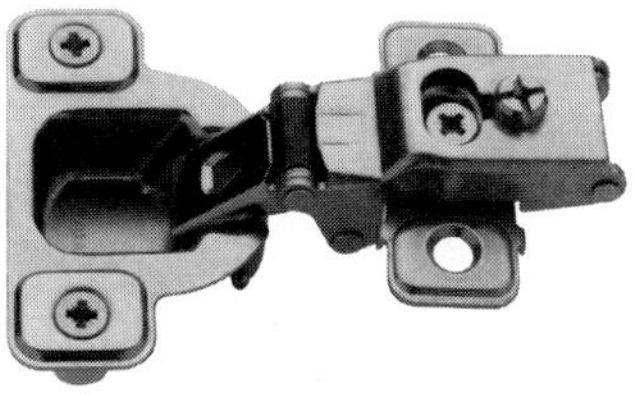

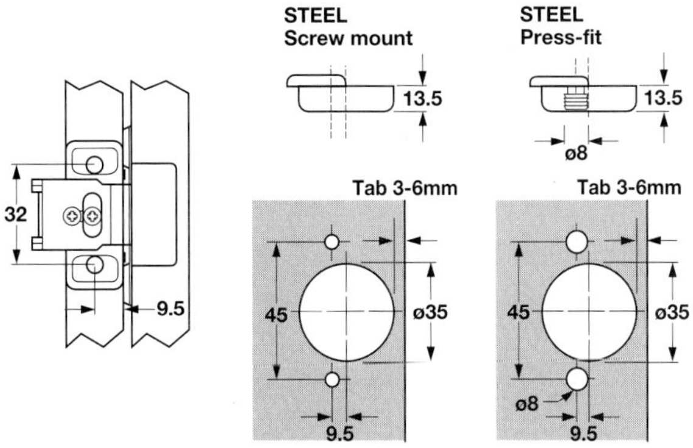

Finish: steel, nickel plated

Cat. No.	screw mount	343.92.600
	press-fit with 8 mm dowels	343.92.605

Packing: 300 pcs.

Kitchen Cabinets, Face Frame Cabinets

- For overlay between 1 1/4" & 1 3/8"
  Hinge can achieve full overlay
- Available with or without mounting plate
  Easy installation, mounting plate fits in 32 mm system
- 110º opening
  Improved access to cabinet interior
- Vertical and horizontal adjustment
  Easy alignment of doors
- With spring

Hinges,
Flap and Lid Stays
Associated Fittings

3

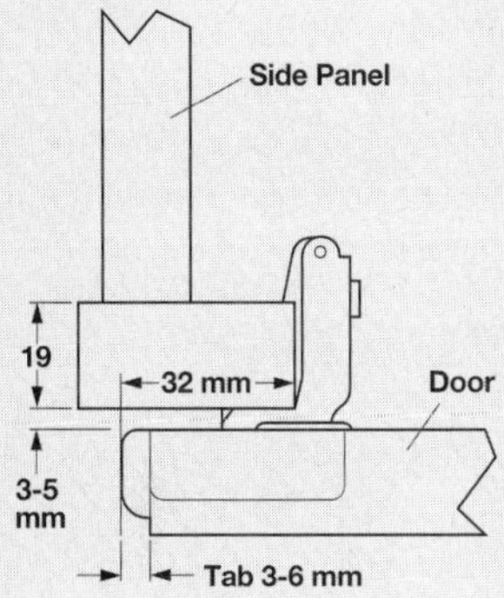

Dimensional data not binding.
We reserve the right to alter specifications without notice.

HÄFELE

Aximat® Hinges

- Hinges **without speed mount system**
- Door thicknesses from **16 - 20 mm** (5/8" to 3/4)
- Hole depth 13, 13.5 and 15.8 mm
- Separate installation of cup and hinge arm

Inset door **with exposed axle 7 mm dia.**

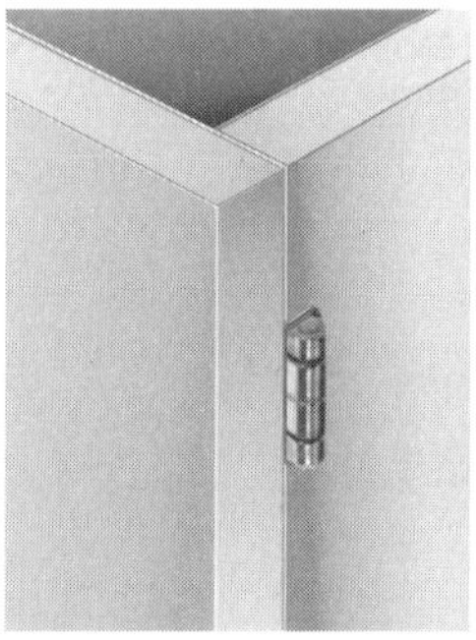

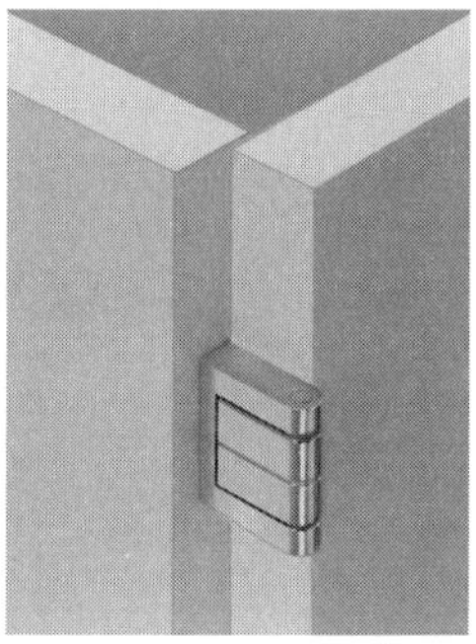

Side panel, center panel and twin mounting **with exposed axle 7 mm dia.**

* Hinges for **screw-mounting** or **press-fitting**, see following pages

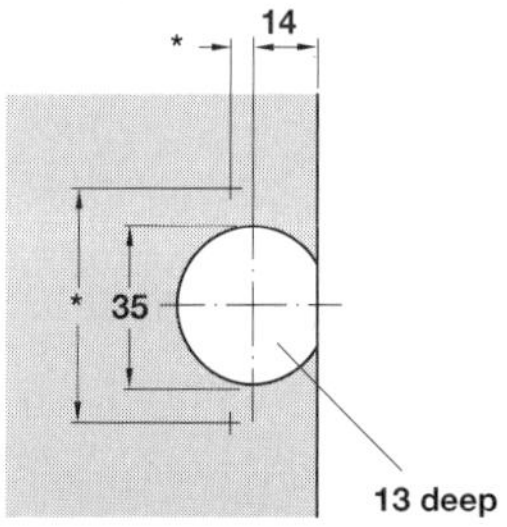

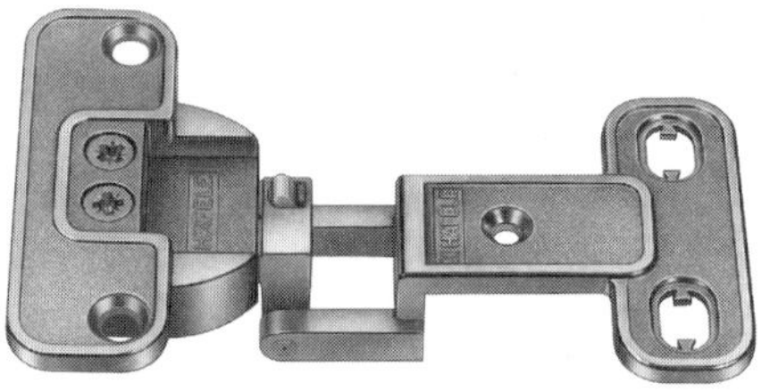

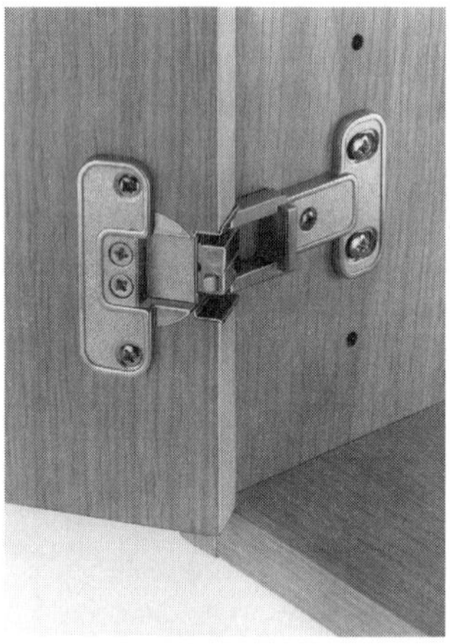

Aximat for inset doors

Aximat for overlay glass doors

Aximat for inset glass doors

* Hinges for **screw-mounting** or **press-fitting**, see following pages

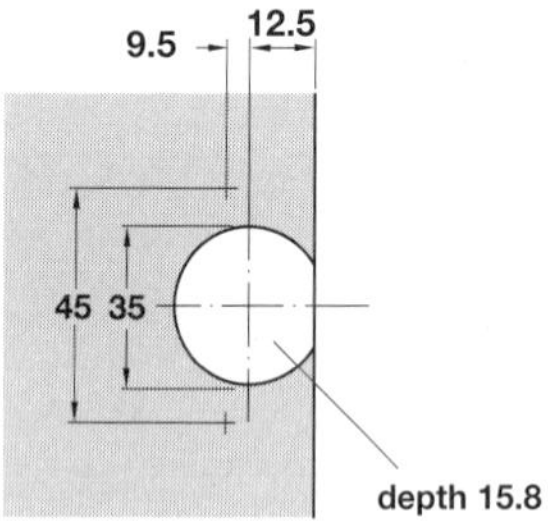

Single-side mounting on 16 and 19 mm cabinet side panels, **with exposed axle 4 mm dia.**

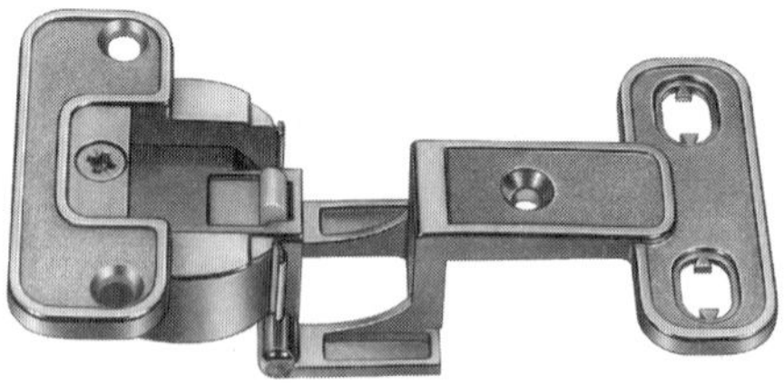

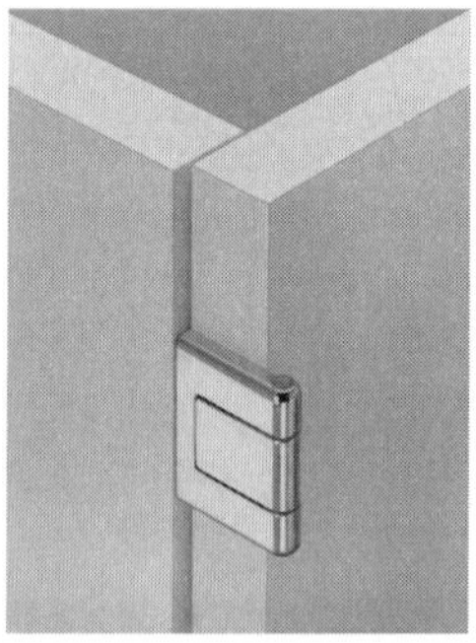

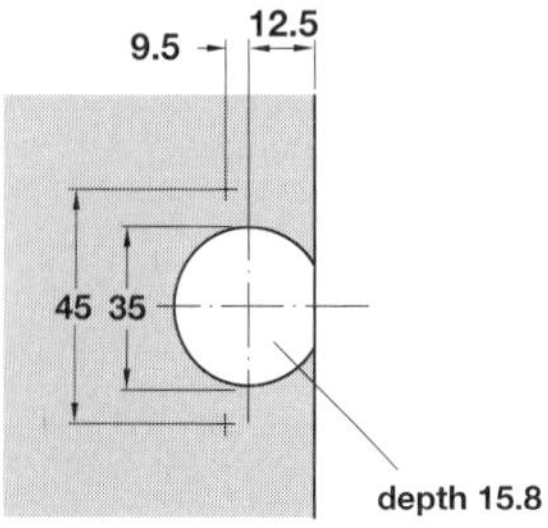

Single-side and center panel mounting on 16 and 19 mm cabinet side panels, **with concealed axle**

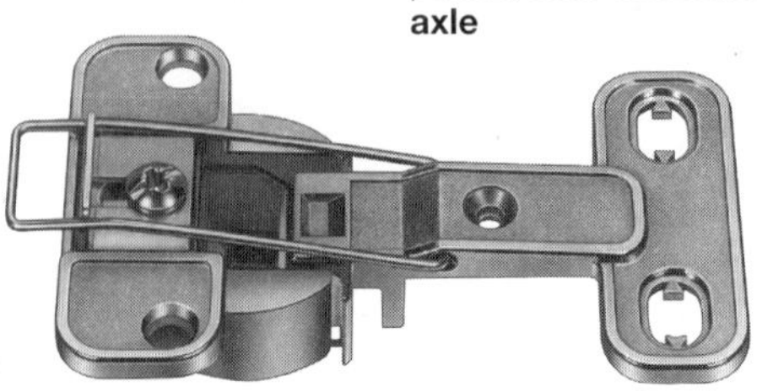

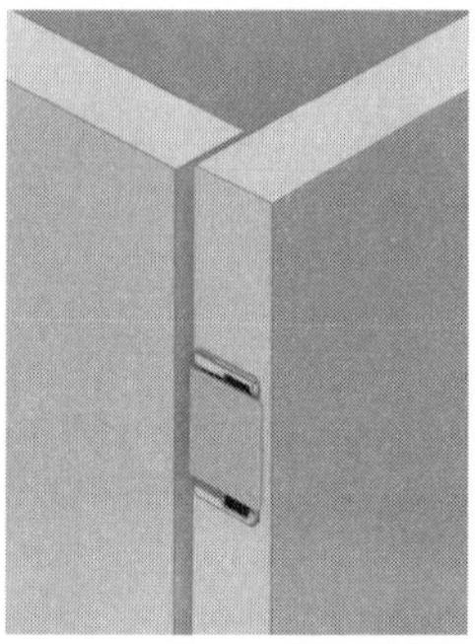

3 Hinges, Flap and Lid Stays Associated Fittings

The hinge requirement is determined by weight and shape of door.

Always maintain correct door width-to-height ratio: width must be *significantly* less than height.

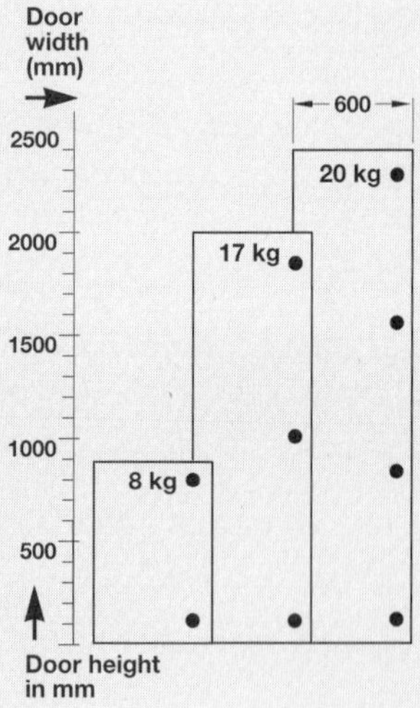

Guide to Aximat®

HÄFELE

Aximat

Hinge type (Self-closing and non self-closing)	Opening angle	Screw-mount 52/5.5	Screw-mount 45/9.5	Press-fit 52/5.5	Press-fit 45/9.5	Axle 7	Axle 4	Con-cealed axle	
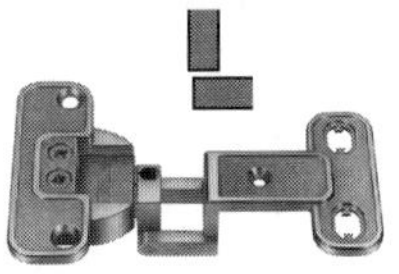	250°	•		•	•	•			
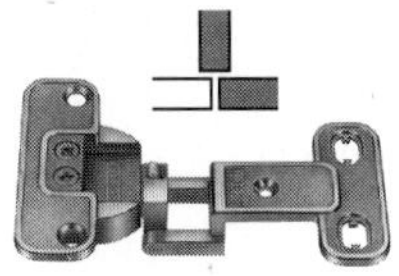	180°	•		•	•	•			
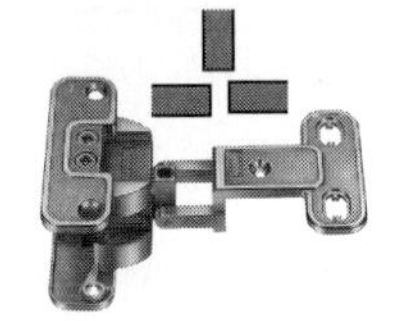	180°	•		•	•	•			
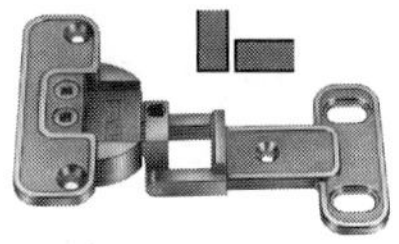	180°	•		•	•	•			
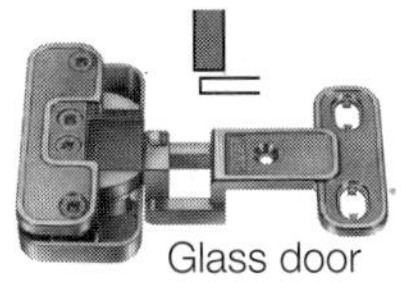 Glass door	180° 250°	•				•			
 Glass door	180°	•				•			
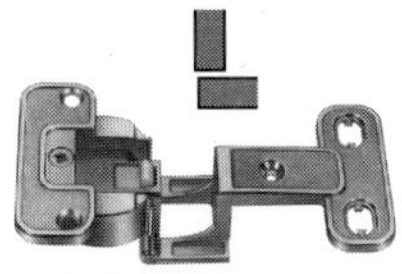	270°		•		•		•		
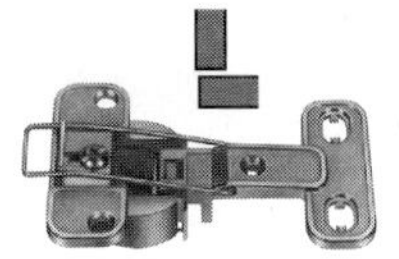	140°		•		•			•	

Hinges,
Flap and Lid Stays
Associated Fittings

3

Dimensional data not binding.
We reserve the right to alter specifications without notice.

Dimensions in mm

HÄFELE

Aximat® With Exposed Axle, 7 mm

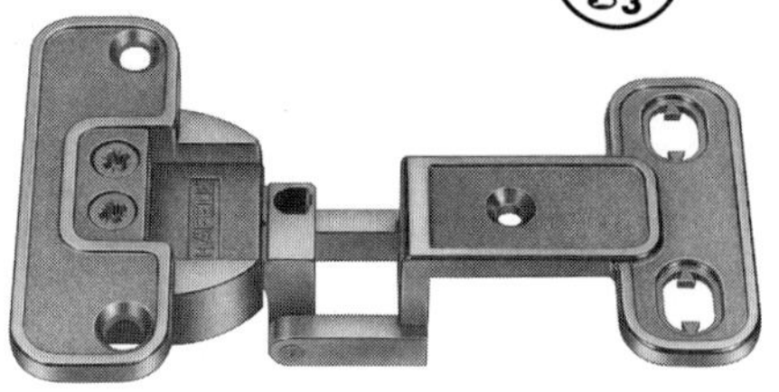

Opening angle: 250°

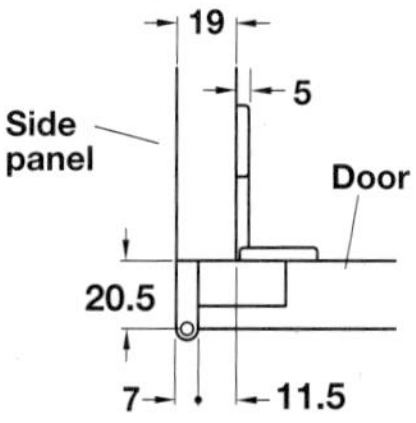

Aximat **hinge** with exposed **7 mm** axle
- Side panel thicknesses from 19 mm (3/4")
- Door thicknesses to 20.5 mm (3/4")
- Horizontal adjustment to 3 mm
- Vertical adjustment ± 2 mm
- All-metal: zinc die-cast, nickel-plated

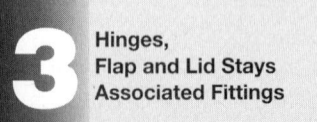

3 Hinges, Flap and Lid Stays Associated Fittings

Accessories found on page **3.56**

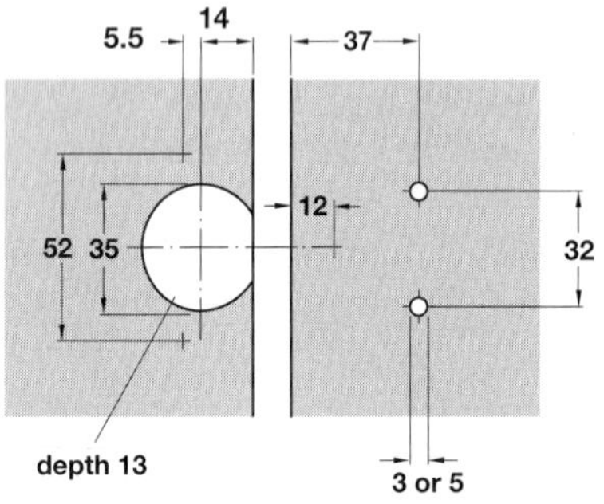

Screw-mount

Mounting	Door overlay	Cat. No. self-closing
Side panel mounting	11.5 mm	343.05.738

Packing: 50 pcs.

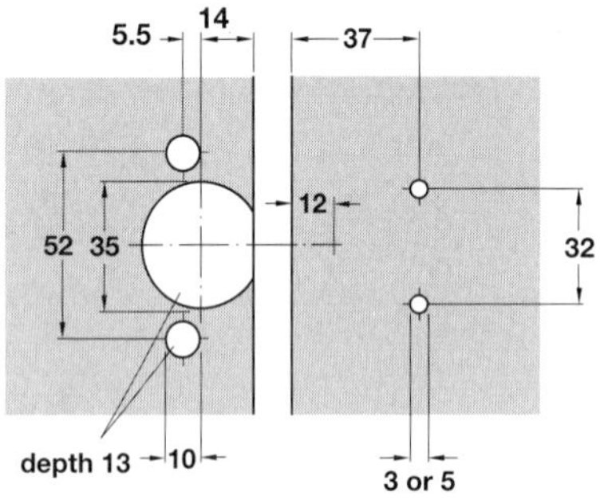

Press-fit, 52/5.5 hole pattern

Mounting	Door overlay	Cat. No. self-closing
Side panel mounting	11.5 mm	343.08.739

Packing: 50 pcs.

Mounting screws:
Hospa particle board screws **raised head** with PZ 2 cross slot
Finish:
steel, nickel-plated

Length	Cat. No.
15 mm	015.55.639
17 mm	015.55.648
20 mm	015.55.657

Packing: 1000 pcs.

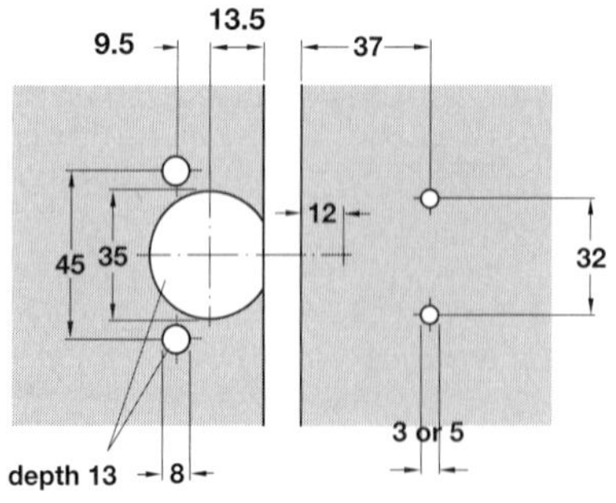

Press-fit in, 45/9.5 hole pattern

Mounting	Door overlay	Cat. No. self-closing
Side panel mounting	11.5 mm	343.08.935

Packing: 50 pcs.

Mounting screws:
Varianta screws **cylinder head** with PZ 2 cross slot
Finish:
steel, nickel-plated

Length	**3** mm dia. hole
10.5 mm	013.20.618
13.5 mm	013.20.636
16.0 mm	013.20.645
	5 mm dia. hole
10.5 mm	013.20.716
13.5 mm	013.20.734
16.0 mm	013.20.743

Packing: 1000 pcs.

Dimensional data not binding. We reserve the right to alter specifications without notice.

Dimensions in mm

Aximat® With Exposed Axle, 7 mm

HÄFELE

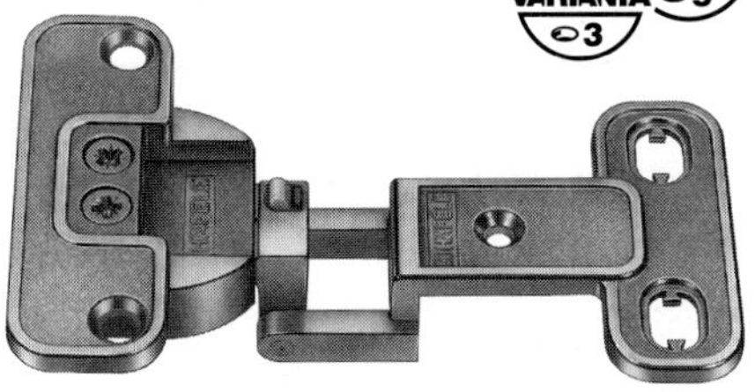

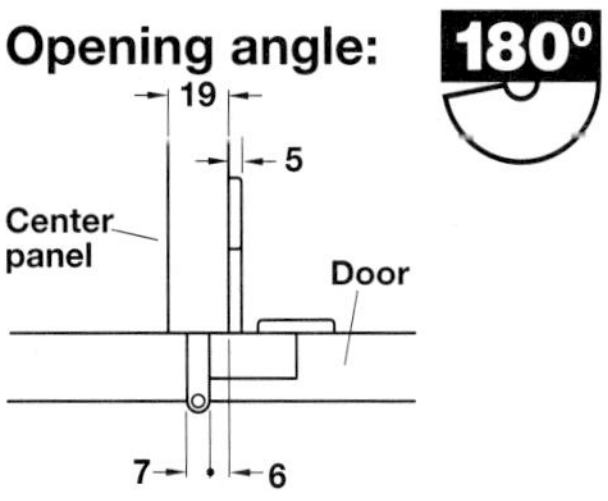

Aximat **center panel hinge** with exposed **7 mm** axle
- Side panel thicknesses from 19 mm (3/4")
- Door thicknesses to 20.5 mm (3/4")
- Horizontal adjustment to 3 mm
- With vertical adjustment ± 2 mm
- All-metal: zinc die-cast, nickel-plated

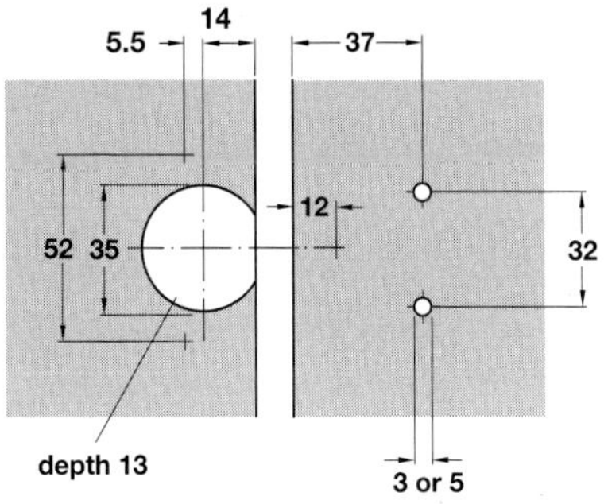

Screw-mount

Mounting	Door overlay	Cat. No. self-closing
Center panel mounting	6 mm	343.05.729

Packing: 50 pcs.

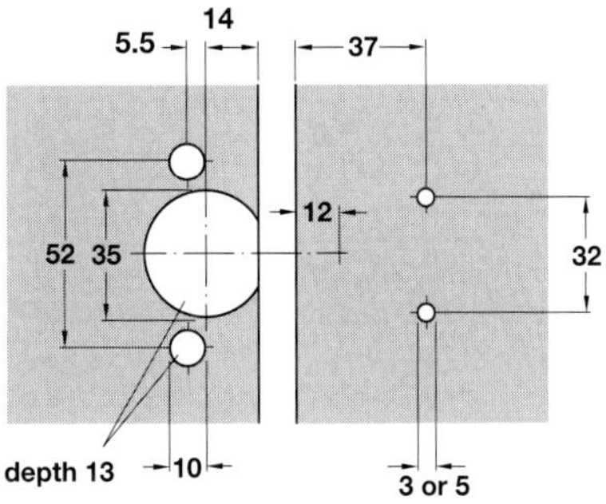

Press-fit, 52/5.5 hole pattern

Mounting	Door overlay	Cat. No. self-closing
Center panel mounting	6 mm	343.08.720

Packing: 50 pcs.

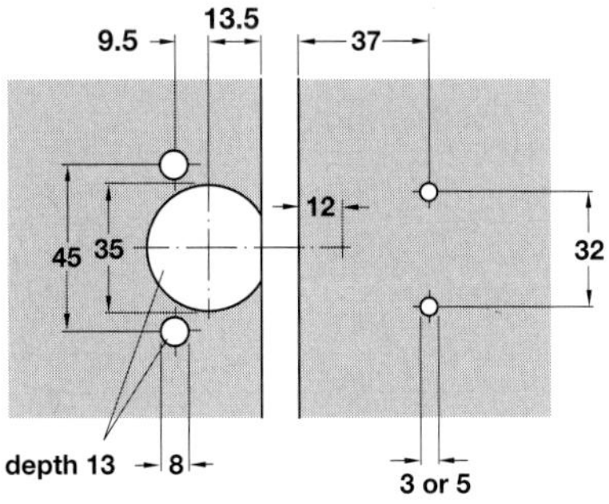

Press-fit, 45/9.5 hole pattern

Mounting	Door overlay	Cat. No. self-closing
Center panel mounting	6 mm	343.08.926

Packing: 50 pcs.

Hinges, Flap and Lid Stays Associated Fittings 3

Accessories found on page **3.56**

Mounting screws:
Hospa particle board screws **raised head** with PZ 2 cross slot
Finish: steel, nickel-plated

Length	Cat. No.
15 mm	015.55.639
17 mm	015.55.648
20 mm	015.55.657

Packing: 1000 pcs.

Mounting screws:
Varianta screws **cylinder head** with PZ 2 cross slot
Finish: steel, nickel-plated

Length	**3** mm dia. hole
10.5 mm	013.20.618
13.5 mm	013.20.636
16.0 mm	013.20.645
	5 mm dia. hole
10.5 mm	013.20.716
13.5 mm	013.20.734
16.0 mm	013.20.743

Packing: 1000 pcs.

Dimensional data not binding. We reserve the right to alter specifications without notice.

Dimensions in mm

HÄFELE

Aximat® With Exposed Axle, 7 mm

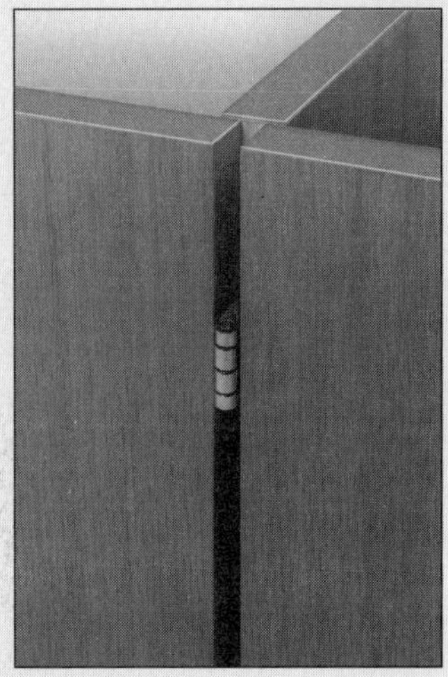

Opening angle: 180°

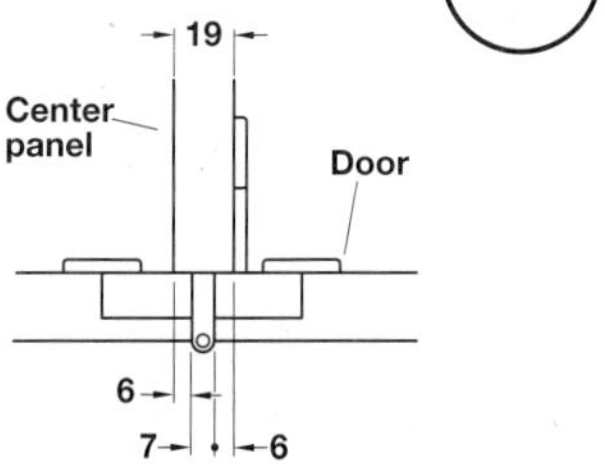

Aximat **twin hinge** with exposed **7 mm** axle
- Side panel thicknesses from 19 mm (3/4")
- Door thicknesses to 20.5 mm (3/4")
- Horizontal adjustment to 3 mm
- Vertical adjustment ± 2 mm
- All-metal: zinc die-cast, nickel-plated

3 Hinges, Flap and Lid Stays Associated Fittings

Accessories found on page **3.56**

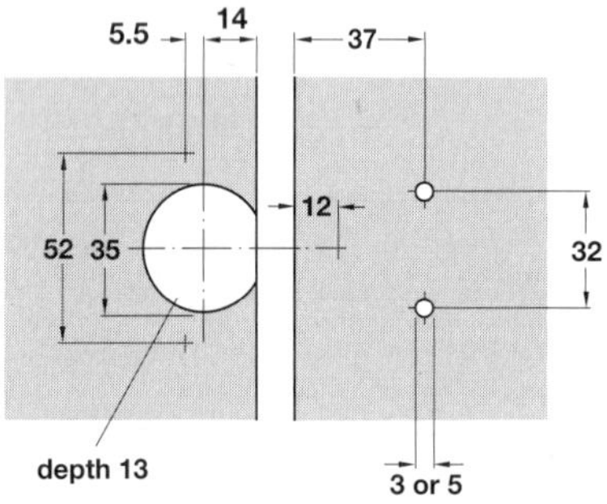

Screw-mount

Mounting	Door overlay	Cat. No. self-closing
Twin mounting	6 mm	343.05.756

Packing: 50 pcs.

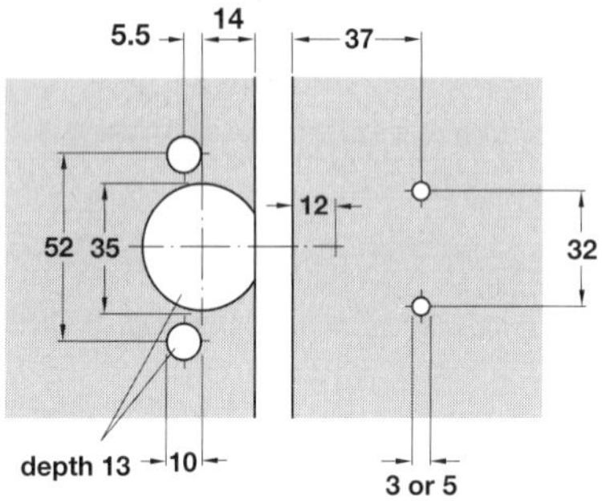

Press-fit, 52/5.5 hole pattern

Mounting	Door overlay	Cat. No. self-closing
Twin mounting	6 mm	343.08.757

Packing: 50 pcs.

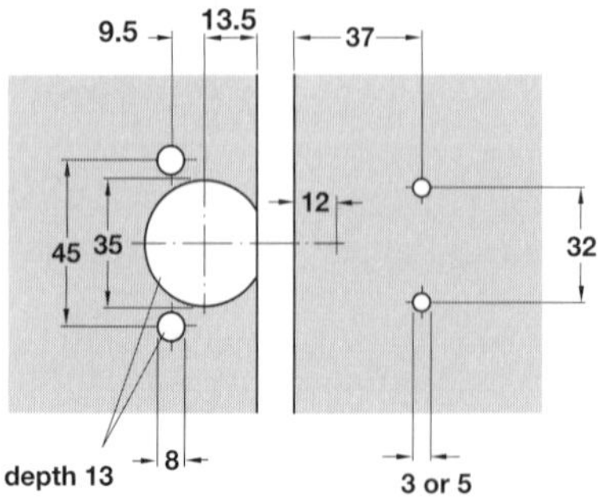

Press-fit, 45/9.5 hole pattern

Mounting	Door overlay	Cat. No. self-closing
Twin mounting	6 mm	343.08.953

Packing: 50 pcs.

Mounting screws:
Hospa particle board screws
raised head with
PZ 2 cross slot
Finish:
steel, nickel-plated

HOSPA Φ3,5

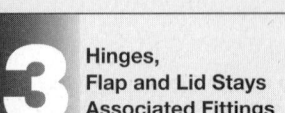

Length	Cat. No.
15 mm	015.55.639
17 mm	015.55.648
20 mm	015.55.657

Packing: 1000 pcs.

Mounting screws:
Varianta special screws
cylinder head with
PZ 2
cross slot
Finish:
steel, nickel-plated

VARIANTA 3 / VARIANTA 5

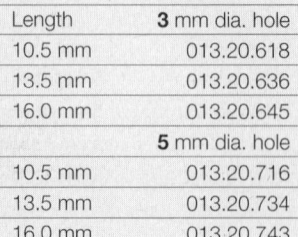

Length	**3** mm dia. hole
10.5 mm	013.20.618
13.5 mm	013.20.636
16.0 mm	013.20.645
	5 mm dia. hole
10.5 mm	013.20.716
13.5 mm	013.20.734
16.0 mm	013.20.743

Packing: 1000 pcs.

Dimensions in mm

Aximat® for Inset Doors, Axle 7 mm

Opening angle:

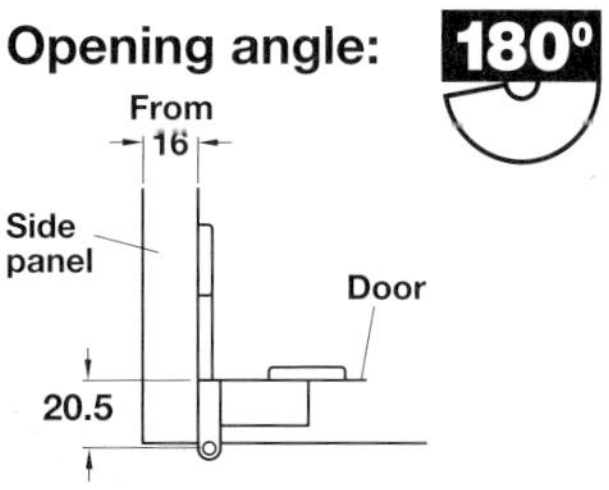

Aximat **hinge** for inset doors, with exposed **7 mm** axle and metal trim* for the door cutout

- Side panel thicknesses from 16 mm (5/8")
- Door thicknesses to 20.5 mm (3/4")
- Horizontal adjustment to 3 mm
- Vertical adjustment ± 2 mm
- All-metal: zinc die-cast, nickel-plated

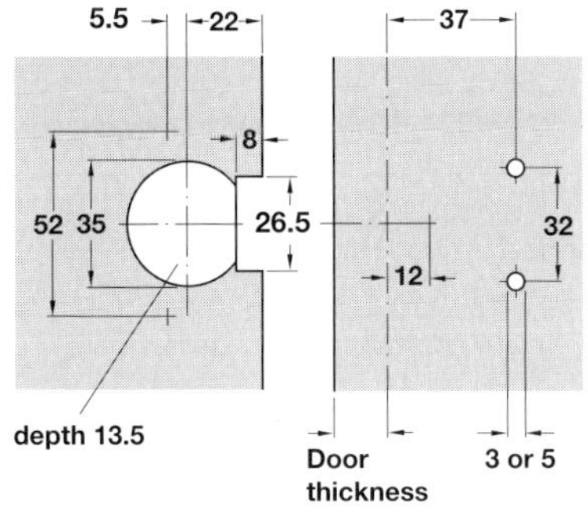

Screw-mount

Mounting	Cat. No. self-closing
Inset mounting	343.05.747

Packing: 50 pcs.

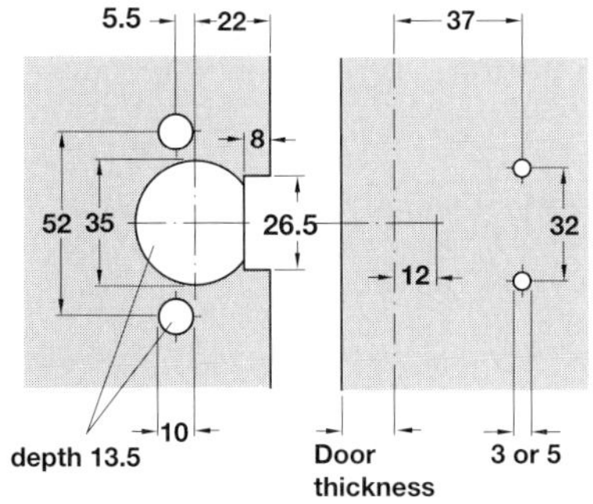

Press-fit, 52/5.5 hole pattern

Mounting	Cat. No. self-closing
Inset mounting	343.08.748

Packing: 50 pcs.

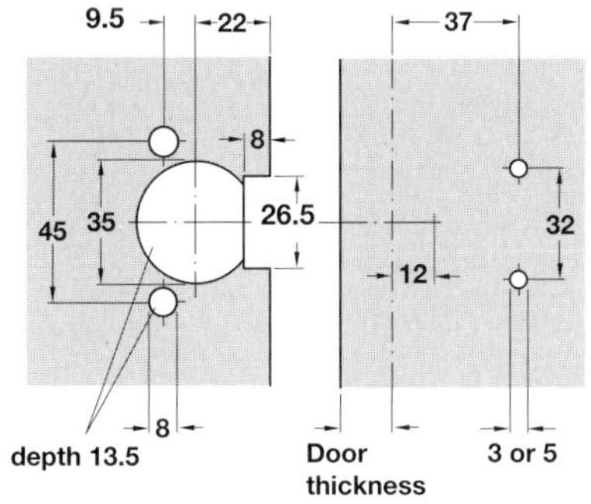

Press-fit , 45/9.5 hole pattern

Mounting	Cat. No. self-closing
Inset mounting	343.08.944

Packing: 50 pcs.

Hinges, Flap and Lid Stays Associated Fittings **3**

Cup hole with door cutout

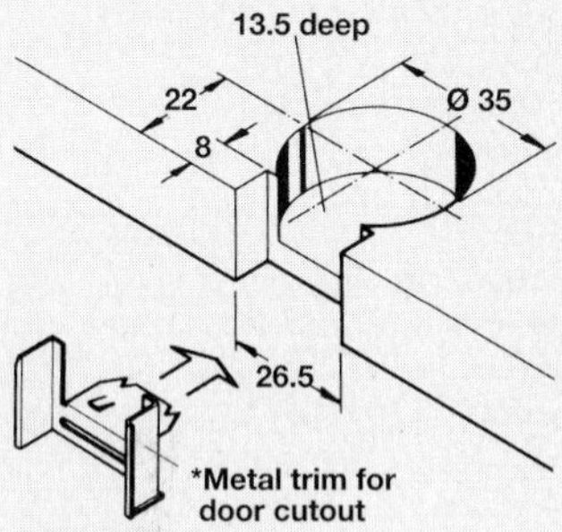

Mounting screws:
Hospa particle board screws **raised head** with PZ 2 cross slot
Finish: steel, nickel-plated

Length	Cat. No.
15 mm	015.55.639
17 mm	015.55.648
20 mm	015.55.657

Packing: 1000 pcs.

Mounting screws:
Varianta special screws **cylinder head** with PZ 2 cross slot
Finish: steel, nickel-plated

Length	**3** mm dia. hole
10.5 mm	013.20.618
13.5 mm	013.20.636
16.0 mm	013.20.645
	5 mm dia. hole
10.5 mm	013.20.716
13.5 mm	013.20.734
16.0 mm	013.20.743

Packing: 1000 pcs.

Dimensional data not binding. We reserve the right to alter specifications without notice.

Dimensions in mm

HÄFELE

Aximat® for Glass Doors, Axle 7 mm

Opening angle: 180° and 250°

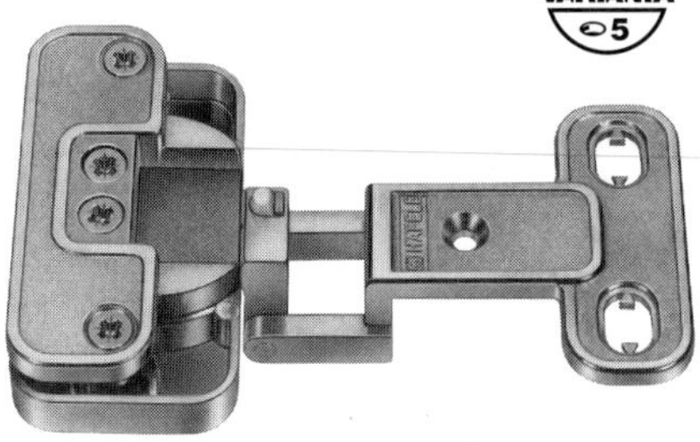

Aximat **glass door hinge** with exposed **7 mm** axle
Complete with trim cap and plastic shims.

- Side panel thicknesses from 19 mm (3/4")
- Glass thicknesses 5 – 6 mm
- Horizontal adjustment to 3 mm
- Vertical adjustment ± 2 mm
- Plastic shims
- All-metal: zinc die-cast, nickel-plated

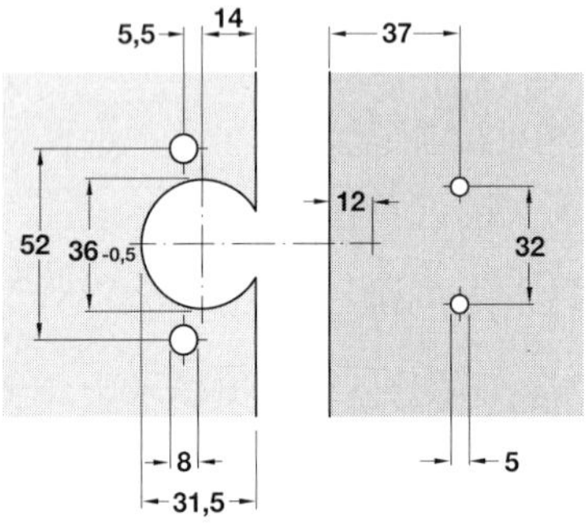

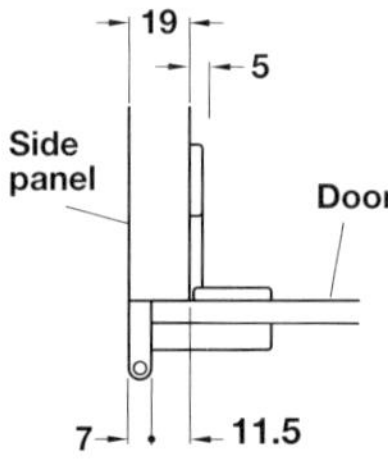

Corner hinge, screw-mounted

Mounting	Door overlay	Max. door opening angle	Cat. No. self-closing
Side panel mounting	11.5 mm	**250°**	343.03.734

Packing: 10 pcs. (complete with mounting hardware)

Mounting screws:
Varianta special screws
cylinder head with PZ 2 cross slot
Finish: steel, nickel-plated

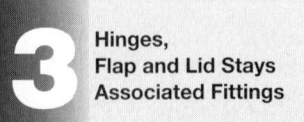

Length	**3** mm dia. hole
10.5 mm	013.20.618
13.5 mm	013.20.636
16.0 mm	013.20.645
	5 mm dia. hole
10.5 mm	013.20.716
13.5 mm	013.20.734
16.0 mm	013.20.743

Packing: 1000 pcs.

Opening angle: 180°

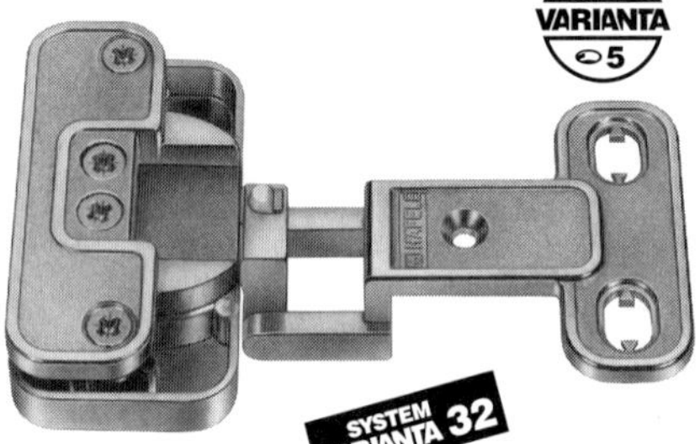

Aximat **glass door hinge,** inset, with exposed **7 mm** axle.
Complete with trim cap and plastic shims.

- Side panel thicknesses from 19 mm (3/4")
- Door thicknesses 5 – 6 mm
- Horizontal adjustment up to 3 mm
- Vertical adjustment ± 2 mm
- All-metal: zinc die-cast, nickel-plated

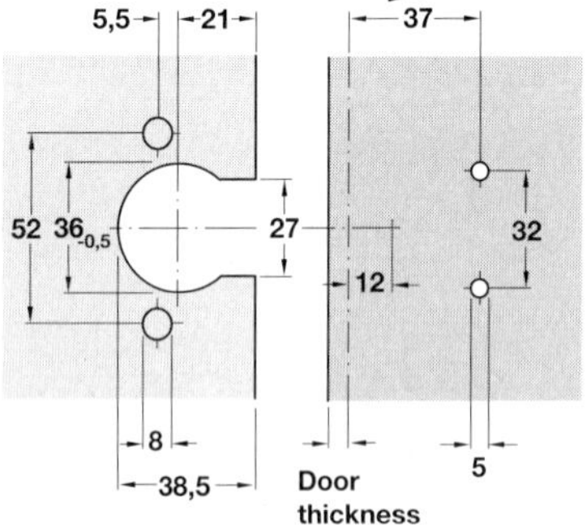

Dimensions in mm

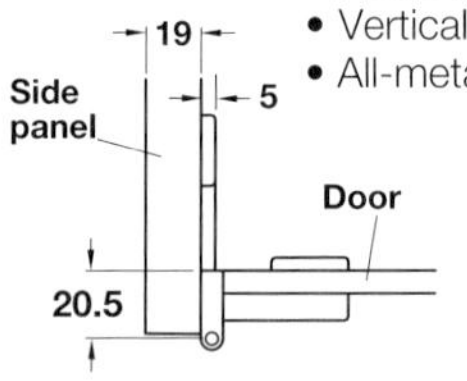

Screw-mount, inset doors

Mounting	Cat. No. self-closing
Inset mounting	343.03.743

Packing: 10 pcs. (complete with mounting hardware)

Aximat® With Exposed Axle, 4 mm

HÄFELE

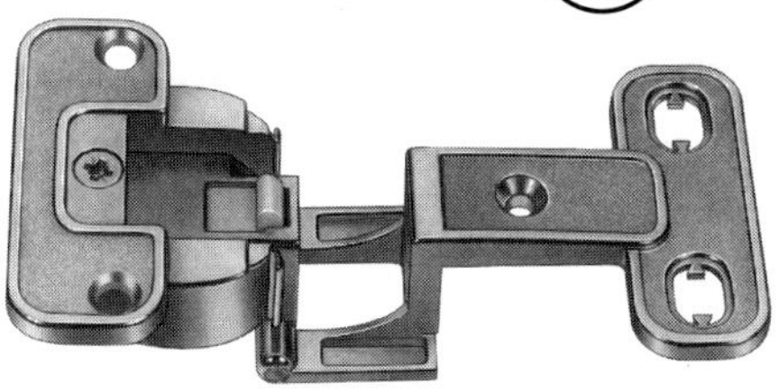

Opening angle: 270°

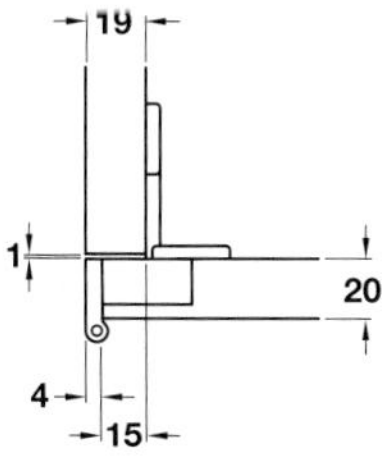

Aximat **hinge** with exposed **4 mm** axle
- Side panel thicknesses from 19 mm (3/4")
- Door thicknesses to 20 mm (3/4")
- Horizontal adjustment up to 3 mm
- Vertical adjustment ± 2 mm
- All-metal: zinc die-cast, nickel-plated + black

SYSTEM VARIANTA 32

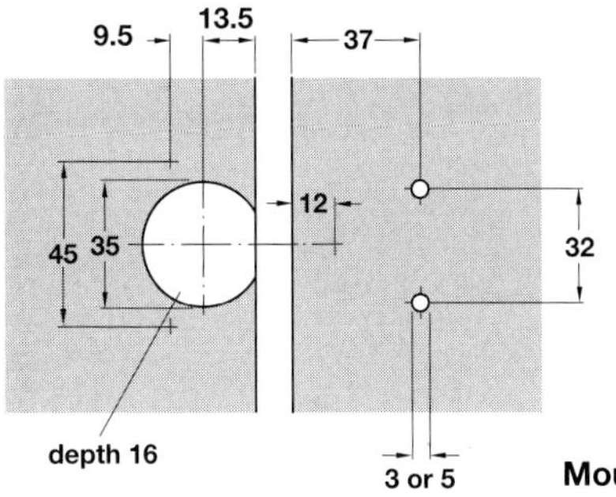

Screw-mount, overlay doors, self-closing

Mounting	Side panel thickness	Cat. No. black	Cat. No. nickel
Side panel mounting	19 mm	343.11.325	343.11.727

Packing: 50 pcs.

Mounting screws:
Varianta, black 5/13.5 mm
Finish: steel, black

Cat. No.	013.20.334

Packing: 500 pcs.

Mounting screws:
Ziip-R **raised head** with combination cross slot & phillips 2 black
Finish: steel, black

Cat. No.	010.83.043

Packing: 1,000 pcs.

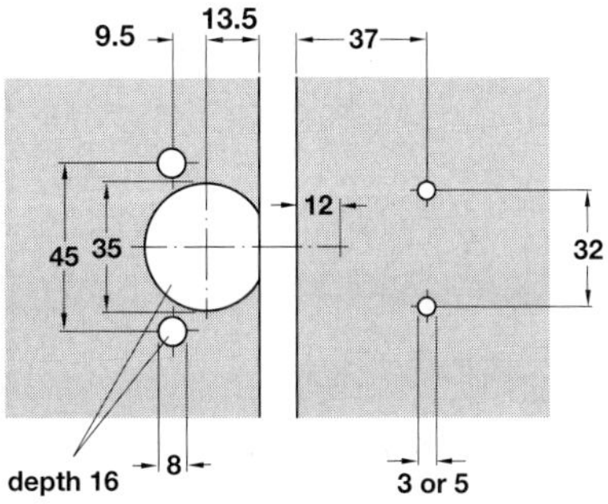

Press-fit, 45/9.5 hole pattern

Mounting	Side panel thickness	Cat. No. self-closing
Side panel mounting	19 mm	343.13.721

Packing: 50 pcs.

Hinges, Flap and Lid Stays Associated Fittings 3

Accessories found on page **3.56**

Mounting screws:
Hospa particle board screws **raised head** with PZ 2 cross slot
Finish: steel, nickel-plated

Length	Cat. No.
15 mm	015.55.639
17 mm	015.55.648
20 mm	015.55.657

Packing: 1000 pcs.

Mounting screws:
Varianta special screws **cylinder head** with PZ 2 cross slot
Finish: steel, nickel-plated

Length	**3** mm dia. hole
10.5 mm	013.20.618
13.5 mm	013.20.636
16.0 mm	013.20.645
	5 mm dia. hole
10.5 mm	013.20.716
13.5 mm	013.20.734
16.0 mm	013.20.743

Packing: 1000 pcs.

Dimensional data not binding. We reserve the right to alter specifications without notice.

Dimensions in mm

HÄFELE

Aximat® With Concealed Axle

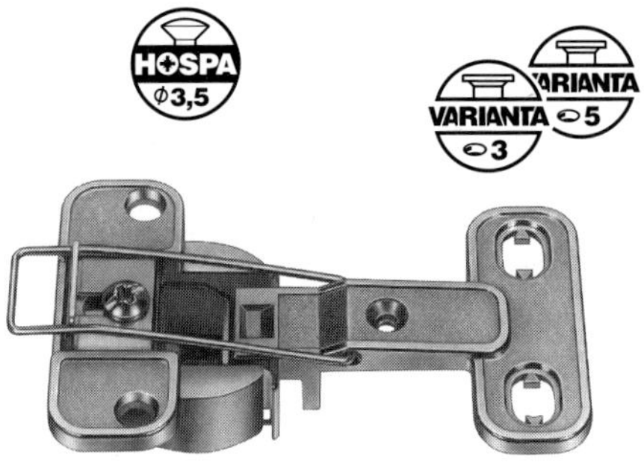

Opening angle: 140°

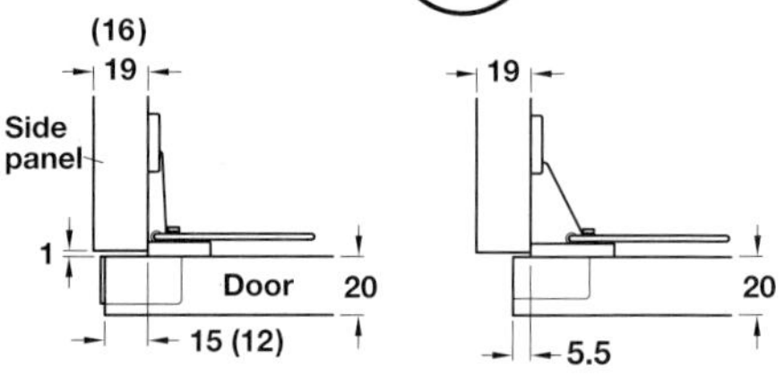

Aximat **hinge** with concealed axle, including axle trim and angle hinge restraint.

- Side panel thicknesses from 16 mm (5/8")
- Door thicknesses to 20 mm (3/4")
- Horizontal adjustment to 3 mm
- Vertical adjustment ± 2 mm
- All-metal: zinc die-cast, nickel-plated

SYSTEM VARIANTA 32

3 Hinges, Flap and Lid Stays Associated Fittings

Accessories found on page **3.56**

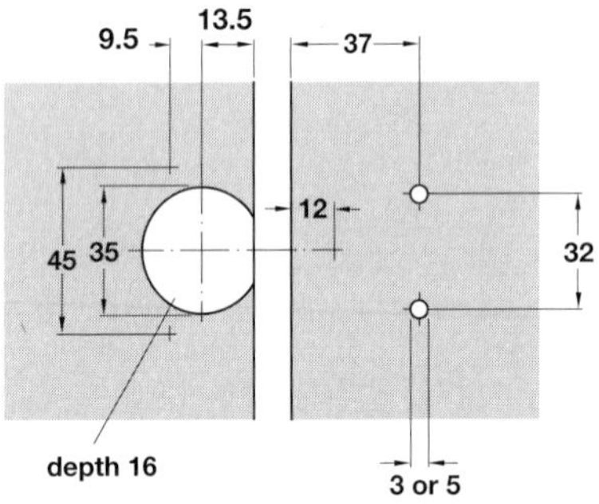

Screw-mount, overlay doors

Mounting	Side panel thickness	Cat. No. self-closing
Side panel mounting	16 mm	343.29.710
Side panel mounting	19 mm	343.29.729
Center panel mounting	19 mm	343.29.747

Packing: 50 pcs.

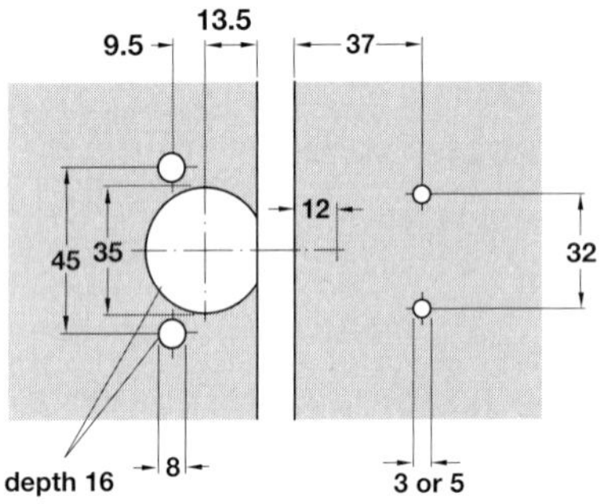

Press-fit, 45/9.5 hole pattern

Mounting	Side panel thickness	Cat. No. self-closing
Side panel mounting	16 mm	343.29.916
Side panel mounting	19 mm	343.29.925
Center panel mounting	19 mm	343.29.943

Packing: 50 pcs.

Mounting screws:
Hospa particle board screws **raised head** with PZ 2 cross slot
Finish: steel, nickel-plated

Length	Cat. No.
15 mm	015.55.639
17 mm	015.55.648
20 mm	015.55.657

Packing: 1000 pcs.

Mounting screws:
Varianta special screws **cylinder head** with PZ 2 cross slot
Finish: steel, nickel-plated

Length	**3** mm dia. hole
10.5 mm	013.20.618
13.5 mm	013.20.636
16.0 mm	013.20.645
	5 mm dia. hole
10.5 mm	013.20.716
13.5 mm	013.20.734
16.0 mm	013.20.743

Packing: 1000 pcs.

Hinges for wood doors: single-side mounting on **16/19** mm side panel and **overlay doors**

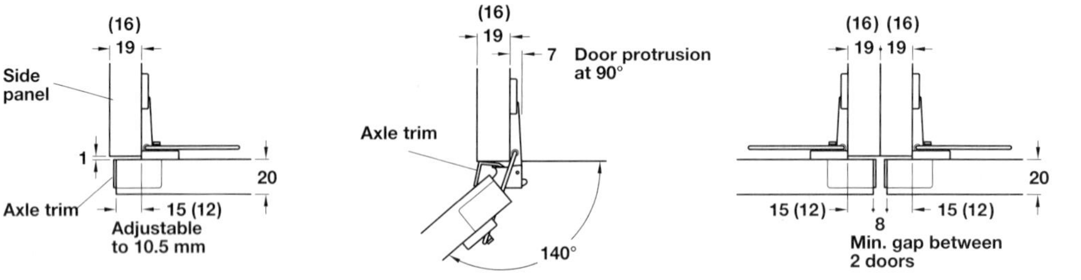

Door closed

Door open

Hinges for wood doors: for side panel thickness **19** mm, single-side and center panel mounting, **overlay doors**

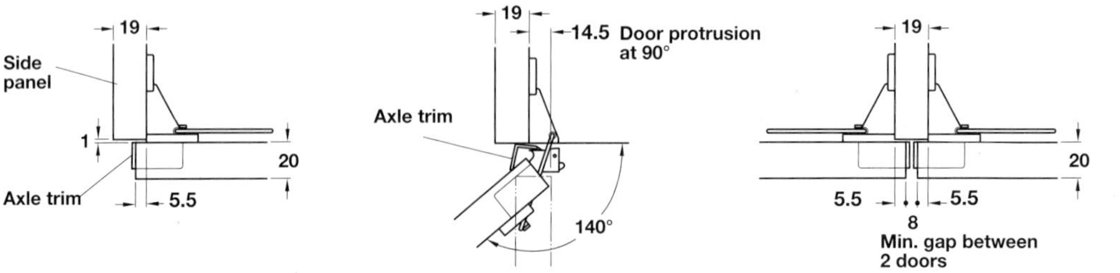

Door closed

Door open

Dimensions in mm

Aximat®-SM Hinges

HÄFELE

- All hinges with **speed mount features**
- All with the same hole pattern, hole depth **16 mm** (5/8") for door thicknesses from **19 - 20 mm** (3/4")
- Separate installation of cup and hinge arm
- Mounted to the side of the door, no tools required.

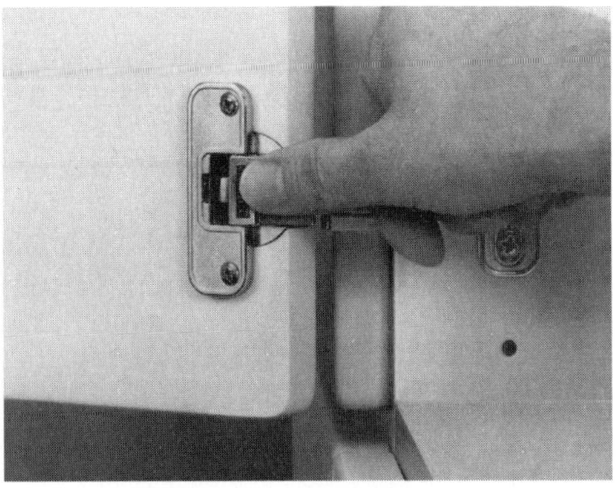

Assembly: to join door to cabinet, just insert hinge into cup and apply thumb pressure, as shown, to secure.

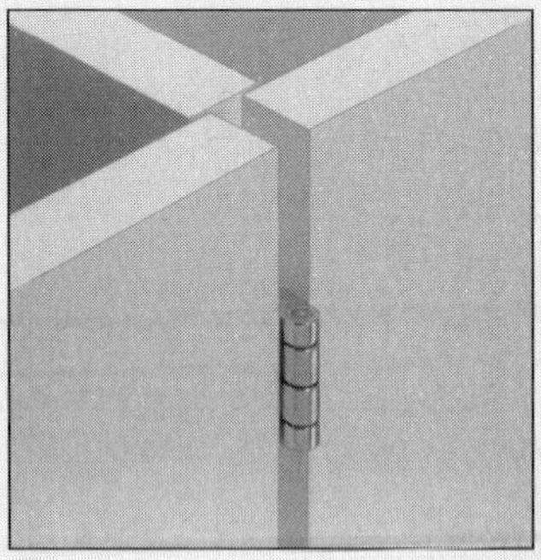

Hinges, **screw-mount** or **press-fit**, see following pages

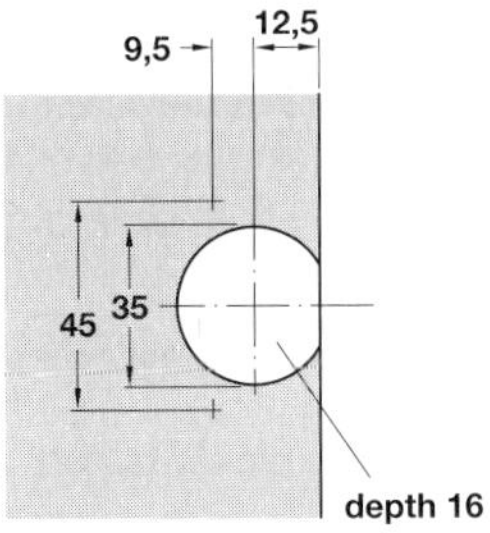

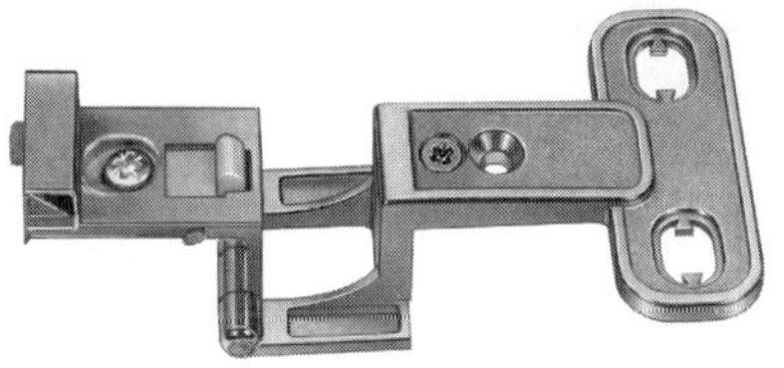

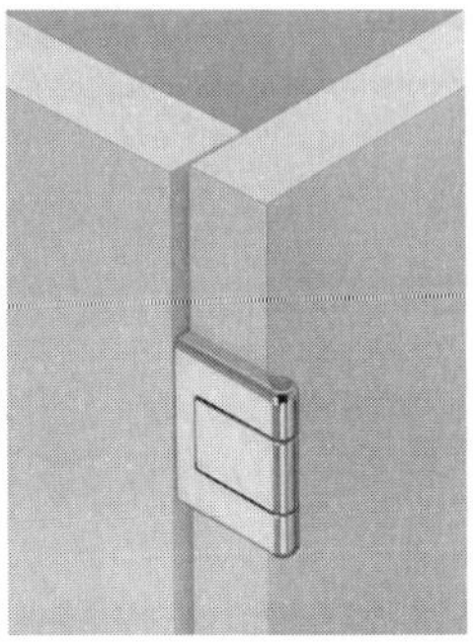

4 mm dia. exposed axle model
Mounts on 16 or 19mm cabinet side panels.

The hinge requirement is determined by weight and shape of door.

Always maintain correct door width-to-height ratio: width must be *significantly* less than height.

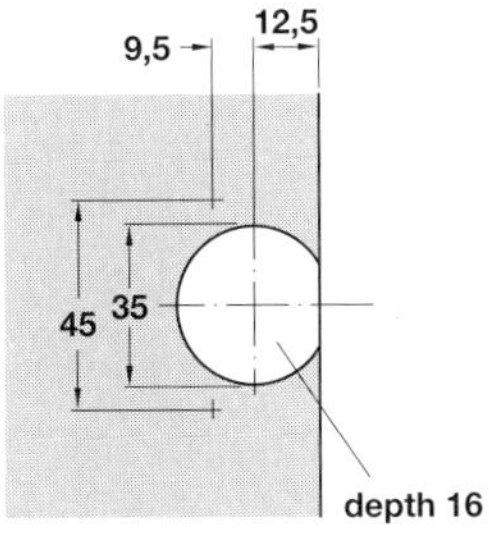

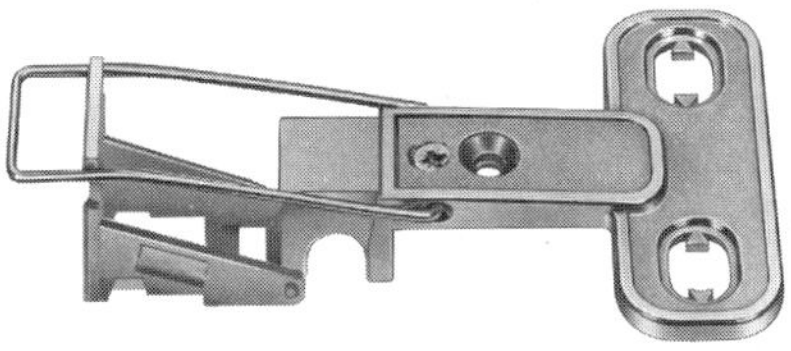

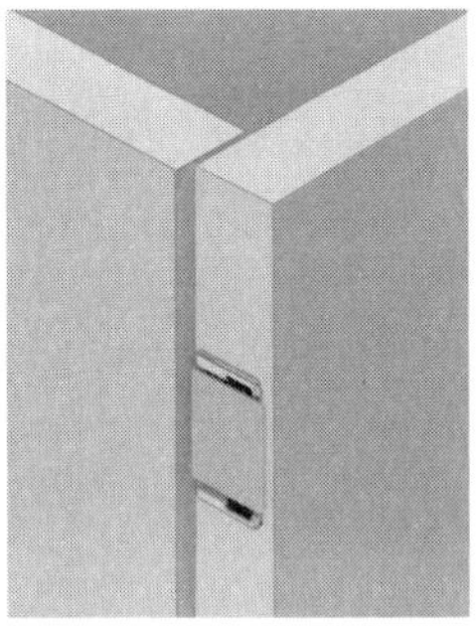

Concealed axle model
Mounts on 16 or 19mm cabinet side panels.

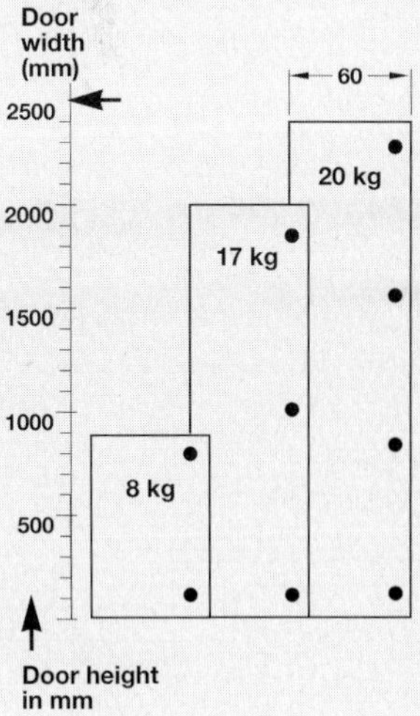

Disassembly: to release hinge joint, twist flat-blade screwdriver in the cup hole to spread wire clip. This feature prevents unintentional hinge release.

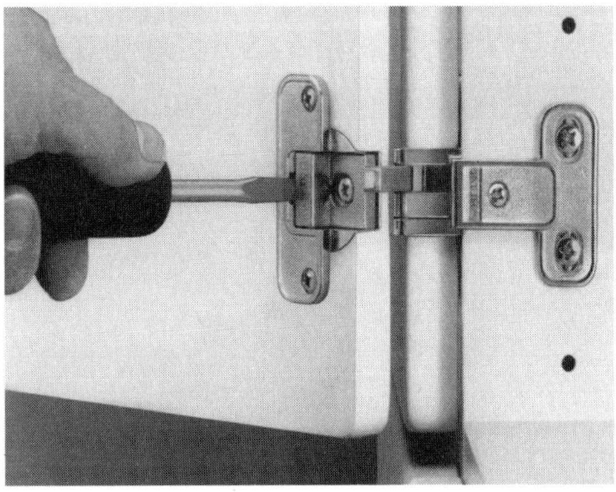

Table is based on 19 mm particle board.

Guide to Aximat®- SM

(Self-closing and non self-closing)	Opening angle	Screw-mount 45/9.5	Press-fit 45/9.5	Axle 7	Axle 4	Con-cealed axle
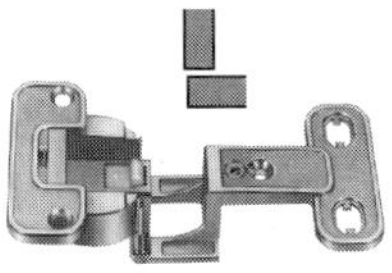	 270°	•	•		•	
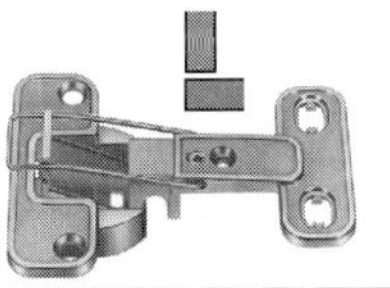	 140°	•	•			•

Dimensional data not binding. We reserve the right to alter specifications without notice.

HÄFELE

Aximat®-SM With Exposed Axle, 4 mm

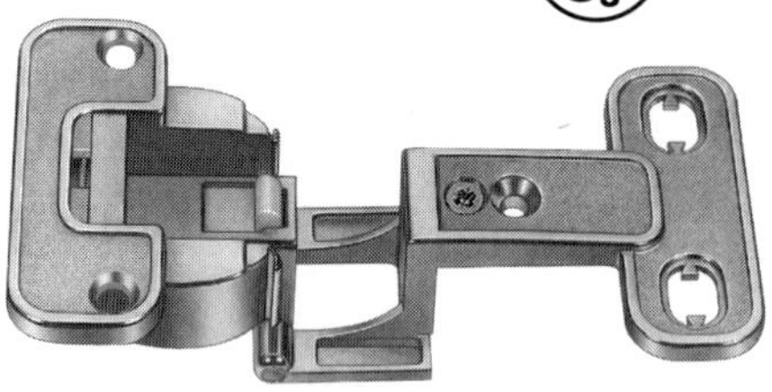

Opening angle: 270°

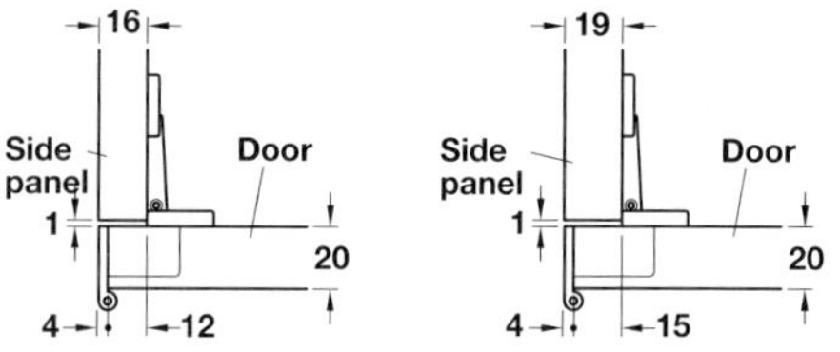

Aximat **hinge** with exposed **4 mm** axle for speed mounting to the side of the door

- Side panel thicknesses from 16 mm (5/8")
- Door thicknesses to 20 mm (3/4")
- Horizontal adjustment to 3 mm
- Vertical adjustment ± 2 mm
- All-metal: zinc die-cast, nickel-plated and black

SYSTEM VARIANTA 32

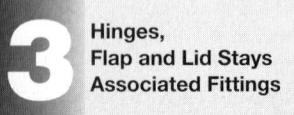

Mounting screws:
for black hinges
Finish: steel, black

Length	Cat. No.
13.5 mm	013.20.334

Packing: 1000 pcs.

Wood screw:
Hospa **raised head** with phillips 2 black
Finish: steel, black

Cat. No.	010.83.043

Packing: 1000 pcs.

Mounting screws:
Hospa particle board screws **raised head** with PZ 2 cross slot
Finish: steel, nickel-plated

Length	Cat. No.
15 mm	015.55.639
17 mm	015.55.648
20 mm	015.55.657

Packing: 1000 pcs.

Mounting screws:
Varianta special screws **cylinder head** with PZ 2 cross slot
Finish: steel, nickel-plated

Length	3 mm dia. hole
10.5 mm	013.20.618
13.5 mm	013.20.636
16.0 mm	013.20.645
	5 mm dia. hole
10.5 mm	013.20.716
13.5 mm	013.20.734
16.0 mm	013.20.743

Packing: 1000 pcs.

Dimensional data not binding. We reserve the right to alter specifications without notice.

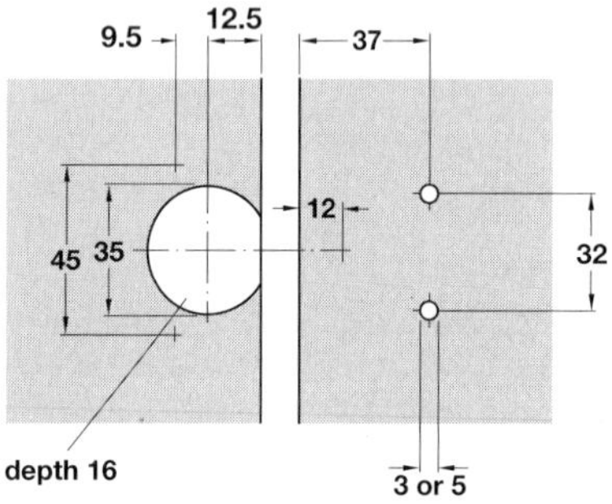

Screw-mount, overlay doors, self-closing

Mounting	Side panel thickness	Cat. No. black	Cat. No. nickel-plated
Side panel mounting	16 mm		344.81.715
Side panel mounting	19 mm	344.81.320	344.81.724

Packing: 50 pcs.

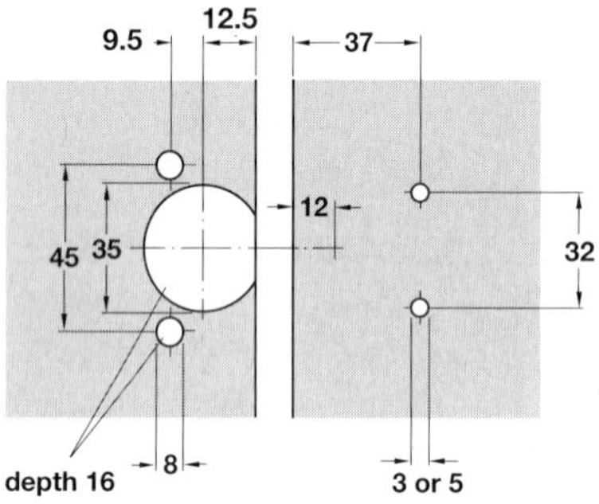

Press-fit, 45/9.5 hole pattern

Mounting	Side panel thickness	Screws	Cat. No. self-closing
Side panel mounting	16 mm		344.81.760
Side panel mounting	19 mm		344.81.779
Side panel mounting	19 mm	Pre-mounted Euro screws	344.81.771

Packing: 50 pcs.

Hinges for wood doors: single-side mounting on **16** mm side panel, **overlay doors**

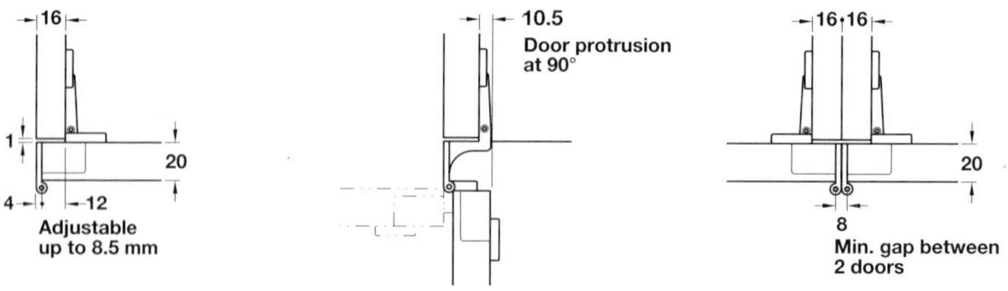

Hinges for wood doors: single-side mounting on **19** mm side panel, **overlay doors**

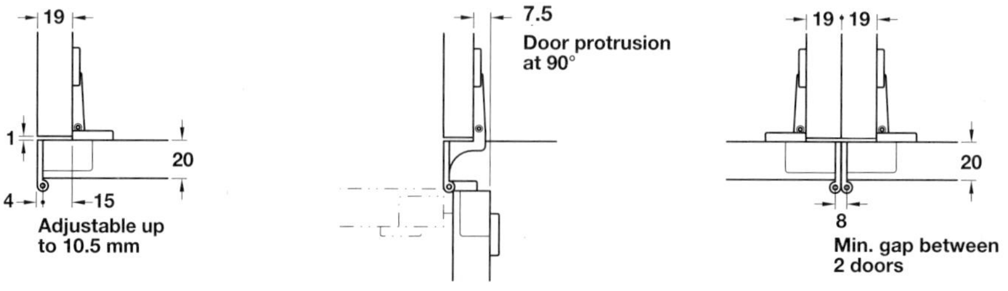

Dimensions in mm

Aximat®-SM With Concealed Axle

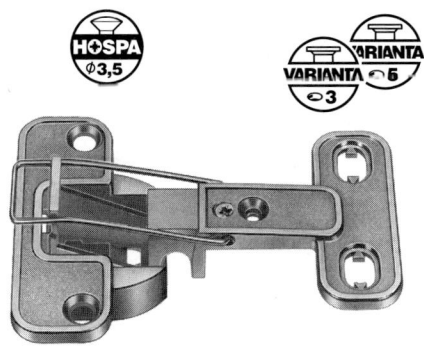

HÄFELE

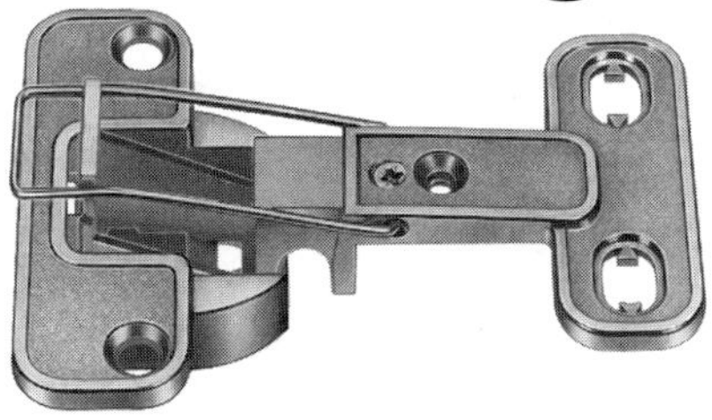

SYSTEM VARIANTA 32

Opening angle: 140°

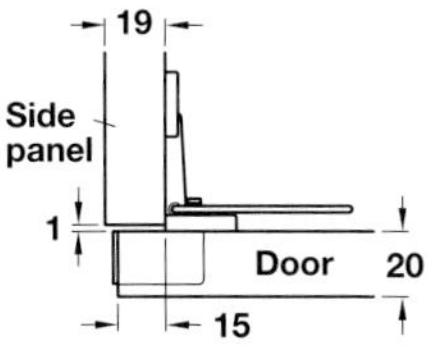

Aximat **hinge** with concealed axle for speed mounting to the cabinet side. Axle trim and hinge restraint included.

- Side panel thicknesses from 16 mm (5/8")
- Door thicknesses 19 to 21 mm (3/4")
- Horizontal adjustment to 3 mm
- Vertical adjustment ± 2 mm
- All-metal: zinc die-cast, nickel-plated

Hinges, Flap and Lid Stays Associated Fittings 3

Accessories found on page **3.56**

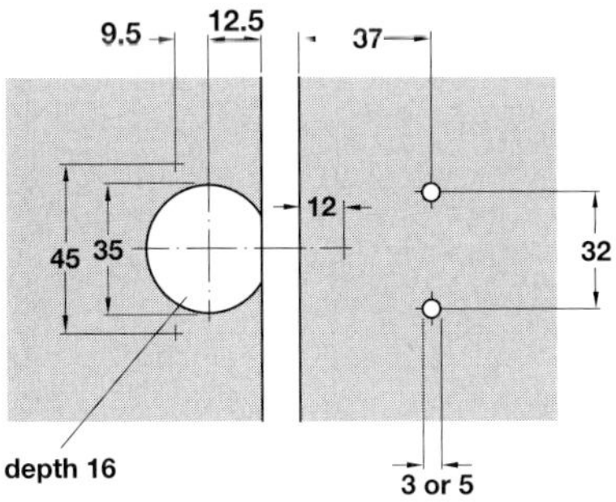

Screw-mount, overlay doors

Mounting	Side panel thickness	Cat. No. self-closing
Side panel mounting	19 mm	344.83.728

Packing: 50 pcs.

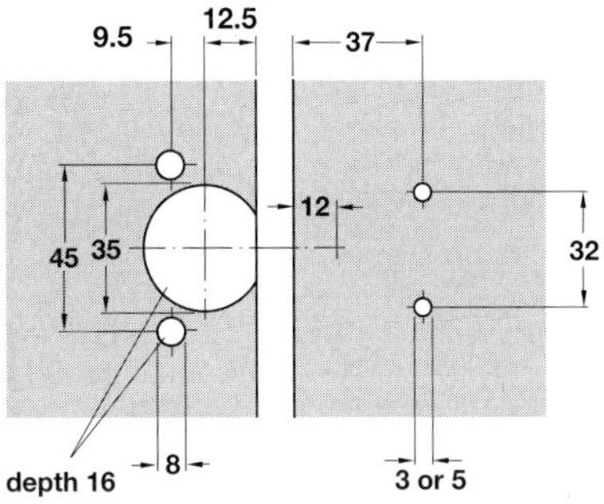

Press-fit, 45/9.5 hole pattern

Mounting	Side panel thickness	Cat. No. self-closing
Side panel mounting	19 mm	344.83.773

Packing: 50 pcs.

Mounting screws:
Hospa particle board screws **raised head** with PZ 2 cross slot
Finish: steel, nickel-plated

Length	Cat. No.
15 mm	015.55.639
17 mm	015.55.648
20 mm	015.55.657

Packing: 1000 pcs.

Hinges for wood doors: single-side mounting on **19** mm side panel, **overlay doors**

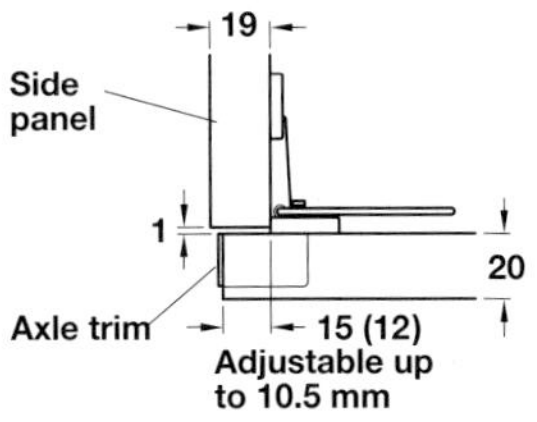

Door closed

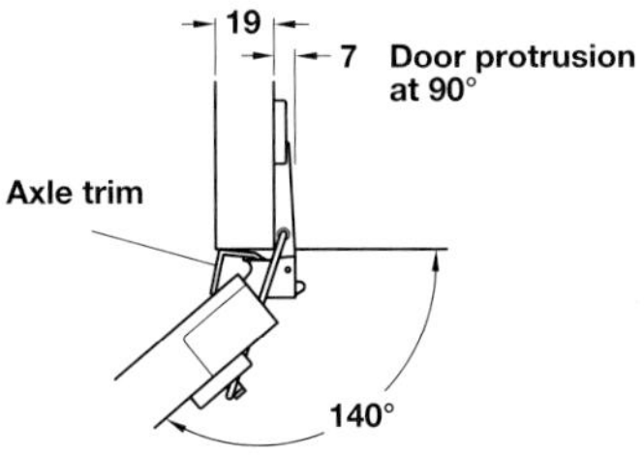

Door open

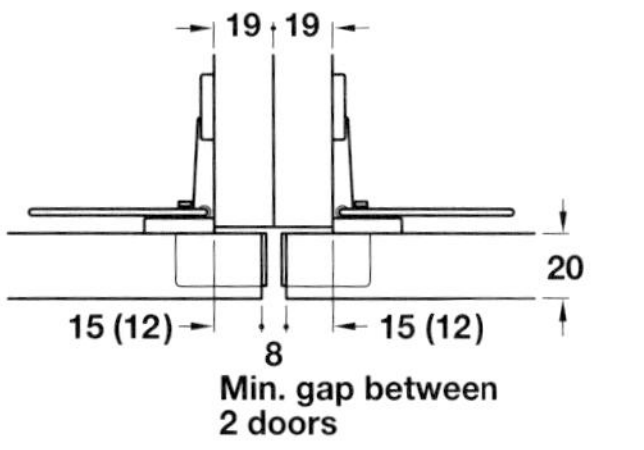

Mounting screws:
Varianta special screws **cylinder head** with PZ 2 cross slot
Finish: steel, nickel-plated

Length	3 mm dia. hole
10.5 mm	013.20.618
13.5 mm	013.20.636
16.0 mm	013.20.645
	5 mm dia. hole
10.5 mm	013.20.716
13.5 mm	013.20.734
16.0 mm	013.20.743

Packing: 1000 pcs.

HÄFELE

Aximat® and Aximat®-SM Accessories

The clothes protector reduces the opening angle to 180°

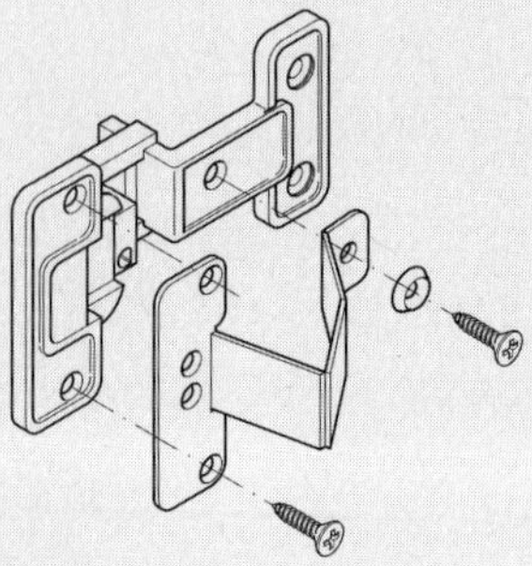

Clothes protector

for Aximat and Aximat-SM hinges with exposed **4** mm axle.
Finish: cover: plastic
washer: aluminum

Hole pattern	Cat. No.
45/9.5 mm	343.10.097

Packing: 50 pcs.

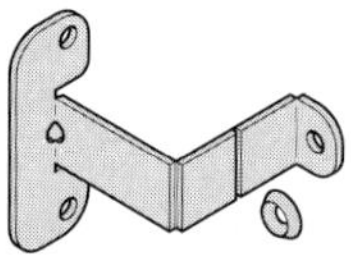

Clothes protector

for Aximat and Aximat-SM hinges with exposed **7** mm axle.
Finish: cover: plastic
washer: aluminum

Hole pattern	Cat. No.
45/9.5 mm	343.04.080
52/5.5 mm	343.04.099

Packing: 50 pcs.

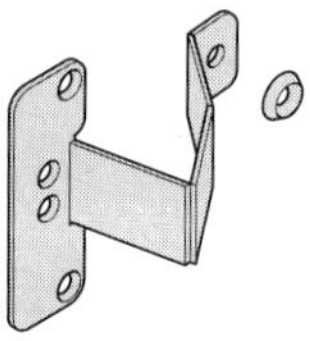

Shims spacer for Aximat hinges, to reduce cup depth with 13 mm thick doors.
Finish: plastic

Hole pattern	Cat. No.
45/9.5 mm	343.07.081
52/5.5 mm	343.07.090

Packing: 50 and 200 pcs.

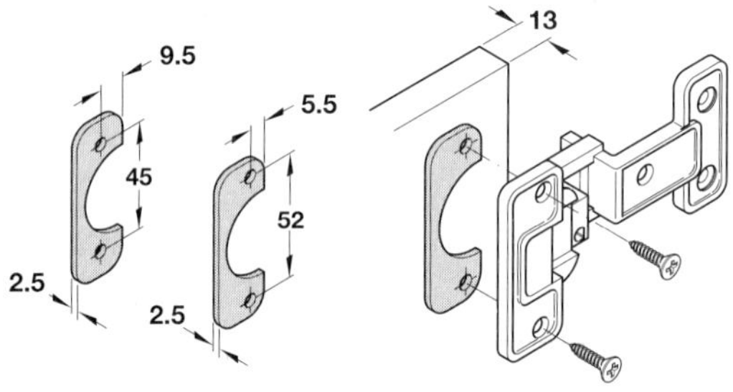

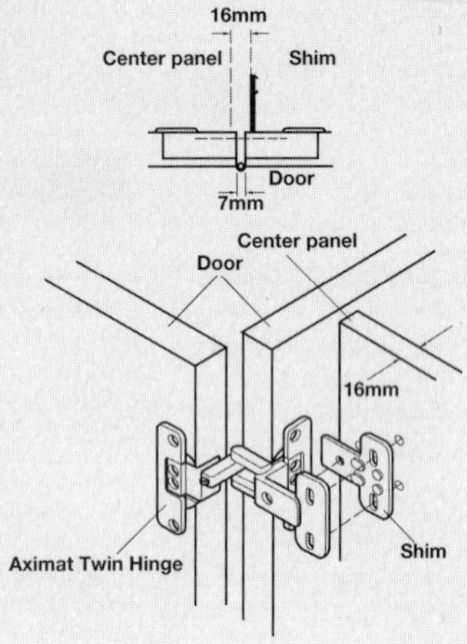

Shim

for Aximat to convert the overlay

Finish: Plastic, gray

Cat. No.	343.04.011

Packing: 100 pcs.

For Example:

1 plate moves hinge 1.5 mm to inside,

2 plates convert a 19 mm hinge to a 16 mm overlay.

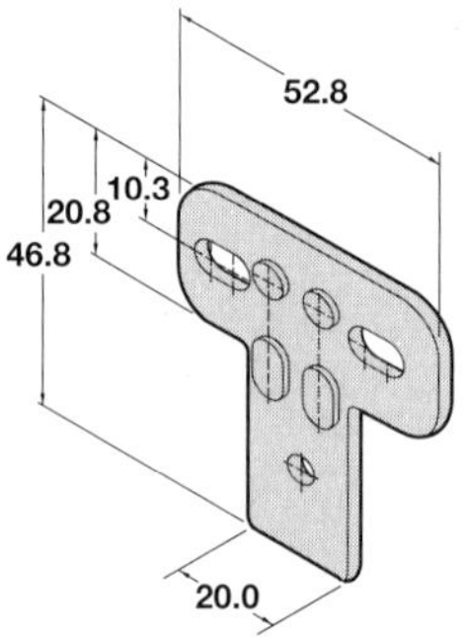

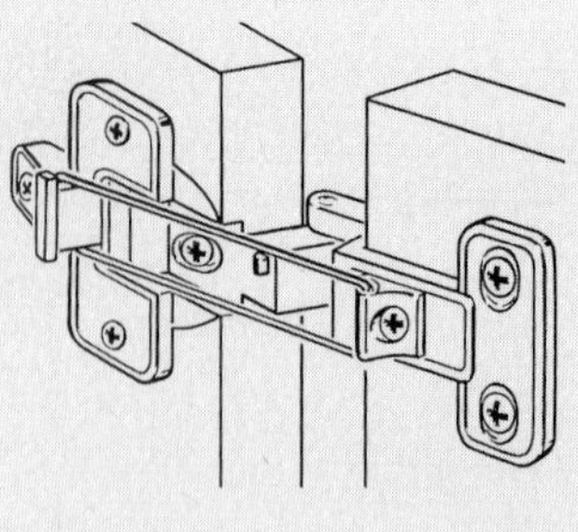

The angle hinge restraint reduces the opening angle to 120°

Hinge restraint, 120°

for Aximat-SM hinges with **7** mm axle.
Finish: steel, nickel-plated screw-mount
elements: zinc die-cast, nickel-plated

Cat. No.	343.04.008

Packing: 50 and 200 pcs.

Hinge restraint, 120°

for Aximat-SM hinges with **4** mm axle.
Finish: steel, nickel-plated screw-mount
elements: zinc die-cast, nickel-plated

Cat. No.	343.10.006

Packing: 50 and 200 pcs.

HOSPA Ø3,5

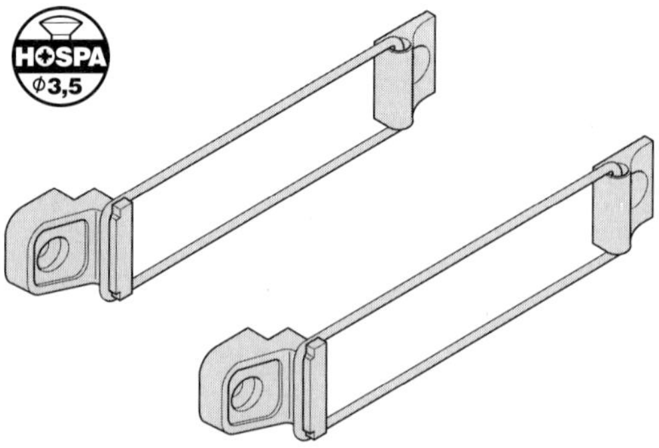

Axle trim

for Aximat hinges with concealed axle.
Finish: plastic, nickel-plated

Cat. No.	343.28.795

Packing: 50 and 200 pcs.

Trim also available in RAL colors silver gray 7001 and light gray 7035. Min. order 1,000.

Axle trim

for Aximat-SM hinges with concealed axle.
Finish: plastic, nickel-plated

Cat. No.	344.82.061

Packing: 50 and 200 pcs.

Varidoor Hinge

HÄFELE

Opening angle: 120°

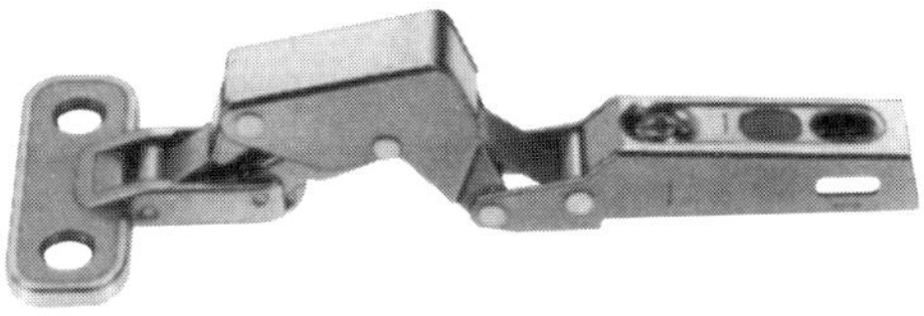

- Door thickness up to 16mm (5/8")
- 3-way adjustable
- Self-closing
- All-metal:
  Cup: zinc die-cast
  Hinge arm: steel, nickel-plated

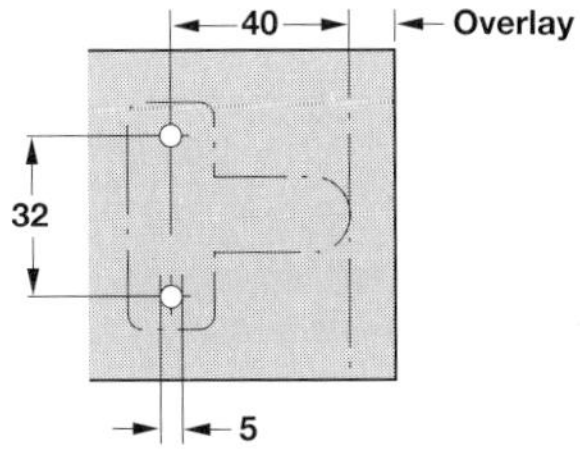

Overlay	Cat. No.
Variable overlay 0 to 13 mm	343.35.601

Packing: 20 pcs.

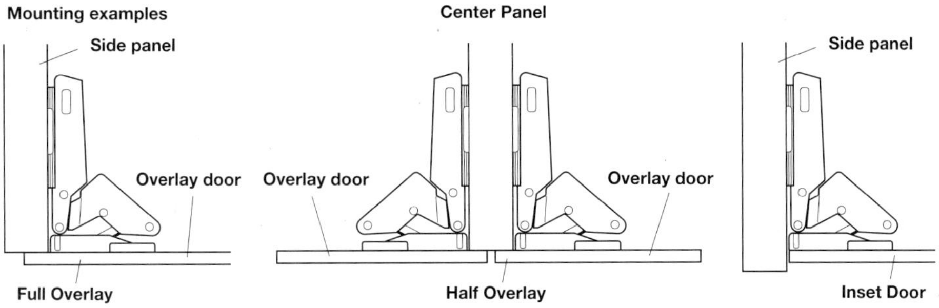

Hinges, Flap and Lid Stays Associated Fittings **3**

- No cup hole drilling required
- Especially suited for thin doors (made of steel or MDF)
- 3 mm door protrusion inside cabinet at 90° opening

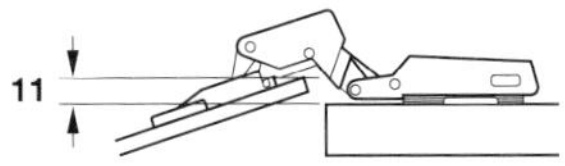

Fixing Materials:
Varianta screws cylinder head withPZ 2 cross slot
Finish:
steel, nickel-plated

Length	3 mm dia. hole
10.5 mm	013.20.618
13.5 mm	013.20.636
16.0 mm	013.20.645
	5 mm dia. hole
10.5 mm	013.20.716
13.5 mm	013.20.734
16.0 mm	013.20.743

Packing: 1000 pcs.

- Wing mounting plate, screw-mount
- Verticle adjustment
- Pre-mounted hinge mounting screw
- Finish: steel, nickel-plated

Hole pattern
(for overlay door)

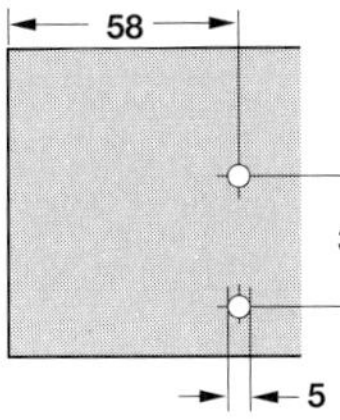

Reinforcement	Model No.	Cat. No.
None	**0**	343.36.608

Packing: 20 pcs.

Dimensional data not binding.
We reserve the right to alter specifications without notice.

HÄFELE

Easy Mount Concealed Hinges

Max. door opening angle: 90°

Easy mount hinge, **screw-mounted.**
- Door thickness 16 mm (5/8")
- Side panel thickness 16 to 22 mm (5/8" - 7/8")
- Horizontal adjustment, oblong holes
- Vertical adjustment, oblong holes
- Self-closing
- All-metal: steel, zinc-plated

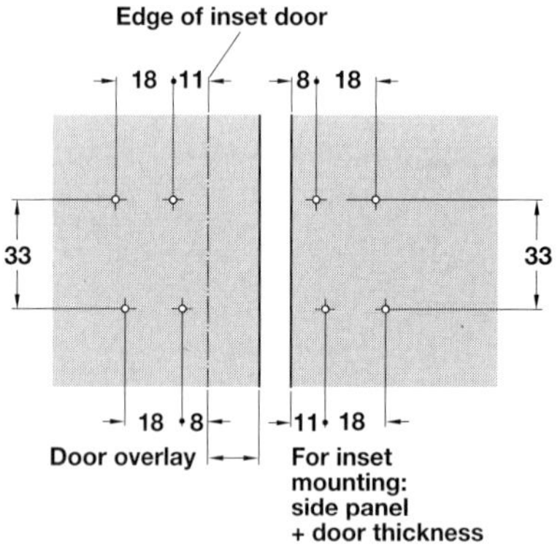

		non self-closing	self-closing
Cat. No.	nickel-plated	343.34.917	343.33.910
	bronzed		343.33.116

Packing: 100 pcs.

Shim

Reinforcement 2 mm, hole pattern as above
Finish: white plastic

Cat. No.	343.34.793

Packing: 500 pcs.

Examples of corner gaps - for single-side, overlay door mountings:

Side panel thick-ness (mm)	No. of shims	Gap (mm)	Door overlay (mm)
16	3	2	14
17	2	1	16
18	2	2	16
19	2	3	16
20	-	-	20
21	-	1	20
22	-	2	20

If side or center panels are thinner than those shown in the table, insert a shim under the hinge mounting plate.
Shims can also be used to achieve wider corner spacing or gaps.
The shims are stackable.

3 Hinges, Flap and Lid Stays Associated Fittings

Mounting screws:
Hospa particle board screws
Pan head with PZ 2 cross slot
Finish:
steel, nickel-plated

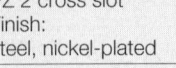

Length	Cat. No.
13 mm	015.71.624
15 mm	015.71.633
17 mm	015.71.642

Packing: 1000 pcs.

Sample installations

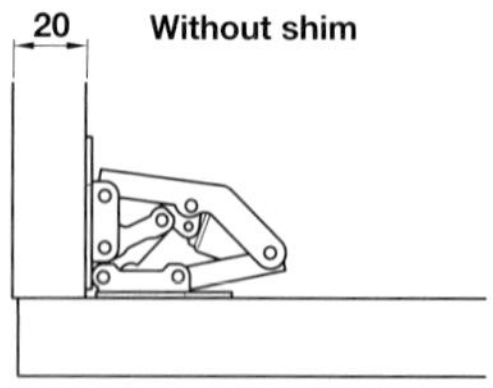

Corner mounting

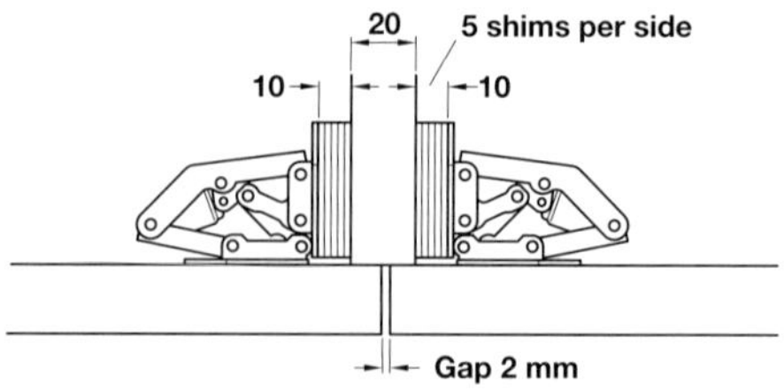

Center panel mounting

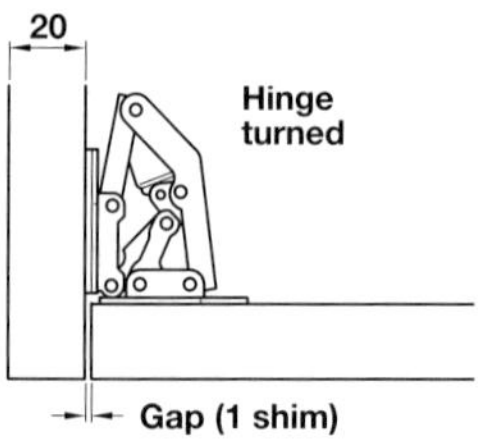

Inset mounting

Dimensions in mm

Dimensional data not binding. We reserve the right to alter specifications without notice.

Easy Mount Concealed Hinges

HÄFELE

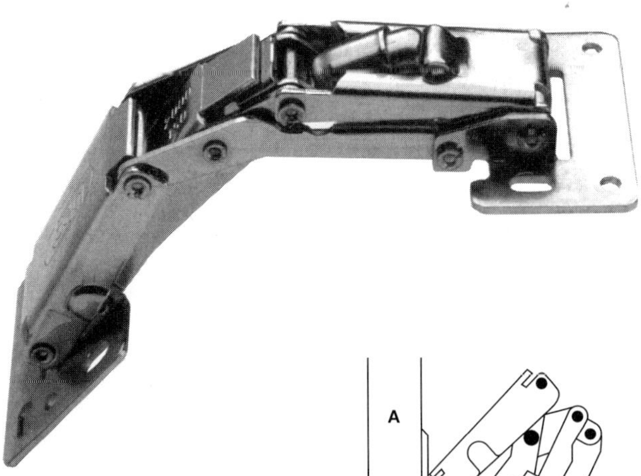

Easy Mount Hinge, screw-mounted
- Door thicknesses 16 - 19 mm (5/8-3/4")
- Side panel thickness 16 - 22 mm (5/8-7/8")
- Horizontal adjustment, oblong holes
- Vertical adjustment, oblong holes
- Self-closing

Opening angle: 150°

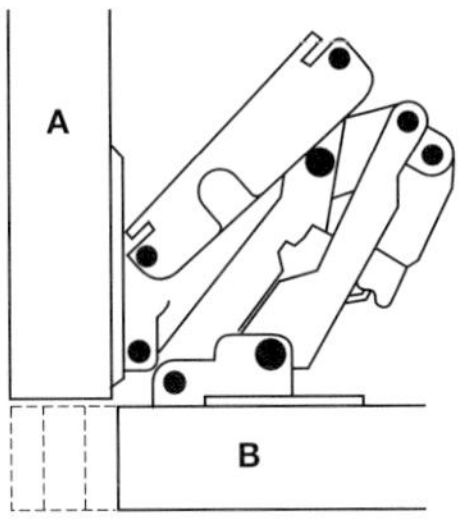

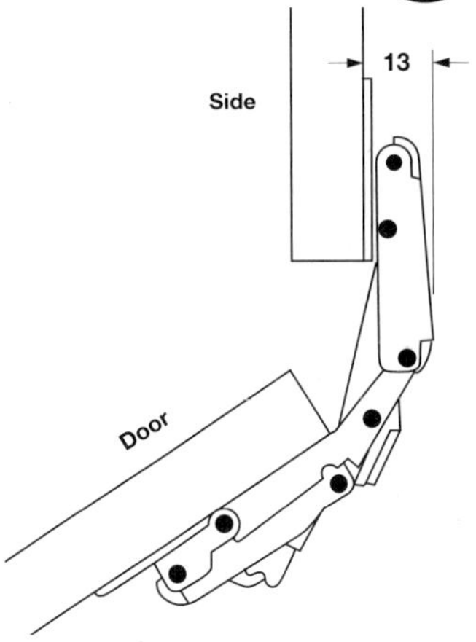

Finish: steel, nickel-plated

Cat. No.	343.33.730

Packing: 100 pcs.

Opening angle: 170°

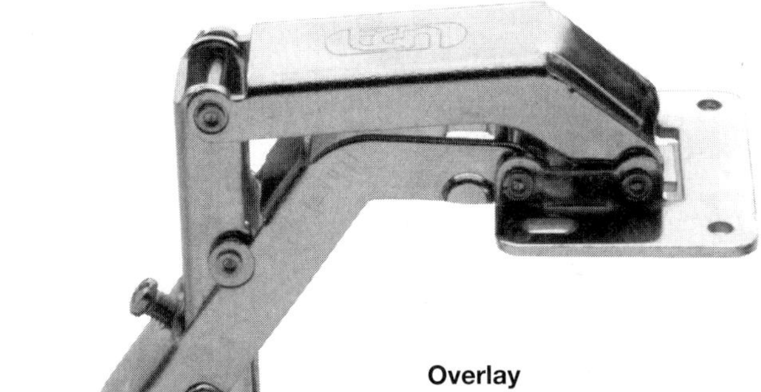

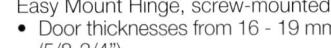

Easy Mount Hinge, screw-mounted
- Door thicknesses from 16 - 19 mm (5/8-3/4")
- Side panel thickness from 16 - 22 mm (5/8-7/8")
- Horizontal adjustment, oblong holes
- Vertical adjustment, oblong holes
- Self-closing

Overlay

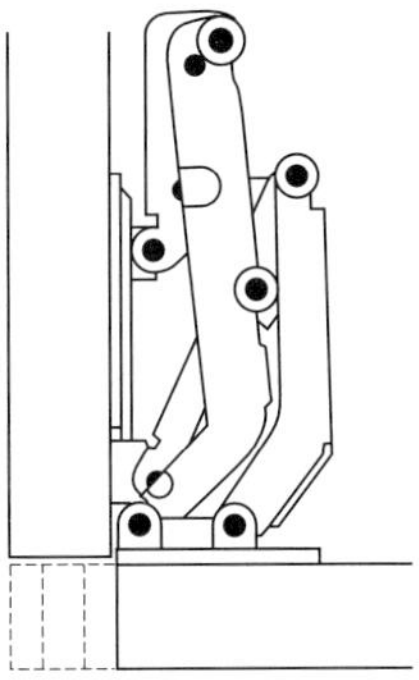

Inset

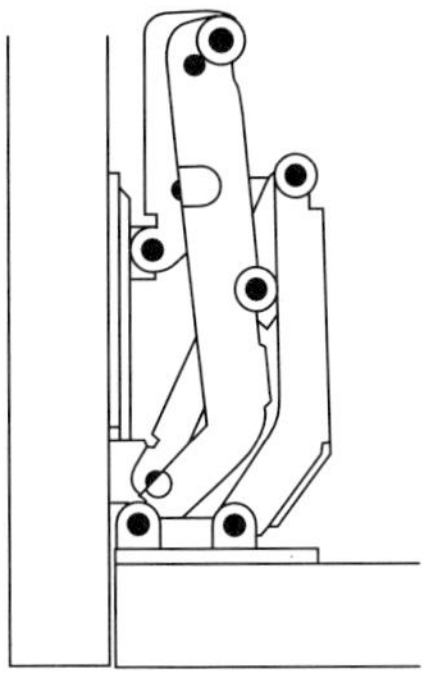

Mounting screws:
Hospa particle board screws
Pan head with
PZ 2 cross slot
Finish:
steel, nickel-plated

HOSPA ⌀3.5

Length	Cat. No.
13 mm	015.71.624
15 mm	015.71.633
17 mm	015.71.642

Packing: 1000 pcs.

Finish: steel, nickel-plated

Cat. No.	343.33.740

Packing: 100 pcs.

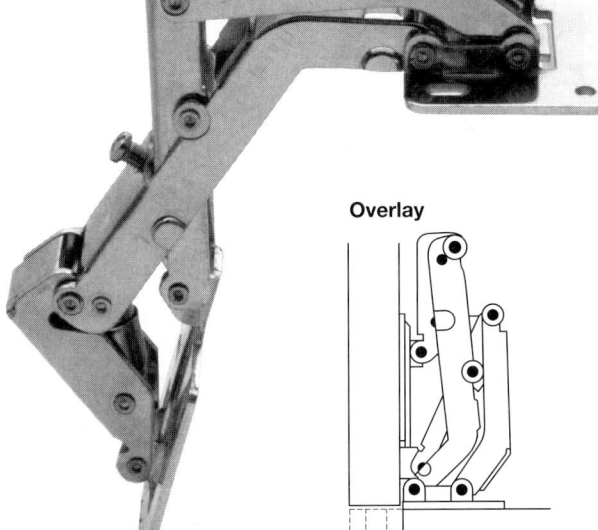

HÄFELE

GS Miter Hinges for Doors and Flaps

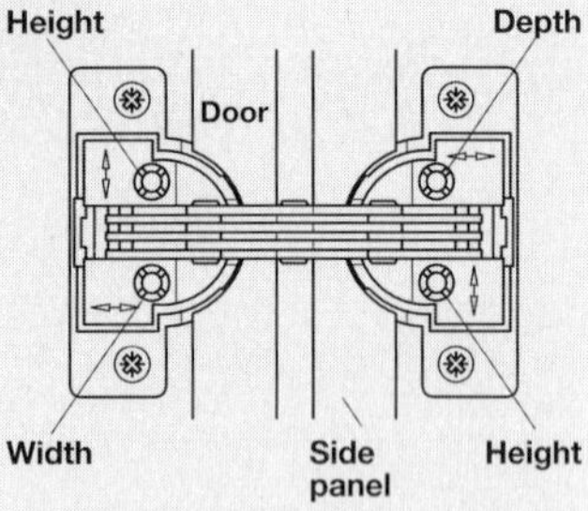

Three-way adjustable:
3 mm in height, **1.5 mm** in depth and width

Mounting screws:
Hospa particle board screws
raised head with
PZ 2 cross slot
Finish: steel, nickel-plated

HOSPA Φ3,5

Length	Cat. No.
15 mm	015.55.639
20 mm	015.55.657
25 mm	015.55.675

Packing: 1000 pcs.

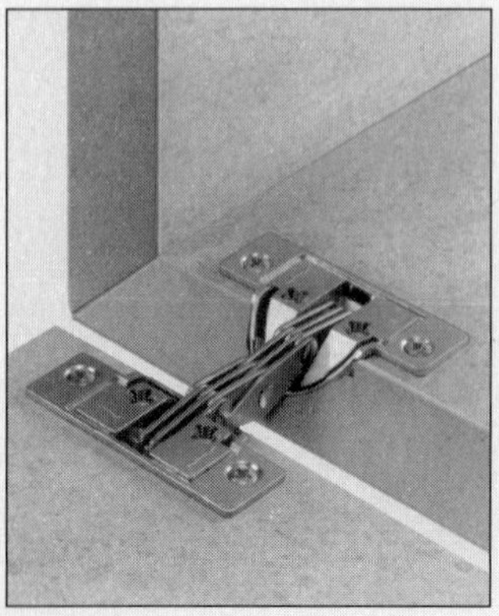

GS 45/90 **miter hinge,**
screw-mounted
All-metal

Opening angle: 135°

HOSPA Φ3,5

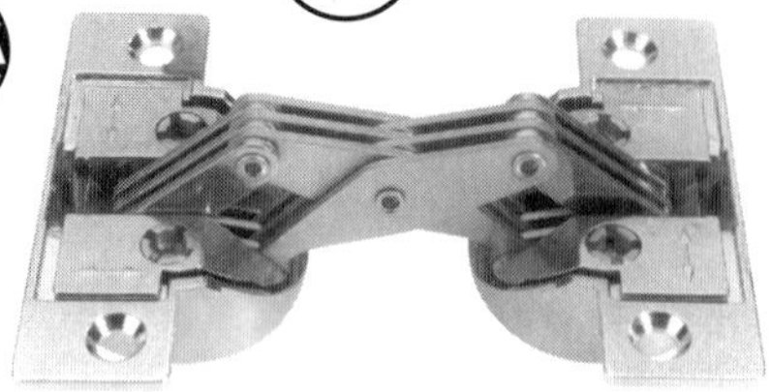

- Chamfer: **45°**
- Three-way adjustable
- Door thickness: 16 to 22 mm
- Side panel thickness: 16 to 22 mm
- Cup: zinc die-cast, nickel-plated
- Hinge arm: steel, nickel-plated

Cat. No.	325.00.708

Packing: 60 pcs.

Hole pattern

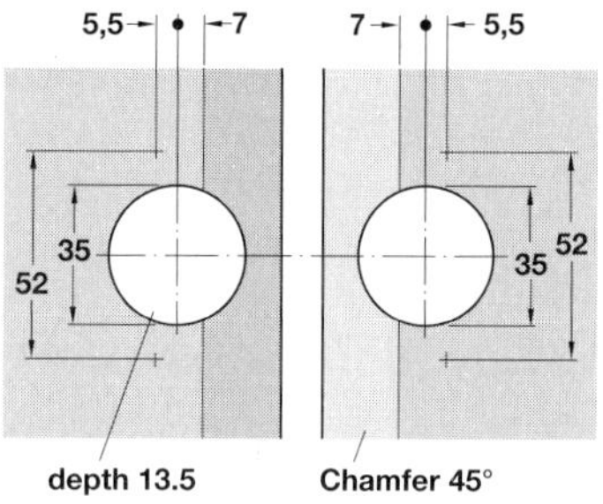

Sample installation:

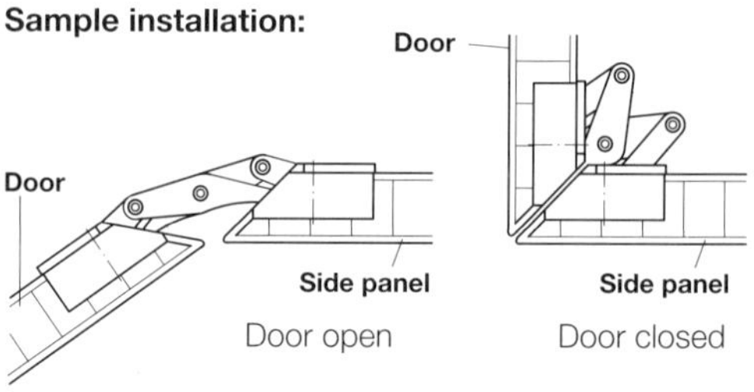

GS 22.5/135 **miter hinge,**
screw-mounted
All-metal

Opening angle: 120°

HOSPA Φ3,5

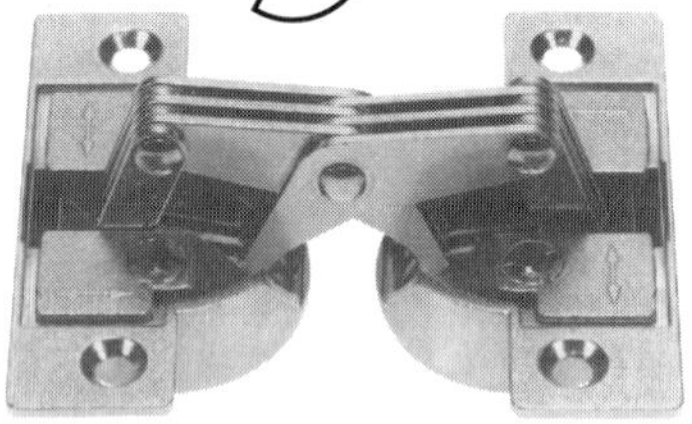

- Chamfer: **22.5°**
- Three-way adjustable
- Door thickness: 16 to 22 mm
- Side panel thickness: 16 to 22 mm
- Cup: zinc die-cast, nickel-plated
- Hinge arm: steel, nickel-plated

Cat. No.	325.00.726

Packing: 60 pcs.

Hole pattern

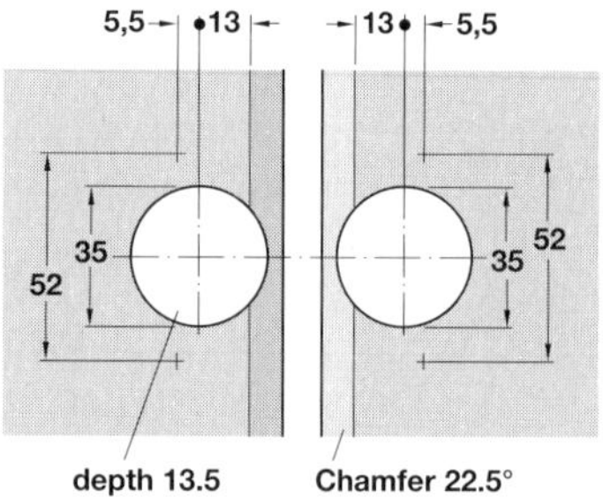

Sample installation:

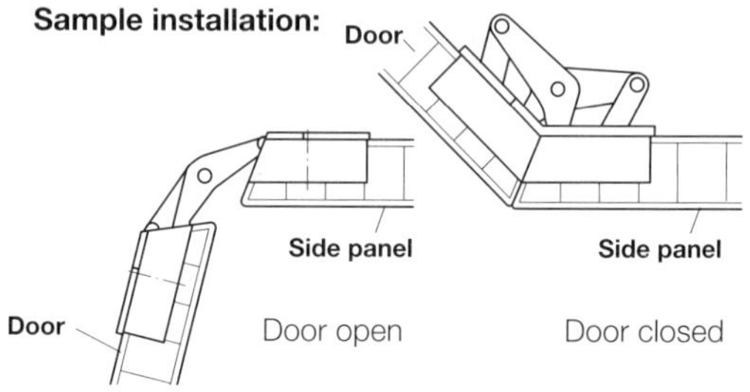

Miter flap hinge,
screw-mounted
All-metal

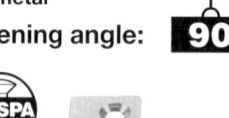

Opening angle: 90°

HOSPA Φ3,5

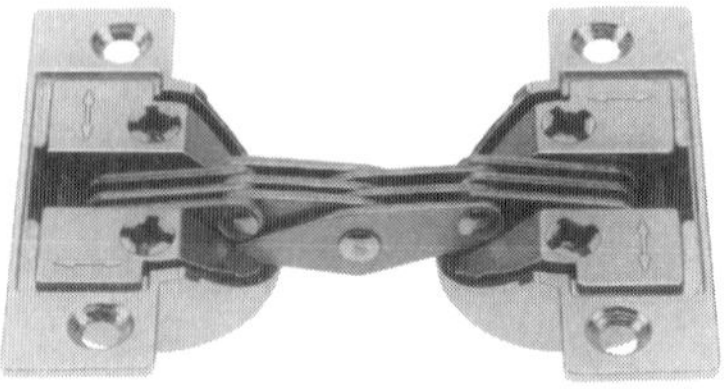

- Chamfer: **45°**
- Three-way adjustable
- Flap thickness: 16 to 22 mm
- Side panel thickness: 16 to 22 mm
- Cup: zinc die-cast, nickel-plated
- Hinge arm: steel, nickel-plated

Cat. No.	325.02.702

Packing: 60 pcs.

Hole pattern:

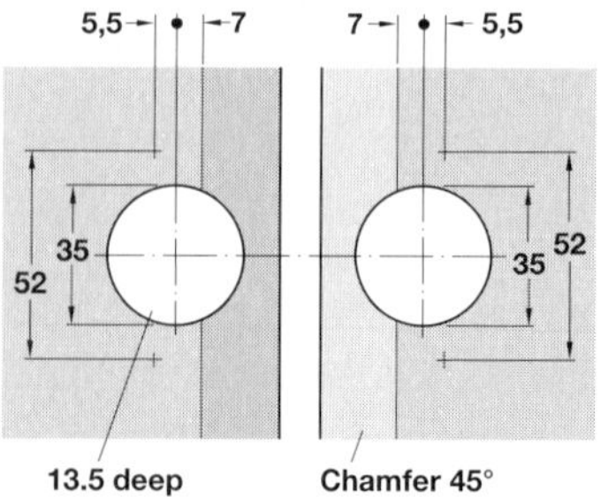

Sample installation:

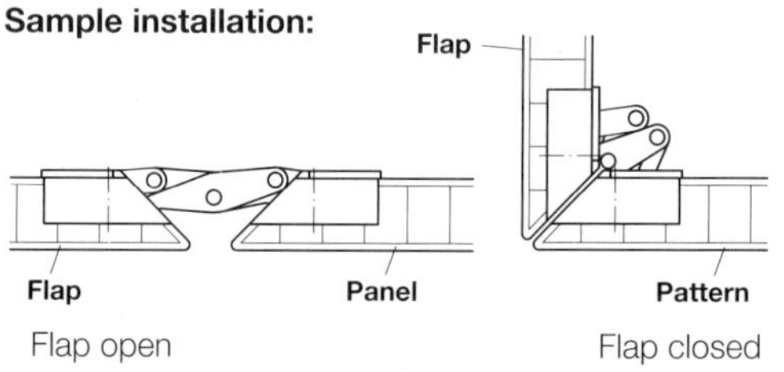

Dimensions in mm

Dimensional data not binding.
We reserve the right to alter specifications without notice.

Pie-cut Corner Hinge

HÄFELE

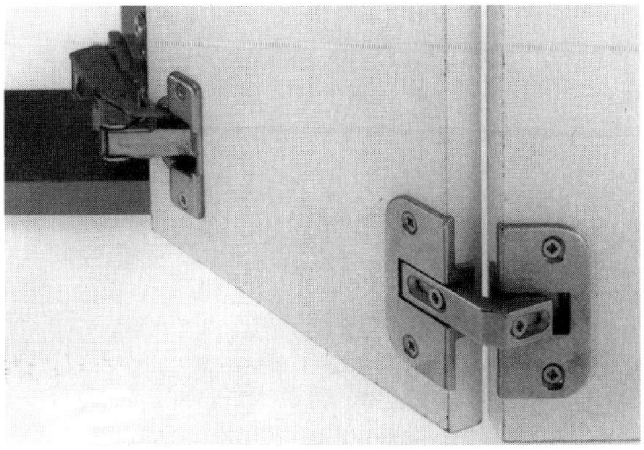

Max. opening angle

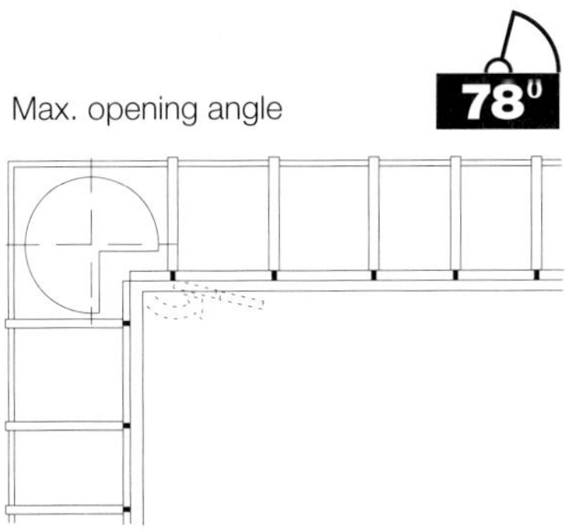

Specially designed for kitchen corner cabinets with revolving shelves.

At long last. A rugged hinge designed for revolving-shelf kitchen cabinet installations. The pie-cut corner hinge meets all design requirements for thre-way adjustability, quick mounting, concealed installation and strudy construction. Adjustable to allow a small air circulation gap.

Pie-cut corner hinges, with two 35 mm cup holes, screw-mounted
Door thickness variable 15-24 mm
Hole size: 35 mm dia., depth 11 mm

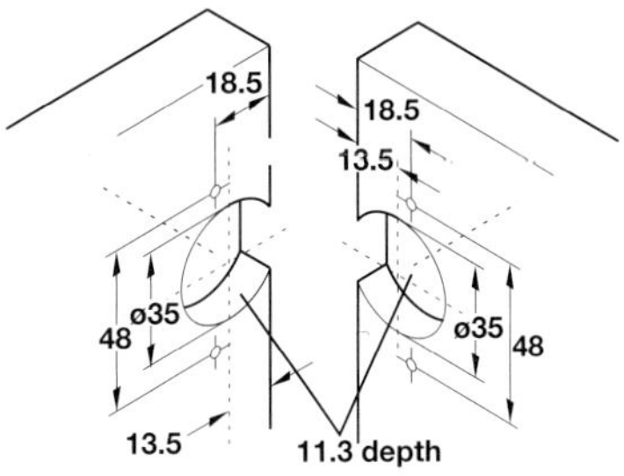

Dimensions in mm

Finish: zinc die-cast, nickel-plated

Cat. No.	343.90.700

Packing: 100 pcs.

Mounting screws:
Hospa particle board screws
countersunk head
40 mm dia. with Z cross slot
Finish: steel, nickel-plated

HOSPA Ø4,0

length	Cat. No.
15 mm	015.35.824
17 mm	015.35.833

Packing: 1000 pcs.

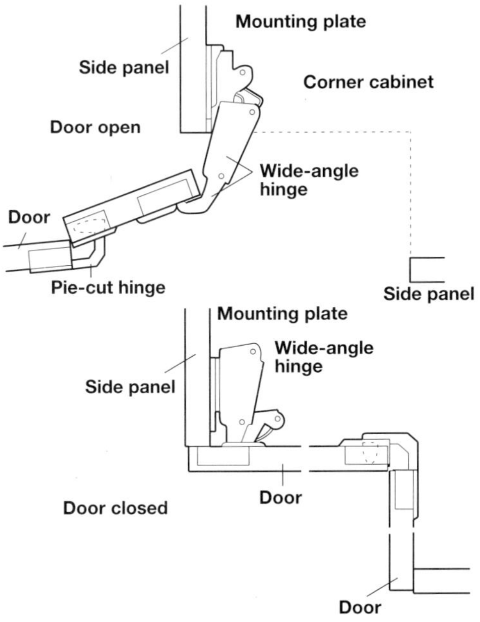

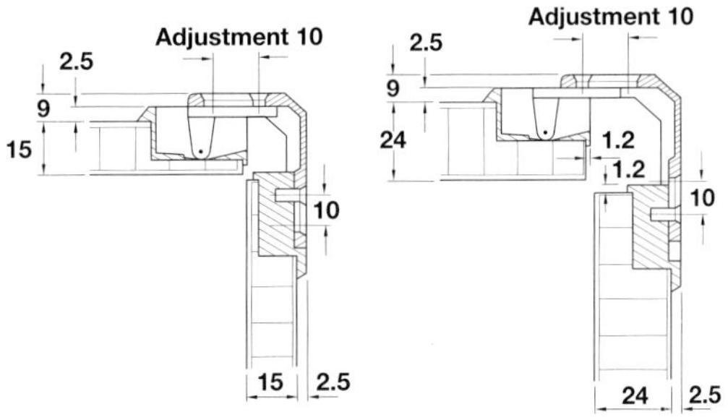

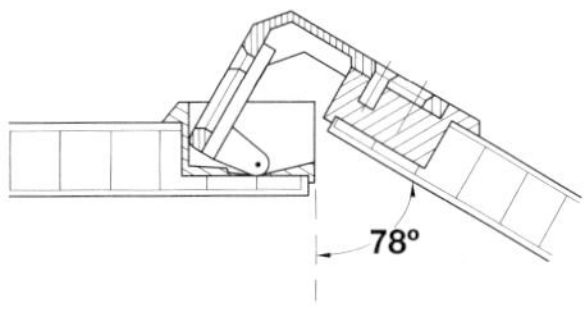

Dimensional data not binding.
We reserve the right to alter specifications without notice.

HÄFELE

Concealed Hinges

Hole pattern, Zysa hinges

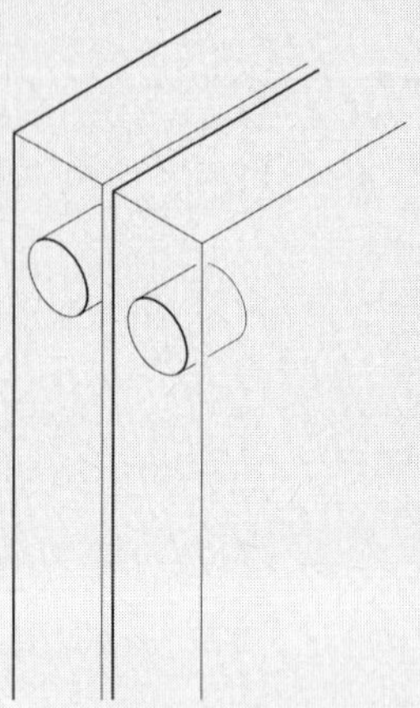

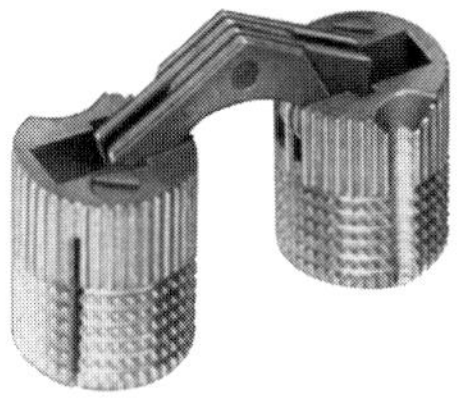

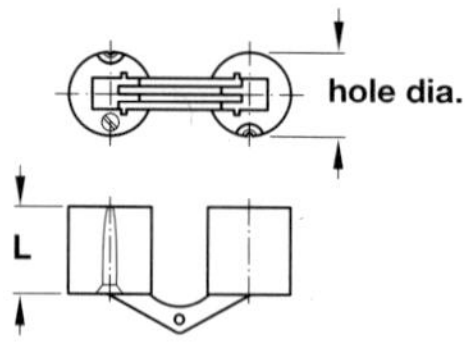

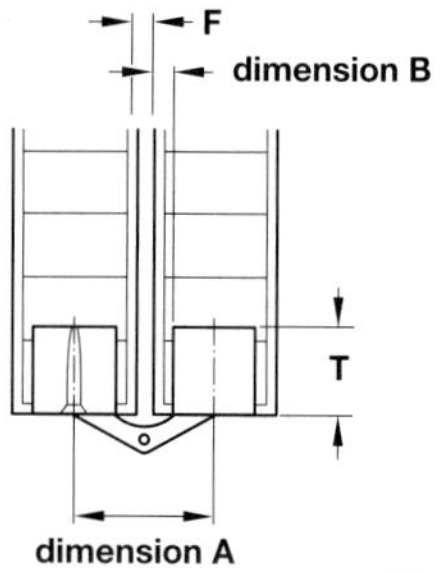

Zysa hinges
Finish: brass, matt

HOSPA ϕ3,5 * e.g. required screw

max. opening angle 180°

Wood thickness	**14 -19**	**17 - 22**	**20 - 26**	**22 - 28**	**24 - 32**	**31 - 40**
Screw*	dia. 2.5	dia. 3.0	dia. 3.5	dia. 3.5	dia. 4.0	dia. 4.5
Length **L**	11	13.5	15.5	16.5	17.5	25
Hole dia.	10	12	14	16	18	24
Hole depth **T**	11	13.5	15.5	16.5	17.5	25
Dimension **A**	16.5	20	23	25	27	36.5
Dimension **B**	2	2.2	3	3	3	3.5
Joint **F**	2.5	3.5	3	3	3	3.5
Cat. No.	341.22.506	341.23.503	341.13.507	341.11.503	341.12.500	341.14.504
Packing:	48 pcs.	48 pcs.	24 pcs.	24 pcs.	24 pcs.	12 pcs.

3 Hinges, Flap and Lid Stays Associated Fittings

Important notice:

- Nonhanded: can be used left or right
- Tighten the tensioning screw to ensure a secure grip in wood
- Additional holding power for exceptionally high loads is achieved by installing a particle board or wood screw through exposed end
- Extremely accurate drilling a must

Butting, inset door:

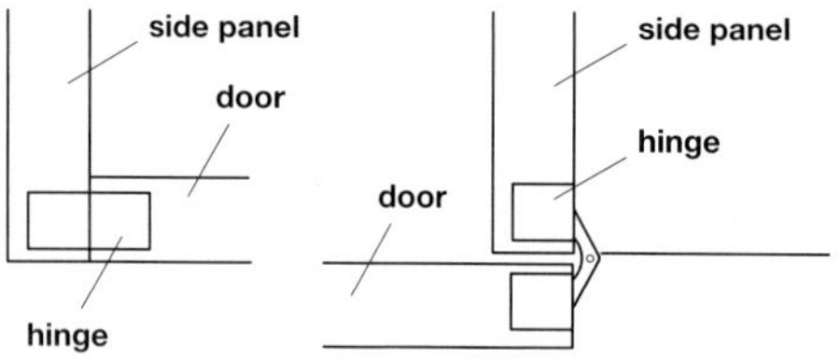

Door closed Door open

Butting, overlay door:

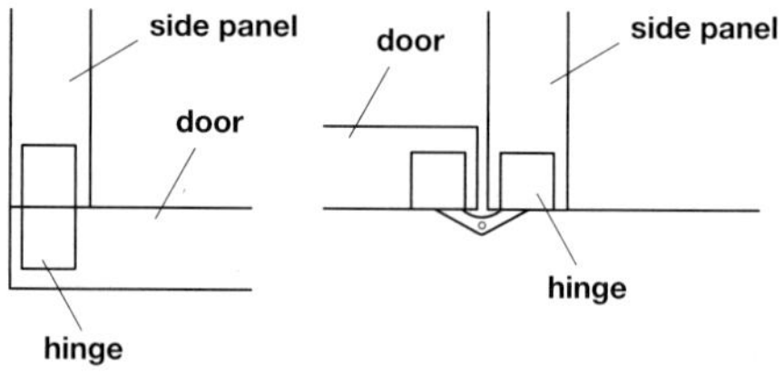

Door closed Door open

Joining two panels:

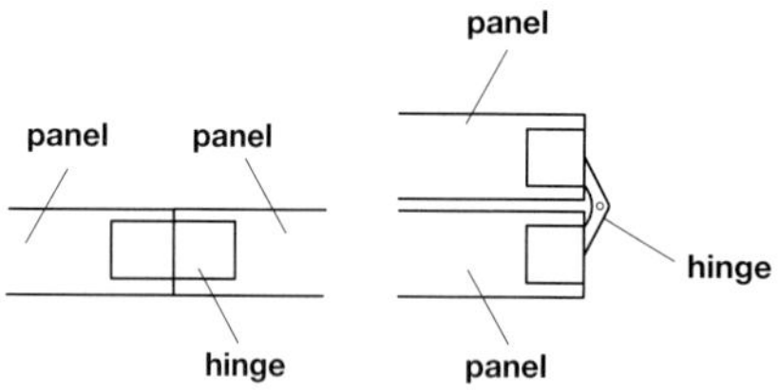

Panel closed Panel open

Butting overlay doors:

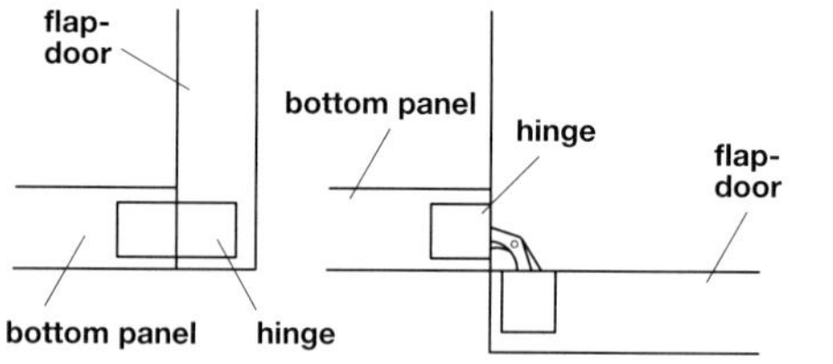

Flap-door closed Flap-door open

Typical folding door installation:

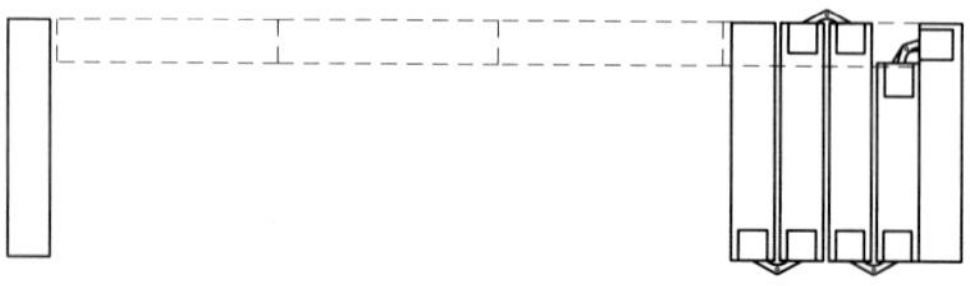

Dimensional data not binding.
We reserve the right to alter specifications without notice.

Dimensions in mm

Concealed Hinges

max. opening angle

180°

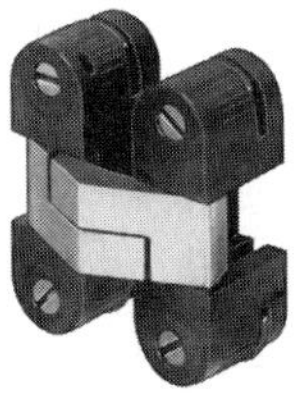

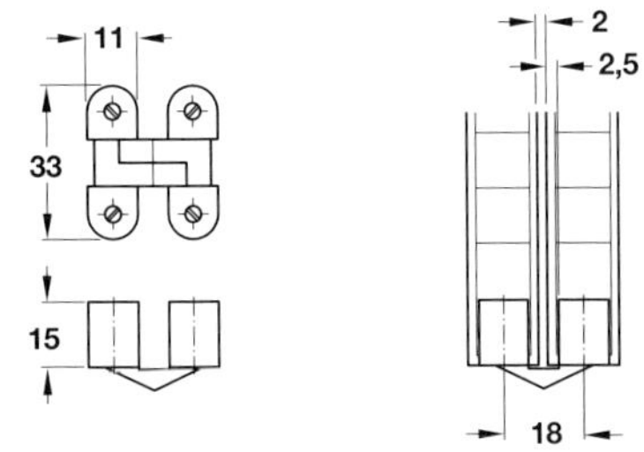

Vidi hinges
Wood thickness **from 16 mm** (5/8")
Finish: brown plastic case
nickel-plated steel linkage

Cat. No.	341.01.016

Packing: 40 pcs.

Vidi hinges are anchored by anchor blades

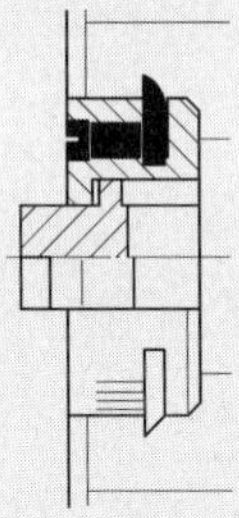

max. opening angle

180°

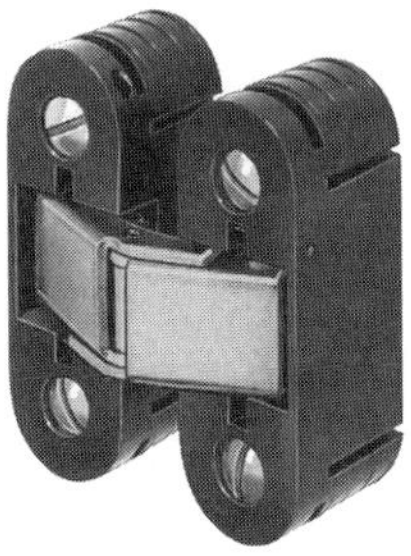

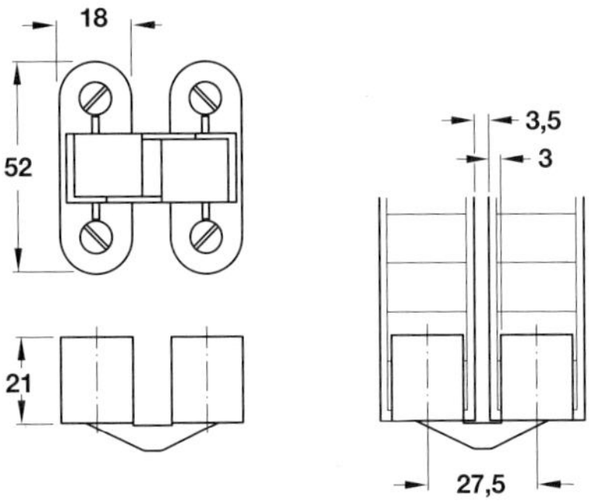

Vidi-Super hinge
Wood thickness **from 24 mm** (1")
Finish: plastic case
brass linkage

Cat. No.	white	341.00.706
	brown	341.00.108
	black	341.00.304

Packing: 24 pcs.

Hole pattern for
Vidi and Vidi–Super hinges

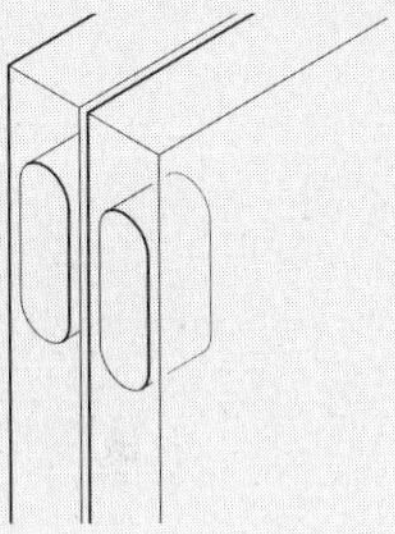

Vidi-Super hinges are anchored by expanding the hinge body

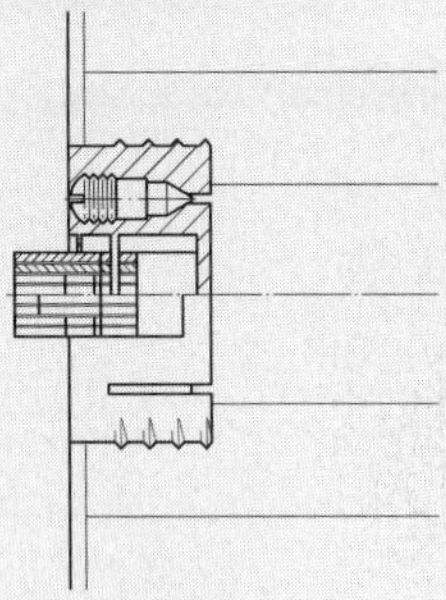

max. opening angle

180°

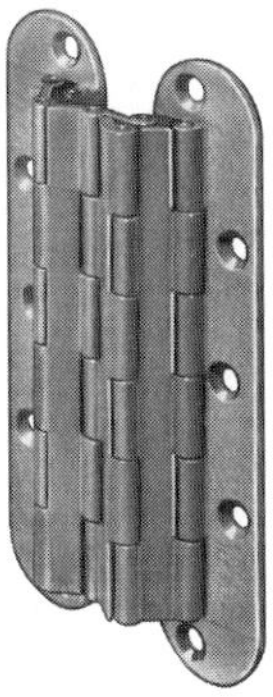

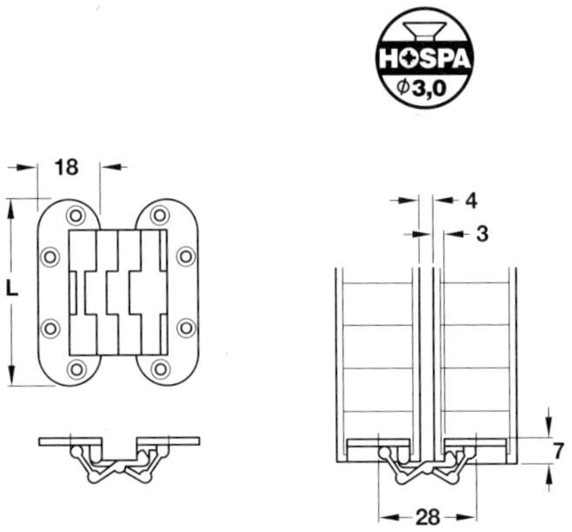

Sepa hinges
Wood thickness **from 24 mm** (1")
Finish: brass, matt

L = Length	Cat. No.
41 mm	341.15.501
52 mm	341.16.508
88 mm	341.17.505

Packing: 10 pcs.

Dimensions in mm

Hole pattern, Sepa hinges

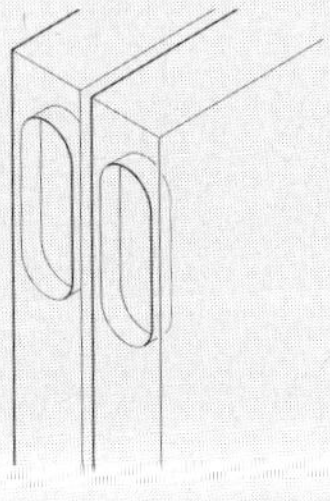

Dimensional data not binding.
We reserve the right to alter specifications without notice.

HÄFELE

Concealed Hinges

Hole pattern, Vici hinges

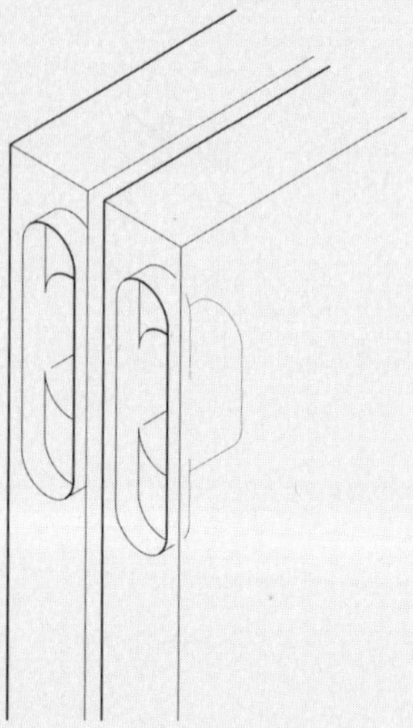

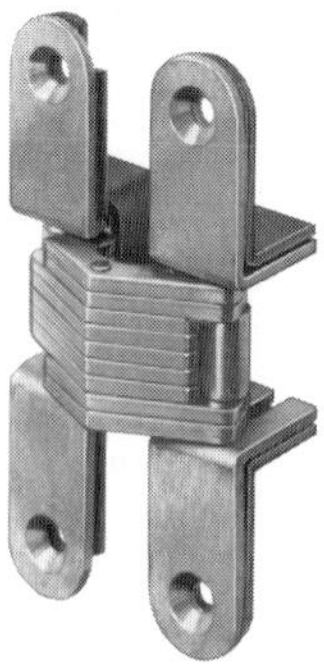

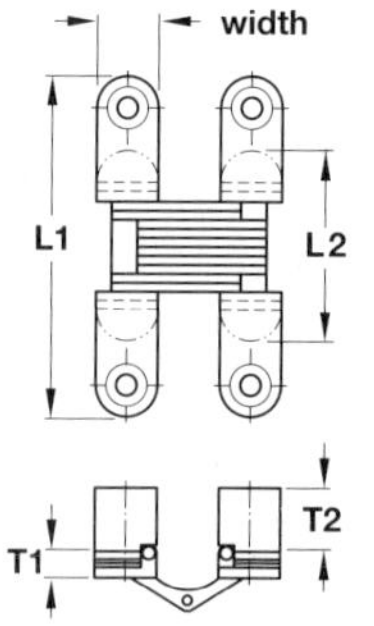

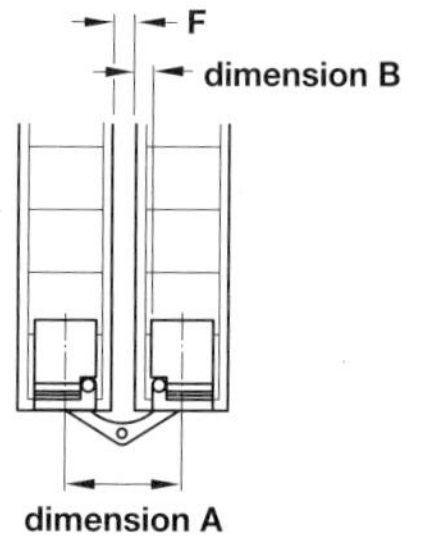

Vici hinges
Finish: brass, matt polished

HOSPA ϕ3,0 * e.g. required screws

max. opening angle 180°

Wood thickness	**17 - 20**	**14 - 16**	**18 - 20**	**20 - 24**
Screw*	dia. 3.0	dia. 3.0	dia. 3.0	dia. 3.5
Width	12	10	12	15
Length **L1**	38.5	44.5	64.5	82
Length **L2**	24.5	28.5	34.5	44
Depth **T1**	1.5	4.5	4.5	5
Depth **T2**	15.5	8	13	14.5
Dimension **A**	22	17	24	26
Dimension **B**	2.5	2	3	2.5
Joint **F**	5	3	6	6
Cat. No.	341.03.538	341.03.547	341.03.565	341.03.574
Packing:	20 pcs.	20 pcs.	20 pcs.	12 pcs.

3 Hinges, Flap and Lid Stays Associated Fittings

Hole pattern, Soss hinges

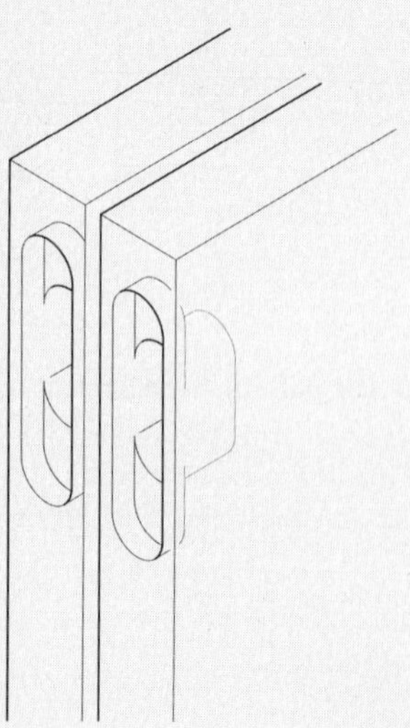

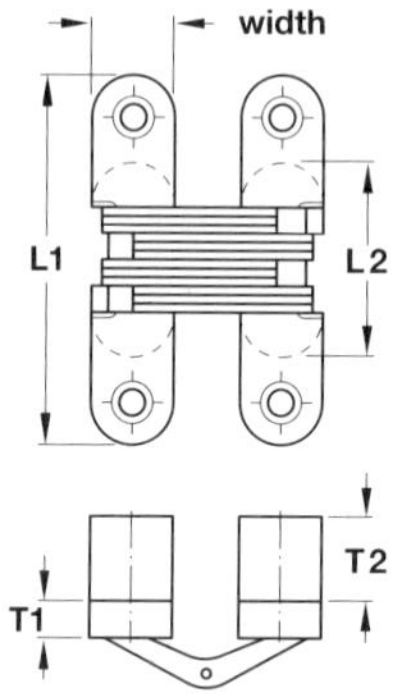

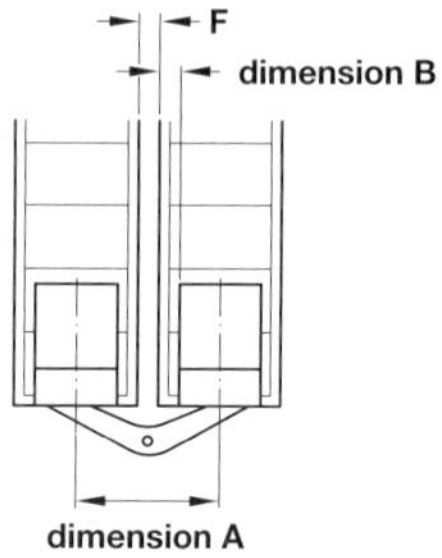

Soss hinges
Finish: case: zinc die-cast, brass-plated
Linkage: steel, brass-plated

max. opening angle 180°

Wood thickness	**13 - 16**	**19 - 24**	**19 - 25**	**22 - 26**	**28 - 34**	**35 - 38**	**41 - 45**
Width	10	13	13	16	19	25.5	28.5
Length **L1**	42	44.5	60	70	95.5	117.5	117.5
Length **L2**	22	20	31	36.5	53	65.5	79
Depth **T1**	5.5	5	7	7	9	12	10
Depth **T2**	7	13.5	11.5	16	17.5	24.5	30
Dimension **A**	17	21.5	21	27	33	44	51.5
Dimension **B**	1.5	3	3	3	4.5	5	6
Joint **F**	4	2.5	2	5	6	8.5	11
Cat. No.	341.07.518	341.07.527	341.07.536	341.07.545	341.07.554	341.07.563	341.07.572
Packing:	24 pcs.	24 pcs.	12 pcs.	4 pcs.	2 pcs.	2 pcs.	2 pcs.

Fastening screws are included.

Dimensional data not binding. We reserve the right to alter specifications without notice.

Dimensions in mm

Glass Door Hinge

This is an all-metal Econo Version of a non-bore glass door hinge

All-Metal Hinge, with catch
Screw-mounted to side of cabinet.
Vertical adjustment with oblong holes
Opening angle 180°

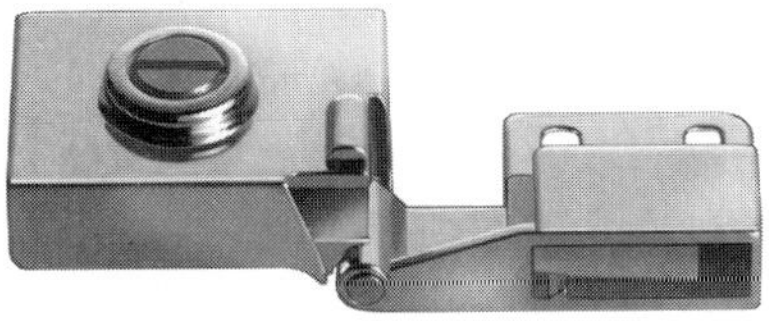

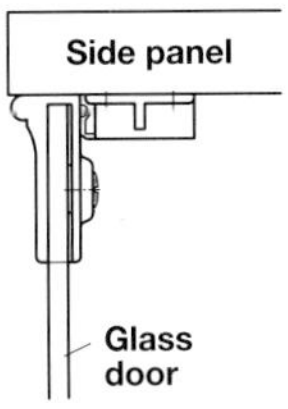

Opening angle:

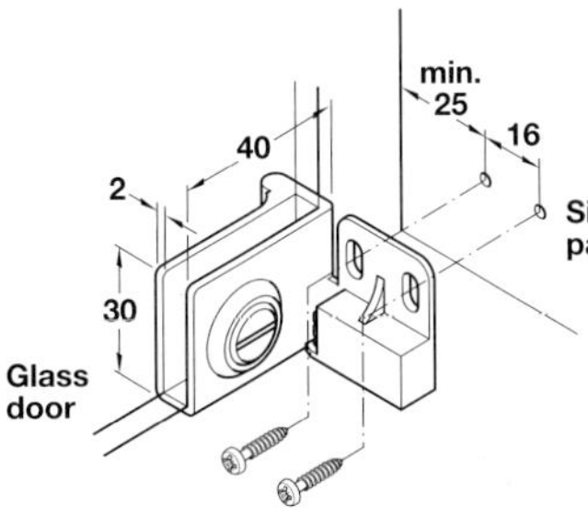

Finish: zinc die-cast, textured matt

Cat. No.	textured black pl	361.93.340
	textured brass pl	361.93.840
	textured chrome pl	361.93.240

Packing: 50 pairs (1 pair = 1 left, 1 right hinge)

min. 2.5 mm gap between glass and panels

For glass thicknesses 3-5 mm

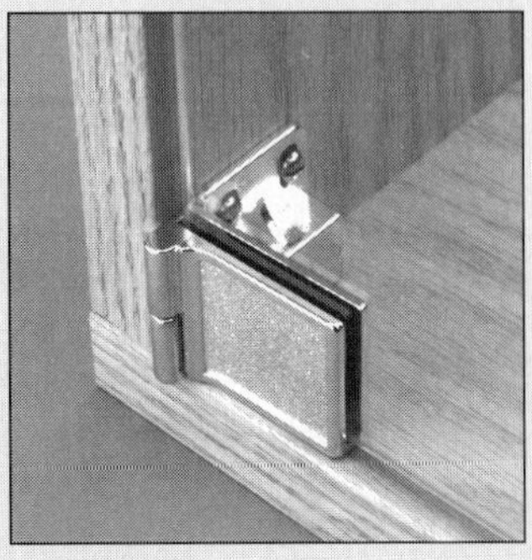

Overlay Hinges, with catch
In and out adjustment, oblong holes
Opening angle 200°

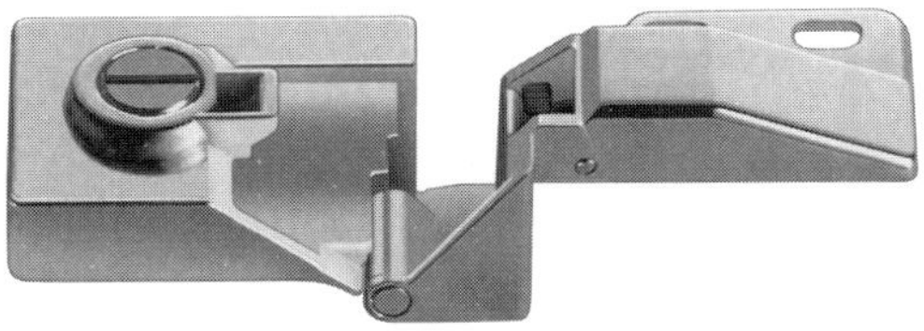

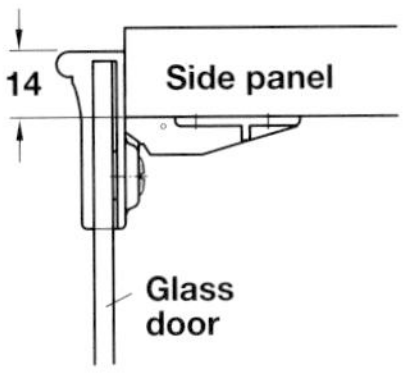

Opening angle:

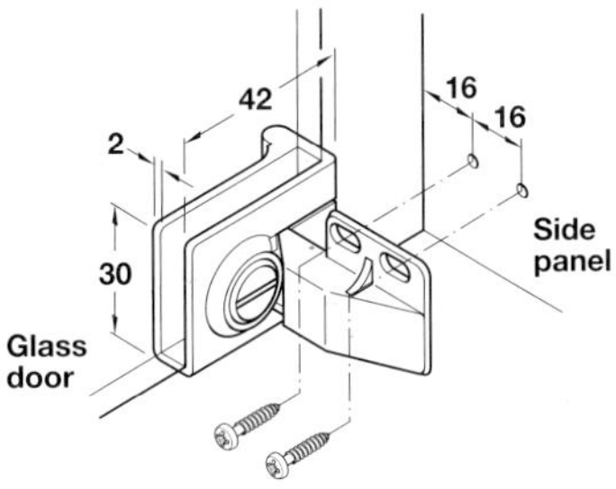

Finish: zinc die-cast

Cat. No.	textured black pl	361.93.341
	textured brass pl	361.93.841
	textured chrome pl	361.93.241

Packing: 50 pairs (1 pair = 1 left, 1 right hinge)

14 mm overlay on side panel
5 mm overlay on top & bottom edge

- Fastening screws are not included
- Includes foam rubber pads.

Glass Door Pull with plastic screw
• Glass thickness max. 5 mm

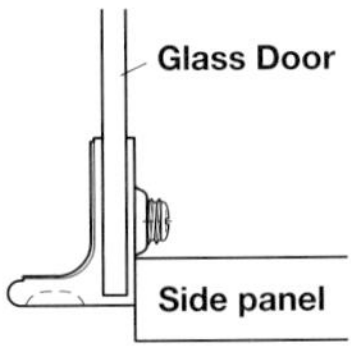

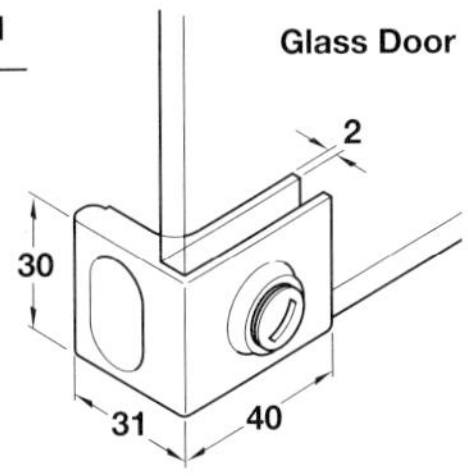

No hole in glass required

Finish: zinc die-cast

Cat. No.	textured chrome polished	154.25.210
	textured gold polished	154.25.810
	textured black matt	154.25.310

Packing: 1 and 20 pcs.

Dimensions in mm

Dimensional data not binding.
We reserve the right to alter specifications without notice.

HÄFELE

Glass Door Hinges

Glass hinge closed

Glass hinge open

Stylish **solid brass** hinges. Installation requires drilling a hole in glass. Door and side panel components installed separately. Door component detaches by removing mounting screw.

To determine the exact tab distance for your application, please make a trial mounting with 1/4" wood material.

All-Metal Glass Door Hinge

Vertical adjustment using oblong mounting holes, horizontal adjustment with arm fixing screw. Two hinges required per door. Maximum glass door thickness 1/4"

- For glass doors with hole. For small and medium size doors.
- Small hinge, easily adjustable
- Easy to install
- Glass thicknesses 4.5 - 6.5 mm
- Arm can be detached from mounting plate

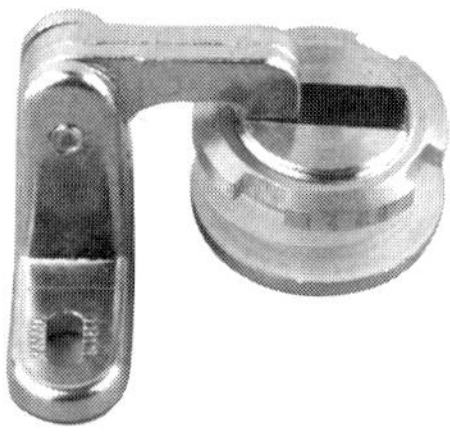

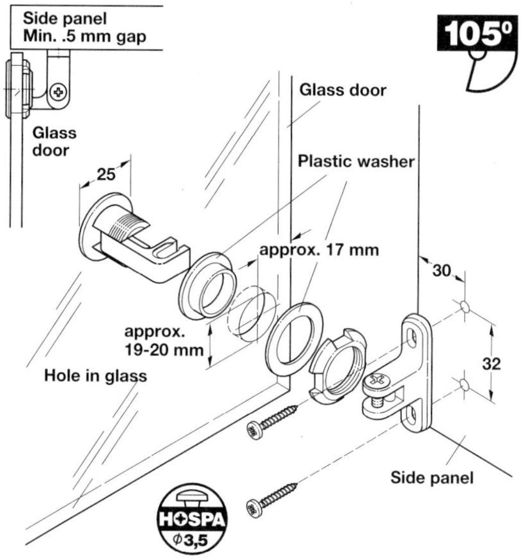

Finish: chrome and brass
Arm: zinc die-cast, plated: door parts, brass

Cat. No.	Chrome	361.48.200
	Brass	361.48.800

Packing: 40 pcs.

Claronda Glass Door Hinge, screw-mounted

- Reversible: can be used left or right
- For glass thicknesses 4.5 to 6.5 mm
- For inset doors

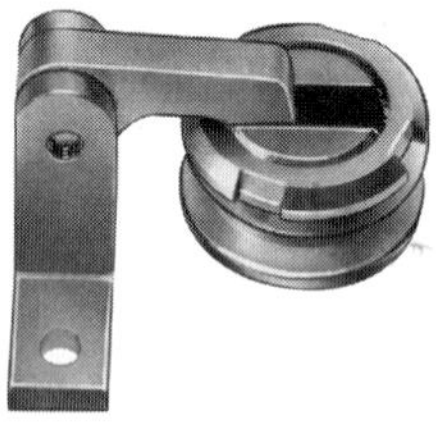

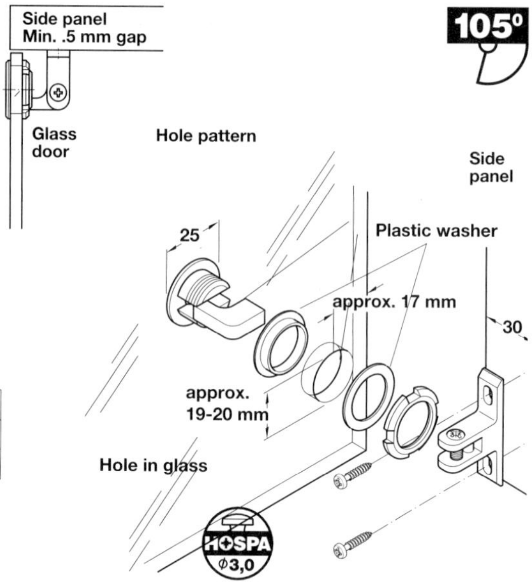

Finish: solid brass

Cat. No.	chrome-plated, polished	361.47.207
	nickel-plated, polished	361.47.707
	brass polished	361.47.805

Packing: 50 pcs. (two hinges per mounting)

Glass Door Hinges

HÄFELE

Glass Door Hinge, screw-mounted
- Reversible: can be used left or right
- For glass thicknesses 6.0 to 8.0 mm
- For insert doors

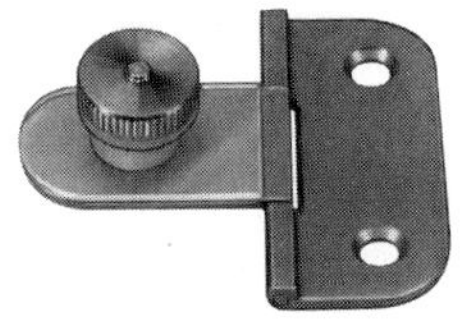

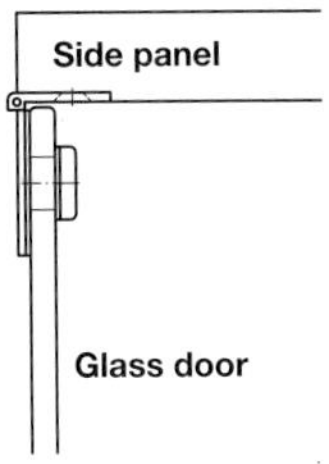

Opening angle:

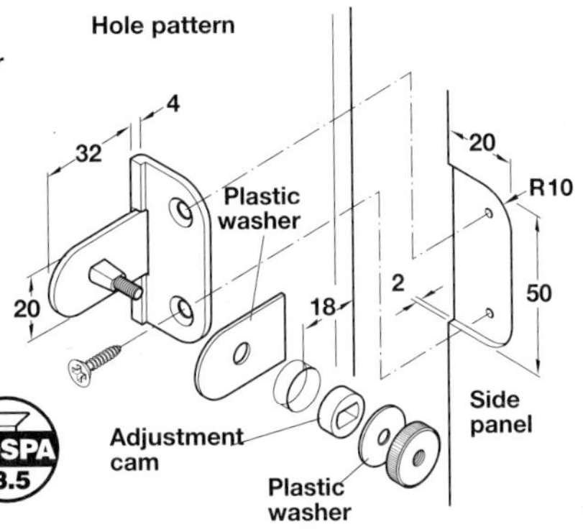

HOSPA Ø3.5

Finish: brass

Cat. No.		
Cat. No.	nickel-plated, matt	361.85.501
	brass matt	361.85.609

Packing: 20 pcs.

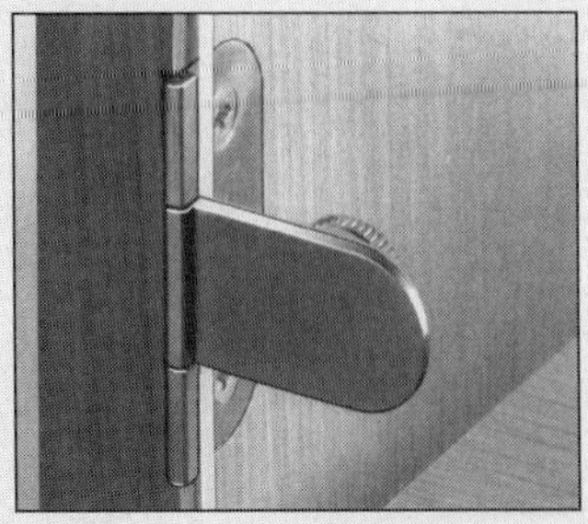

All-metal, exposed-knuckle hinges with 3mm horizontal adjustment. Installation requires drilling a hole in glass. Thumbscrew secures glass.

Glass Door Hinge, screw-mounted
- Glass thickness **6** - **8** mm
- 1 left and 1 right hinge per mounting
- For inset doors

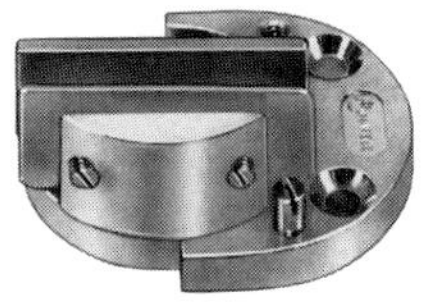

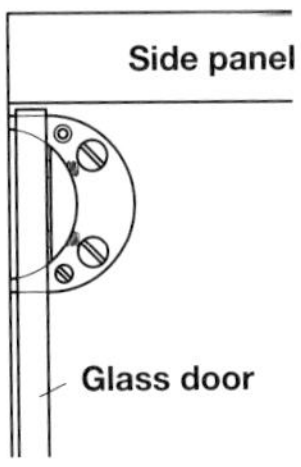

Opening angle:

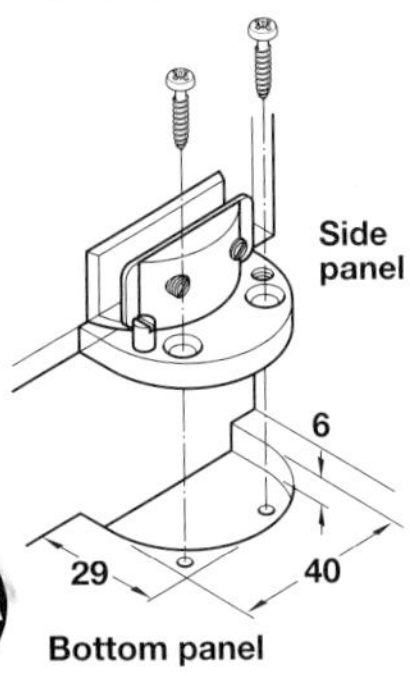

HOSPA Ø3,5

Finish: zinc die-cast

Cat. No.		
Cat. No.	nickel-plated matt	361.49.603
	nickel-plated polished	361.49.701
	chrome-plated	361.49.201
	brass-plated	361.49.809

Packing: 20 pcs, (50% right / 50% left)

Dimensions in mm

Hinges, Flap and Lid Stays Associated Fittings **3**

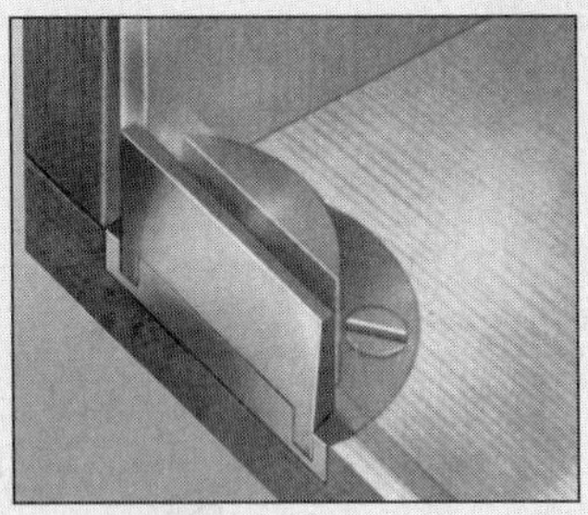

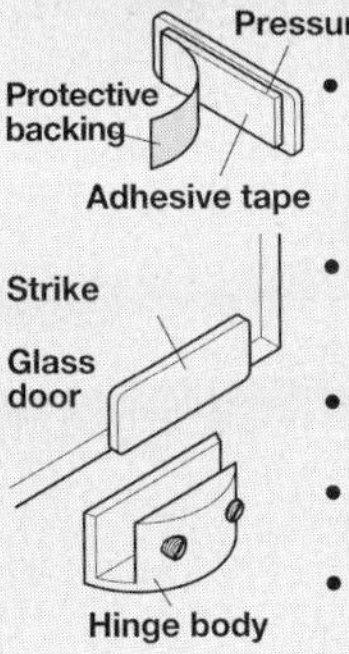

- Remove protective backing from adhesive tape
- Position pressure plate on glass door
- Attach hinge body to base
- Adjust glass door
- Tighten mounting screws

HÄFELE

Non-Bore Glass Door Hinges For Audio Cabinets, Light-Weight Glass Doors

Dimensions shown on mounting diagrams are only approximate. Please conduct trial mounting to determine your exact dimensions.

Magnetic catches see pages **2.82 - 2.88**

Simplex-Inset glass door hinge

screw-mounted to side of cabinet

- Opening angle 110°
- Self-adhesive pressure plates and screws included
- Packaged in pairs for left or right-hand installation
- Glass thickness to 5 mm (3/16")

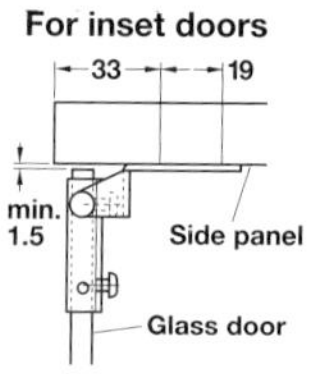

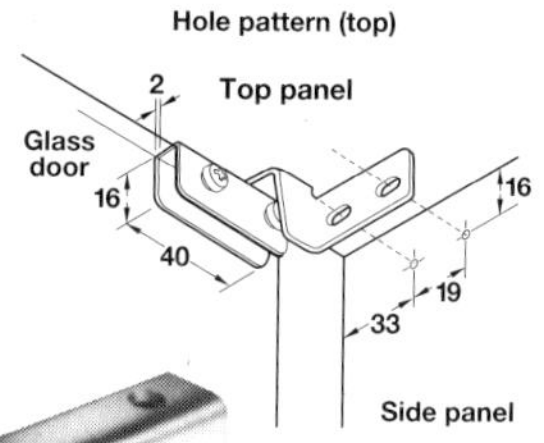

Finish: steel

Cat. No.	chrome-plated	361.33.221
	brass-plated	361.33.829
	black	361.33.329

Packing: 100 pairs (50 right and 50 left)

Simplex Side-overlay glass door hinge

screw-mounted to side of cabinet
Overlays side 15 mm, does not overlay top and bottom

- Opening angle 180°
- Self-adhesive pressure plates and screws included
- Packaged in pairs for left or right-hand installation
- Glass thickness to 5 mm (3/16")

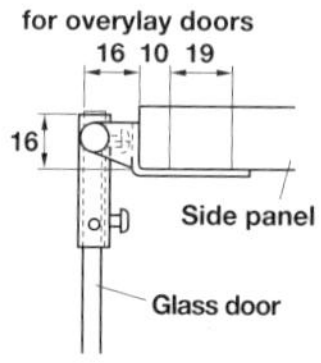

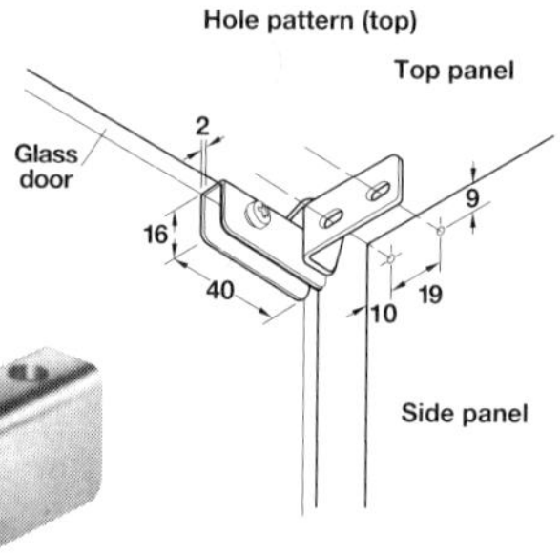

Finish: steel

Cat. No.	chrome-plated	361.33.212
	brass-plated	361.33.810
	black	361.33.310

Packing: 100 pairs (50 right and 50 left)

Simplex All-overlay glass door hinge

screw-mounted to side of cabinet
Overlays top, bottom 5 mm, right and left 5 to 8 mm

- Opening angle 180°
- For large overlay glass doors
- Packaged in pairs for left or right-hand installation
- Glass thickness from 4 mm (5/32") to 6.3 mm 1/4")

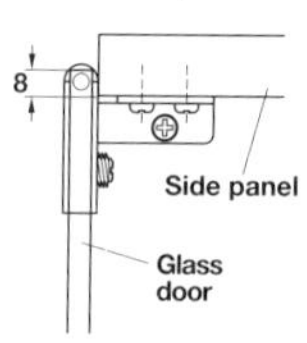

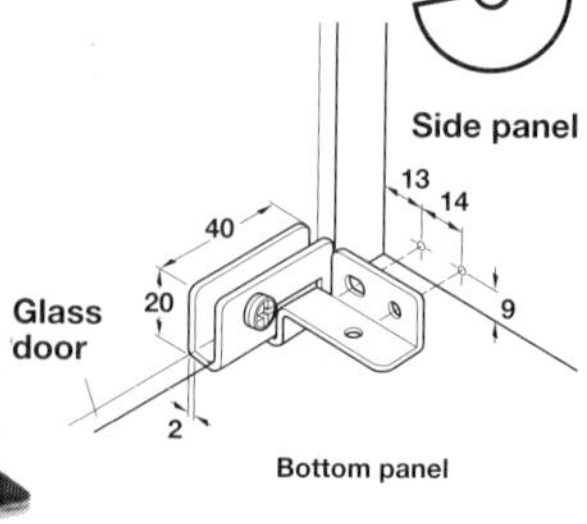

Finish: steel

Cat. No.	chrome-plated	361.42.266
	brass-plated	361.42.864
	black	361.42.364

Packing: 100 pairs (50 right and 50 left)

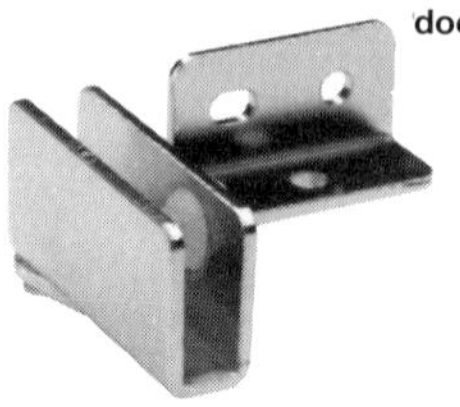

Dimensions in mm

Glass Door Hinge

HÄFELE

- Ideal for RTA industry.
- Easy to install. Glass doors clip easily onto cabinet after hinges are mounted on glass.
- Pivot pins rotate freely in a 5 mm dia. hole. No bushings required.
- Door clearance spacing incorporated into hinge.

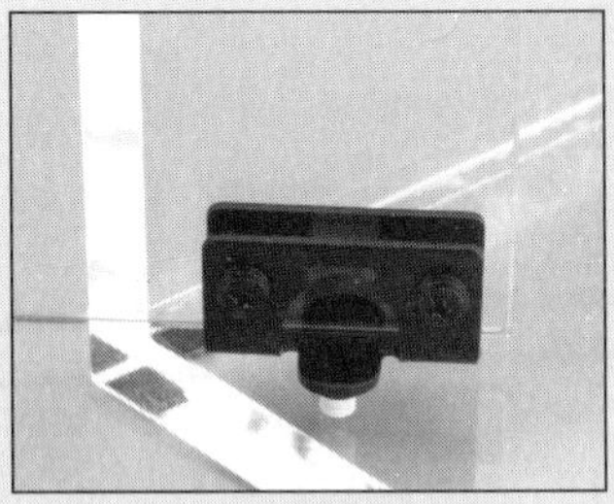

Simplex Hinge, SM
A Simplex Speed Mount hinge for glass doors thickness **6.5 mm (1/4")**

Spring-loaded

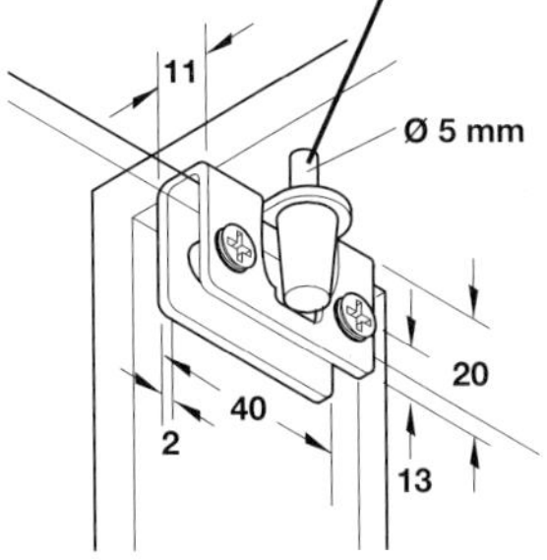

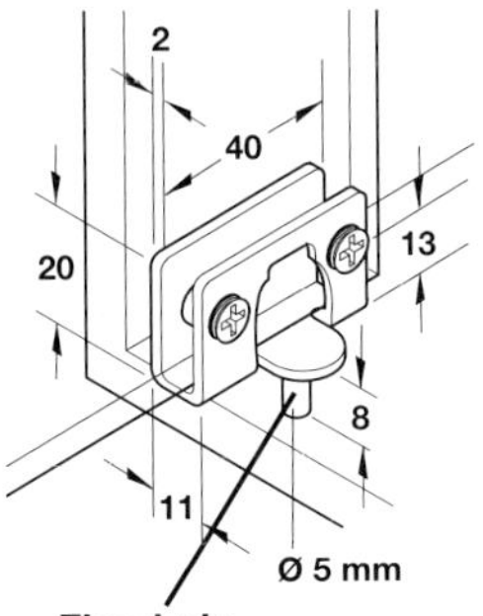

Fixed pin

Finish: steel, black

Cat. No.	361.44.300

Packing: 40 pairs/no inserts included

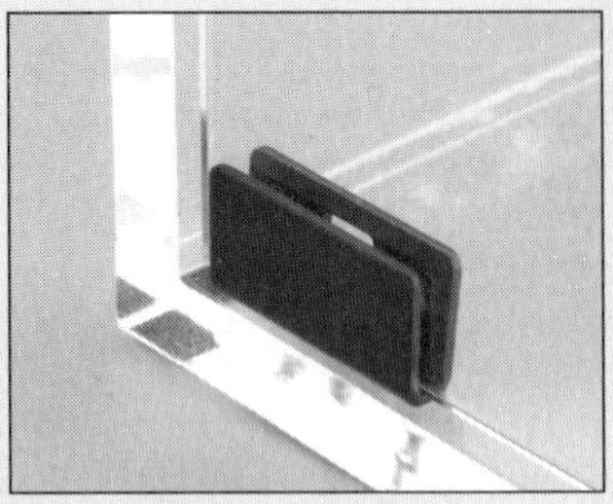

Magnetic catches see pages **2.82 - 2.88**

Dimensions shown on mounting diagrams are only approximate. Please conduct a trial mounting to determine your exact dimensions

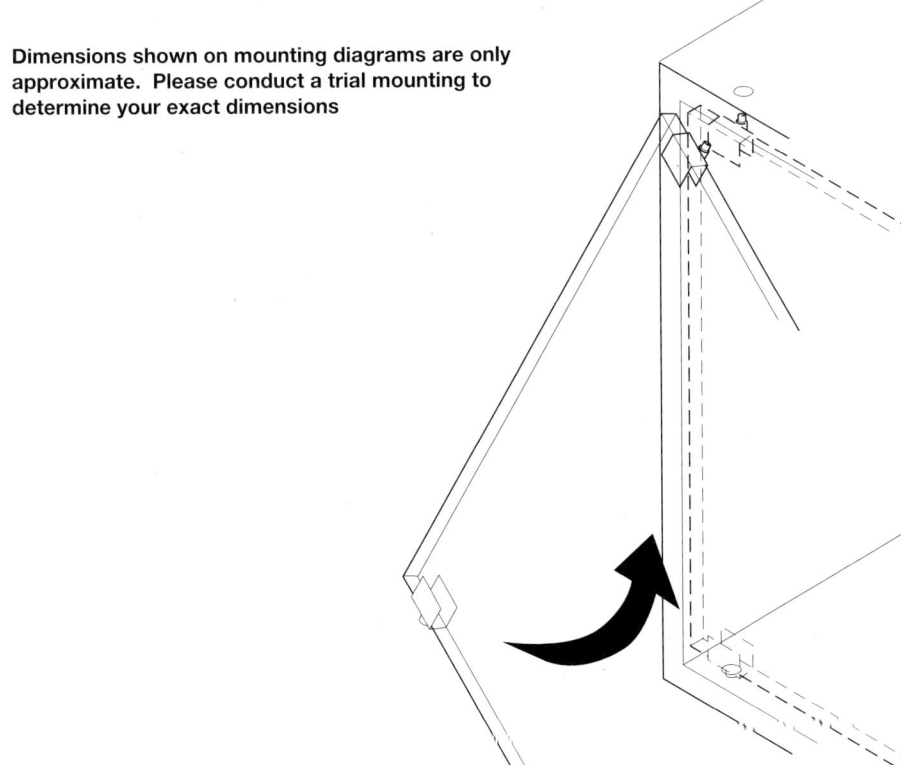

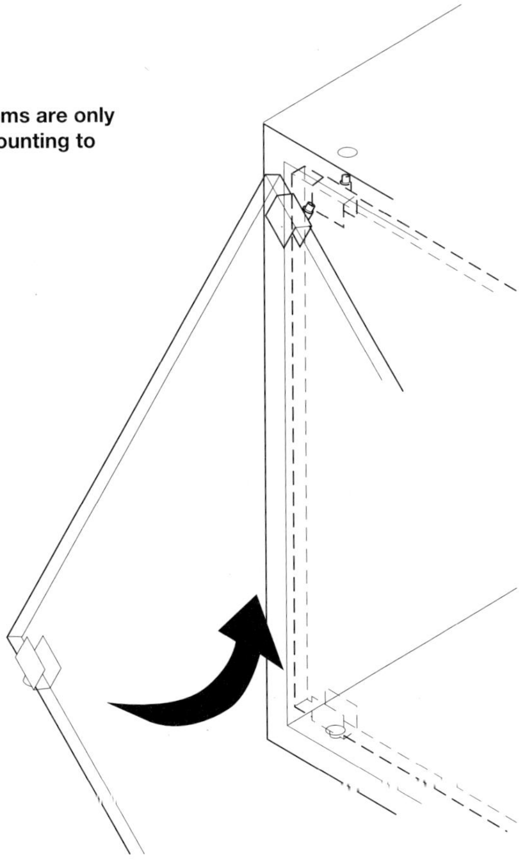

HÄFELE

Non-Bore Glass Door Hinges For Audio Cabinets, Light-Weight Glass Doors

Dimensions shown on mounting diagrams are only approximate. Please conduct tril mounting to determine your exact dimensios.

Magnetic catches see pages **2.82 - 2.88**

Simplex-Inset glass door hinge

with press-fit bushing

- Opening angle 110°
- Self-adhesive pressure plates and screws included
- Packaged in pairs for left or right-hand installation
- Glass thickness to 5 mm (3/16")

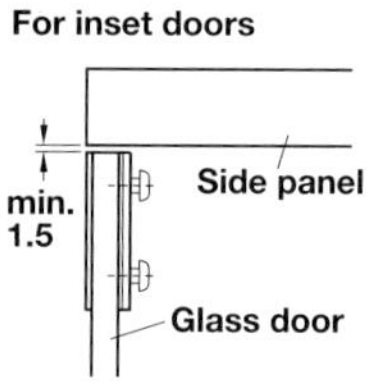

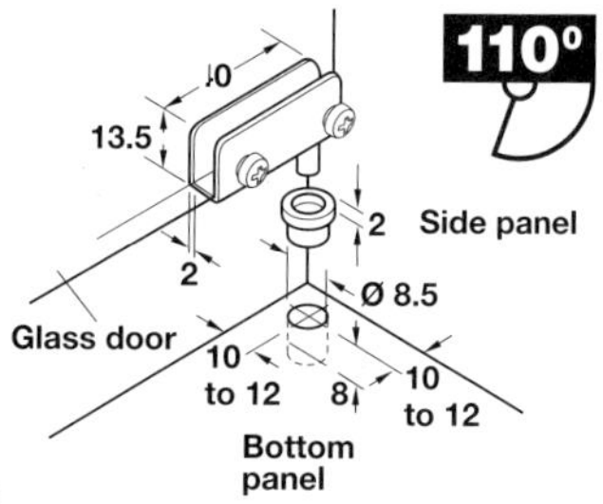

Finish: steel, bushings: plastic, black

Cat. No.	chrome-plated	361.42.202
	brass-plated	361.42.800
	black	361.42.300

Packing: 50 pairs (1 pair = 1 left, 1 right)

Simplex-Inset glass door hinge

with press-fit bushing

- Opening angle 110°
- Self-adhesive pressure plates and screws included
- Packaged in pairs for left or right-hand installation
- Glass thickness to 6.5 mm

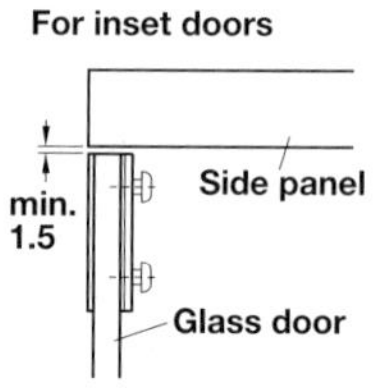

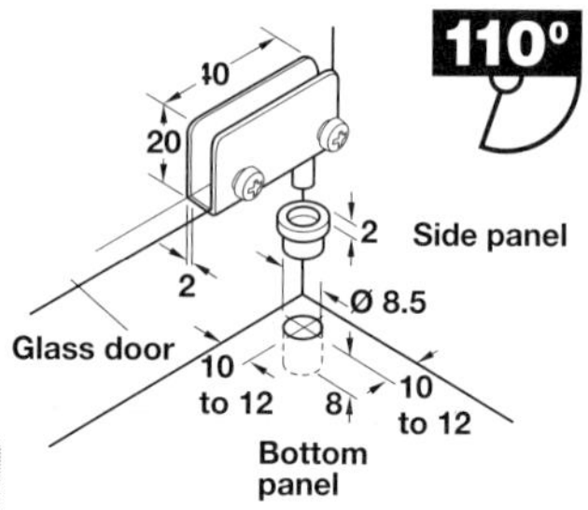

Finish: steel, bushings: plastic, black

Cat. No.	chrome-plated	361.42.211
	brass-plated	361.42.819
	black	361.42.319

Packing: 50 pairs (1 pair = 1 left, 1 right)

Decorative glass door hinge

with press-fit bushing

- Opening angle 110°
- Steel set screw with plastic pad
- Packaged in pairs for left or right-hand installation
- Glass thickness to 6 mm

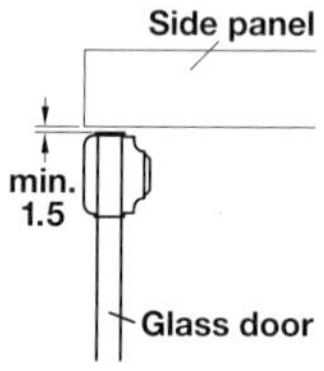

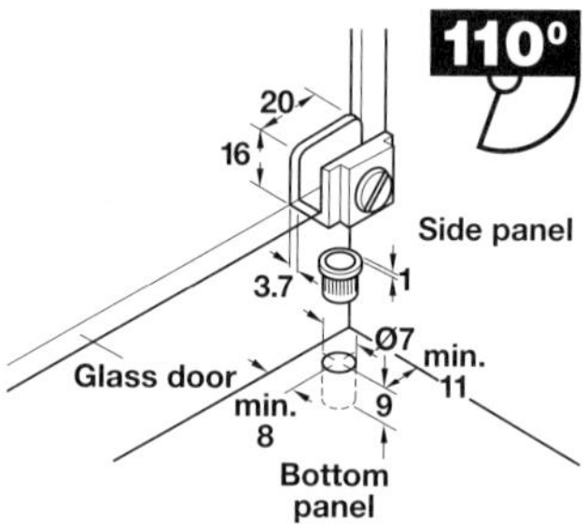

Finish: zinc die-cast, matt black;
fastening screw, steel; bushing, plastic

Cat. No.	361.88.315

Packing: 50 pairs

Glass door hinge with closed end

and press-fit bushing

- Opening angle 110°
- Steel set screw with plastic pad
- Glass thickness to 6 mm

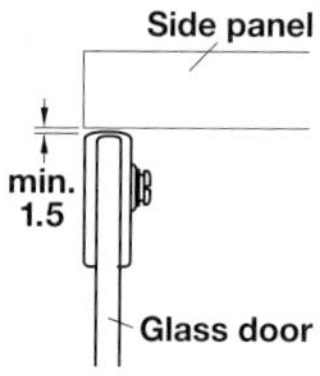

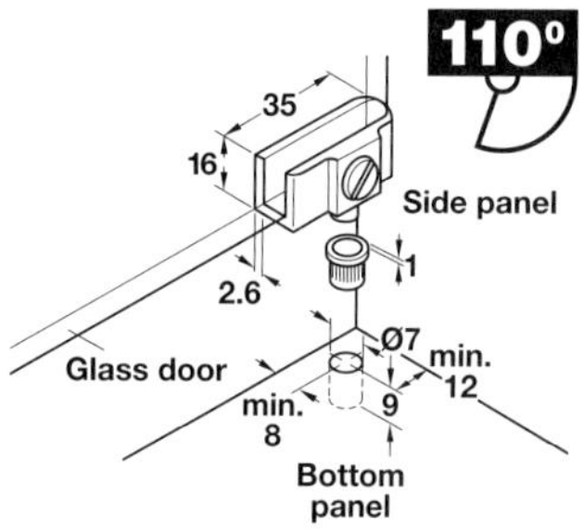

Finish: zinc die-cast, matt black;
fastening screw, steel; bushing, plastic

Cat. No.	361.88.324

Packing: 50 pairs

Dimensions in mm

HÄFELE

Non-Bore Glass Door Hinges For Audio Cabinets, Light-Weight Glass Doors

Inset glass door hinge with exposed knuckle

Available with or without catch

- Opening angle 180°
- Steel set screw with plastic pad
- Glass thickness to 6 mm

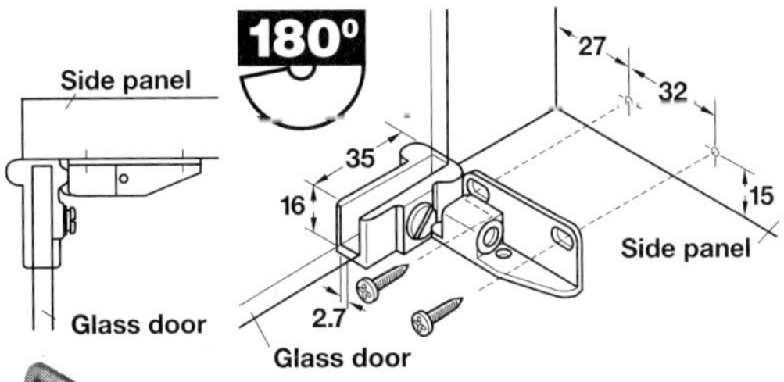

Finish: zinc die-cast, matt black; set screw: steel with plastic pad

Cat. No.	with catch	361.90.351
	without catch	361.90.306

Packing: 50 pairs

Inset glass door hinge with exposed knuckle

and upright mounting flange,
Available with or without catch

- Opening angle 180°
- Steel set screw with plastic pad
- Glass thickness up to 6 mm

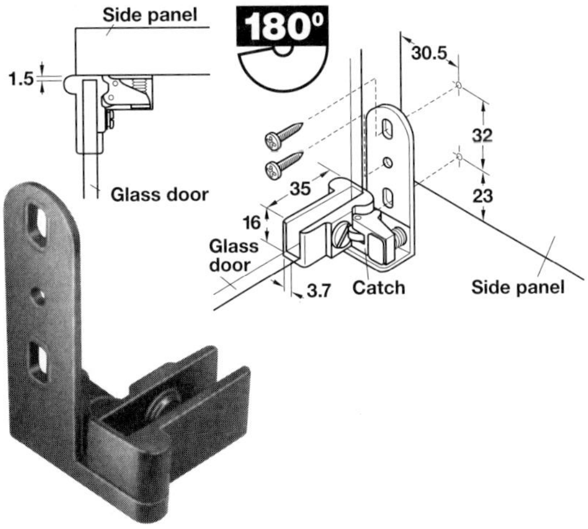

Finish: zinc die-cast, matt black; set screw: steel with plastic pad

Cat. No.	with catch	361.89.303
	without catch	361.89.358

Packing: 50 pairs

Glass door hinge with mounting flange

screw-mounted to side of cabinet

- Opening angle 180°
- Steel set screw with plastic pad
- Glass thickness to 6 mm

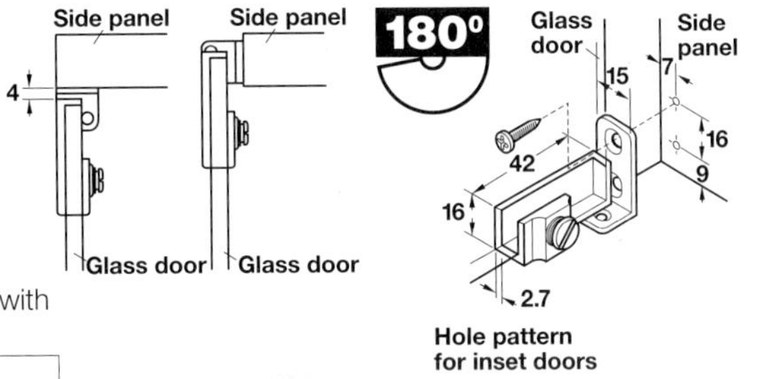

Finish: zinc die-cast, matt black; set screw: steel; with plastic pad

Cat. No.	361.91.303

Packing: 50 pairs

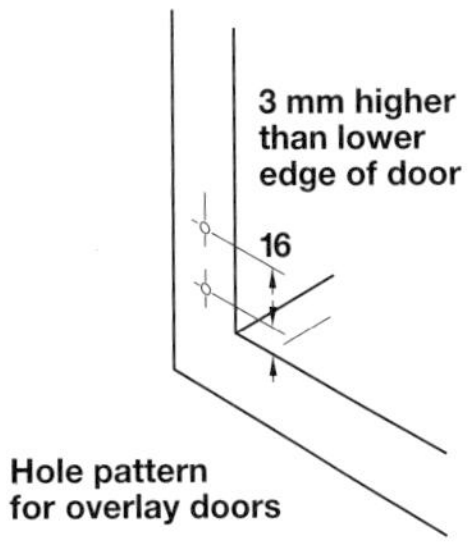

Glass door pull

- For inset glass doors
- Glass thickness 5 mm

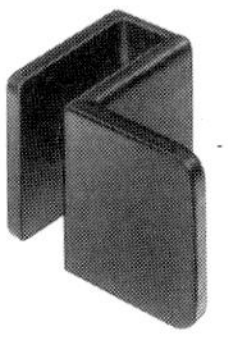

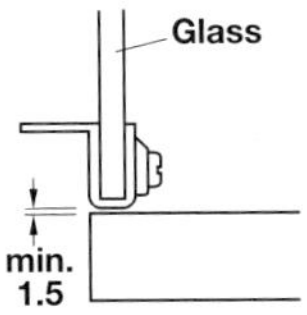

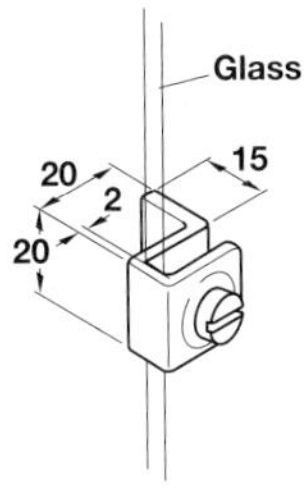

Finish: zinc die-cast, black matt; set screw: steel

Cat. No.	154.22.303

Packing: 25 pcs.

Dimensions in mm

Hinges,
Flap and Lid Stays
Associated Fittings

3

Dimensions shown on mounting diagrams are only approximate. Please conduct trial mounting to determine your exact dimensions.

Magnetic catches see pages **2.82 - 2.88**

HÄFELE

Wooden Door and Lid Hinges for Audio Cabinets

Simplex-wood-mini, door hinges
with press-fit bushing
- Opening angle 110°
- Plastic bushings and screws included
- Wood thickness 14 mm to 19 mm

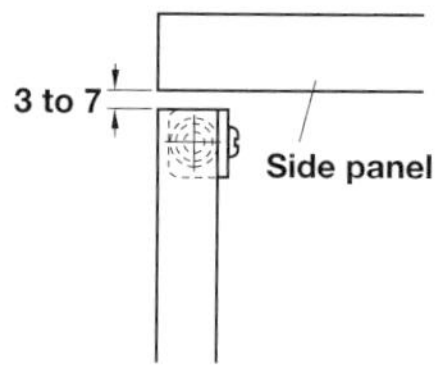

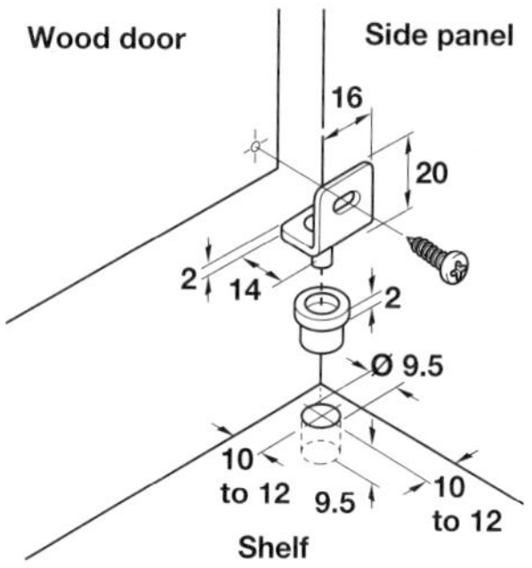

Finish: steel; bushing: plastic, black

Cat. No.	361.34.398

Packing: 100 pairs (50 right and 50 left)

3 Hinges, Flap and Lid Stays Associated Fittings

Dimensions shown on mounting diagrams are only approximate. Please conduct tril mounting to determine your exact dimensions.

Magnetic catches see pages **2.82 - 2.88**

Simplex-wood, door hinges
with press-fit bushing
- Opening angle 110°
- Plastic bushings and screws included
- Wood thickness 14 mm to 19 mm
- Packaged in pairs for left or right-hand installation

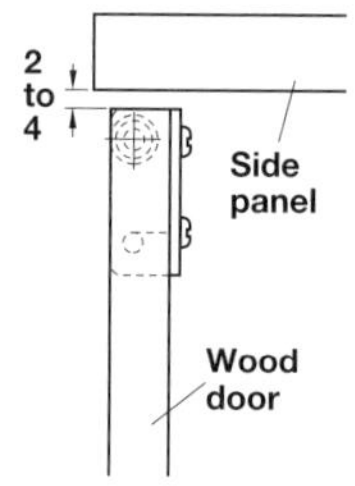

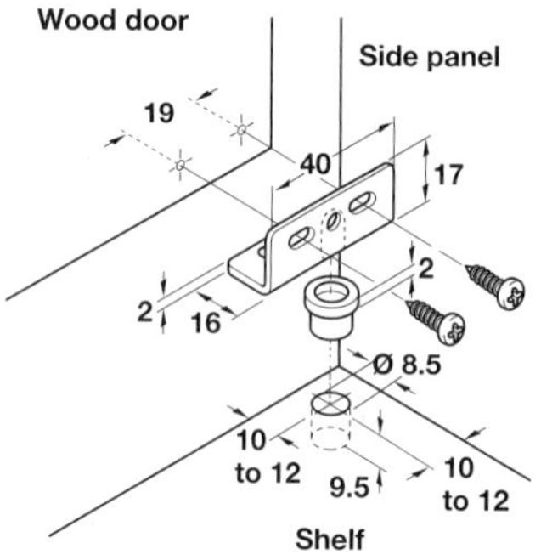

Finish: steel; bushing: plastic, black

Cat. No.	chrome-plated	361.42.293
	brass-plated	361.42.891
	black	361.42.391

Packing: 100 pairs (50 right and 50 left)

Furniture Hinges

HÄFELE

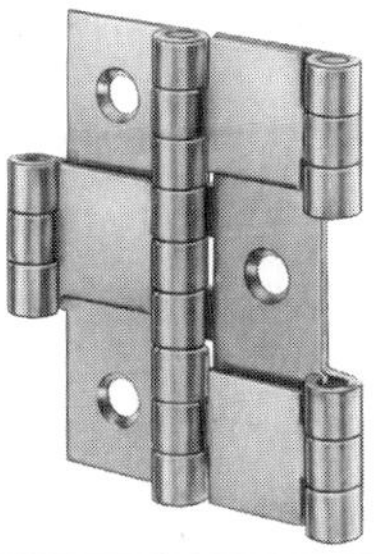

Screen hinges
3-part, pivotable in both directions
Finish: brass, polished

Φ2,5

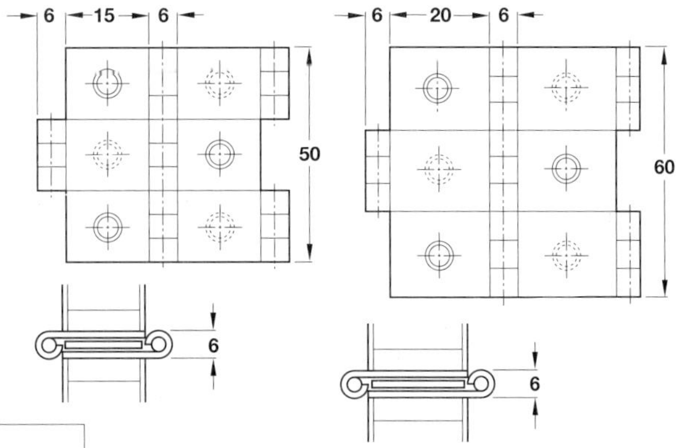

Wood thickness	Cat.No. 15 mm	20 mm
	341.20.806	341.20.815

Packing: 12 pcs.

Neuform cranked hinges
for butting, overlay doors
Finish: solid brass

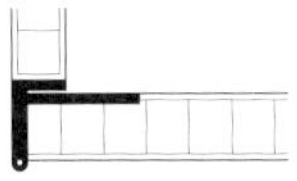

HOSPA Φ3,5

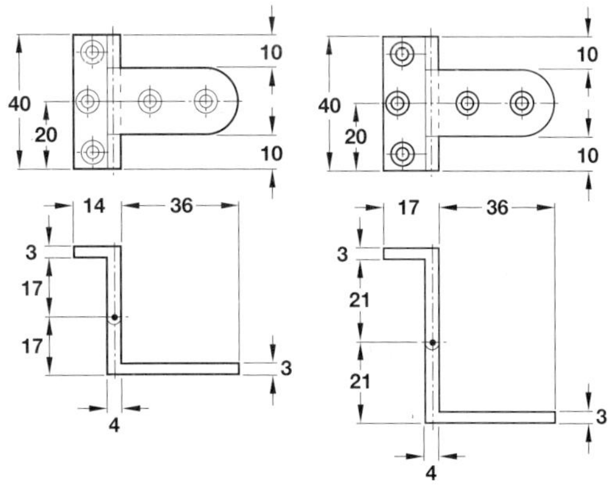

Barrel length: 40 mm

	Cat. No.	
Door thickness Side panel thickness	**15 – 16 mm** from 14 mm	**19 – 20 mm** from 17 mm
polished	307.05.803	307.04.806
nickel-plated, polished	307.05.705	307.04.708
burnished	307.05.107	307.04.100

Packing: 20 pcs.

Neuform twin hinges
Finish: solid brass

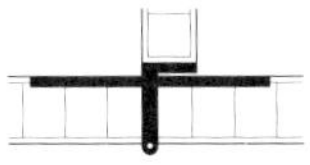

HOSPA Φ3,5

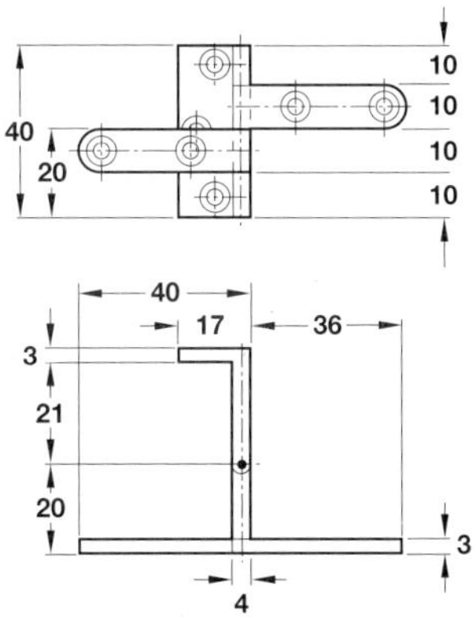

Barrel length: 40 mm

	Cat. No.
Door thickness Side panel thickness	**19 – 20 mm** from 17 mm
polished	307.34.804
nickel-plated, polished	307.34.706
burnished	307.34.108

Packing: 20 pcs.

Cranked hinges
For butting, front-hung doors
Finish: solid brass

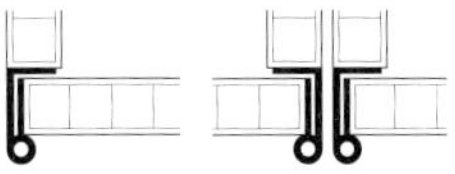

HOSPA Φ3,0

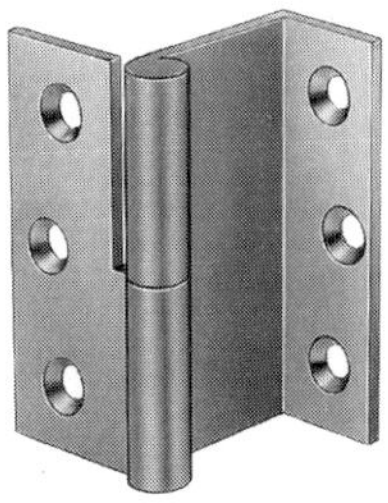

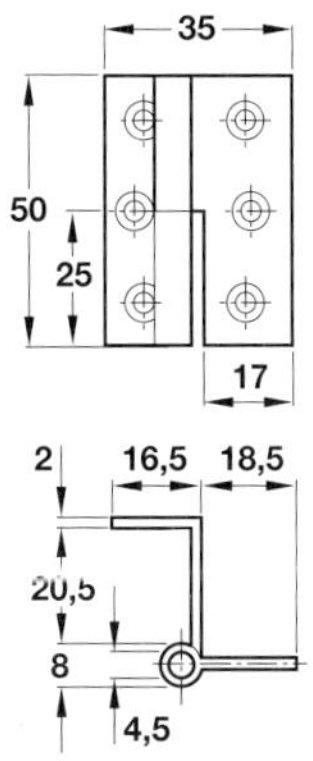

Barrel length: 50 mm
Side panel thickness: optional

Door thickness	Cat. No. **20 -21 mm** left	right
polished	307.01.832	307.01.823
nickel-plated, matt	307.01.636	307.01.627

Packing: 20 pcs.

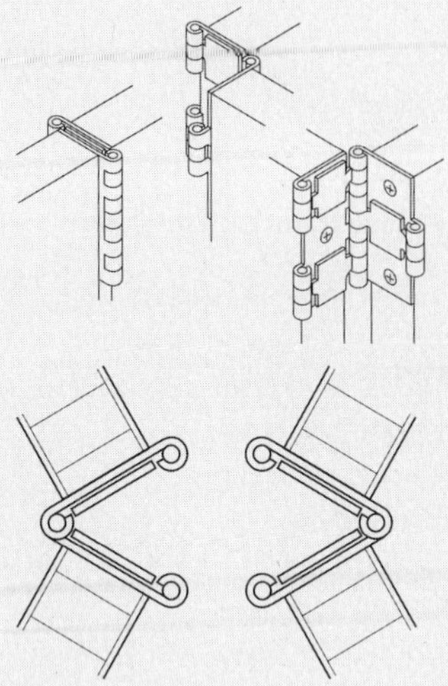

Hinges,
Flap and Lid Stays
Associated Fittings

3

Mounting screws:
Hospa particle board screws
countersunk head with
PZ 2 cross slot
Finish: Steel, galvanized

HOSPA Φ3,0

Length	Cat. No.
13 mm	015.31.522
15 mm	015.31.531
17 mm	015.31.540

Packing: 1000 pcs.

Hospa particle board screws
countersunk head with
PZ 2 cross slot
Finish: Steel, galvanized

HOSPA Φ3,5

Length	Cat. No.
13 mm	015.31.620
15 mm	015.31.639
17 mm	015.31.648

Packing: 1000 pcs.

Dimensional data not binding.
We reserve the right to alter
specifications without notice.

Dimensions in mm

HÄFELE

Solid Brass Cast Hinges

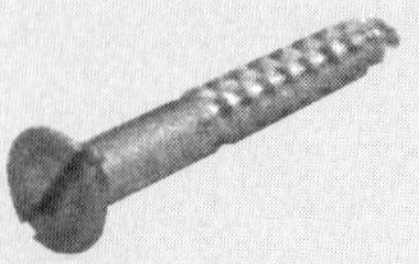

Raised Head Countersunk wood screw

Finish: brass, unfinished

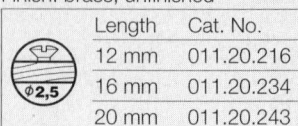

	Length	Cat. No.
Φ2,5	12 mm	011.20.216
	16 mm	011.20.234
	20 mm	011.20.243

Packing: 200 pcs.

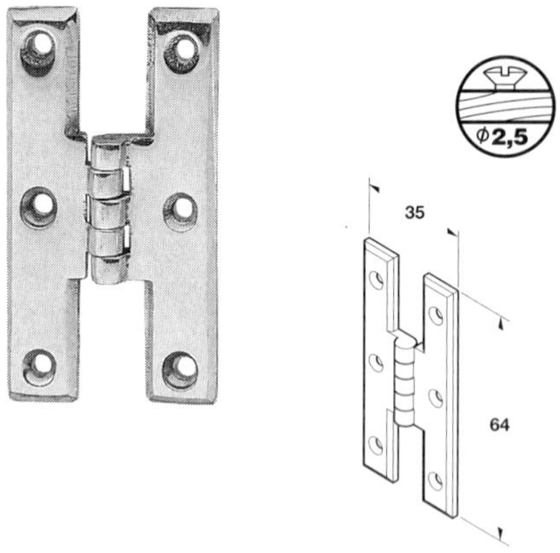

Finish: polished & lacquered

Cat. No.	354.49.819

Packing: 25 pairs

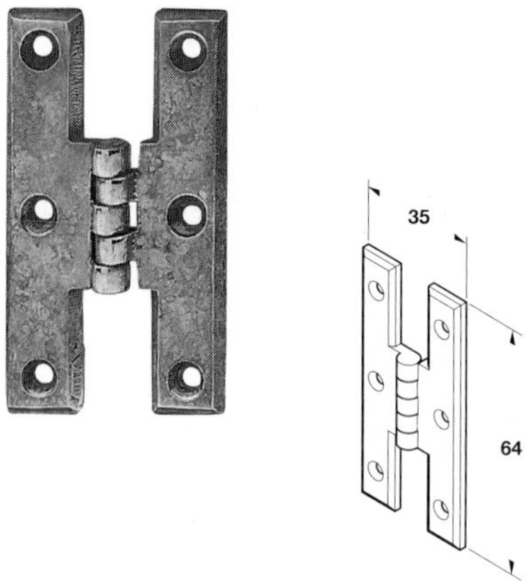

Finish: antique brass

Cat. No.	354.49.113

Packing: 25 pairs

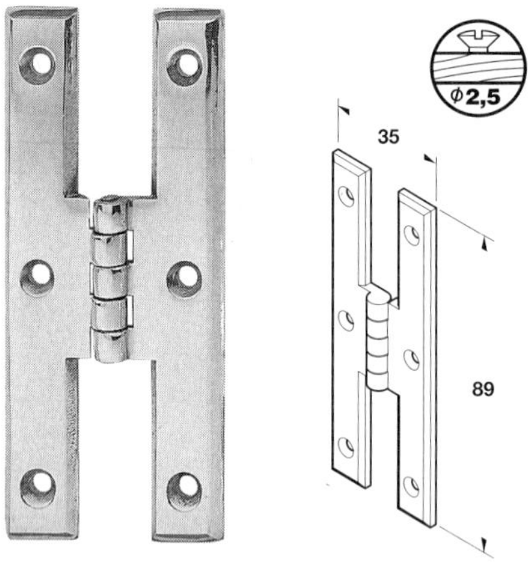

Finish: polished and lacquered

Cat. No.	354.49.828

Packing: 25 pairs

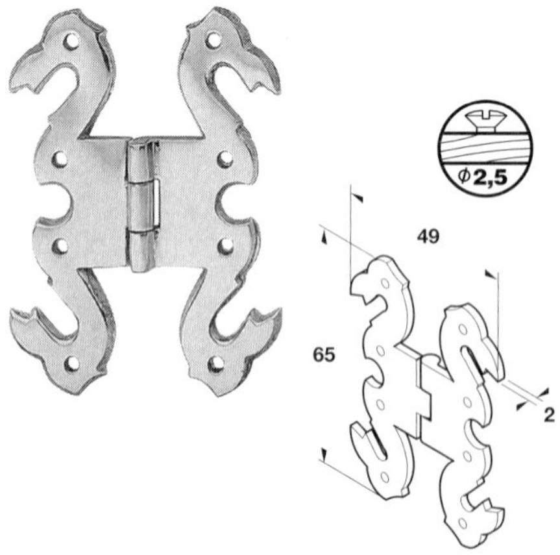

Finish: polished & lacquered

Cat. No.	120.11.817

Packing: 25 pairs

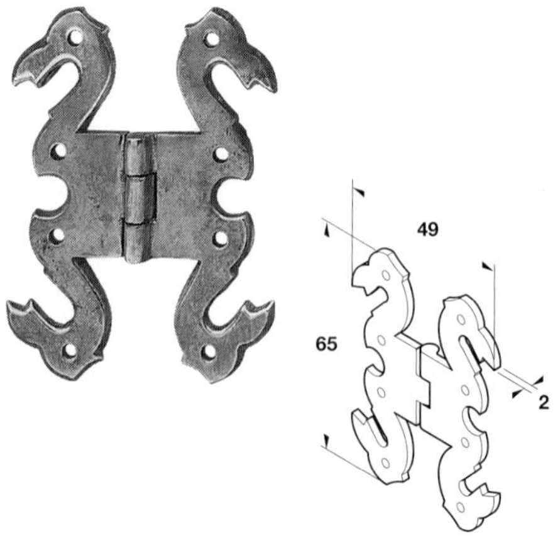

Finish: antique brass

Cat. No.	120.10.114

Packing: 25 pairs

Butt Hinges

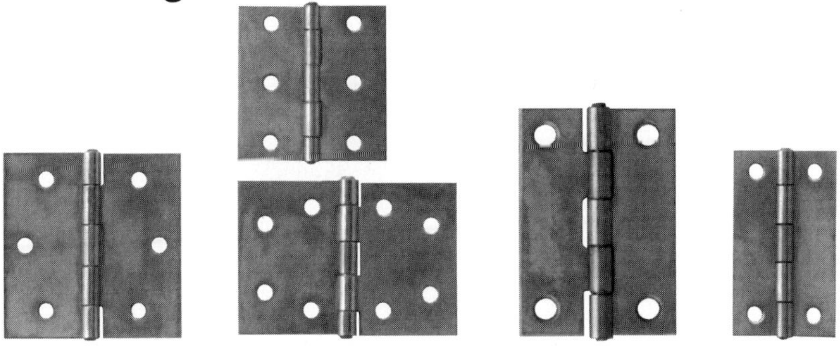
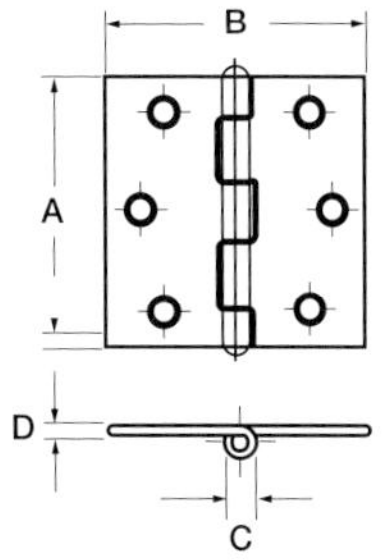

Hinges with fixed pin, 5 Knuckles
Finish: steel, yellow chromated

Cat. No.	Dimension A B (approx.)	Knuckle Dia. (approx.)	Material thickness (approx.)	Holes per wing
354.12.905	50 x 35	5.5	1.2	2
354.12.906	50 x 50	5.5	1.0	3
354.12.907	50 x 75	6.8	1.2	4
354.12.908	60 x 35	5.9	1.4	2
354.12.909	60 x 60	6.2	1.4	3

Packing: 100 pcs.

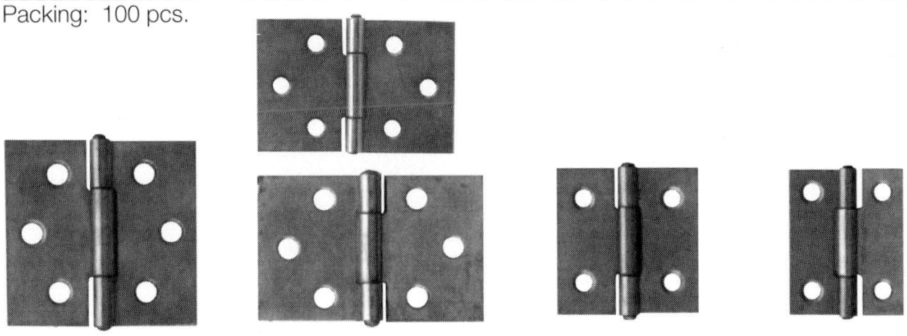
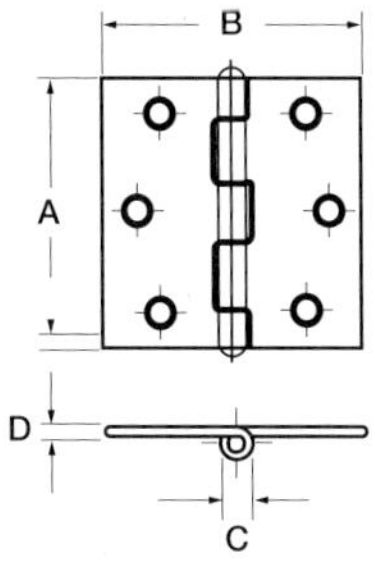

Hinges with fixed pin, 3 Knuckles
Finish: steel, yellow chromated

Cat. No.	Dimension A B (approx.)	Knuckle Dia. (approx.)	Material thickness (approx.)	Holes per wing
354.12.900	30 x 23	4.3	1.0	2
354.12.901	30 x 30	4.5	1.0	2
354.12.902	30 x 47	4.9	1.0	3
354.12.903	40 x 40	4.9	1.0	3
354.12.904	40 x 60	6.0	1.2	3

Packing: 100 pcs.

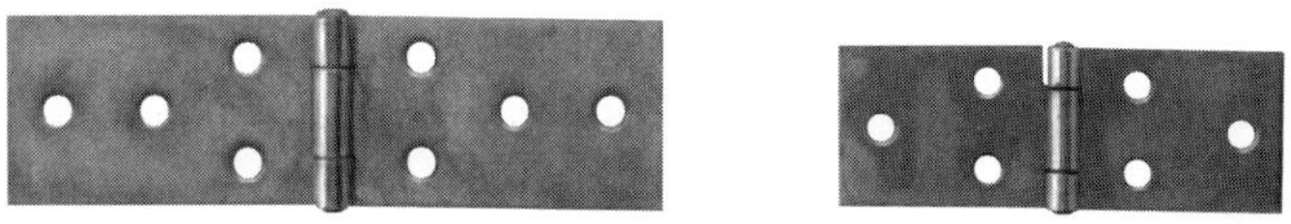
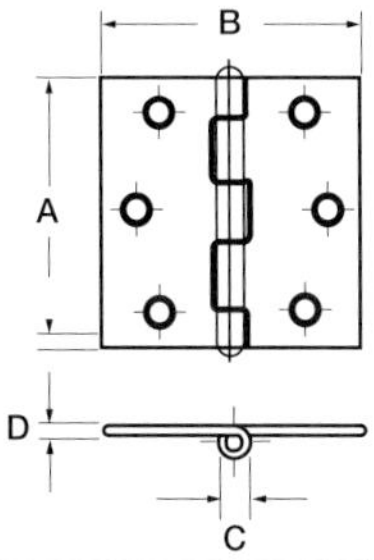

Hinges with fixed pin, 3 Knuckles
Finish: steel, yellow chromated

Cat. No.	Dimension A B (approx.)	Knuckle Dia. (approx.)	Material thickness (approx.)	Holes per wing
354.12.910	28 x 80	6.5	1.3	3
354.12.911	33 x 120	7.3	1.4	4

Packing: 100 pcs.

Decorative Butt Hinge

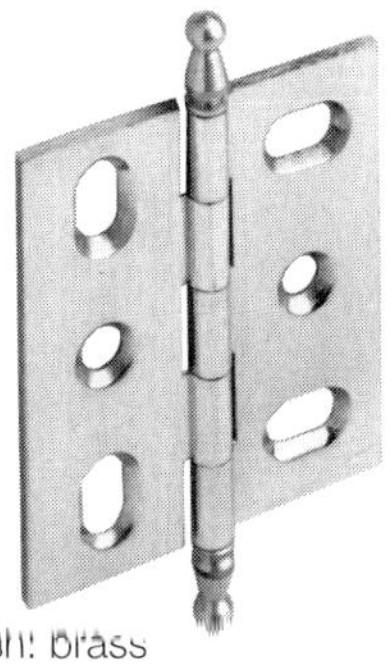
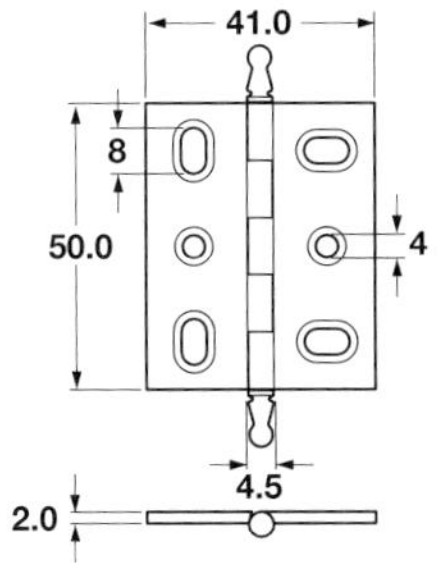

Finish: brass

Cat. No.	antique brass	354.22.130
	polished and lacquered	354.22.830

Packing: 20 pcs. (does not include screws)

Screws for 40 x 60 and larger
Finish: zinc-plated

3.0 x 13	015.31.326
3.0 x 15	015.31.335
3.0 x 17	015.31.344

Packing: 1000 pcs.

Finish: chromated

3.0 x 13	015.33.320
3.0 x 17	015.33.348

Packing: 1000 pcs.

- 2-way adjustable

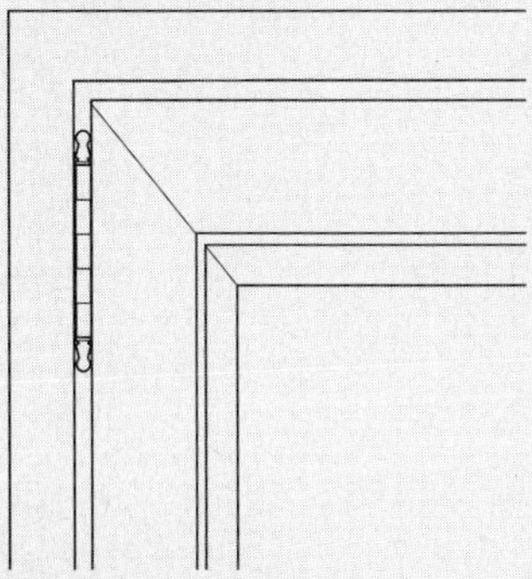

Shaker style furniture with raised panel doors.
- Highly decorative
- Solid brass
- 2-way adjustable

HÄFELE

Nylon Hinges

Tough, low-cost hinge solutions

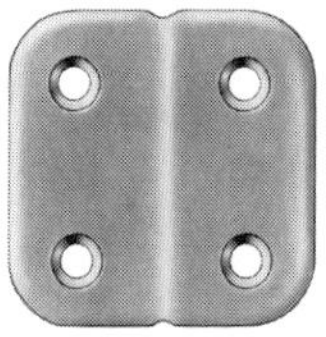

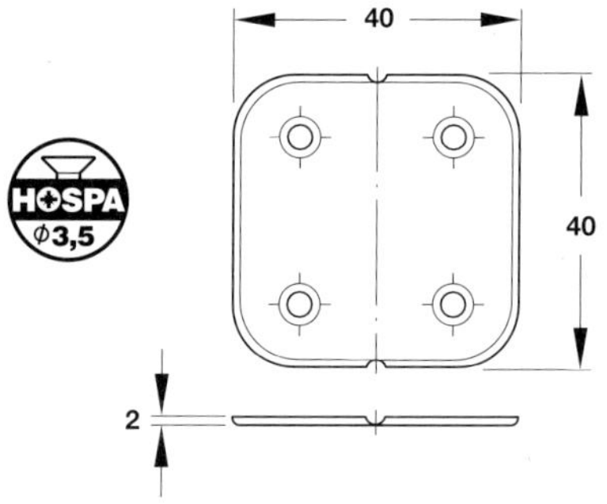

Finish: nylon

Cat. No.	40 mm x 40 mm	white	351.93.723
	40 mm x 40 mm	brown	351.93.125

Packing: 100 pcs.

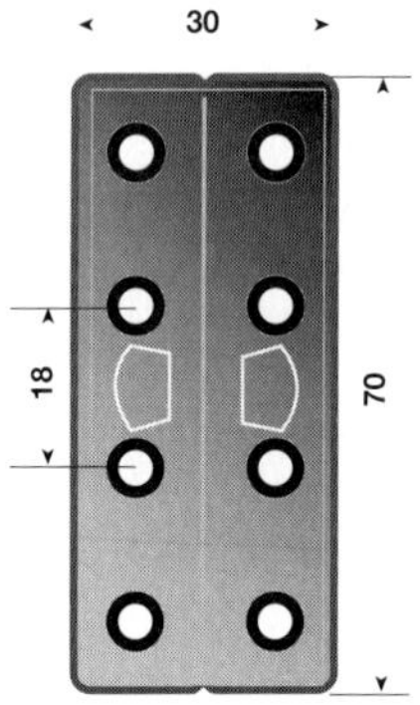

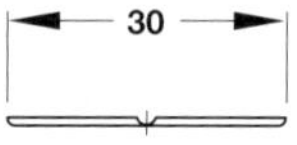

Finish: nylon

Cat. No.	30 mm x 70 mm	white	351.93.741
	30 mm x 70 mm	brown	351.93.143

Packing: 100 pcs.

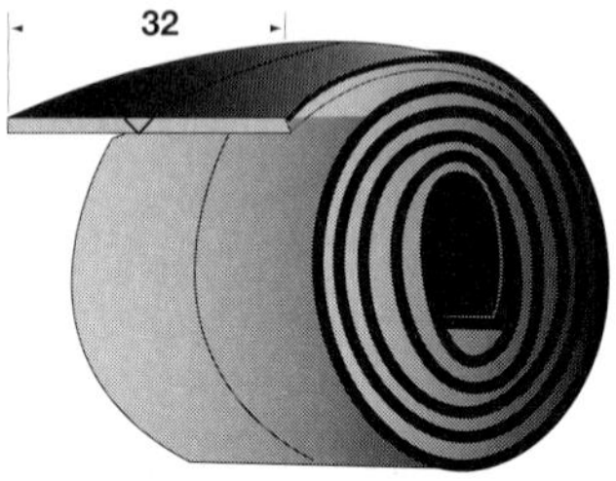

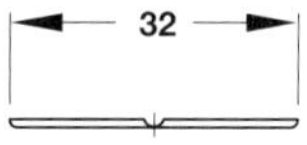

Finish: nylon, natural plastic color

Cat. No.	32 mm x 100 m	351.94.006

Packing: 5 meter roll

Pivot Hinges

HÄFELE

Pivot hinge
- screw-mounted
- max. door opening angle = 180°
- without stop

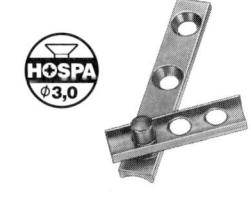

HOSPA Φ3,0

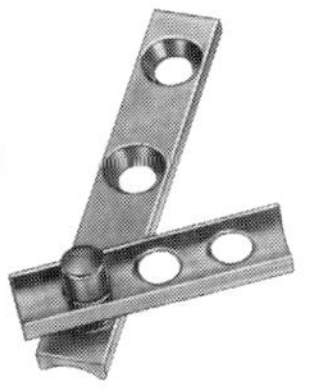

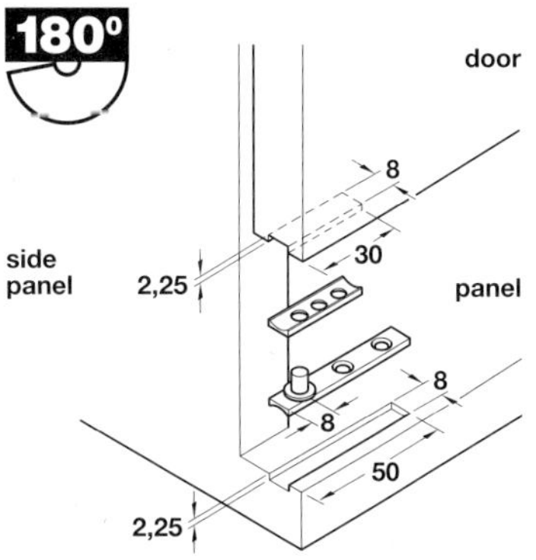

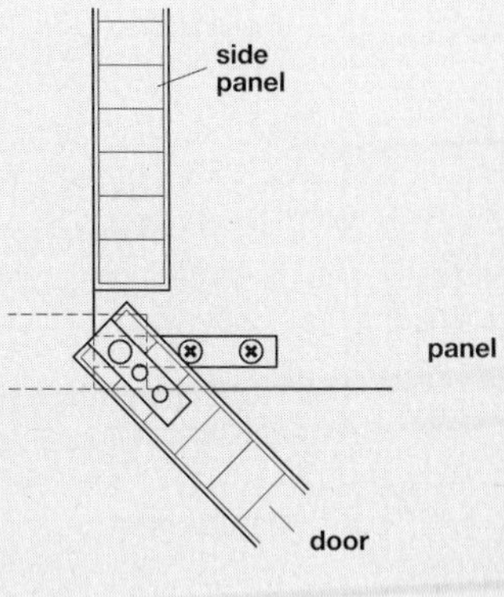

Finish: steel, brass-plated

Length	Cat. No.
50 mm	361.01.505

Packing: 20 pairs

Pivot hinge
- screw-mounted
- max. door opening angle = 180°
- without stop

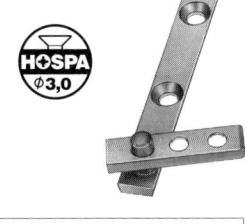

HOSPA Φ3,0

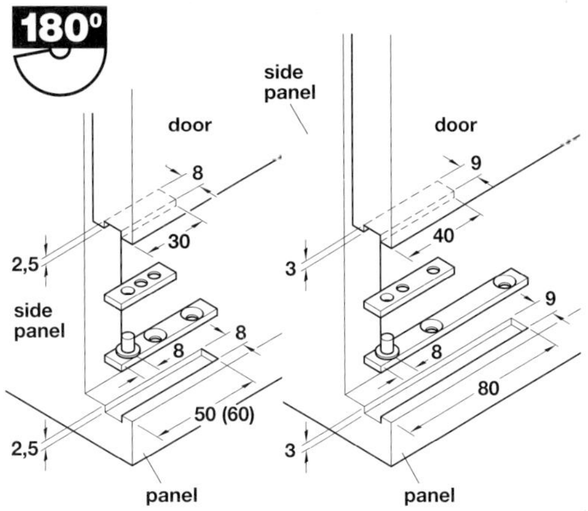

Finish: steel, brass-plated

Length	Cat. No.
50 mm	361.21.507
60 mm	361.21.516
80 mm	361.21.534

Packing: 20 pairs

Hinges,
Flap and Lid Stays
Associated Fittings

3

Corner pivot hinge
- screw-mounted
- max. door opening angle 250°
- **straight**
- without stop
- with outer knuckle

HOSPA Φ3,5

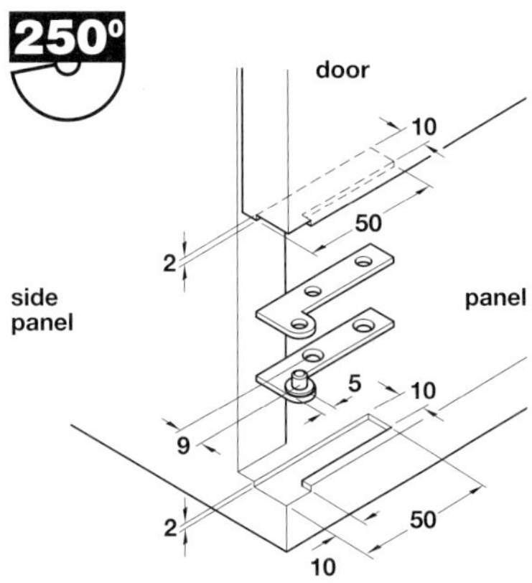

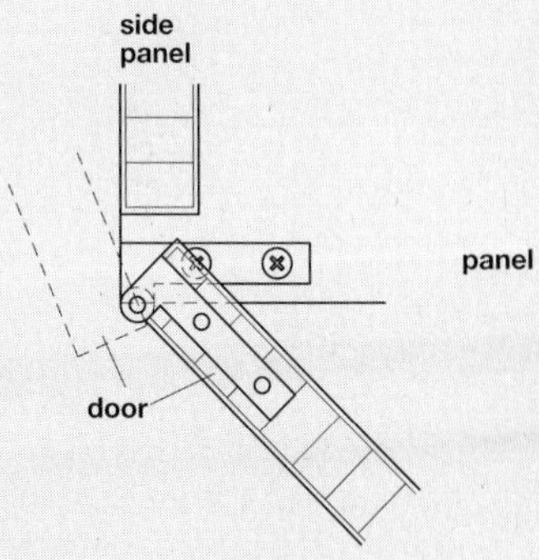

Finish: brass, polished

Length	Cat. No.
50 mm	362.10.803

Packing: 25 pairs

Corner pivot hinge
- screw-mounted
- max. door opening angle 180°
- **cranked**
- without stop
- with outer knuckle

HOSPA Φ3,5

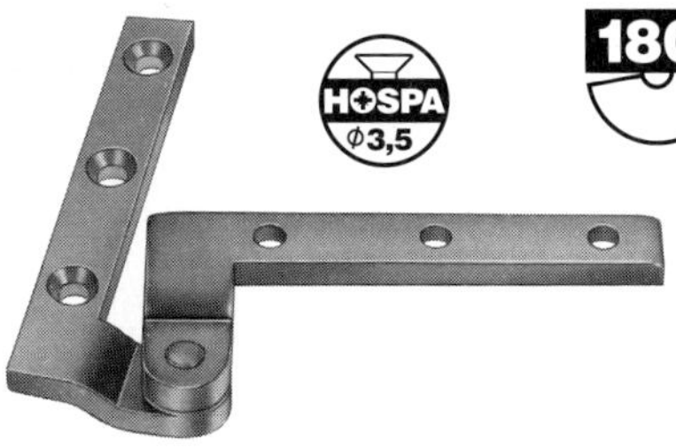

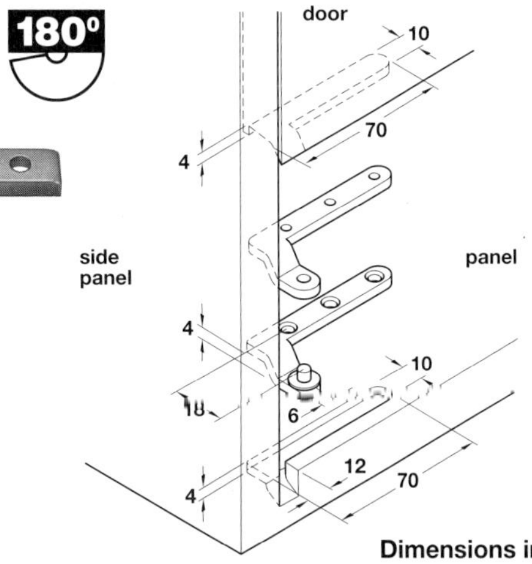

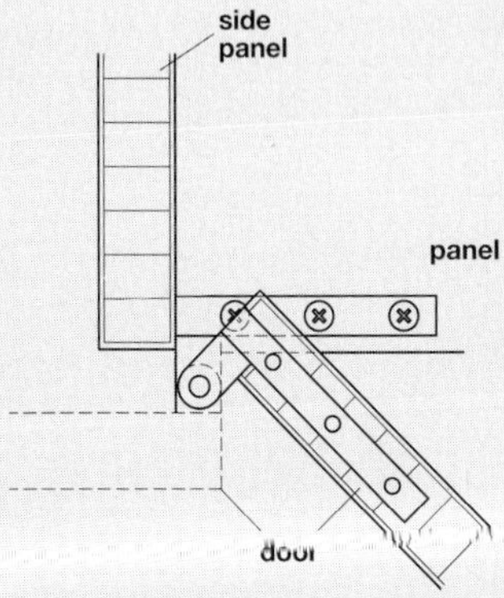

Finish: brass, matt

Length	Cat. No.
70 mm	362.01.500

Packing: 5 pairs

Dimensions in mm

Dimensional data not binding.
We reserve the right to alter specifications without notice.

HÄFELE

Pivot Hinges

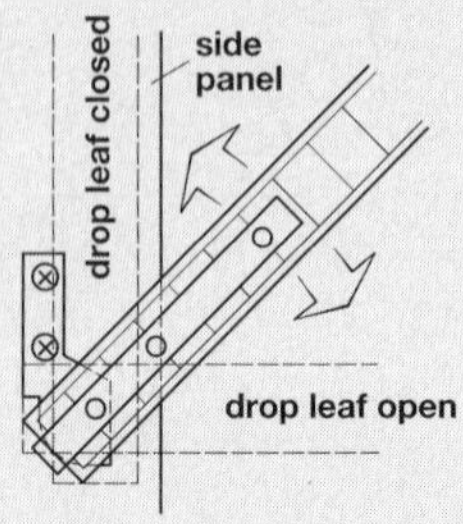

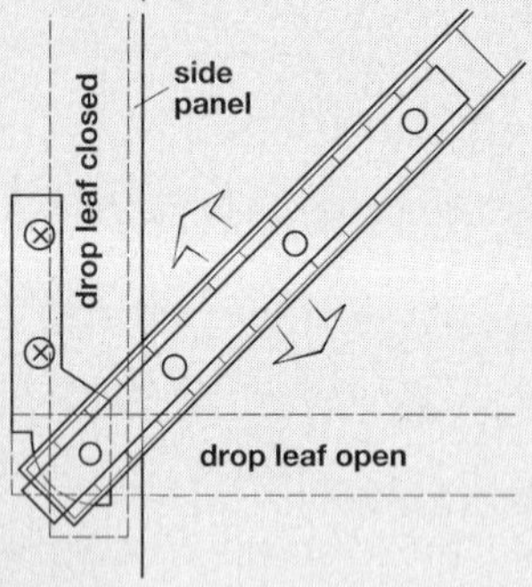

3 Hinges, Flap and Lid Stays Associated Fittings

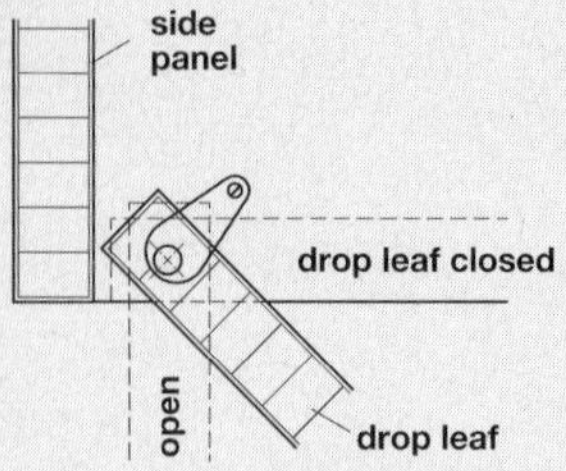

Note:

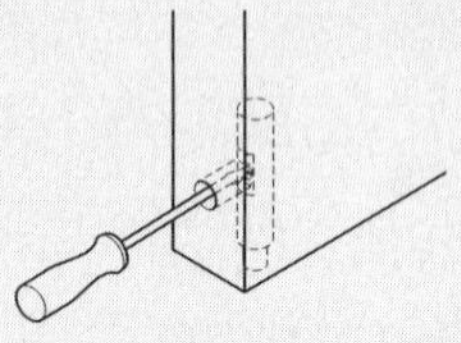

To detach door, insert a small screwdriver into hole located in door edge. Then, use screwdriver to lift spring-loaded pin inside lower bushing.
Important: be sure to match holes in door and bushing.

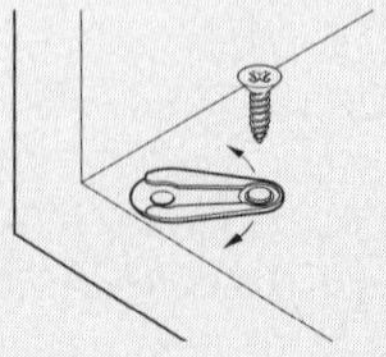

To increase or reduce gap, turn tab on its pivot bearing. Once adjusted as desired, secure tab in position using a small wood screw as shown.

Desk pivot hinge, mounts on drop leaves
- screw-mounted
- max. opening angle = 90°
- with stop

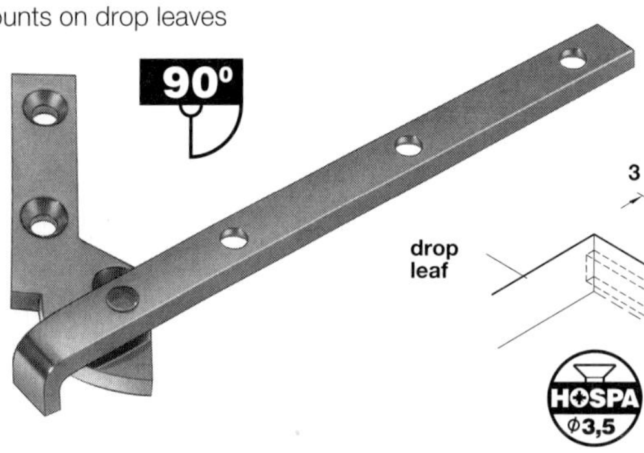

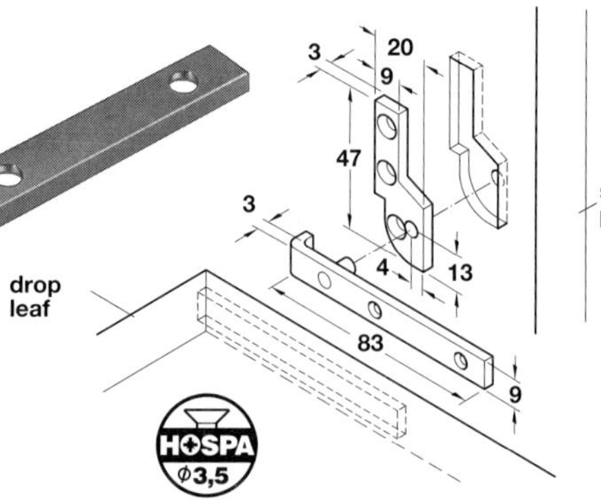

Finish: brass, polished

Length	Cat. No.
80 mm	361.50.802
150 mm	361.50.820

Packing: 5 pairs

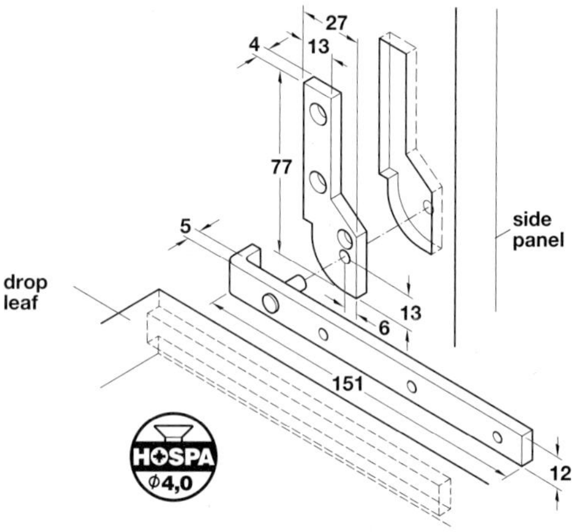

Pivot hinge
- press-fit type
- max. opening angle = 140° approx.
- door thickness 12 – 21 mm
- both pins spring-loaded: no tools required for installation
- detachable
- for inset doors

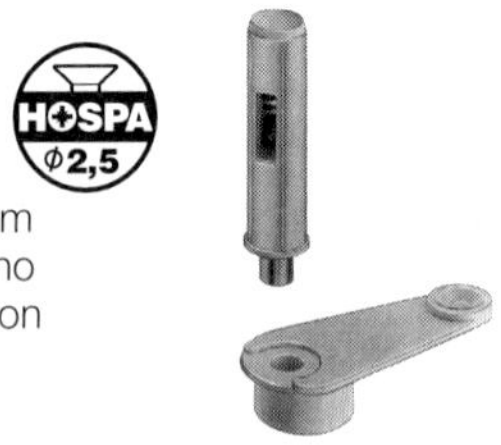

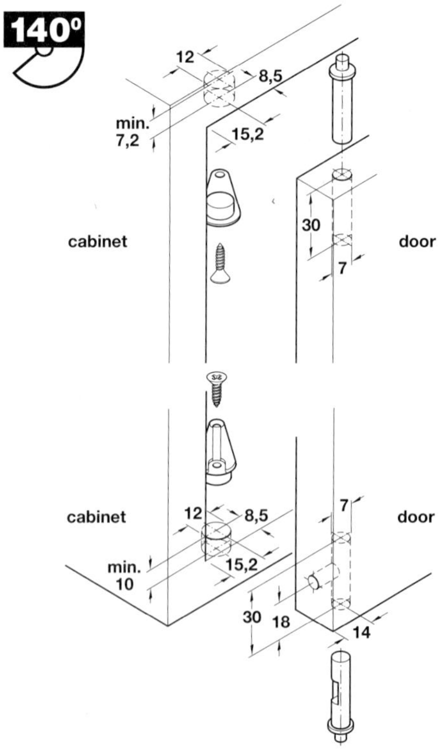

Finish: plastic, steel pivot

Color	Cat. No.
white	361.22.710
brown	361.22.110
black	361.22.310

Packing: 200 pairs (2 pins/2 bushings)

Dimensional data not binding. We reserve the right to alter specifications without notice.

Dimensions in mm

Furniture Hinges

Self-supporting hinges

for folding and sewing-machine tables, flush-mounted

Finish: brass

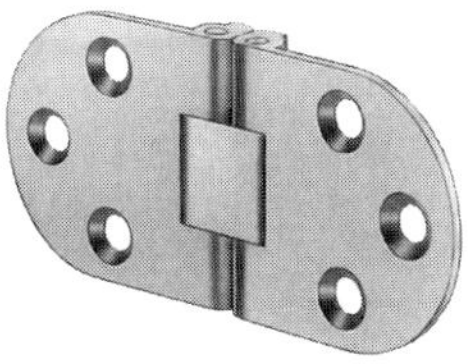

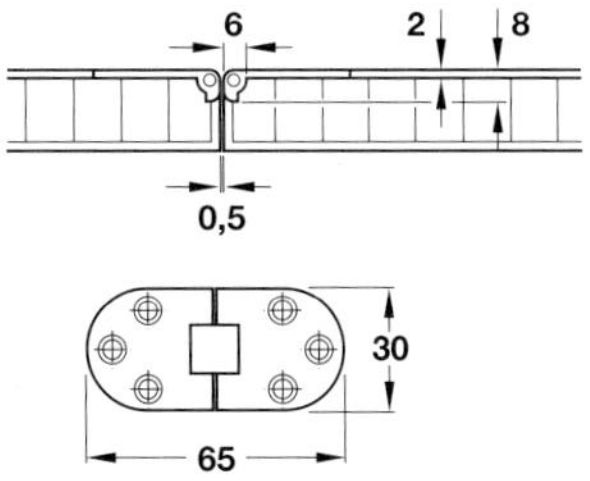

Finish	Cat. No.
nickel-plated, polished	341.32.708
matt	341.32.502
polished	341.32.806
burnished	341.32.100

Packing: 50 pcs.

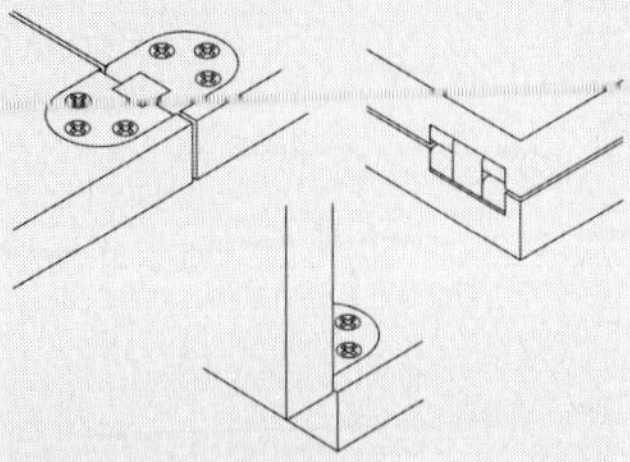

Mounting screws:

Hospa particle board screws **countersunk head** with PZ 2 cross slot

Finish: steel, galvanized

Length	Cat. No.
13 mm	015.31.620
15 mm	015.31.639
17 mm	015.31.648

Packing: 1000 pcs.

Folding table hinges

flush-mounted
for panel thicknesses **19 to 22 mm**
internal hinge
Distance between panels approx. 5 mm

Finish: steel, brass-colored

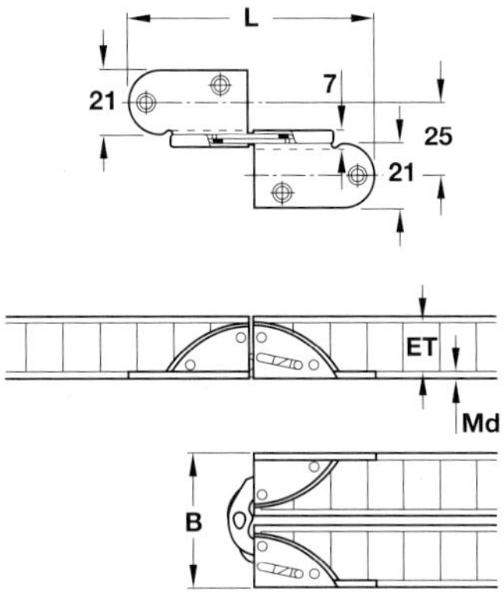

Material thickness	Mortise depth **ET**	Hinge dimensions **L x B**	Material thickness **Md**	Cat. No.
19	16	85 x 47	1,5	341.30.508
22	19	85 x 51	1,5	341.30.526

Packing: 100 pcs.

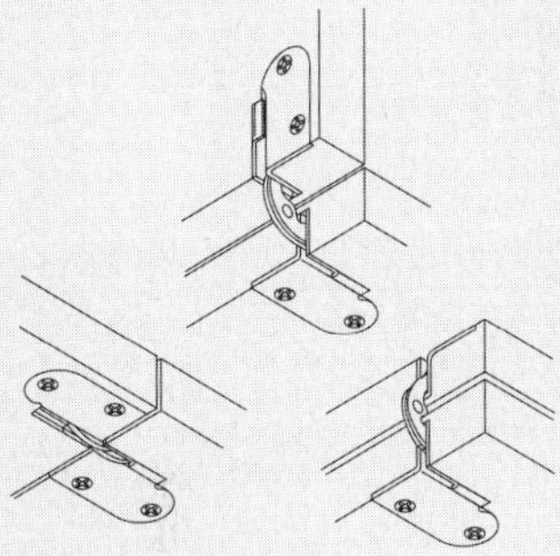

Mounting screws:

Hospa particle board screws **countersunk head** with PZ 2 cross slot

Finish: steel, galvanized

Length	Cat. No.
13 mm	015.31.522
15 mm	015.31.531
17 mm	015.31.540

Packing: 1000 pcs.

Card table hinges

Two-way table-leaf hinges
flush-mounted
Wood thicknesses **from 18 mm**

Finish: steel

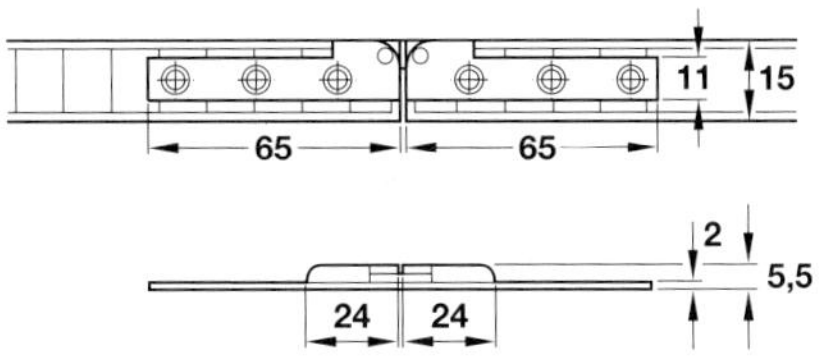

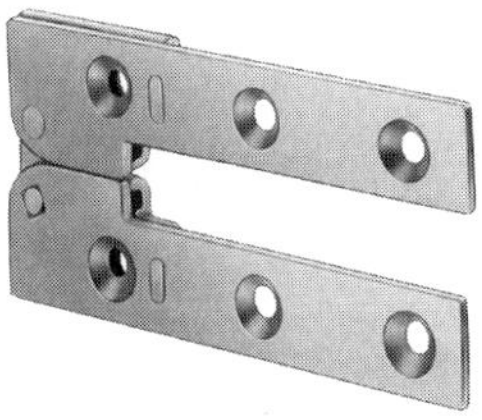

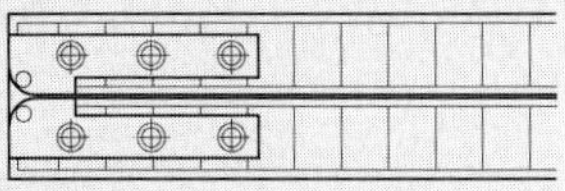

Finish	Cat. No.
nickel-plated	364.20.701
brass-plated	364.20.505

Packing: 20 pcs.

Dimensional data not binding. We reserve the right to alter specifications without notice.

Dimensions in mm

HÄFELE

Plano Flap Hinge®

No projecting parts
on the cabinet or the flap

Mounting screws:
Countersunk wood screws

slotted
Finish:
brass, plain

Length	Cat. No.
12 mm	011.00.214
16 mm	011.00.232
20 mm	011.00.241

brass, nickel-plated

Length	Cat. No.
12 mm	011.04.212
16 mm	011.04.230
20 mm	011.04.249

Packing: 200 pcs.

Plano Medial flap hinge
screw-mounted
metal/plastic

Opening angle: 90°

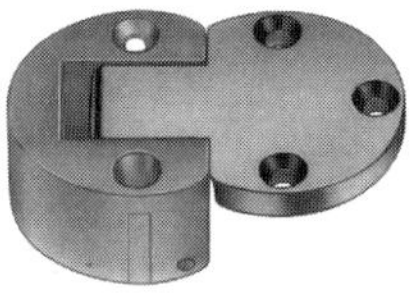

Brass arm

Hole pattern:

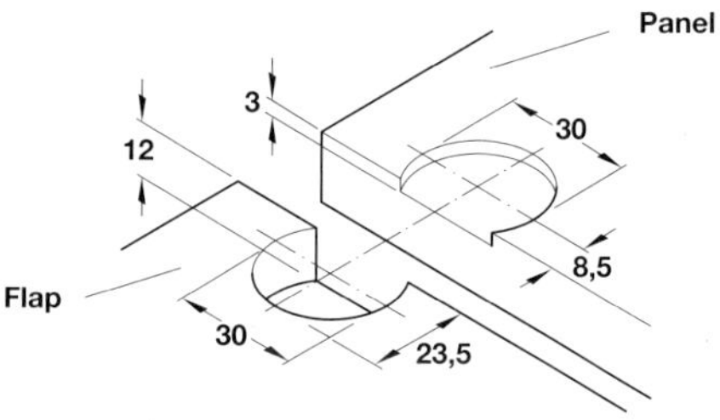

Sample installations

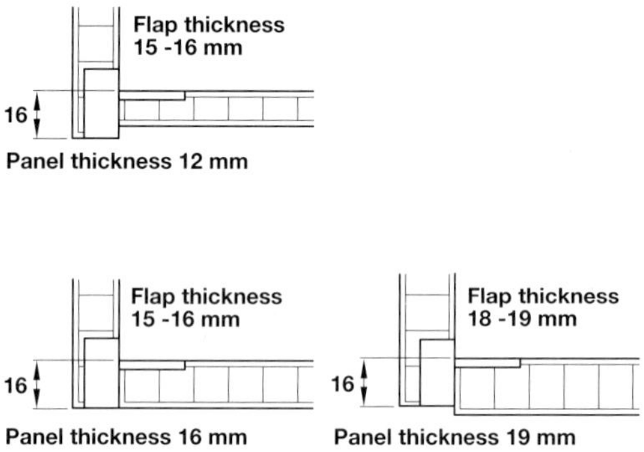

Plastic/Zinc die-cast	Cat. No.
white/chrome-plated	342.75.226
brown/gold-plated	342.75.520

Packing: 50 pcs.

Plano Medial **flap hinge**
screw-mounted
all-metal

Opening angle: 90°

Brass arm

Hole pattern:

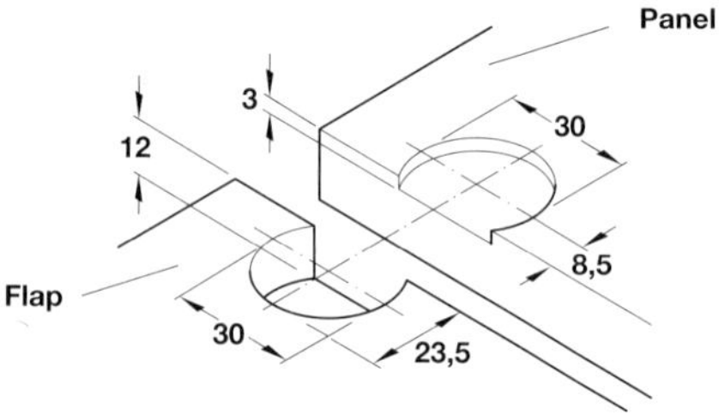

Sample installations

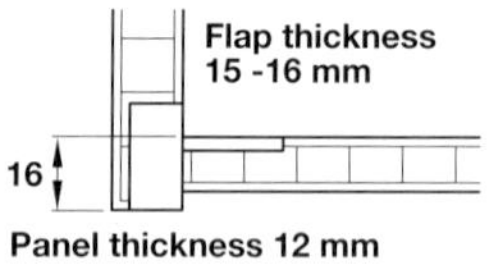

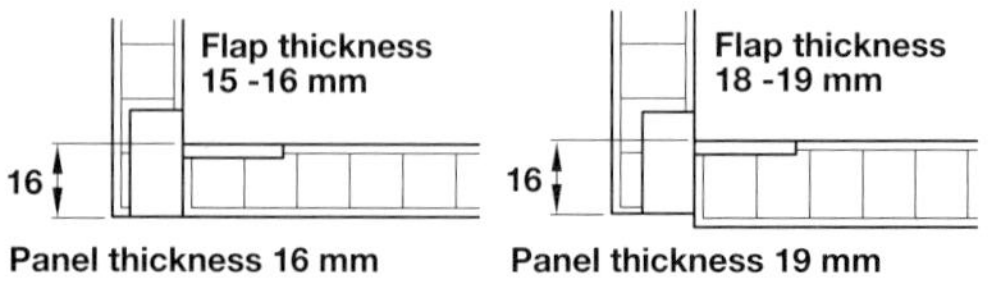

Zinc die-cast	Cat. No.
Nickel-plated	342.75.628
Gold-plated	342.75.824
Burnished	342.75.128

Packing: 50 pcs.

Dimensions in mm

Flap Hinges

HÄFELE

All-Metal Flap Hinge, three-way adjustable and detachable. The two cups can be released and detached for added shipping and installation convenience..

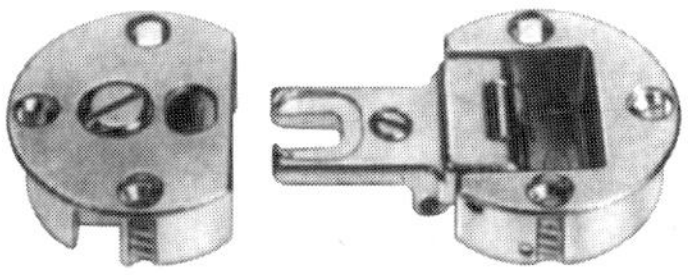

Opening angle 

Finish: zinc die-cast

Cat. No.		
	nickel-plated	342.66.709
	brass-plated	342.66.503
	bronzed	342.66.101

Packing: 100 pcs.

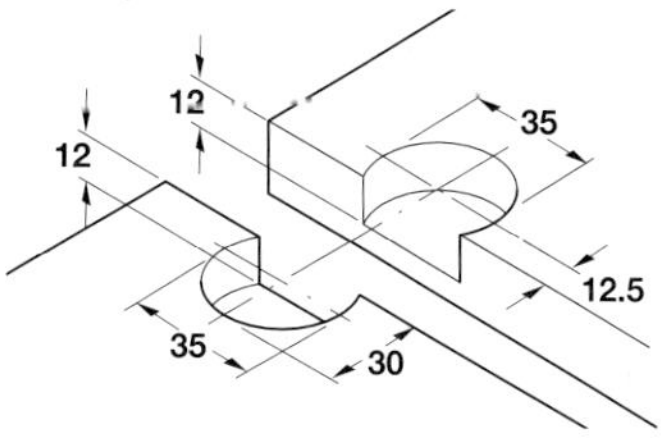

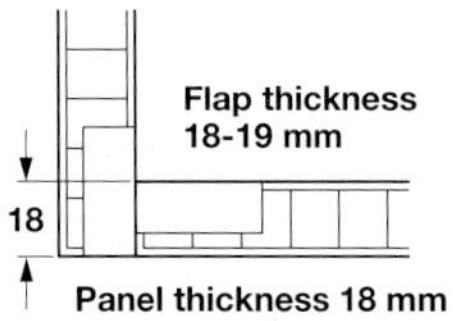

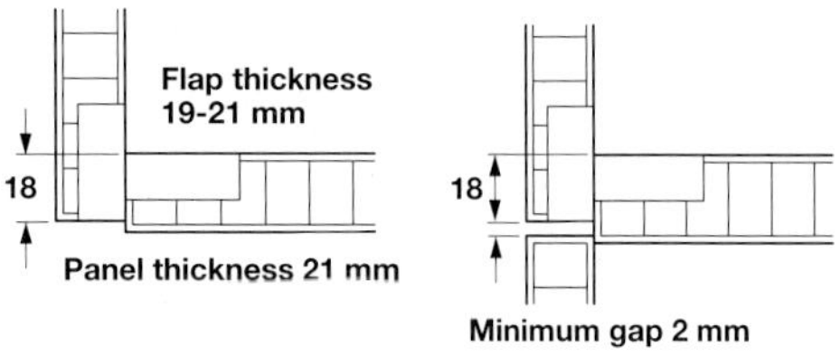

There is a 1 mm gap between flap and shelf when the flap is lowered.

All-Metal Flap Hinge, with plastic, recessed cup and zinc die-cast screw-mounted flange.

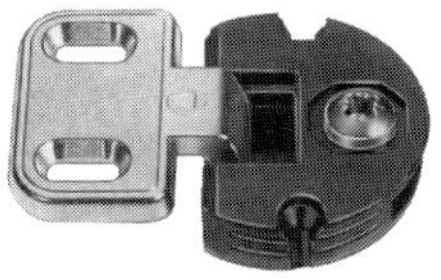

Opening angle 

Finish: Cups, plastic

Arm and flange: Zinc die-cast

Cat. No.		
	black, nickel-plated	342.76.303
	nickel-plated	342.76.705

Packing: 100 pcs.

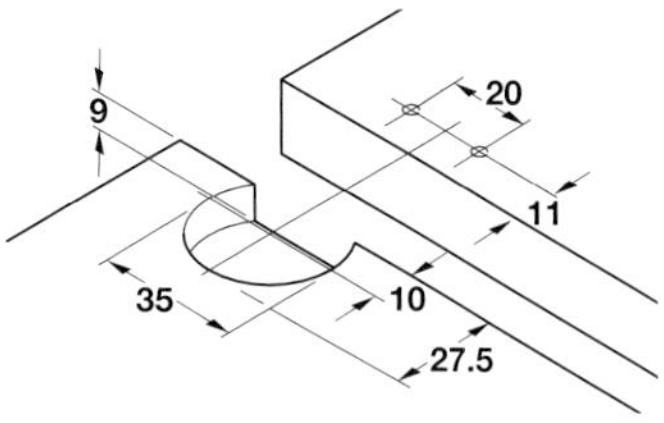

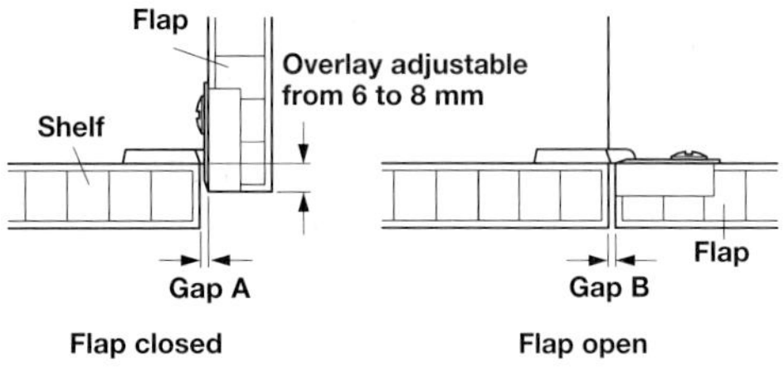

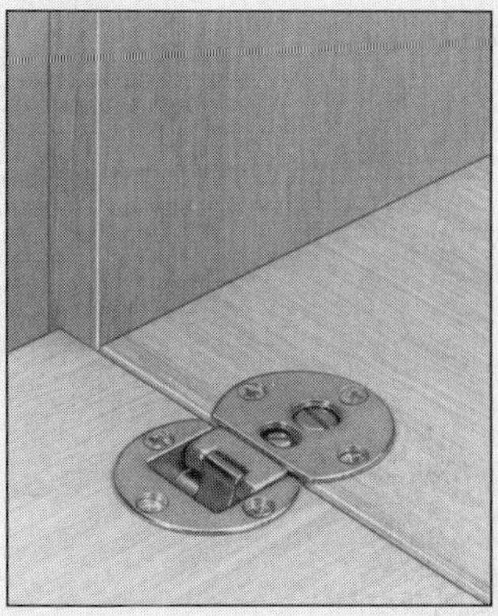

- Including fastening screws

**Hinges,
Flap and Lid Stays
Associated Fittings**

3

Mounting screws:
Countersunk wood screws

slotted
Finish:
brass, plain

Length	Cat. No.
12 mm	011.00.214
16 mm	011.00.232
20 mm	011.00.241

brass, nickel-plated

Length	Cat. No.
12 mm	011.04.212
16 mm	011.04.230
20 mm	011.04.249

Packing: 200 pcs.

HÄFELE

Flap Hinges

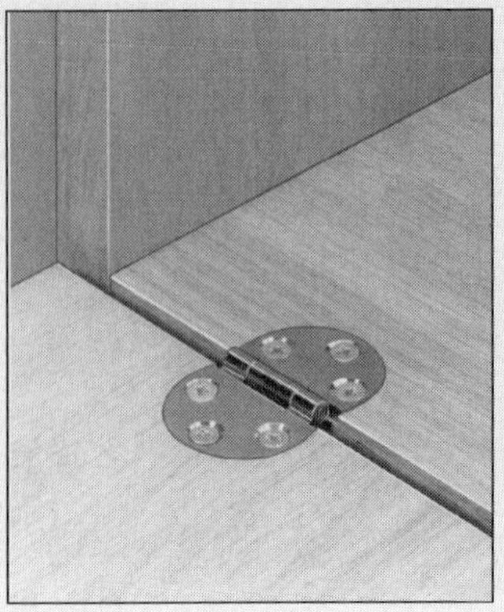

Steel Flap Hinge

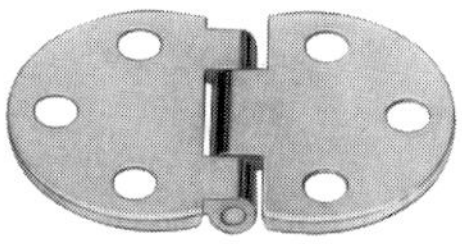

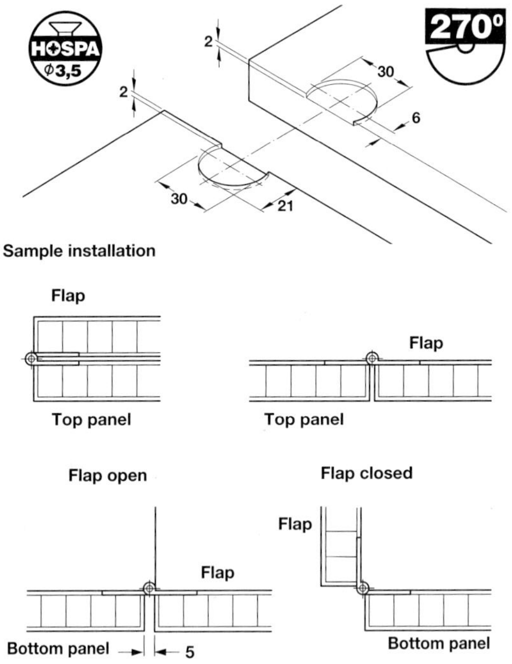

Finish: steel

Cat. No.		
	nickel-plated, polished	342.62.701
	brass-plated, polished	342.62.809
	burnished	342.62.103

Packing: 100 pcs.

3 Hinges, Flap and Lid Stays Associated Fittings

Brass Flap Hinge

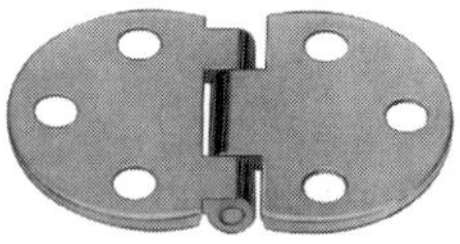

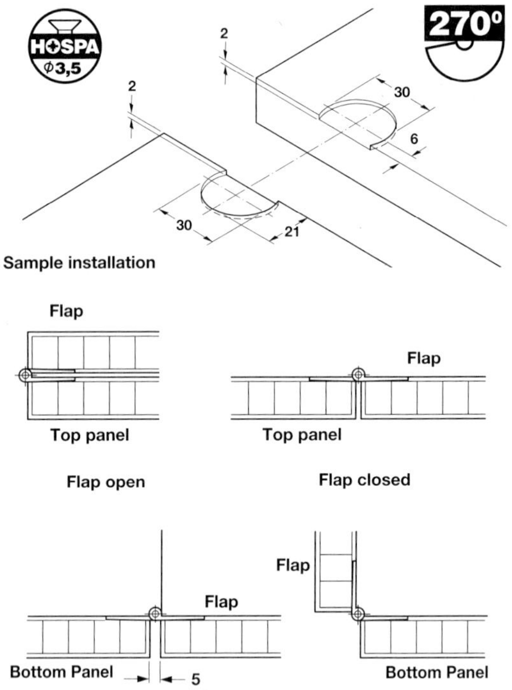

Finish: brass

Cat. No.		
	nickel-plated	342.63.600
	matt	342.63.502
	burnished	342.63.100

Packing: 100 pcs.

Dimensions in mm

Mounting screws:
Hospa particle board screws
Countersunk head
with PZ 2 cross slot
Finish: steel

Length	Cat. No.
15 mm	015.35.637
17 mm	015.35.646
20 mm	015.35.655

Packing: 1000 pcs.

Dimensional data not binding.
We reserve the right to alter specifications without notice.

Fall-ex® Flap Stays with Brake

Reversible: can be installed left or right

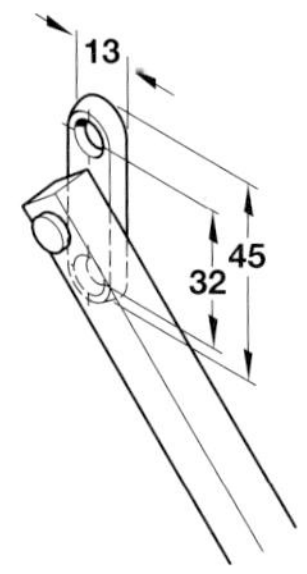

Side panel mounting

SYSTEM VARIANTA 32

Twist piston rod to adjust braking action:
- clockwise to reduce
- counter-clockwise to increase

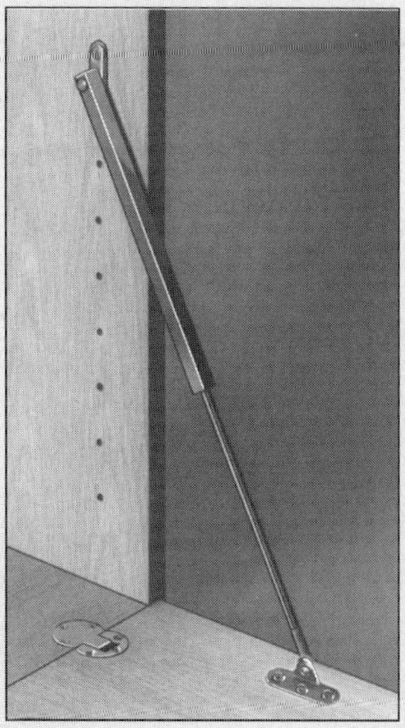

Finish: steel, nickel-plated
Square tube: brass, nickel-plated

Length (mm)	Cat. No.
250	372.17.753
325	372.17.762
450	372.17.771

Packing: 10 pcs.

Dimensions in mm

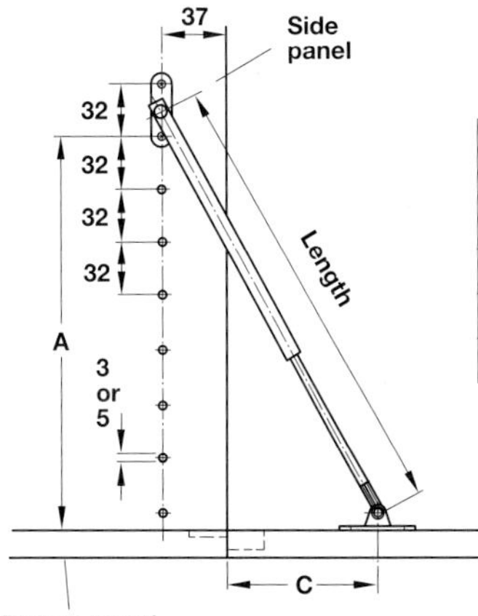

Flap open

Vertical mounting:

Length (mm)	Inside Cabinet Height	Dimension A	Dimension C
250	300 to 400	214.5	Trial
325	350 to 450	288.0	Trial
450	400 to 500	406.5	Trial

Flap

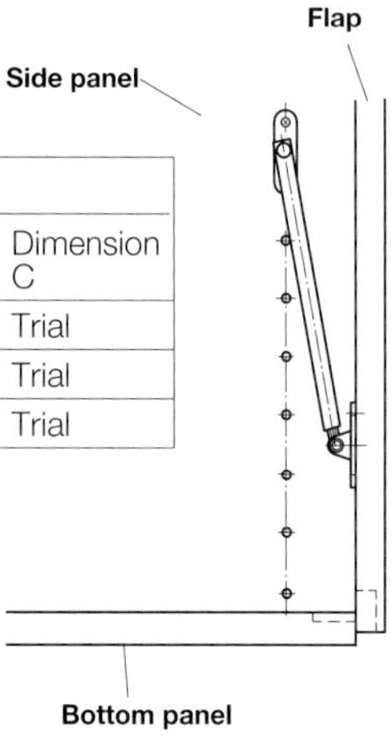

Flap closed

Mounting screws:
Varianta screws
Flat head with PZ 2 cross slot
Finish: steel, nickel-plated

Length	3mm dia.hole	5 mm dia. hole
10,5 mm	013.15.617	013.15.715
13,5 mm	013.15.626	013.15.724
16,0 mm	013.15.635	013.15.733

Packing: 100 and 1000 pcs.

Mounting screws:
Hospa particle board screws
Countersunk head with PZ 2 cross slot
Finish: steel, nickel-plated

Length	Cat. No.
20 mm	015.55.844
25 mm	015.55.853
30 mm	015.55.862

Packing: 1000 pcs.

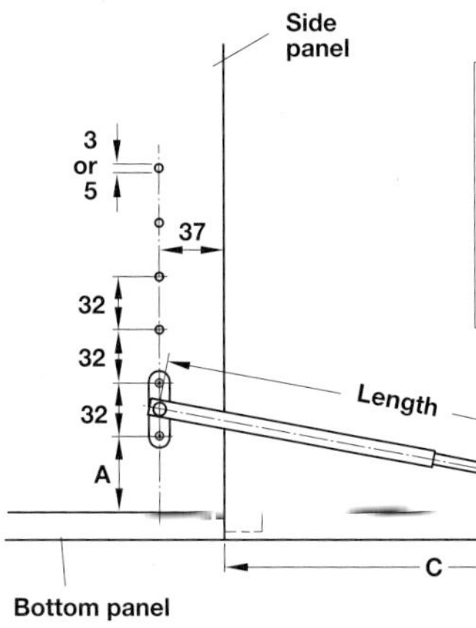

Flap open

Horizontal mounting:

Length (mm)	Inside Cabinet Height	Dimension A	Dimension C
250	300 to 400	22.5	Trial
325	350 to 450	54.5	Trial
450	400 to 500	118.5	Trial

Flap

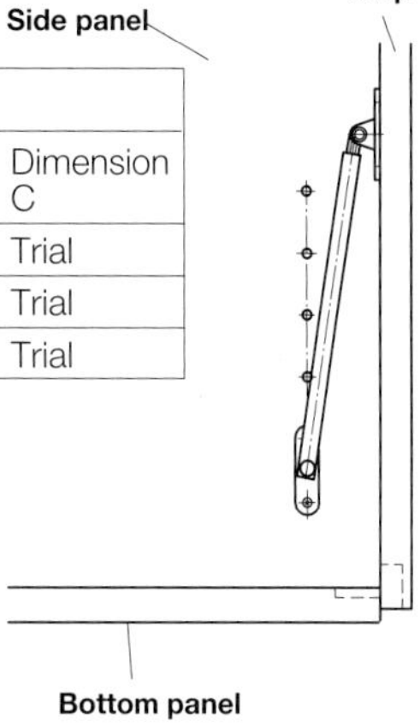

Flap closed

Keep brake piston rod free of oil, grease and other contaminants at all times.

Dimensional data not binding. We reserve the right to alter specifications without notice.

HÄFELE

Dorana-stop Flap Stays with Brake

Braking action is adjustable using adjustment screw. Loosen to increase; tighten to reduce

Dorana-stop flap stays with brake
screw-mounted
left and right-handed models available

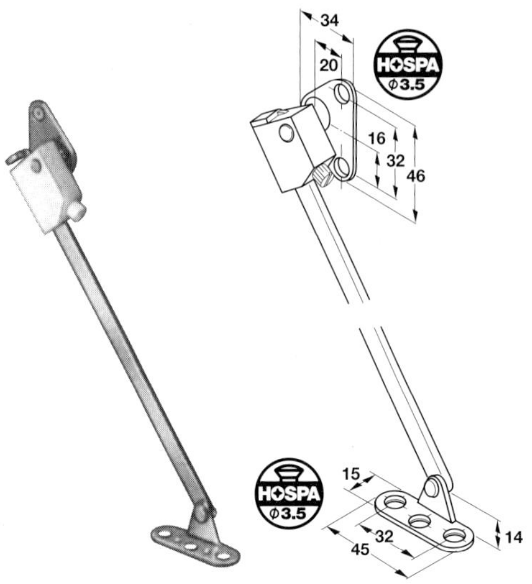

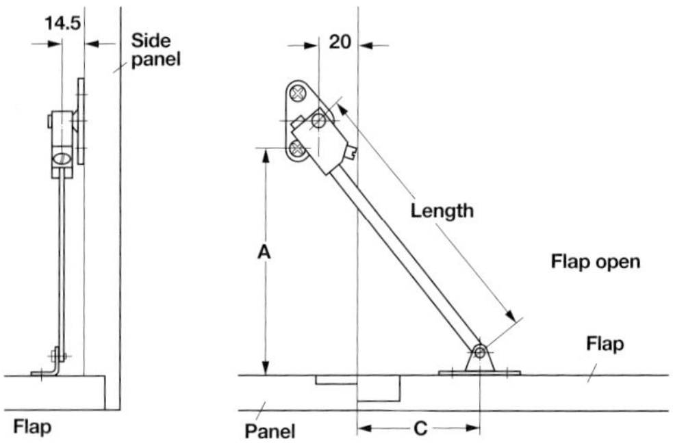

Vertical mounting

Length (mm)	Inside Cabinet Height (mm)	Dimension A (mm)	Dimension C (mm)
160	250 to 350	127	Determine by trial mounting
190	300 to 400	151	
220	350 to 450	175	
250	400 to 500	222	
280	450 to 550	222	

3 Hinges, Flap and Lid Stays Associated Fittings

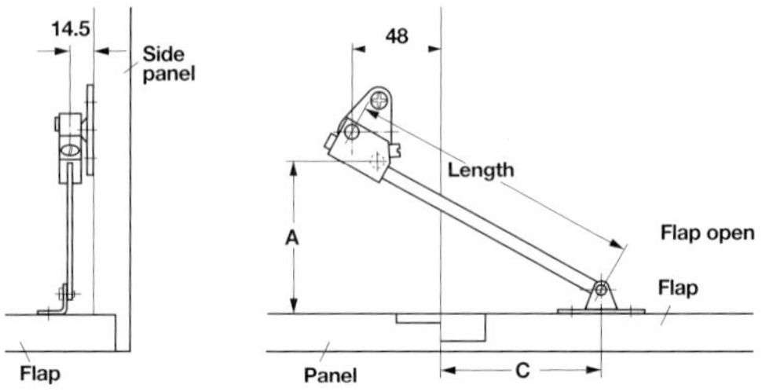

Horizontal mounting

Length (mm)	Inside Cabinet Height (mm)	Dimension A (mm)	Dimension C (mm)
160	200 to 300	82	Determine by trial mounting
190	230 to 330	105	
220	260 to 360	127	
250	290 to 430	148	
280	320 to 460	171	

Keep brake piston rod free of oil, grease and other contaminants at all times.

Finish: plastic/steel		Cat. No. white/nickel-plated left	white/nickel-plated right	brown/nickel-plated left	brown/nickel-plated right	black/nickel-plated left	black/nickel-plated right
Length	160 mm	365.86.713	365.86.704	365.86.115	365.86.106	365.86.311	365.86.302
	190 mm	365.86.731	365.86.722	365.86.133	365.86.124	365.86.339	365.86.320
	220 mm	365.86.759	365.86.740	365.86.151	365.86.142	365.86.357	365.86.348
	250 mm	365.86.777	365.86.768	365.86.179	365.86.160	365.86.375	365.86.366
	280 mm	365.86.795	365.86.786	365.86.197	365.86.188	365.86.393	365.86.384

Packing: 100 each

Dimensions in mm

Dorana-stop Flap Stays with Brake

HÄFELE

Dorana-stop flap stays with brake
screw-mounted, system hole installation
left and right-handed models available

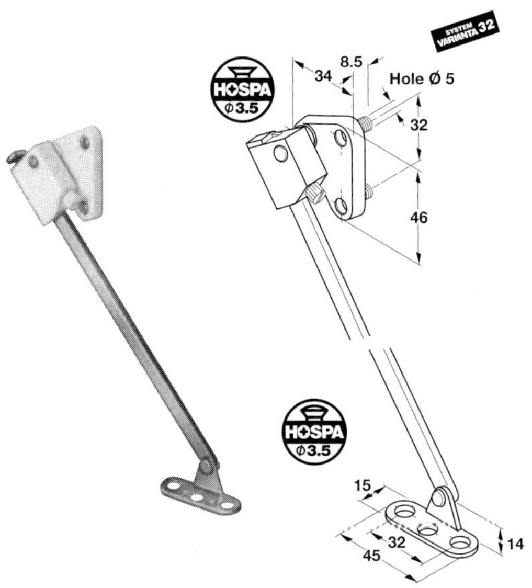

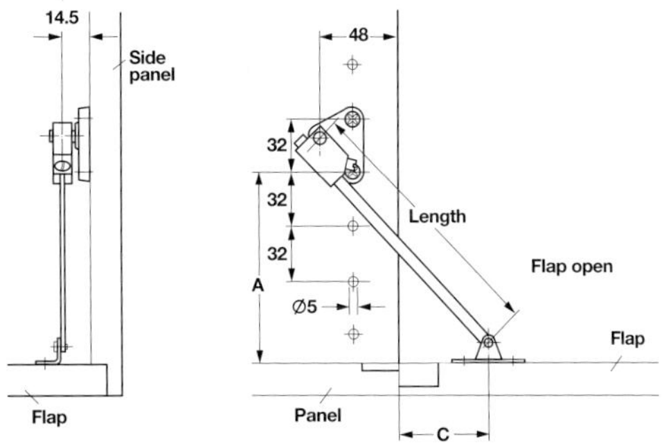

Vertical mounting

Length (mm)	Inside Cabinet Height (mm)	Dimension A (mm)	Dimension C (mm)
160	250 to 350	to 114	Determine by trial mounting
190	300 to 400	to 145	
220	350 to 450	to 170	

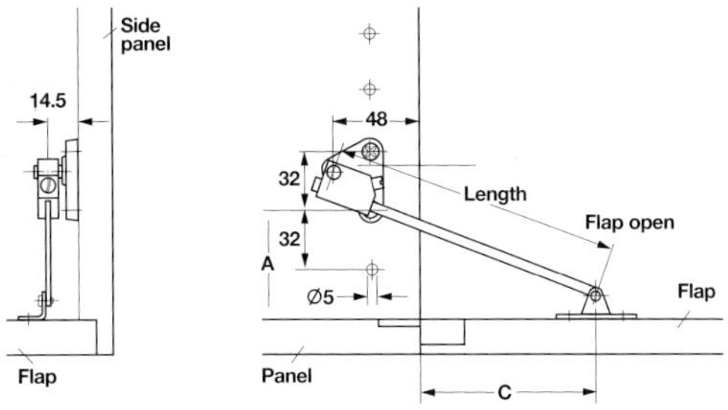

Horizontal mounting

Length (mm)	Inside Cabinet Height (mm)	Dimension A (mm)	Dimension C (mm)
160	200 to 300	from 58	Determine by trial mounting
190	230 to 330	from 83	
220	260 to 400	from 104	

Finish:		Cat. No.	
plastic/steel		white/nickel-plated	
		left	right
Length	160 mm	365.91.714	365.91.705
	190 mm	365.91.732	365.91.723
	220 mm	365.91.750	365.91.741

Packing: 20 pcs. each

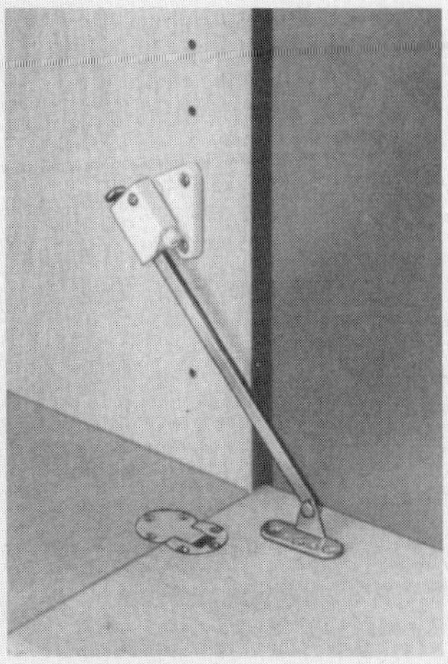

Braking action is adjustable using adjustment screw. Loosen to increase; tighten to reduce.

Keep brake rod free of oil, grease and other contaminants at all times.

HÄFELE

Dorana-stop Flap Stays with Brake

Braking action is adjustable using adjustment screw. Loosen to increase; tighten to reduce.

3 Hinges, Flap and Lid Stays Associated Fittings

Keep brake rod free of oil, grease and other contaminants at all times.

Dorana-stop flap stays with brake and magnetic catch
screw-mounted, system hole installation
left and right-handed models available

SYSTEM VARIANTA 32

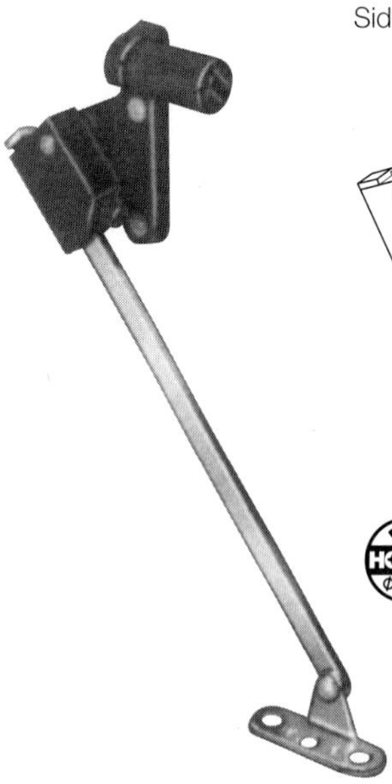

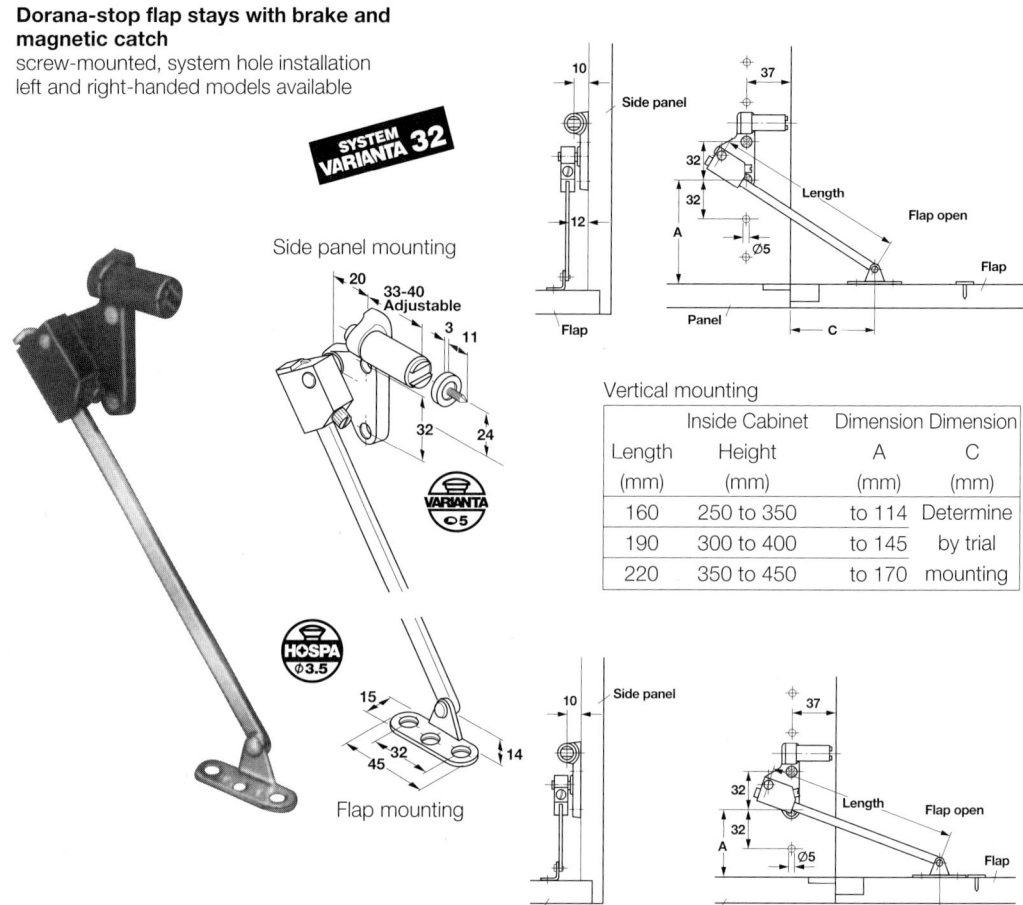

Side panel mounting

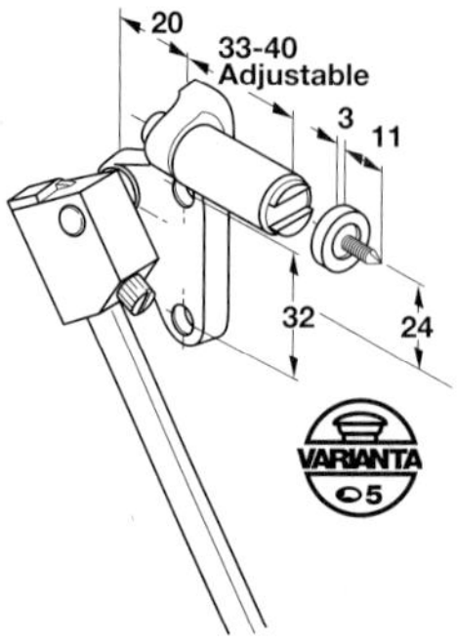

VARIANTA Ø5

HOSPA Ø3.5

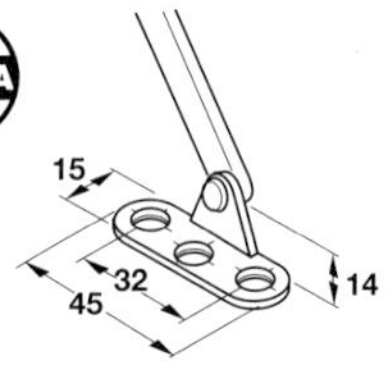

Flap mounting

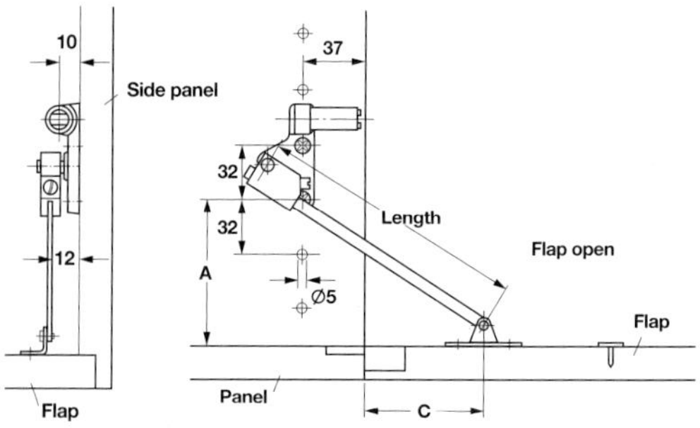

Vertical mounting

Length (mm)	Inside Cabinet Height (mm)	Dimension A (mm)	Dimension C (mm)
160	250 to 350	to 114	Determine
190	300 to 400	to 145	by trial
220	350 to 450	to 170	mounting

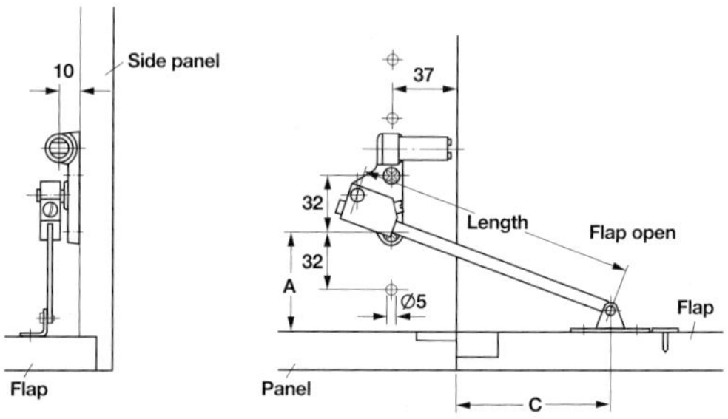

Horizontal mounting

Length (mm)	Inside Cabinet Height (mm)	Dimension A (mm)	Dimension C (mm)
160	200 to 300	from 58	Determine
190	230 to 330	from 83	by trial
220	260 to 400	from 104	mounting

Cat. No.

Finish: steel/plastic white/nickel-plated		left	right
Length	160 mm	365.92.711	365.92.702
	190 mm	365.92.739	365.92.720
	220 mm	365.92.757	365.92.748

Packing: 20 pcs. each

Dimensional data not binding. We reserve the right to alter specifications without notice.

Dimensions in mm

HÄFELE

Stopmatic Flap Stays with Brake

Stopmatic S flap stay with brake
all-metal, screw-mounted.
Reversible: can be used left or right.

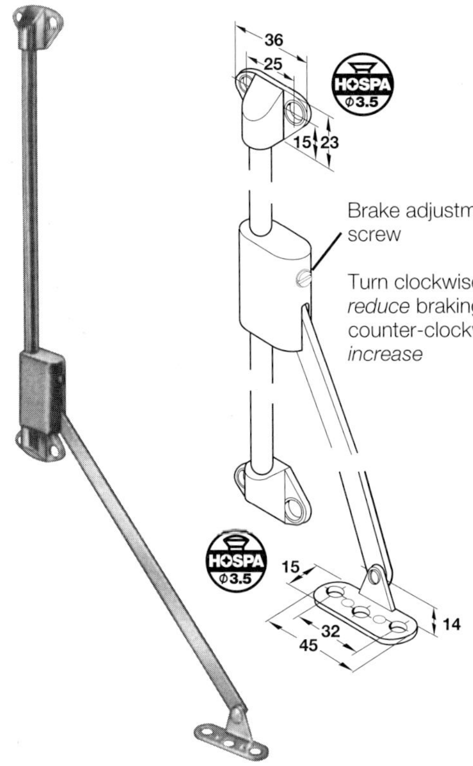

Application drawing

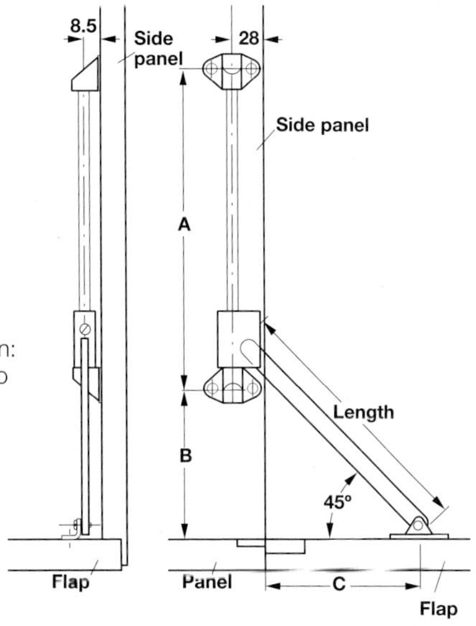

Length (mm)	Inside Cabinet Height (mm)	Dimension A (mm)	Dimension B (mm)	Dimension C (mm)
200	350 to 450	238	115	Determine by trial mounting
250	450 to 550	288	140	
300	550 to 650	338	165	

Finish:	Cat. No.
zinc die-cast/steel	nickel-plated
Length 200 mm	365.74.713
250 mm	365.74.722
300 mm	365.74.731

Packing: 50 pcs.

Stopmatic, **with** magnetic catch

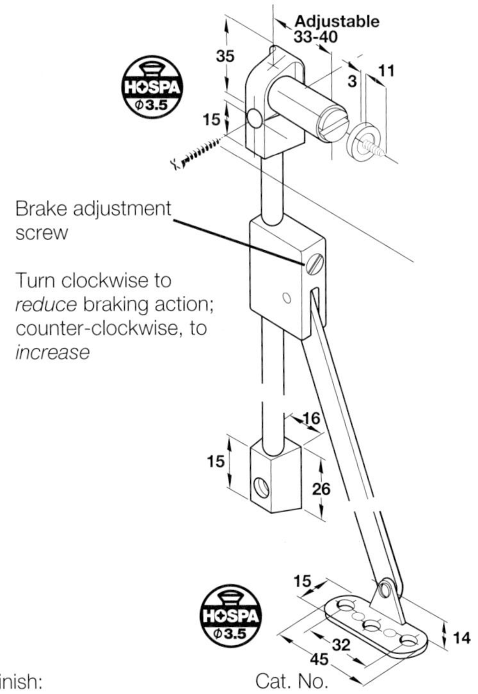

installs in pre-drilled holes

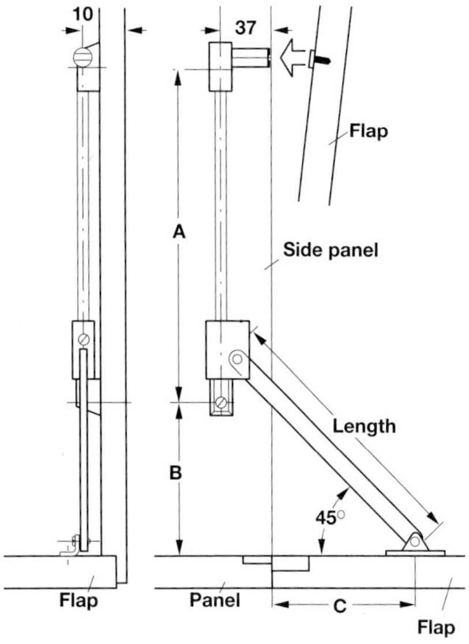

Finish:	Cat. No.
zinc die-cast/steel	nickel-plated
Length 200 mm	365.73.716
250 mm	365.73.725
300 mm	365.73.734

Packing: 50 pcs.

Length (mm)	Inside Cabinet Height (mm)	Dimension A (mm)	Dimension B (mm)	Dimension C (mm)
200	350 to 450	238	115	Determine by trial mounting
250	450 to 550	288	140	
300	550 to 650	338	165	

Dimensions in mm

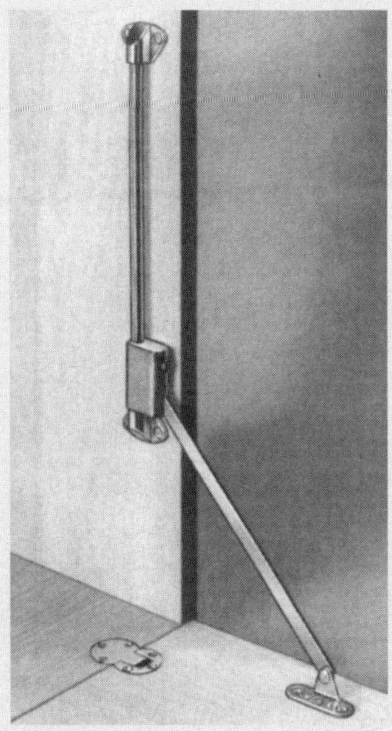

Hinges,
Flap and Lid Stays
Associated Fittings
3

- These flap stays can be used in left or right-hand installations: just reverse position of foot and magnetic catch as needed.

Mounting screws HOSPA Φ3,0
3.0 x 30 mm
Finish: steel, nickel-plated

Cat. No.	015.55.586

Packing: 1000 pcs.

Keep brake piston rod free of oil, grease and other contaminants at all times.

HÄFELE

Flap Stays

Keep brake piston rod free of oil, grease and other contaminants at all times.

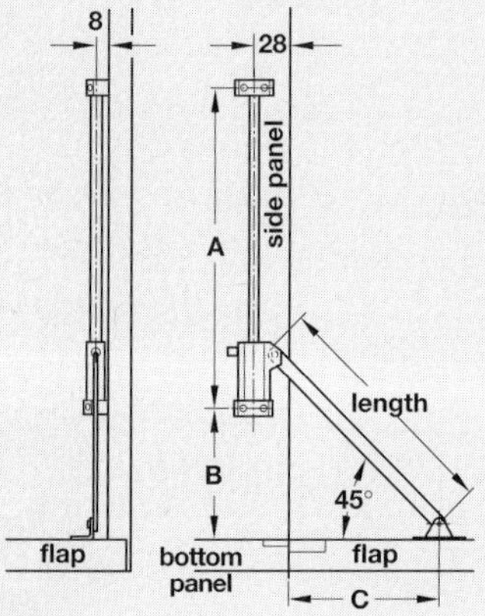

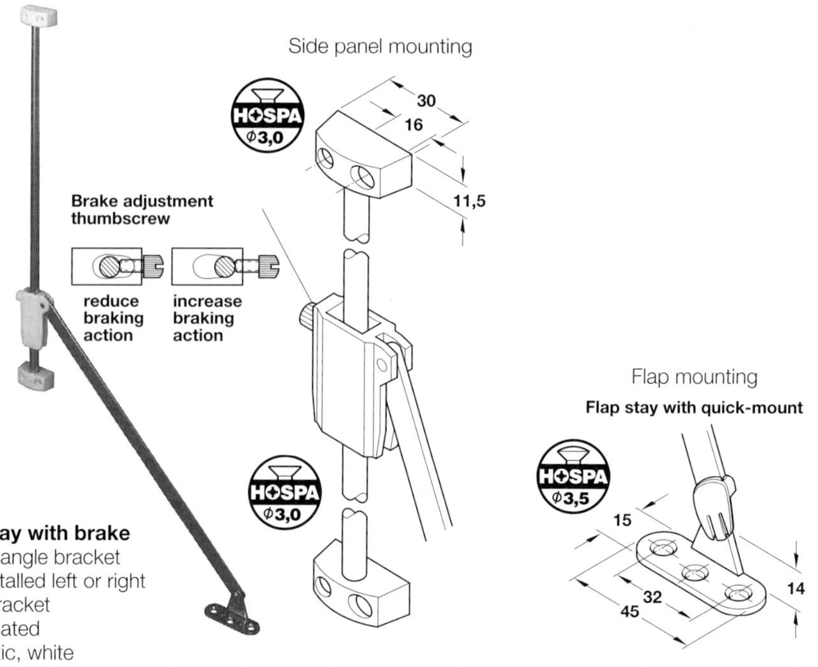

"Stopmatic" flap stay with brake
with screw-mounted angle bracket
reversible: can be installed left or right
quick-mount angle bracket
Finish: steel, nickel-plated
Housing: plastic, white

Length	Inside Cabinet Ht.	Dimension A	B	C	Cat. No. **with** quick-mount
200	350–450	225	125	determine	365.40.600
250	450–550	275	150	by trial	365.40.620
300	550–650	325	175	mounting	365.40.640

Packing: 10 pcs.

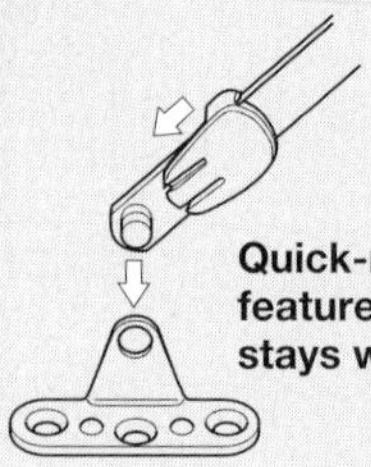

Quick-mount feature for flap stays with brakes

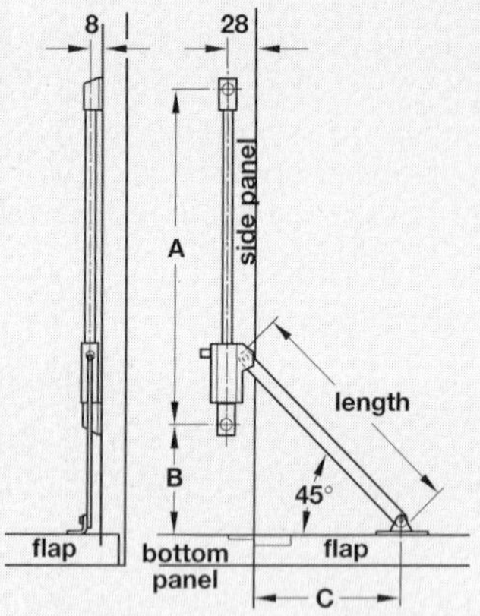

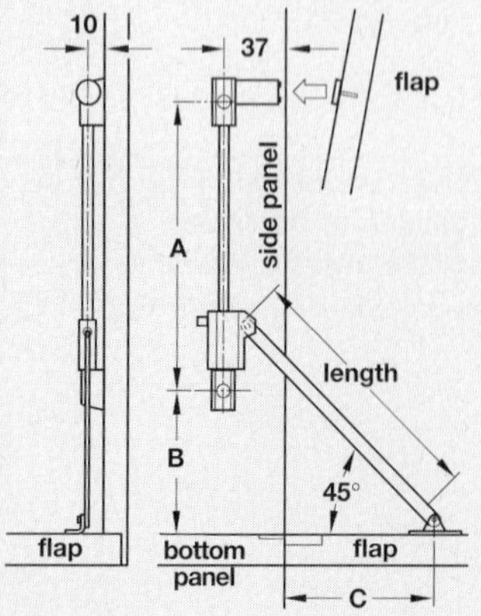

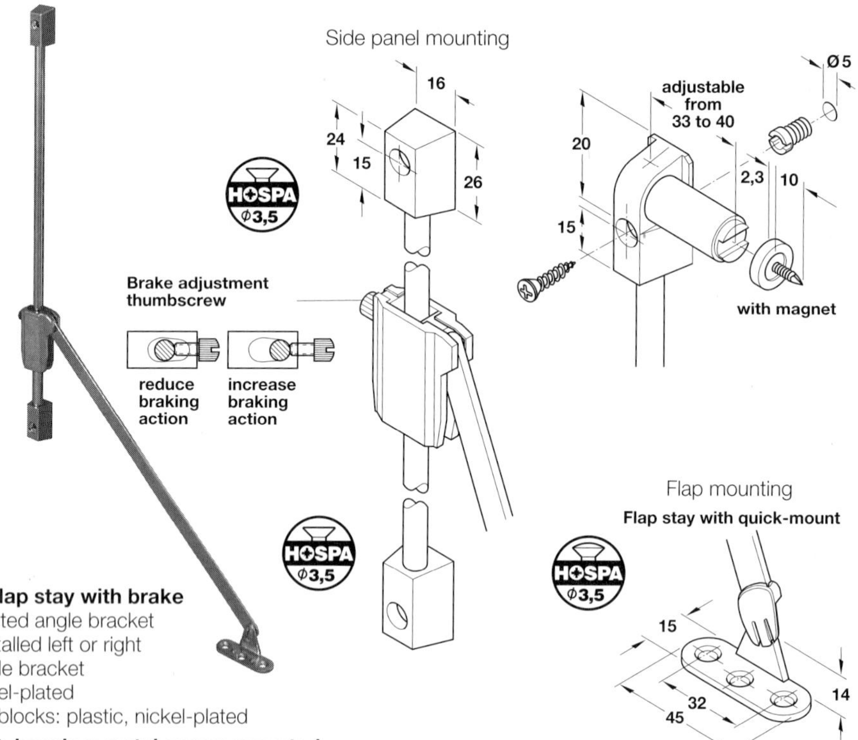

"Stopmatic S" flap stay with brake
with screw-mounted angle bracket
reversible: be installed left or right
quick-mount angle bracket
Finish: steel, nickel-plated
Mounting blocks: plastic, nickel-plated

Without magnet, housing: metal screw-mounted

Length	Inside Cabinet Ht.	Dimension A	B	C	Cat. No. **with** quick-mount
200	350–450	238	115	determine	365.44.600
250	450–550	288	140	by trial	365.44.620
300	550–650	338	165	mounting	365.44.640

With magnet for screw-mounting

Length	Inside Cabinet Ht.	Dimension A	B	C	Cat. No. **with** quick-mount
200	350–450	238	115	determine	365.45.600
250	450–550	288	140	by trial	365.45.620
300	550–650	338	165	mounting	365.45.640

Packing: 10 pcs.

Dimensional data not binding.
We reserve the right to alter specifications without notice.

Dimensions in mm

Long-Stop Flap Stay with Brake

Long-stop flap stay with brake, provides extra support for unusually long flaps; all-metal, screw-mounted
left and right-handed models available

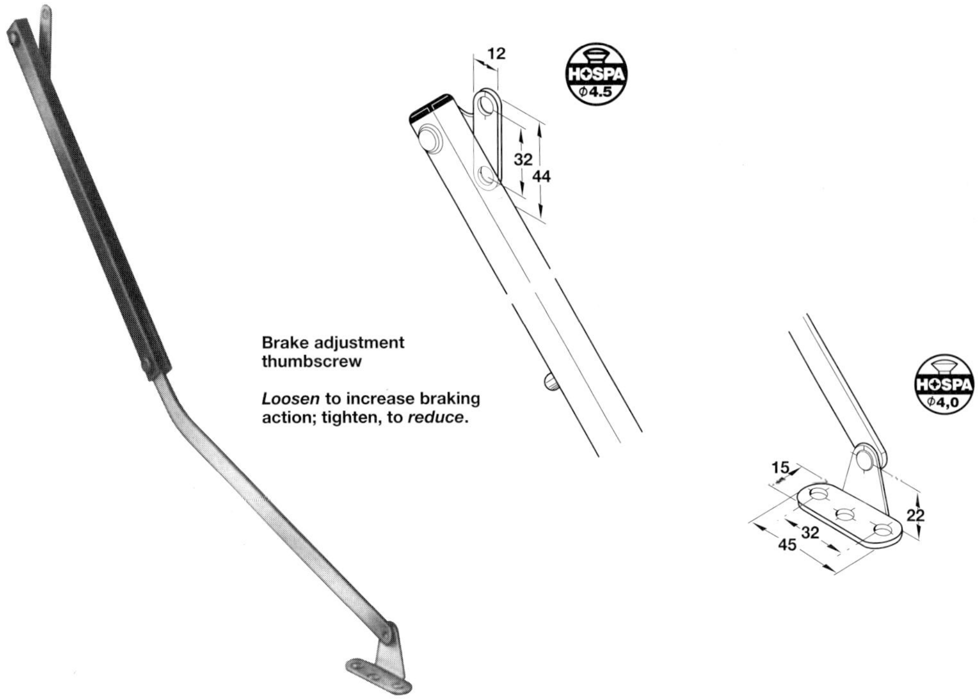

HÄFELE

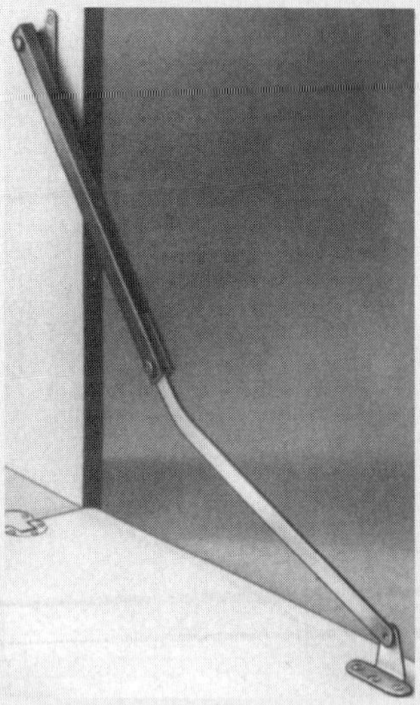

Braking action is adjustable using adjustment screw. Loosen to increase; tighten to reduce.

Hinges, Flap and Lid Stays Associated Fittings 3

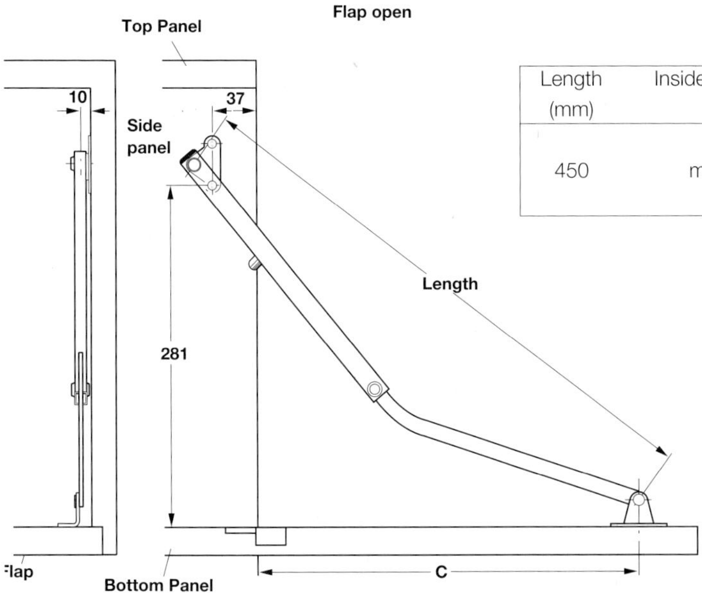

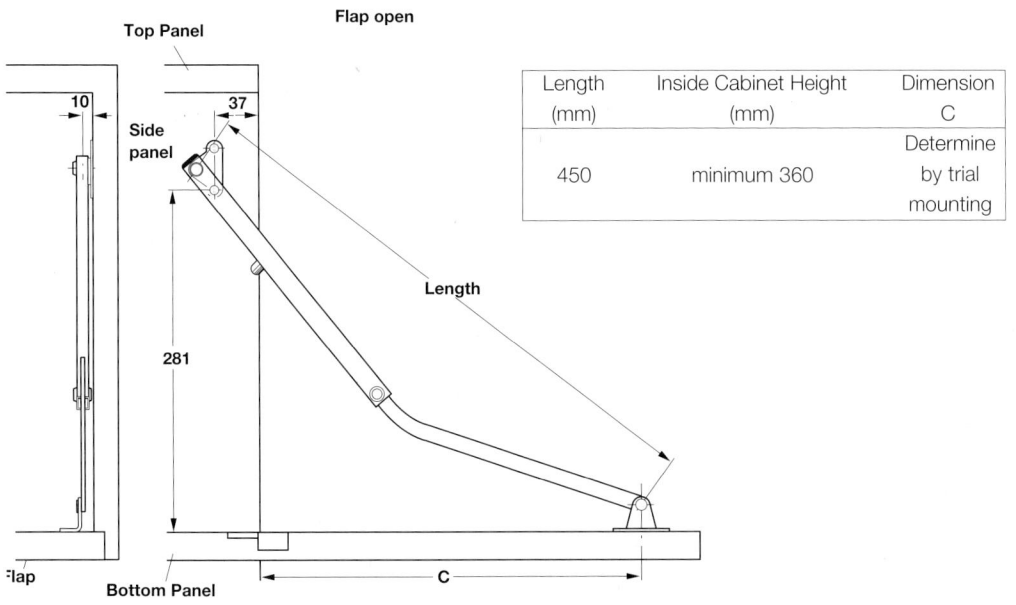

Length (mm)	Inside Cabinet Height (mm)	Dimension C
450	minimum 360	Determine by trial mounting

Finish:	Cat. No.			
aluminum/steel	silver anodized/nickel-plated		brown anodized/bronzed	
	left	right	left	right
Length 450 mm	365.66.613	365.66.604	365.66.113	365.66.104
Packing:	1 pc.			

Dimensional data not binding. We reserve the right to alter specifications without notice.

Dimensions in mm

Flap Stays

"Slow" flap stay, screw-mounted
reversible: can be installed left or right

Braking action adjustable using adjustment screws which attach plastic block to side panel. Loosen or tighten as needed.

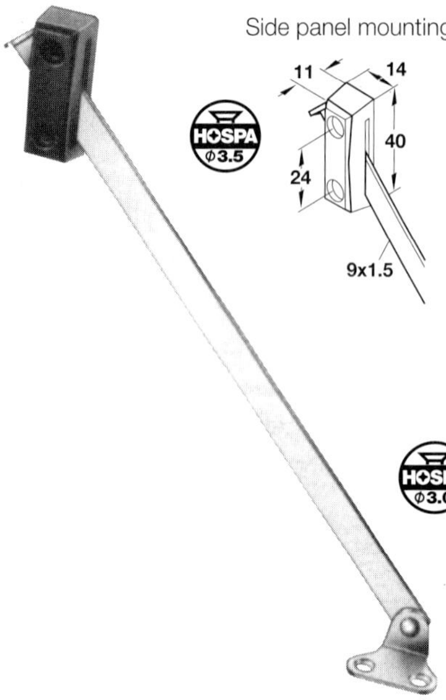

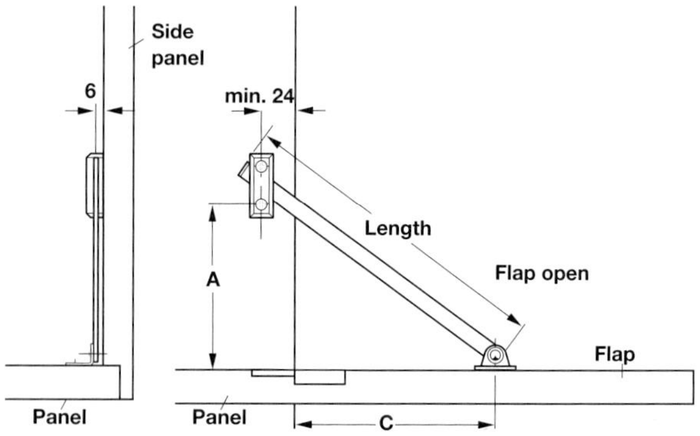

Flap mounting

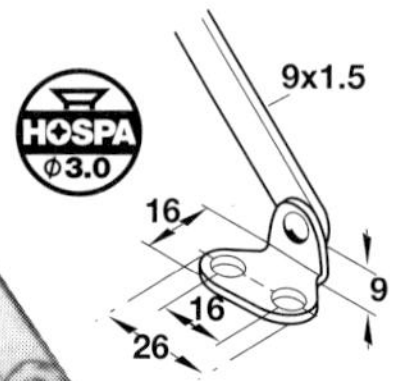

Length (mm)	Inside cabinet Depth (mm)	Dimension A (mm)	Dimension C (mm)
150	min. 130	70	Determine
200	min. 170	105	by trial
250	min. 210	140	mounting

- These reversible flap stays come configured for right-hand installation

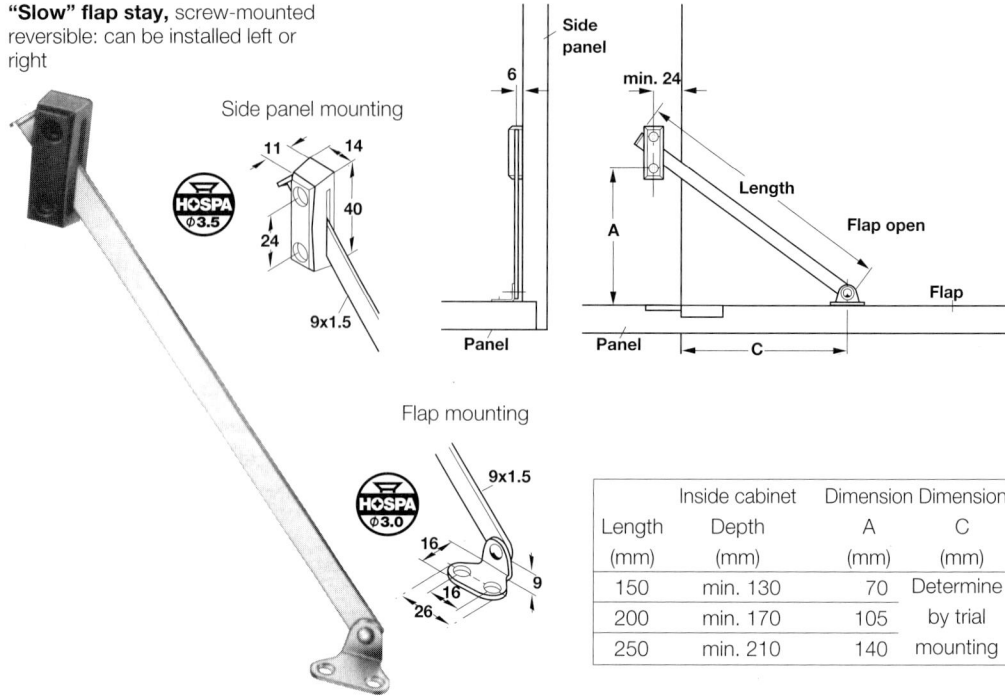

Finish: Cat. No.

steel/plastic		white/nickel-plated	brown/nickel-plated
Length	150 mm	365.80.828	365.80.720
	200 mm	365.80.846	365.80.748
	250 mm	365.80.855	365.80.757

Packing: 50 pcs.

Flap stay with catch, screw-mounted
Reversible: can be installed left or right

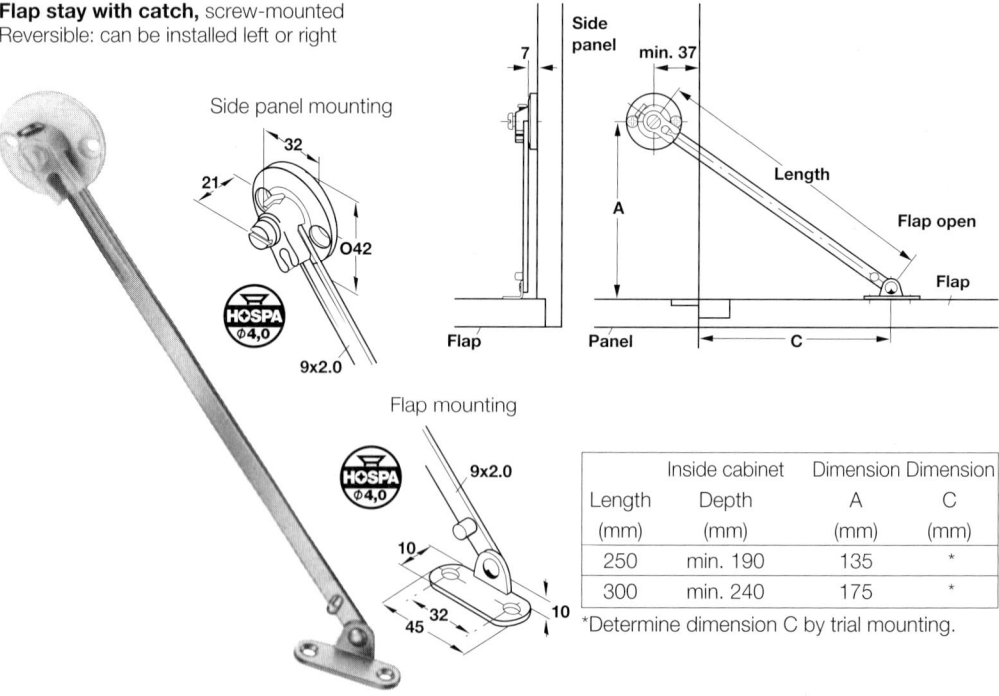

To adjust braking action, loosen or tighten screw on stay, as needed.

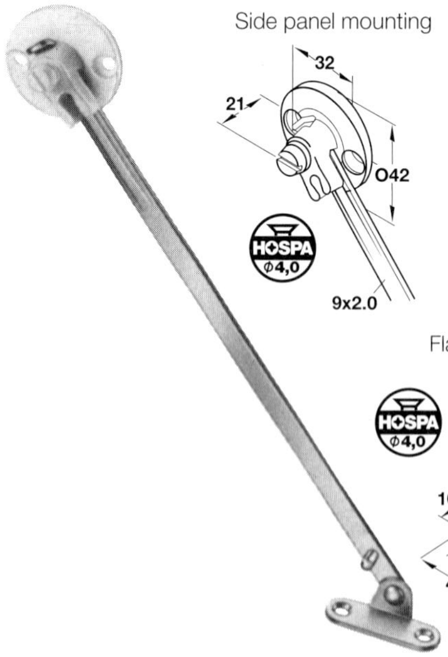

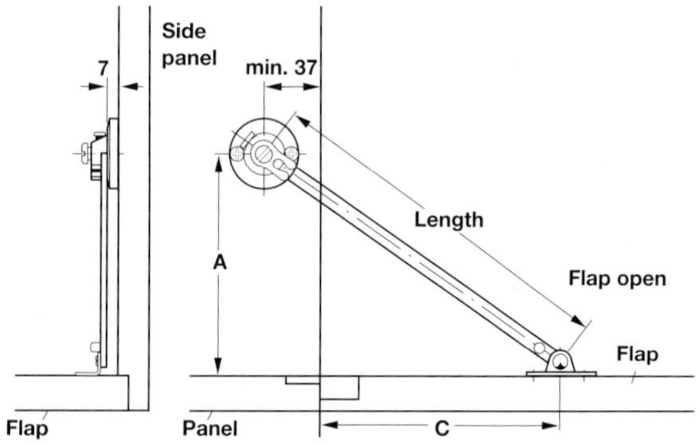

Flap mounting

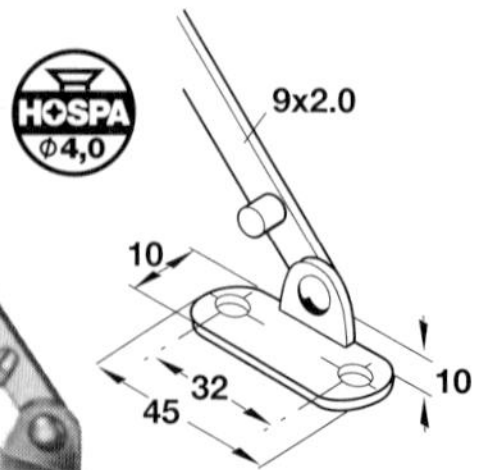

Length (mm)	Inside cabinet Depth (mm)	Dimension A (mm)	Dimension C (mm)
250	min. 190	135	*
300	min. 240	175	*

*Determine dimension C by trial mounting.

Finish: Cat. No.

steel/plastic		white/nickel-plated	brown/nickel-plated
Length	225 mm	365.75.710	365.75.112
	275 mm	365.75.729	365.75.121

Packing: 200 pcs.

Dimensional data not binding. We reserve the right to alter specifications without notice.

Dimensions in mm

Flap Brake

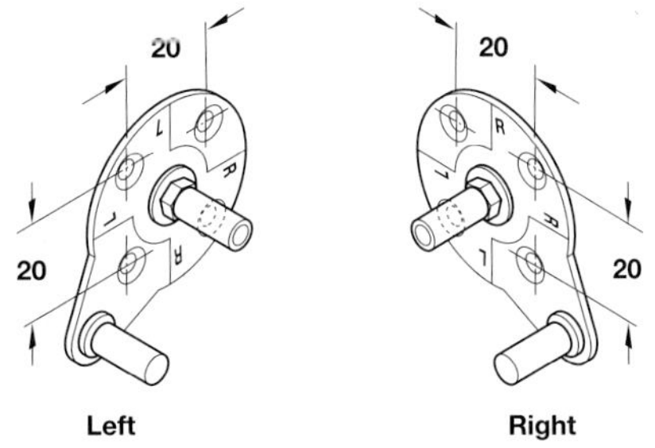

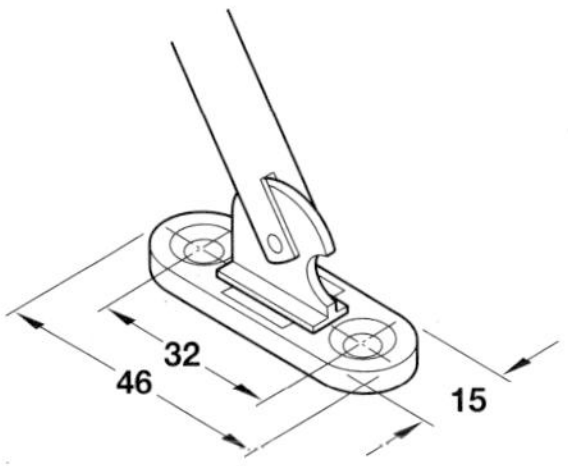

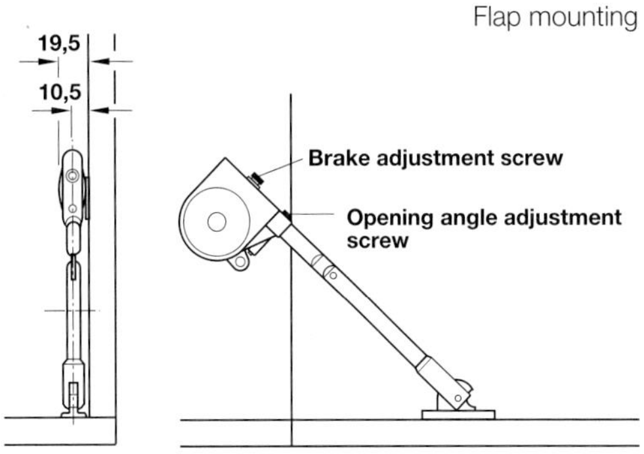

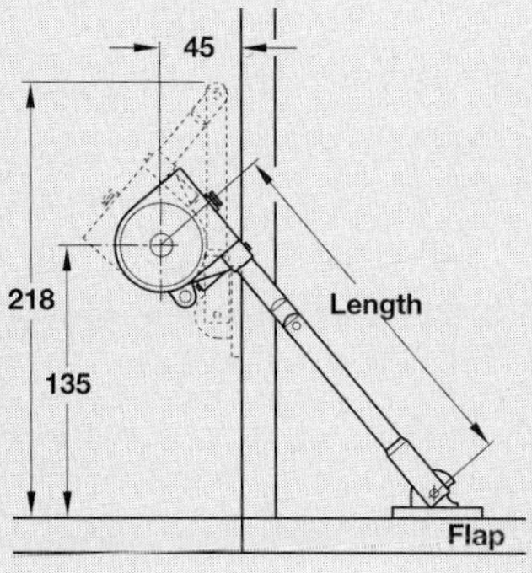

Flap Stay
speed mount bracket
Reversible: can be installed left or right
Finish: plastic, black/steel, nickel-plated

Length	Cat. No.
200 mm	365.30.300

Packing: 20 pcs, including fastening screws

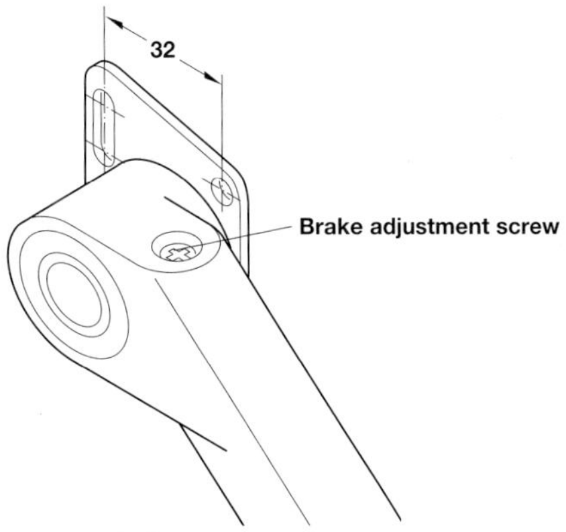

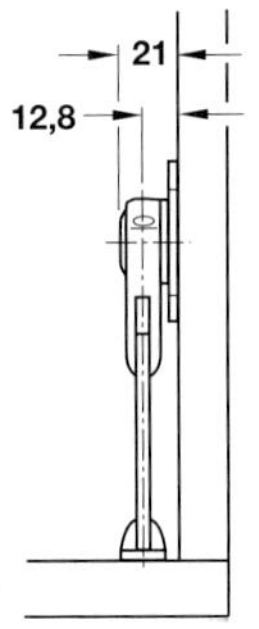

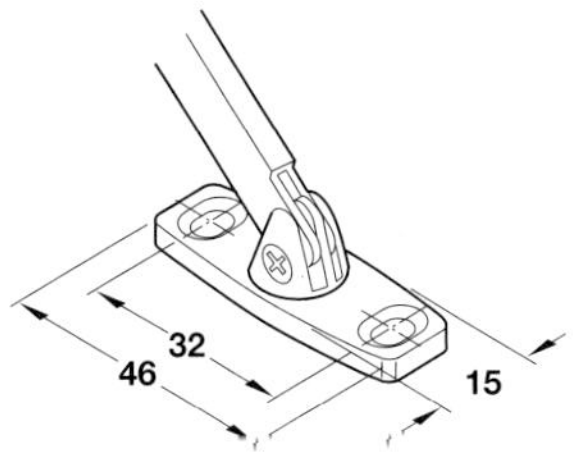

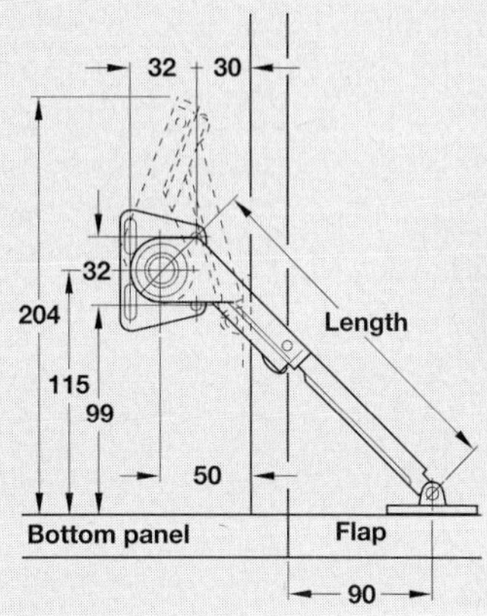

Flap Stay
Finish: steel, nickel-plated

Length		Cat. No.
200 mm	left	365.30.601
	right	365.30.600

Packing: 20 pcs, including fastening screws

Dimensions in mm

Dimensional data not binding.
We reserve the right to alter specifications without notice.

Flap Stays

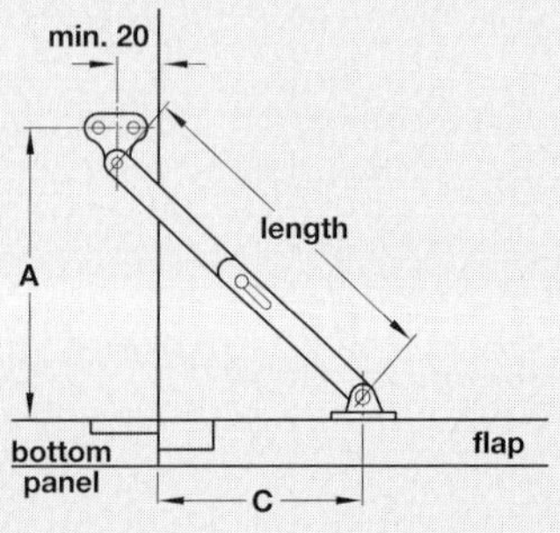

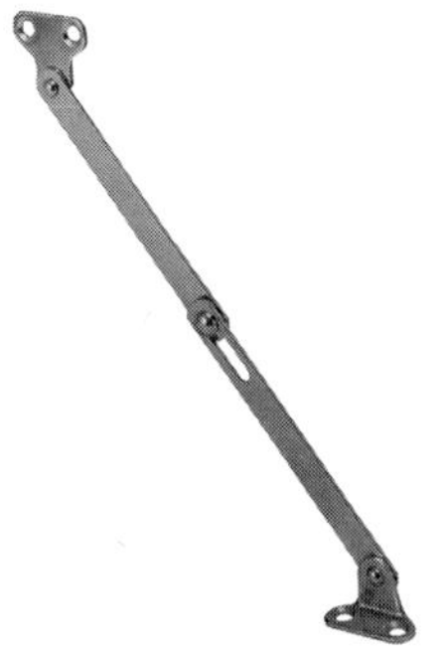

Side panel mounting

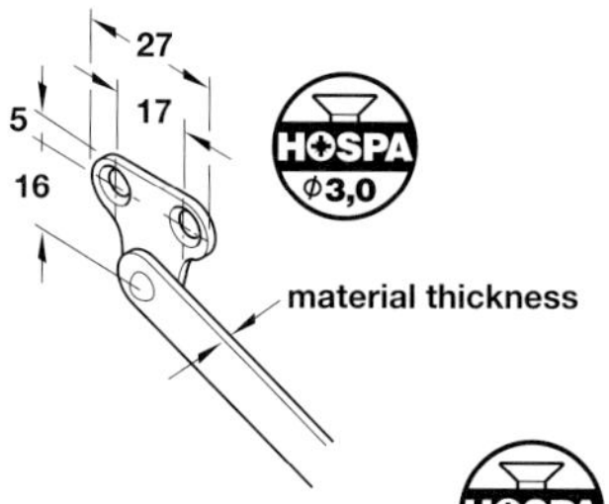

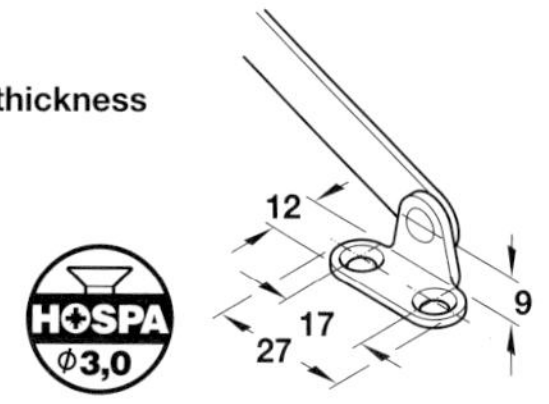

Flap mounting

Flap stay
slotted arm provides sliding action,
reversible: can be installed left or right

Finish: steel, nickel-plated

Length	Inside cabinet height	Dimension A	Dimension C	Material thickness	Cat.No.
150	min. 125	135	determine by trial mounting	10 x 1.5	365.00.722
200	min. 170	160		10 x 2.0	365.10.728
250	min. 200	190		10 x 2.0	365.10.737

Packing: 50 pcs.

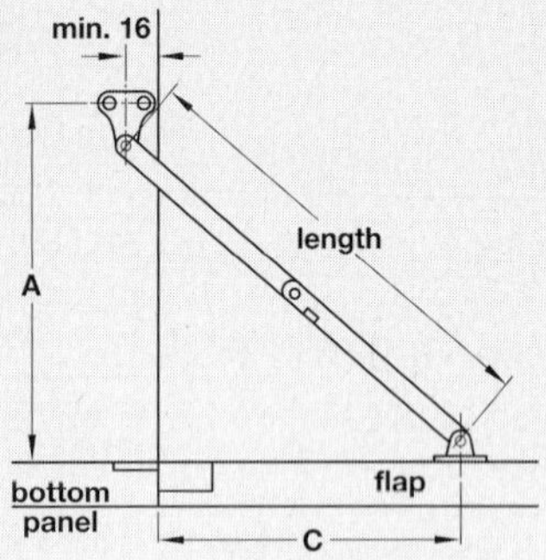

Side panel mounting

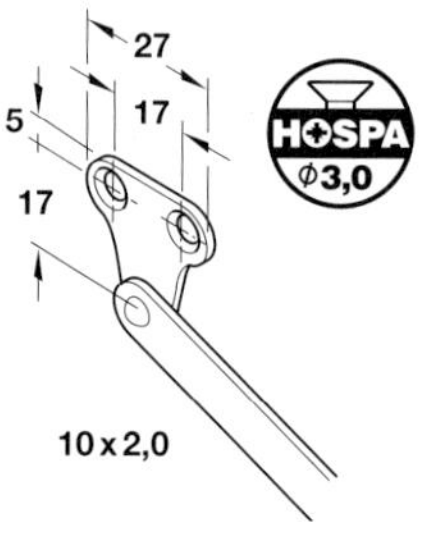

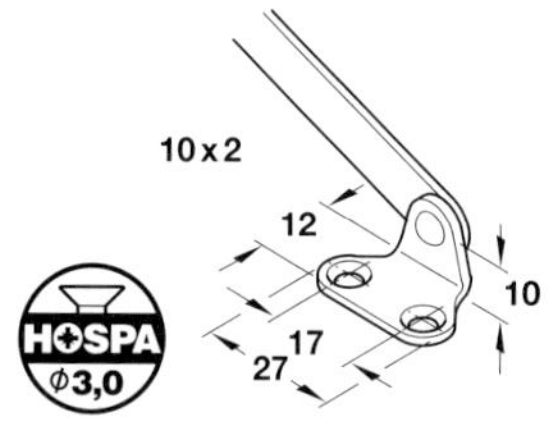

Flap mounting

Flap stay
with stop

Finish: steel, nickel-plated

Length	Inside cabinet height	Dimension A	Dimension C	Cat. No. Left	Cat. No. Right
150	min. 135	125	determine by trial mounting	365.60.737	365.60.728
200	min. 170	160		365.60.755	365.60.746
250	min. 200	190		365.60.773	365.60.764

Packing: 50 pcs.

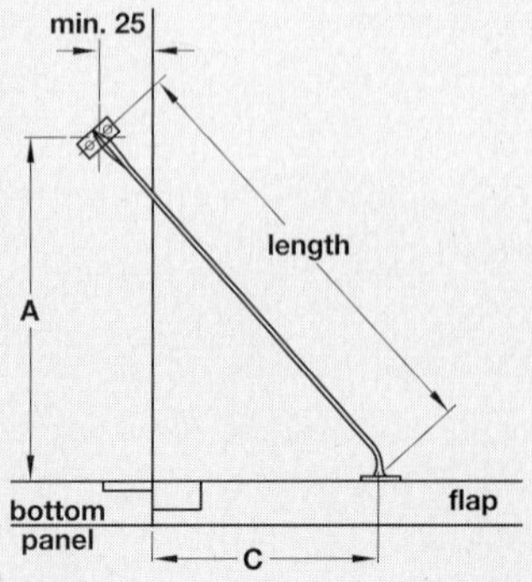

Can also be used to limit door opening.

Dimensional data not binding. We reserve the right to alter specifications without notice.

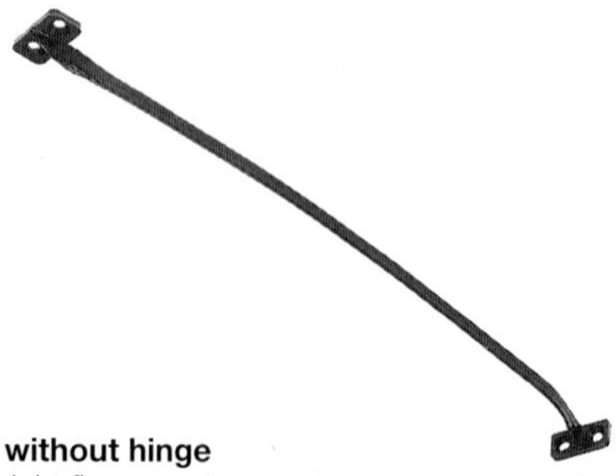

Side panel mounting

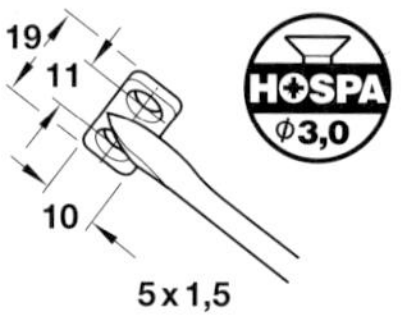

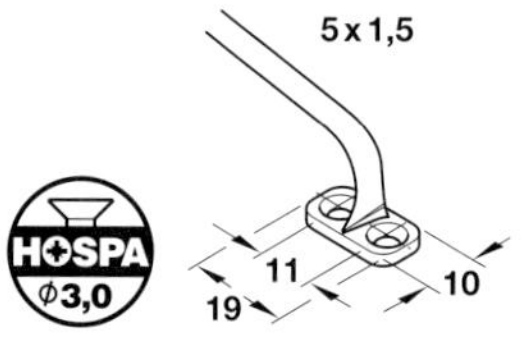

Flap mounting

Flap stay without hinge
for light-weight flaps
Reversible: can be installed left or right

Finish: plastic

Length	Dimension A	Dimension C	Cat. No. White	Cat. No. Brown
200	155	127	366.73.702	366.73.104

Packing: 100 pcs.

Dimensions in mm

Easy Mount Flap Hinges

HÄFELE

Max. Opening Angle: 80°

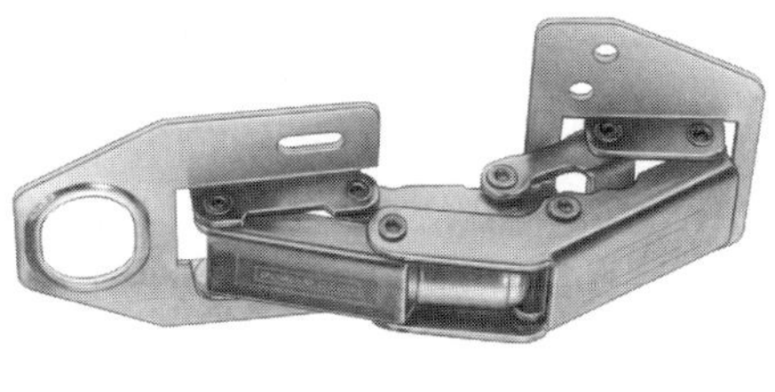

Easy-Mount hinge **screw-mounted**.
- Flap thickness min. 16 mm (5/8")
- Top panel thickness min. 16 mm (5/8")
- Adjustable, oblong holes
- Side adjustment through cam
- Spring-loaded
- All-metal: steel zinc-plated

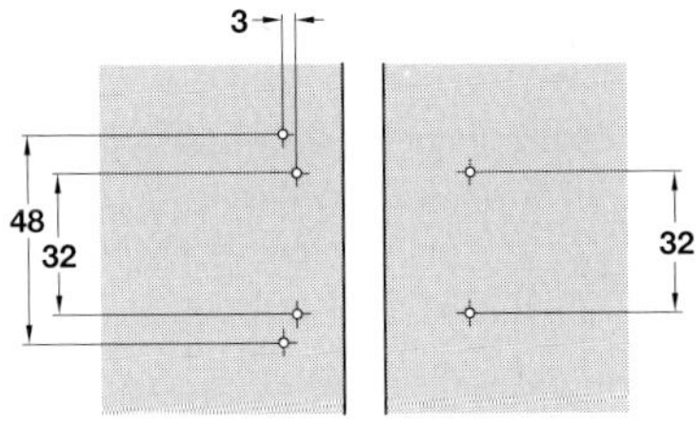

Cat. No.	343.33.956

Packing: 50 pcs.

Hinges, Flap and Lid Stays Associated Fittings 3

Must be ordered separately:
Cam Disk

Finish: Plastic, brown

Cat. No.	343.33.009

Packing: 10 pcs.

Mounting diagram:

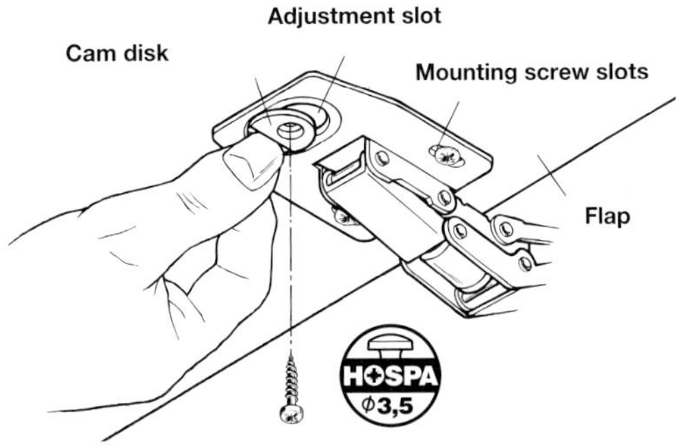

- Press cam disk into oblong hole located on arm/wing
- Mount hinge on cabinet
- Mount flap loosely to hinge, centering screws in oblong holes
- Adjust cam disk (±2 mm)
- Tighten screws

Mounting screws:
Hospa particle board screws
3.0 mm pan head
with PZ 2 cross slot
Finish:
Steel, galvanized

Length	Cat. No.
15 mm	015.71.535
17 mm	015.71.544
20 mm	015.71.553

Packing: 1000 pcs.

Mounting screws:
Hospa particle board screws
3.5 mm pan head
with PZ 2 cross slot
Finish:
Steel, galvanized

Length	Cat. No.
15 mm	015.71.633
17 mm	015.71.642
20 mm	015.71.651

Packing: 1000 pcs.

Mounting diagram

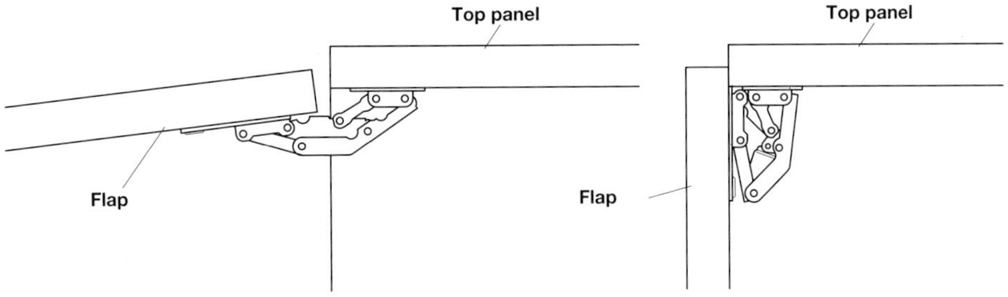

Flap open　　Flap closed

Dimensional data not binding.
We reserve the right to alter specifications without notice.

Dimensions in mm

HÄFELE

Easy-On Hinge With Lid Support

- No drilling necessary, screw-mount hinge
- Ideal for boat, RV and kitchen
- Hinge and lid support in one.
- No separate installation of lid stay

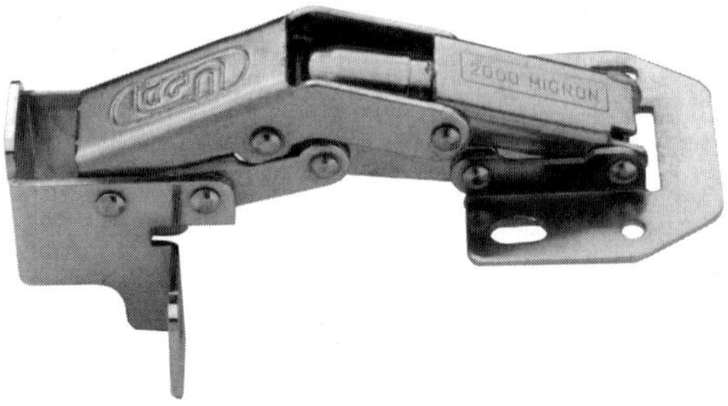

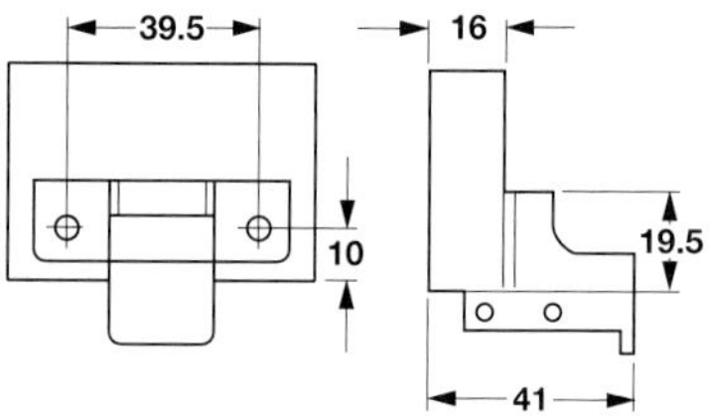

B = 16 mm = face frame thickness
F = 2 mm = minimum gap
A = max. 18 mm = door overlay
C = max. 20 mm = door thickness

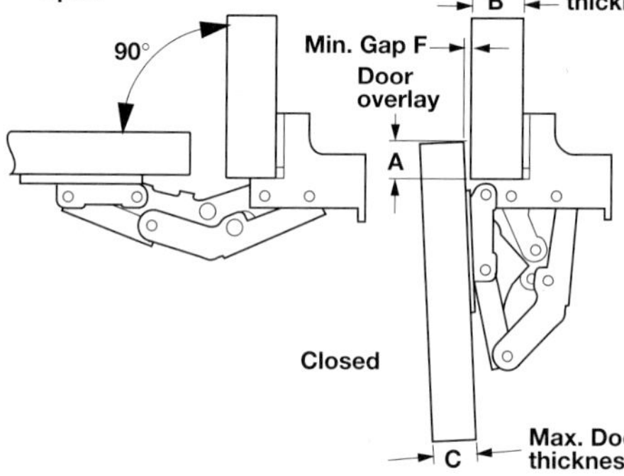

Finish: nickel-plated

Cat. No.	343.33.710

Packing: 100 pcs.

Dimensions in mm

Lid Supports

Lid stay
With safety catch
All-metal

Finish: nickel-plated

Cat. No.		
	left-handed	366.30.770
	right-handed	366.30.761

Packing: 50 pcs.

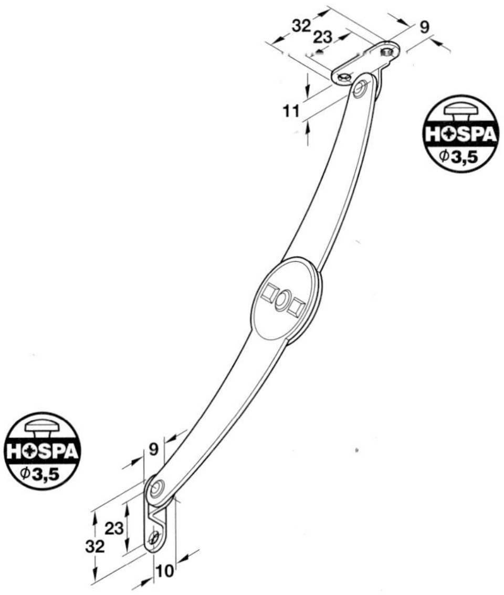

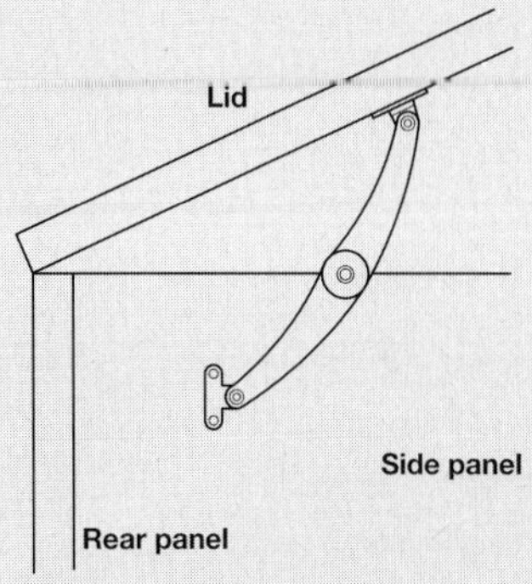

Audio cabinet lid stay featuring spring-loaded joint and dependable safety stop. For cabinet lid, flap-door and flap stay applications. Note: when used as a flap stay, it is necessary to reverse handing; the right-hand stay is installed left, and vice versa.

Lid stay
With safety catch
Plastic material

Finish: plastic, beige

Cat. No.		
	left-handed	366.32.498
	right-handed	366.32.489

Packing: 100 pcs.

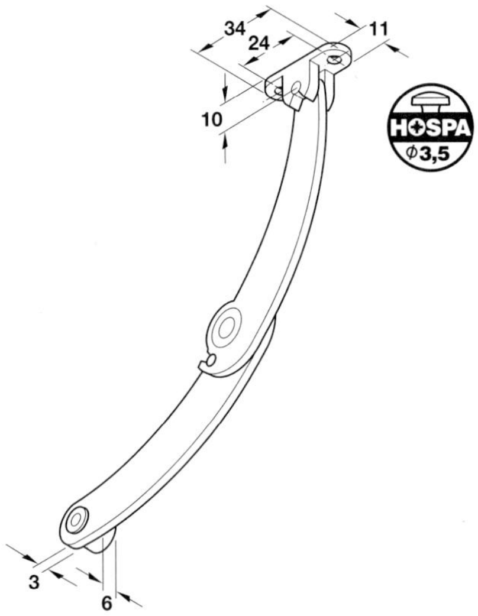

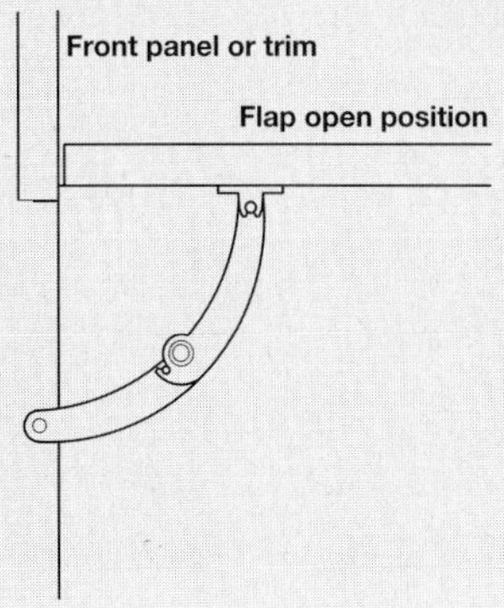

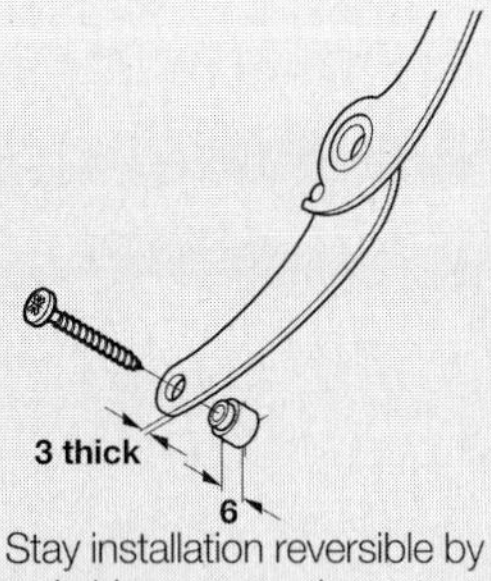

Stay installation reversible by switching spacer sleeve to opposite side.

Cara-Top Lid stay
For light-duty use with adjustable spring.
Reversible: Can be installed left or right.
Metal mounting plate rotates 180° to switch from left to right.

Finish: plastic, black/steel, zinc-plated

Cat. No.	373.53.334

Packing: 100 pcs.

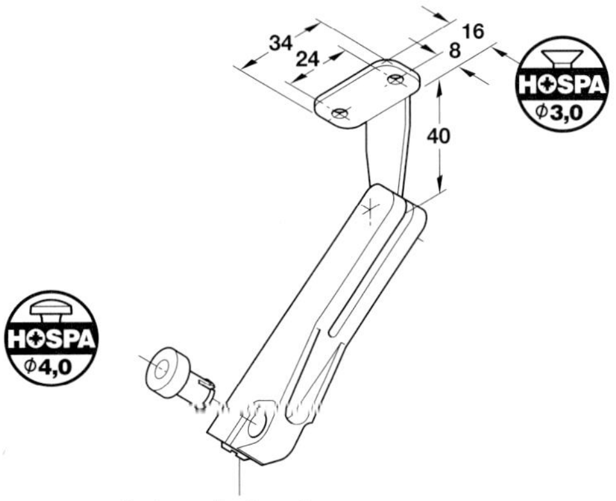

Spring adjustment screw

Lid in open position

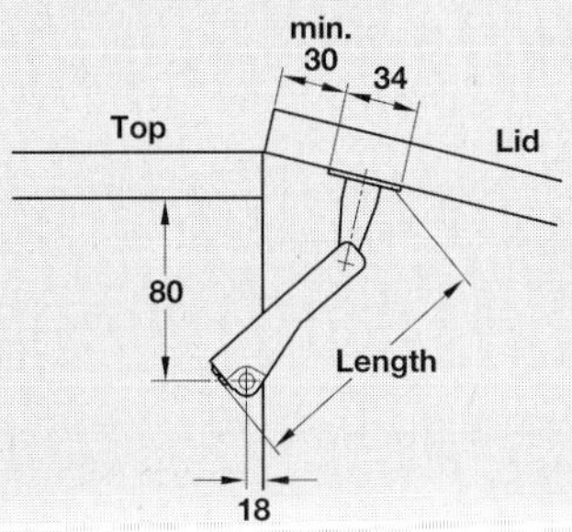

Dimensional data not binding.
We reserve the right to alter specifications without notice.

Dimensions in mm

HÄFELE

Fall-ex® Lid Stays

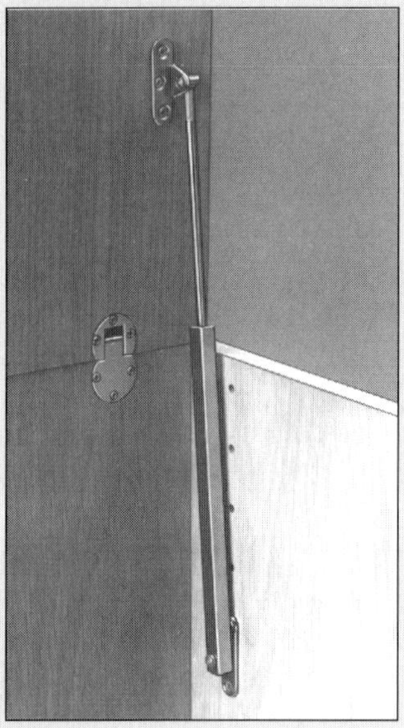

3 Hinges, Flap and Lid Stays Associated Fittings

Mounting screws:
Hospa particle board screws
Raised head with
PZ 2 cross slot
Finish:
steel, nickel-plated

Length	Cat. No.
20 mm	015.55.844
25 mm	015.55.853
30 mm	015.55.862

Packing: 1000 pcs.

Mounting screws:
Varianta screws
Flat head with
PZ 2 cross slot
Finish:
steel, nickel-plated

Length	3 mm dia. hole	5 mm dia. hole
10,5 mm	013.15.617	013.15.715
13,5 mm	013.15.626	013.15.724
16,0 mm	013.15.635	013.15.733

Packing: 100 and 1000 pcs.

Keep brake piston rod free of oil, grease and other contaminants at all times.

Reversible: can be installed left or right

Finish: steel, nickel-plated
Square tube: brass, nickel-plated

Length (mm)	Cat. No.
250	372.17.253
325	372.17.262
450	372.17.271

Packing: 10 pcs.

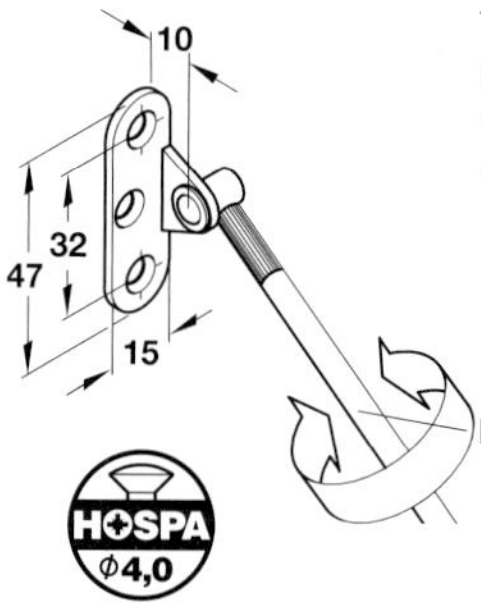

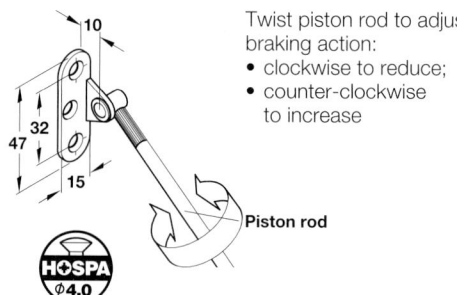

Twist piston rod to adjust braking action:
- clockwise to reduce;
- counter-clockwise to increase

Side panel mounting

SYSTEM VARIANTA 32

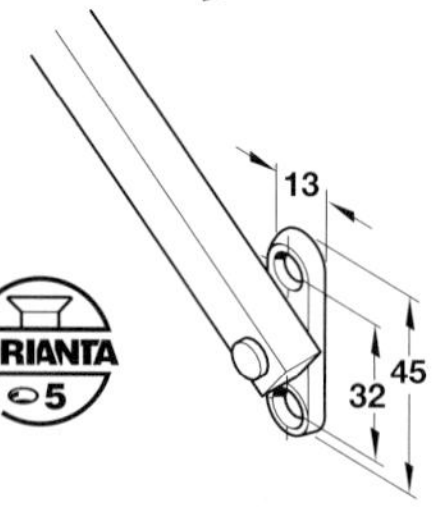

Dimensions in mm

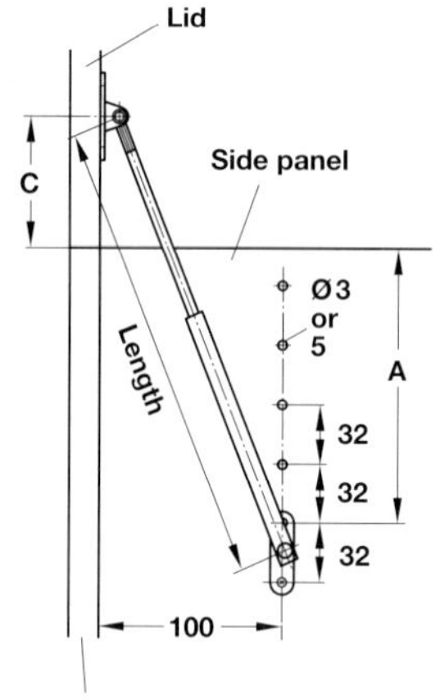

Lid open

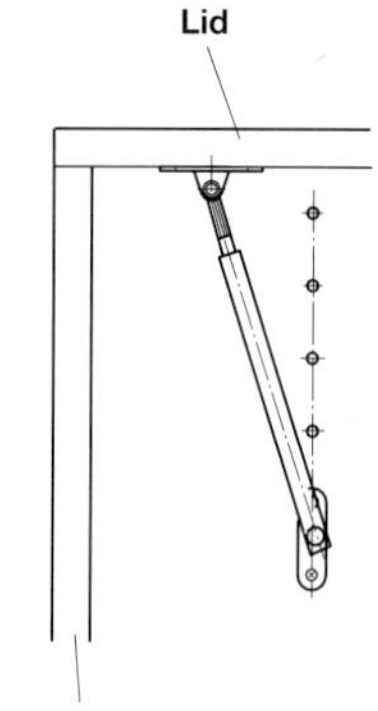

Lid closed

Length (mm)	Lid height	Dimension A	Dimension C
250	up to 300	145	Trial
325	up to 450	185	Trial
450	over 450	255	Trial

Dimensional data not binding.
We reserve the right to alter specifications without notice.

Lid Stays

HÄFELE

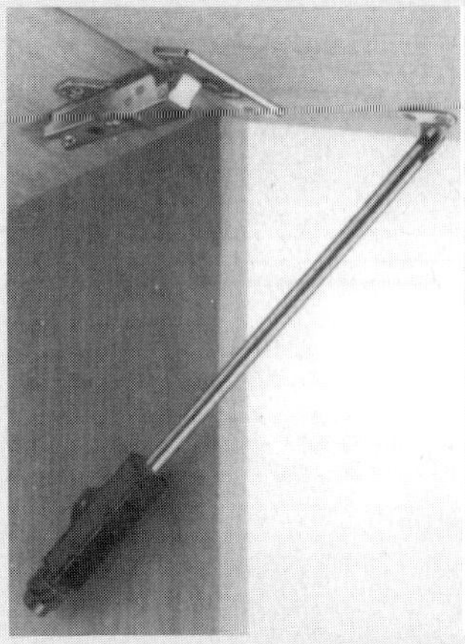

- Braking action infinitely adjustable using adjustment collar. Clockwise to reduce braking action; counter-clockwise to increase.

Hinges, Flap and Lid Stays Associated Fittings **3**

- As door is opened, end cap snaps over adjustment collar to lock door in open position.

Master-stop lid stay with brake
screw-mounted
reversible: can be installed left or right

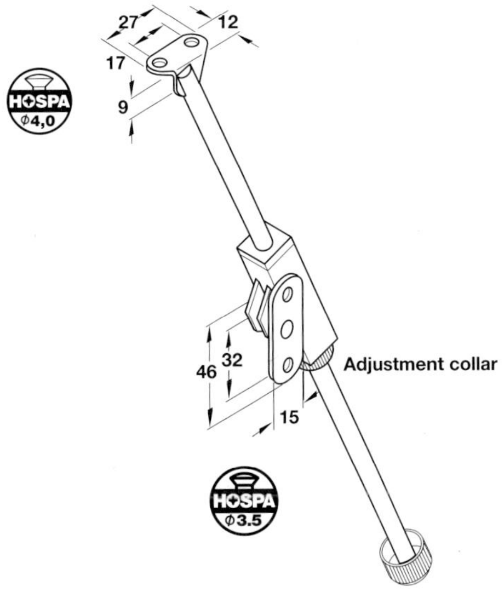

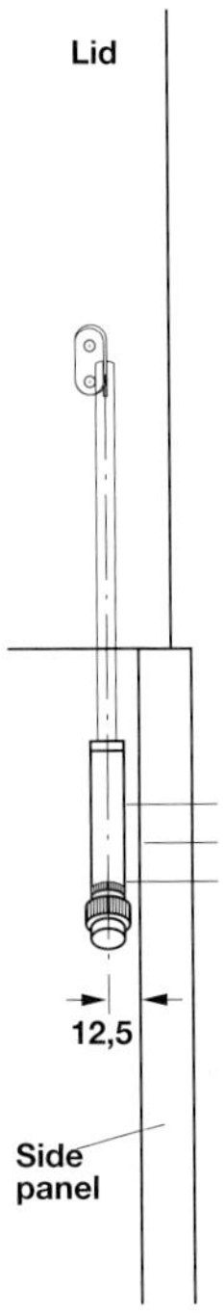

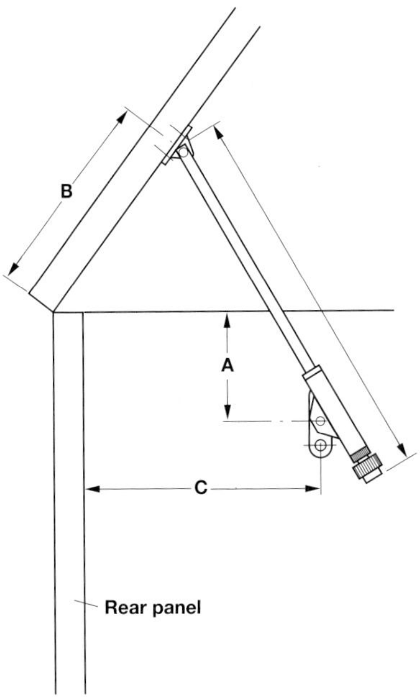

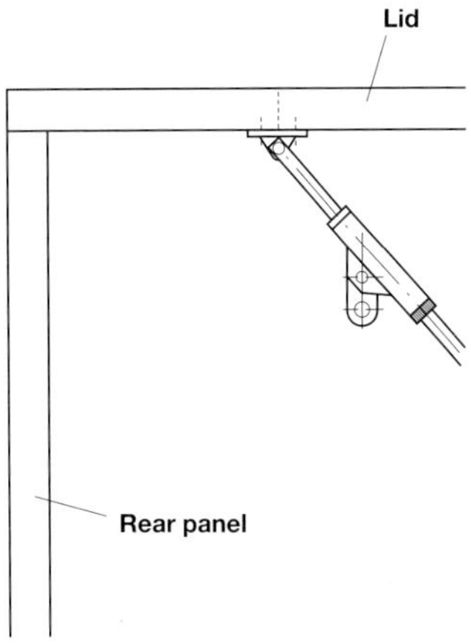

Length (mm)	Dimension A (mm)	Dimension B (mm)	Dimension C (mm)
145	Determine by trial mounting		
260	depending on lid opening		
330	angle.		

Keep brake piston rod free of oil, grease and other contaminants at all times.

Finish:		Cat. No.	
plastic/steel		black/nickel-plated	black/bronzed
Length	260 mm	373.74.324	373.74.128
	330 mm	373.74.333	373.74.137

Packing: 25 pcs.

Dimensions in mm

Dimensional data not binding.
We reserve the right to alter specifications without notice.

HÄFELE

Lid Stays

Lid in open position

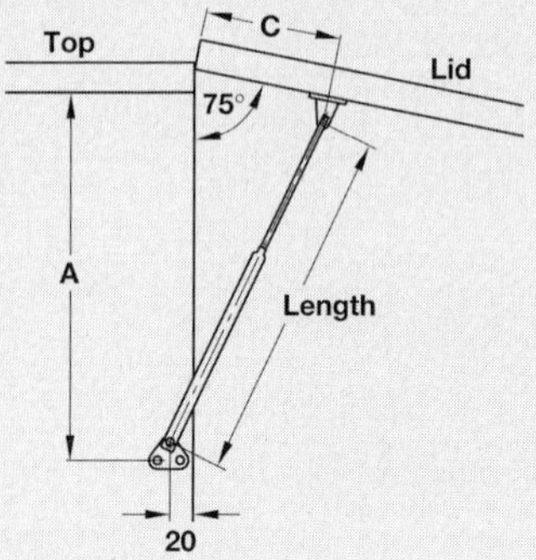

Dual-purpose intergrated spring holds lid securely in open or closed position. Use one or two stays, depending on lid weight.

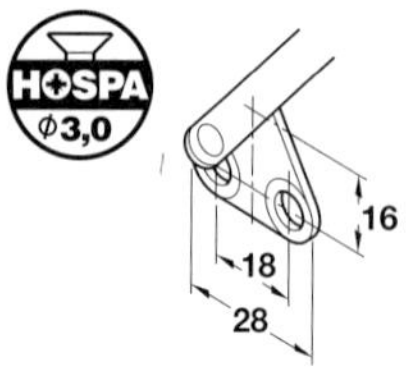

Side panel attachment

Lid attachment

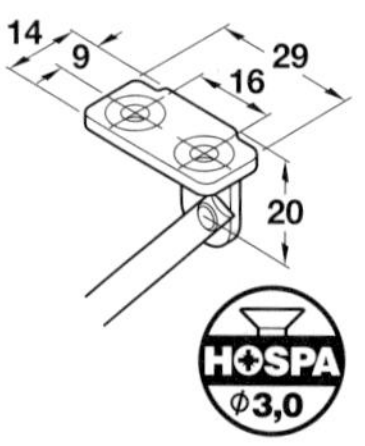

Firmatop Lid Stay
reversible: can be installed left or right handed

Length	Finish	Dimension A	Dimension C	Cat. No.
130	Steel zinc-plated	150	Determine	373.58.788
250	Brass chrome plated	260	by trial	373.58.919
250	Brass polished	260	installation	373.58.811

Packing: 20 pcs.

Lid in open position

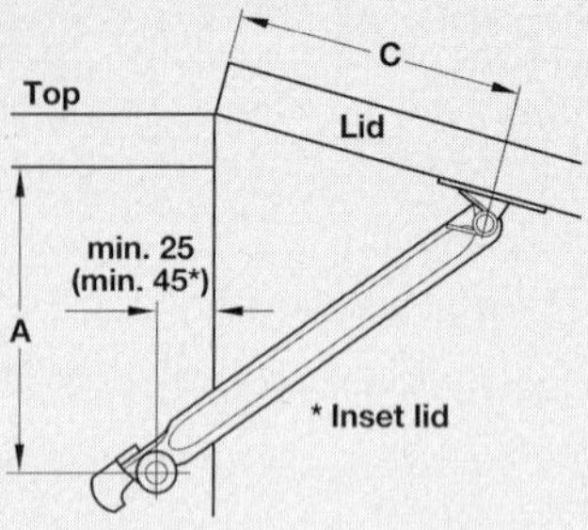

Light lids, one stay; for heavier lids, use two stays.
- To release, lift lid slightly.

Lid attachment

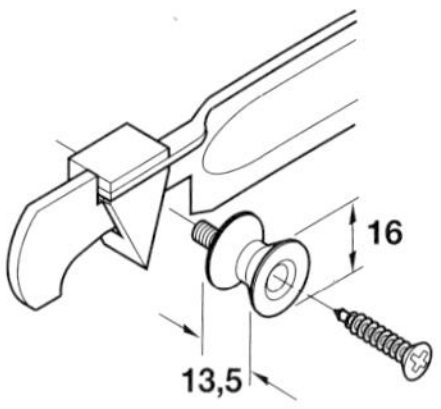

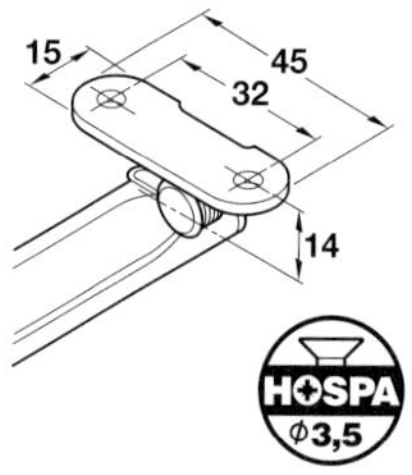

Side panel attachment

Side panel attachment
Finish: Steel, nickel-plated

Length	Lid height	Dimension A Inset lid	Dimension A Overlay lid	Dimension C	Cat. No. left	Cat. No. right
150	max. 250	80	80	Determine	366.37.715	366.37.706
200	max. 500	120	120	by trial	366.37.733	366.37.724
250	max. 1000	160	160	mounting	366.37.751	366.37.742

Packing: 10 pcs.

Dimensional data not binding. We reserve the right to alter specifications without notice.

Dimensions in mm

Lid Stays

HÄFELE

Lid attachment

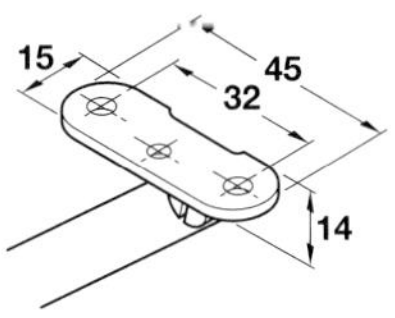

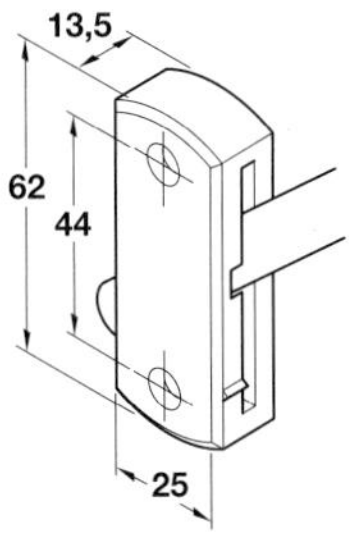

HOSPA Ø3,5

Side panel attachment

Lid stay

Finish: Steel, nickel-plated

Length	Lid height	Dimension A Inset lid	overlay lid	Dimension C	Cat. No. left	right
200	max. 500	90	70	Determine by	373.73.710	373.73.701
250	over 500	120	120	trial mounting	373.73.738	373.73.729

Packing: 25 pcs.

Lid in open position

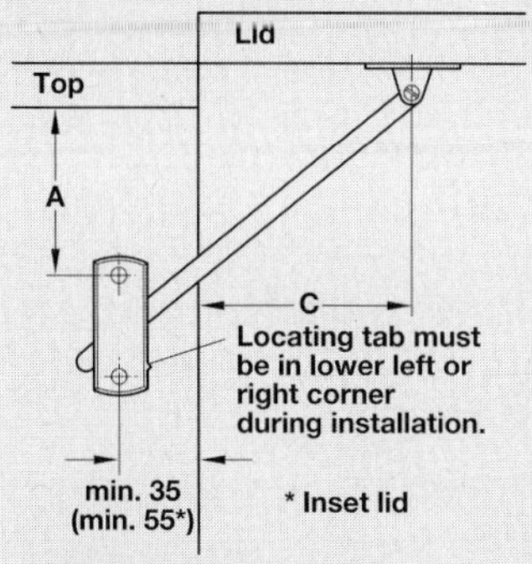

- To lock, lift lid until lid stay engages.
- Lift slightly to release stay.

Hinges, Flap and Lid Stays Associated Fittings 3

Lid attachment

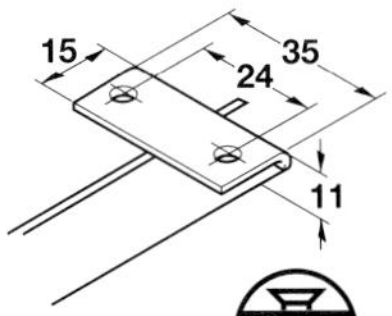

HOSPA Ø3.0

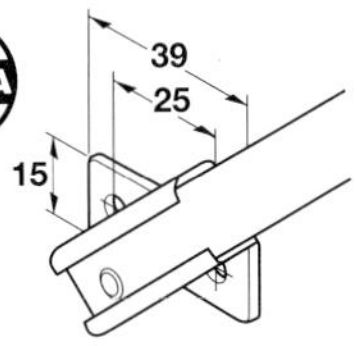

HOSPA Ø3.0

Side panel attachment

Arretop lid stay

with automatic lock; can be installed left or right
Finish: steel, nickel-plated

Size	Cabinet Depth	Dimension A	Dimension C	Cat. No.
200	210	150	Determine by trial mounting	373.70.611
250	260	180		373.70.620
300	310	230		373.70.639

Packing: 10 pcs.

Lid in open position

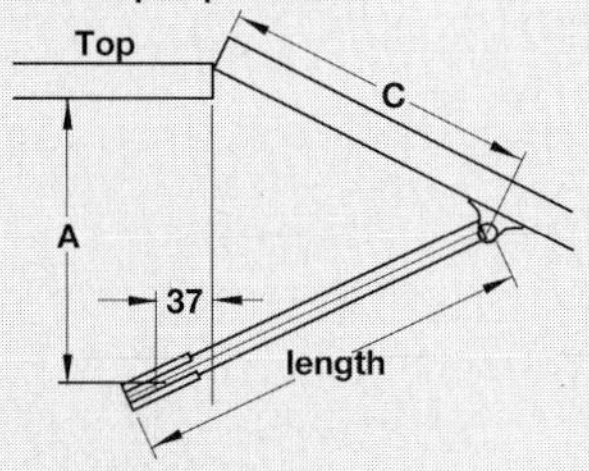

- Open to approx. 75° until lid stay engages
- Lift lid slightly to release

HÄFELE

Lid Stays

Lid in open position

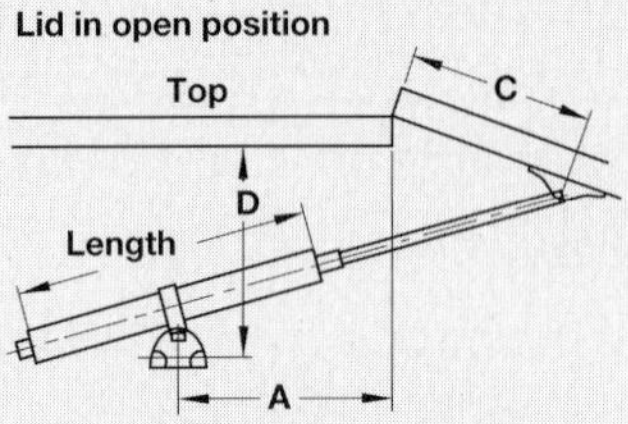

- Apply slight pressure to close lid
- Trial mounting recommended
- Snaps into a locked position when fully extended
- Speed-adjustable
- Does not support lid during upward movement
- Left and Right-handed models available

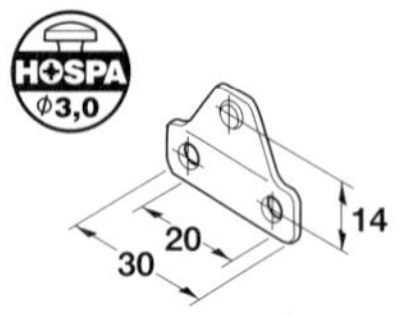

Side panel attachment

Lid attachment

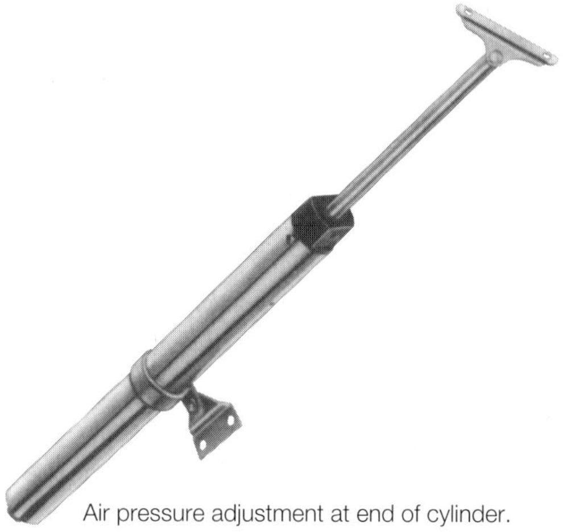

Air pressure adjustment at end of cylinder.

Berolina lid stay
for vertical lids
Finish: steel, nickel-plated

Length	Cabinet depth	Dimension A	Dimension C		Cat. No. left	right
220	min. 270	145	145	determine by trial mounting	372.03.795	372.03.740

Packing: 1 pc.

Lid in open position

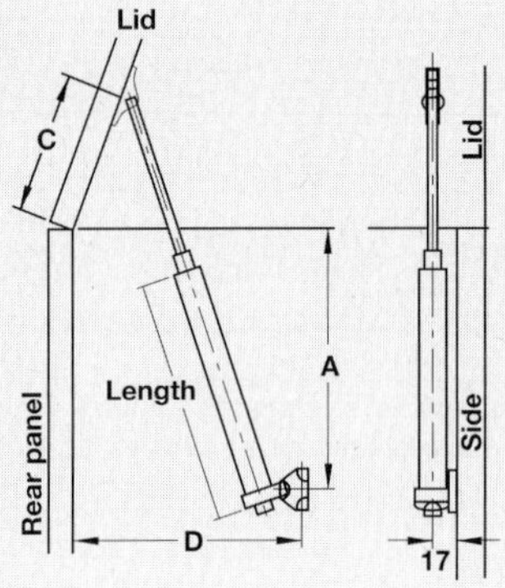

- Apply light pressure to close lid

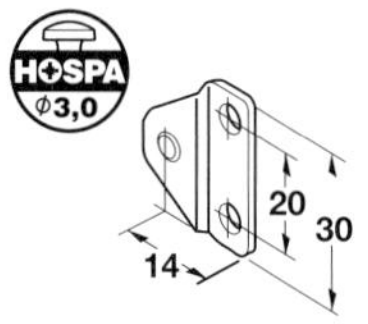

Side panel attachment

Lid attachment

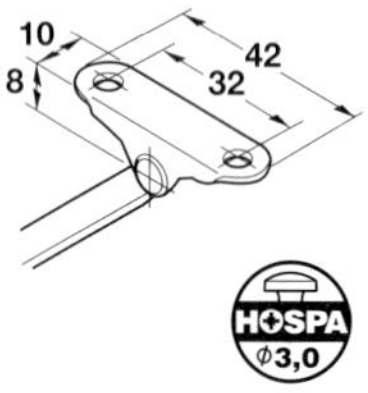

pressure adjustment at end of cylinder.

Berolina lid stay
for horizontal lids
Finish: steel, nickel-plated

Length	Cabinet depth	Dimension A	Dimension C	Dimension D	Cat. No. left	right
180	min. 230	195	100	determine by	372.04.783	372.04.738
220	min. 270	235	125	trial mounting	372.04.792	372.04.747

Packing: 1 pc.

Dimensional data not binding.
We reserve the right to alter specifications without notice.

Dimensions in mm

Lid Stays

Lid mounting

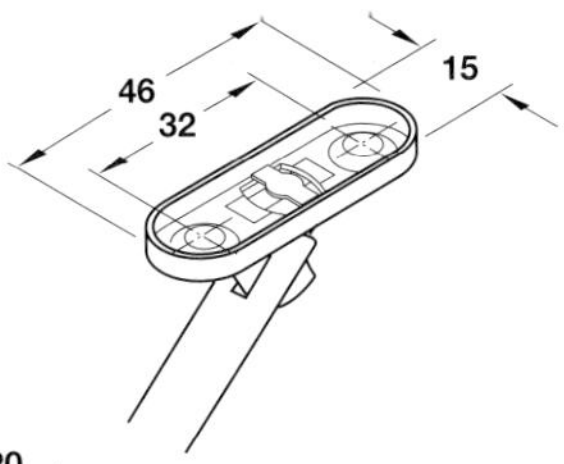

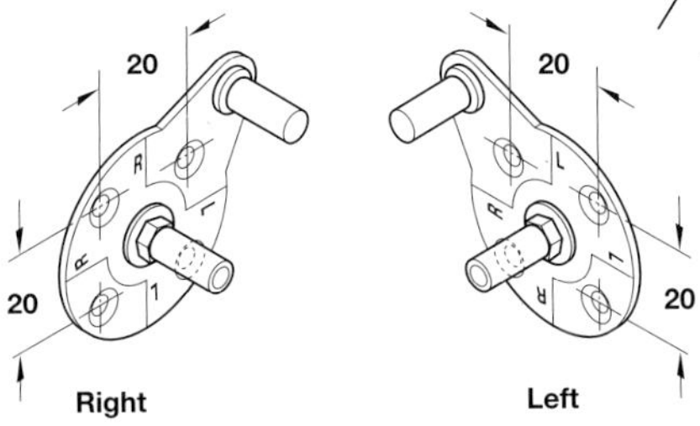

Side panel mounting

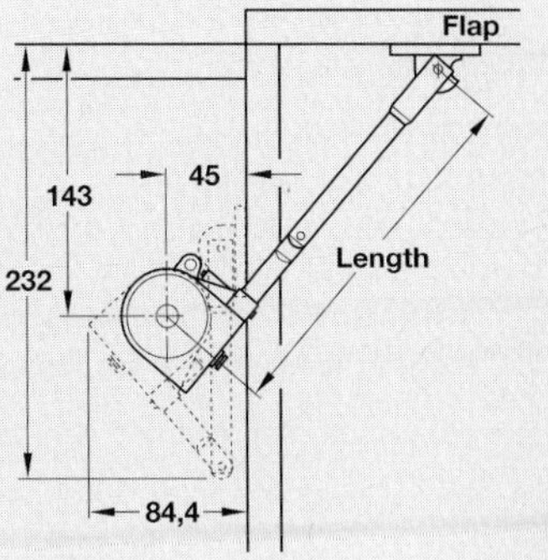

Lid Stay
lid bracket attachment
reversible: can be installed left or right
Finish: plastic/steel, nickel-plated

Length	Color	Cat. No.
200 mm	black	365.31.300
	white	365.31.700

Packing: 20 pcs, including fastening screws

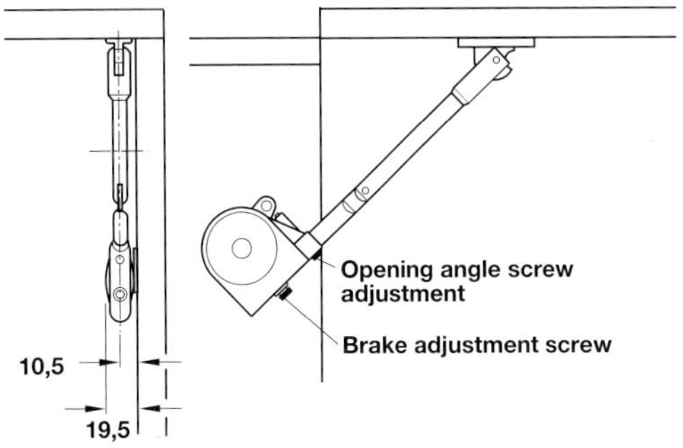

Lid mounting

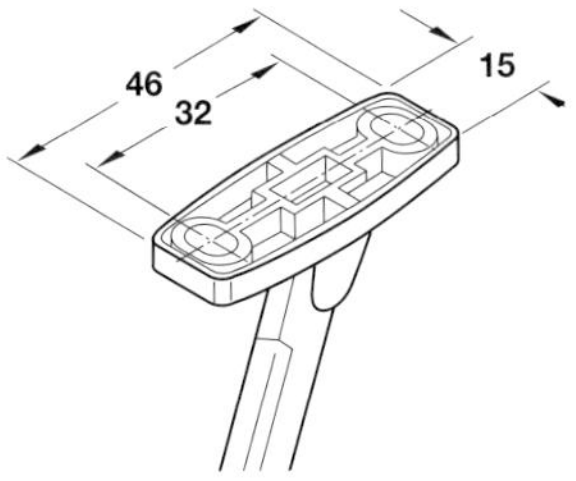

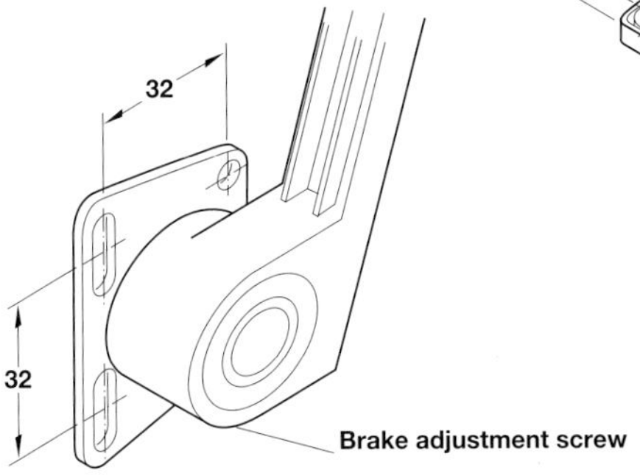

Side panel mounting

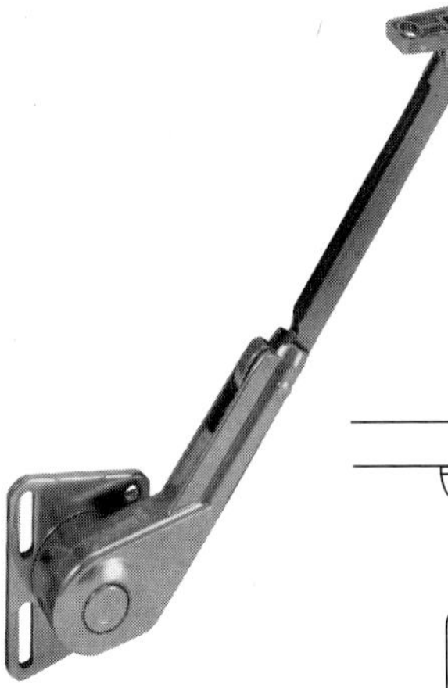

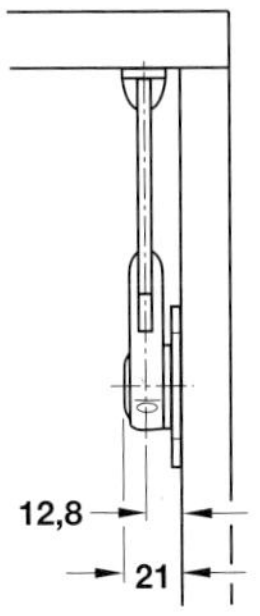

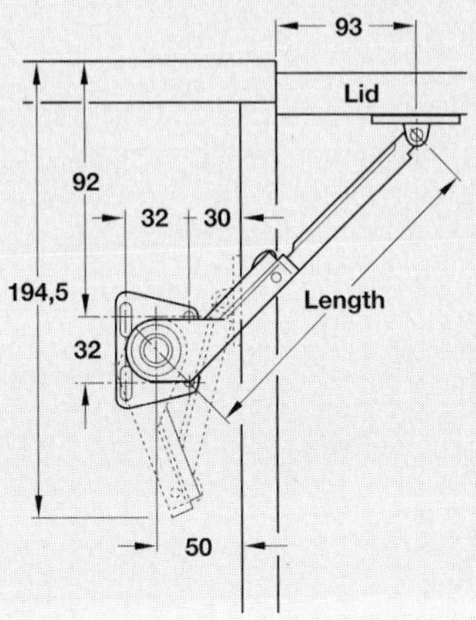

Lid Stay
Finish: steel, nickel-plated

Length		Cat. No.
200 mm	left	365.31.601
	right	365.31.600

Packing: 20 pcs, including fastening screws

Dimensions in mm

Dimensional data not binding.
We reserve the right to alter specifications without notice.

Lid Stays

Lid in open position

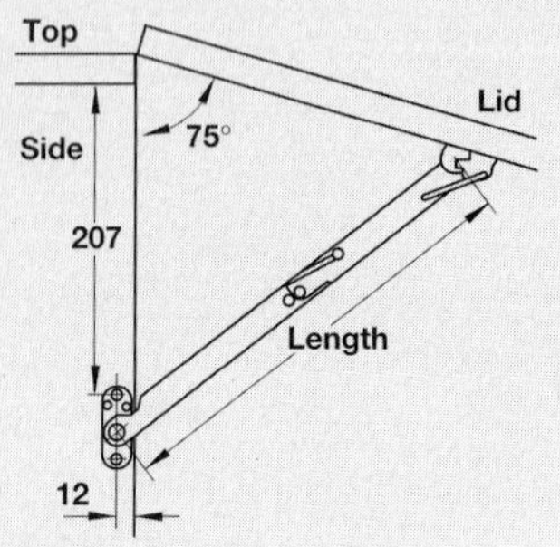

- Raise lid slightly to release lid stay
- Can be used to limit door opening angle
- Trial mounting recommended

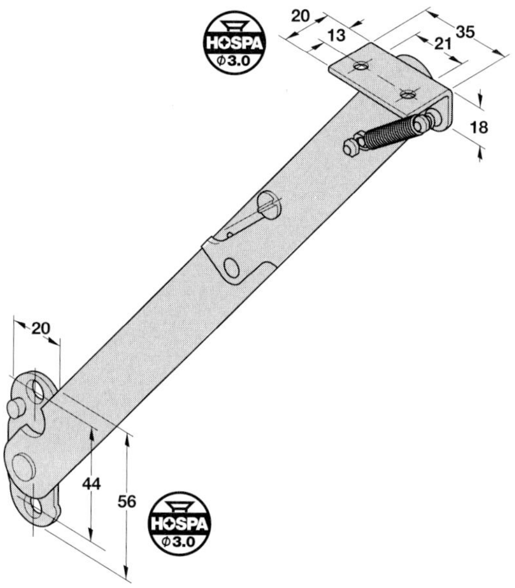

Lid stay
Finish: steel, nickel-plated

Length	Cat. No. left	right
300	366.35.711	366.35.702

Packing: 40 pcs.

Lid in open position

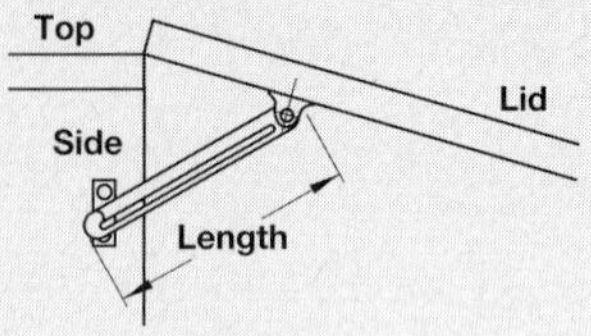

- Can be used to limit door opening angle

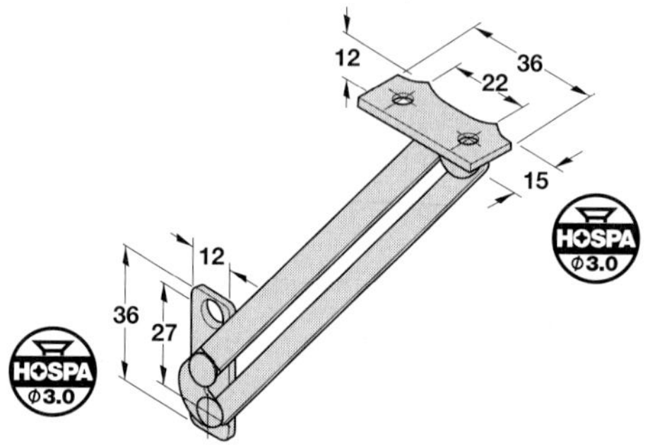

Lid stay with guide slot
Finish: steel

Length		Cat. No. left	right
150	nickel-plated	366.40.776	366.40.767
150	brass-plated	366.40.570	366.40.561

Packing: 50 pcs.

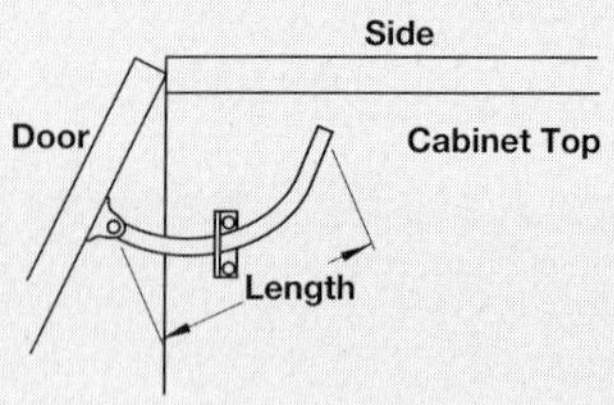

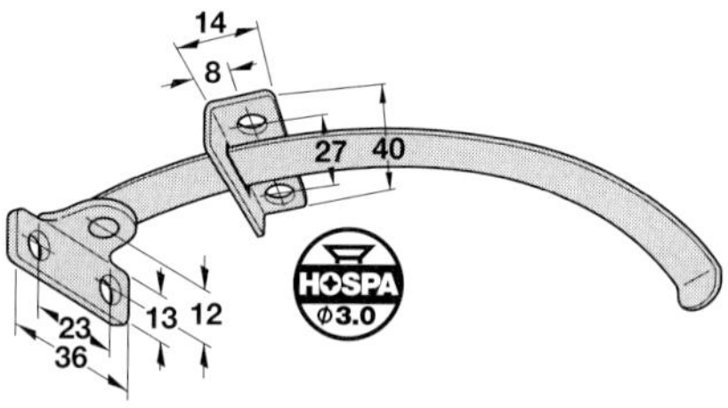

Lid stay
used as door restraint
Finish: steel, nickel-plated

Length	Cat. No. left	right
150	371.32.755	371.32.700

Packing: 50 pcs.

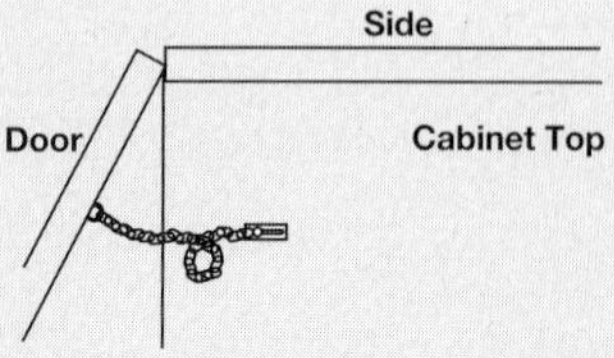

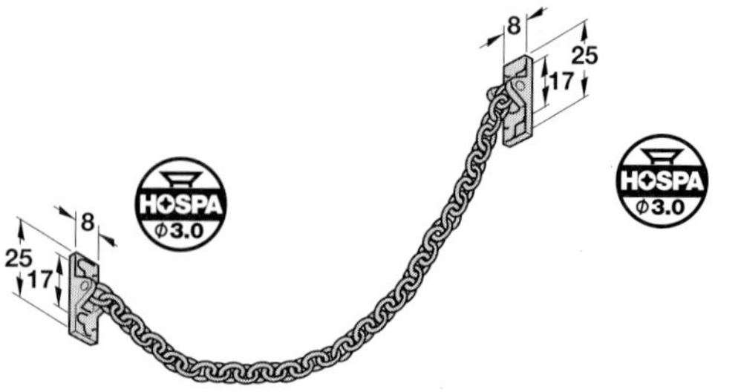

Decorative door restraint chain
with mounting plates
Finish: brass, polished

Length	Cat. No.
200	372.35.813

Packing: 10 pcs.

Dimensional data not binding.
We reserve the right to alter specifications without notice.

Dimensions in mm

Brass Lid Stays

Sliding Stay, for slant-front desk lids

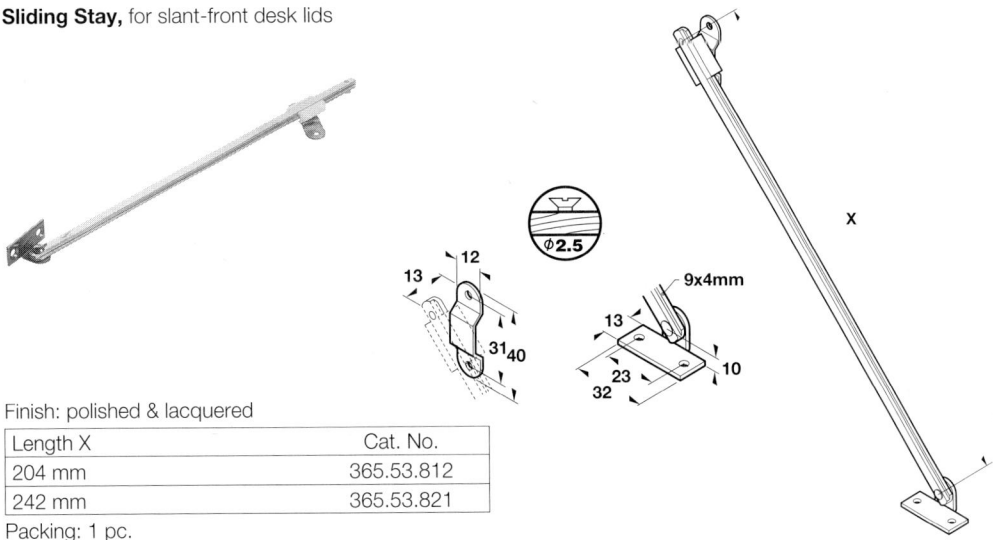

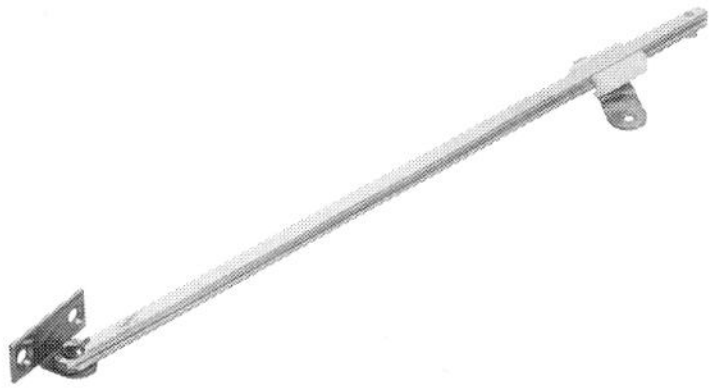

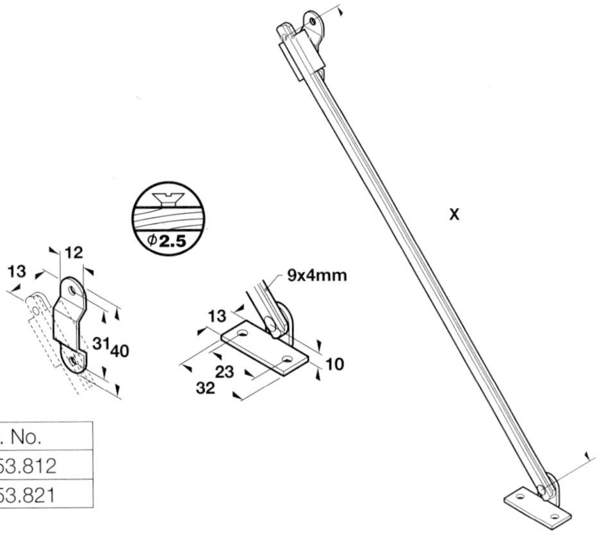

Finish: polished & lacquered

Length X	Cat. No.
204 mm	365.53.812
242 mm	365.53.821

Packing: 1 pc.

Folding Lid Stay

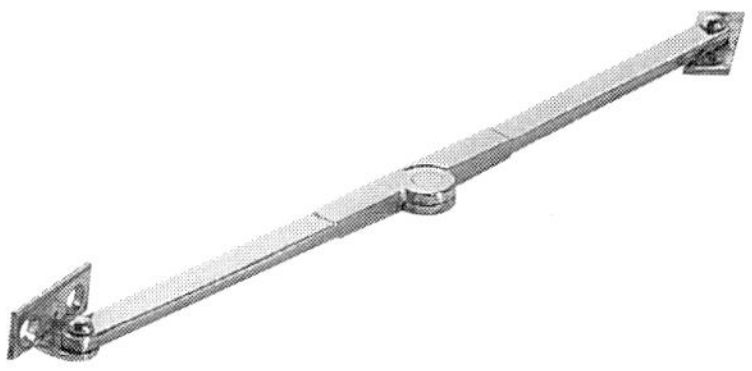

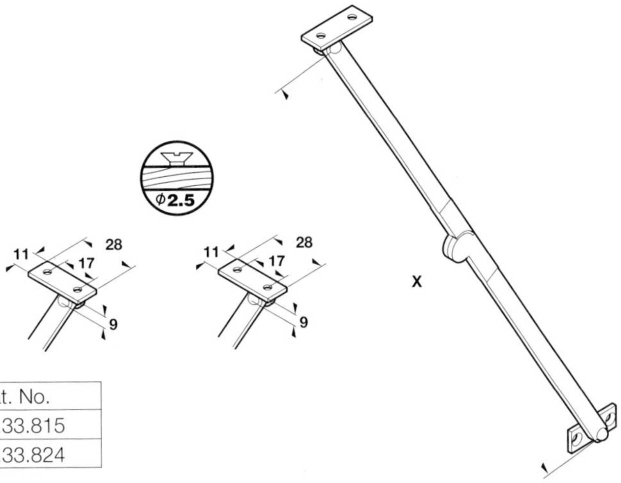

Finish: polished & lacquered

Length X	Cat. No.
195 mm	366.33.815
300 mm	366.33.824

Packing: 1 pc.

Lockable Door Stay

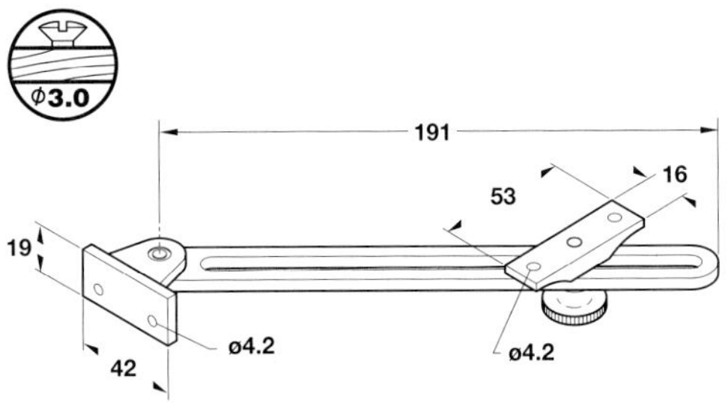

Finish: polished & lacquered

Cat. No.	805.06.814

Packing: 1 pc.

HÄFELE

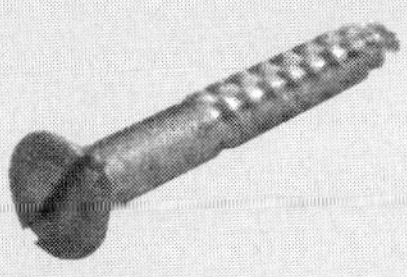

Raised Head Countersunk wood screw

Finish: brass, unfinished

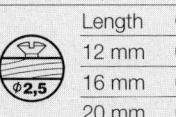

	Length	Cat. No.
Φ2,5	12 mm	011.20.216
	16 mm	011.20.234
	20 mm	011.20.243

Packing: 200 pcs.

Raised Head Countersunk wood screw

Finish: brass, unfinished

	Length	Cat. No.
Φ3.0	12 mm	011.20.412
	16 mm	011.20.430
	20 mm	011.20.449

Packing: 200 pcs.

- Locks in open position

- Thumbscrew adjustment controls door movement

HÄFELE

Bench Seat Hinges, Folding Table Fittings

- Hinge design ensures safe retention of seat top in raised position at an angle of 95°
- Guarantees generous degree of forward movement (approx. 110 mm)
- Unrestricted opening even of fully upholstered seats, as no joint is required between the seat and back
- Hinge joints incorporate a stop to prevent the open seat slamming against the fitting
- Springs for seat tops weighing 8 and 12 kg counterbalance the weight of the seat top and assist opening
- Screw holes in the bench side panel and seat top are at 32 mm intervals

Left-hand hinge, without spring (raised)

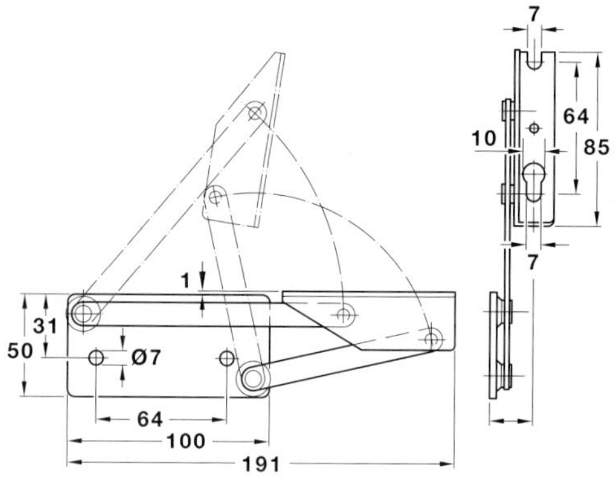

Bench seat hinge
for light-weight seat tops, **without spring**
Finish: steel

Cat. No.	yellow chromated	643.01.506
	white epoxy	643.01.700

Packing: 10 pairs

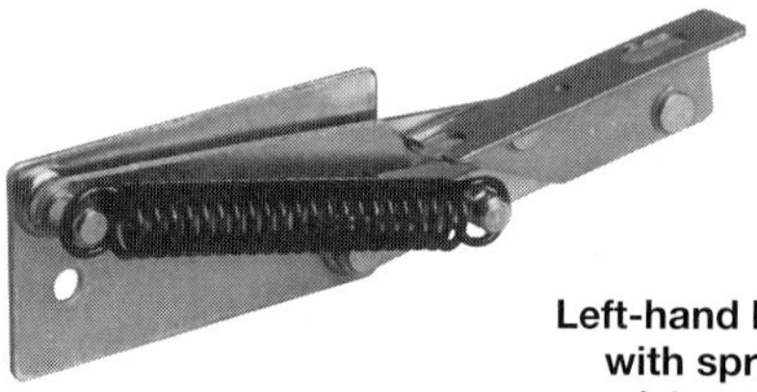

Left-hand hinge, with spring (closed)

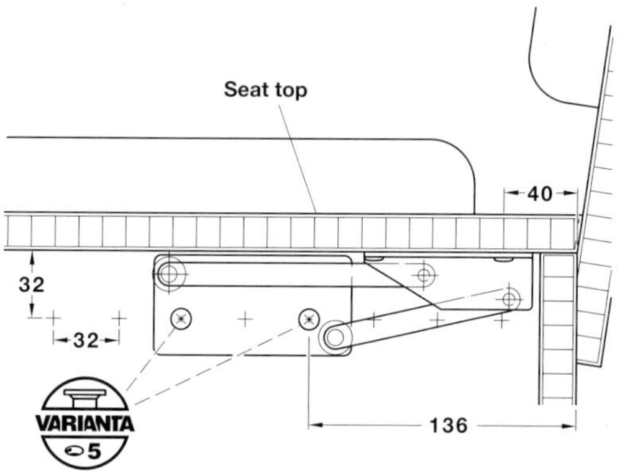

Bench seat hinge
with spring
Finish: steel

Seat top weight		approx. **8 kg**	approx.**12 kg**
Cat. No.	yellow chromated	643.01.515	643.01.524
	white epoxy	643.01.730	643.01.740

Packing: 1 and 10 pairs

Dimensional data not binding.
We reserve the right to alter specifications without notice.

Dimensions in mm

Flap Stay »FLAP-EX«

This hinge is particularly suitable for installing in bathroom and laboratory cabinets with front flaps.

The door is opened under spring tension by **approx. 27°** by simply applying pressure directly to the door. When the door is closed, the flap is pushed back into the cabinet where it is secured by means of the **Mini Latch catch.**

This flap hinge is designed for installation in cabinet sizes from 820 mm high, 400 mm wide and an inside cabinet depth of at least 270 mm.

Important:
the hinge with the coil springs is designed to support a **particle board front** with the maximum dimensions 590 mm high, 400 mm wide and 19 mm thick and a maximum **weight when full** of **5 kg (11lbs)**.

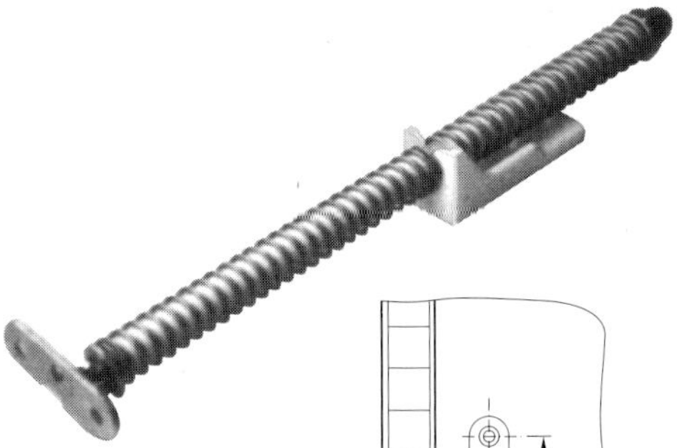

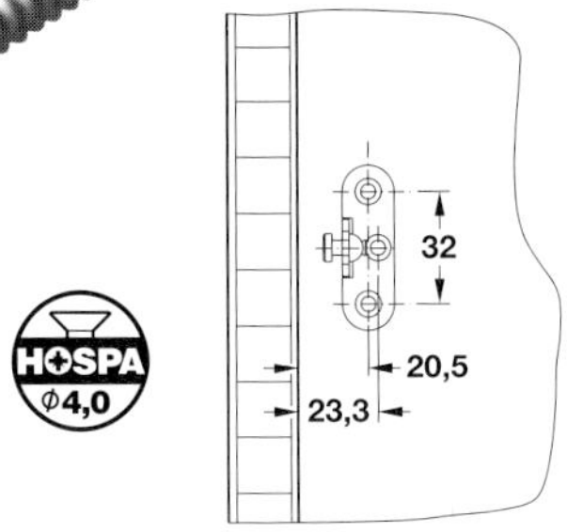

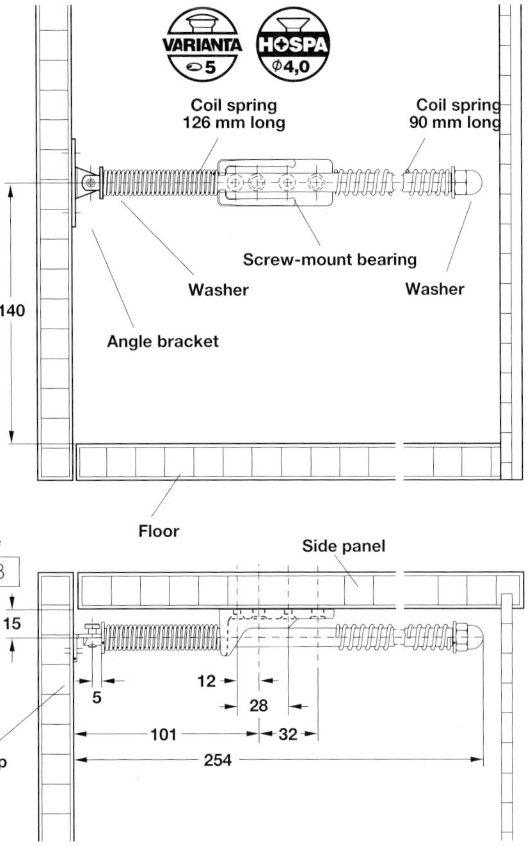

Dimensions in mm

For installation of the front flap, the following are required in addition:
2 cup hinges
as well as **Mini Latch catch, see below**.

Flap hinge »FLAP-EX«
completely assembled, consisting of:
- 1 screw-mount angle bracket, steel, nickel-plated
- 1 round rod with plastic sleeve, 2 washers
- 2 coil springs: front =126 mm long
  rear = 90 mm long

1 screw-mount bearing, packed loose: plastic, white

Cat. No.	365.52.708

Packing: 10 pcs.

Mounting instructions:
screw angle bracket to front panel and screw-mount bearing to cabinet side panel; see mounting drawing on the right.
Push round rod into the screw-on bearing between the two coil springs.

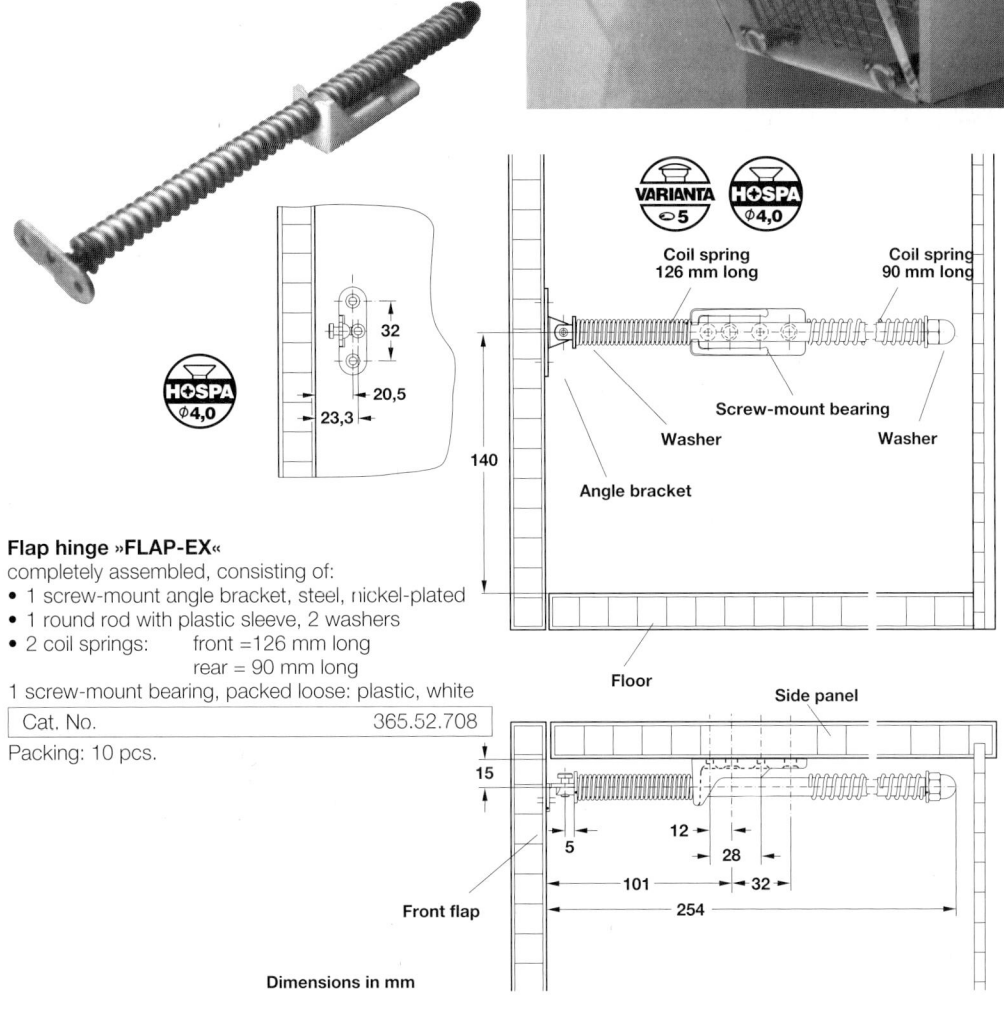

Automatic spring catch Mini Latch, screw-mount, with strike

Finish
Catch: steel, nickel-plated
Strike: plastic, white

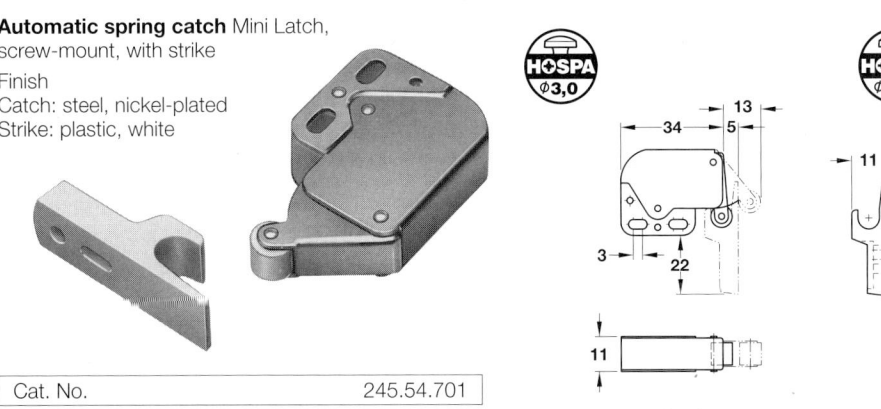

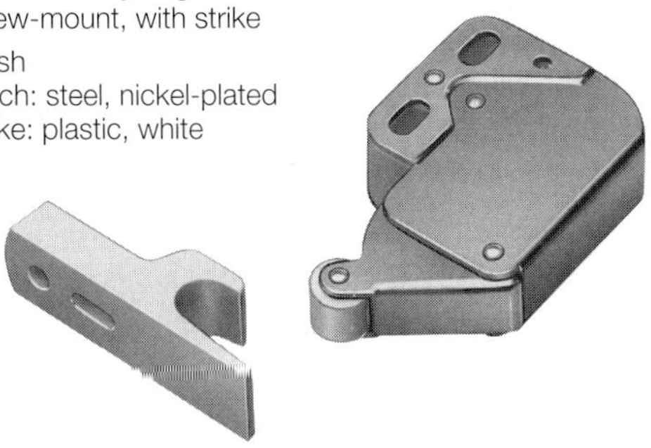

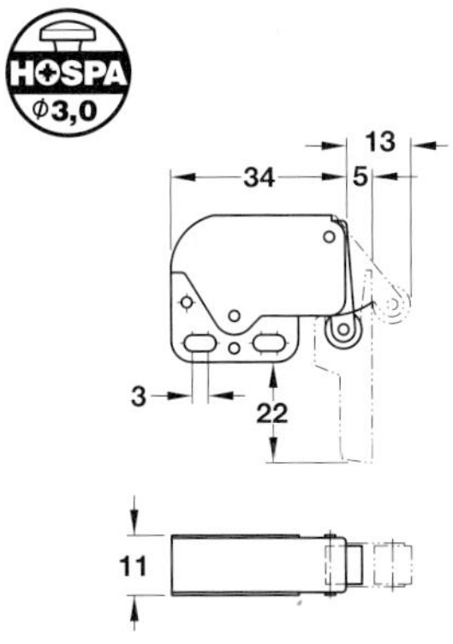

Catch

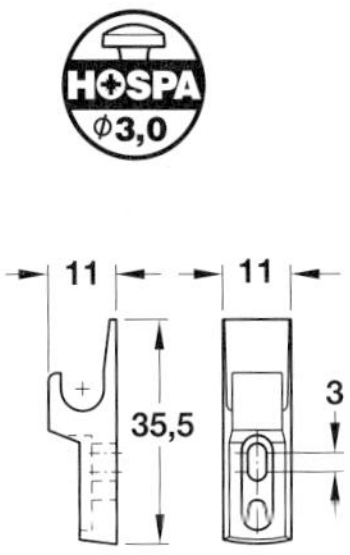

Strike

Cat. No.	245.54.701

Packing: 50 pcs.

The door is **opened** by pushing against the door panel. The pressure triggers the release spring in the fitting. The door opens auto-matically.
To **close** the door, slightly press against the door panel.

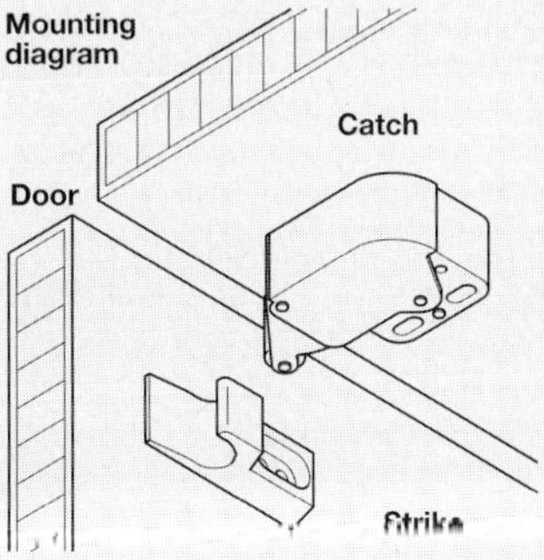

HÄFELE

Synchronous scissor-action hinge

With this mechanism, both doors of a cabinet can be opened sychronously in a single pull - even when equipped with stop strips. With the articulated rods, when the right-hand door is pulled forward the left-hand door lags behind - without collision.

The **opening angle** of both doors is limited to **110°** using cup hinges.

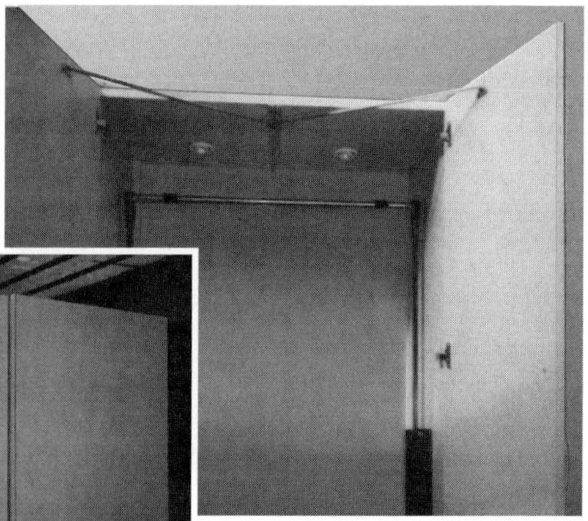

During closing, the left-hand door is pushed forward by spring tension. This ensures that both doors can be closed without problems.

Mounting sequence:
the aluminum running track is designed for maximum installation depth and can be cut to length as required.

- Cut running track to length according to installation depth and the installed stop strip; see sketch below.
- Screw running track into the center of the cabinet to the upper shelf.
- Screw articulated rods on left and right on both doors, see dim. X below.

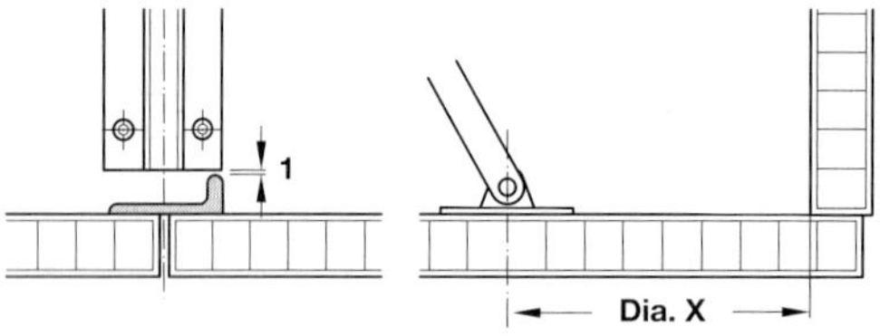

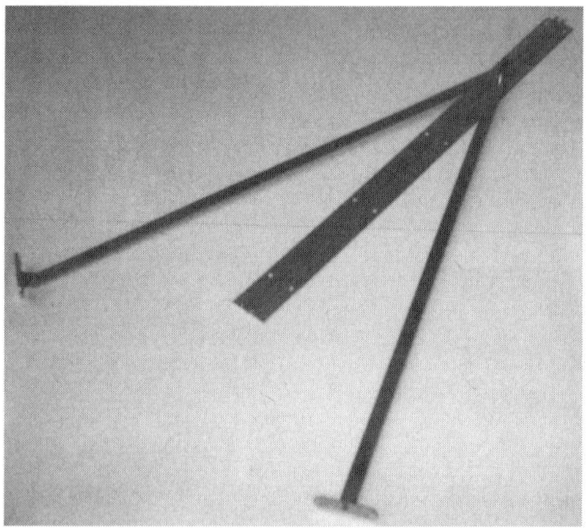

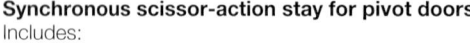

Synchronous scissor-action stay for pivot doors
Includes:
- 1 guide running track (for cutting to size) 530 mm long: aluminium, unfinished, with white plastic glide
- 2 art. rods each w. pivot bearing: steel, nickel-plated

Size	Cabinet width	Door width	Installation depth*	Contr. arm length	Dim. X	Cat. No.
1	700 mm	350 mm	min. 380 mm	440 mm	100 mm	371.02.710
	800 mm	400 mm	min. 350 mm	440 mm	120 mm	
2	900 mm	450 mm	min. 450 mm	540 mm	130 mm	371.02.720
	1000 mm	500 mm	min. 400 mm	540 mm	130 mm	
3	1100 mm	550 mm	min. 500 mm	640 mm	130 mm	371.02.730
	1200 mm	600 mm	min. 450 mm	640 mm	130 mm	

Packing: 1 and 25 pcs.

Important:

we recommend using only hinges for corner mounting with an opening angle of no more than 110°.

The synchronous hinge must be screwed onto the top panel, and the **articulated rod with spring** must always be screwed to the door with the stop strip.

If **cabinet dimensions** deviate from the table, a **test installation** should be carried out. In doing so see that **dimension X** is minimum.

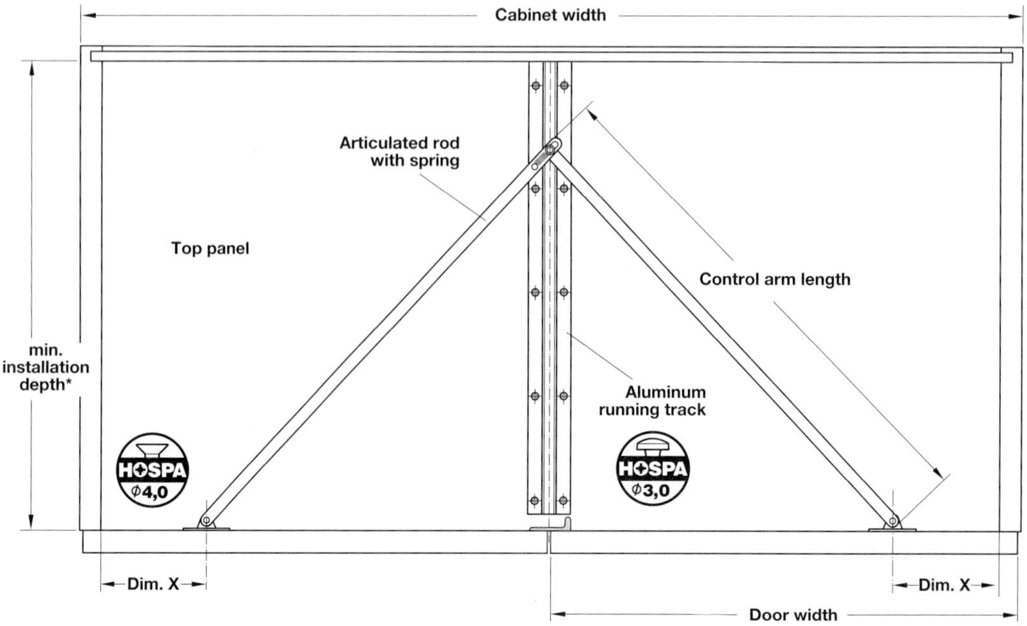

Dimensional data not binding.
We reserve the right to alter specifications without notice.

Chest Fittings

HÄFELE

Draw pull catches
Order strike separately

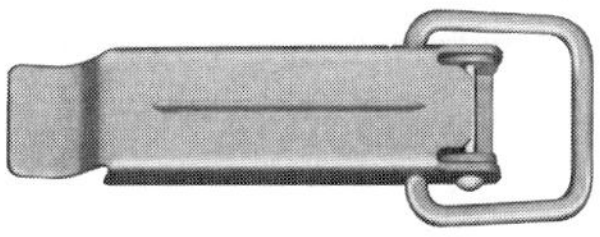

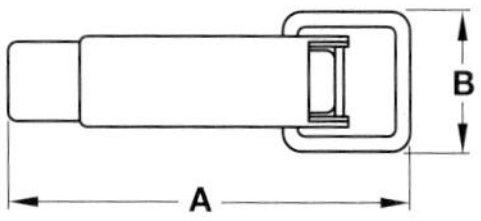

Finish: steel, black

overall length A	max. width B	wire clamp Ø	Cat. No.
55	22	3	380.53.306
75	30	4	380.53.315

Packing: 100 pcs.

Strikes for draw pull catches

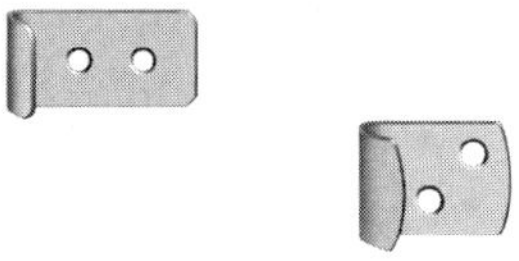

Finish: steel, black

length	width	thickness	Cat. No.
28	13	1.3	380.65.306
24	18	2.0	380.65.315

Packing: 100 pcs.

Dimensions in mm

Applications:

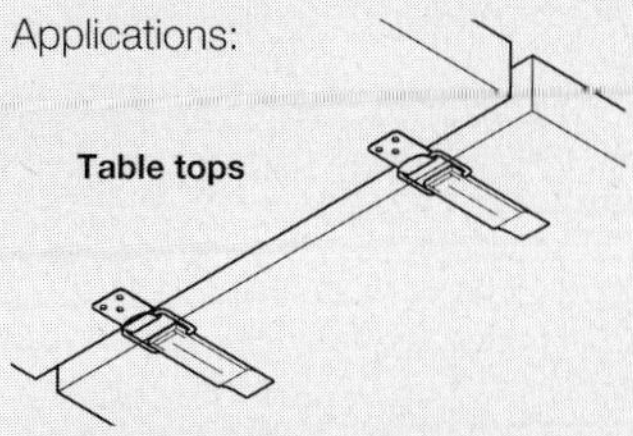

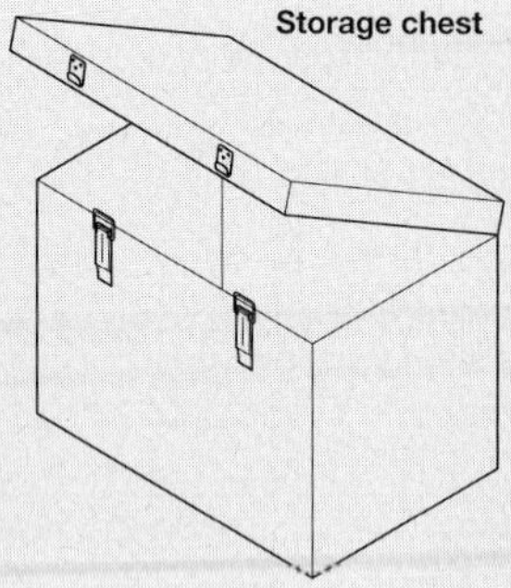

**Hinges,
Flap and Lid Stays
Associated Fittings**

3

Dimensional data not binding.
We reserve the right to alter specifications without notice.

HÄFELE

Metric Conversion Chart

Length

For our purposes, the basic metric units of *length* are the **millimeter and the meter.**

To convert inches to millimeters, multiply inches x 25.4

Inches	To	Millimeters
1/16"		1.59 mm
1/8"		3.18 mm
3/16"		4.76 mm
1/4"		6.35 mm
3/8"		9.53 mm
1/2"		12.70 mm
5/8"		15.88 mm
3/4"		19.05 mm
7/8"		22.23 mm
1"		25.40 mm
2"		50.80 mm
4"		101.60 mm
6"		152.40 mm
8"		203.20 mm
10"		254.00 mm
12"		304.80 mm
16"		406.40 mm
18"		457.20 mm
21"		533.40 mm
24"		609.60 mm
27"		685.80 mm
30"		762.00 mm
33"		838.20 mm
36"		914.40 mm
39"		990.60 mm
48"		1219.20 mm

To convert millimeters to inches, divide millimeters by 25.4

Millimeters	To	Inches
1 mm		1/16"
3 mm		1/8"
6 mm		1/4"
8 mm		5/16"
10 mm		3/8"
12 mm		1/2"
16 mm		5/8"
19 mm		3/4"
22 mm		7/8"
25.4 mm		1"
32 mm		1 1/4"
100 mm		4"
305 mm		12"
500 mm		19 3/4"
1000 mm		39 3/8"

*Inches are expressed to the nearest 16th.

To convert meters to feet, multiply meters by 3.3

Meters	To	Feet
1 meter		3' 3 3/8"
2 meters		6' 6 3/4"
2.5 meters		8' 2 1/2"
4 meters		13' 1 1/2"
6 meters		19' 8 1/4"

Weight

The basic metric unit of *weight* is the **kilogram.**

To convert kilograms to pounds, multiply kilograms x 2.2

Kilograms	To	Pounds
1 kg		2.2 lbs.
10 kg		22 lbs.
50 kg		110 lbs.

Volume

The basic metric unit of *volume* is the **liter.**

To convert liters to gallons, multiply liters x 0.26

Liters	To	Gallons
1 liter		0.26 gallons
4 liter		1 gallon
15 liter		4 gallons

Product Guide - Sliding Door Systems

HÄFELE

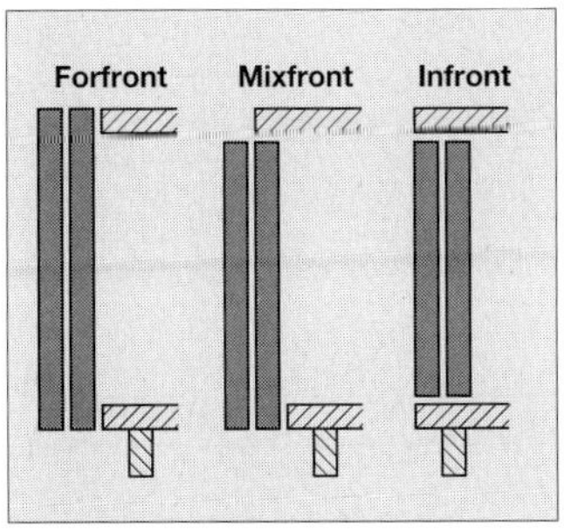

Sliding Doors for Cabinets
Pages **4.2 - 4.18**

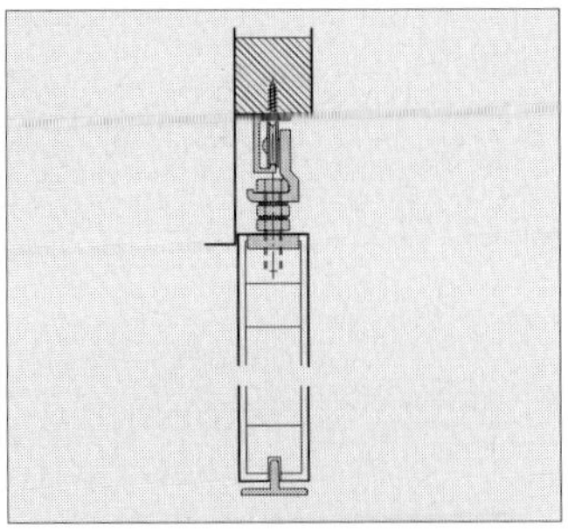

Heavy-duty Sliding Systems
Pages **4.19-4.26**

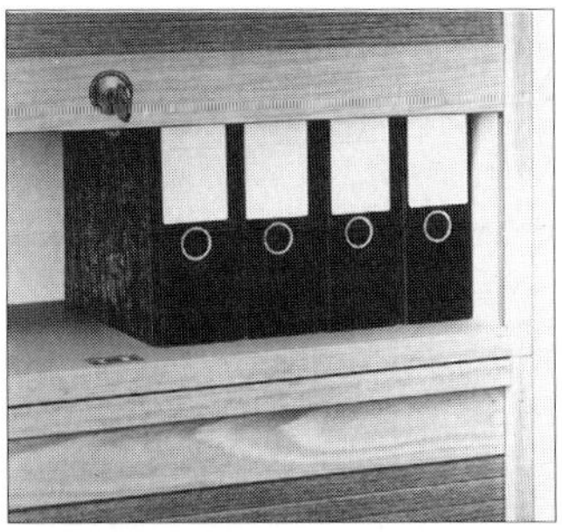

Roller Shutter Systems
Pages **4.27 - 4.30**

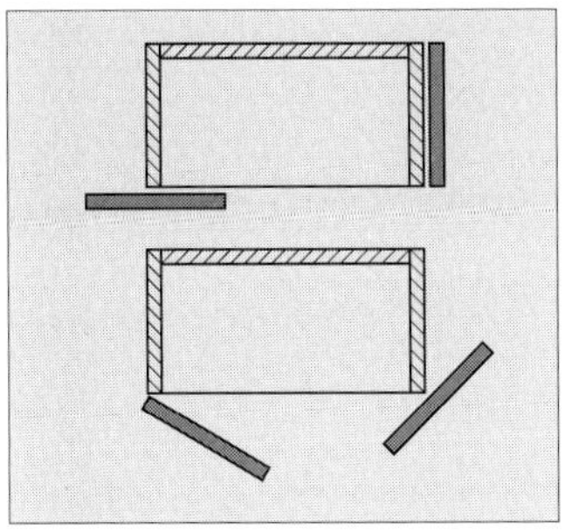

Pivoting Pocket Door Systems
Pages **4.30 - 4.44**

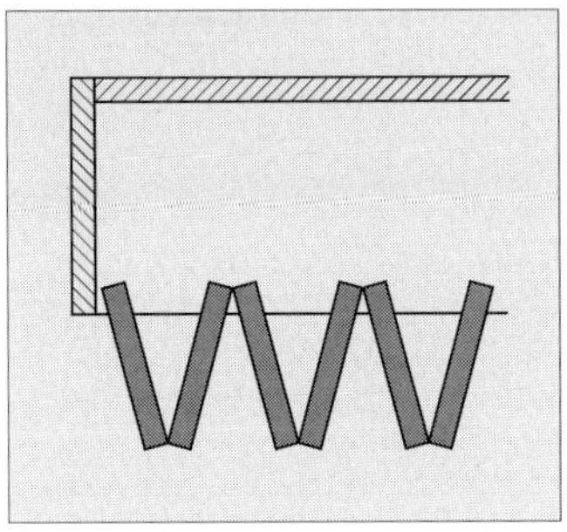

Sliding, Folding Door Systems
Pages **4.45 - 4.52**

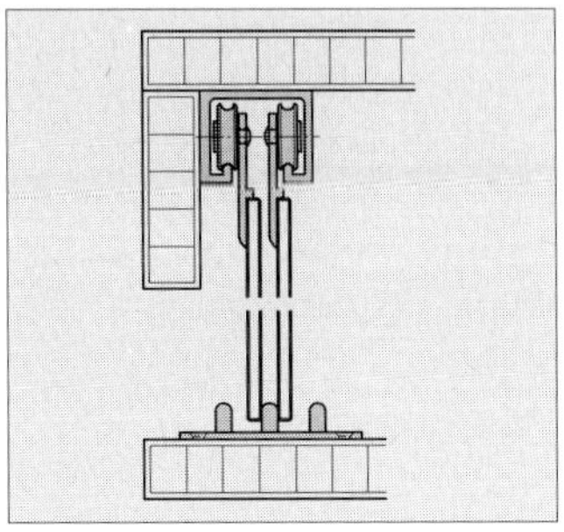

Sliding Systems for Glass
Pages **4.52 - 4.57**

Product Guide For:

- Drawer Slides
- Television Support Mechanisms

See Page 4.58

Guide and Glide Fittings for Sliding Doors

- Guide bolts for sliding doors
- Inexpensive and easy to install
- Provides for smooth and quiet operation.

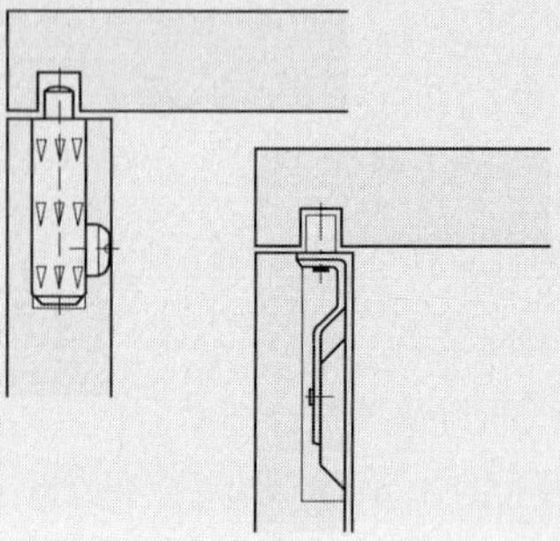

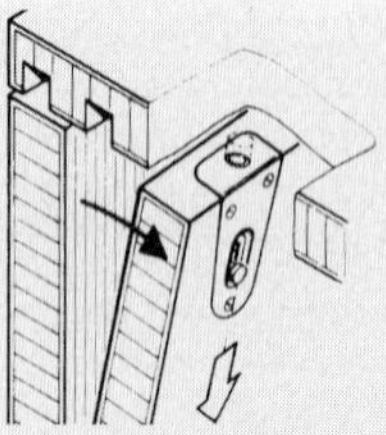

Guide bolt with spring-loaded pin

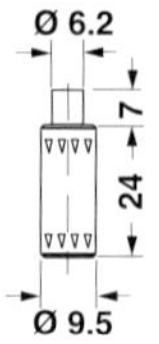

Finish: nylon, white

Cat. No.	402.90.006

Packing: 1000 pcs.

Guide bolt with screw-adjusted pin

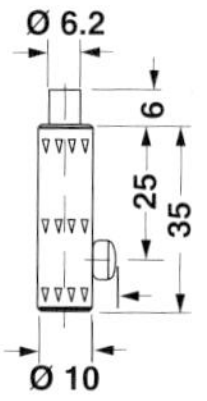

Finish: nylon, white

Cat. No.	402.95.001

Packing: 100 pcs.

Guide bolt with brass roller

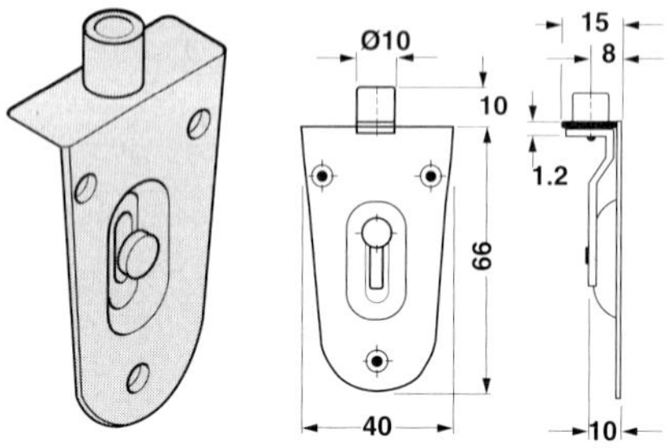

HOSPA Φ3.0

Finish: steel, nickel-plated

Cat. No.	405.20.910

Packing: 50 pcs.

4 Sliding Door Hardware
Drawer Slides
Television Supports

- Tracks for these glides can be found on page 4.3

Glide, screw mounted **A**

HOSPA Φ3.0

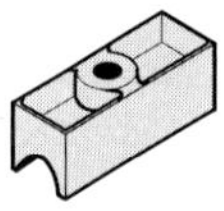

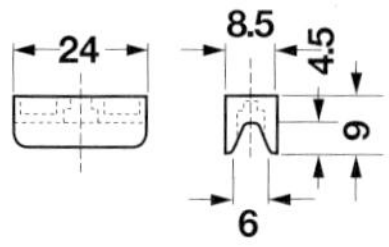

Finish: nylon, natural

Cat. No.	402.00.002

Packing: 100 pcs.

Glide with plastic-coated ball-bearing roller, recess mounted, load bearing capacity **20 kg (44 lbs.)** **B**

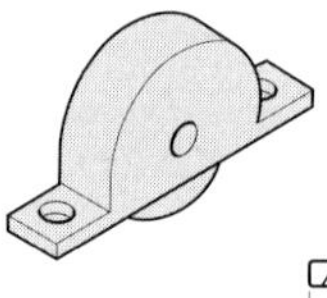

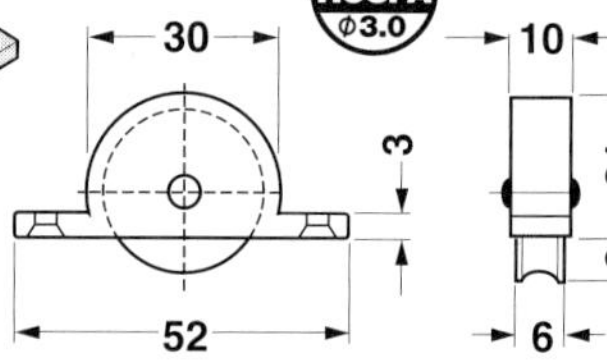

Finish: plastic, brown

Cat. No.	404.29.105

Packing: 50 pcs.

Glide, with brass roller , press-fit type **C**

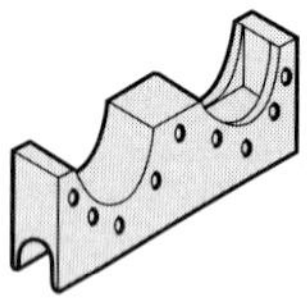

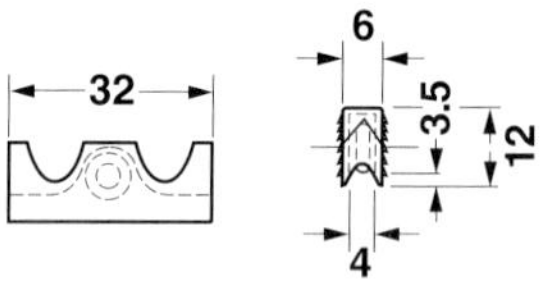

Finish: nylon, natural

Cat. No.	402.50.002

Packing: 50 pcs.

Glide, glued or screw mounted **D**

HOSPA Φ3.0

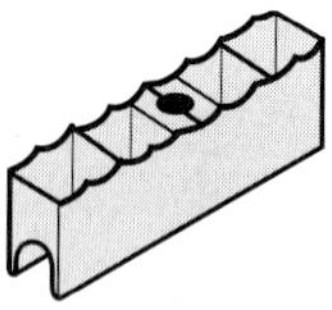

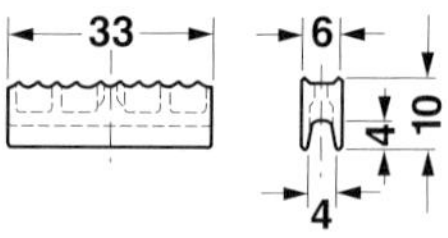

Finish: nylon, natural

Cat. No.	402.10.017

Packing: 500 pcs.

Glide, with nylon roller, press-fit type **E**

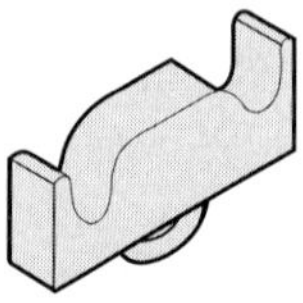

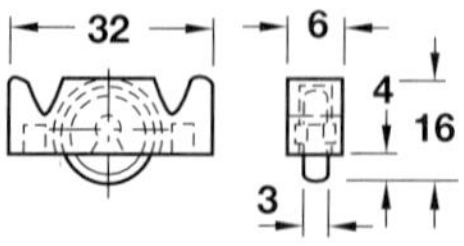

Finish: nylon, natural

Cat. No.	402.51.009

Packing: 1000 pcs.

Glide, press-fit **F**

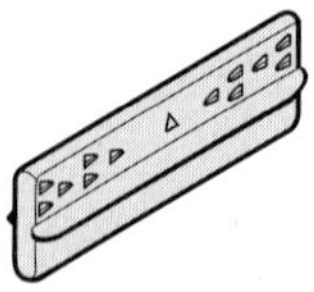

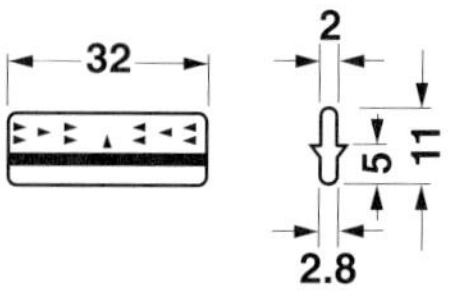

Finish: nylon, natural

Cat. No.	402.06.013

Packing: 500 pcs.

Dimensional data not binding.
We reserve the right to alter specifications without notice.

Dimensions in mm
Inches are approximate

Guide and Support Tracks for Sliding Doors

HÄFELE

- Economically priced elements for sliding doors.
- Low-friction, low-noise.

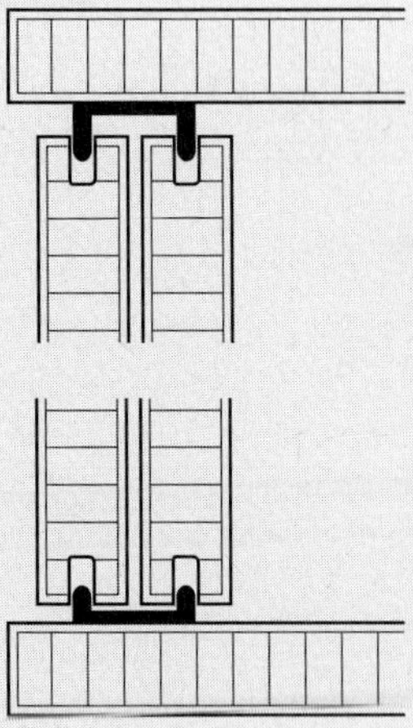

Double door guide track, upper
Without screw-holes, for tack gun attachment
Door panel weight up to **10 kg (22 lbs.)**
Recommended wood thickness 16 mm (5/8")

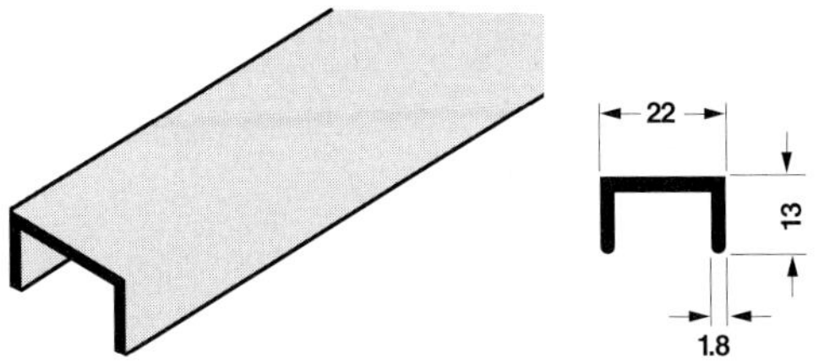

Finish: Plastic, white

Cat. No.	401.32.705

Packing: lengths of 2.5 meters

Double door guide track, upper
Without screw-holes, for tack gun attachment
Door panel weight up to **10 kg (22 lbs.)**
Recommended wood thickness 19 mm (3/4")

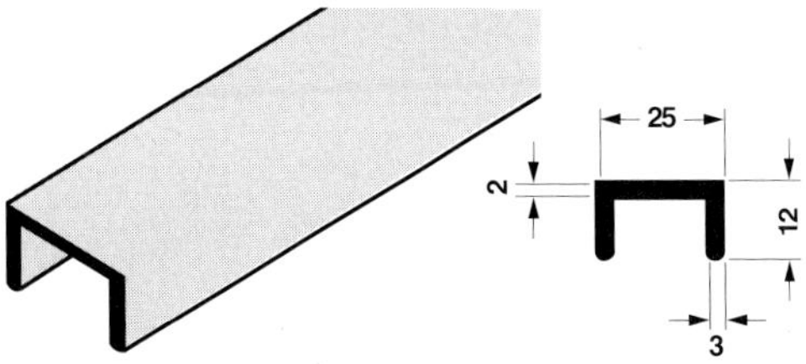

Finish: plastic, white

Cat. No.	401.32.714

Packing: lengths of 2.5 meters

Double door support track, lower
Without screw-holes, for tack gun attachment
Door panel weight up to 10 kg
Recommended wood thickness 16 mm (5/8")

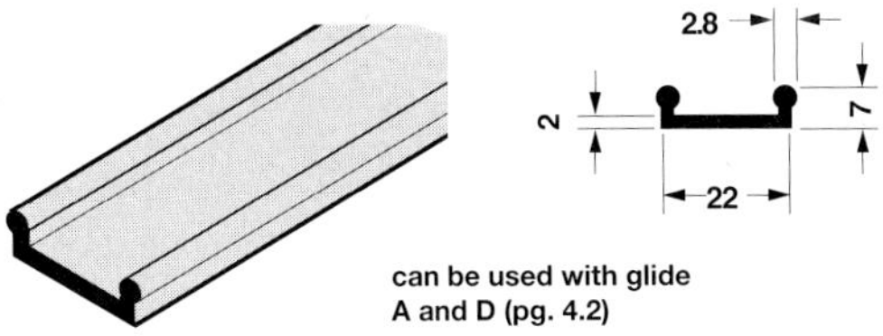

can be used with glide A and D (pg. 4.2)

Finish: plastic, white

Cat. No.	401.33.702

Packing: lengths of 2.5 meters

Double door support track, lower
Without screw-holes, for tack gun attachment
Door panel weight up to 10 kg
Recommended wood thickness 19 mm (3/4")

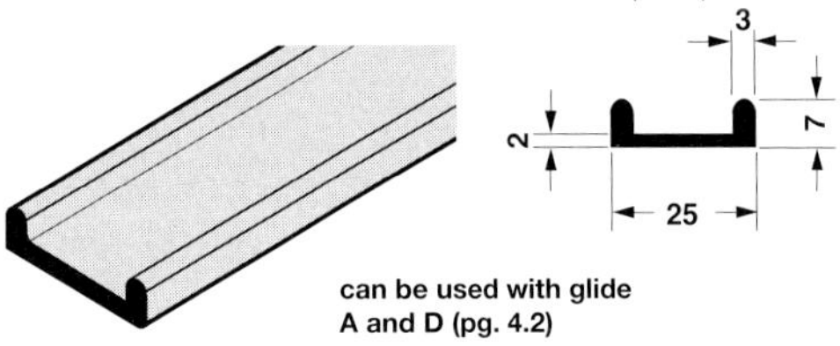

can be used with glide A and D (pg. 4.2)

Finish: plastic, white

Cat. No.	401.33.711

Packing: lengths of 2.5 meters

Sliding Door Hardware
Drawer Slides
Television Supports
4

- See glides on page 4.2
- Lower guide fittings for sliding doors
- Inexpensive and easy to install
- Provides smooth and quiet operation

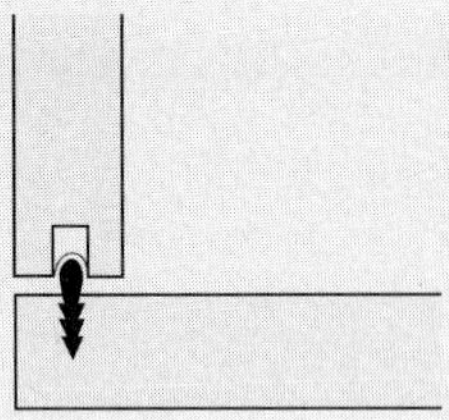

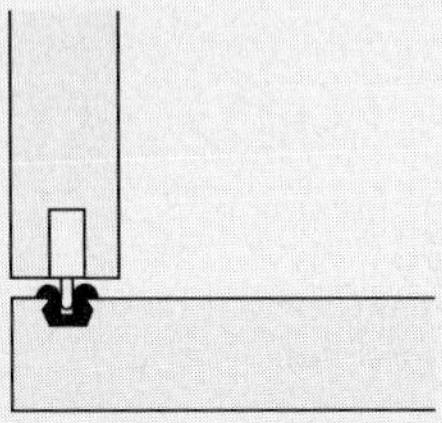

Support track, press-fit in groove

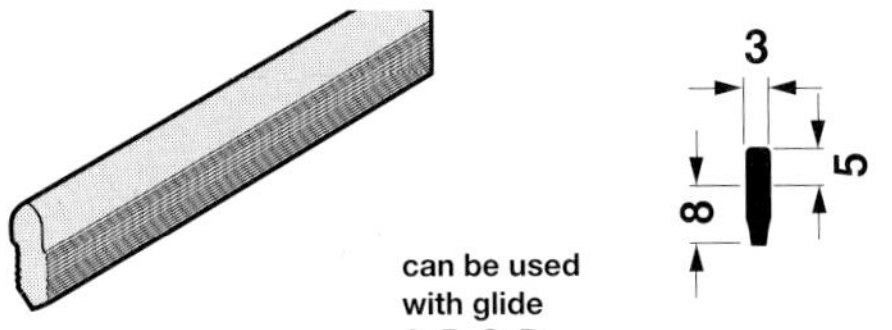

can be used with glide A, B, C, D (pg. 4.2)

Finish: plastic

Cat. No.		
	brown	401.01.102
	white	401.01.700

Packing: in rolls of 50 meters

Support track, press-fit in groove

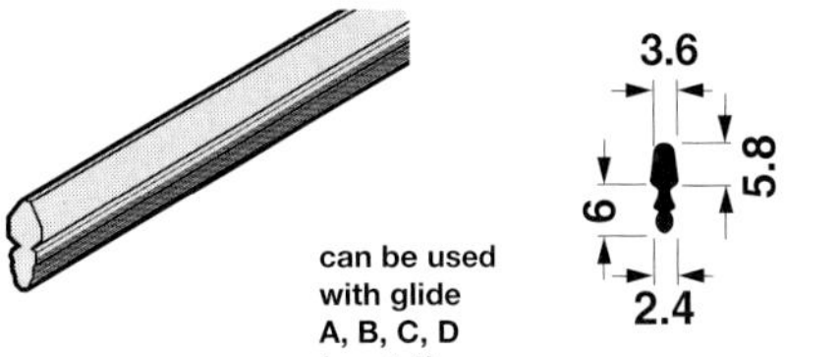

can be used with glide A, B, C, D (pg. 4.2)

Finish: plastic

Cat. No.		
	brown	401.02.109
	white	401.02.707

Packing: in rolls of 50 meters

Support track, with flanged edge, press-fit type

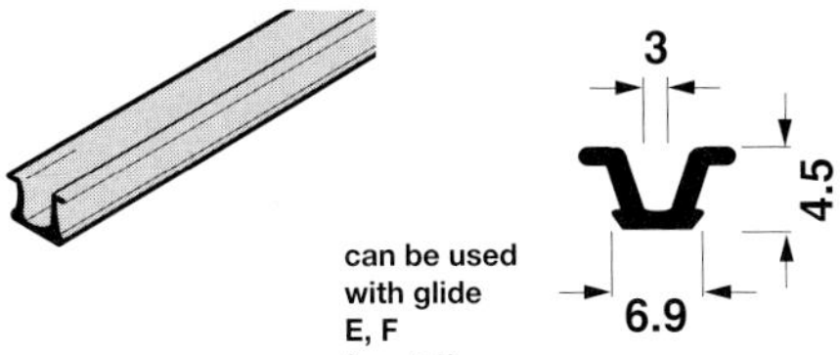

can be used with glide E, F (pg. 4.2)

Finish: plastic

Cat. No.		
	brown	401.11.108
	white	401.11.706

Packing: in lengths of 2.5 meters

Dimensions in mm
Inches are approximate

Dimensional data not binding. We reserve the right to alter specifications without notice.

HÄFELE

Guide and Glide Fittings for Sliding Doors

- These sliding door fittings form combinations for siding doors with bottom rollers and upper glides. The support track with flanged edges is designed for mounting at the top and bottom of the cabinet.
- The bottom runner guides run smoothly in the guide track with low friction.

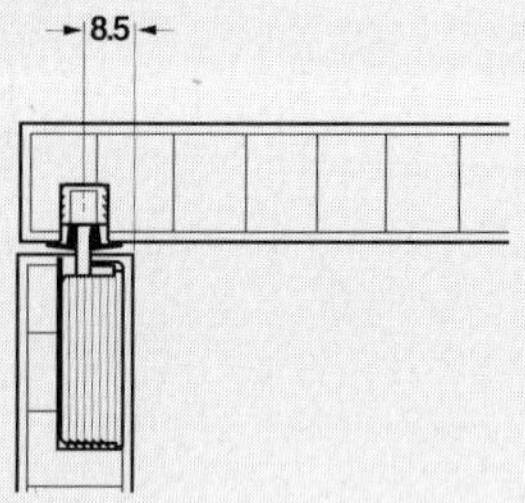

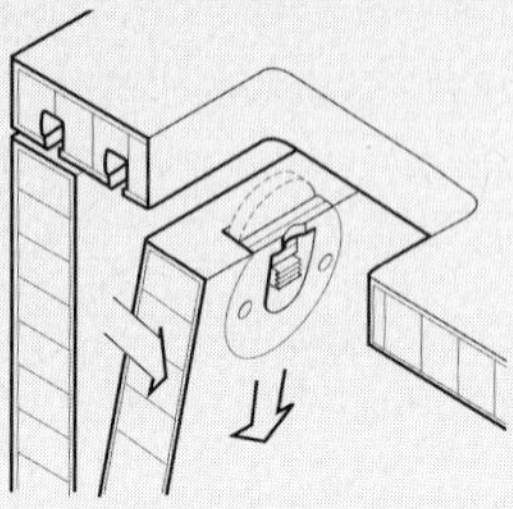

Guide Track, press-fit type
For top and bottom

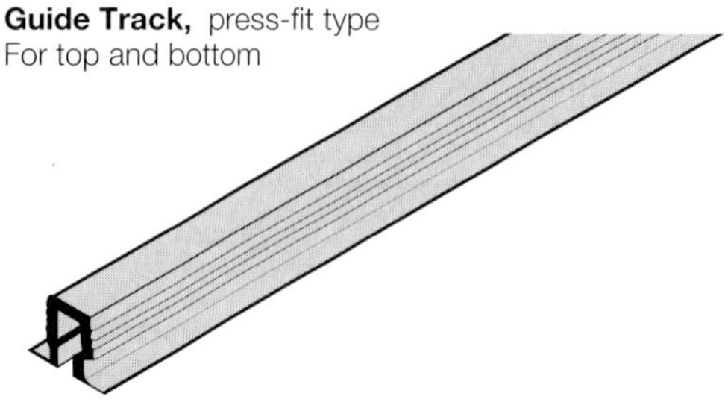

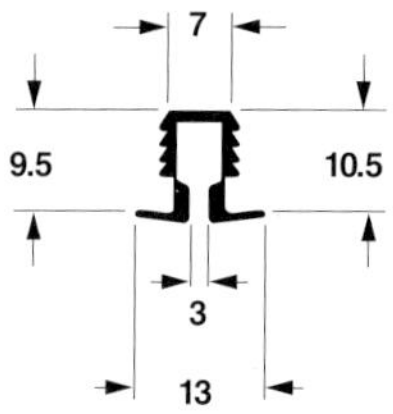

Finish: plastic

Cat. No.	white	404.14.702
	brown	404.14.104

Packing: 30 M in lengths of 3 meters

Upper glide/guide with adjustable guide, lockable at 5mm and 8mm, press fit

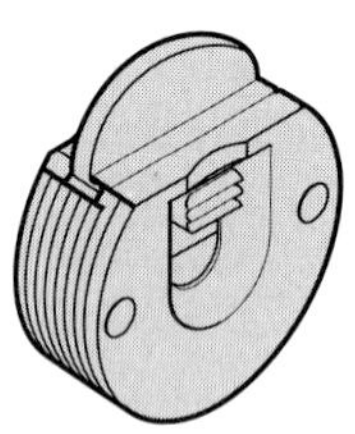

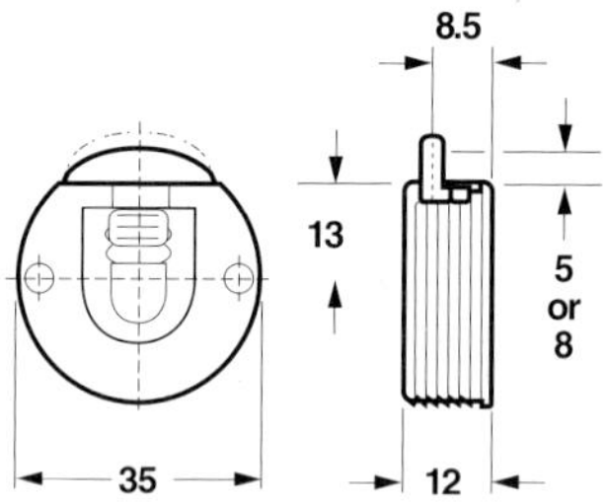

Finish: plastic

Cat. No.	brown	404.19.118
	white	404.19.716

Packing: 100 pcs.

Bottom guide with steel spindle, nylon roller and guide, press-fit

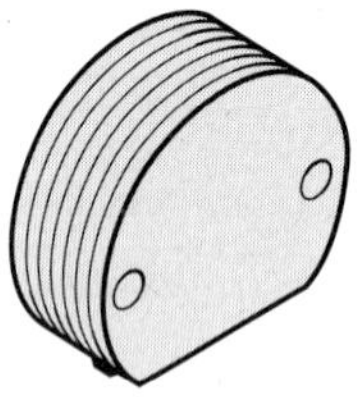

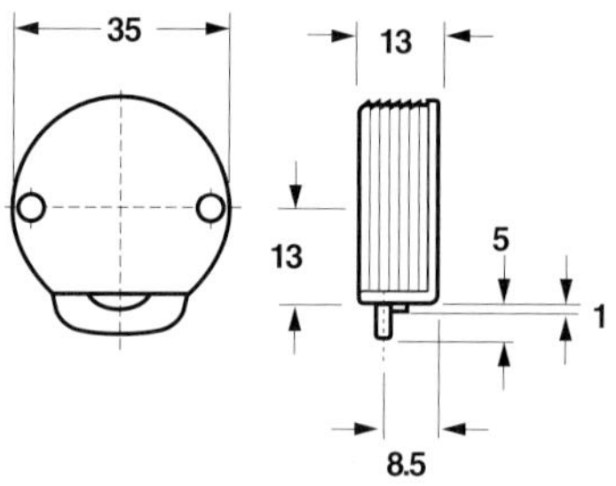

Finish: plastic

Cat. No.	brown	404.20.120
	white	404.20.728

Packing: 100 pcs.

Bottom guide with vertically adjustable steel spindle, nylon roller and guide, press-fit

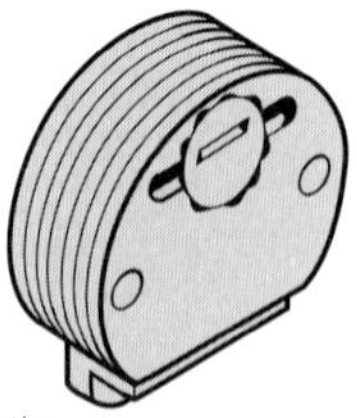

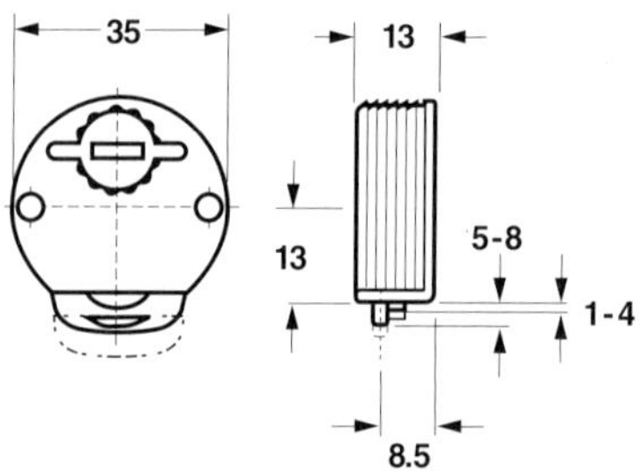

Finish: plastic

Cat. No.	brown	404.20.139
	white	404.20.737

Packing: 100 pcs.

Guide mount
Finish: plastic

Cat. No.	brown	404.06.004

Packing: 100 pcs.

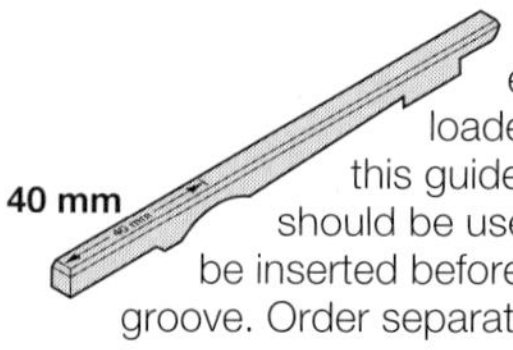

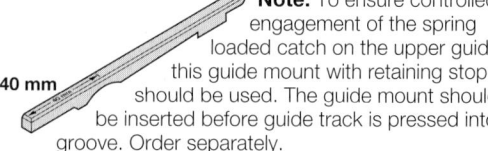

Note: To ensure controlled engagement of the spring loaded catch on the upper guide, this guide mount with retaining stop should be used. The guide mount should be inserted before guide track is pressed into groove. Order separately.

Dimensional data not binding. We reserve the right to alter specifications without notice.

Dimensions in mm
Inches are approximate

Guide and Roller Fittings for Sliding Doors

Glide track, with flanged edges and barbed shoulders
Press-fit for top and bottom of cabinet

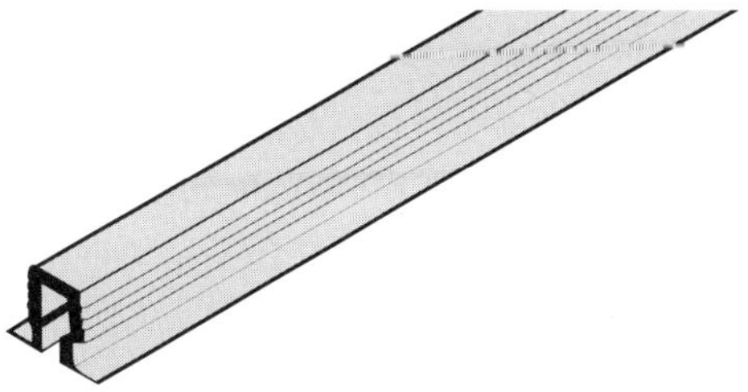

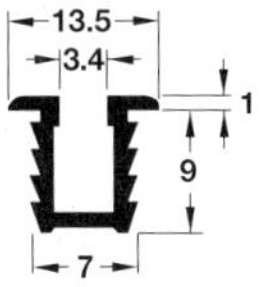

Finish: plastic

Cat. No.	white	404.14.702
	brown	404.14.104

Packing: 30 m in lengths of 3 meters

Glide, spring-loaded to be pressed in and screw-mounted to the sliding door

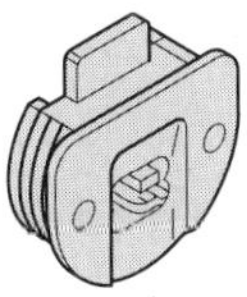

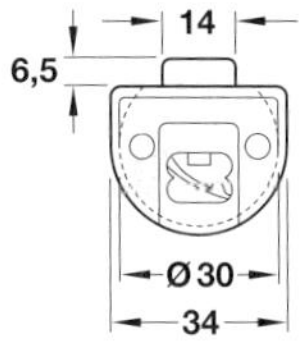

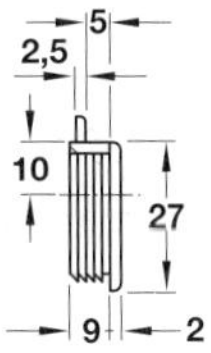

Finish: plastic

Cat. No.	404.21.154

Packing: 500 pcs.

Guide, lockable to be pressed in and screw-mounted to the sliding door

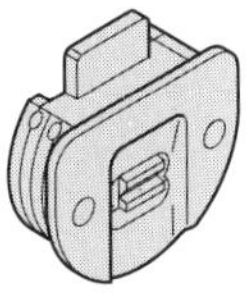

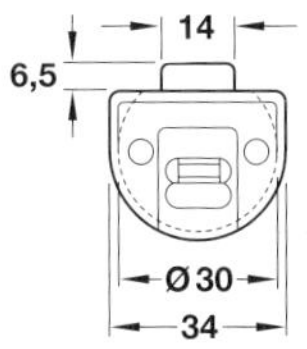

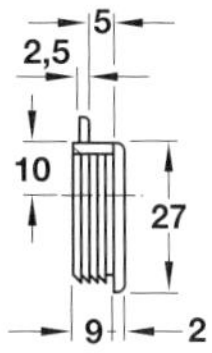

Finish: plastic

Cat. No.	404.21.109

Packing: 500 pcs.

Lower roller with double bearing mounted axle, to be pressed in and screw-mounted to the sliding door

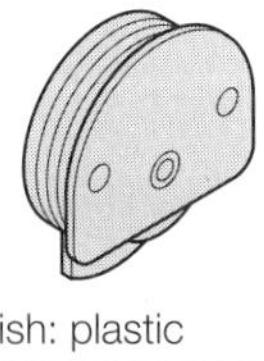

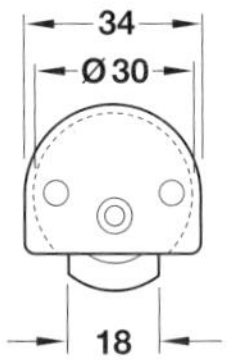

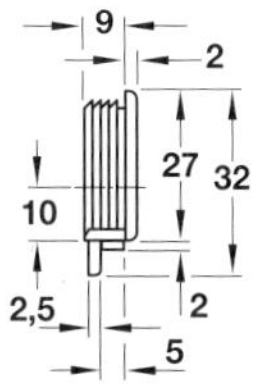

Finish: plastic

Cat. No.	brown	404.22.106

Packing: 500 pcs.

Lower roller, vertically adjustable with double bearing mounted axle, screw-mounted to the sliding door

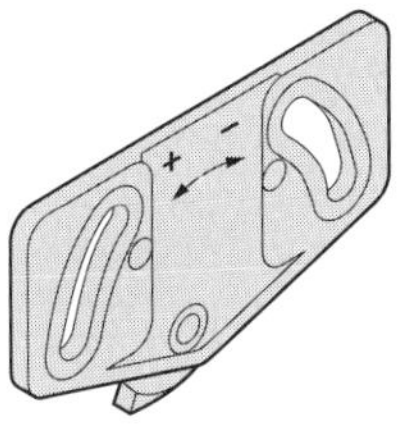

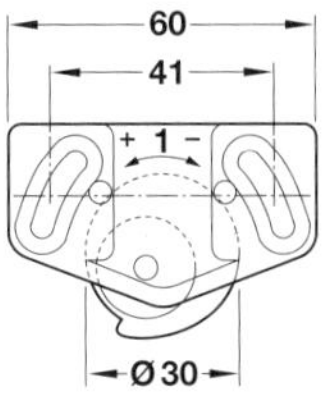

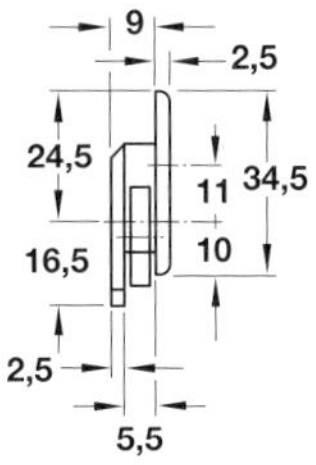

Finish: plastic

Cat. No.	brown	404.22.151

Packing: 500 pcs.

- These sliding door fittings form combinations for sliding doors with bottom rollers and upper glides. The same plastic, flanged track is designed to be used both at the top and bottom of the cabinet.
- The bottom runner guide glides virtually friction-free in the track recess.

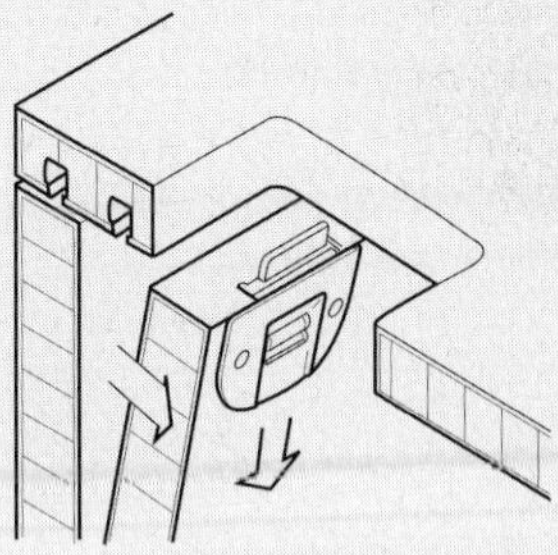

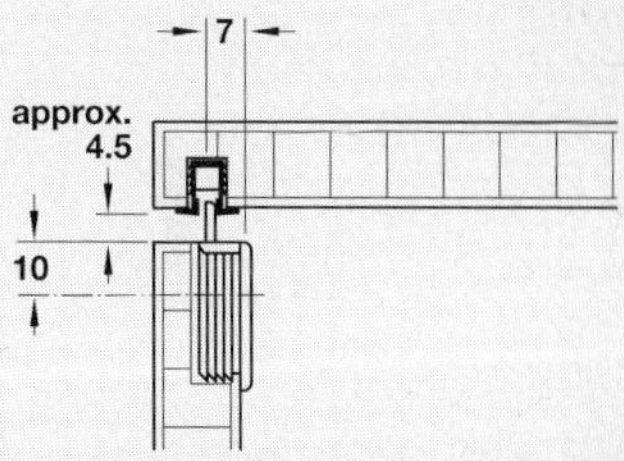

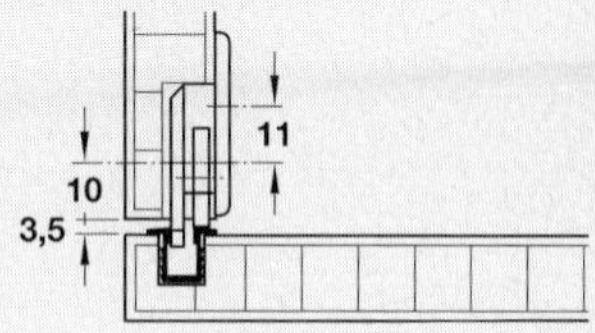

Dimensional data not binding.
We reserve the right to alter specifications without notice.

Dimensions in mm
Inches are approximate

HÄFELE

"Rolluna" is a sliding door fitting for heavy doors in interior decorating applications.
Up to 55 kg (121 lbs.)

Two upper guide tracks are mounted side by side for double or multi-panel doors.

Mounting screws:
Hospa chipboard screws
countersunk head
with cross slot
PZ 2
Finish:
steel, nickel-plated

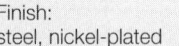

Length	Cat. No.
15 mm	015.35.824
17 mm	015.35.833
20 mm	015.35.842

Packing: 1000 pcs.

"Rolluna" Sliding Door Fitting

Guide track
without screw-holes

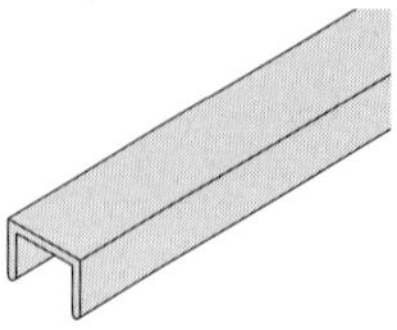

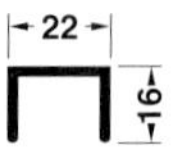

Finish: aluminum, unfinished

Cat. No.	2.5 m long	404.30.019
	5.0 m long	404.30.037

Glide
with plastic roller and sound-damping rubber stop

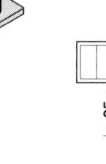

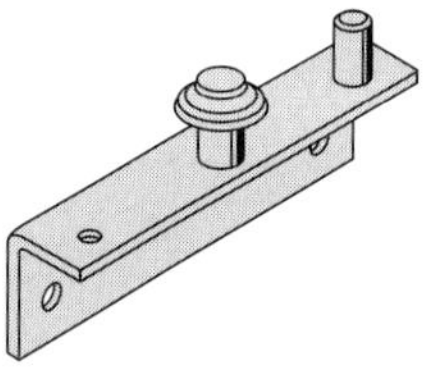

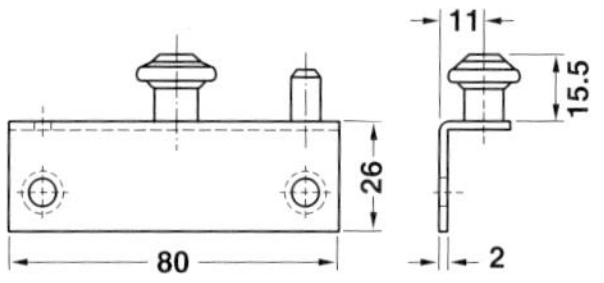

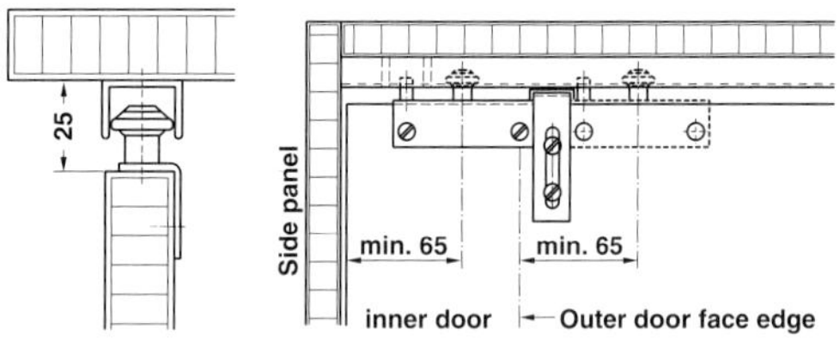

Finish: steel, galvanized

Cat. No.	404.32.900

Packing: 5 pairs

End stop
complete with sleeve screw for mounting in guide track

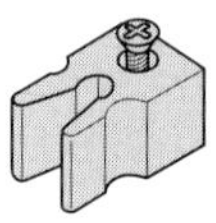

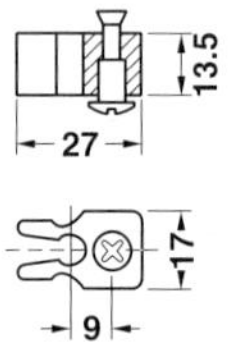

Finish: plastic, black

Cat. No.	404.32.004

Packing: 10 pcs.

Safety stop
(anti-derailment device) for single-panel sliding doors, screw-mounted

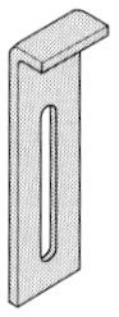

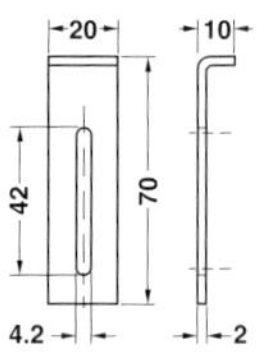

Finish: steel, galvanized

Cat. No.	404.32.988

Packing: 2 pcs.

Note:
If multi-panel doors are employed, we recommend fitting the special follower which also serves as a safety (anti-derailment) stop (see below)

Follower/safety stop
with rubber buffer, screw-mounted

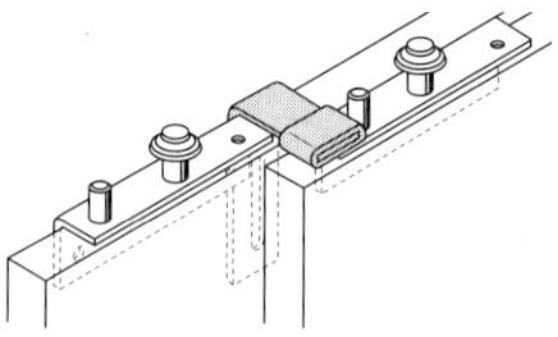

Finish: steel, galvanized

Cat. No.	404.32.997

Packing: 2 pcs.

Running Gear
with plastic-coated, ball-bearing mounted roller, recessed and screw-mounted

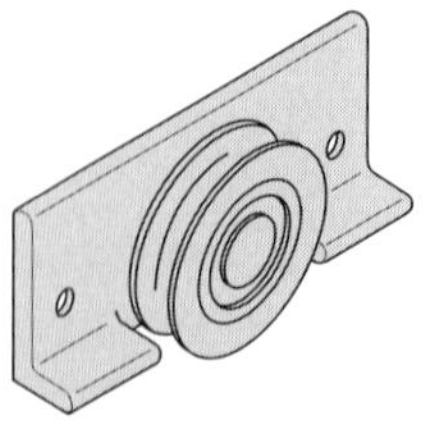

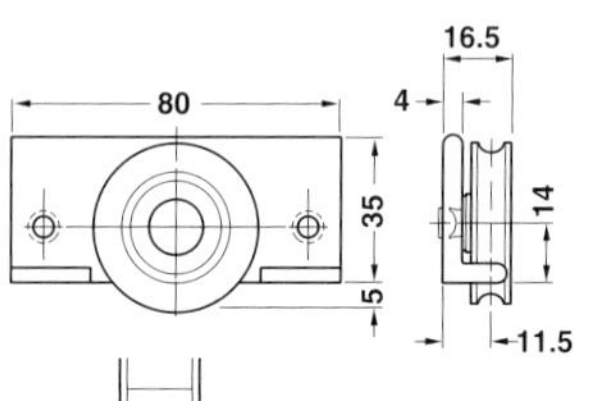

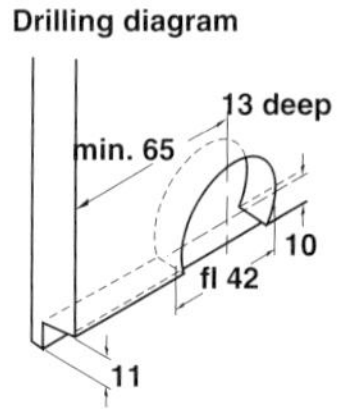

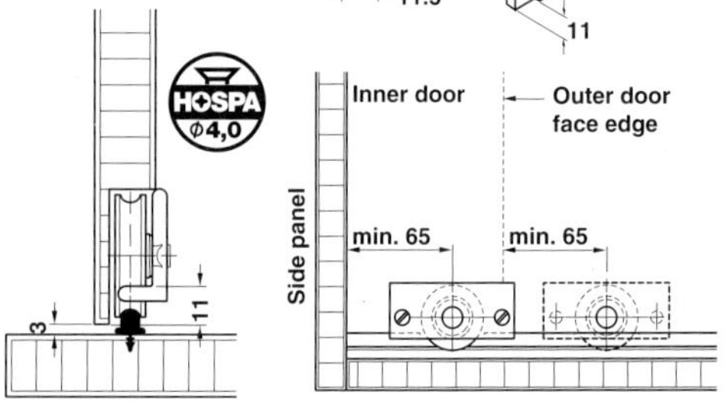

Finish: aluminum, unfinished

Cat. No.	404.32.951

Packing: 10 pcs.

Support track
press-fit type

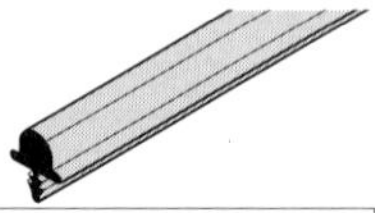

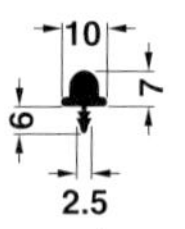

Finish: aluminum, unfinished

Cat. No.	2.5 m long	404.31.016
	5.0 m long	404.31.034

Dimensional data not binding.
We reserve the right to alter specifications without notice.

Dimensions in mm

HÄFELE

"Hangar" Sliding Door Fitting

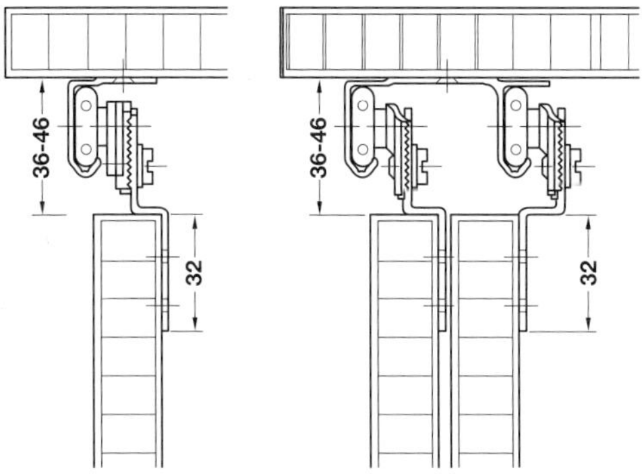

Note: If double doors of 19 mm (3/4") thickness are used, the rear running gear mounting plates must be repositioned (see mounting diagram–left). Doors up to 35 mm (1 3/8") thick can be hung with mounting plates positioned in this way (see diagram below)

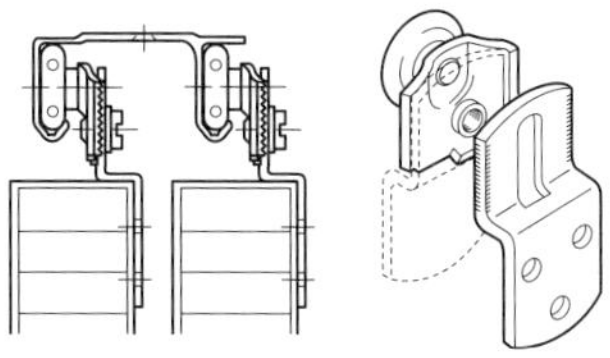

For wood thickness from 19 mm (3/4") - 35 mm (1 3/8")

- "Hangar" is a sliding door fitting for light to medium-weight doors.
- Double or multiple doors can be hung on parallel tracks allowing independent travel.
- Choice of single or double upper tracks for the runners.

Single upper track, with screw-holes

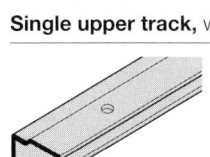

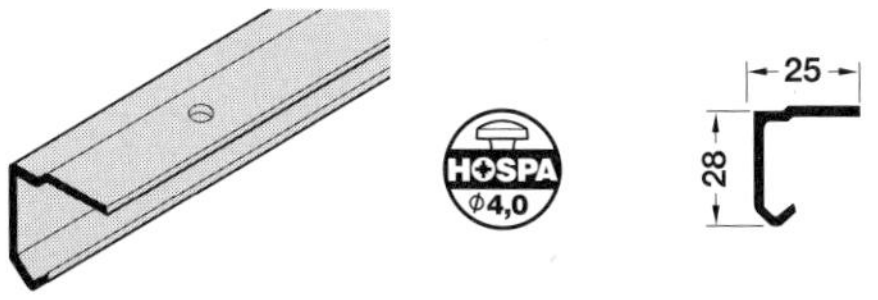

Finish: aluminum, unfinished

Cat. No.	407.10.003

Packing: in lengths of 6 m

Double upper track, with screw-holes

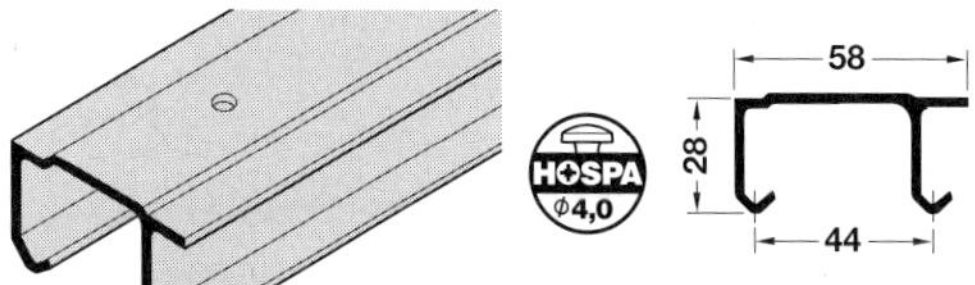

Finish: aluminum, unfinished

Cat. No.	407.11.000

Packing: in lengths of 6 m

Running gear, with ball-bearing mounted nylon roller and mounting bracket for attachment to side of door panel. For door weight max. 14 kg (30 lbs)

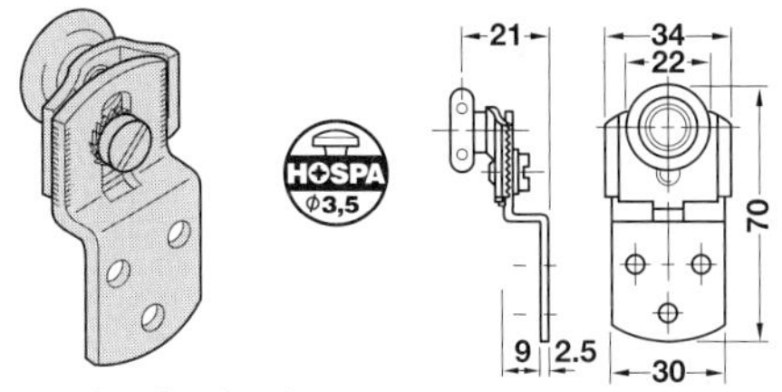

Finish: steel, galvanized

Cat. No.	407.13.906

Packing: 10 pcs.

Double upper running gear, with screw-holes. For door weight max. 28 kg (60 lbs)

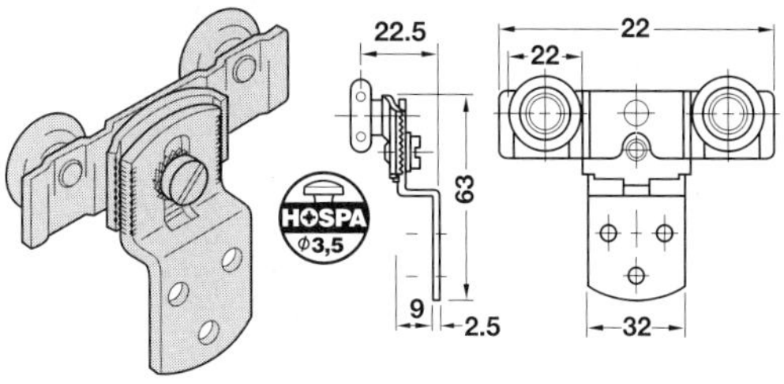

Finish: steel, galvanized

Cat. No.	407.14.903

Packing: 10 pcs.

Sliding Door Hardware
Drawer Slides
Television Supports

4

Follower, comprising nylon press-fit sleeve, rubber buffer with fastening screw and galvanized steel stop plate

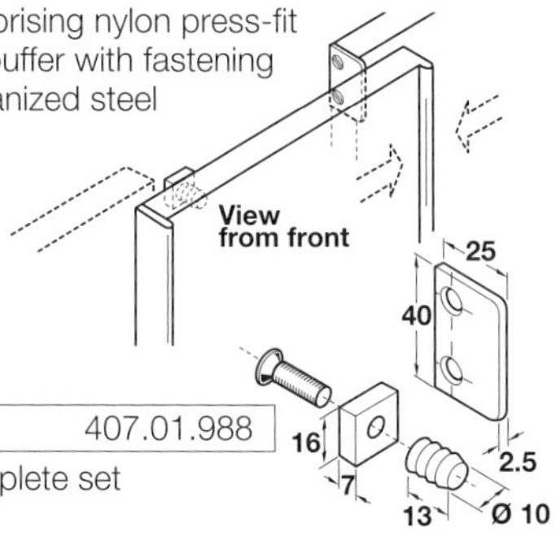

Cat. No.	407.01.988

Packing: 1 complete set

Guide, recessed and screw-mounted in cabinet bottom

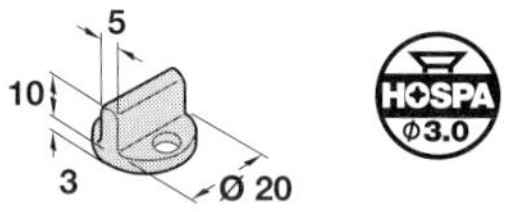

Finish: plastic, natural-colored

Cat. No.	407.01.942

Packing: 100 pcs.

Single guide, two-part screw-mounted

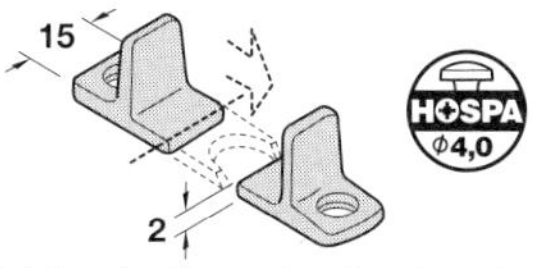

Finish: plastic, natural-colored

Cat. No.	407.01.960

Packing: 10 pcs.

Double guide, screw-mounted. Adjustable for door thicknesses between 19 and 35 mm (3/4"-1 3/8").

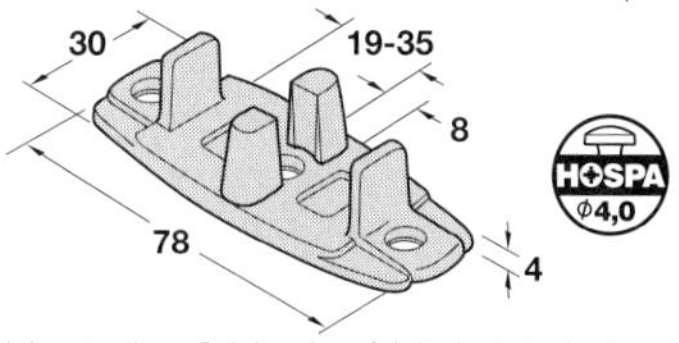

Finish: steel, unfinished; w/nickel-plated, zinc die-cast end cap

Cat. No.	407.01.951

Packing: 10 pcs.

Rubber bumper, screw-mounted

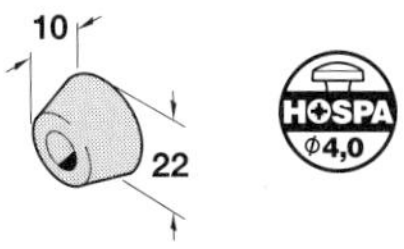

Finish: black

Cat. No.	407.01.933

Packing: 100 pcs. each

Rubber bumper, plug-fit type

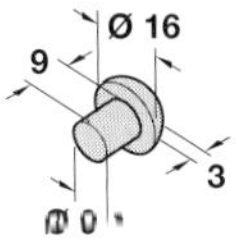

Finish: white

Cat. No.	406.24.100

Packing: 10 pcs.

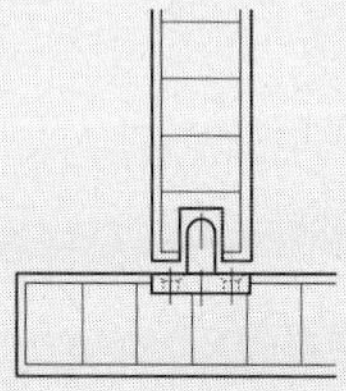

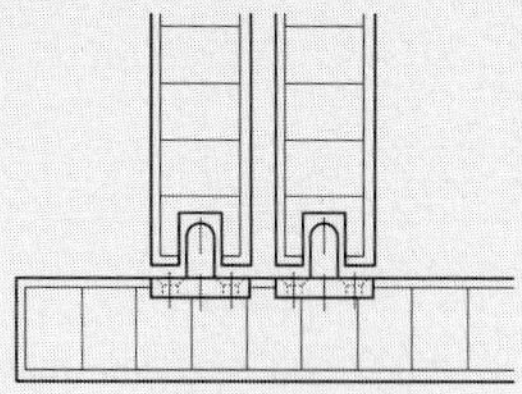

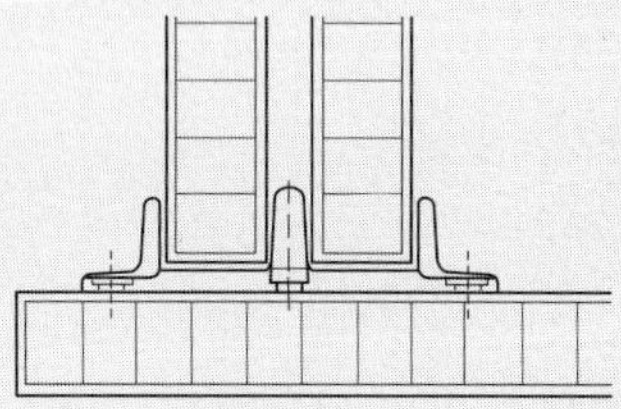

Dimensional data not binding. We reserve the right to alter specifications without notice.

Dimensions in mm

HÄFELE

Clipo® 15/H Sliding Door Fittings

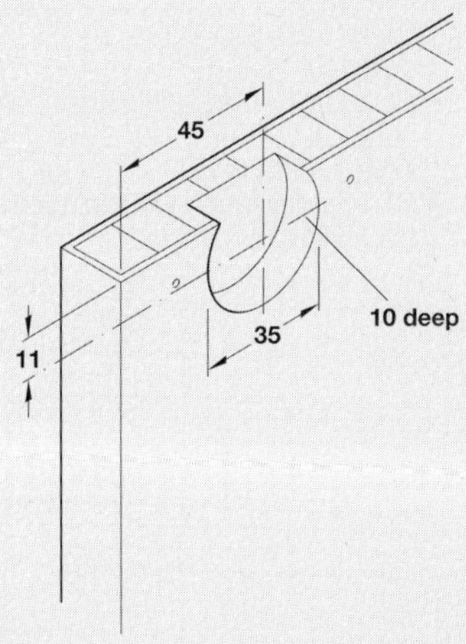

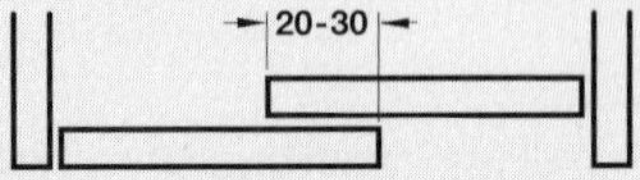

- max. **15 kg. (32 lbs)** door weight for **wooden doors**
- door thicknesses of **13, 16 and 19 mm (1/2, 5/8 and 3/4")**
- running gears **with clip** and plastic rollers and metal shafts
- housing suitable for **screw-mounting** or **press-fitting**
- also available as complete fitting sets

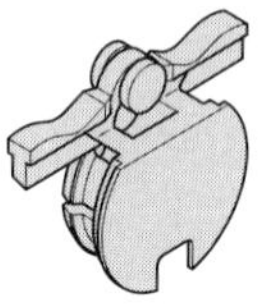

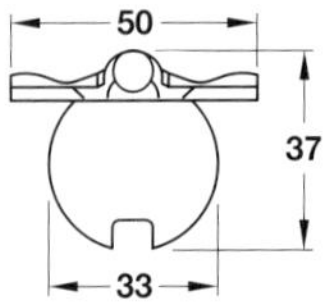

Running gear with clip for quick mounting
Finish: plastic, anthracite

Cat. No.	405.83.908

Packing: 100 pcs.

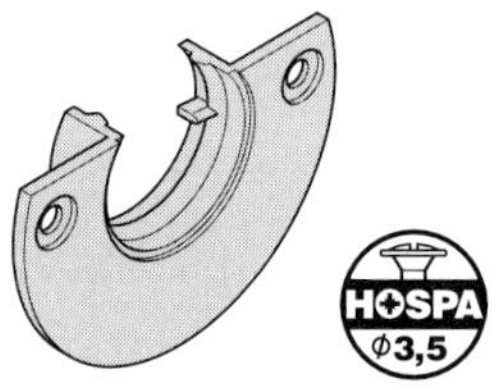

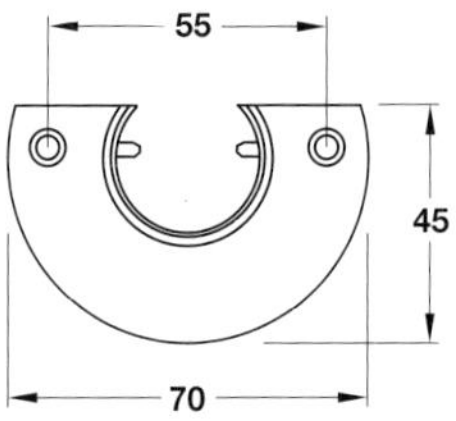

Housing for **screw-mounting**
Finish: plastic, anthracite

Cat. No.	405.83.800

Packing: 100 pcs.

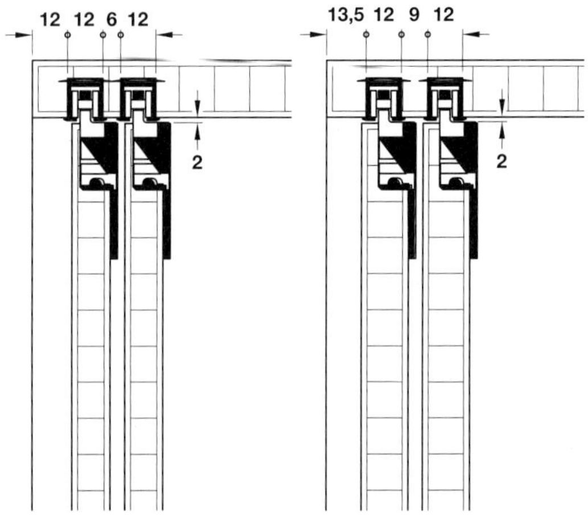

4 Sliding Door Hardware
Drawer Slides
Television Supports

Advantages:
- quick door mounting
- no guide rails in the floor
- application as Infront and Mixfront
- no wooden cover rail necessary

Clipo-Infront

for sliding doors running in a cabinet

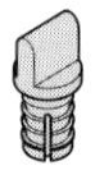

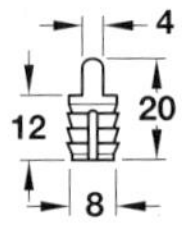

Guide for mounting in drilled holes
Finish: plastic, anthracite

Cat. No.	405.83.104

Packing: 50 pcs.

Complete fitting set	**door weight max. 15 kg (32 lbs)**
Includes:	**2 doors**
Running gear with clip	4 pcs.
Housing for screw-mounting	4 pcs.
Stopper with retaining spring	4 pcs.
Guide for mounting in drilled holes	2 pcs.
Cat. No.:	**405.82.214**
Packing: 1 set	

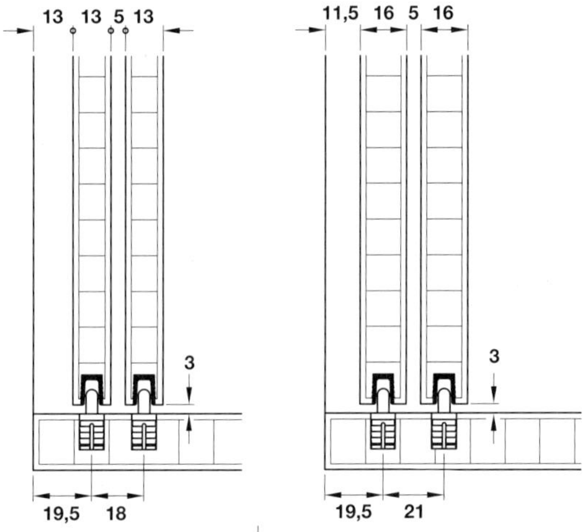

1/2" doors **5/8" doors**

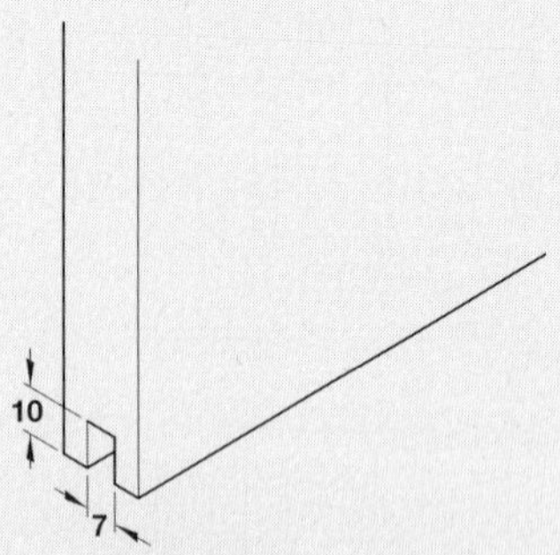

Clipo-Mixfront for sliding doors running in the top of the cabinet and at the bottom running in front of the cabinet

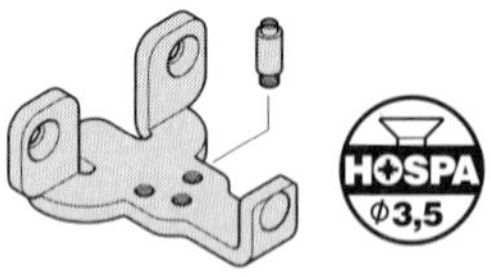

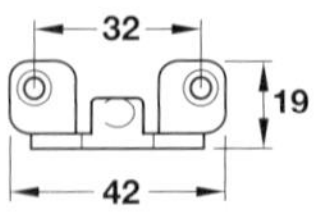

Guide screw-mounted, adjustable
Finish: steel, black

Cat. No.	405.83.113

Packing: 25 pcs.

Complete fitting set	**door weight max. 15 kg (32 lbs)**
Includes:	**2 doors**
Running gear with clip	4 pcs.
Housing screw-mounted	4 pcs.
Stopper with retaining spring	4 pcs.
Guide screw-mounted	1 pc.
Cat. No.:	**405.82.116**
Packing: 1 set	

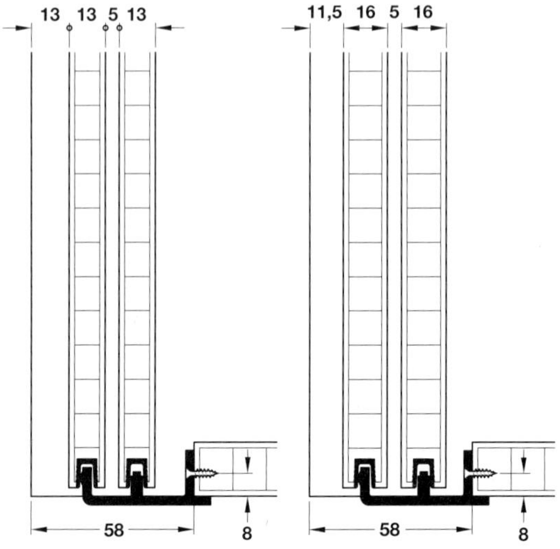

* **Important:**
The complete fitting set is always delivered **without rails**, please order separately.
See rails page **4.9**

Dimensions in mm
Inches are approximate

Clipo® 15/H Sliding Door Fittings

HÄFELE

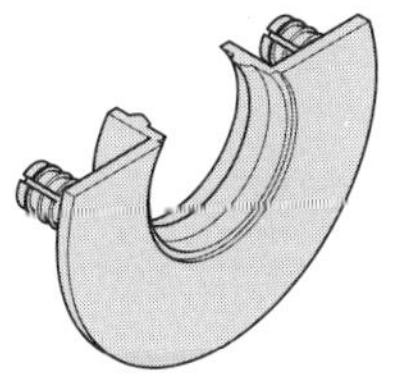
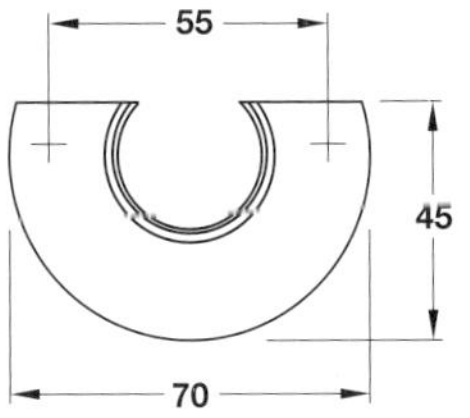

Housing, press-fit
Finish: plastic, anthracite

Cat. No.	405.83.819

Packing: 100 pcs.

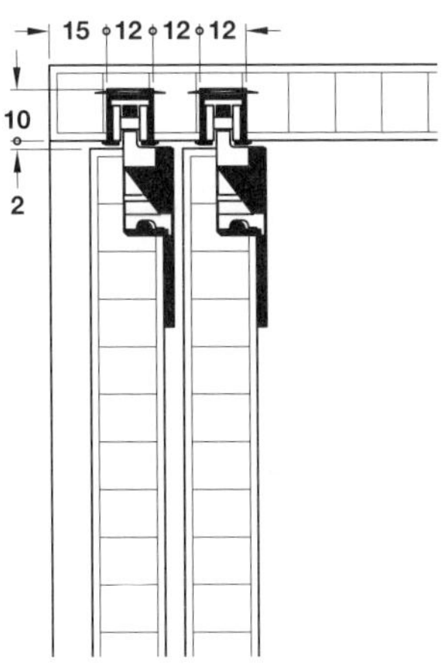

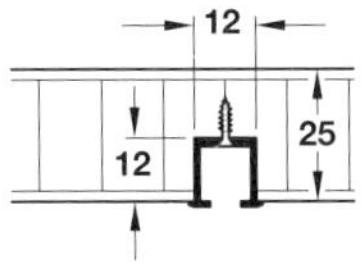

A **min. cabinet top thickness of 25 mm (1")** is required for mounting the single guide rail with screw holes.

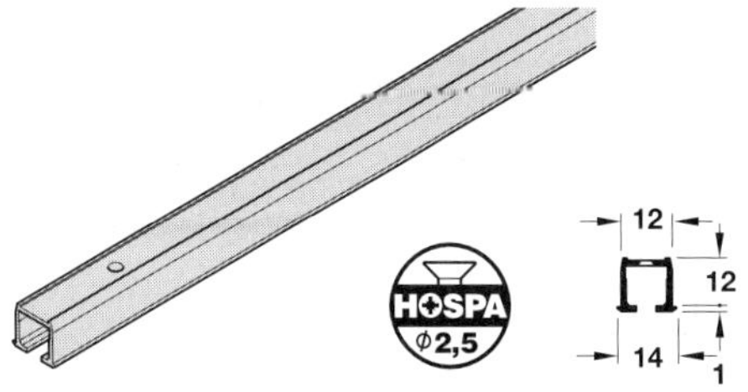

Single guide rail, upper, with screw holes
Finish: aluminum, unfinished

Packing	Cat. No.
2.5 m long	405.87.013

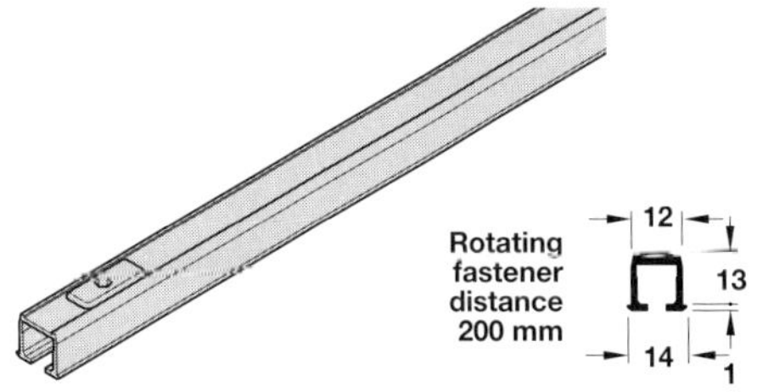

Single guide rail, upper, with rotating fasteners
Finish: aluminum, unfinished

Packing	Cat. No.
2.5 m long	405.86.016

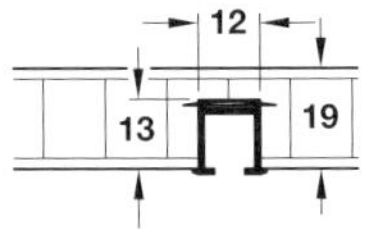

A **min. cabinet top thickness of 19 mm (3/4")** is required for mounting the single guide rail with rotating fasteners.

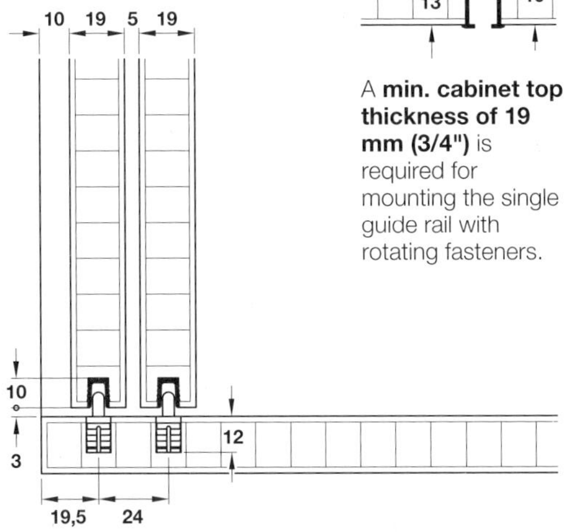

3/4" doors

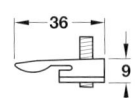

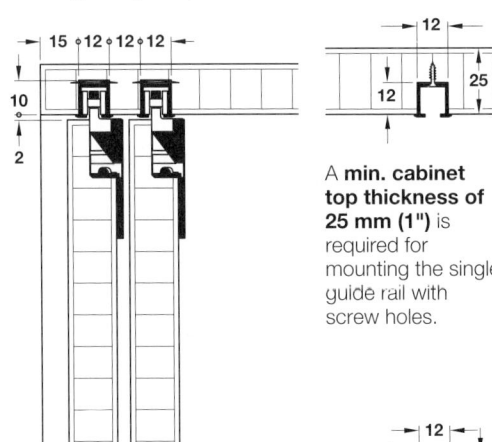

Stopper with retaining spring, for upper guide rails
Finish: plastic, natural colored

Cat. No.	405.83.131

Packing: 100 pcs.

*** Important**
The complete fitting set is always delivered **without guide rails**, please order separately.

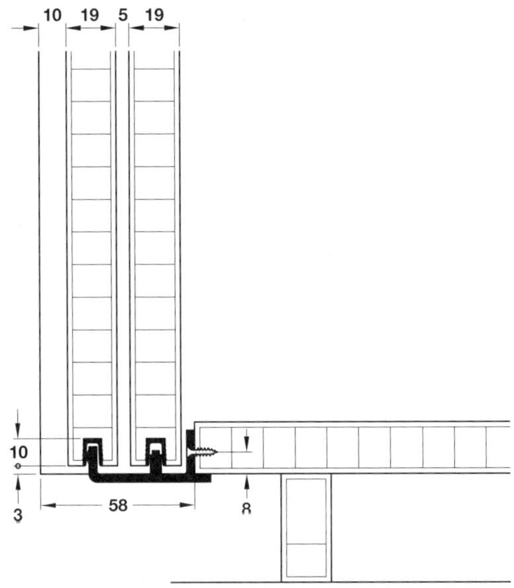

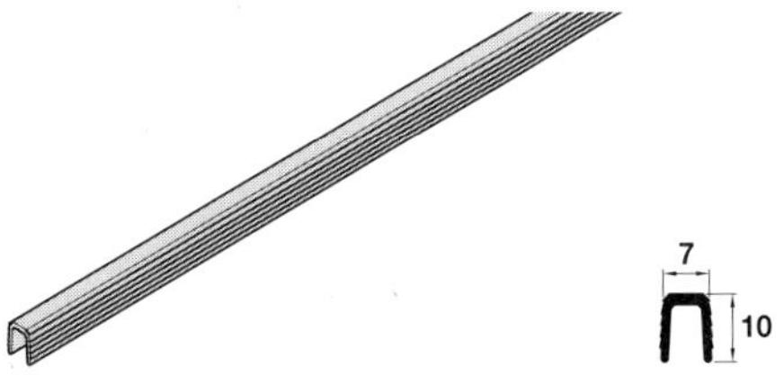

Guide rail, lower, barbed
Finish: plastic, anthracite

Packing	Cat. No.
2.5 m long	405.98.516

Dimensions in mm
Inches are approximate

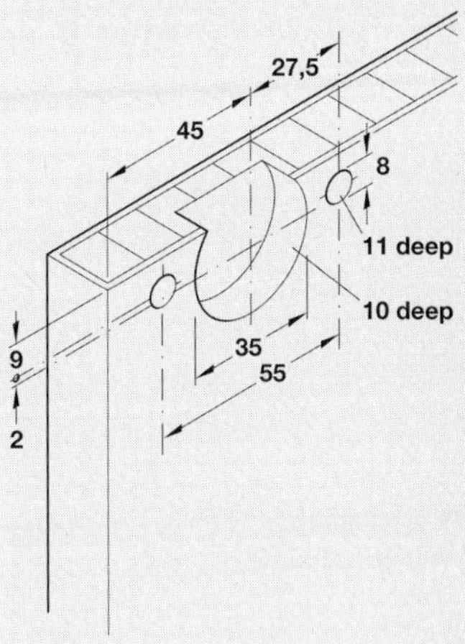

Sliding Door Hardware
Drawer Slides
Television Supports
4

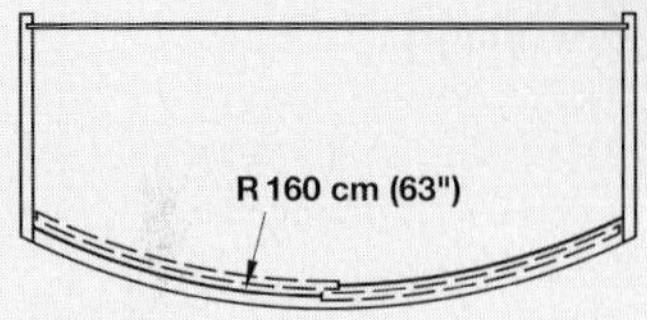

Semicircular arches from **160 cm** radius possible, manually press the single guide rail **with screw holes** into the precut groove.

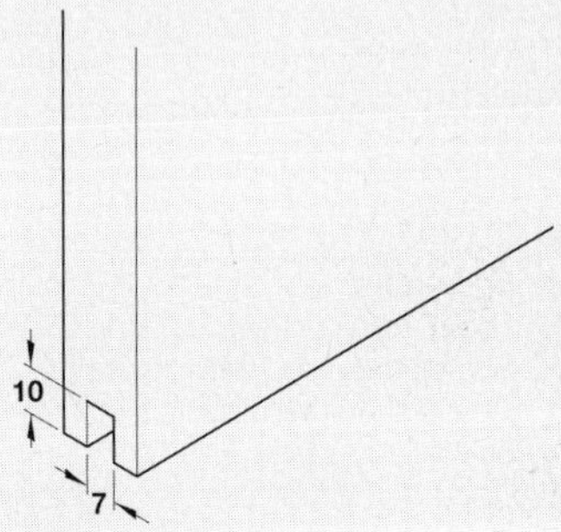

HÄFELE

Clipo® 15/H Sliding Door Fittings

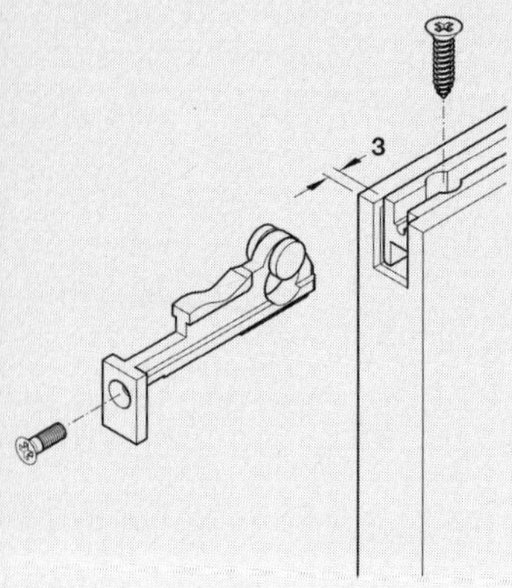

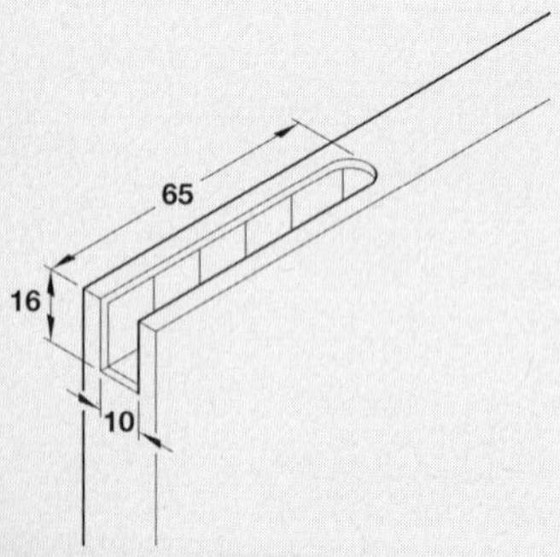

- max. **15 kg. (32 lbs)** door weight for **wooden doors**
- door thicknesses of **16 and 19 mm (5/8 and 3/4")**
- running gears **for insertion** with plastic rollers and metal shafts
- housing suitable for **press-fitting** in grooved edge
- also available as complete fitting sets

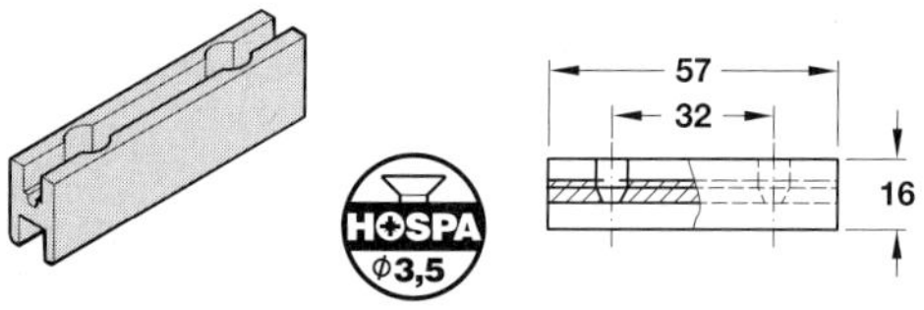

Housing for **insertion** in a grooved edge and screw-mounting
Finish: aluminum, anodized

Cat. No.	405.83.828

Packing: 100 pcs.

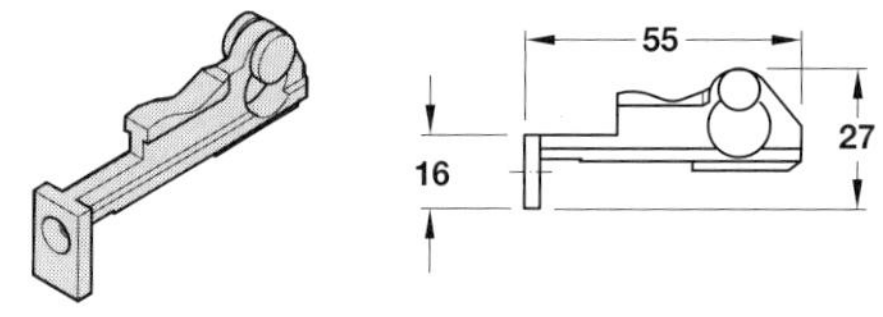

Running gear for insertion
Finish: plastic, anthracite

Cat. No.	405.83.917

Packing: 100 pcs.

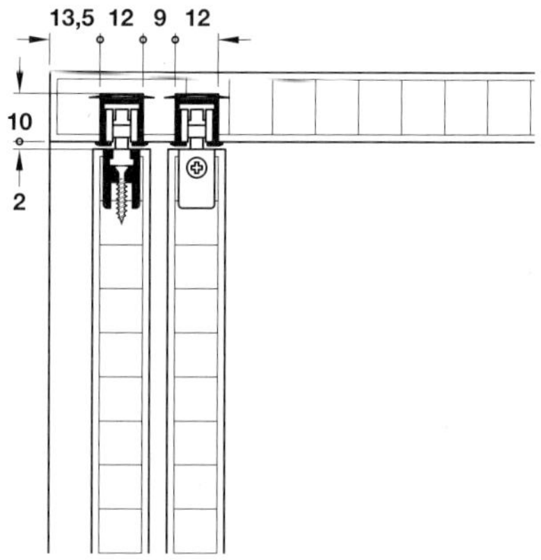

4 Sliding Door Hardware Drawer Slides Television Supports

Advantages:
- quick door mounting
- no guide rails in the floor
- application as Infront and Mixfront
- no wooden cover rail necessary

Clipo-Infront

for sliding doors running in a cabinet

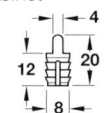

Guide for mounting in drilled holes
Finish: plastic, anthracite

Cat. No.	405.83.104

Packing: 50 pcs.

Complete fitting set	door weight **max. 15 kg (32 lbs)**
Includes:	**2 doors**
Running gear for insertion	4 pcs.
Housing screw-mounted	4 pcs.
Stopper with retaining spring	4 pcs.
Guide mounted in drilled holes	2 pcs.
Cat. No.	**405.82.232**
Packing: 1 set	

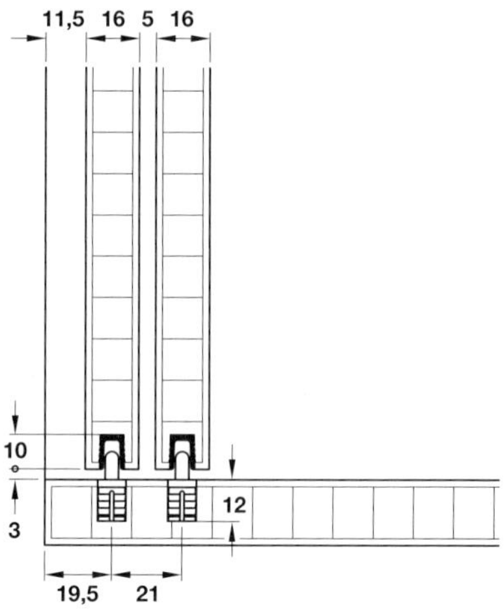

5/8" door

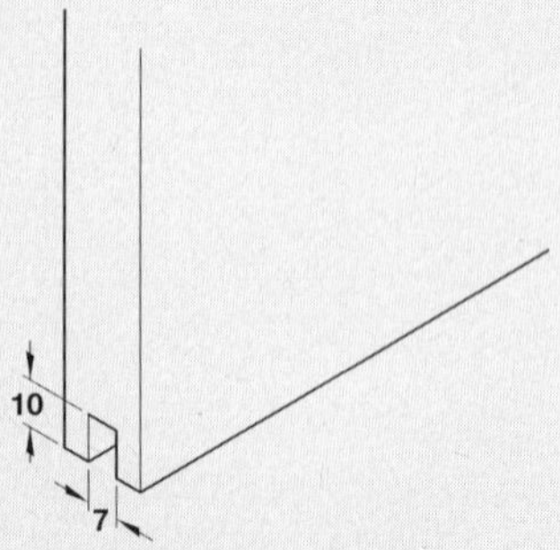

Clipo-Mixfront

for sliding doors running in the top of the cabinet and at the bottom running in front of the cabinet

Guide screw-mounted, adjustable
Finish: steel, black

Cat. No.	405.83.113

Packing: 25 pcs.

Complete fitting set	door weight **max. 15 kg (32 lbs)**
Includes:	**2 doors**
Running gear for insertion	4 pcs.
Housing screw-mounted	4 pcs.
Stopper with retaining spring	4 pcs.
Guide screw-mounted	1 pc.
Cat. No.	**405.82.134**
Packing: 1 set	

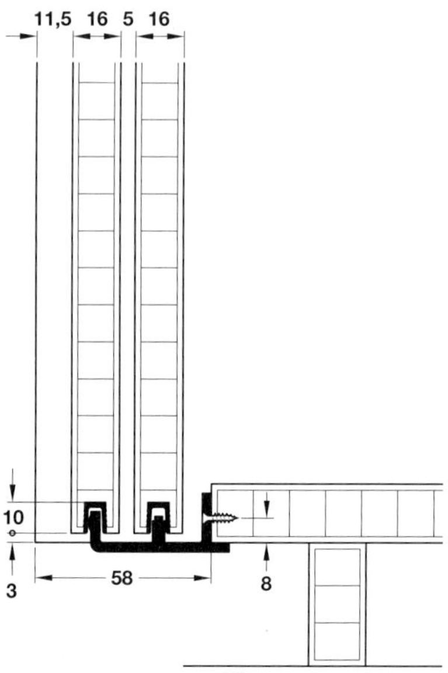

* **Important**
The complete fitting set is always delivered **without rails**, please order separately.
See rails on page **4.11**

Dimensional data not binding. We reserve the right to alter specifications without notice.

Dimensions in mm
Inches are approximate

Clipo® 15/H Sliding Door Fittings

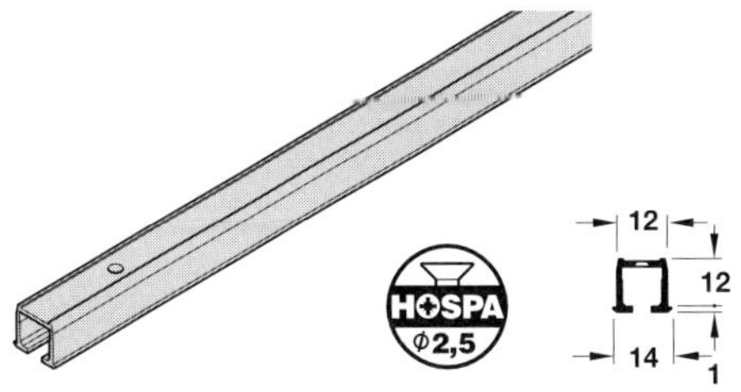

Single guide rail, upper, with screw holes
Finish: aluminum, unfinished

Cat. No.	405.87.013

Packing: 2.5 m long

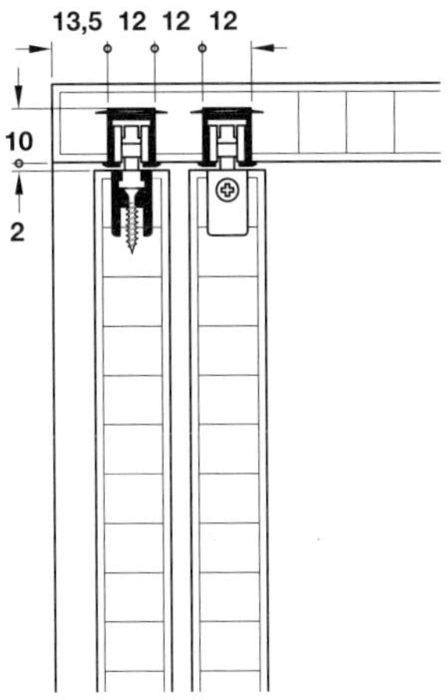

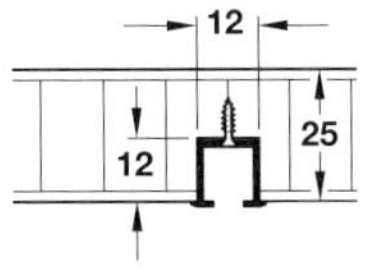

A **min. cabinet top thickness of 25 mm (1")** is required for mounting the single guide rail with screw holes.

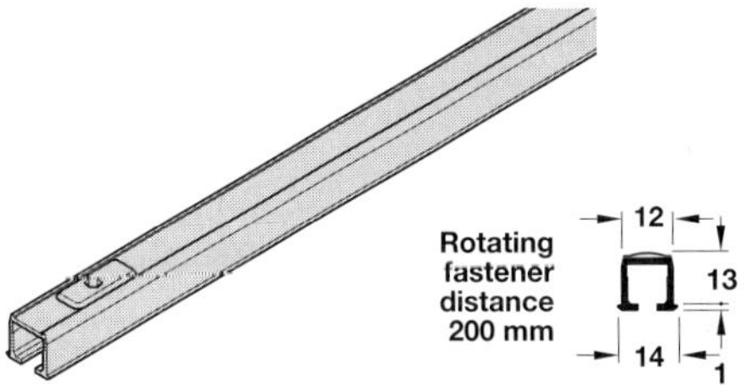

Single guide rail, upper, with rotating fasteners
Finish: aluminum, unfinished

Cat. No.	405.86.016

Packing: 2.5 m long

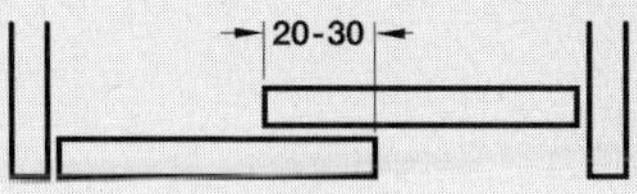

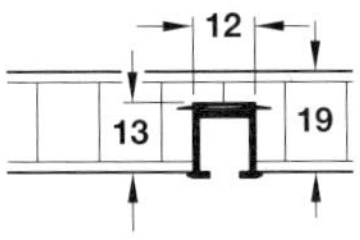

A **min. cabinet top thickness of 19 mm (3/4")** is required for mounting the single guide rail with rotating fasteners.

Sliding Door Hardware
Drawer Slides
Television Supports
4

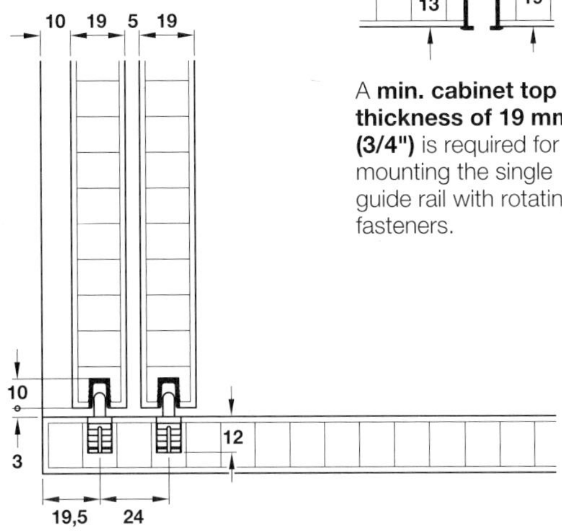

3/4" doors

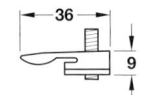

Stopper with retaining spring, for upper guide rails
Finish: plastic, natural colored

Cat. No.	405.83.131

Packing: 100 pcs.

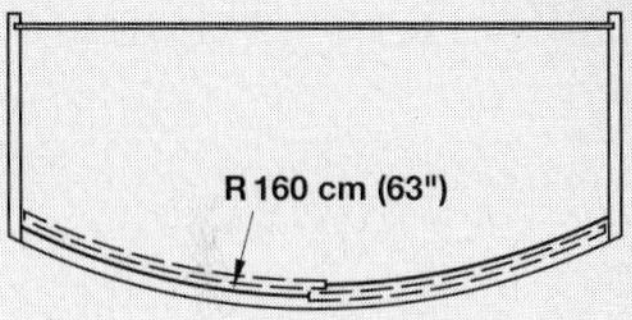

Semicircular arches from **160 cm** radius possible, manually press the single guide rail **with screw holes** into the precut groove.

* **Important**
The complete fitting set is always delivered **without guide rails**, please order separately.

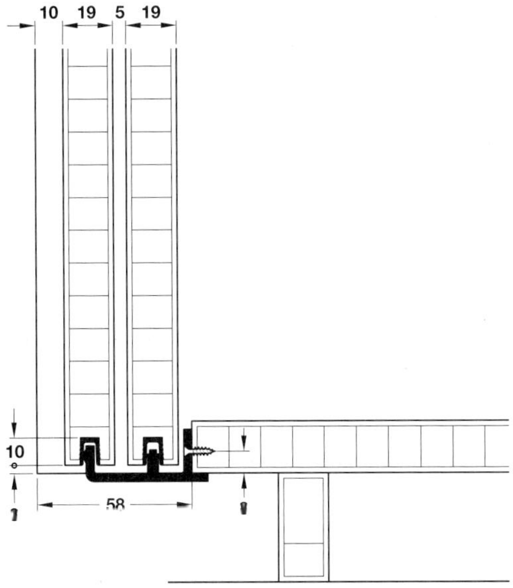

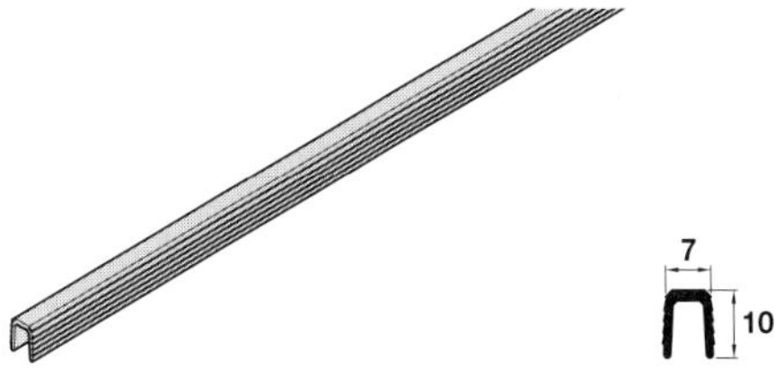

Guide rail, lower, barbed
Finish: plastic, anthracite

Cat. No.	405.98.516

Packing: 2.5 m long

Dimensions in mm
Inches are approximate

Dimensional data not binding.
We reserve the right to alter specifications without notice.

HÄFELE

Sliding Door Fitting Combino Forefront 20 and 35

- for door thickness **16 – 20 mm (5/8"-3/4")**
- comfortable height adjustment +/- 2 mm on the roller gear
- no tools necessary to mount door – door is mounted with the spring button system
- runner tracks fit four different cabinet types
- recommended door overlap = 30 mm

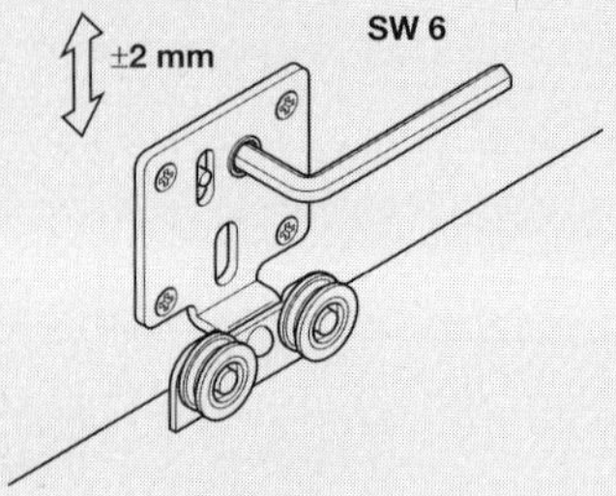

Complete hardware set	Door weight max. 20 kg (44 lbs.)	
	for 2 doors	**3 doors**
Includes:		
guide, inner door	2 pcs.	4 pcs.
guide, outer door	2 pcs.	2 pcs.
rubber buffer		2 pcs.
guide buffer	4 pcs.	4 pcs.
gear, single roller		
• inner door	2 pcs.	4 pcs.
• outer door	2 pcs.	2 pcs.
stopper, without spring	2 pcs.	1 pcs.
stopper, with spring	2 pcs.	3 pcs.
Cat. No.	**405.91.124**	**405.91.133**
Packing:	1 set including Varianta fixing screws 6.3 x 13 mm	

Complete hardware set	Door weight max. 35 kg (77 lbs.)	
	for 2 doors	**3 doors**
Includes:		
guide, inner door	2 pcs.	4 pcs.
guide, outer door	2 pcs.	2 pcs.
rubber buffer		2 pcs.
guide buffer	4 pcs.	4 pcs.
gear, single roller		
• inner door	2 pcs.	4 pcs.
• outer door	2 pcs.	2 pcs.
stopper, without spring	2 pcs.	1 pcs.
stopper, with spring	2 pcs.	3 pcs.
Cat. No.	**405.91.222**	**405.91.231**
Packing:	1 set including Varianta fixing screws 6.3 x 13 mm	

For cabinets with more doors, please order the appropriate numbers of sets:
for example, for five doors, order
1 hardware set for 2 doors PLUS
1 hardware set for 3 doors

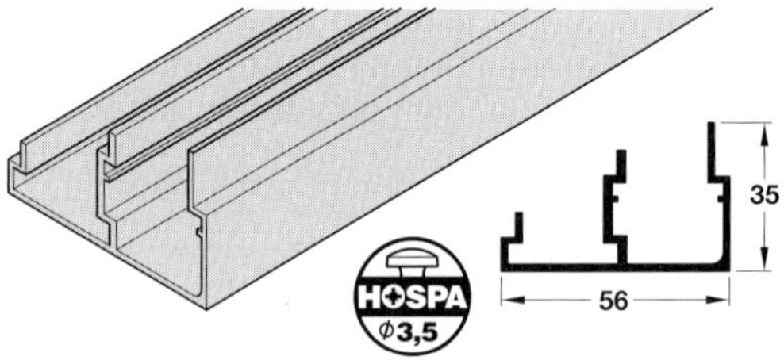

Upper guide tracks with holes for screw-mounting
Finish: aluminum, unfinished

Packing	Cat. No.
2.5 m	405.97.019
6.0 m	405.97.037

4 Sliding Door Hardware
Drawer Slides
Television Supports

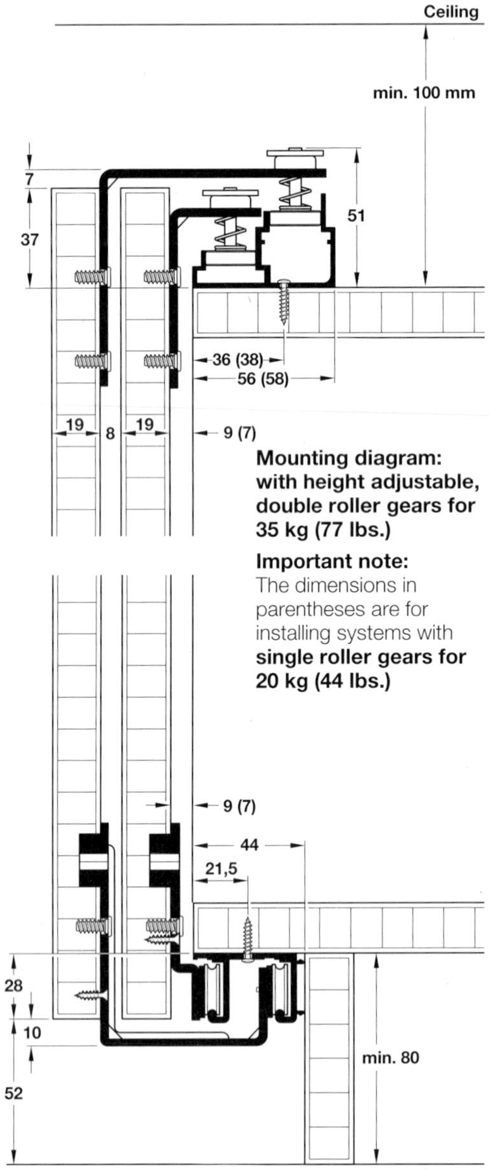

Mounting diagram: with height adjustable, double roller gears for 35 kg (77 lbs.)

Important note:
The dimensions in parentheses are for installing systems with **single roller gears for 20 kg (44 lbs.)**

Screw-mounting position for the upper guide track while **installing** systems with height adjustable **single roller gears**

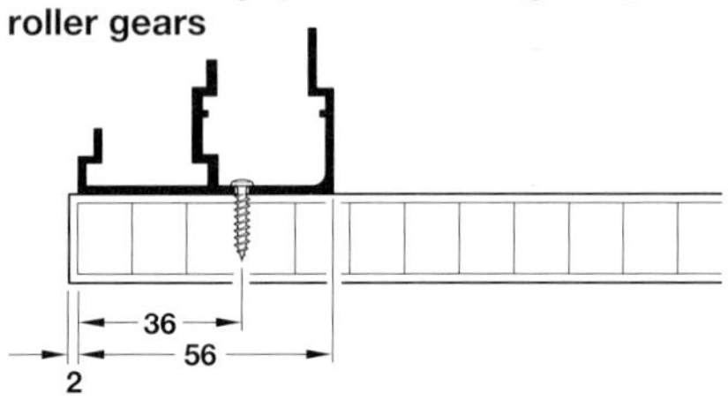

for **double roller gears,** the upper cabinet panel and the track are flush

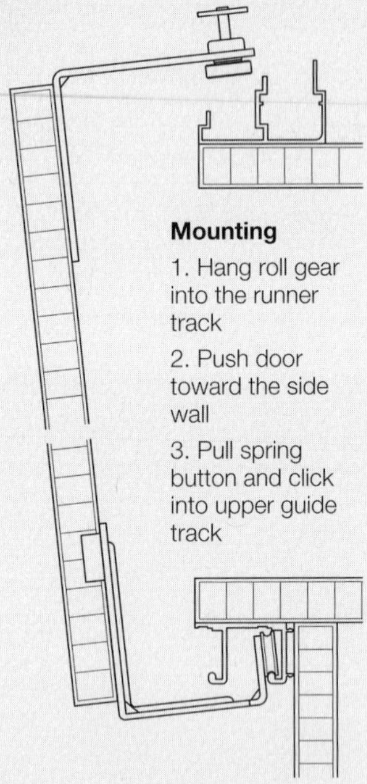

Mounting

1. Hang roll gear into the runner track
2. Push door toward the side wall
3. Pull spring button and click into upper guide track

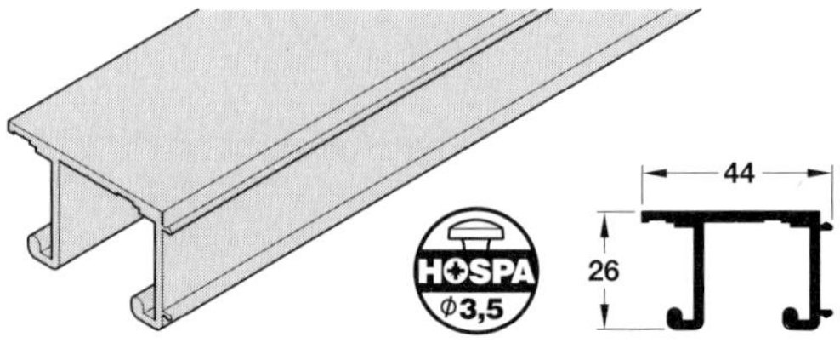

Double runner track, bottom with holes for screw-mounting
Finish: aluminum, unfinished

Packing	Cat. No.
2.5 m	406.31.963
6.0 m	406.31.981

Important Note:
Tracks and center door stoppers are not included in the complete hardware sets. Please order separately.

Dimensional data not binding.
We reserve the right to alter specifications without notice.

Dimensions in mm

Sliding Door Fitting Combino Forefront 20 and 35

For ordering individual parts

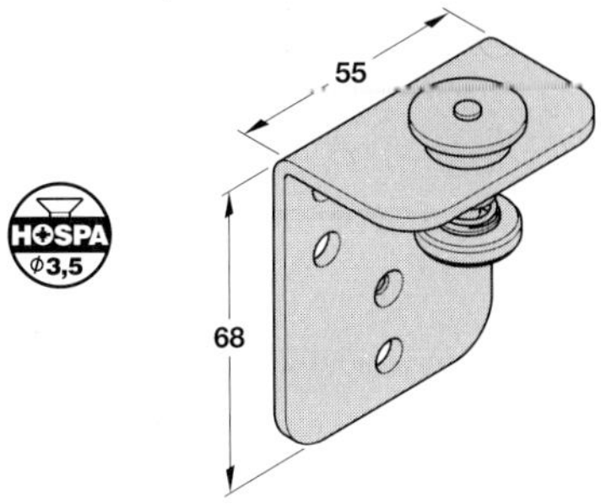

Guide
for inside door, with spring button
Finish: steel, zinc-plated

Cat. No.	405.93.815

Packing: 20 pcs.

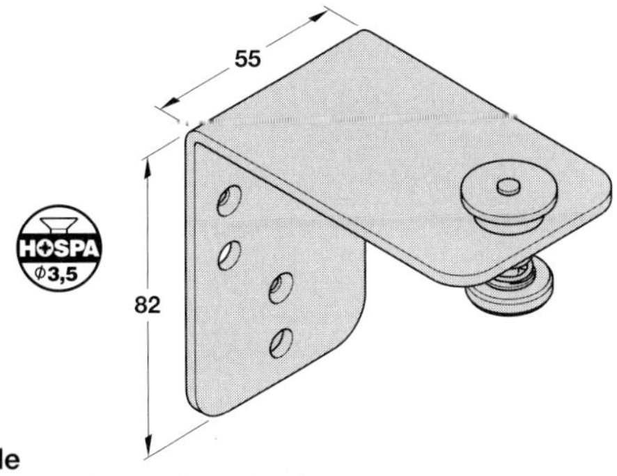

Guide
for outside door, with spring button
Finish: steel, zinc-plated

Cat. No.	405.93.824

Packing: 20 pcs.

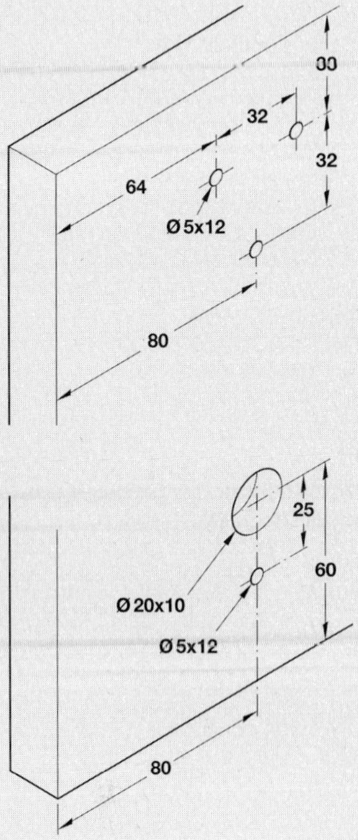

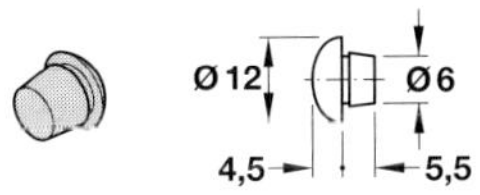

Rubber buffer, black
to be recessed into the door edge

Cat. No.	406.24.101

Packing: 100 pcs.

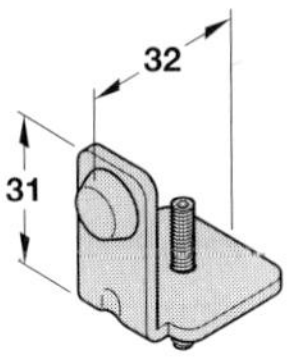

Guide buffer
for upper guide track
Finish: steel, zinc-plated

Cat. No.	405.93.011

Packing: 40 pcs.

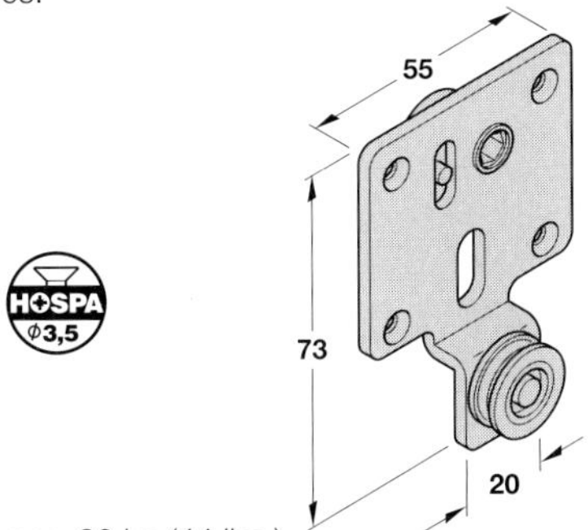

Single roller gear, 20 kg (44 lbs.)
for inside door, with height adjustment +/- 2 mm
Finish: steel, zinc-plated

Cat. No.	405.93.931

Packing: 20 pcs.

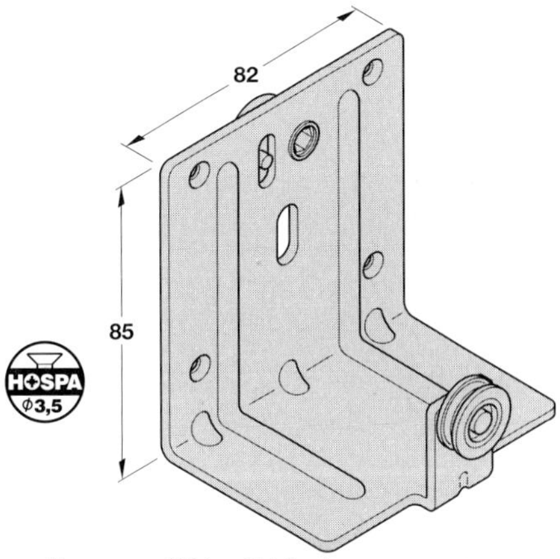

Single roller gear, 20 kg (44 lbs.)
for outside door, with height adjustment +/- 2 mm
Finish: steel, zinc-plated

Cat. No.	405.93.940

Packing: 20 pcs.

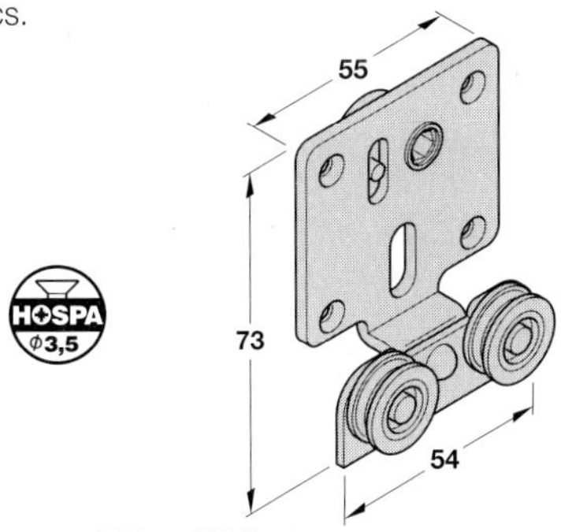

Double roller gear, 35 kg (77 lbs.)
for inside door, with height adjustment +/- 2 mm
Finish: steel, zinc-plated

Cat. No.	405.93.959

Packing: 20 pcs.

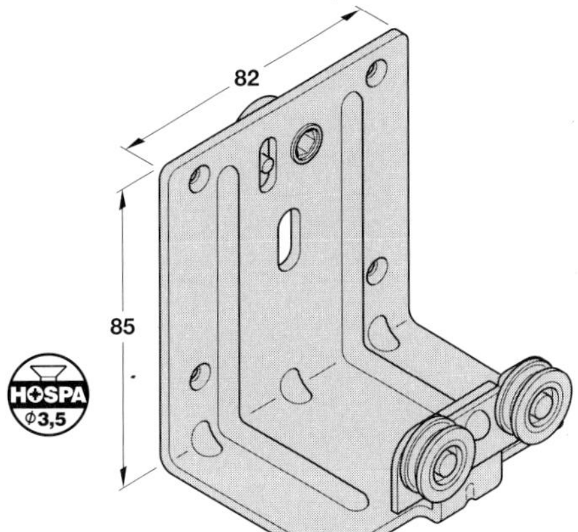

Double roller gear, 35 kg (77 lbs.)
for outside door, with height adjustment +/- 2 mm
Finish: steel, zinc-plated

Cat. No.	405.93.968

Packing: 20 pcs.

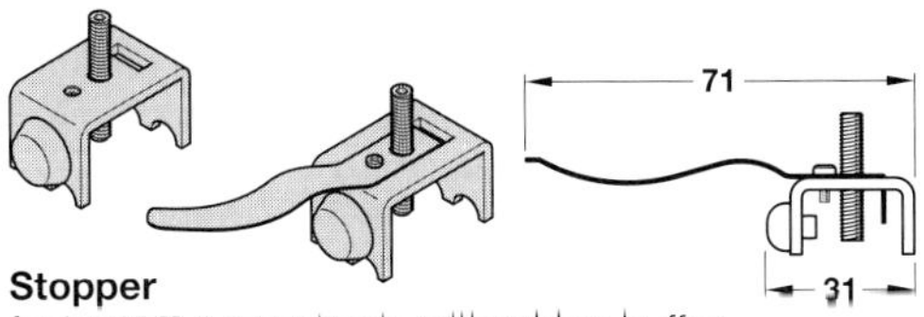

Stopper
for bottom runner track, with rubber buffer
Finish: steel, zinc-plated

Cat. No.		
	without spring	406.32.077
	with spring	406.32.068

Packing: 20 pcs.

Sliding Door Hardware
Drawer Slides
Television Supports
4

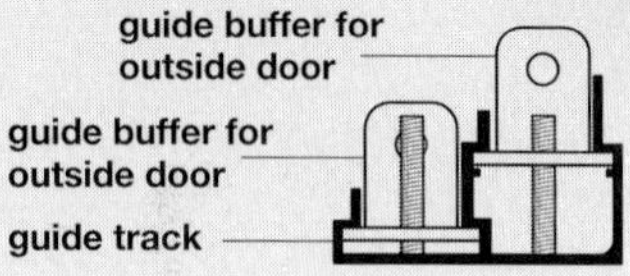

push stops into place before mounting the tracks

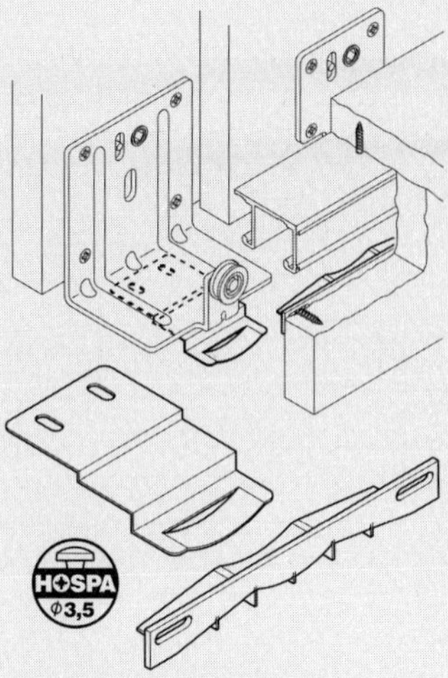

Center door stopper
for cabinets with 3 doors
Finish:
Spring part: steel, nickel-plated
Stopper: plastic

Cat. No.	406.32.080

Packing: 1 pc.

Dimensional data not binding.
We reserve the right to alter specifications without notice.

Dimensions in mm
Inches are approximate

HÄFELE

Sliding Door Fittings Combino Infront 20 and 35

- for door thickness 16–20 mm (5/8"-3/4")
- comfortable height adjustment (+/- 2 mm) on the roller gear
- vertical adjustment of +/- 1.25 mm on the guide
- no tools necessary to mount door – door is mounted with the spring button system
- runner tracks fit four different cabinet typed
- elegant clip-on aluminum cover profile available
- recommended door overlap: 30 mm

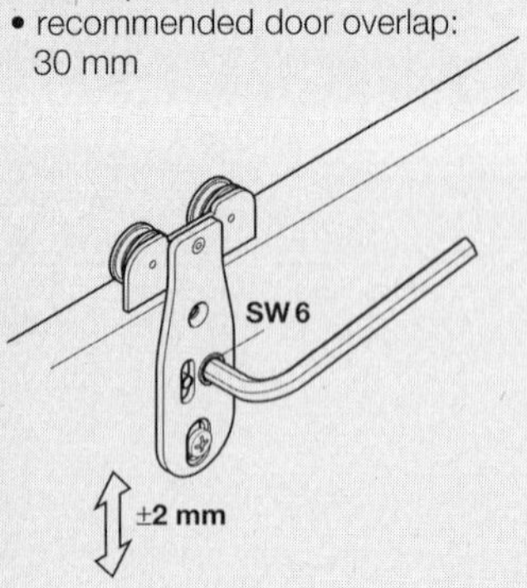

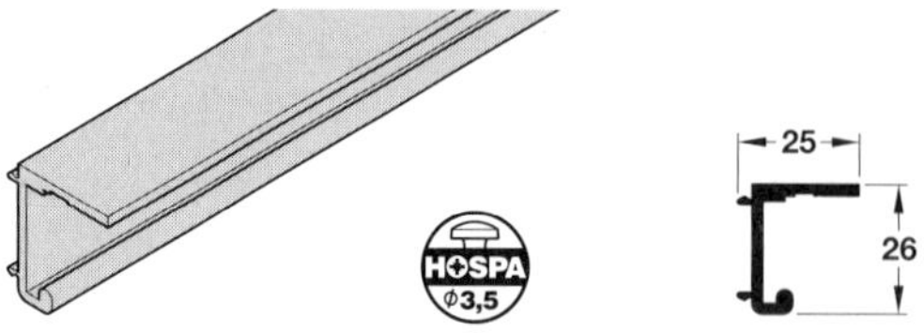

Single runner track, top, with holes for screw-mounting

Finish: aluminum, unfinished

Packing	Cat. No.
2.5 m	406.30.966
6.0 m	406.30.984

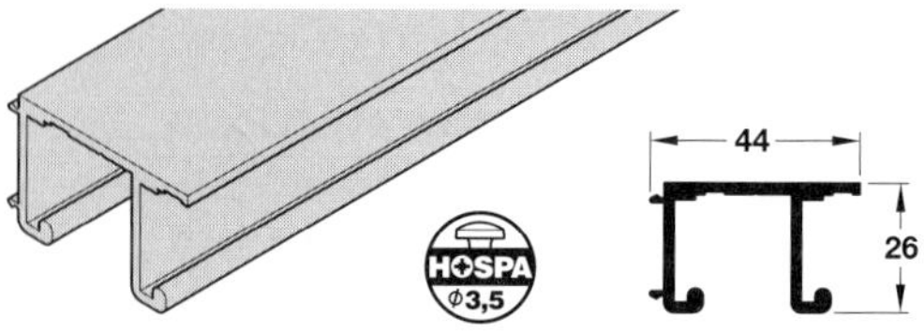

Double runner track, top, with holes for screw-mounting

Finish: aluminum, unfinished

Packing	Cat. No.
2.5 m	406.31.963
6.0 m	406.31.981

Complete hardware sets	door weight **max. 20 kg (44 lbs.)**		door weight **max. 35 kg (77 lbs.)**
for:	**2 doors**	**3 doors**	**2 doors**
height adjustment (h.a.):	**no**	**yes**	**yes**
Includes:			
single roller gear without h.a.	4 pcs.		
single roller gear with h.a.		4 pcs.	
double roller gear with h.a.			4 pcs.
stoppers, with & without spring	2 pcs. each	2 pcs. each	2 pcs.
guide for guide track with 7.5 mm dia. bolt	2 pcs.	2 pcs.	2 pcs
Cat. No. for gear with plastic coated ball bearings	**405.91.679**	**405.91.624**	**405.91.722**
Packing: 1 set, including Varianta mounting screws 6.3 x 13 mm			

4 **Sliding Door Hardware**
Drawer Slides
Television Supports

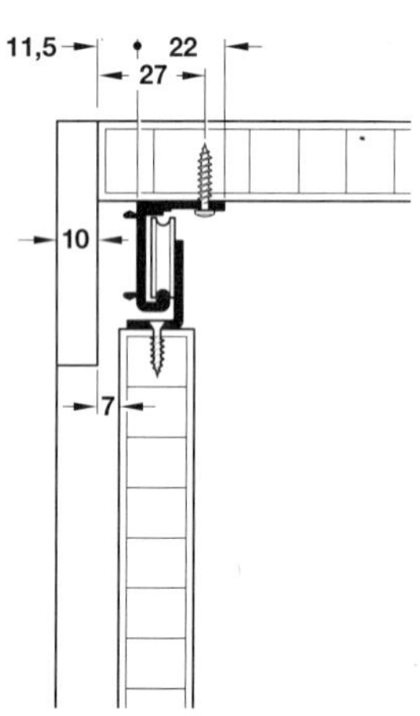

Mounting diagram:
with single roller gear fastens to edge of door

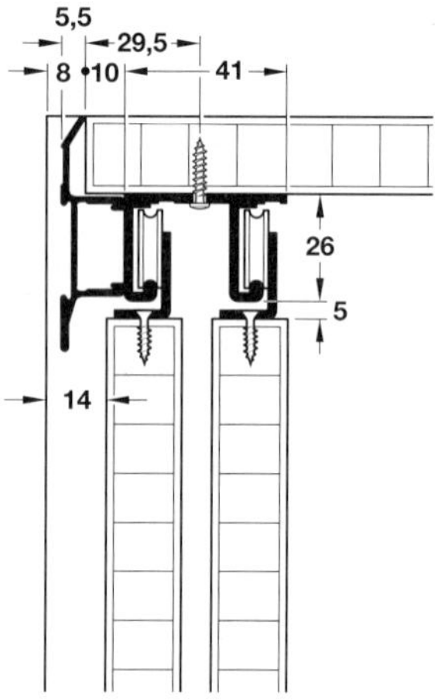

Mounting diagram:
with single roller gear fastens to edge of door

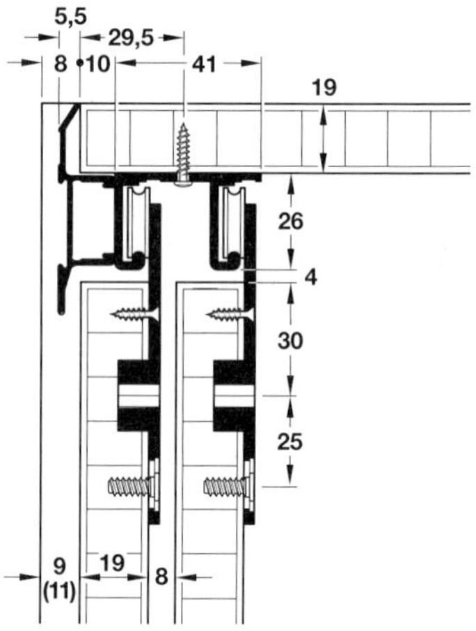

Mounting diagram:
with height adjustable single and double roller gears fastens to inside of door

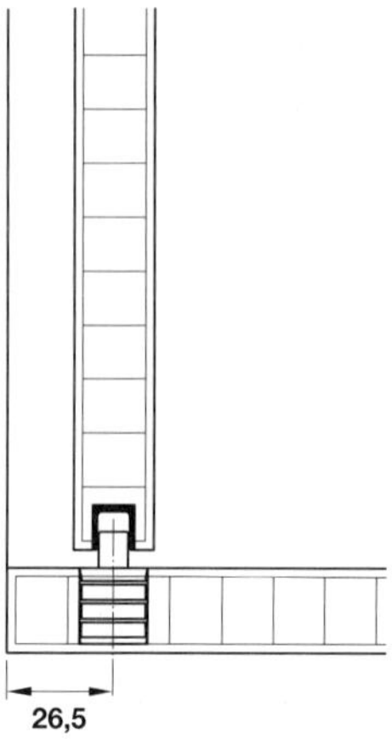

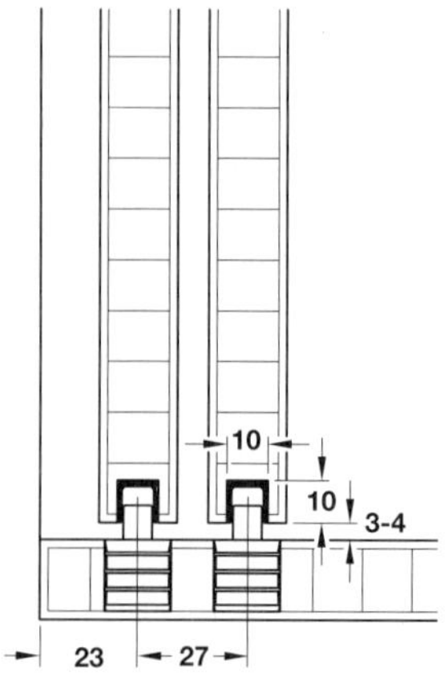

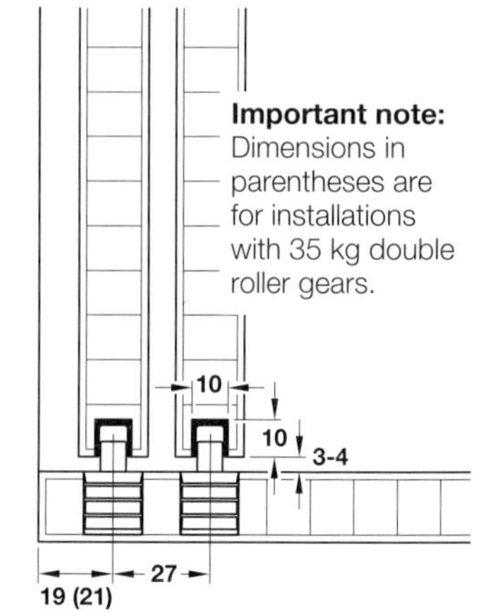

Important note:
Dimensions in parentheses are for installations with 35 kg double roller gears.

Important note:
Tracks are not included in the complete hardware sets. Please order separately.

Dimensions in mm

Sliding Door Fittings Combino Infront 20 and 35

For ordering individual parts

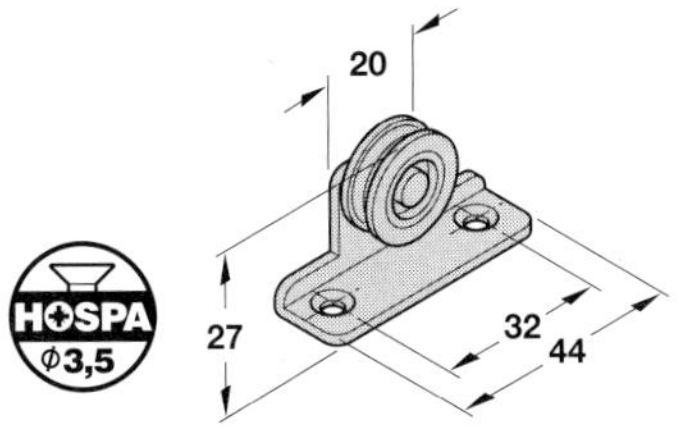

20 kg (44 lbs.) single roller gear
Finish: steel, zinc-plated

Cat. No.	with ball bearings	406.33.921

Packing: 40 pcs.

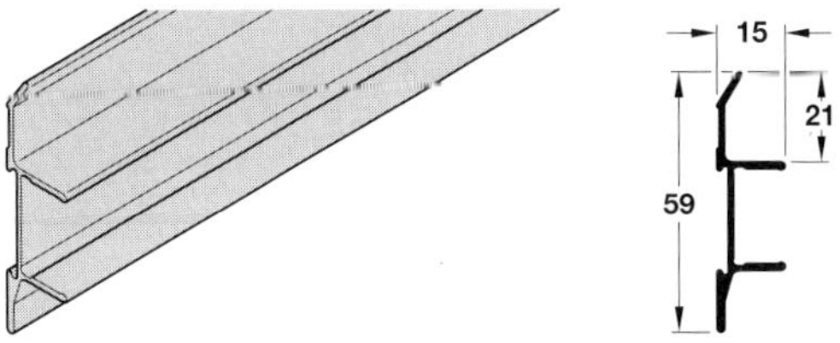

Cover profile
to be clipped onto the runner tracks
Finish: aluminum, anodized

Packing	Cat. No.
2.5 m	406.34.919
6.0 m	406.34.937

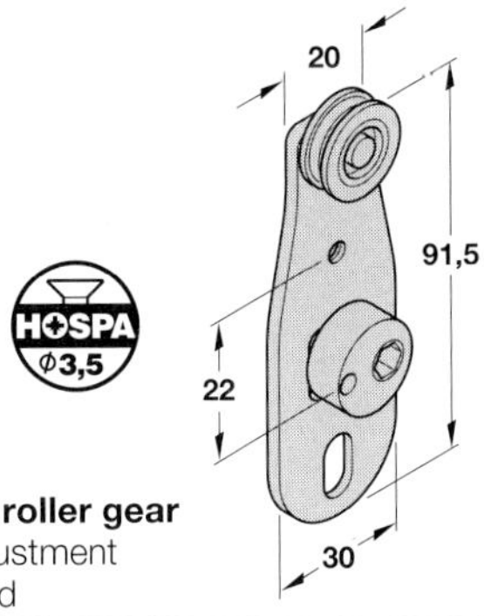

20 kg (44 lbs.) single roller gear
with ±2 mm height adjustment
Finish: steel, zinc-plated

Cat. No.	with ball bearings	405.93.913

Packing: 40 pcs.

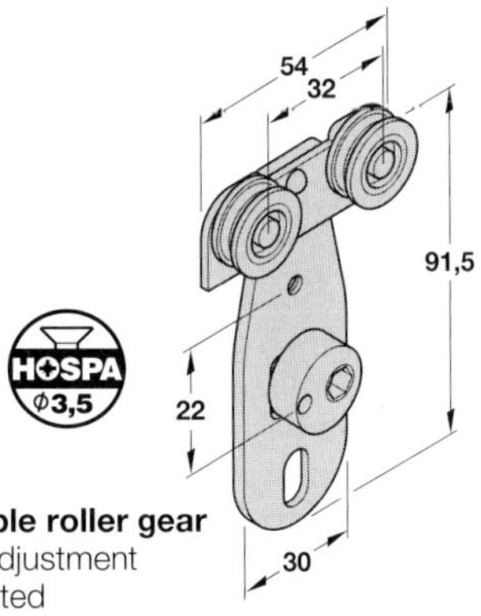

35 kg (77 lbs.) double roller gear
with ±2 mm height adjustment
Finish: steel, zinc-plated

Cat. No.	with ball bearings	405.93.922

Packing: 40 pcs.

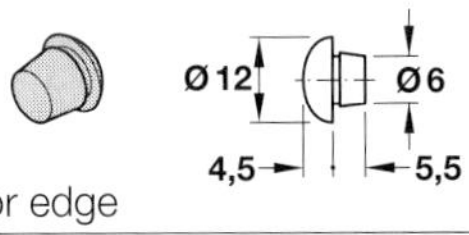

Rubber buffer, black
to be recessed into the door edge

Cat. No.	406.24.101

Packing: 100 pcs.

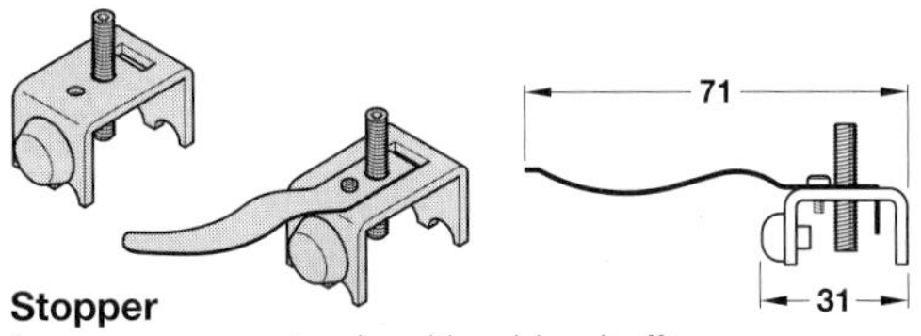

Stopper
for upper runner track, with rubber buffer
Finish: steel, zinc-plated

Cat. No.	without spring	406.32.077
	with spring	406.32.068

Packing: 20 pcs.

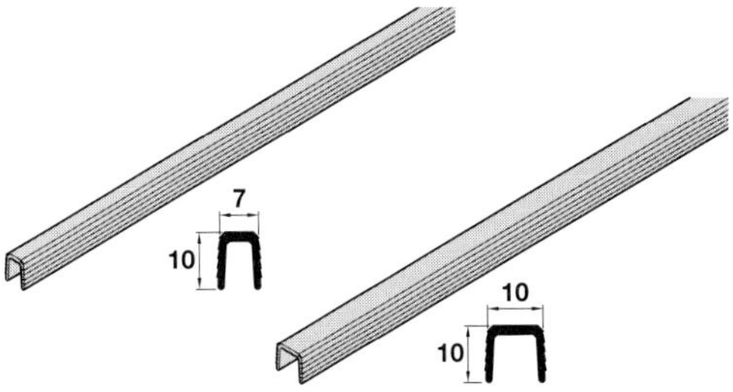

Lower guide track, barbed
Finish: plastic, gray

Packing	Cat. No. groove width 7 mm	groove width 10 mm
2.5 m	405.90.510	405.99.513

* For complete hardware set

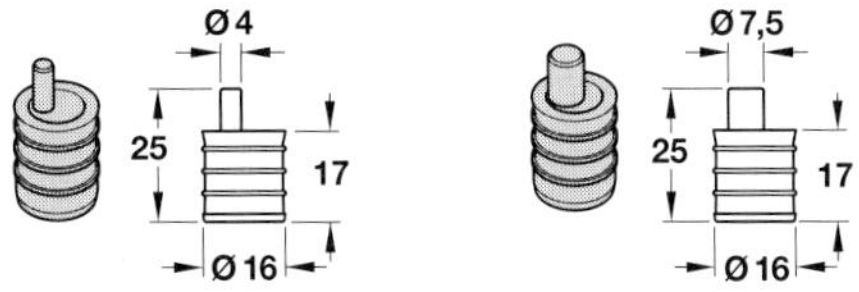

Guide for lower guide track
Finish: plastic, ivory

Cat. No.	with **4 mm Ø** bolt	406.32.022
	with **7.5 mm Ø** bolt	406.32.013

Packing: 20 pcs.

- Can stick labels or decorative strips into the cover profile

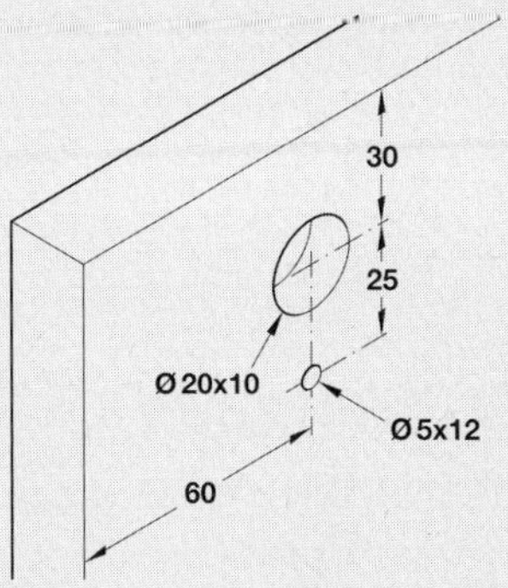

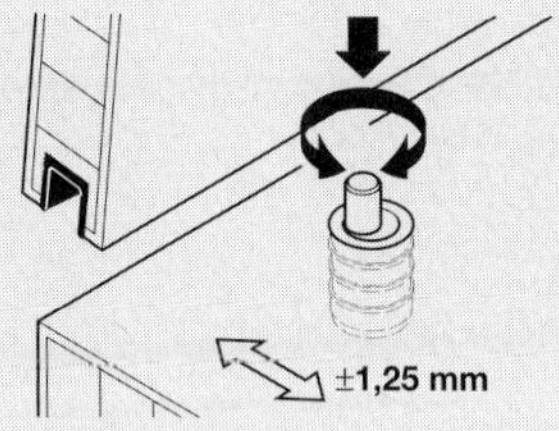

By pressing and simultaneous turning , the guide bolt can be adjusted by ±1.25 mm; this permits vertical adjustments of the door.

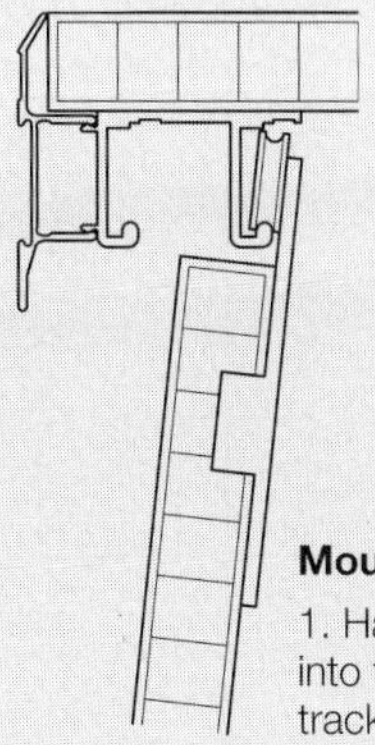

Mounting
1. Hang the gear into the runner track

2. Press bolt and swing door into place …
3. … until the bolt clicks into the guide track.

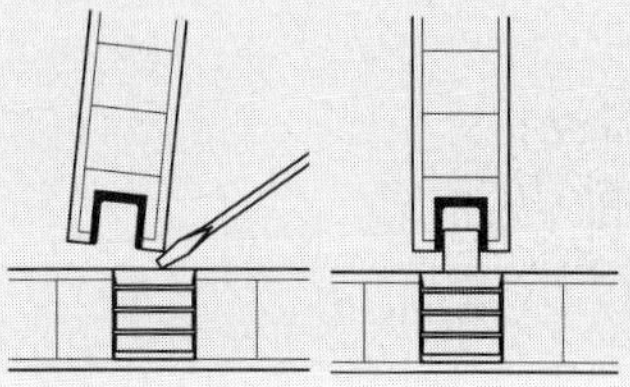

Dimensional data not binding. We reserve the right to alter specifications without notice.

Dimensions in mm

HÄFELE

For wood thickness from 19 mm (3/4")

"Hawa-roll-away" is a sliding door fitting for medium to heavy weight doors in room interiors; light and quiet running plastic-coated rollers with precision-made ball bearings; maintenance-free.

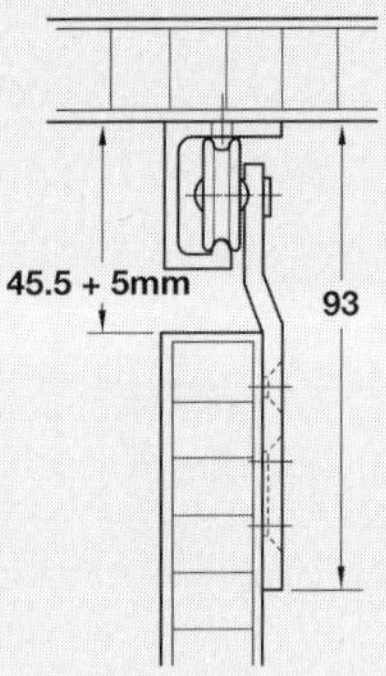

Two upper tracks are mounted side by side for double or multiple doors.

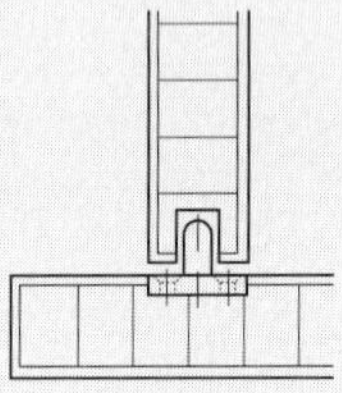

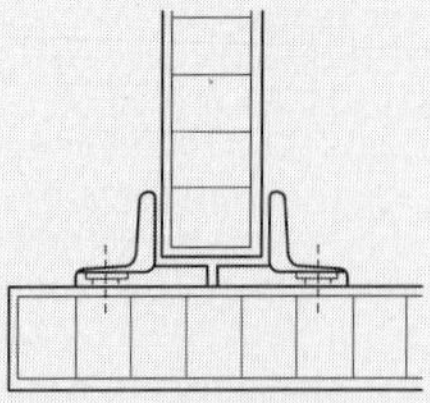

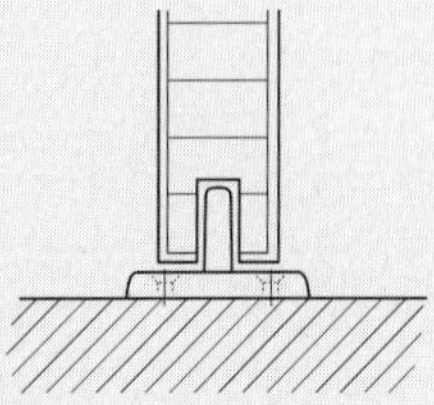

Dimensional data not binding. We reserve the right to alter specifications without notice.

Hawa-roll-away® Sliding Door Fitting

Upper track with screw-holes

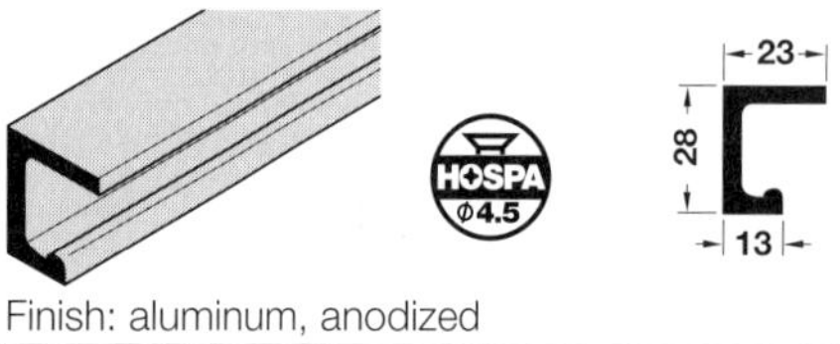

Finish: aluminum, anodized

Cat. No.		
	2.5 m long	942.14.250
	3.5 m long	942.14.350
	6.0 m long	942.14.600

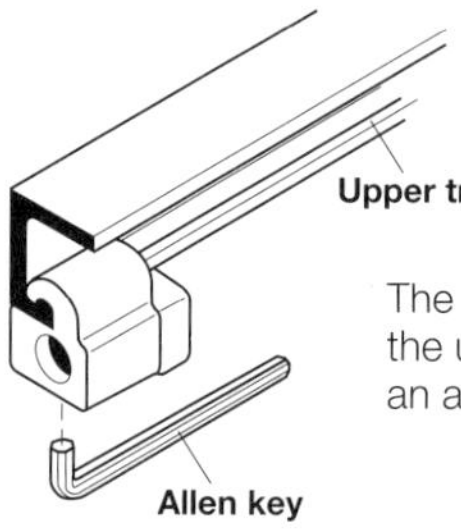

The track stopper is slipped onto the upper track and secured with an allen key.

Track stopper for infinitely adjustable mounting in upper track

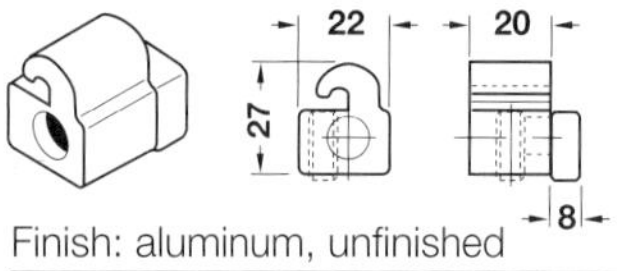

Finish: aluminum, unfinished

Cat. No.	942.14.041

Packing: 2 pcs.

Door weights up to 20 kg (44 lbs), running gear, with ball bearing mounted roller, complete with mounting plate for attachment to side of door; vertical adjustment slot.

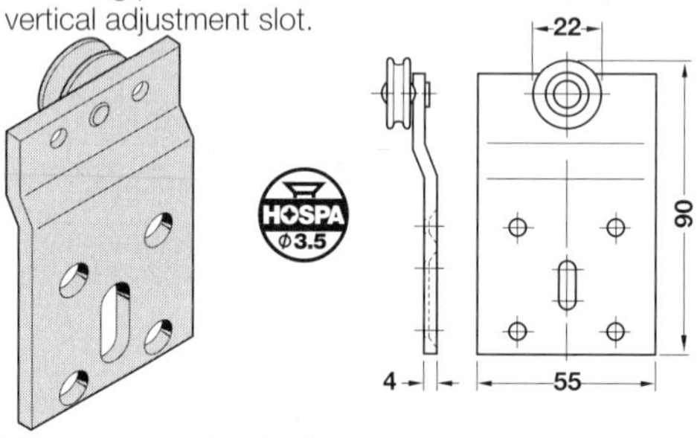

Finish: steel, galvanized

Cat. No.	407.65.017

Packing: 2 pcs.

Door weights up to 40 kg (88 lbs), running gear, with ball bearing mounted roller, complete with mounting plate for attachment to side of door; vertical adjustment slot.

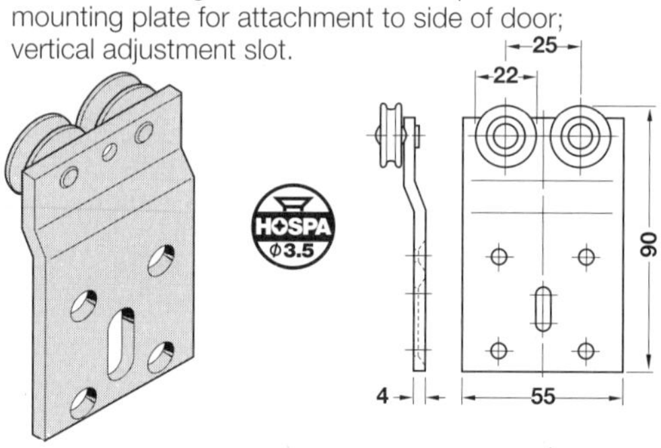

Cat. No.	407.65.035

Packing: 2 pcs.

Guide, recessed and screw-mounted in cabinet floor

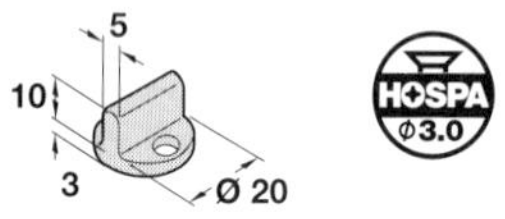

Finish: plastic, natural-colored

Cat. No.	407.01.942

Packing: 100 pcs.

Single guide, two-part screw-mounted

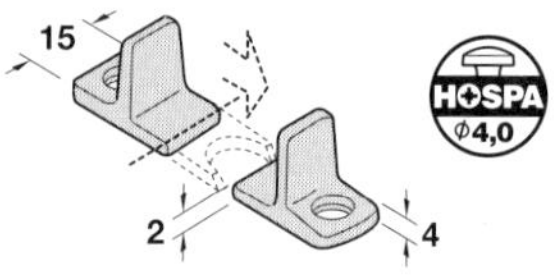

Finish: plastic, natural-colored

Cat. No.	407.01.960

Packing: 2 pcs. each

Rubber buffer, screw-mounted

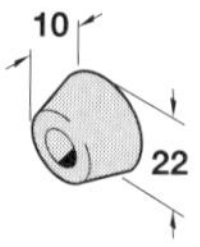

Finish: black

Cat. No.	407.01.933

Packing: 10 pcs. each

Guide, for very smooth sliding operation

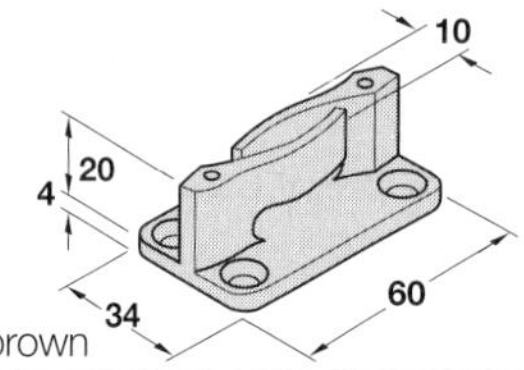

Finish: plastic, brown

Cat. No.	407.01.190

Packing: 1 pc.

Rubber buffer, plug-fit type

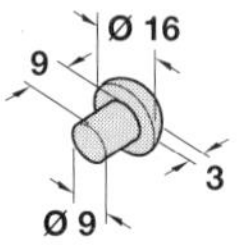

Finish: white

Cat. No.	406.24.100

Packing: 10 pcs.

Dimensions in mm

Hawa-Dorado-Infront Sliding Door Fitting

- For door thicknesses from 19-25 mm (3/4-1")
- Max weight per door **40 kg. (88 lbs)**
- Twin-double rollers
- Easy adjustability ± 3 mm
- For easy ordering complete sets are available
- All 35 mm drilling

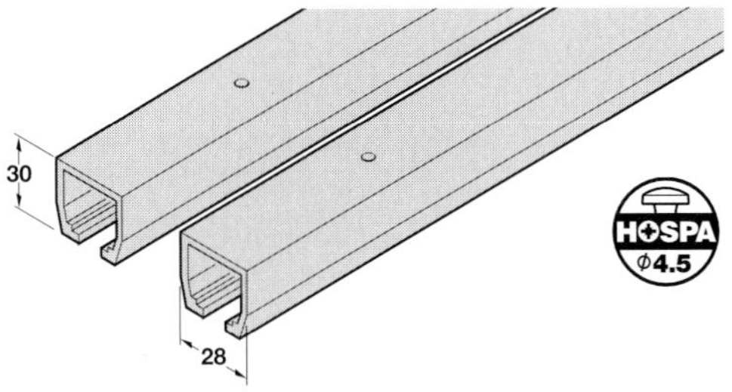

Complete Set of Fittings		
	Cat. No. Overlapping	
Set of fittings for	**2 doors**	**3 doors**
Door weights up to **40 kg (88 lbs.)**	**406.70.120**	**406.70.139**
One set comprises:		
Running gear for inner/outer doors	4 units	6 units
Track buffers for both doors	3 units	4 units
Allen key, SW 3	1 unit	1 unit
Twin guide, for both doors	1 unit	1 unit
Single guide for inner door		1 unit
Rubber buffer	2 units	2 units

For multiple door layouts, order as follows:
4 doors 2 sets of 2-door fitting
5 doors 1 set each 2-door and 3-door fittings

No tracks (lower or upper) are included in set packing. Please order separately.

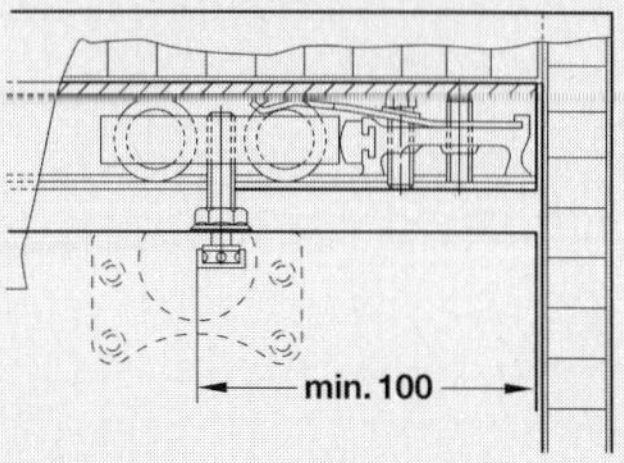

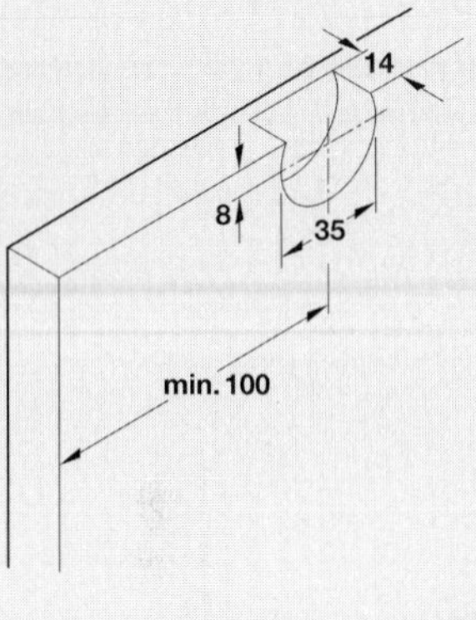

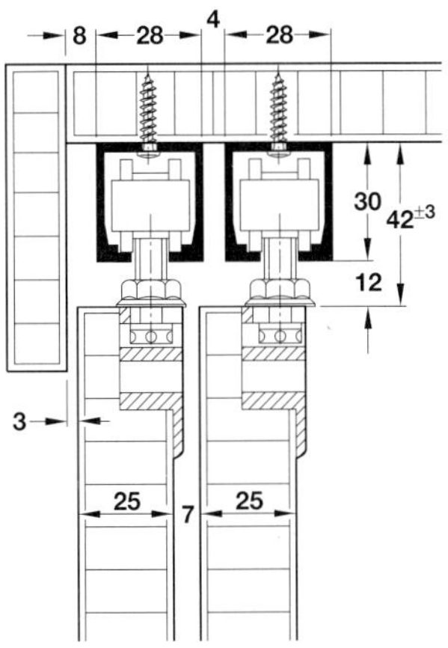

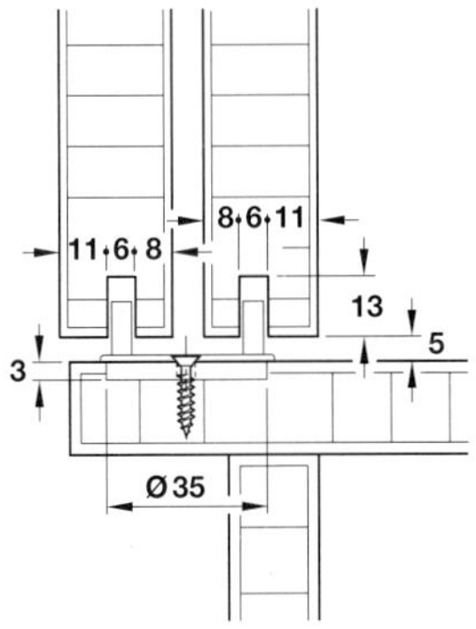

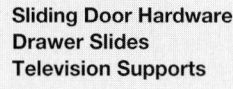

Sliding Door Hardware
Drawer Slides
Television Supports
4

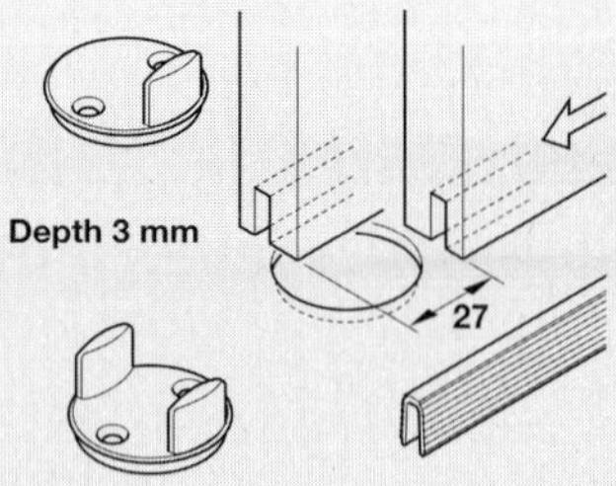

Minimum door overlap=27 mm

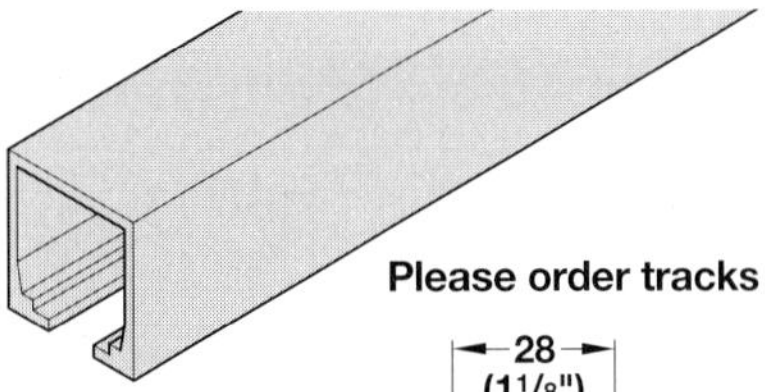

Please order tracks separately

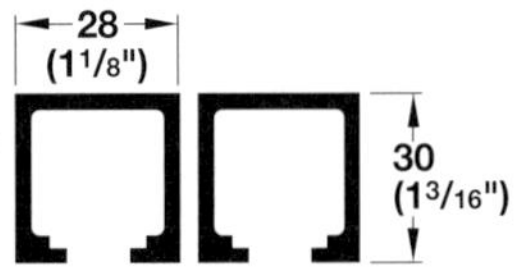

Two upper tracks are mounted side-by-side for overlapping or multiple doors.

Tracks
2 tracks, side-by-side are needed for overlapping doors. Upper track with screw-holes
Finish: aluminum, anodized

Finish: aluminum, anodized

Cat. No.	1.4 m (4' 7")	407.56.867
	1.6 m (5' 3")	407.56.876
	1.8 m (5' 11")	407.56.885
	2.0 m (6' 7")	407.56.894
	3.0 m (0' 10⅛")	407.56.011
	4.0 m (13' 1½")	407.56.951
	6.0 m (19' 8¼")	407.56.931

Packing: 1 pc.

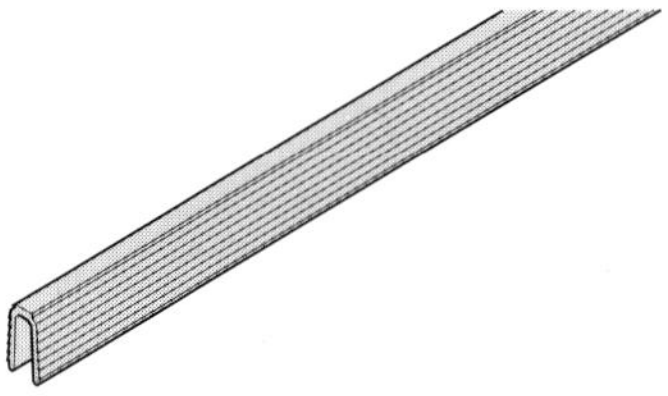

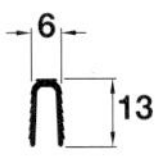

Lower guide, press-fit (use glue)

Finish: plastic, brown

Cat. No.	406.73.103

Packing: 3.0 m

Dimensional data not binding. We reserve the right to alter specifications without notice.

Dimensions in mm

HÄFELE

Hawa Dorado-Infront Sliding Door Fitting

Individual Parts

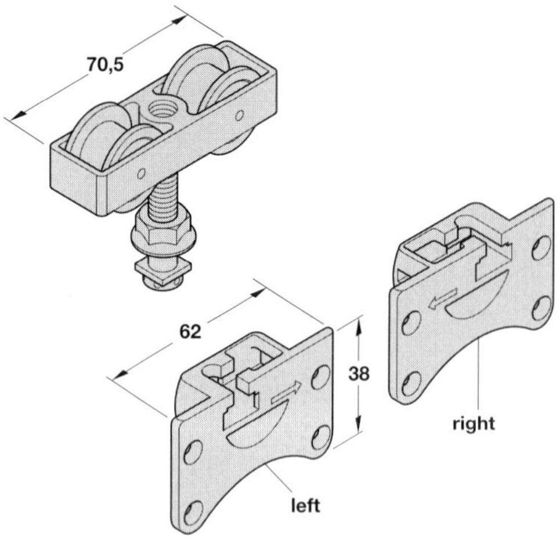

Running gear
For inner and outer doors, vertically adjustable ±3 mm, with 2 friction-bearing mounted tandem runner assembles in white plastic and a nickel-plated zinc die-cast. Suitable for door weights up to 40 kg. (88 lbs.)
Complete with mounting materials.

	Cat. No.
left	406.70.901
right	406.70.900

Packing: 1 pc. includes mounting material

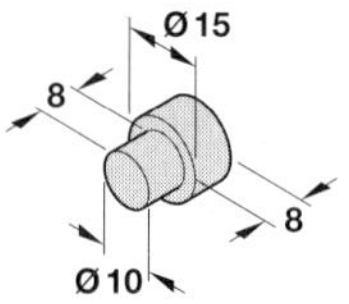

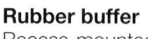

Rubber buffer
Recess-mounted in edge of door.
finish: white

Cat. No.	406.70.980

Packing: 1 pc.

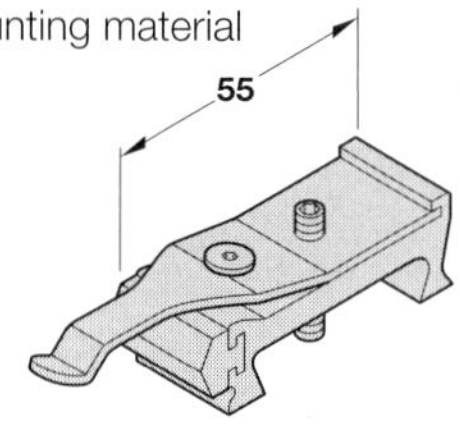

Track-mounted buffer
For inner and outer doors, steplessly adjustable.
Finish: zinc die-cast w/adjustable steel spring and retainer

Cat. No.	407.56.018

Packing: 1 pc.

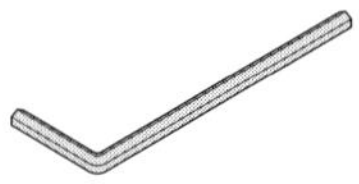

Allen key M3
To secure buffer in twin track.
Finish: steel

Cat. No.	008.28.035

Packing: 3000 pc.

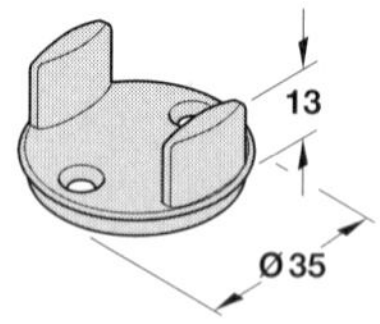

Twin guide
For both doors.
Screw-mounted in ø35 mm recess in cabinet floor.
Guides CTC distance = 29 mm
Complete w/mounting materials.
Finish: plastic, brown

Cat. No.	406.70.920

Packing: 1 pc. with mounting material

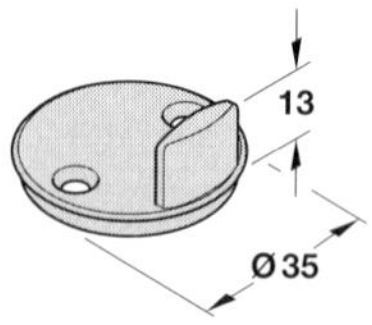

Single guide
For inner door.
Screw-mounted in ø35 mm recess in cabinet floor.
Complete w/mounting materials
Finish: plastic, brown

Cat. No.	406.70.921

Packing: 1 pc. includes mounting material

Dimensions in mm

Hawa Junior 40 Sliding Door Fitting

HÄFELE

Hawa Junior 40 is a vertically adjustable sliding door fitting for light to medium weight interior doors. Tandem rollers made of high-grade polyamide and mounted in an aluminum carriage ensuring exceptionally light and silent action. All parts are corrosion-resistant and are suitable for use in rooms with a humid atmosphere.

1 Complete Set, for a single sliding door without upper tracks includes the following components:

Fitting Set for single sliding door without upper tracks

Cat. No.	940.40.001

Packing: 1 set

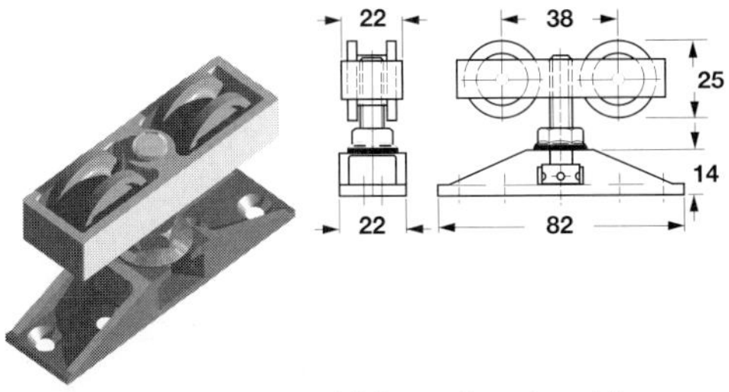

Running Gear, 2 units, high-grade polyamide tandem rollers with sleeve bearings, aluminum carriage and zinc die-cast mounting plate. Complete with mounting materials.

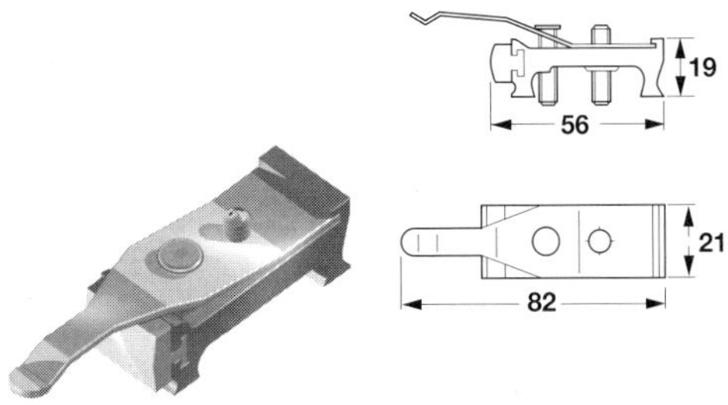

Track Stopper, 1 unit for positioning in upper track. Zinc die-cast housing with adjustable steel spring and rubber bumper.

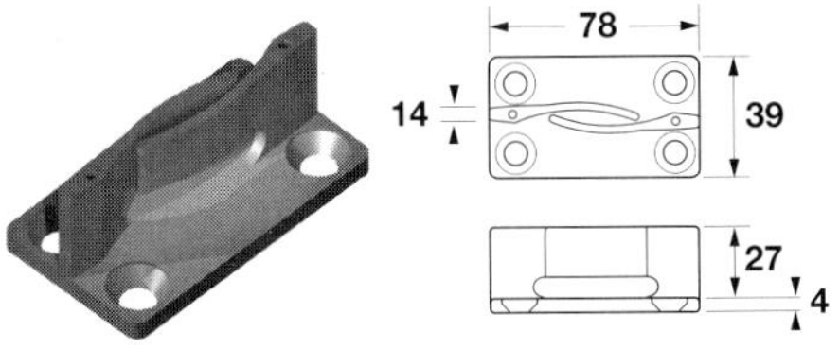

Guide, 1 unit in brown plastic for screw mounting to floor, complete with mounting materials.

Rubber Bumper, 1 unit, screw-mounted, complete with mounting materials.

Upper Track, with screw holes ordered separately for set or sets from above:

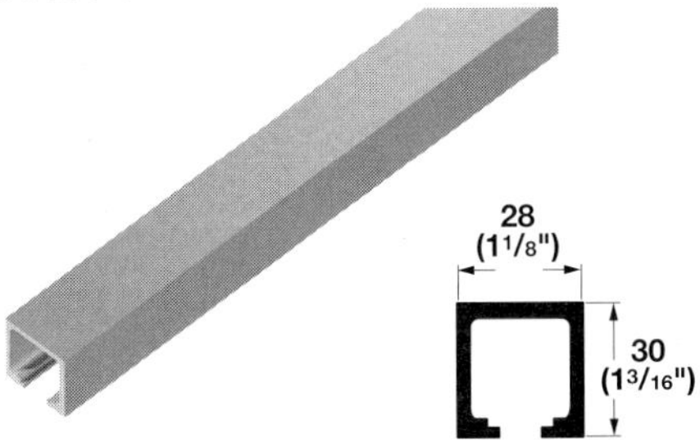

Finish: aluminum, anodized

Cat. No.		
	1.4 m (4' 7")	407.56.867
	1.6 m (5' 3")	407.56.876
	1.8 m (5' 11")	407.56.885
	2.0 m (6' 7")	407.56.894
	3.0 m (9' 10 1/8")	407.56.941
	4.0 m (13' 1 1/2")	407.56.951
	6.0 m (19' 8 1/4")	407.56.931

Packing: 1 pc.

Complete Sets, including:
Upper Track, Running Gear, Track Stopper, Guide, and Rubber Bumper.

Door panel width	Track length	Cat. No.
60-80 cm (2'–2' 7")	1.4 m (4' 7")	407.56.143
70-90 cm (2' 4"–2' 11")	1.6 m (5' 3")	407.56.161
80-100 cm (2' 7"–3' 3")	1.8 m (5' 11")	407.56.189
90-110 cm (2' 11"–3' 7")	2.0 m (6' 7")	407.56.205

Packing: 1 set

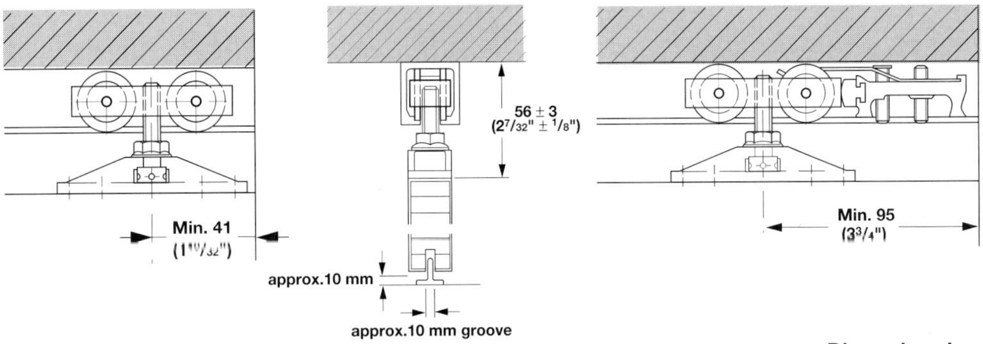

Dimensions in mm
Inches are approximate

Door weights up to 40 kg (88 lbs.) Wood Thicknesses from 22 mm (7/8 in.)

Sliding Door Hardware
Drawer Slides
Television Supports
4

Two upper tracks can be mounted side by side for double or multiple doors.

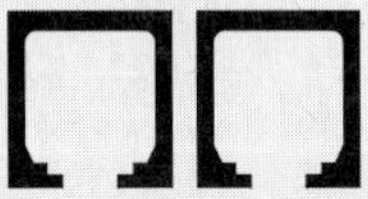

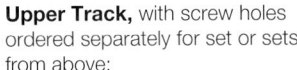

Supplementary Track Stopper
If the sliding door is required to stop at both ends, we recommend installing an additional track stopper.

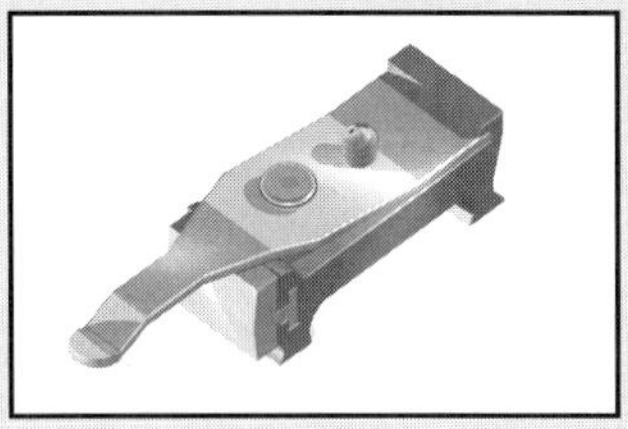

Finish: zinc die-cast housing, steel spring, rubber bumper

Cat. No.	940.40.041

Packing: 1 pc.

HÄFELE

Hawa Junior 80 Sliding Door Fitting

Hawa Junior 80 is a vertically adjustable sliding door fitting for heavy weight interior doors. Tandem rollers made of high-grade polyamide and mounted in an aluminum carriage ensuring exceptionally light and silent action. All parts are corrosion-resistant and are suitable for use in rooms with a humid atmosphere.

Door weights up to 80 kg (176 lbs.) Wood Thicknesses from 25 mm (1 in.)

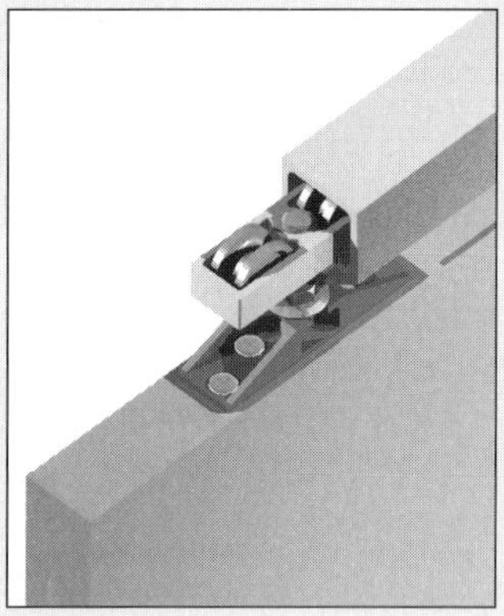

Two upper tracks can be mounted side by side for double or multiple doors.

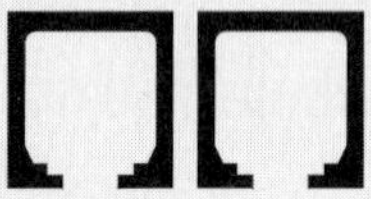

Supplementary Track Stopper
If the sliding door is required to stop at both ends, we recommend installing an additional track stopper.

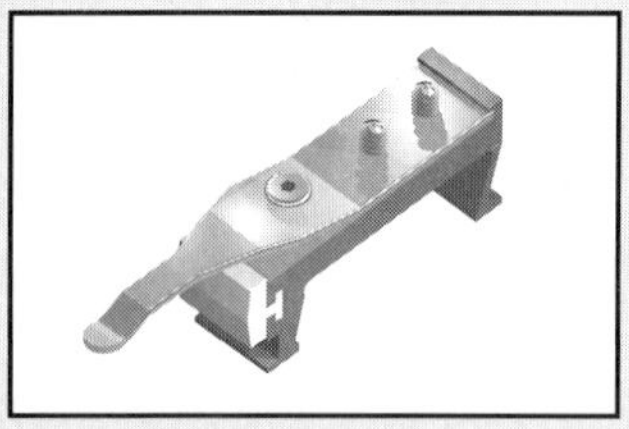

Finish: zinc die-cast housing, steel spring, rubber bumper

Cat. No.	940.80.041

Packing: 1 pc.

1 Complete Set, for a single sliding door without upper tracks includes the following components:

Fitting Set for single sliding door without upper tracks

Cat. No.	940.80.001

Packing: 1 set

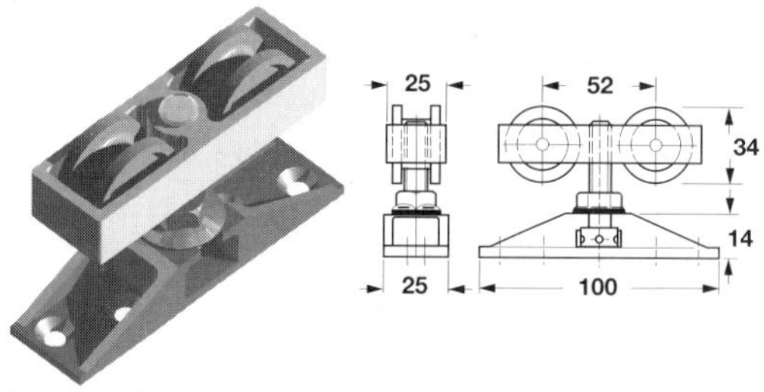

Running Gear, 2 units, high-grade polyamide tandem rollers with sleeve bearings,aluminum carriage and zinc die-cast mounting plate. Complete with mounting materials.

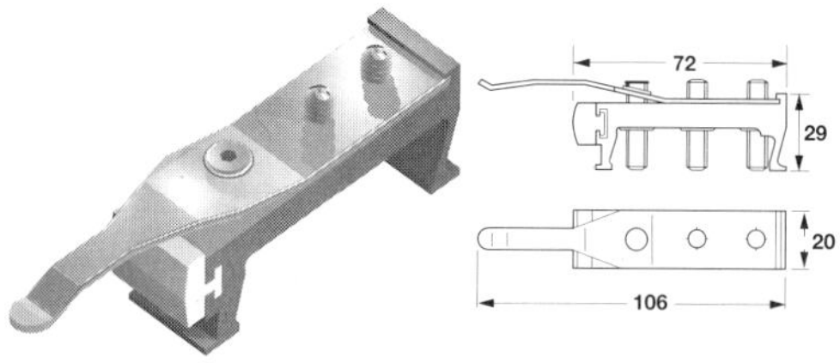

Track Stopper, 1 unit for positioning in upper track. Zinc die-cast housing with adjustable steel spring and rubber bumper.

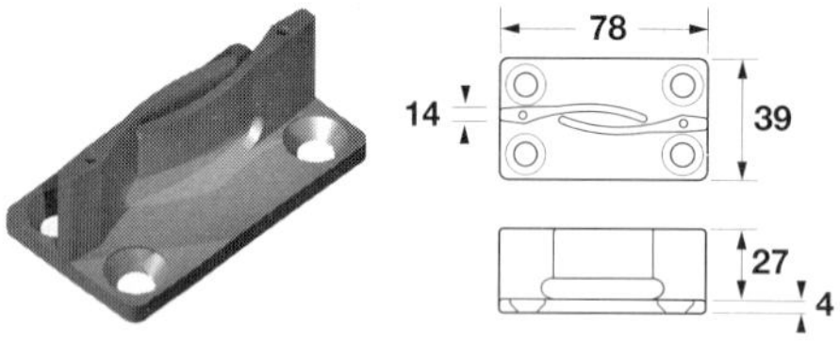

Guide, 1 unit in brown plastic for screw mounting to floor, complete with mounting materials.

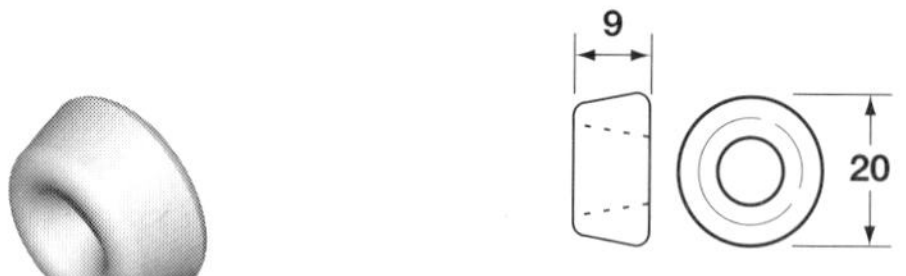

Rubber Bumper, 1 unit, screw-mounted, complete with mounting materials.

Upper Track, ordered separately for set or sets from above:

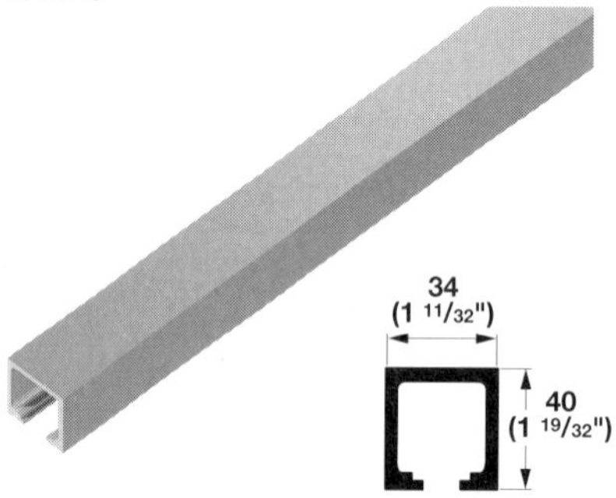

Upper Track, with screw holes.
Finish: aluminum, anodized

Cat. No.		
	1.4 m (4' 7")	407.59.868
	1.6 m (5' 3")	407.59.877
	1.8 m (5' 11")	407.59.886
	2.0 m (6' 7")	407.59.895
	2.2 m (7' 3")	407.59.902
	2.5 m (8' 2")	407.59.911
	3.0 m (9' 10⅛")	407.59.941
	4.0 m (13' 1½")	407.59.951
	6.0 m (19' 8¼")	407.59.931

Packing: 1 pc.

Complete Sets, for a single sliding door, including:
Upper Track, Running Gear, Track Stopper, Guide, and Rubber Bumper.

Door panel width	Track length	Cat. No.
60-80 cm (2'-2' 7")	1.4 m (4' 7")	407.59.144
70-90 cm (2' 4"-2' 11")	1.6 m (5' 3")	407.59.162
80-100 cm (2' 7"-3' 3")	1.8 m (5' 11")	407.59.180
90-110 cm (2' 11"-3' 7")	2.0 m (6' 7")	407.59.206
100-120 cm (3' 3"-3' 11")	2.2 m (7' 3")	407.59.224
120-140 cm (3' 11"-4' 7")	2.5 m (8' 2")	407.59.251

Packing: 1 set

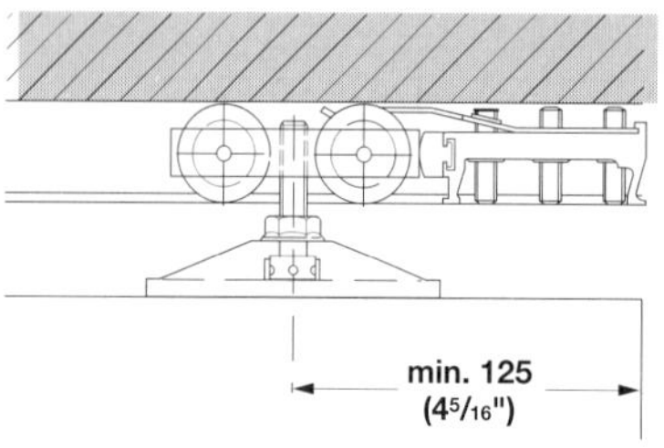

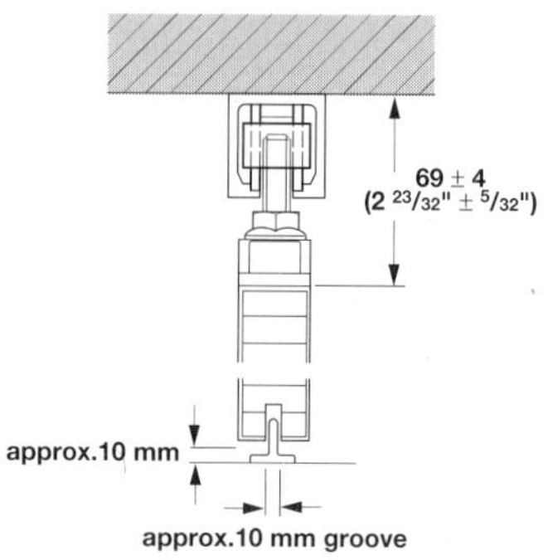

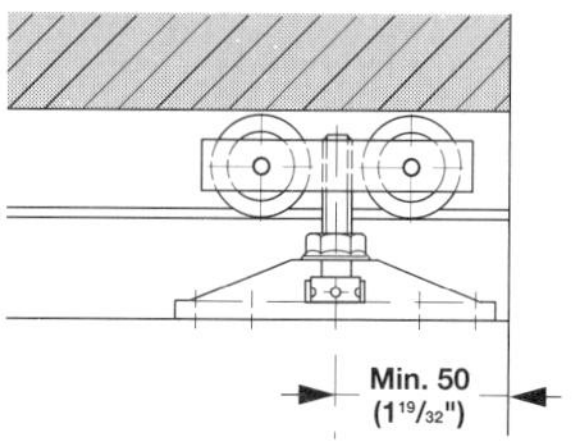

Dimensions in mm
Inches are approximate

Dimensional data not binding. We reserve the right to alter specifications without notice.

HÄFELE

Hawa Junior 160 Sliding Door Fitting

Hawa Junior 160 is a vertically adjustable sliding door fitting for particularly heavy weight interior doors. Tandem rollers made of high-grade polyamide and mounted in an aluminum carriage ensuring exceptionally light and silent action. All parts are corrosion-resistant and are suitable for use in rooms with a humid atmosphere.

Door weights up to 160 kg (352 lbs.) Wood Thicknesses from 35 mm (1 3/8 in.)

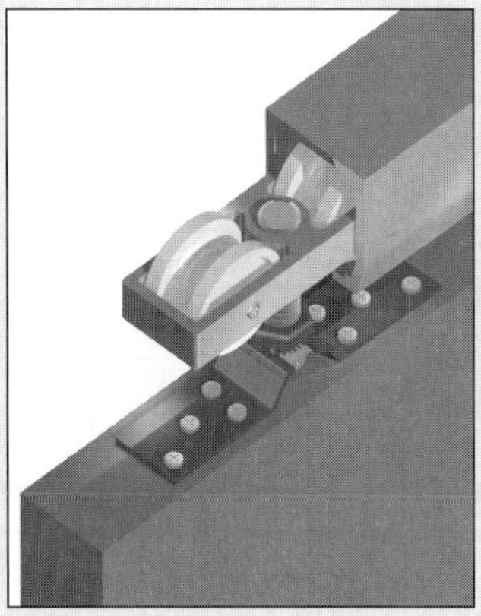

1 Complete Set, for a single sliding door without upper tracks includes the following components:

Fitting Set for single sliding door without upper tracks

Cat. No.	941.60.001

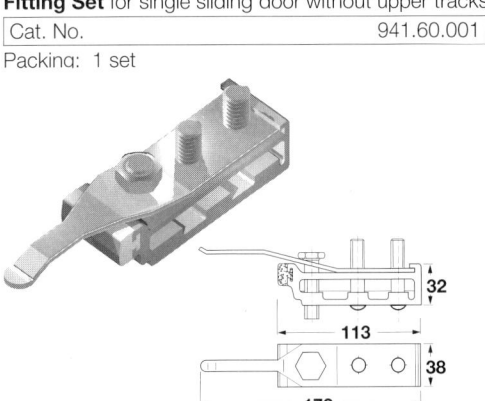

Packing: 1 set

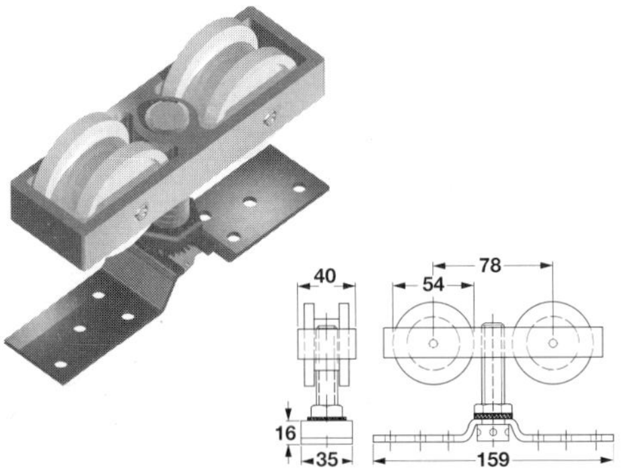

Running Gear, 2 units, high-grade polyamide tandem rollers with sleeve bearings,aluminum carriage and galvanized steel mounting plate. Complete with mounting materials.

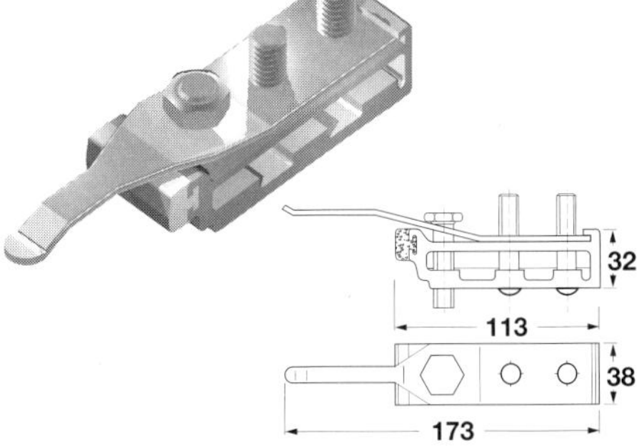

Track Stopper, 1 unit for positioning in upper track. Zinc die-cast housing with adjustable steel spring and rubber bumper.

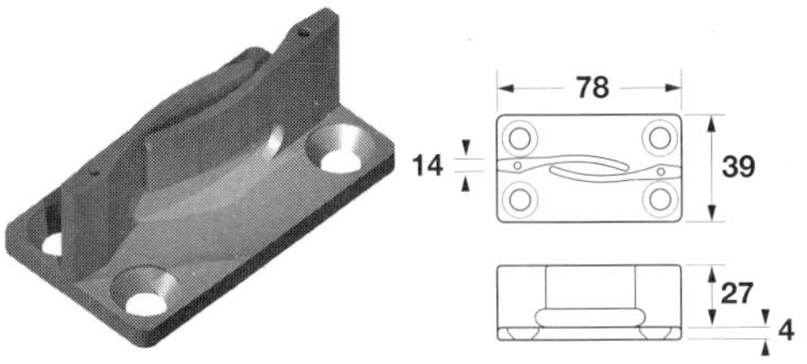

Guide, 1 unit in brown plastic, screw-mounted to floor, complete with mounting materials.

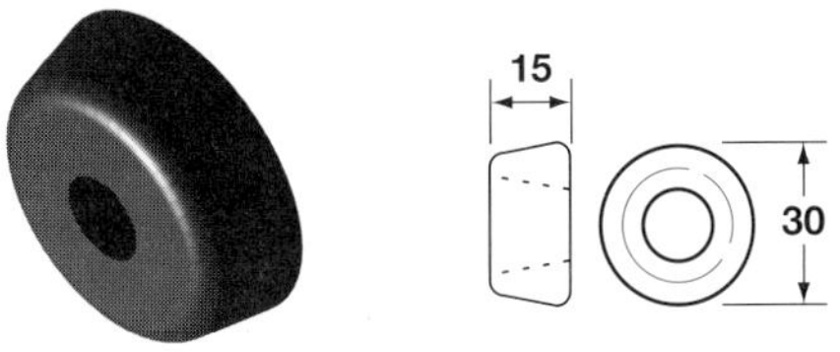

Rubber Bumper, 1 unit, screw-mounted, complete with mounting materials.

Sliding Door Hardware
Drawer Slides
Television Supports
4

Two upper tracks can be mounted side by side for double or multiple doors.

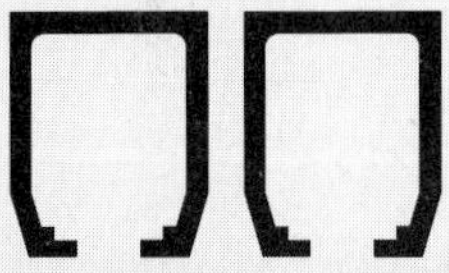

Upper Track, ordered separately for set or sets from above:

Upper Track, with screw holes.

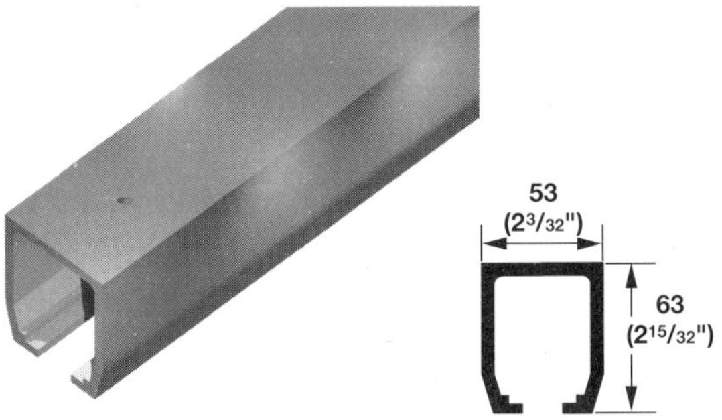

Finish: aluminum, anodized

Cat. No.	3 m (9' 10 1/8")	407.57.911
	4 m (13' 1 1/2")	407.57.921
	6 m (19' 8 1/4")	407.57.931

Packing: 1 pc.

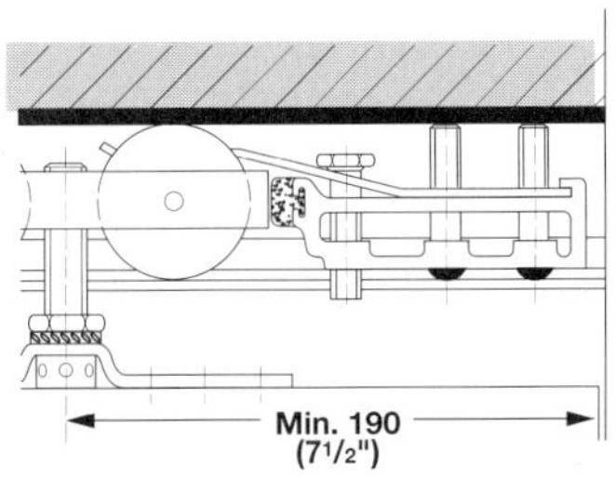

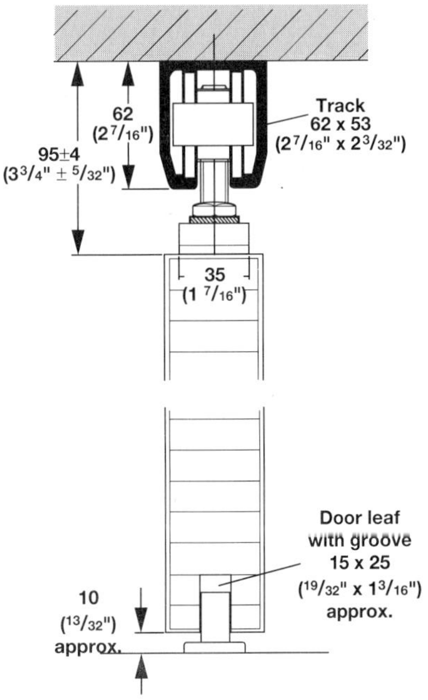

Supplementary Track Stopper
If the sliding door is required to stop at both ends, we recommend installing an additional track stopper.

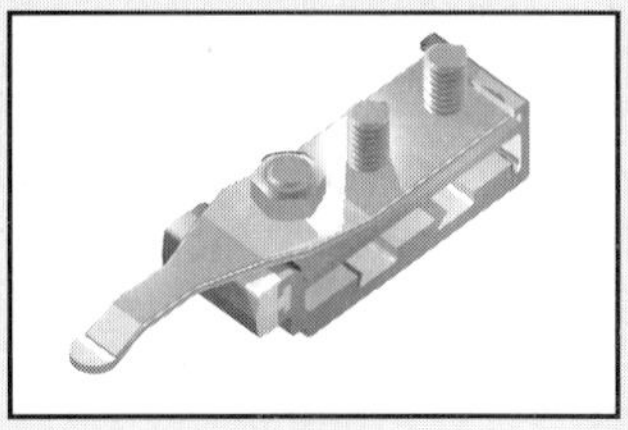

Finish: zinc die-cast housing, steel spring, rubber buffer

Cat. No.	941.60.041

Packing: 1 pc.

Dimensional data not binding. We reserve the right to alter specifications without notice.

Dimensions in mm
Inches are approximate

HÄFELE

Hawa Symmetric 80 Sliding Door Fitting

Hawa Junior 80 is a vertically adjustable sliding door fitting for heavy weight interior doors. It allows simultaneous opening and closing of bi-parting sliding doors. Tandem rollers made of high-grade polyamide and mounted in an aluminum carriage ensure exceptionally light and silent action. All parts are corrosion-resistant and are suitable for use in rooms with a humid atmosphere.

Door weights up to 80 kg (176 lbs.) Wood Thicknesses from 25 mm (1 in.)

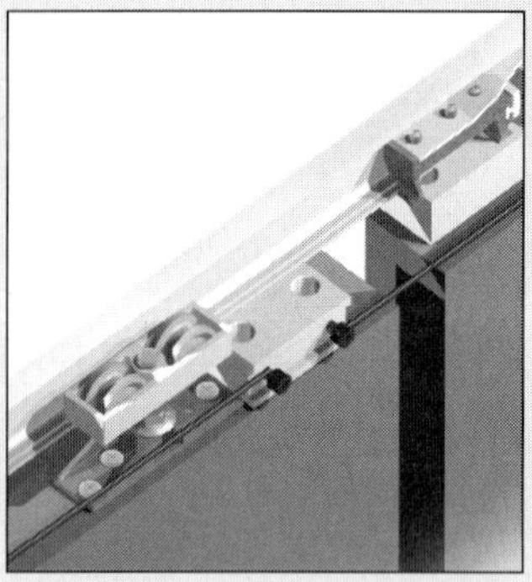

1 Complete Set, for one set of bi-parting doors without upper tracks includes the following components:

Fitting Set for 1 set of bi-parting doors

Cat. No.	940.80.006

Packing: 1 set

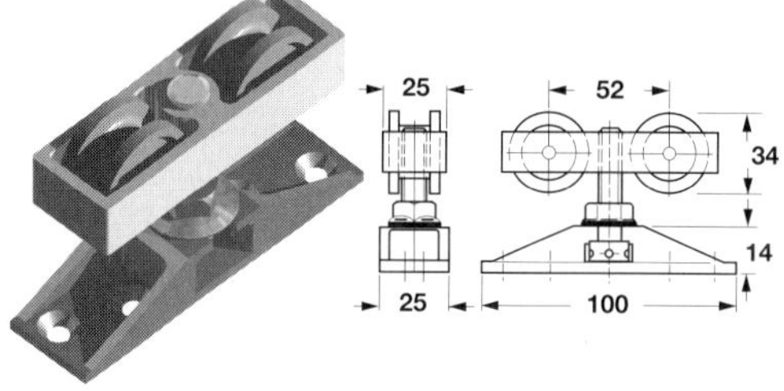

Running Gear, 4 units, high-grade polyamide tandem rollers with sleeve bearings, aluminum carriage and zinc die-cast mounting plate. Complete with mounting materials.

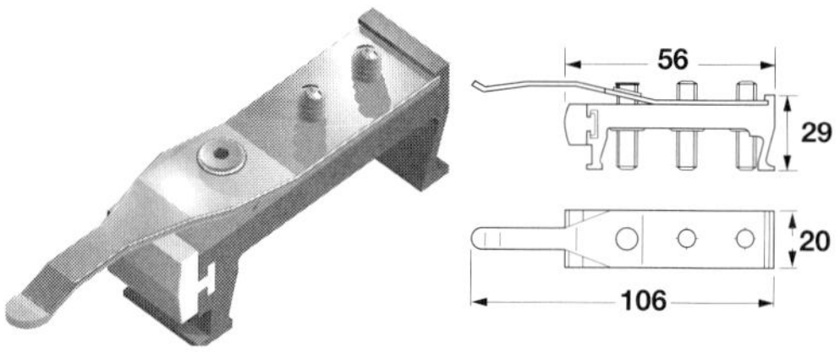

Track Stopper, 1 unit for positioning in upper track. Zinc die-cast housing with adjustable steel spring and rubber bumper.

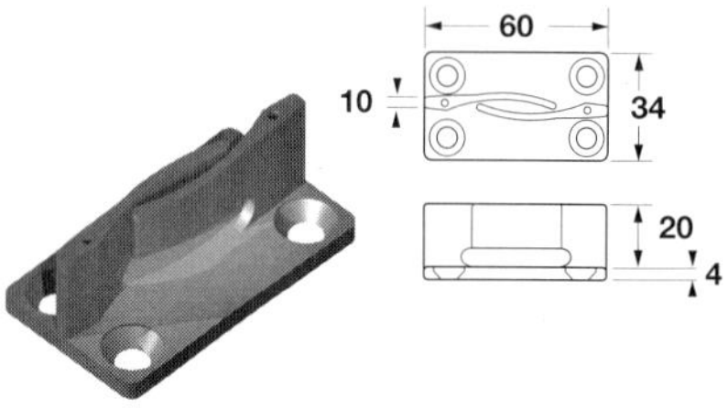

Guides, 2 units in brown plastic for mounting to cabinet floor, complete with mounting materials.

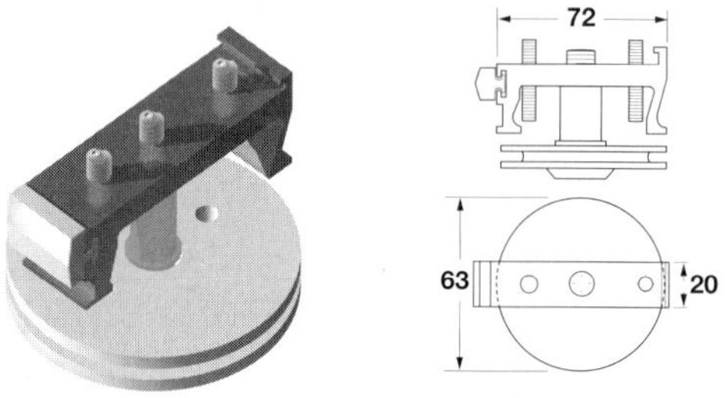

End Stops, with deflection roller 2 units, zinc die-cast housing, plastic roller.

Steel Cable, 10 m (32' 9 3/4") Cable is calculated for 2 sliding doors of each max. 1200 mm (2' 11 1/4") width.

Vertical Adjustment pin, 1 unit, steel Not shown.

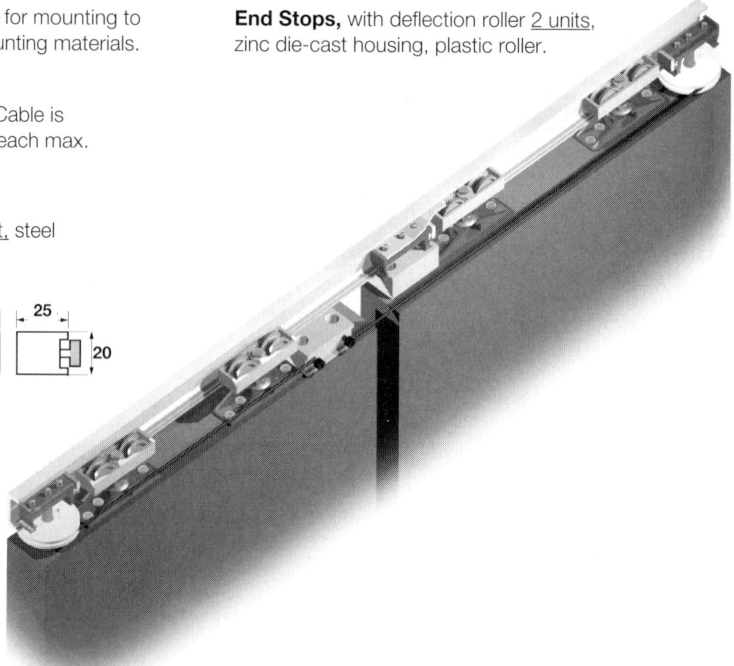

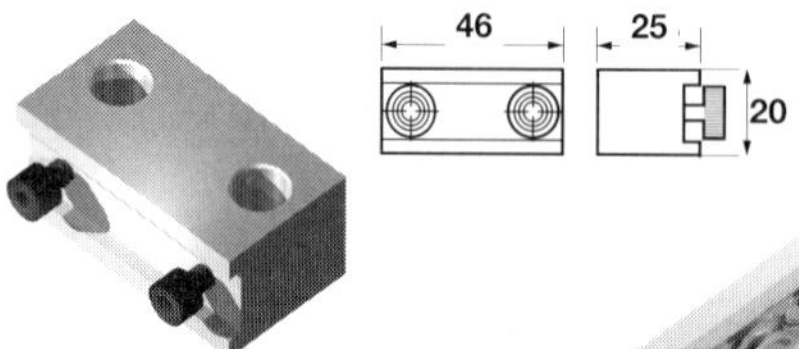

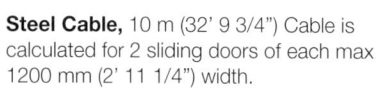

Clamps, for mounting steel cables, 2 units, zinc die-cast housing.

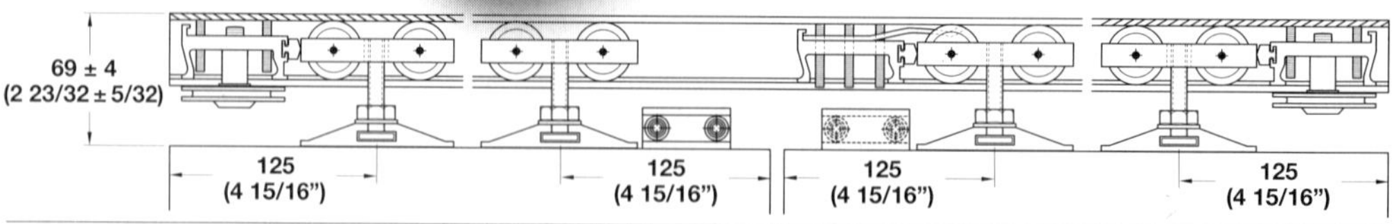

Upper Track, with screw holes, ordered separately.

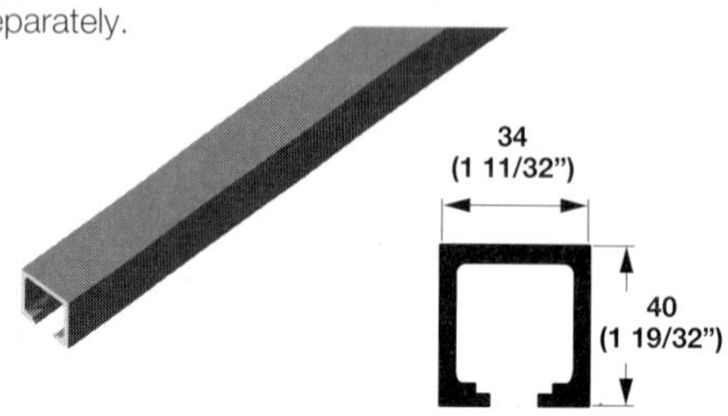

Upper Track, with screw-holes
Finish: aluminum, anodized

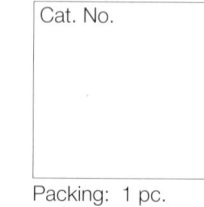

Cat. No.		
	2.0 m (6' 6¾")	407.59.895
	2.2 m (7' 2⅝")	407.59.902
	2.5 m (8' 2½")	407.59.911
	3.0 m (9' 10⅛")	407.59.941
	4.0 m (13' 1½")	407.59.951
	6.0 m (19' 8¼")	407.59.931

Packing: 1 pc.

Dimensions in mm
Inches are approximate

Freeslide Sliding Door Fittings

HÄFELE

Sliding Door Fitting

Freeslide for sliding doors mounts flush to the cabinet front, enabling the doors to slide to the right or left beyond the cabinet body.
The doors are accurately guided without using expensive tracks or running gear and can also be complemented with a synchronizing unit.
Capacity: 30 kg (66 lbs.) each pair
Finish: steel, galvanized

Mounting Detail

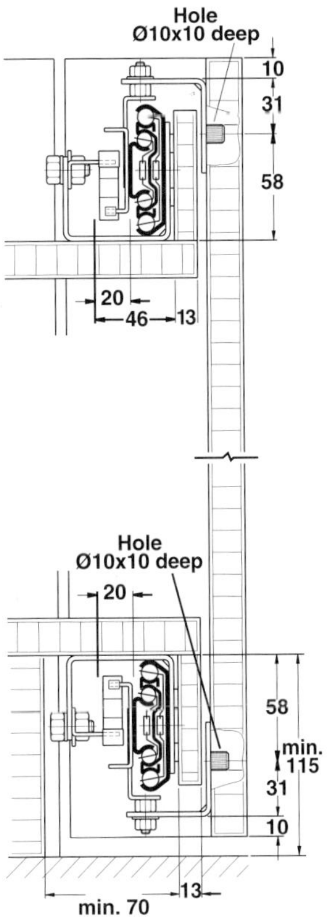

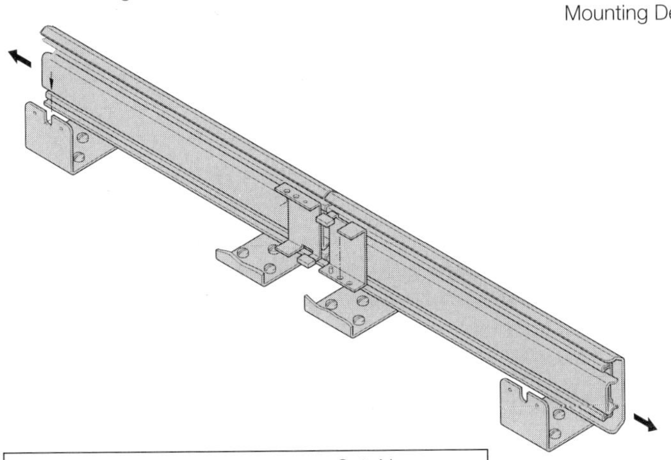

Door width	Cat. No.
450 mm (17¾")	407.30.452
500 mm (19¾")	407.30.505

Packing: 1 Set (for 1 sliding door panel)

Special advantages:

- Simple assembly of the running tracks, thus reduced assembly costs
- Running tracks with integrated closing device
- The running tracks are prepared for installing the synchronizing unit.
- Allows for access into the complete interior of cabinet
- Closing device, laterally and vertically adjustable

Sliding Door Hardware
Drawer Slides
Television Supports
4

Freeslide Synchronizing Unit

To be used with Freeslide Sliding Door Fitting to synchronize the door action.
Capacity: 30 kg (66 lbs.) each pair
Finish: steel, galvanized

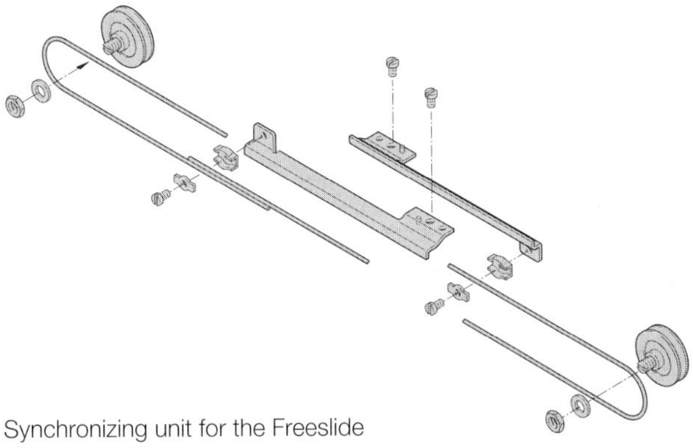

Synchronizing unit for the Freeslide sliding door fitting

Cat. No.	407.30.005

Packing: 1 Set (for 1 pair of sliding doors)

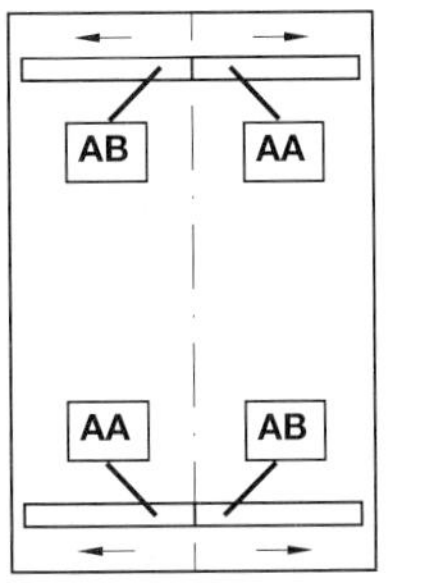

Door panel width	Guide track		Installation dimensions in mm				
	AA	AB	L	A	B	C	D
450	1 St.	1 St.	430	300	75	388	45
500	1 St.	1 St.	480	350	75	388	45

*For single door cabinets, dimension B must be enlarged to include the door overhang.

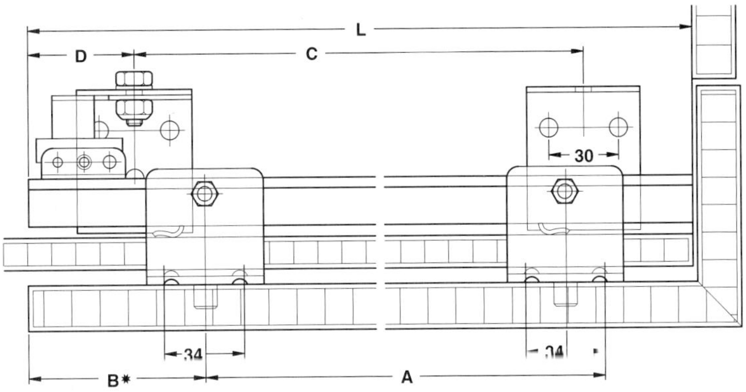

Dimensions in mm

Dimensional data not binding.
We reserve the right to alter specifications without notice.

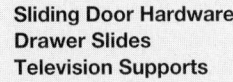

HÄFELE

Hawa-Confort Sliding Door Guides; Door Seal Profile

- Designed for wall mounting, eliminating all the problems arising with traditional floor-mounting methods from such factors as uneven or weak floors, carpets, tiles or underfloor heating.
- After installation, the door and cladding panel are easily aligned by lateral adjustment of the guide elements.

Hawa-Confort lower guide for sliding doors, single-element

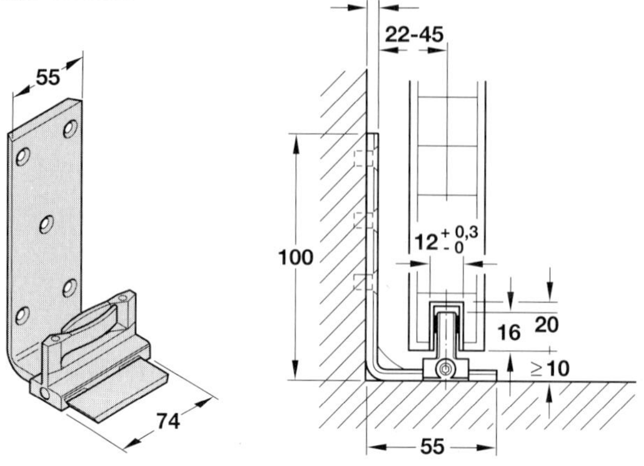

Finish: bracket: aluminum, bronze anodized
Guide: zinc die-cast with 5M set screw

Cat. No.	940.40.071

Packing: 1 pc.

Hawa-Confort lower guide for sliding doors, double-element

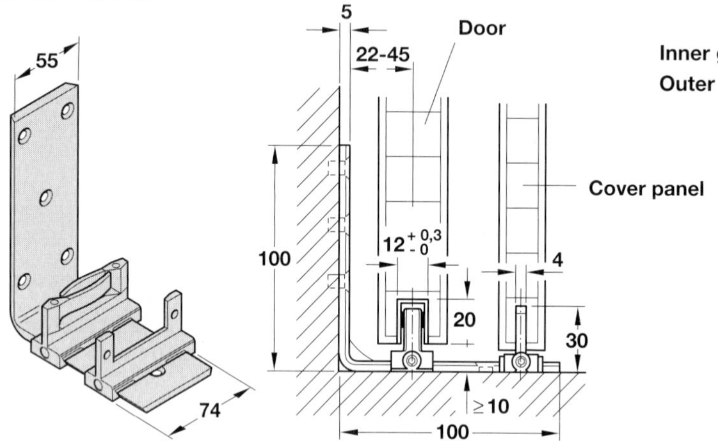

Inner guide - for sliding door
Outer guide - bracket attaches cover panel to floor.

Finish: bracket: aluminum, bronze anodized
Guide: zinc die-cast with 5M set screws

Cat. No.	940.40.072

Packing: 1 pc.

4 Sliding Door Hardware
Drawer Slides
Television Supports

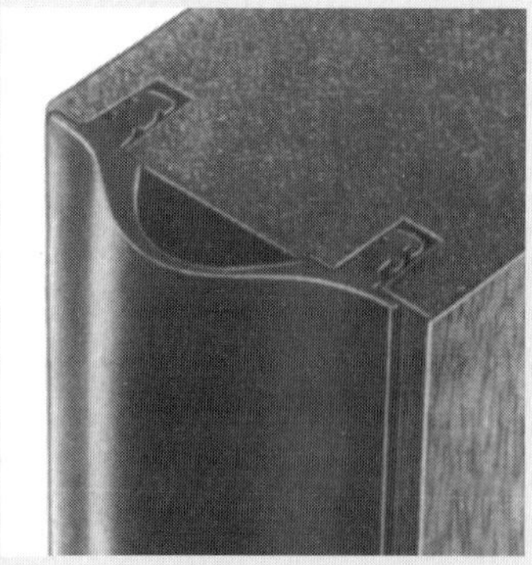

Sealing and buffer profile for sliding doors

Installed in two grooves in the edge of sliding doors. This profile strip absorbs impact noise and prevents possible damage from over-forceful closing, and seals the door when closed.

Finish: neoprene, white, brown and black

Cat. No.		
	white	940.00.549
	brown	940.00.521
	black	940.00.530

Packing: 5 m

Groove patterns

The door requires two grooves to accommodate the profile (see diagram, below).
The height of the profile is determined by the interval between the grooves.

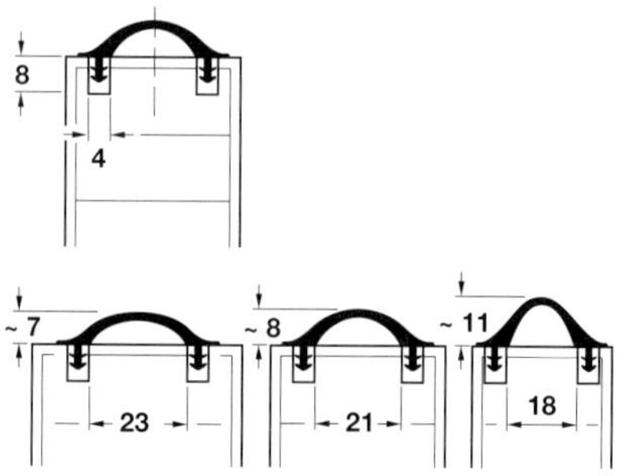

Dimensional data not binding. We reserve the right to alter specifications without notice.

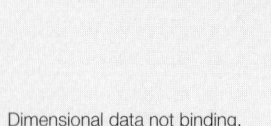

Dimensions in mm
Inches are approximate

Sliding Door Accessories

HÄFELE

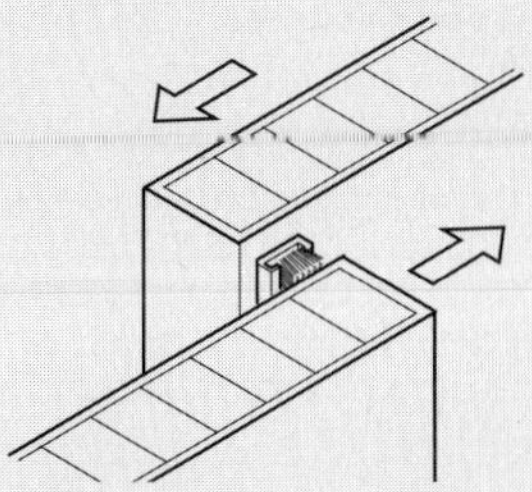

Dust cover profile with brush of artificial fiber
screw-mounted to cabinet sliding doors

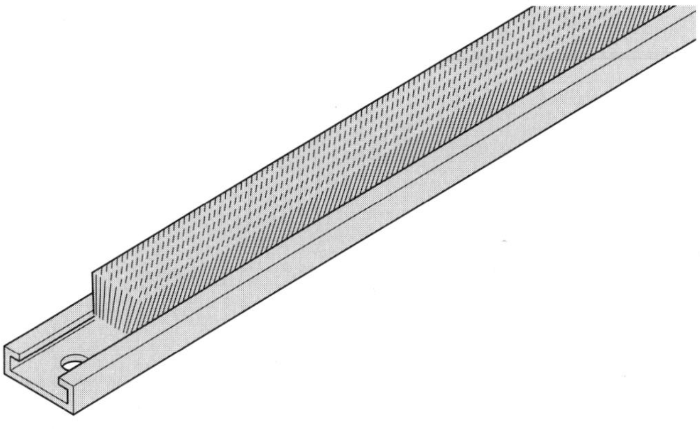

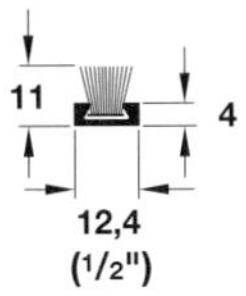

Finish: aluminum, unfinished

Cat. No.	406.41.807

Packing: 2.5 meters

Dust cover profile with brush of artificial fiber
to be glued on cabinet sliding doors

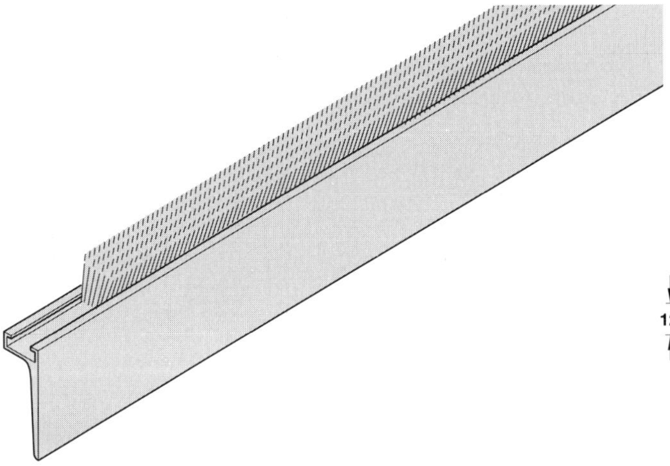

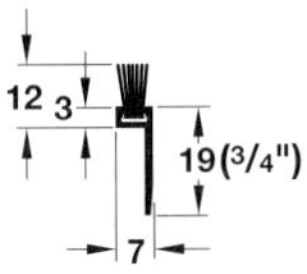

Finish: plastic, brown

Cat. No.	406.01.107

Packing: 2.5 meters

Dimensions in mm

Sliding Door Hardware
Drawer Slides
Television Supports
4

Dimensional data not binding.
We reserve the right to alter
specifications without notice.

HÄFELE

Planofit Door Straightening System

For wood thickness from 16 mm (5/8")

- Adds rigidity to wooden sliding doors of 16 mm (5/8") thickness and upwards, and up to 2600 mm (8'6") in height, and prevents warping in either direction.
- It can also be used to straighten warped doors.

The system components are set into two cup recesses, **∅35 mm x 12.5 mm deep,** and a groove, 10 mm wide x 8 mm deep.
The threaded rod should be shortened according to the door height, i.e. length = distance from recess center to recess center plus 33 mm.
The length of the trim strip = the distance from recess center to recess center less 44 mm.

The components should be assembled before installation.
After the fitting has been installed, the aluminum trim strip is knocked into the groove and secured with retaining plates.
When the locking element has been removed from the tensioning component, the door can be straightened with an M 10 open-ended wrench.

4
Sliding Door Hardware
Drawer Slides
Television Supports

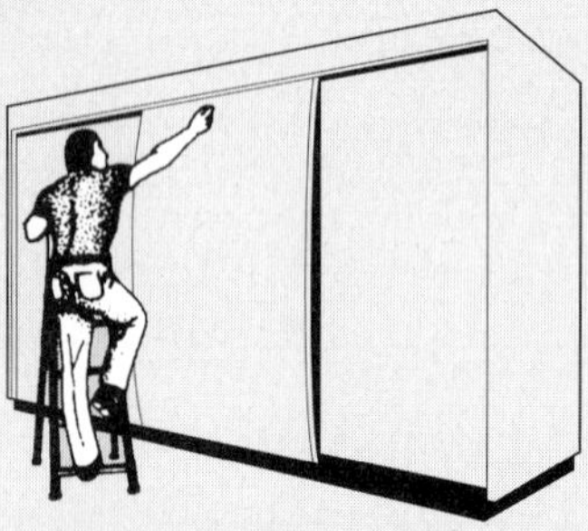

Ideal for large, heavy, sliding doors. If installed in a new door, restraightening can be carried out any time.

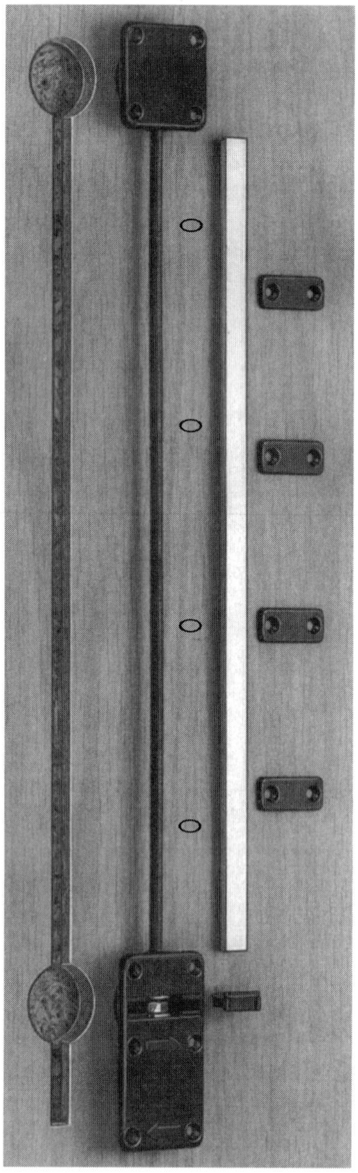

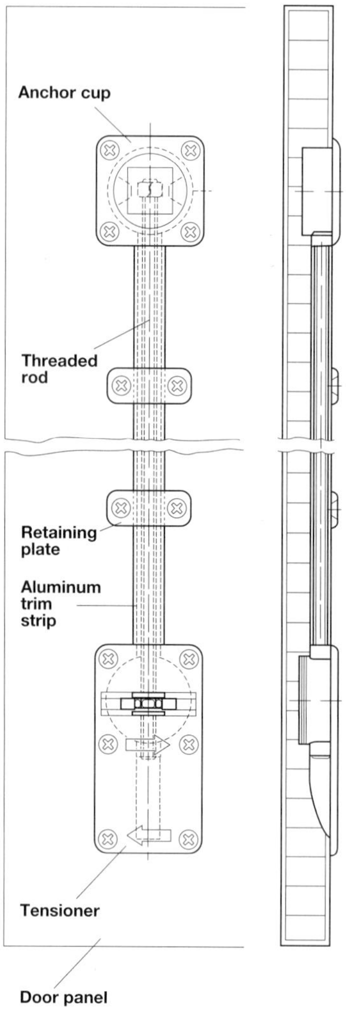

Mounting diagram

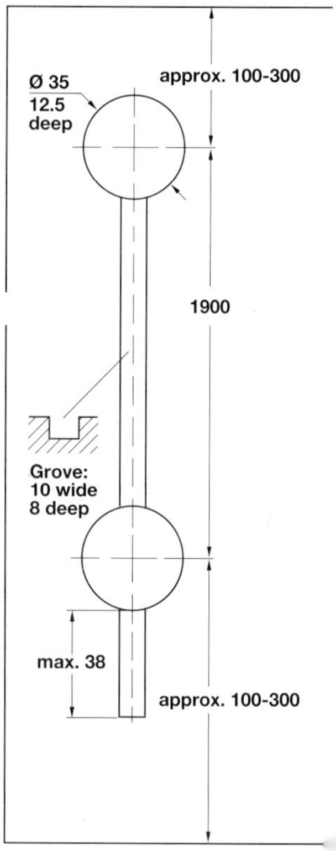

HOSPA ∅3,5

We recommend installing two straightening fittings per door.

Planofit door straightening system.
A complete set includes the following components:

1 Anchor cup, black plastic
1 Tensioner, black plastic with galvanized steel nut
1 Threaded rod, 1927 mm long, steel
1 Trim strip, 1852 mm long, unfinished aluminum
4 Retaining plates, black plastic
4 Rubber O rings

Cat. No.	406.99.123

Packing: 2 sets

Bulk pack (w/o retaining plates and O-rings)

Cat. No.	406.99.153

Packing: 50 sets

Open-ended wrench, M 10, for adjustments

Cat. No.	008.20.646

Packing: 1 pc.

Retaining plates, black plastic

Cat. No.	406.99.394

Packing: 500 pcs.

Rubber O-rings, black, used as spacer rings, to be pushed onto threaded rod

Cat. No.	406.99.214

Packing: 200 pcs.

Dimensional data not binding.
We reserve the right to alter specifications without notice.

Dimensions in mm
Inches are approximate

Plastic Roller Shutters

Version 1
with 90° arc

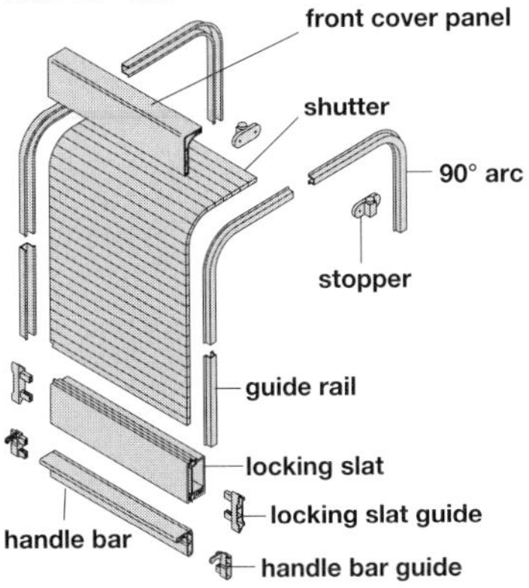

Version 2
with roller shutter coil

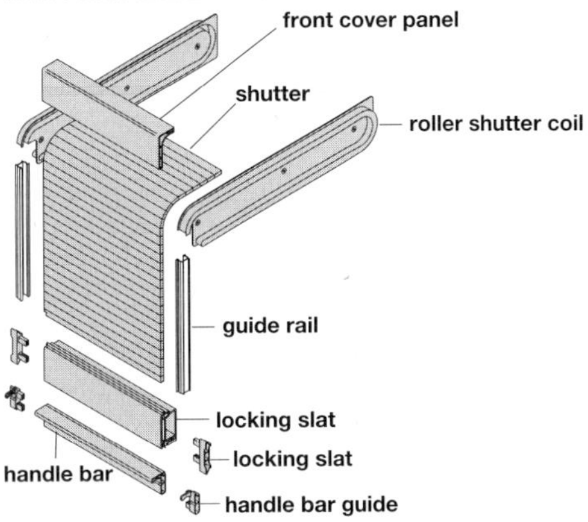

This roller shutter includes roller shutter slats which have been inserted into each other. Additionally, the slats are strengthened on the back with special tape. A sectional profile reveals excellent rolling properties. Furthermore, the roller shutter slats can be inserted into one another easily by hand when making the shutters from scratch. Both horizontal and vertical applications allow the shutters to run well. The narrow rolling radius of R=35 mm saves room.

If you make your own shutters, version 1 or version 2, you need the following accessories listed below PLUS further parts depending on the version – please see pages 4.28 and 4.29.

Textile Tape
We recommend for roller shutters
up to 80 cm (31") width: 2 strips
up to 120 cm (47") width: 3 strips

Accessories/general

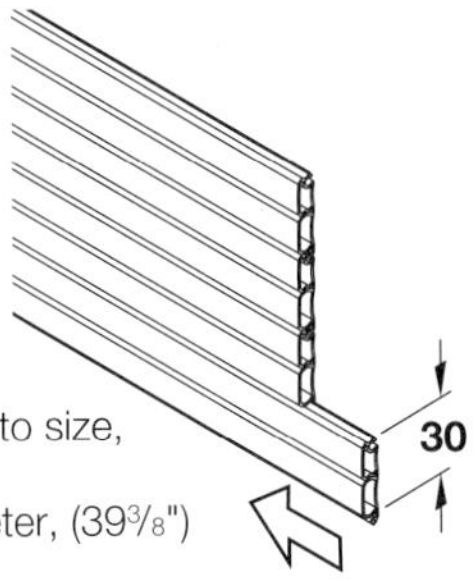

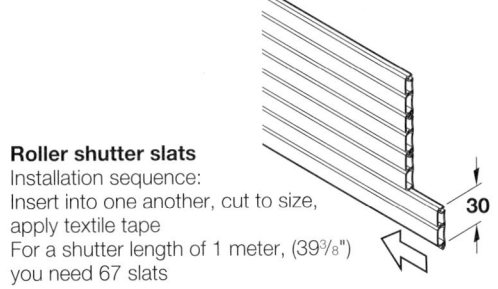

Roller shutter slats
Installation sequence:
Insert into one another, cut to size, apply textile tape
For a shutter length of 1 meter, (39³/₈") you need 67 slats

Finish: plastic

Color	Cat. No.
white	442.50.700
gray	442.50.500

Packing: 1 pc. (2.5 meters long)

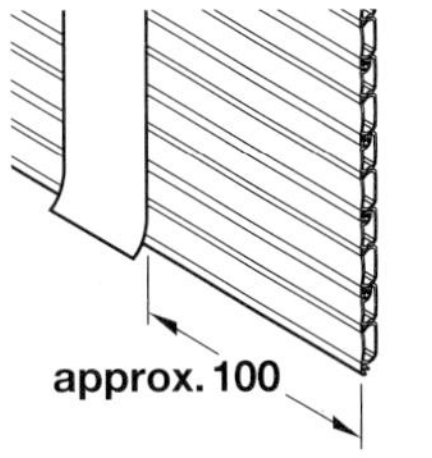

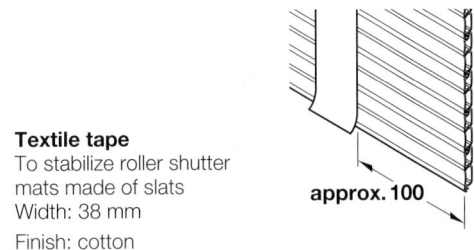

Textile tape
To stabilize roller shutter mats made of slats
Width: 38 mm

Finish: cotton

Cat. No.	442.01.087

Packing: 1 roll (10 meters long)

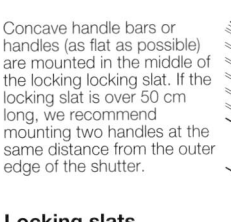

Concave handle bars or handles (as flat as possible) are mounted in the middle of the locking locking slat. If the locking slat is over 50 cm long, we recommend mounting two handles at the same distance from the outer edge of the shutter.

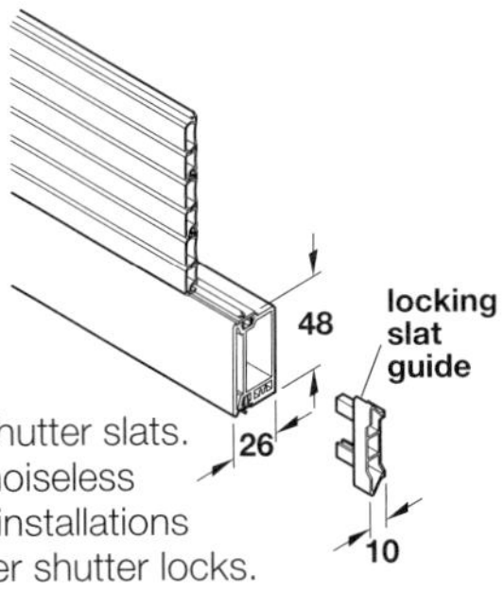

Locking slats
To be inserted in roller shutter slats. With soft sealing lip for noiseless closing. Appropriate for installations of regularly available roller shutter locks.

Finish: plastic, sealing lip is made of soft PVC

Color	Cat. No.
white	442.58.700
gray	442.58.500

Packing: 1 pc. (2.5 meters long)

Locking slat guide
To be inserted into the locking slat

Finish: plastic, natural color

Cat. No.	442.58.780

Packing: 10 pcs.

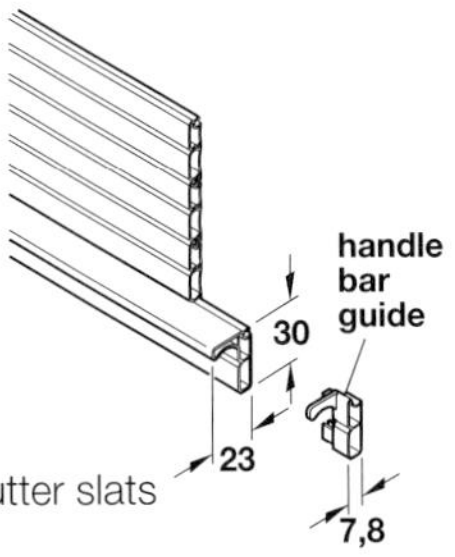

Handle bar
To be inserted into roller shutter slats

Finish: plastic

Color	Cat. No.
white	442.52.700
gray	442.52.500

Packing: 1 pc. (2.5 meters long)

Handle bar guide
To be inserted into handle bar

Finish: plastic, natural color

Color	Cat. No.
white	442.52.780
gray	442.52.580

Packing: 10 pairs

Maximum roller shutter slat lengths: For built-in shutters in horizontal and vertical positions, we recommend the following maximum slat lengths:

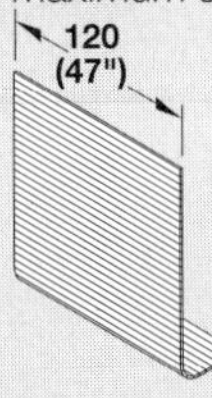

The maximum slat width is **120 cm** for roller slats that are positioned horizontally, but where the whole roller shutter is used primarily to go up and down ...

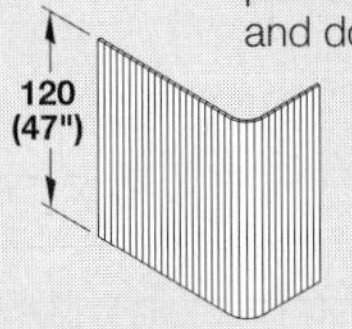

... or if the slats are positioned vertically.

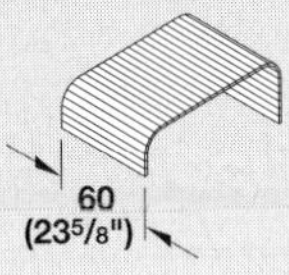

The maximum slat width is **60 cm** for roller slats that are positioned horizontally, but where the whole roller shutter is used primarily to go back and forth.

At a minimum order quantity of 2000 M, the roller shutter slats and mats can be delivered in fixed measurements or custom colors.

To paint, please use Polyurethane based paints only. In order to be able to get the edges painted properly, hang the shutters over something round. The sealing profile of the locking slat (not paintable) can be removed during painting.

The locking slat (guide) cannot be moved around 90° arcs.

For locks for the locking slat, please see page ...

Dimensional data not binding.
We reserve the right to alter specifications without notice.

Dimensions in mm

HÄFELE

Plastic Roller Shutters, Version 1

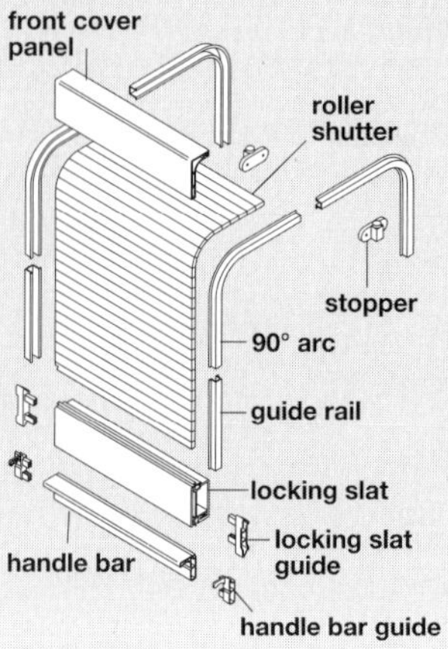

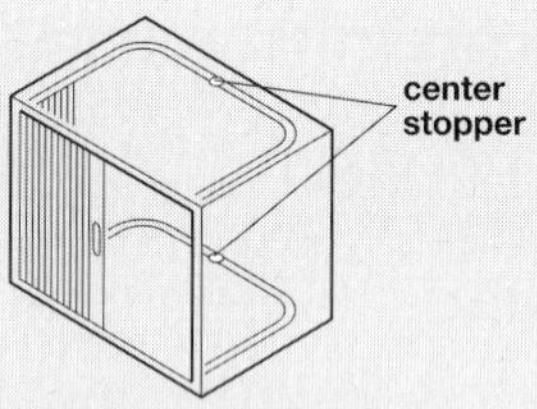

- stops the opened roller shutter and prevents banging

The weight balancing hardware to be installed at the back of the cabinet is suitable for **a roller shutter width of 216 – 1000 mm (8½"-39⅜")** and for **a usable cabinet height of at most 1800 mm (71").** The adjustable power spring functions as an aid for raising and lowering the roller shutters.

For heavy roller shutters, we recommend a trial installation.

Version 1 (On page 4.27 you will find some general accessories for this version)

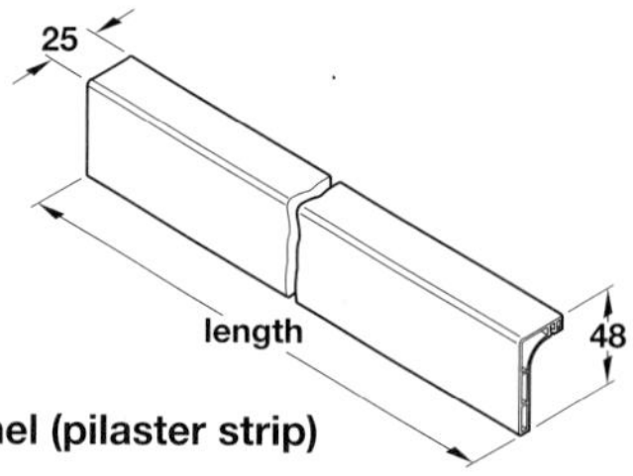

Front cover panel (pilaster strip)
screw-on type

Finish: plastic

Color	Cat. No.
white	442.53.700
gray	442.53.500

Packing: 1 pc. (2.5 meters long)

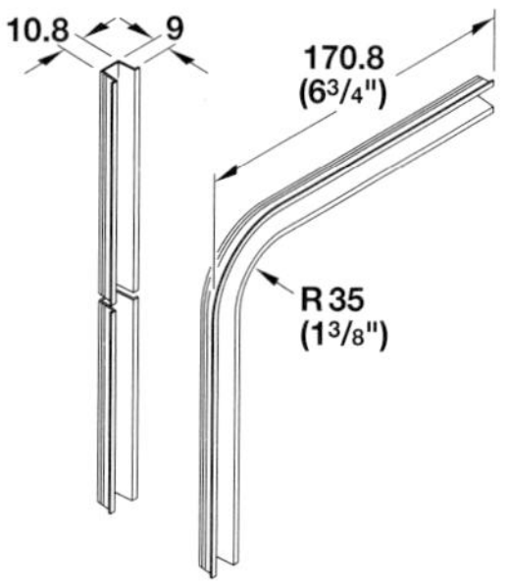

Runner guide
with ridge, mortise-type

Finish: plastic

Color	Cat. No.
white	442.54.700
brown	442.54.100
gray	442.54.500

Packing: 1 pc. (2.5 meters long)

90° Arc
with ridge, radius = 35 mm, mortise-type
fits runner guide

Finish: plastic

Color	Cat. No.
white	442.55.700
brown	442.55.100
gray	442.55.500

Packing: 40 pcs.

(For large enough order quantities, it is possible to obtain arcs with a greater radius.)

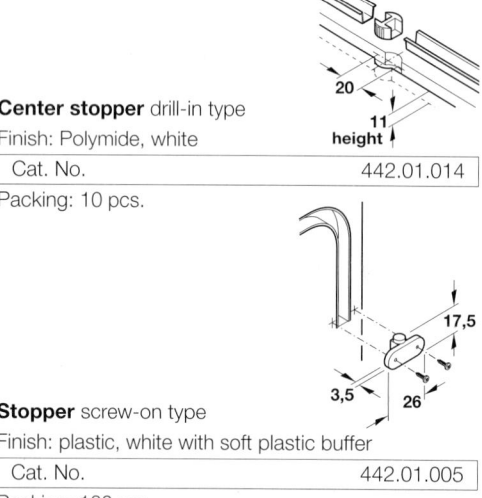

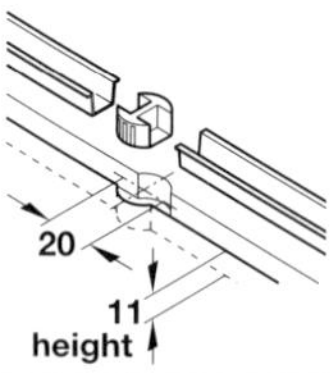

Center stopper drill-in type

Finish: Polymide, white

Cat. No.	442.01.014

Packing: 10 pcs.

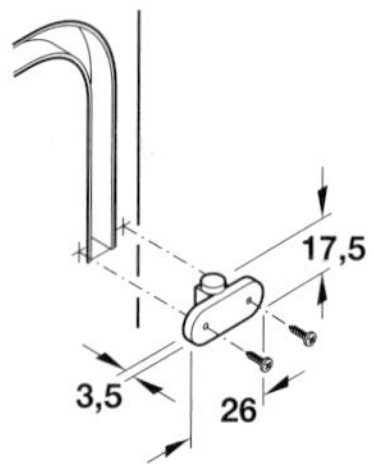

Stopper screw-on type

Finish: plastic, white with soft plastic buffer

Cat. No.	442.01.005

Packing: 100 pcs.

Weight-balancing hardware for cabinets with roller shutters that have a reversing arc
includes:
1 pair weight balancers
2 steel ropes, 1600 mm (63") long each, with eyelets
1 set fixing materials
1 installation instructions

Finnish: steel, zinc-plated
side wheels: plastic, black

Cat. No.	442.09.903

Packing: 1 set

Important:
- Minimum roller shutter width **= 216 mm (8½")**
- pull ropes must be fastened **exactly in the center** of the roller shutter's bottom edge
- The mounting position for the adjustment hardware, which depends on the size of the roller shutter, is shown in the installation instructions. Please follow instructions carefully!

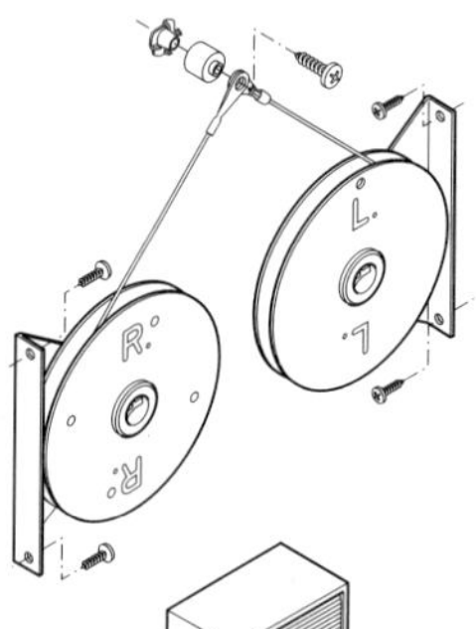

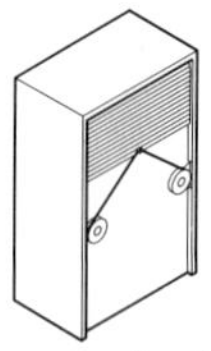

example of installed hardware

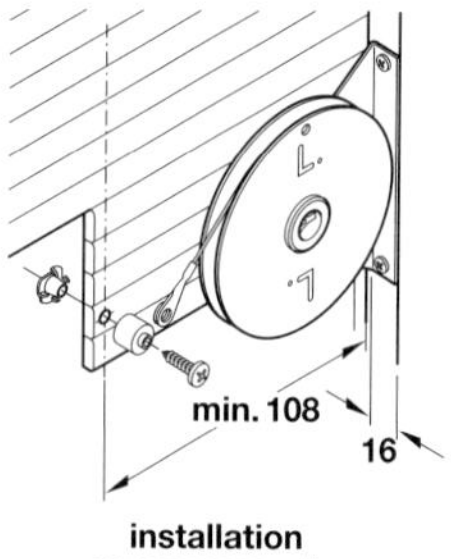

installation measurements

Size of Roller Shutters

Length of the roller shutter
= inner height of cabinet + 30 mm

The end of the closed roller shutter must reach over the arc in order to avoid sliding out of place diagonally.

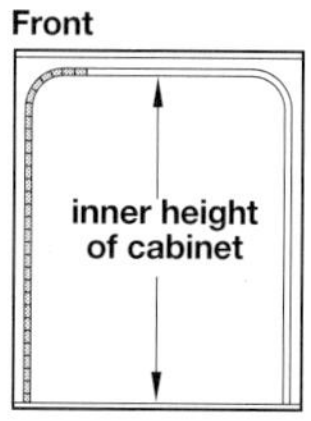

Width of roller shutter
= inside width of cabinet + 12 mm

Width of locking slat
= inside width of cabinet – 4.5 mm

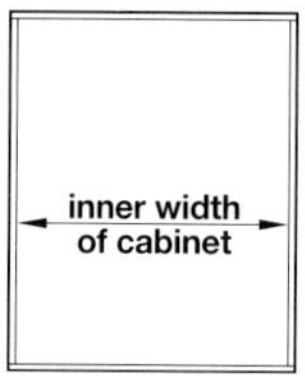

Dimensions in mm

Dimensional data not binding. We reserve the right to alter specifications without notice.

Plastic Roller Shutters, Version 2

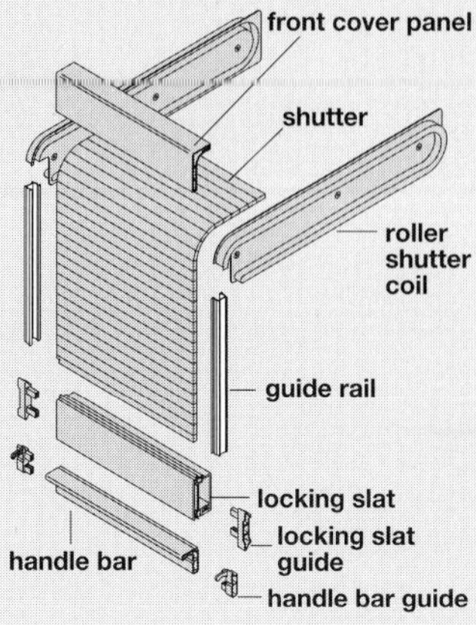

Version 2 (on page **4.27 and 4.28**, you will find general accessories suitable for this version)

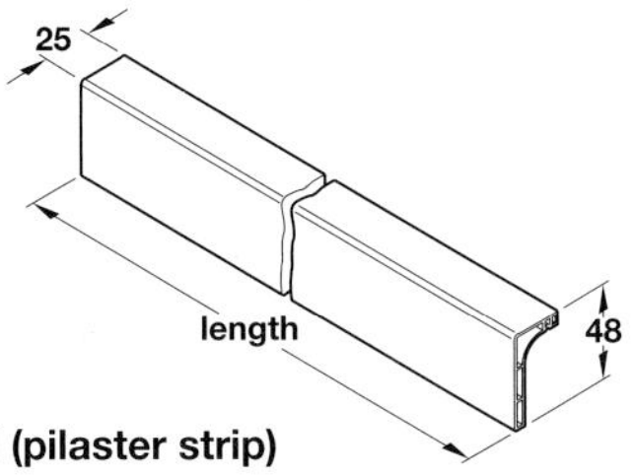

Front cover panel (pilaster strip)
screw-mounted

Finish: plastic

Color	Cat. No.
white	442.53.700
gray	442.53.500

Packing: 1 pc. (2.5 m long)

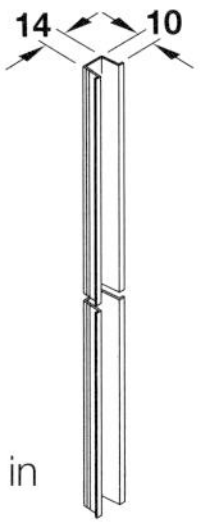

Guide rail
with ridge, mortise-type, can only be used in conjunction with roller shutter coil

Finish: plastic

Color	Cat. No.
white	442.56.700
gray	442.56.500

Packing: 1 pc. (2.5 m long)

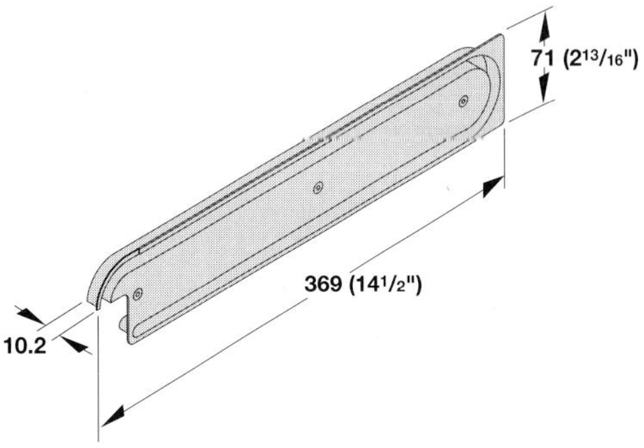

Roller shutter coil
to be inserted in cabinet side panel

Finish: plastic

Color	Cat. No.
black	442.57.310

Packing: 1 pair

Sliding Door Hardware
Drawer Slides
Television Supports
4

Size of Roller Shutters

Length of the roller shutter
= inside height of cabinet + 30 mm

The end of the closed roller shutter must reach over the arc in order to avoid sliding out of place diagonally.

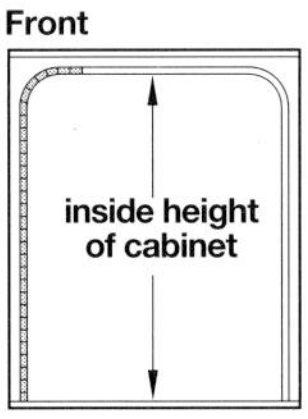

Width of roller shutter
= inside width of cabinet + 12 mm

Width of locking slat
= inside width of cabinet – 4.5 mm

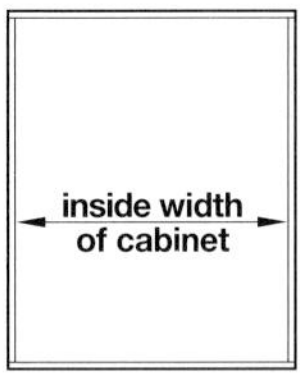

Dimensional data not binding.
We reserve the right to alter specifications without notice.

Dimensions in mm

HÄFELE

Counterbalancing Mechanism

Counterbalancing mechanism
for roller-shutter. With adjustable spring-loading function to hold the shutter in any position, preventing unintentional opening or closing. Suitable for shutter widths of 216-1000 mm (8½"-39⅜") and max. shutter travel of 1800 mm (71"). A trial installation is recommended for heavy-weight shutters.

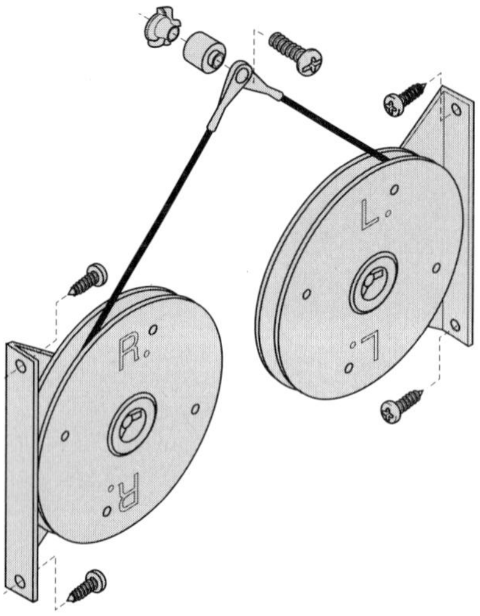

One set includes:
- 1 Pair counterbalancing drums
- 2 Steel cables, each 1600 mm (63") long
- Fastening materials and mounting instructions.

Cat. No.	442.09.903

Packing: 1 set

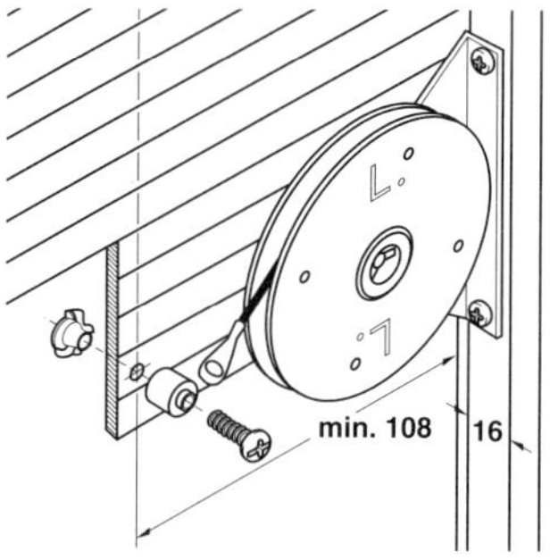

Typical installatior

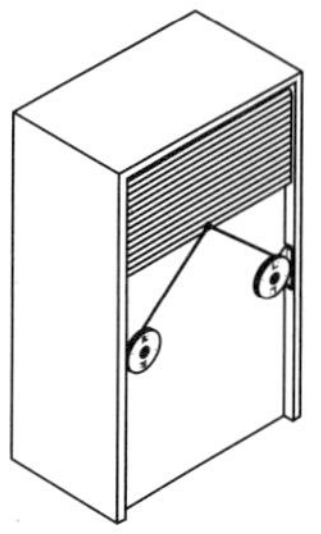

Caution: On minimum-width shutters (216 mm) (8½"), the cable must be secured in the center of the lower edge of the shutter.

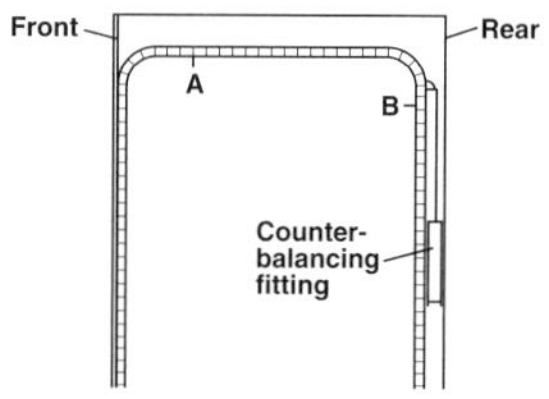

Shutter length
The required shutter length can be calculated by using the following formula:

A = without counterbalance
L = cabinet height + 100 mm (4")

B = with counterbalance
L = cabinet height + cabinet depth

4 Sliding Door Hardware
Drawer Slides
Television Supports

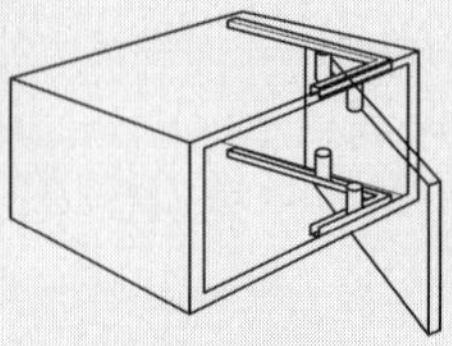

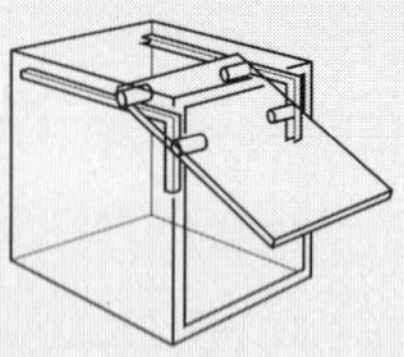

Pivot Sliding Door Fittings

Pivot sliding door fitting
for lightweight doors and flaps on audio cabinets and office furniture with door heights up to 800 mm (31½").

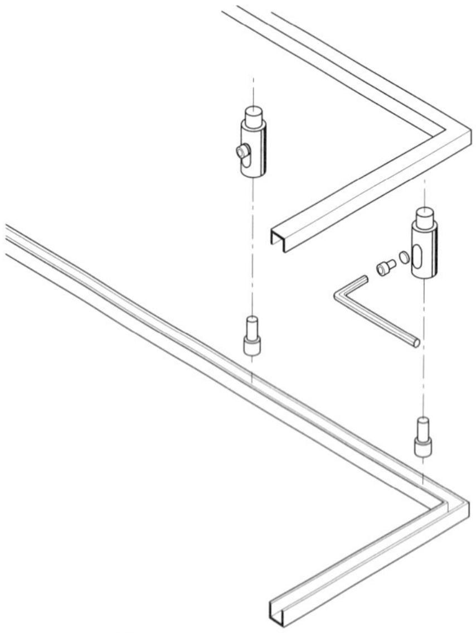

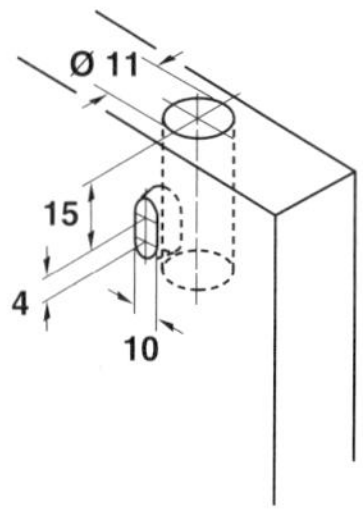

Note: Pin locations must be determined by trial installation.

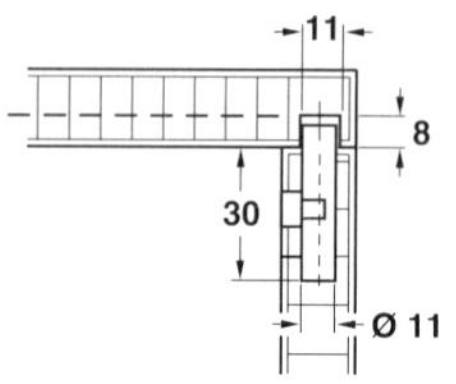

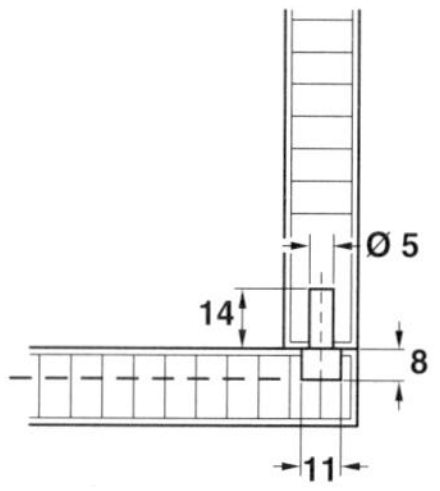

The complete fitting includes:
1 Pair plastic U-tracks in lengths of 575 (22⅝") and 140 mm (5½") each, recess-mounted in upper and lower cross-members.
2 Lower glide bolts (steel), recess-mounted in under- edge of door.
2 Upper glide bolts (steel), adjustable in sleeves and recess-mounted in top edge of door.
These items are secured with socket-head screws, tightened with an allen key.

Cat. No.	408.01.009

Packing: 1 set

Dimensions in mm

Dimensional data not binding. We reserve the right to alter specifications without notice.

WF Pocket Door Slide System Components

Components listed below are needed for each door.

Maximum Door Height up to 711 mm (28")
Maximum Door Thickness up to 32 mm (1¼")
Minimum Pocket Width:
Door thickness ⅝–⅞" (16–22 mm) = 1¾" (45 mm)
Door thickness ⅞–1¼" (22–32 mm) = 2¼" (57 mm)

Recommended for...
Entertainment systems, office furniture systems, etc...where the wood follower strip is finished (by the customer) to match the inside of the cabinet.

Ball-bearing Slide

Finish: steel, black

Length		Max. Retraction		Cat. No.
mm	in.	mm	in.	
304	12	224	8 ¾	408.10.302
354	14	274	10 ¾	408.10.357
404	16	324	12 ¾	408.10.400
454	18	374	14 ¾	408.10.455
504	20	424	16 ¾	408.10.508
554	22	474	18 ¾	408.10.553
604	24	524	20 ¾	408.10.606

Packing: 20 pcs.

Inset Application

Duomatic Hinge, 35 mm, height adjustable
For use with door thickness of 16–22 mm (⅝–⅞ in.)
Finish: steel, nickel-plated

Cat. No.	329.01.509

Packing: 20 and 600 pcs.

Mounting Plate, for 35 mm hinge, height adjustable
For use with door thickness of 16–22 mm (⅝–⅞ in.)
Finish: steel, nickel-plated

Cat. No.	329.80.626

Packing: 20 and 600 pcs.

Inset Application - Thick Door

Duomatic Hinge, 40 mm, 11 mm crank
For use with door thickness of 22–32 mm (⅞–1¼ in.)
Finish: steel, nickel-plated

Cat. No.	329.05.614

Packing: 300 pcs.

Mounting Plate, for 40 mm hinge, height adjustable
For use with door thickness of 22–32 mm (⅞–1¼ in.)
Finish: zinc, nickel-plated

Cat. No.	329.80.626

Packing: 600 pcs.

Pivot Roller, ∅ 20 mm x 12 mm
Finish: black, nylon

Cat. No.	418.09.300

Packing: 10 pcs.

Hospa Screws
Panhead Screws 4 x 13 mm
Finish: zinc-plated

Cat. No.	013.03.304

Packing: 200 pcs.

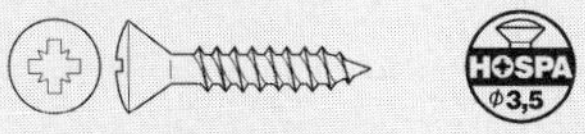

Hospa Screws
Countersunk Screws 3.5 x 15 mm
Finish: nickel-plated

Cat. No.	015.55.639

Packing: 1000 pcs.

Sliding Door Hardware
Drawer Slides
Television Supports
4

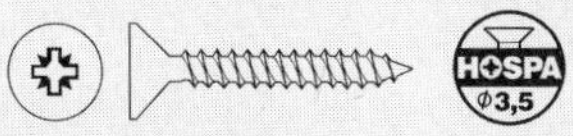

Hospa Screws
Countersunk Screws 3.5 x 25 mm
Finish: zinc-plated

Cat. No.	015.31.675

Packing: 1000 pcs.

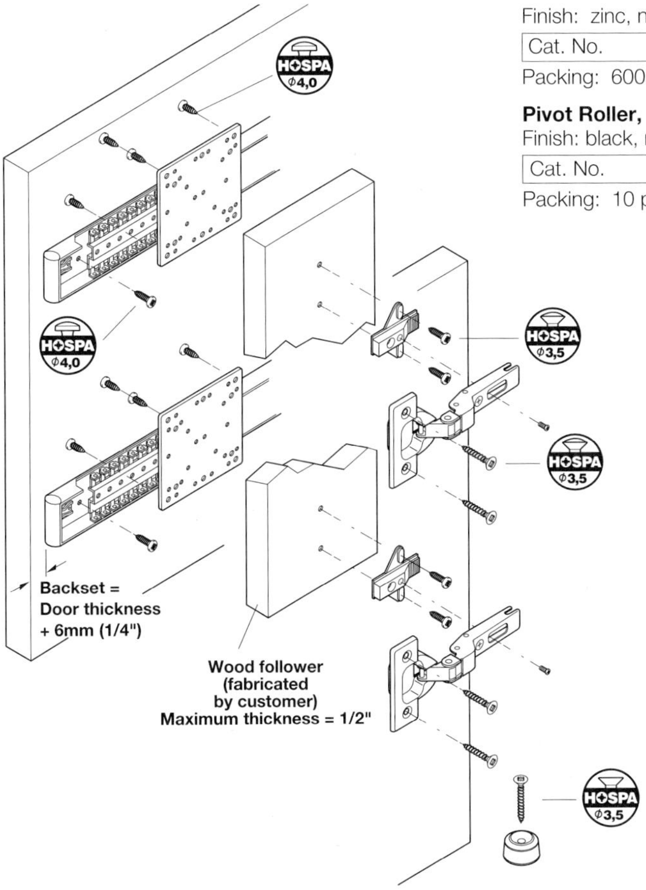

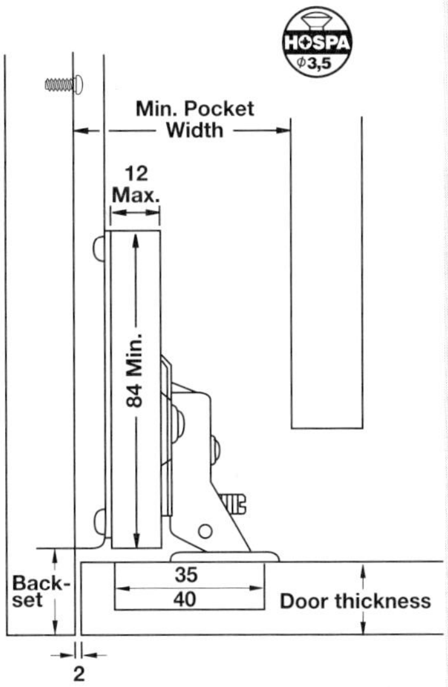

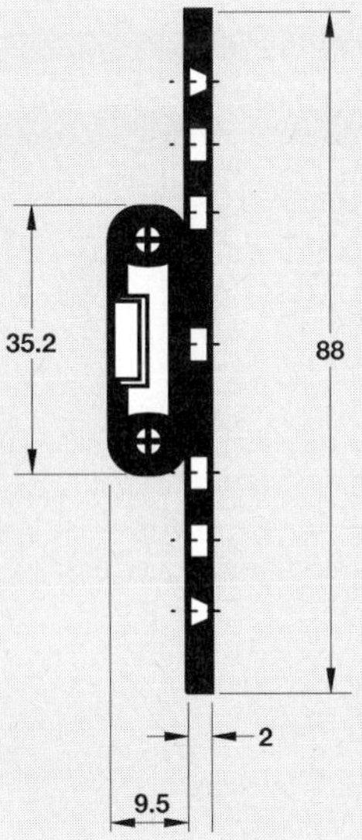

Dimensional data not binding.
We reserve the right to alter specifications without notice.

Dimensions in mm
Inches are approximate

HÄFELE

MF Pocket Door Slide System Components

Recommended for...
Entertainment systems, office furniture systems, institutional furniture where the follower strip is supplied at pre-cut length.

Hospa Screws
Panhead Screws 4 x 13 mm
Finish: steel, zinc-plated

Cat. No.	013.03.304

Packing: 200 pcs.

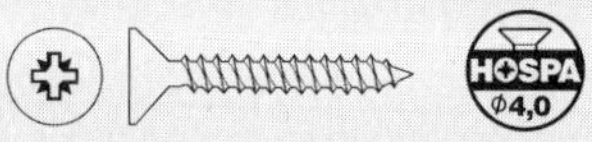

Hospa Screws
Countersunk Screws 4.0 x 17 mm
Finish: steel, nickel-plated

Cat. No.	015.35.833

Packing: 1000 pcs.

M4 Screws 5 mm

Finish: steel, zinc-plated

Cat. No.	020.05.210

Packing: 5000 pcs.

4 Sliding Door Hardware
Drawer Slides
Television Supports

M4 Screws 6 mm

Finish: steel, black

Cat. No.	020.46.059

Packing: 2000 pcs.

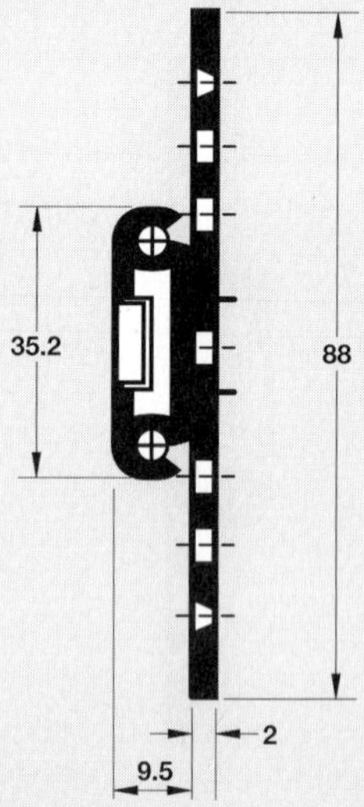

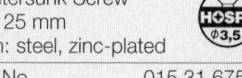

Hospa Screws
Countersunk Screw
3.5 x 25 mm
Finish: steel, zinc-plated

Cat. No.	015.31.675

Packing: 1000 pcs.

Dimensional data not binding.
We reserve the right to alter specifications without notice.

Components listed below are needed for each door.

Maximum Door Height up to 32" (813 mm)
Maximum Door Thickness up to 1¼" (32 mm)
Minimum Pocket Width:
Door thickness ⅝–⅞" (16–22 mm) = 1¾" (45 mm)
Door thickness ⅞–1¼" (22–32 mm) = 2¼" (57 mm)

Ballbearing Slide
Finish: steel, black

Length mm	Length in.	Max. Retraction mm	Max. Retraction in.	Cat. No.
304	12	224	8 ¾	408.10.302
354	14	274	10 ¾	408.10.357
404	16	324	12 ¾	408.10.400
454	18	374	14 ¾	408.10.455
504	20	424	16 ¾	408.10.508
554	22	474	18 ¾	408.10.553
604	24	524	20 ¾	408.10.606

Packing: 20 pcs.

Pivot Roller, Ø 20 mm x 12 mm
Finish: black, nylon

Cat. No.	418.09.300

Packing: 10 pcs.

Metal Follower
Finish: steel, black

Min. Door Height mm	Min. Door Height in.	CTC Hinges mm	CTC Hinges in.	(L) Length mm	(L) Length in.	Cat. No.
508	20	406	16	357	14	408.18.317
610	24	508	20	457	18	408.18.326
711	28	610	24	559	22	408.18.335

Packing: 40 pcs.

Inset Door Application

Duomatic Hinge, 35 mm, 8 mm crank
For use with door thickness of 16–22 mm (⅝–⅞")
Finish: nickel-plated

Cat. No.	329.01.518

Packing: 300 pcs.

Mounting Plate, 35 mm dia., height adjustable
Finish: zinc, nickel-plated

Cat. No.	329.80.653

Packing: 20 and 600 pcs.

Inset Application - Thick Door

Duomatic Hinge, 40 mm, 1 mm crank
For use with door thickness of 22–32 mm (⅞–1¼")
Finish: steel, nickel-plated

Cat. No.	329.05.632

Packing: 300 pcs.

Mounting Plate, 40 mm dia., height adjustable
For use with door thickness of 22–32 mm (⅞–1¼")
Finish: zinc, nickel-plated

Cat. No.	329.80.626

Packing: 20 and 600 pcs.

Overlay Door Application (Max. overlay = 10 mm (⅜"))

Duomatic Hinge, 40 mm, 11 mm crank
For use with door thickness of 16–19 mm (⅝–¾")
Finish: steel, nickel-plated

Cat. No.	329.05.614

Packing: 300 pcs.

Mounting Plate, 40 mm dia., height adjustable
For overlay use
Finish: zinc, nickel-plated

Cat. No.	329.80.626

Packing: 20 and 600 pcs.

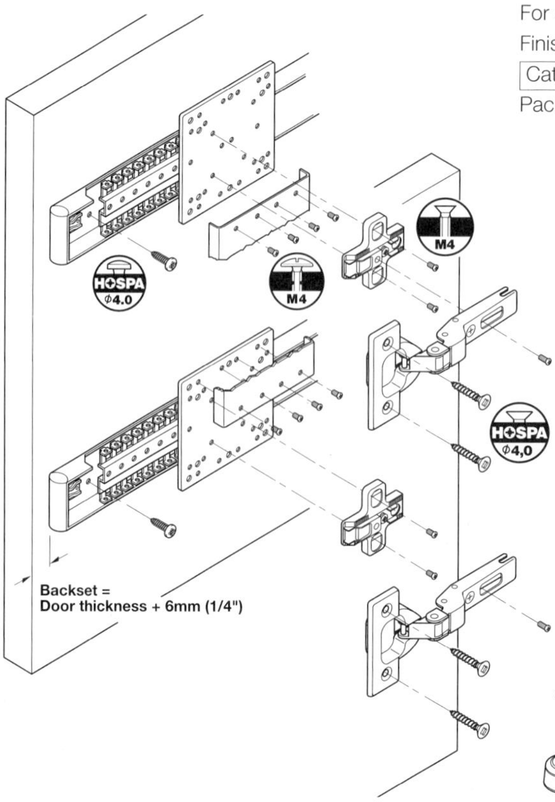

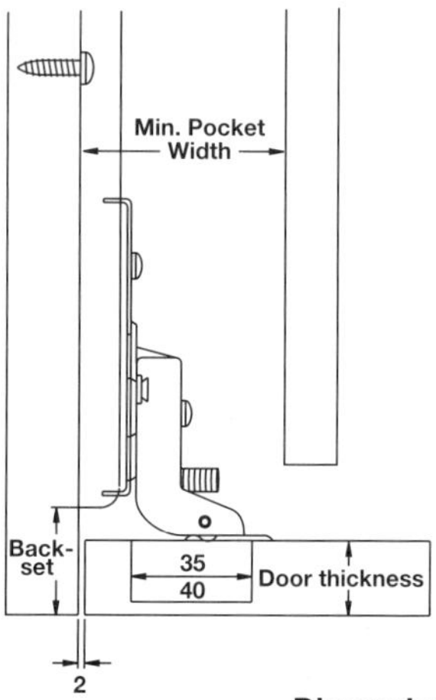

Dimensions in mm
Inches are approximate

MF Pocket Door Slide System – Complete Sets

For inset door thickness 16–22mm (5/8"– 7/8"), using 35 mm cup hinges

Includes:
- 2 pc. Slide
- 1 pc. Metal Follower
- 2 pc. 35mm Hinges
- 2 pc. Mounting Plates
- 2 pc. Pivot Roller

- 8 pc. Slide Screws — HOSPA ϕ4,0
- 4 pc. Hinge Screws — HOSPA ϕ4,0
- 4 pc. Hinge Mtg. Plate Screws — M4
- 8 pc. Metal Follower Screws — M4
- 2 pc. Pivot Roller Screws — HOSPA ϕ3,5

Max. height of door		Min. height of door		Length of slide		Length of Metal Follower		Complete Set
mm.	in.	mm.	in.	mm.	in.	mm.	in.	Cat. No.
610	24	508	20	356	14	356	14	408.19.109
610	24	508	20	406	16	356	14	408.19.118
610	24	508	20	457	18	356	14	408.19.127
610	24	508	20	508	20	356	14	408.19.136
610	24	508	20	559	22	356	14	408.19.145
610	24	508	20	610	24	356	14	408.19.154
711	28	610	24	356	14	457	18	408.19.207
711	28	610	24	406	16	457	18	408.19.216
711	28	610	24	457	18	457	18	408.19.225
711	28	610	24	508	20	457	18	408.19.234
711	28	610	24	559	22	457	18	408.19.243
711	28	610	24	610	24	457	18	408.19.252
813	32	711	28	356	14	559	22	408.19.305
813	32	711	28	406	16	559	22	408.19.314
813	32	711	28	457	18	559	22	408.19.323
813	32	711	28	508	20	559	22	408.19.332
813	32	711	28	559	22	559	22	408.19.341
813	32	711	28	610	24	559	22	408.19.350

Packing: 1 set = 1 door

- **For thick doors 22mm – 32mm (7/8"–1 1/4") use the 40mm Hinge, Cat. No. 329.05.632, and 40mm Mtg. Plate, Cat. No. 329.80.626**
- **For overlay applications. Door thickness from 16mm – 19mm (5/8"–3/4"). Maximum overlay = 10mm (3/8") use the 40mm Overlay Hinge, Cat. No. 329.05.614, and 40mm Mtg. Plate, Cat. No. 329.80.626**

Dimensions in mm
Inches are approximate

HÄFELE

RP 42/60 Pocket Door Slide System Components

Maximum Door Weight up to 14 kg (30 lbs.)
Maximum Door Thickness up to 32 mm (1¼")
RP 42 Maximum Door Height 1067 mm (42")
RP 60 Maximum Door Height 1524 mm (60")
Minimum Pocket Width:
Door thickness 16-22 mm (5/8–7/8") = 57 mm (2¼")
Door thickness 22-32 mm (7/8–1¼") = 67 mm (2 5/8")

Recommended for...
- Entertainment systems, office furniture systems, etc.

Hospa Screws
Panhead Screws 4 x 13 mm
Finish: steel, zinc-plated

Cat. No.	013.03.304

Packing: 200 pcs.

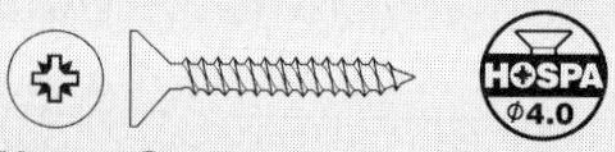

Hospa Screws
Countersunk Screws 4.0 x 17 mm
Finish: steel, nickel-plated

Cat. No.	015.35.833

Packing: 1000 pcs.

M4 Screws x 5 mm
Finish: steel, zinc-plated

Cat. No.	020.05.210

Packing: 25,000 pcs.

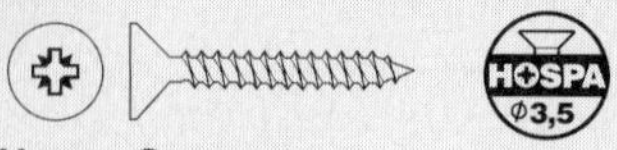

Hospa Screws
Countersunk Screws 3.5 x 25 mm
Finish: steel, nickel-plated

Cat. No.	015.31.675

Packing: 1000 pcs.

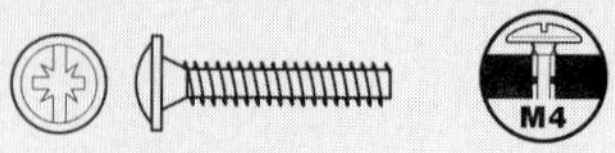

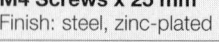

M4 Screws x 25 mm
Finish: steel, zinc-plated

Cat. No.	022.35.252

Packing: 1000 pcs.

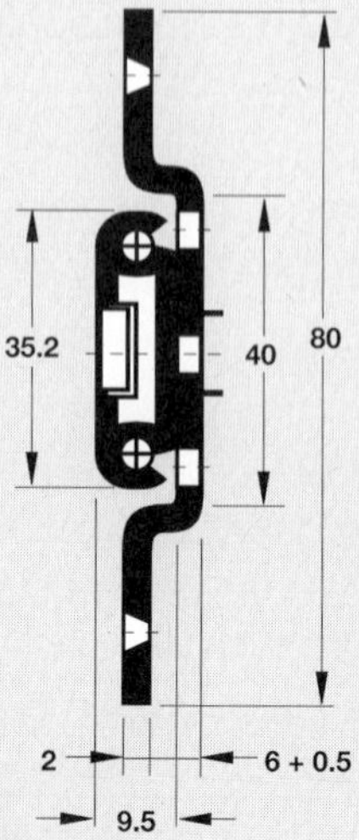

Dimensional data not binding. We reserve the right to alter specifications without notice.

Components listed below are needed for each door.

Ballbearing Slide
Finish: steel, black

Length mm	Length in.	Max. Retraction mm	Max. Retraction in.	Cat. No.
304	12	224	8 3/4	408.11.309
354	14	274	10 3/4	408.11.354
404	16	324	12 3/4	408.11.407
454	18	374	14 3/4	408.11.452
504	20	424	16 3/4	408.11.505
554	22	474	18 3/4	408.11.550
604	24	524	20 3/4	408.11.603

Packing: 20 pcs.

Pivot Roller, Ø 20 mm x 12 mm
Finish: nylon, black

Cat. No.	418.09.300

Packing: 10 pcs.

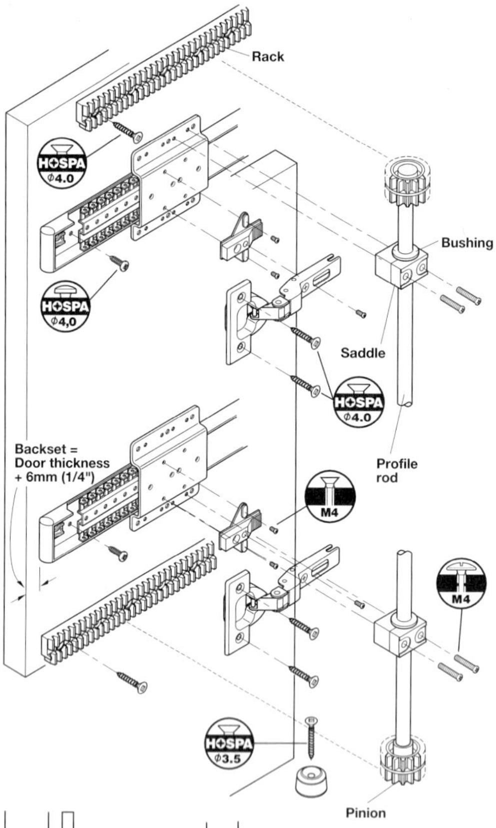

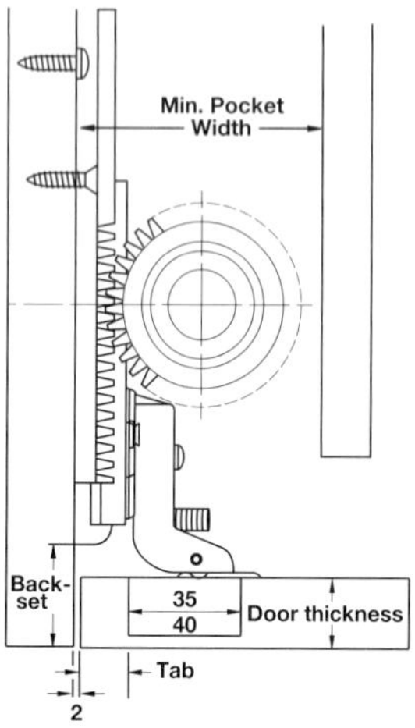

Inset Door Application

Duomatic Hinge, 35 mm, 8 mm crank
For use with door thickness of 16–22 mm (5/8–7/8")
Finish: steel, nickel-plated

Cat. No.	329.01.518

Packing: 300 pcs.

Mounting Plate, 35 mm dia., height-adjustable
For use with door thickness of 16–22 mm (5/8–7/8")
Finish: zinc, nickel-plated

Cat. No.	329.80.653

Packing: 600 pcs.

Inset Application – Thick Door

Duomatic Hinge, 40 mm, 1 mm crank
For use with door thickness of 22–32 mm (7/8–1¼")
Finish: steel, black

Cat. No.	329.05.632

Packing: 300 pcs.

Mounting Plate, 40 mm dia., height-adjustable
For use with door thickness of 22–32 mm (7/8–1¼")
Finish: zinc, nickel-plated

Cat. No.	329.80.626

Packing: 20 and 600 pcs.

Overlay Door Application (Max. overlay = 10 mm (3/8"))

Duomatic Hinge, 40 mm, 11 mm crank
For use with door thickness of 16–19 mm (5/8–3/4")
Finish: steel, nickel-plated

Cat. No.	329.05.614

Packing: 300 pcs.

Mounting Plate, 40 mm dia., height-adjustable
For overlay use
Finish: zinc, nickel-plated

Cat. No.	329.80.626

Packing: 20 and 600 pcs.

Pinion Wheel
Finish: pvc, black

Cat. No.	408.14.382

Packing: 100 pcs.

Saddle and Bushing
Finish: pvc, black

Cat. No.	408.14.390

Packing: 50 prs.

Rack, 532 mm (21")
Finish: pvc, black

Cat. No.	408.14.337

Packing: 100 pcs.

Profile Rod RP42, 1100 mm (43")
Finish: steel, nickel-plated

Cat. No.	226.67.116

Packing: 1 pc.

Profile Rod RP60, 1600 mm (63")
Finish: steel, nickel-plated

Cat. No.	226.67.161

Packing: 1 pc.

Dimensions in mm
Inches are approximate

RP 42/60 Pocket Door Slide System – Complete Sets

RP 42 – For inset door thickness 16–22mm (5/8"– 7/8"), using 35 mm hinges

Includes:
- 2 pc. Ball Bearing Slides
- 1 pc. Profile Rod 43"
- 2 pc. 35mm Hinge
- 2 pc. Mounting Plates
- 2 pc. Pinions
- 4 pr. Saddles & Bushings
- 2 pc. Rack
- 2 pc. Pivot Roller

- 8 pc. Slide Screws
- 12 pc. Hinge and Rack Screws
- 4 pc. Hinge Mtg. Plate Screws
- 8 pc. Saddle & Bushing Screws
- 2 pc. Pivot Roller Screws

Max. height of door mm.	in.	Min. height of door mm.	in.	Length of slide Quantity 2 pcs. mm.	in.	Complete Set Cat. No.
1067	42	813	32	356	14	408.20.102
1067	42	813	32	406	16	408.20.111
1067	42	813	32	457	18	408.20.120
1067	42	813	32	508	20	408.20.139
1067	42	813	32	559	22	408.20.148
1067	42	813	32	610	24	408.20.157

Packing: 1 set = 1 door

RP 60 – For inset door thickness 16–22mm (5/8"– 7/8"), using 35 mm hinges

Includes:
- 3 pc. Ball Bearing Slides
- 1 pc. Profile Rod 63"
- 3 pc. 35mm Hinge
- 3 pc. Mounting Plates
- 2 pc. Pinions
- 6 pr. Saddles & Bushings
- 2 pc. Rack
- 2 pc. Pivot Roller

- 12 pc. Slide Screws
- 14 pc. Hinge and Rack Screws
- 6 pc. Hinge Mtg. Plate Screws
- 12 pc. Saddle & Bushing Screws
- 2 pc. Pivot Roller Screws

Max. height of door mm.	in.	Min. height of door mm.	in.	Length of slide Quantity 3 pcs. mm.	in.	Complete Set Cat. No.
1524	60	1067	42	356	14	408.20.200
1524	60	1067	42	406	16	408.20.219
1524	60	1067	42	457	18	408.20.228
1524	60	1067	42	508	20	408.20.237
1524	60	1067	42	559	22	408.20.246
1524	60	1067	42	610	24	408.20.255

Packing: 1 set = 1 door

Sliding Door Hardware
Drawer Slides
Television Supports

4

- **For thick doors 22mm – 32mm (7/8"–1 1/4") use the 40mm Hinge, Cat. No. 329.05.632, and 40mm Mtg. Plate, Cat. No. 329.80.626**
- **For overlay applications. Door thickness from 16mm – 19mm (5/8"–3/4"). Maximum overlay = 10mm (3/8") use the 40mm Overlay Hinge, Cat. No. 329.05.614, and 40mm Mtg. Plate, Cat. No. 329.80.626**

Dimensional data not binding. We reserve the right to alter specifications without notice.

Dimensions in mm
Inches are approximate

HÄFELE

XL-Slide Pocket Door System

Pocket Door Slides with cables attached.
Finish/materials: steel, black zinc-electroplated; plastic, black; steel cable, black nylon coated; roller, black.

- Especially suited for use in larger door cabinets such as those found in home theater applications.
  For use with doors up to 60" high, 24" wide and weighing up to 35 pounds.
- Will handle doors up to 1¼" thick.
- No jigs or fixtures are required to locate slide top and bottom.
  Integral location tabs locates slides in cabinet.
- Adjustment screws allow maximum adjustability.
  Adjustment for cable tensioning conveniently located at front of slide.
  Easily accessible from front of cabinet by installer or end user.
- Steel cable is black nylon coated to reduce friction and enhance appearance.

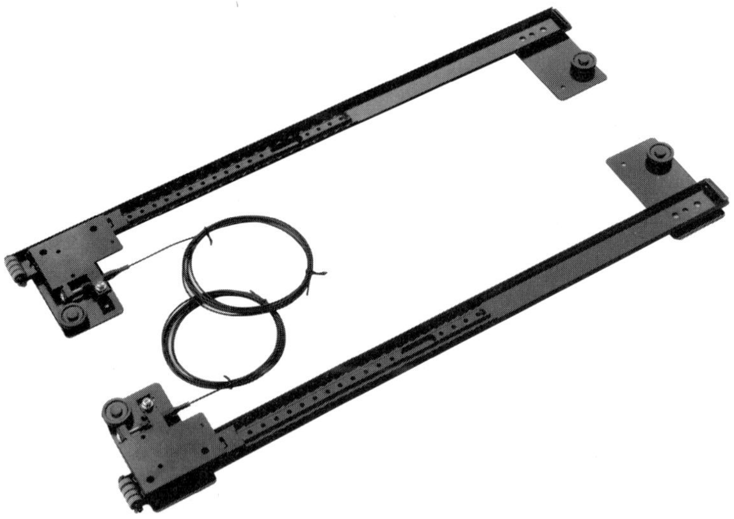

Length		Travel		Cat. No.
mm	inches	mm	inches	
410	16	295	11.5	408.24.315
461	18	345	13.5	408.24.324
511	20	396	15.5	408.24.333
562	22	447	17.5	408.24.342
613	24	498	19.5	408.24.351
664	26	549	21.5	408.24.360

Packing: 1 set = 1 door

Note: Accessory pack on page **4.37** required to complete assembly.

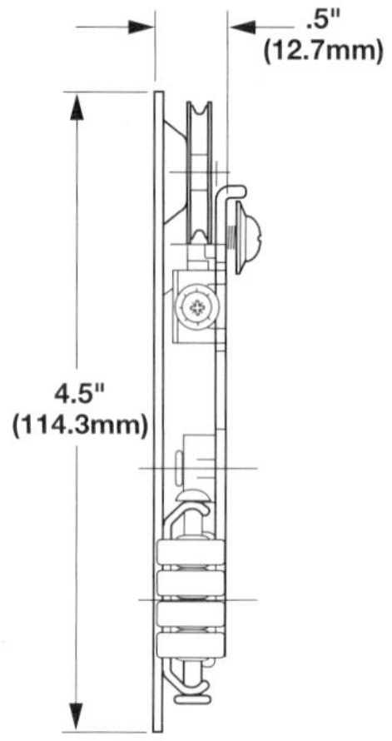

- Cable runs parallel with slide to ensure smooth operation. Excess pressure on slide is eliminated.
- Positive out-stop on slide keeps door in alignment in closed position.
- Soft rubber roller on slide front protects door front from scratches and marring.
- Minimal installation and adjustment time means lower production costs.
- 32 mm compatible

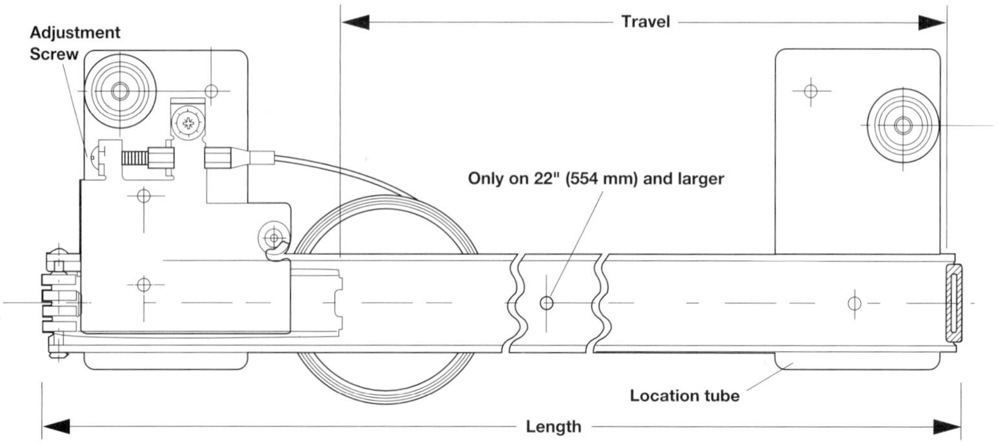

Patent pending.

Dimensional data not binding. We reserve the right to alter specifications without notice.

Dimensions in mm
Inches are approximate

XL-Slide Pocket Door System

Typical Installation.

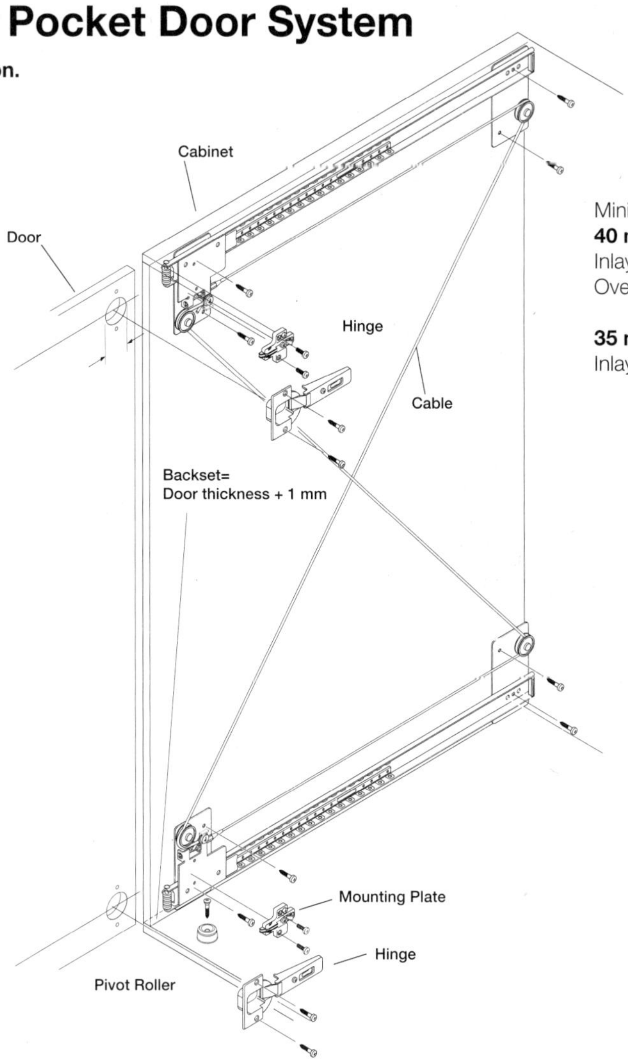

Minimum pocket width:

40 mm hinges
Inlay door = 64mm (2 1/2")
Overlay door = 50mm (2")

35 mm hinges
Inlay door = 45mm (1 3/4")

40mm - Inlay Door Accessory Pack (Door thickness 19mm - 32mm)

Set includes:
4 - 020.05.210 - M4 x 5mm - Hinge plate mounting screws
4 - 015.55.639 - 3.5 x 15mm - Hinge mounting screws
2 - 418.09.300 - Pivot roller
1 - 015.31.675 - Pivot roller mounting screw
10 - 013.03.304 - Slide mounting screws
2 - 329.05.632 - Duomatic 95°, 40mm cup hinge for inset doors
2 - 329.60.624 - Duomatic clip mounting plate, with single screw adjustment

Cat. No.	408.24.002

Packing: 1 set = 1 door

40mm - Overlay Door Accessory Pack (Door thickness 19mm - 22mm, max. overlay - 7mm)

Set includes:
4 - 020.05.210 - M4 x 5mm - Hinge plate mounting screws
4 - 015.55.639 - 3.5 x 15mm - Hinge mounting screws
2 - 418.09.300 - Pivot roller
1 - 015.31.675 - Pivot roller mounting screw
10 - 013.03.304 - Slide mounting screws
2 - 329.05.614 - Duomatic 95°, 40mm cup hinge for overlay doors
2 - 329.60.624 - Duomatic clip mounting plate, with single screw adjustment

Cat. No.	408.24.011

Packing: 1 set = 1 door

35mm - Inlay Door Accessory Pack (Door thickness 16mm -19mm)

Set includes:
4 - 020.05.210 - M4 x 5mm - Hinge plate mounting screws
4 - 015.55.639 - 3.5 x 15mm - Hinge mounting screws
2 - 418.09.300 - Pivot roller
1 - 015.31.675 - Pivot roller mounting screw
10 - 013.03.304 - Slide mounting screws
2 - 329.01.518 - Duomatic 95°, 35mm cup hinge for inset doors
2 - 329.60.651 - Duomatic clip mounting plate, with single screw adjustment

Cat. No.	408.24.020

Packing: 1 set = 1 door

Dimensions in mm
Inches are approximate

HÄFELE

- Complete mounting instructions included with slides.

For touch latch applications, requiring a free-swinging hinge (not self-closing), order separately the following articles in place of the 40mm hinges supplied:

Overlay application

Cat. No.	329.04.617

Packing: 1 pc.

Inset application

Cat. No.	329.04.635

Packing: 1 pc.

HÄFELE

Hawa-Turnaway Fiero 25/35 Pivot Sliding Door Fitting

The Hawa-Turnaway 25/35 pivot sliding door fitting neatly resolves the problem of "what to do with the door" when it is open by allowing it to retract into the side of the cabinet. The new Hawa-Turnaway 25 and 35 were designed with many years of experience from the previous Hawa- Turnaway X fittings.
They fully comply with all the recent developments in furniture design.
• Rapid, precise installation of the fitting is assured by the series-drilled holes at 32 mm intervals

H = Inside height
T = Maximum door travel (retraction)
D = Inside cabinet depth. For maximum door travel (Dimension T) this amount of inside cabinet depth is required.

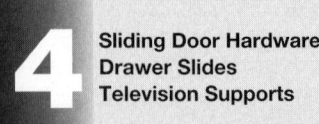

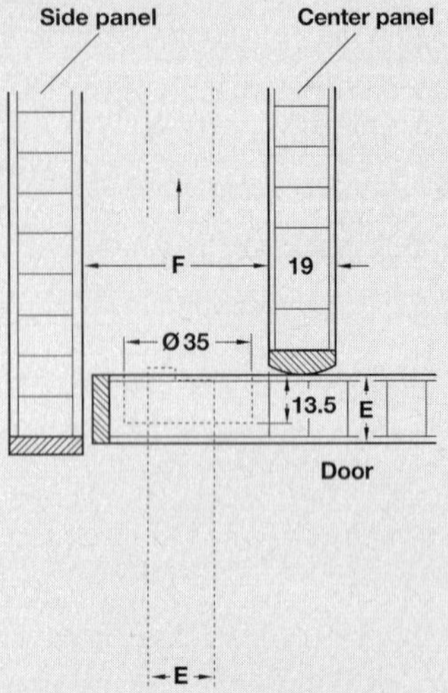

Space requirements for slide-in pocket (F):

Wood thickness of door (E)	Space required (F)
19 mm (3/4")	45 mm (1 3/4")
25 mm (1")	47 mm (1 7/8")
28 mm (1 1/8")	50 mm (2")

Hawa-Turnaway Fiero 25
Door weight up to **25 kg (55 lbs.)**
For wood thicknesses from 19 to 28 mm (3/4"-1 1/8")
• Door height from 900 – 2250 mm (35 7/16"-88 1/2")
• Divider panel 19 mm (3/4") (for hardware installation)

Fiero/25

Inside height: Dim. "H"		**Dim. "T"**		**Dim. "D"**		**Left**	**Right**
mm	inches	mm	inches	mm	inches		
900-1200	35 7/16"-47 1/4"	470	18 1/2"	565	22 1/4"	407.70.125	407.70.027
1200-1800	47 1/4"-70 7/8"	500	19 11/16"	595	23 7/16"	407.70.134	407.70.036
1800-2250	70 7/8"-88 1/2"	530	20 7/8"	625	24 5/8"	407.70.143	407.70.045

Packing: 1 set

Hawa-Turnaway Fiero 35
Door weight up to **35 kg (77 lbs.)**.
For wood thicknesses from 19 to 28 mm (3/4"-1 1/8")
• Door height from 2250 – 2850 mm (88 1/2"-112 3/16")
• Divider panel 19 mm (3/4") (for hardware installation)

Fiero/35

Inside height: Dim. "H"		**Dim. "T"**		**Dim. "D"**		**Left**	**Right**
mm	inches	mm	inches	mm	inches		
2250-2850	88 1/2"-112 3/16"	530	20 7/8"	625	24 5/8"	407.70.152	407.70.054

Packing: 1 set

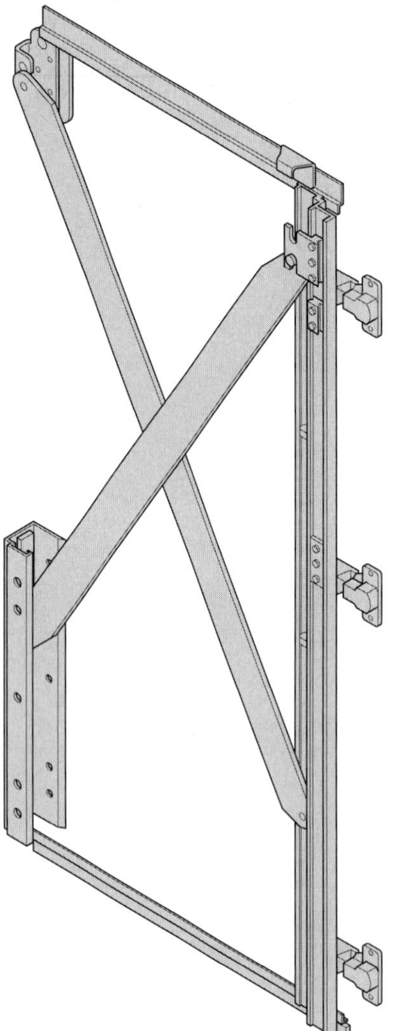

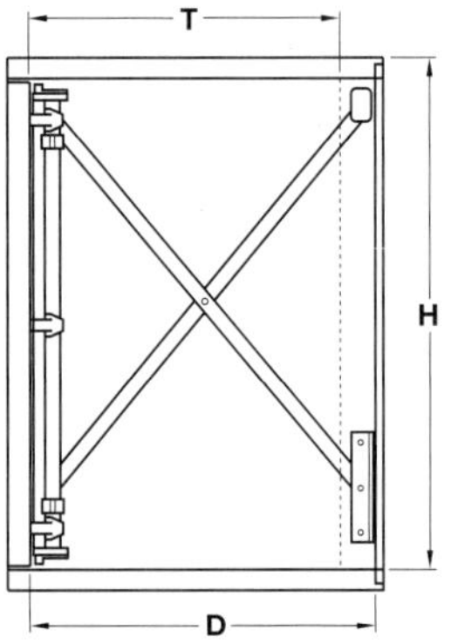

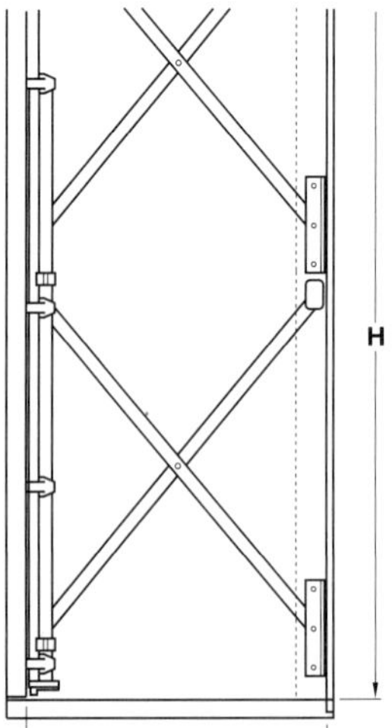

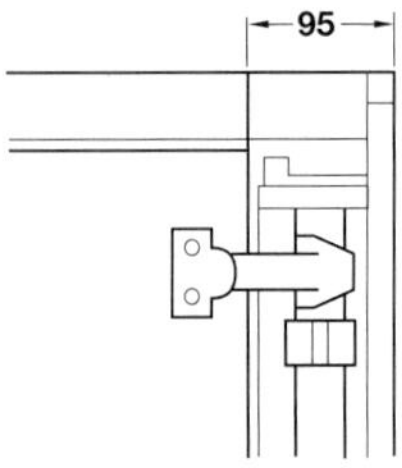

Precise mounting instructions are supplied with every fitting

Dimensional data not binding.
We reserve the right to alter specifications without notice.

Dimensions in mm
Inches are approximate

Hawa-Turnaway 15/X1 Pivot Sliding Door Fitting

HÄFELE

Hawa-Turnaway 15/X1
- Door weight up to **15 kg (33 lbs.)**
- Door height from 600 – 1050 mm (23 5/8"-41 3/8")
- Door thickness from 16 – 38 mm (5/8"-1 1/2")

15/X1

Inside height: Dim. "H"		Dim. "T"		Dim. "D"		Left	Right
mm	inches	mm	inches	mm	inches		
500-550	19 11/16"-21 11/16"	365	14 3/8"	420	16 9/16"	407.71.113	407.71.015
550-600	21 11/16"-23 5/8"	405	15 15/16"	460	18 1/8"	407.71.122	407.71.024
600-650	23 5/8"-25 5/8"	435	17 1/8"	490	19 5/16"	407.71.131	407.71.033
650-700	25 5/8"-27 9/16"	475	18 11/16"	530	20 7/8"	407.71.140	407.71.042
700-750	27 9/16"-29 9/16"	505	19 7/8"	560	22 1/16"	407.71.159	407.71.051
750-800	29 1/2"-31 1/2"	545	21 7/16"	600	23 5/8"	407.71.168	407.71.060
800-1050	31 1/2"-41 3/8"	575	22 5/8"	630	24 13/16"	407.71.177	407.71.079

Packing: 1 set

*** Hinges**
for door thickness from 28 – 35 mm

Cat. No.	407.71.908

Packing: 2 pcs.

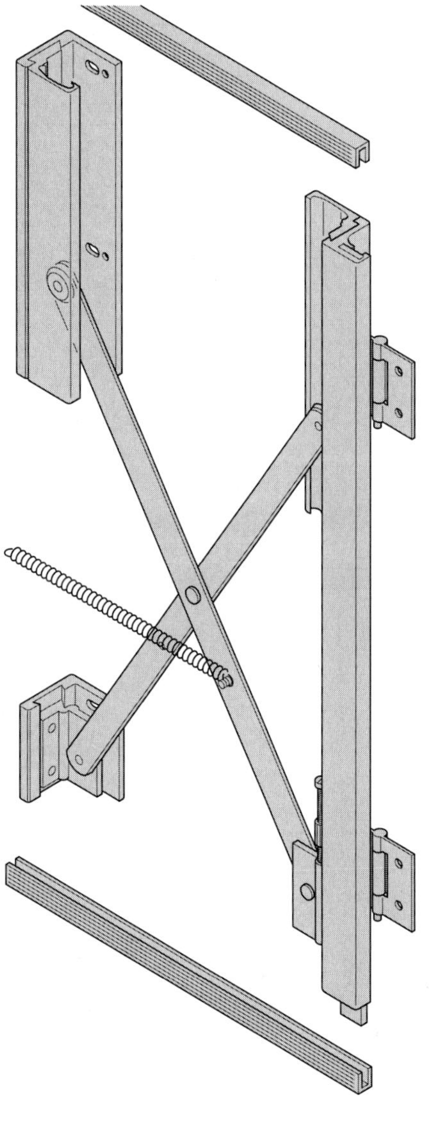

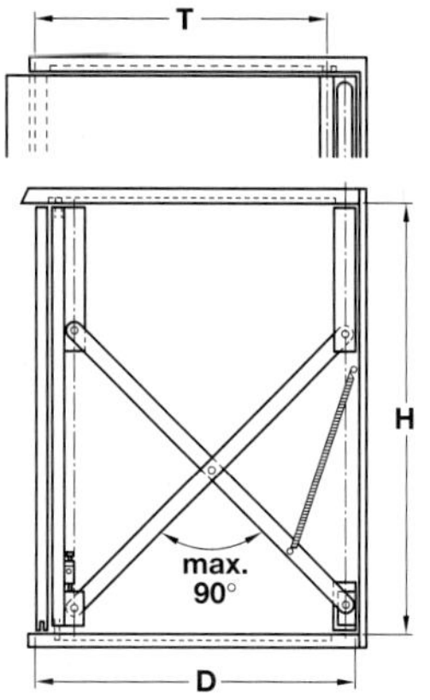

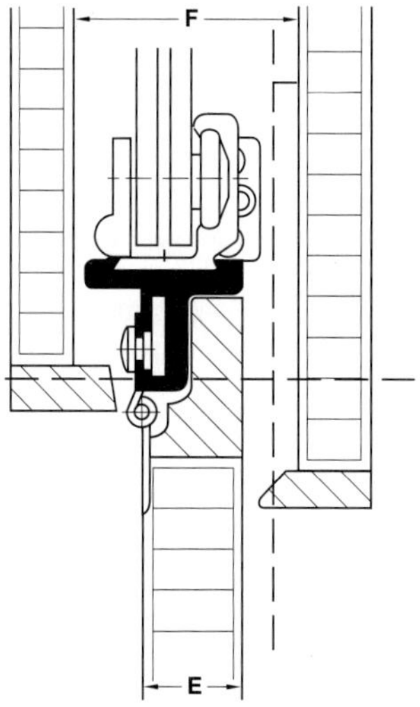

Space requirements for slide-in pocket (F):

Wood thickness of door (E)	Space required (F)
16 mm (5/8")	50 mm (2")
19 mm (3/4")	50 mm (2")
25 mm (1")	58 mm (2 1/4")
32 mm (1 1/4")	73 mm (2 7/8")
38 mm (1 1/2")	75 mm (3")

Dimensions in mm
Inches are approximate

H = Inside height
T = Maximum door travel (retraction)
D = Inside cabinet depth. For maximum door travel (Dimension T) this amount of inside cabinet depth is required.

Hawa-Turnaway 15/X1, for door weights up to 15 kg. The Hawa-Turnaway 15/X1 is the light-duty version of this scissor hinge series. It is designed for door heights up to 105 cm and is therefore suitable for television and audio cabinets, counters, desks, etc...In function and precision it is identical to the heavier-duty models.

Note
Plan drawings in a 1:1 scale are available upon request.

Adjust top clearance of door, i.e. loosen hinge arm at lower front of upright, adjust door clearance with vertical adjustment screw. Retighten screws.

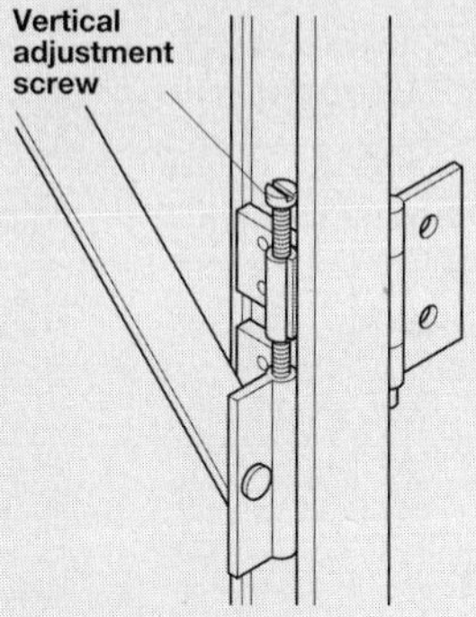

HÄFELE

Hawa-Turnaway 25/X2 and 35/X3 Pivot Sliding Door Fitting

Hawa-Turnaway 25/X2
for door weights up to **25 kg (55 lbs.)**.
This fitting with one scissor assembly is designed for short and light doors.

- Door height from 1050 – 1800 mm (41 3/8"-70 7/8")
- Door thickness from 19 – 45 mm (3/4"-1 3/4")

25/X2

Inside height: Dim. "H"		Dim. "T"		Dim. "D"		Left	Right
mm	inches	mm	inches	mm	inches		
1050-1200	41 3/8"-47 1/4"	700	27 9/16"	765	30 1/8"	407.72.165	407.72.067
1200-1500	47 1/4"-59 1/16"	780	30 11/16"	845	33 1/4"	407.72.174	407.72.076
1260-1800	49 5/8"-70 7/8"	820	32 5/16"	885	34 7/8"	407.72.183	407.72.085

Packing: 1 set

Hawa-Turnaway 35/X3
for door weights up to **35 kg (77 lbs.)**.
This fitting with one reinforced scissor assembly is designed for large and heavy doors.

- Door height from 1260 – 2450 mm (49 5/8"-96 1/2")

35/X3

Inside height: Dim. "H"		Dim. "T"		Dim. "D"		Left	Right
mm	inches	mm	inches	mm	inches		
1260-2450	49 5/8"-96 1/2"	820	32 5/16"	885	34 7/8"	407.73.153	407.73.055

Packing: 1 set

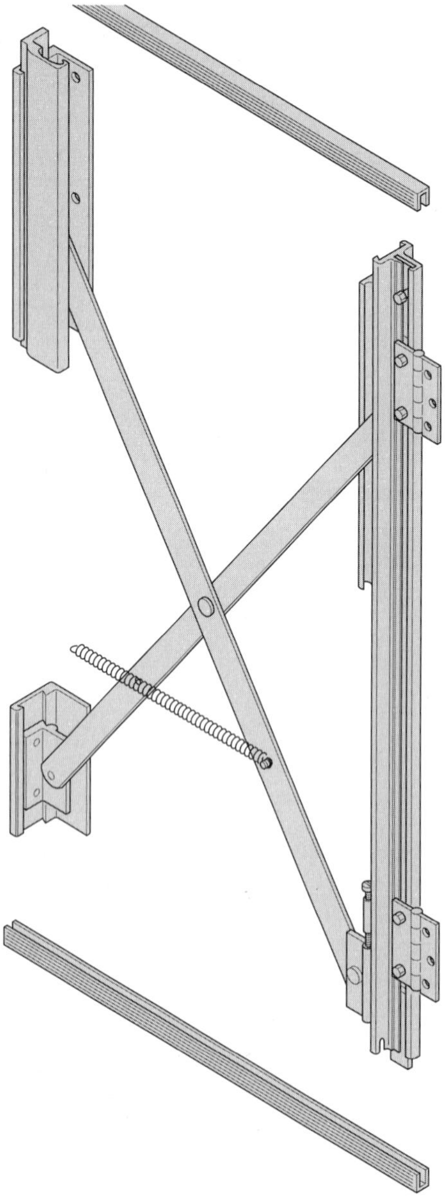

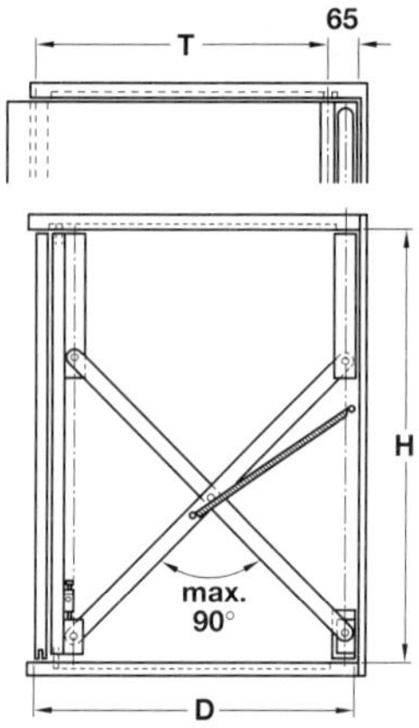

H = Inside height
T = Maximum door travel (retraction)
D = Inside cabinet depth. For maximum door travel (Dimension T) this amount of inside cabinet depth is required.

Hawa-Turnaway 35/X3:
In the event of a door width not exceeding 600 mm (2'), the door weight may be as much as 40 kg. (88 lbs.).

Note
Plan drawings in a 1:1 scale are available upon request.

Adjust top clearance of door, i.e. loosen hinge arm at lower front of upright, adjust door clearance with vertical adjustment screw. Retighten screws.

Vertical adjustment screw

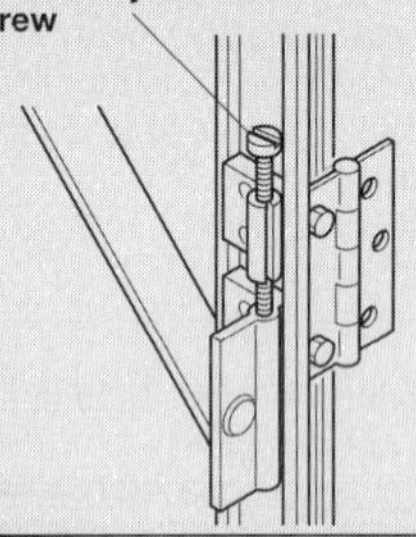

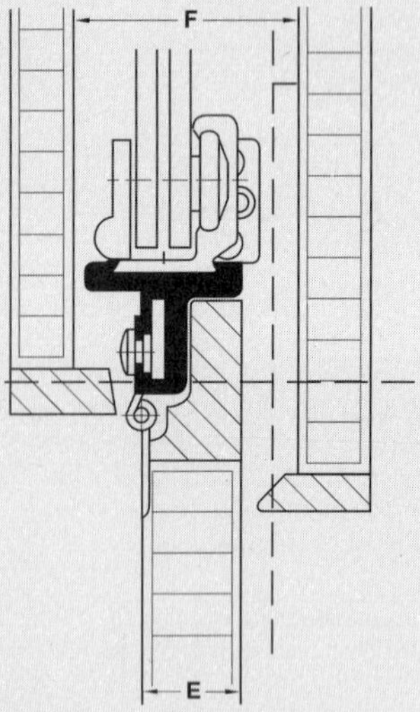

Space requirements for slide-in pocket (F):

Wood thickness of door (E)	Space required (F)
19 mm (3/4")	52 mm (2 1/16")
22 mm (7/8")	52 mm (2 1/16")
25 mm (1")	58 mm (2 5/16")
28 mm (1 1/8")	62 mm (2 7/16")
30 mm (1 3/16")	71 mm (2 3/4")
35 mm (1 3/8")	75 mm (3")
38 mm (1 1/2")	75 mm (3")
45 mm (1 3/4")	85 mm (3 3/8")

Dimensional data not binding. We reserve the right to alter specifications without notice.

Dimensions in mm
Inches are approximate

Hawa-Turnaway 30/X4 Pivot Sliding Door Fitting

H = Inside height
T = Maximum door travel (retraction)
D = Inside cabinet depth. For maximum door travel (Dimension T) this amount of inside cabinet depth is required.

Hawa-Turnaway 30/X4, for door weights up to **30 kg (66 lbs.)**. This fitting includes an upright guide and two scissor assembles arranged one above the other (see diagram). Two adjustable hinges per scissor assembly are secured to the upright guide.

- Door weight 30 kg (66 lbs.)
- Door heights from 2450 – 2800 mm (96 1/2"-110 1/4")
- Door thickness from 19 – 44 mm (3/4"-1 3/4")

30/X4

Inside height: Dim. "H"		Dim. "T"		Dim. "D"		Left	Right
mm	inches	mm	inches	mm	inches		
2450-2800	96 1/2"-110 1/4"	820	32 5/16"	885	34 7/8"	407.73.377	407.73.279

Packing: 1 set each

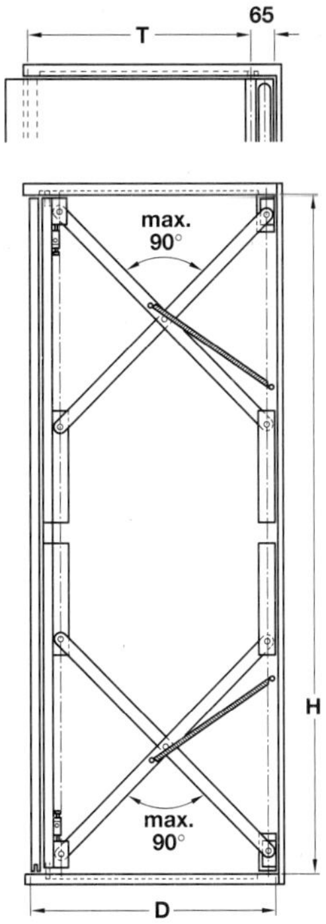

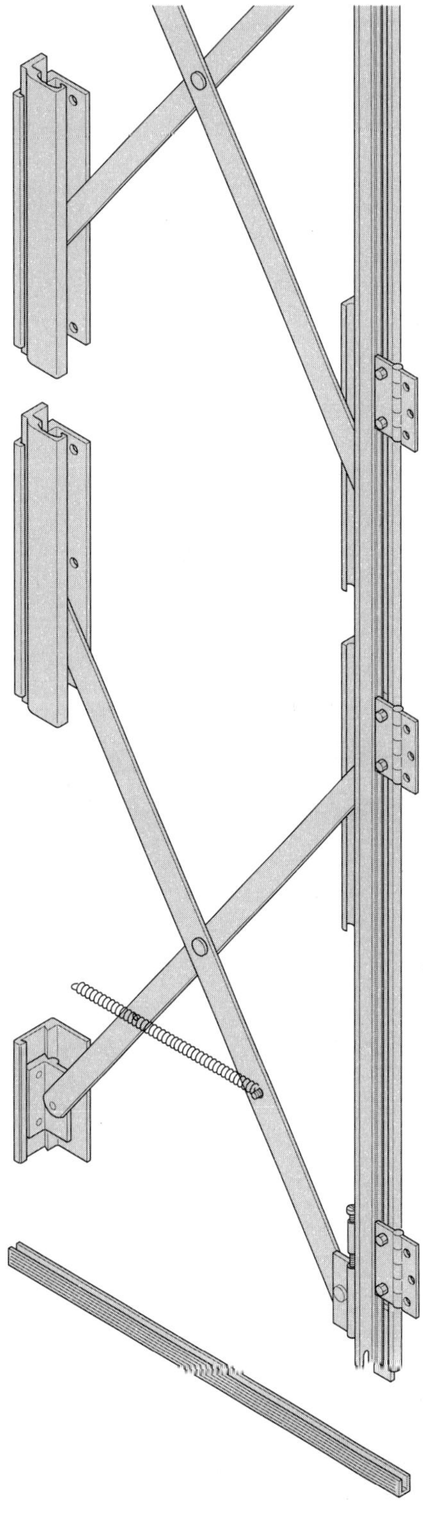

Adjust top clearance of door, i.e. loosen hinge arm at lower front of upright, adjust door clearance with vertical adjustment screw. Retighten screw.

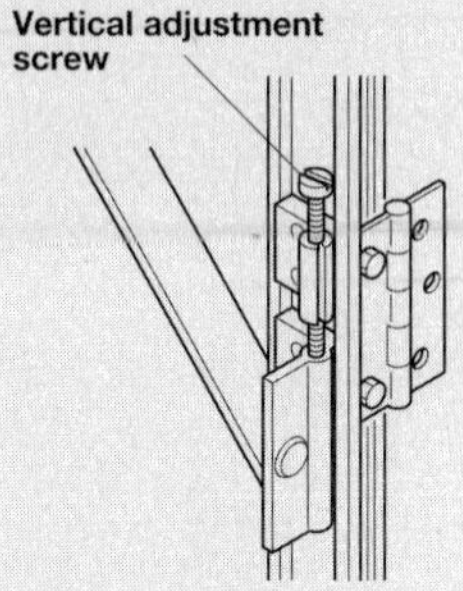

Sliding Door Hardware
Drawer Slides
Television Supports

4

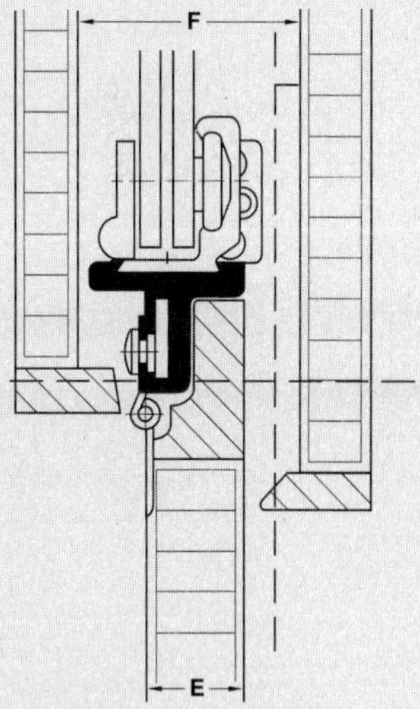

Space requirements for slide-in pocket (F):

Wood thickness of door (E)	Space required (F)
19 mm (3/4")	52 mm (2 1/16")
22 mm (7/8")	52 mm (2 1/16")
25 mm (1")	58 mm (2 5/16")
28 mm (1 1/8")	62 mm (2 7/16")
30 mm (1 3/16")	71 mm (2 3/4")
35 mm (1 3/8")	75 mm (3")
38 mm (1 1/2")	75 mm (3")
45 mm (1 3/4")	85 mm (3 3/8")

Dimensional data not binding. We reserve the right to alter specifications without notice.

Dimensions in mm
Inches are approximate

HÄFELE

Hawa-Turnaway 40/X5 Pivot Sliding Door Fitting

H = Inside height
T = Maximum door travel (retraction)
D = Inside cabinet depth. For maximum door travel (Dimension T) this amount of inside cabinet depth is required.

Hawa-Turnaway 40/X5:
In the event of a door width not exceeding 600 mm (2'), the door weight may be as much as 50 kg. (110 lbs.).

Adjust top clearance of door, i.e. loosen hinge arm at lower front of upright, adjust door clearance with vertical adjustment screw. Retighten screw.

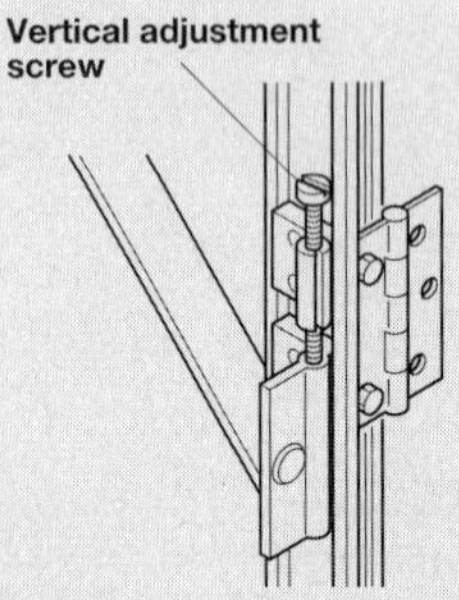

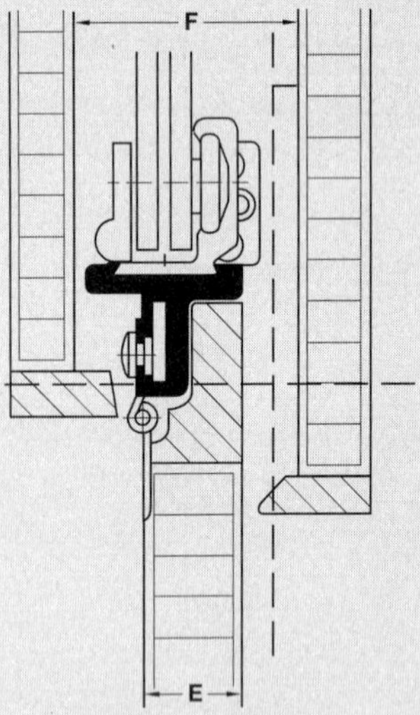

Space requirements for slide-in pocket (F):

Wood thickness of door (E)	Space required (F)
19 mm (3/4")	52 mm (2 1/16")
22 mm (7/8")	52 mm (2 1/16")
25 mm (1")	58 mm (2 5/16")
28 mm (1 1/8")	62 mm (2 7/16")
30 mm (1 3/16")	71 mm (2 3/4")
35 mm (1 3/8")	75 mm (3")
38 mm (1 1/2")	75 mm (3")
45 mm (1 3/4")	85 mm (3 3/8")

Dimensional data not binding. We reserve the right to alter specifications without notice.

Hawa-Turnaway 40/X5, for door weights up to **40 kg (88 lbs.)**. This fitting includes an upright guide and **two reinforced** scissor assembles arranged one above the other (see diagram). Two adjustable hinges per scissor assembly are secured to the upright guide.

- Door weight 40 kg (88 lbs.)
- Door heights from 2450 – 2800 mm (96 1/2"-110 1/4")
- Door thickness from 19 – 44 mm (3/4"-1 3/4")

40/X5

Inside height: Dim. "H"		Dim. "T"		Dim. "D"		Left	Right
mm	inches	mm	inches	mm	inches		
2450-2800	96 1/2"-110 1/4"	820	32 5/16"	885	34 7/8"	407.73.537	407.73.439

Packing: 1 set each

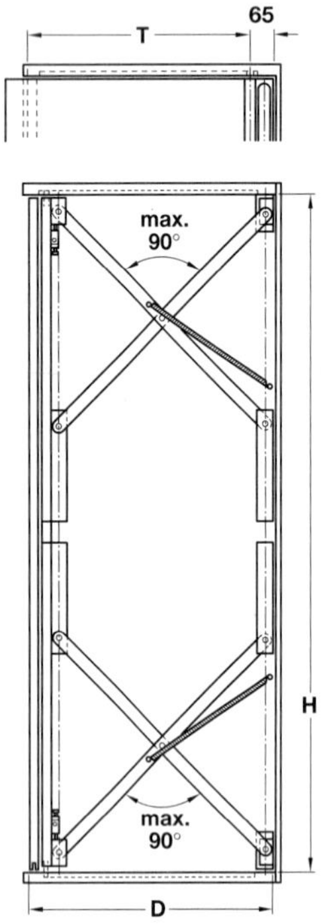

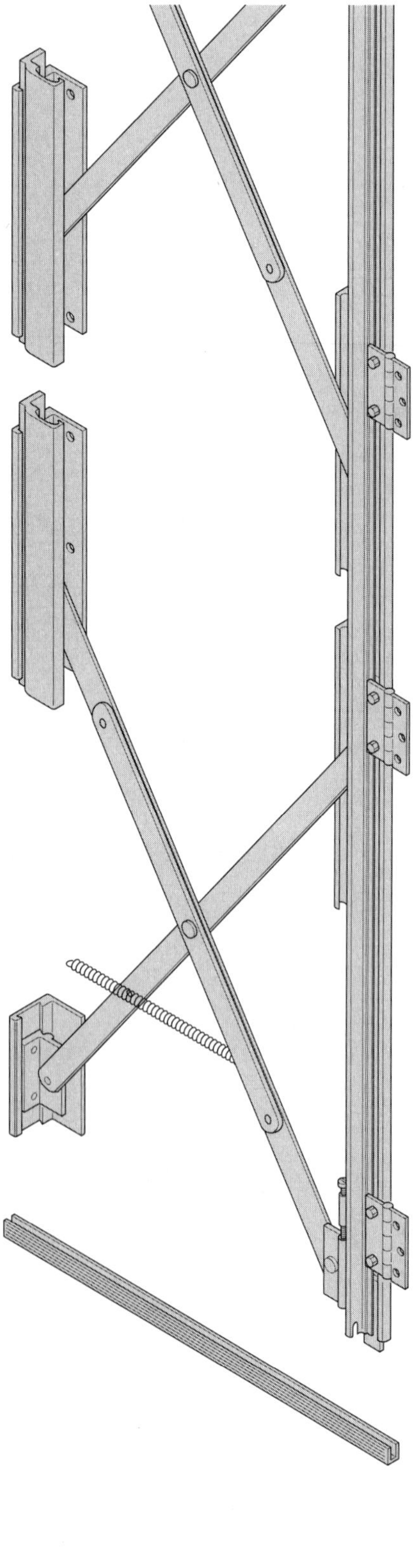

Dimensions in mm
Inches are approximate

Hawa Bi-Folding Door Fitting for Turnaways

HÄFELE

Supplementary hardware for two folding doors to be used in combination with the Hawa Turnaway 25/X2 or 35/X3

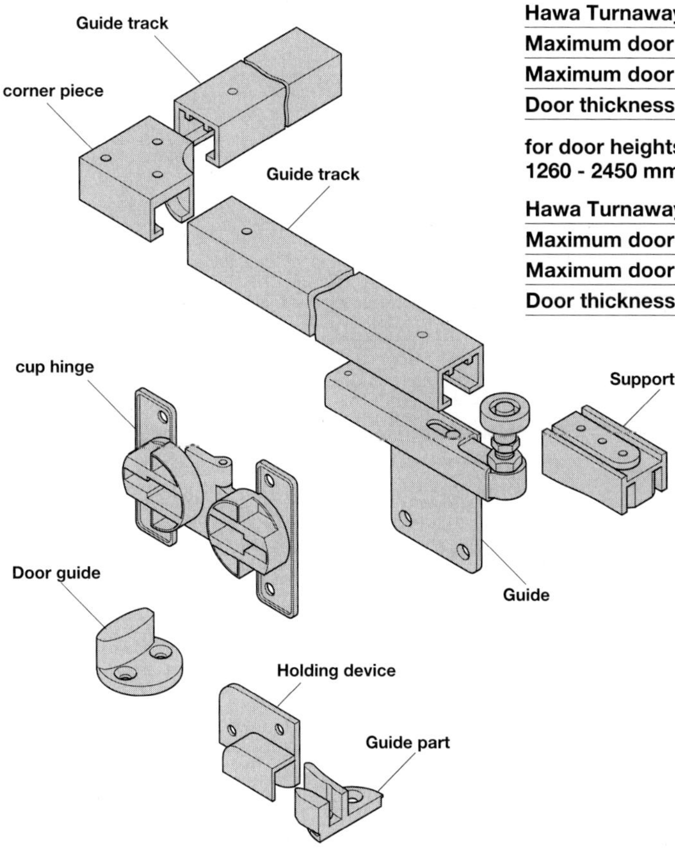

Construction data:

for door heights from 1050 - 1800 mm (41 3/8"-70 7/8")

Hawa Turnaway set	25/X2 (see page **4.40**)
Maximum door width	600 mm (24")
Maximum door weight	15 kg (33 lbs.)
Door thickness	19 - 35 mm (3/4"-1 3/8")

for door heights from 1260 - 2450 mm (49 5/8"-96 1/2")

Hawa Turnaway set	35/X3 (see page **4.40**)
Maximum door width	600 mm (24")
Maximum door weight	20 kg (44 lbs.)
Door thickness	19 - 35 mm (3/4"-1 3/8")

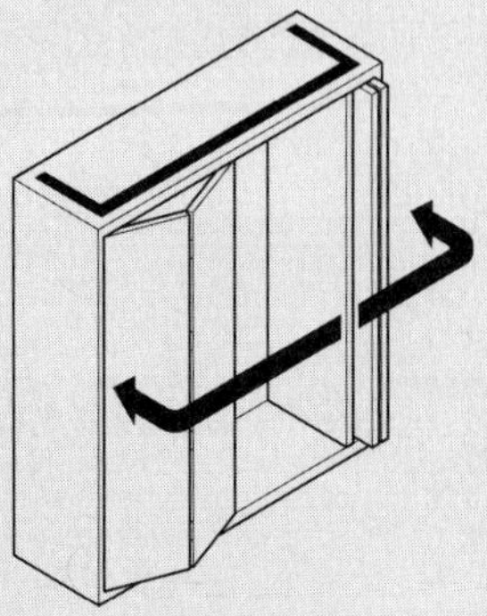

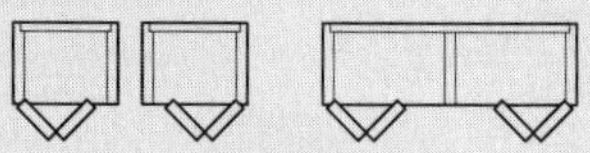

Note:
For planning and installation instructions, please order drawings together with the Hawa turn-away diagrams.

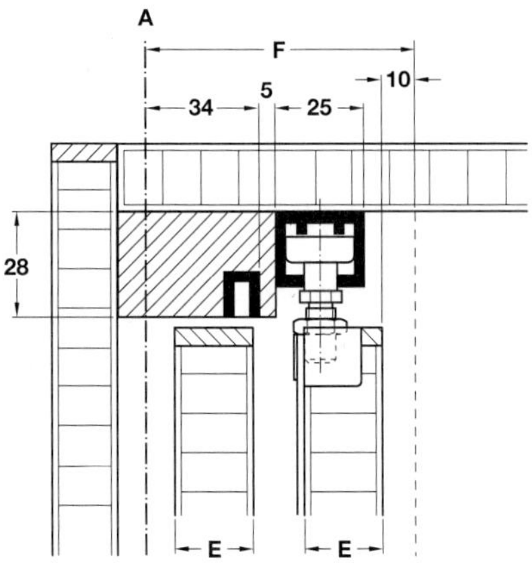

Space requirements for slide-in pocket (F):

Wood thickness of door (E)	Space requirement (F)
mm	
19 mm (3/4")	77 mm (3 1/16")
22 mm (7/8")	77 mm (3 1/16")
25 mm (1")	80 mm (3 3/16")
28 mm (1 1/8")	83 mm (3 1/4")
30 mm (1 3/16")	85 mm (3 3/8")
35 mm (1 3/8")	90 mm (3 9/16")

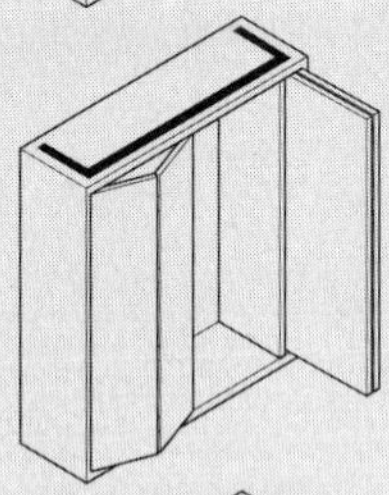

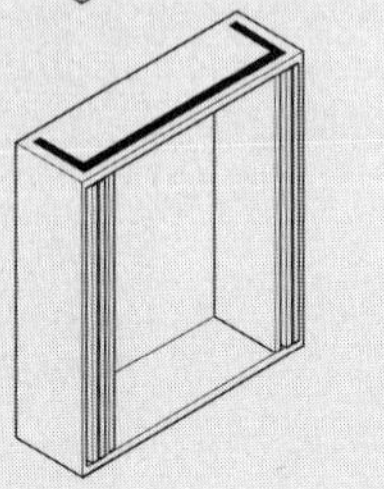

Supplementary fittings for Hawa Folding Turnaway 25/X2 and 35/X3

Version	Cat. No.
right hand	407.73.064
left hand	407.73.162

Packing: 1 set with mounting hardware and installation instructions

Dimensional data not binding. We reserve the right to alter specifications without notice.

Dimensions in mm
Inches approximate

Freeswing Sliding and Pivoting/Sliding Door Fitting

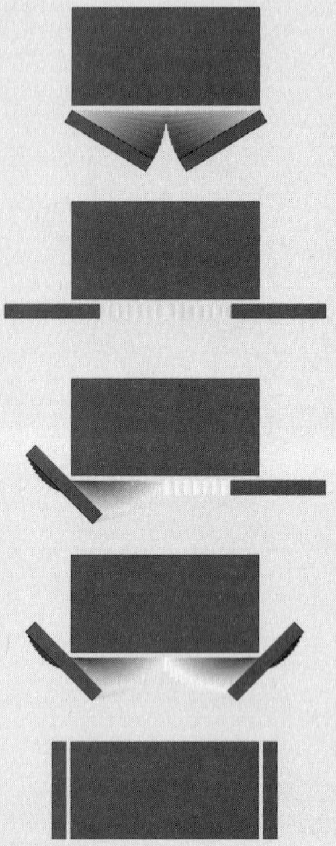

Freeswing offers completely new and exciting design possibilities. The cabinet space can be fully used; no door offset, no part of the door encroaches on the interior as the doors are opened completely outside the cabinet.

- The pivot bearings can be screwed into the Varianta 32 hole system.
- The fitting is suitable for variable door heights, steel pipes and profile rail can be conveniently shortened.
- Running tracks and toothed rails can be shortened in accordance with the door width
- Adjustment is possible by means of the adjusting eccentric in toothed rails and slots in the running tracks.

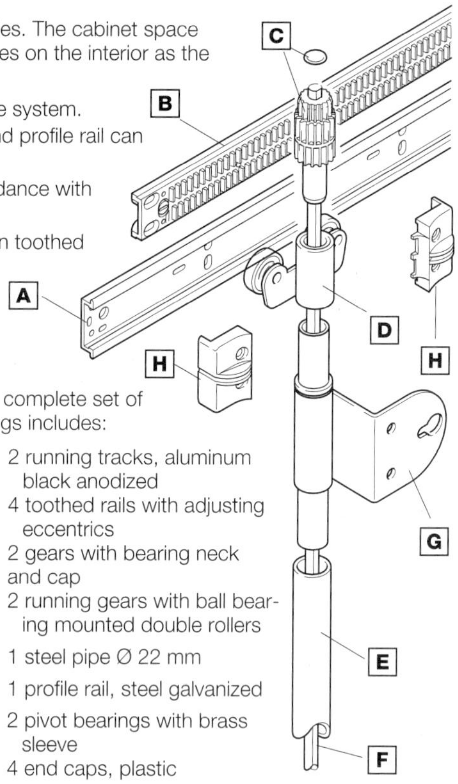

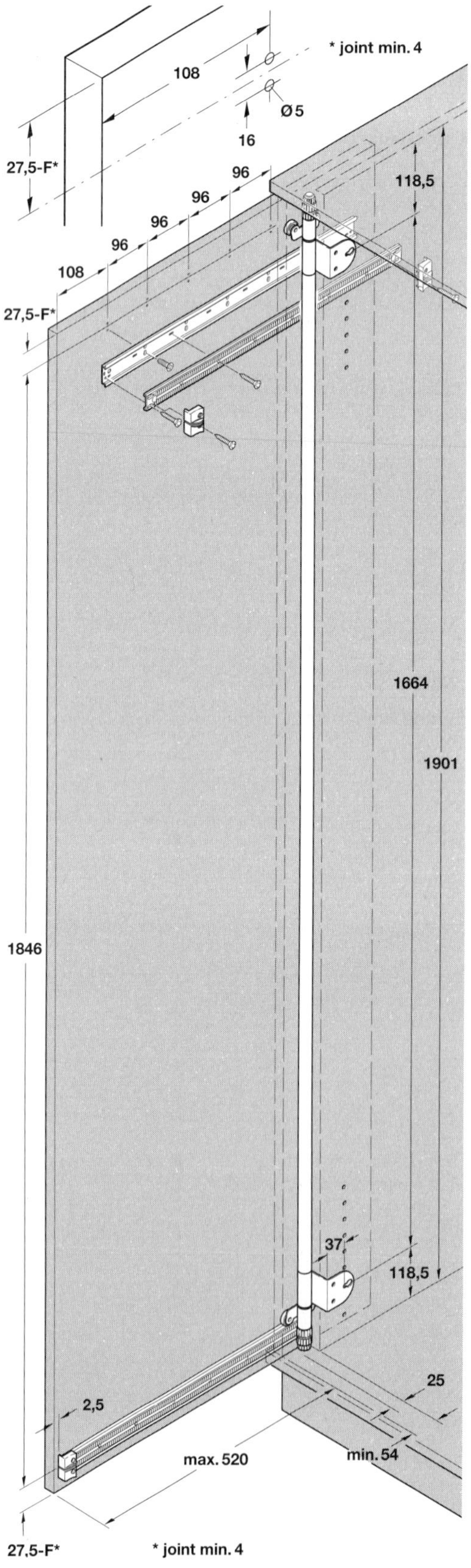

The complete set of fittings includes:

- **A** 2 running tracks, aluminum black anodized
- **B** 4 toothed rails with adjusting eccentrics
- **C** 2 gears with bearing neck and cap
- **D** 2 running gears with ball bearing mounted double rollers
- **E** 1 steel pipe Ø 22 mm
- **F** 1 profile rail, steel galvanized
- **G** 2 pivot bearings with brass sleeve
- **H** 4 end caps, plastic

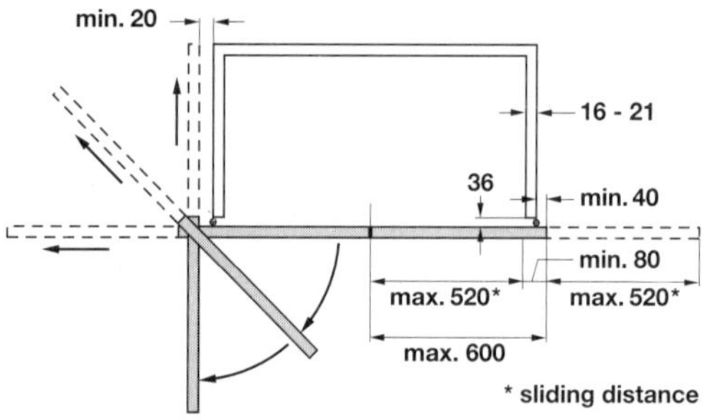

The doors can be simultaneously operated

- **as pivoting doors**
- **as sliding doors**
- **and as pivoting/sliding doors**

Important:
other installation heights are possible by cutting the steel pipe E and the profile rail F to length within a **32 mm** grid.

max. installation height:
1901 mm (75")
max. panel width:
600 mm (24")
weight capacity per door:
30 kg (66 lbs.)

Finish:
steel parts: gray metallic plastic-coated
plastic parts: black

Cat. No.	408.23.540

Packing: 1 set
for 1 panel including assembly instructions and fastening materials

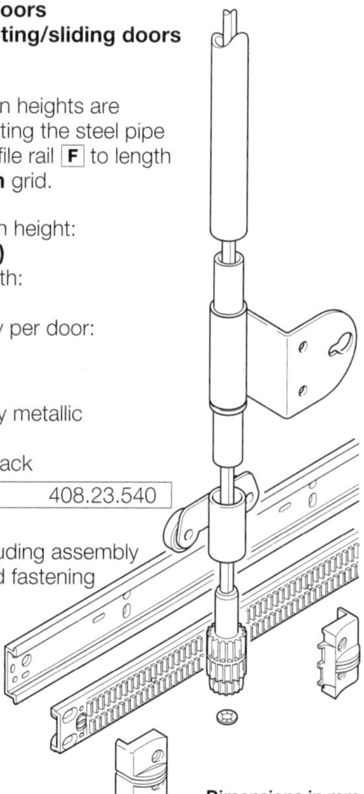

Dimensions in mm
Inches are approximate

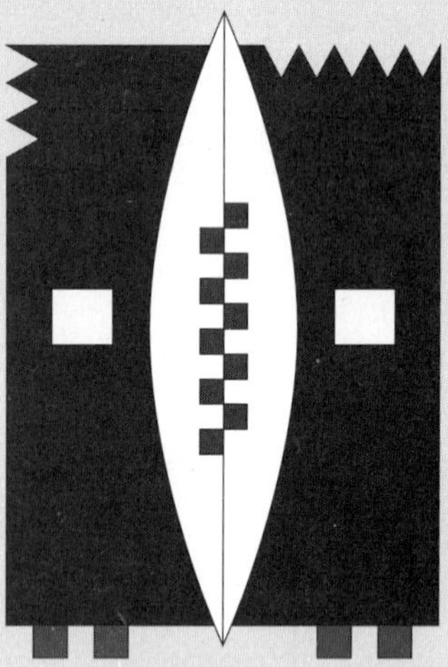

Dimensional data not binding. We reserve the right to alter specifications without notice.

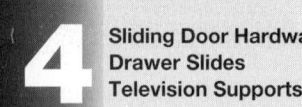

Control Arm for Folding Doors

- For folding doors
- Operates without running tracks or guides
- 32 mm compatible
- Can be used left or right
- **Hinges must be ordered separately**

Guide Levers for Folding Doors

Screw-mounted.
To be used with **120°-135°** hinges
Length: 413 mm (16¼")
Minimum installation depth: 320 mm (12⅝")
Finish: Flat steel rod, nickel-plated
Material dimension: 10 x 2.5 mm

Cat. No.	409.40.700

Packing: 50 pcs.

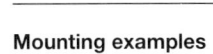

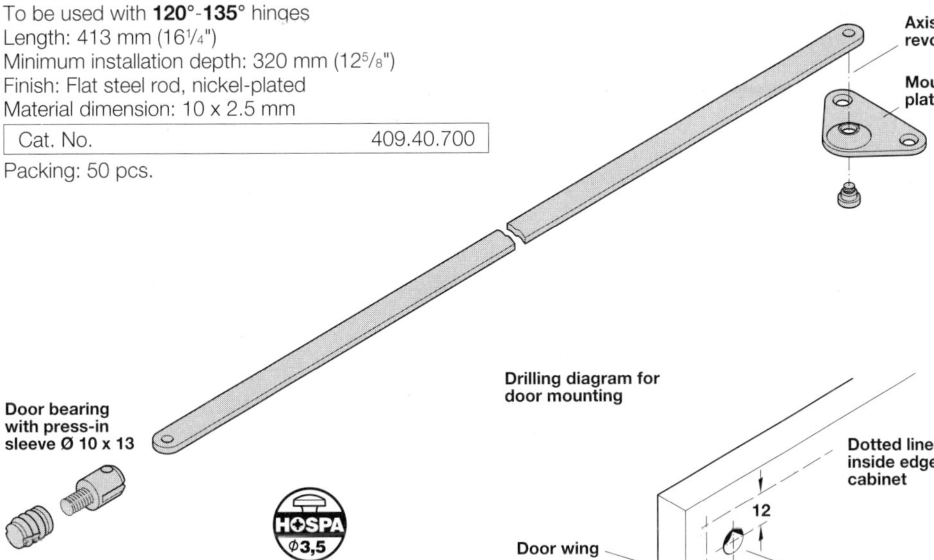

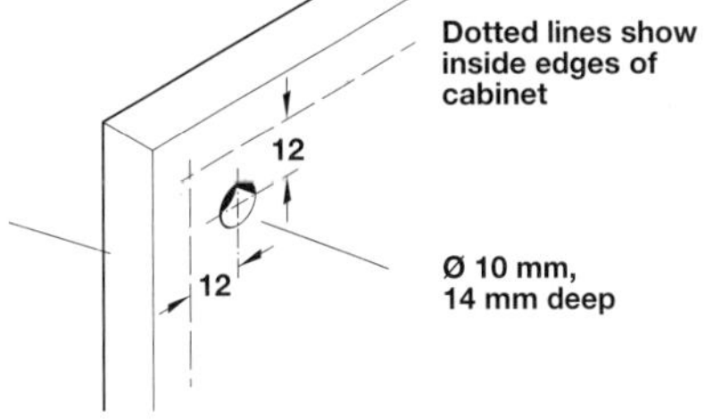

Guide Levers for Folding Doors

Screw-mounted.
To be used with wide angle hinges of **170°** hinges
Length: 397 mm (15⅝")
Minimum installation depth: 330 mm (13")
Finish: Flat steel rod, nickel-plated
Material dimension: 14 x 3 mm

Cat. No.	409.40.710

Packing: 50 pcs.

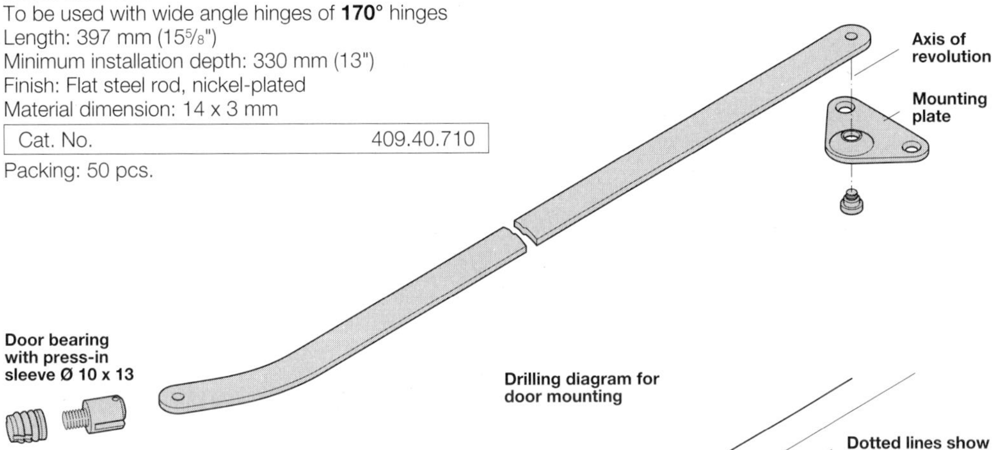

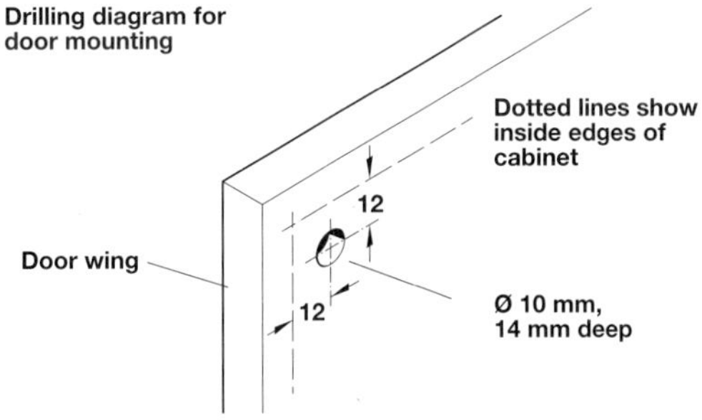

Sliding Door Hardware
Drawer Slides
Television Supports
4

Mounting tips:

- Both door wings must have the same width: 300 mm per wing (for wider doors, a test installation is necessary)
- Mount guide lever to the folding door (see diagram)
- Mark arc "a" with the guide lever while the door is closed
- Mark arc "b" with the guide lever while the door is open all the way
- Arc intersection "c" is the exact rotational axis of the guide lever, and it is the point where the axis is to be screw-mounted
- Hang the guide lever in place and secure with a nut.

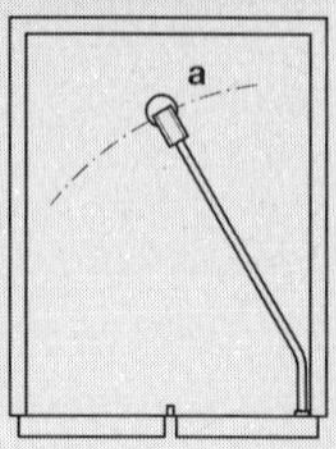

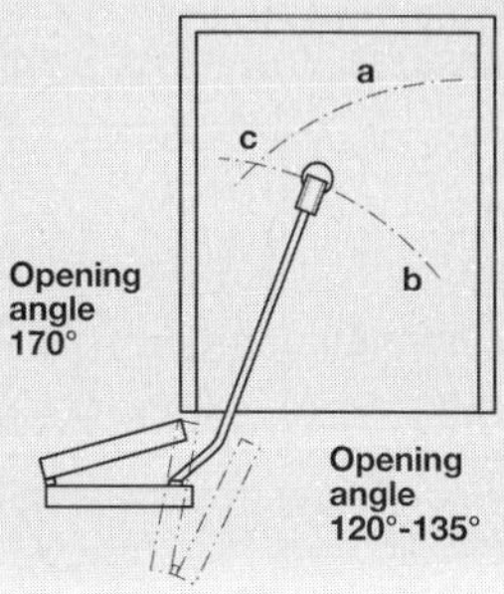

Mounting examples

a) single

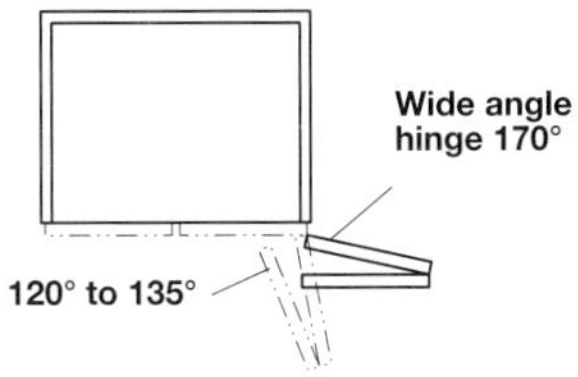

b) double doors

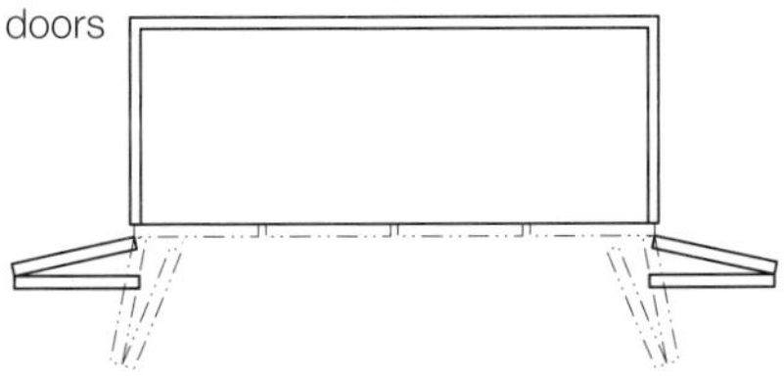

c) corner cabinet

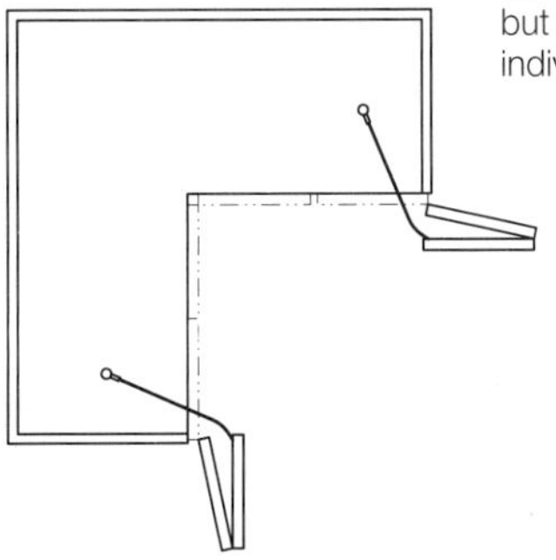

For corner mounting:

Winged doors with 45° mitred front edges will bump into each other, but may be opened individually.

Dimensional data not binding.
We reserve the right to alter specifications without notice.

Dimensions in mm

HÄFELE

Control arm for folding doors

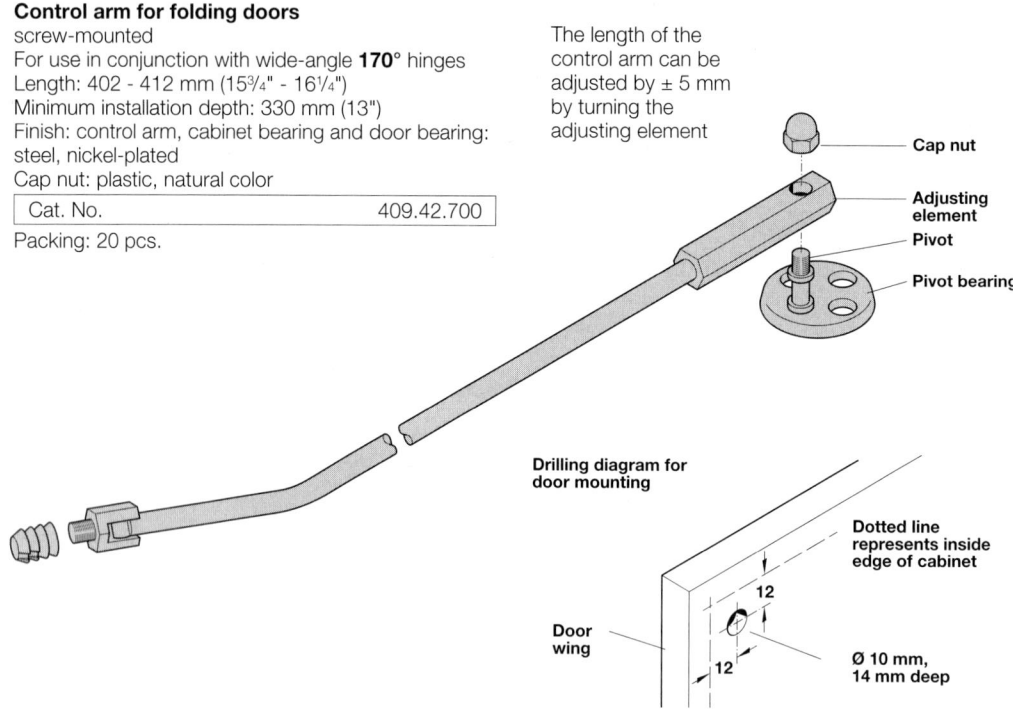

- For folding doors
- Operates without running tracks or guides
- 32 mm compatible
- Can be used left or right
- **Hinges must be ordered separately**
- M6 insert must be ordered separately. See page **0.15**

Control arm for folding doors
screw-mounted
For use in conjunction with wide-angle **170°** hinges
Length: 402 - 412 mm (15¾" - 16¼")
Minimum installation depth: 330 mm (13")
Finish: control arm, cabinet bearing and door bearing: steel, nickel-plated
Cap nut: plastic, natural color

Cat. No.	409.42.700

Packing: 20 pcs.

The length of the control arm can be adjusted by ± 5 mm by turning the adjusting element

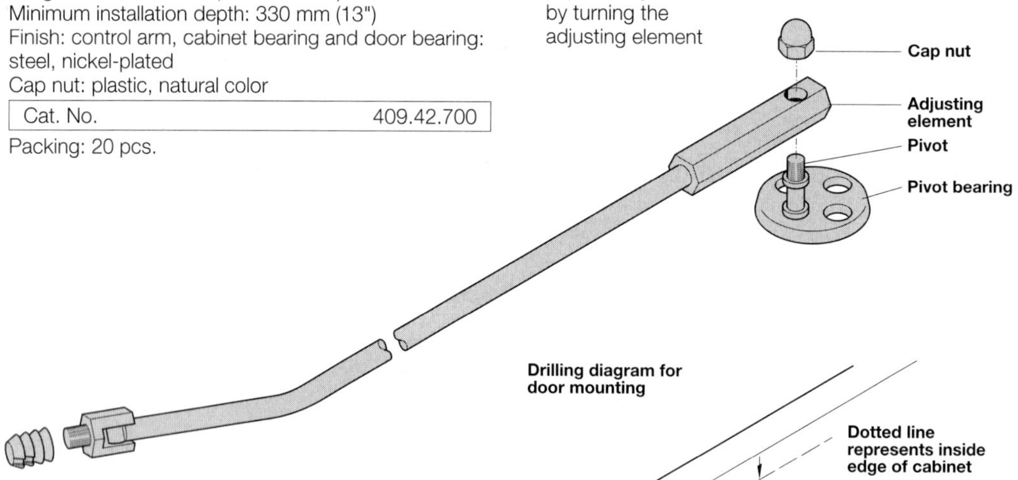

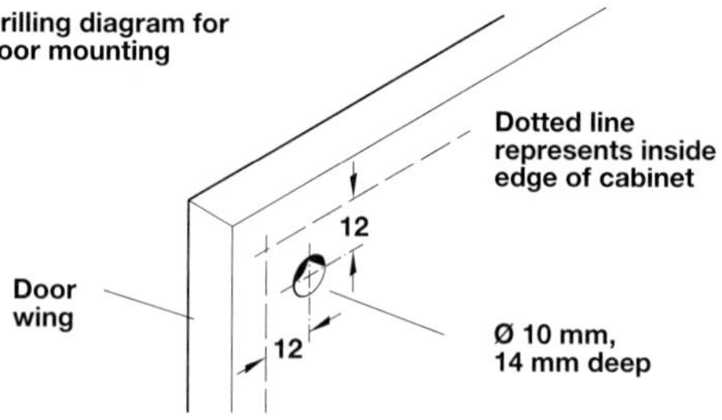

Installation:
- both door panels must be of the same width and should not exceed 300 mm (if wider doors are to be used, a trial installation is necessary)
- mount control arm to folding door (see drilling diagram)
- with door closed, mark arc „a" with control arm
- with door fully open, mark arc „b" with control arm
- screw-mounting of countrol arm pivot at intersection „c" of the arcs
- mount control arm and secure with cap nut

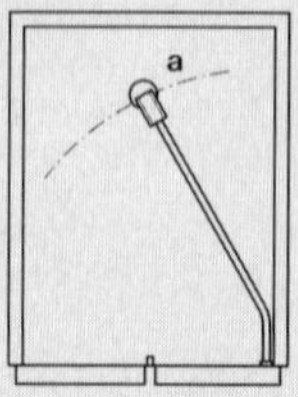

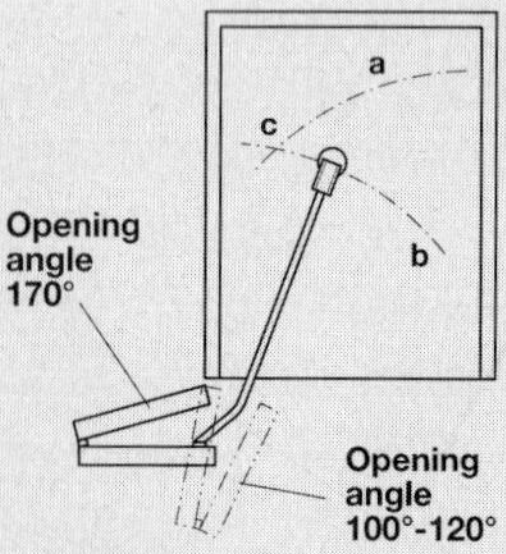

Typical installations

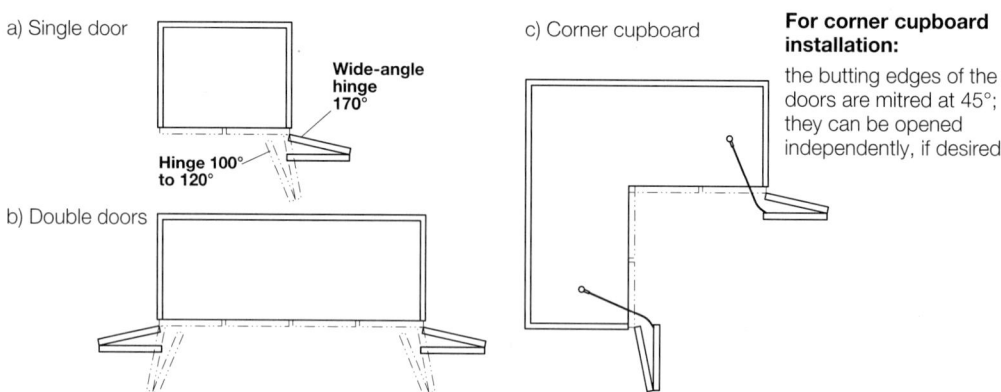

a) Single door

b) Double doors

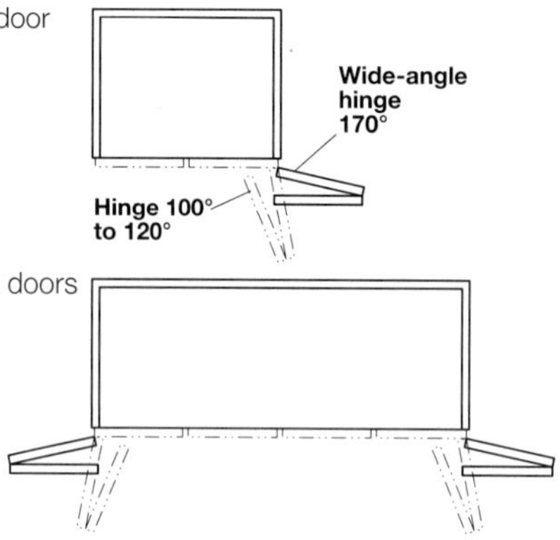

c) Corner cupboard

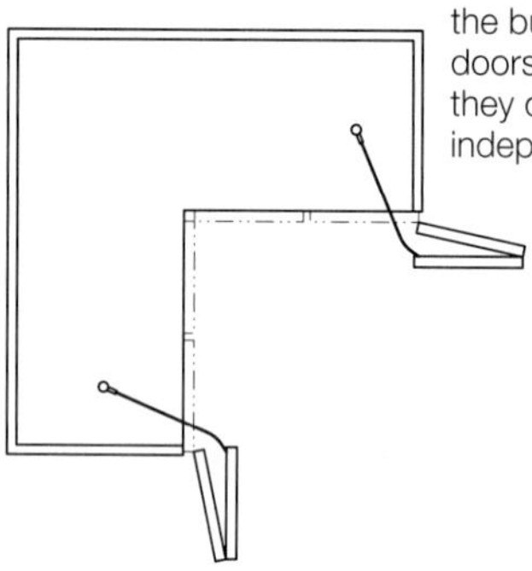

For corner cupboard installation:
the butting edges of the doors are mitred at 45°; they can be opened independently, if desired.

Folding Door System for Cabinet Doors

HÄFELE

Door Guide Bolt
Fits in 35 mm holes

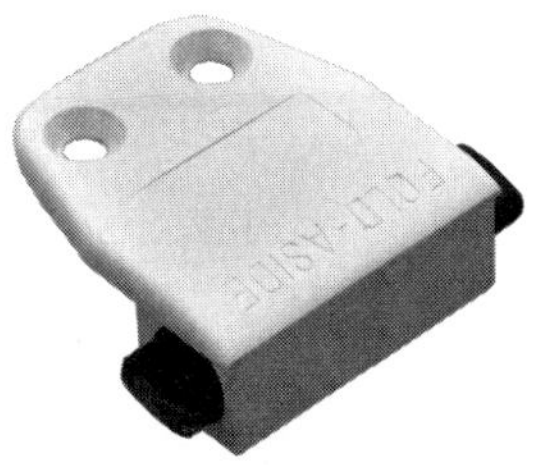

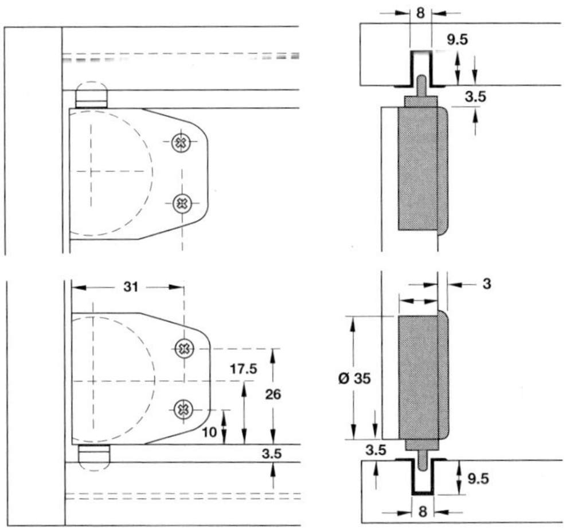

Finish: plastic

Cat. No.		
	white	404.02.702
	brown	404.02.104

Packing: 100 pcs.

Adjustable Stop Pin

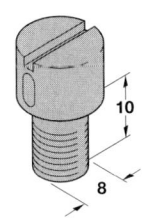

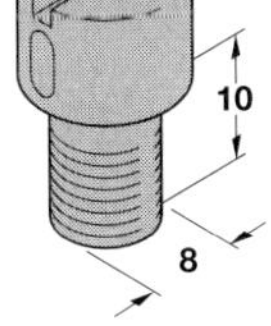

Finish: plastic, black

Cat. No.	404.02.391

Packing: 100 pcs.

Guide Tracks, 7 mm

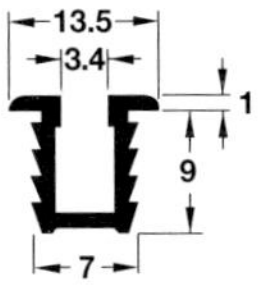

Finish: plastic

Cat. No.		
	white	404.14.702
	brown	404.14.110

Packing: 30 meters in lengths of 3 m (118")

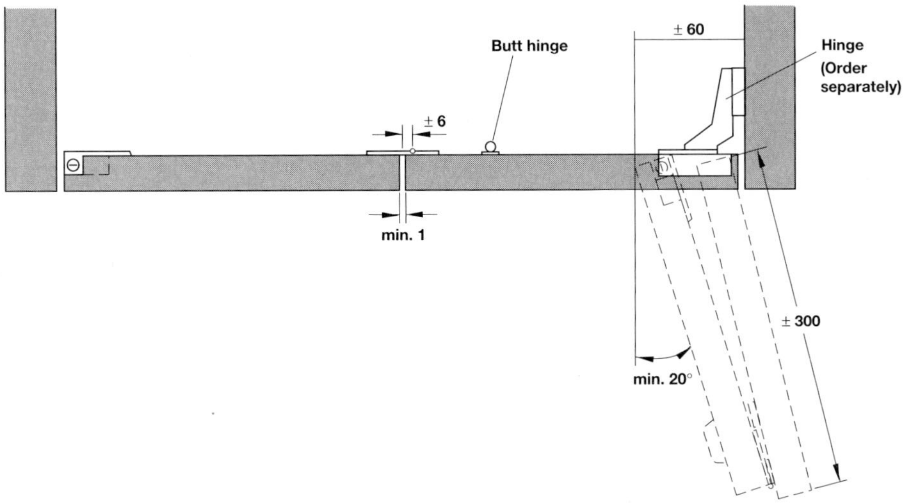

Wide-angle Hinge, for mounting folding doors.

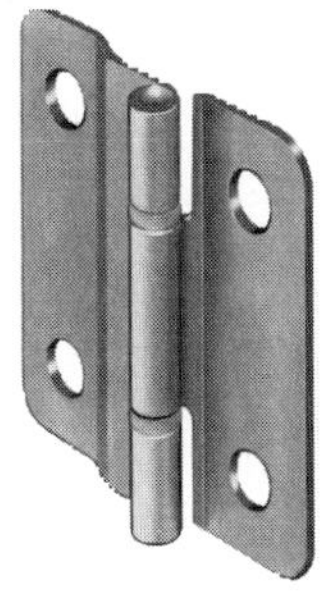

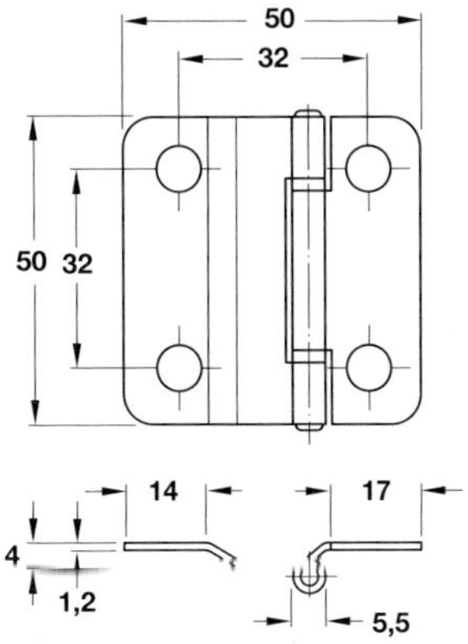

With riveted pin and plastic friction bearings.
Finish: steel, galvanized
Friction bearing: white, plastic

Cat. No.	354.15.911

Packing: 500 pcs.

Dimensions in mm

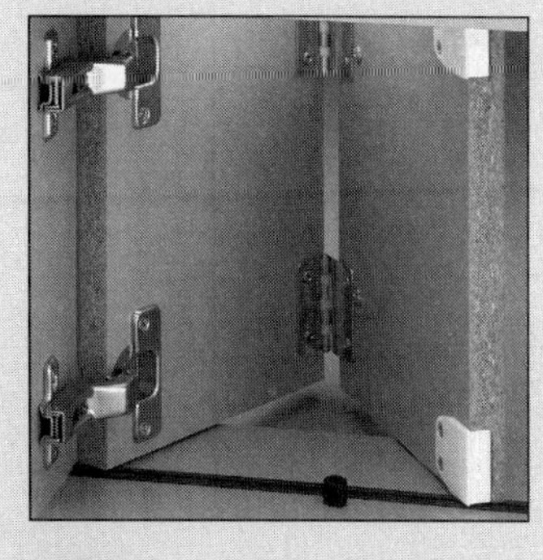

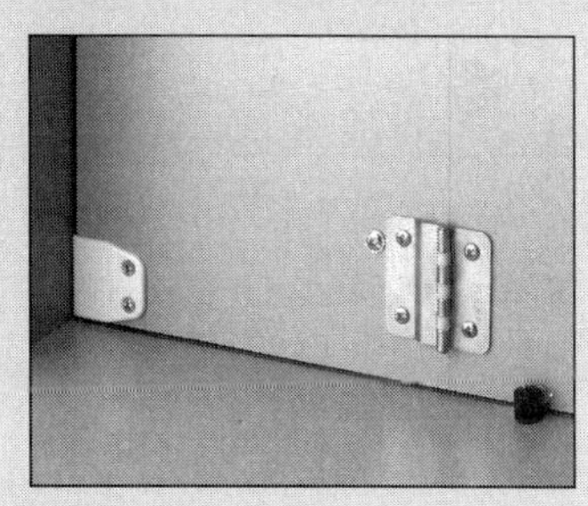

- Inexpensive solution for doors up to **16 kg (35 lbs)**
- Standard drilling dimensions make easy to install ø 35 mm
- Combines the function of hinged and ruding doors which provide easy access to the cabinet.

- **Light weight system for pairs of inset door leaves only.**
- **Application:** Ideal for caravan and mobile home manufacturers.
- **Range**
  Maximum door panel weight
  4 kg (9 lbs.)
  Maximum door thickness
  19 mm (3/4")
  Maximum door panel height
  1 m (36 3/8")
  Maximum door panel width
  300 mm (11 3/4")

Fastening screws:
Varianta special screws
countersunk head
with PZ 2 cross-slots
Finish: steel, nickel-plated

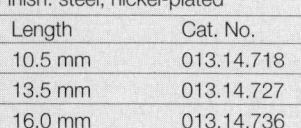

Length	Cat. No.
10.5 mm	013.14.718
13.5 mm	013.14.727
16.0 mm	013.14.736

Packing: 100 or 1000 pcs.

HÄFELE

Leporello Folding Cabinet Door Fitting

The Leporello system is designed for **front-hung folding cabinet doors.**

Load-carrying capacity:
25 kg (55 lbs.) per running gear, for wood thickness from 16 mm (5/8")

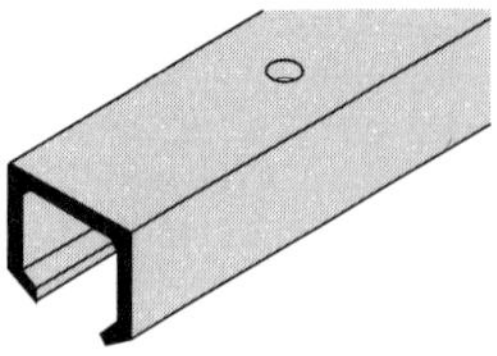

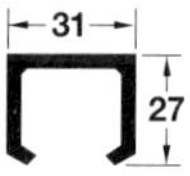

Upper track
Pre-drilled for mounting screws

Finish: aluminum, unfinished

Cat. No.	409.25.924

Packing: in 6 m lengths

Installation note:
Drill recess as shown. Mount fittings in track. Press-fit hinges into recesses and secure with fastening screws.

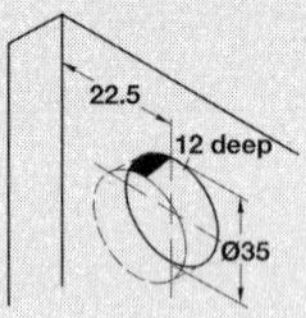

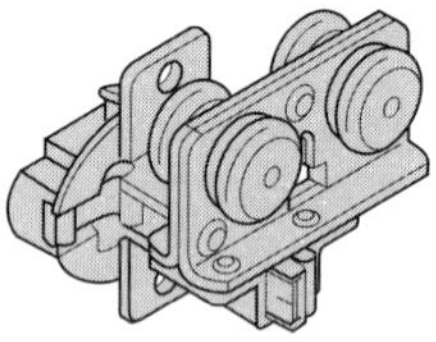

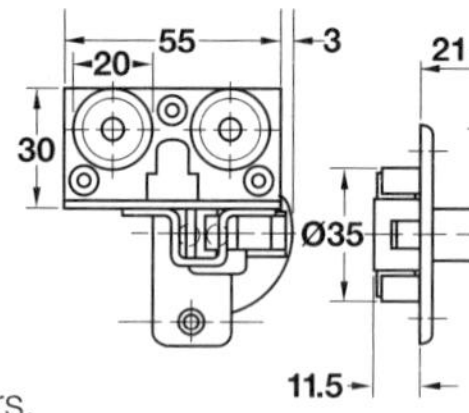

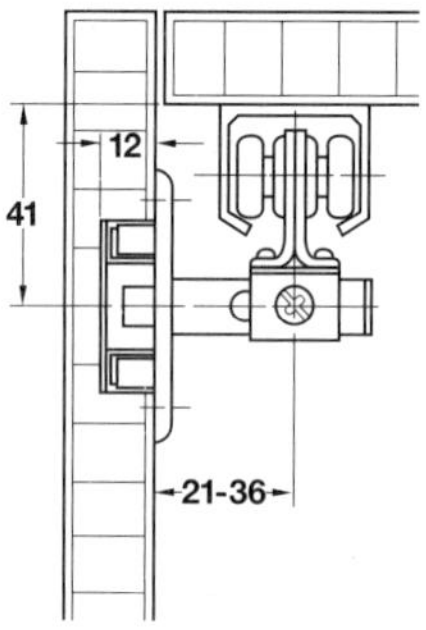

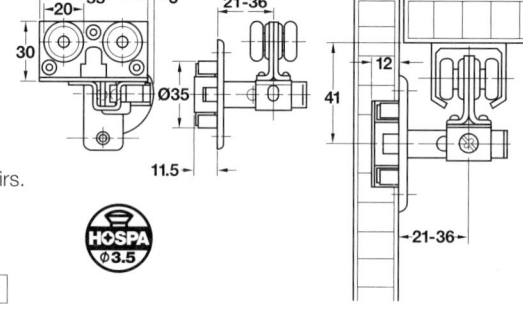

Suspension fitting
With ball-bearing mounted nylon rollers, in tandem pairs.
Boss-type hinge mounting for machine installation.
Reversible from right to left.

Finish: aluminum, unfinished

Cat. No.	409.26.921

Packing: 10 pcs.

4 Sliding Door Hardware
Drawer Slides
Television Supports

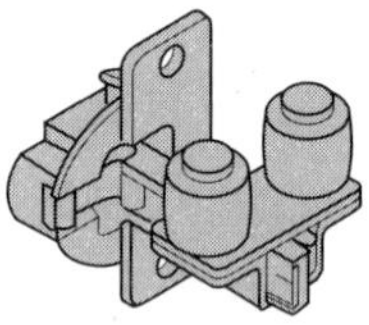

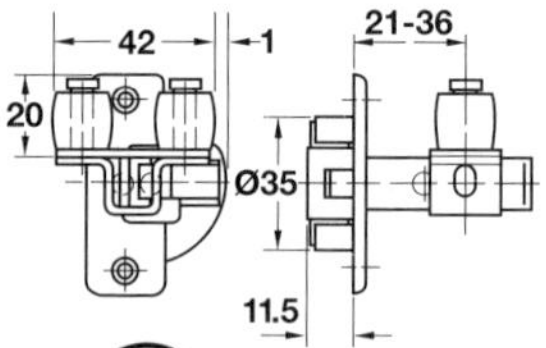

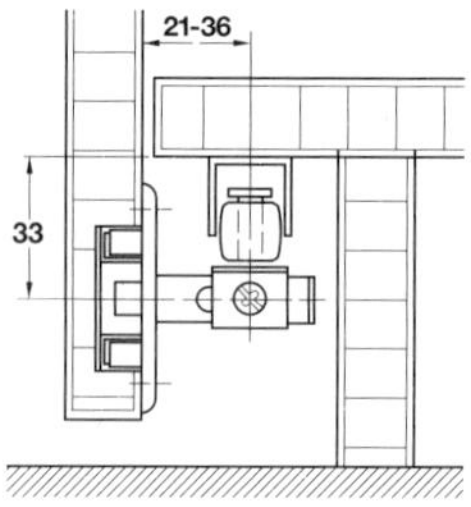

Guide fitting
With friction bearing mounted nylon rollers in pairs.
Boss-type hinge mounting for machine installation.
Reversible from right to left.

Finish: steel galvanized

Cat. No.	409.27.928

Packing: 10 pcs.

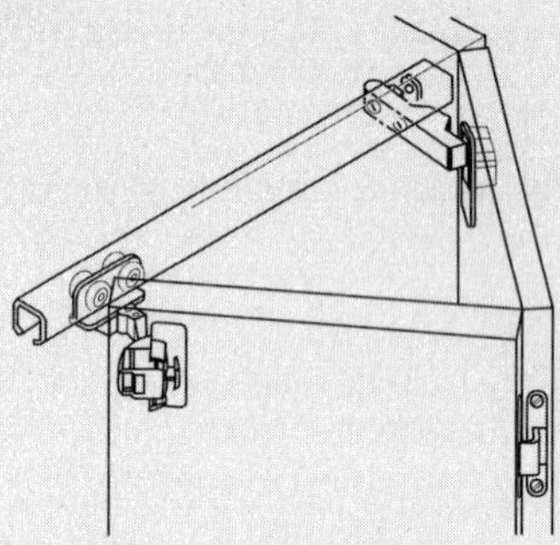

Install door leaves as shown.
Maximum 2 leaves per side.

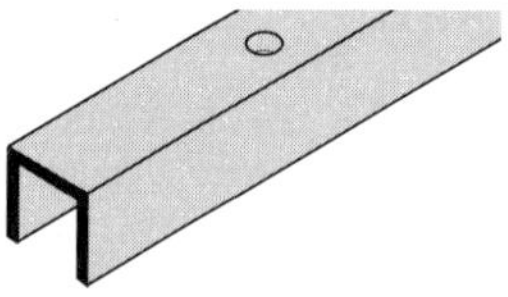

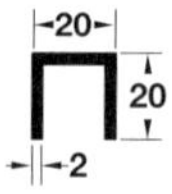

Lower track
Pre-drilled for mounting screws.
Fastens to underside of cupboard floor.

Finish: aluminum, unfinished

Cat. No.	409.25.979

Packing: in 6 m lengths

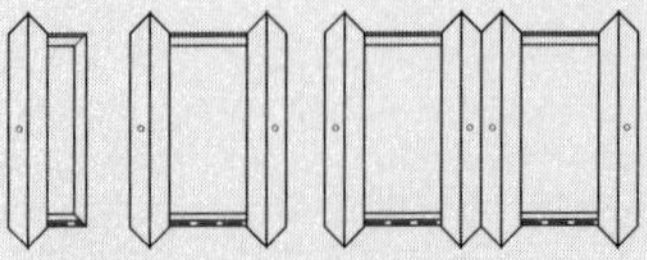

Applications:
Doors can be appropriately matched to architectural and functional demands.
Any type of layout is feasible, e.g. doors attached to left and/or right hand side panels, or twin installations, as shown.
For side panel mountings, boss-type hinges with straight arms should be used. Center panel mountings require cranked hinges.

Typical installation of four-leaf cabinet door (opening to both sides)

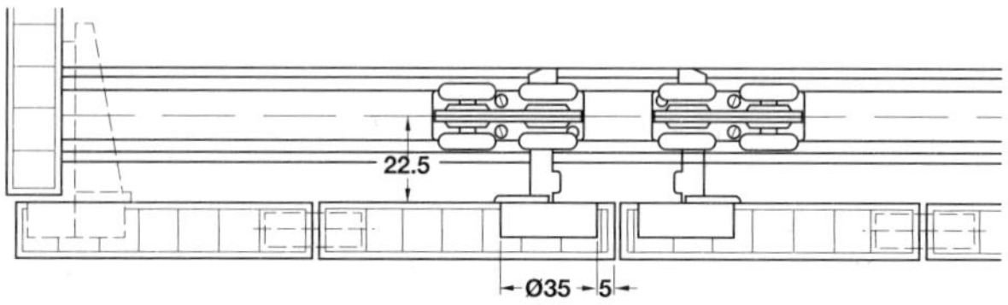

Typical installation of two-leaf cabinet door (opening to one side)

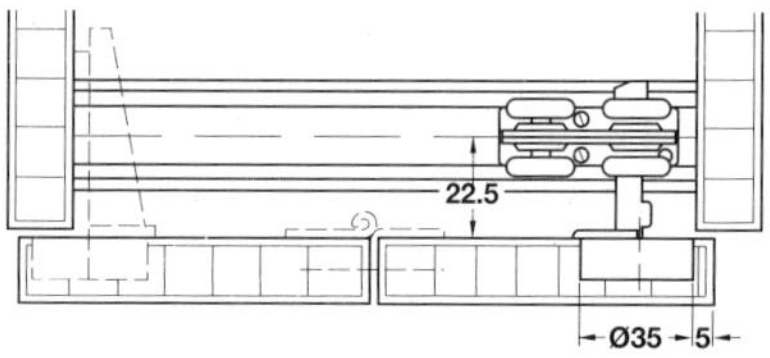

Mounting method varies with type of hinge

The hinges required to fasten the door leaves together appear on page **3.63-3.64** (concealed type) or page **3.75** (screw-mounted butt hinges).

Dimensional data not binding. We reserve the right to alter specifications without notice.

Dimensions in mm

Hawa Bifold 40 Sliding Door Fitting

Hawa Bifold 40 is a new development, based on the well established construction of the Junior 80 sliding door fitting. The Bifold 40 is a high-quality folding door fitting, created especially for large accessible wall units or closets in the home, as well as for wall partitions. The fitting is easy to install, because it requires no grooving or rabbeting.

1 Complete Set, for a 2 piece folding door includes the following components:

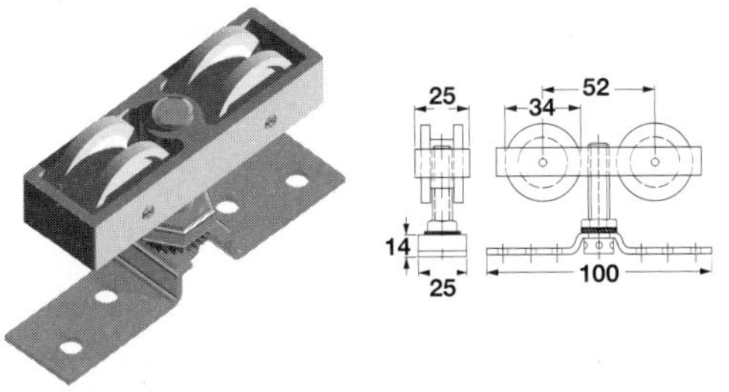

Running Gear, 1 unit, high-grade polyamide tandem rollers with sleeve bearings,aluminum carriage and zinc die-cast mounting plate. Complete with fastening materials.

Fitting Set for single panel

Cat. No.	407.58.003

Packing: 1 set

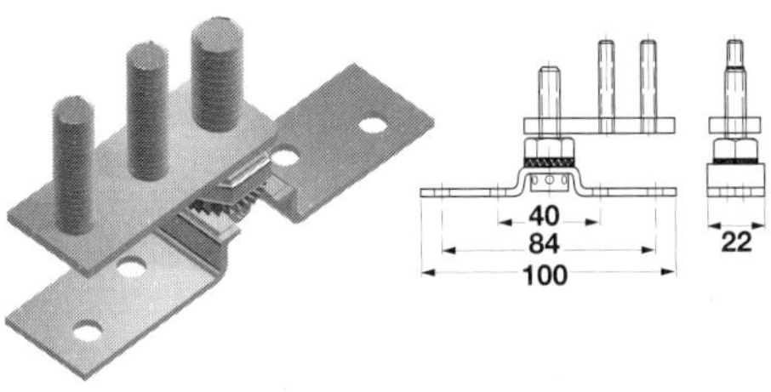

Upper Pivot Hinge, 1 unit consisting of an aluminum support plate with two hex screws 6 x 35 mm to fasten into guide track in a height and side adjustable ± 2 mm mounting bracket with steel pivot bolt.

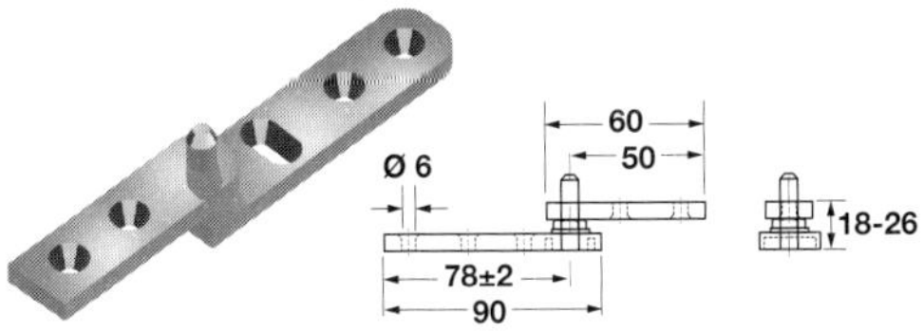

Lower Pivot Hinge, 1 unit consisting of an adjustable ± 2 mm aluminum floor mounting plate with steel pivot bolt and an aluminum door mounting plate.

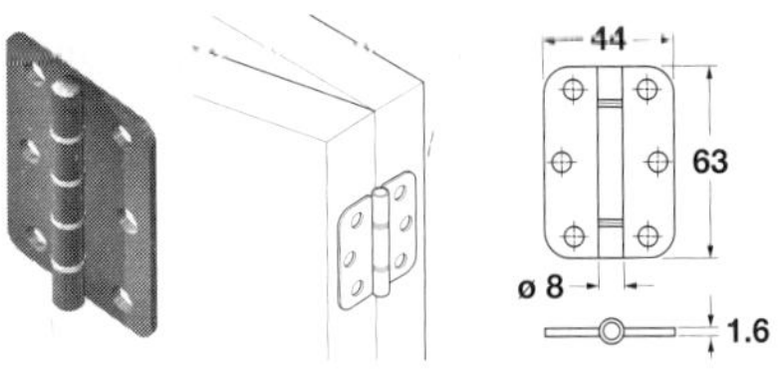

Butt Hinge, 3 units, with removable, galvanized steel pin.

Upper Track and Butt Hinge, ordered separately for set or sets from above:

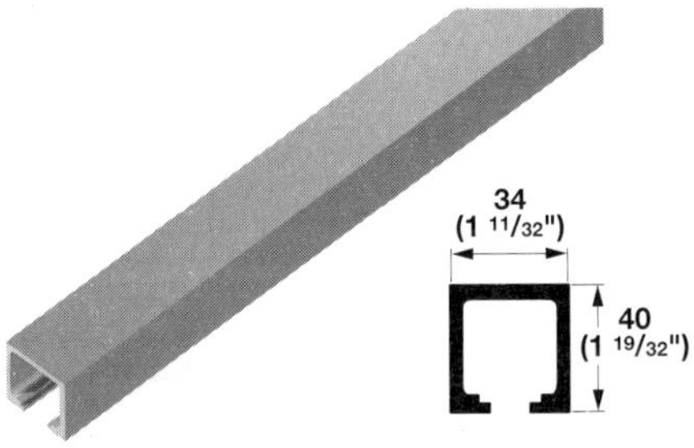

Upper Track, with screw holes.

Finish: aluminum, anodized

Cat. No.		
	1.4 m (4' 7")	407.59.868
	1.6 m (5' 3")	407.59.877
	1.8 m (5' 11")	407.59.886
	2.0 m (6' 7")	407.59.895
	2.2 m (7' 3")	407.59.902
	2.5 m (8' 2")	407.59.911
	3.0 m (9' 10⅛")	407.59.941
	4.0 m (13' 1½")	407.59.951
	6.0 m (19' 8¼")	407.59.931

Packing: 1 pc.

Butt Hinge, 3 units, with removable, galvanized steel pin.

Number of hinges per door panel up to:
2.2 m (86 5/8") = 3 hinges
From 2.2 m (86 5/8")= 4 hinges

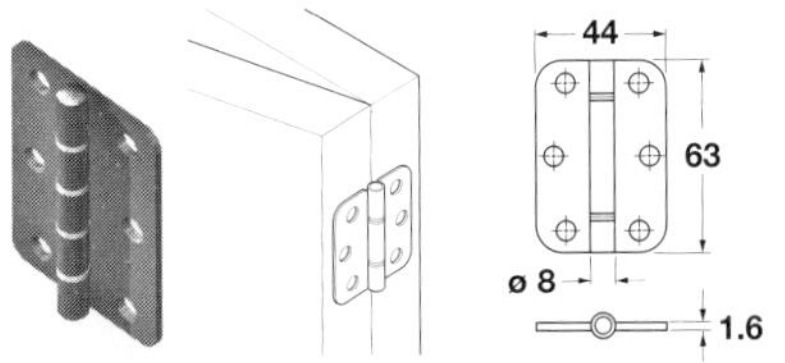

Finish: galvanized steel, nylon bushing

Cat. No.	407.78.989

Packing: 1 pc.

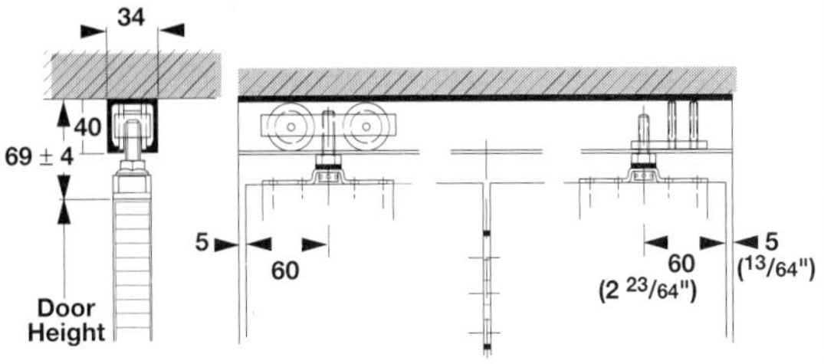

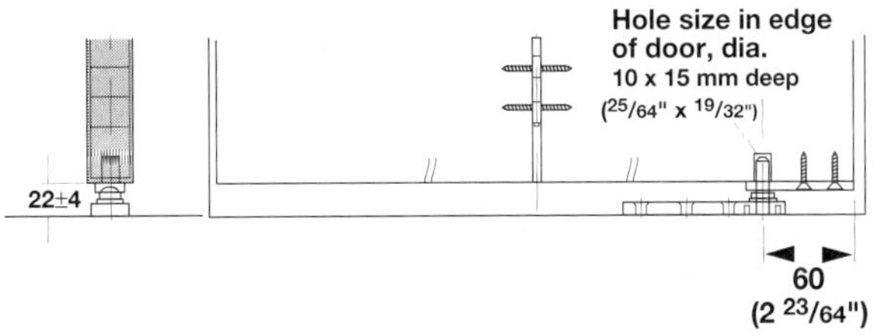

Dimensions in mm
Inches are approximate

HÄFELE

Weights up to 40 kg (88 lbs.) / per panel Wood Thicknesses from 25 mm (1") Max. Door Width 1.2 m (47¼")

Sliding Door Hardware
Drawer Slides
Television Supports
4

- High load capacity
  Maximum panel weight - 40 kg/88 lbs
- All fittings are surface-mounted
  No rabbeting or grooving required.
- Non-corrosive, maintenance-free precision running gear ensure a smooth and silent run.
- No bottom tracks required, only a lower pivot hinge: closets are easily accessible.
- The hardware is left = right interchangeable.

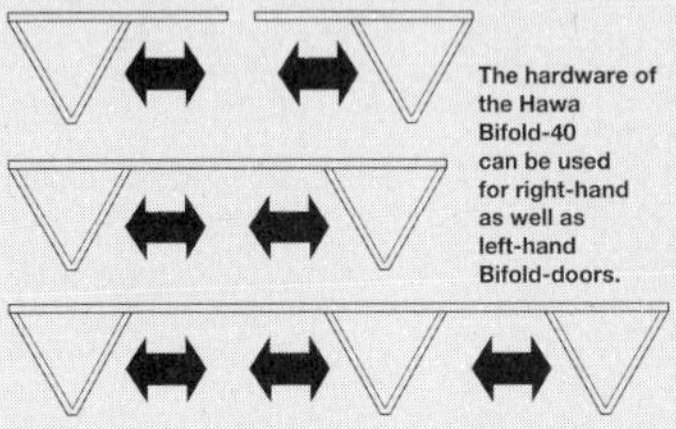

The hardware of the Hawa Bifold-40 can be used for right-hand as well as left-hand Bifold-doors.

Dimensional data not binding. We reserve the right to alter specifications without notice.

HÄFELE

Rollenda® Folding Door Fitting

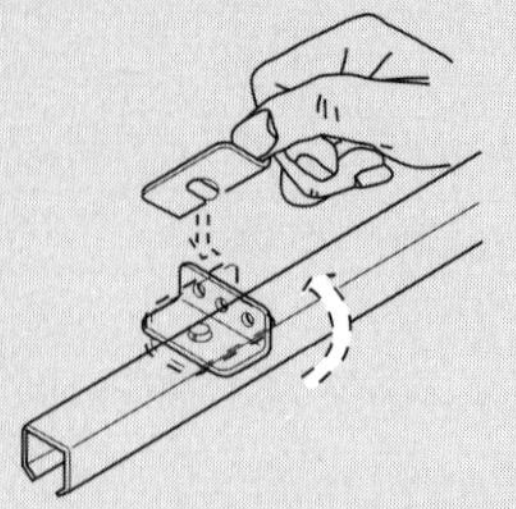

The upper track is designed for wall mounting, if required, with the aid of the mounting bracket. This is attached to the track by inserting the lug in the track aperture at the right angles, then turning the bracket into line with the track to make it secure.

Load-carrying capacity:
25 kg (55 lbs) per running gear, for wood thickness from 20 to 26 mm ($^{25}/_{32}$ – 1$^{1}/_{32}$")

4 **Sliding Door Hardware**
Drawer Slides
Television Supports

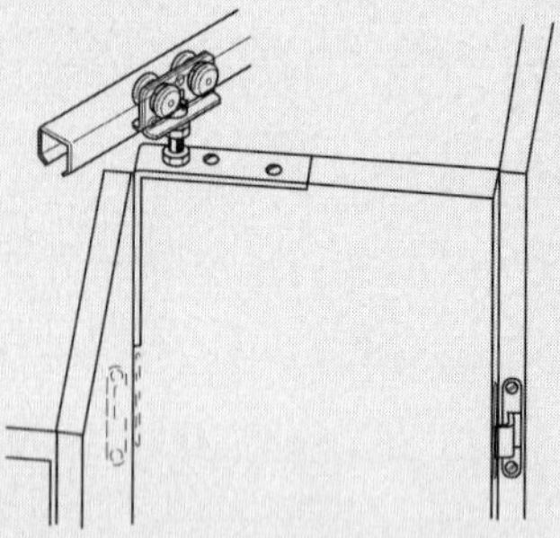

We recommend **Soss hinges** for fastening door leaves together. These can be found in Section **3**.

Upper track
with screw-holes

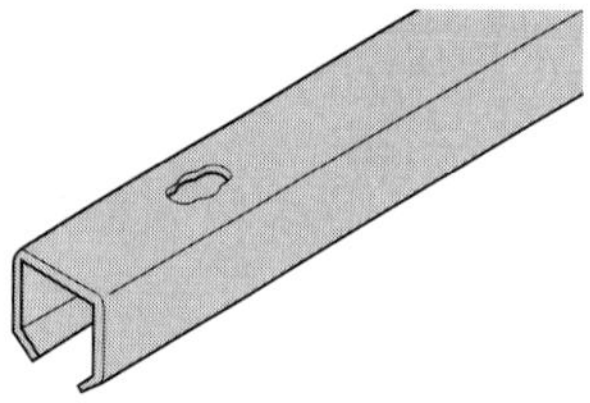

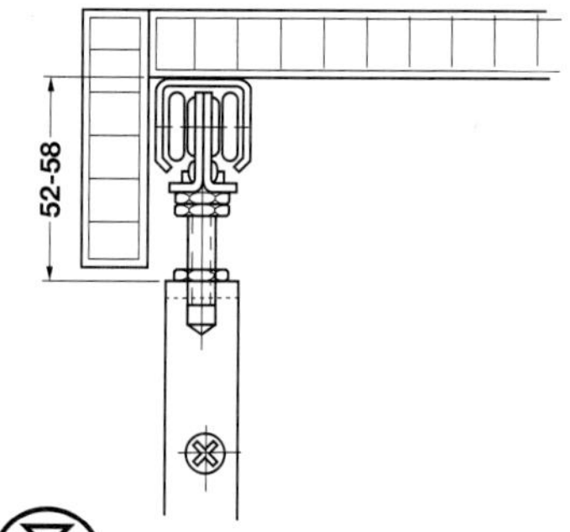

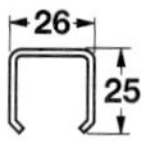

HOSPA Φ6.0

Finish: steel, galvanized

Cat. No.	407.81.904

Packing: in 6 meter lengths

Wall mounting bracket
for upper track

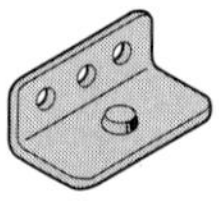

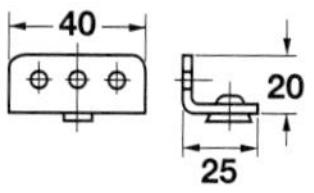

HOSPA Φ4,5

Finish: steel, galvanized

Cat. No.	407.81.995

Packing: 20 pcs.

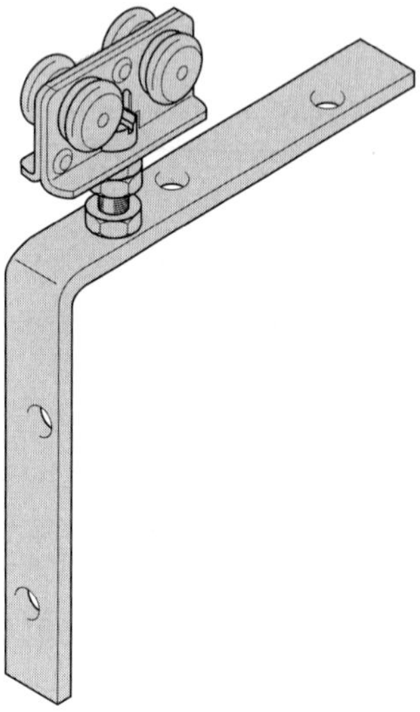

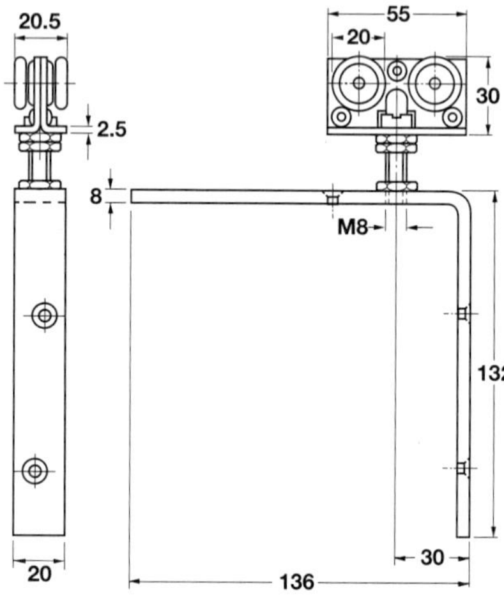

HOSPA Φ4,0

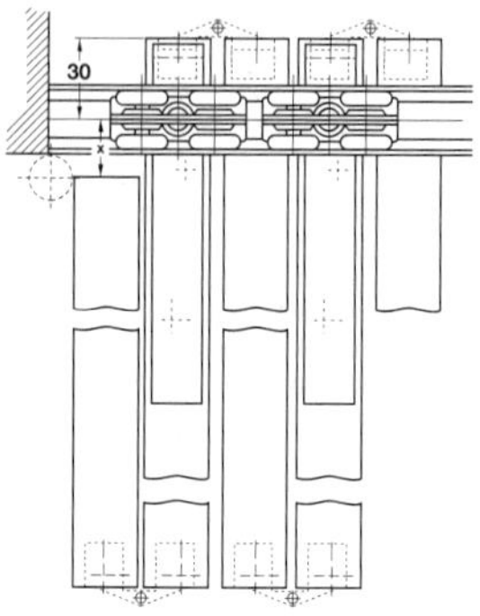

Please note:
the first door leaf (distance a) must **be narrower** than the other leaves (distance b) **by 30 mm plus distance x. Distance x** is calculated as 13 mm (half track width) plus half the diameter of the hinge barrel.

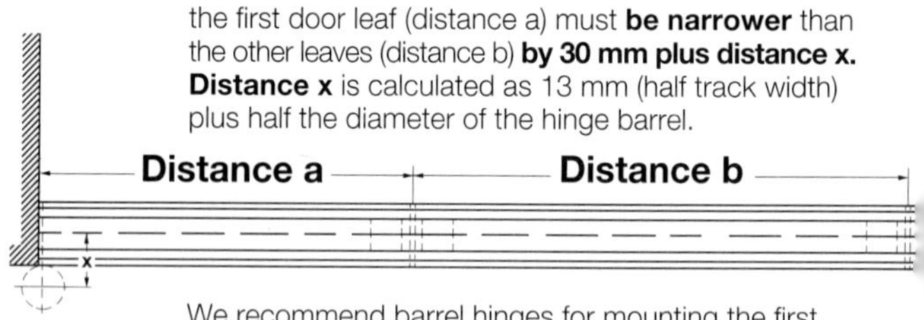

Running gear
with ball bearing-mounted nylon rollers, complete with mounting bracket for attachment to door edge.

Finish: steel, galvanized

Cat. No.	407.89.919

Packing: 1 pc.

We recommend barrel hinges for mounting the first door leaf.

Lower guide
screw-mounted

HOSPA Φ4,0

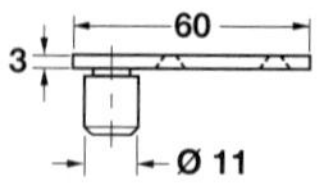

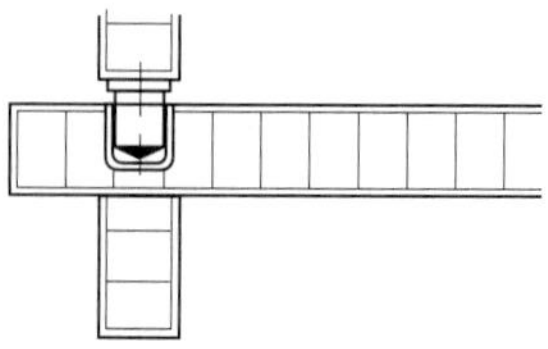

Finish: steel, galvanized, with nylon roller

Cat. No.	407.89.964

Packing: 2 pcs.

Lower guide track
with screw-holes for attachment to cupboard floor

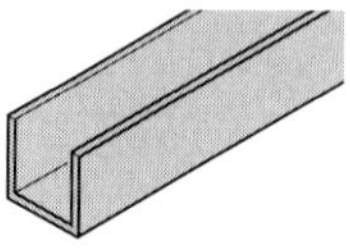

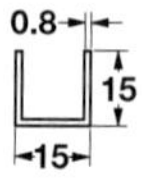

HOSPA Φ3,5

Finish: steel, galvanized

Cat. No.	409.25.960

Packing: in 6 meter lengths

Dimensional data not binding.
We reserve the right to alter specifications without notice.

Dimensions in mm
Inches are approximate

Hawa Planfront 220 Sliding Door Fitting

Hawa Planfront 220 sliding door fitting allows doors to be flush mounted when closed and recessed when opened. For a two-door leaf, a left and right set must be ordered.

1 Complete Set, for a single sliding door includes the following components:

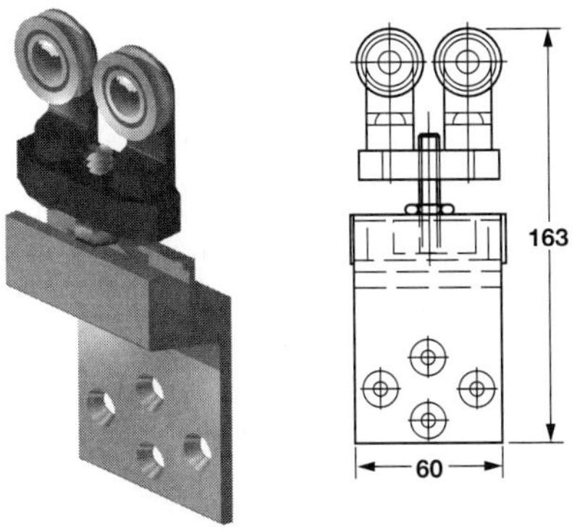

Running Gear, 2 units with ball bearing-mounted rollers, plastic coated, vertically adjustable. complete with mounting plate, carriage and rubber trim caps. Rollers are pivot mounted, and the carriage mount is adjustable in the mounting plate. 35 mm Depth.
Finish: carriage: precision pressure cast, nickel-plated. Mounting plate: aluminum, anodized.

Fitting Set for single sliding door widths up to 1.5 meters (5')

Cat. No.	right opening	407.74.230
	left opening	407.74.338

Packing: 1 pc.

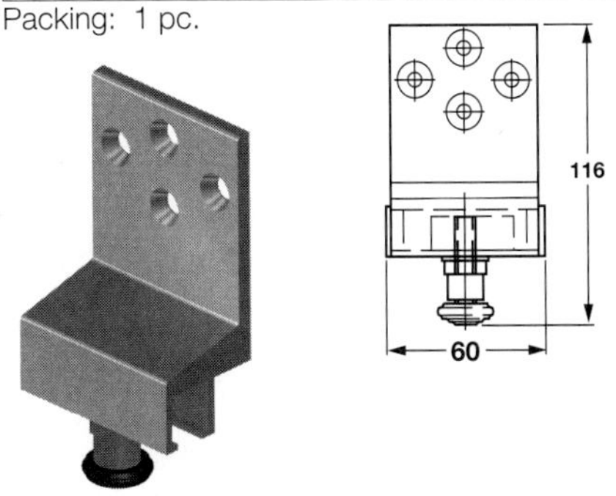

Guide, 1 unit with adjustable roller guide and rubber trim caps. 35 mm Depth.
Finish: aluminum, anodized

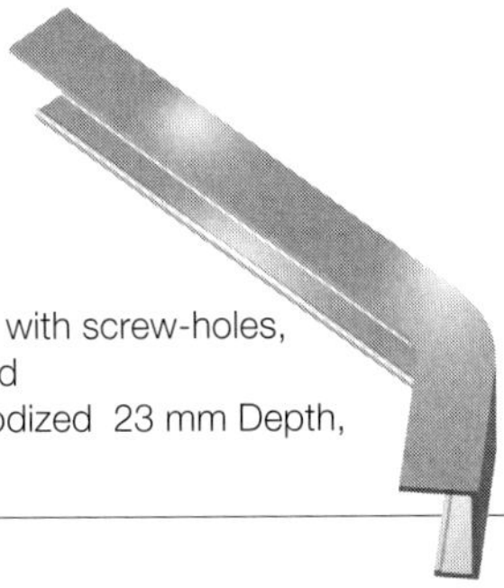

Upper Track, 2 units with screw-holes, pre-curved and aligned
Finish: aluminum, anodized 23 mm Depth, 35 mm Height

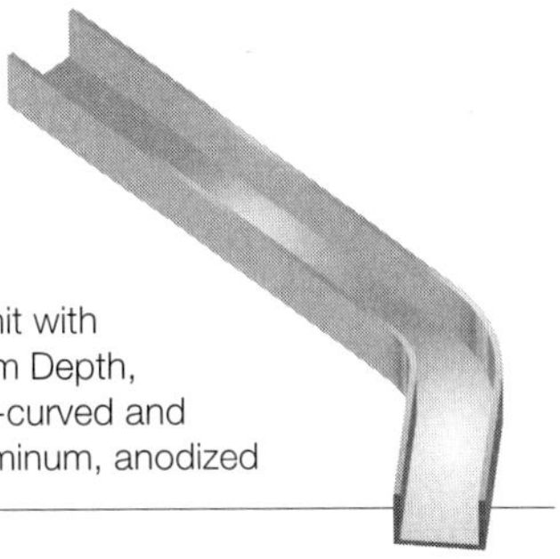

Lower Track, 1 unit with screw-holes, 27 mm Depth, 20 mm Height, pre-curved and aligned Finish: aluminum, anodized

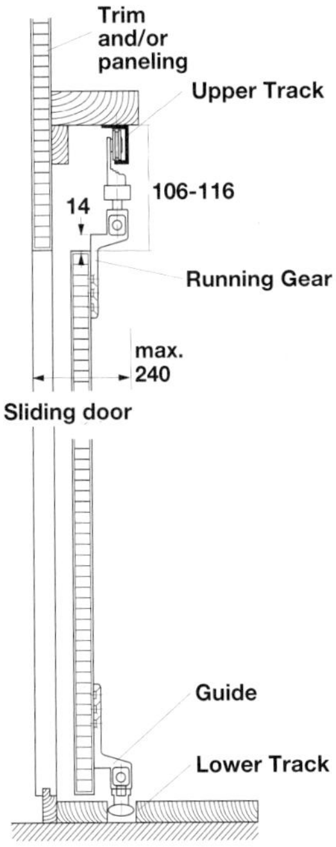

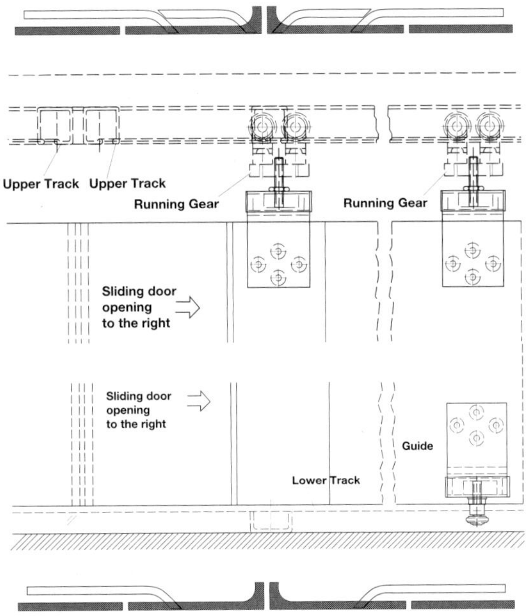

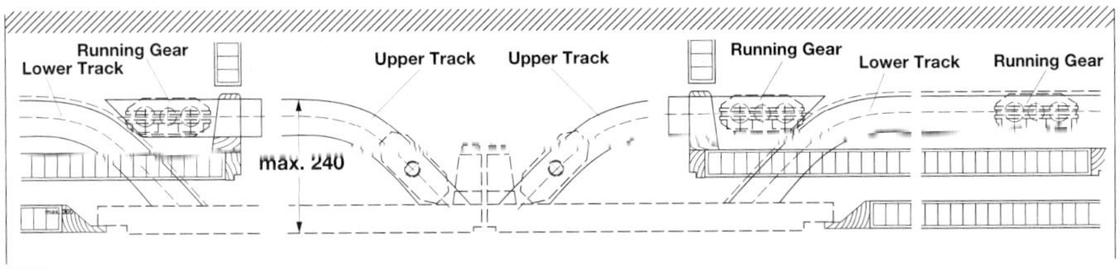

Dimensions in mm
Inches are approximate

Door weights to 70 kg (154 lbs.)
Wood Thicknesses 19 mm (3/4") to 45 mm (1 3/4")
Door panel width 1500 mm (59 1/16")

Ordering note:
The remarks "right opening/left opening" refer to the cabinet as seen from the outside. For two sliding doors, one left and one right opening set should be ordered, appropriate to the door leaf width. Intermediate widths can be accommodated by shortening the upper and lower tracks. For widths larger than 1.5 meters (59 1/16") please inquire.

For detailed mounting instructions and assistance please contact our Architectural Dept. at 1-888-437-7477

HÄFELE

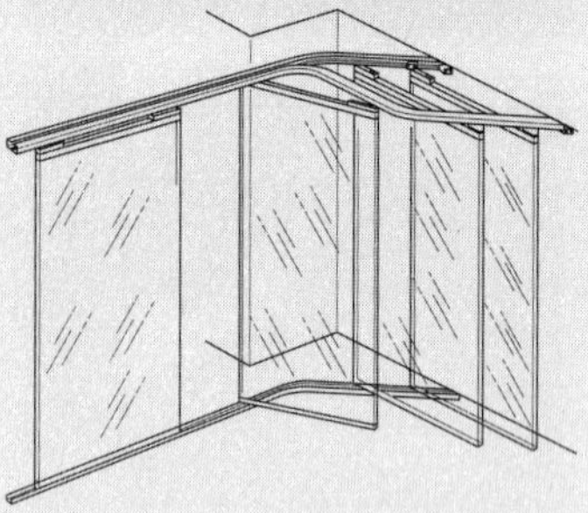

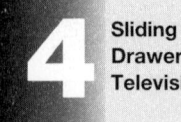

Range of Application
In all places where top quality and quiet operation are a must, e.g., in shopping centers, banks, airports, railway stations, hotels, offices and private residences.

Dimensional data not binding.
We reserve the right to alter specifications without notice.

Hawa Sliding Hardware Systems For Architectural Projects

Our systems allow for multiple panels to slide along a track for parking in a wall recess or against a side wall (see layout options below)

Applications: wood, glass and metal panels

Door Panel weights up to 400 kg (680 lbs)

Special Features of Hawa systems include:
- Extremely smooth running on curved tracks
- Low space requirements in the parking area
- No maintenance after installation

Options Include:
- Aluminum, steel or brass tracks
- Trollys with two point guide facility
- Modular track system
- Glass rail with integrated guide and lock options
- Applications without bottom guide channel

Häfele offers a complete range of architectural hardware for domestic and international projects, along with comprehensive planning and technical services.

Contact the Häfele Architectural Products Group for details at **1-888-437-7477**

Glass

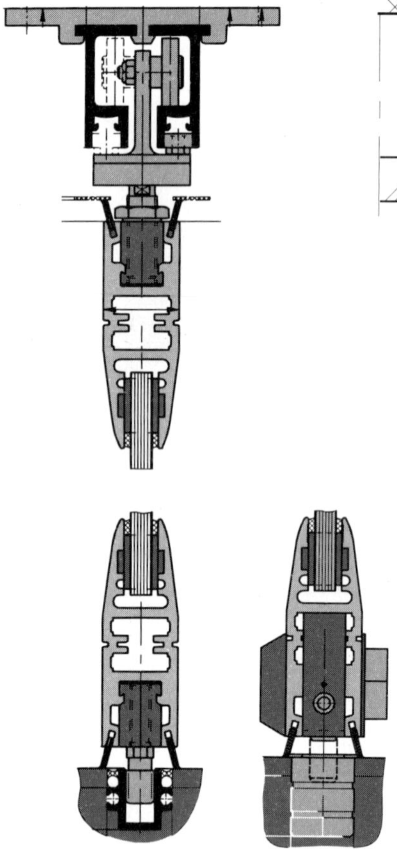

Wood

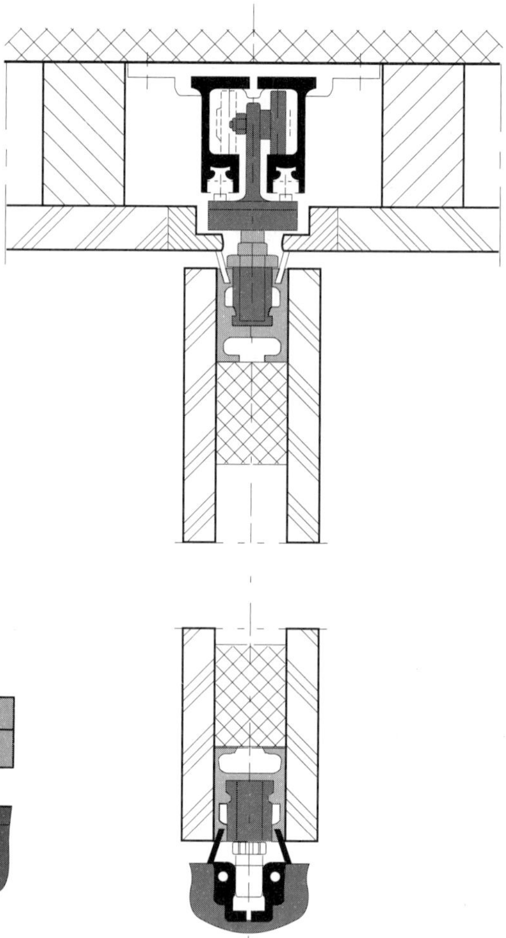

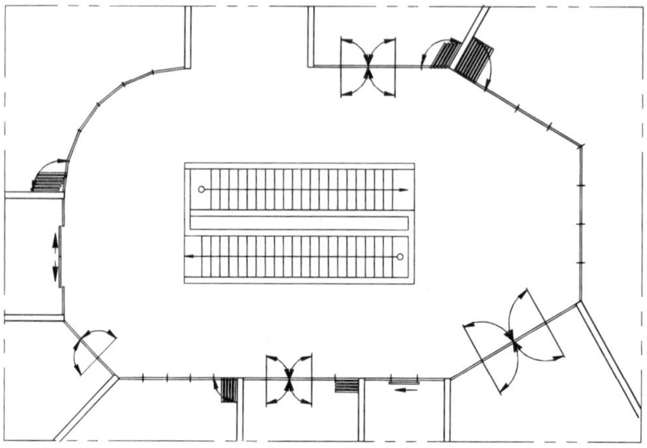

Floorplan Examples

For details and planning assistance contact a Häfele Architectural Product Specialist

Labora Sliding Glass Door Fitting

HÄFELE

For 6 – 8 mm (15/64 – 5/16") glass thickness

- For doors up to 80 cm (31½") in width use 2 runners. The maximum load rating is **15 kg (33 lbs.)** per runner.
- For larger doors, add additional runners.
- We strongly recommend the use of 4 runners for doors wider than 80 cm (31½").
- Runners must be spaced evenly.

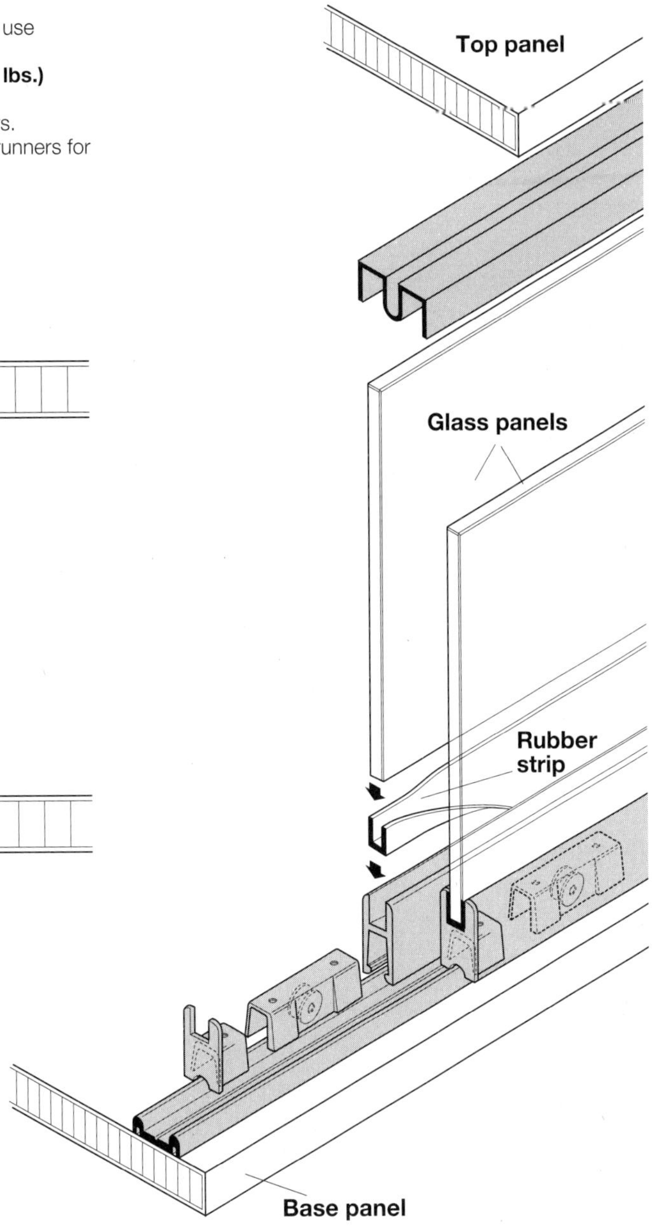

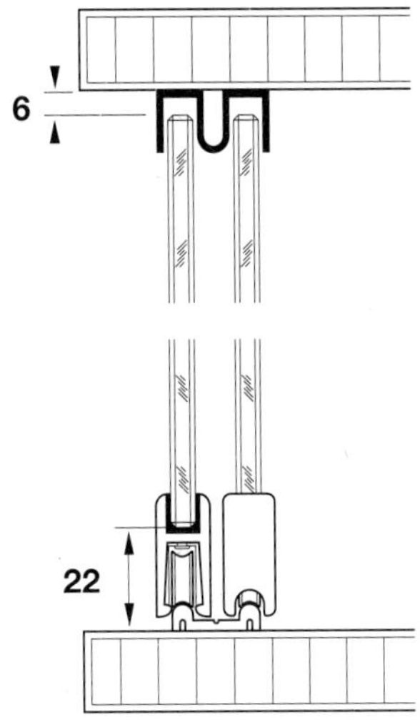

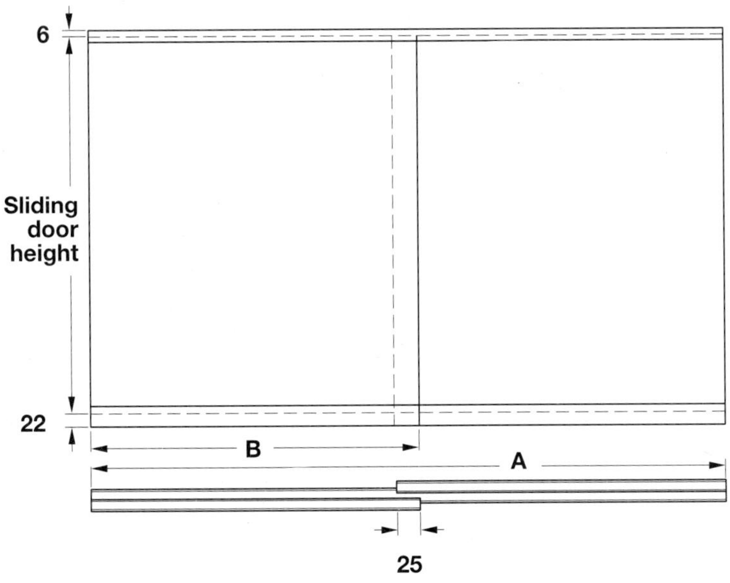

Dimension A: Overall width of glass door

Dimension B: Width of individual door panel

This is calculated as half dimension **A** plus the required overlap (usually 25mm) (1"), e.g. 1000 ÷ 2 = 500 mm + 25 = 525 mm.

Dimensions in mm
Inches are approximate

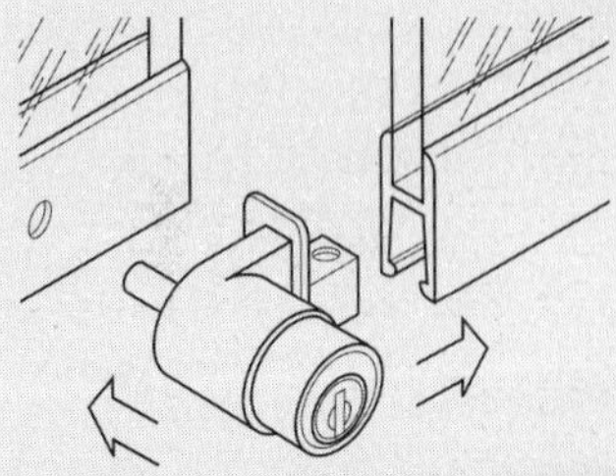

End cap pushbutton cylinder locks can be installed in the ends of the runner housing profile if required.

This pushbutton cylinder is shown on opposite page.

HÄFELE

Labora Sliding Glass Door Fitting

- Specially developed to fit into the runner housing profile of the Labora system.
- Doors are locked by engaging lock bolt into hole on opposite door profile.
- When ordering, please specify left or right hand closing and keying options.

Cylinder locks for two-door cabinets using the Labora sliding glass door system

End cap pushbutton cylinder lock for installation in the end of the sliding glass door runner profile.

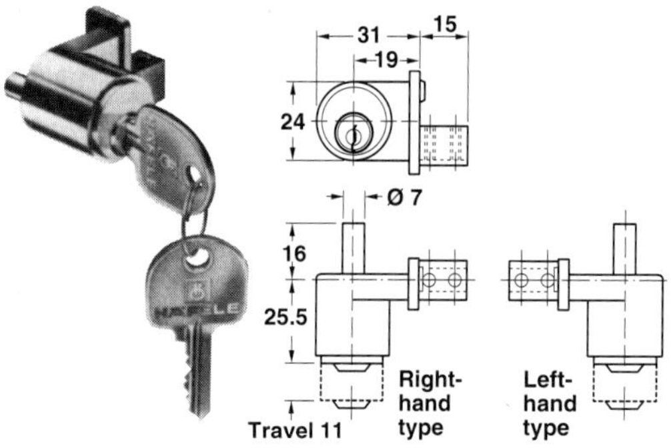

Finish: zinc die-cast case and brass cylinder, matt chrome-plated
5 Pin levers = 10,000 key changes.
Accessories: 2 keys

Keyed differently:

Cat. No.	left	233.13.813
	right	233.13.804

Keyed alike: key change H1

Cat. No.	left	233.13.868
	right	233.13.859

Master Key System:

Cat. No.	233.13.88X*

Packing: 1 pc. each

Double guide track, without screw-holes

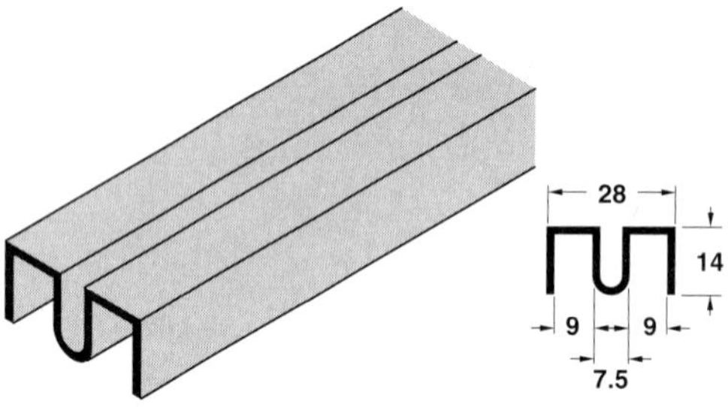

Finish: aluminum, silver anodized

Cat. No.	415.08.963

Packing: lengths of 5 meters

Runner housing profile

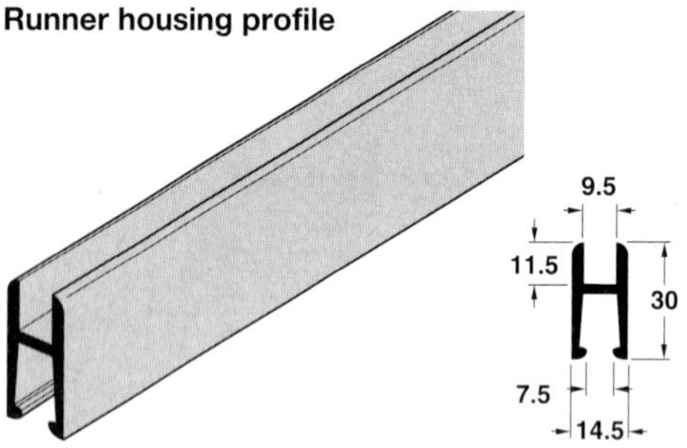

Finish: aluminum, silver anodized

Cat. No.	415.08.927

Packing: lengths of 5 meters

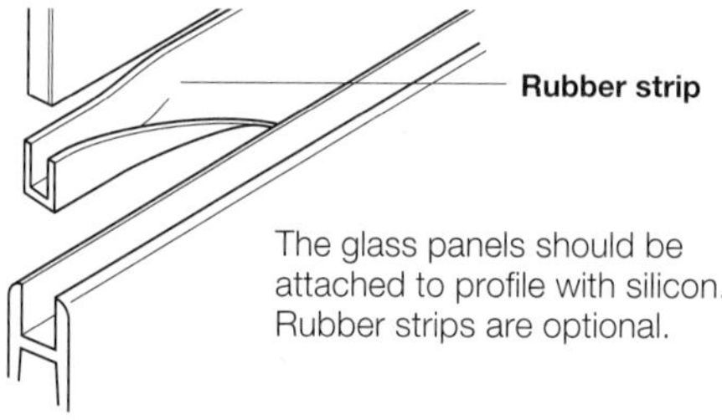

The glass panels should be attached to profile with silicon. Rubber strips are optional.

Rubber strip 32 x 1.5 mm
Glass thickness 6 mm plus

Cat. No.	416.10.002

Rubber strip 32 x 1.0 mm
Glass thickness 8 mm plus

Cat. No.	416.10.011

Packing: rolls of 2 meters

Runner, without end cap
for installation in runner housing profile

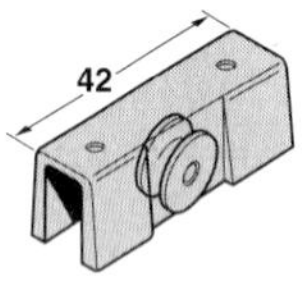

Finish: steel, unfinished

Cat. No.	415.08.954

Packing: 10 pcs.

Runner, with notched end cap
for installation in runner housing profile

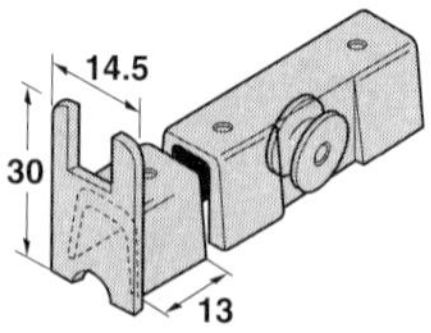

Finish: steel, unfinished; w/nickel-plated, zinc die-cast end cap

Cat. No.	415.08.945

Packing: 10 pcs.

Runner, with plain end cap
for installation in runner housing profile

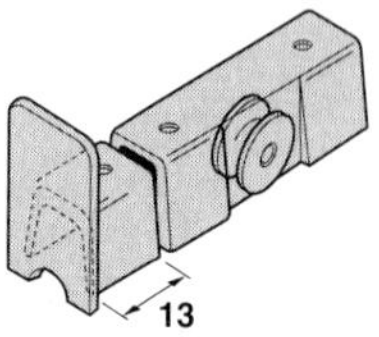

Finish: steel, unfinished; w/nickel-plated, zinc die-cast end cap

Cat. No.	415.08.918

Packing: 10 pcs.

Double supporting track, without screw-holes

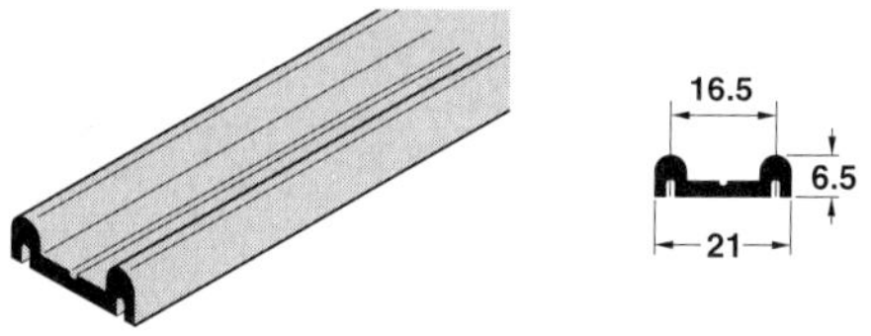

Finish: aluminum, silver anodized

Cat. No.	415.08.936

Packing: lengths of 5 meters

Rubber buffer, for bonding to edge of glass panel, 6–8 mm glass

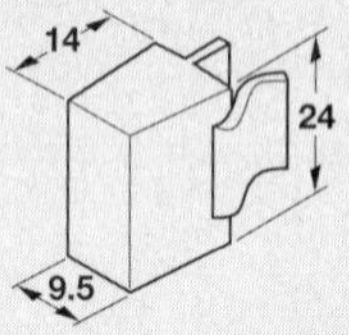

Finish: brass, nickel-plated with rubber bumper

Cat. No.	416.08.001

Packing: 10 pcs. each

Rubber buffer, screw-mounted

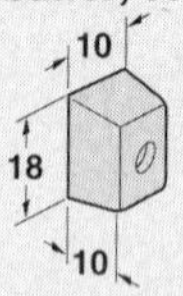

Cat. No.	416.07.005

Packing: 10 pcs.

Dust strip, adhesive-mounted

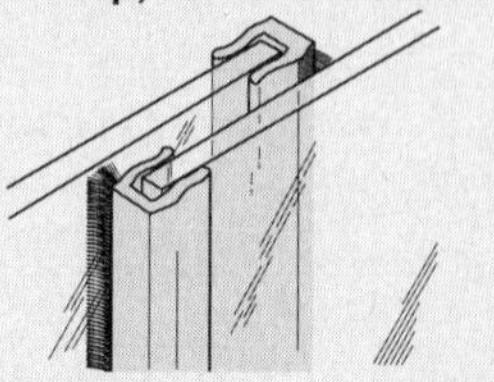

Finish: profile brass, nickel-plated; with jute bristles

Cat. No. for 6–7 mm glass	416.12.015

Packing: lengths of 10 meters

Dimensional data not binding. We reserve the right to alter specifications without notice.

Dimensions in mm
Inches are approximate

Sliding Door Fittings For Glass Doors – Novum 1

Can also be used to hang writing boards for conference rooms.

Sliding door fitting for glass doors
to be used with one-winged, free-hanging glass doors with the following requirements:
- weight of wings up to **40 kg (88 lbs.)** per meter
- wing height up to 1 m (39³⁄₈")
- glass thickness of 4 – 8 mm

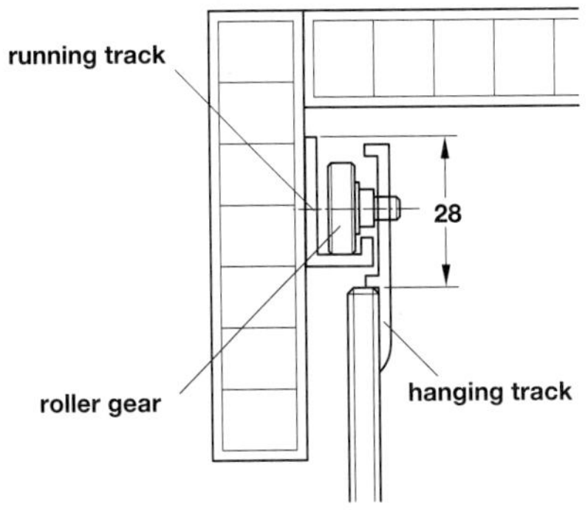

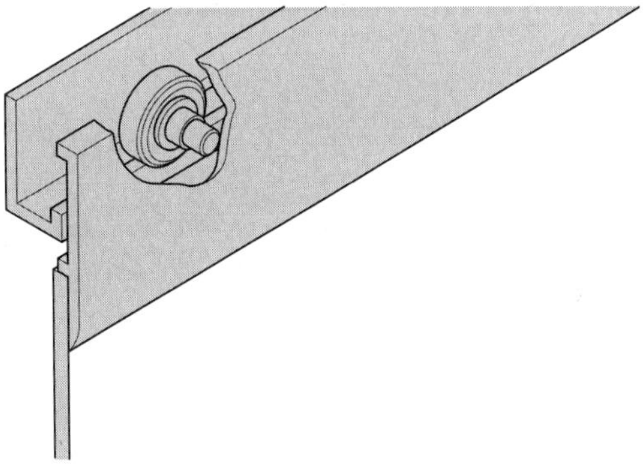

Mounting:
- roughen up the track surface before applying glue
- glass pane and hanging track must be glued together with the special two-package system adhesive

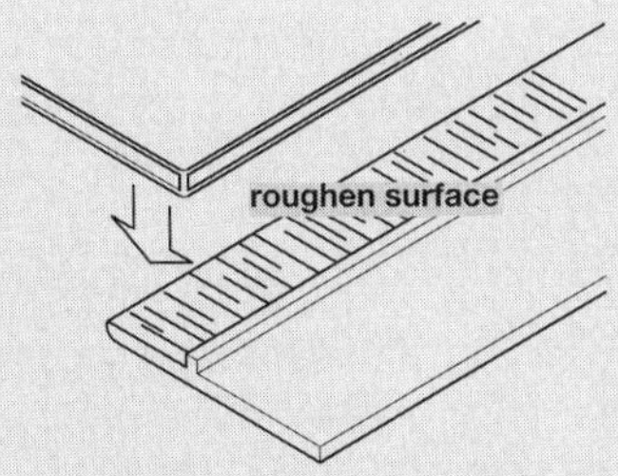

- Hang the hanging track together with the glass pane into the running track

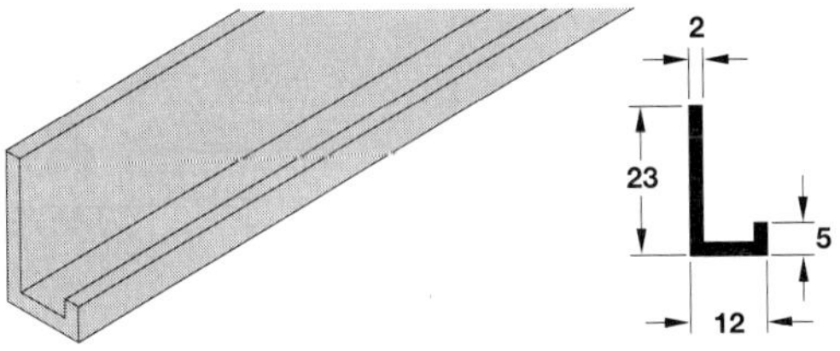

Running track
without holes, to be screw-mounted on the side
Finish: brass, nickel-plated, polished

Cat. No.	418.08.717

Packing: 5 meters

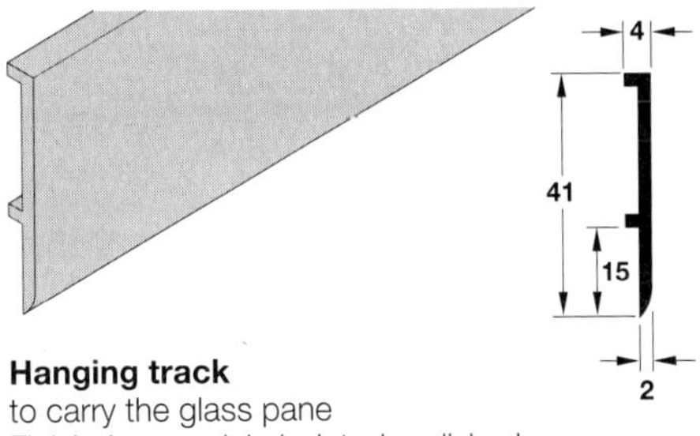

Hanging track
to carry the glass pane
Finish: brass, nickel-plated, polished

Cat. No.	418.08.726

Packing: 5 meters

Adhesive, 2 package system
"UHU Plus" to glue the glass pane onto the hanging track

Cat. No.	003.03.024

Packing: 1 package with bonding material and hardening agent, Content: 33 ml

Number of roller gears

Length of track	Roller gears
up to 1000 mm	2
from 1000 mm	4

The roller gears need to be riveted to the hanging track

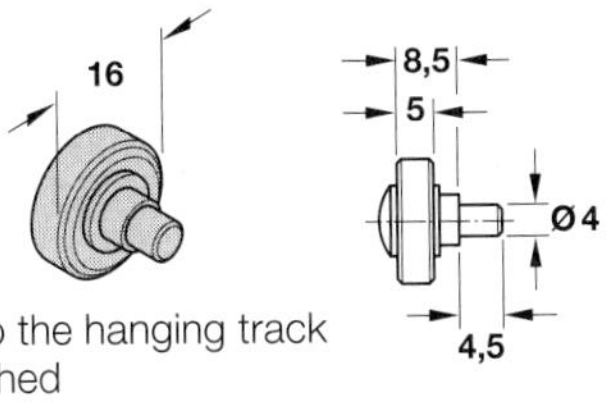

Roller gear
to be mounted onto the hanging track
Finish: steel, unfinished

Cat. No.	418.08.833

Packing: 2 pcs.

Distance a = 1/10 of the track's length

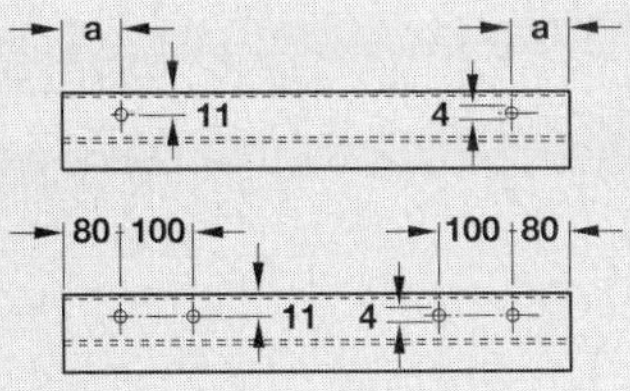

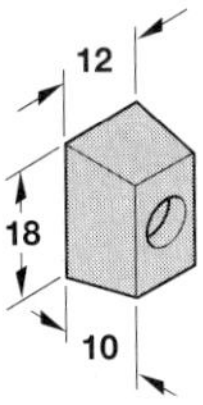

Rubber buffer
screw-mounted

Cat. No.	416.07.005

Packing: 10 pcs.

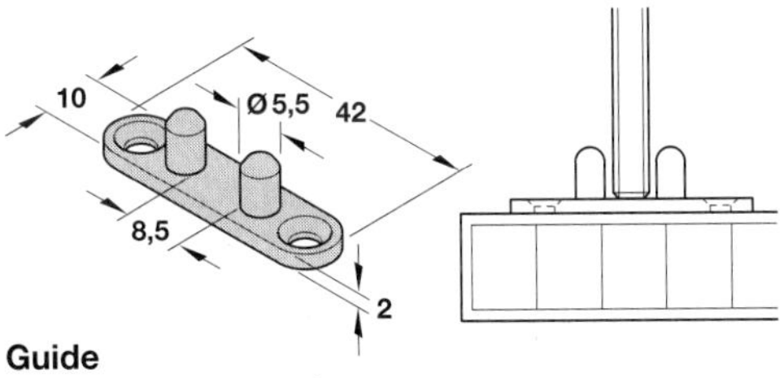

Guide
to be screw-mounted
Finish: steel, nickel-plated

Cat. No.	418.08.057

Packing: 10 pcs.

Length of the hanging track
Runner track length: 2 + overhang
example:
1000 mm ÷ 2 = 500 + 25 = 525 mm

Hanging tracks are also available cut to size with pre-mounted roller gears

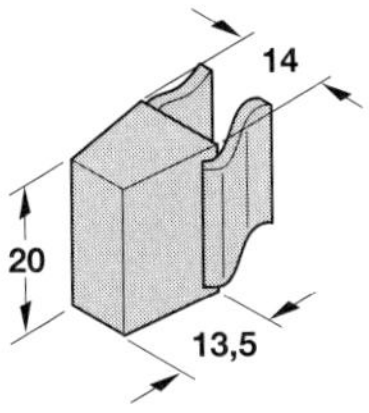

Rubber buffer
clip onto the edge of a 6 mm thick glass pane
Finish of spring: brass, nickel-plated

Cat. No.	418.08.001

Packing: 10 pcs.

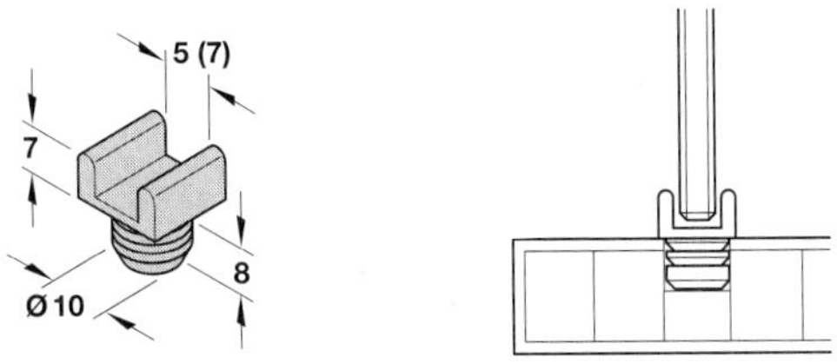

Guide
to be bored into the floor
Finish: plastic, clear

Glass thickness	Cat. No.
3 – 5 mm	400.41.414
5 – 7 mm	400.41.423

Packing: 10 pcs.

Dimensions in mm

Dimensional data not binding.
We reserve the right to alter specifications without notice.

Sliding Door Fittings for Glass Doors - Novum 2

Can also be used to hang writing boards for conference rooms.

Sliding door fitting for glass doors
to be used with two-winged, free-hanging glass doors with the following requirements:
- weight of wings up to **(40 kg (88 lbs.)** per meter
- wing height up to 1 meter (39³⁄₈")
- glass thickness of 4-6 mm

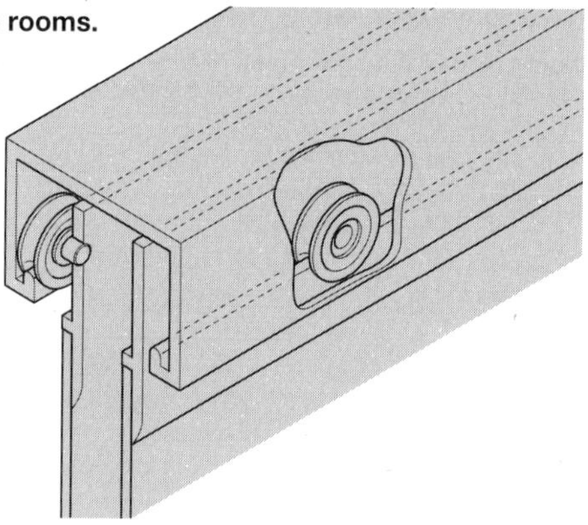

Mounting:
- Roughen up the track surface before applying glue
- Glass pane and hanging track must be glued together with the special two-package system adhesive

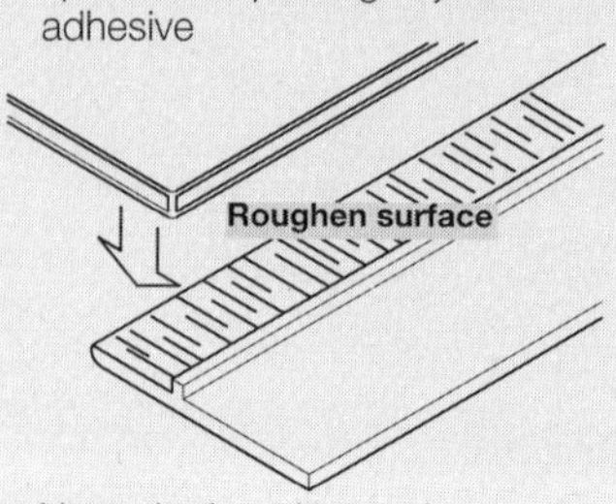

- Hang the hanging track together with the glass pane into the running track

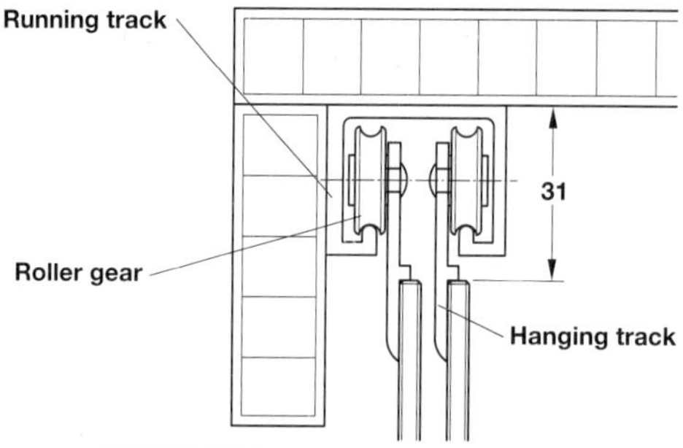

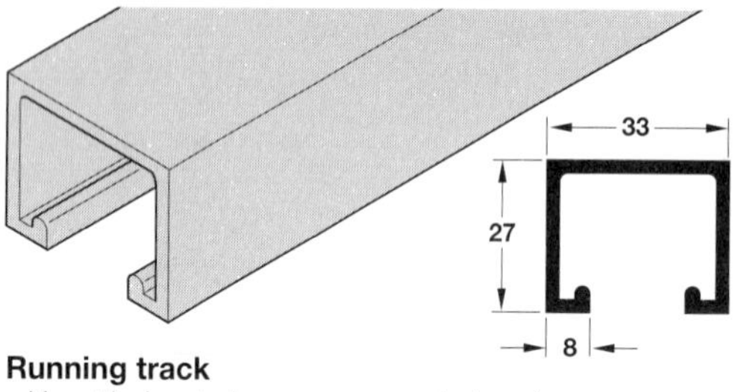

Running track
without holes, to be screw-mounted under the top panel
Finish: brass, nickel plated, polished

Cat. No.	418.58.717

Packing: 5 meter

Hanging track
to carry the glass pane
Finish: brass, nickel plated, polished

Cat. No.	418.58.726

Packing: 5 meter

Adhesive, 2 package system
"UHU Plus" to glue the glass pane onto the hanging track. Any other 2 component polyurethane glue can be used

Cat. No.	003.03.024

Packing: 1 package with bonding material and hardening agent
Content: 33 ml

4 Sliding Door Hardware
Drawer Slides
Television Supports

Number of roller gears:

Length of track	roller gears
up to 1000 mm	2
from 1000 mm	4

The roller gears need to be riveted to the hanging track

Dimension "a" = 1/10 of the tracks length

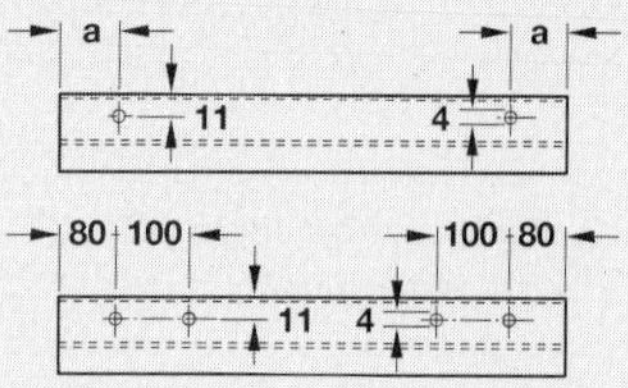

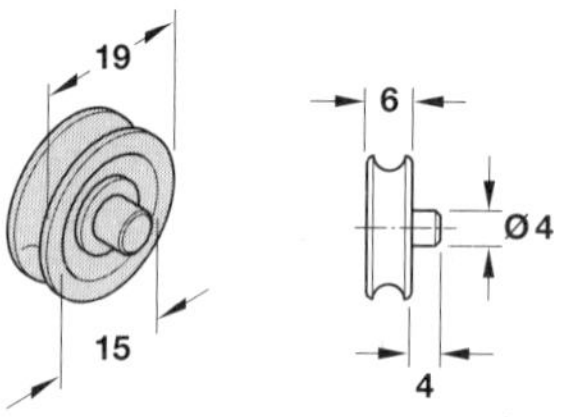

Roller gear
concave shape, with ball bearings and axle to be mounted to the hanging track
Finish: steel, unfinished

Cat. No.	418.58.833

Packing: 2 pcs.

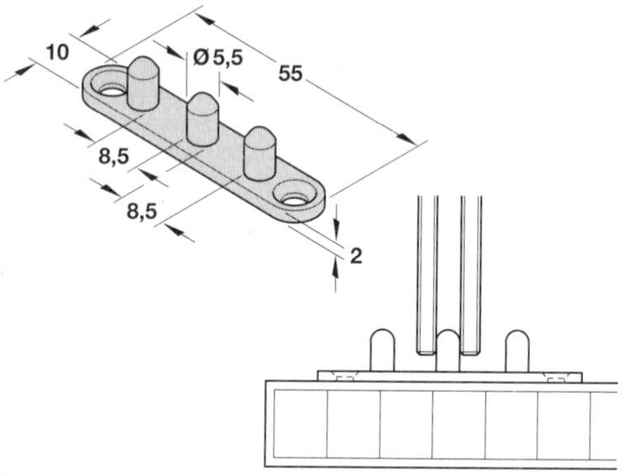

Guide
to be screw-mounted onto the floor
Finish: steel, nickel-plated

Cat. No.	418.58.057

Packing: 1 pc. or 10 pcs.

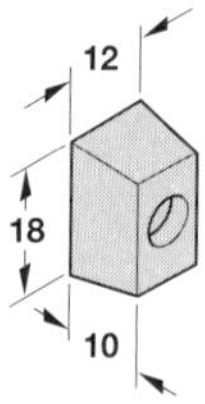

Rubber buffer
screw-mounted

Cat. No.	416.07.005

Packing: 1 pc. or 10 pcs.

Length of hanging track
Runner track length: 2 + overhang
example:
1000 mm ÷ 2 = 500 + 25 = 525 mm

Hanging tracks are also available cut to size with pre-mounted roller gears.

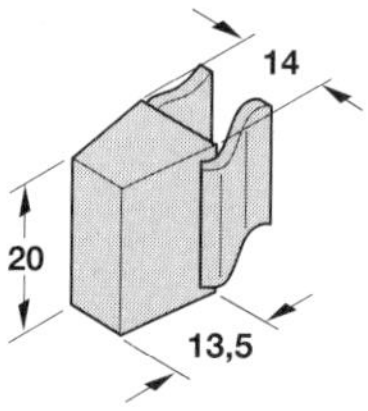

Rubber buffer
clip onto the top edge of a 6 mm thick glass pane

Cat. No.	416.08.001

Packing: 1 pc. or 10 pcs.

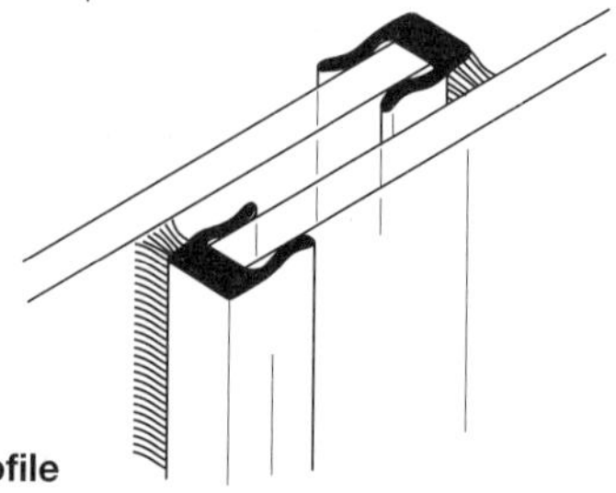

Dust cover profile
clip onto the edge of a 6 mm thick glass pane
Finish: aluminum, silver anodized with jute brushes

Cat. No.	416.13.905

Packing: 5 meter

Dimensions in mm

HÄFELE

Hawa Junior 80 Sliding Glass Door Fitting

Hawa Junior 80 is a vertically adjustable sliding door fitting for glass doors. Tandem rollers made of high-grade polyamide and mounted in an aluminum carriage, ensure light and silent action. The top of the glass door is clamped in a special shoe, which mounts to the roller carriage. At the bottom, the door is controlled by a guide, screwed to the floor. All parts are corrosion-resistant for use in rooms with a humid atmosphere.

Door weights to 80 kg (176 lbs.) Glass Thicknesses 10 mm (3/8") to 12.7 mm (1/2")

1 Complete Set, for one glass panel sliding door without upper tracks includes the following components:

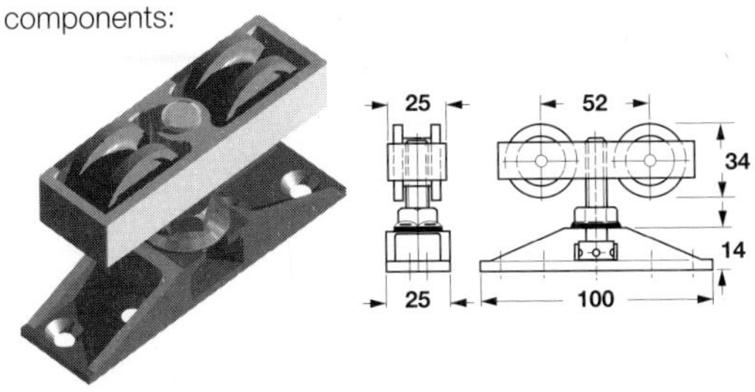

Running Gear, 2 units, high-grade polyamide tandem rollers with sleeve bearings,aluminum carriage and zinc die-cast mounting plate. Complete with fastening materials.

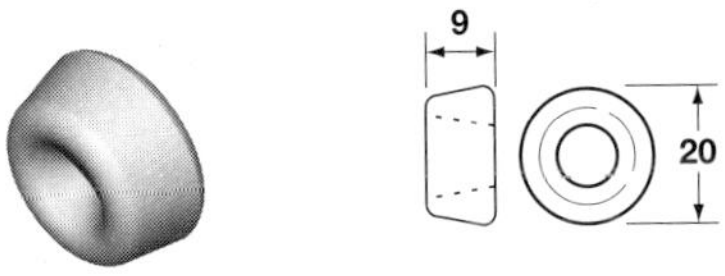

Rubber Bumper, 1 unit screw-mounted, complete with fastening materials.

Fitting Set for single sliding door without upper tracks

Cat. No.	940.80.009

Packing: 1 pc.

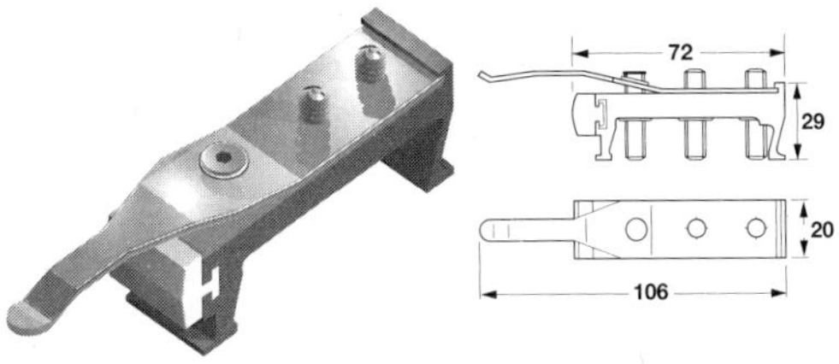

Track Stopper, 1 unit for positioning in upper track. Zinc die-cast housing with adjustable steel spring and rubber bumper.

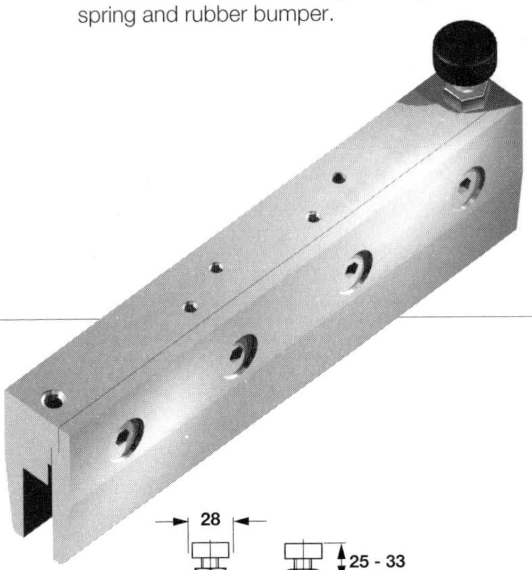

Upper Track, Clamping Shoe and Guide, ordered separately for set or sets from above:

Upper Track, with screw holes.

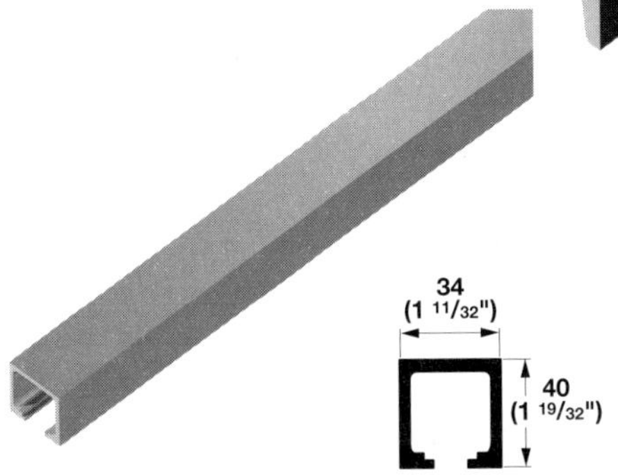

Finish: aluminum, anodized

Cat. No.		
	1.4 m (4' 7")	407.59.868
	1.6 m (5' 3")	407.59.877
	1.8 m (5' 11")	407.59.886
	2.0 m (6' 7")	407.59.895
	2.2 m (7' 3")	407.59.902
	2.5 m (8' 2")	407.59.911
	3.0 m (9' 10 1/8")	407.59.941
	4.0 m (13' 1 1/2")	407.59.951
	6.0 m (19' 8 1/4")	407.59.931

Packing: 1 pc.

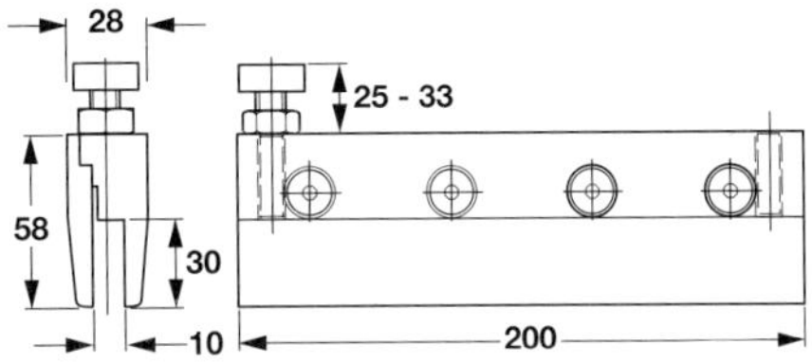

Clamping Shoe, for glass door, complete with set screws and plastic liner strips.
Finish: aluminum, non-anodized

Cat. No.	940.80.028

Packing: 2 pcs. (for 1 panel) with screws for mounting included.

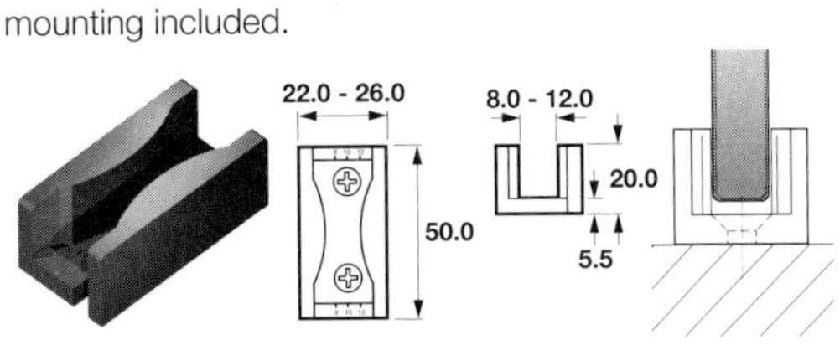

Guide, screw-mounted to floor, adj., 10 -12.7 mm
Finish: plastic, black

Cat. No.	940.80.039

Packing: 1 pc.

Complete Sets, including:
Upper Track, Running Gear, Track Stopper, and Rubber Buffer. (Does not include clamping shoe and guide. Order separately.)

Door panel width	Track length	Cat. No.
60-80 cm (2'-2' 7")	1.4 m (4' 7")	407.59.144
70-90 cm (2' 4"-2' 11")	1.6 m (5' 3")	407.59.162
80-100 cm (2' 7"-3' 3")	1.8 m (5' 11")	407.59.180
90-110 cm (2' 11"-3' 7")	2.0 m (6' 7")	407.59.206
100-120 cm (3' 3"-3' 11")	2.2 m (7' 3")	407.59.224
120-140 cm (3' 11"-4' 7")	2.5 m (8' 2")	407.59.251

Packing: 1 set

Dimensions in mm

Two upper tracks can be mounted side by side for double or multiple doors.

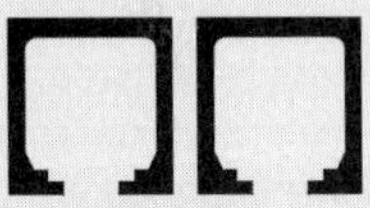

Supplementary Track Stopper
If the sliding door is required to stop at both ends, we recommend installing an additional track stopper.

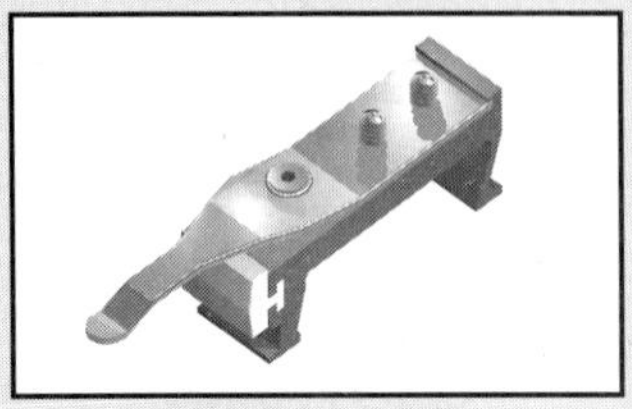

Finish: zinc die-cast housing, steel spring, rubber buffer

Cat. No.	940.80.041

Packing: 1 pc.

Dimensional data not binding. We reserve the right to alter specifications without notice.

HÄFELE

Product Guide - Drawer Slides

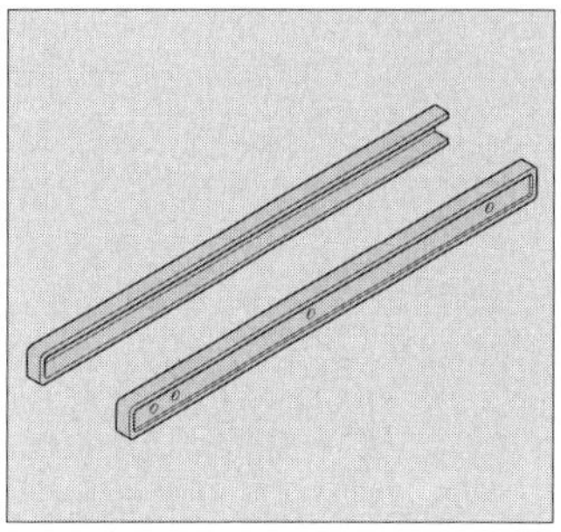

Drawer Guides
Pages **4.59 - 4.62**

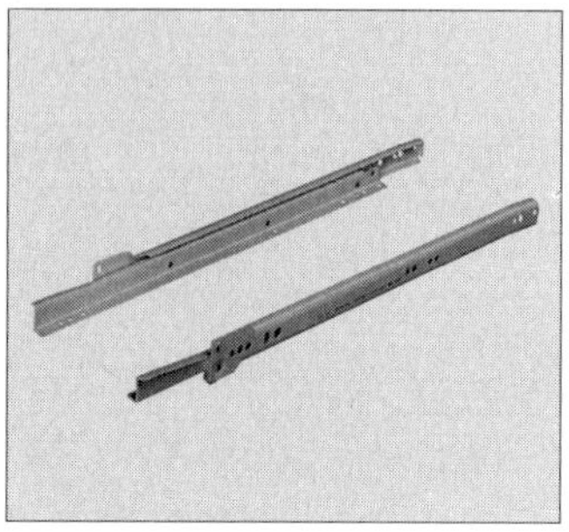

Epoxy-coated Drawer Slides
Pages **4.63 - 4.71**

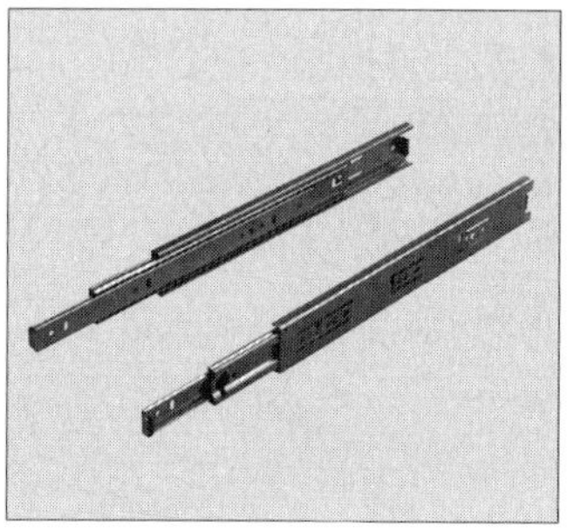

Ball-bearing Drawer Slides
Pages **4.72 - 4.96**

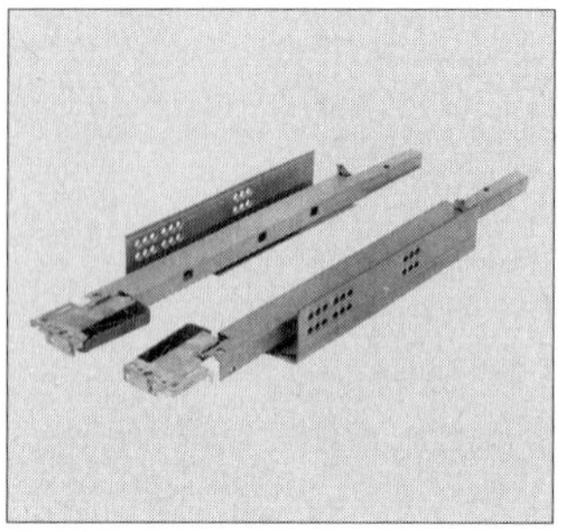

Concealed Undermount Drawer Slides
Pages **4.75 - 4.78**

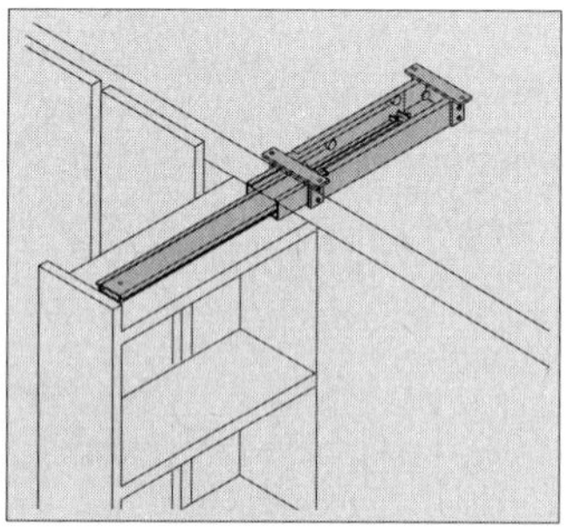

Heavy-duty Pull-out Systems
Pages **4.97 - 4.102**

Television Support Mechanisms
Pages **4.103 - 4.111**

Drawer Guides

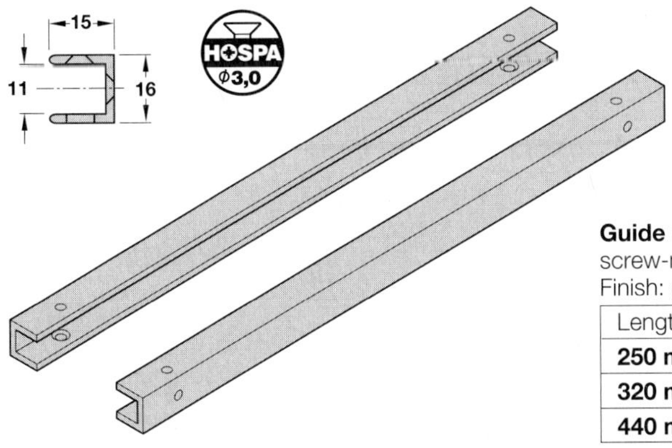

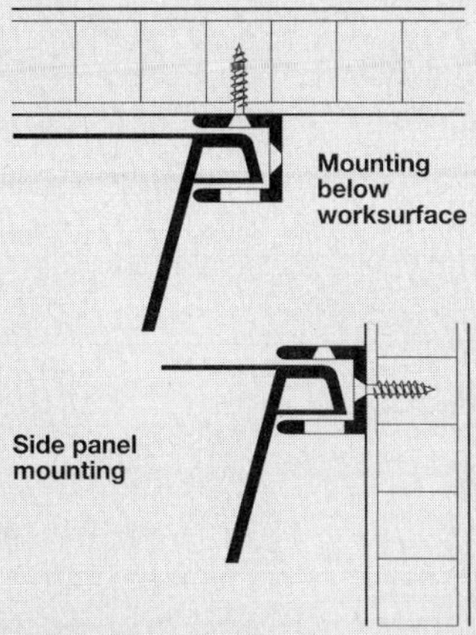

Guide rails

screw-mounted.
Finish: plastic, white

Length	Cat. No.
250 mm (9⅞")	430.31.710
320 mm (12⅝")	430.31.720
440 mm (17$^{5}/_{16}$")	430.31.730

Packing: 40 pcs.

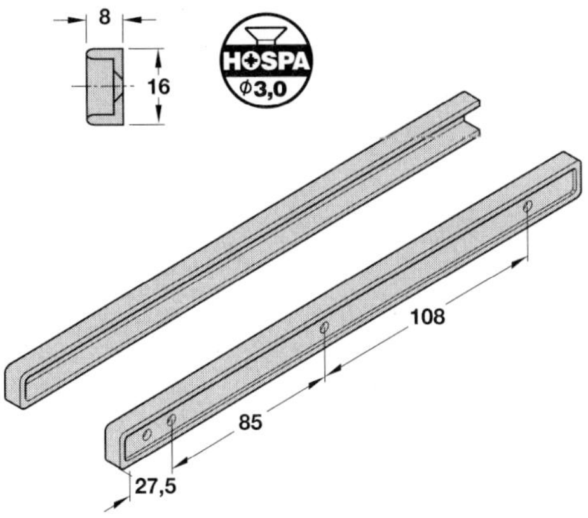

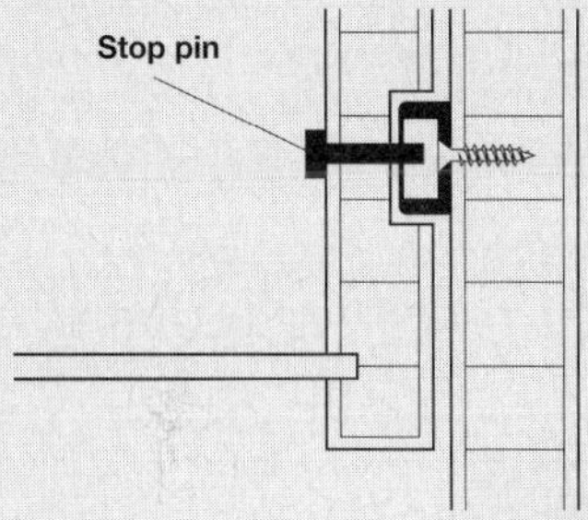

Guide rails, 248 mm (9¾") long

screw-mounted, for drawers with a **17 mm groove.**
Finish: plastic, brown

Cat. No.	430.16.100

Packing: 20 pcs.

Mounting tip:
increased loading capacity when mounting the closed end of rail to the front. This also permits the use of stop pins (included) to secure the drawer.

Sliding Door Hardware
Drawer Slides
Television Supports
4

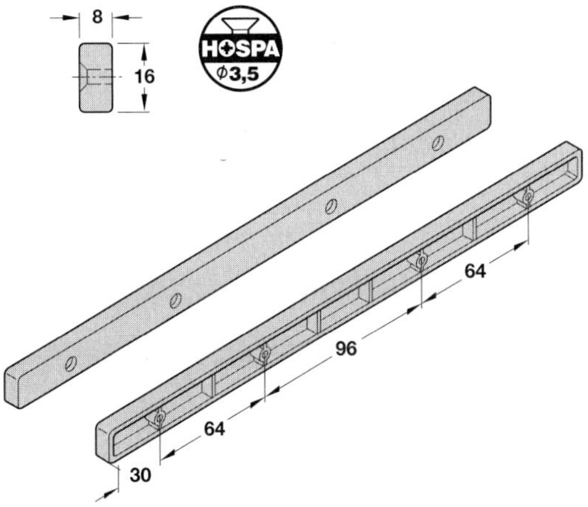

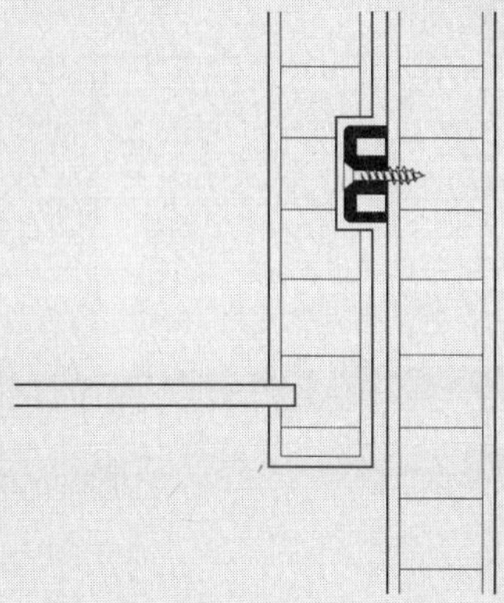

Guide rails, 285 mm (11¼") long

screw-mounted, for drawers with a **17 mm groove.**
Finish: plastic, white

Cat. No.	430.15.701

Packing: 20 pcs.

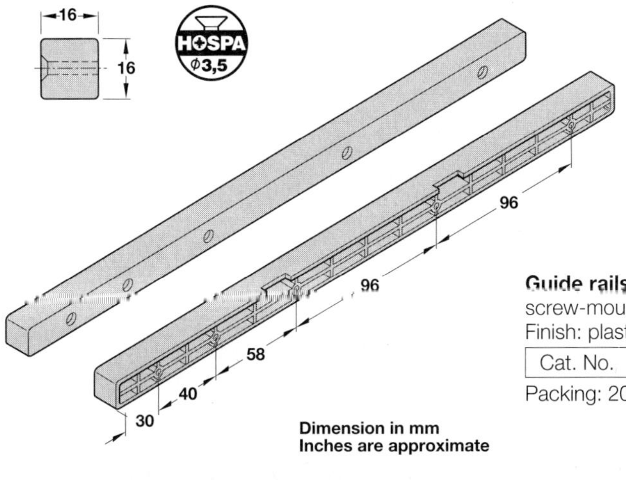

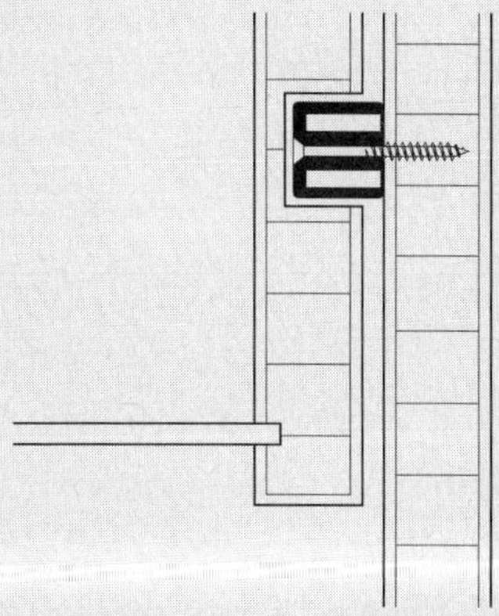

Guide rails, 350 mm (13¾") long

screw-mounted, for drawers with a **17 mm groove.**
Finish: plastic, white

Cat. No.	430.15.710

Packing: 20 pcs.

Dimension in mm
Inches are approximate

Dimensional data not binding.
We reserve the right to alter specifications without notice.

HÄFELE

Drawer Guides

Baskets can be removed from the cabinet, even if the door offers restricted access (e.g. inset doors).

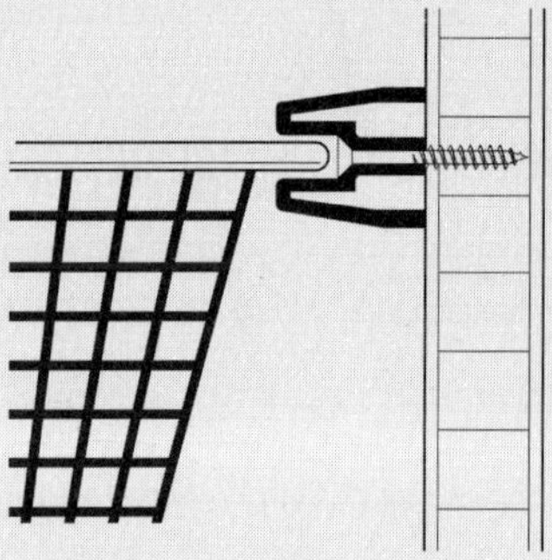

Wire baskets suitable for these guides can be found in group 5.

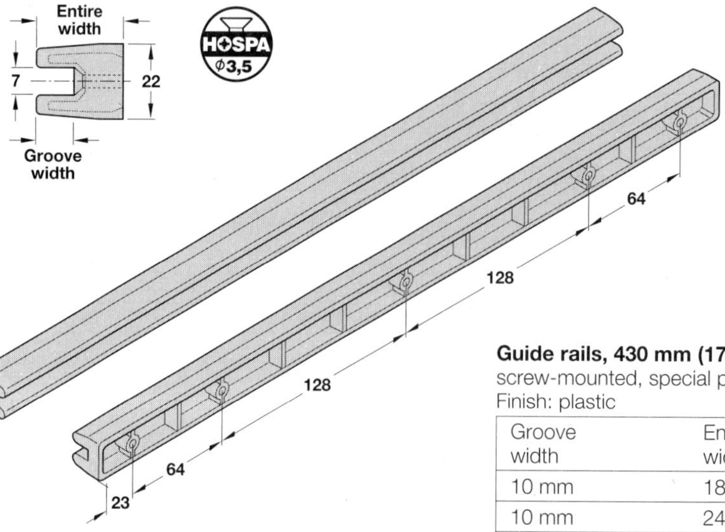

Guide rails, 430 mm (17") long

screw-mounted, special profile for wire baskets.
Finish: plastic

Groove width	Entire width	Cat.No. white
10 mm	18 mm	430.34.718
10 mm	24 mm	430.34.724
10 mm	26 mm	430.34.726

Packing: 40 pcs.

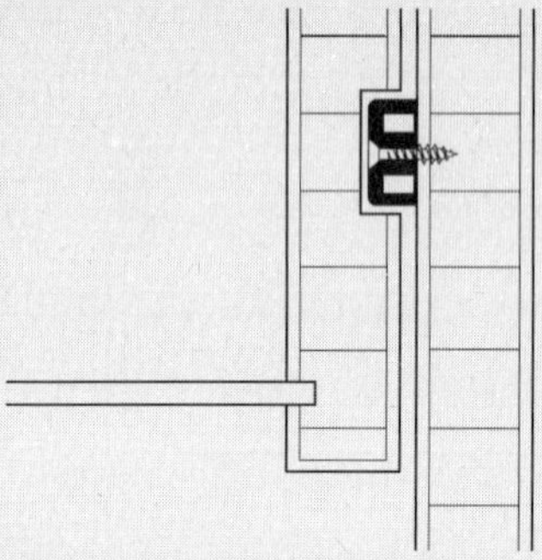

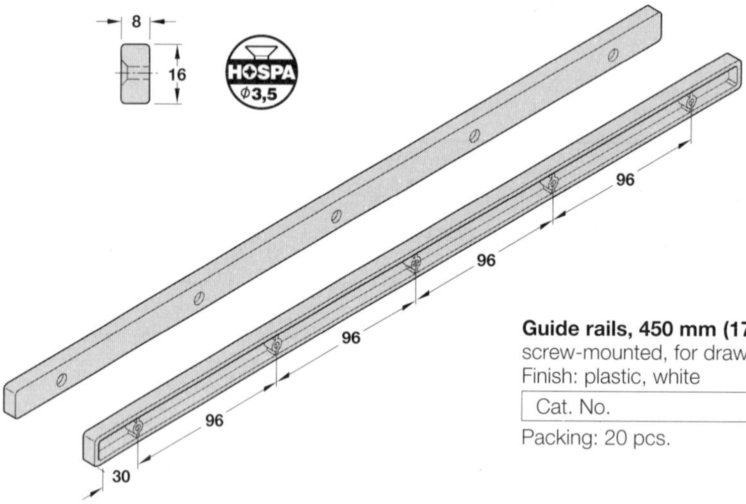

Guide rails, 450 mm (17¾") long

screw-mounted, for drawers with a **17 mm groove.**
Finish: plastic, white

Cat. No.	430.15.738

Packing: 20 pcs.

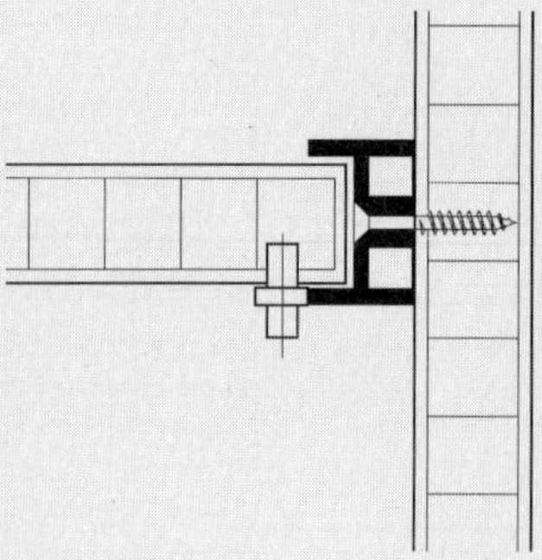

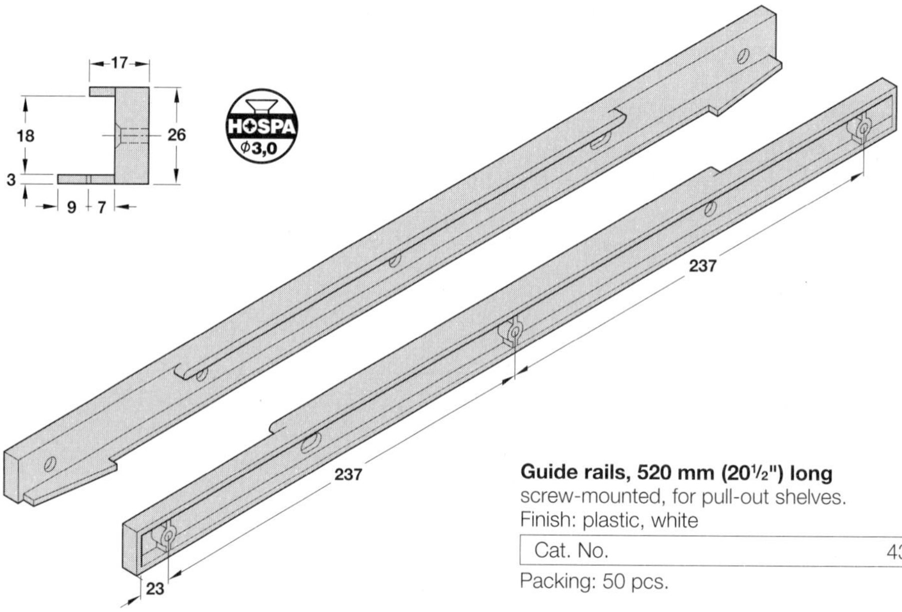

Guide rails, 520 mm (20½") long

screw-mounted, for pull-out shelves.
Finish: plastic, white

Cat. No.	430.10.700

Packing: 50 pcs.

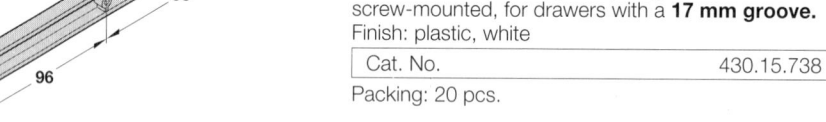

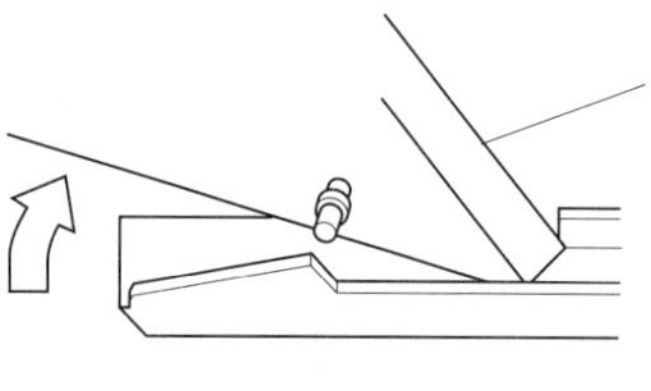

A lock in the profile of this guide is designed so that a stop (wood dowel) inserted in the shelf prevents unintentional removal. If required the shelf can be lifted over the lock and removed.

Dimensional data not binding. We reserve the right to alter specifications without notice.

Dimension in mm
Inches are approximate

Drawer Guides

HÄFELE

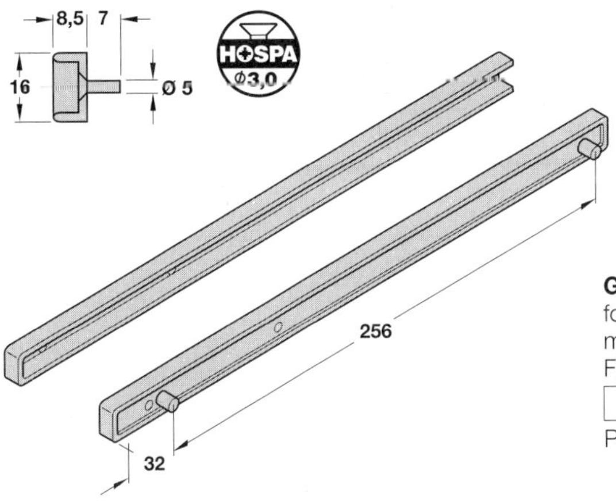

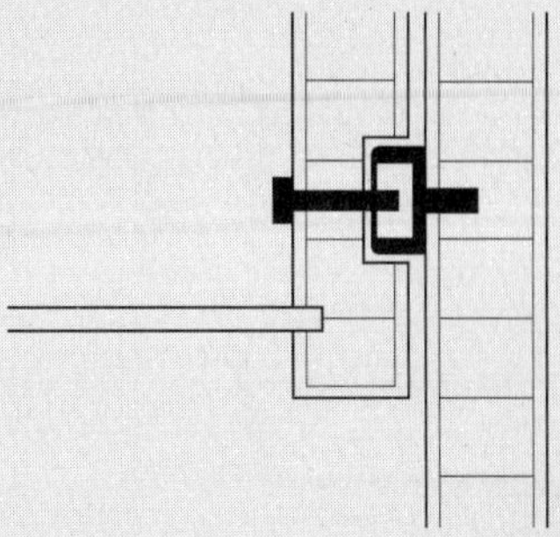

Guide rails, 300 mm (11¾") long
for insertion in **Ø 5 mm** holes and additional screw-mounting in drawers with a **17 mm groove.**
Finish: plastic, brown

Cat. No.	430.18.104

Packing: 20 pcs.

SYSTEM VARIANTA 32

Mounting tip:
increased loading capacity when mounting the closed end of rail to the front. This also permits the use of stop pins (included) to secure the drawer.

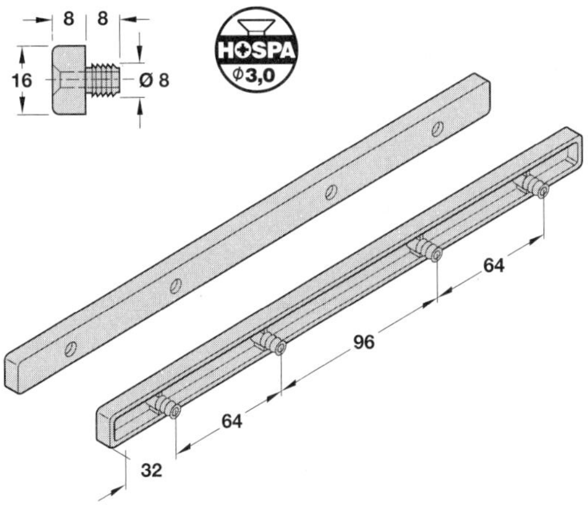

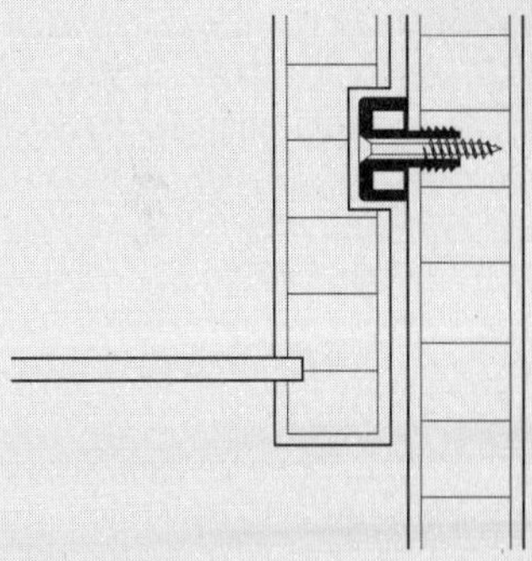

Guide rails, 288 mm (11⅜") long
for insertion in **Ø 8 mm** holes and additional screw-mounting in drawers with a **17 mm groove.**
Finish: plastic, white

Cat. No.	430.15.756

Packing: 20 pcs.

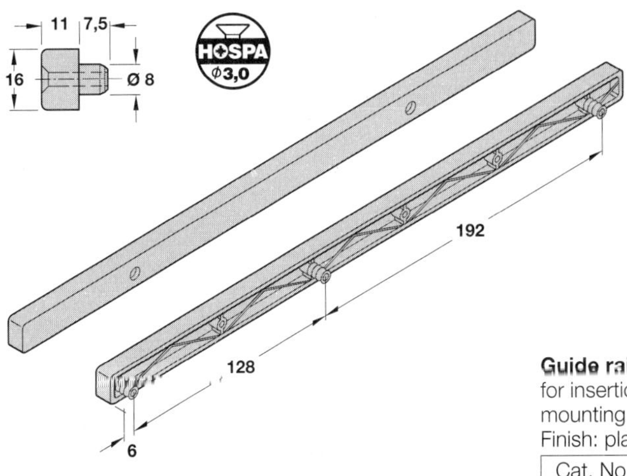

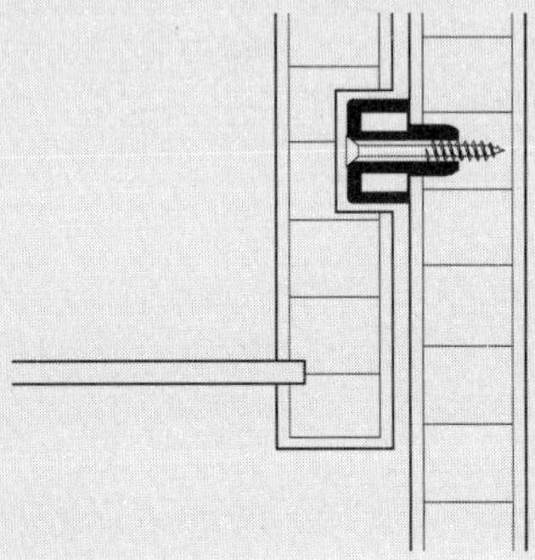

Dimension in mm
Inches are approximate

Guide rails, 350 mm (13¾") long
for insertion in **Ø 8 mm** holes and additional screw-mounting in drawers with a **17 mm groove.**
Finish: plastic, white

Cat. No.	430.15.765

Packing: 350 pcs.

Dimensional data not binding.
We reserve the right to alter specifications without notice.

Drawer Guides

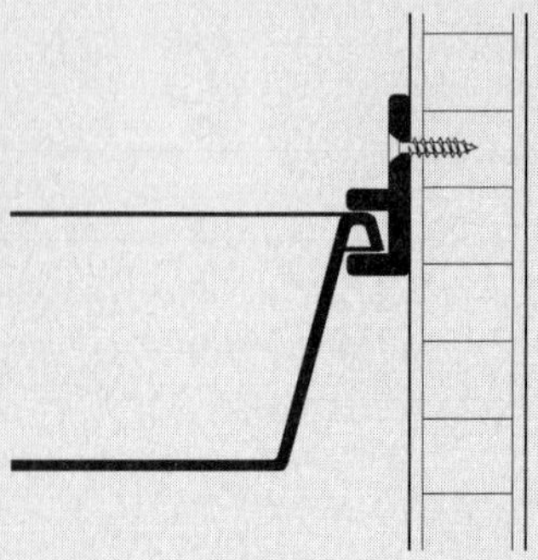

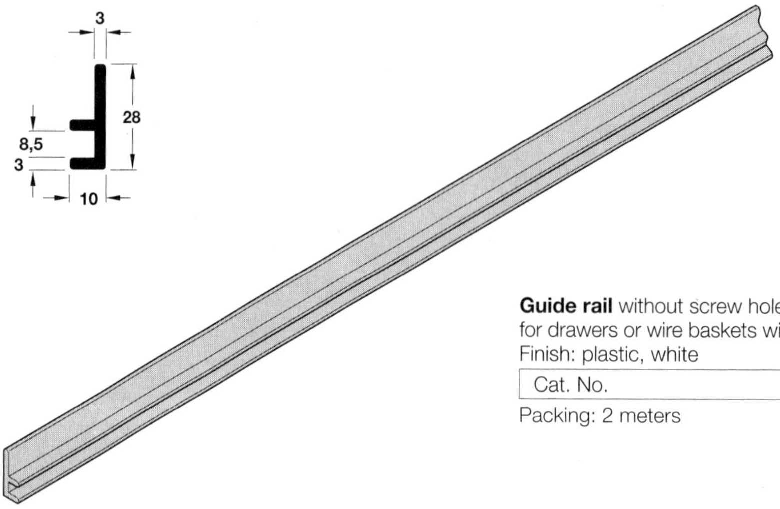

Guide rail without screw holes, screw or staple-mount for drawers or wire baskets with side mounted runners.
Finish: plastic, white

Cat. No.	401.60.709

Packing: 2 meters

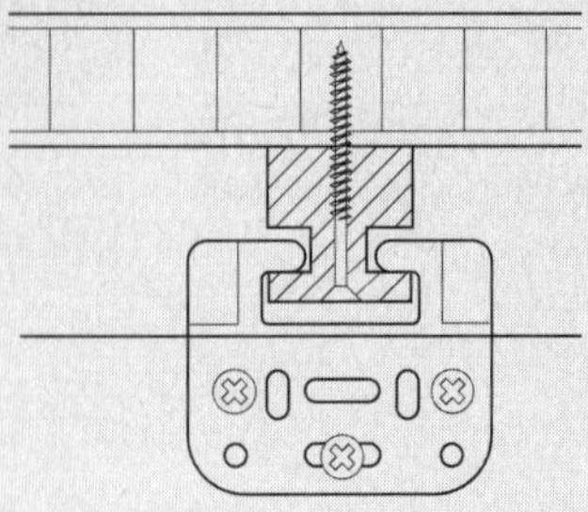

Optional top or bottom mounting.

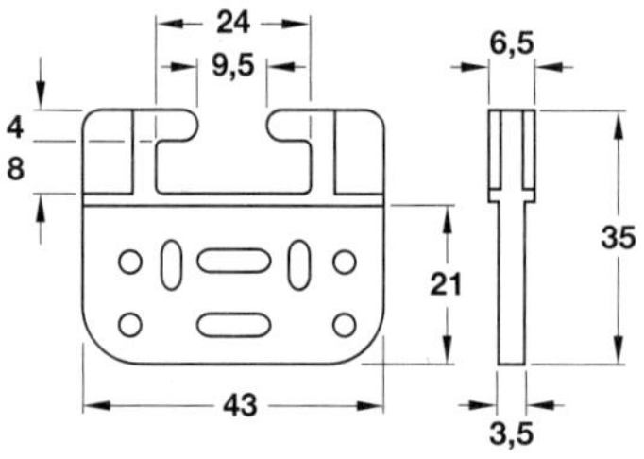

HOSPA Ø3,5

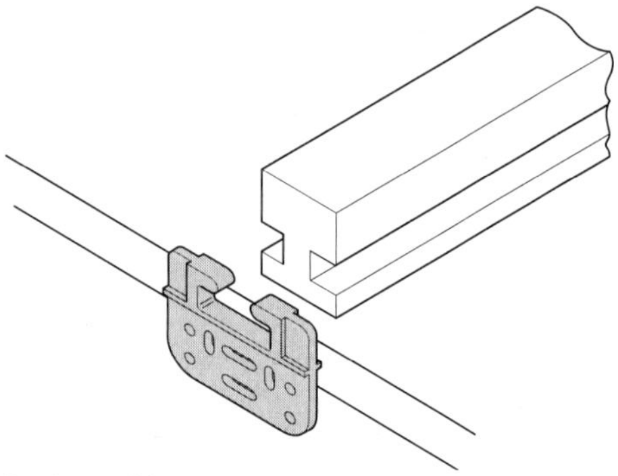

Centre guide
screw-mounted to the rear drawer panel, for drawers that cannot be supported along the entire side length.
Finish: natural plastic

Cat. No.	430.11.007

Packing: 100 pcs.

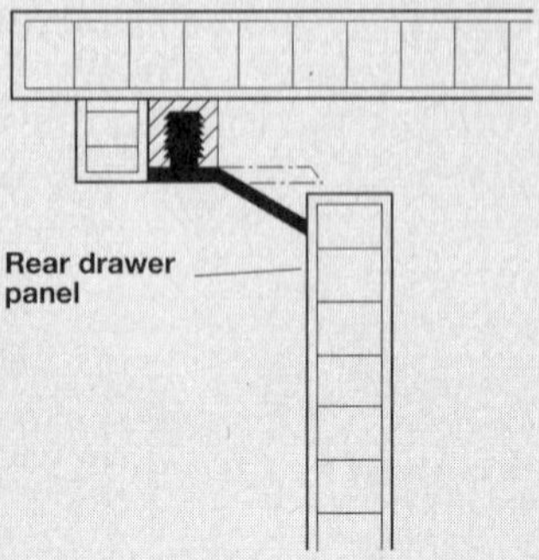

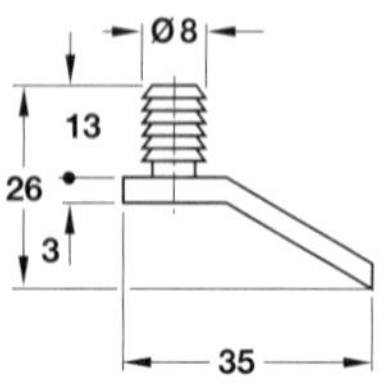

To remove drawer, press the stop lever upward.

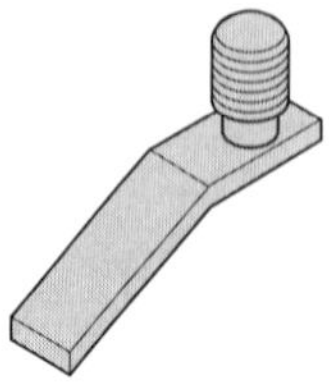

Drawer stop
press-fit
Finish: natural plastic

Cat. No.	430.09.150

Packing: 1000 pcs.

Dimensions in mm

Dimensional data not binding.
We reserve the right to alter specifications without notice.

Drawer Runners, Single-Extension Side-Mount

HÄFELE

Basic, economic drawer runners designed for standard drawers which are not generally subjected to heavy loadings and are less wide than deep (front-to-back). They are best installed in the upper third of the drawer side panel. Detent at rear secures in extended position.

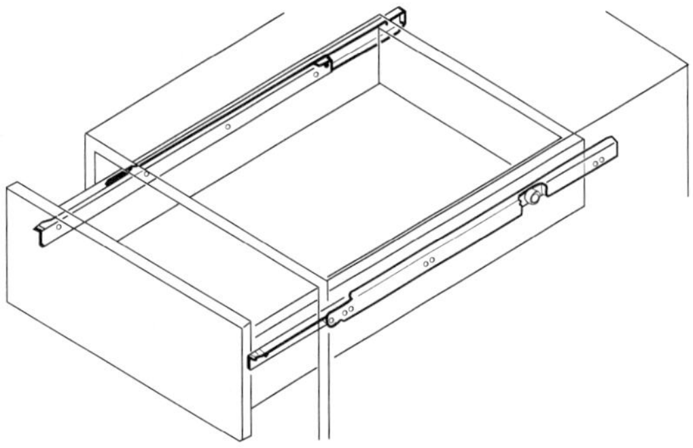

Side-Mount, F-Slide
Soft-Roller

- load carrying capacity, max. 25 kg (55 lbs.)/pair
- rollers: 4 friction bearing-mounted nylon rollers
- single-extension unit
- side-mounted

Finish: powder-coated, white RAL 9010
powder-coated, brown RAL 8011
powder-coated, black RAL 9005

Installed length		Extended length		Cat. No.		
inch	mm	inch	mm	white	brown	black
12	300	9	230	423.33.317	423.33.335	423.33.308
14	350	11	280	423.33.362	423.33.380	423.33.353
16	400	12	300	423.33.415	423.33.433	423.33.406
18	450	14	350	423.33.460	423.33.488	423.33.451
20	500	16	400	423.33.513	423.33.531	423.33.504
22	550	18	450	423.33.568	423.33.586	423.33.559
24	600	20	500	423.33.611		

Packing: 20 pairs, bulk packing on request

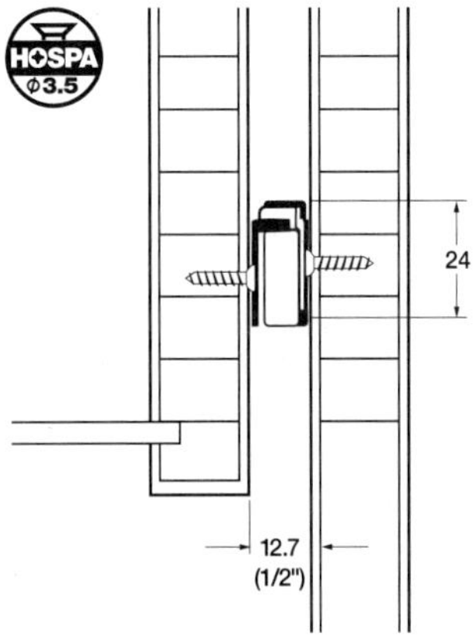

Sliding Door Hardware
Drawer Slides
Television Supports

4

Mounting Screws:
Hospa chipboard screw
Countersunk head
Size Ø 3.5 x 13 mm length
Finish: steel, zinc-plated

Cat. No.	015.31.620

Packing: 1000 pcs.

For system hole mounting
Varianta special screw
Countersunk head
Size Ø 6.0 mm
Finish: steel, nickel-plated

Length	Cat. No.
10.5 mm	013.14.718
13.5 mm	013.14.729
16.0 mm	013.14.738

Packing: 1000 pcs.

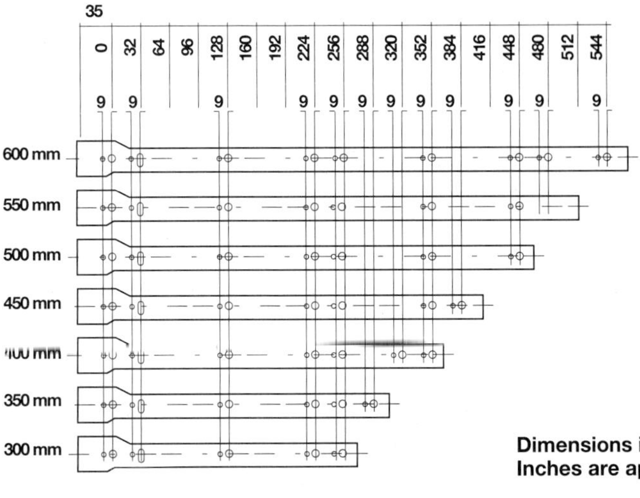

Dimensions in mm
Inches are approximate

Dimensional data not binding.
We reserve the right to alter specifications without notice.

HÄFELE

Drawer Runners, Single-Extension Bottom-Mount

A basic drawer runner with friction bearing-mounted plastic rollers, particularly economical model for mass-produced furniture. For standard drawers which are not generally subjected to heavy loadings and are less wide than deep (front-to-back).

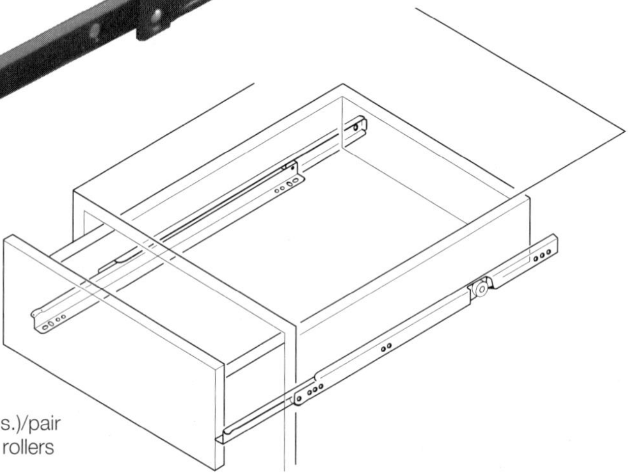

4 **Sliding Door Hardware**
Drawer Slides
Television Supports

Bottom-Mount
Soft roller

- load carrying capacity up to 25 kg (55 lbs.)/pair
- rollers: 4 friction bearing-mounted nylon rollers
- single-extension unit
- side-mounted

Finish: powder-coated white RAL 9010
powder-coated brown RAL 8011
powder-coated black RAL 9005

Installed length		Extended length		Cat. No.		
inch	mm	inch	mm	white	brown	black
12	300	9	230	423.34.314	423.34.332	423.34.305
14	350	11	280	423.34.369	423.34.387	423.34.350
16	400	12	300	423.34.412	423.34.430	423.34.403
18	450	14	350	423.34.467	423.34.485	423.34.458
20	500	16	400	423.34.510	423.34.538	423.34.501
22	550	18	450	423.34.565	423.34.583	423.34.556
24	600	20	500	423.34.618		

Packing: 20 pairs, bulk packing on request

HOSPA Ø3.5

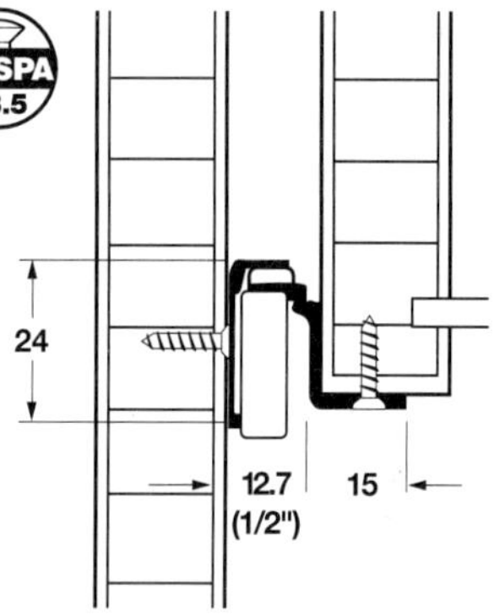

Mounting Screws:
Hospa chipboard screw
Countersunk head
Size Ø 3.5 x 13 mm length
Finish: steel, zinc-plated

Cat. No.	015.31.620

Packing: 1000 pcs.

SYSTEM VARIANTA 32

For system hole mounting.
Varianta special screw
Countersunk head
Size Ø 6.0 mm

Finish: steel, nickel-plated

Length	Cat. No.
10.5 mm	013.14.718
13.5 mm	013.14.727
16.0 mm	013.14.736

Packing: 1000 pcs.

Dimensional data not binding. We reserve the right to alter specifications without notice.

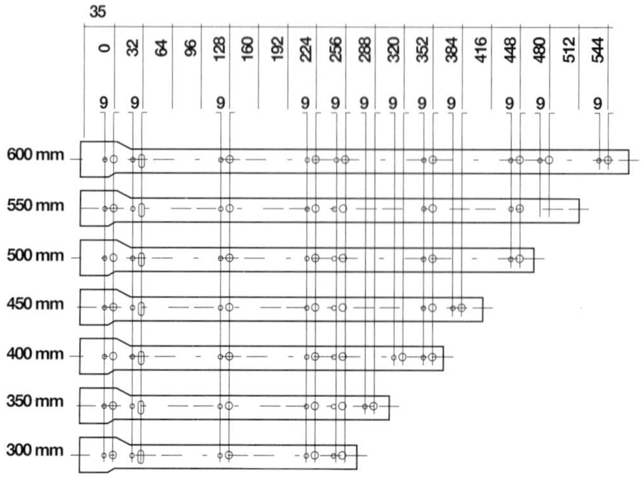

Dimensions in mm
Inches are approximate

Self-Closing Drawer Runners, Single-Extension Bottom-Mount

The drawer runners depicted on this page are roller guide, single-extension systems, offering effortless, non-twist, silent running. The special profile on the left-hand side with the captive roller guidance system ensures absolute lateral stability (see below). Manufacturing tolerances are compensated by the right-hand profile. A bevel, incorporated in the U-profile, prevents the rollers from being damaged by fouling screw-heads. The glides are equipped with double extension stop. The inlet-slant of the carcass and drawer slides guarantees, that the drawer closes automatically in the last third of insertion.

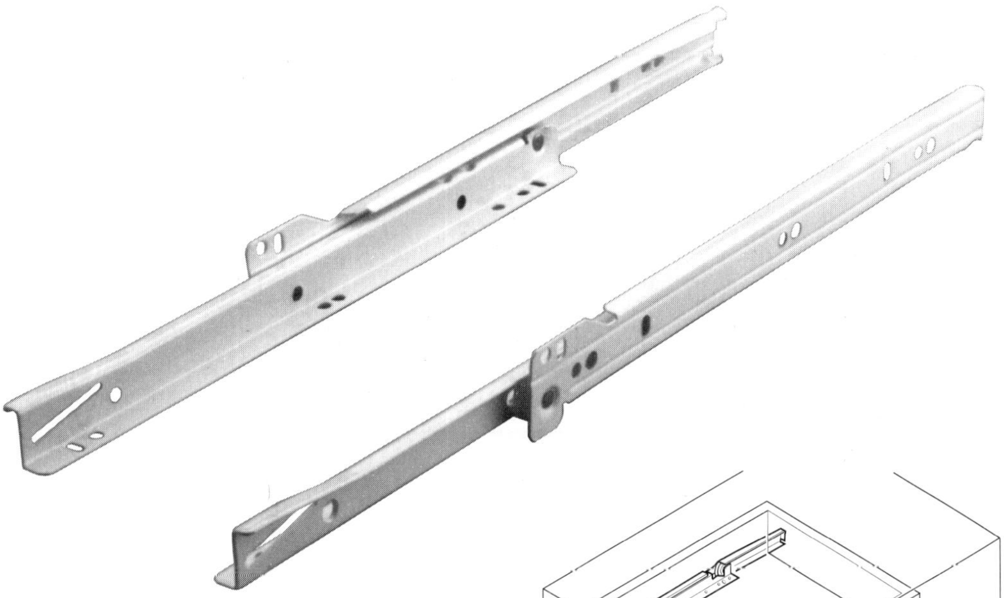

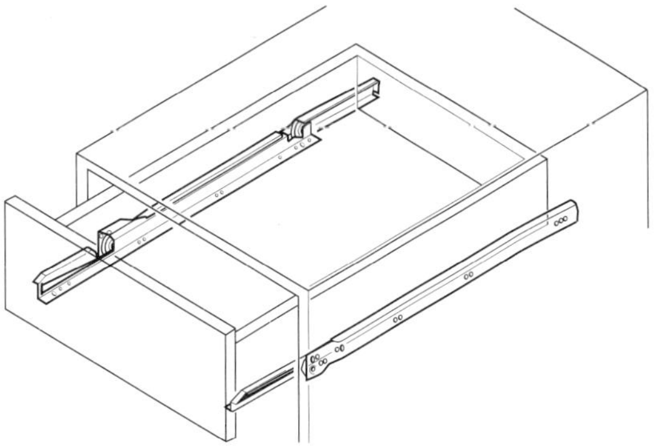

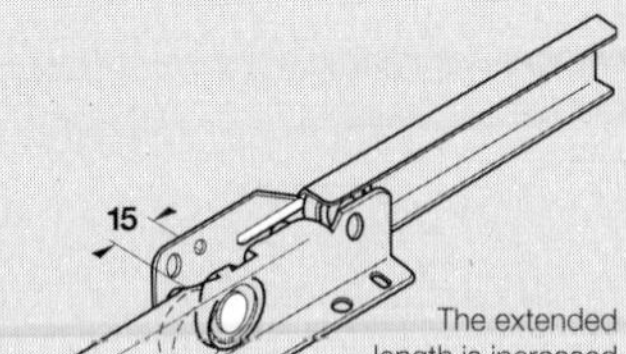

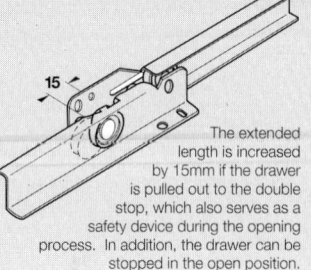

The extended length is increased by 15mm if the drawer is pulled out to the double stop, which also serves as a safety device during the opening process. In addition, the drawer can be stopped in the open position.

Self-closing
Soft-Roller

- load carrying capacity up to 30 kg (66 lbs.)/pair
- rollers: 4 friction bearing-mounted nylon rollers
- single-extension unit
- base mounted
- self-closing

Finish: steel, powder coated

Installed length		Extension length		Cat. No.	
inch	mm	inch	mm	Beige	White
12	300	8	212	423.36.327	423.36.318
14	350	10	262	423.36.372	423.36.363
16	400	12	312	423.36.425	423.36.416
18	450	13	352	423.36.470	423.36.461
20	500	15	396	423.36.523	423.36.514
22	550	17	436	423.36.578	423.36.569
24	600	18	474	423.36.621	423.36.612

Packing: 20 pairs, bulk pack on request

HOSPA ø3.5

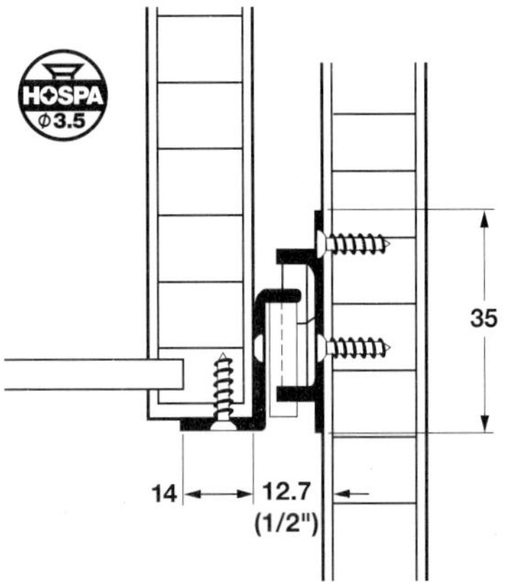

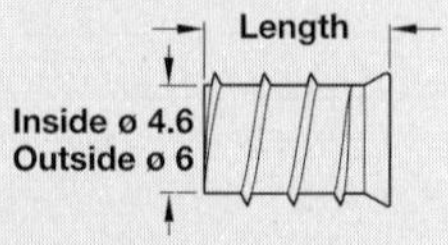

Varianta special screw

Countersunk head with cross-slots for ø 5mm system holes

Finish: steel, nickel plated

Length	Cat. No.
8 mm	013.14.719
10.5 mm	013.14.718
13.5 mm	013.14.727
16.0 mm	013.14.736

Packing: 500 pcs.

Screws sold separately.

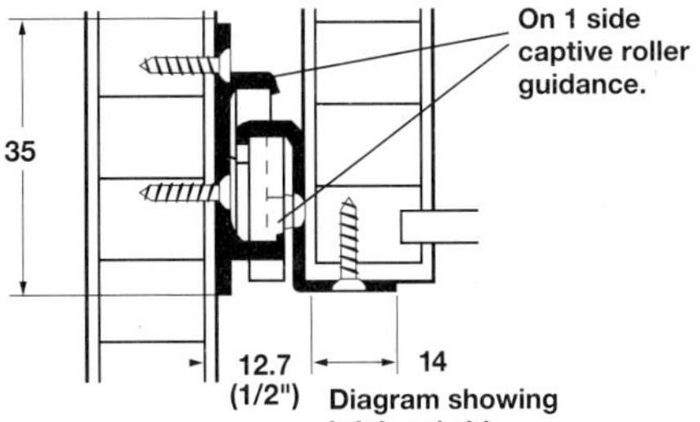

Diagram showing left hand side

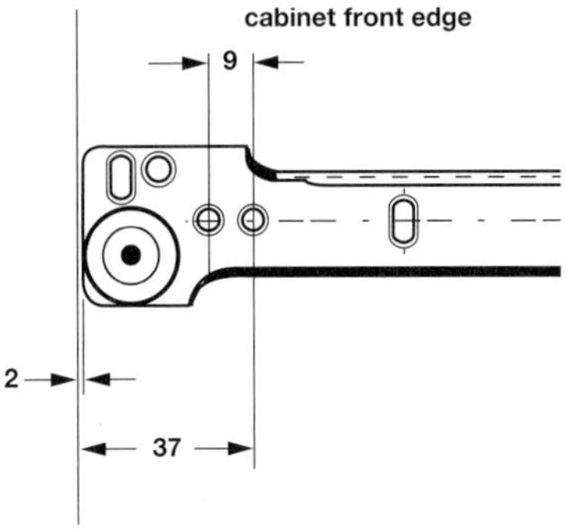

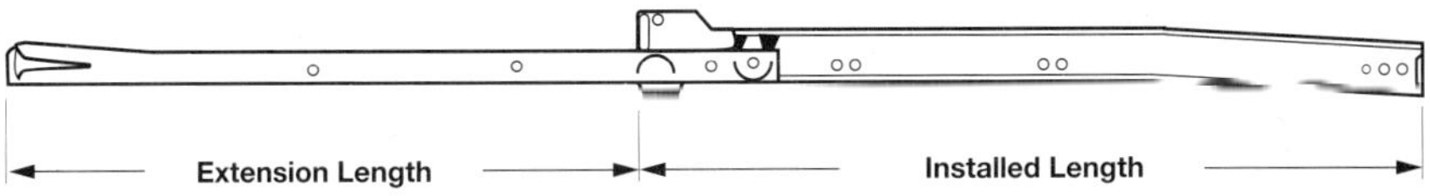

Dimensions in mm
Inches are approximate

Dimensional data not binding. We reserve the right to alter specifications without notice.

HÄFELE

Drawer Runners, Single-Extension Bottom-Mount

The drawer runners shown on this page are roller guide, single-extension systems, offering effortless, non-twist, silent operation. The special profile on the left-hand side with the captive roller guidance system ensures absolute lateral stability (see below). Manufacturing tolerances are compensated by the right-hand profile. A bevel, incorporated in the U-profile, prevents the rollers from being damaged by screw snagging against heads. The glides are equipped with double extension stop.

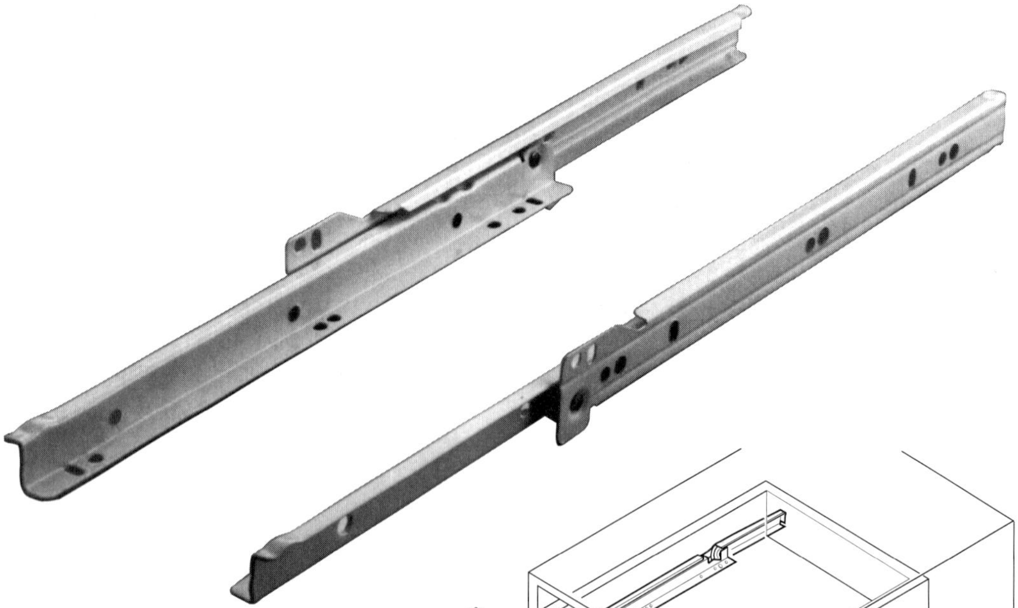

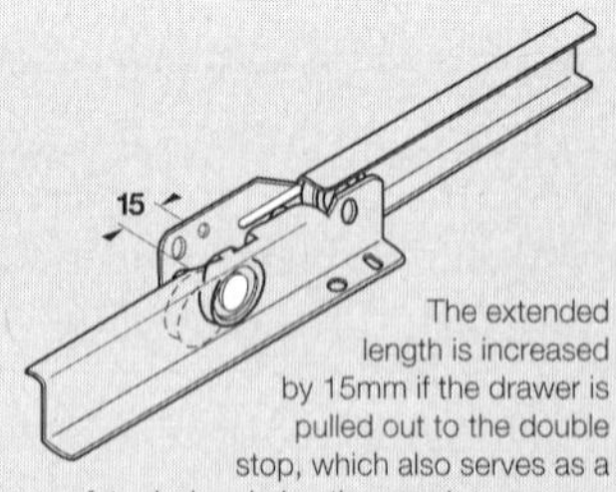

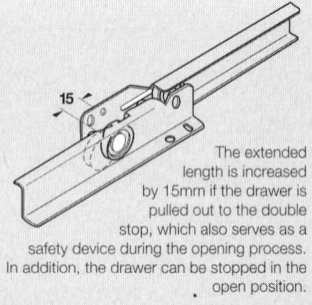

The extended length is increased by 15mm if the drawer is pulled out to the double stop, which also serves as a safety device during the opening process. In addition, the drawer can be stopped in the open position.

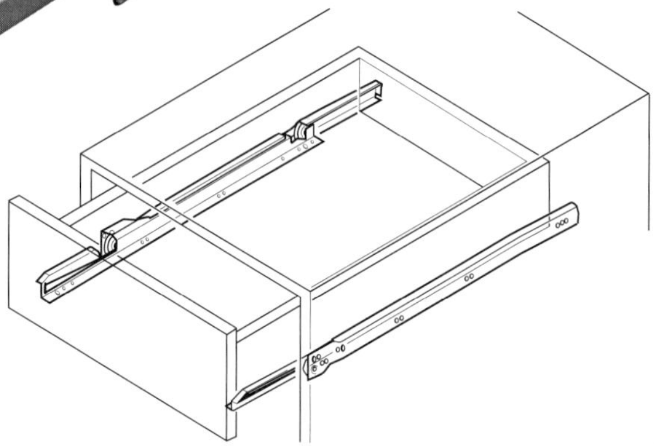

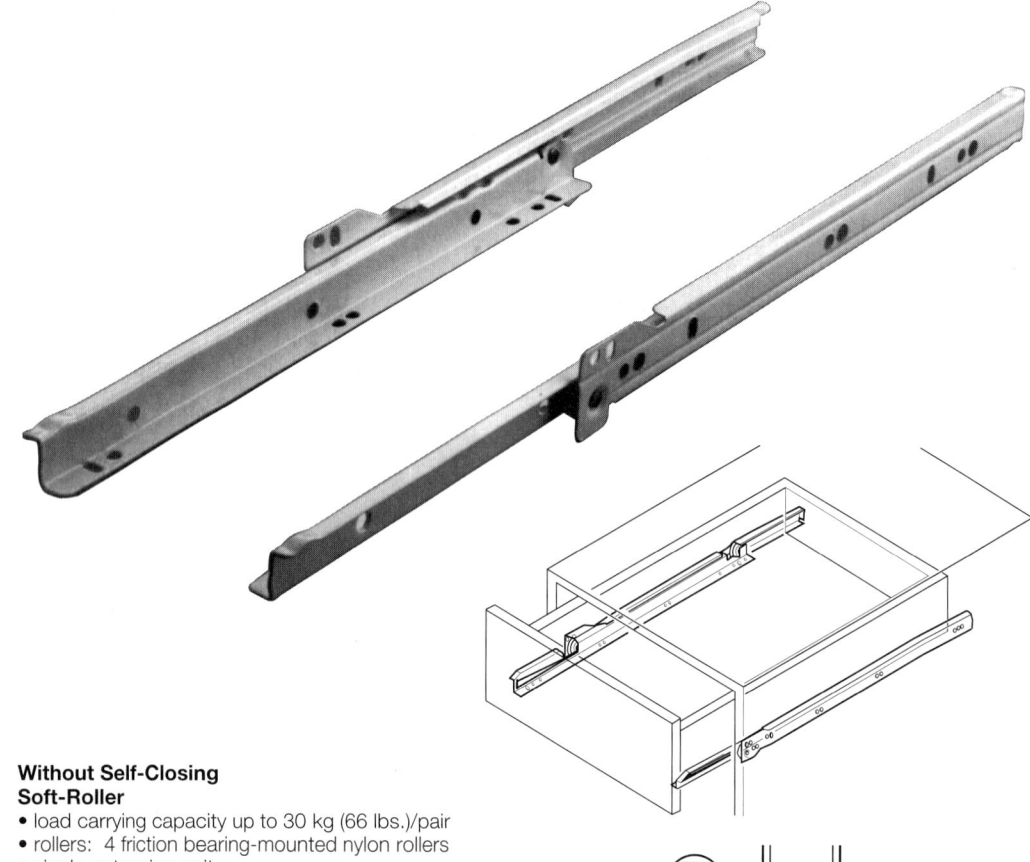

Without Self-Closing
Soft-Roller

- load carrying capacity up to 30 kg (66 lbs.)/pair
- rollers: 4 friction bearing-mounted nylon rollers
- single-extension unit
- Base-mounted
- self-closing

Finish: steel, powder-coated white RAL 9010

Installed length		Extension length		Cat. No.
inch	mm	inch	mm	White
12	300	8	212	423.35.311
14	350	10	262	423.35.366
16	400	12	312	423.35.419
18	450	13	352	423.35.464
20	500	15	396	423.35.517
22	550	17	436	423.35.562
24	600	18	474	423.35.615

Packing: 20 pairs, bulk packing available on request

HOSPA ⌀3,5

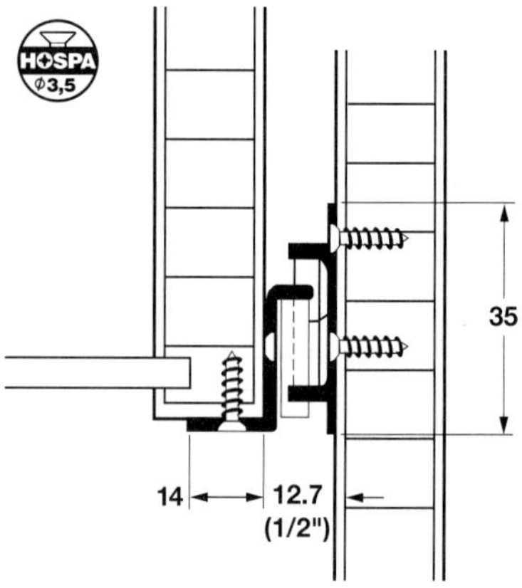

VARIANTA ⌀5

Varianta special screw

Countersunk head with cross-slots Z for series-drilled, ⌀ 5mm holes
Finish: steel, nickel plated

Length	Cat. No.
8 mm	013.14.719
10.5 mm	013.14.718
13.5 mm	013.14.727
16.0 mm	013.14.736

Packing: 500 pcs.

Screws sold separately.

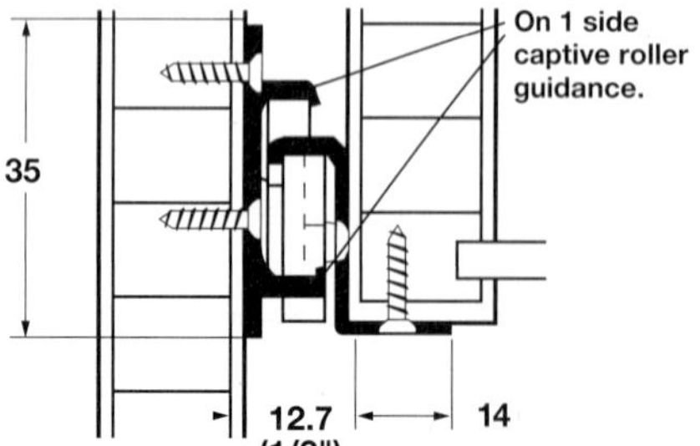

Diagram showing left hand side

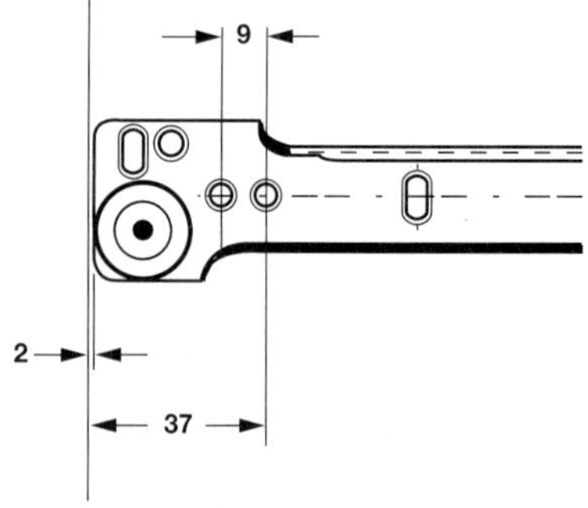

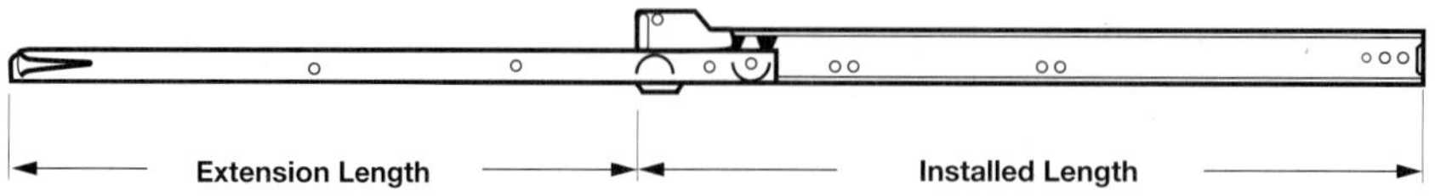

Dimensional data not binding. We reserve the right to alter specifications without notice.

Dimensions in mm
Inches are approximate

Rear Mounting Brackets for Epoxy Slides

Adjustable Rear Mounting Bracket, for use with self-closing slides, 423.36 series.
Use for face-frame applications.

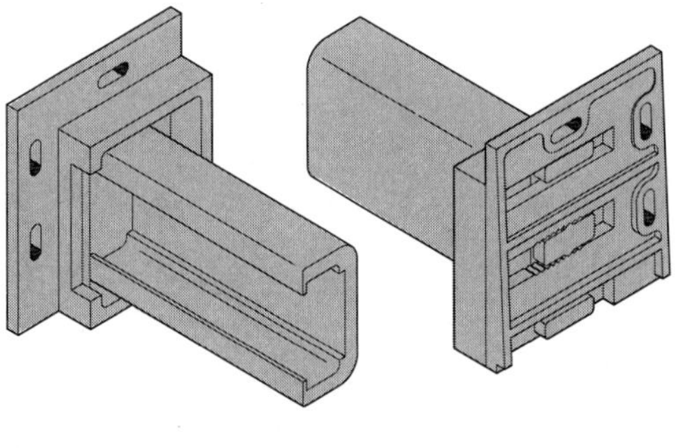

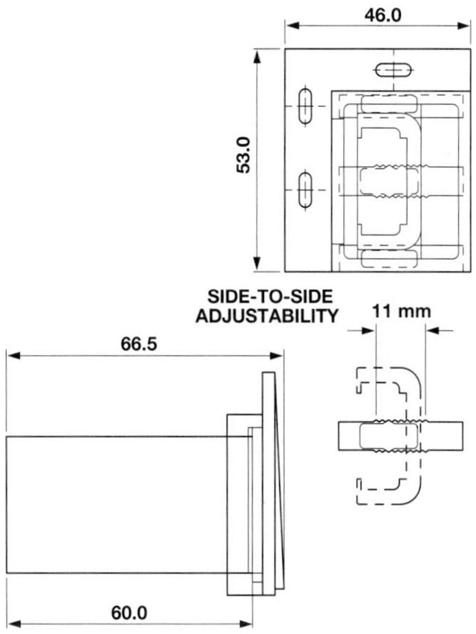

Finish: plastic

Cat. No.	421.86.916

Packing: 1 set

Rear Mounting Bracket, for use with non-self-closing slides, 423.33, 423.34, 423.35 series.
Use for face-frame applications.

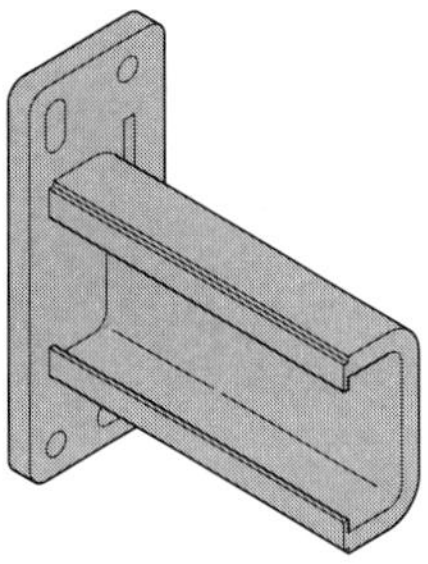

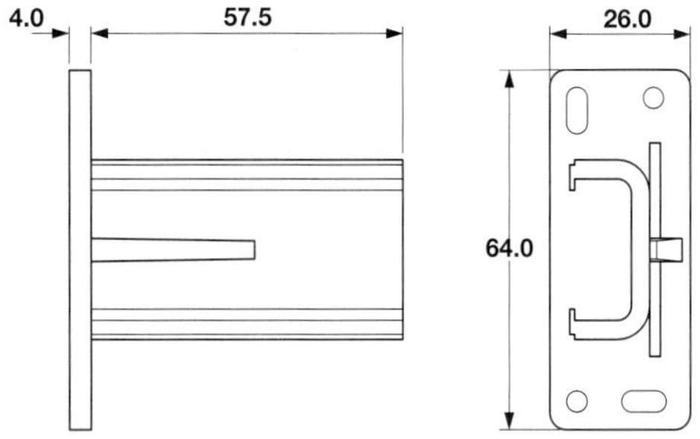

Finish: plastic

Cat. No.	421.71.906

Packing: 1 pc.

Distance Spacers for Drawer Runners, screw-mounted in ø5 mm system holes. Stackable.

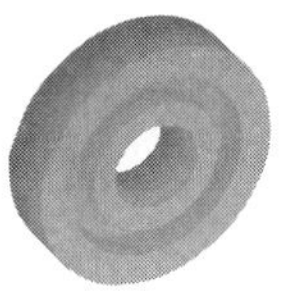

HOSPA ϕ3,5

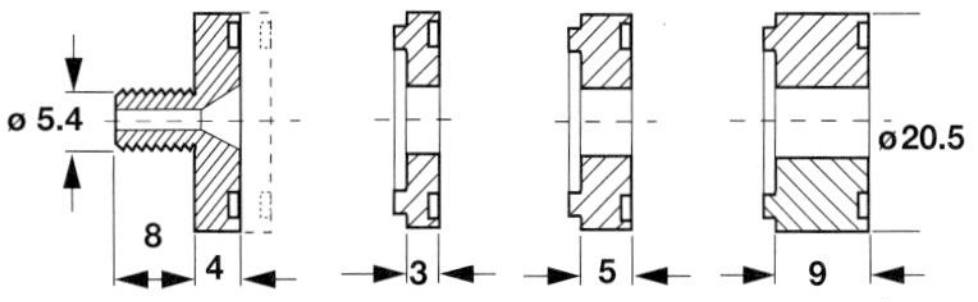

Finish: plastic, white

Cat. No.	4 mm with plug, 5 mm	037.93.708
	3 mm	037.93.717
	5 mm	037.93.726
	9 mm	037.93.735

Packing: 100 pcs.

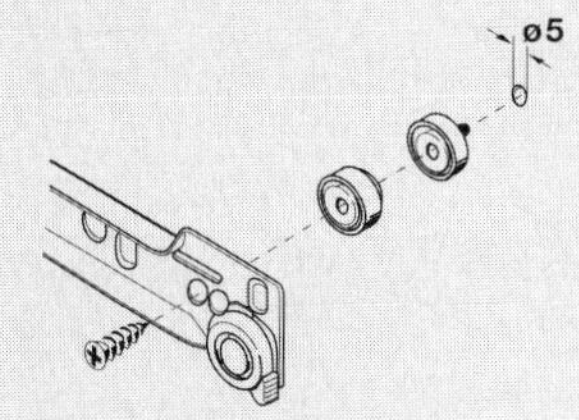

Dimensional data not binding. We reserve the right to alter specifications without notice.

HÄFELE

Self-closing, Drawer Runners, Full-Extension, Premium

- Patented middle rail reinforcement
- **High lateral stability** due to specially designed profiles
- Special cabinet rail shape prevents scraping of the rollers
- Middle rail return prevention
- patented buffer and pull-out prevention clip
- can be combined in 32 mm system holes with the partial extensions; Cat. Nos. 421.75., 421.79. and 421.80
- 32 mm-compatible

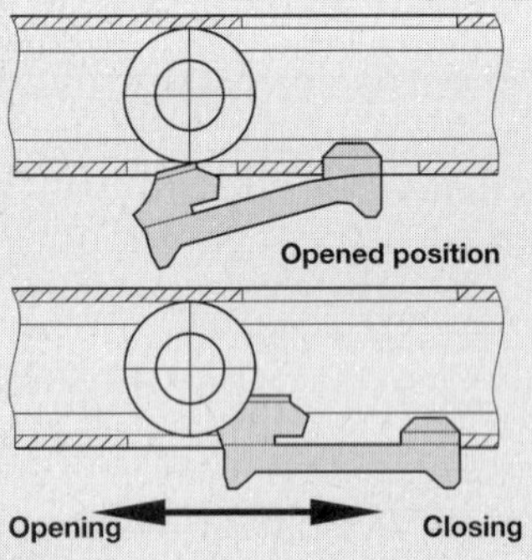

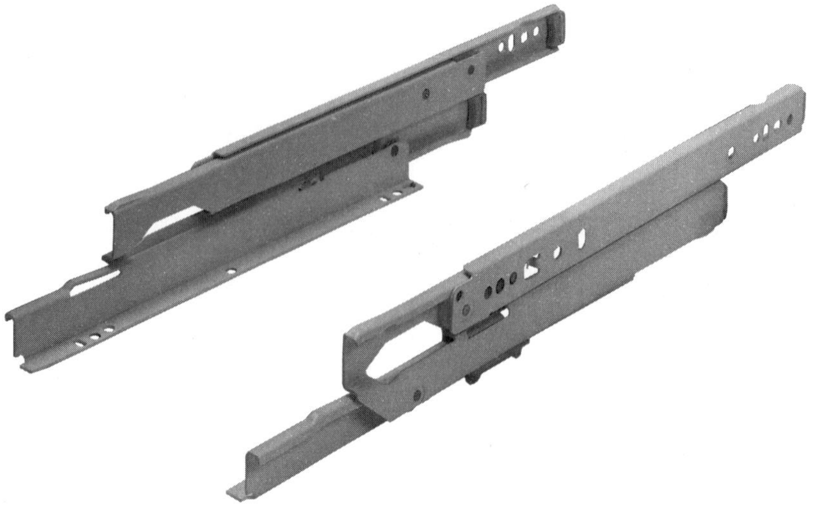

Mounting tip: drawer insertion
- withdraw middle rail up to return prevention
- Lift drawer rail rollers above middle rail rollers
- Push guide in until it stops

Important:
Open the withdrawal prevention before removing the drawer entirely.

Note: depending on application, this slide can carry up to 150 lbs.

Soft-Roller 45

- load capacity max. 45 kg (100 lbs.)/pair
- rollers: 2 quiet-action rollers, 6 friction bearing-mounted nylon rollers
- full-extension
- bottom-mount
- self-retracting
- double captive

Finish: steel, white RAL 9010, epoxy-coated

Installed length	Extended length	Cat. No.
200 mm (8")	200 mm (8")	423.46.721
250 mm (10")	250 mm (10")	423.46.776
300 mm (12")	300 mm (12")	423.46.791
350 mm (14")	370 mm (14½")	423.46.736
400 mm (16")	420 mm (16½")	423.46.741
450 mm (18")	470 mm (18½")	423.46.746
500 mm (20")	520 mm (20½")	423.46.751
550 mm (22")	570 mm (22½")	423.46.756
600 mm (24")	620 mm (24½")	423.46.761

Packing: 1 pair

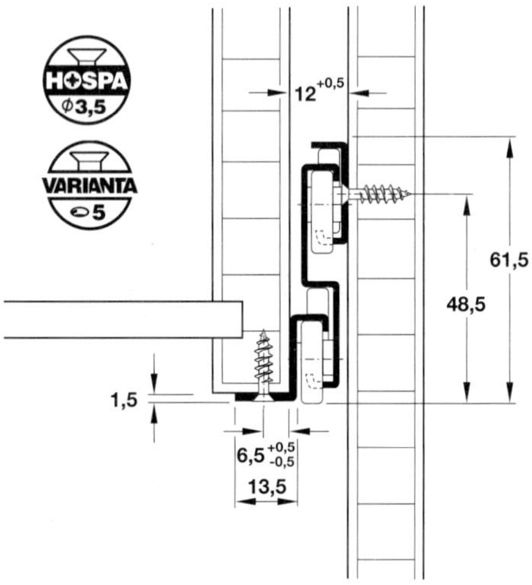

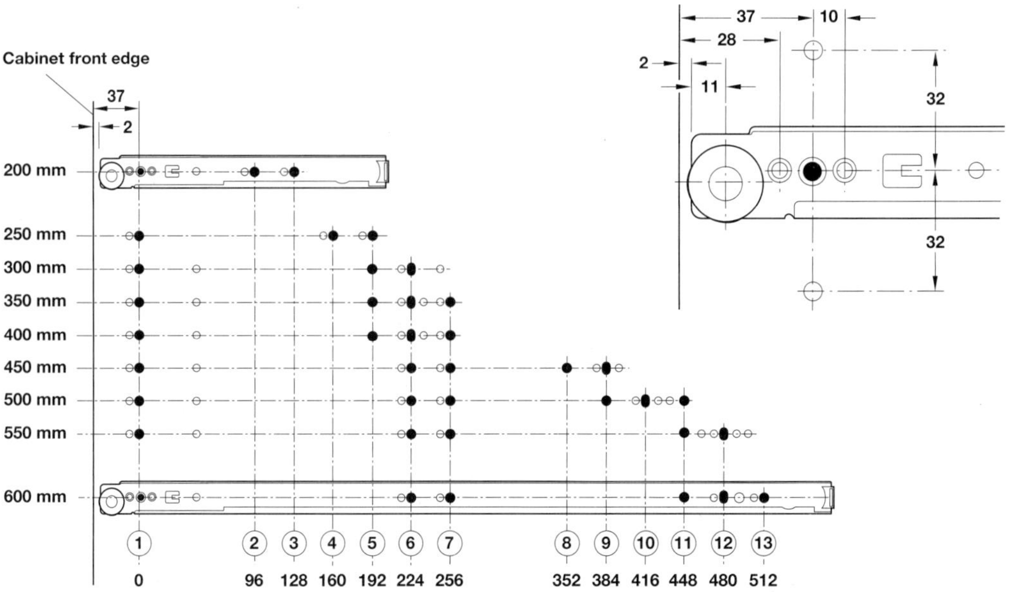

Dimensions in mm
Inches are approximate

Dimensional data not binding. We reserve the right to alter specifications without notice.

Drawer Runners, Full-Extension, Econo

HÄFELE

- New epoxy-coated full-extension soft-roller drawer slide.
- Stop lock device. Retention mechanism on the drawer members allows easy and quick insertion of the drawer.
- Dynamic load capacity of 30 kg (66 lbs.).

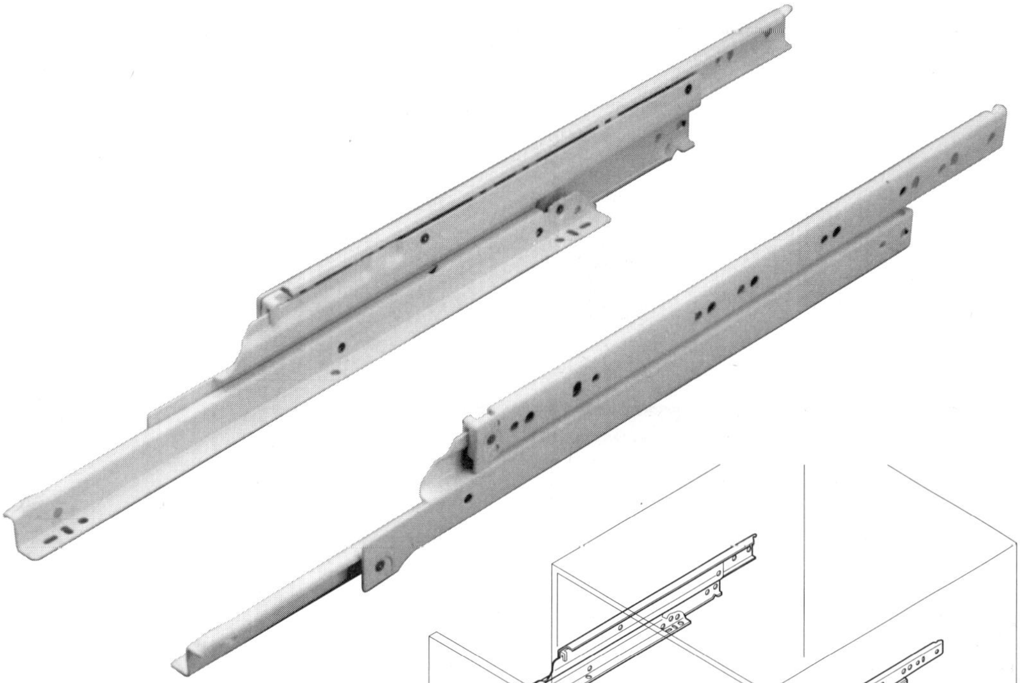

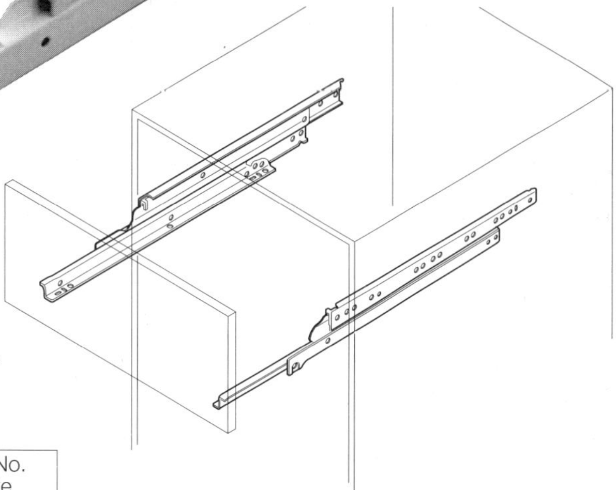

Sliding Door Hardware
Drawer Slides
Television Supports

4

Soft-Roller 30

- load carrying capacity max. 30 kg (66 lbs.)/pr
- rollers: 8 friction bearing-mounted nylon rollers
- fully-extended
- base-mounted

Finish: steel, epoxy-coated

Installed length inch	mm	Extension length inch	mm	Capacity	Cat. No. white (RAL 9001)
12	300	12	300	30 kg	423.25.324
14	350	14	350	30 kg	423.25.379
16	400	16	400	30 kg	423.25.422
18	450	18	450	30 kg	423.25.477
20	500	20	500	30 kg	423.25.520
22	550	22	550	30 kg	423.25.575
24	600	24	600	30 kg	423.25.628

Packing: 10 pairs bulk packaging per request

Runners can be mounted with Varianta special screws in Ø 5 mm system holes.

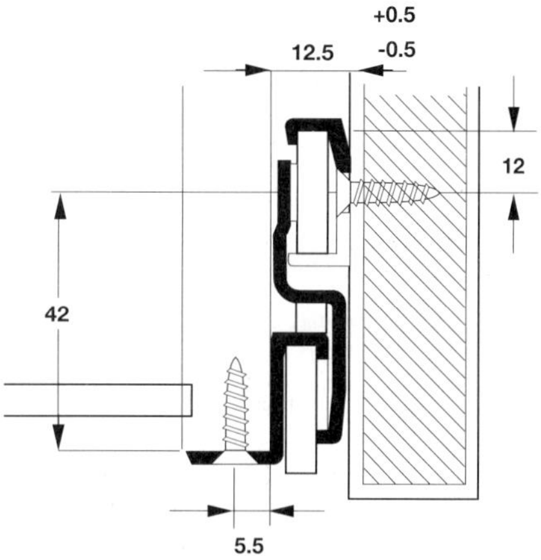

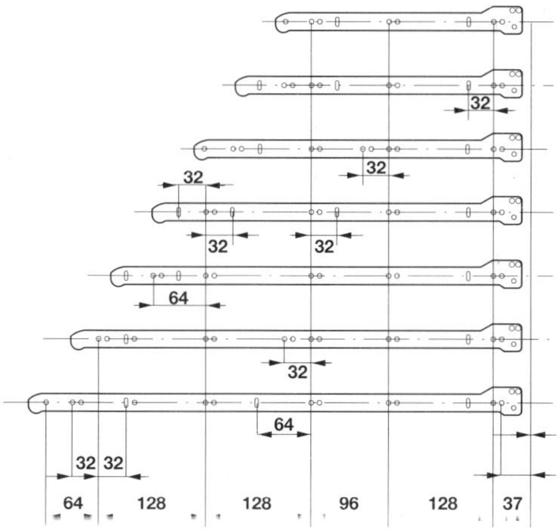

Dimensional data not binding. We reserve the right to alter specifications without notice.

Dimensions in mm

HÄFELE

Shelf Runners, Computer Keyboard

Laterally secure runners for extending keyboard shelves a load carrying capacity of 30 kg (66 lbs.), with locking facility in extended position.

- Ideal for pull-out keyboard trays or utility shelves.

Soft-Roller
- load carrying capacity up to 30 kg (66 lbs.)/pair
- rollers: 4 friction bearing-mounted nylon rollers
- single-extension unit
- shelf mounting

Finish: steel, light gray epoxy-coated to RAL 7035

Installed length	Extension length	Cat. No.
400 mm (16")	295 mm (11 5/8")	421.25.404

Packing: 1 pair

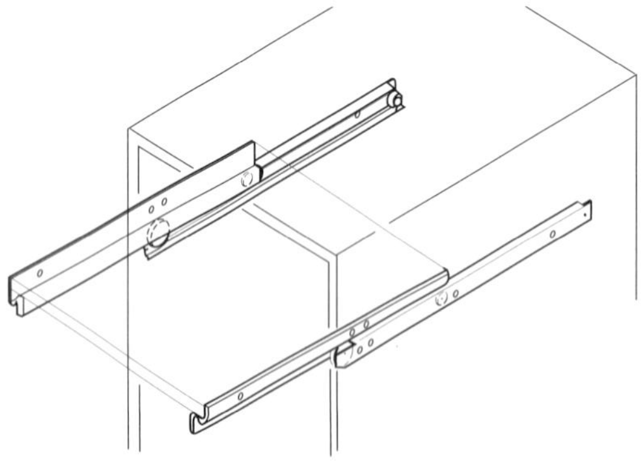

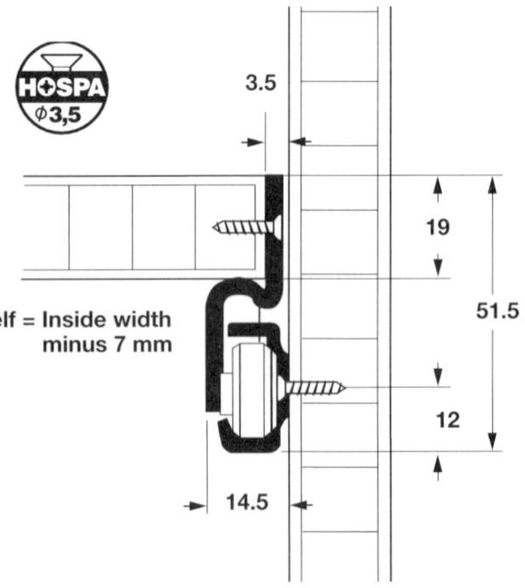

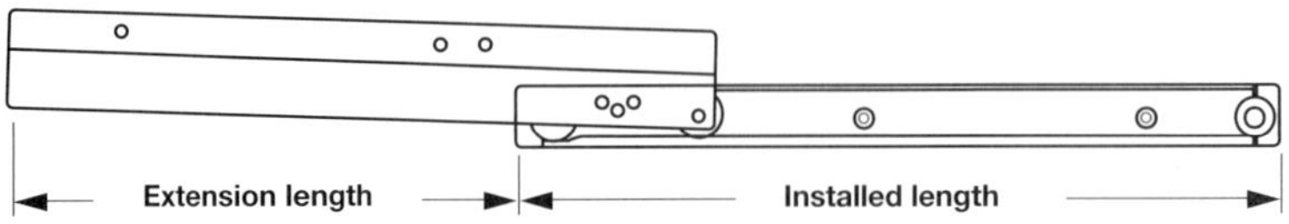

Dimensional data not binding. We reserve the right to alter specifications without notice.

Dimensions in mm
Inches are approximate

Shelf Runners, Self-closing

HÄFELE

Keyboard pullouts
- Top mounting brackets for shelf
  Easy to install, secure connection between slide and shelf
- Fits 32 mm hole pattern
  Cabinet can be pre-drilled for faster installation
- Nylon rollers with washer between profile and roller
  Smooth, quiet operation

Soft roller
- Load carrying capacity up to 25 kg (55 lbs.)/pair
- Single-extension
- self-closing

Finish: epoxy-coated, black

Installed length	Extension length	Cat. No.
350 mm (13¾")	260 mm (10¼")	421.23.335
400 mm (15¾")	310 mm (12¼")	421.23.340
450 mm (17¾")	360 mm (14¼")	421.23.345

Packing: 20 pairs per box

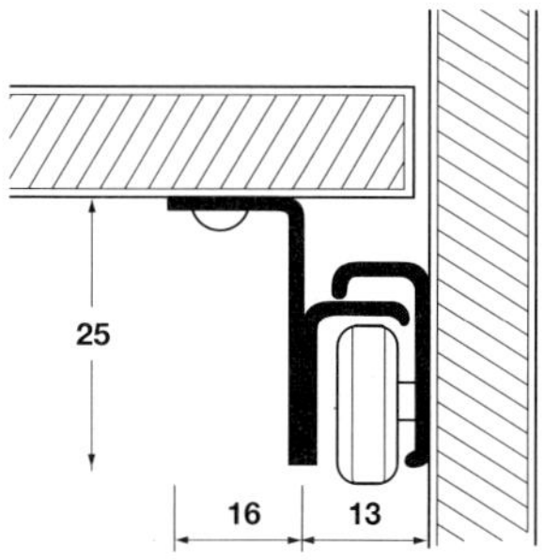

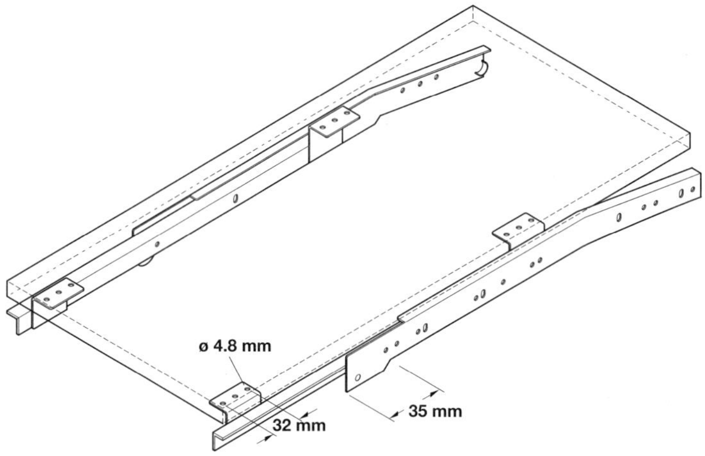

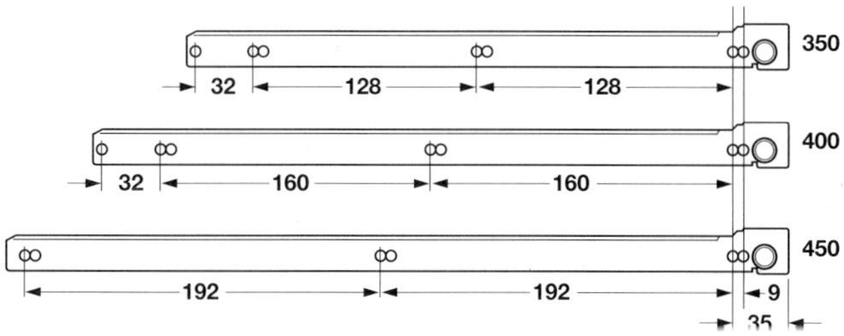

Dimensions in mm
Inches are approximate

Dimensional data not binding. We reserve the right to alter specifications without notice.

HÄFELE

17 mm Ball-bearing Slides

- Suitable for the needs of the furniture manufacturing and custom fitted kitchen industries.
- Lateral play is virtually eliminated when the groove mounting method is employed.
- Precision-running, ball-mounted single-stage extension.
- This runner here is small, stylish and space-saving.
- Easy-to-mount.

Mounting note:
- An M4 metal screw is sufficient to secure the guide rail in the drawer groove.
- No additional fastening (e.g. with wood screws) is required, since the load imposed by the drawer is carried by the groove.

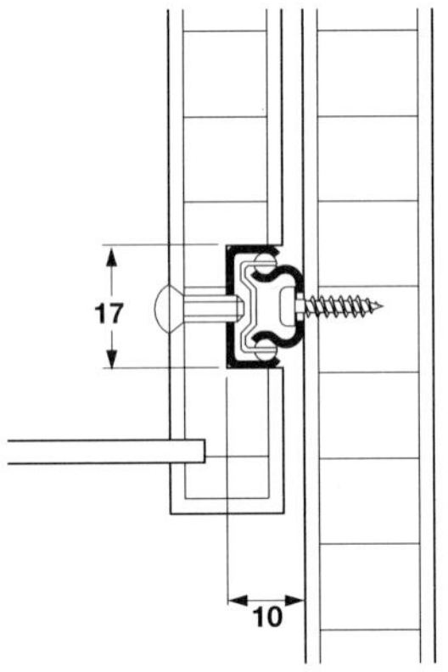

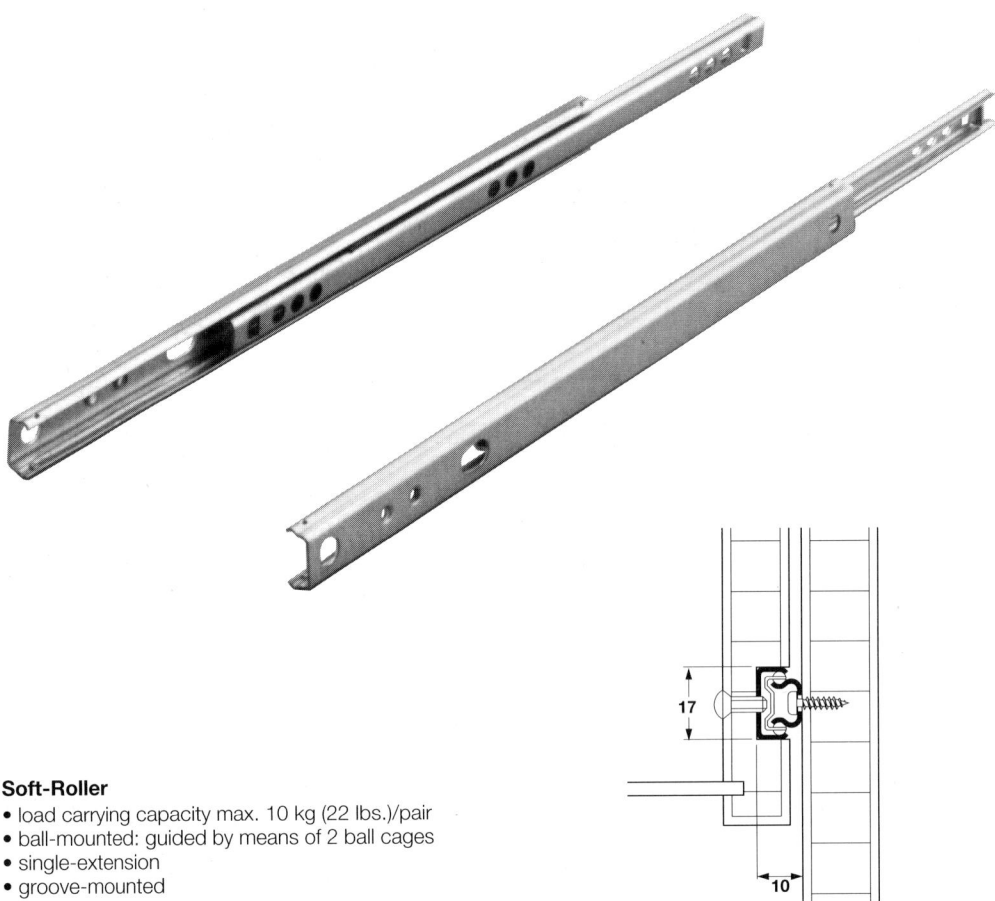

Soft-Roller
- load carrying capacity max. 10 kg (22 lbs.)/pair
- ball-mounted: guided by means of 2 ball cages
- single-extension
- groove-mounted

Finish: steel, galvanized

Drawer depth min.	max.	Installed length	Extension loss	Cat. No.
184 mm ($7\frac{1}{4}$")	- 288 mm ($11\frac{3}{8}$")	182 mm ($7\frac{3}{16}$")	50 mm (2")	420.58.186
216 mm ($8\frac{1}{2}$")	- 354 mm (14")	214 mm ($8\frac{7}{16}$")	74 mm (3")	420.58.211
246 mm ($9\frac{3}{4}$")	- 410 mm ($16\frac{1}{8}$")	246 mm ($9\frac{11}{16}$")	77 mm ($3\frac{1}{8}$")	420.58.257
312 mm ($12\frac{1}{4}$")	- 520 mm ($20\frac{1}{2}$")	310 mm ($12\frac{3}{16}$")	100 mm (4")	420.58.319
344 mm ($13\frac{1}{2}$")	- 550 mm ($21\frac{3}{4}$")	342 mm ($13\frac{11}{16}$")	102 mm ($4\frac{1}{8}$")	420.58.355
376 mm ($14\frac{3}{4}$")	- 635 mm (25")	374 mm ($14\frac{11}{16}$")	104 mm ($4\frac{3}{16}$")	420.58.373

Packing: 100 pair/box

Mounting screws
Hospa chipboard screws
pan head with
PZ2 cross slots
Finish:
steel, galvanized

HOSPA Φ3,5

Length	Cat. No.
15 mm	015.71.633
17 mm	015.71.642
20 mm	015.71.651

Packing: 1000 pcs.

Mounting screws
Threaded screws M4
flat head with
PZ2 combi-slots
Finish:
steel, galvanized

M4

Length	Cat. No.
10 mm	022.35.109
12 mm	022.35.127
15 mm	022.35.154
18 mm	022.35.181

Packing: 100 and 1000 pcs.

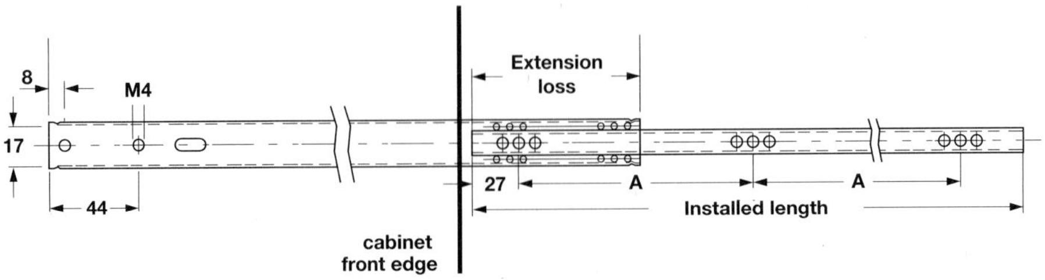

Dimensional data not binding. We reserve the right to alter specifications without notice.

Dimensions in mm
Inches are approximate

27mm Ball-bearing Slides

HÄFELE

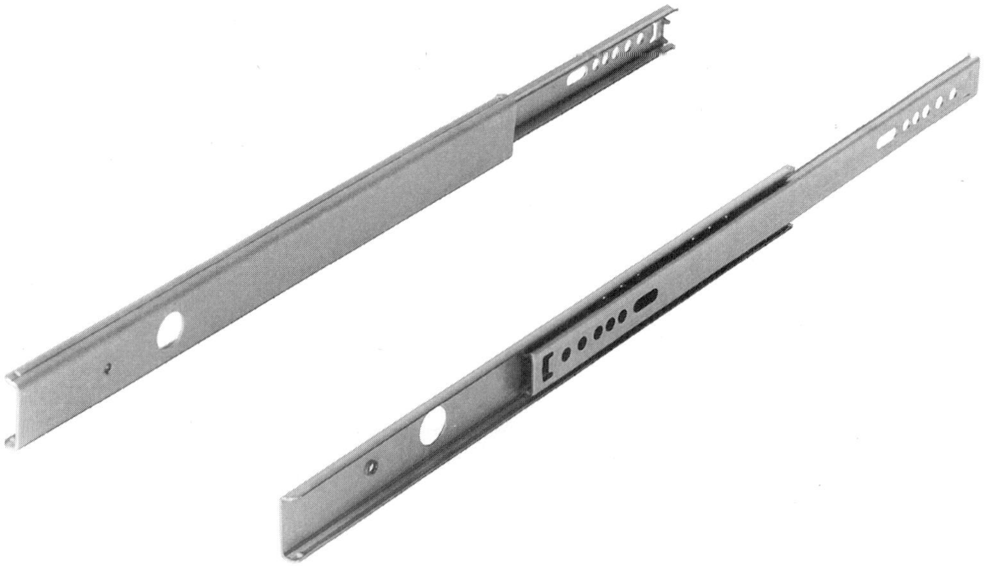

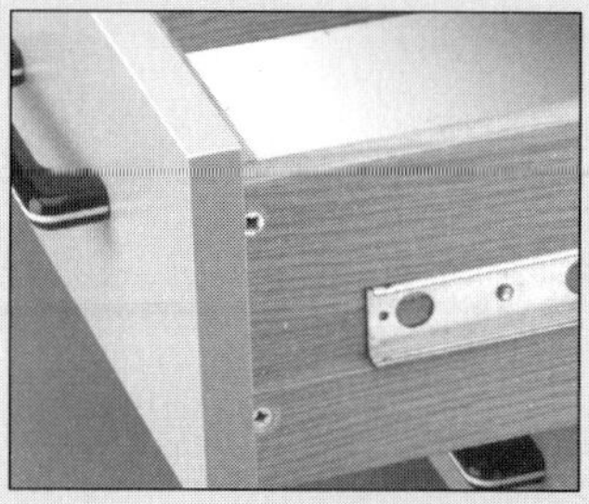

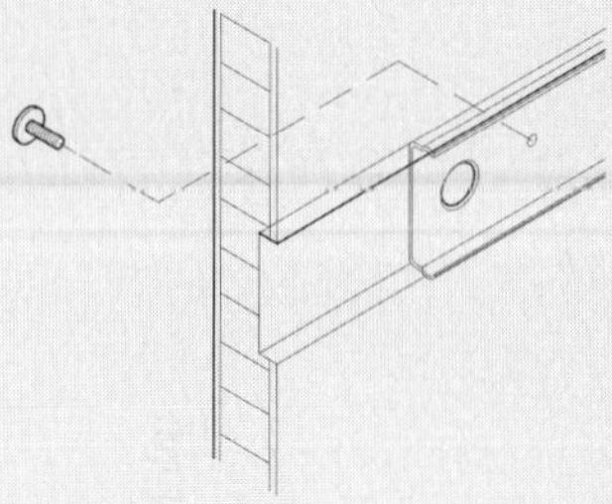

Soft-Roller
- load carrying capacity up to 15 kg (33 lbs.)/pair
- ball-mounted: guided by means of 2 ball cages
- single-extension
- groove-mounted

Finish: steel, galvanized

Drawer depth **min.**	**max.**	Installed length	Extension loss	Cat. No.
278 mm (11")	- 482 mm (19")	278 mm (11")	74 mm (3")	420.57.278
310 mm ($1\frac{3}{16}$")	- 538 mm ($21\frac{1}{4}$")	310 mm ($1\frac{3}{16}$")	81 mm ($3\frac{1}{4}$")	420.57.312
342 mm ($13\frac{1}{2}$")	- 588 mm ($23\frac{1}{4}$")	342 mm ($13\frac{1}{2}$")	97 mm ($3\frac{3}{4}$")	420.57.349
374 mm ($14\frac{3}{4}$")	- 648 mm ($25\frac{1}{2}$")	374 mm ($14\frac{3}{4}$")	98 mm ($3\frac{7}{8}$")	420.57.376
406 mm (16")	- 690 mm ($27\frac{1}{4}$")	406 mm (16")	122 mm ($4\frac{3}{4}$")	420.57.401

Packing: 50 pair/box

Sliding Door Hardware
Drawer Slides
Television Supports

4

- Self-positioning in groove.
- Only one fixing screw needed to attach to drawer.
- One-piece slide.
- Slides are recessed, resulting in more usable drawer space.
- Extremely economical.

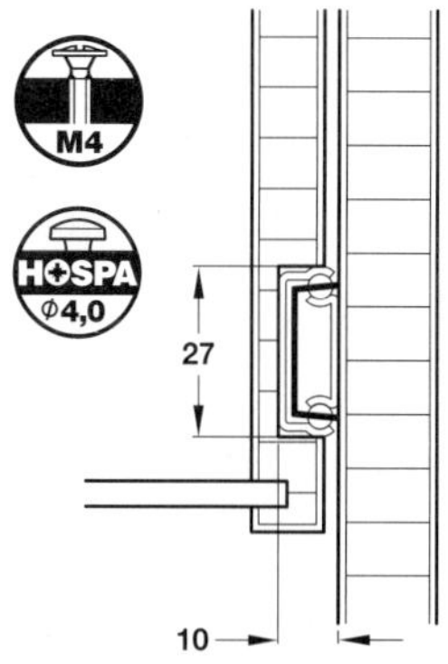

A note on groove mounting:
An M4 metal screw is sufficient to secure the guide rail in the drawer groove.
No additional fastening (e.g. with wood screws) is required, since the load imposed by the drawer is carried by the groove.

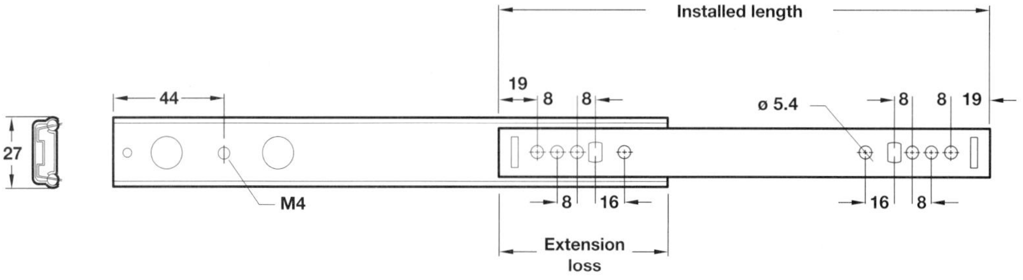

Dimensional data not binding. We reserve the right to alter specifications without notice.

Dimensions in mm
Inches are approximate

HÄFELE

37mm Ball-bearing Slides

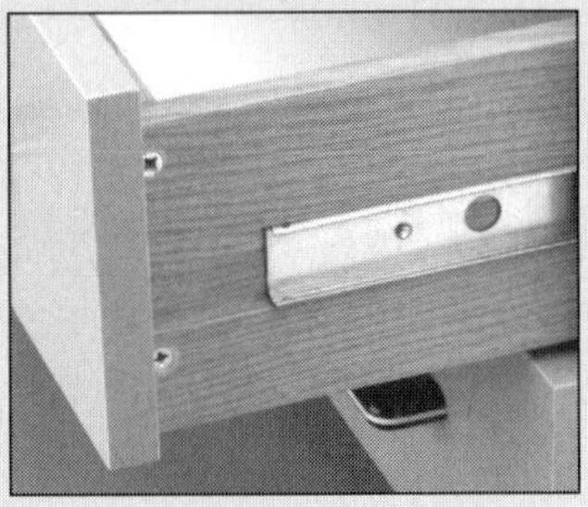

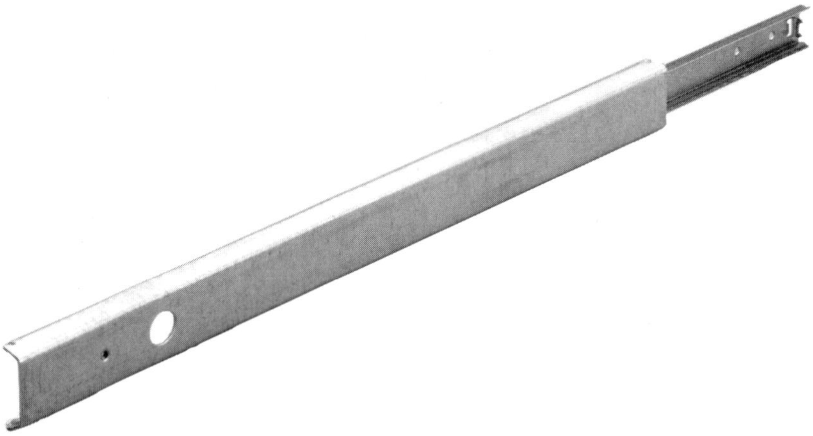

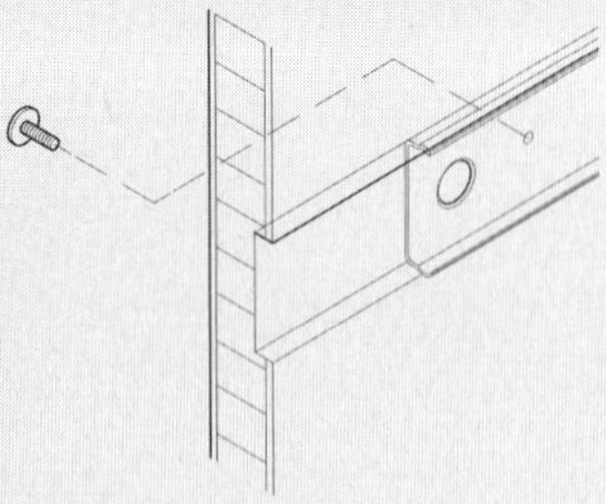

Sliding Door Hardware
Drawer Slides
Television Supports

- Self-positioning in groove.
- Only one fixing screw needed to attach to drawer.
- Fast assembly.
- Slides are recessed, resulting in more usable drawer space.
- Maximum lateral stability.

Soft-Roller
- load carrying capacity max. 25 kg (55 lbs.)/pair
- ball-mounted: guided by means of 2 ball cages
- single-extension
- groove-mounted

Finish: steel, galvanized

Drawer depth min.	max.	Installed length	Extension loss	Cat. No.
214 mm (8$\frac{1}{2}$")	- 340 mm (13$\frac{3}{8}$")	214 mm (8$\frac{1}{2}$")	88 mm (3$\frac{1}{2}$")	420.96.214
246 mm (9$\frac{3}{4}$")	- 405 mm (16")	246 mm (9$\frac{3}{4}$")	88 mm (3$\frac{1}{2}$")	420.96.246
278 mm (11")	- 470 mm (18$\frac{1}{2}$")	278 mm (11")	88 mm (3$\frac{1}{2}$")	420.96.278
310 mm (1$\frac{3}{16}$")	- 535 mm (21")	310 mm (1$\frac{3}{16}$")	88 mm (3$\frac{1}{2}$")	420.96.310
342 mm (13$\frac{1}{2}$")	- 600 mm (23$\frac{5}{8}$")	342 mm (13$\frac{1}{2}$")	88 mm (3$\frac{1}{2}$")	420.96.342
398 mm (15$\frac{3}{4}$")	- 680 mm (26$\frac{3}{4}$")	398 mm (15$\frac{3}{4}$")	100 mm (4")	420.96.398
473 mm (18$\frac{3}{4}$")	- 780 mm (30$\frac{3}{4}$")	473 mm (18$\frac{3}{4}$")	100 mm (4")	420.96.473

Packing: 30 pair/box

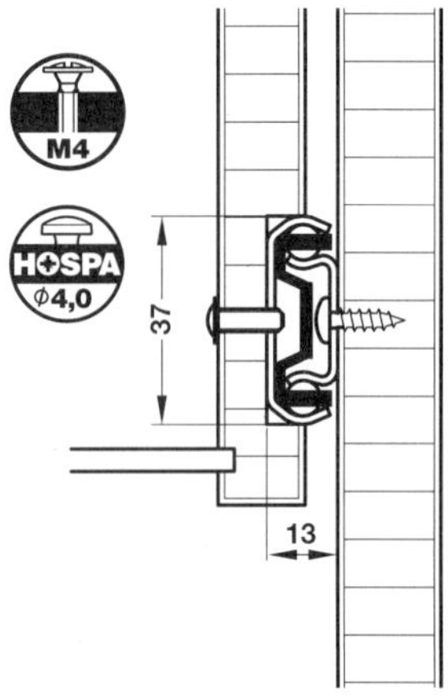

A note on groove mounting:
An M4 metal screw is sufficient to secure the guide rail in the drawer groove.
No additional fastening (e.g. with wood screws) is required, since the load imposed by the drawer is carried by the groove.

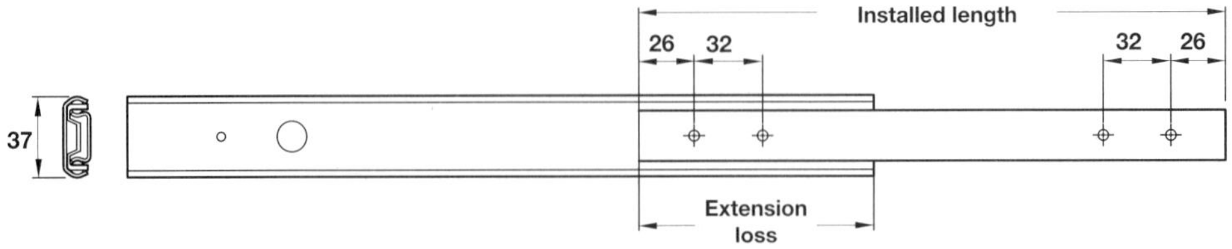

Dimensional data not binding. We reserve the right to alter specifications without notice.

Dimensions in mm
Inches are approximate

Concealed Undermount Slides - Single-Extension

HÄFELE

"Undermount 2000"

- Maximum lateral and vertical stability
- Quiet, smooth operation
- Self-closing feature
- Height adjustable
- Low profile

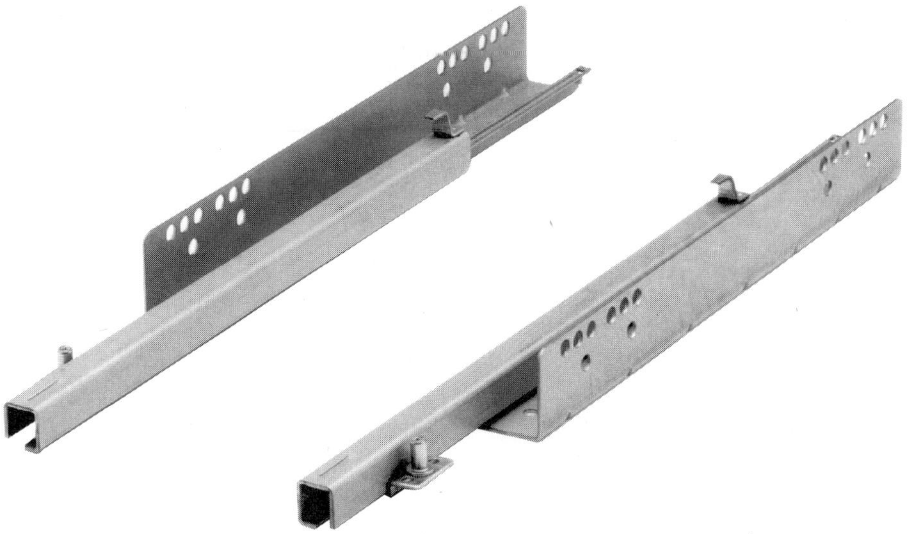

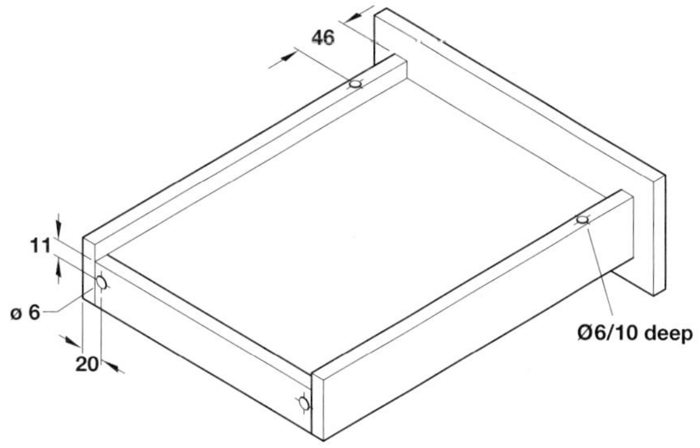

Soft-Roller

- Load capacity max. 30 kg (66 lbs.)/pair
- Roller bearings
- Single-extension
- Bottom-mount
- Self-closing

Finish: steel, electroplated

Slide Length	Drawer Length	Extension Loss	Cat. No.
10" 260 mm	250 mm	93 mm	423.55.925
12" 310 mm	300 mm	93 mm	423.55.930
14" 360 mm	350 mm	93 mm	423.55.935
16" 410 mm	400 mm	93 mm	423.55.940
18" 460 mm	450 mm	93 mm	423.55.945
20" 510 mm	500 mm	93 mm	423.55.950
22" 560 mm	550 mm	93 mm	423.55.955
24" 610 mm	600 mm	93 mm	423.55.960

Packing: 10 pairs

SYSTEM VARIANTA 32

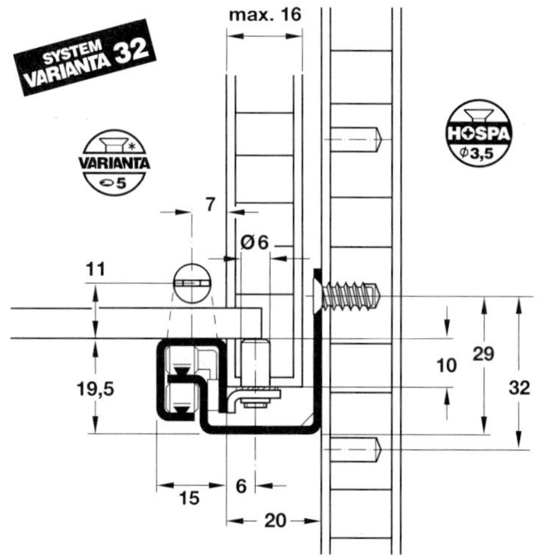

Min. Installation depth = drawer depth + 15 mm

Front edge of cabinet

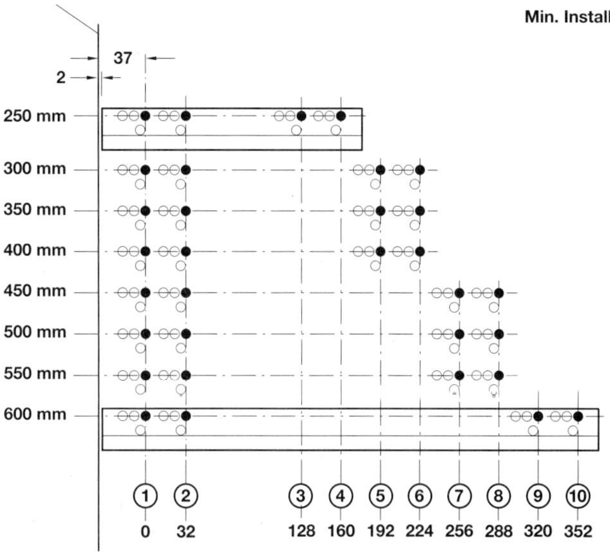

Hole pattern of cabinet member

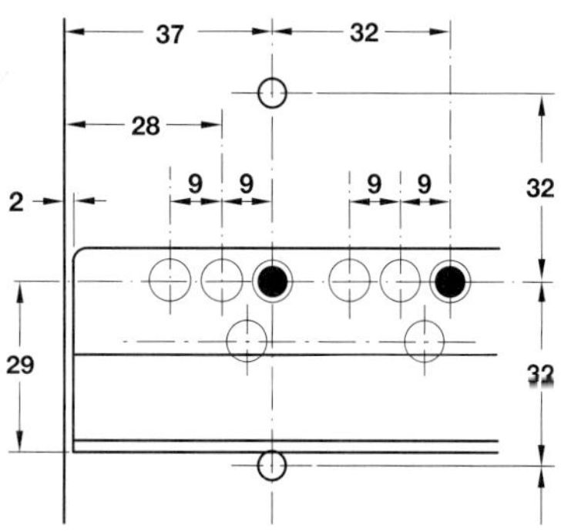

Dimensions in mm
Inches are approximate

Sliding Door Hardware
Drawer Slides
Television Supports

4

Fixing Screws:

Varianta Screws
Flathead with cross-slot PZ 2 for **Wood**
Finish:
steel, nickel-plated

Length (mm)	Cat. No. Ø5 mm
10.5	013.14.718
13.5	013.14.727
16.0	013.14.736

Packing: 500 pcs.

Hospa Screws
Countersunk with cross-slot PZ2
Finish:
Steel, zinc-plated

Length	Cat. No.
13 mm	015.31.620
15 mm	015.31.639
17 mm	015.31.648

Packing: 1000 pcs.

Dimensional data not binding. We reserve the right to alter specifications without notice.

HÄFELE

Concealed Undermount Slides, Full-Extension

"Undermount 2000"
- Maximum lateral and vertical stability
- Quiet, smooth operation
- Self-closing feature
- Height adjustable
- Low profile

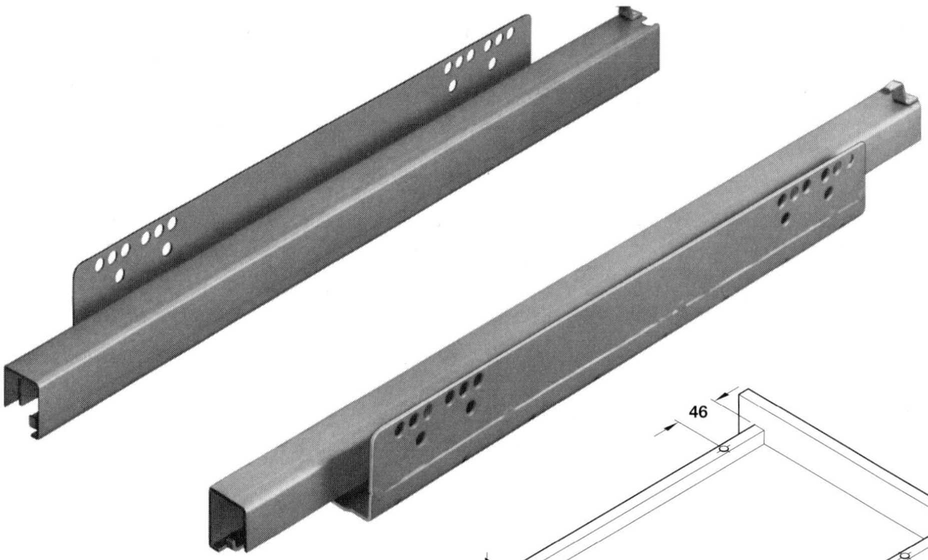

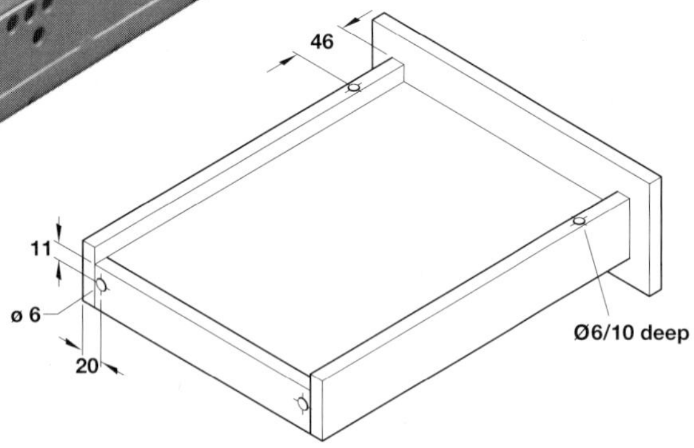

Soft-Roller
- Load carrying capacity max. 30 kg (66 lbs.) /pair
- Plastic carriage with rollers
- Full extension
- Base-mounted
- Self-retracting

Finish: steel, electrolytic

Guide length	Drawer depth	Over-travel	Cat. No.
10" 260 mm	250 mm	15 mm	423.57.926
12" 310 mm	300 mm	15 mm	423.57.931
14" 360 mm	350 mm	15 mm	423.57.936
16" 410 mm	400 mm	15 mm	423.57.941
18" 460 mm	450 mm	15 mm	423.57.946
20" 510 mm	500 mm	15 mm	423.57.951
22" 560 mm	550 mm	15 mm	423.57.956
24" 610 mm	600 mm	15 mm	423.57.961

Packing: 10 pairs

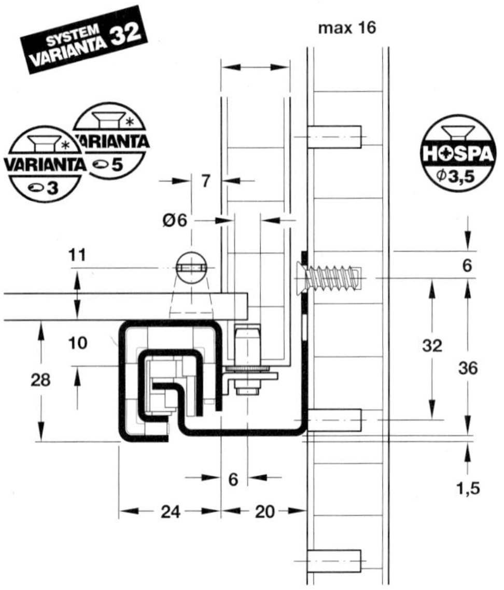

Min. Installation depth = drawer depth + 15 mm

Fixing Screws:

Varianta Screws
Flathead with cross-slot PZ 2 for **Wood**
Finish:
Steel, nickel-plated

Length (mm)	Cat. No. Ø 5 mm
10.5	013.14.718
13.5	013.14.727
16.0	013.14.736

Packing: 500 pcs.

Hospa Screws
Countersunk with cross-slot PZ2
Finish:
Steel, zinc-plated

Length	Cat. No.
13 mm	015.31.620
15 mm	015.31.639
17 mm	015.31.648

Packing: 1000 pcs.

Front edge of cabinet

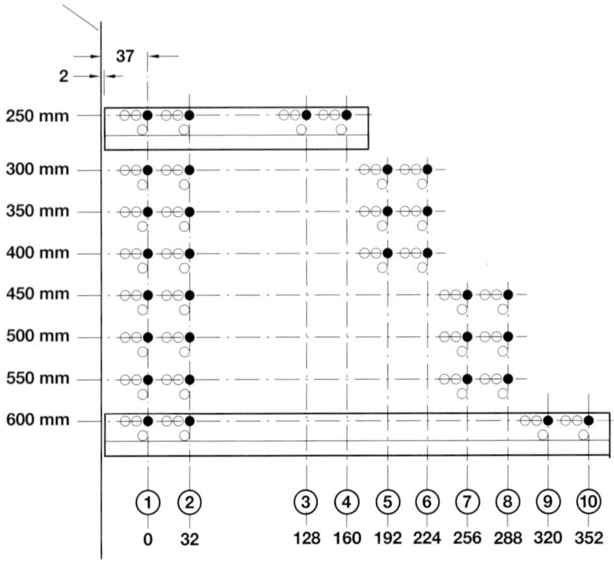

Hole pattern of cabinet member

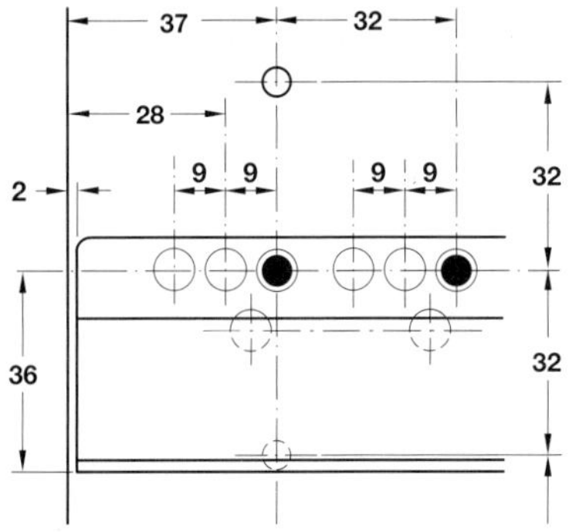

Dimensional data not binding. We reserve the right to alter specifications without notice.

Dimensions in mm
Inches are approximate

Concealed Undermount Slides, Single-Extension With Quick Release Latch

HÄFELE

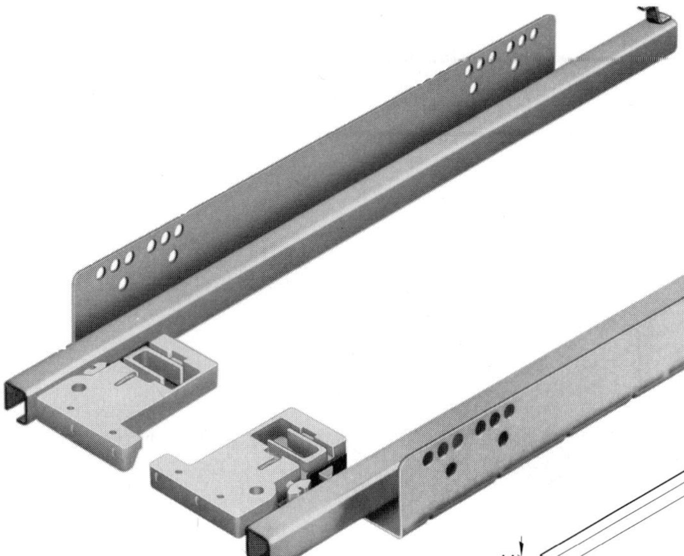

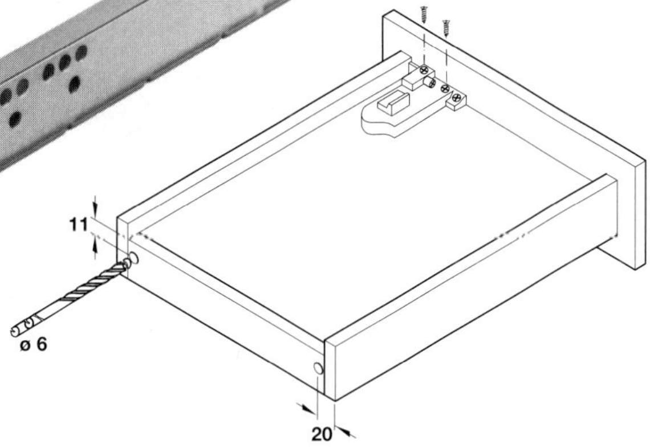

"Undermount 2000"

- Maximum lateral and vertical stability
- Quiet and smooth operation
- Self-closing feature
- Height adjustable ± 3 mm
- Quick attachment and release through plastic coupling
- Side adjustment of ± 2.5 mm
- Low profile

Soft-Roller

- Load carrying capacity max. 30 kg (66 lbs.) /pair
- Plastic carriage with rollers
- Single-extension
- base-mounted
- Self-retracting

Finish: steel, electrolytic

Slide length	Drawer depth	Extension loss	Cat. No.
10" 260 mm	250 mm	93 mm	423.55.826
12" 310 mm	300 mm	93 mm	423.55.831
14" 360 mm	350 mm	93 mm	423.55.836
16" 410 mm	400 mm	93 mm	423.55.841
18" 460 mm	450 mm	93 mm	423.55.846
20" 510 mm	500 mm	93 mm	423.55.851
22" 560 mm	550 mm	93 mm	423.55.856
24" 610 mm	600 mm	93 mm	423.55.861

Packing: 1 pair including quick release latch

SYSTEM VARIANTA 32

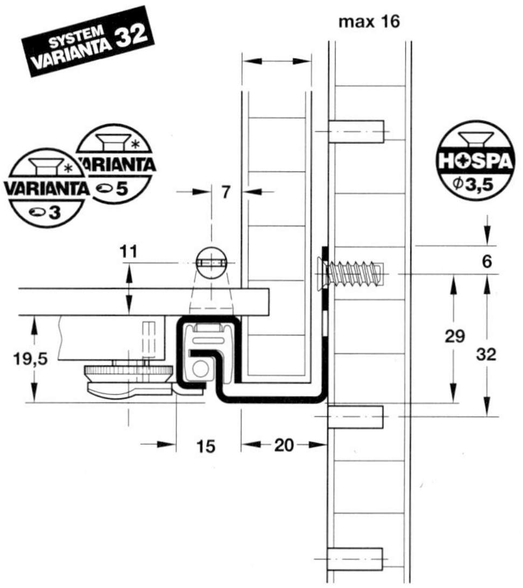

Min. Installation depth = drawer depth + 15mm

Sliding Door Hardware
Drawer Slides
Television Supports

4

Fixing Screws:

Varianta Screws
Flathead with cross-slot PZ 2 for **Wood**
Finish:
Steel, nickel-plated

Length (mm)	Cat. No. Ø 5 mm
10.5	013.14.718
13.5	013.14.727
16.0	013.14.736

Packing: 500 pcs.

Hospa Screws
Countersunk with cross-slot PZ2
Finish:
Steel, zinc-plated

Length	Cat. No.
13 mm	015.31.620
15 mm	015.31.639
17 mm	015.31.648

Packing: 1000 pcs.

Front edge of cabinet

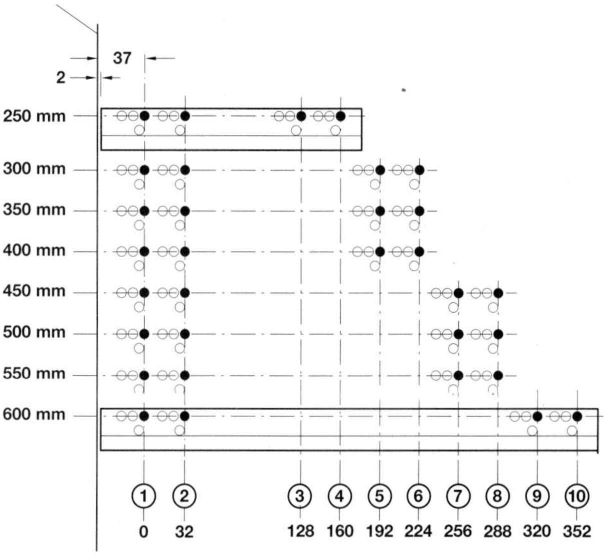

Hole pattern of cabinet member

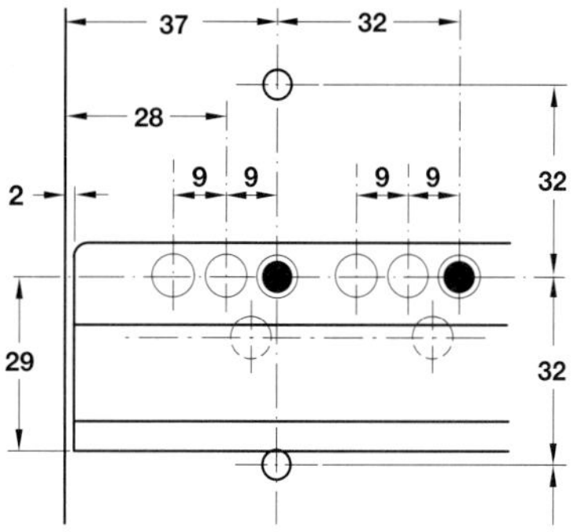

Dimensions in mm
Inches approximate

Dimensional data not binding. We reserve the right to alter specifications without notice.

HÄFELE

Concealed Undermount Slides, Full-Extension With Quick Release Latch

"Undermount 2000"

- Maximum lateral and vertical stability
- Quiet, smooth operation
- Self-closing feature
- Height adjustable ± 3 mm
- Quick attachment and release through plastic coupling
- Side adjustment ± 2.5 mm
- Low profile

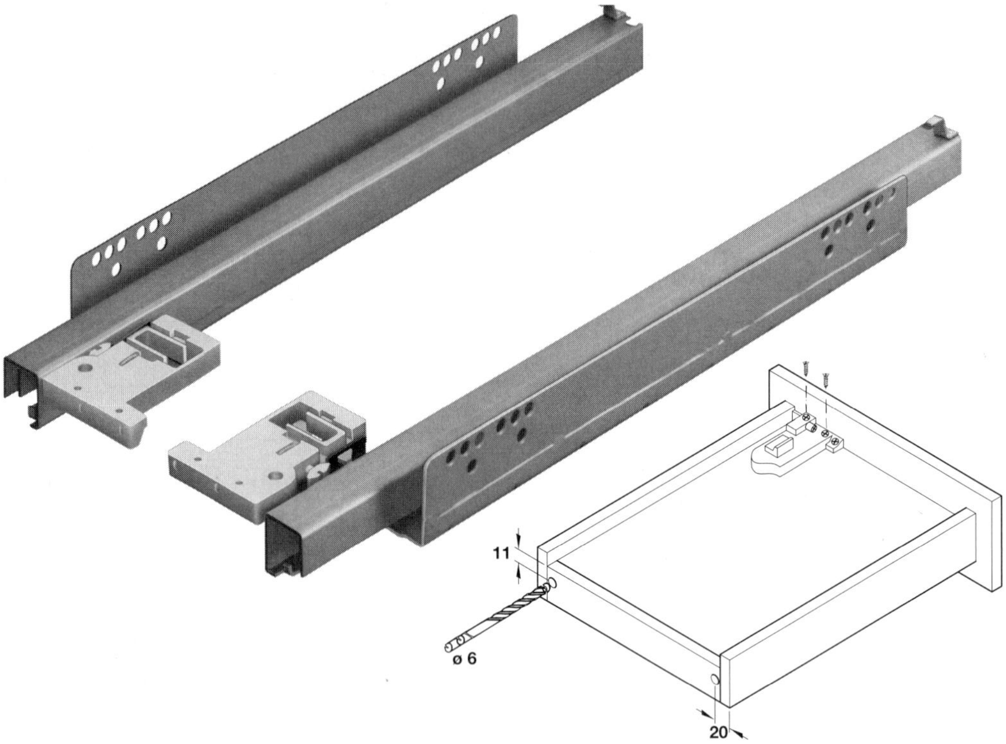

Fixing Screws:

Varianta Screws
Flathead with cross-slot PZ 2 for **Wood**
Finish:
Steel, nickel-plated

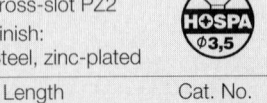

Length (mm)	Cat. No. Ø5 mm
10.5	013.14.718
13.5	013.14.727
16.0	013.14.736

Packing: 500 pcs.

Hospa Screws
Countersunk with cross-slot PZ2
Finish:
Steel, zinc-plated

Length	Cat. No.
13 mm	015.31.620
15 mm	015.31.639
17 mm	015.31.648

Packing: 1000 pcs.

Soft-Roller

- Load carrying capacity max. 30 kg (66 lbs.) /pair
- Plastic carriage with rollers
- Full-extension
- Base-mounted
- Self-retracting

Finish: steel, electrolytic

Slide length	Drawer length	Over-travel	Cat. No.
10" 260 mm	250 mm	15 mm	423.57.826
12" 310 mm	300 mm	15 mm	423.57.831
14" 360 mm	350 mm	15 mm	423.57.836
16" 410 mm	400 mm	15 mm	423.57.841
18" 460 mm	450 mm	15 mm	423.57.846
20" 510 mm	500 mm	15 mm	423.57.851
22" 560 mm	550 mm	15 mm	423.57.856
24" 610 mm	600 mm	15 mm	423.57.861

Packing: 10 pairs including quick release latch

SYSTEM VARIANTA 32

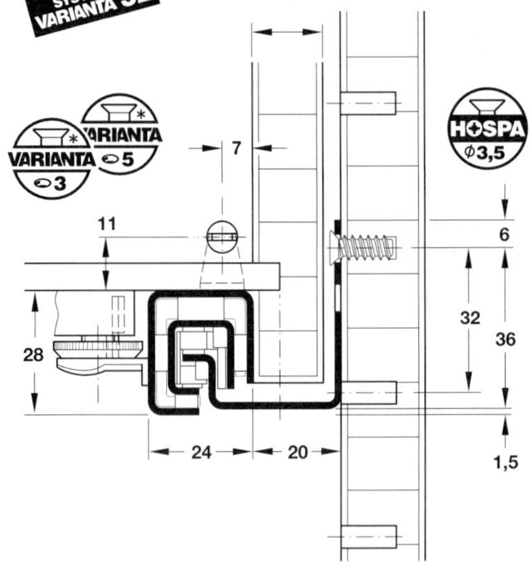

Min. Installation depth = drawer depth + 15 mm

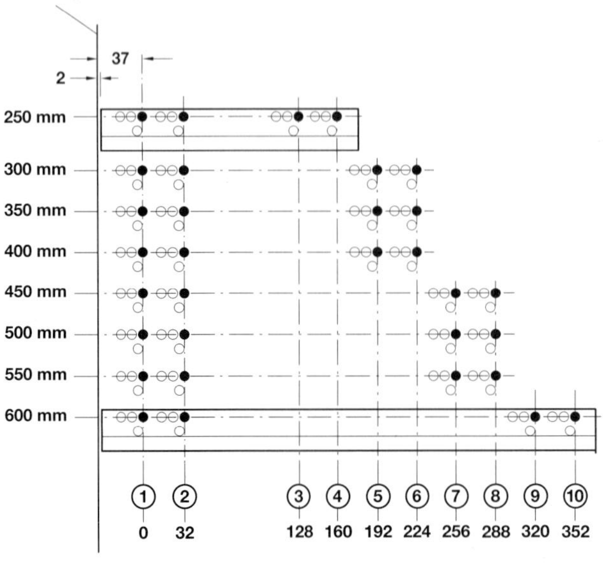

Hole pattern of cabinet member

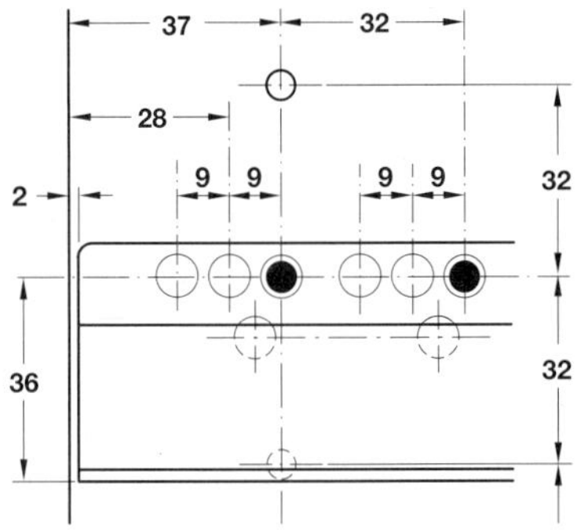

Dimensional data not binding. We reserve the right to alter specifications without notice.

Dimensions in mm
Inches are approximate

Drawer Runners with Fold-Down Front Bracket

HÄFELE

- easy hook-in key-hole attachment
- adjustment slots for horizontal/ vertical adjustment of front plate

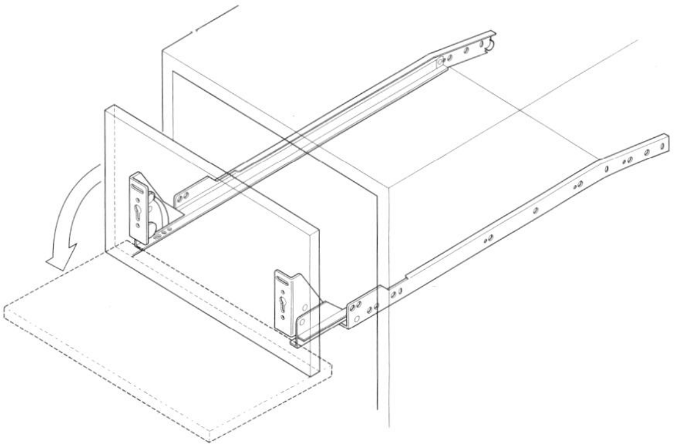

Soft-Roller
- self-closing
- weight capacity 30 kg. (66 lbs.)
- 90° to 180°
- positive lock closed position
- single-extension

Finish: steel, brown

Length	Cat. No.
400 mm (16")	423.48.140

Packing: 15 pairs

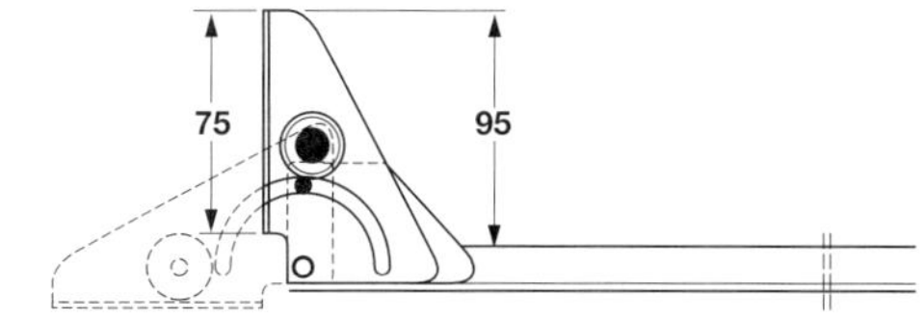

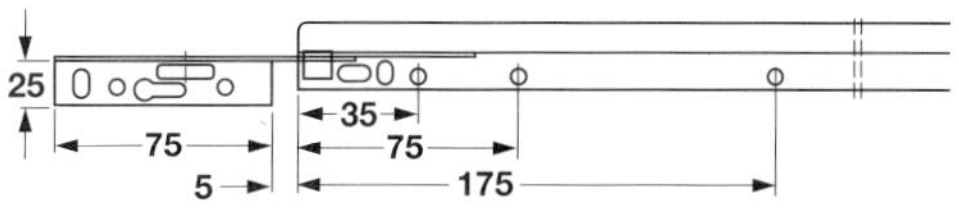

Fold-Down Bracket for Drawer Fronts

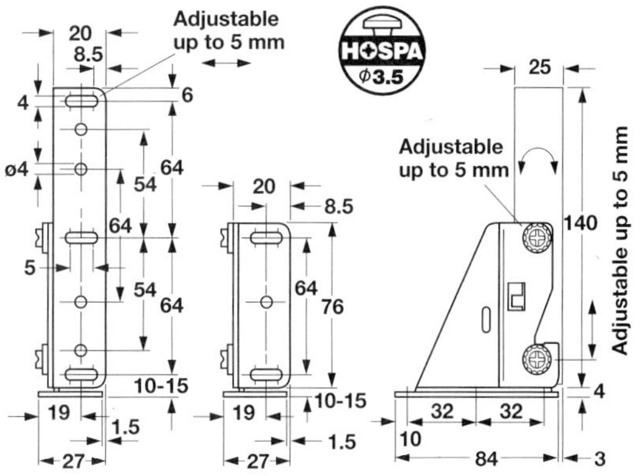

- Screw-mounted to drawer base, this element permits infinitely variable vertical and horizontal alignment of the front panel.
- All adjustments occur only within the element itself, and are thus independent of the drawer guide.
- Front panel or trim can be removed from the foot component along with the adjuster.

Finish: steel, white plastic-coated to RAL 9010

Trim height	Bracket height	Cat. No.
up to 160 mm	76 mm	421.39.711
from 160 mm	140 mm	421.39.720

Packing: 1 pair

Dimensions in mm

Dimensional data not binding. We reserve the right to alter specifications without notice.

HÄFELE

- Drawer fronts remain stationary when one side is pulled open.
- Safe to operate, with built-in front stops.
- Exceptional running action and absolute lateral stability due to a double-sided roller guidance system.
- Easy to install by means of a special drawer profile and an installation template.
- Hold-in detent.

Anceps Two-Way Drawer System

"Anceps" is a two-way drawer runner system. Comprising a roller guided, single-extension system of 12 kg (26 lbs.) load carrying capacity, it is intended especially for installation in room dividers, and islands.

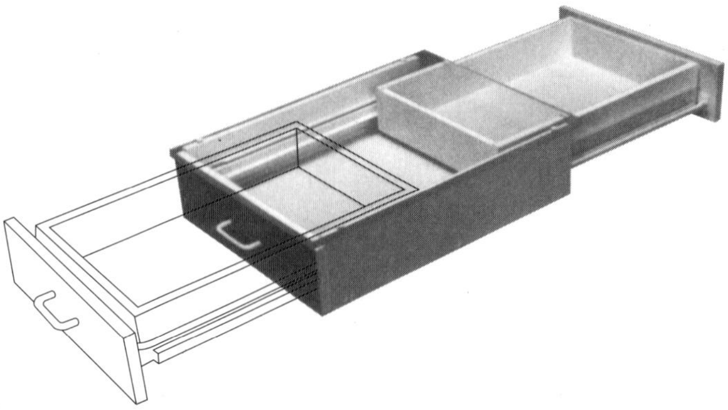

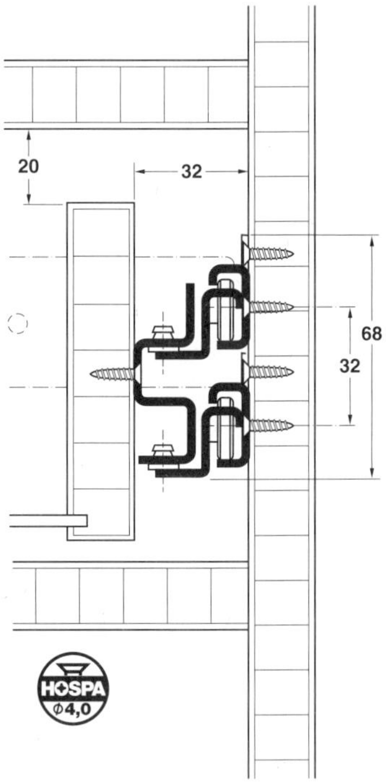

HOSPA Φ4,0

Cabinet depth 510 – 600 mm (21 inch - 24 inch)

Finish: steel, white epoxy-coated to RAL 9010

Installed length	Extension length	Cat. No.
502 mm (19¾")	400 mm (15¾")	420.53.529

Packing: 1 set

"Anceps" drawer system function:

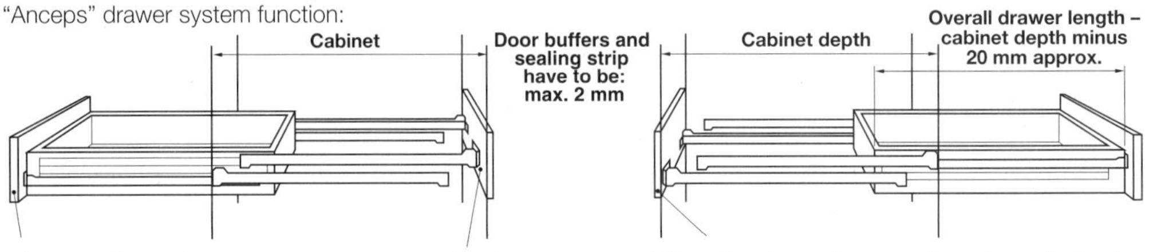

When the drawer is opened on one side . . . . . . the drawer front on the other side remains in side, filling the opening as if the drawer were closed.

When the drawer is closed again . . . . . . it can be pulled out on the other side, leaving the other drawer front in the opposing opening.

"Anceps" Soft-Roller

- load carrying capacity up to 12 kg (26 lbs.) /pair
- rollers: 8 friction bearing-mounted nylon rollers
- single-extension
- side mounting

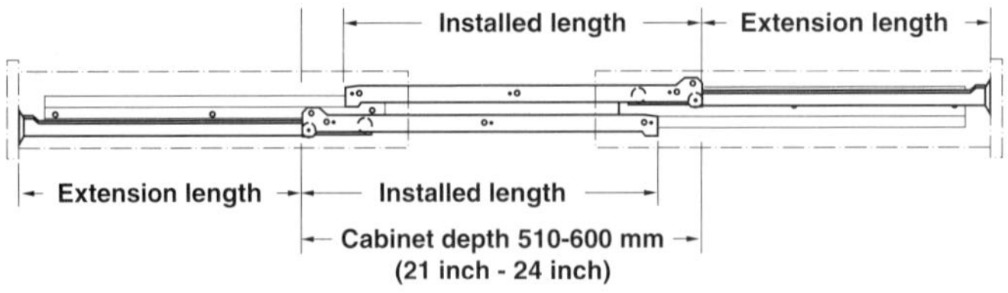

Installation template

Slide templates into position flush in front and back of cabinet side and mark accordingly (adjustable for all lengths.)

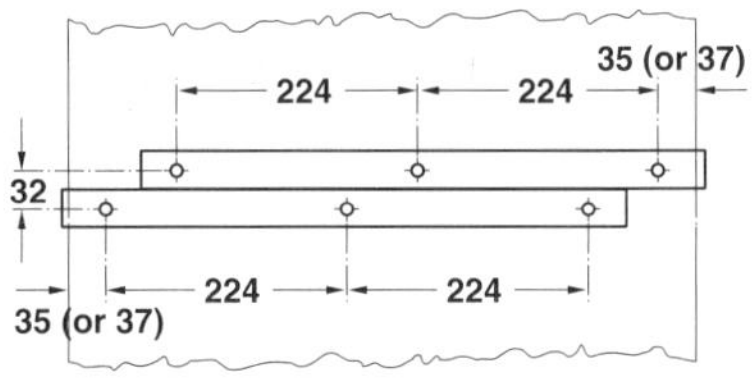

Finish: steel, zinc-plated

Cat. No.	420.53.001

Packing: 1 pair

Mount cabinet profile exactly parallel, 32 mm apart center to center

4 Sliding Door Hardware
Drawer Slides
Television Supports

Dimensions in mm
Inches are approximate

Drawer Slides, Product Review

Accuride® from HÄFELE

	Description	Accuride Type	Load Capacity	Extension	Ball Bearing	Page
	Center-Mount Slide zinc-plated	1029	**35 lbs.**	3/4	steel	4.82
	Keyboard/Pencil Drawer Slide zinc-plated, black	2009	**75 lbs.**	3/4	steel	4.83
	Box Drawer Slide zinc-plated zinc-plated, black	2037	**50 lbs.**	3/4	polymer	4.84
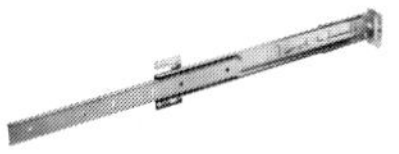	Box Drawer Slide zinc-plated	214	**75 lbs.**	3/4	steel	4.85
	Telescoping Slide zinc-plated	2132	75 lbs.	3/4	steel	4.86
	Telescoping Slide zinc-plated zinc-plated, black epoxy powder coated, white	3832	**100 lbs.**	full	steel	4.87
	Telescoping Slide zinc-plated zinc-plated, black	3834	**90 lbs.**	1" over-travel	steel	4.88
	Telescoping Slide zinc-plated zinc-plated, black	7432	**100 lbs.**	full	steel	4.89
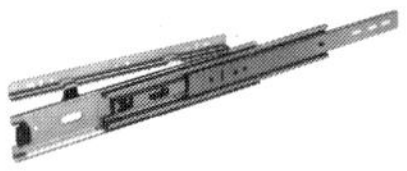	Telescoping, Medium-Duty File Drawer Slide zinc-plated zinc-plated, black	3017	**100 lbs.**	1" over-travel	polymer	4.90
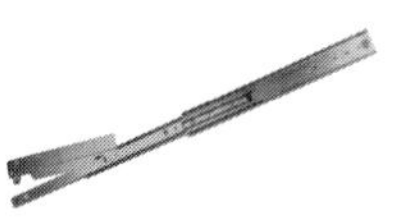	Telescoping, Heavy-Duty File Drawer Slide zinc-plated	3640	**200/*75 lbs.**	1" over-travel	steel	4.91
	Heavy-Duty Pull-Out Slide zinc-plated	301-2590	**130 lbs.**	7/8" over-travel	steel	4.92
	Progressive, Medium-Duty File Drawer Slide zinc-plated zinc-plated, black	4033	**110 lbs.**	full	polymer	4.93
	Progressive, Heavy-Duty File Drawer Slide zinc-plated zinc-plated, black	4034	**150 lbs.**	1 1/2" over-travel	steel	4.94
	Over the Top Flipper Door Slide zinc-plated, black	115	**30 lbs.**	3/4	steel	4.95
	Two-Way Drawer System zinc-plated	2002	**50 lbs.**	3/4	steel	4.96

Dimensions in mm

HÄFELE

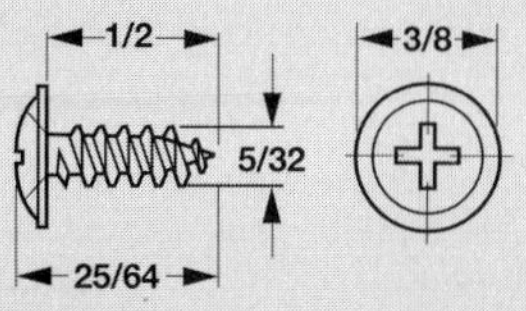

Accuride special screws for all Accuride slide models. The ideal screw for installing drawer slides with a special premounted washer and the Phillips drive size 2 for Ø 1/8" holes.

Finish	Cat. No.
zinc-plated	013.03.902
black	013.03.304
white	013.03.706

Packing: 200 pcs.

Varianta Special Screw:
For mounting in system holes
Countersunk head
Size Ø 6.0

SYSTEM VARIANTA 32

Finish: steel, zinc-plated

Size	Cat. No.
10.5 mm length	013.14.718
13.5 mm length	013.14.727
16.0 mm length	013.14.736

Packing: 500 pcs.

* Rating if used as bottom-mounted slide.

HÄFELE

Precision Ball-Bearing Slides

- For kitchen cabinets, bedroom, and dining room furniture applications.
- Features concealed center bottom mount (no side clearance required)
- Adjustable rear mounting bracket
- Friction disconnect.

Accuride® from HÄFELE

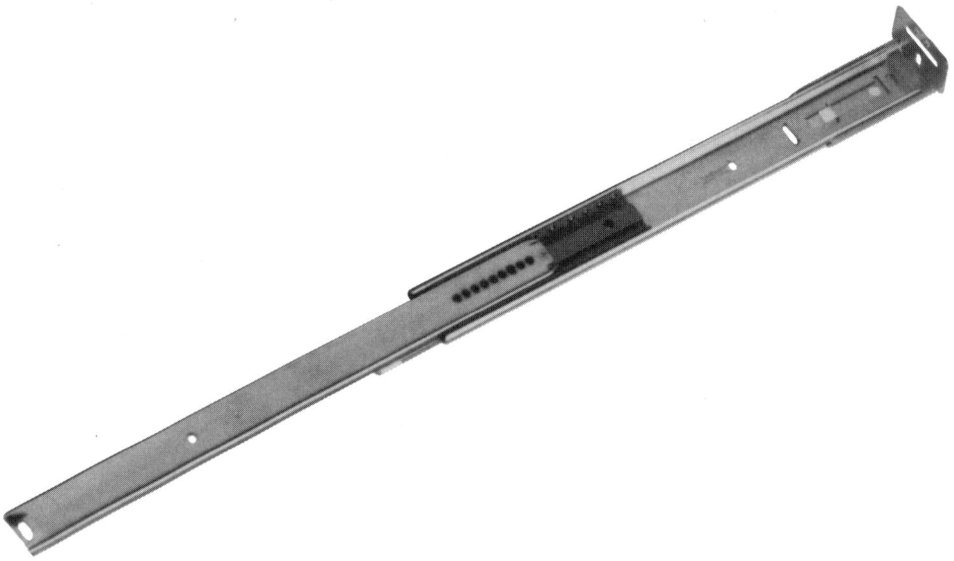

Accuride Model 1029/35 lbs.
Center-Mount Slide

- weight capacity up to 16 kg (35 lbs.) /pair
- single-extension
- bottom-mounted

Finish: steel, zinc-plated

for drawer depth		for cabinet depth		cabinet member		drawer extension		Cat. No.
inch	mm	inch	mm	inch	mm	inch	mm	
12 5/8-14 1/2	321-368	15-16 1/2	381-419	14 7/8	378	10 1/2	267	422.00.359
14 5/8-16 1/2	371-419	17-18 1/2	432-470	16 7/8	429	12	305	422.00.402
16 5/8-16 1/2	422-470	19-20 1/2	482-521	18 7/8	479	12 1/2	318	422.00.457
18 5/8-20 1/2	473-521	21-22 1/2	533-572	20 7/8	530	14 1/2	368	422.00.500
20 5/8-22 1/2	524-572	23-24 1/2	584-622	22 7/8	581	16 1/2	419	422.00.555

Packing: 20 pcs.

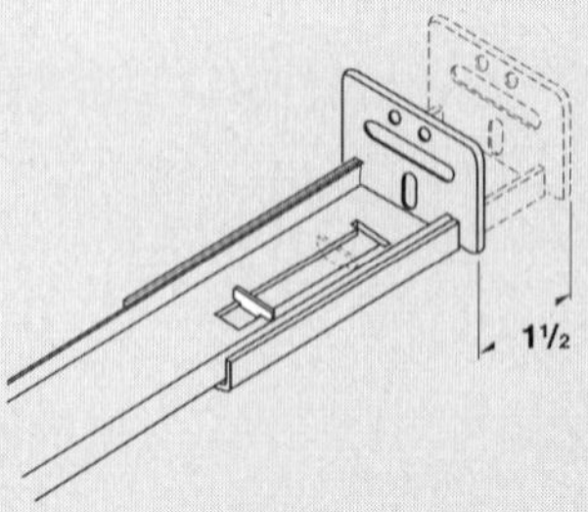

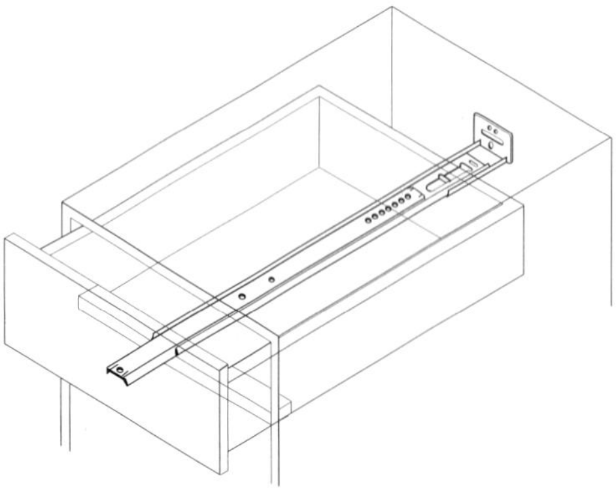

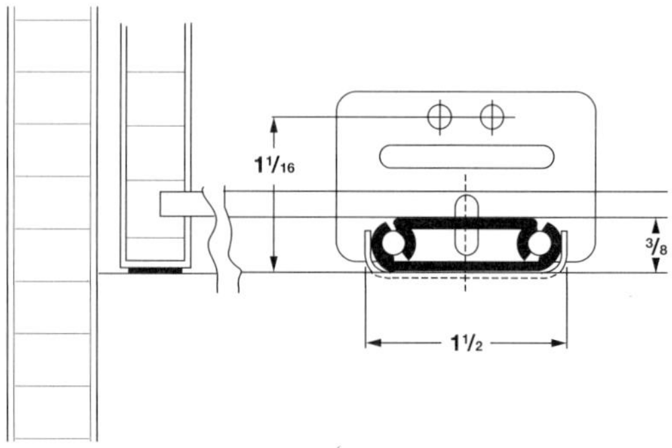

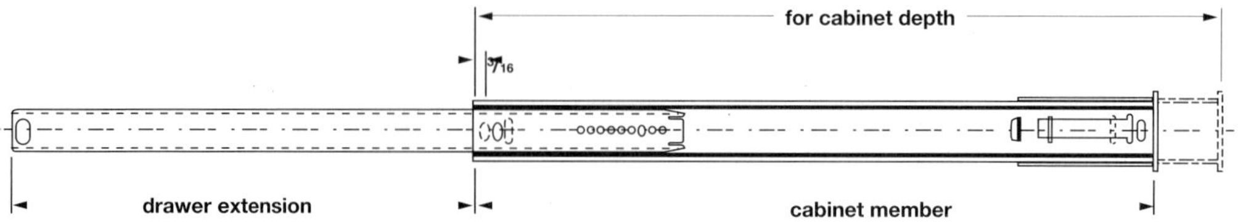

Dimensional data not binding. We reserve the right to alter specifications without notice.

Dimensions in inches
mm are approximate

Precision Ball-Bearing Slide

HÄFELE

Accuride® from **HÄFELE**

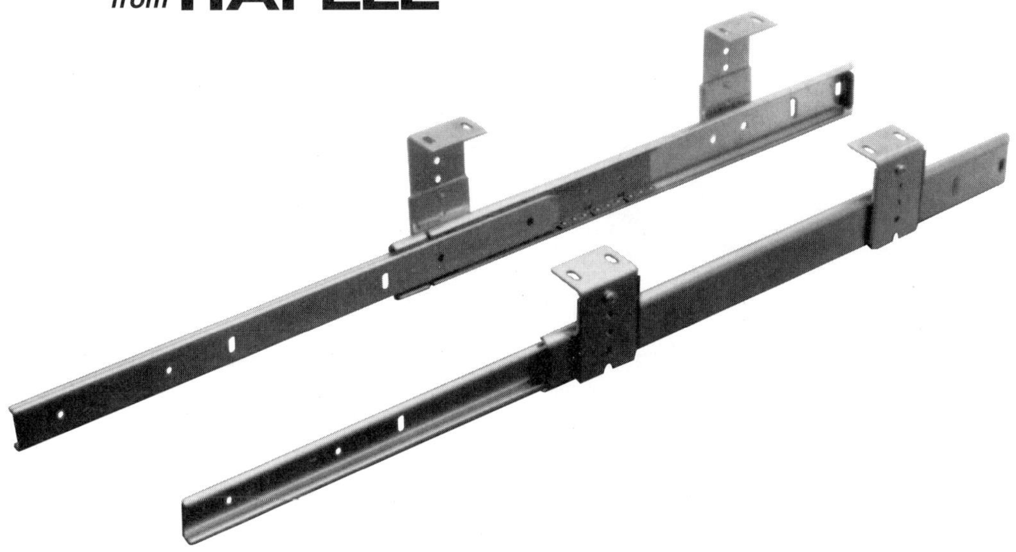

- For computer keyboard, printer shelf and pencil drawer applications.
- Features easy top or bottom mounting, with mounting brackets that are height adjustable and reversible.
- Detent out with lever disconnect.

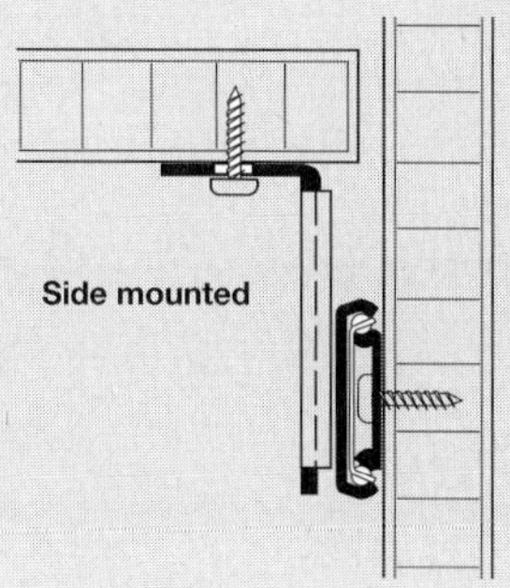

Accuride Model 2009/75 lbs.
Keyboard/Pencil Drawer Slide

- weight capacity up to 34 kg (75 lbs.) /pair
- single-extension
- under-mount

Finish: steel, zinc-plated, black

Installed length		Extension length		Distance **A**		Distance **B**		Distance **C**		Cat. No.
inch	mm	inch	mm	inch	mm	inch	mm	inch	mm	zinc-plated black
12	305	9	228	8 1/2	216	5 61/64	151	9 61/64	253	422.14.317
14	356	11	279	8 1/2	216	7 61/64	202	11 61/64	304	422.14.362
16	406	12	305	8 1/2	253	9 61/64	253	13 61/64	354	422.14.415
18	457	13	344	8 1/2	216	11 61/64	304	15 61/64	405	422.14.460
20	508	15	381	8 1/2	216	13 61/64	354	17 61/64	456	422.14.513
22	559	16	419	16 1/2	419	15 61/64	405	19 61/64	507	422.14.568
24	610	17	445	16 1/2	419	17 61/64	456	21 61/64	558	422.14.611

Packing: 10 pairs

Sliding Door Hardware
Drawer Slides
Television Supports
4

- The angle brackets and fastening screws are unassembled to allow for maximum installation flexibility.

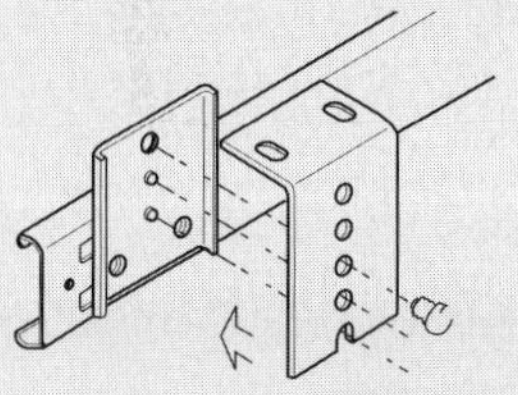

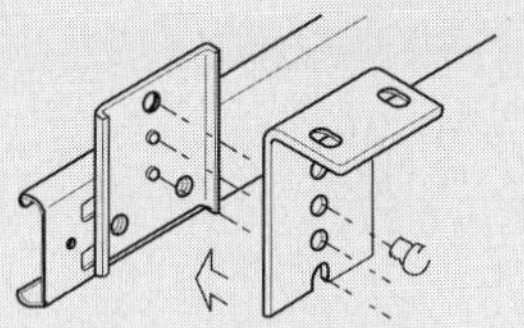

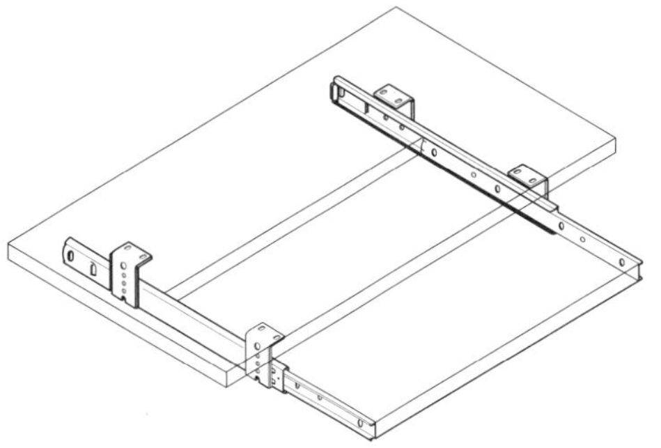

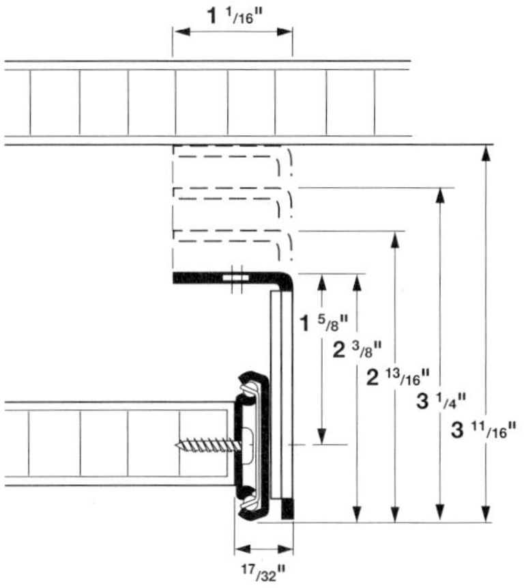

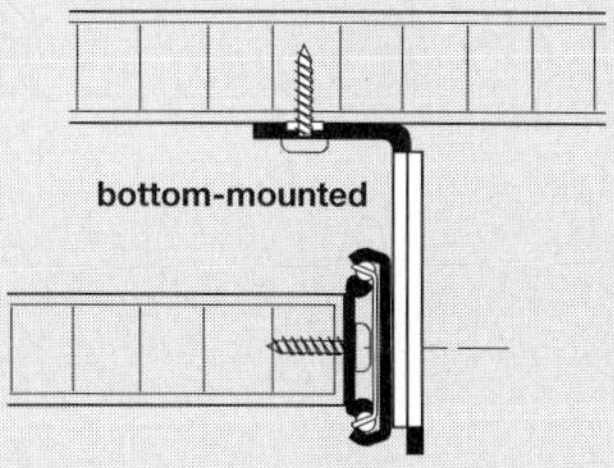

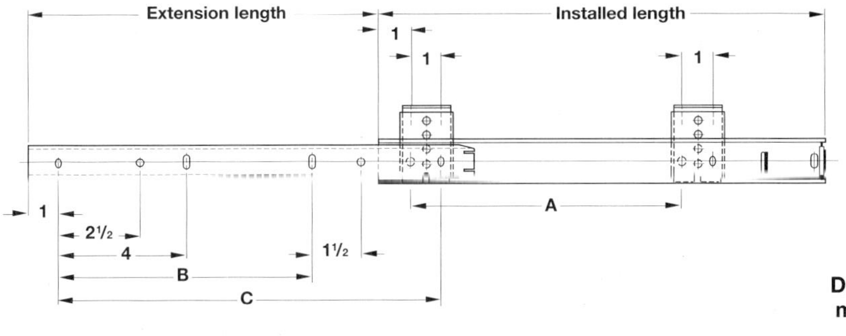

Dimensional data not binding. We reserve the right to alter specifications without notice.

Dimensions in inches
mm are approximate

HÄFELE

Precision Ball-Bearing Slides

- For desk/credenza box drawer applications.
- Features tolerance-asborbing mounting brackets
- Polymer ball bearings for quiet movement
- Easy rail disconnect
- Unhanded slides.

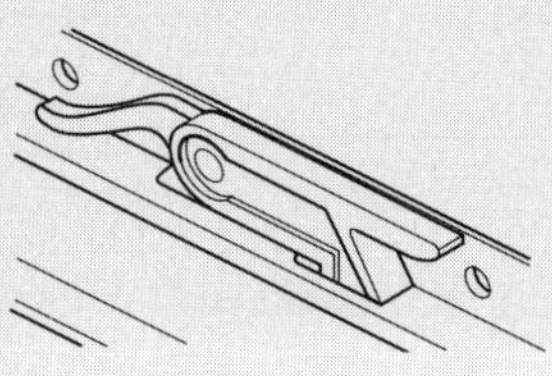

Accuride® from HÄFELE

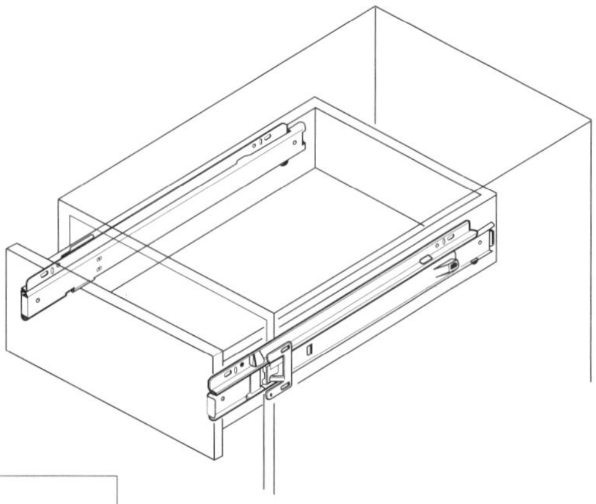

Accuride Model 2037/50 lbs.
Box Drawer Slide

- weight capacity up to 23 kg (50 lbs.) /pair
- single-extension unit
- side-mounted, rail disconnect

Finish: steel, zinc-plated and zinc-plated black

Installed length		Extension length		Cat. No.	
inch	mm	inch	mm	zinc-plated	zinc-pl. black
12	300	8	203	422.02.308	422.02.317
14	356	10	254	422.02.353	422.02.362
16	406	12	305	422.02.406	422.02.415
18	457	14	356	422.02.451	422.02.460
20	508	16	406	422.02.504	422.02.513
22	559	18	457	422.02.559	422.02.568
24	610	19	483	422.02.602	422.02.611

Packing: 10 pairs

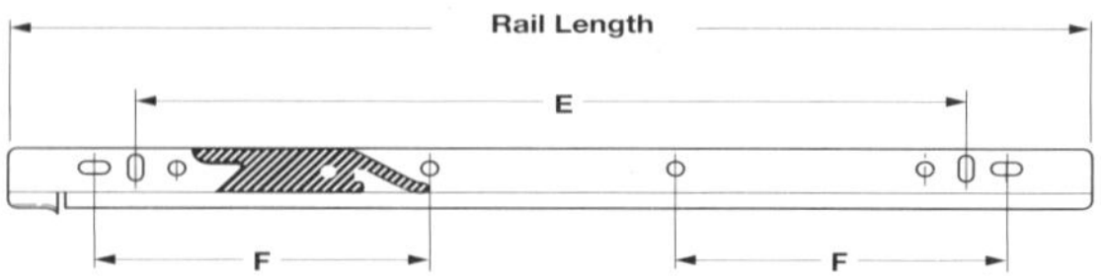

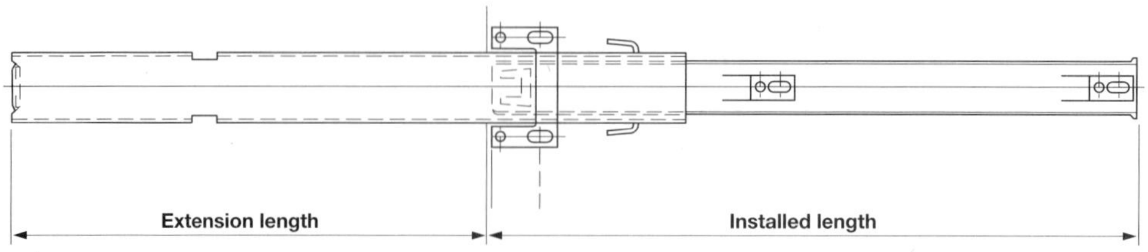

Dimensions in inches
mm are approximate

Precision Ball-Bearing Slides

HÄFELE

Accuride® from **HÄFELE**

- For kitchen cabinet drawers, commercial and residential furniture applications.
- Features tolerance-absorbing mounting brackets
- Easy friction disconnect
- Unhanded slides

Accuride Model 214/75 lbs.
- weight capacity up to 34 kg (75 lbs.) /pair
- single-extension unit
- side mounted

Finish: steel, zinc-plated

for Cabinet depth		Cabinet member length		Extension length		Distance A		Distance B		Cat. No. zinc-plated
inch	mm	inch	mm	inch	mm	inch	mm	inch	mm	
12 1/8	308-346	12	305	7 3/4	197	5 63/64	152	9 63/64	254	422.03.305
14 1/8	359-397	14	356	9 3/4	248	7 63/64	203	11 63/64	304	422.03.350
16 1/8	410-448	16	406	11 3/4	298	9 63/64	254	13 63/64	355	422.03.403
18 1/8	460-498	18	457	13 3/4	349	11 63/64	304	15 63/64	406	422.03.458
20 1/8	511-549	20	508	15 3/4	400	13 63/64	355	17 63/64	457	422.03.501
22 1/8	562-600	22	559	17 3/4	451	15 63/64	406	19 63/64	507	422.03.556
24 1/8	613-651	24	610	18 3/4	476	17 63/64	457	21 63/64	558	422.03.609
26 1/8	664-702	26	660	19 3/4	502	19 63/64	507	23 63/64	609	422.03.654

Packing: 25 pairs

Sliding Door Hardware
Drawer Slides
Television Supports

4

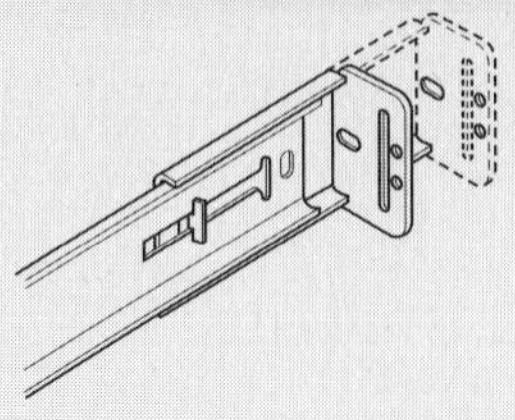

Order separately
Mounting brackets for face-frame cabinets

Cat. No.	422.03.001

Packing: 50 pcs.

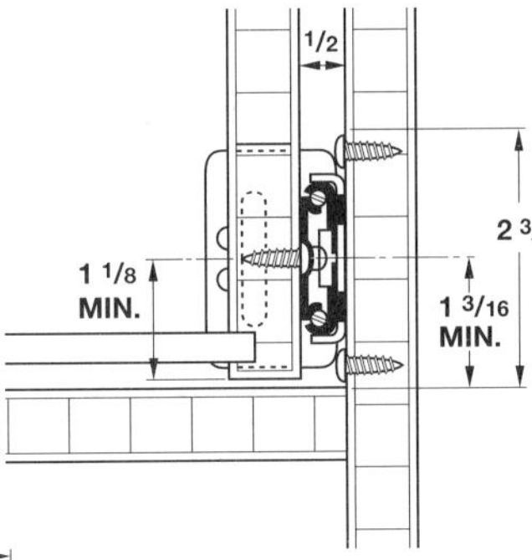

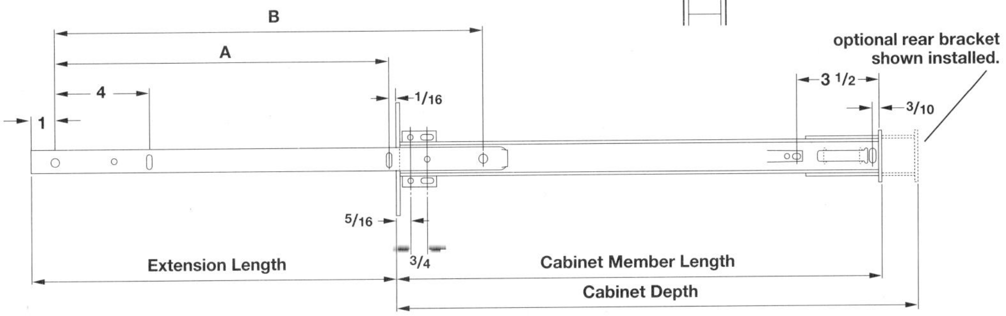

Dimensions in inches
mm are approximate

Dimensional data not binding. We reserve the right to alter specifications without notice.

HÄFELE

Precision Ball-Bearing Slides

- Low cost
- 3/4 extension
- Hold-in detent
- Steel ball bearings
- Low profile
- Easy lever disconnect – no rails
- Mounting tabs provide flexibility
- 32 mm hole pattern to match popular 3832A pattern
- Unhanded

Accuride® from HÄFELE

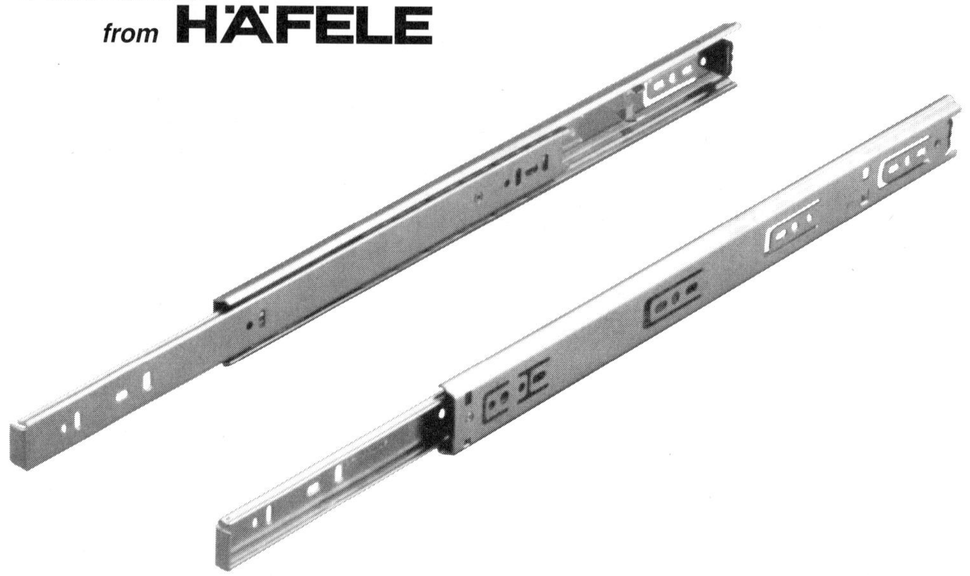

Accuride Model 2132/75 lbs.
- weight capacity up to 34 kg (75 lbs.) /pair
- 3/4 extension unit
- side-mounted

Finish: steel, zinc-plated

mm	inch	Extension length inch	mm	Cat. No.
305	12	8 1/4	210	422.32.930
356	14	10 1/4	260	422.32.935
407	16	11 1/4	281	422.32.940
458	18	13 1/4	331	422.32.945
508	20	14 3/4	376	422.32.950
559	22	16 1/4	451	422.32.955
610	24	17 3/4	451	422.32.960
661	26	19 1/4	488	422.32.965

Packing: 10 pairs

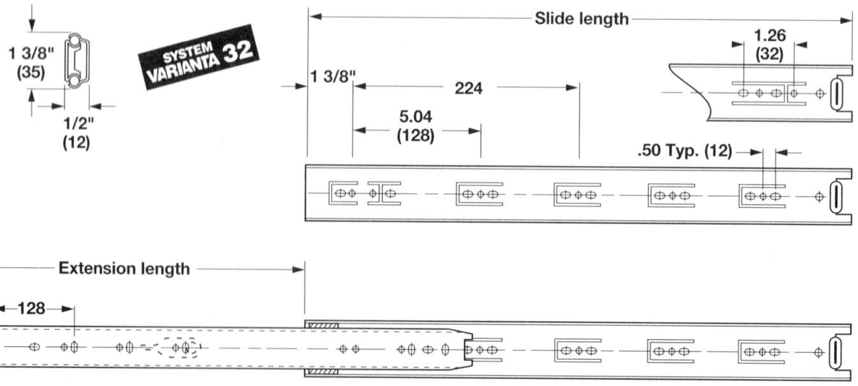

Dimensional data not binding. We reserve the right to alter specifications without notice.

Dimensions in mm
Inches are approximate

Precision Ball-Bearing Slide

HÄFELE

Accuride® from **HÄFELE**

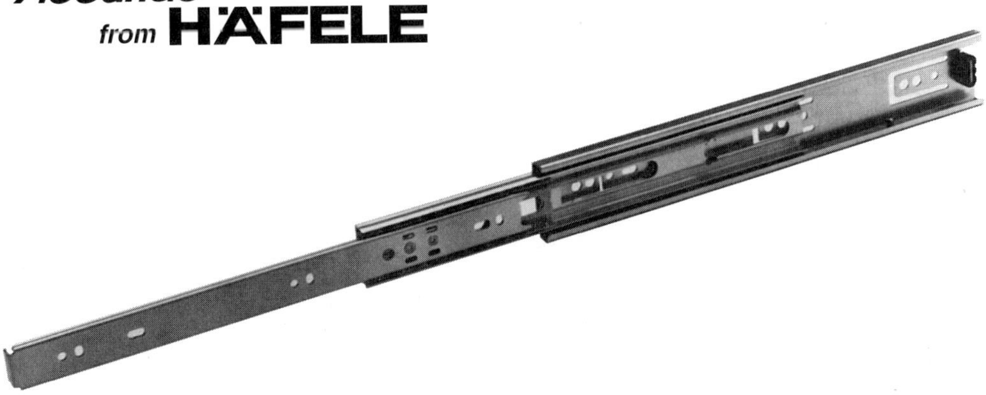

- Full-extension, telescoping slide
- For 32mm casegood construction
- For commercial and residential furniture applications.
- For kitchen cabinets where full-extension is required.
- Features low profile for shallow drawers.
- Hold-in detent
- Unhanded slides
- Easy lever disconnect

SYSTEM VARIANTA 32

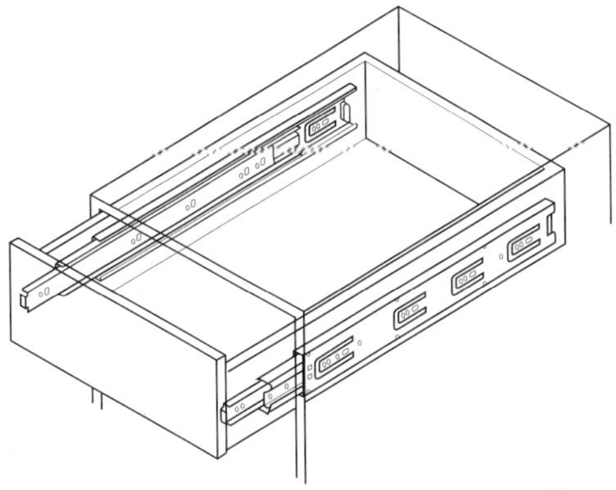

Accuride Model 3832A/100 lbs
Telescoping Drawer slide

- weight 45 kg (100 lbs) per pair
- telescopic extension
- side-mounting

Finish: steel, zinc-plated, zinc-plated black, white epoxy

Installed Length		Extension length		Distance		Cat. No.		
inch	mm	inch	mm	A mm	B	zinc	black	white epoxy
10	250	10	250		131	422.04.259	422.04.268	422.04.277
12	300	12	300		163	422.04.302	422.04.311	422.04.320
14	350	14	350		163	422.04.357	422.04.366	422.04.375
16	400	16	400	96	163	422.04.400	422.04.419	422.04.428
18	450	18	450	128	163	422.04.455	422.04.464	422.04.473
20	500	20	500	192	163	422.04.508	422.04.517	422.04.526
22	550	22	550	224	163	422.04.553	422.04.562	422.04.571
24	600	24	600	256	163	422.04.606	422.04.615	422.04.624
26	650	26	650	320	163	422.04.651	422.04.660	422.04.679
28	700	28	700	320	163	422.04.704	422.04.713	422.04.722

Packing: 10 pairs

Sliding Door Hardware
Drawer Slides
Television Supports

4

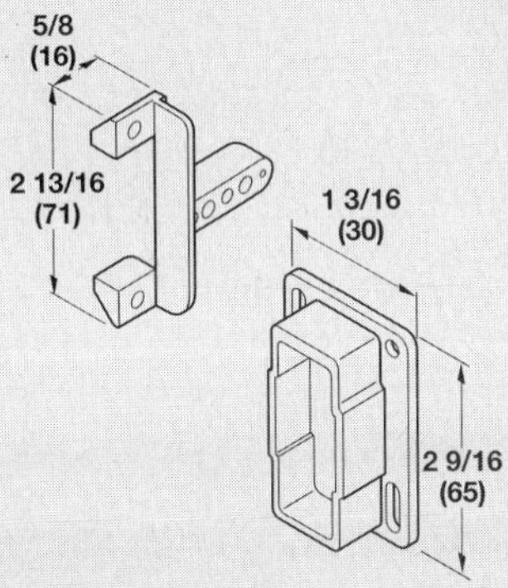

Order separately:
Mounting brackets for face-frame cabinets, including:
2 front-brackets and 2 rear brackets
Finish: nylon, white

Cat. No.	422.05.005

Packing: 1 set

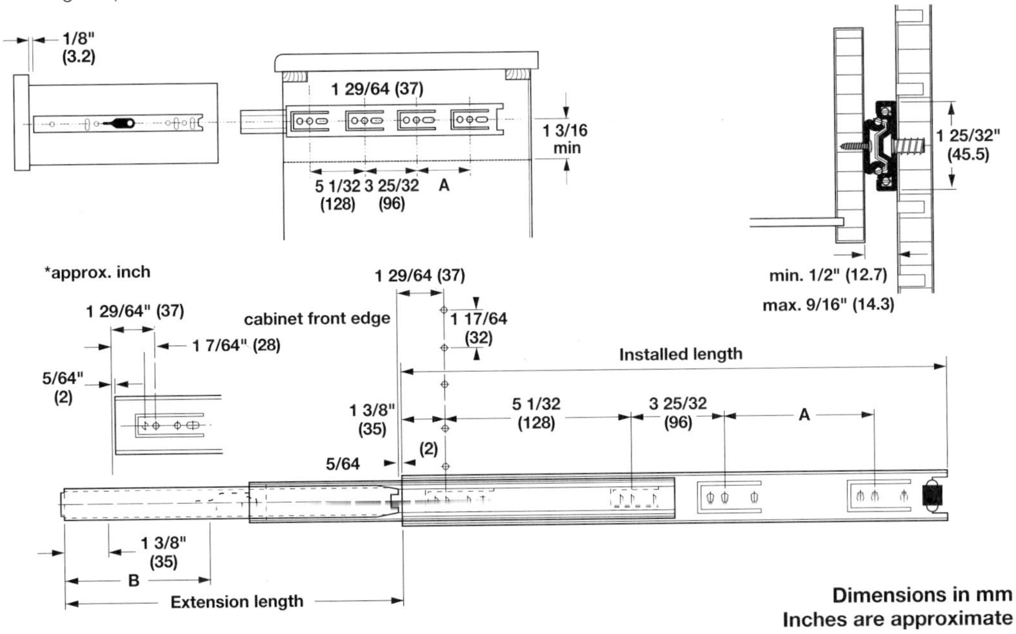

Dimensions in mm
Inches are approximate

Dimensional data not binding.
We reserve the right to alter specifications without notice.

HÄFELE

Precision Ball-Bearing Slide

- full-extension, telescoping slide with 1" overtravel
- For 32mm casegood construction
- For commercial and residential furniture applications.
- For kitchen cabinets where full-extension is required.
- Features low profile for shallow drawers.
- Hold-in detent
- Unhanded slides
- Easy lever disconnect

Accuride® from HÄFELE

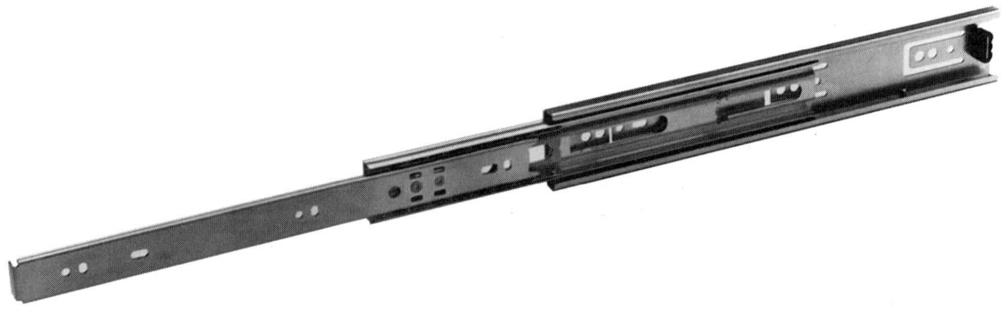

SYSTEM VARIANTA 32

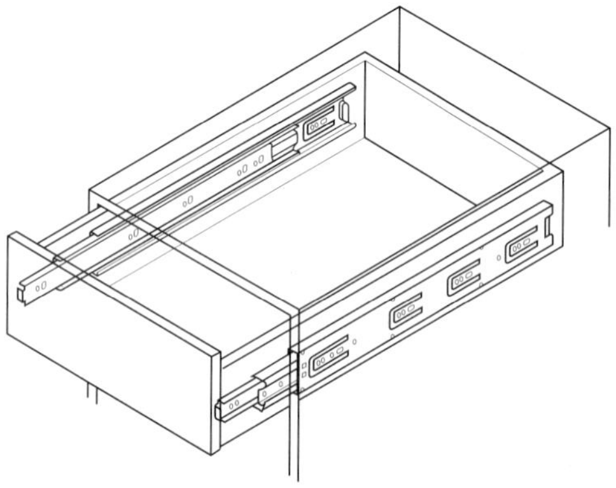

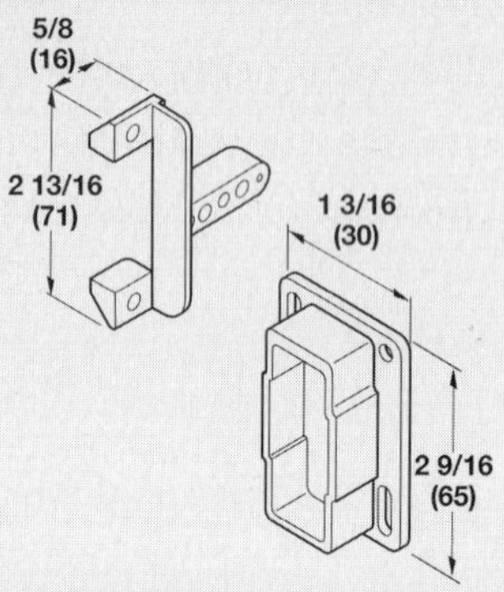

Order separately:
Mounting brackets for face-frame cabinets, including:
2 front-brackets and 2 rear brackets
Finish: nylon, white

Cat. No.	422.05.005

Packing: 1 set

Accuride Model 3834A/90 lbs
Telescoping Drawer slide
- weight 41 kg (90 lbs) per pair
- telescopic extension, with overtravel
- side-mounted

Finish: steel, zinc-plated, zinc-plated black and steel

Installed Length		Extension length		Distance		Cat. No.	
inch	mm	inch	mm	A mm	B	zinc	black
12	300	13	330		163	422.16.302	422.16.311
14	350	15	381		163	422.16.352	422.16.366
16	400	17	432	96	163	422.16.400	422.16.419
18	450	19	483	128	163	422.16.455	422.16.464
20	500	21	533	192	163	422.16.508	422.16.517
22	550	23	584	224	163	422.16.553	422.16.562
24	600	25	635	256	163	422.16.606	422.16.615
26	650	27	686	320	163	422.16.651	422.16.660
28	700	29	737	320	163	422.16.704	422.16.713

Packing 10 pairs

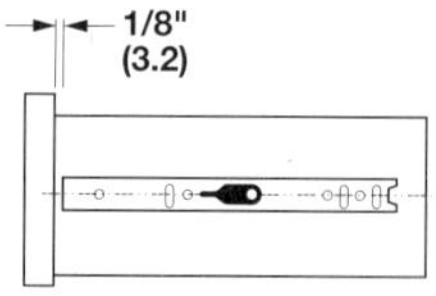

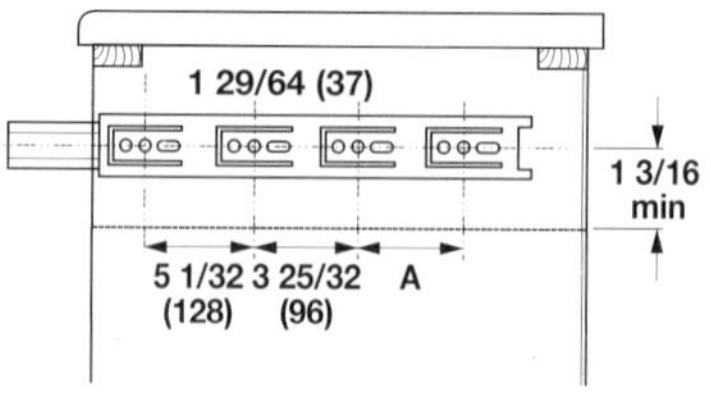

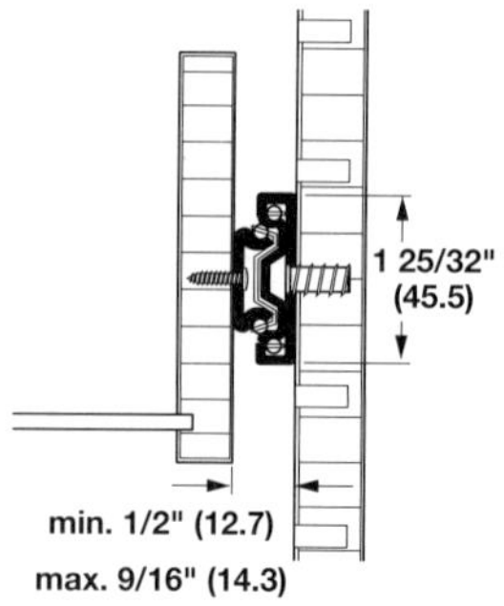

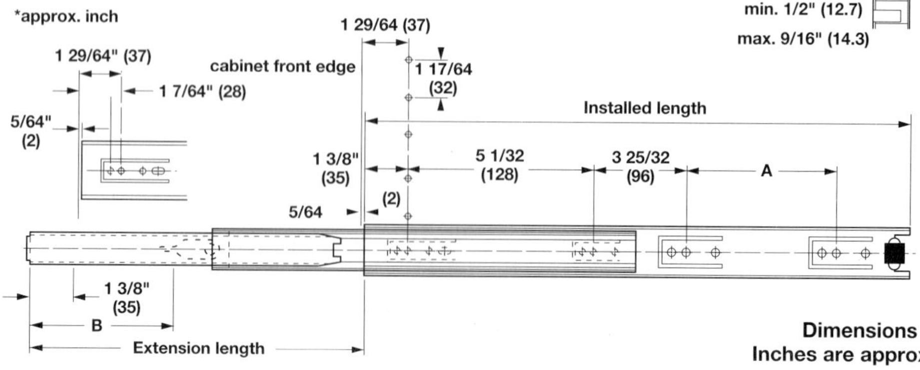

Dimensions in mm
Inches are approximate

Dimensional data not binding.
We reserve the right to alter specifications without notice.

Precision Ball-Bearing Slide

HÄFELE

Accuride® from **HÄFELE**

SYSTEM VARIANTA 32

- 100 lb. (45 kg) load rating.
- full-extension, progressive action. Full drawer access with smooth, consistent movement.
- Low profile - 2.35" (60 mm).
- Steel ball-bearings. Increased strength & stability.
- Hold-in detent. Prevents drawer bounce back and roll out.
- Can be mounted in either traditional or 32 mm cabinets.
- Rail mounted. Easy drawer installation and removal.

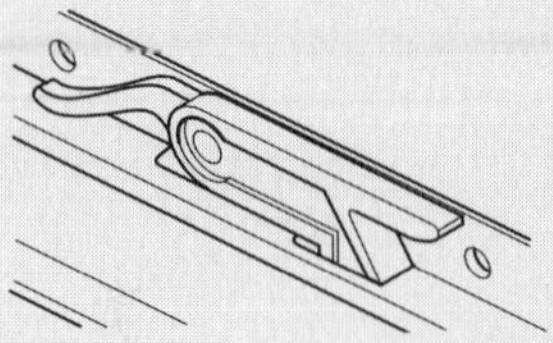

Accuride Model 7432/100 lbs (45 kg)

- weight 45 kg (100 lbs.)
- full-extension, progressive action
- side-mounting, rail disconnect

Finish: steel, zinc-plated and zinc-plated black

Installed Length inch	mm	Extension Length inch	mm	Rail Length inch	mm	Cat. No. zinc-plated	zinc-plated black
12"	300 mm	12"	304 mm	10 9/16"	268 mm	422.29.930	422.29.330
14"	350 mm	14"	355 mm	10 9/16"	268 mm	422.29.935	422.29.335
16"	400 mm	16"	405 mm	13 1/16"	332 mm	422.29.940	422.29.340
18"	450 mm	18"	455 mm	13 1/16"	332 mm	422.29.945	422.29.345
20"	500 mm	20"	505 mm	16 7/8"	428 mm	422.29.950	422.29.350
22"	550 mm	22"	555 mm	20 5/8"	524 mm	422.29.955	422.29.355
24"	600 mm	24"	605 mm	20 5/8"	524 mm	422.29.960	422.29.360
26"	650 mm	26"	655 mm	24 7/16"	620 mm	422.29.965	422.29.365
28"	700 mm	28"	705 mm	24 7/16"	620 mm	422.29.970	422.29.370

Packing: 5 pairs

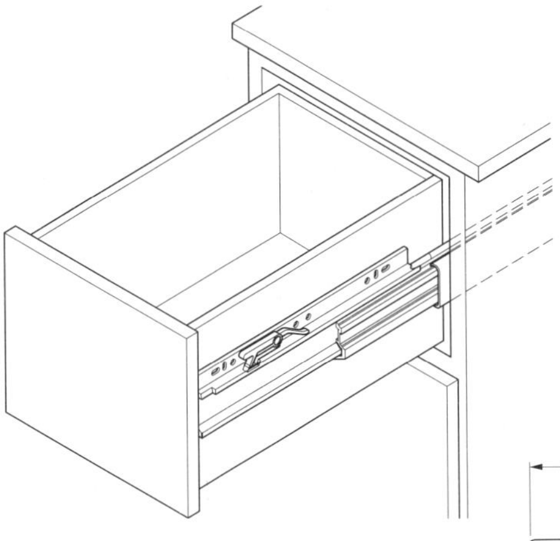

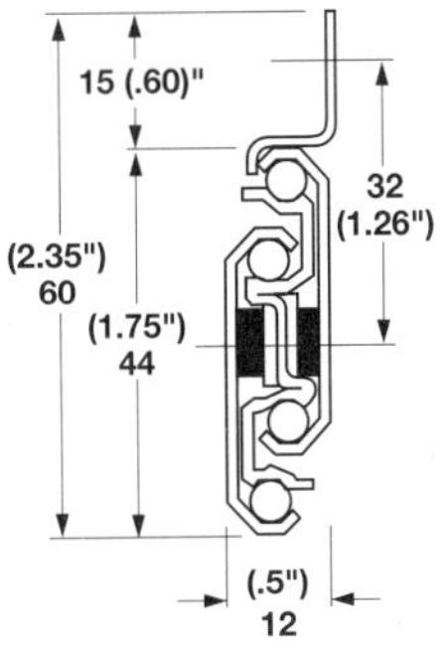

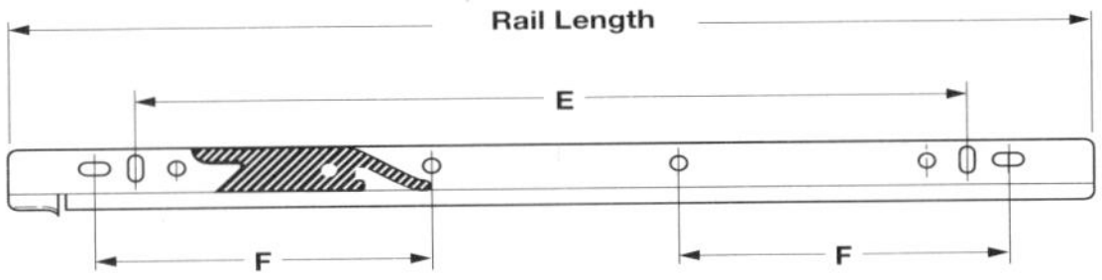

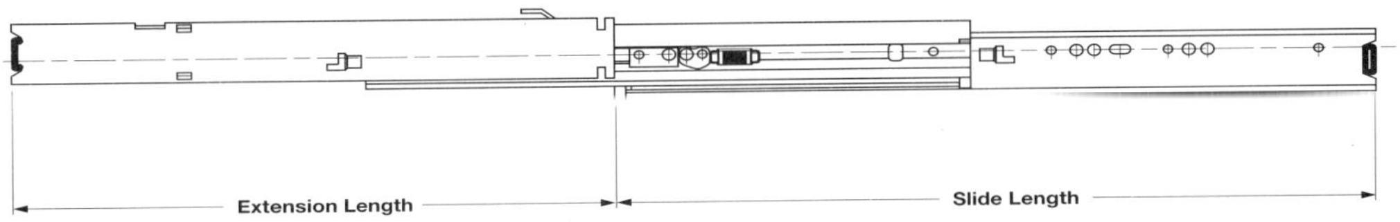

Dimensional data not binding.
We reserve the right to alter specifications without notice.

Dimensions in mm
Inches are approximate

HÄFELE

Precision Ball-Bearing Slides

Accuride® from HÄFELE

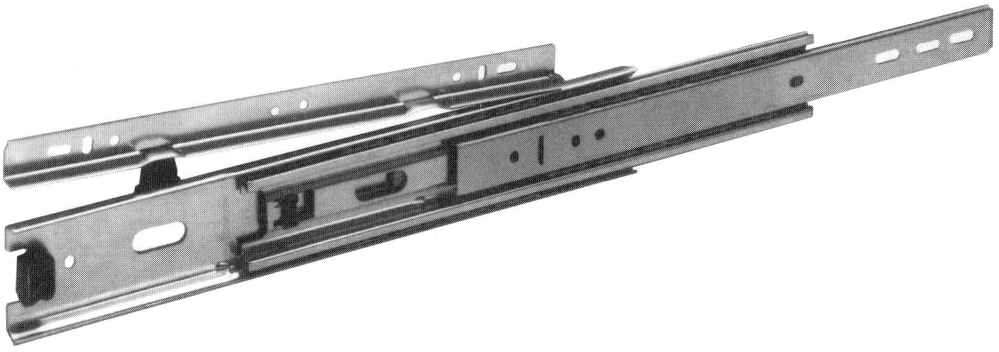

Telescoping medium duty file drawer slide

- Full-extension, telescoping slide with 1" overtravel.
- For desk/credenza box and file drawer applications.
- Features polymer ball bearings for quiet movement.
- Low profile for shallow drawers
- Hold-in detent
- Easy rail disconnect
- 32 mm compatible

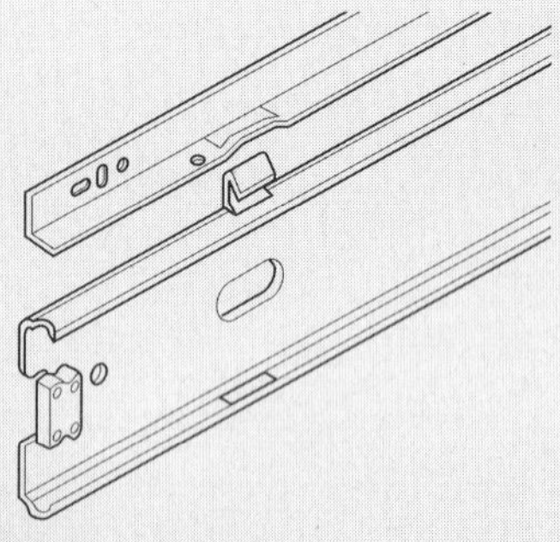

SYSTEM VARIANTA 32

Accuride 3017/100 lbs.

- weight capacity up to 45 kg/pair
- telescopic extension
- side mounting,rail disconnect

Finish: steel, zinc-plated and zinc-plated black

Installed length		Extension length		Distance A		Distance B		Distance C		Distance D		Distance E		Cat. No.	
inch	mm	inch	mm	inch	mm	inch	mm	inch	mm	inch	mm	inch	mm	zinc-plated	zinc-pl. black
12	300	13	330			6	152	8 3/32	206	9 1/32	230	9 7/8	251	422.06.306	422.06.315
14	356	15	381			8	203	10 3/32	256	11 3/64	281	11 55/64	301	422.06.351	422.06.360
16	406	17	432			10	254	12 3/32	307	13 3/64	331	13 55/64	352	422.06.404	422.06.413
18	457	19	483	10	254	12	305	14 3/32	358	15 3/64	382	15 55/64	403	422.06.459	422.06.468
20	508	21	533	11	279	14	356	16 3/32	409	17 3/64	433	17 55/64	454	422.06.502	422.06.511
22	559	23	584	12	305	16	406	18 3/32	460	19 3/64	484	19 55/64	505	422.06.557	422.06.566
24	610	25	635	13	330	18	457	20 3/32	510	21 3/64	535	21 55/64	555	422.06.600	422.06.619

Packing: 10 pair

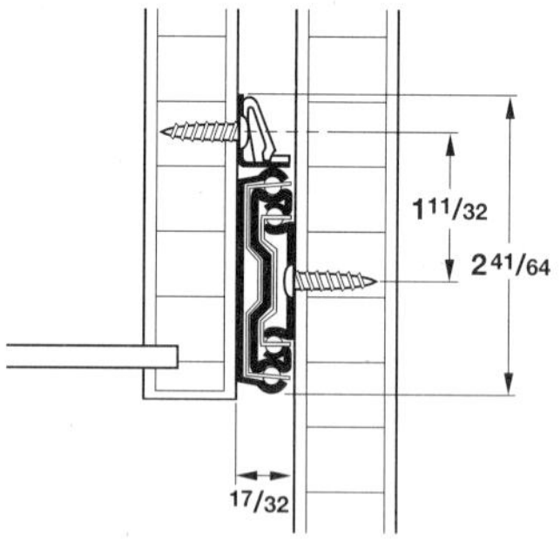

for installed length		Distance F		Distance G	
inch	mm	inch	mm	inch	mm
12	300	4	102	7 9/16	192
14	356	3 1/2	89	7 9/16	192
16	406	3 1/2	89	10 5/64	256
18	457	3 1/2	89	10 5/64	256
20	508	3 1/2	89	13 55/64	352
22	559	6 1/2	165	17 41/64	448
24	610	6 1/2	165	17 41/64	448

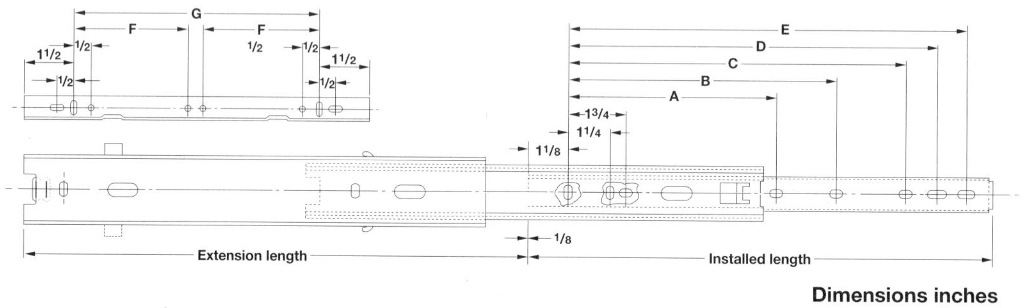

Dimensions inches
mm are approximate

Dimensional data not binding.
We reserve the right to alter specifications without notice.

Precision Ball-Bearing Slides

Accuride® from HÄFELE

HÄFELE

- Heavy-duty, full-extension, telescoping slide with 1" overtravel.
- For large store fixtures, library, and institutional furniture applications.
- Features unhanded slides
- Oversized ball bearings for heavy loads
- Hold-in detent
- Easy disconnect mounting brackets.
- 32 mm compatible

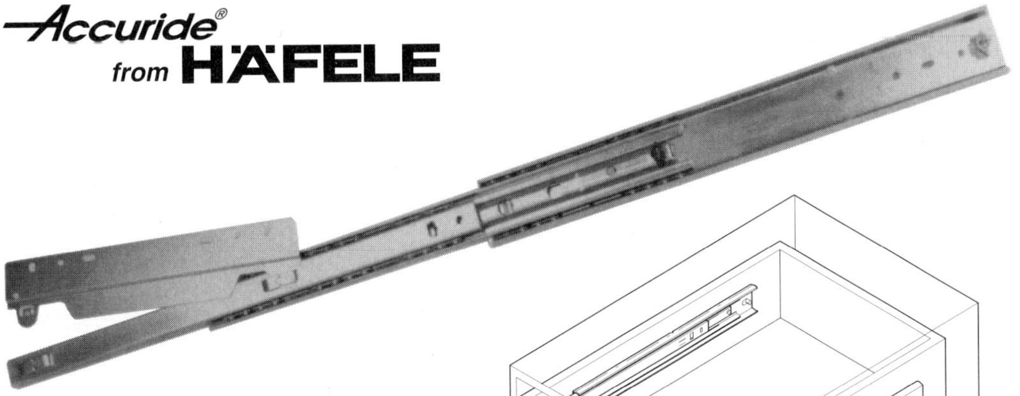

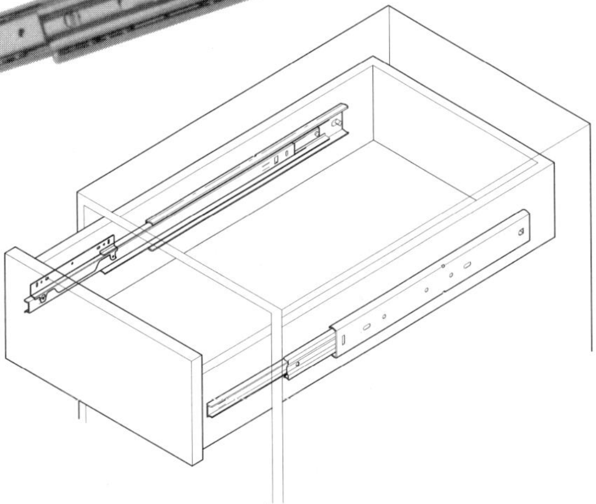

SYSTEM VARIANTA 32

Accuride model 3640/200 lbs. side mounted (at 18")
75 lbs. bottom mounted (at 16")

- weight capacity up to:
  90 kg (200 lbs.)/pair side-mounted
  34 kg (75 lbs.)/pair bottom-mounted
- telescopic extension
- side mounting, or bottom mounting, rail disconnect

Rail Dimensions

installed length	H	J	K
16"	10.00	-	8.50
18"-20"	12.00	-	10.50
22"-24"	14.00	7.00	12.50
26"-28"	17.00	8.50	15.50

Finish: steel, zinc-plated

Installed length	Extension length	Distance A	Distance B	Distance C	Distance D	Distance E	Distance F	Distance G	Cat. No. zinc-plated
16	17		9 21/64	11 3/64	12 3/64	13 3/64	1	8 1/2	422.07.401
18	19	7 1/2	11 21/64	13 3/64	14 3/64	15 3/64	1 1/2	10 1/2	422.07.456
20	21	8 1/2	13 21/64	15 3/64	16 3/64	17 3/64	1 1/2	10 1/2	422.07.509
22	23	9 1/2	15 21/64	17 3/64	18 3/64	19 3/64	2	12 1/2	422.07.554
24	25	10 1/2	17 21/64	19 21/64	20 3/64	21 3/64	2	12 1/2	422.07.607
26	27	11 1/2	19 21/64	21 3/64	22 3/64	23 3/64	2 1/2	15 1/2	422.07.652
28	29	12 1/2	21 21/64	23 3/64	24 3/64	25 3/64	2 1/2	15 1/2	422.07.705

Packing: 5 pairs

Sliding Door Hardware
Drawer Slides
Television Supports

4

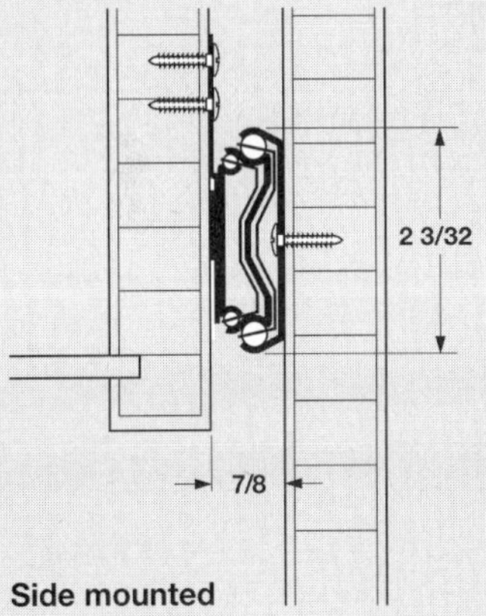

Side mounted

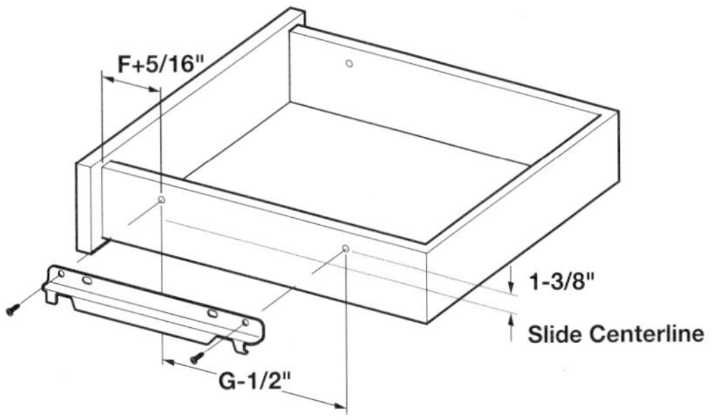

Note: Do not tighten screws completely.

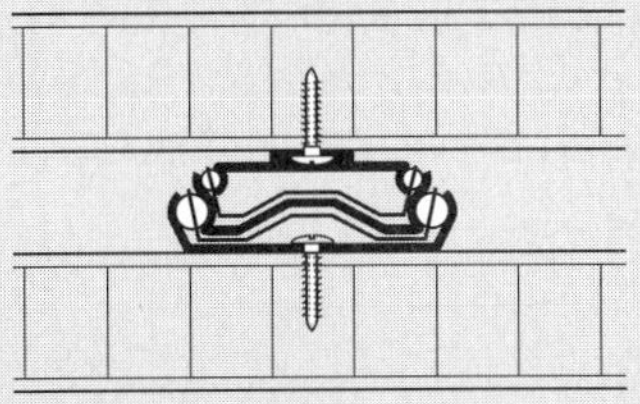

Bottom mounted

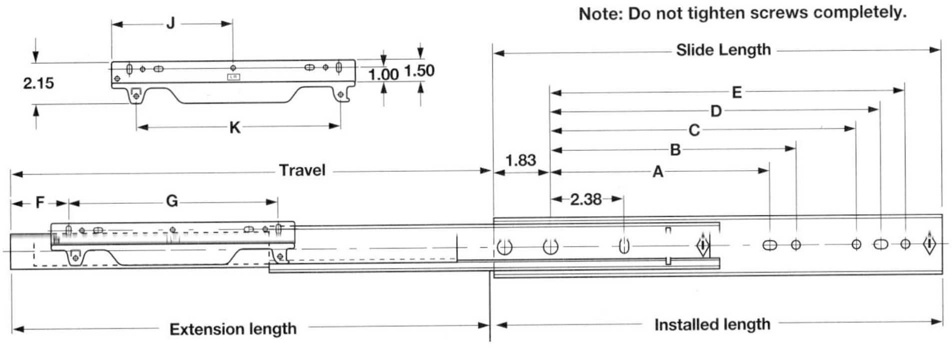

Dimensional data not binding. We reserve the right to alter specifications without notice.

Dimensions in inches

HÄFELE

Precision Ball-Bearing Slides

Accuride
from HÄFELE

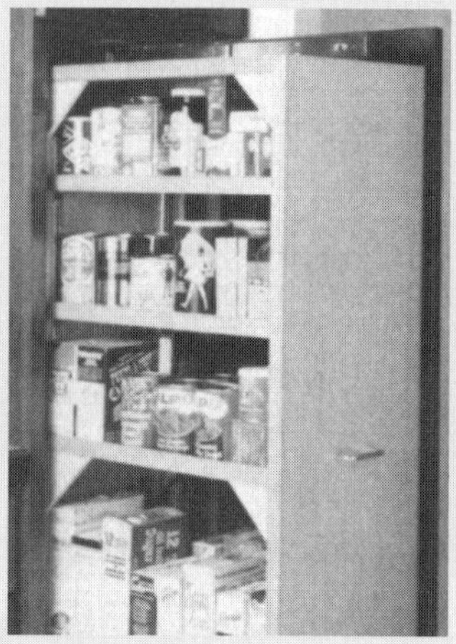

- Heavy-duty pull-out slide
- full-extension slide with 7/8" overtravel
- For kitchen pantry slide-out units, TV shelves, store fixtures, and institutional furniture applications.
- Features hold-in detent
- Easy installation
- With top and bottom mounting brackets.

Accuride Model: 301-2590/130 lbs.
- weight capacity up to (60 kg) pair
- full-extension, with overtravel
- base-mounted

Finish: steel, zinc-plated

Installed length		Extension length		Distance A		Distance B		Distance C		Cat. No. zinc-plated
inch	mm	inch	mm	inch	mm	inch	mm	inch	mm	
16	406	16 7/8	429	4	102	10	254	14	356	422.08.408
18	457	18 7/8	479	4	102	12	305	16	406	422.08.453
20	508	20 7/8	530	7	179	11	279	18	457	422.08.506
22	559	22 7/8	581	7	179	13	330	20	508	422.08.551

Packing: 5 pair

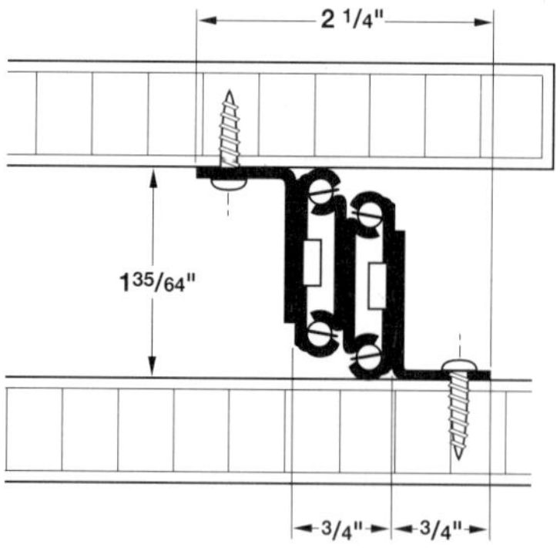

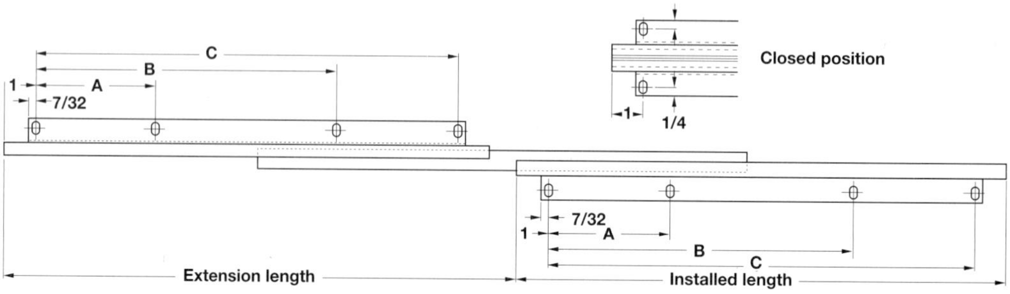

Dimensional data not binding.
We reserve the right to alter specifications without notice.

Dimensions in inches
mm are approximate

Precision Ball-Bearing Slides

HÄFELE

Accuride® from HÄFELE

Accuride Model 4033/100 lbs.
- weight capacity up to 45 kg/pair
- progressive movement
- full-extension
- side-mounted

Rail Dimensions

Installed length	Rail length	Distance **F**	Distance **E**
12-14	10.54	4	7.56
15-18	13.06	4	10.08
19-21	16.84	4	13.86
22-25	20.62	7	17.64
26	24.40	7	21.42

Finish: steel, zinc-plated and zinc-plated black

Installed length		Extension length		A		B		C		D		Cat. No	
inch	mm	inch	mm	inch	mm	inch	mm	inch	mm	inch	mm	zinc-plated	zinc-pl. balck
12	300	12 1/4	312	8 13/16	224							422.23.307	422.23.316
14	350	14 7/32	361	8 13/16	224							422.23.352	422.23.361
16	400	16 5/32	410	8 13/16	224	12 1/2	320					422.23.405	422.23.414
18	450	18 1/8	460	8 13/16	224	14	352					422.23.450	422.23.469
20	500	20	509	8 13/16	224	16 3/8	416					422.23.503	422.23.512
22	550	21 15/16	558	8 13/16	224	14	352	17 5/8	448	19	480	422.23.558	422.23.567
24	600	24 3/8	620	8 13/16	224	14	352	19	480			422.23.601	422.23.610
26	650	26 5/16	669	8 13/16	224	14	352	21 1/2	544			422.23.656	422.23.665

Packing: 5 pairs

SYSTEM VARIANTA 32

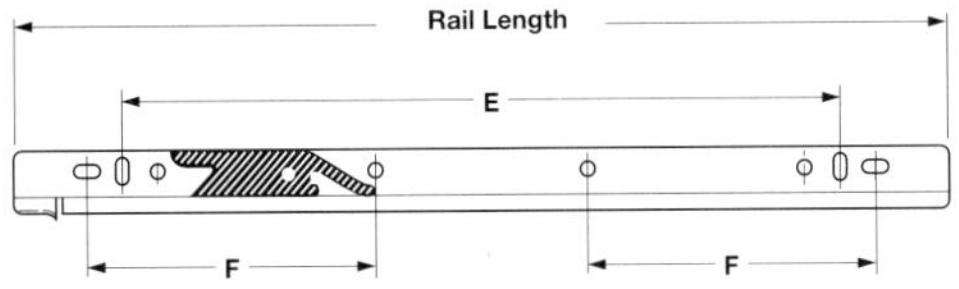

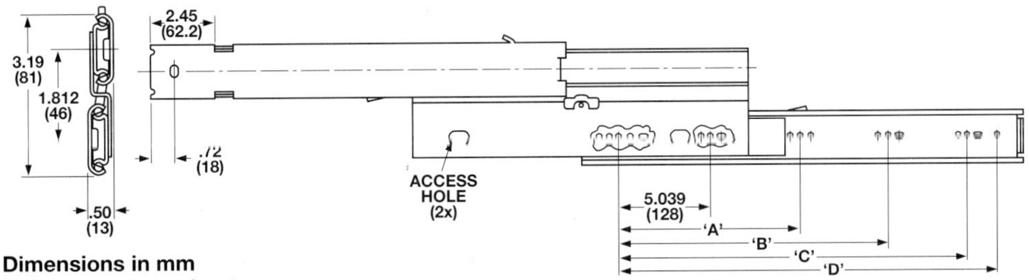

Dimensions in mm
Inches are approximate

Progressive Heavy-Duty File Drawer Slide
- Full-extension, progressive slide.
- For file drawer applications in desk, credenzas.
- Also store fixtures and institutional furniture.
- Features handed slides
- Polymer ball-bearings
- Hold-in detent
- Easy rail disconnect
- Side mount only
- 32mm and traditional hole pattern.
- Runners can be mounted with Varianta special screws in ø 5 mm system holes.

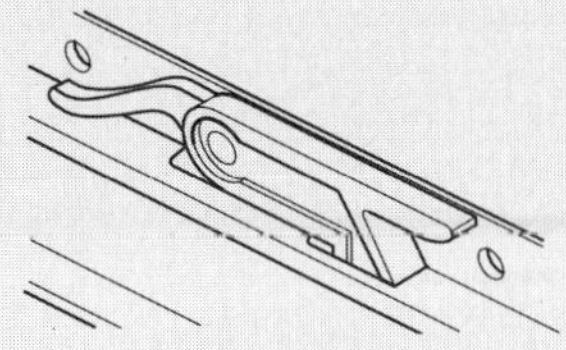

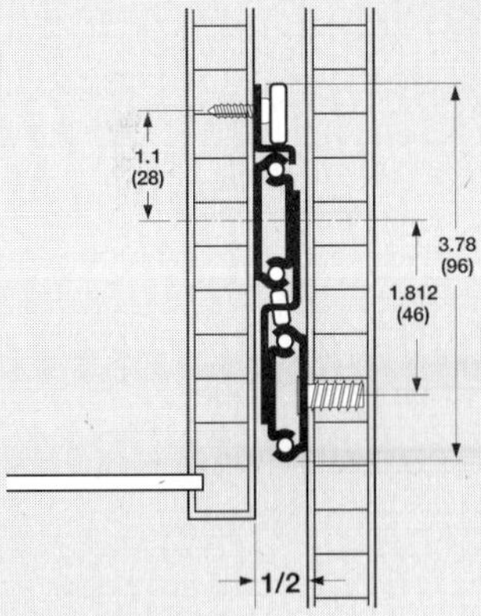

Dimensional data not binding.
We reserve the right to alter specifications without notice.

HÄFELE

Precision Ball-Bearing Slides

Accuride® from HÄFELE

Progressive Heavy-Duty File Drawer Slide

- Full-extension, progressive slide with **1 1/2" overtravel.**
- For file drawer applications in desk, credenzas, and lateral files.
- Also store fixtures and institutional furniture.
- Features handed slides, steel ball-bearings
- Hold-in detent
- Easy rail disconnect
- Side mount only
- 32mm and traditional hole pattern.
- Runners can be mounted with Varianta special screws in ø 5 mm system holes.

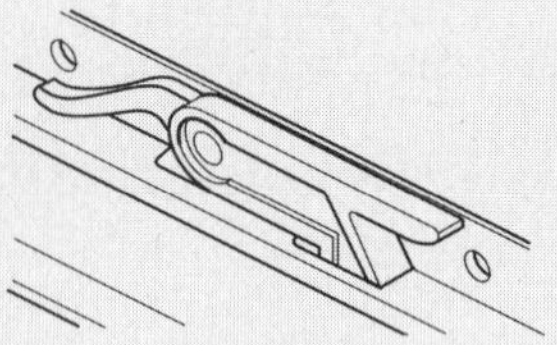

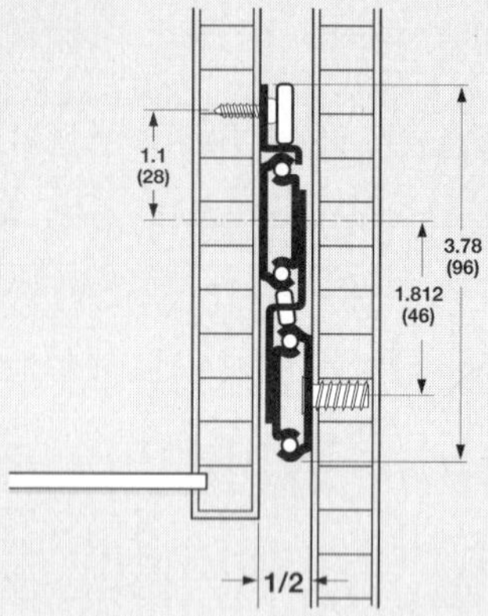

Accuride Model 4034/150 lbs.
- weight capacity up to 60 kg/pair
- progressive movement
- full-extension with 1 1/2" overtravel
- side-mounting

Rail Dimensions

Installed length	Extension length	Distance **F**	Distance **E**
12-14	10.54	4	7.56
15-18	13.06	4	10.08
19-21	16.84	4	13.86
22-25	20.62	7	17.64
26-28	24.40	7	21.42

Finish: steel, zinc-plated and zinc-plated black

Installed length		Extension length		A		B		C		D		Cat. No	
inch	mm	inch	mm	inch	mm	inch	mm	inch	mm	inch	mm	zinc-plated	zinc-pl. balck
12	300	13 1/4	337	8 13/16	224							422.17.309	422.17.318
14	350	15 7/32	386	8 13/16	224							422.17.354	422.17.363
15 3/4	400	17 5/8	448	8 13/16	224	12 1/2	320					422.17.407	422.17.416
17 3/4	450	19 5/8	498	8 13/16	224	14	352					422.17.452	422.17.461
20	500	21 1/2	547	8 13/16	224	16 3/8	416					422.17.505	422.17.514
21 21/32	550	23 29/64	596	8 13/16	224	14	352	17 5/8	448	19	480	422.17.550	422.17.569
23 21/32	600	25 25/64	645	8 13/16	224	14	352	19	480			422.17.603	422.17.612
25 19/32	650	27 5/16	694	8 13/16	224	14	352	21 1/2	544			422.17.658	422.17.667
27 9/16	700	29 1/4	743	8 13/16	224	14	352	21 1/2	544	24	608	422.17.701	422.17.710

Packing: 5 pairs

SYSTEM VARIANTA 32

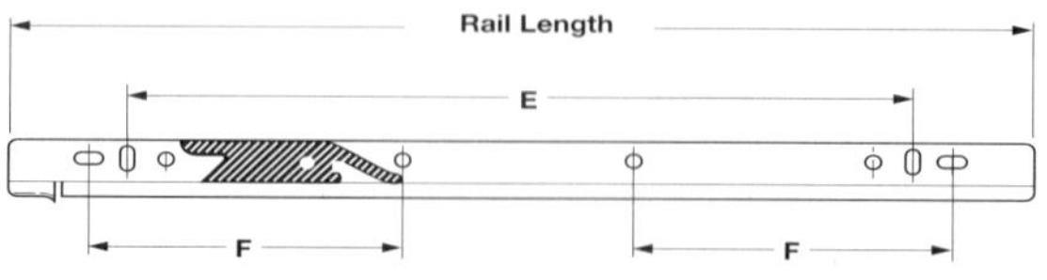

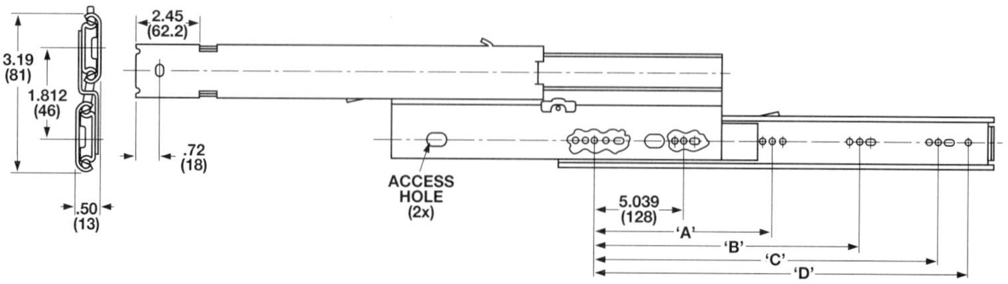

Dimensions in mm
Inches are approximate

Dimensional data not binding. We reserve the right to alter specifications without notice.

Precision Ball-Bearing Slides

HÄFELE

Accuride® from HÄFELE

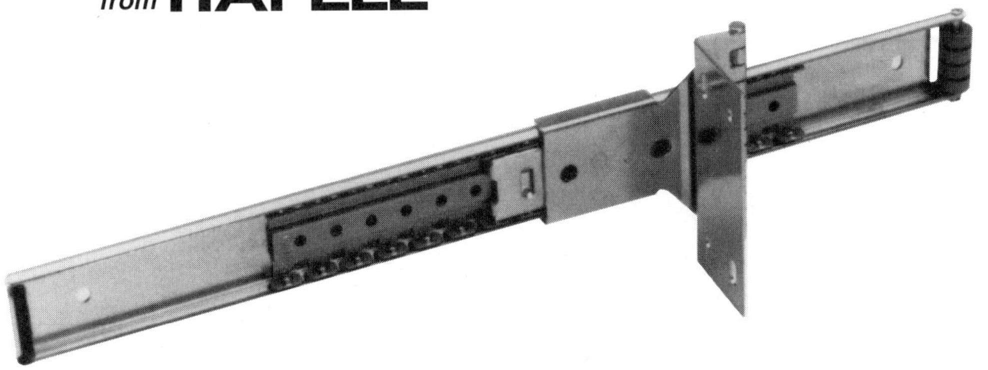

- The "Over the Top" Flipper Door slide is ideally suited for upper file cabinets, audio-video wall units, and entertainment centers.

Accuride Model: 115 / 30 lbs.
Over the Top Flipper Door Slide

Finish: steel, zinc plated black

Installed length inch	Installed length mm	Extension length inch	Extension length mm	Cat. No. zinc-plated black
14	356	10 5/8	270	408.21.369
16	406	12	305	408.21.412
18	457	13 5/8	346	408.21.467

Packing: 10 pairs

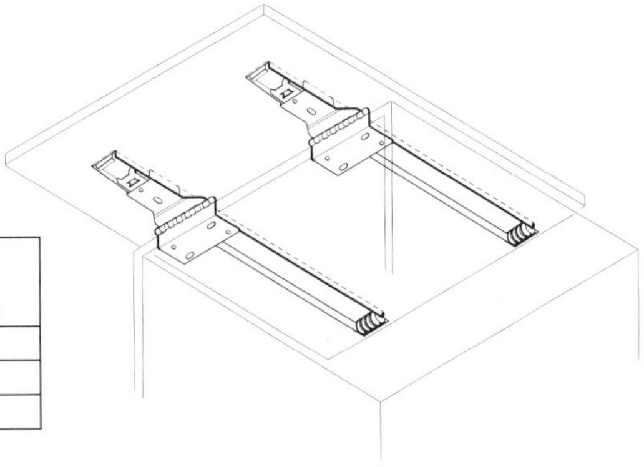

Sliding Door Hardware
Drawer Slides
Television Supports
4

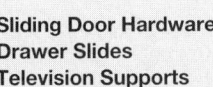

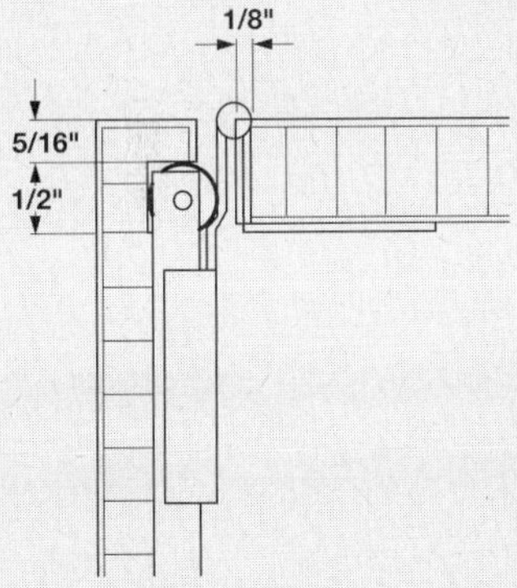

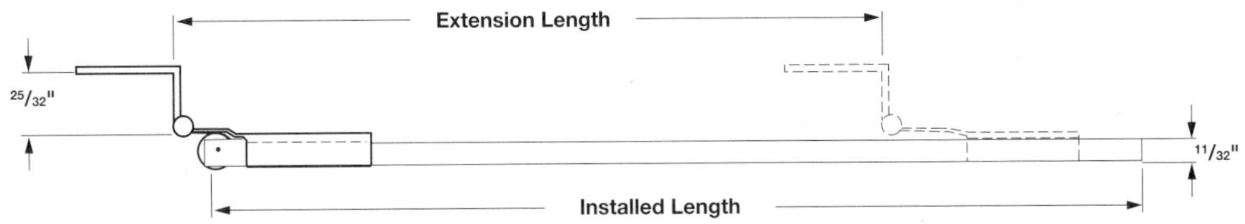

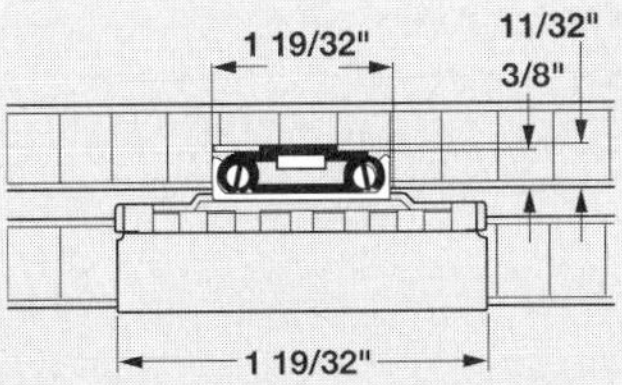

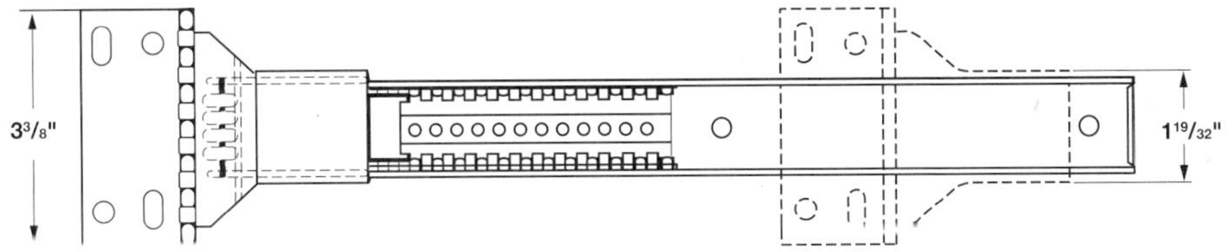

Dimensional data not binding.
We reserve the right to alter specifications without notice.

Dimensions in inches
mm are approximate

HÄFELE

Two-Way Drawer System

Designed especially for installation in room dividers, e.g. kitchen islands, medical carts, pass-through shelves.

Can be used wherever access is needed from both sides of the unit.

Accuride® from HÄFELE

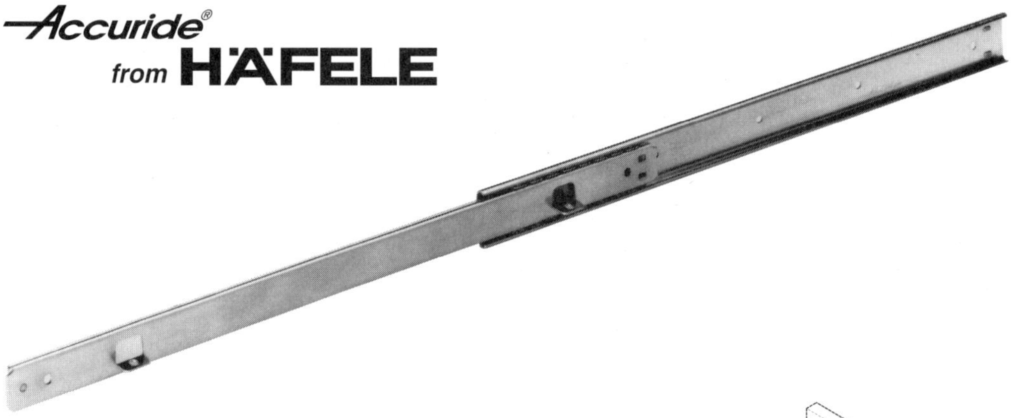

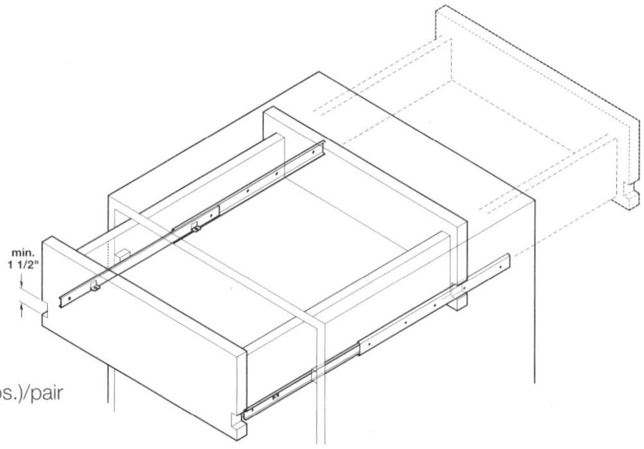

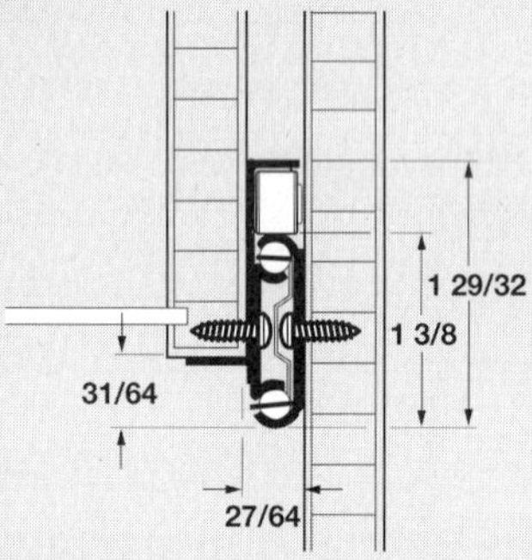

Accuride Model 2002/50 lbs.
- load carrying capacity up to 22 kg (50 lbs.)/pair
- single-extension
- side-mounted

Finish: steel, zinc-plated

Installed length inch	mm	Extension length inch	mm	Cat. No. zinc-plated
18	457	12	328	422.15.458
20	508	14	379	422.15.501
22	559	15	404	422.15.556
24	610	16	430	422.15.609

Packing: 5 pairs

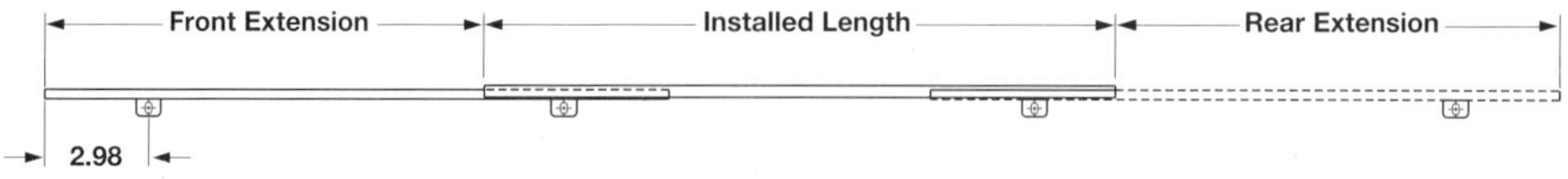

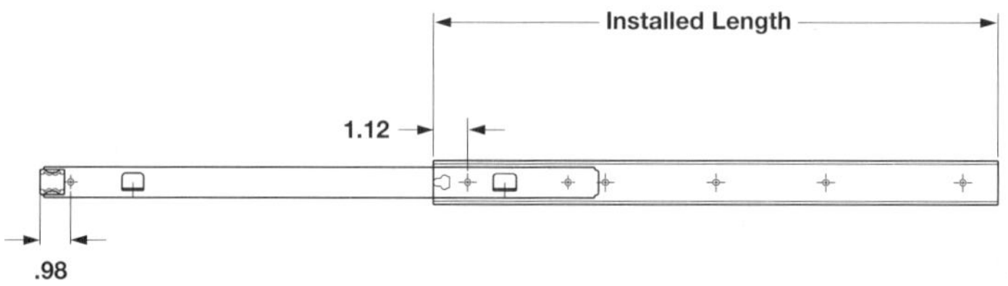

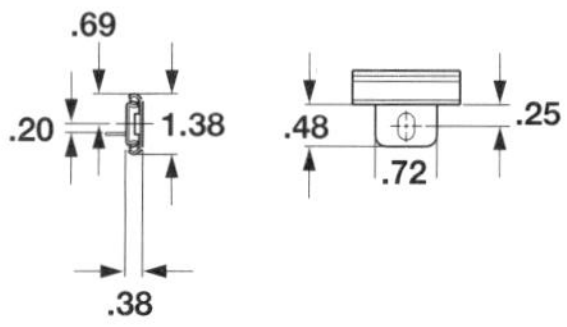

Dimensional data not binding. We reserve the right to alter specifications without notice.

Dimensions in inches
mm are approximate

Pull-Out Runners for Display Panels

Suspension-mounted display pull-out fittings

- Fully extending, 30 mm overtravel.
- Load carrying capacity: 50 kg (110 lbs.)
- 8 ball-bearing mounted rollers.
- Rubber buffers at ends of rails ensure soft braking action.

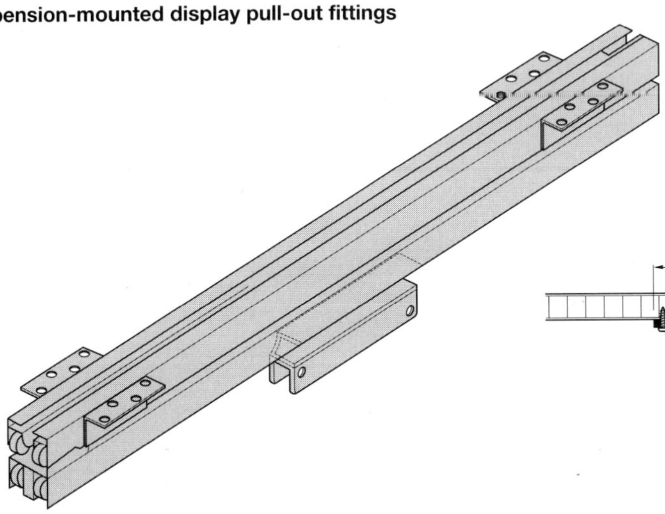

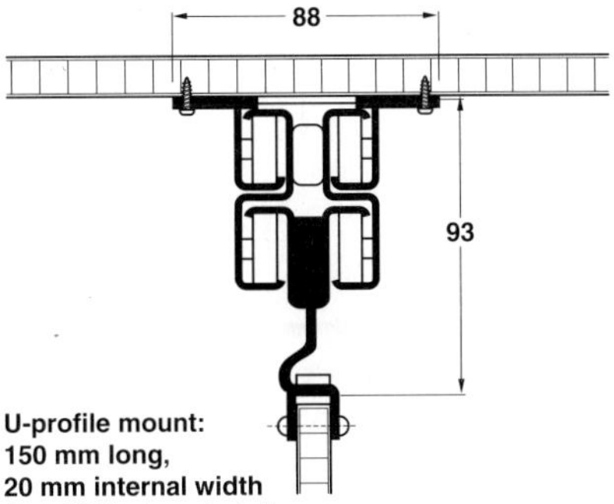

U-profile mount:
150 mm long,
20 mm internal width
(For 3/4 inch material)

Finish: steel, brown powder coated.
RAL 8014

Installed length	Extension length	Cat. No. **Capacity 50 kg**
500 mm	530 mm	421.53.506
700 mm	730 mm	421.53.702
900 mm	930 mm	421.53.908
1000 mm	1030 mm	421.53.999

Packing: 1 pc.

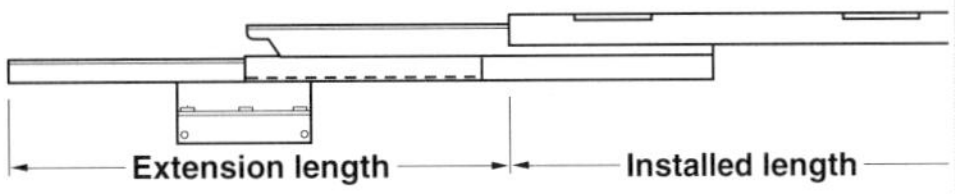

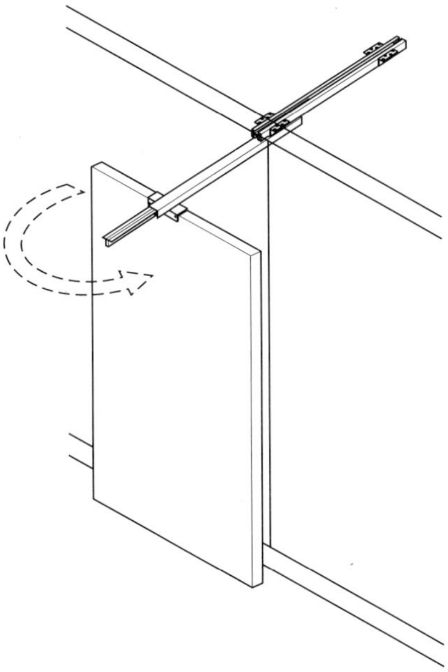

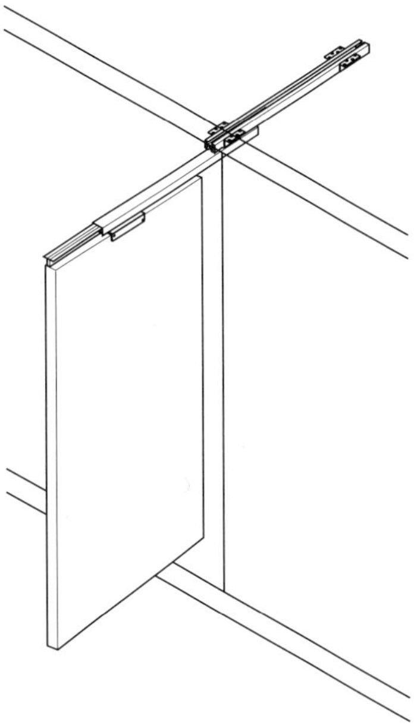

Dimensional data not binding.
We reserve the right to alter specifications without notice.

Dimensions in mm

HÄFELE

Tiratell Pull-Out Cabinet System

A multi-purpose runner system, available in two versions, i.e.
- **tiratell 12,** for cabinet widths up to 250 mm (19 15/16")
- **tiratell 21,** for cabinet widths from 250 to 350 mm (9 13/16 - 13 3/4"). (Two tiratell fittings can be mounted side-by-side for cabinet widths over 350 mm.) (13 3/4")

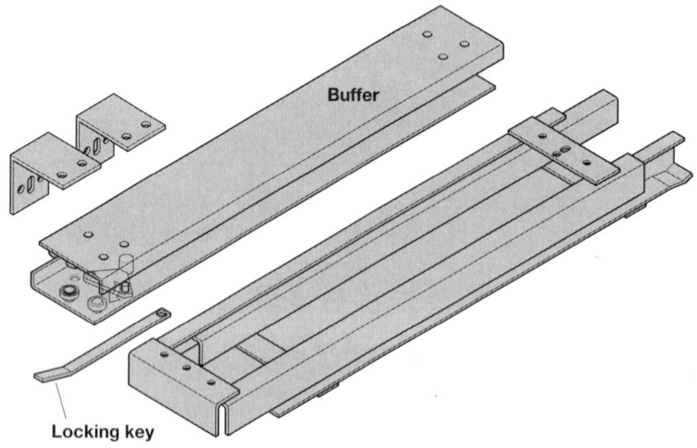

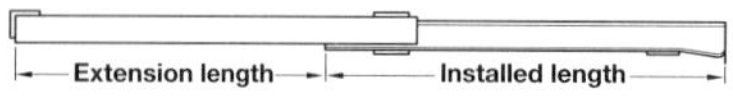

- The weight rating is approximate and can change depending where load is applied.

Tiratell pull-out cabinet system
Technical data:
Single extension unit, load carrying capacity **100 kg.** (220 lbs.)
Rollers: 4 ball-bearing mounted steel rollers with polyamid caps.
Top runner is fitted with four friction bearing mounted polyamid rollers and two rubber buffers. Safety retainer accommodating the front buffer can be released with the accompanying key.
Please order top runner separately. See article numbers below.

Finish: steel, galvanized

Model	tiratell 12	tiratell 21
Installed length	500 mm	
Extension length	385 mm	
Installed width	120 mm	215 mm
For cabinet width	max. 250 mm	250-350 mm
Cat. No.	421.45.102	421.45.111

Packing: 1 pc.

Top runner, for lateral stability
Mounting on underside of cabinet or side panel
Finish: steel, galvanized

Cat. No.	421.45.166

Packing: 1 pc.

Mounting bracket
for side panel mounting of top runner including fastening screw
Finish: steel, galvanized

Cat. No.	421.45.095

Packing: 1 pc.

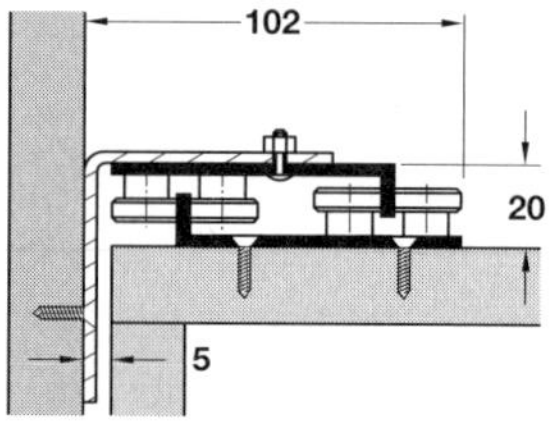

or:

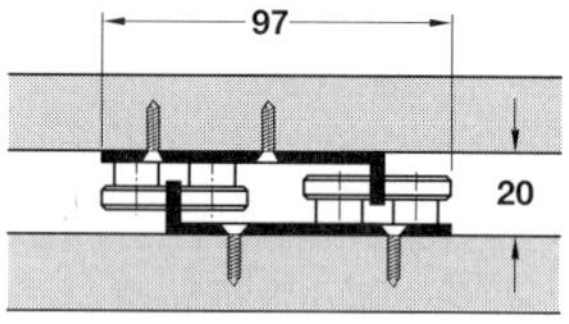

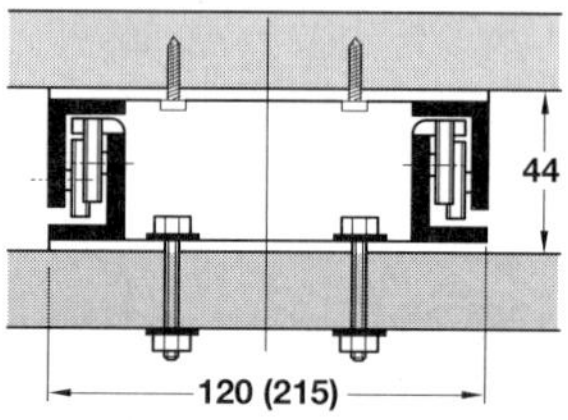

Sectional drawings above show:
top: side panel mounting using angle brackets
center: mounting on underside of cabinet ceiling
bottom: mounted on carcase floor

Dimensional data not binding. We reserve the right to alter specifications without notice.

Dimensions in mm

Pull-Out Cabinet System

For tall cabinets found in pharmacies, etc.

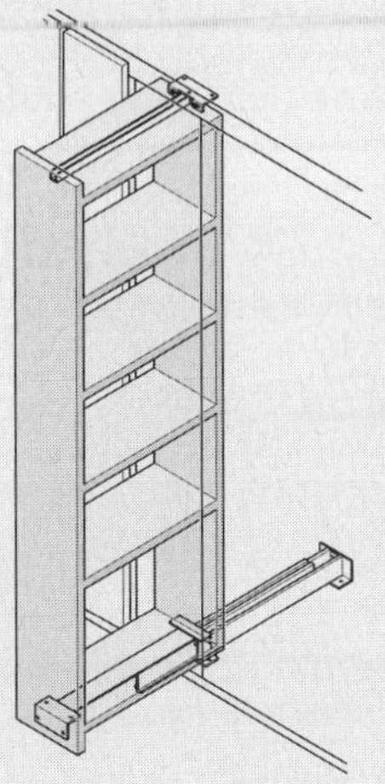

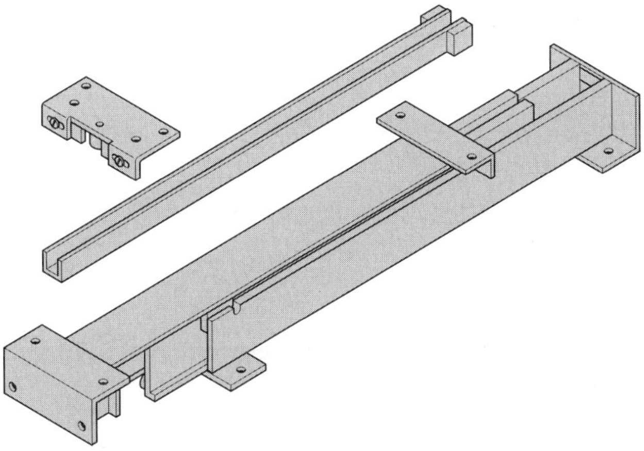

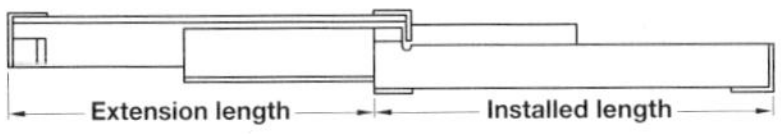

Pull-out cabinet system and top runner
Technical data:
Differential extension type, load carrying capacity:
150 kg. (330 lbs.) (530 mm long)
125 kg. (275 lbs.) (860 mm long)
Rollers:
8 ball-bearing mounted steel rollers
2 friction bearing mounted steel rollers
1 friction bearing mounted cylinder steel roller
Rubber buffers on the rails and runner ensure silent action; return guide and retainer provide for the accurate closure of the cabinet pull-out; safety stop
Top runner is included in package.

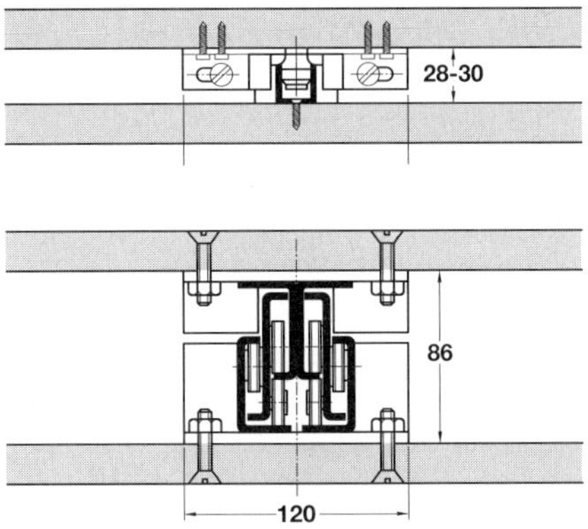

Finish: steel, galvanized

Capacity	Installed length	Extension length	Cat. No.
170 kg.	482 mm	438 mm	421.48.489
170 kg.	532 mm	478 mm	421.48.532
170 kg.	582 mm	528 mm	421.48.587
150 kg.	682 mm	628 mm	421.48.685
125 kg.	862 mm	808 mm	421.48.863

Packing: 1 pc.

- The weight rating is approximate and can change depending where load is applied.

HÄFELE

Heavy-Duty Cabinet Pull-Out System

- Differential feature provides smooth, silent operation
- Nylon glides between tracks to prevent rubbing noise
- Cross-members for added lateral stability
- Effortless, high-grade steel ball-bearing action
- Positive stop in closed position
- Adding another pull-out system double load capacity to 200 kg. (400 lbs.)

- The additional upper guide track is recommended for increased stability

Upper guide track for added stability
System includes guide track and guide roller. Enclosed track end serves as positive stop for guide roller.
Finish: steel, galvanized

Installed length	Cat. No.
420 mm	421.57.406
470 mm	421.57.451
520 mm	421.57.504
570 mm	421.57.559
620 mm	421.57.602
670 mm	421.57.657
720 mm	421.57.700
770 mm	421.57.755
820 mm	421.57.808
870 mm	421.57.853
920 mm	421.57.906
970 mm	421.57.951
1020 mm	421.57.997

Packing: 1 pc.

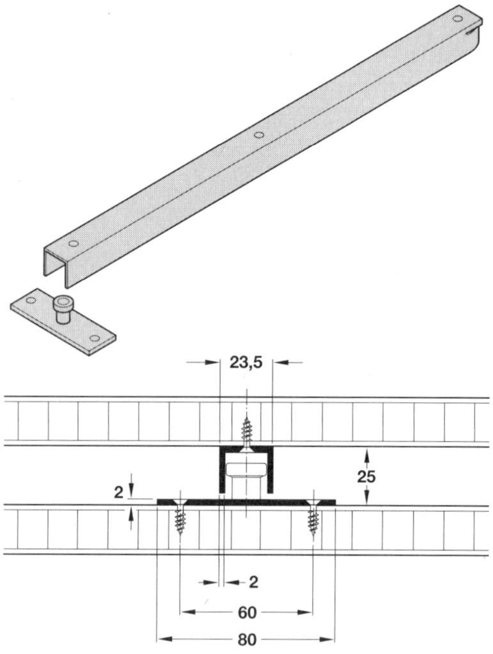

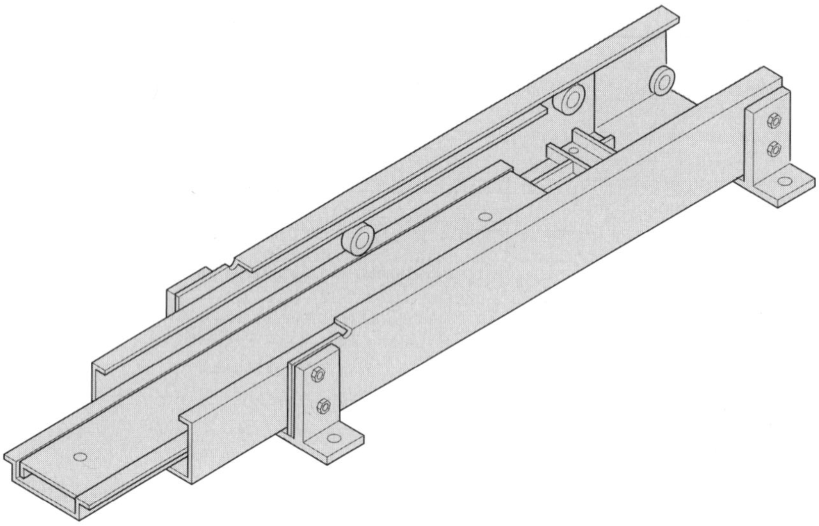

Heavy-duty Pantry Pull-out System, Floor-mounted
single-extension
Action:
- 4 steel ball-bearing roller
- 2 steel ball-bearing rollers, nylon tread
- 4 polyamide rollers

Load capacity: **100 Kg (200 lbs.)**
Finish: steel, zinc-plated; polyamide roller

Installed length	Extension	Cat. No.
400 mm	385 mm	421.56.409
450 mm	435 mm	421.56.454
500 mm	485 mm	421.56.507
550 mm	535 mm	421.56.552
600 mm	585 mm	421.56.605
650 mm	635 mm	421.56.650
700 mm	685 mm	421.56.703
750 mm	735 mm	421.56.758
800 mm	785 mm	421.56.801
850 mm	835 mm	421.56.856
900 mm	885 mm	421.56.909
950 mm	935 mm	421.56.954
1000 mm	985 mm	421.56.990

Packing: 1 pc.

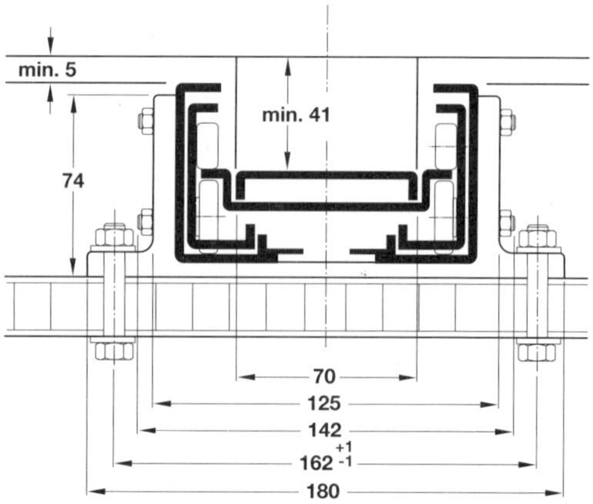

Load capacity specification applies to lengths up to 600 mm. Increasing length reduces load capacity by up to 20%.

Dimensions in mm

Sliding Cabinet System

HÄFELE

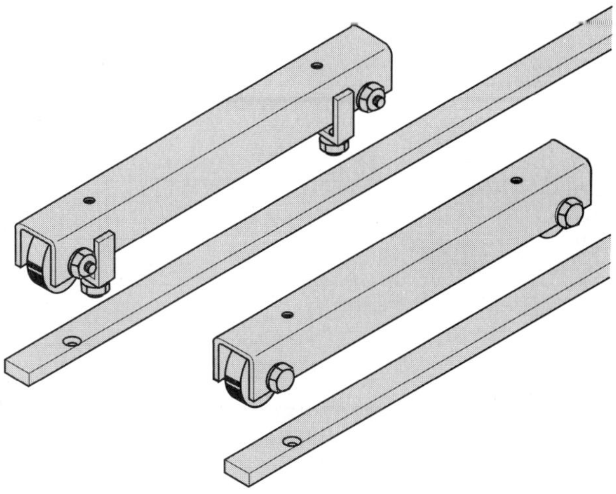

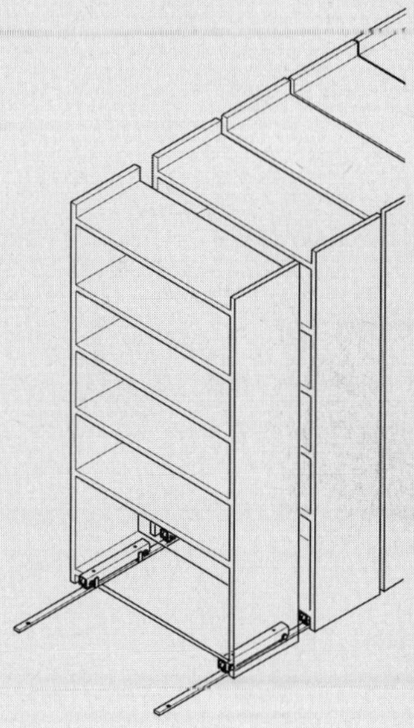

Sliding cabinet system, storage of large volumes of small items, easy access with minimum loss of storage space.

Technical data:
Load bearing capacity: **220 kg** (485 lbs.) per roller unit
(two roller units per cabinet required).
Running gear includes: 2 ball-bearing mounted, compressed webbing rollers
Lateral guides: 2 ball-bearing mounted, steel rollers
Frame: steel, brown enameled
Track: steel, galvanized

Sliding cabinet running gear
Standard length: 350 mm (13¾")

Catalog No.	421.59.928

Packing: 2 pcs.

Roller track
Standard length: 3000 mm (118")

Catalog No.	421.59.062

Packing: 1 pc.

Mounting note: To ensure proper lateral control, the running gear must always be mounted under the cabinet section so that the guide rollers are on the inside, i.e. towards the center of the cabinet.

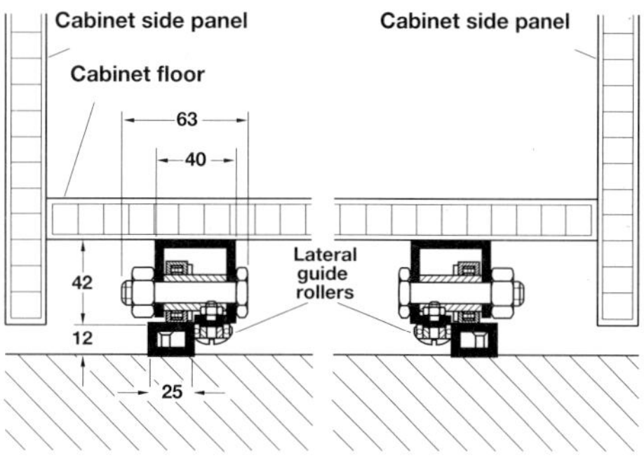

Dimensions in mm

HÄFELE

Tirator Pull-Out Cabinet Runner

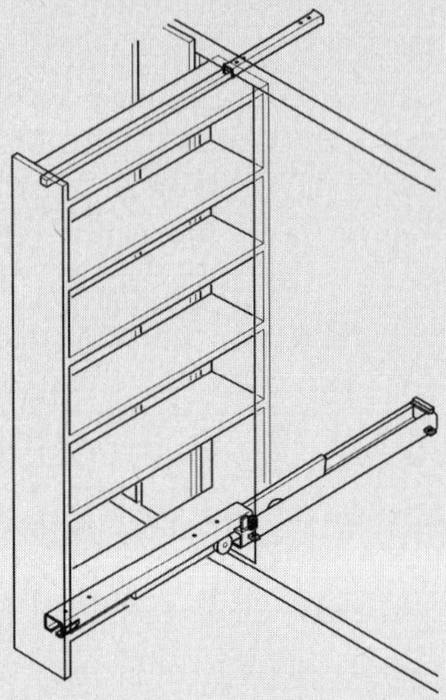

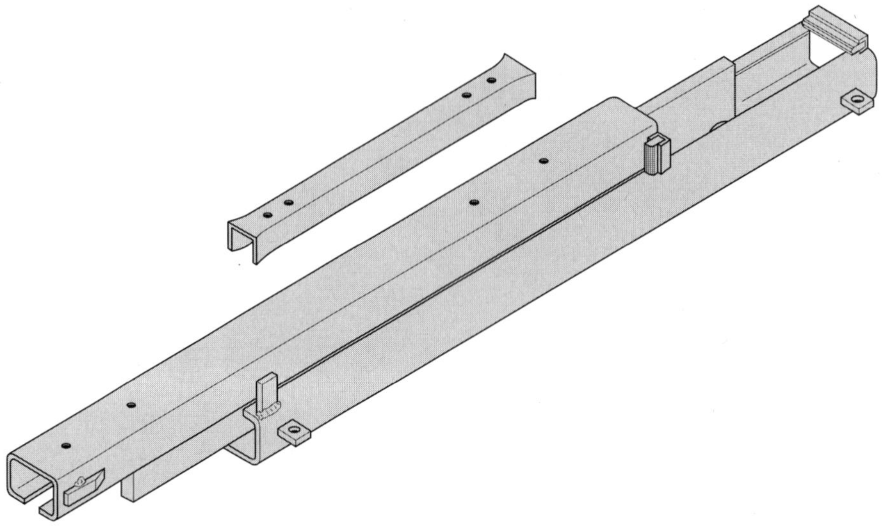

Tirator pull-out cabinet system, suitable for heavily loaded, tall cabinets (load bearing capacity 250 kg) of of the type found in offices, filing rooms, pharmacies and hospitals. The runner is available in three standard lengths (900, 1000 and 1200 mm) and comes complete with upper guide and runner fastening bolts.

Technical data: Differential, single extension type.
Load bearing capacity: **250 kg** (550 lbs.)
Rollers: 10 ball-bearing mounted steel rollers.
Rubber buffers for stopping purposes.
Finish: steel, grey enameled

Installed length	900 mm	1000 mm	1200 mm
Extension length	approx. 840 mm	approx. 940 mm	approx. 1140 mm
Load bearing capacity	250 kg (550 lbs.)		
Cat. No.	421.47.197	421.47.222	421.47.277

Packing: 1 pc.

Mounting note: The upper guide rail is intended to accommodate a 23 x 23 mm hardwood batten, which should be prepared on site and mounted on top of the pull-out unit.

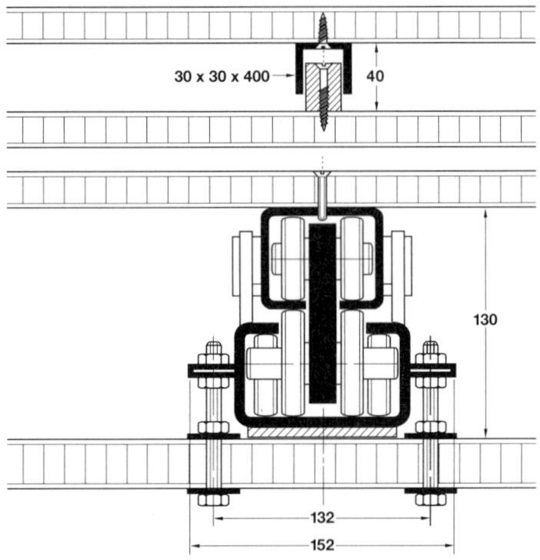

Dimensional data not binding. We reserve the right to alter specifications without notice.

Dimensions in mm

Television Extension Swivels

HÄFELE

Low profile television extension swivel (110 lbs)

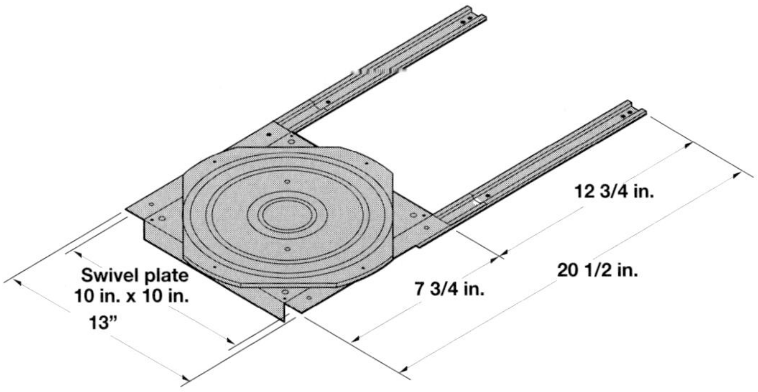

Low profile, swivel pull-out fitting extends 7 3/4 inch. 12 3/4" long x 13" wide x 1" high. Swivel plated size 10" square. Ball-bearing action on both extension and swivel. 110 lb. load capacity. Sold without installation screws.

Finish: zinc

Cat. No.	421.60.912

Packing: 10 pcs.

High profile television extension swivel (150 lbs.)

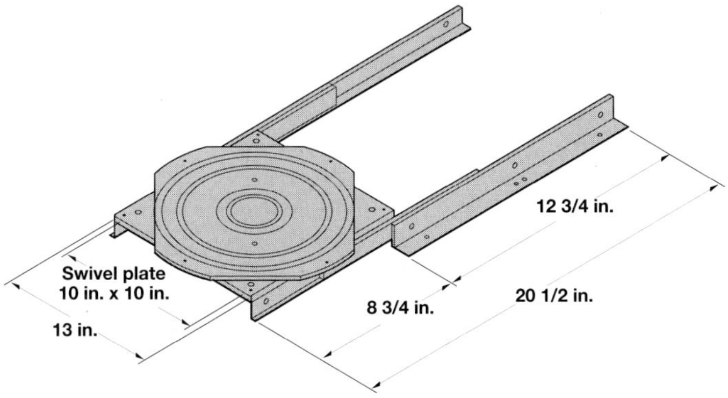

Best selling swivel pull-out fitting, extends 8 3/4 inch. 12 3/4" long x 13" wide x 1 7/8" high. Swivel plated size 10" square. 150 lb. load capacity. Sold without installation screws.

Finish: zinc

Cat. No.	421.60.921

Packing: 10 pcs.

High profile television extension swivel (110 lbs.)

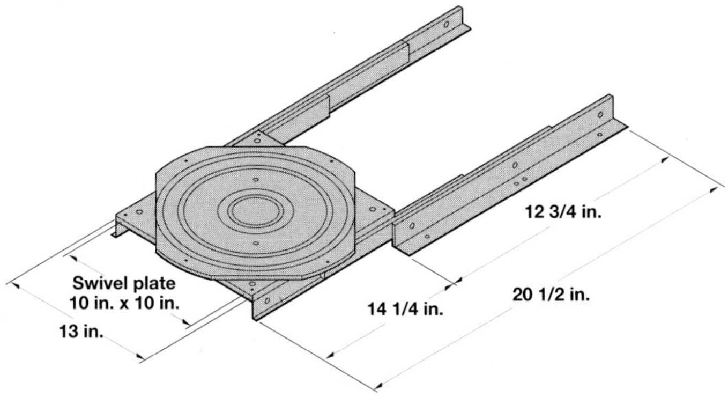

High profile television extension swivel

Full extension, swivel pull-out fitting, extends 14 1/4 inch. 12 3/4" long x 13" wide x 1 7/8" high. Swivel plate size 10" square. Ball-bearing action on both extension and swivel. Sold without installation screws.

110 load capacity. Sold w/o screws.

Finish: zinc

Cat. No.	421.60.930

Packing: 5 pcs.

Mounting to shelf (slides) must be done with through-bolt.

Note: Depending on installation and where load is actually placed, the weight rating can change. (leverage effect) For commercial applications, please conduct your own test.

Dimensional data not binding. We reserve the right to alter specifications without notice.

Extending Television Turntables

- For heavy TVs up to 90 kg (200 lbs.)
- Low profile
- Brown color blends well with wood.

Fixing to shelf (slides) must be done with through-bolt.

Note: Depending on installation and where load is actually placed, the weight rating can change. (leverage effect) For commercial applications, please conduct your own test.

Extending TV turntable 90 kg (200 lbs)

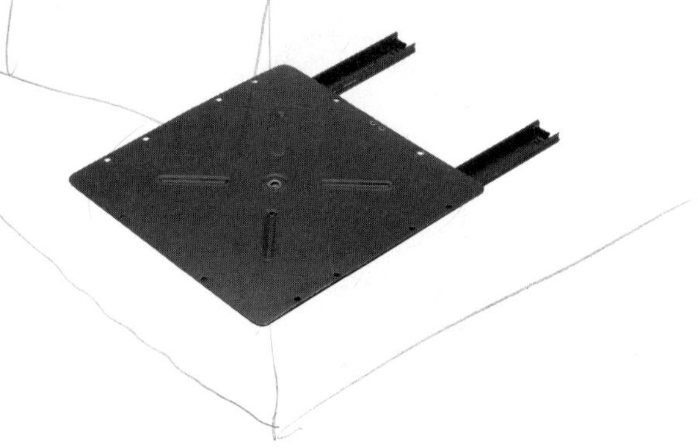

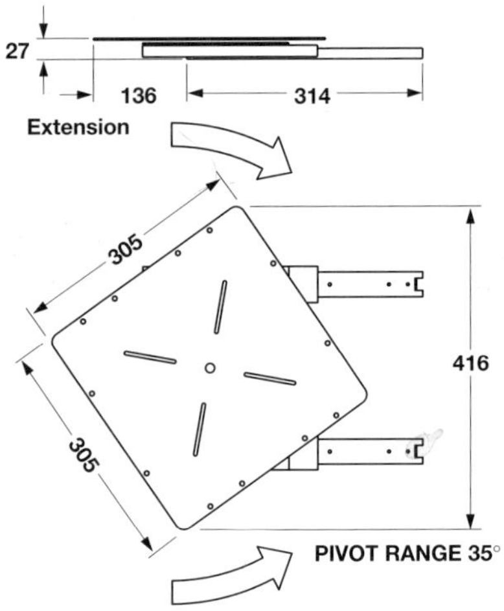

Measurements in mm

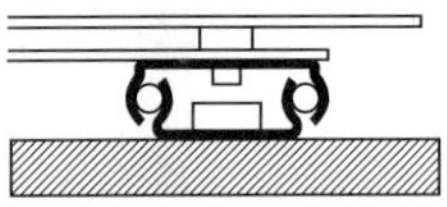

Finish: steel, painted brown

Cat. No.	421.96.110

Packing: 6 pcs.

Extending TV turntable 55 kg (125 lbs)

- Economical model for the contract furniture industry
- Low profile slide and swivel

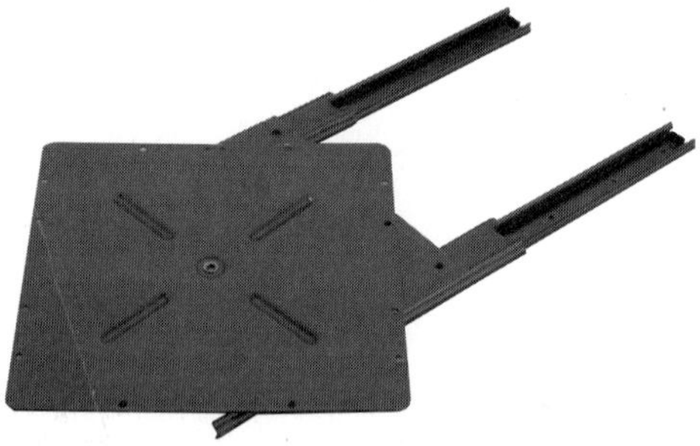

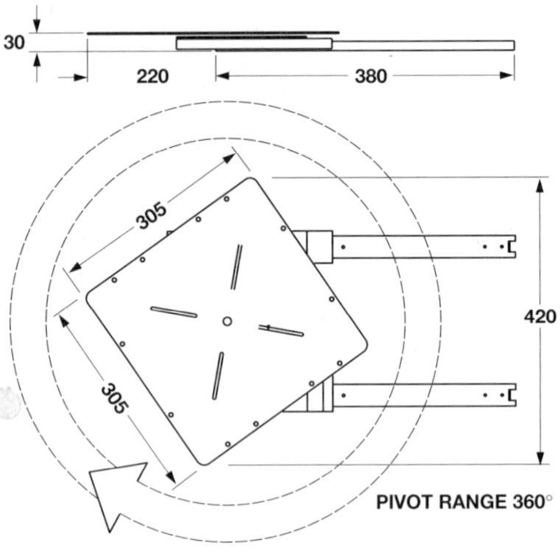

Measurements in mm

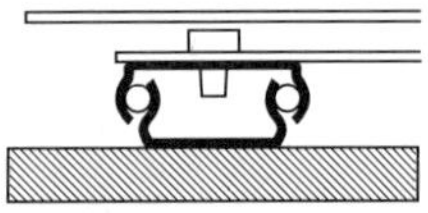

Finish: steel, painted brown

Cat. No.	421.96.118

Packing: 6 pcs.

Extending TV turntable 90 kg (200 lbs)

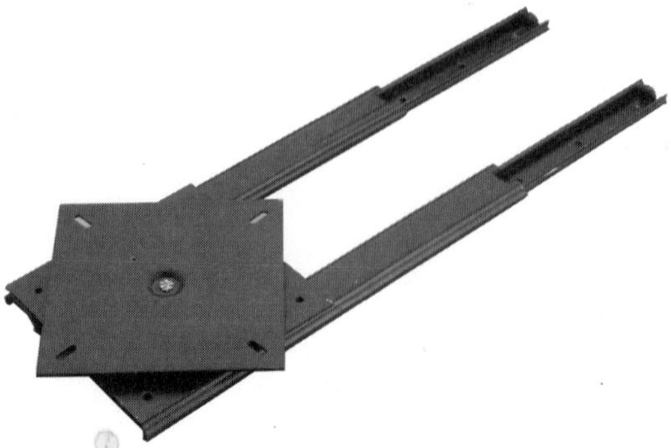

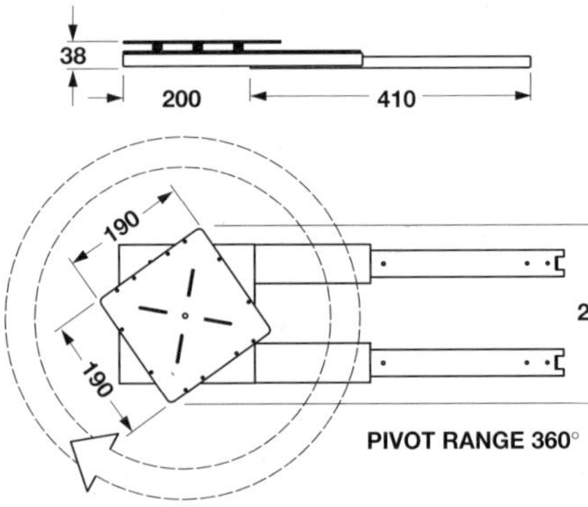

Note: Top plate must be manufactured separately

Measurements in mm

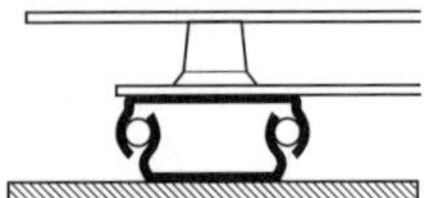

Finish: steel, painted brown

Cat. No.	421.96.109

Packing: 6 pcs.

Extending Television Turntables

TV swivel full-extension 60 kg (132 lbs.)

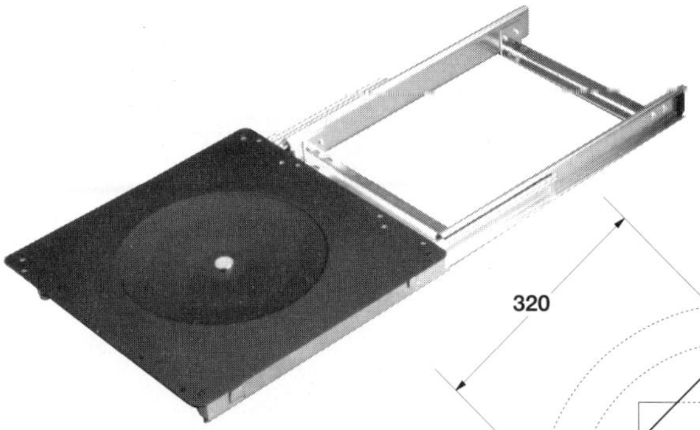

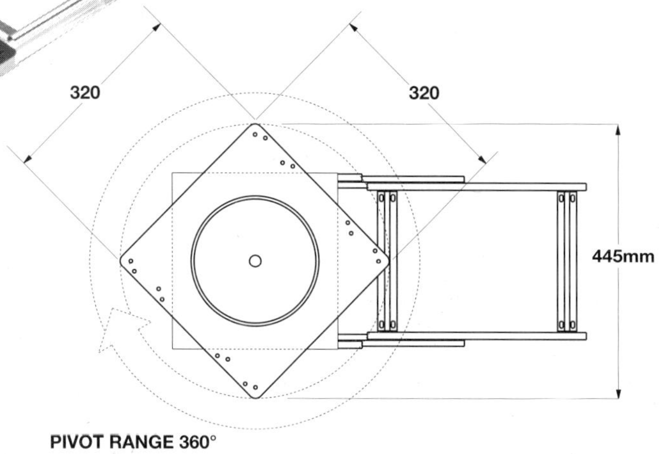

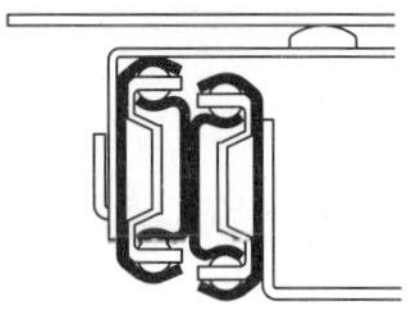

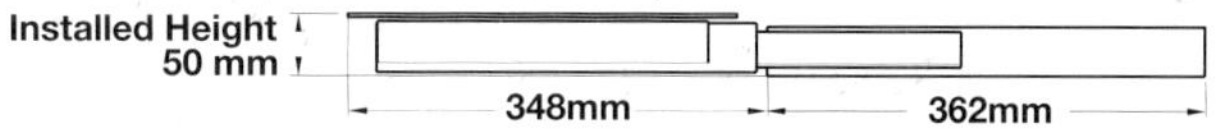

Finish: Slides; steel, galvanized, Platform; steel, black

Cat. No.	423.93.300

Packing: 1 pc.

TV swivel full extension 60 kg (132 lbs.)

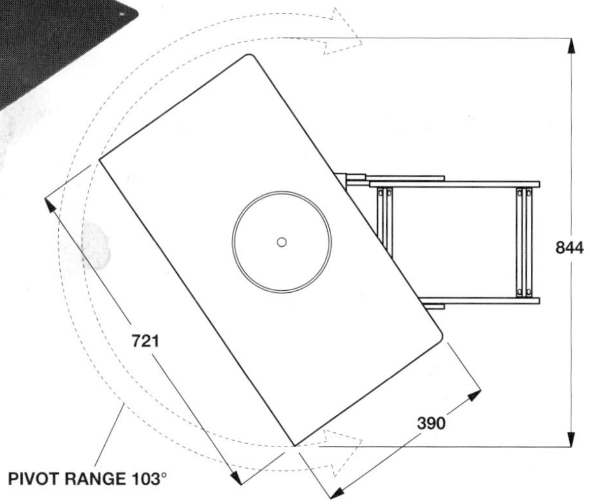

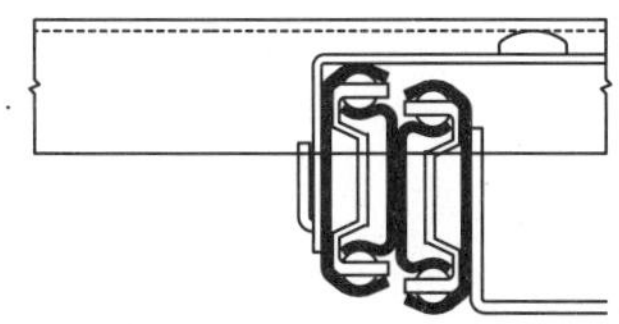

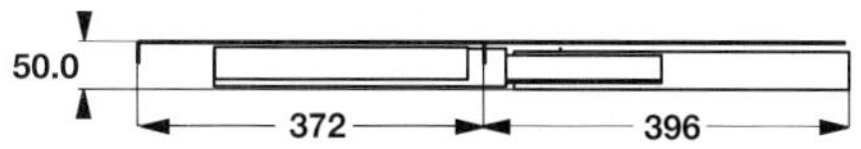

Finish: Slides; steel, galvanized, Platform; steel, black

Cat. No.	423.93.310

Packing: 1 pc.

Dimensions in mm

- Full extension TV turntable
- Entertainment centers, computer terminals.
- Dynamic load rating of 60 kg (132 lbs).
- Durable, long lasting
- Ball cage guided runners
- Smooth and quiet operation
- Platform designed to carry custom top plate of individual size.
- Platform can be rotated 360°.

Mounting to shelf (slides) must be done with through-bolt.

Note: Depending on installation and where load is actually placed, the weight rating can change. (leverage affect) For commercial applications, please conduct your own test.

- Full-extension TV turntable
- Entertainment centers, computer terminals.
- Dynamic load rating of 60 kg (132 lbs).
- Durable, long lasting
- Ball cage guided runners
- Smooth and quiet operation
- Full-size platform
- No need to manufacture platform for TV
- Pull-out strip for easy operation.

Mounting to shelf (slides) must be done with through-bolt.

Note: Depending on installation and where load is actually placed, the weight rating can change. (leverage affect) For commercial use, please conduct your own test.

HÄFELE

TV Swivel, Single-Extension

Mounting to shelf (slides) must be done with through-bolt.

Note: Depending on installation and where load is actually placed, the weight rating can change. (leverage effect) For commercial applications, please conduct your own test.

TV Swivel 360°, 60 kg (132 lbs.)

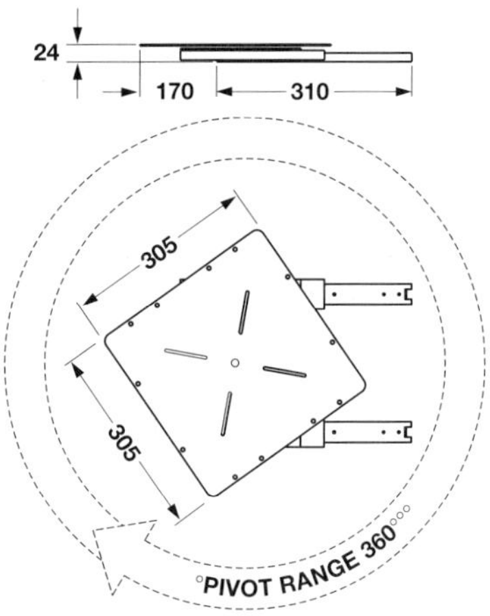

Finish: galvanized platform, black

Cat. No.	423.93.320

Packing: 2 pcs.

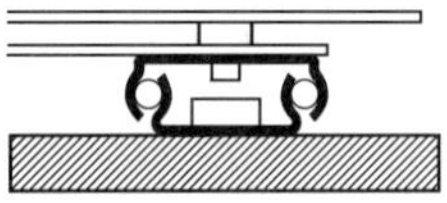

4
Sliding Door Hardware
Drawer Slides
Television Supports

TV Turntables

Super-Color V Extending TV Turntable

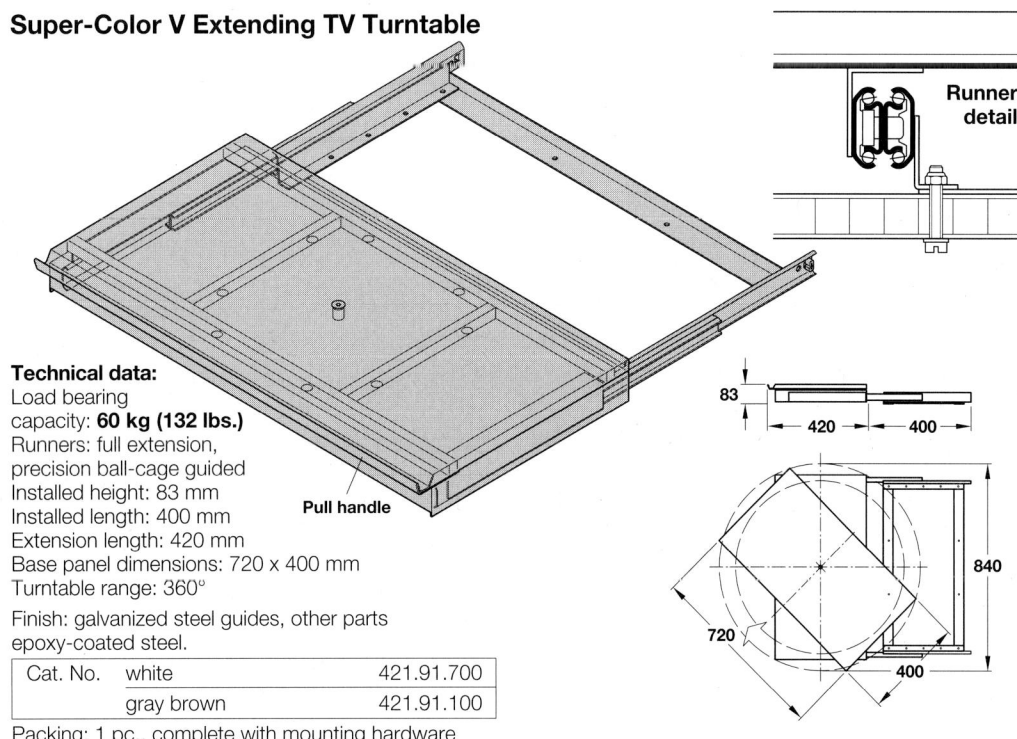

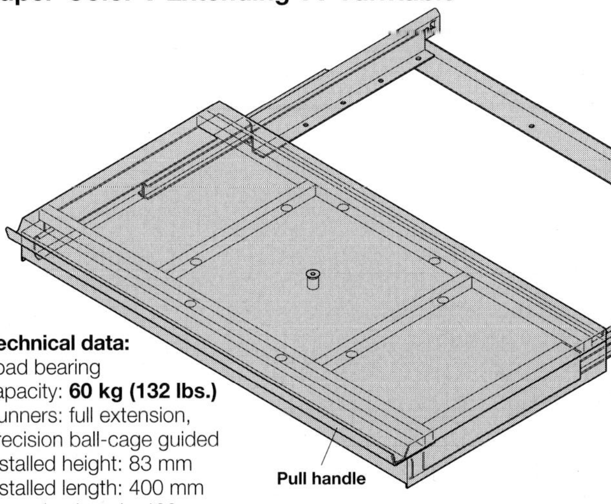

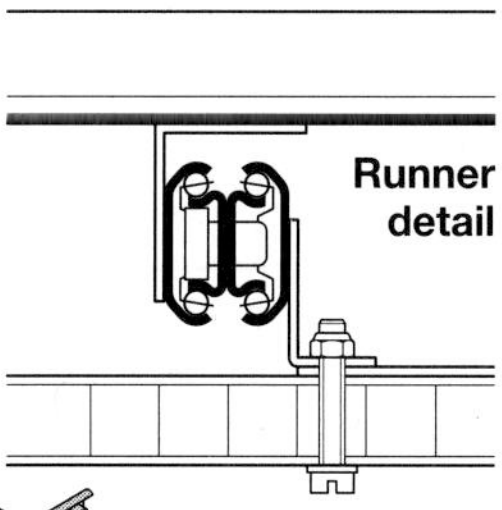

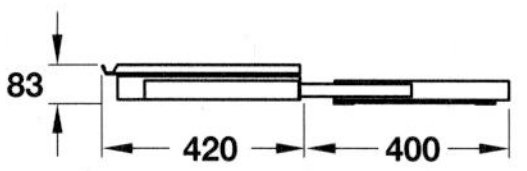

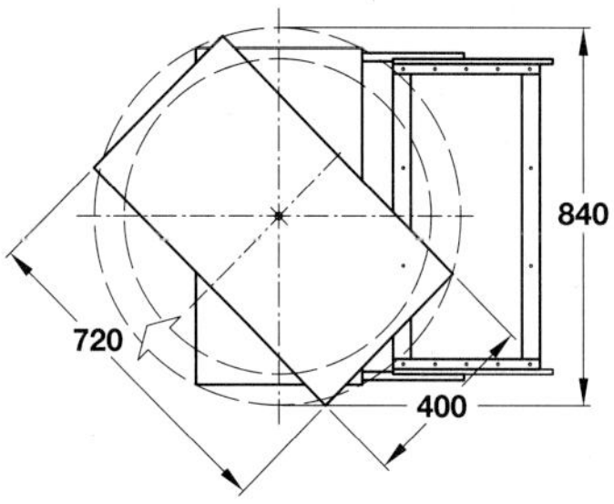

Technical data:
Load bearing capacity: **60 kg (132 lbs.)**
Runners: full extension, precision ball-cage guided
Installed height: 83 mm
Installed length: 400 mm
Extension length: 420 mm
Base panel dimensions: 720 x 400 mm
Turntable range: 360°

Finish: galvanized steel guides, other parts epoxy-coated steel.

Cat. No.	white	421.91.700
	gray brown	421.91.100

Packing: 1 pc., complete with mounting hardware

- Handle operated from top
- Comes complete with shelf

Mounting to shelf (slides) must be done with through-bolt.

Important Notice:

To ensure safe operation of the TV swivels, the following safety precautions must be taken:

1. The shelf holding the TV must be securely connected to the cabinet.
2. Slides must be attached with through bolts and lock nuts to shelf.
3. Wood screws can only be used to mount the front of the slides to the shelf.

HÄFELE

TV Turntables

- All TV swivels feature precision ball-bearing slides for quiet, smooth operation

Important Notice:

To ensure safe operation of the TV swivels, the following safety precautions must be taken:

1. The shelf holding the TV must be securely connected to the cabinet.
2. Slides must be attached with through bolts and lock nuts to shelf.
3. Wood screws can only be used to mount the front of the slides to the shelf.

Mounting at rear

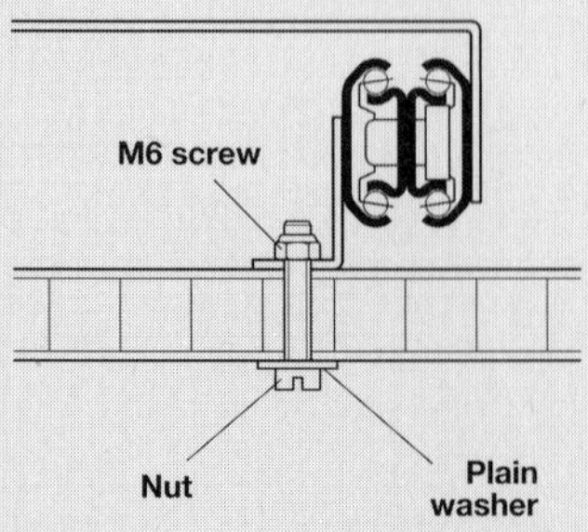

Dimensional data not binding. We reserve the right to alter specifications without notice.

Colorette Extending TV Turntable

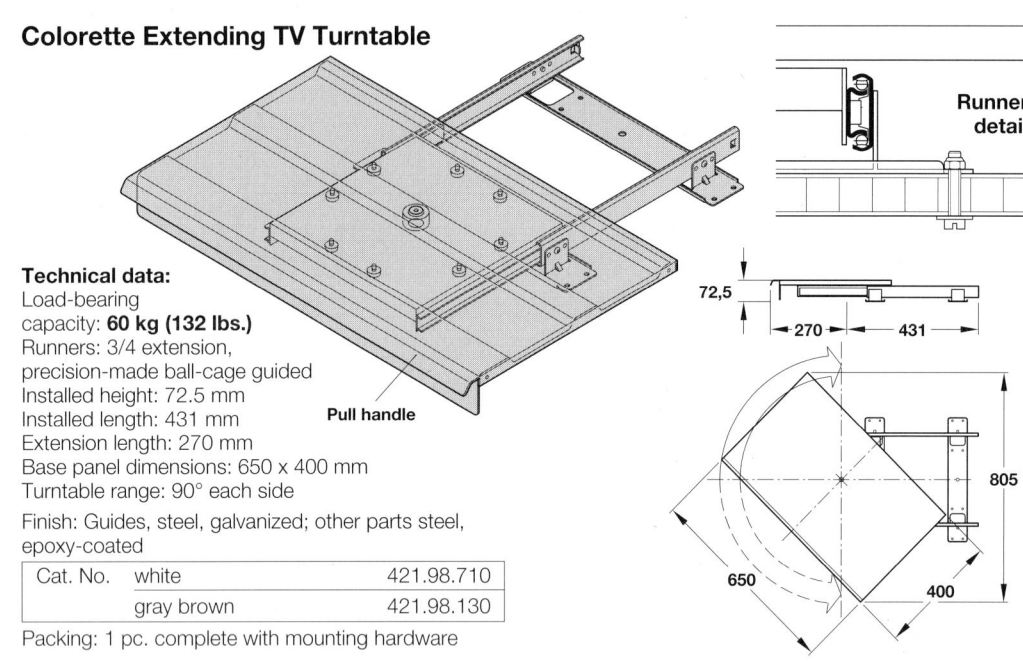

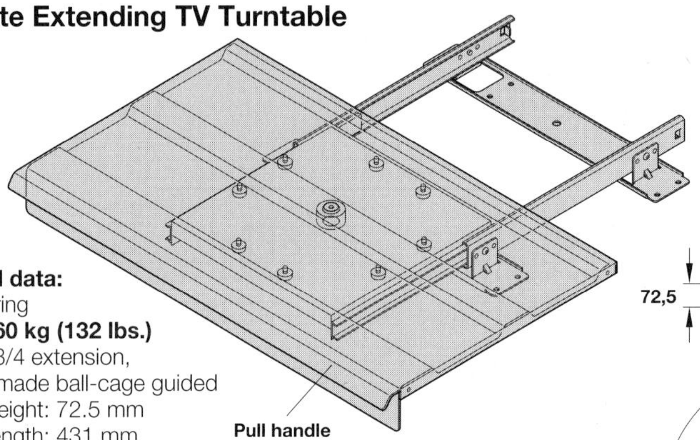

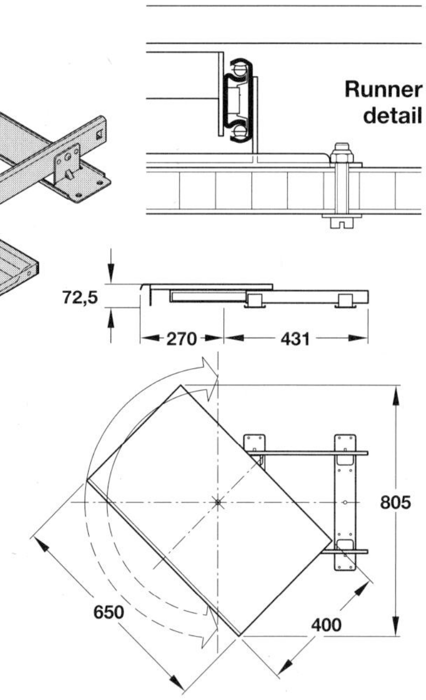

Technical data:
Load-bearing capacity: **60 kg (132 lbs.)**
Runners: 3/4 extension, precision-made ball-cage guided
Installed height: 72.5 mm
Installed length: 431 mm
Extension length: 270 mm
Base panel dimensions: 650 x 400 mm
Turntable range: 90° each side

Finish: Guides, steel, galvanized; other parts steel, epoxy-coated

Cat. No.	white	421.98.710
	gray brown	421.98.130

Packing: 1 pc. complete with mounting hardware

Color E Extending TV Turntable

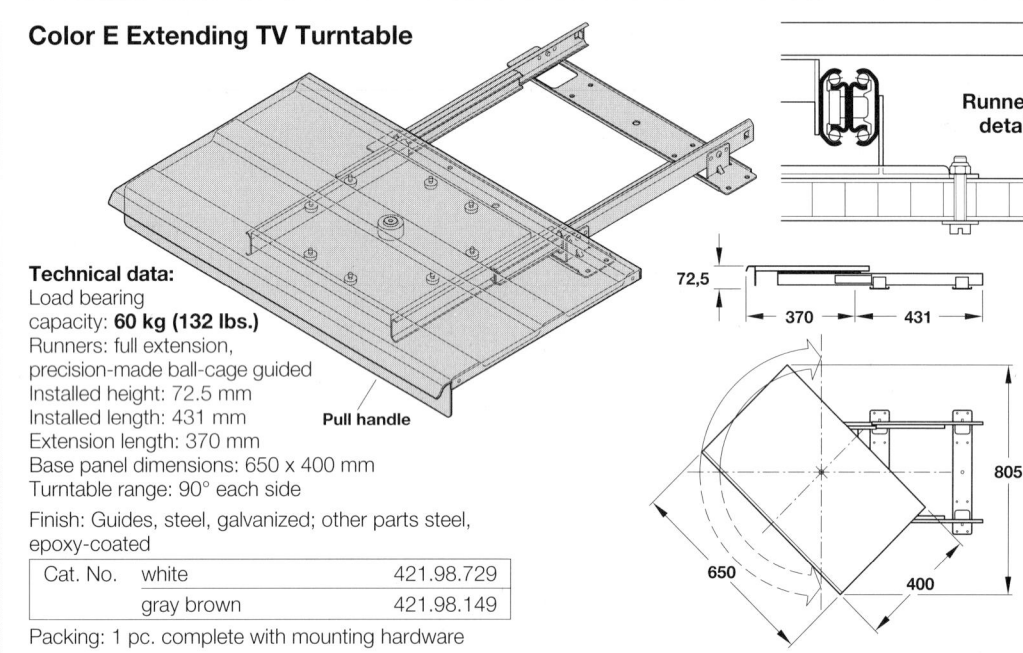

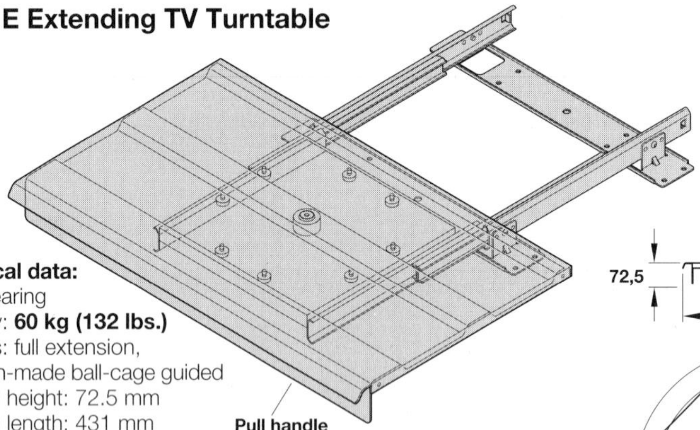

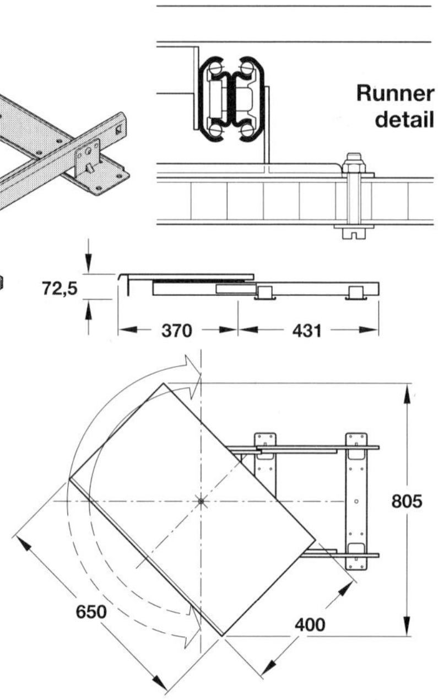

Technical data:
Load bearing capacity: **60 kg (132 lbs.)**
Runners: full extension, precision-made ball-cage guided
Installed height: 72.5 mm
Installed length: 431 mm
Extension length: 370 mm
Base panel dimensions: 650 x 400 mm
Turntable range: 90° each side

Finish: Guides, steel, galvanized; other parts steel, epoxy-coated

Cat. No.	white	421.98.729
	gray brown	421.98.149

Packing: 1 pc. complete with mounting hardware

Colorvaria V Extending TV Turntable

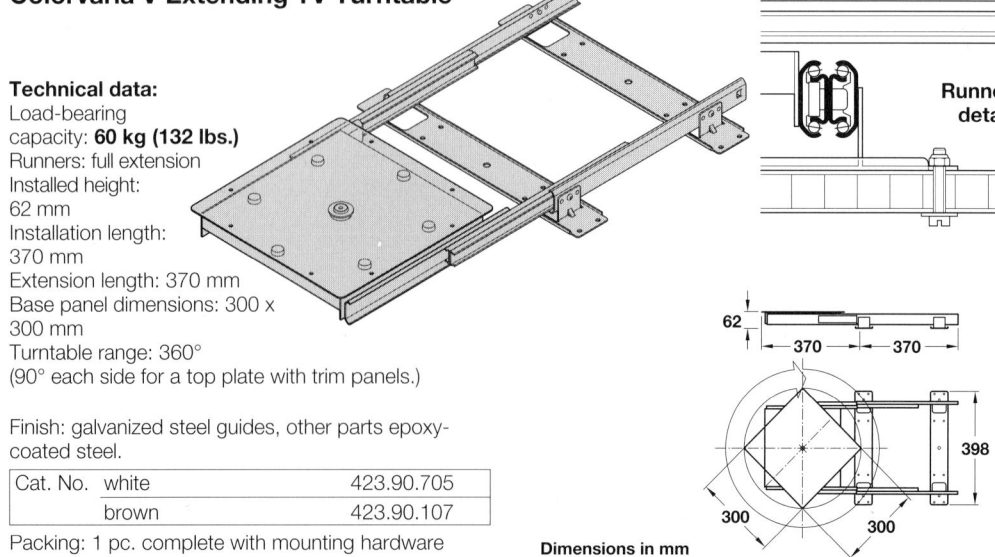

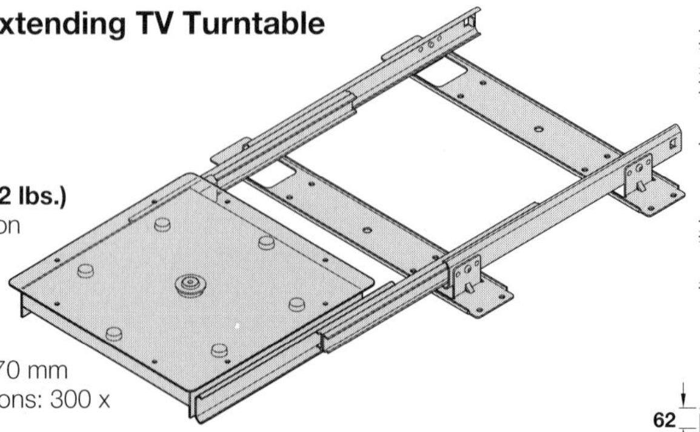

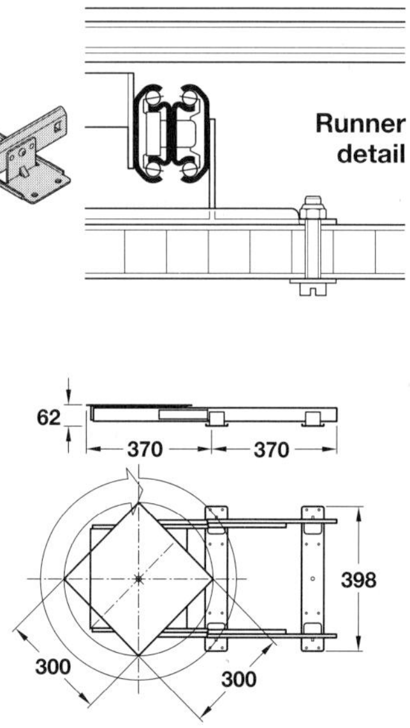

Technical data:
Load-bearing capacity: **60 kg (132 lbs.)**
Runners: full extension
Installed height: 62 mm
Installation length: 370 mm
Extension length: 370 mm
Base panel dimensions: 300 x 300 mm
Turntable range: 360°
(90° each side for a top plate with trim panels.)

Finish: galvanized steel guides, other parts epoxy-coated steel.

Cat. No.	white	423.90.705
	brown	423.90.107

Packing: 1 pc. complete with mounting hardware

Dimensions in mm

Call 1-800-423-3531 anywhere in the US and Canada

Heavy-duty T.V. Pull-out Swivel Slide

HÄFELE

Accuride®
from HÄFELE

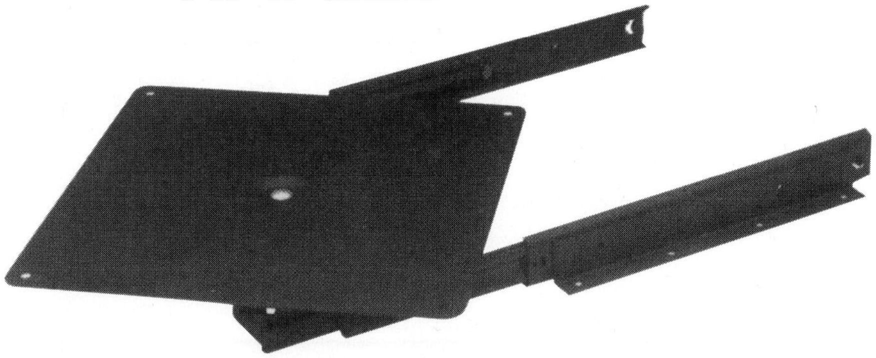

- Designed to support large televisions with ease.
- Sturdy support brackets provide an extraordinary degree of stability, even at maximum extension.
- 16 square inch mounting plate with support rollers mounted underneath reduces unwanted rocking.

Accuride Model CB3620-258 TV

Technical Data

- Load Rating 180lbs* (82kg)
- Travel 14" (356mm)
- Plate Dimensions 16" x 16" (406mm x 406mm)
- Height 2.42 ± .10 (62mm)
- Mounting Bracket. Slide members rest on the cabinet
- Extension: Full
- Finish: Black zinc plating
- Steel ball-bearings
- Hold-in detent
- Silenced stops, in and out
- All necessary mounting hardware included

*For best results we recommend a TV no larger than 30-32" diagonal and a maximum weight of 82kg (180lbs) including mounting shelf.

Finish: steel, black zinc-plating

Cat. No.	423.91.300

Packing: 1 pc. (complete with all mounting hardware)

Sliding Door Hardware
Drawer Slides
Television Supports

4

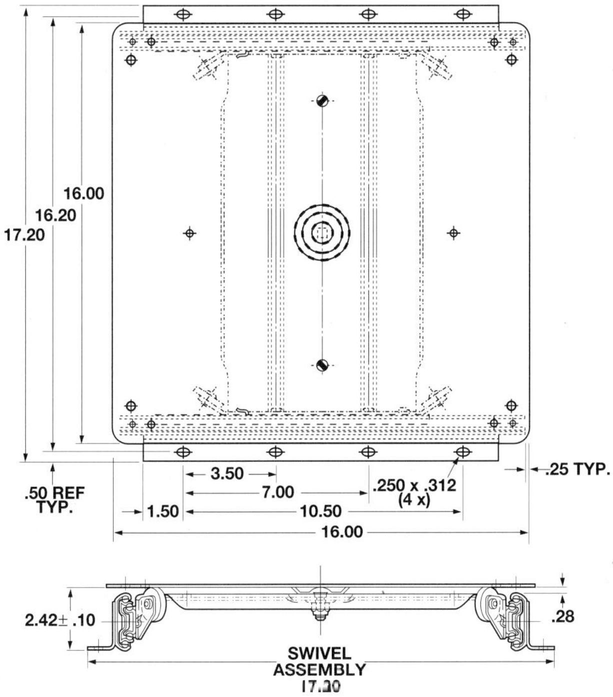

Dimensional data not binding.
We reserve the right to alter specifications without notice.

HÄFELE

TV Pivot Arms

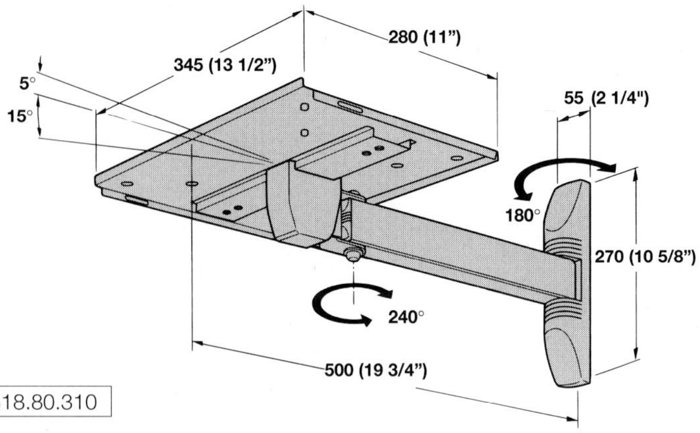

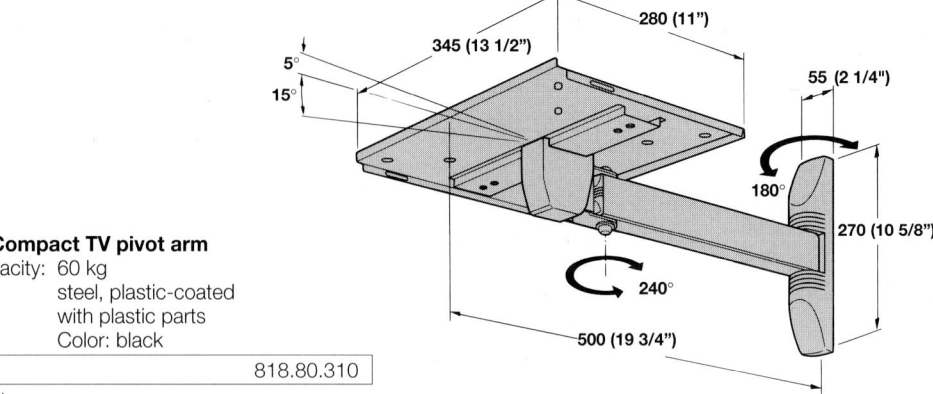

Unispace-Compact TV pivot arm

Loading capacity: 60 kg
Finish: steel, plastic-coated with plastic parts
Color: black

Cat. No.	818.80.310

Packing: 1 piece

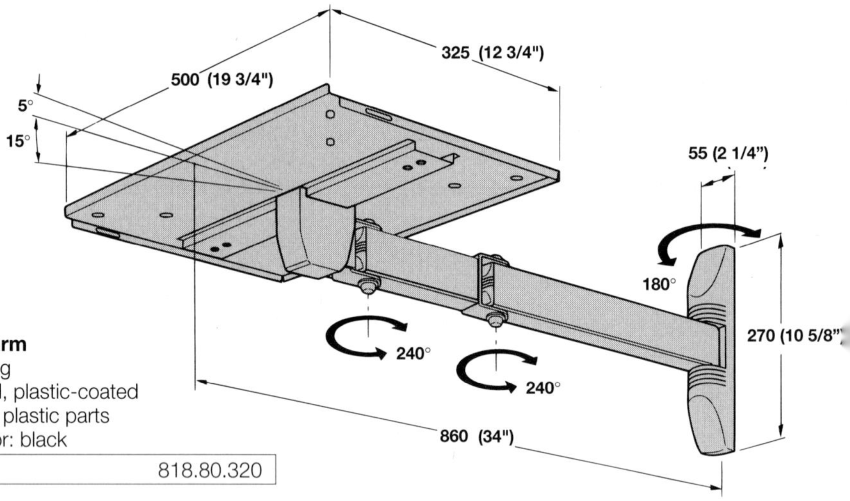

Flexispace TV pivot arm

Loading capacity: 60 kg
Finish: steel, plastic-coated with plastic parts
Color: black

Cat. No.	818.80.320

Packing: 1 piece

TV Pivot Arms

- for living rooms, kitchens, offices and TV rooms
- for hotels and restaurants, sport and club houses, hospitals, airports
- for TV units, monitors, video equipment, microwave units, radios, musical equipment

4 Sliding Door Hardware
Drawer Slides
Television Supports

- GS and TÜV tested
- 5 year guarantee
- pivotable, adjustable tilting angle and simple positioning
- easily assembled according to instructions and template
- additional unit fastening with supplied nylon safety belt, the unit can also be screw-mounted
- hidden cable conduits
- locking mechanism prevents unintentional adjustment

Note: Depending on installation and where load is actually placed, the weight rating can change. (leverage effect) For commercial use, please conduct your own test.

Dimensional data not binding. We reserve the right to alter specifications without notice.

Dimensions in mm
Inches are approximate

TV Pivot Arms

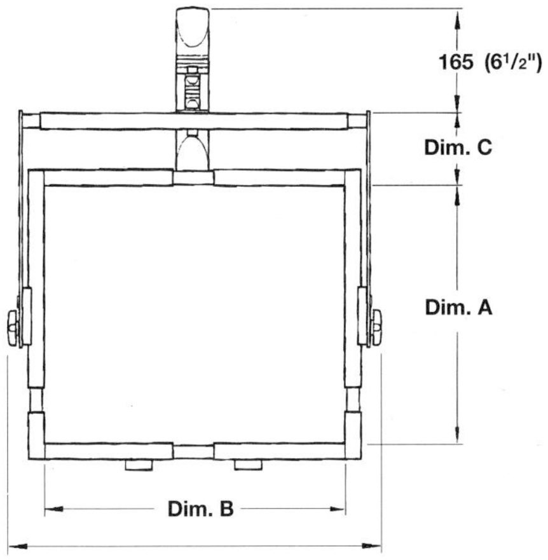

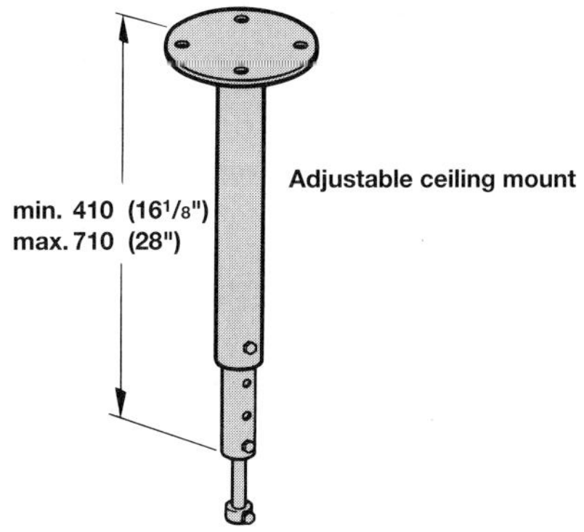

Note: Depending on installation and where load is actually placed, the weight rating can change. (leverage affect) For commercial applications, please conduct your own test.

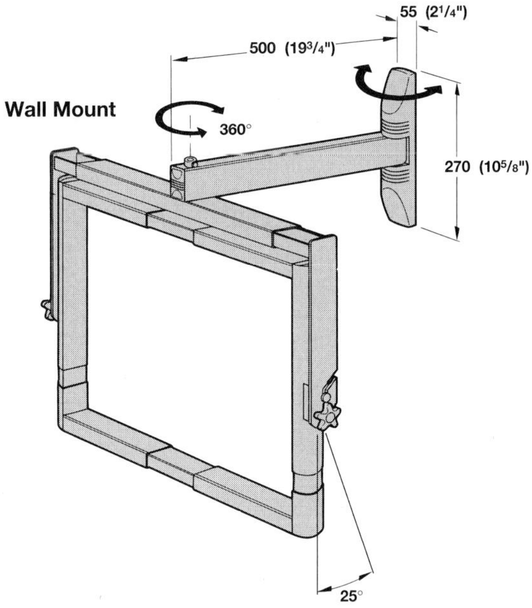

Maxispace TV pivot arm
Loading capacity: 75 kg (165 lbs.)
Finish: steel, epoxy powder-coated with plastic parts
Color: black

Mounting	Dim. A	Adjusting range Dim. B	Dim. C	Cat. No.
Wall	250 - 410 (9 7/8"-16 1/8")	300 - 496 (11 7/8"-19 1/2")	88 (3 1/2")	818.80.330
	370 - 640 (14 1/2"-25 1/8")	445 - 750 (17 1/2"-29 1/2")	113 (4 1/2")	818.80.340
Ceiling	250 - 410 (9 7/8"-16 1/8")	300 - 496 (11 7/8"-19 1/2")	88 (3 1/2")	818.80.331
	370 - 640 (14 1/2"-25 1/8")	445 - 750 (17 1/2"-29 1/2")	113 (4 1/2")	818.80.341

Packing: 1 pc.

VCR carrier
suitable for video units having:
max. width: 475 mm (18 11/16")
max. height: 120 mm (4 11/16")

Additional unit fastening with supplied nylon safety belt possible.

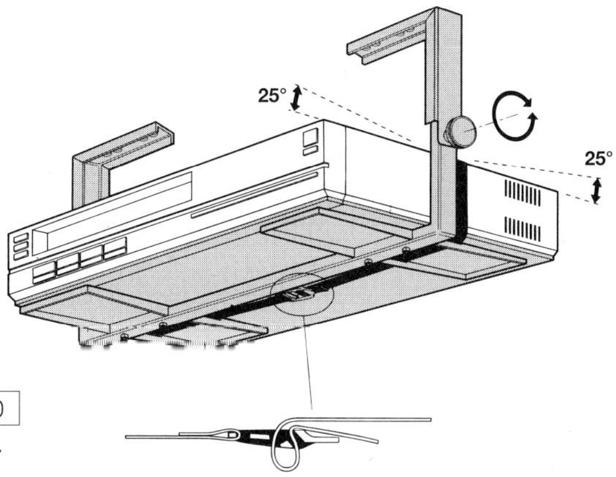

VCR carrier for TV pivot arms
Finish: steel, epoxy powder-coated with plastic parts
Color: black

Cat. No.	818.81.300

Packing: 1 pc. (complete with mounting material incl. cable clips)

Dimensions in mm
Inches are approximate

Dimensional data not binding. We reserve the right to alter specifications without notice.

Lift Systems

- Unique push/latch mechanism easily adjusts from the lower/upper position to the mid-position.
- Mid-position stop is removable to allow use in other applications, i.e., computer monitors, overhead projectors, A/V display projectors.
- Requires very little mounting space.
- Supports up to maximum weight of 18kg (39.7 lbs.)
- Minimum effort required to lift maximum weight to full height

3-Step Support
with gas piston, incl. midstep/free arm position
Support arms detachable for shipping.
Stroke 340 mm.
Finish: Profile rail, anodized aluminum, brown; steel support arms and brackets, epoxy-coated, brown.

Support Capacity to 8 kg (17.6 lbs.)

Cat. No.	421.67.117

Support Capacity 8 to 14 kg (17.6 lbs. to 30.9 lbs.)

Cat. No.	421.67.126

Support Capacity 14 to 18 kg (30.9 lbs. to 39.7 lbs.)

Cat. No.	421.67.135

Packing: 1 pc.

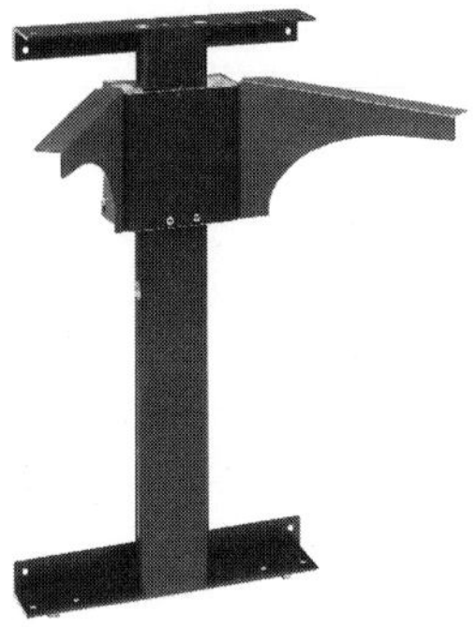

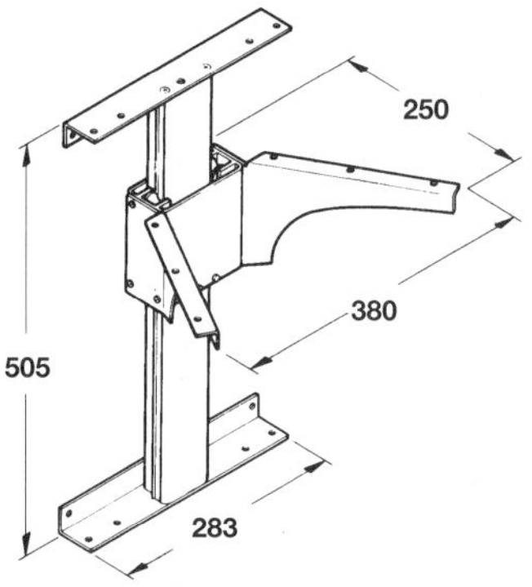

4 Sliding Door Hardware
Drawer Slides
Television Supports

- Can be positioned anywhere within travel range by use of remote control switch.
- Extremely quiet operation.

Support Electric Lift
Electrical operated. Can be stopped anywhere within the travel range. Support arms detachable for shipping. 110 V/60 Hz. transformer to 24 V/DC Motor switch, plug, and remote control included.
Stroke 350 mm.
Finish: Profile rail, anodized aluminum, brown; steel support arms and brackets, epoxy-coated, brown.

Lift force 25 kg (55 lbs.)

Cat. No.	421.68.105

Packing: 1 pc.

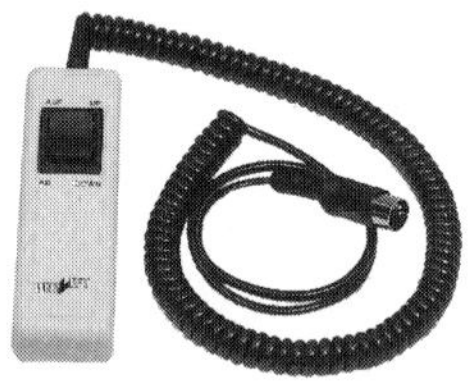

Remote Control
with cable (included).

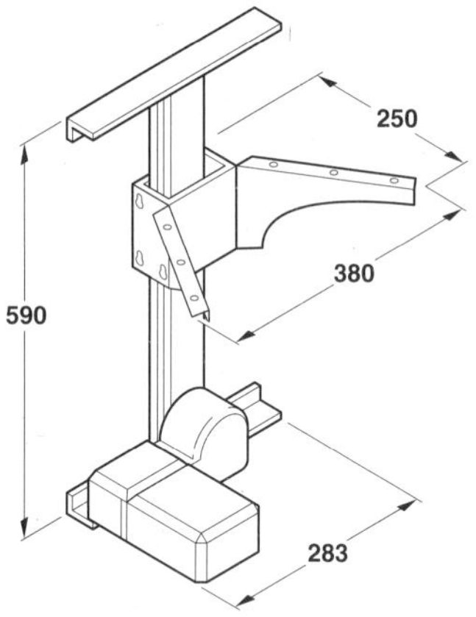

Dimensional data not binding. We reserve the right to alter specifications without notice.

Product Guide - Kitchen Accessory Systems

HÄFELE

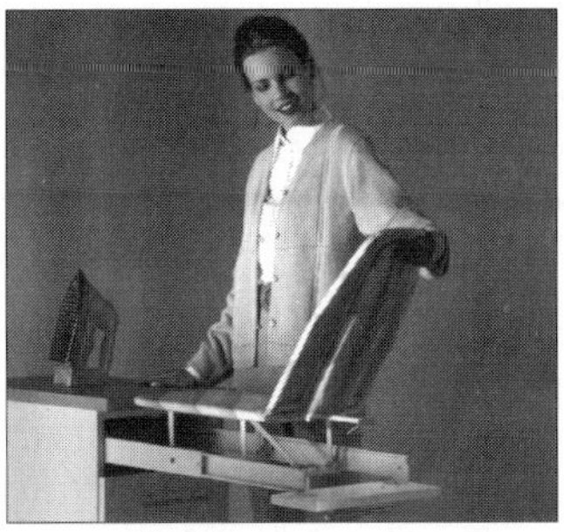

Built-in Ironing Boards
Pages **5.2 - 5.3**

Pull-out Table Systems
Pages **5.4 - 5.6**

Foldaway Systems
Page **5.7**

Revolving Corner Unit Systems
Pages **5.8 - 5.21**

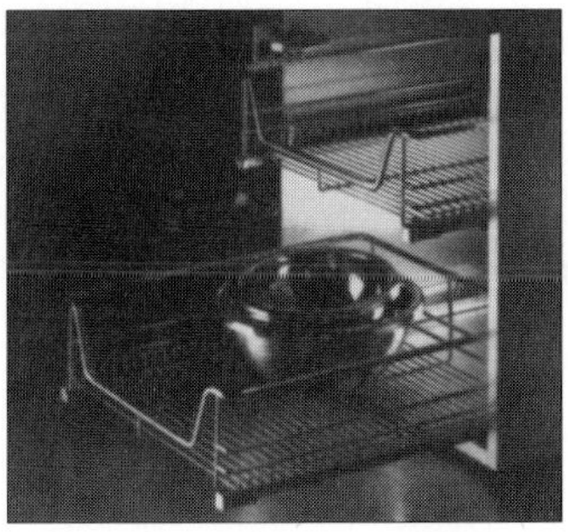

Base Cabinet Pull-out Systems
Pages **5.22 -5.32**

Wire Basket Storage Systems
Pages **5.27 - 5.31**

Waste and Recycling Bins
Pages **5.35 - 5.39**

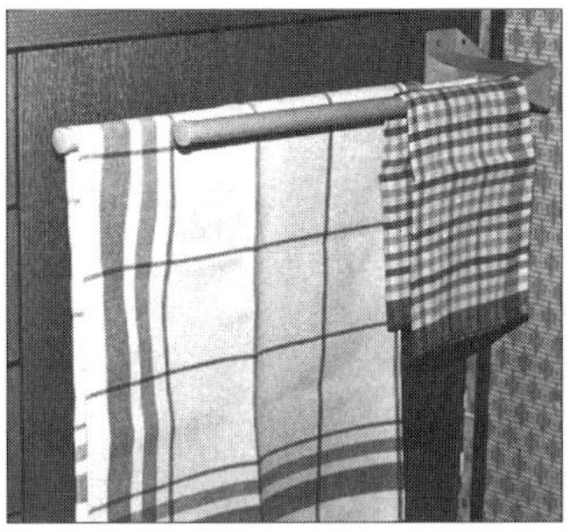

Pull-out Towel Racks
Pages **5.41 - 5.42**

Pantry Pull-out Systems
Pages **5.51 - 5.61**

Drawer Inserts
Pages **5.44 - 5.49**

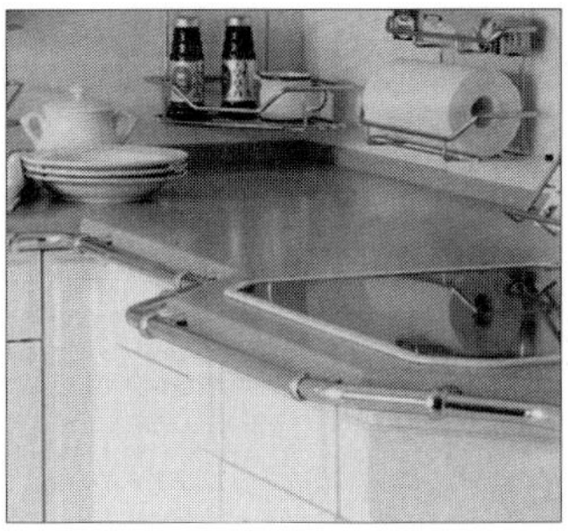

Kitchen Railing System
Pages **5.62 - 5.65**

Backsplash Storage System
Pages **5.66 - 5.68**

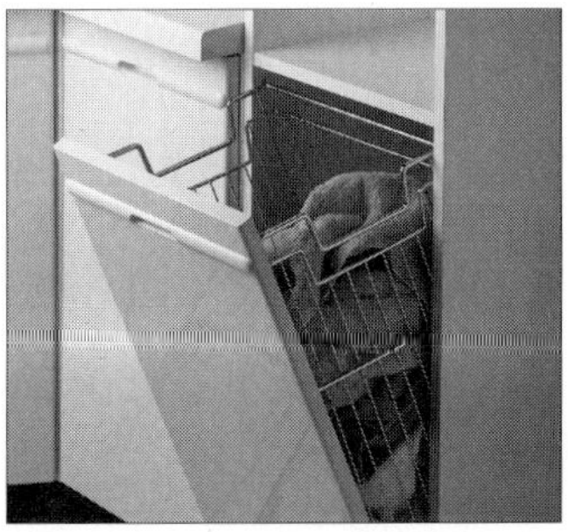

Laundry Hampers
Pages **5.84 - 5.85**

Countertop Supports
Pages **5.91 - 5.92**

Dimensional data not binding.
We reserve the right to alter specifications without notice.

HÄFELE

Built-In Ironing Boards

Fold Away Ironing Board

Complete with cover and mounting screws.
54" high x 14 1/4" wide x 3" deep.

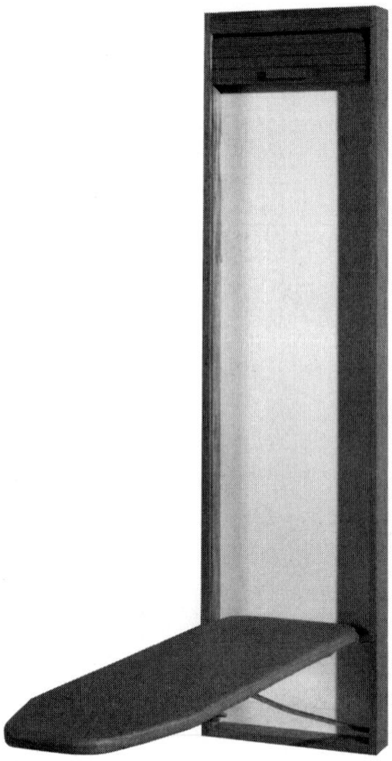

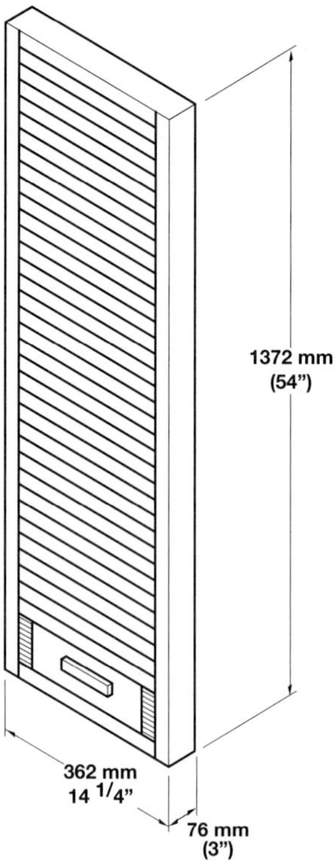

Finish: case/door	Cat. No.
white Melamine/white painted birch	568.65.700
honey-stained red oak veneer/honeystained red oak	568.65.800
unfinished red oak veneer/unfinished red oak	568.65.400

Packing: 1 pc.

Note:
Can be surface-mounted or recess-mounted into the wall. Comes with instructions.

- Use in laundry room, sewing room, condos, apartments, R.V.'s, house boats, etc.
- Fully finished cabinet and door.
- Easy and convenient to install.
- Built-in safety feature prevents ironing board from opening unexpectedly.
- Slim line design--does not take up a lot of room when mounted.
- Large ironing surface - 11 1/2" x 41 1/2".

Replacement cover for ironing board

100% cotton with metallized silver finish

Cat. No.	568.65.990

Packing: 1 pc.

HÄFELE

Built-In Ironing Boards

Ironfix built-in ironing board
Complete set including fastening hardware: comprising 2 cabinet rails, 1 collapsible ironing board support system with mounted 2-part extending runners, folding ironing board, integrated sleeve board and 1 pull track.
Finish: steel, epoxy-coated, fabric ironing board cover in striped design.

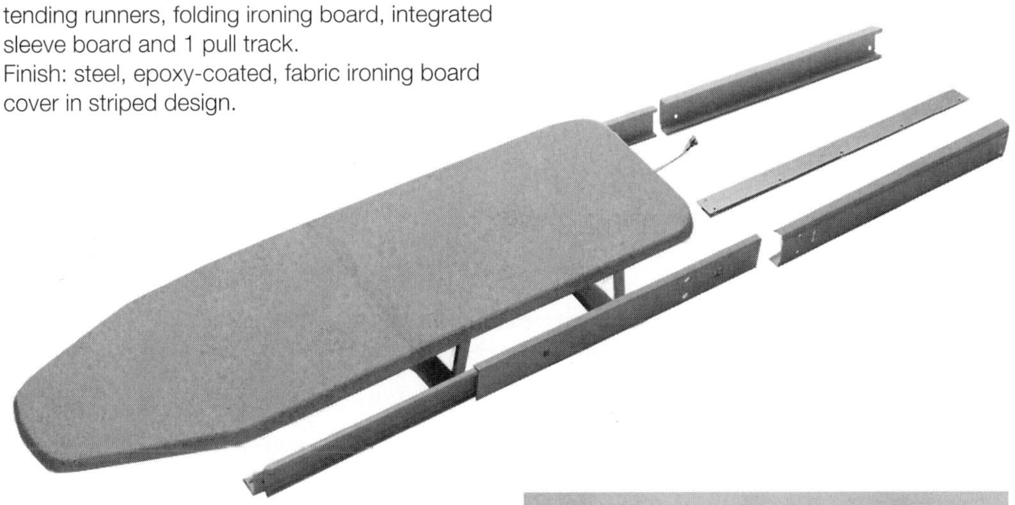

Ironfix built-in ironing board
- Fits into cabinet drawer for maximum space savings
- Infinitely variable width adjustment for inside built-in widths between 362 and 500 mm
- Inside cabinet depth 500 mm
- Integrated sleeve board
- Hinging front section permits trousers, shirts to be pulled easily over the board
- Durable finish – all hardware components made of plastic-coated metal
- Automatically extending support for the ironing surface when the drawer is opened
- Operating and assembly instructions are included with every ironing board.

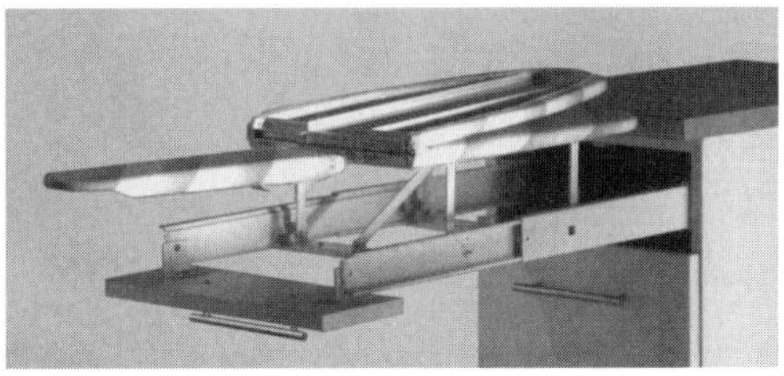

Simply fold back the front section of the ironing board and you have a sleeve board ready for use.

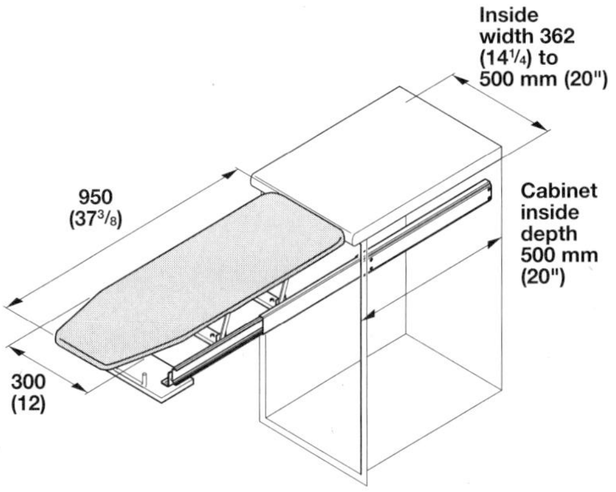

If you require the ironing board to be at the same height as the countertops, observe the following dimensions:

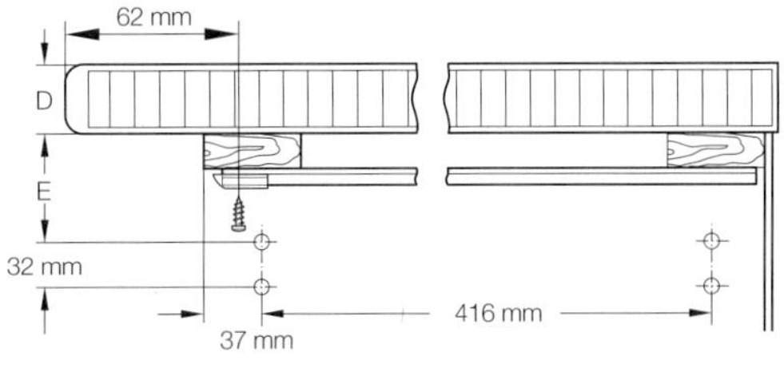

D (mm)	20	30	40	50
E (mm)	86	76	66	66

Color	white
Cat. No.	568.60.701

Packing: 1 pc.

Kitchen Accessory Systems **5**

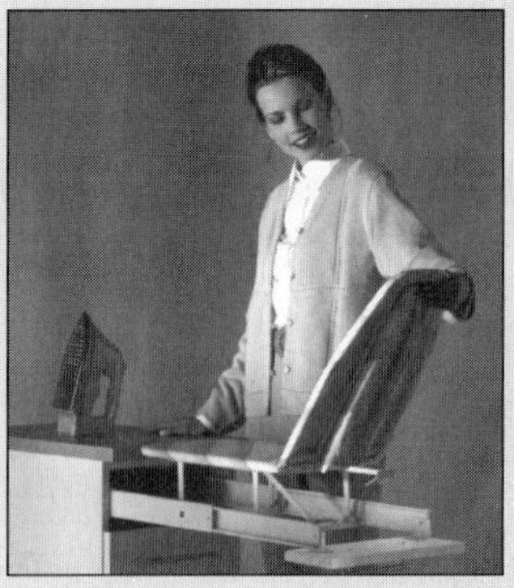

For installation in a face frame cabinet it is necessary to attach a longer cable for Ironfix to operate properly. Finish: steel, galvanized	
Cat. No.	568.60.70x
Packing: 1 pc.	

Replacement cover for ironing board
with elastic drawstring, natural white cotton with gray stripes, foam-backed.

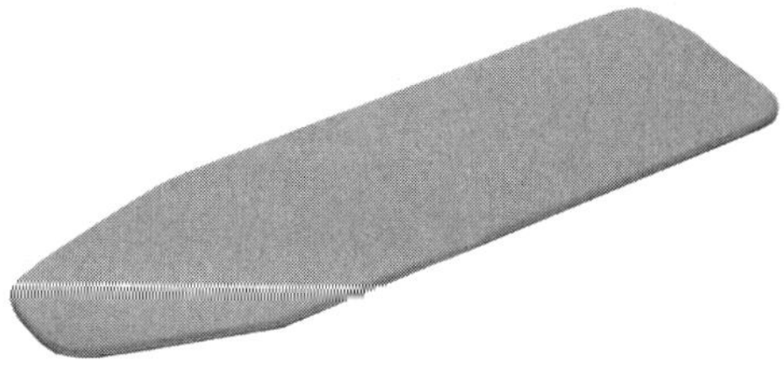

Cat. No.	568.60.907

Packing: 1 pc.

Replacement cover for sleeve board
with elastic drawstring, natural white cotton with gray stripes, foam-backed.

Cat. No.	568.60.916

Packing: 1 pc.

Dimensions in mm
Inches are approximate

Dimensional data not binding.
We reserve the right to alter specifications without notice.

HÄFELE

Pull-out Table Systems

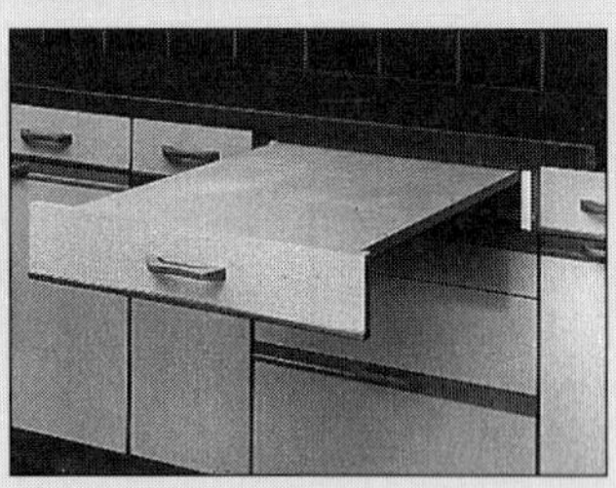

Advantages
- A drawer front panel can be screw mounted directly onto the table front panel
- The system can be subsequently installed in place of a drawer or between two cabinets
- Once installed the fitting is not visible

Rapid pull-out table, cantilever
600 mm ($23\frac{5}{8}$") wide cabinets
Load capacity: **100 kg (220 lbs.)** (for evenly distributed loads)
consisting of:
- housing with tabletop
- 4 telescopic guides
- front panel

Finish: wood
tabletop: with Melamine plastic coating, white
telescopic guides: beech

Cat. No.	505.58.702

Packing: 1 pc.

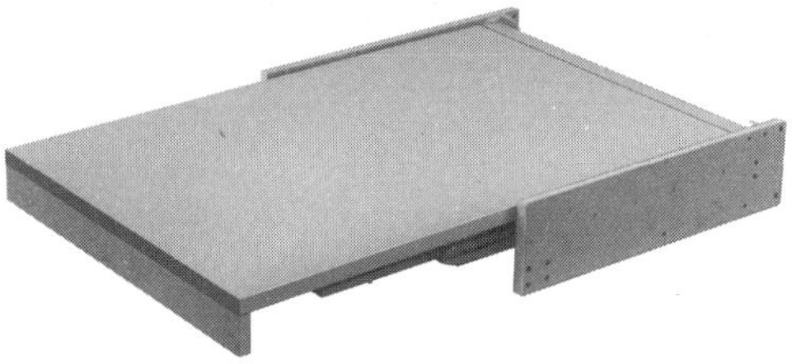

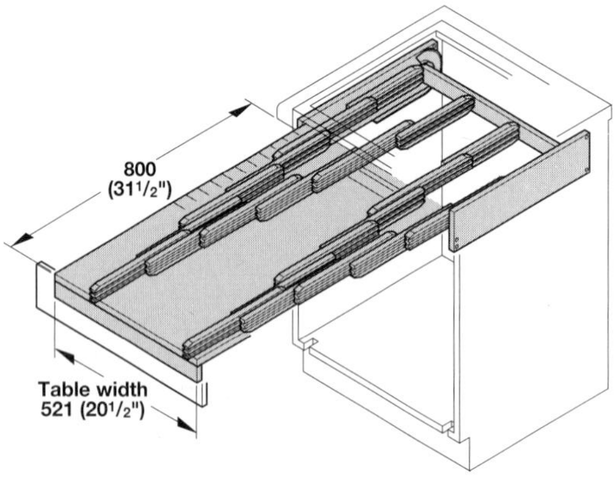

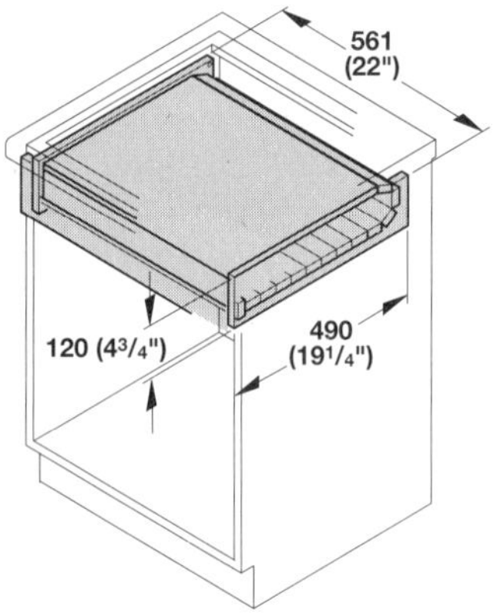

Kombi-Rapid pull-out table, cantilever
600 mm ($23\frac{5}{8}$") wide cabinets
Load capacity: **80 kg (176 lbs.)** (for evenly distributed loads)
consisting of:
- housing with tabletop and extension leaf
- 2 telescopic guides
- drawer with cutlery insert

Finish: wood
tabletop: Melamine laminated white
cutlery insert: plastic 500 x 400 mm
telescopic guides: beech

Cat. No.	505.58.711

Packing: 1 pc.

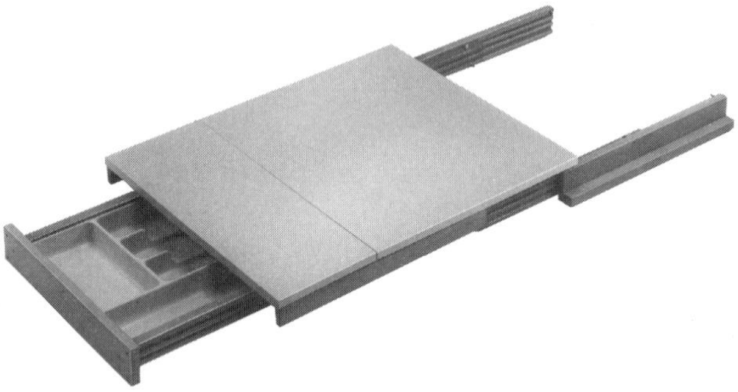

The drawer with the cutlery insert can be used whether the table is extended or stowed.

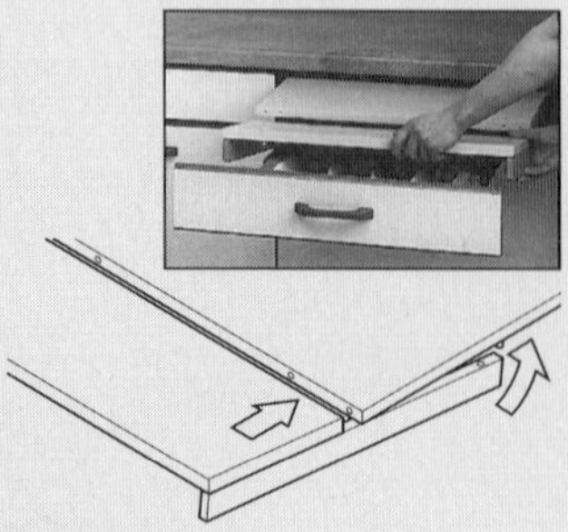

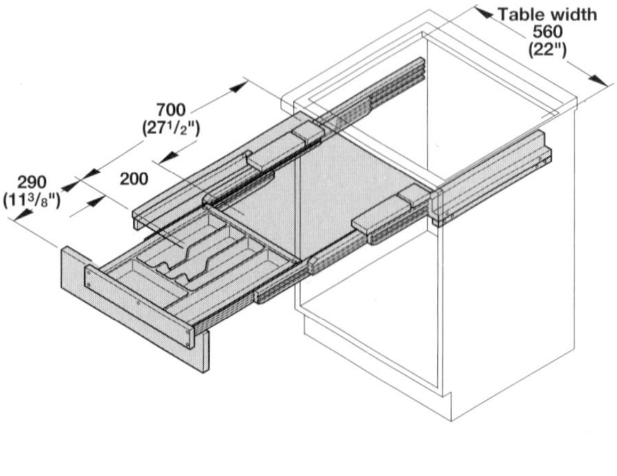

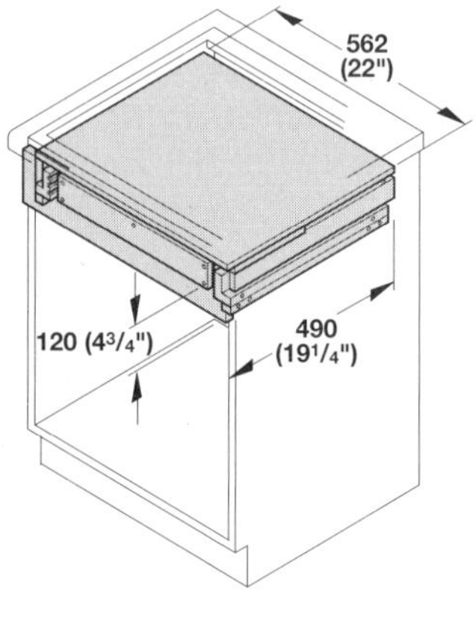

Dimensional data not binding. We reserve the right to alter specifications without notice.

Dimensions in mm
Inches are approximate

Pull-out Tables

Pull-out Presto Table System
600 mm (23 5/8") wide cabinet
consisting of:
• Housing with tabletop and trim panel
• 2 extending guides
Finish: wood, Melamine laminated, white

Cat. No.	505.59.709

Packing: 1 set

Leg Assembly (required)
Presto table system
vertically adjustable between 640 and 850 mm (25 1/8" and 33 1/2")
Finish: Steel, plastic coated white

Cat. No.	505.59.772

Packing: 1 pair

• A drawer or door front can be screw mounted directly to the table trim panel.
• The space beneath the table can be used for folding chairs, waste bins, etc...

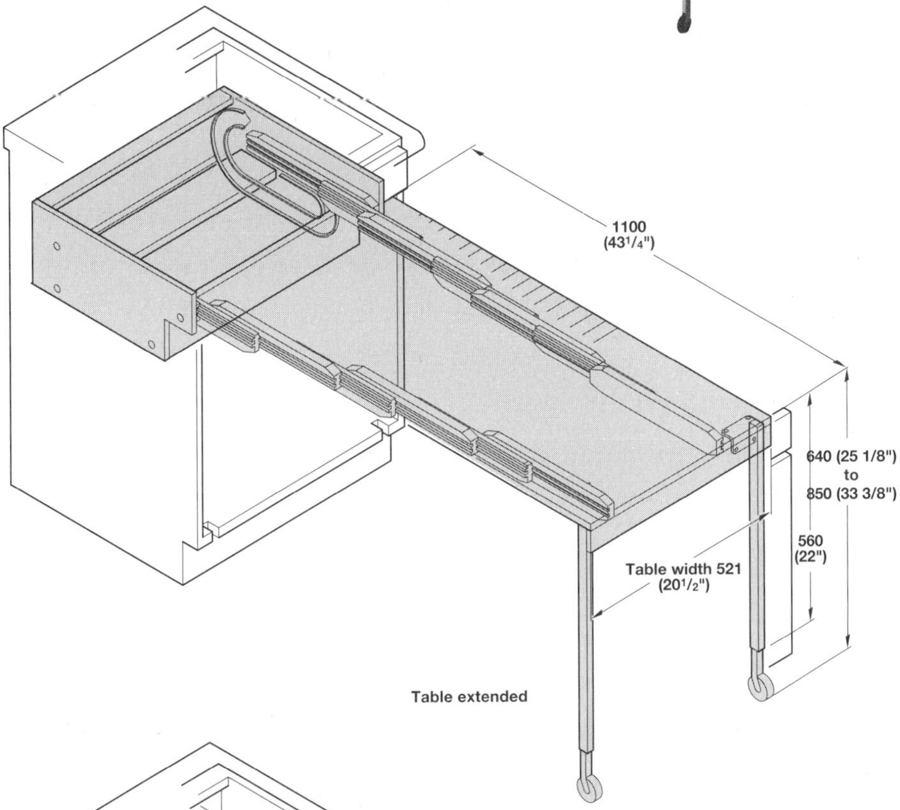

Table extended

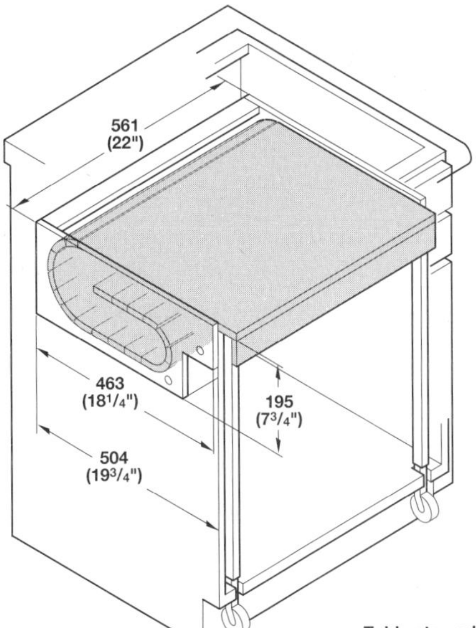

Table stowed

Detailed mounting instructions are supplied with each set .

Dimensional data not binding.
We reserve the right to alter specifications without notice.

Dimensions in mm
Inches are approximate

HÄFELE

Pull-out Table Systems

Detailed mounting instructions are included with every set.

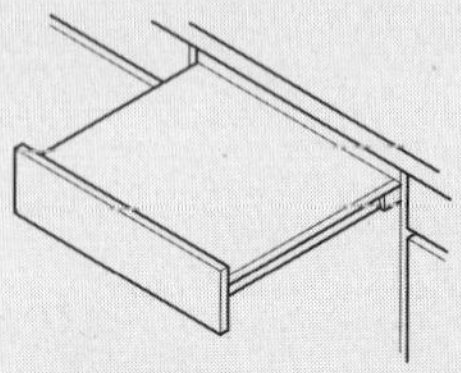

Pull-out table systems, with fixed front panel. The panel either projects above the level of the table...

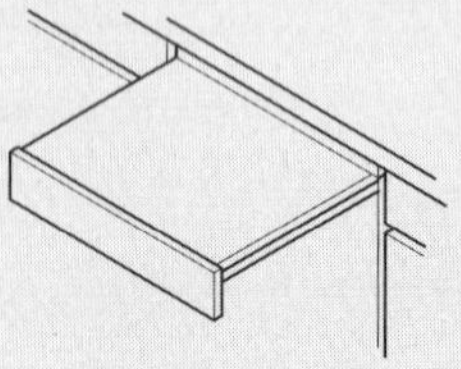

...or is mounted flush with the tabletop, in which case a shallow trim is required above the pull-out front.

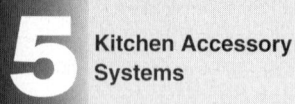

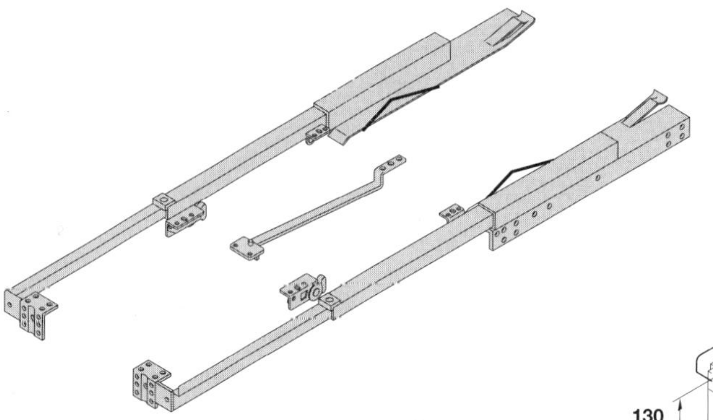

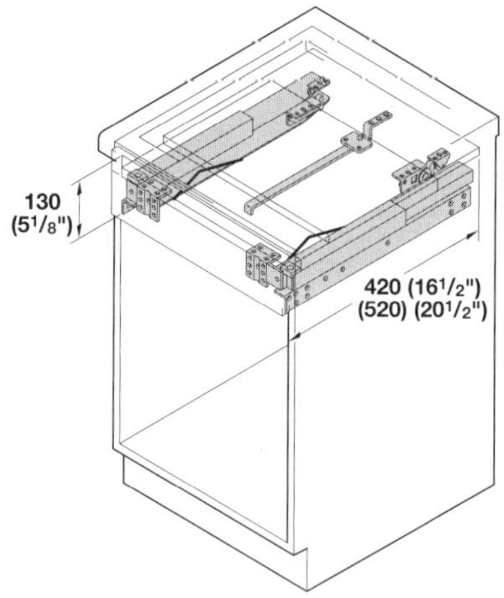

Pull-out Table System, cantilever, for 2-part tabletop (max. thicknesses 18 mm)
Load bearing capacity: 80 kg. (176 lbs) evenly dist.

Cabinet depth	Cat. No.
500 mm (20")	505.70.502
600 mm (24")	505.70.600

Packing: 1 set

Dimensions in parentheses are for 600 mm (24") installed depth.

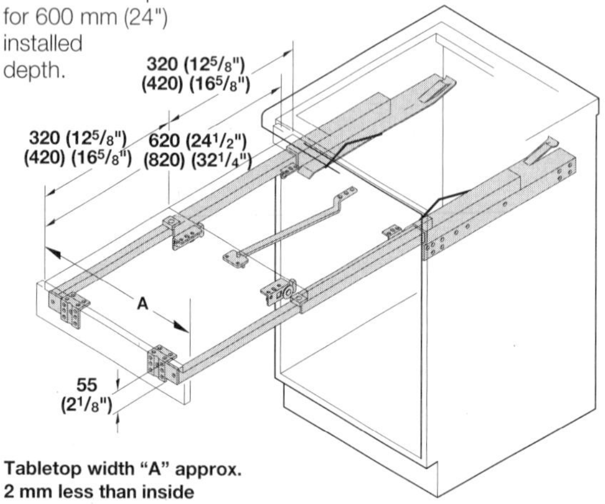

Tabletop width "A" approx. 2 mm less than inside cabinet width

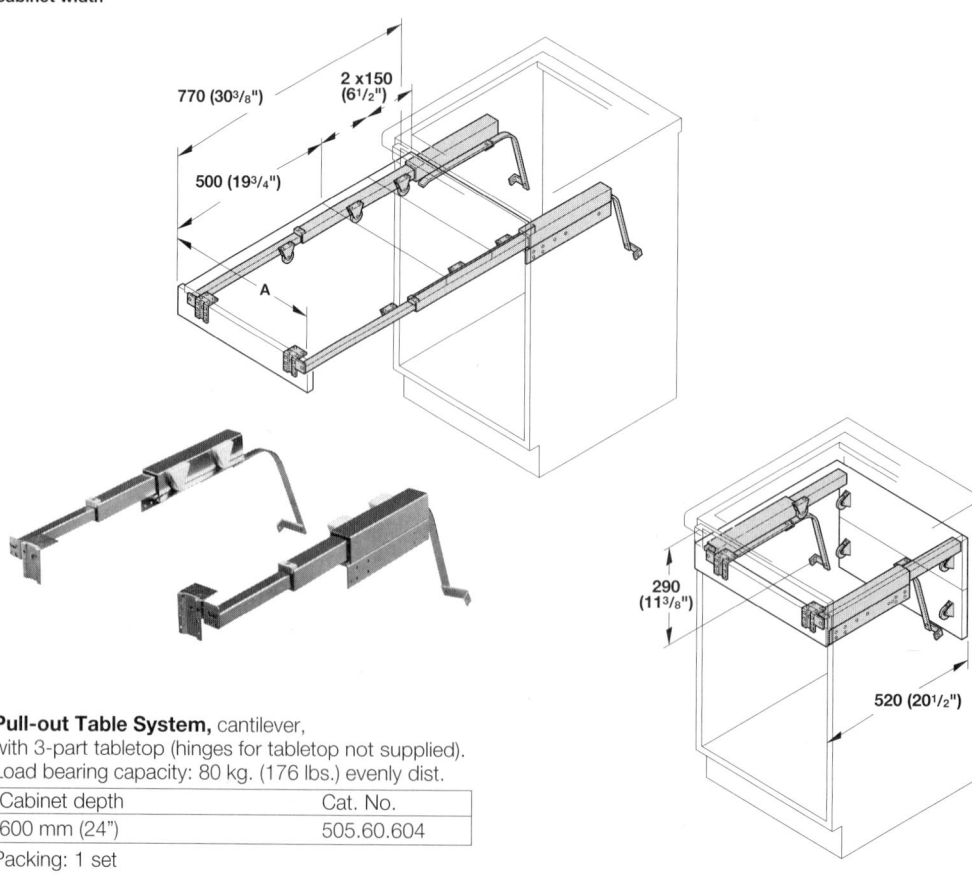

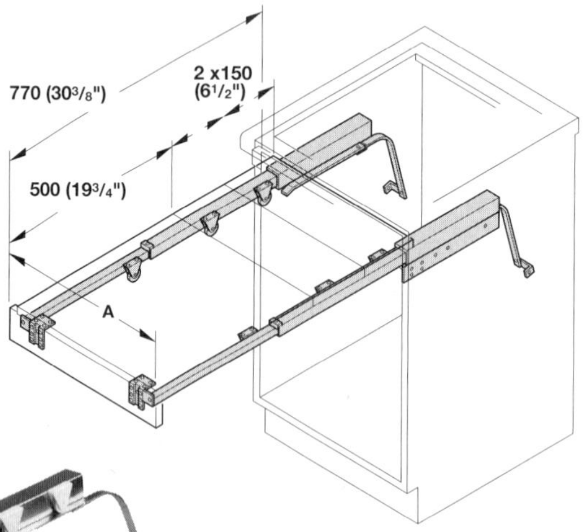

- The inner tabletop sections fold downward on tracks when the table is closed, occupying a minimum of space against the rear panel of the cabinet.

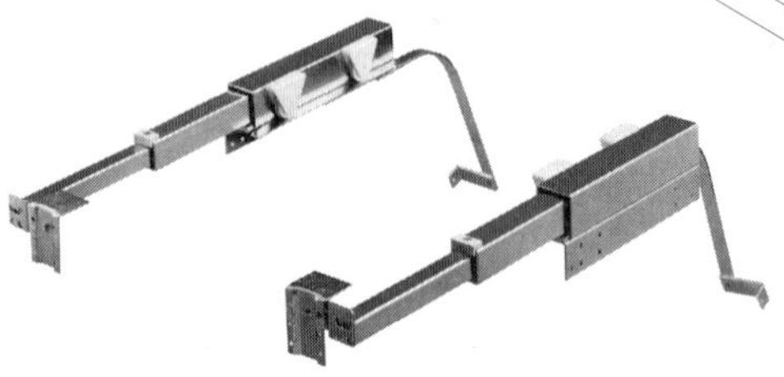

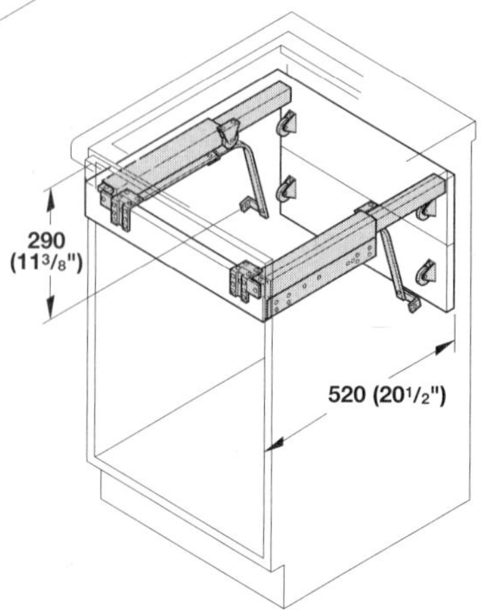

Pull-out Table System, cantilever, with 3-part tabletop (hinges for tabletop not supplied).
Load bearing capacity: 80 kg. (176 lbs.) evenly dist.

Cabinet depth	Cat. No.
600 mm (24")	505.60.604

Packing: 1 set

Dimensional data not binding. We reserve the right to alter specifications without notice.

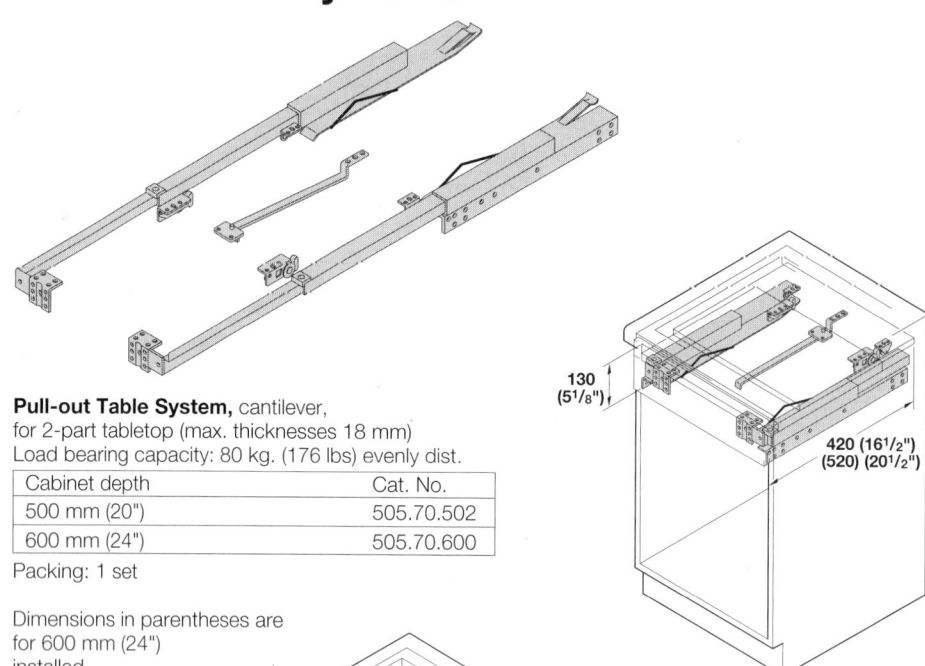

Dimensions in mm
Inches are approximate

HÄFELE

Foldaway Systems

Lift-Up mechanism
with locking mechanism
Cabinet widths of 300 mm (11⅞") to 600 mm (23⅝")
and shelf depth of 420 mm (16½")
Load bearing capacity: 12 kg (26 lbs)
Set consists of:
- 2 mechanisms (left and right)
- 2 locking devices
- 2 tension springs
- 4 plastic distance washers and 4 plastic appliance spacers

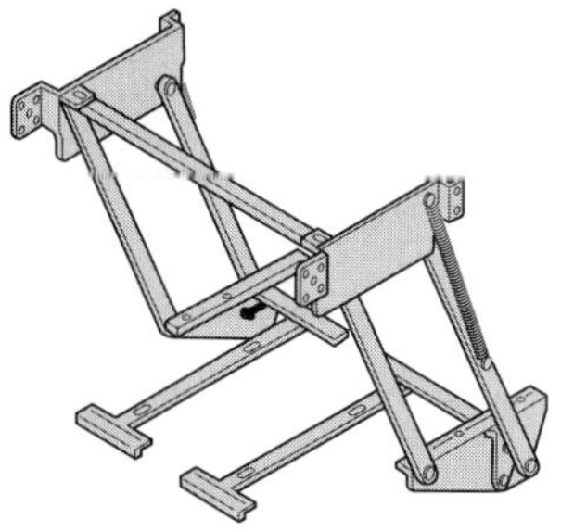

- Latch locks in down as well as up position.
  – Prevents shelf from banging against the lower cabinet door from the inside when closed.
- Mounting instructions are provided with each set.

Finish: steel, plastic-coated, white

Minimum Inside Cabinet		For Storage Of		
Height-including swing arc	Depth	Max. Height Up To	Max. Depth Up To	Cat. No.
470 mm (18½")	450 mm (17¼")	305 mm (12")	292 mm (11½")	504.24.710
		202 mm (8")	406 mm (16")	
570 mm (22½")	500 mm (19¼")	394 mm (15½")	336 mm (13¼")	504.24.701
		342 mm (13½")	406 mm (16")	

Packing: 1 set

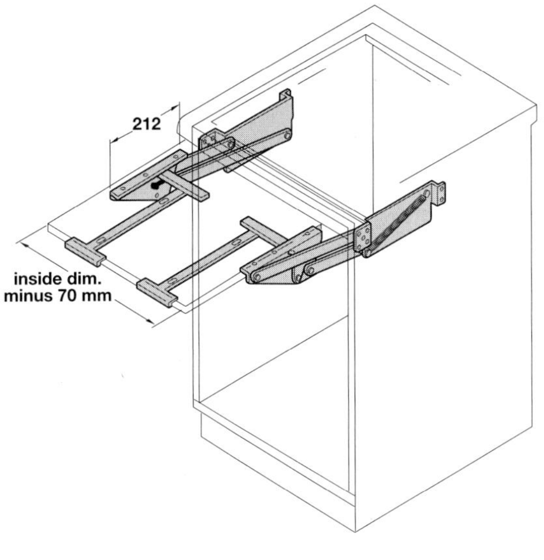

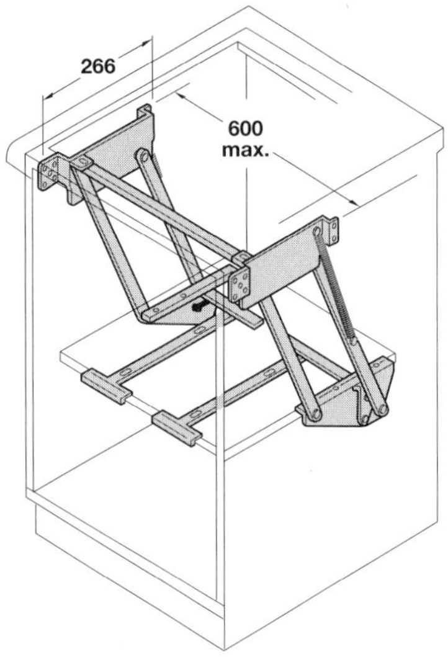

Kitchen Accessory Systems

5

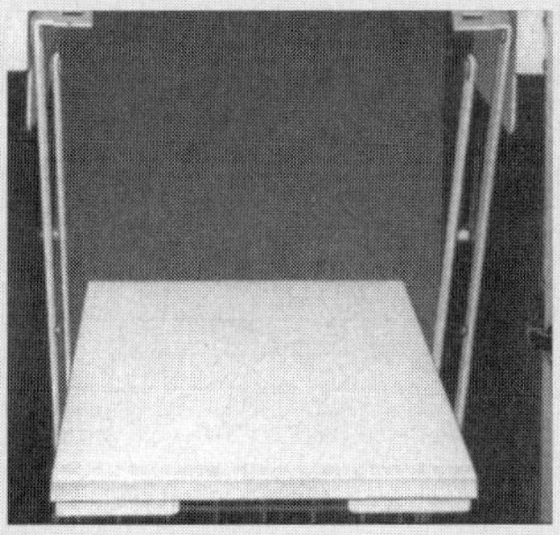

Dimensions for storage of items:

Cat. No. 504.24.710

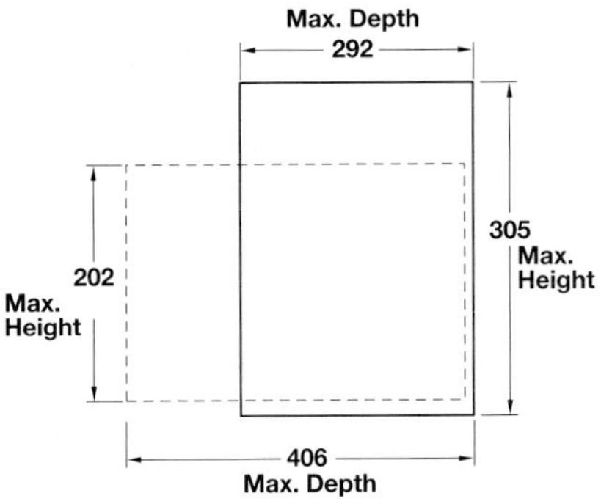

Cat. No. 504.24.701

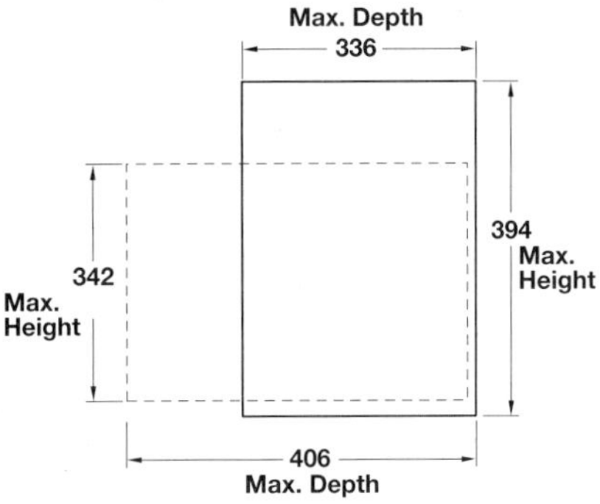

Minimum inside dimensions including swing arc:

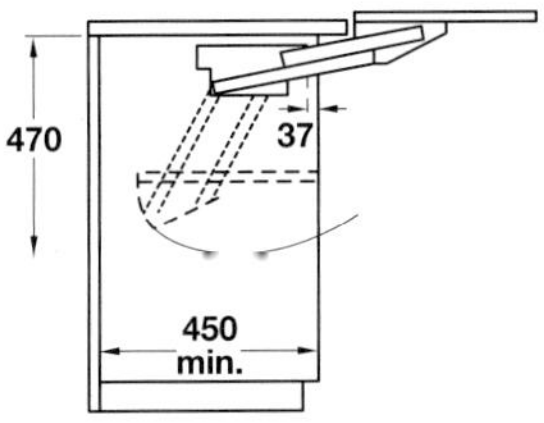

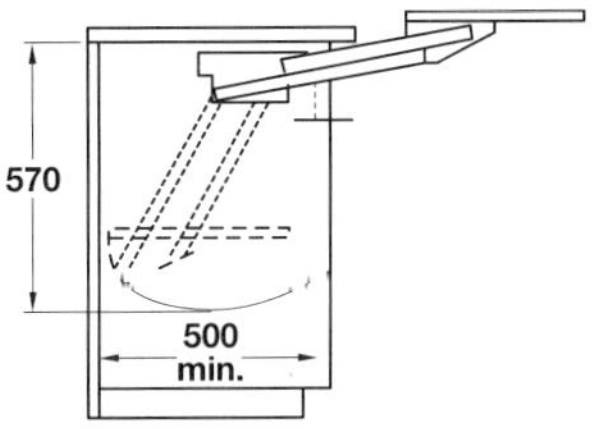

Dimensional data not binding.
We reserve the right to alter specifications without notice.

Dimensions in mm
Inches are approximate

HÄFELE

Revolving Corner Unit Systems

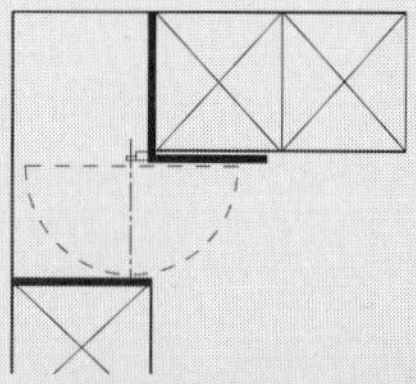

For the attaching of customer-supplied half moon revolving shelves made of wood to a central upright at any height

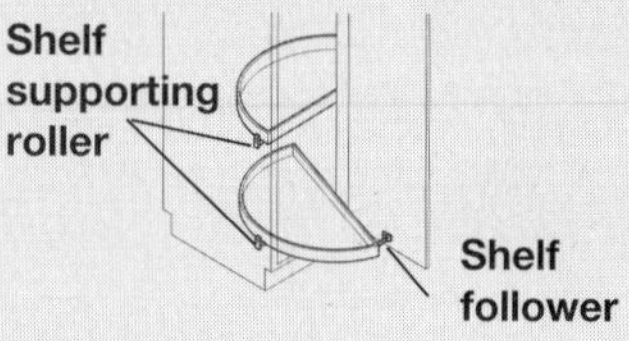

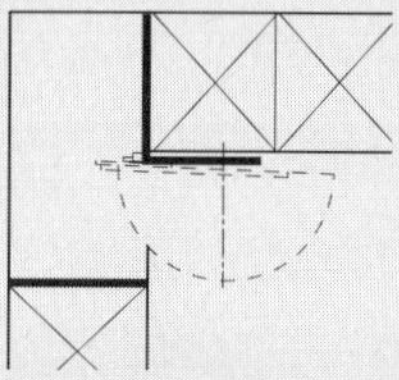

For cabinets with front mounted doors, shelves can be installed in any required number and at any height by attachment to a central upright.

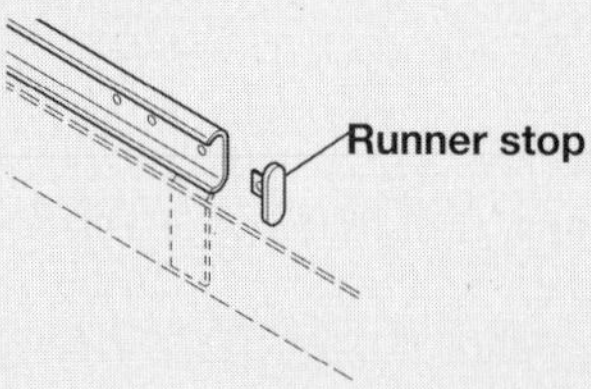

The runner stop can be installed on either side.

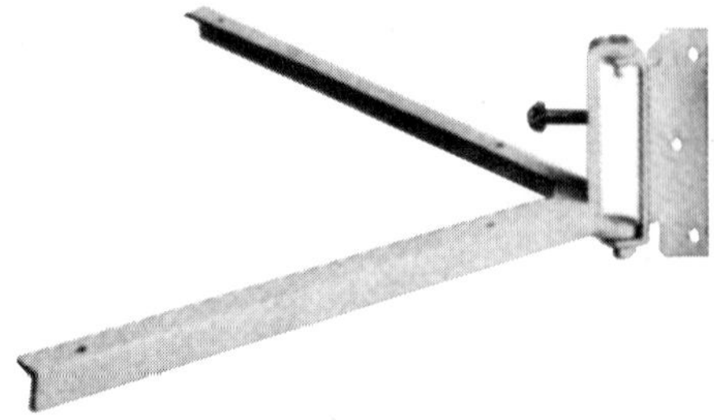

Revolving hardware,
Complete system includes: mounting bracket with V-shaped shelf support.
Finish: Steel, plastic-coated, white

Cat. No.	501.07.027

Packing: 25 sets

Installed dimensions for user provided shelves (overall dimensions optional):

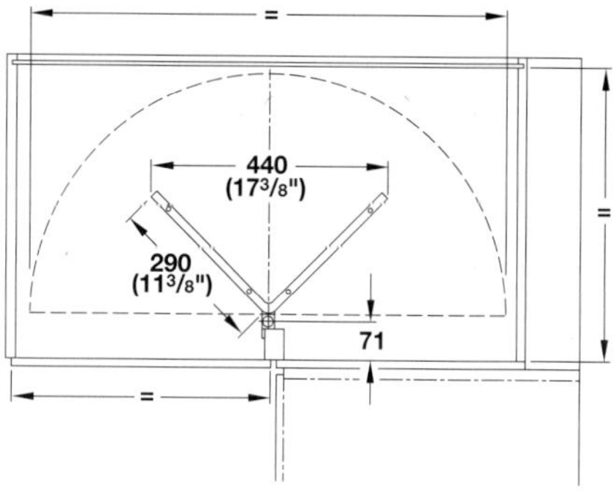

Shelf follower 2-part, screw mounted
Causes shelf to revolve automatically as cabinet door opens.
Finish: Nickel-plated steel

Cat. No.	501.07.125

Packing: 2 pcs.

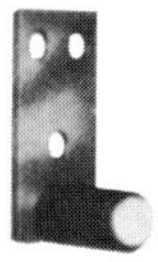

Shelf support roller, screw-mounted.
Supports and guides shelf as it revolves
Finish: Nickel-plated steel; plastic roller

Cat. No.	501.07.107

Packing: 2 pcs.

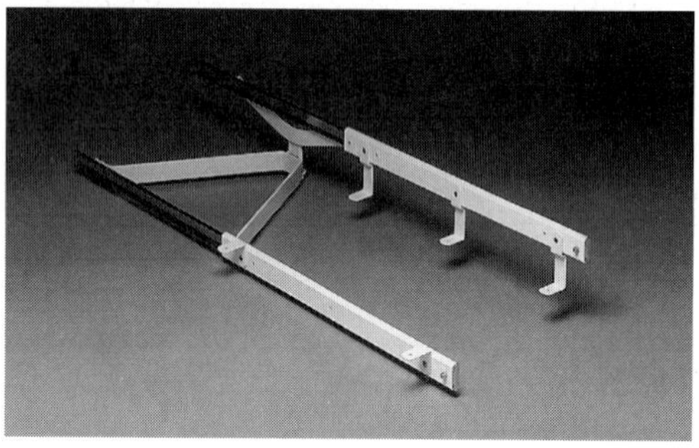

Revolving/extended system
Complete system includes: revolving element with shelf support arms and extension runners.
Finish: steel, plastic coated white

Cat. No.	541.63.709

Packing: 5 pcs.

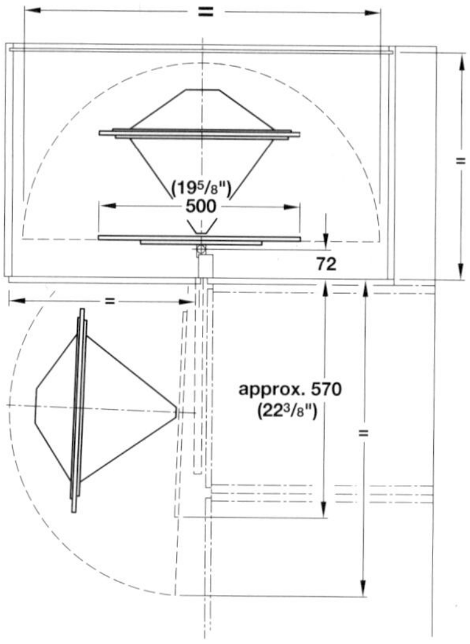

Dimensional data not binding.
We reserve the right to alter specifications without notice.

Dimensions in mm
Inches are approximate

1/4 Turn Systems

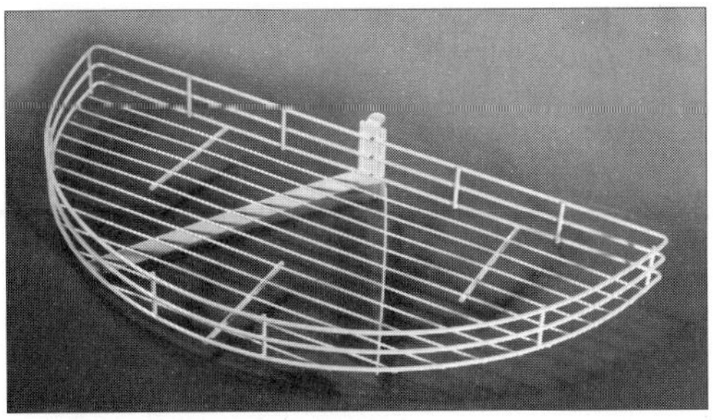

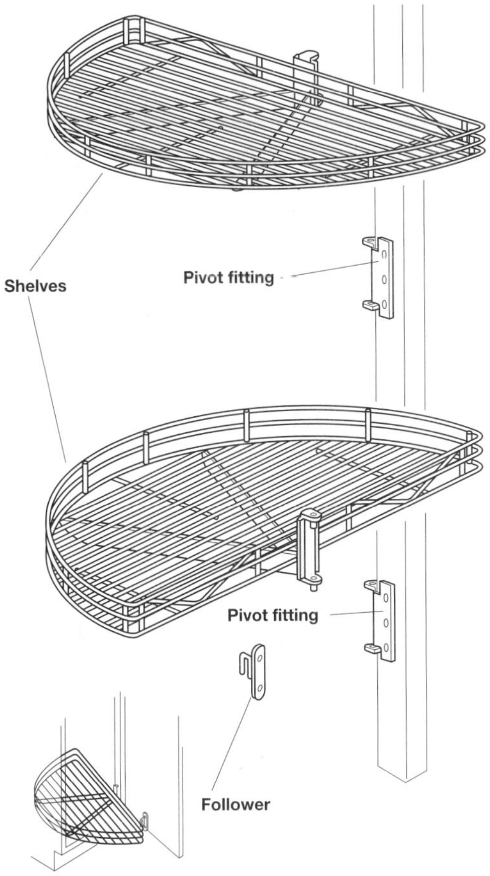

1/4 turn fitting set
complete with two half moon wire shelves, 2 pivot systems and 1 follower
Finish: steel, plastic-coated, white
follower: plastic, white

for cabinet door width from mm (inch)	Size	Cat. No.
370 (14½")	650 x 330 mm	541.25.718
425 (16¾")	770 x 390 mm	541.25.727
490 (19¼")	890 x 450 mm	541.25.745

Packing: 1 set

Installed dimensions for minimum door widths:

from 370 mm (14½")

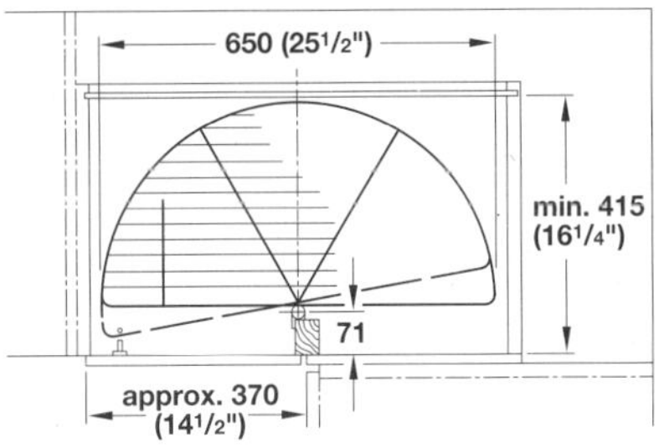

from 425 mm (16¾")

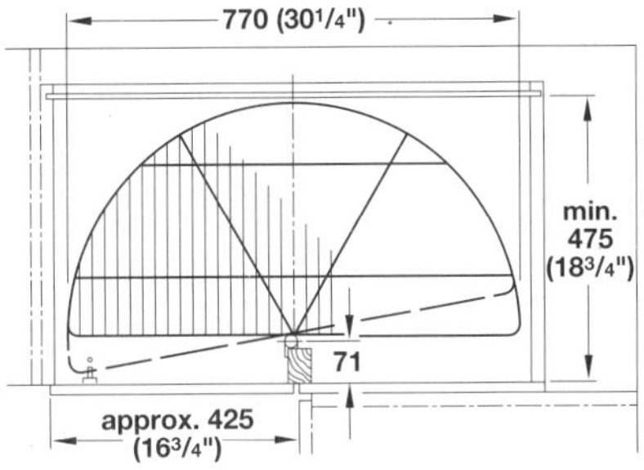

from 490 mm (19¼")

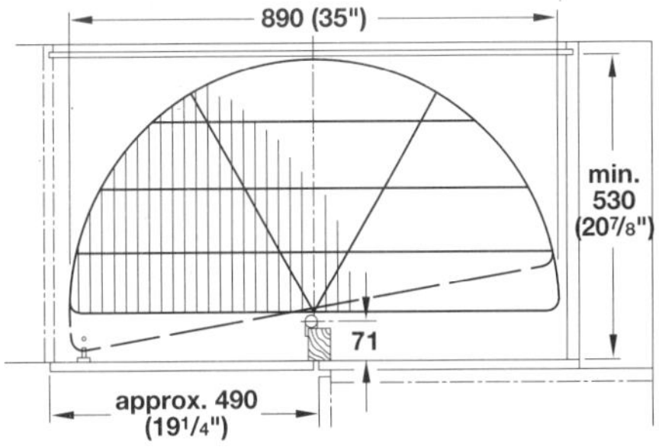

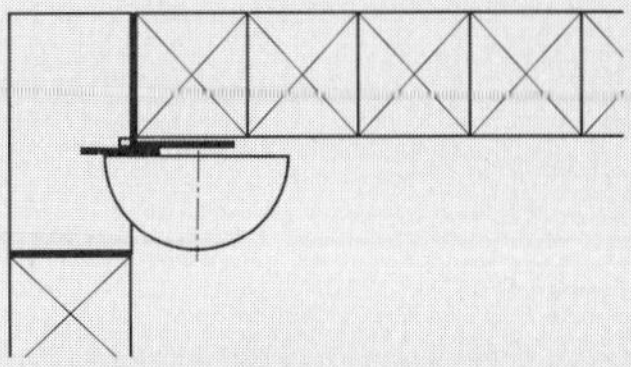

- Because the pivot systems are attached to a center upright at any height, there are no installation height limitations.

Installation
with center upright minimum
60 mm depth

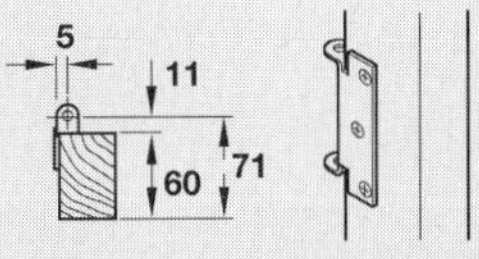

Kitchen Accessory Systems **5**

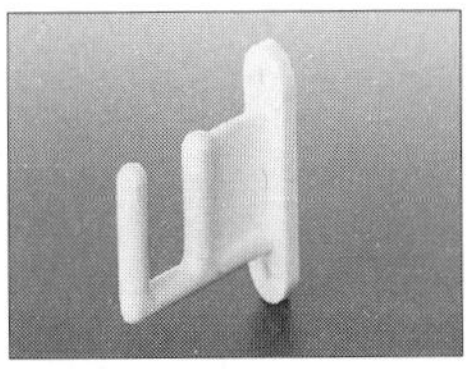

Follower
Finish: plastic, white

Cat. No.	541.63.905

Packing: 1 pc.

Optional Follower is screw-mounted to the inside of the cabinet door. It is hooked in the sidewall of the shelf and revolves automatically as the door is opened.

Dimensional data not binding.
We reserve the right to alter specifications without notice.

Dimensions in mm
Inches are approximate

HÄFELE

1/4 Turn Systems

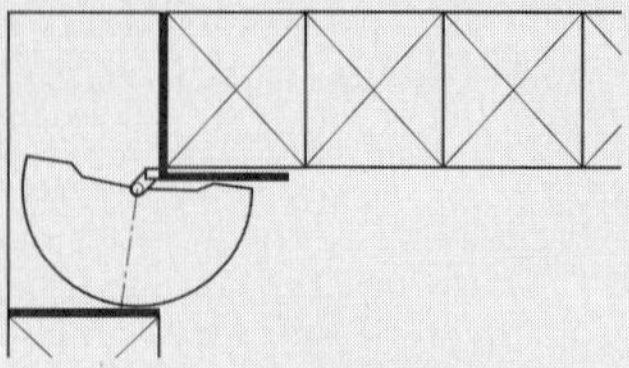

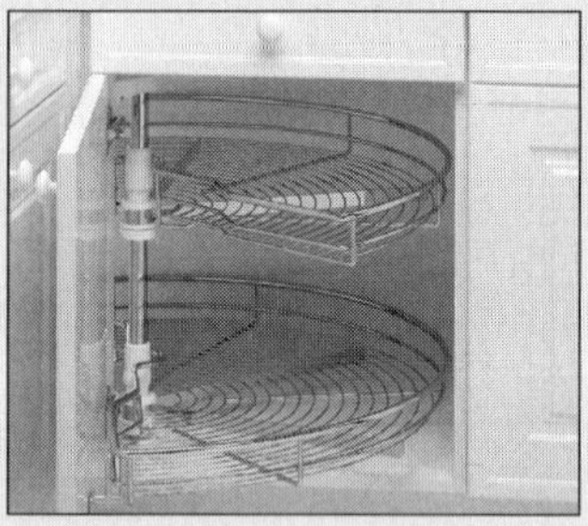

Installation
Using a center upright
50 mm deep

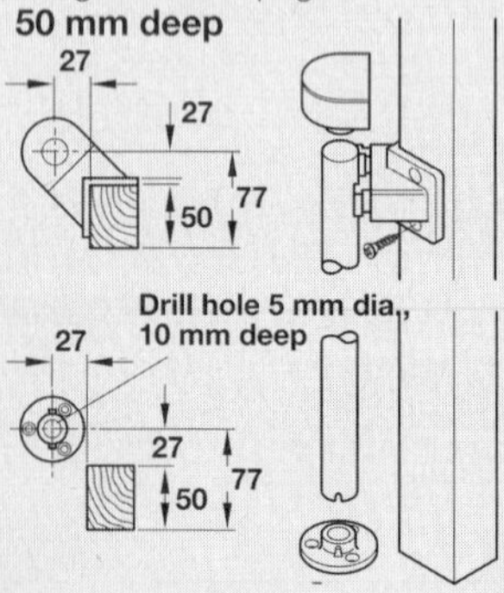

5 Kitchen Accessory Systems

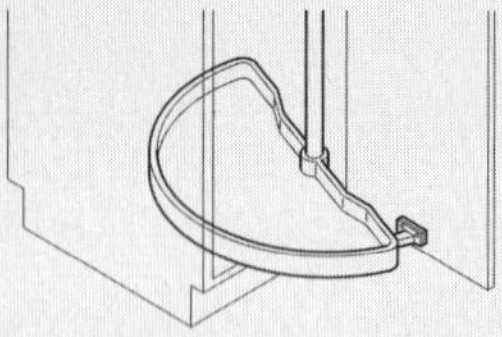

Installation
Using a center upright
60 mm in depth

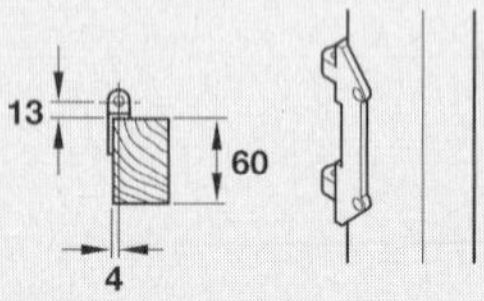

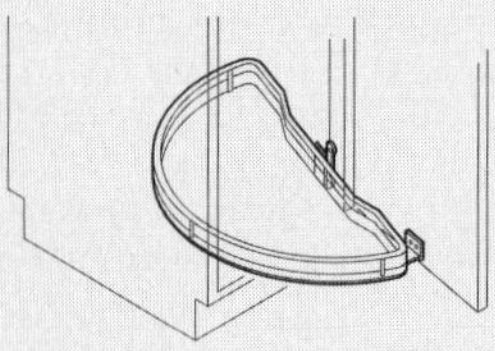

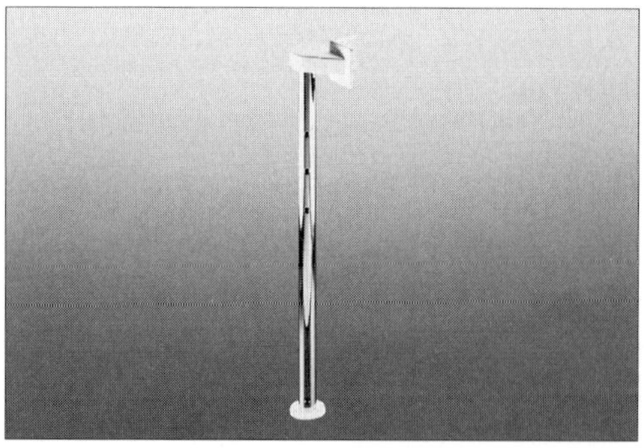

1/4 Turn post, 495 mm (19½") high with upper bearing to be screw-mounted to a center upright and lower bearing to be screw-mounted to the cabinet bottom.
Complete system includes: central post with four locations for the shelf support ring, upper and lower bearing.
Finish: post steel, chrome plated
bearings: plastic white

Cat. No.	541.19.292

Packing: 1 set

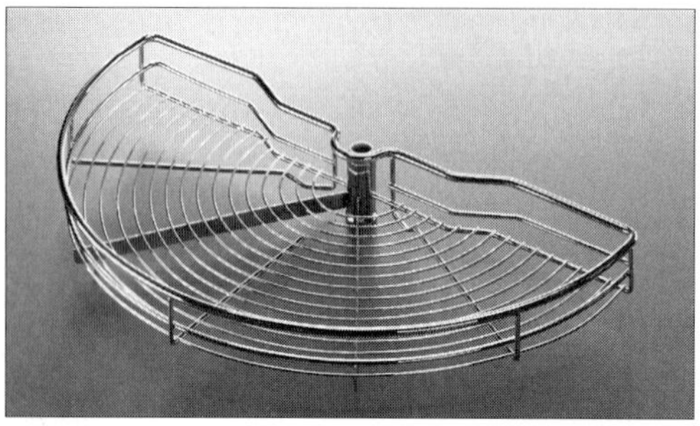

Half moon revolving shelf
Spindle bearing with clamping sleeve, complete with support ring and pin for mounting to center post.
Finish: steel, chrome-plated;
bearings: plastic white

cabinet door width mm	Dimensions mm	Cat. No.
440 (17¼")	750 x 420 x 80	541.19.229
490 (19¼")	850 x 475 x 80	541.19.247

Packing: 1 pc.

Ordered separately as needed:

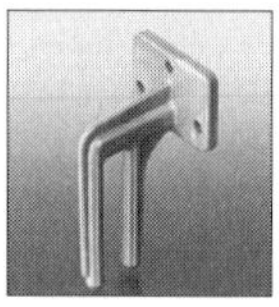

Shelf follower for half moon revolving shelf 541.19.229/247 for cabinets with doors.

Advantage: allows shelf to revolve automically as door opens.
Finish: Polyamide, aluminum colored

Cat. No.	541.19.283

Packing: 1 pc.

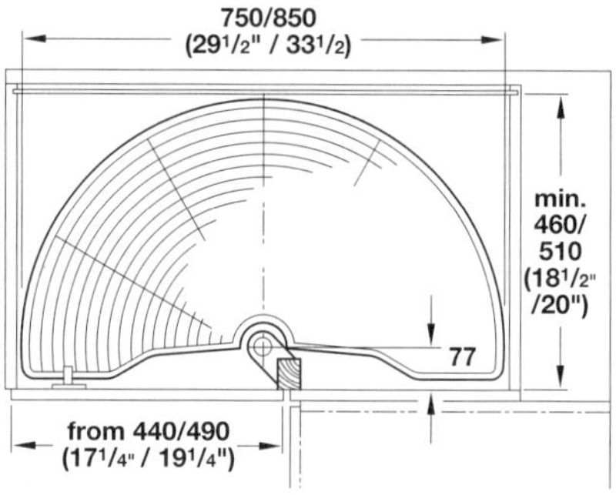

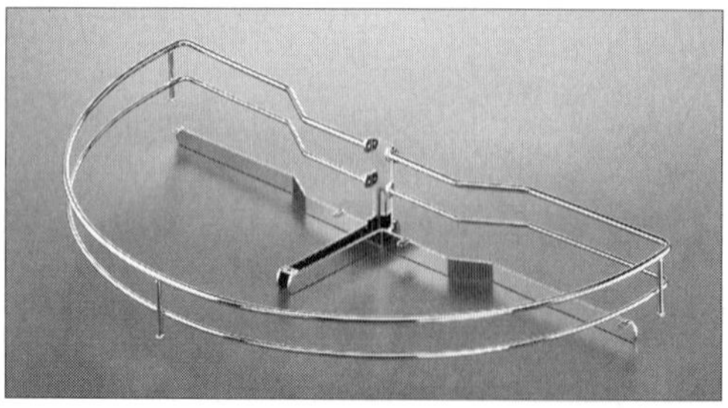

Half moon wire fence 1/4 turn
for wood shelves (not supplied)
Shelf revolves in bearing screw-mounted to center upright
Finish: steel, chrome plated
bearing, plastic

for cabinet door width mm	Dimensions mm	Cat. No.
425 (16¾")	782 x 425 x 105	541.03.230

Packing: 1 pc.

Shelf follower
for fence 541.03.230,
or base units with doors.

Advantage: allows shelf to revolve automatically as door opens.
Finish: steel chrome plated,
roller: plastic, white

Cat. No.	541.03.285

Packing: 10 pcs.

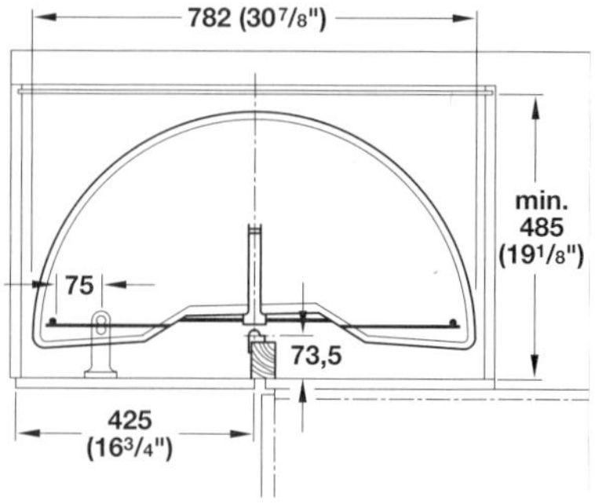

Dimensional data not binding.
We reserve the right to alter specifications without notice.

Dimensions in mm
Inches are approximate

1/4 Turn Wire Shelf Corner Unit Systems

1/4 turn/extending wire shelf with fence
Complete with pivot/extending fitting (can be mounted left or right) and follower roller.
Finish: Steel, plastic-coated white

For cabinet door width from mm	inch	Dimensions mm	Cat. No.
425	$16^{3}/_{4}$	770 x 400	541.26.724
490	$19^{1}/_{2}$	890 x 460	541.26.742

Packing: 1 pc.

The pivot fitting, which is designed for left or right hand mounting, is screw to the center upright at any desired height.

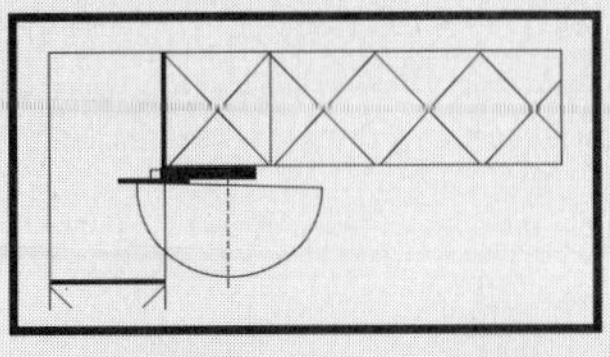

Installation using a center upright 60 mm deep

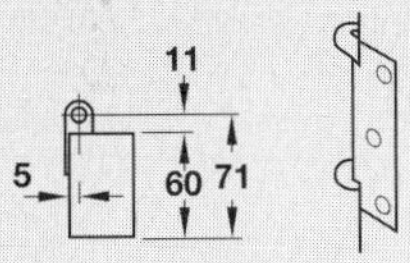

Installed dimensions for minimum door width:

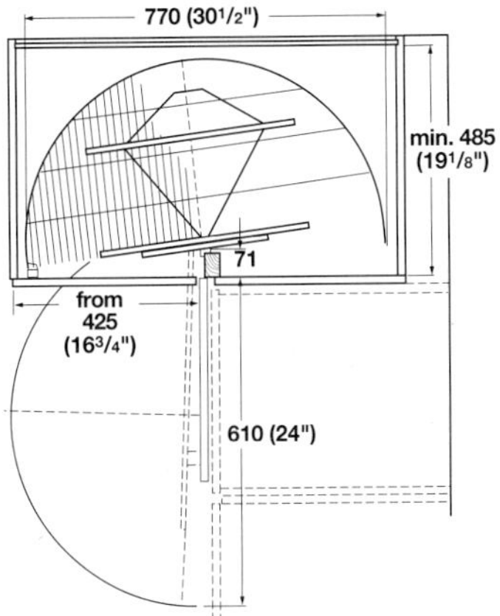

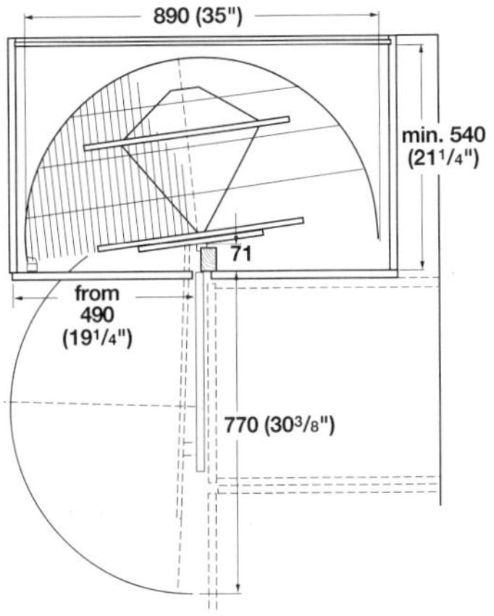

Kitchen Accessory Systems **5**

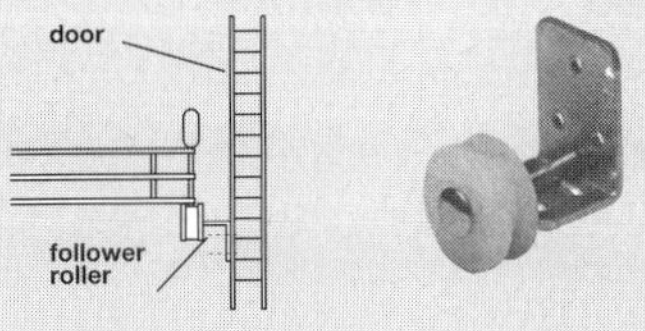

These revolving/extending half moon wire shelves are delivered with a follower roller, that is screwed to the inside of the door, causing the shelf to revolve as the door opens, from where it can be extended forwards on the supporting roller.

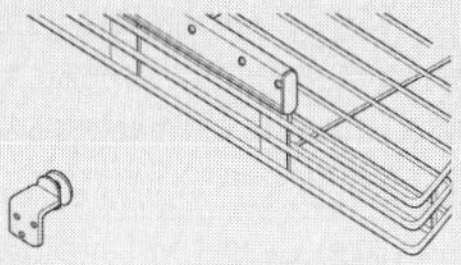

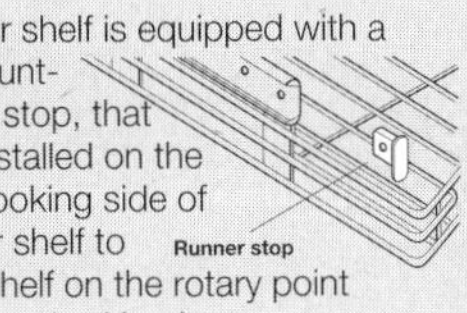

The runner shelf is equipped with a screw mounted runner stop, that is to be installed on the outward looking side of the runner shelf to stop the shelf on the rotary point when it's pushed back.

Dimensional data not binding. We reserve the right to alter specifications without notice.

Dimensions in mm
Inches are approximate

HÄFELE

Dual Function Slide-Out For Blind Base Corner Units

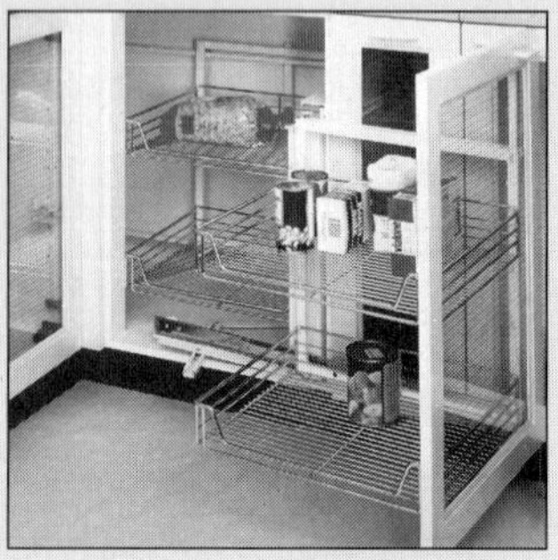

- Available left or right hand mounting. The illustration here shows the right hand version.
- Cabinet door mounts to frame.

Function diagram

1. Closed position

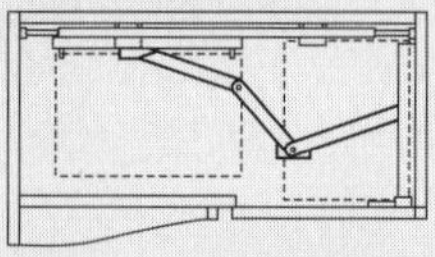

2. Slide-out

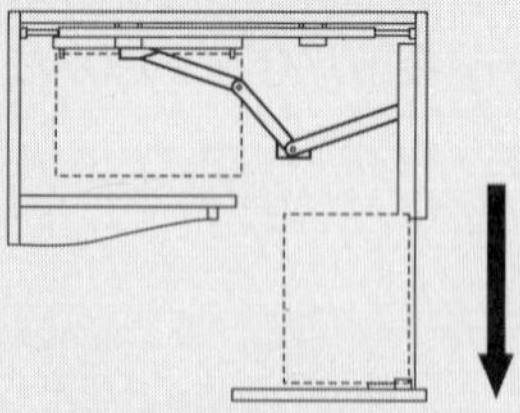

3. Turn and Slide out

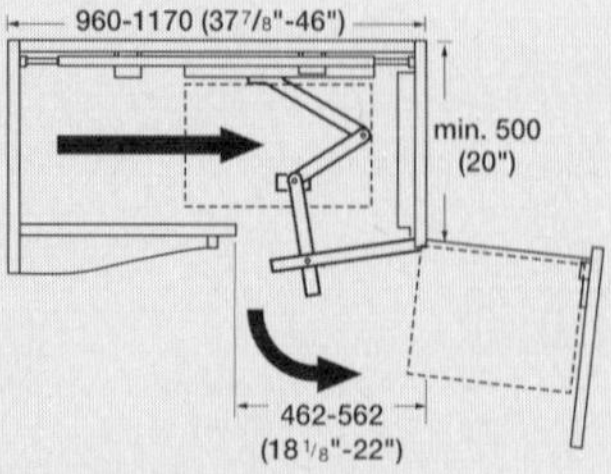

dotted lines=baskets

Dimensional data not binding. We reserve the right to alter specifications without notice.

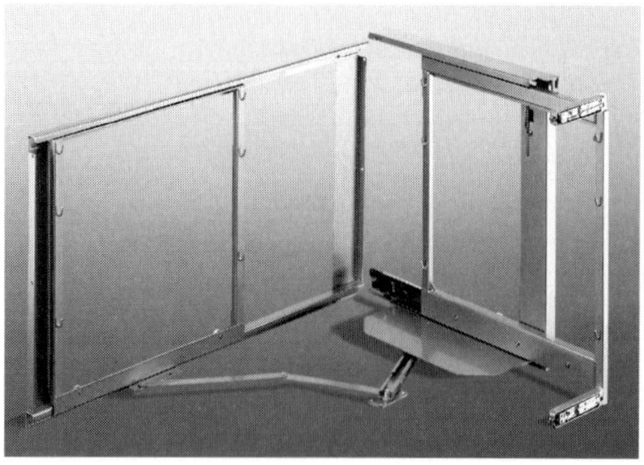

Base corner unit system
inside height of 580–680 mm (23–27")
Finish: steel, epoxy-coated
Slide, steel galvanized

Finish	Right hand	Left hand
white Ral 9010	546.17.711	546.17.702
silver Ral 9006	546.17.917	546.17.908

Packing: 1 pc. (including mounting template)

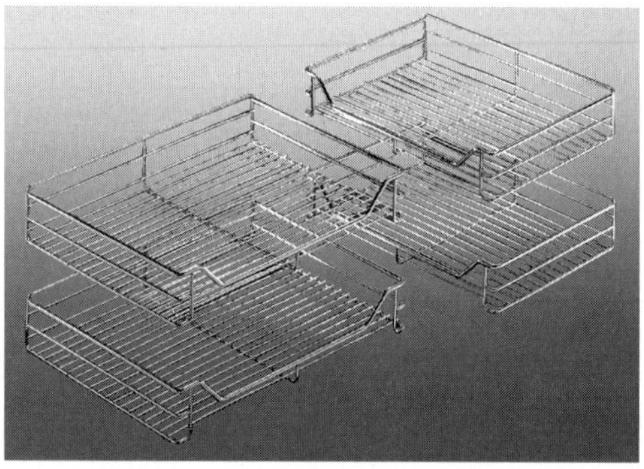

Storage Baskets for base corner unit system.
Size: 340 x 472 x 90 mm
Finish: steel wire, chrome-plated

Cat. No.	546.17.257

Packing: 1 pc. (4 baskets per unit recommended)

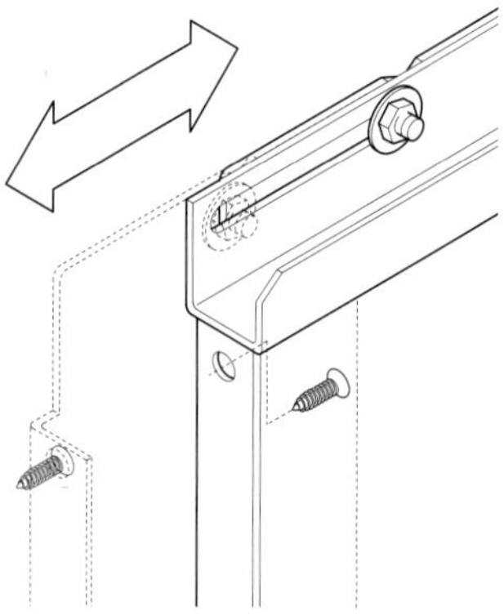

When the fitting is fixed to the cabinet bottom, it is in addition secured at the top of the sidewalls with the adjustable brackets as shown.

Dimensions in mm
Inches are approximate

HÄFELE

Revolving Corner Unit Systems for Internal Revolving Doors

Revolving corner unit systems for base cabinets

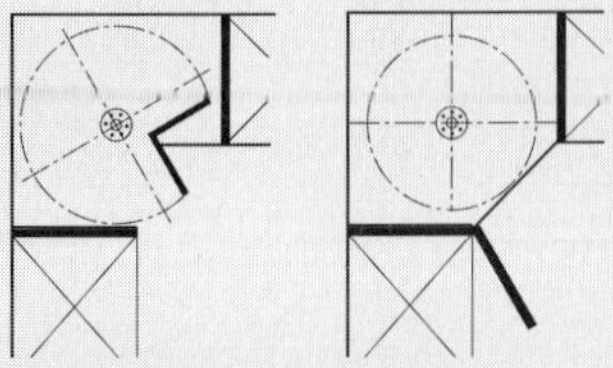

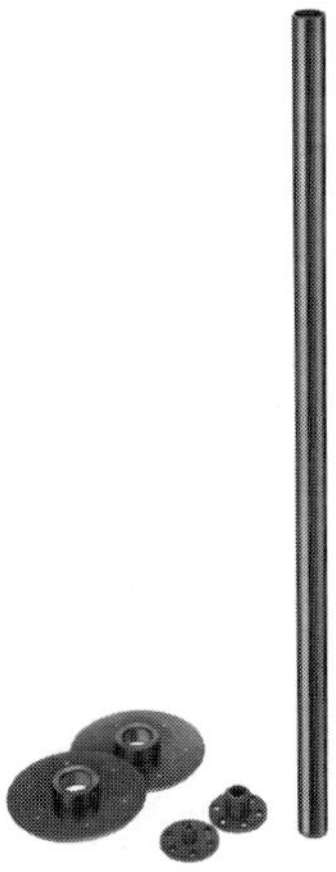

Revolving fitting with self centering cam for **customer provided three quarter round or full-round revolving wood shelves.**

Consist of:
- post
- upper and lower bearing
- 2 mounting plates as supports for the revolving shelves (can be screwed onto the post at any height)

Finish:

Post:	steel, zinc-plated
Bearings:	plastic, white
Mounting plates:	steel, zinc-plated

Height	Cat. No.
700 mm (27½")	501.01.007
750 mm (29½")	501.01.016

Packing: 1 pc.

Mounting plates for mounting additional wood shelves

Finish: steel, zinc-plated

Cat. No.	501.01.909

Packing: 1 pc.

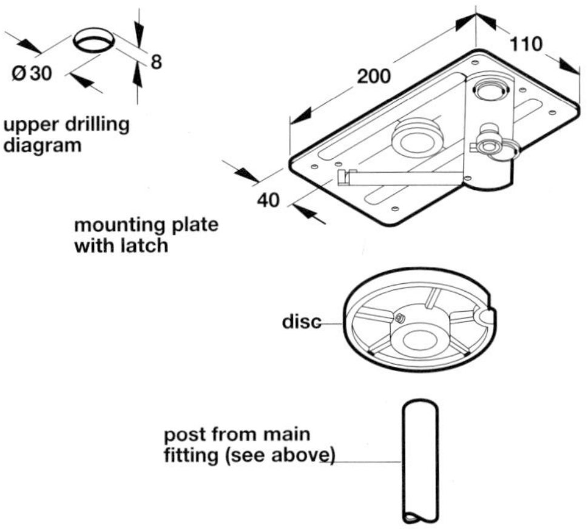

Door catch

Screw-mounted underneath the cabinet top or cabinet crossbar as upper bearing for the fitting (in place of standard upper bearing)

Consist of:
- mounting plate with latch
- disc (with latching recess) which must be secured to post

Finish:

Mounting plate:	steel, zinc-plated
Disc:	plastic, white

Cat. No.	501.10.711

Packing: 1 set

Kitchen Accessory Systems 5

If an internally revolving door is used, the bottom shelf must be set lower than the others in order to ensure that all the kitchen cabinet doors are of the same height (see diagram).

Cross section

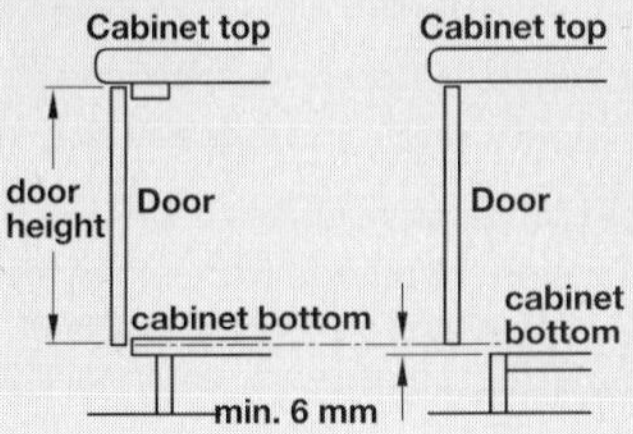

The dimensions of base corner cabinets are not subject to restrictions

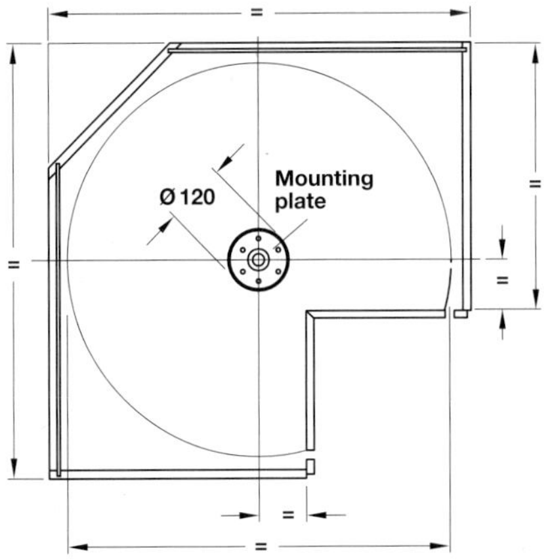

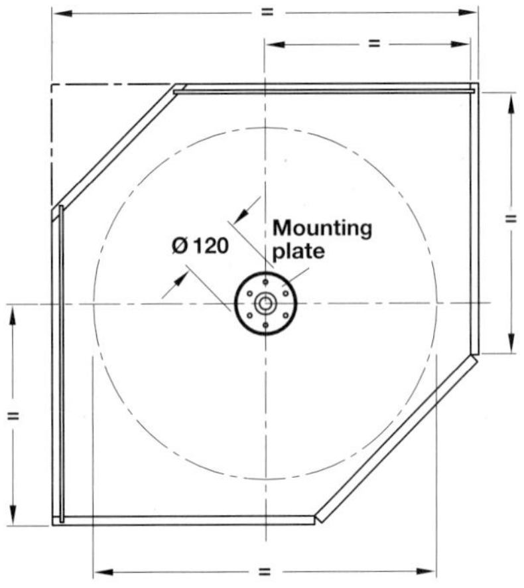

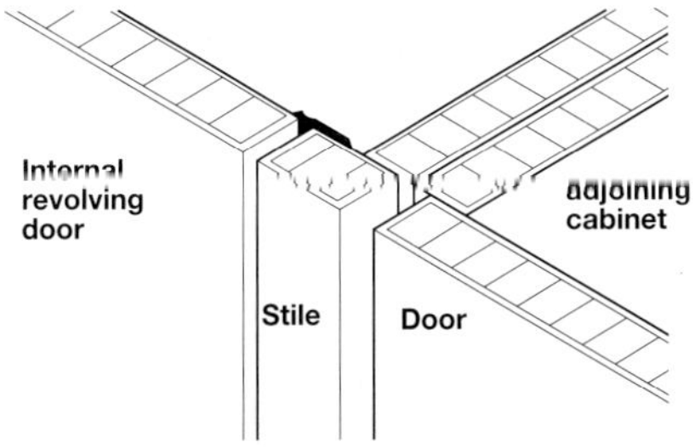

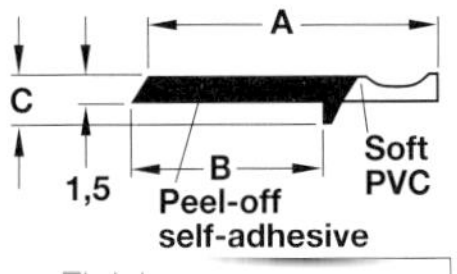

Door sealing profile, self-adhesive

Finish: plastic with soft PVC lip

		Finish		
Size AxB	Dimension C	White	Brown	Beige
17.8 x 11	0.8	716.60.707	716.60.109	716.60.403
22.5 x 12	1.5	716.60.716	716.60.118	716.60.412

Packing: 2.5 meters

Dimensional data not binding. We reserve the right to alter specifications without notice.

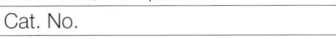

HÄFELE

Revolving Corner Systems

- For use in corner cabinets.
- Nylon bearings for durability
- Adjustable post
- Easy to install

• By adding BP to Cat. No., 10 sets are packed to a box.

Pie Cut Shelf Set

IIncludes: 2 trays and hardware.
Finish:
Shelves: High impact white polystyrene,
Post: steel chrome plated
Bearings: nylon
Adjustable post fits 23¼" - 33" high cabinets.

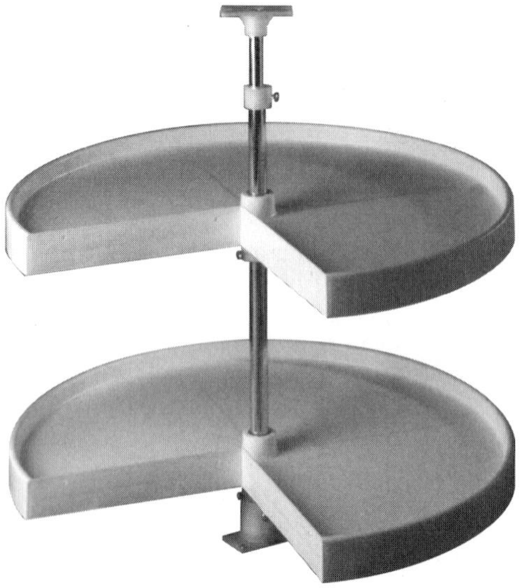

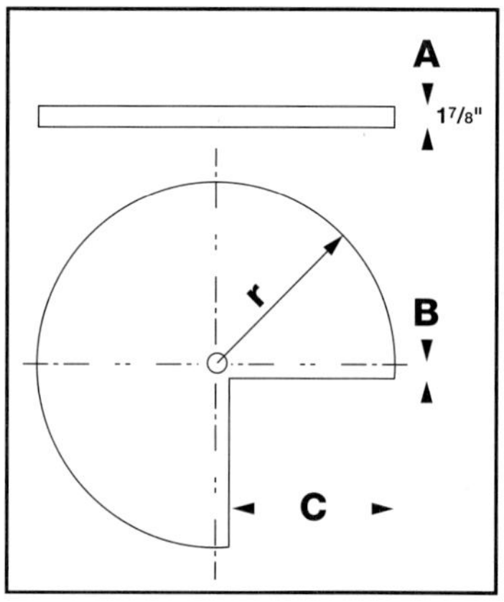

Size	r=radius	A	B	C	White	Almond
24"	12"	1⅞"	1½"	10½"	542.10.721	542.10.420
28"	14"	1⅞"	3½"	10½"	542.10.730	542.10.430

Packing: 1 and 10 sets*

- For use in corner cabinets.
- Trays rotate independently.
- Lock-in position
- Nylon bearings for durability
- Adjustable post
- Easy to install

** By adding BP to Cat. No., 10 sets are packed to a box for the 24 and 28" sizes and 5 sets for the 32" size.

Kidney Shelf Set

IIncludes: 2 trays and hardware.
Finish:
Shelves: high impact white polystyrene 32" diameter – high impact polystyrene over particle board
Post: steel chrome-plated
Bearings: nylon
Adjustable post fits 23¼" – 33" high cabinets.

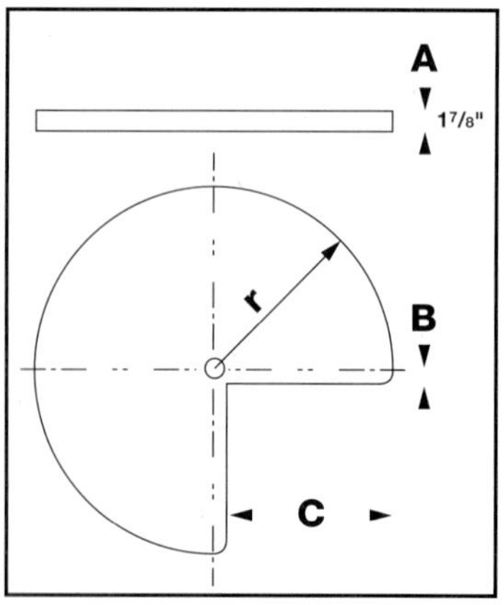

Size	r=radius	A	B	C	White	Almond
24"	12"	1⅞"	2"	10"	542.11.728	542.11.420
28"	14"	1⅞"	4"	10"	542.11.737	542.11.430
32"	16"	2⅛"	4⅛"	11⅞"	542.11.740	N/A

Packing: 24" and 28" – 1 and 10 sets**
32" – 1 and 5 sets**

Dimensions in mm
Inches are approximate

HÄFELE

Revolving Corner Unit Systems Three-quarter Round

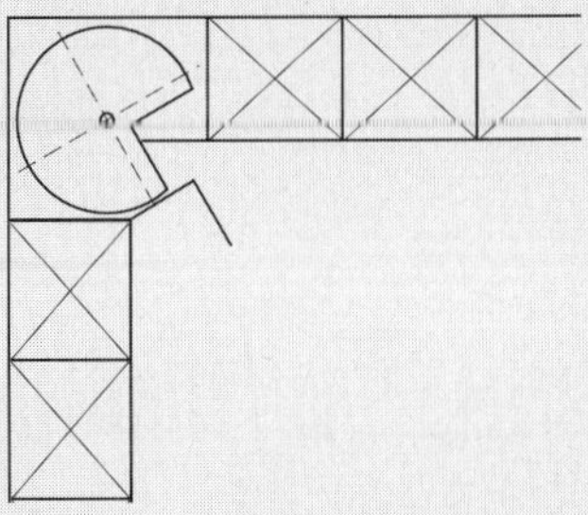

Three-quarter round revolving system.
Minimum installation height: 710 mm (28") to 780 mm (30 3/4")
The complete set includes:
- 1 post, 700 mm (27 1/2") high, with welded lower mounting plate and vertical adjusting element
- 2 shelves
- 2 shelf bearings, 3-part
- 2 self-centering cams

Finish: Post, steel chrome-plated; shelves, steel epoxy-coated, white; adjusting-element, steel galvanized; upper post bearing, polyamide, white

for corner cabinets	800 x 800 mm	900 x 900 mm
Dimensions	Ø 700 mm	Ø 820 mm
Cat. No.	541.59.830	541.59.849

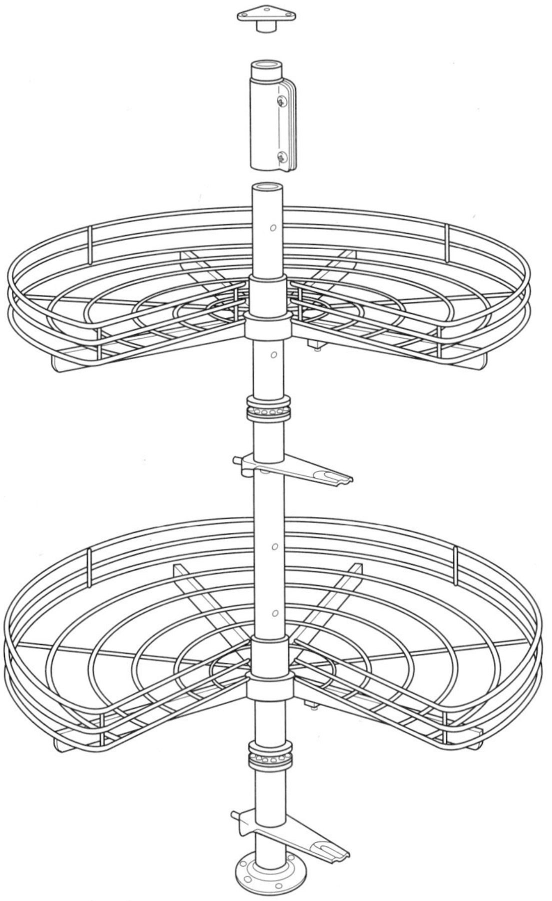

The ball-bearing mounted wire shelves rotate independently around a fixed center post. Self-centering cams keep shelves at the correct position when door is closed.

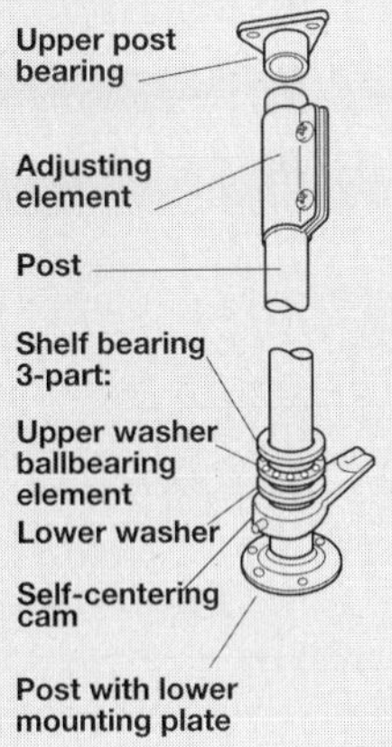

Installed dimensions for corner cabinets 800 x 800 mm (31 1/2" x 31 1/2")

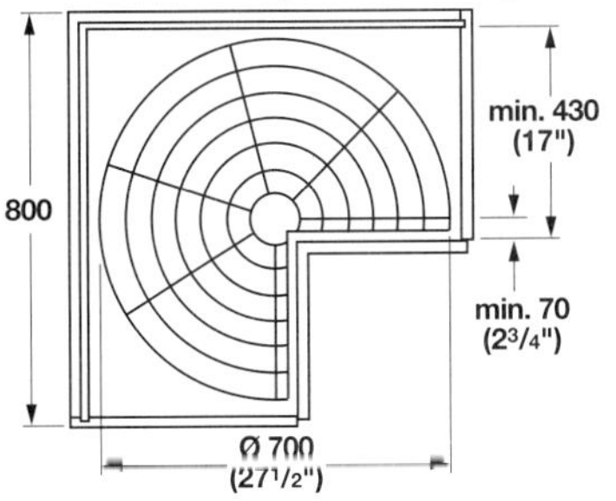

Installed dimensions for corner cabinets 900 x 900 mm (35 1/2" x 35 1/2")

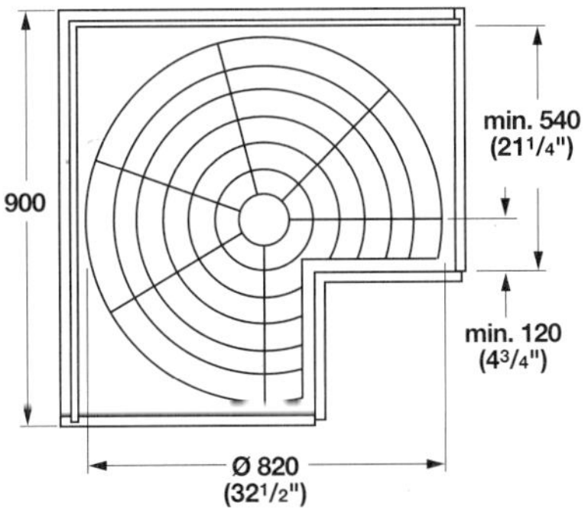

Dimensions in mm
Inches are approximate

Dimensional data not binding. We reserve the right to alter specifications without notice.

HÄFELE

Revolving Corner Unit Systems
Three-quarter Round

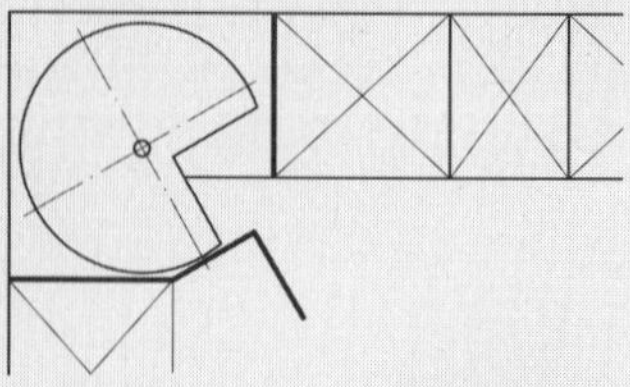

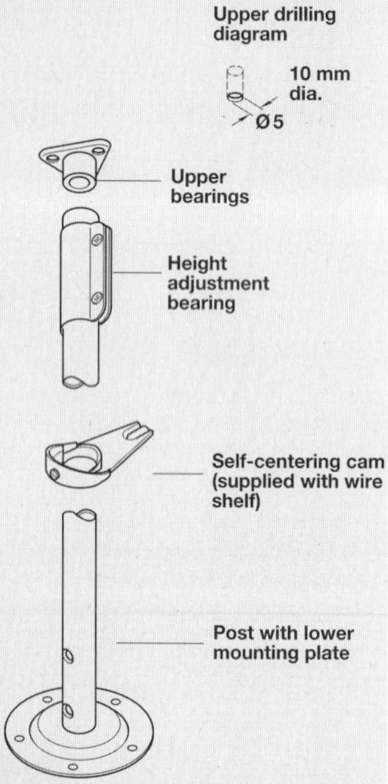

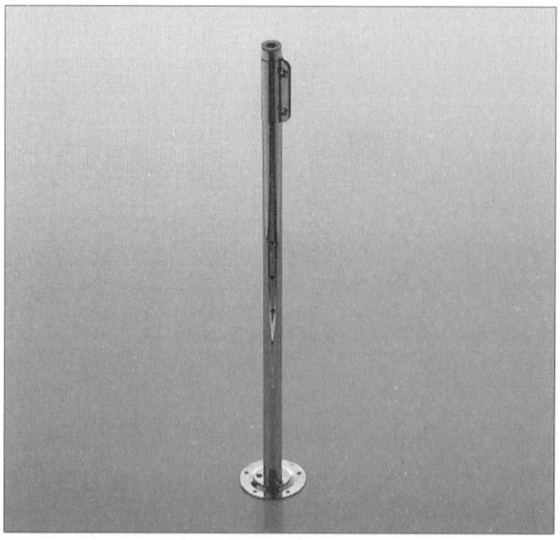

Center Post
vertically adjustable 725 (28 1/2") to 765 mm (30 1/8")
with upper and lower bearings and vertical adjustment bearing
Capable of accommodating 3 shelves
Finish:
Post: steel, chrome plated
Height-adjustable bearing: steel, galvanized
Upper bearing: plastic, white

Cat. No.	541.17.234

Packing: 1 pc.

Three-quarter round, revolving wire shelf with wire surround and complete with ball bearing and self-centering cam.
Height: 80 mm (3 1/8")
Finish: steel, chrome-plated

for corner floor units	Diameter	Cat. No.
800 x 800 mm	Ø 700 (27 1/2")	541.18.222
900 x 900 mm	Ø 820 (34 1/4")	541.18.231

Packing: 1 pc.

Installed dimensions for 800 x 800 mm corner base units

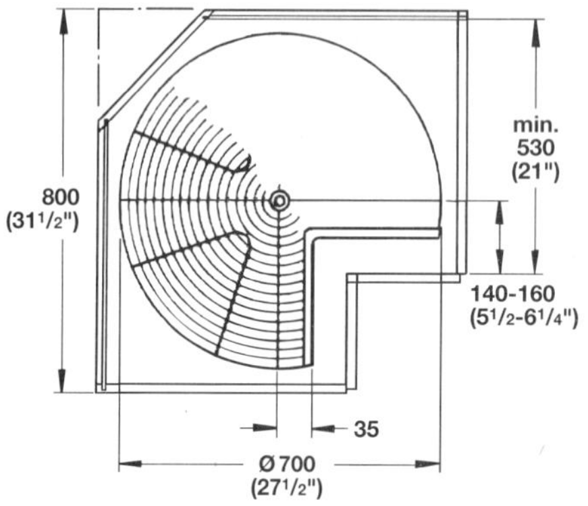

Installed dimensions for 900 x 900 mm corner base units

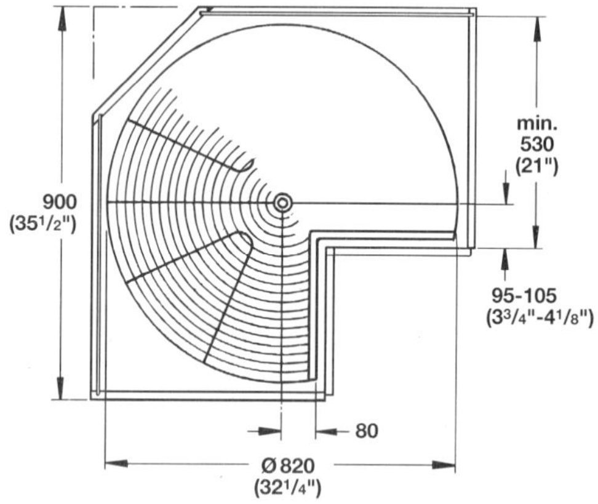

Dimensional data not binding.
We reserve the right to alter specifications without notice.

Dimensions in mm
Inches are approximate

Revolving Corner Unit Systems

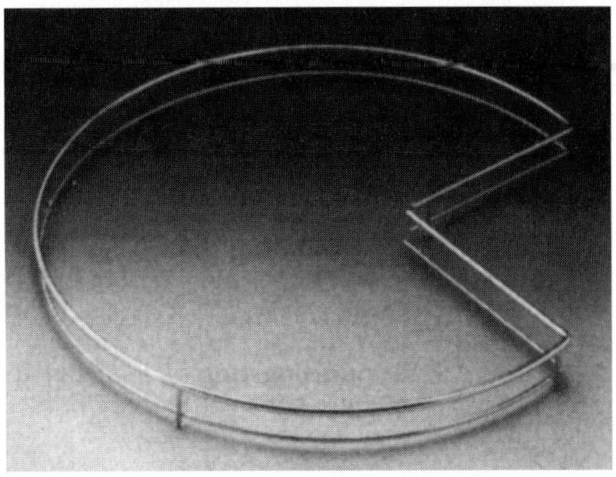

Wire Surround Fence
for screw mounting to three-quarter round, customer-supplied wood shelf
For 900 x 900 mm (36 x 36") corner units
Diameter: 810 mm (31 7/8")
Height: 62 mm (2 1/2")
Finish: steel, chrome-plated

Cat. No.	541.02.233

Packing: 1 pc.

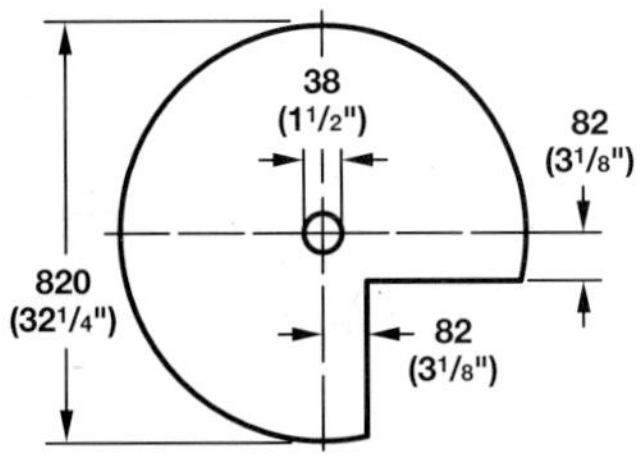

Cutout and hole for wood shelf

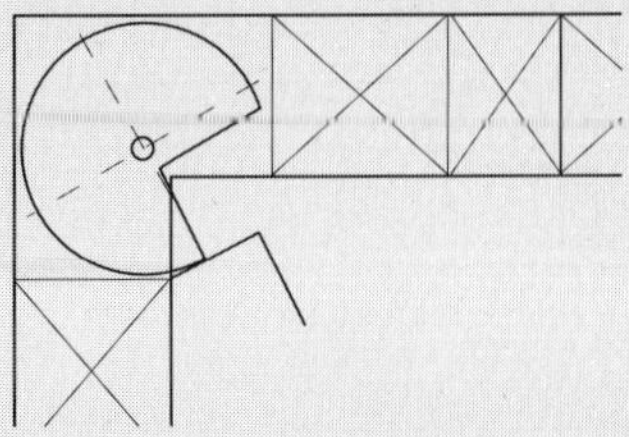

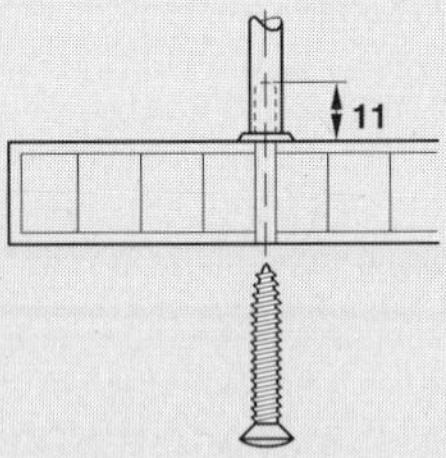

Wire fences are secured to wood shelves with **raised head screws**
Size: Ø 4.2 x 32 mm
Finish: steel, galvanized

Cat. No.	023.27.460

Packing: 100 pcs.

Shelf support for mounting to Post 541.17.234 supports three-quarter round, revolving wood shelf complete with retaining pin
Finish: steel, epoxy-coated, white

Cat. No.	541.02.706

Packing: 1 pc.

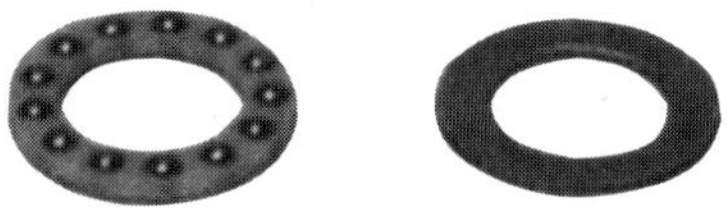

Ball bearing with support washer for installation on Post 541.17.234

Cat. No.	541.56.919

Packing: 1 pc.

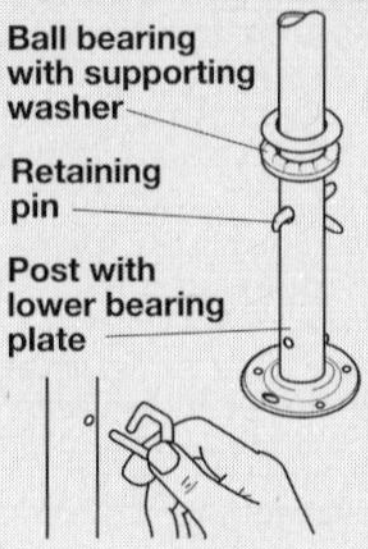

Dimensions in mm
Inches are approximate

HÄFELE

Revolving Corner Unit Systems - Self Closing

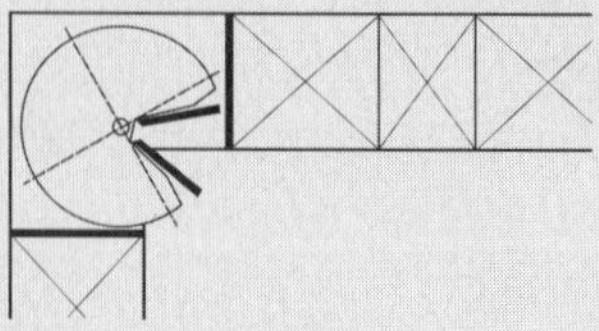

- For front mounted, internally revolving folding doors.
- Three dimensional adjustment.
- When opened, the folding doors are drawn inward by a cam system and revolve through the interior of the cabinet with the fittings.
- An integral, adjustable pneumatic damping device ensures that the doors close quietly.

It is essential that the cabinet floor is set lower than the others in order to ensure that all the base cabinet doors are the same height (see diagram).

Cross section

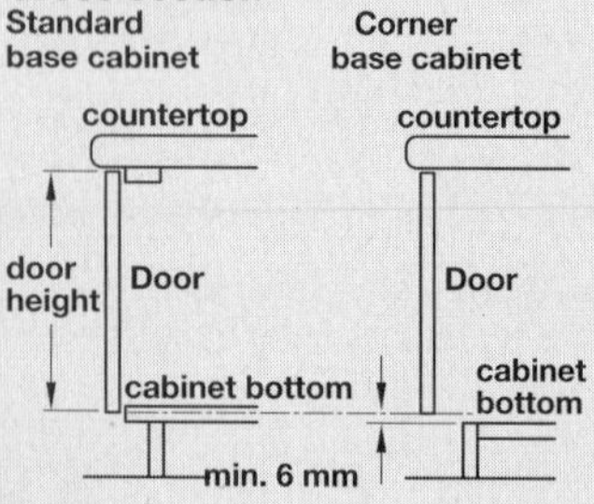

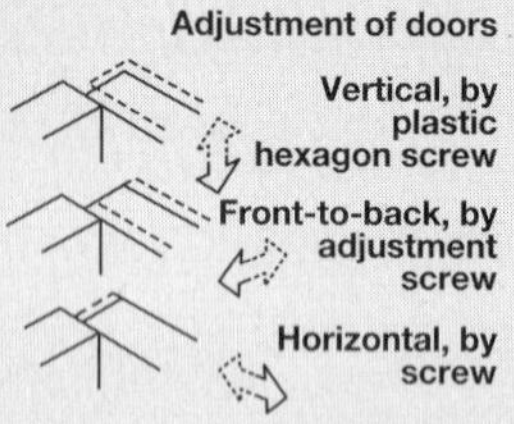

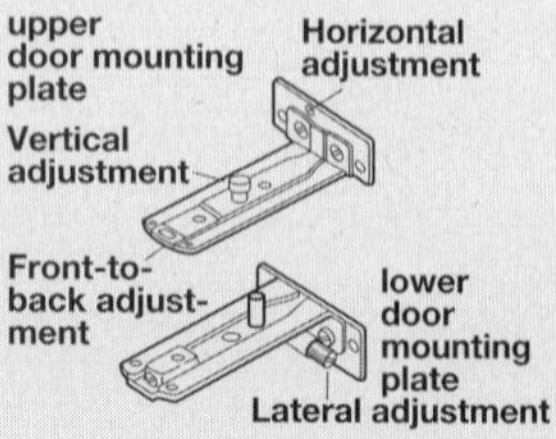

Dimensional data not binding. We reserve the right to alter specifications without notice.

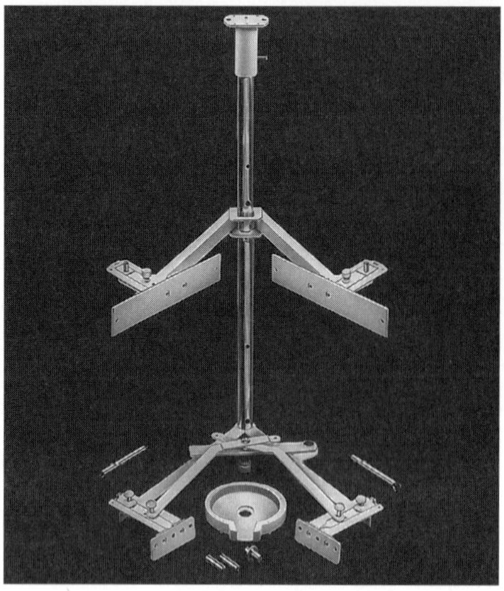

Folding/revolving fitting with pneumatic damping, vertical adjustable from 710 to 750 mm (28-29 1/2") for max. 2 three-quarter round revolving shelves

Fitting complete with:
- upper post bearing
- pre-drilled tubular post with pre-installed folding assembly
- 4 door mounting plates
- 2 retaining pins for shelves
- 2 coil springs
- cam disc and knock-in pin for lower post bearing

Finish: post, coil springs and retaining pins, galvanized steel; all other parts plastic and metal parts, white

For corner unit	For door opening	Cat. No.
800 x 800	250 x 250 (10 x 10)	541.35.750
36" x 36"	12" x 12" slab door	541.35.750
900 x 900	350 x 350 (14 x 14)	541.35.760
36" x 36"	12" x 12" frame & panel door	541.35.770

Packing: 1 set (with mounting instructions and template for door parts)

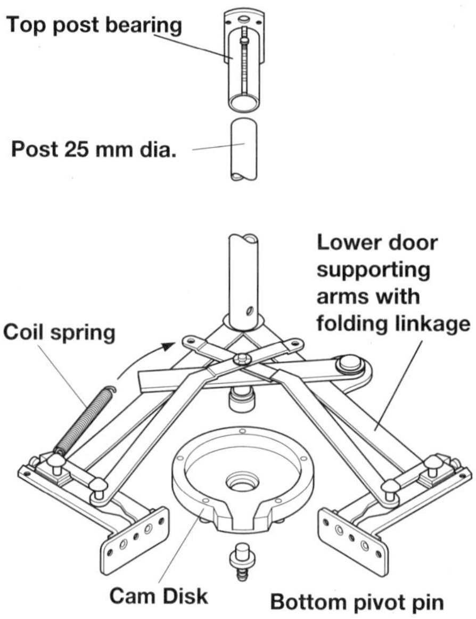

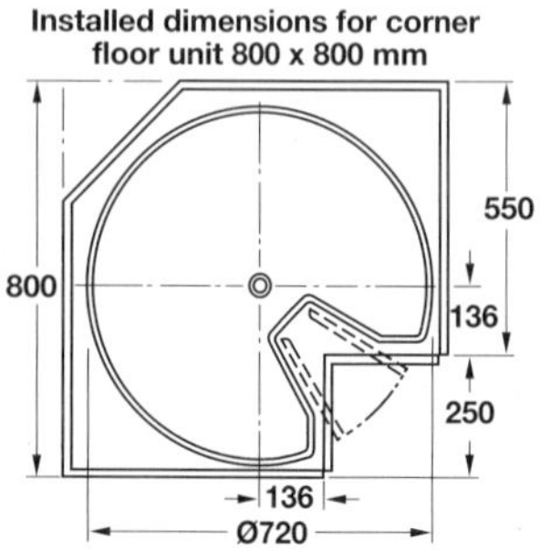

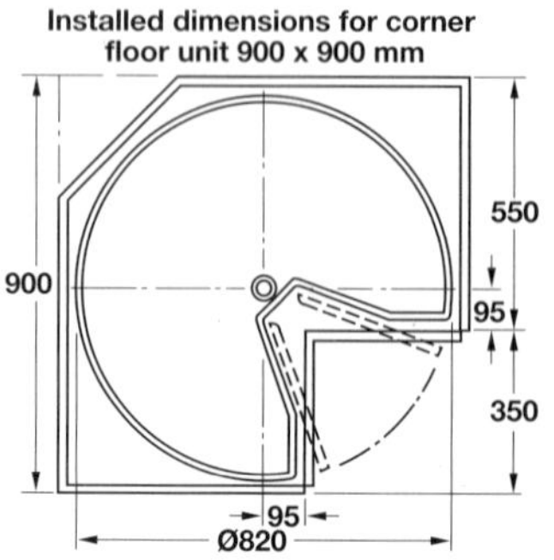

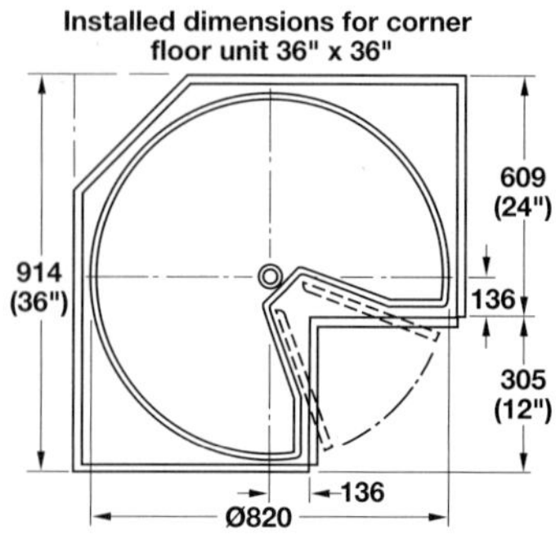

Dimensions in mm
Inches are approximate

HÄFELE

Revolving Corner Unit Trays for 541.35 Revolving Corner Unit Fitting

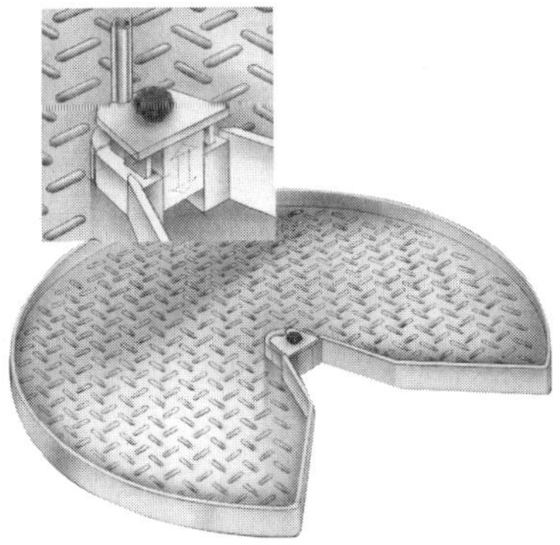

Plastic adapter
for three-quarter round revolving shelf
(1 required per shelf)
Finish: plastic, white

Cat. No.	542.16.796

Packing: 1 pc.

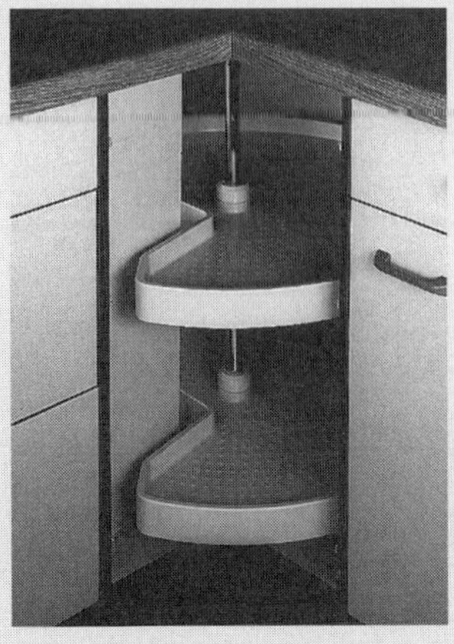

- Shelf installs without tools for fast installation.
- Handles heavy loads.

Three-quarter round revolving shelf
for folding/revolving fitting (requires plastic adapter)
Finish: plastic, white

For corner units		Size		Cat. No.
mm	inches	mm	inches	
800 x 800	31 1/2" x 31 1/2"	Ø 710	Ø 28"	542.16.714
914 x 914	36" x 36"	Ø 820	Ø 32 1/4"	542.16.732
900 x 900	35 1/2" x 35 1/2"	Ø 820	Ø 32 1/4"	542.16.732

Packing: 1 pc.

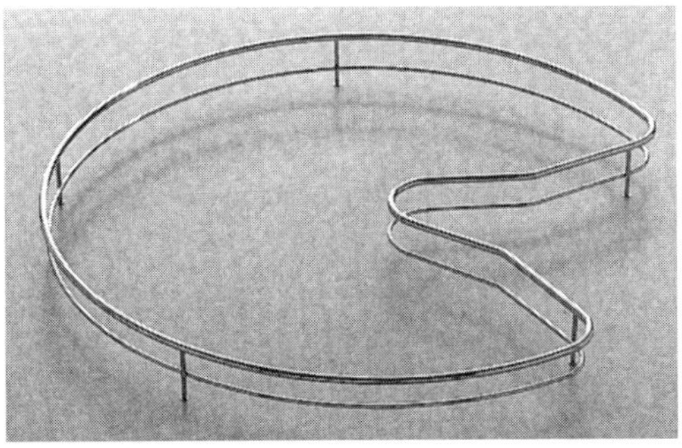

Shelf support
for customer-supplied wood revolving shelves complete with clamping rings
Finish: plastic, white

Cat. No.	541.35.796

Packing: 2 pcs.

Three-quarter wire border
for customer-supplied revolving wood shelves with shelf support 541.35.796
Finish: steel, chrome-plated

For corner units		Size		Cat. No.
mm	inches	mm	inches	
800 x 800	31 1/2" x 31 1/2"	Ø 685	Ø 27"	541.04.228
900 x 900	35 1/2" x 35 1/2"	Ø 785	Ø 31"	541.04.237
914 x 914	36" x 36"	Ø 785	Ø 31"	541.04.237

Packing: 1 pc.

Three-quarter round revolving shelf
double wall with clamping sleeve
Finish: steel, chrome-plated

For corner units		Size		Cat. No.
mm	inches	mm	inches	
800 x 800	31 1/2" x 31 1/2"	Ø 700	Ø 27 1/2""	541.11.228
900 x 900	35 1/2" x 35 1/2"	Ø 800	Ø 31 1/2"	541.11.232
914 x 914	36" x 36"	Ø 800	Ø 31 1/2"	541.11.232

Packing: 1 pc.

Dimensions in mm
Inches are approximate

HÄFELE

Revolving Corner Systems – Full Round

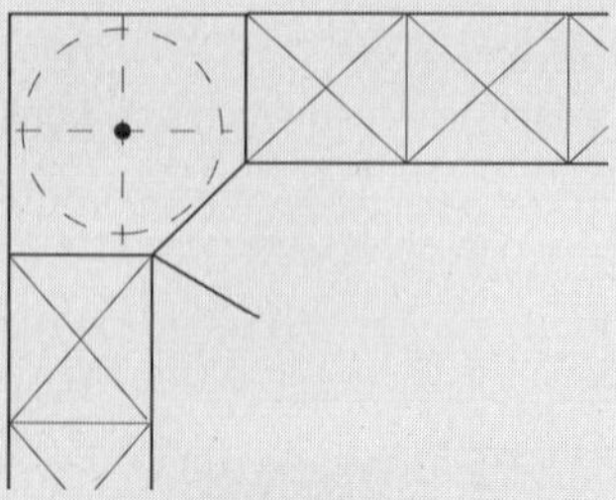

- For corner cabinet installations
- Durable nylon bearings
- Adjustable post
- Easy to install

Full Round Shelf Sets
Includes: 2 trays and hardware, or 3 trays and hardware.
Finish:
Shelf: high impact white polystyrene; 32" diameter-high impact polystyrene over particle board
Pedestal: chrome plated steel post
Bearings: nylon
Adjustable post fits 23¼"– 33" for two tray sets.
Adjustable post fits 27"– 45" for three tray sets.

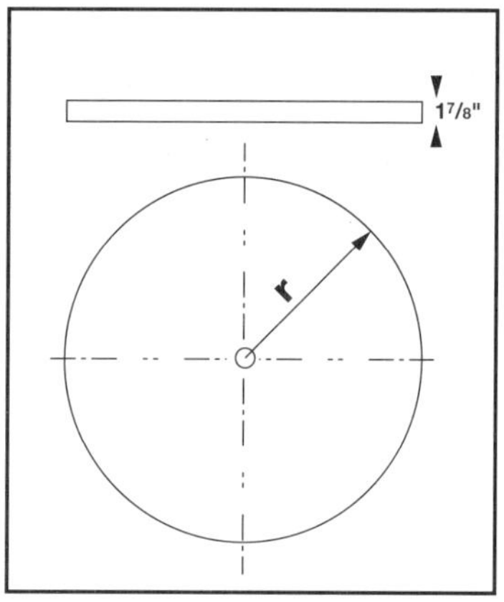

Size	Trays	Post	r=radius	White	Almond
18"	2	23¼-33"	9"	542.12.716	542.18.410
18"	3	27-45"	9"	542.12.743	542.18.440
20"	2	23¼-33"	10"	542.19.720	542.19.420
24"	2	23¼-33"	12"	542.12.725	542.18.420
28"	2	23¼-33"	14"	542.12.734	542.18.430
32"	2	23¼-33"	16"	542.12.700	N/A

Packing: 1 set*

* By adding BP to the Catalog Number, 10 sets are packed to a box for the 18–28" sizes and 5 sets for the 32" size.

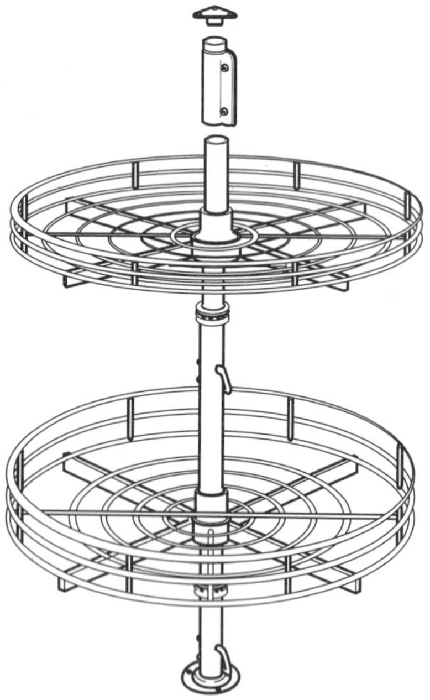

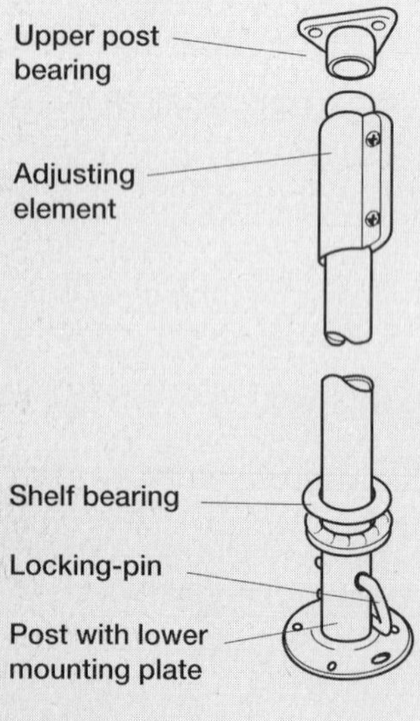

Installed dimensions for corner cabinets

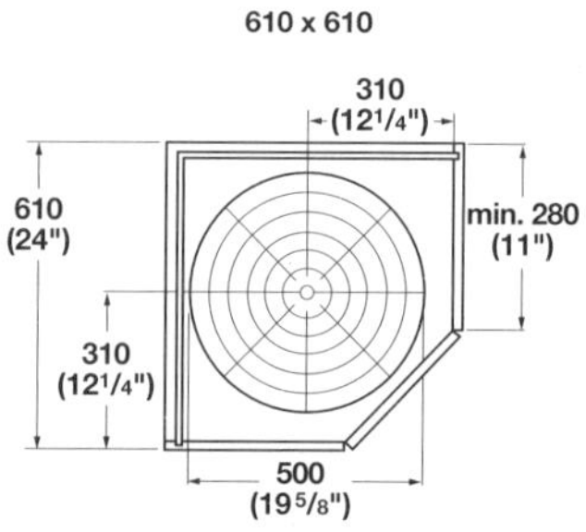

Full round revolving fitting set
Minimum installed height 710 mm (28") to 780 mm (30 3/4") Complete with 1 post 700 mm (27½") high with welded lower mounting plate and vertical adjusting element, 2 shelves, 2 steel bearings, three part, 2 locking pins.
Finish: post: steel, chrome-plated
shelves: steel, epoxy-coated, white
adjusting element: steel, galvanized
upper post bearing: plastic, white

For corner cabinet	Diameter mm (inch)	Cat. No.
610 x 610 mm	500 (19⅝")	541.29.814

Packing: 1 set

Dimensional data not binding. We reserve the right to alter specifications without notice.

Dimensions in mm
Inches are approximate

Revolving Corner Unit Systems - Full Round

HÄFELE

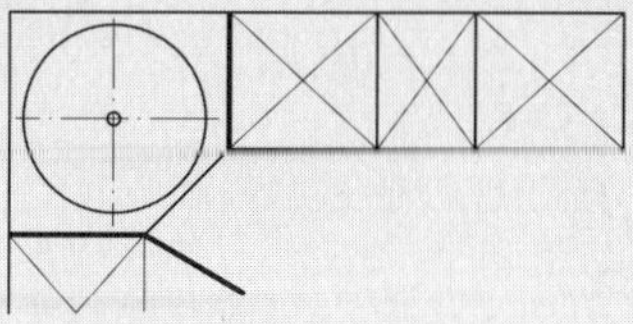

Corner floor unit revolving systems with circular revolving shelves
- for cabinets with front mounted diagonal doors
- fixed center post
- shelves turn independently

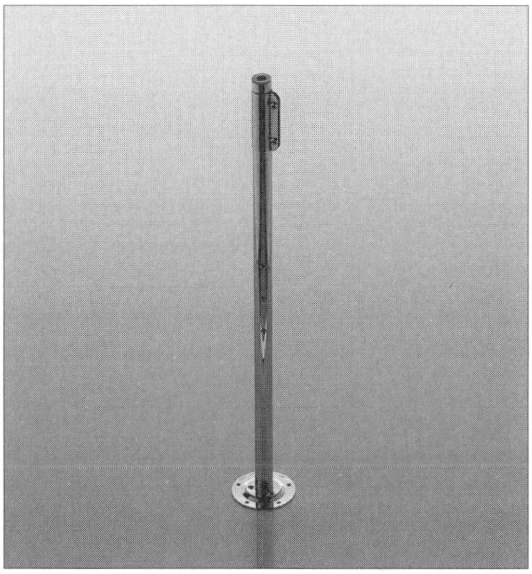

Center post, vertically adjustable from 725 mm (28$^{1}/_{2}$") to 765 mm (30$^{1}/_{8}$")
with upper and lower bearings and vertical adjustment bearing, capable of accommodating 3 shelves.

Finish:

post:	steel, chrome-plated
height adjustment bearing:	steel, galvanized
upper bearing:	plastic, white
Cat. No.	541.17.234

Packing: 1 set

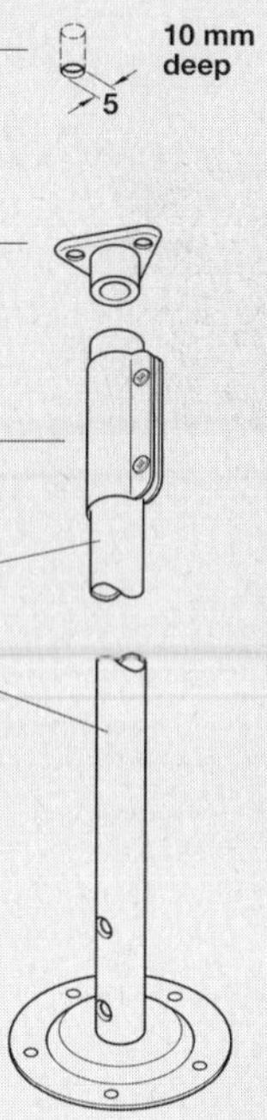

Circular revolving shelf with wire fence,
complete with support and positioning device
Finish: steel, chrome-plated

For cabinets 900 x 900 mm
Dimensions: Ø 750 mm (29$^{1}/_{2}$"), 80 mm (3$^{1}/_{8}$") high

Cat. No.	541.12.239

Packing: 1 pc.

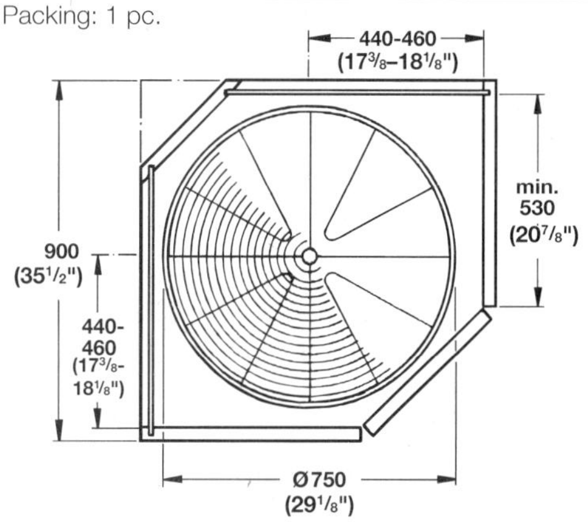

Kitchen Accessory Systems 5

Dimensional data not binding. We reserve the right to alter specifications without notice.

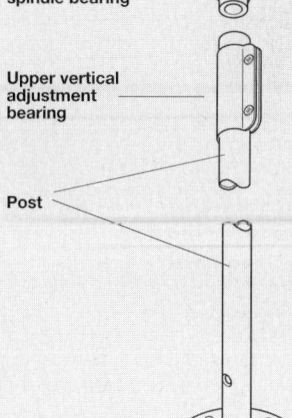

Dimensions in mm
Inches are approximate

HÄFELE

Base Cabinet Pull-Out Units

Under-sink storage unit
Complete fitting includes parallel runners, screwed-mounted to cabinet floor.

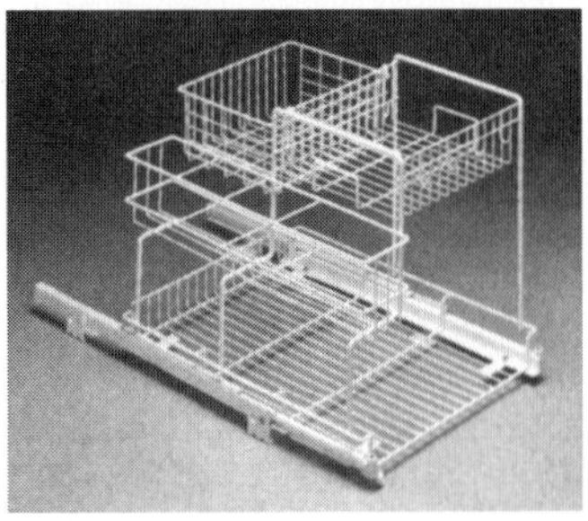

Finish: steel, plastic-coated, white

Cat. No.	545.47.705

Packing: 1 pc.

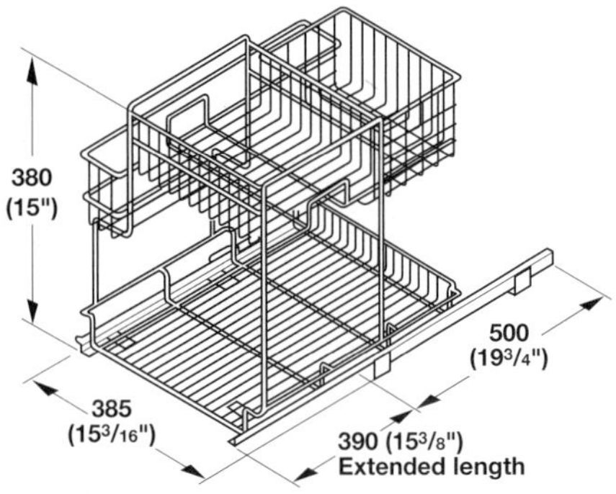

Under-sink storage unit
Can be installed left or right.
Complete fitting includes upper and lower runners to be screw-mounted to cabinet side panel.

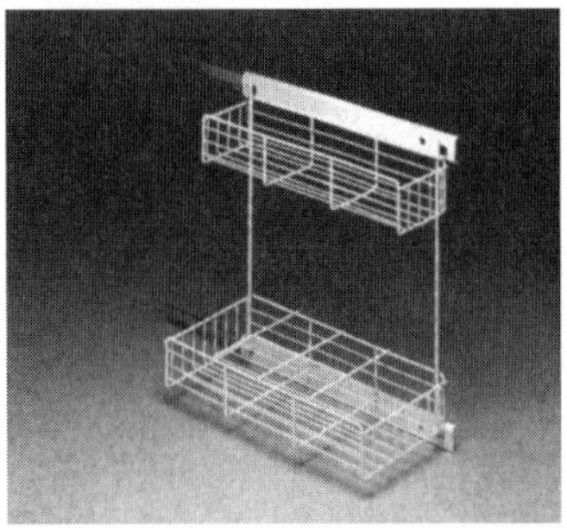

Finish: steel, plastic-coated, white

Cat. No.	545.48.702

Packing: 1 pc.

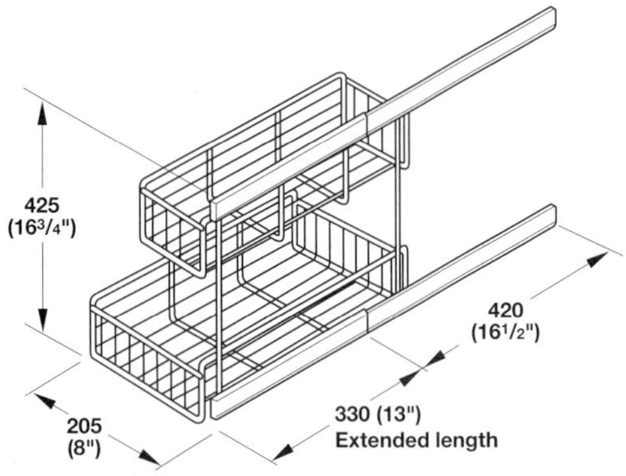

5 Kitchen Accessory Systems

Under-sink storage unit
Can be installed left or right.
Complete fitting includes upper and lower runners to be screw-mounted to cabinet side panel.

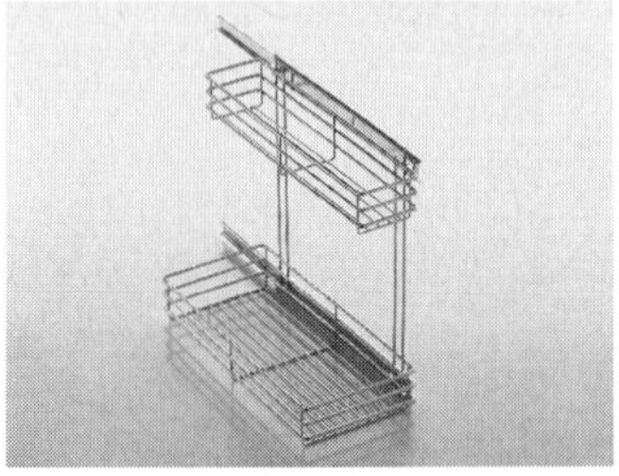

Finish: steel, chrome plated; runner, steel galvanized

Cat. No.	545.48.239

Packing: 1 pc.

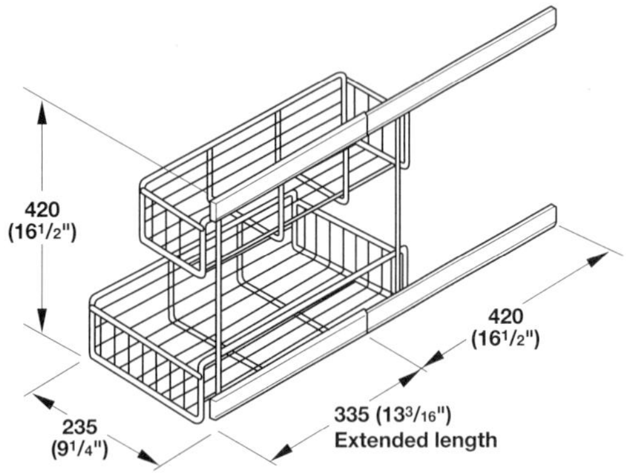

Lockable, pull-out compartment
for cleaning supplies, complete with runners
Dimensions: 206 (8 1/8") x 470 (18 1/2") x 450 (17 7/8") mm

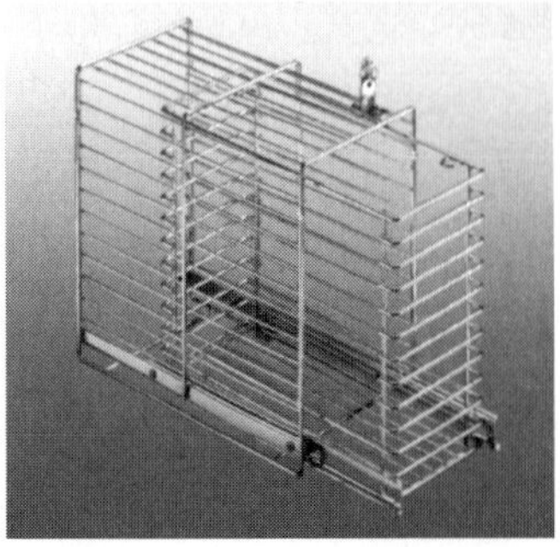

Finish: steel, chrome-plated

Cat. No.	545.48.248

Packing: 1 pc.

- key can be kept handy in a wall unit, out of the reach of children
- pull-out compartment provides much more convenient access to cleaning supplies

Dimensions listed in the following order:
width x depth x height

Dimensional data not binding.
We reserve the right to alter specifications without notice.

Dimensions in mm
Inches are approximate

Base Cabinet Pull-out Units

HÄFELE

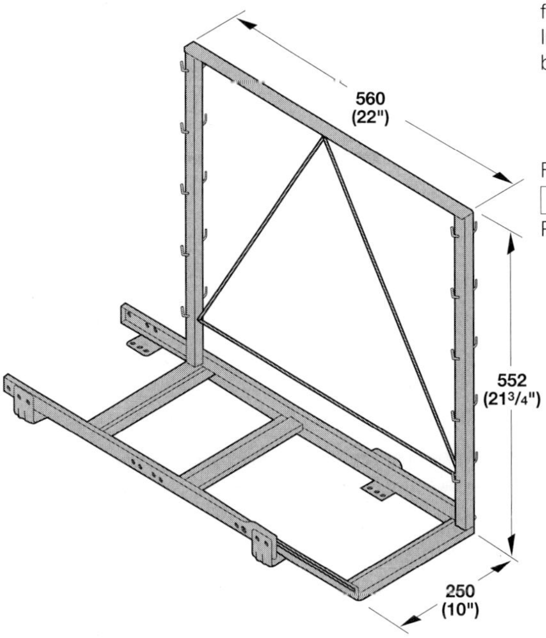

Vario-Pull, pull-out frame
for bottom mounting
Includes: one frame, one pair of soft rollers, four bottom mounting brackets and fastening hardware

Finish: steel, epoxy coated, white

Cat. No.	545.54.728

Packing: 1 pc.

- Baskets can be mounted to both sides of frame or frame can be mounted all the way to one side for one sided use, left or right.

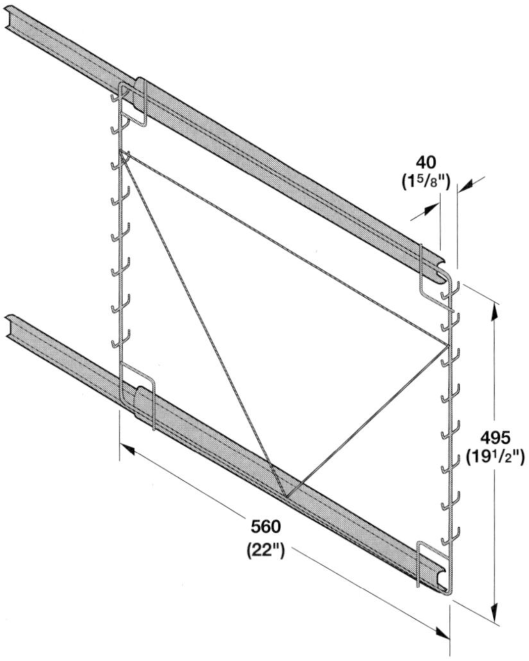

Vario-Pull, pull-out frame
for side mounting
Includes: one frame, one pair of ball bearing slides, four 15 mm spacers

Finish: steel, epoxy coated, white

Cat. No.	545.51.727

Packing: 1 pc.

- Frame can be mounted left or right.

Kitchen Accessory Systems 5

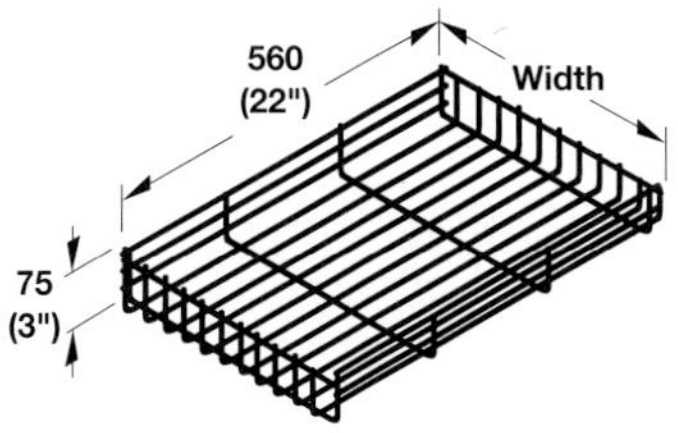

Hook-on Basket

Finish: steel, epoxy coated, white

Basket Width mm	Cat. No.
98 (4")	545.42.719
137 (5 3/8")	545.42.728
175 (6 7/8")	545.42.737
216 (8 1/2")	545.42.746
292 (11 1/8")	545.42.755
368 (14 1/2")	545.42.764

Packing: 1 pc.

Dimensions in mm
Inches are approximate

Dimensional data not binding.
We reserve the right to alter specifications without notice.

HÄFELE

Base Cabinet Storage Systems

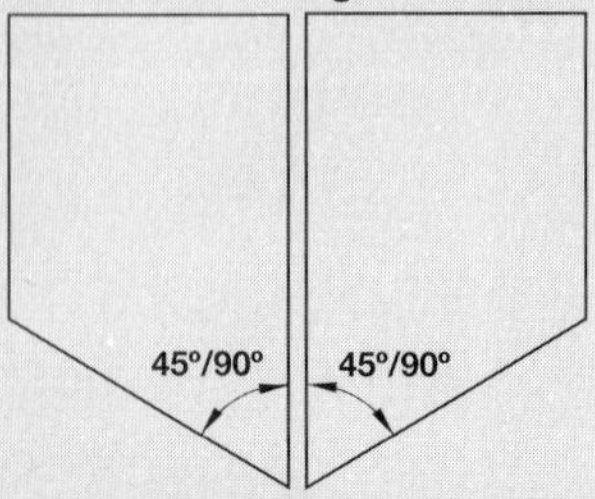

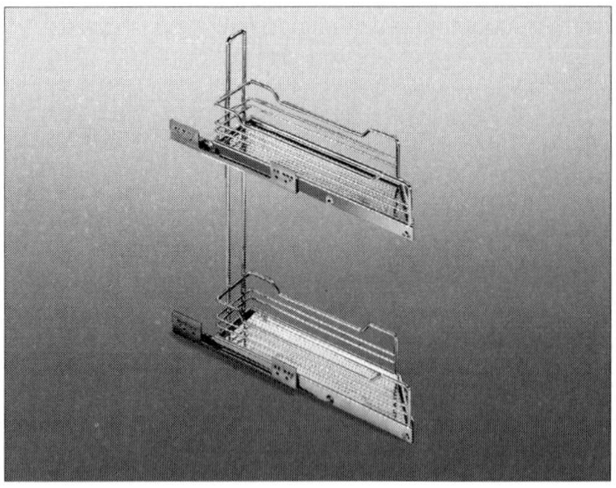

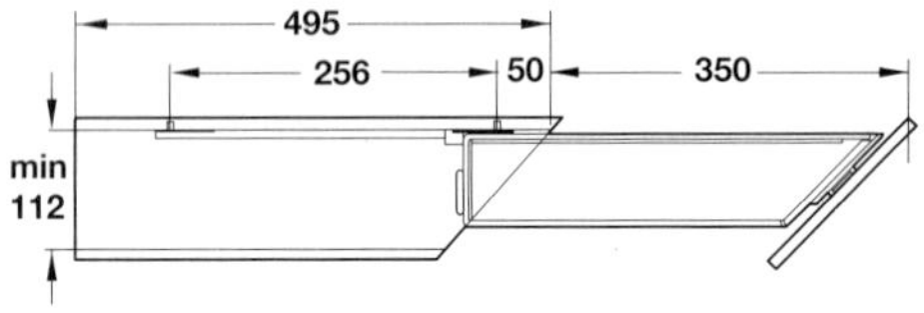

Base cabinet pull-out system
Minimum inside cabinet width: 112 mm (4 1/2")
Minimum inside cabinet depth: 495 mm (19 1/2")
Minimum inside cabinet height: 580 mm (22 3/4")
width x depth x height =
104 x 466 x 541 mm (4 1/8" x 18 3/8" x 21 1/4")
complete with slides and front connections
Finish: steel, chrome-plated

		Cat. No.
45°	left	545.61.221
	right	545.61.220
90°*	left	545.61.211
	right	545.61.210

Packing: 1 pc.
(not shown)

Refrigerator Door Attachment Mechanism

- The action of the sliding mechanism allows you to open the cabinet door while the appliance door is being opened.

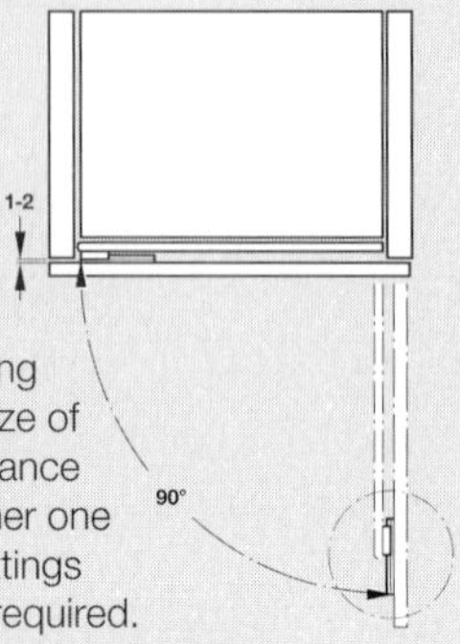

Depending on the size of the appliance door either one or two fittings may be required.

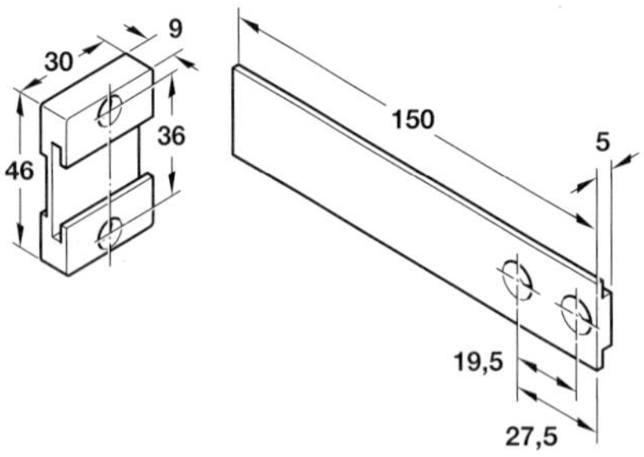

Mechanism for attaching an appliance door to a hinged front panel.
Finish: plastic, brown

Cat. No.	568.16.007

Packing: 1 set (4 fastening screws included)

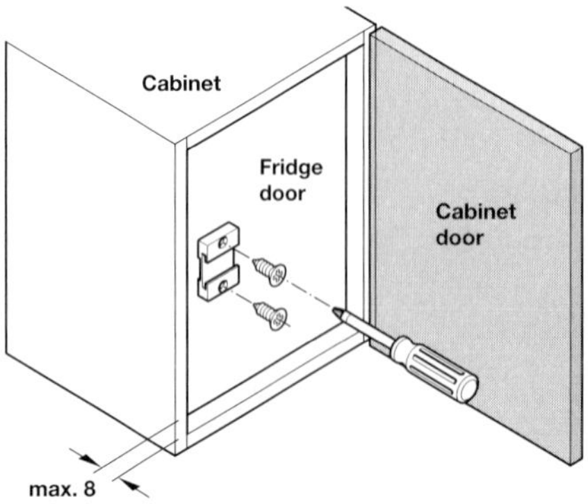

Attach the guide to the outer side of the refrigerator door.

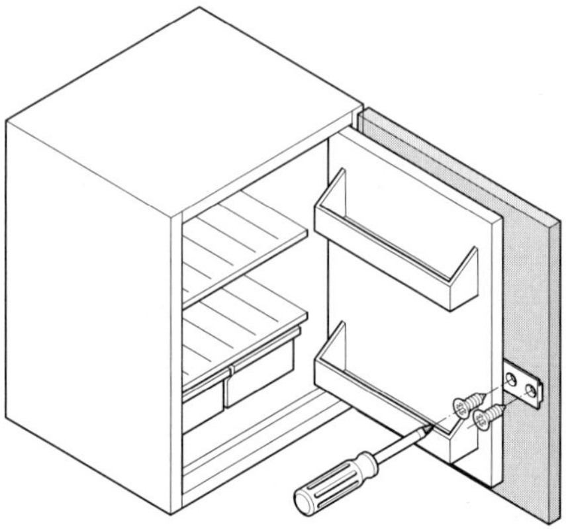

Open the refrigerator door to 90° and insert the rail into the guide. Now screw on the rail perfectly level to the inner side of the cabinet door.

Dimensions in mm
Inches are approximate

Base Cabinet Pull-Outs

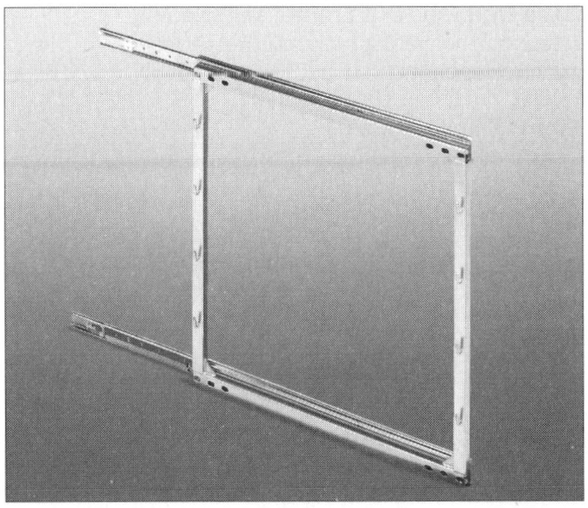

Base Unit Pull-Out Frame, self-closing

inside cabinet width: basket width + 33 mm (1 1/4")
inside cabinet depth: min. 500 mm (19 3/4")

Frame Dimensions:
Depth: 480 mm (18 1/2")
Width: 37 mm (1 1/2")
Finish: steel, epoxy coated

silver, RAL 9006

Inside cabinet Height min. mm (inch)	Height frame	Cat. No. Left	Right
510 (20)	500 mm	545.59.241	545.59.251
610 (24)	600 mm	545.59.242	545.59.252
680 (26 7/8)	668 mm	545.59.243	545.59.253

white, RAL 9010

Inside cabinet Height min. mm (inch)	Height frame	Cat. No. Left	Right
510 (20)	500 mm	545.59.741	545.59.751
610 (24)	600 mm	545.59.742	545.59.752
680 (26 7/8)	668 mm	545.59.743	545.59.753

Packing: 1 pc.

Left

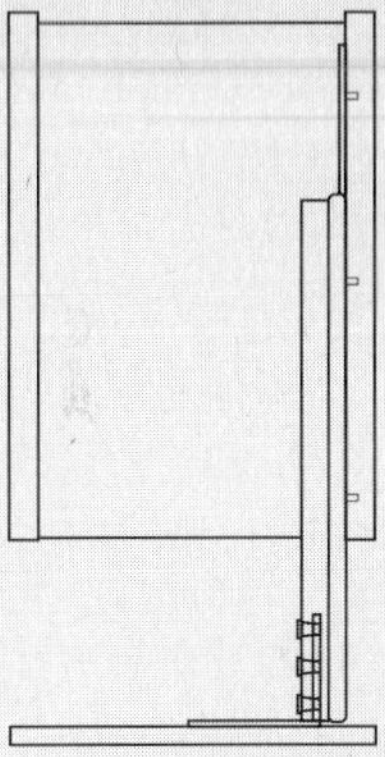

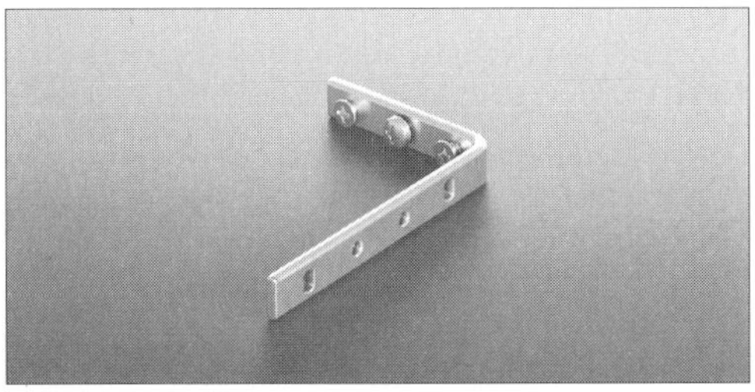

Front Bracket

Finish: steel, epoxy coated

Angle	Silver, epoxy RAL 9006	White RAL 9010
90°	545.59.293	545.59.793

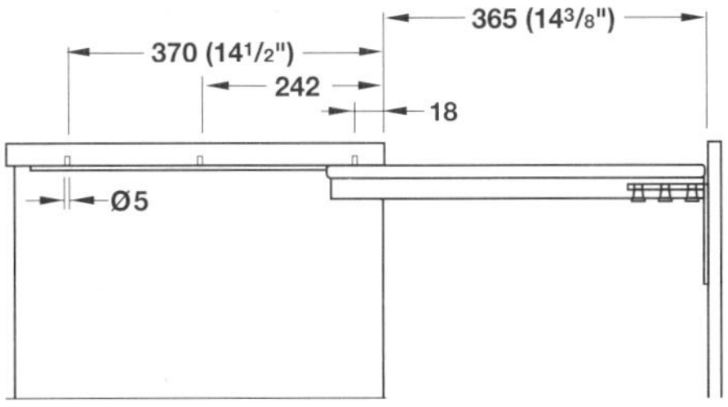

Kitchen Accessory Systems **5**

Right

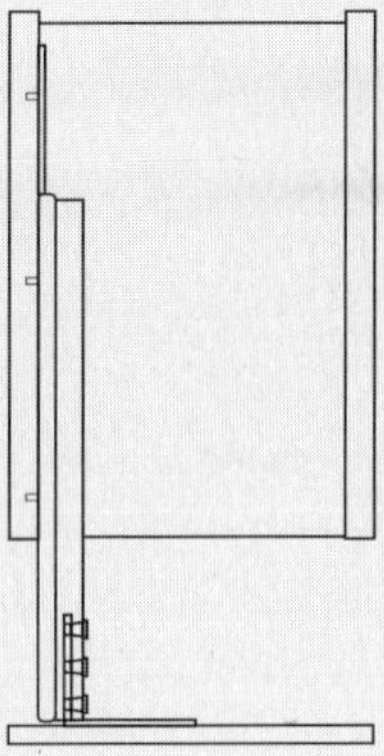

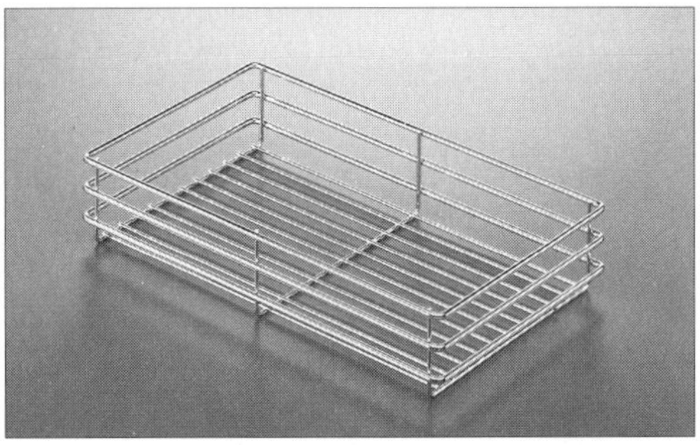

Storage Basket

Basket dimensions:
Width: 470 mm (18 1/2")
Height: 75 mm (3")
Finish: steel, chrome-plated

Width mm (inch)	Cat. No.
110 (4 3/8)	545.60.208
160 (6 1/4)	545.60.217
210 (8 1/4)	545.60.244
320 (12 1/2)	545.60.253

Packing: 1 pc.

Storage Basket

Basket dimensions:
Width: 480 mm (18 7/8")
Height: 75 mm (3")
Finish: steel, epoxy coated
white RAL 9010

Width mm (inch)	Cat. No.
110 (4 3/8)	545.52.019
160 (6 1/4)	545.52.028
190 (7 1/2)	545.52.037
220 (8 5/8)	545.76.313
310 (12 1/4)	545.52.046

Packing: 1 pc.

Dimensions in mm
Inches are approximate

HÄFELE

Base Cabinet Pull-Outs

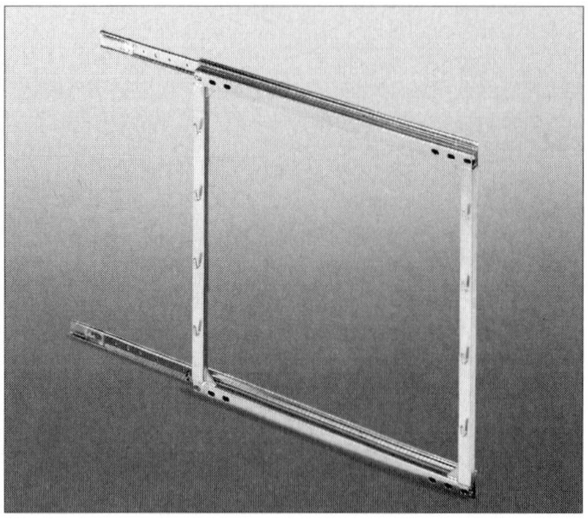

Base Unit Pull-Out Frame, self-closing

inside cabinet width: min. 262 mm (10³/₈")
inside cabinet depth: min. 500 mm (19³/₄")

Frame Dimensions
Depth: 480 mm (18¹/₂")
Width: 37 mm (1¹/₂")
Finish: Steel, epoxy coated

silver, RAL 9006

Inside cabinet Height min. mm	Height frame	Left	Right
510 (20")	500 mm	545.59.241	545.59.251
610 (24")	600 mm	545.59.242	545.59.252
680 (26⁷/₈")	668 mm	545.59.243	545.59.253

white, RAL 9010

Inside cabinet Height min. mm	Height frame	Left	Right
510 (20")	500 mm	545.59.741	545.59.751
610 (24")	600 mm	545.59.742	545.59.752
680 (26⁷/₈")	668 mm	545.59.743	545.59.753

Packing: 1 pc.

Left

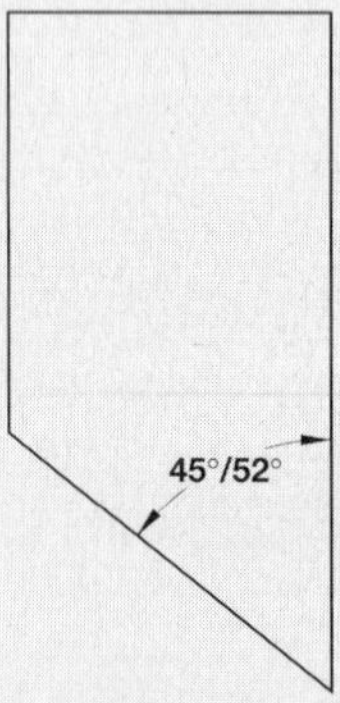

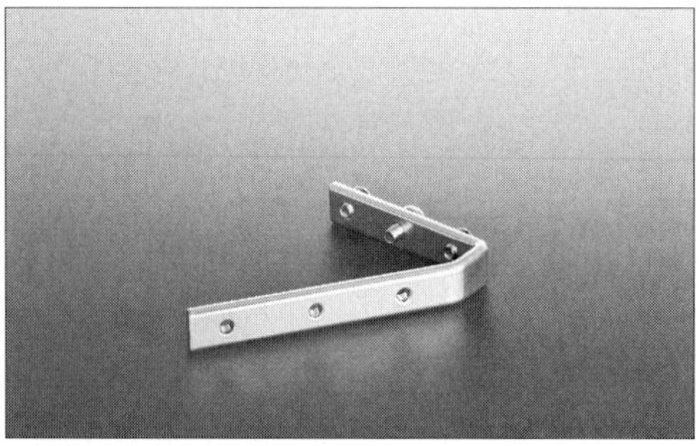

Front Bracket

Finish: steel, epoxy coated

Angle	Silver RAL 9006	White RAL 9010
55°	545.59.292	545.59.792
45°	545.59.291	545.59.791

Packing: 1 pc.

5 Kitchen Accessory Systems

Right

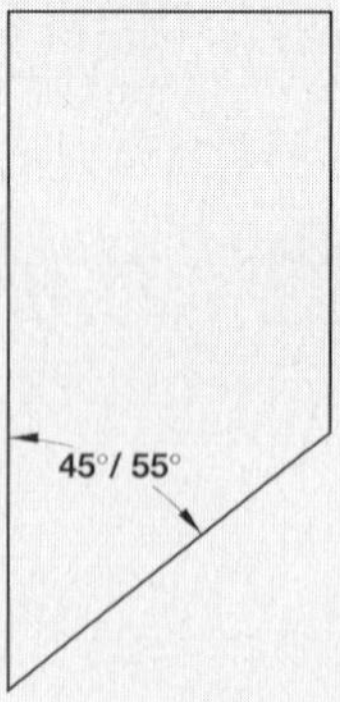

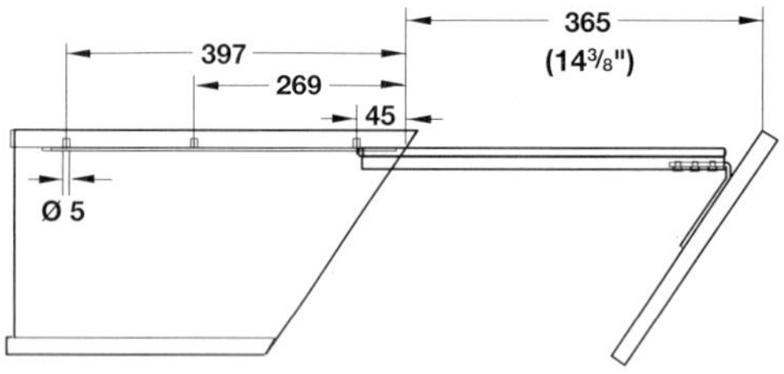

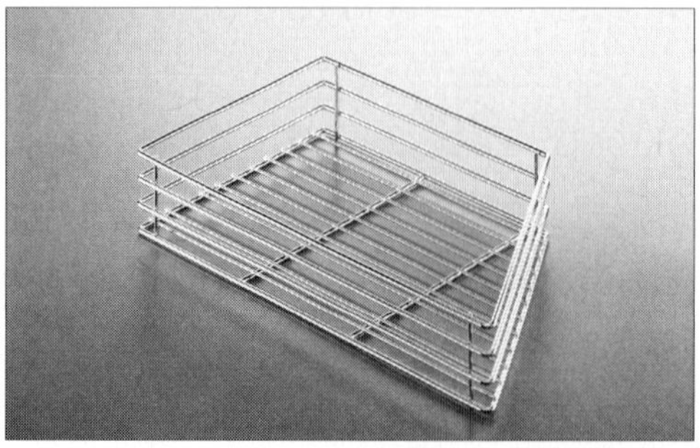

Storage Basket

Size: 228 x 467 x 74 mm (L x W x H)
Finish: steel

For Angle		chrome-plated	epoxy coated white RAL 9010
55°	right	545.60.226	545.60.726
	left	545.60.235	545.60.735
45°	right	545.60.224	545.60.724
	left	545.60.234	545.60.734

Packing: 1 pc.

Dimensions in mm
Inches are approximate

Dimensional data not binding.
We reserve the right to alter specifications without notice.

HÄFELE

Base Cabinet Storage Drawers

4-sided wire-fence, hinged, 120 mm (4¾") high x 550 mm (21⅝") deep
Finish: steel, epoxy coated or plated

Cab. Size	Actual Width	Cat. No. white	Cat. No. chrome plated
15 in.	301 mm	540.87.713	540.87.213
18 in.	377 mm	540.87.722	540.87.222
21 in.	453 mm	540.87.731	540.87.231
24 in.	511 mm	540.87.740	540.87.240
27 in.	588 mm	540.87.759	540.87.259
30 in.	664 mm	540.87.768	540.87.268
33 in.	740 mm	540.87.777	540.87.277
36 in.	816 mm	540.87.786	540.87.286
39 in.	890 mm	540.87.795	540.87.295
42 in.	969 mm	540.87.802	540.87.302

Packing: 1 pc.

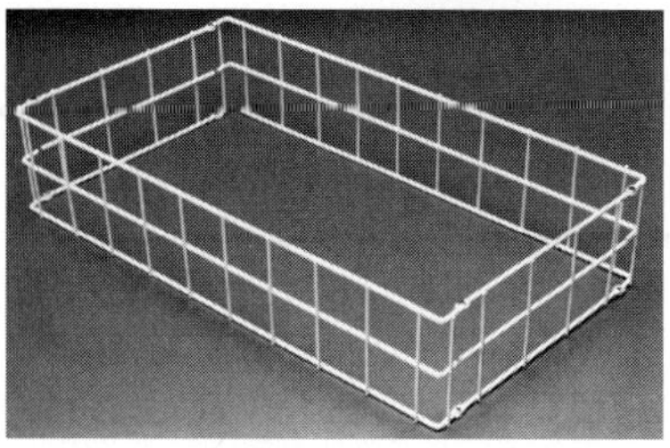

- Designed for U.S. cabinet widths 15-42 inches.
- Ideal for use in base cabinets behind doors

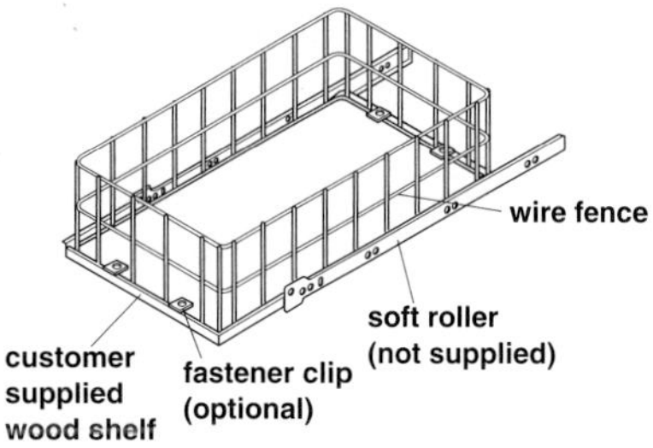

Slides are not supplied and must be ordered separately. For fastening frames to pullout shelves we recommend fasteners below

---

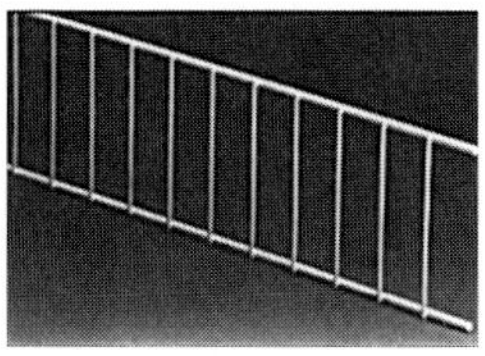

Wire fence, can be cut to size.
2110 mm (83") length x160 mm (6¼") height
Finish: steel, epoxy coated, white

Cat. No.	540.99.731

Packing: 1 pc.

Kitchen Accessory Systems 5

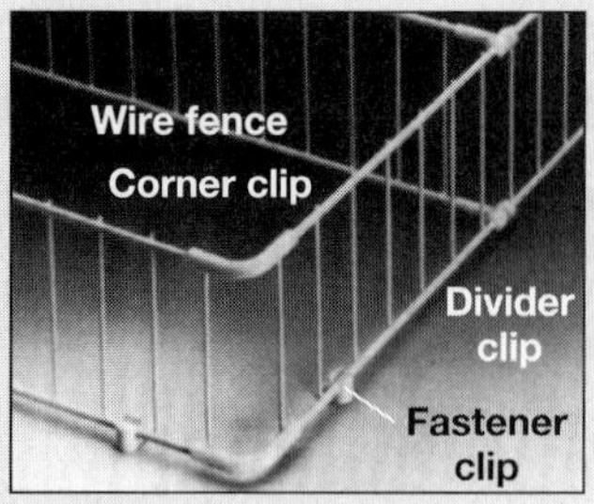

- Required length can be cut to size

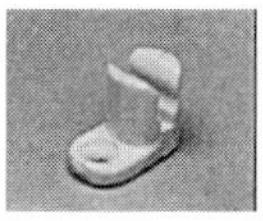

Fastener clip
screw-mounted
Finish: plastic, white

Cat. No.	540.67.711

Packing: 100 pcs.

Fastening clip press-fit
Finish: plastic, white

Cat. No.	540.67.702

Packing: 100 pcs.

Fastener block
screw-mounted
Finish: plastic, white

Cat. No.	540.67.720

Packing: 100 pcs.

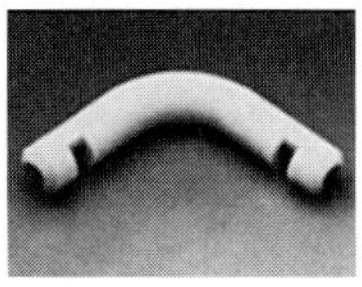

Corner clip to connect the wire frame 540.99.731 at right angles
Finish: plastic, white

Cat. No.	540.99.795

Packing: 100 pcs.

Divider clip
Finish: plastic, white

Cat. No.	545.87.601

Packing: 100 pcs.

Dimensions in mm
Inches are approximate

Dimensional data not binding. We reserve the right to alter specifications without notice.

HÄFELE

Wire Basket Pull-Out Storage System

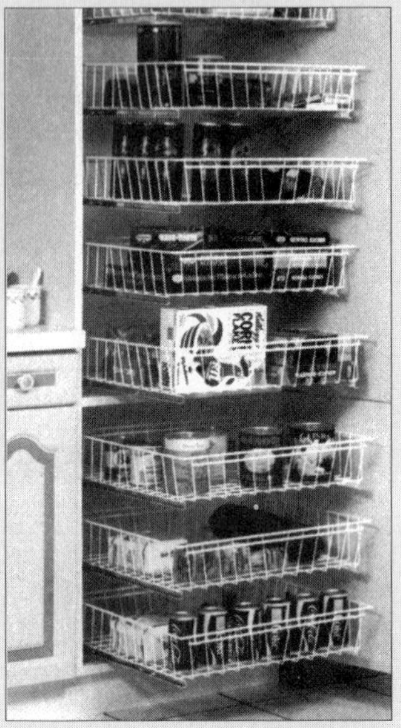

Complete with Soft-Roller drawer runners.

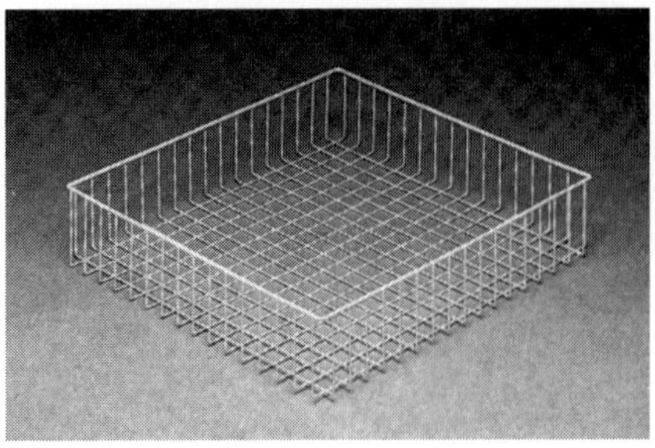

Wire basket pull-out storage system sets
cabinet depth min. 550 mm (21 5/8").
complete with 1 basket, 1 pair Soft-Roller drawer runners, 8 basket fixing brackets with Hospa-screws, 4 spacers, 15 mm thick.
Load capacity: 20 kg (44 lbs.)
Soft-Roller extension length: 447 mm (17 5/8")
Finish: steel/steel-wire, epoxy-coated, white
brackets and spacers: plastic, white

Installation width* mm	inch	Overall width mm	inch	Cat. No.
255	10	242	9 1/2	540.20.718
331	13	318	12 1/2	540.20.727
407	16	394	15 1/2	540.20.736
483	19	470	18 1/2	540.20.745

Packing: 1 set

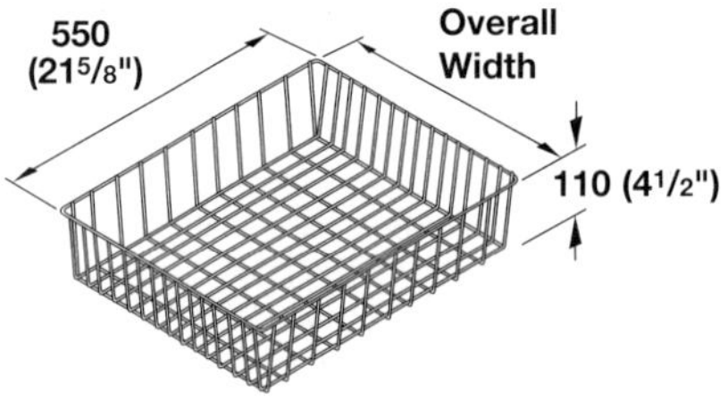

*** Installed width without spacers. The spacers permit the system installation width to be expanded on each side from 3 mm to 21 mm (max.).**

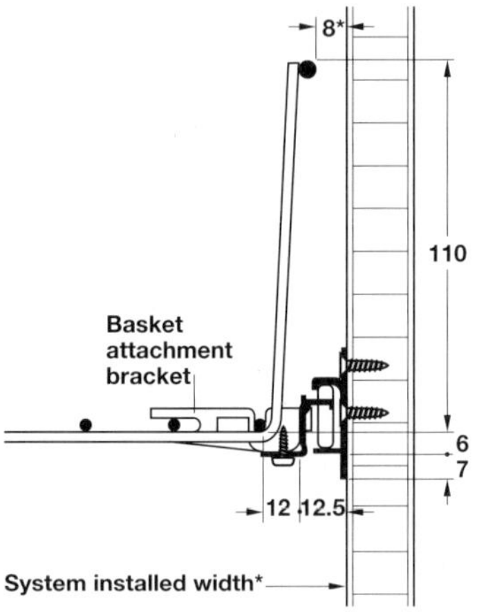

5 Kitchen Accessory Systems

Optional bottom-mount bracket
For Soft-Roller drawer runners bracket.
4 each required per basket.
Finish: steel, plastic-coated, white

Cat. No.	540.20.905

Packing: per set of 4 pcs.
with screws

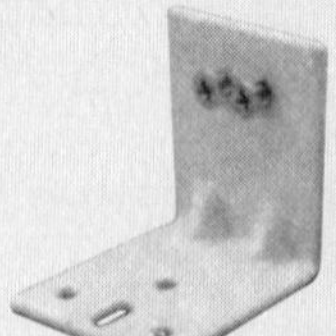

Stackable spacers
for adequate clearance for the projecting door hinges on the hinge-side of the cabinet

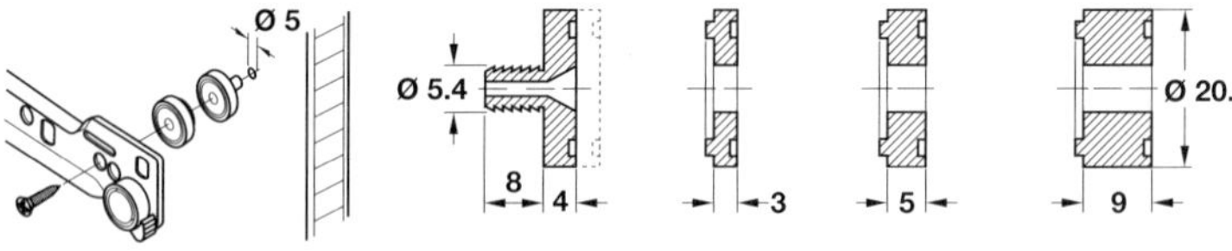

Finish: plastic, white

Cap thickness:	4 mm	3 mm	5 mm	9 mm
Cat. No.	037.93.708	037.93.717	037.93.726	037.93.735

Packing: 100 pcs

Total spacer thickness not to exceed 21 mm

Dimensional data not binding.
We reserve the right to alter specifications without notice.

Dimensions in mm
Inches are approximate

HÄFELE

Wire Basket Pull Outs

Wire basket with steel rim for 24" inside cabinet width, with use of optional 423.35 slides only.

586 (23") width x 300 (11⅞") depth

Height mm	Packing	Cat. No.
200 (7⅞")	10 pcs.	540.41.717
300 (11⅞")	10 pcs.	540.41.726
500 (19⅞")	5 pcs.	540.41.735

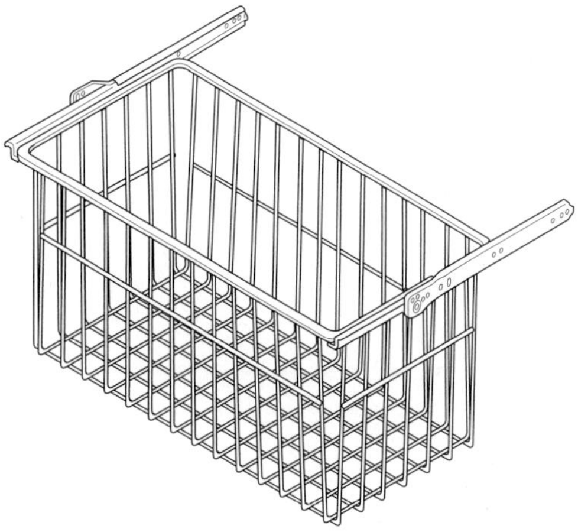

586 (23") width x 350 (13⅞") depth

Height mm	Packing	Cat. No.
100 (4")	10 pcs.	540.41.646
200 (7⅞")	10 pcs.	540.41.655
300 (11⅞")	5 pcs.	540.41.664
500 (19⅞")	5 pcs.	540.41.673

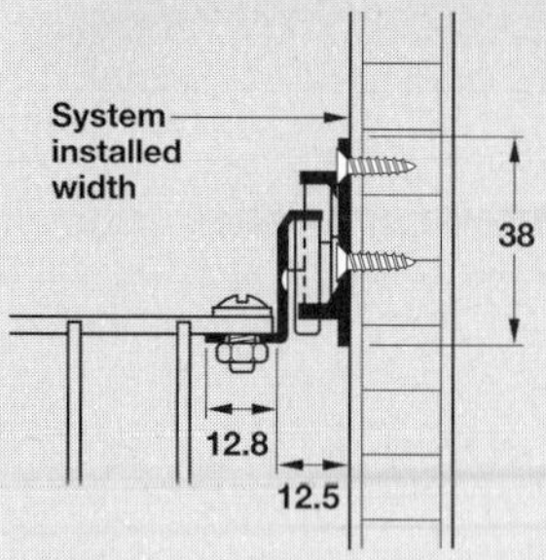

586 (23") width x 400 (15¾") depth

Height mm	Packing	Cat. No.
100 (4")	10 pcs.	540.41.744
200 (7⅞")	10 pcs.	540.41.753
300 (11⅞")	5 pcs.	540.41.762
500 (19⅞")	5 pcs.	540.41.771

Screws and nuts for attaching baskets to rollers

M4 Screw x 10mm Length

Cat. No.	022.35.109

Packing: 100 and 1000 pcs.

M4 Nuts

Cat. No.	034.11.943

Packing: 100 pcs.

Six screws and nuts required per basket

Softroller Slider
for basket Catalog No. 540.41.
Load Bearing Capacity: 30kg (66lbs.)/pair
Finish: Steel, epoxy coated, white
rollers, nylon, white

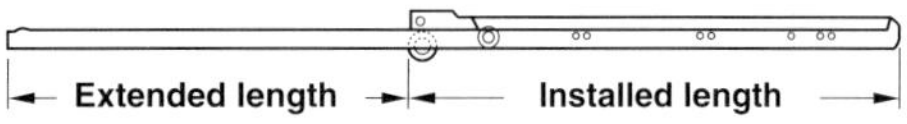

Installed length	300 mm	350 mm	400 mm
Extension length	212 mm	262 mm	312 mm
Cat. No. (non self-closing)	423.35.311	423.35.366	423.35.419
Cat. No. (self-closing)	423.36.318	423.36.363	423.36.416

Packing: 20 pairs

Kitchen Accessory Systems 5

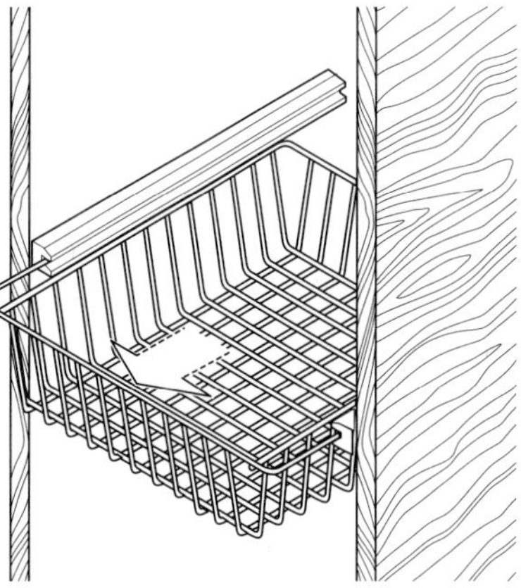

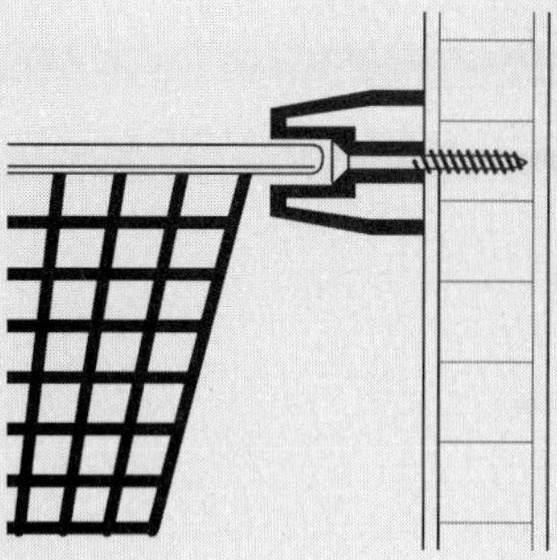

Wire basket with rim for use with 430.34 series track
Height: 120 mm (4¾")
Finish: steel wire, epoxy-coated, white

Width mm	Depth mm	Cat. No.
380 (15")	430 (17")	540.46.025
430 (17")	430 (17")	540.46.052
450 (17¾")	450 (17¾")	540.46.061
530 (20⅞")	430 (17")	540.46.007
380 (15")	450 (17¾")	540.46.089
495 (19½")	500 (19⅝")	540.46.098

Packing: 1 pc.

- Baskets can be slid out from cabinets with doors due to extra width of guide rail track.

Tracks for wire baskets Cat. No. 540.46 series
Length: 430 mm (17")
Finish: plastic, white

Width	Cat. No.
26 mm	430.34.726
24 mm	430.34.724
18 mm	430.34.718

Packing: 1 pair

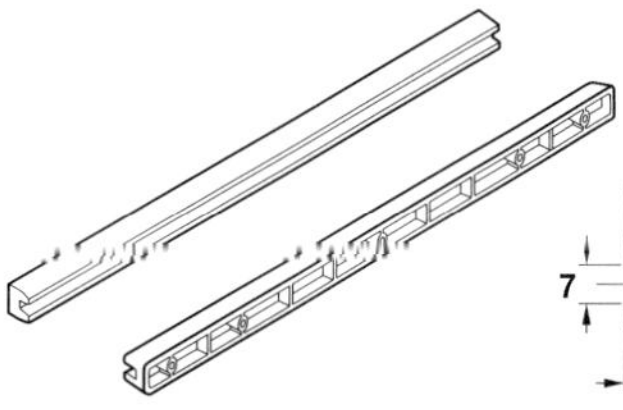

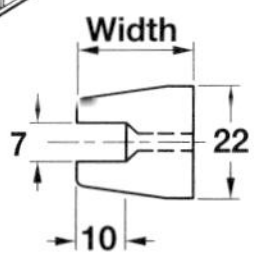

Dimensional data not binding. We reserve the right to alter specifications without notice.

Dimensions in mm
Inches are approximate

HÄFELE

Wire Basket Pull-out Systems

Overall height including slide = basket height + 15 mm

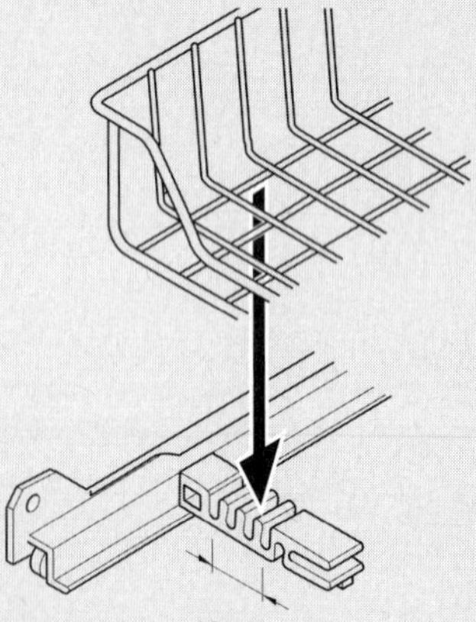

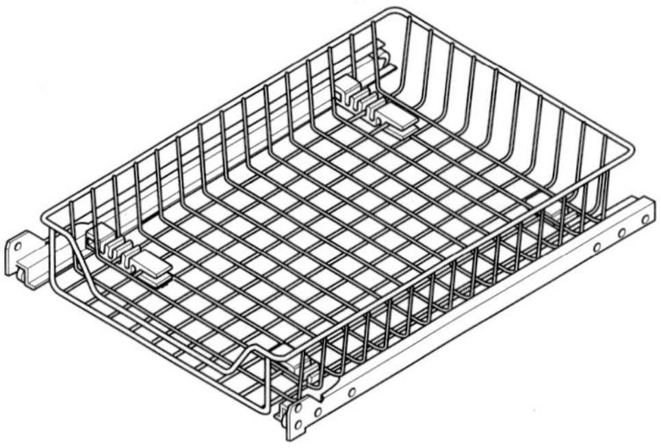

Pull-out baskets low front
and special width adjustable (+/- 16 mm) softroller slides that clip onto the bottom of the basket. Installed depth 500 mm (19 3/4") load capacity approximately 15 kg (33 lb.)

Finish:		
	basket:	steel, chrome-plated
	cabinet slide	steel, plastic coated white RAL 9010
	drawer slide:	steel, plastic coated silver RAL 9006

for outside cabinet width (mm) inch	basket size width x depth x height (mm)	for inside widths from to	Cat. No.
300 11 3/4"	226 x 500 x 80	243-273	547.04.228
400 15 3/4"	330 x 500 x 80	343-378	547.04.237
450 17 3/4"	390 x 500 x 80	403-438	547.04.246
500 19 3/4"	428 x 500 x 80	444-468	547.04.255
550 21 5/8"	488 x 500 x 80	498-528	547.04.264
600 23 5/8"	530 x 500 x 80	539-558	547.04.273

Packing: 1 pc.

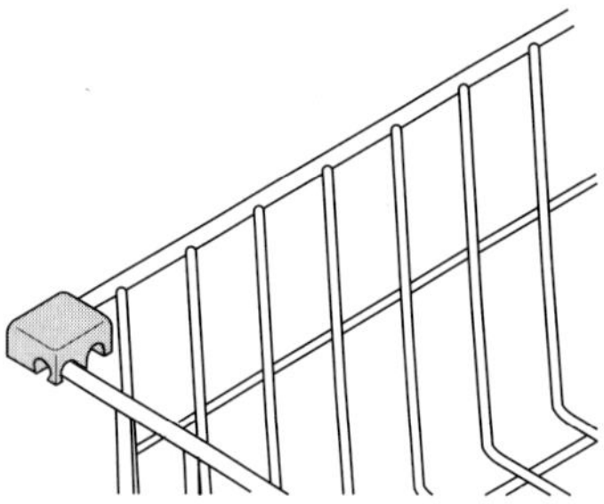

Door guard
for baskets, can be used left or right
Finish: plastic

Color	white
Cat. No.	547.08.708

Packing: 10 pcs.

Dimensions in mm
Inches are approximate

Base Cabinet Storage Drawers

HÄFELE

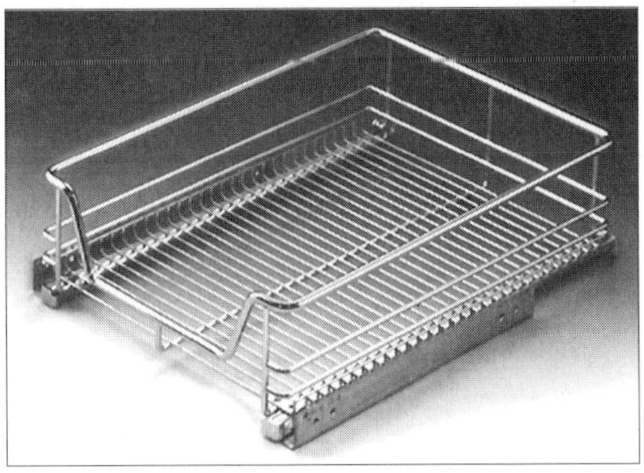

Internal drawer basket
- lower front and ball bearing runners
- Load carrying capacity: **40 kg (88 lbs)**
- Installation depth 495 mm (19½")

Finish: body: steel, chrome plated
runners: steel, galvanized

inside cabinet width	Drawer body W x D x H (mm)	Cat. No.
400 (15¾")	345 x 476 x 120	540.25.222
450 (17¾")	395 x 476 x 120	540.25.231
500 (19¾")	445 x 476 x 120	540.25.240
600 (23⅝")	545 x 476 x 120	540.25.259

Packing: 1 pc.

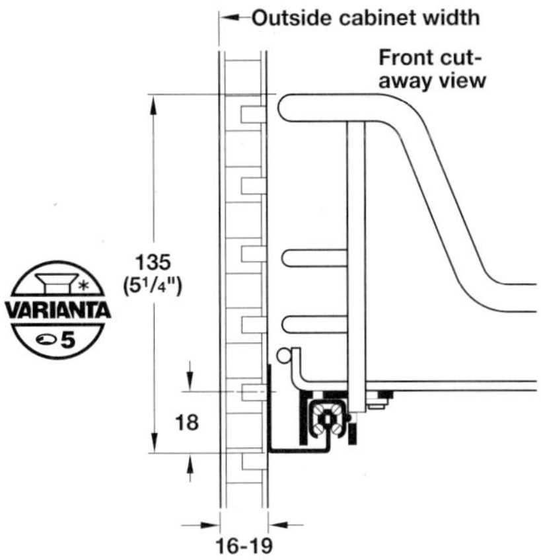

Horizontal adjustment of 3 mm on each side permits installation in cabinets with 16–19 mm thick side panels.

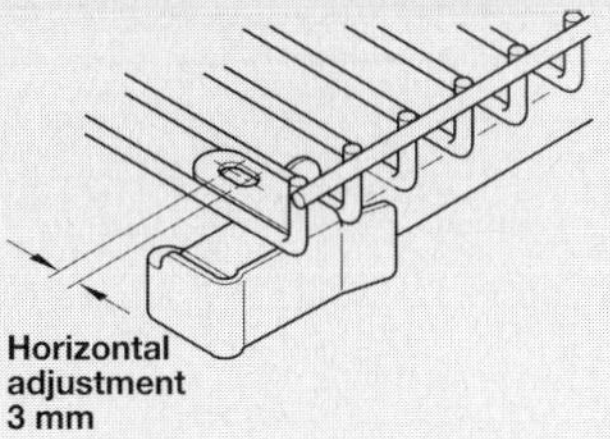

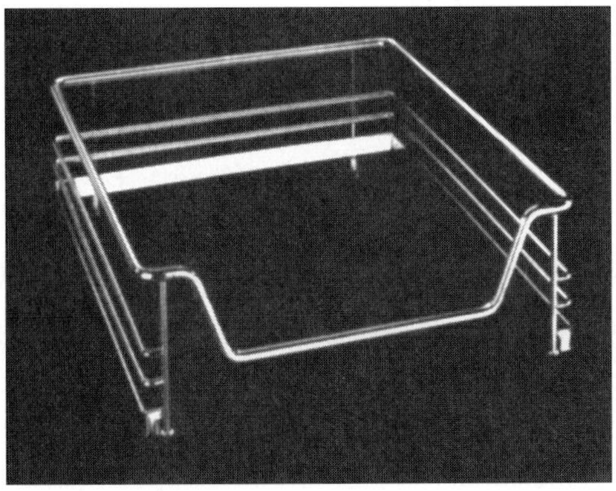

4 Sided chrome wire fence
to be mounted on a pull-out shelf (not supplied)
Finish: steel, chrome plated

Width mm	Cat. No.
345 (13½")	540.96.043
395 (15½")	540.96.052
445 (17½")	540.96.061
545 (21½")	540.96.070

Packing: 1 pc.

Kitchen Accessory Systems **5**

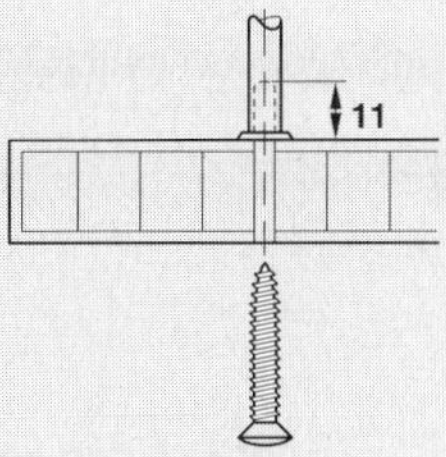

Wire fences are secured to wood shelves with **raised head screws**
Size: Ø 4.2 x 32 mm
Finish: steel, galvanized

Cat. No.	023.27.460

Packing: 100 pcs.

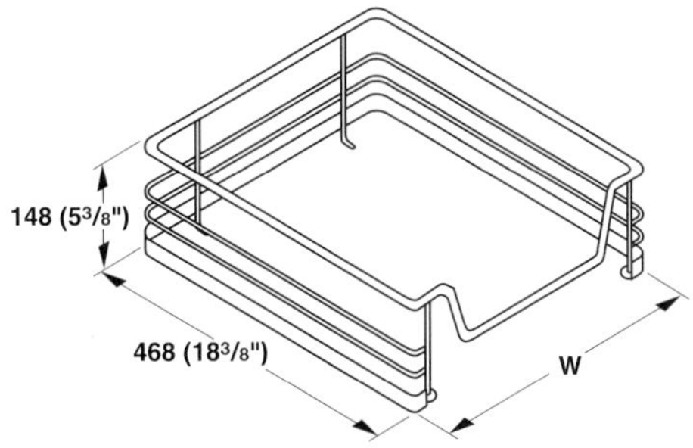

Dimensions in mm
Inches are approximate

HÄFELE

Base Cabinet Storage Drawers

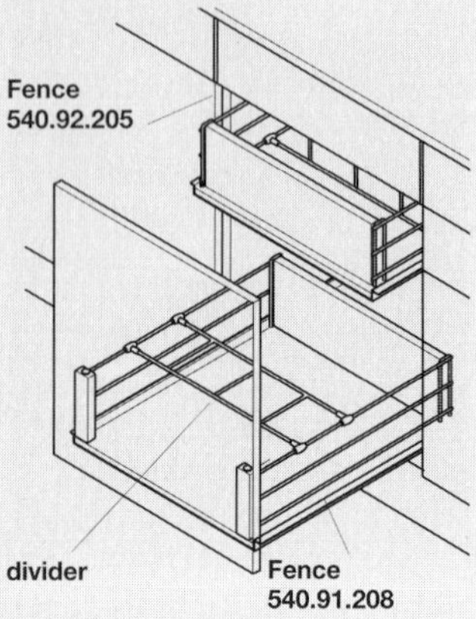

Mounting procedure:

1. Cut drawer base and rear panel to size, making allowance for intended drawer runner type.
2. Secure fence to drawer bottom with raised head metal screws.
3. Secure fence to rear panel. The latter must be secured to the drawer bottom with at least 2 screws to prevent twisting.
4. In case of concealed inner drawers with fence 540.92.205, both drawer fronts and rear panels should be secured as in point 3 above.
5. Secure mounting bracket to drawer front to connect with 3-D bracket on fence.
6. Install and adjust drawer front.

Raised head crossslot metal screws
with cross slots
Size: Ø 4,2 x 32 mm
Finish: steel, nickel-plated

Cat. No.	023.27.460

Packing: 100 pcs.

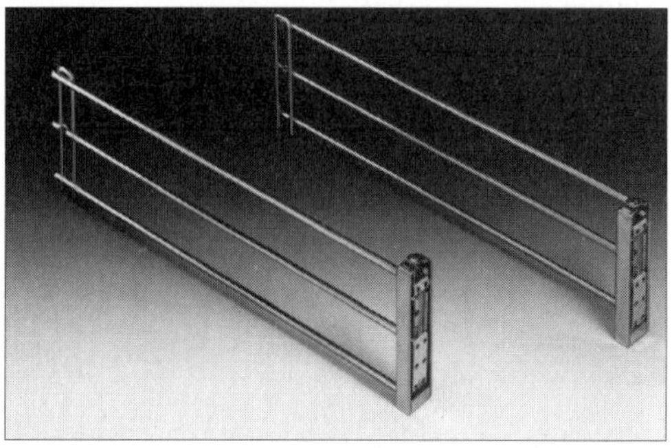

Wire fence with front brackets to attach drawer front. Mounted to drawer bottom, front and rear panel (not supplied)
Without drawer runners.
Finish: steel, chrome-plated

Dimensions mm	inches	Cat. No.
500 x 136	19¾ x 5⅜"	540.91.208

Packing: 1 pair

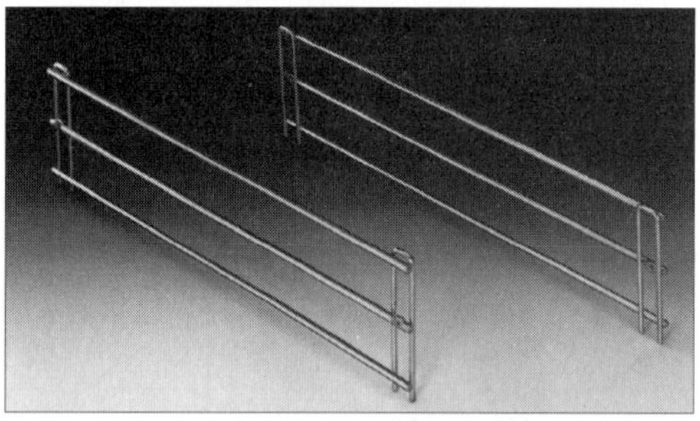

Wire fence with screw-eyes to secure drawer-front and rear panel. Used on a concealed, inner drawer
Finish: steel, chrome-plated

Dimensions mm	inches	Cat. No.
500 x 136	19¾ x 5⅜"	540.92.205

Packing: 2 pcs.

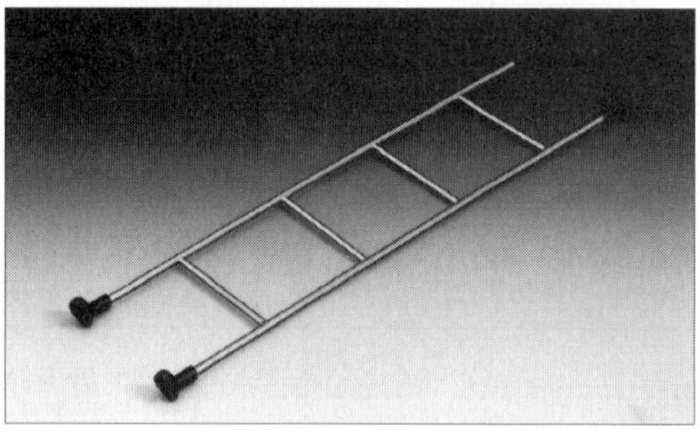

Transverse divider with bottle compartments
Clips into side fences.
Finish: clips: plastic;
bars: steel wire, chrome plated

Cabinet width mm	Dimensions (mm)	Cat. No.
450 (17¾")	399 x 128	540.93.248
500 (19¾")	449 x 128	540.93.257
600 (23⅝")	549 x 128	540.93.266

Packing: 1 pc.

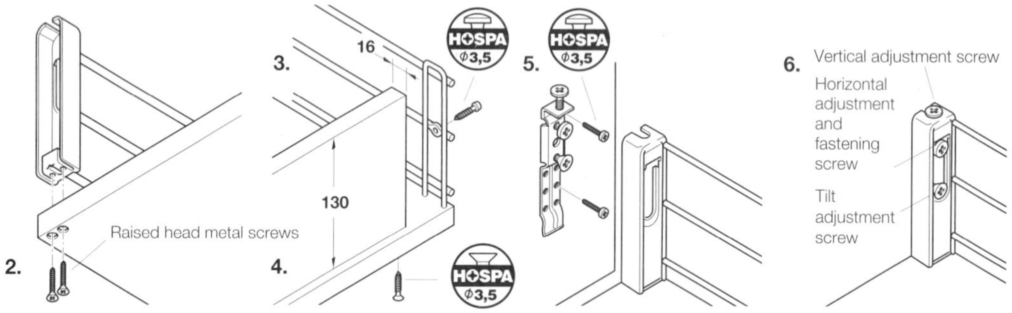

Kitchen canisters
Finish: plastic, white

Size	Width x Depth x Height mm	Cat. No.
1 (small)	185 x 235 x 150 (7½ x 9¼ x 5⅞")	556.71.719
2 (medium)	235 x 285 x 150 (9¼ x 11¼ x 5⅞")	556.71.728
3 (large)	235 x 470 x 150 (9¼ x 18½ x 5⅞")	556.71.737

Packing: 1 pc.

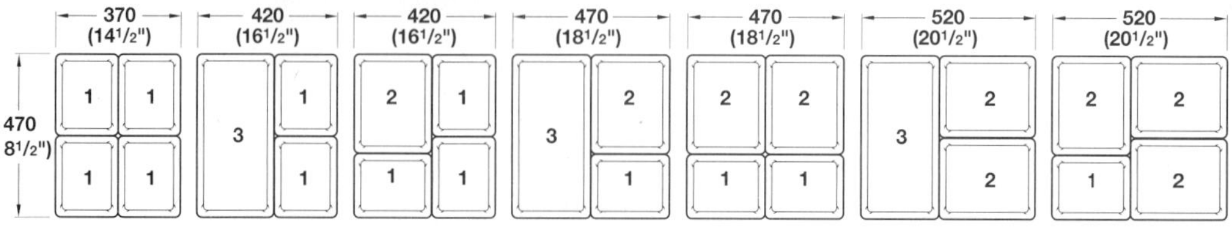

Dimensional data not binding.
We reserve the right to alter specifications without notice.

Metal Drawer Slides

HÄFELE

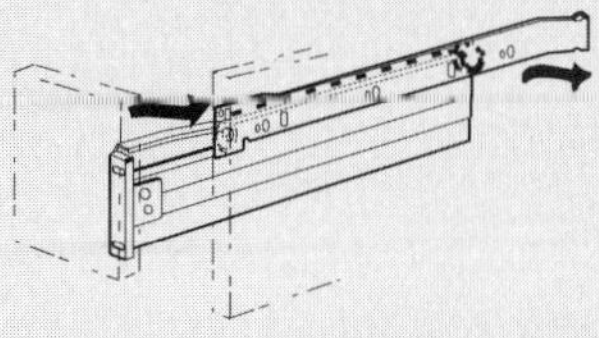

Self-closing, single-extension
Drawer height - 86 mm
Material: steel, epoxy-coated
Load capacity: 20 kg (44 lbs)

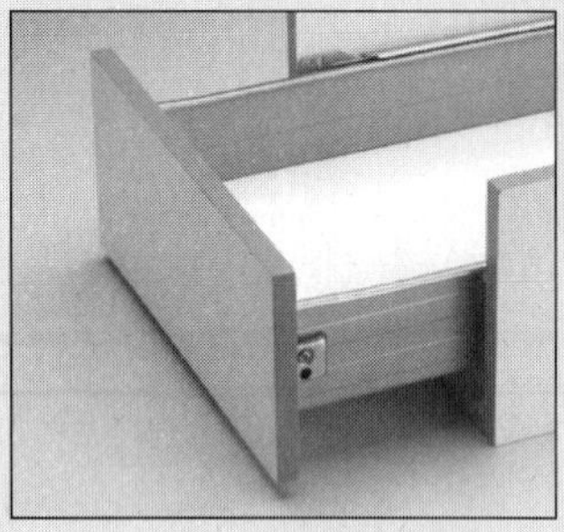

- Use in kitchen and bath drawers, laboratory drawers.
- European design elegant lock.
- Easy installation, no need for drawer sides.
- Front adjustment bracket ±2mm
- Screw on or dowel mounting for easy assembly.

Standard, screw mounted

Color	Height	Length	Cat. No.
white	86 mm	450 mm (17 3/4")	559.71.750
white	86 mm	500 mm (19 3/4")	559.71.769
white	86 mm	550 mm (21 3/4")	559.71.770

silver	86 mm	450 mm (17 3/4")	559.71.956
silver	86 mm	500 mm (19 3/4")	559.71.965

Packing: 1 set = 2 cabinet members
2 drawer sides
2 front mounting brackets

10 sets per box

Automatic, dowel-mounted 10 mm dowels

Color	Height	Length	Cat. No.
white	86 mm	450 mm (17 3/4")	559.71.652
white	86 mm	500 mm (19 3/4")	559.71.661
white	86 mm	550 mm (21 3/4")	559.71.670

silver	86 mm	450 mm (17 3/4")	559.71.858
silver	86 mm	500 mm (19 3/4")	559.71.867

Packing: 1 set = 2 cabinet members
2 drawer sides
2 front mounting brackets

10 sets per box

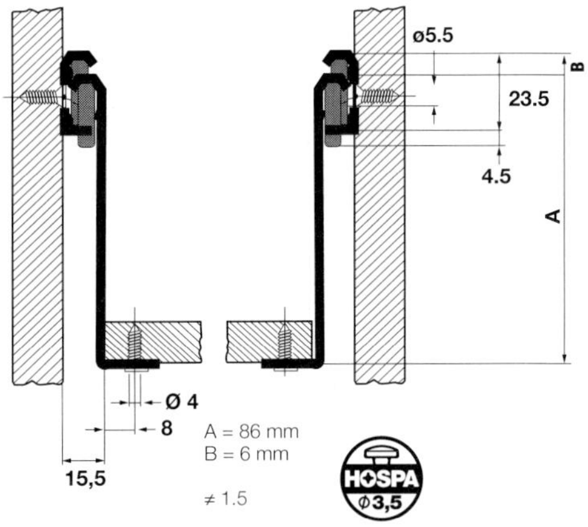

Kitchen Accessory Systems

5

Dimensional data not binding.
We reserve the right to alter specifications without notice.

Dimensions in mm
Inches are approximate

HÄFELE

Vinyl Wrapped Drawer Profiles

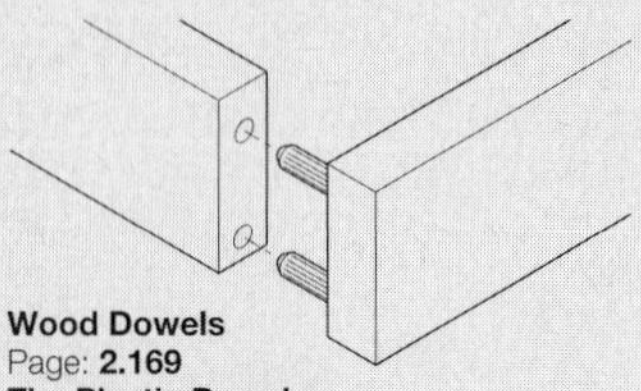

Wood Dowels
Page: **2.169**
The Plastic Dowel
Page: **2.168**

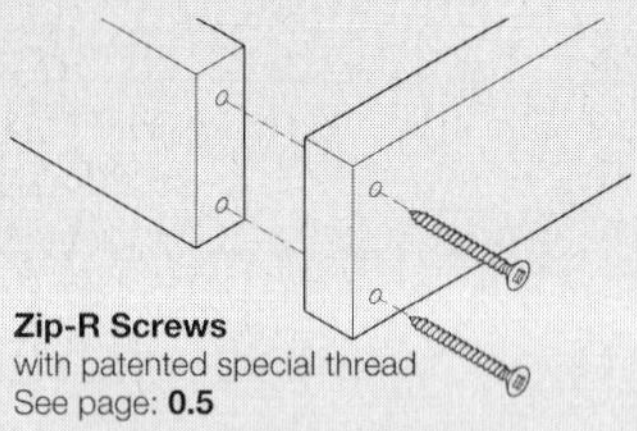

Zip-R Screws
with patented special thread
See page: **0.5**

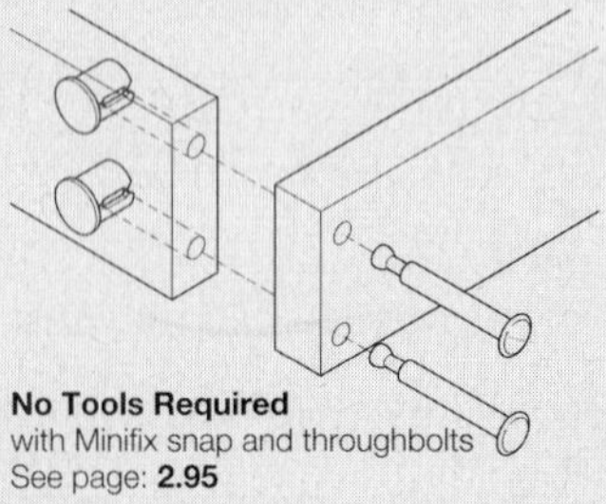

No Tools Required
with Minifix snap and throughbolts
See page: **2.95**

5 Kitchen Accessory Systems

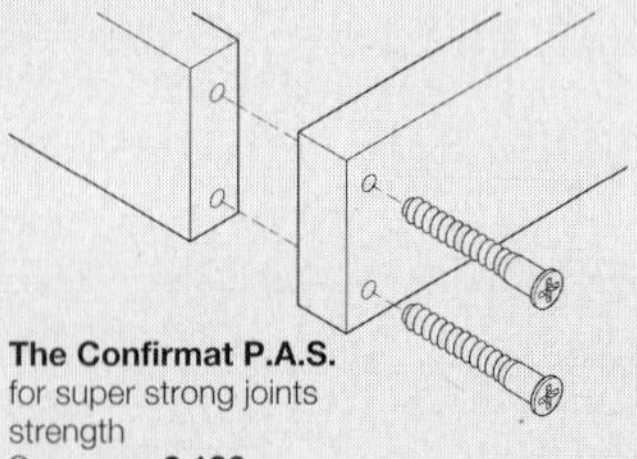

The Confirmat P.A.S.
for super strong joints
strength
See page: **2.136**

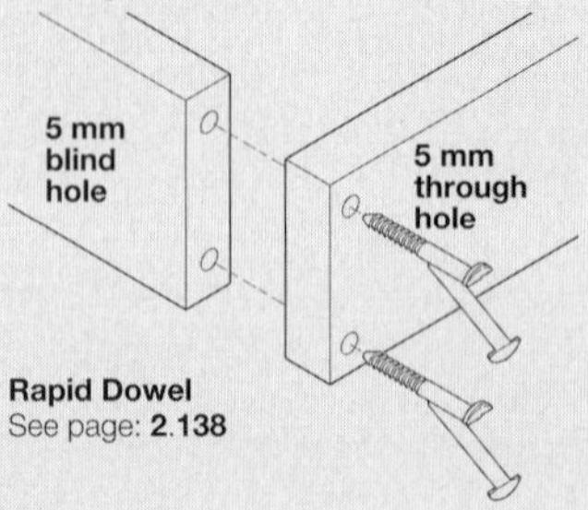

Rapid Dowel
See page: **2.138**

Without Slide Groove

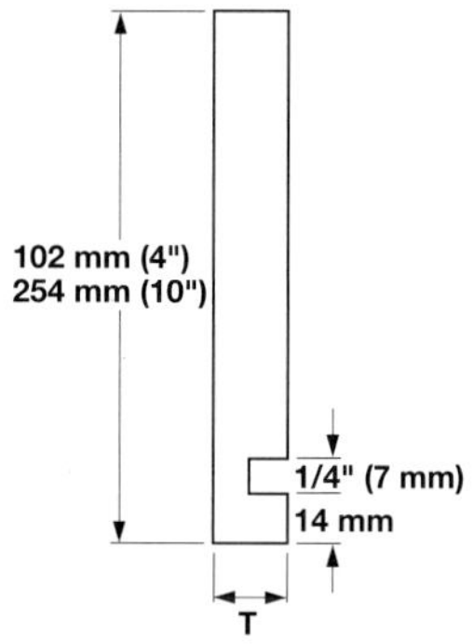

Rigid PVC vinyl: gauge 0.008
Adhesive: vinyl acetate copolymer emulsion

Height	Thickness T	Length	Cat. No. white	Cat. No. wood grain
102 mm (4")	1/2"	4'	557.60.711	557.60.611
254 mm (10")	1/2"	4'	557.60.712	557.60.612
102 mm (4")	5/8"	4'	557.60.721	557.60.621
254 mm (10")	5/8"	4'	557.60.722	557.60.622

Packing: 5 pcs. (ea. 4')

With 17 mm Groove

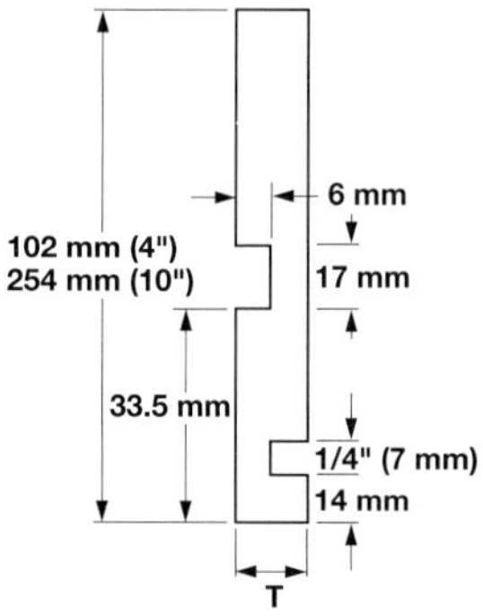

Rigid PVC vinyl: gauge 0.008
Adhesive: vinyl acetate copolymer emulsion

Height	Thickness T	Length	Cat. No. white	Cat. No. wood grain
102 mm (4")	1/2"	4'	557.61.711	557.61.611
254 mm (10")	1/2"	4'	557.61.712	557.61.612
102 mm (4")	5/8"	4'	557.61.721	557.61.621
254 mm (10")	5/8"	4'	557.61.722	557.61.622

Packing: 5 pcs. (ea. 4')

Pre-finished Wood Drawer Profiles
Without Slide Groove

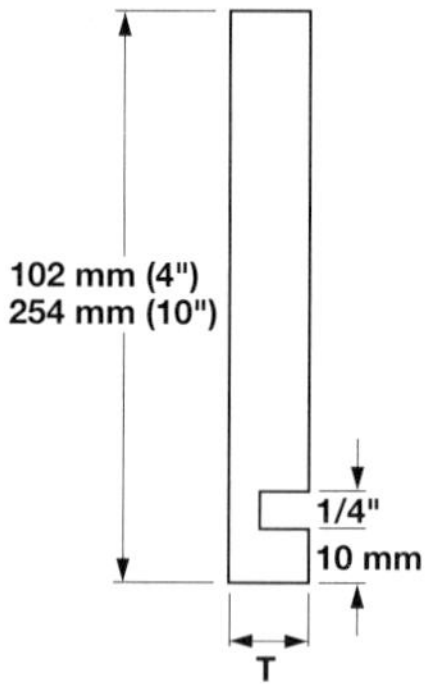

7 ply hardwood, plywood veneer core construction
with ultraviolet cured flatline finish.

Height	Thickness T	Length	Cat. No. maple	Cat. No. red oak
102 mm (4")	1/2"	4'	557.60.111	557.60.311
254 mm (10")	1/2"	4'	557.60.112	557.60.312
102 mm (4")	5/8"	4'	557.60.121	557.60.321
254 mm (10")	5/8"	4'	557.60.122	557.60.322

Packing: 5 pcs. (ea. 4')

Availabe on request: custom heights, lengths, drilling,
colors. Minimum order: 1000 pcs.

Dimensions in mm
Inches are approximate

Waste Bins

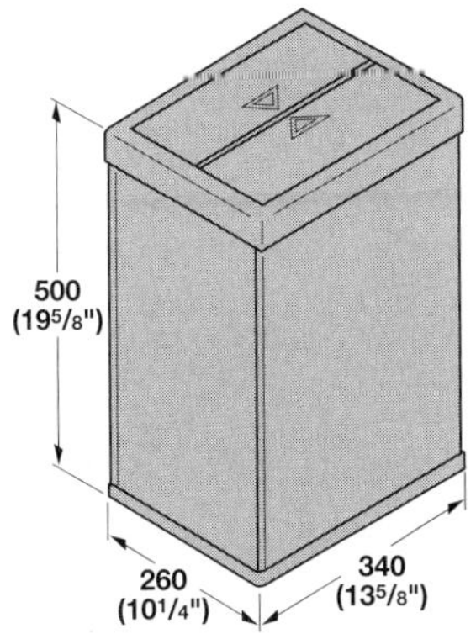

Waste Bin
froo ctanding
Capacity: 41 liters (11 gal.)
Lid: plastic, white
Housing: steel, epoxy coated white

Cat. No.	502.30.718

Packing: 1 pc.

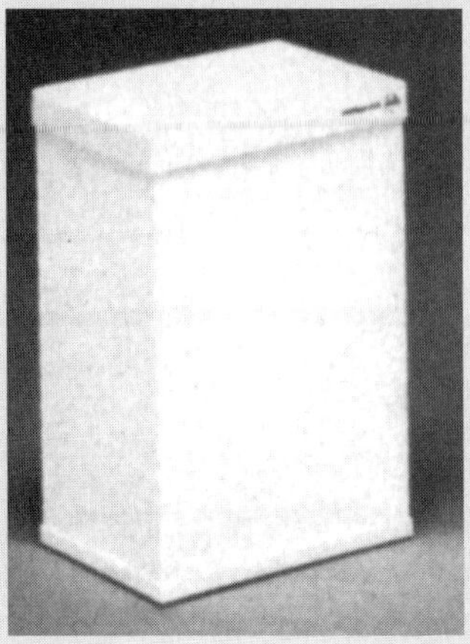

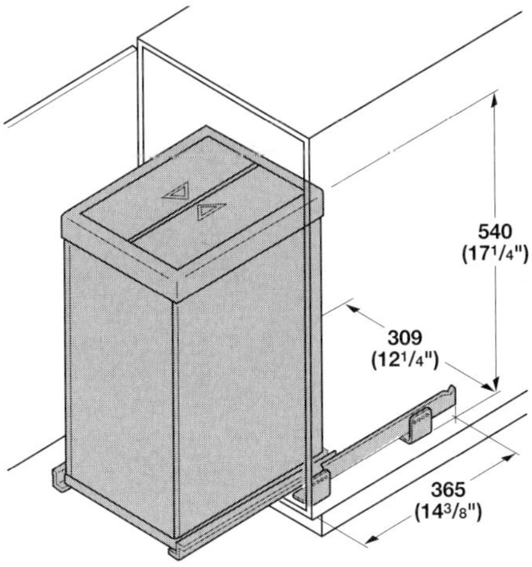

Waste Bin
floor mounted, manual pull-out, 3/4 extension
Capacity: 41 liters (11 gal.)
Lid: plastic, white
Housing: steel, epoxy coated white

Cat. No.	502.29.751

Packing: 1 pc.

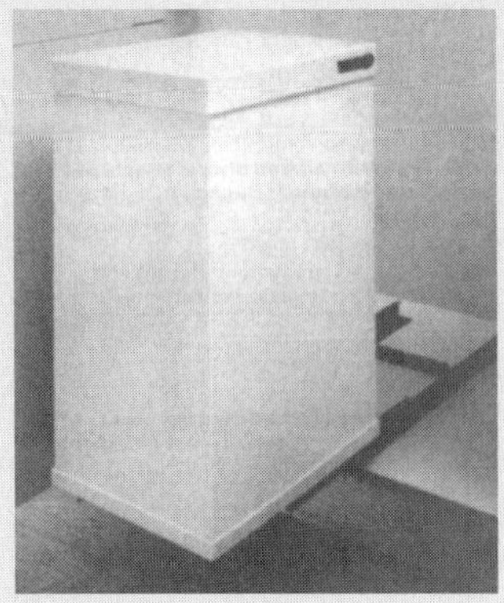

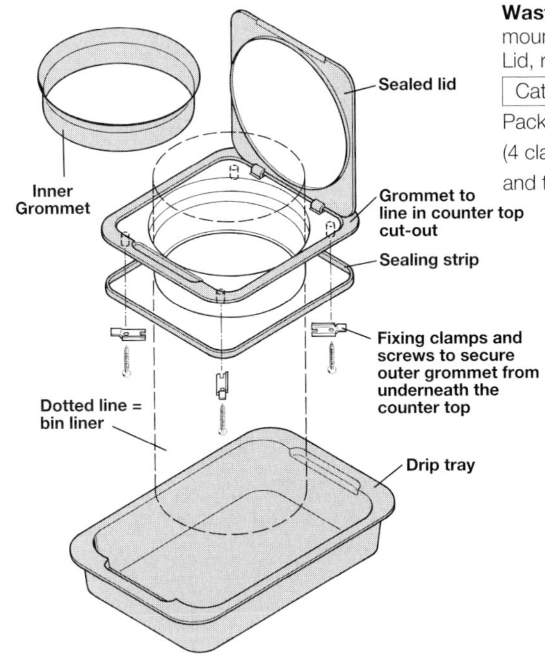

Waste Bin
mounts in countertops up to 40 mm (1½") thick
Lid, ring and tray: plastic, white

Cat. No.	502.54.709

Packing: 1 pc. complete with fastening hardware (4 clamps and screws), mounting instructions and template.

Kitchen Accessory Systems **5**

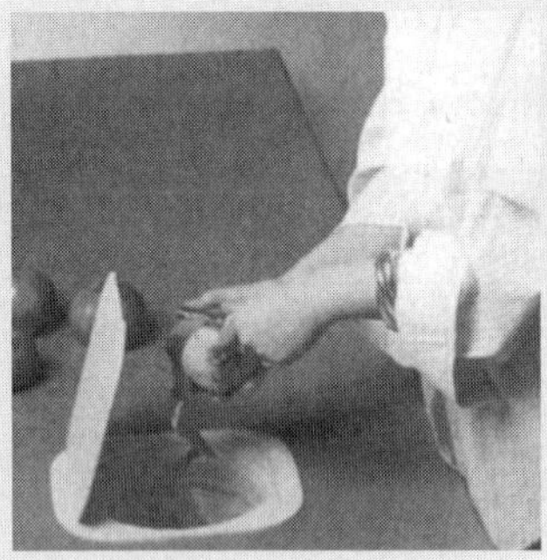

Outer grommet

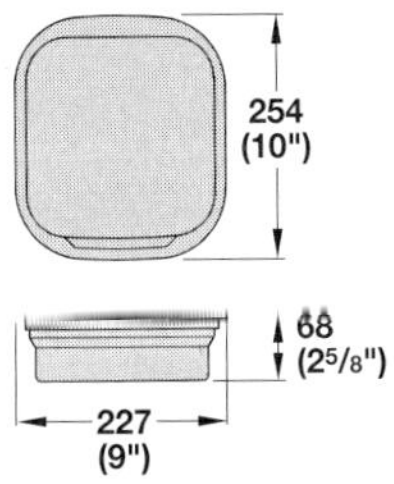

Drip tray

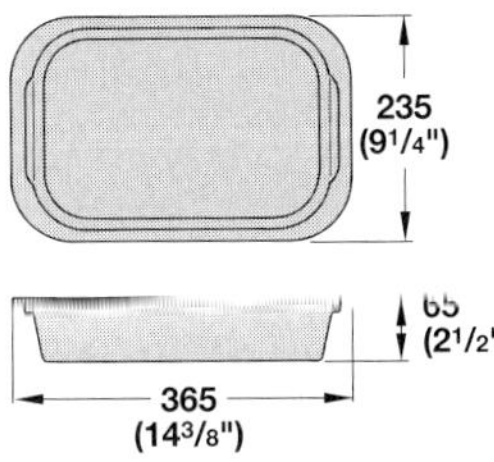

Dimensional data not binding.
We reserve the right to alter specifications without notice.

Dimensions in mm
Inches are approximate

HÄFELE

Waste Bins for Swing Out Behind Doors

- Waste bins can be mounted for left or right hand use.
- Features lid in the cabinet principle, as the door is opened the lid tilts automatically.
- Mounting instructions and accessories packed with each unit.

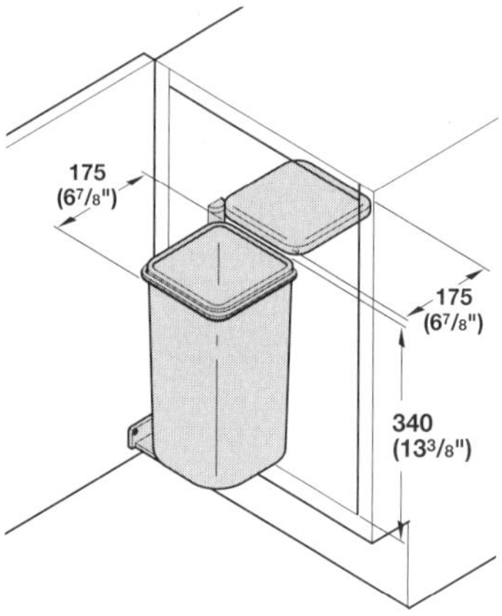

Waste Bin

side panel mounted
cabinet widths over 250 mm (10")
cabinet depths over 192 mm (7½")

MINIMUM 250mm CABINET WIDTH

Capacity:	**5 liters (1.25 gal.)**
Mounting lid & bin:	plastic, white

Cat. No.	502.63.726

Packing: 1 pc.

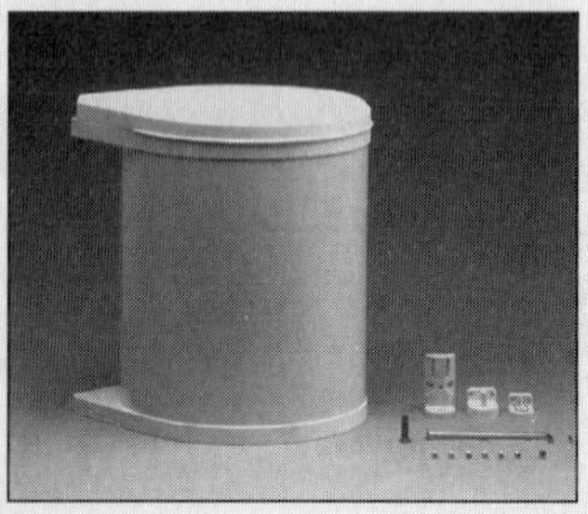

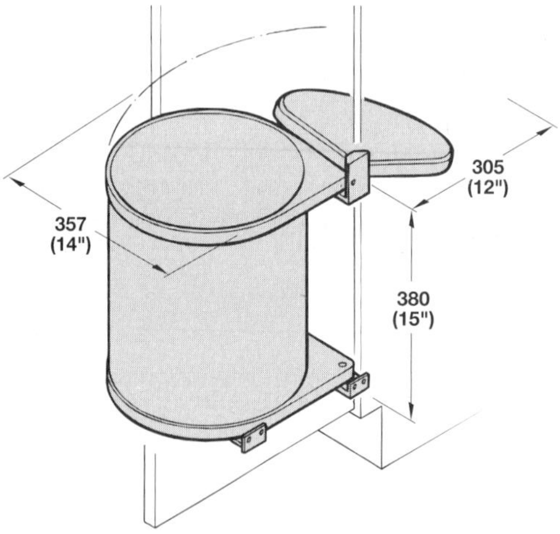

Waste Bin

side panel mounted
cabinet widths over 400 mm (15¾)

MINIMUM 400mm CABINET WIDTH

Capacity:	**15 liters (4 gal.)**
Lid:	plastic, white
Pail:	plastic, light gray

Housing:	Cat. No.
white, plastic-coated	502.12.729
cream, plastic-coated	502.12.425
stainless steel, polished	502.12.023

Packing: 1 pc.

Replacement pails

Capacity:	**15 liters (4 gal.)**
Finish:	plastic, light gray

Cat. No.	502.12.998

Packing: 1 pc.

5 Kitchen Accessory Systems

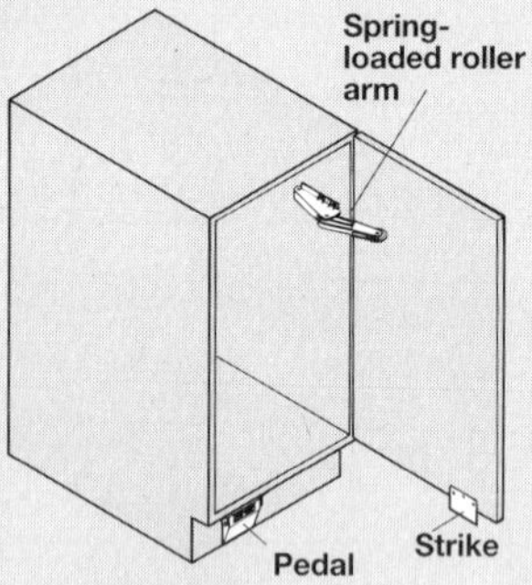

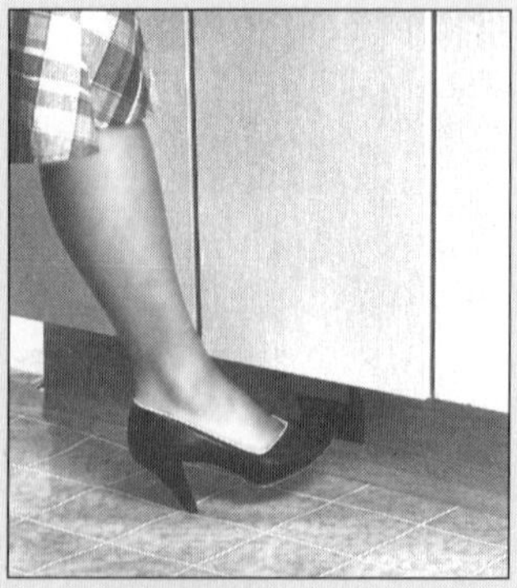

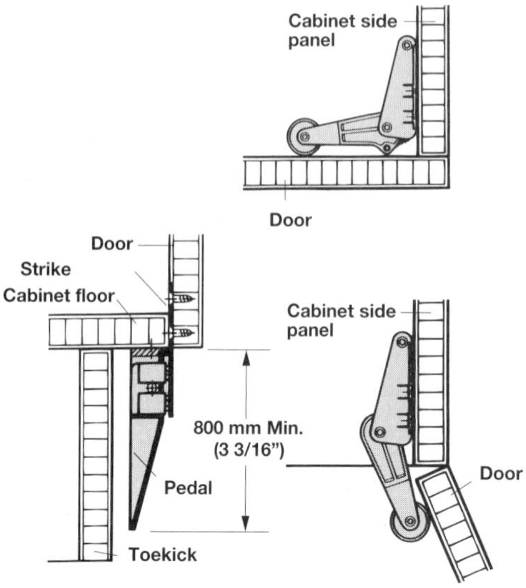

Door Opener for Hinged Base Cabinet Doors

Pedal:	plastic, brown
Strike:	steel, black, lacquered
Spring loaded roller arm:	plastic, white

Cat. No.	502.15.033

Packing: 1 pcs.

Dimensional data not binding. We reserve the right to alter specifications without notice.

Dimensions in mm
Inches are approximate

Waste Bins for Swing-out Doors

Waste Bin for side panel mounted
for cabinet widths over 450 mm (18")
left or right mounting
Capacity: 18 litres (4.75 gallon)
Finish: Lid, plastic, white
Pail, plastic, light gray

Housing	Cat. No.
Stainless Steel	502.62.014
White	502.62.710

Packing: 1 pc.

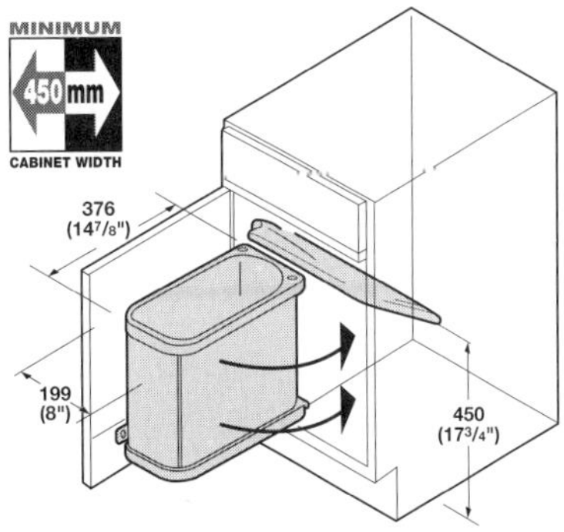

Add on Kit For 502.62.710/014
Attaches to rear of waste bin
For installation depth of over 380 mm (15")
Capacity: 5 litres (1.25 gallon)
Finish: Lid, plastic, white
Pail, plastic, light gray

Catalog No.	502.63.717

Packing: 1 pc.

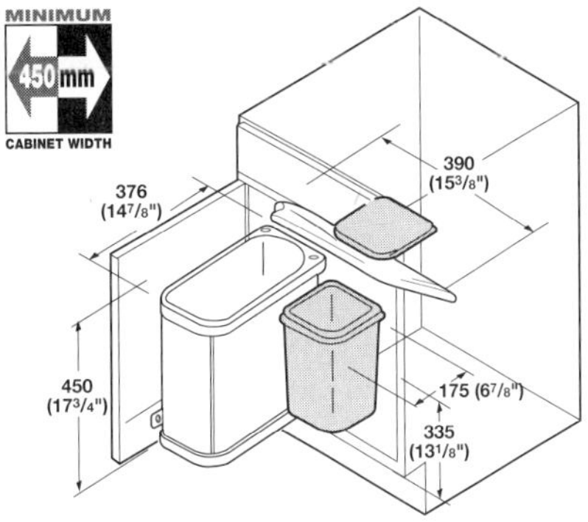

Dimensions in mm
Inches are approximate

HÄFELE

Add-on Kit For Uno hinged doors
- Offers second waste bin
- Allows waste separation
- Extremely easy to install
- Can be mounted with Uno or add later

Kitchen Accessory Systems **5**

Replacement bin
Finish: plastic

Capacity	Color	Cat.No.
18 liter	Light gray	502.61.937

Packing: 1 pc.

Dimensional data not binding.
We reserve the right to alter specifications without notice.

HÄFELE

Pull-out Waste Bins

- Mounts to cabinet bottom
- Features lid in the cabinet principle, as the door is opened the lid tilts automatically.
- Optional pull-out tray for paper recycling can be added above waste bins.

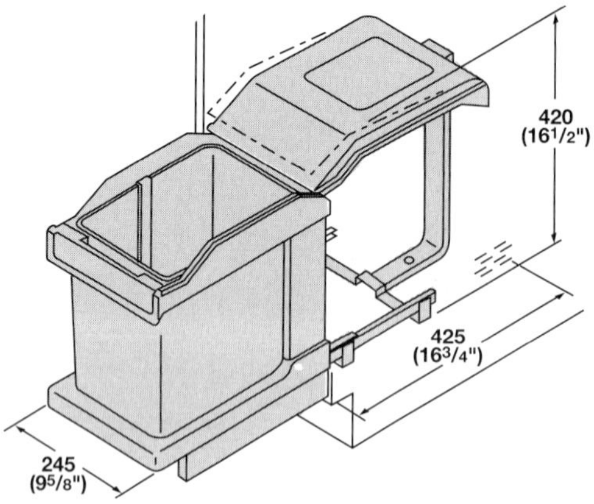

MINIMUM 300 mm CABINET WIDTH

Waste Bin
floor-mounted, manual extension
cabinet widths over 300 mm (11 3/4)
Capacity: 20 liters **(5.25 gal.)**

Holder:	steel, plastic coated white
Cover:	plastic, gray-brown
Pails:	plastic, gray-brown
Cat. No.	502.43.706

Packing: 1 pc.

Replacement Bin
Finish: plastic, brown

Cat. No.	502.43.902

Packing: 1 pc.

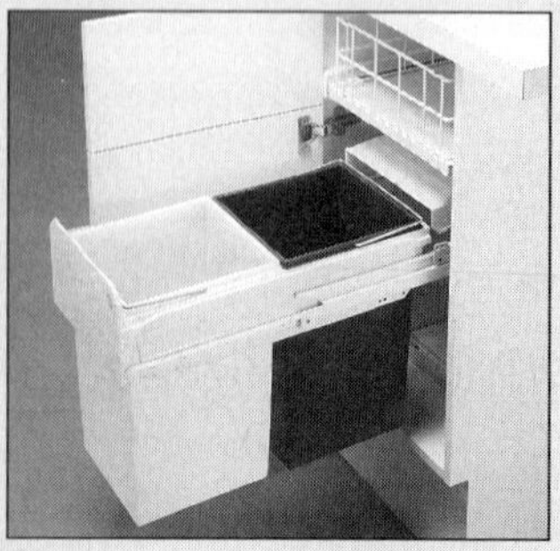

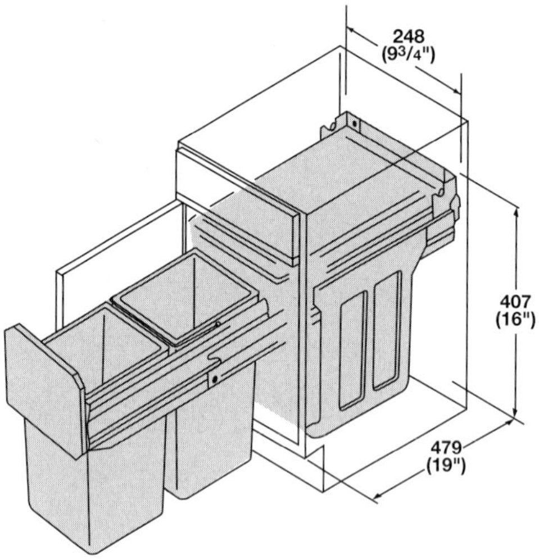

MINIMUM 300 mm CABINET WIDTH

Double Waste Bin
floor-mounted, manual full-extension
cabinet widths over 300 mm (11 3/4")
Capacity: **2 x 15 liters (4 gal.)**

Holder:	steel, plastic coated white
Cover:	plastic, white
Pails:	plastic, yellow and brown
Cat. No.	502.70.767

Packing: 1 pc.

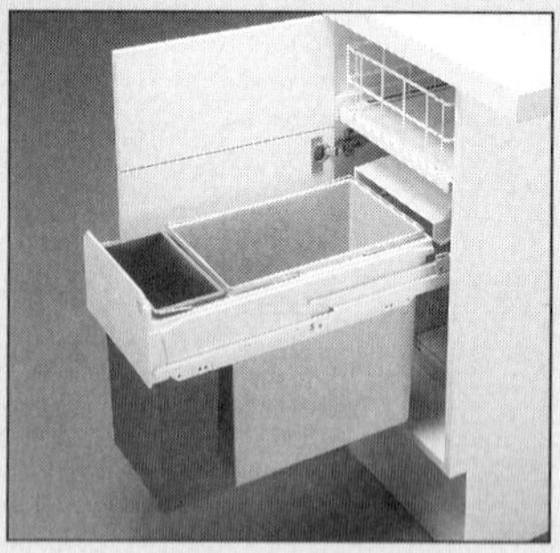

Replacement Bins
Finish: plastic

Capacity	Color	Cat. No.
15 Liters	yellow	502.71.693
15 Liters	brown	502.71.193
7 Liters	green	502.70.098
24 Liters	gray	502.73.599

Packing: 1 pc.

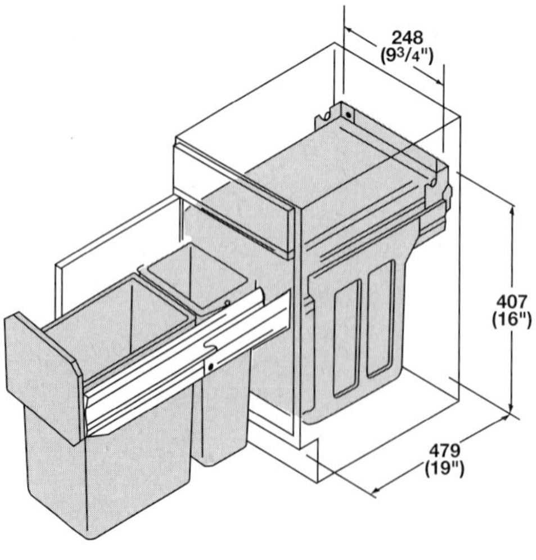

MINIMUM 300 mm CABINET WIDTH

Double Waste Bin
floor-mounted, manual full-extension
cabinet widths over 300 mm (11 3/4")
Capacity: **1 x 24 liters (6.25 gal.)** **1 x 7 liters (1.75 gal.)**

Holder:	steel, plastic coated white
Cover:	plastic, white
Pails:	plastic, gray and green
Cat. No.	502.70.776

Packing: 1 pc.

Dimensional data not binding.
We reserve the right to alter specifications without notice.

Dimensions in mm
Inches are approximate

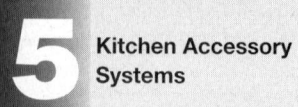

Pull-out Door Mounted Waste Bins

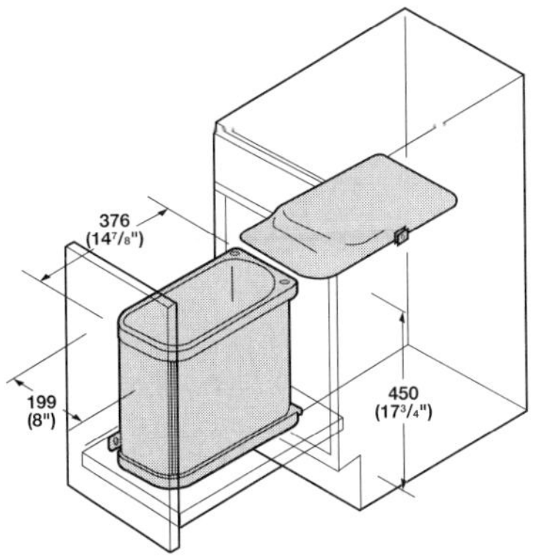

Waste Bin
floor mounted
cabinet widths over 250 mm (9 3/4")
Pull-out shelf & soft roller not supplied.

Capacity:	**18 liters (4.75 gal.)**
Lid:	plastic, white
Pail:	plastic, light gray

Cat. No.	502.61.713

Packing: 1 pc.

Replacement Bin
Finish: plastic, light gray

Cat. No.	18 liter	502.61.937

Packing: 1 pc.

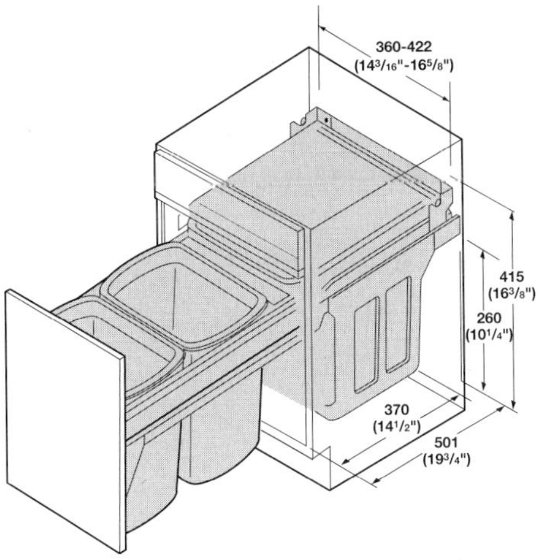

Double Waste Bin
side wall mounted, manual full extension effect
for cabinet widths over 360 mm (14 3/16")
Adjustable inside width
360-422 mm (14 3/16" – 16 5/8")

Capacity:	**2 x 18 liters (4.75 gal.)**
Frame:	steel, plastic coated white
Cover:	plastic, white
Pails:	plastic, light gray

Cat. No.	502.73.780

Packing: 1 pc.

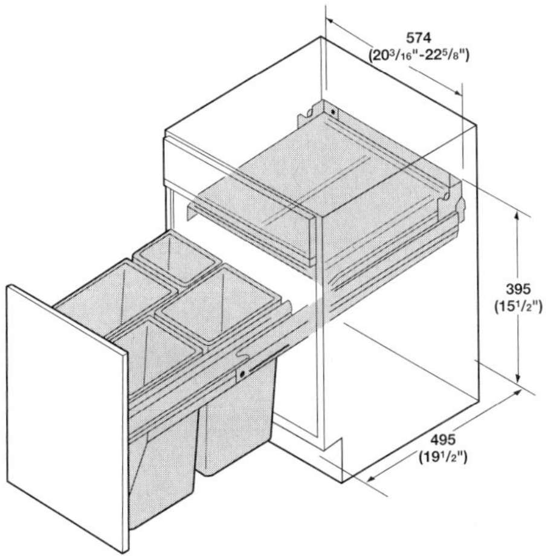

Quadruple Waste Bin
side wall mounted, manual full extension
cabinet widths over 512 mm (20 3/16")
Adjustable inside width
512-574 mm (20 3/16" – 22 5/8")

Capacity:	**2 x 15 liters (4 gal.)**
	1 x 7 liters (1.75 gal.)
	1 x 24 liters (6.25 gal.)
Frame:	steel, plastic coated white
Cover:	plastic, white
Pails:	gray, green, yellow and brown

Cat. No.	502.73.795

Packing: 1 pc.

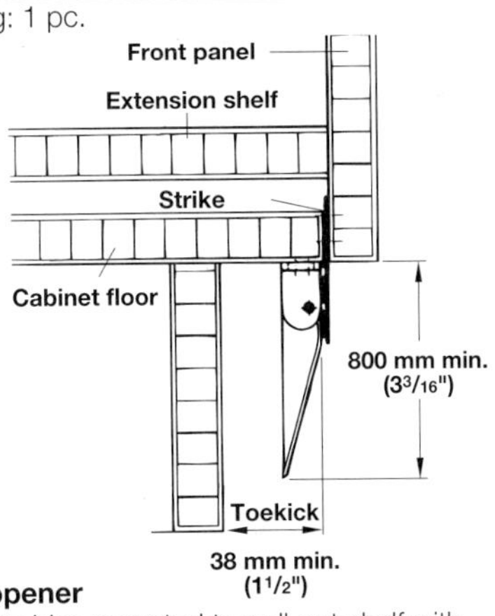

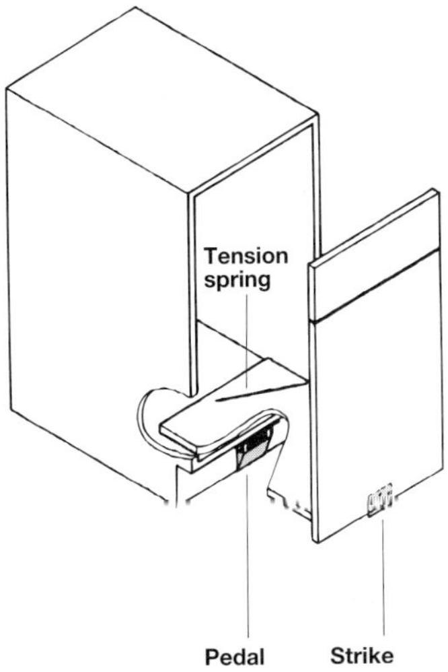

Door opener
for waste bins mounted to pull-out shelf with
door attached

Pedal:	plastic, brown
Strike:	steel, black enameled
Tension spring:	steel wire, bright

Cat. No.	502.15.113

Packing: 1 pc.

HÄFELE

Uno Waste Bin - Pull-Out
- Mounts directly to pull out shelf.
- Bottom Mounting
- Offers narrow width but high capacity.

Replacement Bins
Finish: plastic

Capacity	Color	Cat.No.
15 liter	yellow	502.71.963
15 liter	brown	502.71.193
7 liter	green	502.71.098
24 liter	gray	502.71.599

Packing: 1 pc.

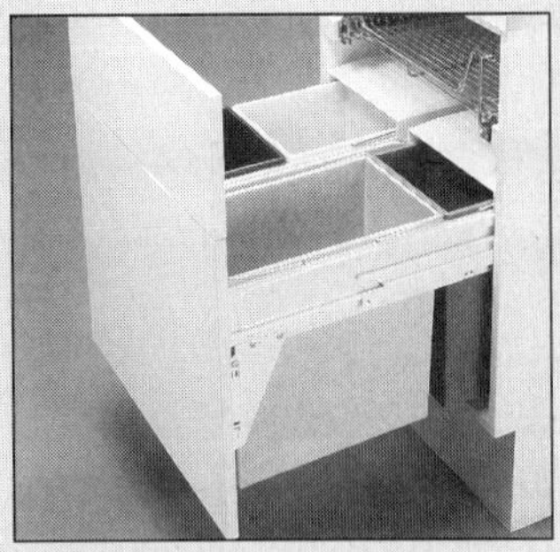

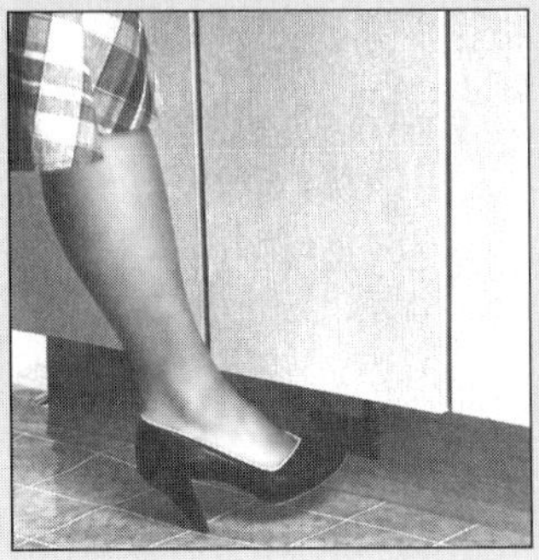

Dimensional data not binding.
We reserve the right to alter specifications without notice.

HÄFELE

Folding Step Stool

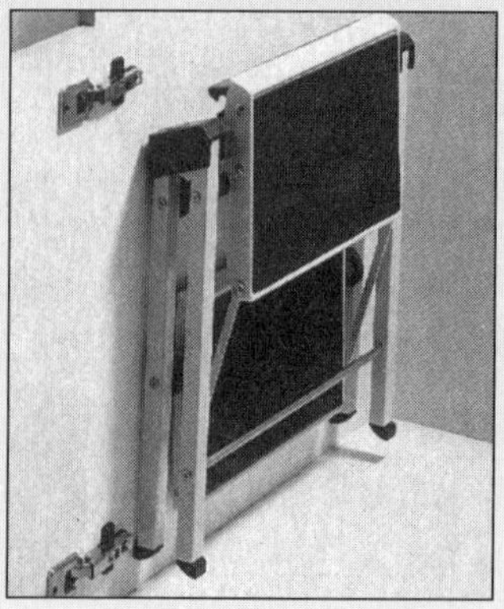

Stepfix can be hung on a side panel using the optional hanging bracket.

- **Stepfix** is a sturdy compact folding step for kitchen use.

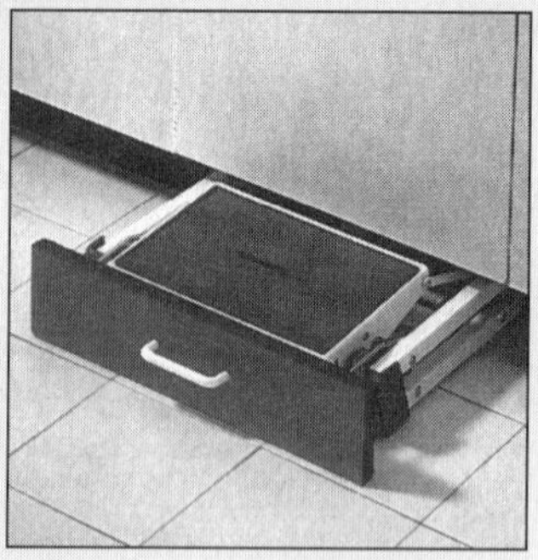

- **Stepfix** has built in rollers permitting it to slide in/out with easy under cabinets when used with optional folding bracket.

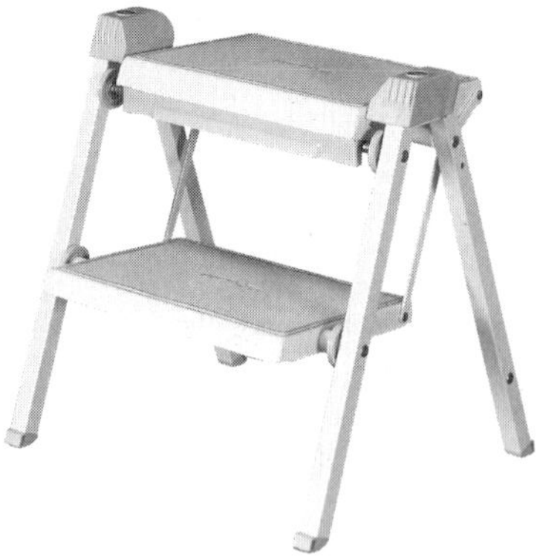

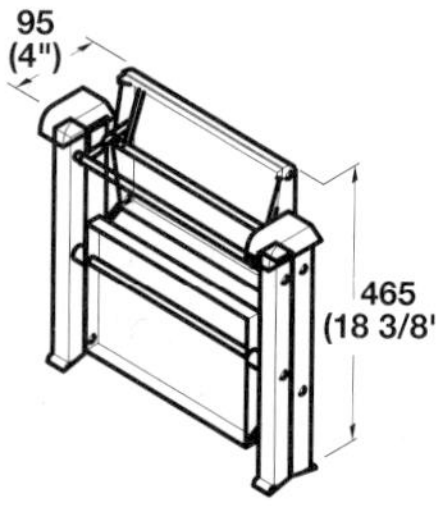

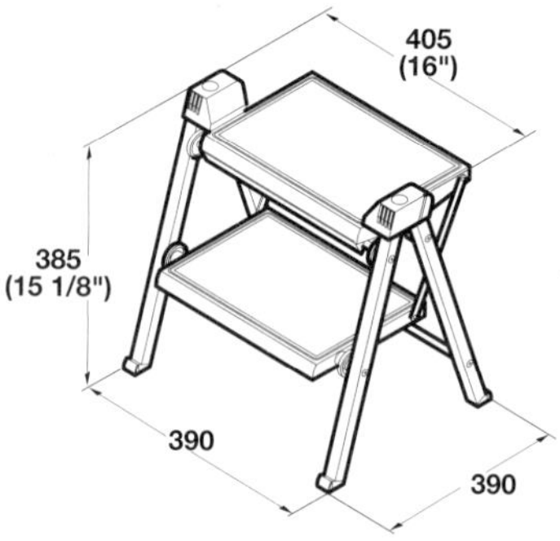

Step stool
With 2 steps 200 x 300 mm (7¾ x 11¾")
covered with non-slip rubber treads
Finish: steel, epoxy-coated
plastic feet

Frame/plastic parts	Cat. No.
silver/black	505.04.210
white/gray	505.04.704

Packing: 1 pc.

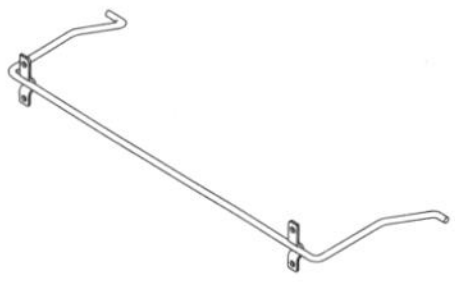

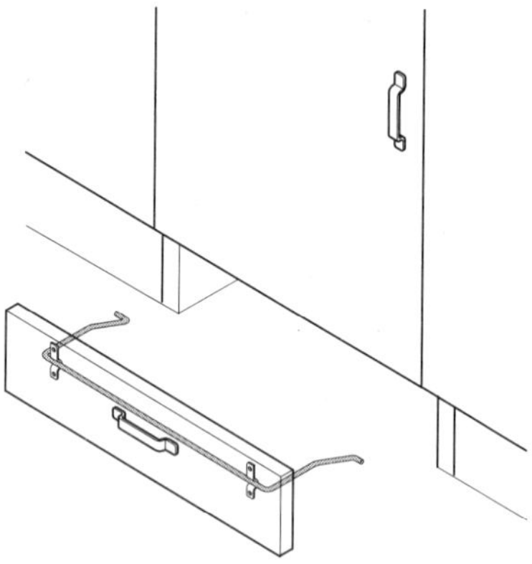

Toekick bracket
Attaches to step stool and toekick. Use to slide under cabinet. A minimum of 100 mm (4") is required.
Finish: steel, galvanized

Cat. No.	505.04.419

Packing: 1 pc.

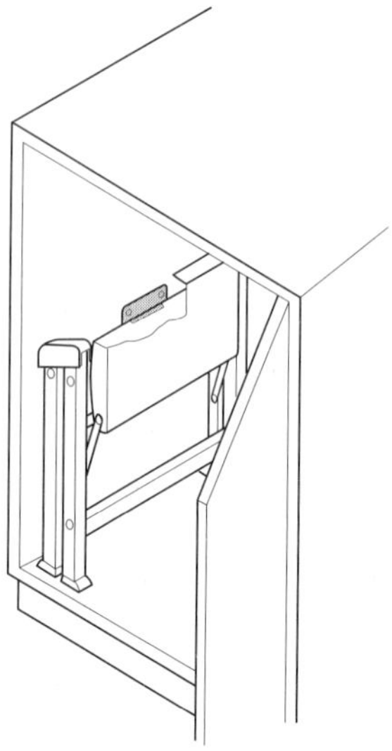

Hanging bracket
Screw-mounting to cabinet side panel to stow step stool.
Length: 140 mm (5½")
Depth: 30 mm (1⅛")
Height: 35 mm (1⅜")
Finish: steel, epoxy-coated, white

Cat. No.	505.04.722

Packing: 1 pc.

Dimensions in mm
Inches are approximate

Pull-out Towel Racks

HÄFELE

Towel Rack, 2 bars
Installed dimensions: (w) x (h)
Under-mount: 65 x 74 mm (2 1/2" x 3")
Side-mount: 93 x 31 mm (3 5/8" x 1 1/4")

Finish: aluminum anodized or epoxy-coated
3 precision plastic rollers

Cat. No.		
	white	510.50.723
	silver anodized	510.50.929
	bronze anodized	510.50.125

Packing: 1 pc.

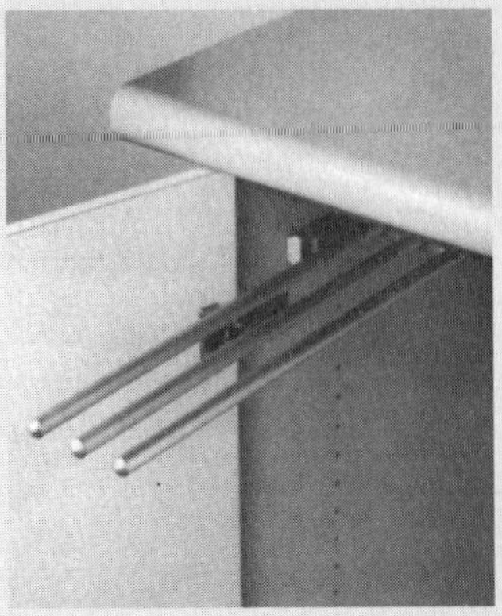

The special design permits for under mounting...

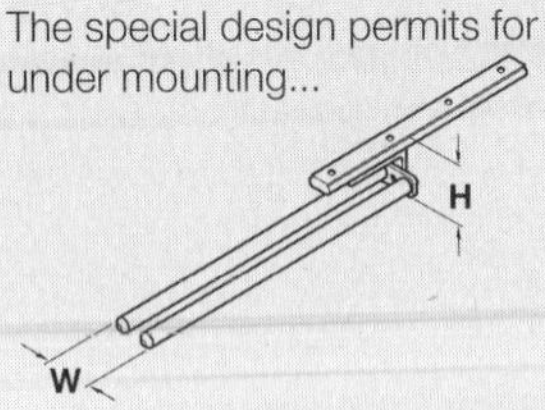

Towel Rack, 3 bars
Under-mount or side-mount feature
Installed dimensions: (w) x (h)
Under-mount: 110 x 74 mm (4 3/4" x 3")
Side-mount: 138 x 31 mm (5 1/2" x 1 1/4"")

Finish: aluminum anodized or epoxy-coated
3 precision plastic rollers

Cat. No.		
	white	510.50.732
	silver anodized	510.50.938
	bronze anodized	510.50.134

Packing: 1 pc.

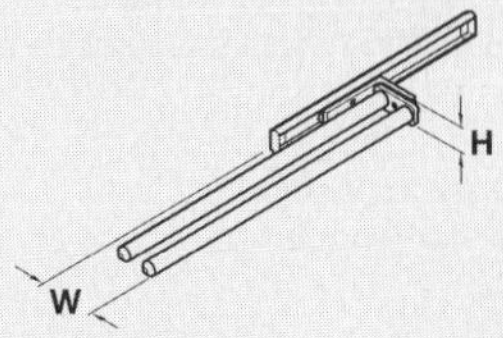

...or side mounting.

Kitchen Accessory Systems 5

Towel Rack, 4 bars
under-mount or side-mount feature
Installed dimensions: (w) x (h)
Under-mount: 158 x 74 mm (6 1/4" x 3")
Side-mount: 183 x 31 mm (5 1/5" x 1 1/4")

Finish: aluminum anodized or epoxy-coated
3 precision plastic rollers

Cat. No.		
	white	510.50.741
	silver anodized	510.50.947
	bronze anodized	510.50.143

Packing: 1 pc.

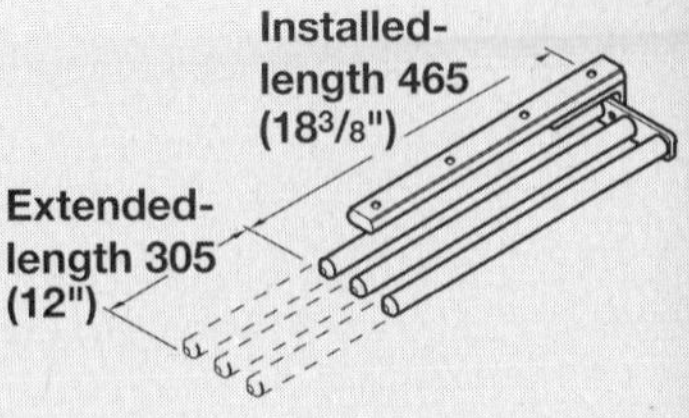

Length of mounting bracket: 410 mm
Length of extending rails: 450 mm

Installation length, extended bar lengths and installed heights of all three models are identical.

Dimensional data not binding. We reserve the right to alter specifications without notice.

Dimensions in mm
Inches are approximate

HÄFELE

Pull-out Towel Rack

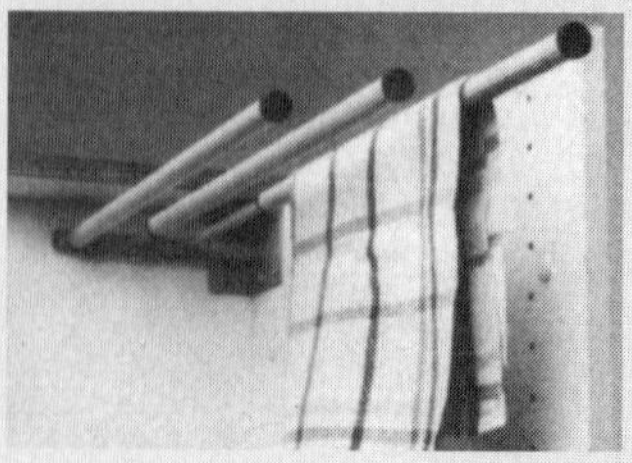

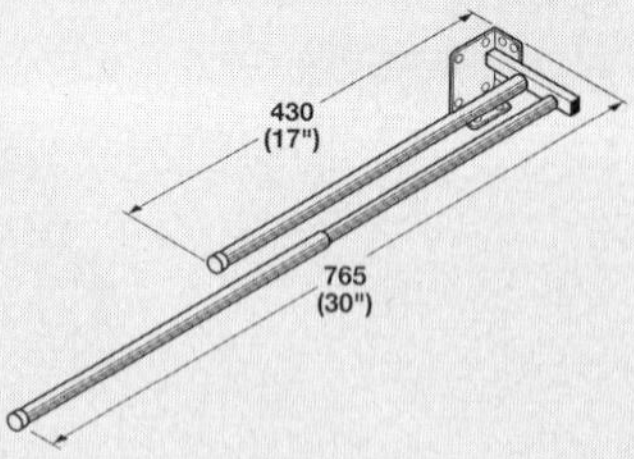

- Can be mounted directly below the countertop, to side or back wall.
- Non-slip pull-out towel bars can be pulled out with ease to a distance of 765 mm (30").
- Bars are prevented from twisting by their square-profiled retaining bar.

Towel rack, rail and 2 bars
installed width: 140 mm (5½")

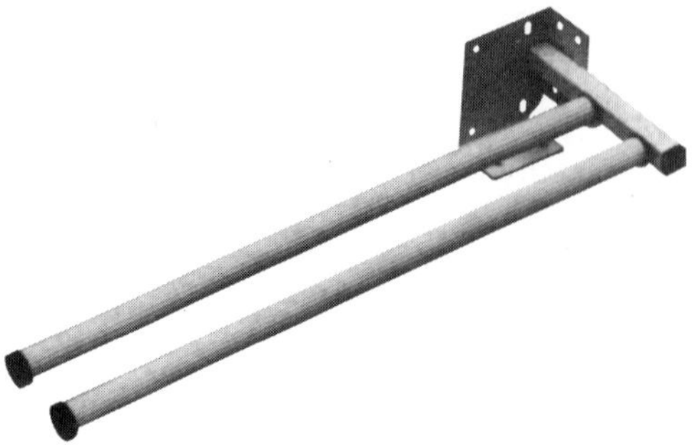

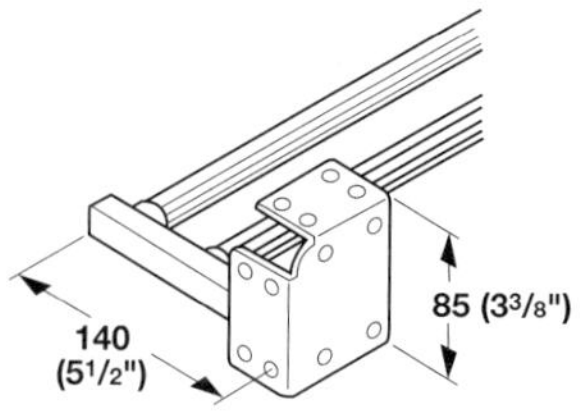

Finish: mounting bracket and inner tube: plastic coated steel, white
outer bar: non-slip ribbed plastic, white

Cat. No.	510.06.725

Packing: 1 pc.

Towel rack, 3 bars
Installed width: 190 mm (7½")

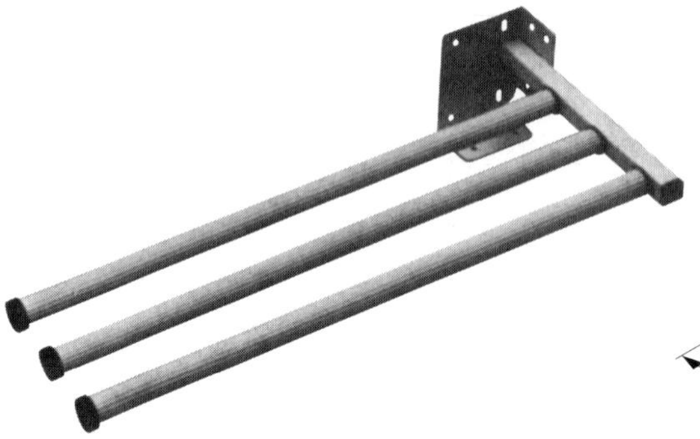

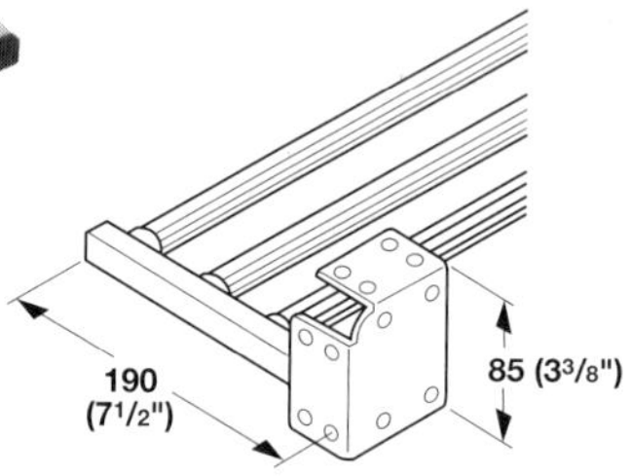

Finish: mounting bracket and inner tube: plastic coated steel, white
outer bar: non-slip ribbed plastic, white

Cat. No.	510.06.752

Packing: 1 pc.

Dimensions in mm
Inches are approximate

Kitchen Matting

HÄFELE

Under-sink Matting
Size: 550 x 1150 mm (21 3/4 x 45 1/2")

Finish: polystyrene, white

Cat. No.	547.91.703

Packing: 1 pc.

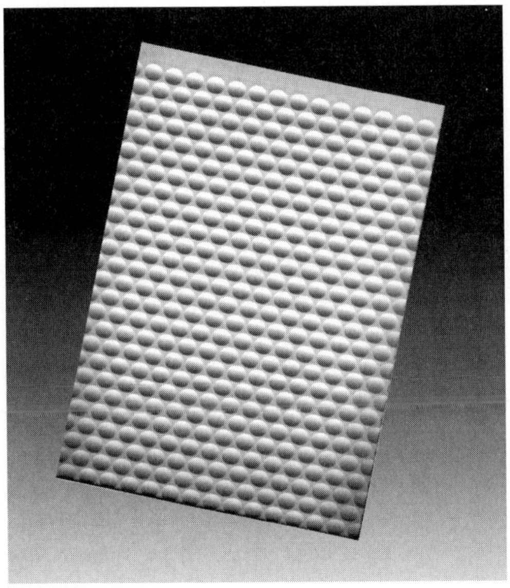

- Cut to size to fit in sink cabinet.
- Unique dimples collect water or other liquids to prevent damage to cabinet.
- Dimples can collect up to 6 liters of water per square meters.

Non-Skid Shelf Liner Mats
Acoustic, heat resistant nap, suitable for food storage.
Size: 1 roll = 10 meters x 1 meter

Finish: synthetic rubber with non-slide surface

Cat. No.	547.90.706

Packing: 1 roll

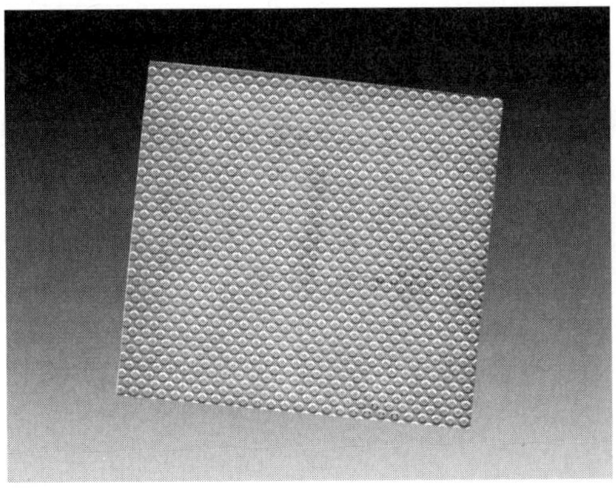

- Cut-to-size non-skid mats prevents sliding or movement of tableware, pots, and other kitchen utensils on pull-out shelves, revolving shelves pull-out drawers, etc.

Dimensions in mm
Inches are approximate

HÄFELE

Cutlery Tray & Spice Drawer Inserts

Cutlery tray insert with diagonal compartments
Material thickness: 3 mm, height: 57 mm (2 1/4")
Finish: plastic, white, high gloss.

Size	Cutlery Tray Dimensions: Width, minimum mm (inch)	Width, maximum mm (inch)	Depth, minimum mm (inch)	Depth, maximum mm (inch)	Cat. No.
1	200 (7 7/8")	240 (9 1/2")	440 (17 1/4")	550 (21 5/8")	556.75.717
2	300 (11 3/4")	340 (13 3/8")	440 (17 1/4")	550 (21 5/8")	556.75.735
3	350 (13 3/4")	390 (15 3/8")	440 (17 1/4")	550 (21 5/8")	556.75.744
4	400 (15 3/4")	440 (17 1/4")	440 (17 1/4")	550 (21 5/8")	556.75.753
5	450 (17 3/4")	490 (19 1/4")	440 (17 1/4")	550 (21 5/8")	556.75.762
6	500 (19 3/4")	540 (21 1/4")	440 (17 1/4")	550 (21 5/8")	556.75.771

Packing: 1 pc.

5 Kitchen Accessory Systems

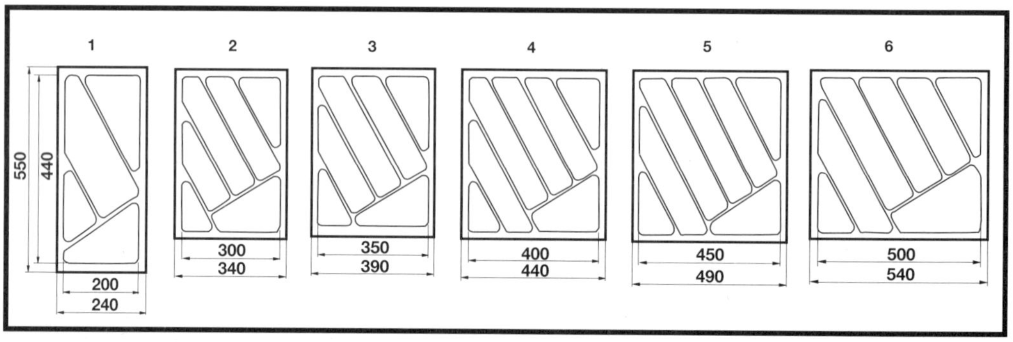

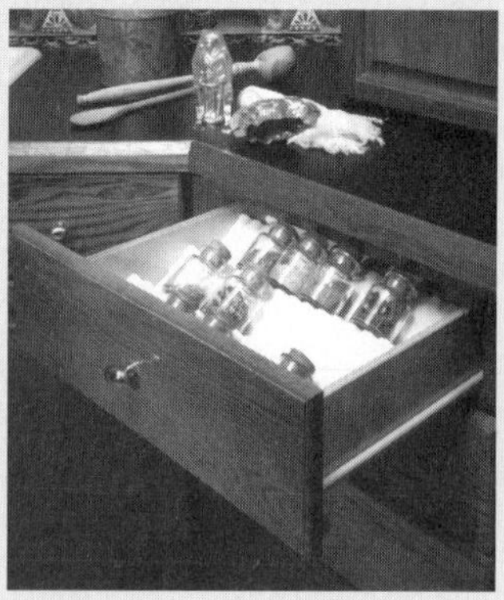

- Ready for trimming to fit drawers up to 1300 mm (51 1/8")

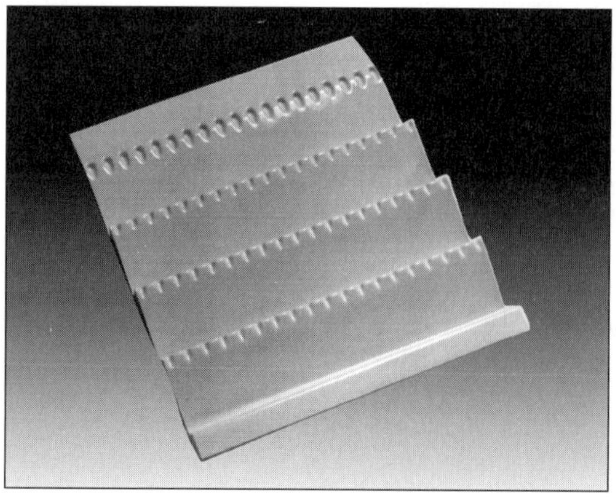

Spice Drawer Insert, for storage of average sized spice jars. A minimum inside drawer height of 3 1/4" is required.
1300 x 550 mm (51 1/8 x 21 5/8")
Material thickness: 3 mm
Finish: plastic, white, gloss

Cat. No.	556.79.706

Packing: 1 pc.

Dimensional data not binding. We reserve the right to alter specifications without notice.

Dimensions in mm
Inches are approximate

Cutlery Tray Inserts

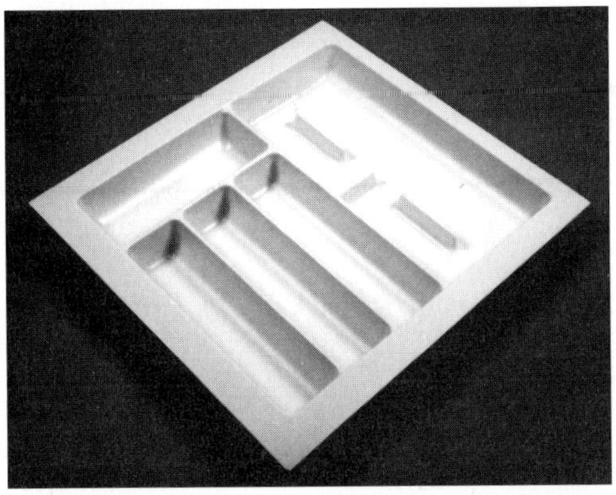

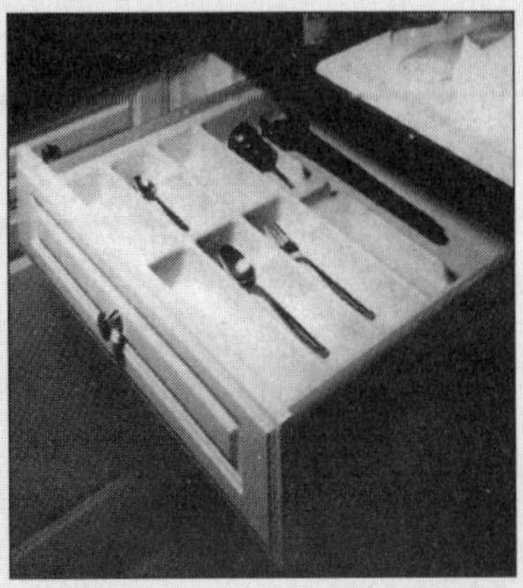

Cutlery Tray
crossways compartments
Material thickness: 2.5 mm Height: 50 mm (2")
Finish: plastic, white gloss

- At the front are crossways compartments with multipurpose compartments at the rear to hold large utensils.

Size	cabinet width	Cutlery Tray Dimensions				Cat. No.
		Width		Depth		
		min.	max.	min.	max.	
	mm (inch)	mm (inch)	mm (inch)	mm (inch)	mm (inch)	
1	300 (11¾")	200 (7⅞")	240 (9½")	440 (17⅜")	540 (21¼")	556.77.830
2	350 (13¾")	250 (10")	290 (11½")	440 (17⅜")	540 (21¼")	556.77.835
3	400 (15¾")	300 (11⅞")	340 (13⅜")	440 (17⅜")	540 (21¼")	556.77.840
4	450 (17¾")	350 (13¾")	390 (15⅜")	440 (17⅜")	540 (21¼")	556.77.845
5	500 (19¾")	400 (15¾")	440 (17⅜")	440 (17⅜")	540 (21¼")	556.77.850
6	550 (21⅝")	450 (17¾")	490 (19⅜")	440 (17⅜")	540 (21¼")	556.77.855
7	600 (23⅝")	500 (19⅝")	540 (21¾")	440 (17⅜")	540 (21¼")	556.77.860

Packing: 1 pc.

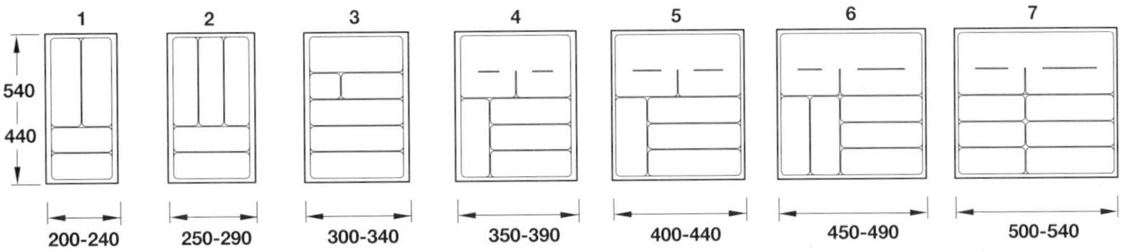

Kitchen Accessory Systems 5

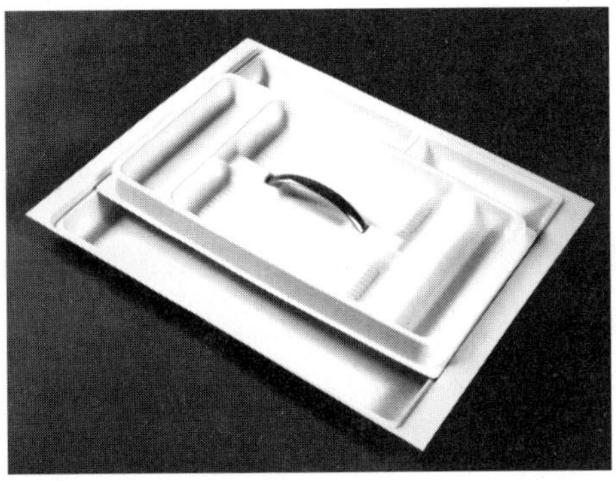

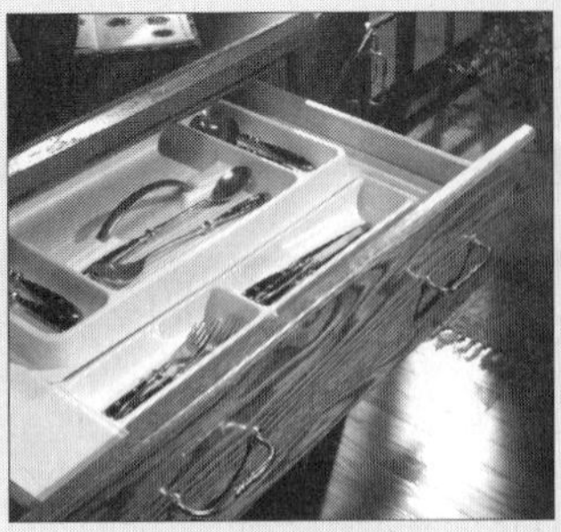

Cutlery Tray
with upper tier and metal handle
Material thickness: 2.5 mm Height: 89 mm (3½")
Finish: plastic, white textured

- Top tier removes easily for dishwasher loading.

Size	for cabinet width	Cutlery Tray Dimensions				Cat. No.
		Width		Depth		
		min.	max.	min.	max.	
	mm (inch)	mm (inch)	mm (inch)	mm (inch)	mm (inch)	
1	450 (17¾")	350 (13¾")	390 (15⅜")	440 (17⅜")	540 (21¼")	556.70.745
2	500 (19¾")	400 (15¾")	440 (17⅜")	440 (17⅜")	540 (21¼")	556.70.750
3	600 (23⅜")	500 (19¾")	540 (21¾")	440 (17⅜")	540 (21¼")	556.70.760

Packing: 1 pc.

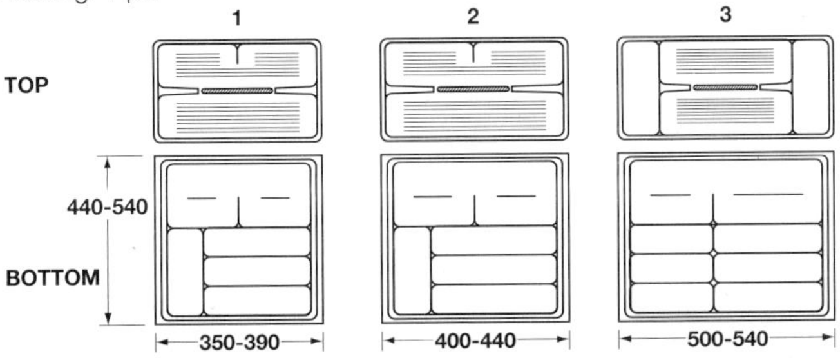

Dimensions in mm
Inches are approximate

Dimensional data not binding.
We reserve the right to alter specifications without notice.

HÄFELE

Cutlery Trays Inserts

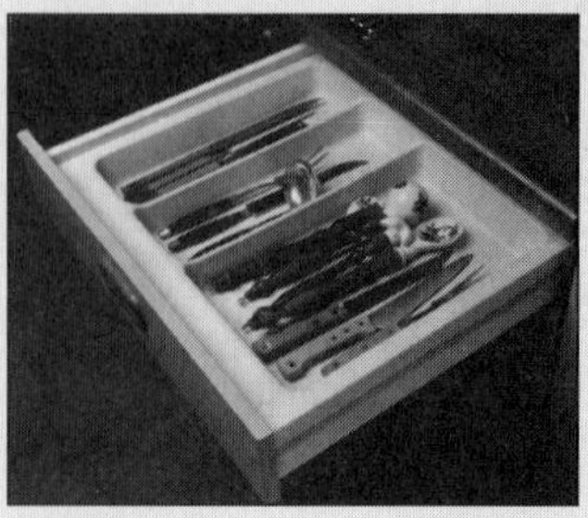

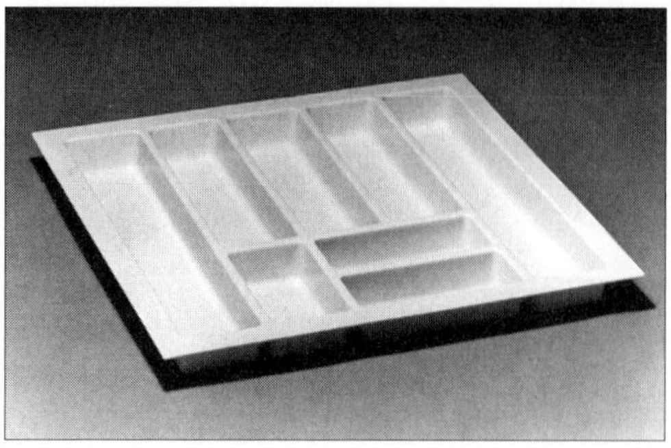

Cutlery Tray Insert
Material: 3 mm, height: 57 mm (2 1/4)
Finish: plastic, white, grained

Size	cabinet width	Cutlery tray dimensions				
		Width		Depth		
		min. mm (inch)	max. mm (inch)	min. mm (inch)	max. mm (inch)	Cat. No.
1	300 (11 3/4)	180 (7)	300 (11 7/8)	451 (17 3/4)	498 (19 1/2)	556.60.752
2	400-450 (15 3/4-17 3/4)	305 (12)	400 (15 3/4)	451 (17 3/4)	498 (19 1/2)	556.60.761
3	500-550 (19 3/4-21 5/8)	405 (16)	500 (19 3/4)	451 (17 3/4)	498 (19 1/2)	556.60.770
4	600 (23 5/8)	505 (19 7/8)	560 (22)	451 (17 3/4)	498 (19 1/2)	556.60.789

Packing: 1 pc.

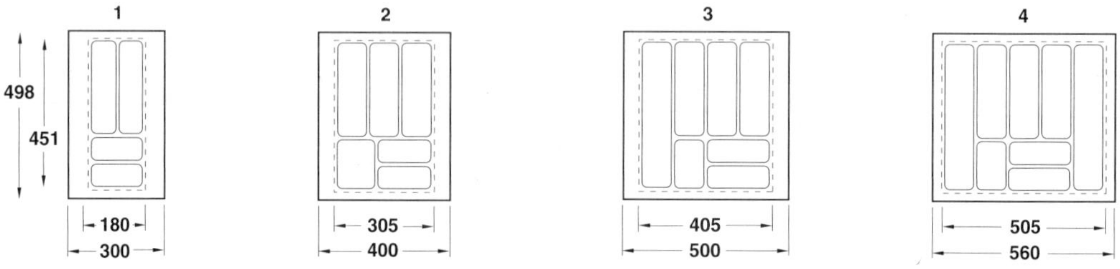

5 Kitchen Accessory Systems

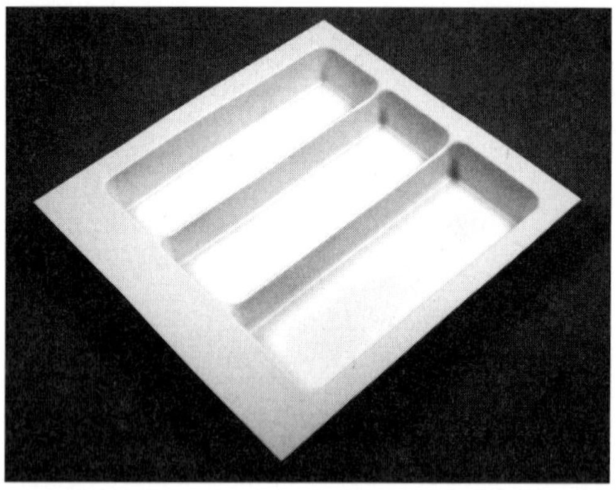

Cutlery Trays
with large compartments
Material thickness: 3 mm, height: 57 mm (2 1/4)
Finish: plastic, white, grained

Size	cabinet width	Cutlery tray dimensions				
		Width		Depth		
		min. mm (inch)	max. mm (inch)	min. mm (inch)	max. mm (inch)	Cat. No.
1	450 (17 3/4)	350 (13 3/4)	390 (15 1/4)	410 (16)	480 (18 7/8)	556.65.748
2	500 (19 3/4)	400 (15 3/4)	440 (17 3/8)	410 (16)	480 (18 7/8)	556.65.757
3	600 (23 3/4)	500 (19 5/8)	540 (21 1/4)	410 (16)	480 (18 7/8)	556.65.766

Packing: 1 pc

Inserts available pre-trimmed to specified dimensions. Minimum orders of 100 per size.

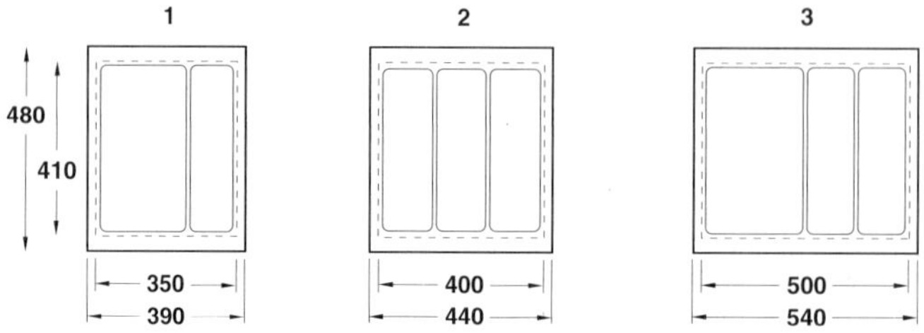

Dimensional data not binding. We reserve the right to alter specifications without notice.

Dimensions in mm
Inches are approximate

Cutlery Trays Inserts

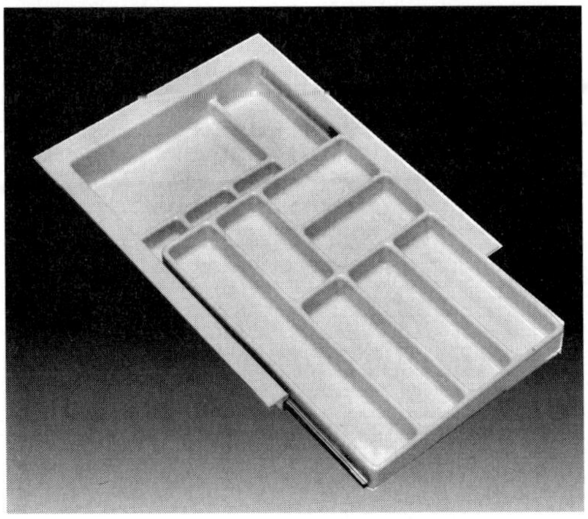

- The top tier slides easily on ball-bearing slides back into the cabinet allowing easy access to the bottom tier.
- For cleaning ease, top tier lifts out.
- Can be trimmed to fit drawers.

Top Tier

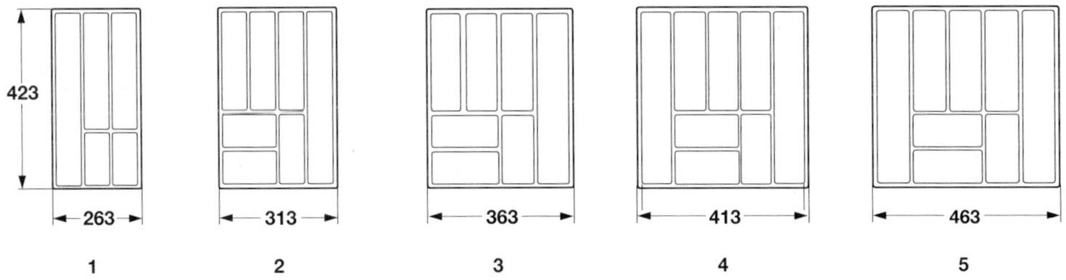

Bottom Tier

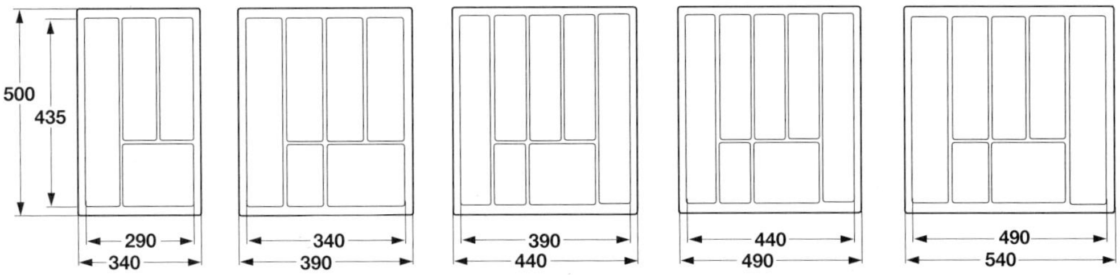

Double Cutlery Tray
with removable top tier
material thickness: 3 mm (1/8")
height: 78 mm (3 1/8")
Finish: plastic, white, gloss

Cutlery Tray Dimensions					
Size	Width		Depth		Cat. No.
	minimum	maximum	minimum	maximum	
1	290 (11 1/2")	340 (13 3/8")	435 (17 1/8")	500 (19 3/4")	556.68.730
2	340 (13 3/8")	390 (15 3/8")	435 (17 1/8")	500 (19 3/4")	556.68.749
3	390 (15 3/8")	440 (17 1/4")	435 (17 1/8")	500 (19 3/4")	556.68.758
4	440 (17 1/4")	490 (19 1/4")	435 (17 1/8")	500 (19 3/4")	556.68.767
5	490 (19 1/4")	540 (21 1/4")	435 (17 1/8")	500 (19 3/4")	556.68.776

Packing: 1 pc.

Dimensional data not binding.
We reserve the right to alter specifications without notice.

Dimensions in mm
Inches are approximate

HÄFELE

Silverware Drawer Kit

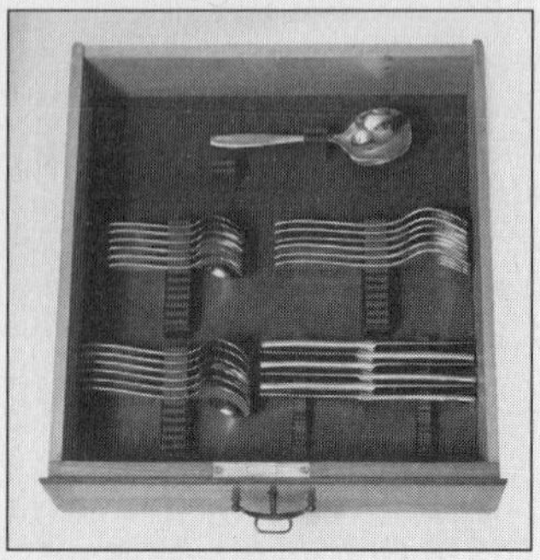

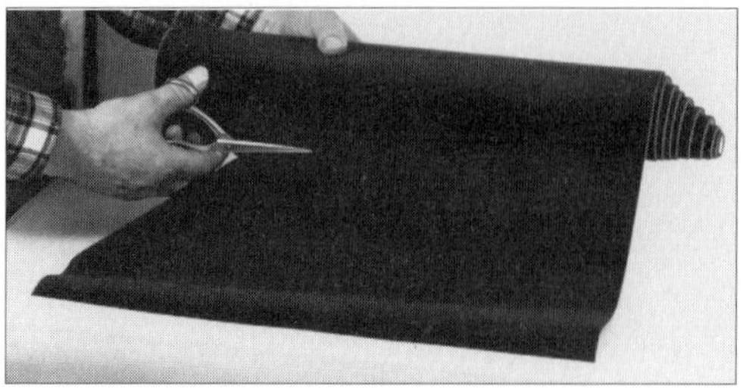

Felt material
drawer liner
Size: 100 x 45 cm (39 3/8 x 17 3/4")
Finish: brown, self-adhesive

Cat. No.	891.21.193

Packing: 1 piece

Assembly instructions:
1. Line the drawer base with self-adhesive felt.
2. Mount the holders (cutlery utensils must lie at right angles to drawer movement).
3. Knife holders; adjoining knives always alternate directions as shown (see photo below).

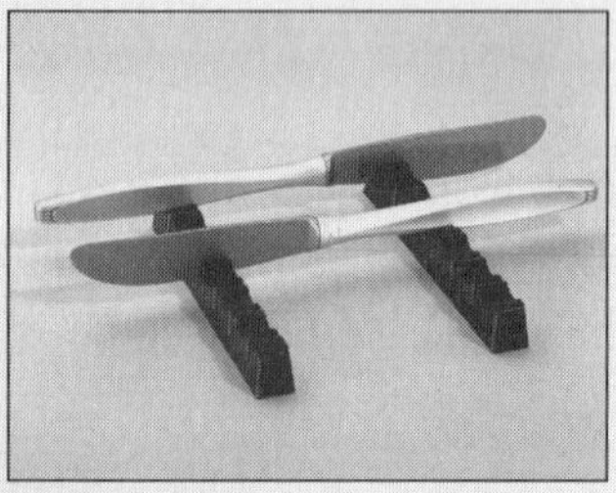

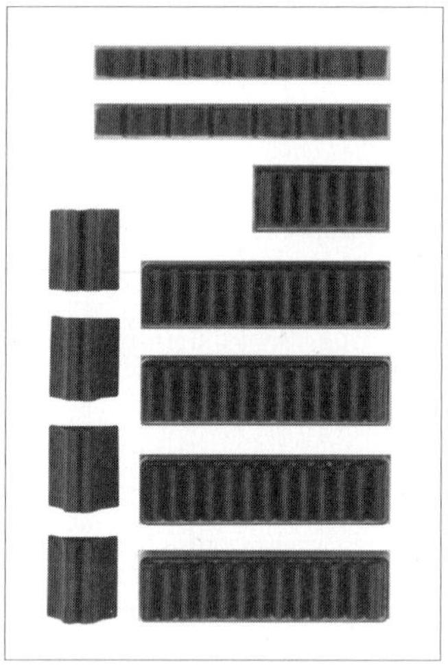

Silverware Cutlery holders, assorted set
Finish: plastic, brown
with felt covering, brown; self-adhesive

Quantity	Cat. No.:
for **50** pieces (12 knives, forks, spoons, teaspoons each; 2 large individual items)	891.21.111
for **70** pieces (12 knives, forks, spoons, teaspoons, pastry forks each; 6 small and 4 large individual items)	891.21.120
for **90** pieces (24 knives, forks each; 12 spoons, teaspoons, pastry forks each; 6 large individual items)	891.21.139

Packing: 1 set

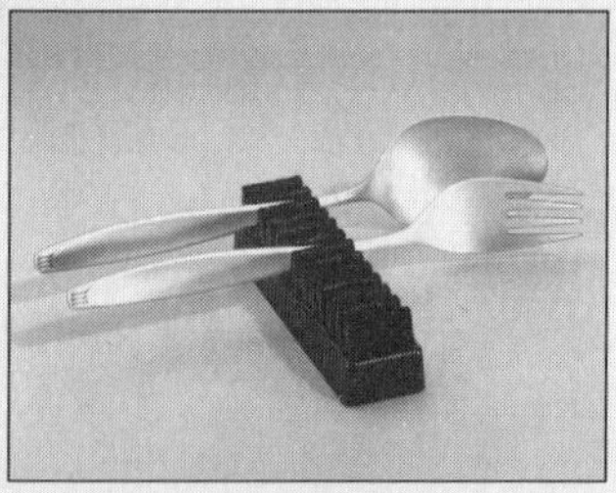

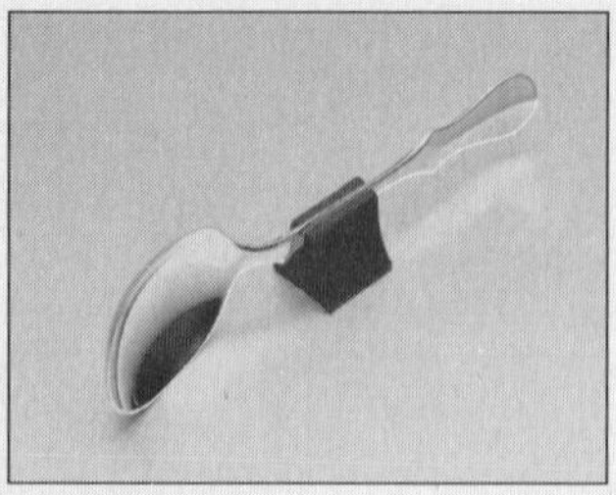

Dimensions in mm
Inches are approximate

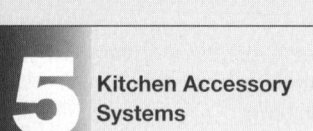

Medical Drawer Inserts

HÄFELE

Drawer inserts
Material: 2.5 mm
Finish: Polystyrene, gloss white

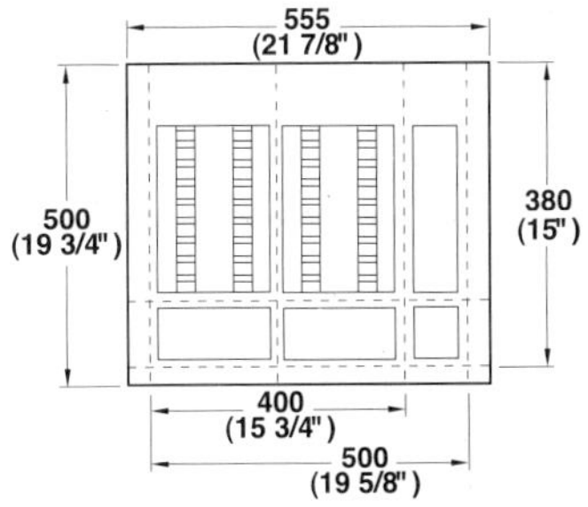

Drawer insert, flat with plastic for dental mirror, tweezers and other medical instruments.
Height: 28 mm (1 1/8")

Cat. No.	556.66.763

Packing: 1 Pc.

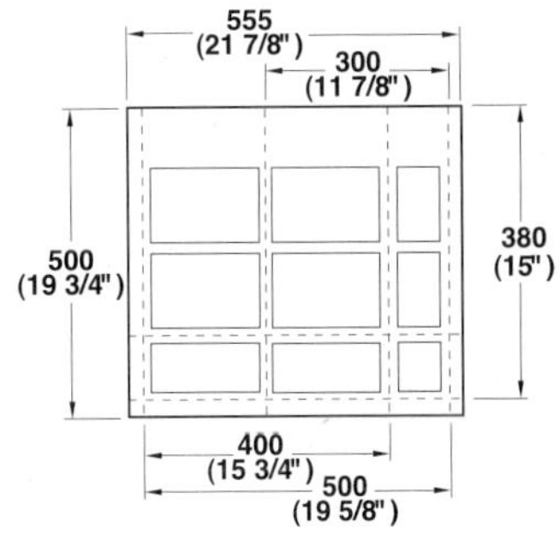

Drawer insert, flat with partitions for different materials and medical instruments
Height: 28 mm (1 1/8")

Cat. No.	556.66.754

Packing: 1 Pc.

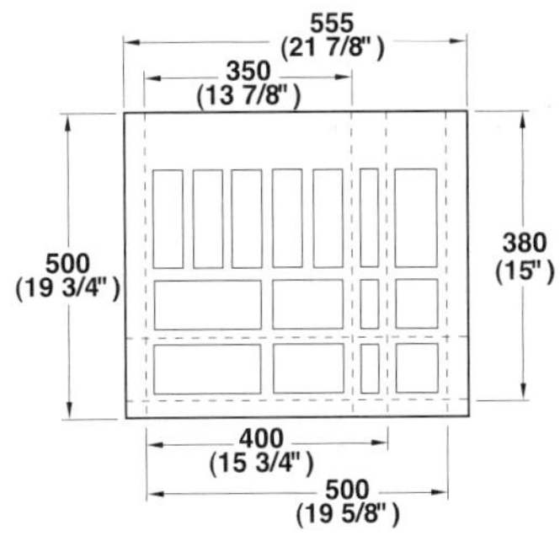

Drawer insert, flat with all-purpose partitions
Height: 28 mm (1 1/8")

Cat. No.	556.66.745

Packing: 1 Pc.

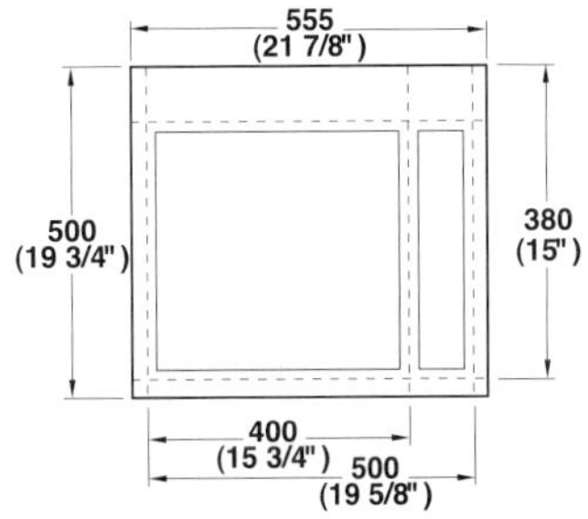

Drawer insert, deep with one large and one small partition.
Height: 57 mm (2 1/4")

Cat. No.	556.66.718

Packing: 1 Pc.

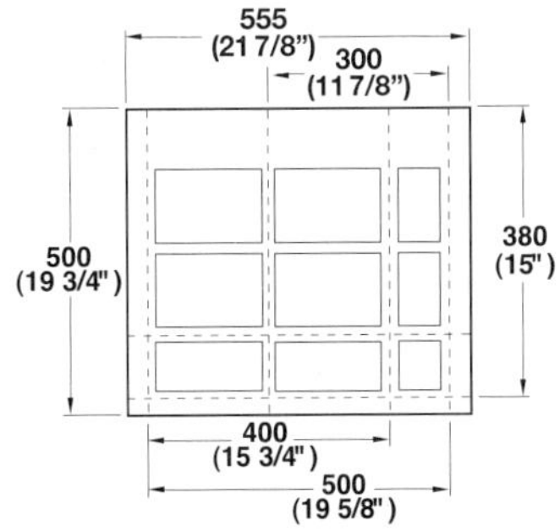

Drawer insert, deep with partitions for materials and medical instruments.
Height: 57 mm (2 1/4")

Cat. No.	556.66.727

Packing: 1 Pc.

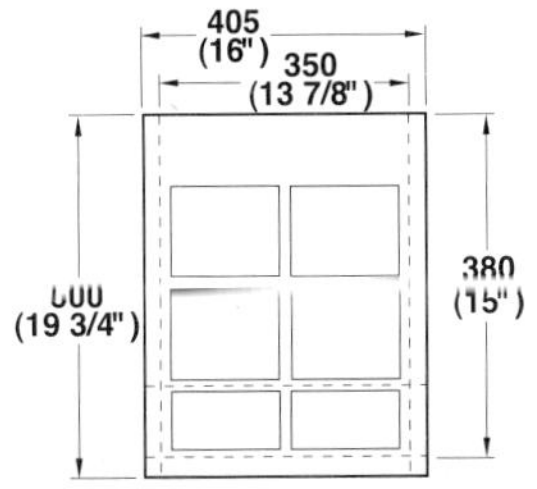

Drawer insert, deep with 6 partitions for materials and medical instruments.
Height: 57 mm (2 1/4")

Cat. No.	556.66.736

Packing: 1 Pc.

Dimensions in mm
Inches are approximate

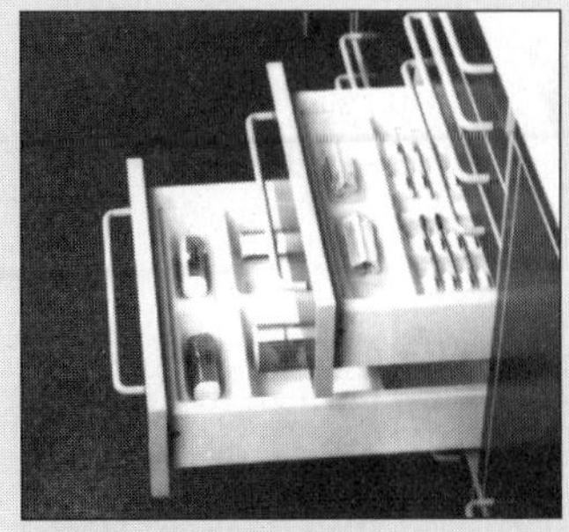

Fixed dimensions: starting at 100 pieces, at no extra cost.

Medical drawer inserts can be trimmed with a circular saw to the measurements indicated by the broken line.

Dimensional data not binding.
We reserve the right to alter specifications without notice.

HÄFELE

Swing-out Pantry Shelf Systems

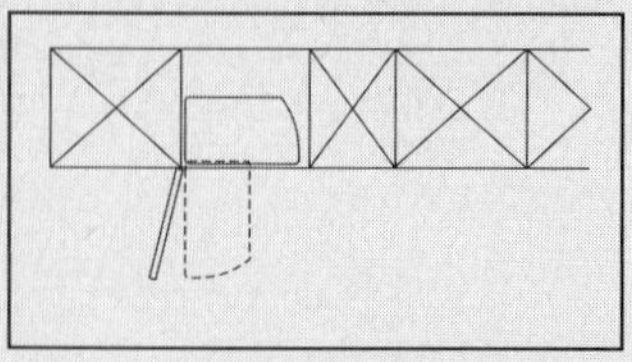

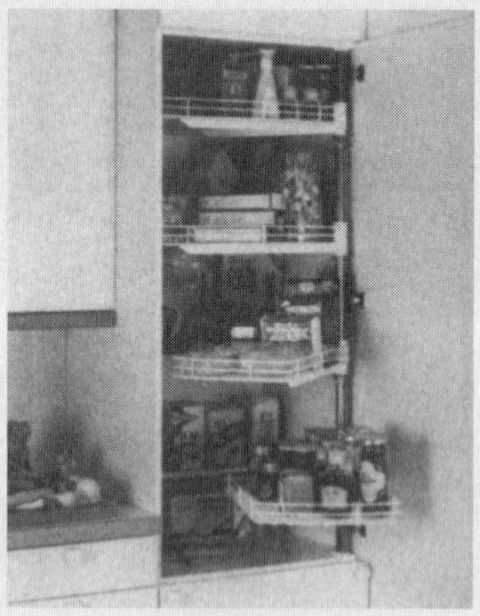

Right hand application shown.

- The post for the revolving shelves is a fixed installation, allowing the shelves to rotate independently.
- Shelves revolve independently around stationary post.

Post, 1745 mm (68 3/4") high
Pre-drilled for revolving shelves
Screw-mounted to cabinet floor and ceiling.

**Note: Different heights can be obtained by shortening the post at the upper end.*

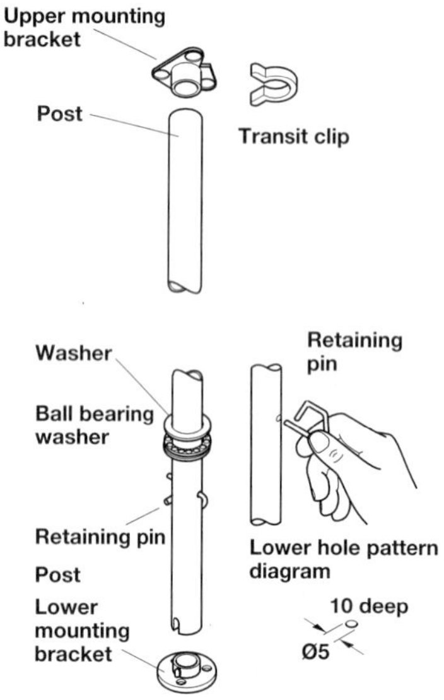

Finish: Post: Ø 25 mm steel, chrome-plated
Mounts and safety device: plastic, white

Cat. No.	545.90.206

Packing: 1pc.

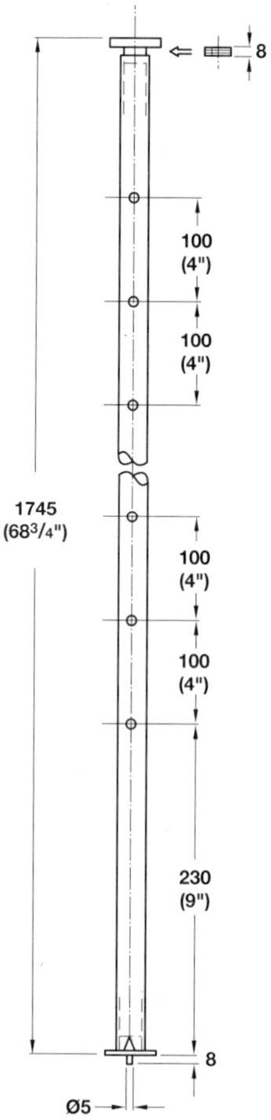

Swing-out Shelf
With wire surround, complete with ball bearing washer and retaining pin.

Finish: steel, plastic-coated, white

For tall units 500 mm wide

Dimensions	448 x 240 x 82 mm	
Type:	left	right
Cat. No.	545.90.733	545.90.724

For tall units 600 mm wide

Dimensions	548 x 330 x 82 mm	
Type:	left	right
Cat. No.	545.90.751	545.90.742

Packing: 1 and 5 pcs.

Installed dimensions for 500 mm unit

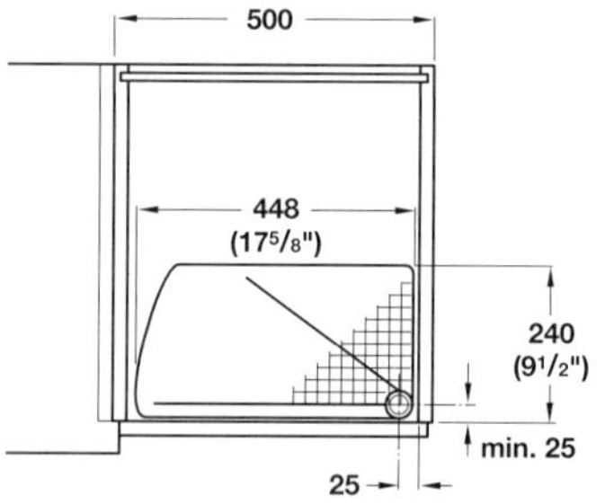

Installed dimensions for 600 mm unit

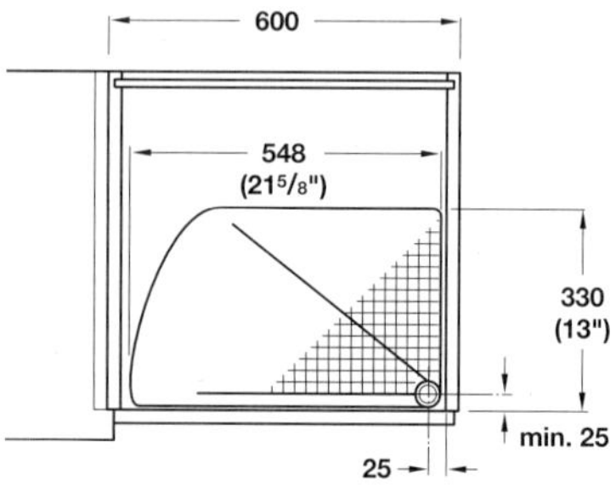

Dimensional data not binding.
We reserve the right to alter specifications without notice.

Dimensions in mm
Inches are approximate

Pantry Pull-Out Units

HÄFELE

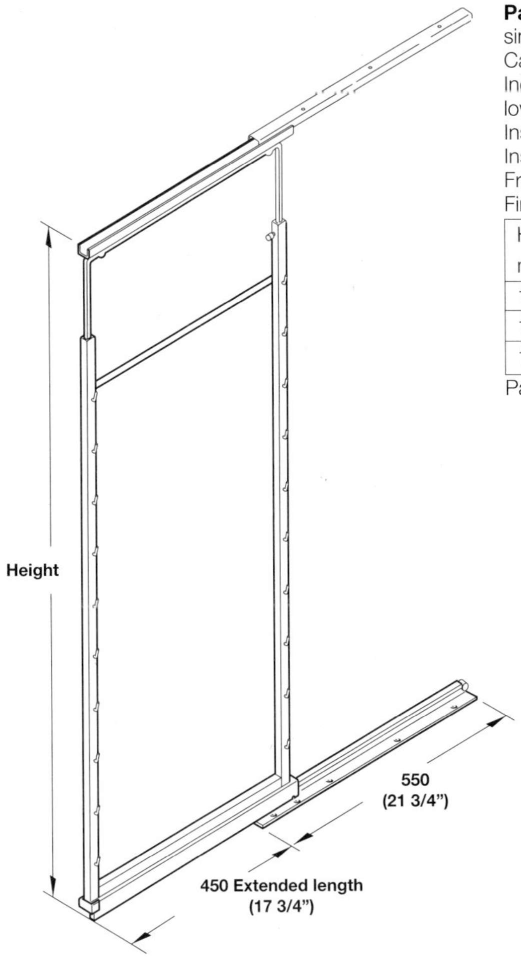

Pantry pull-out set, height-adjustable single-extension
Capacity: **50 kg (110 lbs.)**
Includes frame with hooks on both sides, upper and lower runners.
Inside cabinet width: basket width + 38 mm (1 1/2")
Inside cabinet depth: 550 mm (21 5/8")
Frame dimensions: width: 38 mm (1 1/2")
Finish: steel, epoxy-coated, white

Height mm (inch)	Cat. No.
1000-1350 (39 3/8-53")	545.74.757
1350-1650 (53-65")	545.74.766
1650-2000 (65-78 3/4")	545.74.775

Packing: 1 pc.

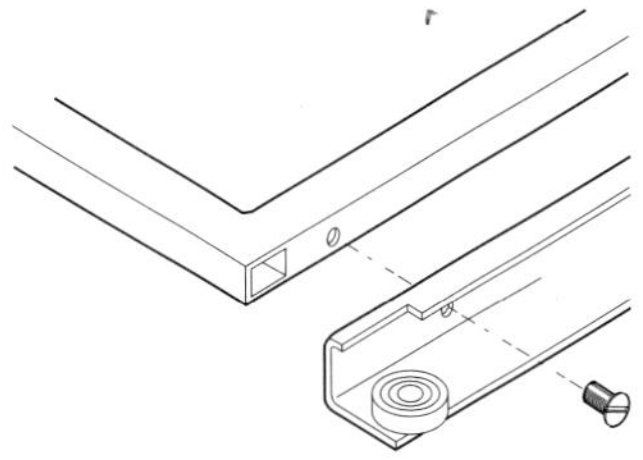

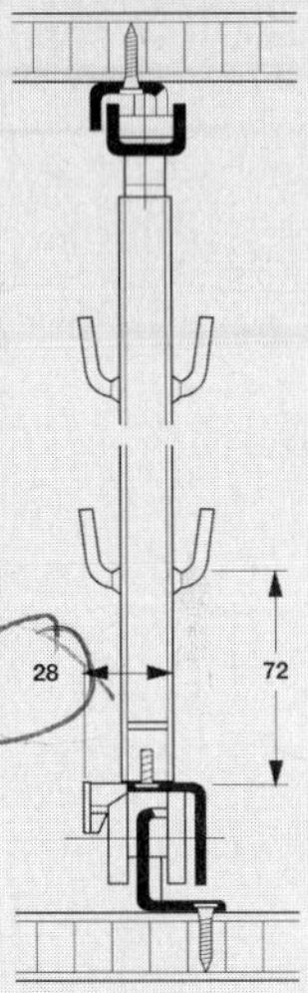

The upper runner can be reversed for mounting left or right.

The mounting of the lower runner on the hanging frame can be reversed to permit installation on either side.

Kitchen Accessory Systems **5**

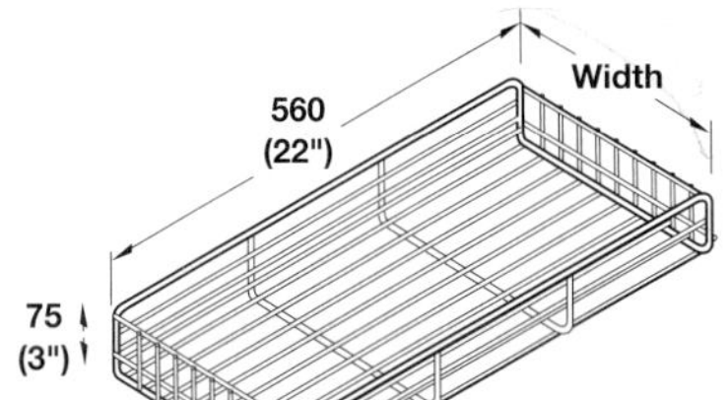

Storage basket
Finish: steel, epoxy-coated, white

Basket width mm (inch)	Cat. No.
98 (4")	545.42.719
137 (5 3/8")	545.42.728
175 (6 7/8")	545.42.737
216 (8 1/2")	545.42.746
292 (11 1/2")	545.42.755
368 (14 1/2")	545.42.764

Packing: 1 pc.

Dimensions in mm
Inches are approximate

HÄFELE

Pantry Pull-out Unit

Detailed assembly installation included.

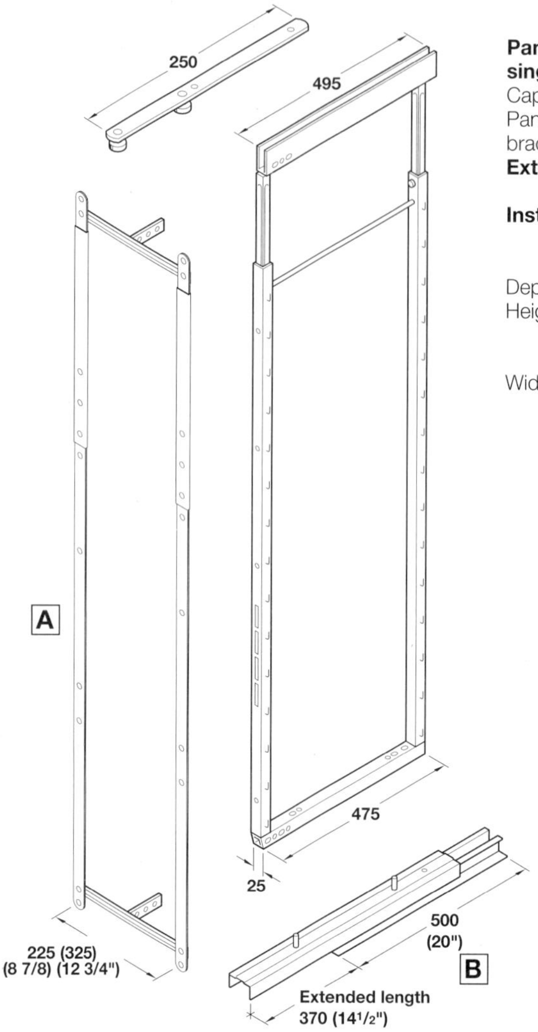

Pantry Pull-out Unit - height-adjustable , single-extension
Capacity: 100 kg (220 lbs.)
Pantry frame includes front frame, front frame fixing brackets and counter frame.
Extension runner must be ordered separately.

Installed dimensions:

Depth:	minimum 500 mm (20")
Height:	1195 - 1685 mm (47 - 66 3/8")
	1590-2080 (62 5/8"- 81 7/8")
	1895-2380 (74 5/8"- 93 7/8")
Width:	260 mm (10 1/4")
	to 360 mm (14 1/8")

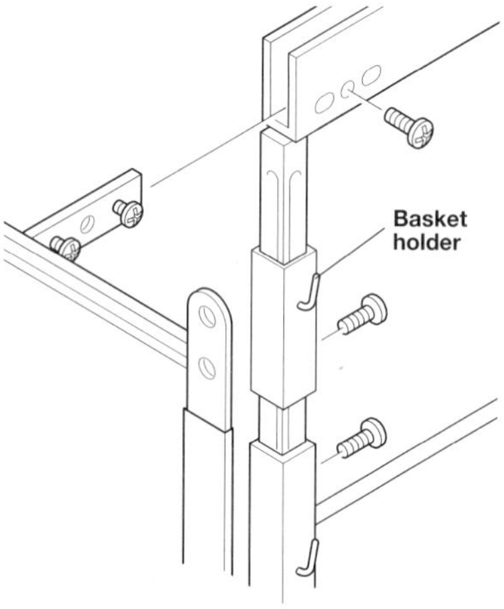

5 Kitchen Accessory Systems

A Pantry frame

Finish: steel, epoxy-coated

Cabinet width mm	Cabinet width inch	Installed height mm	Installed height inch	Cat. No. white Ral 9010	Cat. No. silver Ral 9006
300	12"	1195-1685	47-66 3/8"	546.77.720	546.77.220
300	12"	1590-2080	62 5/8-81 7/8"	546.77.740	546.77.240
300	12"	1895-2380	74 5/8-93 7/8"	546.77.760	546.77.260
400	16"	1195-1685	47-66 3/8"	546.77.730	546.77.230
400	16"	1590-2080	62 5/8-81 7/8"	546.77.750	546.77.250
400	16"	1895-2380	74 5/8-93 7/8"	546.77.770	546.77.270

Packing: 1 set

Basket Holder:
To be used as add-on hooks when pantry frame height is extended.
Height: 125 mm (5")

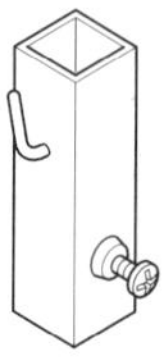

Finish: steel, epoxy-coated

silver RAL 9006	545.84.280
white RAL 9010	545.84.780

Packing: 1 pair (2 pcs.)

B Full Extension Runner for 3/4" extension effect

Includes upper and lower runners.
Finish: steel, epoxy-coated

Color	Cat. No.
White RAL 9010	546.70.790
Silver Epoxy RAL 9006	546.70.290

Packing: 1 pc.

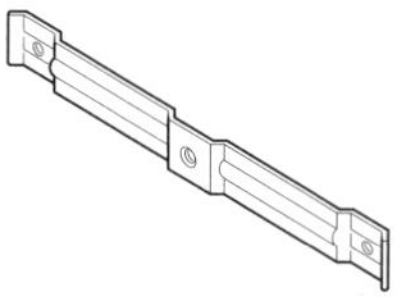

Stabilizer bar:
for attachment to framed doors
Finish: steel, epoxy-coated

Color	300 mm	400 mm
silver RAL 9006	546.76.201	546.76.210
white RAL 9010	546.76.701	546.76.710

Packing: 1 pc.

Dimensions in mm
Inches are approximate

Pantry Pull-out Unit

HÄFELE

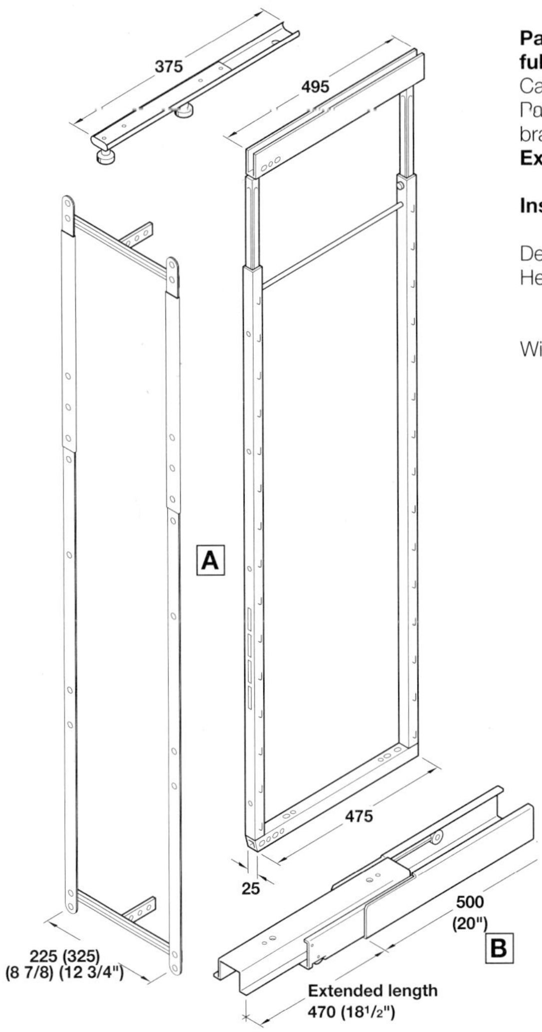

Pantry Pull-out Unit - height-adjustable full extension
Capacity: 100 kg (220 lbs.)
Pantry frame includes front frame, front frame fixing brackets and center frame.
Extension runner must be ordered separately.

Installed dimensions:

Depth:	minimum 500 mm (20")
Height:	1255 - 1745 mm (49¹/₂ - 68³/₄")
	1650 - 2140 mm (64³/₄ - 84¹/₄"
	1955-2440 mm(78¹/₂ - 96")
Width:	260 mm (10¹/₄")
	to 360 mm (14¹/₈")

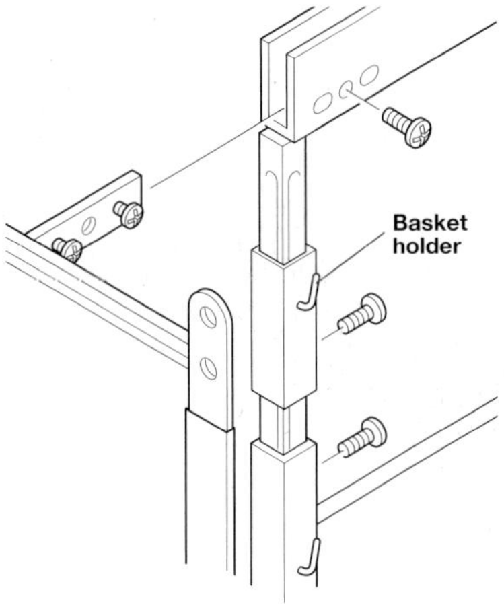

Detailed assembly instruction included.

Kitchen Accessory Systems

5

A Pantry frame

Finish: steel, epoxy-coated

Cabinet width mm	inch	Installed height mm	inch	Cat. No. white Ral 9010	silver Ral 9006
300	12"	1255-1745	49¹/₂-68³/₄"	546.77.720	546.77.220
300	12"	1650-2140	64³/₄-84¹/₄"	546.77.740	546.77.240
300	12"	1955-2440	77-96"	546.77.760	546.77.260
400	16"	1255-1745	49¹/₂-68³/₄"	546.77.730	546.77.230
400	16"	1650-2140	64³/₄-84¹/₄"	546.77.750	546.77.250
400	16"	1955-2440	77-96"	546.77.770	546.77.270

Packing: 1 set

Basket Holder:
To be used as add-on hooks when pantry frame height is extended.
Height: 125 mm (5")

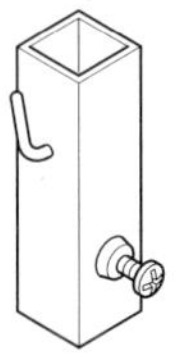

Finish: steel, epoxy-coated

silver RAL 9006	545.84.280
white RAL 9010	545.84.780

Packing: 1 pair (2 pcs.)

B Full Extension Runner

Consists upper and lower runners.
Finish: steel, epoxy-coated

Color	Cat. No.
White RAL 9010	546.71.797
Silver Epoxy RAL 9006	546.71.297

Packing: 1 pc.

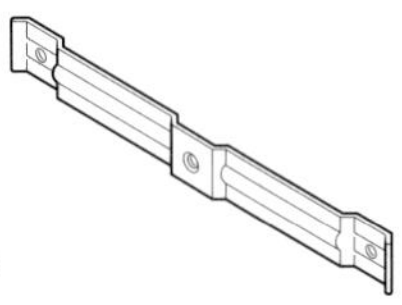

Stabilizer bar:
for attachment to framed doors
Finish: steel, epoxy-coated

Color	300 mm	400 mm
silver RAL 9006	546.76.201	546.76.210
white RAL 9010	546.76.701	546.76.710

Packing: 1 pc.

Dimensions in mm
Inches are approximate

Dimensional data not binding. We reserve the right to alter specifications without notice.

HÄFELE

Storage Baskets

Recommended number of storage baskets

installed height
- 1195-1685 (1255-1745) — 4 baskets
- 1590-2080 (1650-2140) — 6 baskets
- 1895-2380 (1955-2440) — 8 baskets

for Pantry Pull-out Units
with cabinet widths of 300 mm (11¾) and 400 mm (15¾)

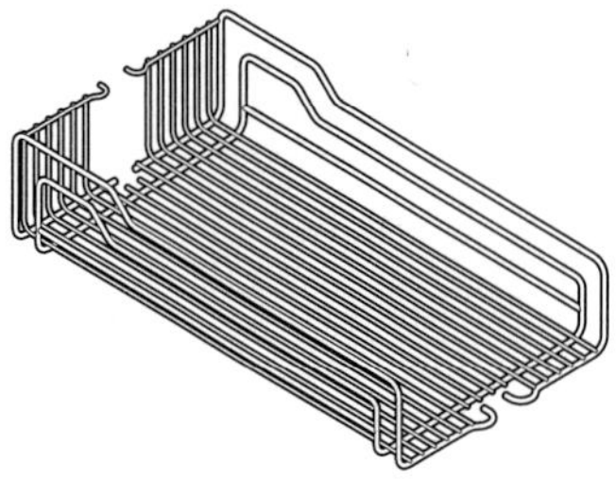

Storage basket (hook-on)
Finish: steel

cabinet width	300 mm	400 mm
width x depth x height (mm)	250 x 467 x 110	350 x 467 x 110
chrome-plated	546.75.204	546.75.213

Packing: 1 pc.

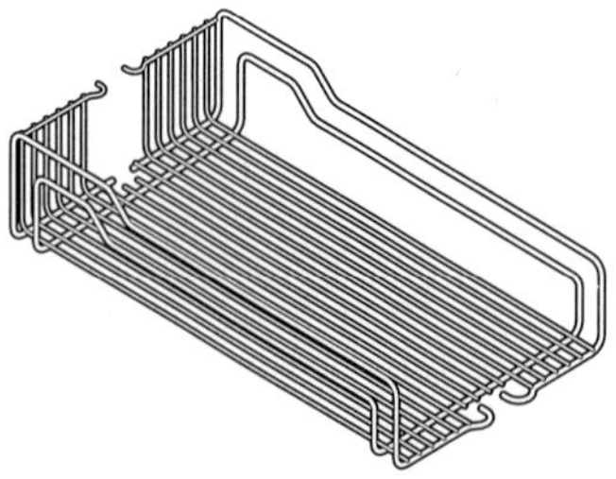

Storage basket (hook-on)
Finish: steel

cabinet width	300 mm	400 mm
width x depth x height (mm)	250 x 467 x 110	350 x 467 x 110
plastic-coated white RAL 9010	546.75.704	546.75.713
chrome-plated	546.75.200	546.75.210

Packing: 1 pc.

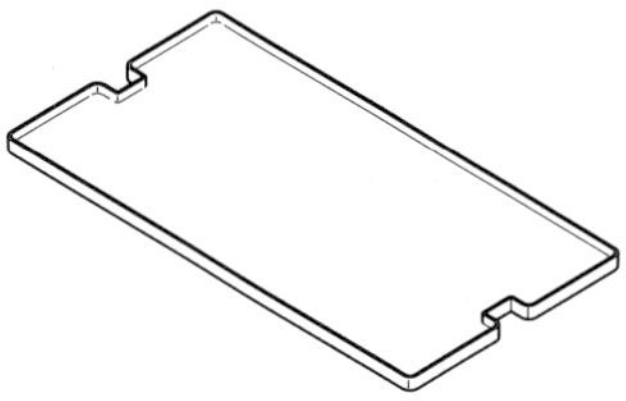

Storage shelf, for storage basket 546.75.
Finish: plastic

for cabinet width	300 mm	400 mm
width x depth x height (mm)	238 x 450 x 12	338 x 450 x 12
white RAL 9010	546.75.780	546.75.781

Packing: 1 pc.

5 Kitchen Accessory Systems

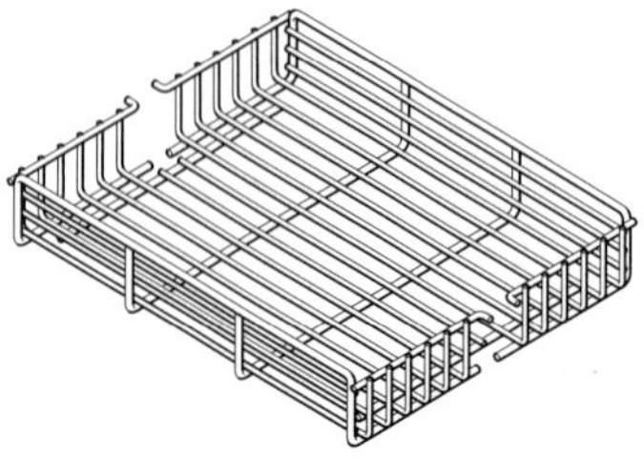

Storage basket (hook-on)
Finish: steel

cabinet width	300 mm	400 mm
width x depth x height (mm)	250 x 468 x 75	350 x 468 x 75
plastic coated white RAL 9010	545.86.711	545.86.720

Packing: 1 pc.

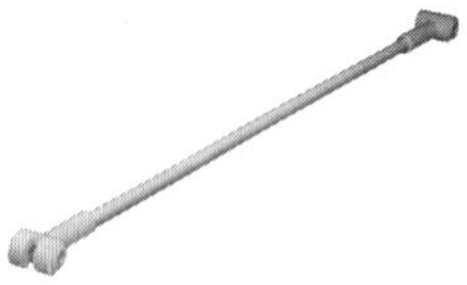

Crossbar and end clips, for use with storage baskets
Finish: end clips: plastic, white or black
Bar: steel, plastic-coated or chrome-plated

for cabinet width	300 mm	400 mm
white/white	545.87.718	545.87.727
chrome-plated/black	545.89.212	545.89.221

Packing: 1 pc.

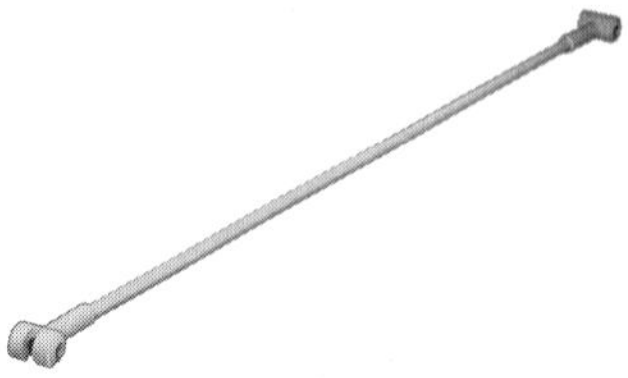

Crossbar and end clips, for use with storage baskets
Finish: fastening clips: plastic; bar: steel, plastic-coated

length	445-473 mm
white	545.87.790

Packing: 1 pc.

Dimensional data not binding. We reserve the right to alter specifications without notice.

Dimensions in mm
Inches are approximate

Storage Baskets

HÄFELE

for Pantry Pull-out Units
with cabinet widths of 300 mm (11¾) and 400 mm (15¾)

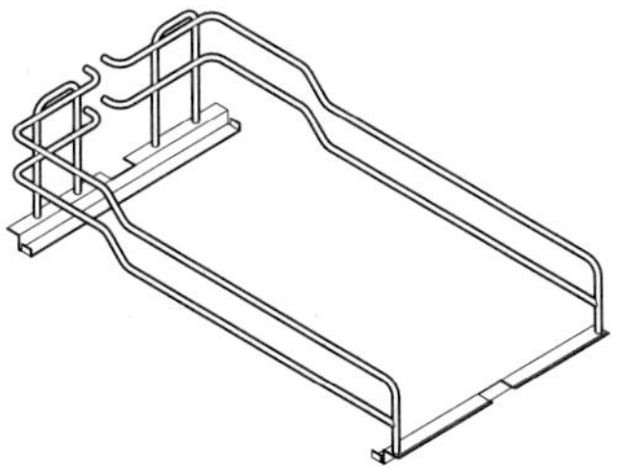

Shelf support (hook-on), steel

for cabinet width	300 mm	400 mm
width x depth x height	250x460x110	350x460x110
chrome-plated	546.75.222	546.75.231

Packing: 1 piece

Customer provide wood liners having the dimensions 249 (349) x 419 x 16 mm can be installed in these shelf supports

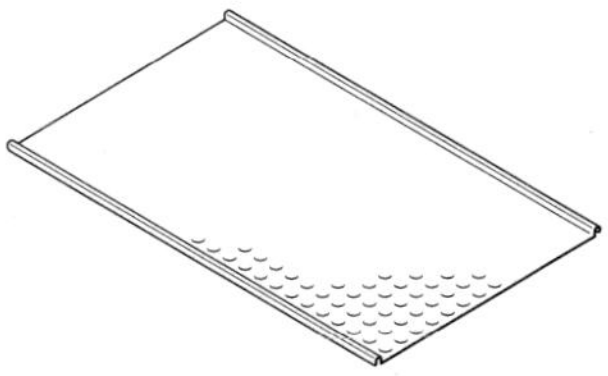

Structured metal shelf, for shelf siupport
Finish: stamped metal

for cabinet width	300 mm	400 mm
width x depth x height	255x422	355x422
white RAL 9010	546.75.740	546.75.759

Packing: 1 piece

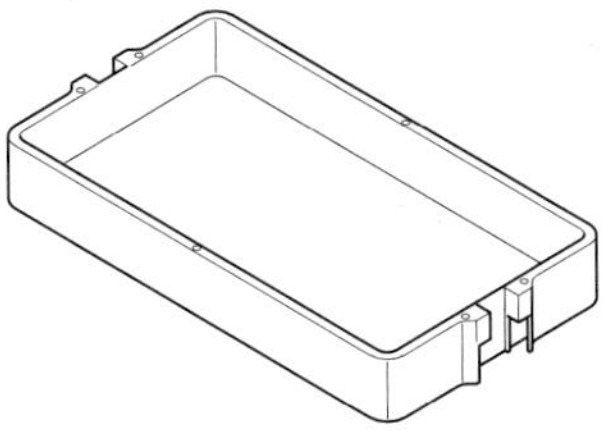

Tray (hook-on), plastic

for cabinet width	300 mm	400 mm
width x depth x height	250x460x70	350x460x70
white RAL 9010	545.86.739	545.86.748

Packing: 1 piece

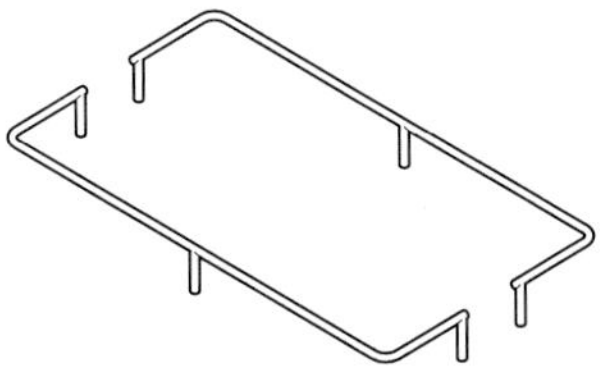

Attachable railing, for tray series 545.86
Finish: steel

for cabinet width	300 mm	400 mm
chrome-plated	545.86.284	545.86.293

Packing: 2 pcs. (including mounting hardware)

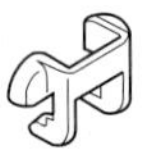

Basket clip, for storage baskets
Finish: plastic

color	Cat. No.
clear	546.75.090

Packing: 10 pcs.

Recommended number of storage baskets

installation height
- 1195-1685 (1255-1745) 4 baskets
- 1590-2080 (1650-2140) 6 baskets
- 1895-2380 (1955-2440) 8 baskets

Kitchen Accessory Systems 5

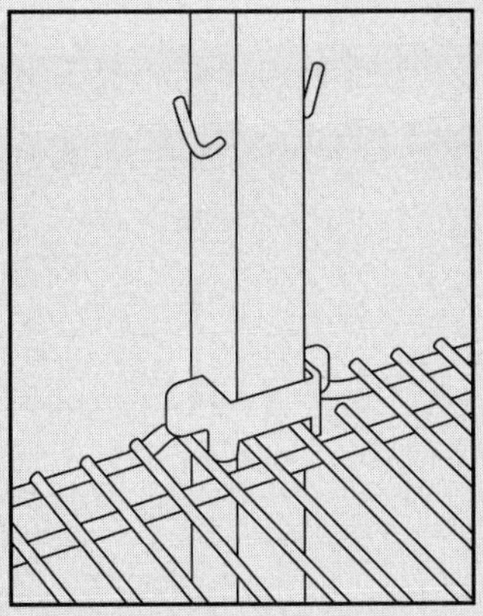

Basket clip holds baskets on pantry pull-out 546.77 during shipping which eliminates the need to pack baskets in separate boxes.

HÄFELE

Pantry Pullout Unit, Full-Extension Slide

Pantry pullout and swivel with full-extension slide
for minimum 445 mm (17 1/2") inside width cabinets.
Includes: frame, upper and lower slide
Load capacity: 50 kg (110 lbs.)
Finish: steel, epoxy coated

white	546.80.720
silver	546.80.920

Packing: 1 pc.

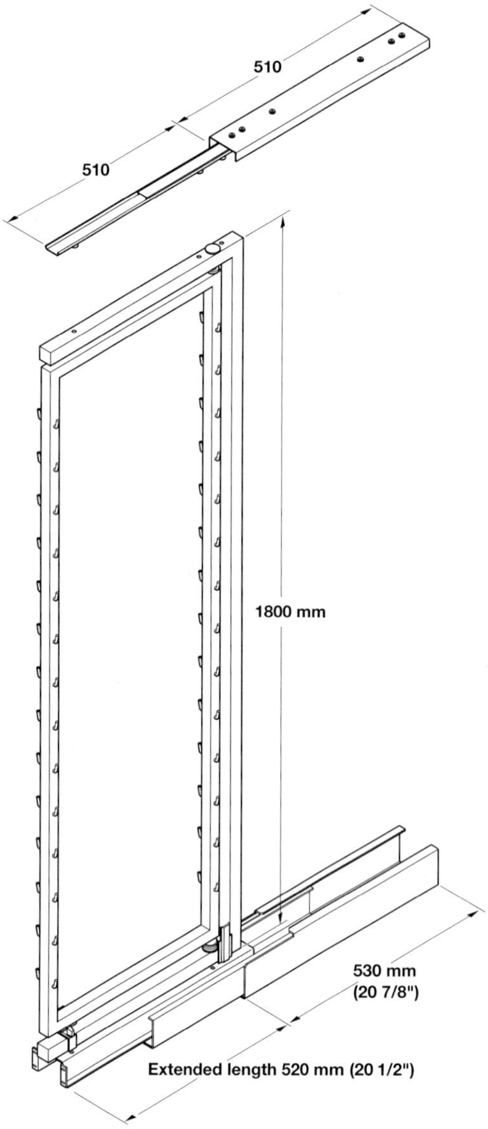

Height:	1800 mm	(71")
Depth:	530 mm	(20 7/8")
Door width:	445 mm	(17 1/2")

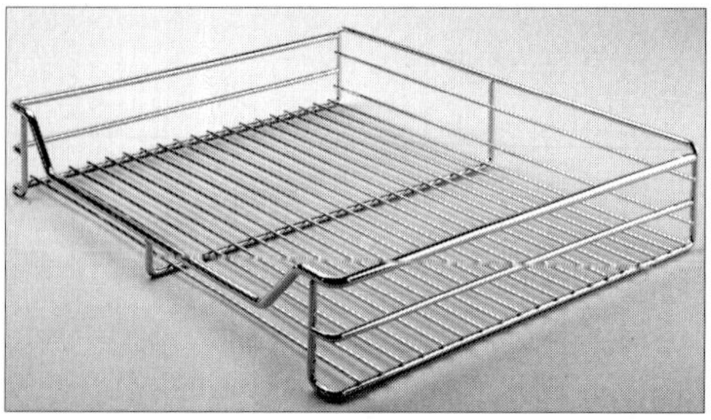

Storage basket
395 x 470 x 80 mm
Finish: steel, chrome plated

Cat. No.	546.81.200

Packing: 1 pc.

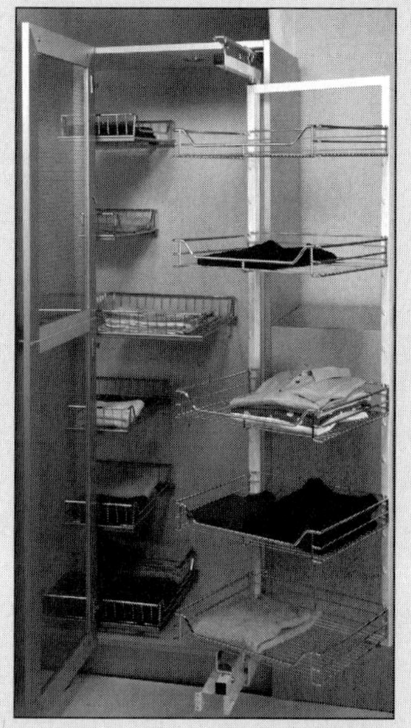

- Can be mounted to right or left side. 1 frame for 2 mounting options
- Installed at bottom of cabinet and to top side of cabinet-- can be used in cabinets 1800 mm or more in height
- Full extension slide with swiveling tubular frame--allows access to all baskets and rear of cabinet

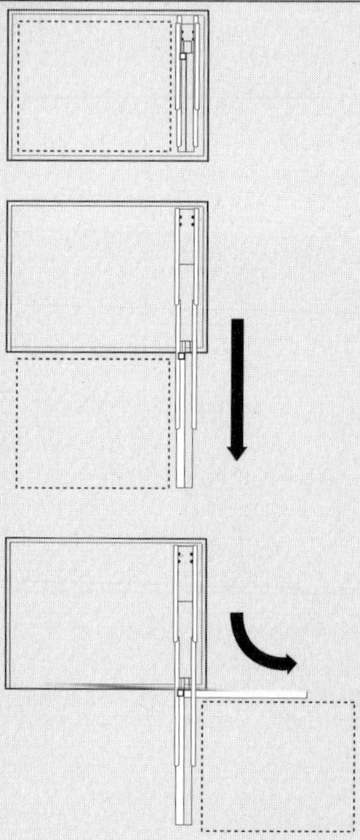

- Adjustable chrome-plated baskets can be rearranged

Dimensional data not binding. We reserve the right to alter specifications without notice.

Dimensions in mm
Inches are approximate

HÄFELE

Duo Swivel Pantry Unit

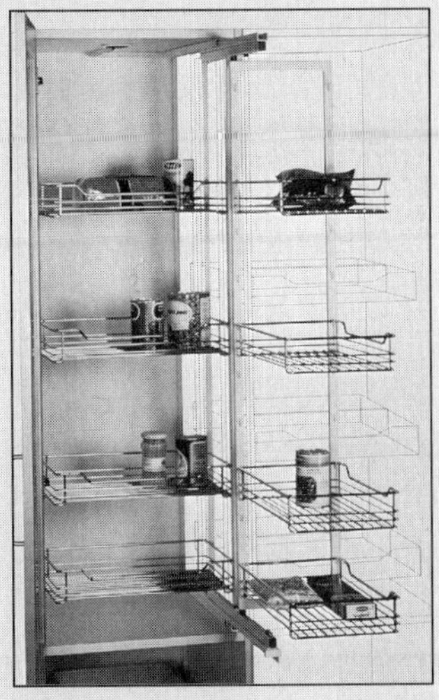

- Very easy to use--accessible to front and back baskets
- Suitable for one or two door cabinets 450 mm or 900 mm
- Lockable pivoting front frame--allows access to rear baskets and locks front part in place.

Duo swivel pantry unit with 3/4 extension slides
Consisting of frame, upper guide and lower rail
Load capacity 50 kg (110 lbs.)
Finish: steel, epoxy-coated

white	546.82.710
silver	546.82.910

Packing: 1 pc.

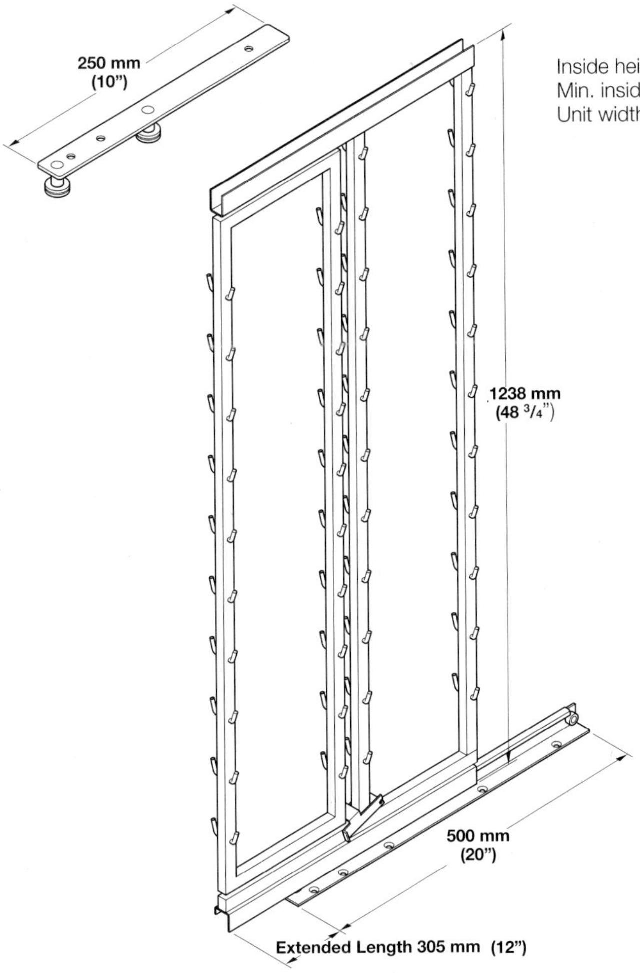

Inside height:	1238 mm (48 3/4")
Min. inside cabinet depth:	500 mm (19 3/4")
Unit width:	450 mm (17 3/4")

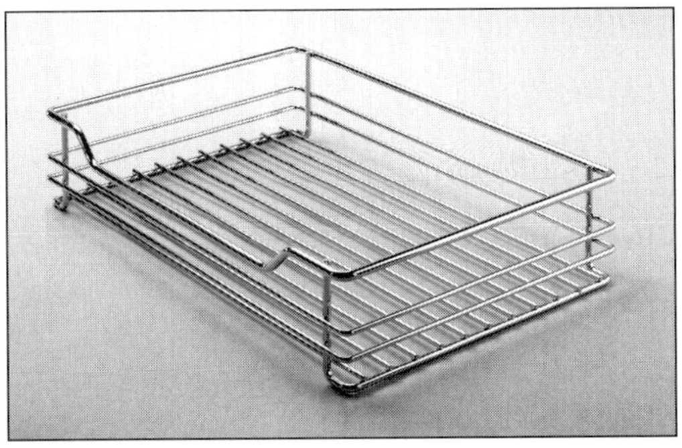

Storage basket
238 x 350 x 70 mm
Finish: steel, chrome plated

Cat. No.	546.83.200

Packing: 1 pc.

Kitchen Accessory Systems 5

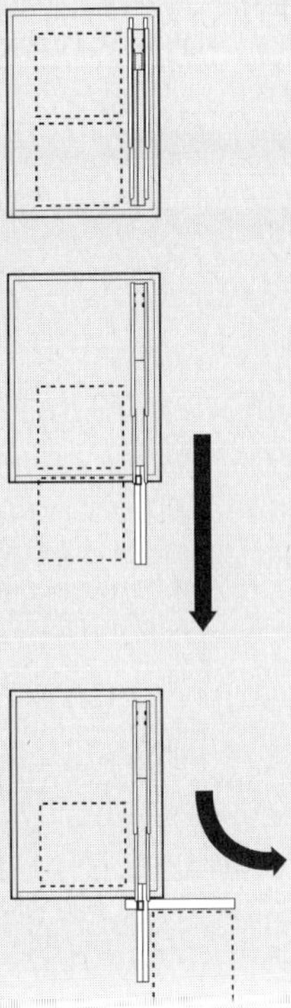

Dimensional data not binding. We reserve the right to alter specifications without notice.

Dimensions in mm
Inches are approximate

HÄFELE

Tall Unit Pantry Pull-Outs for Diagonal Cabinets

Detailed installation instructions are enclosed.

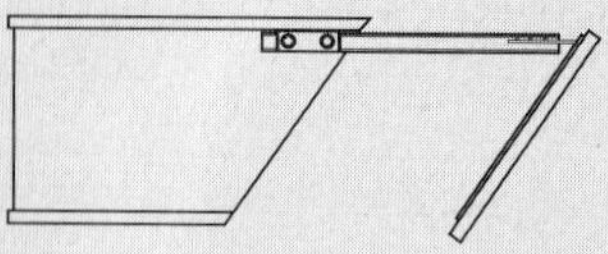

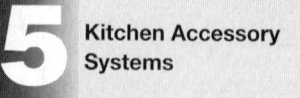

right hand cabinet

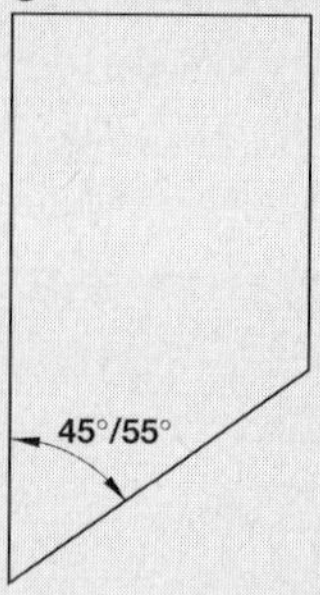

left hand cabinet

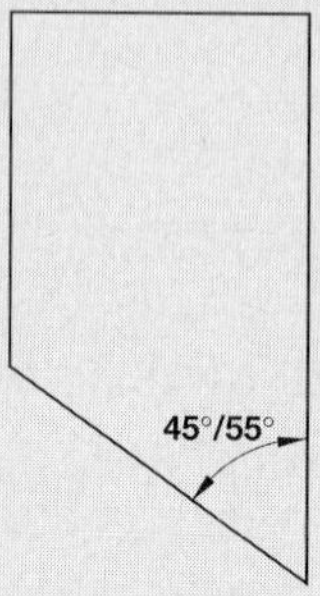

Dimensional data not binding. We reserve the right to alter specifications without notice.

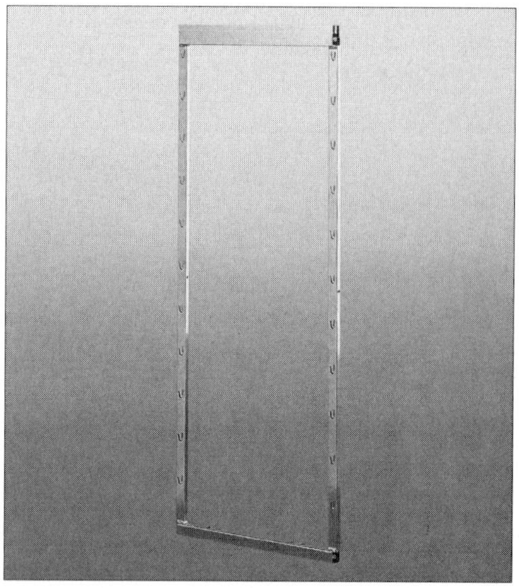

Diagonal tall unit pantry pull-out
Minimum cabinet width 262 mm (10 1/4")
Minimum cabinet depth 495 mm (19 1/2")
Load capacity: 100 kg maximum (220 lbs.)

Support frame for diagonal pantry pull-out for tall units
Width: 25 mm (1")
Depth: 455 mm (18")
Finish: steel, plastic-coated

Min. inside cabinet height mm	inch	Height of frame	white alum. RAL 9006	white RAL 9010
1235	48 5/8	1165	546.78.211	546.78.711
1463	57 5/8	1393	546.78.212	546.78.712
1780	70	1710	546.78.213	546.78.713
2080	82	2010	546.78.214	546.78.714

Packing: 1 pc.

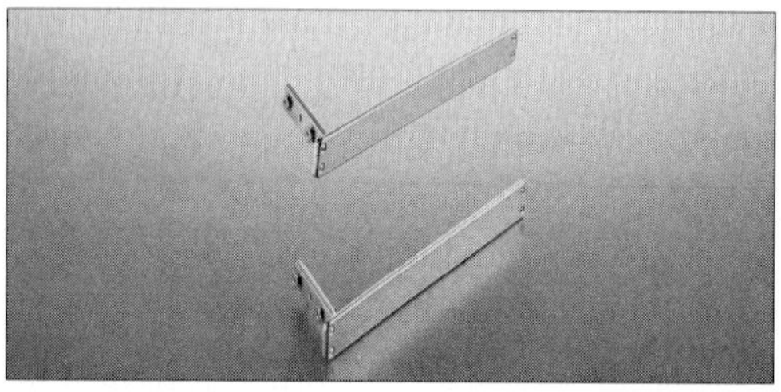

Front bracket
Finish: steel, plastic-coated

Length	Angle	white alum. RAL 9006	white RAL 9010
300 mm	55°	546.78.222	546.78.722
355 mm	45°	546.78.221	546.78.721

Packing: 1 set (2 pcs.)

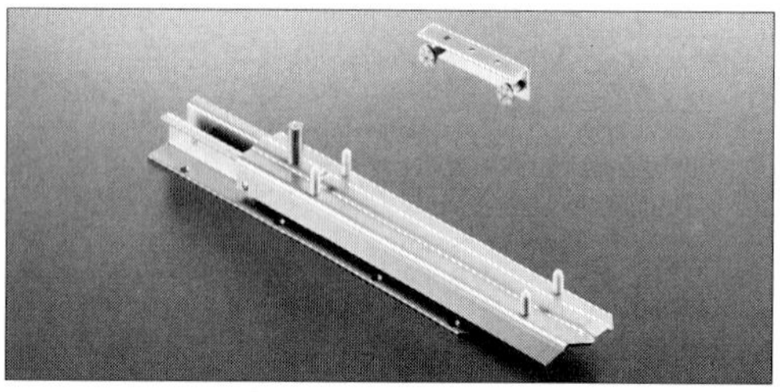

Pull-out slide
Partial-extension slide, complete with upper runner
Load capacity: 100 kg (220 lbs.)
Finish: steel, plastic-coated

color	Cat. No.
white aluminum, RAL 9006	546.78.200
white, RAL 9010	546.78.700

Packing: 1 pc.

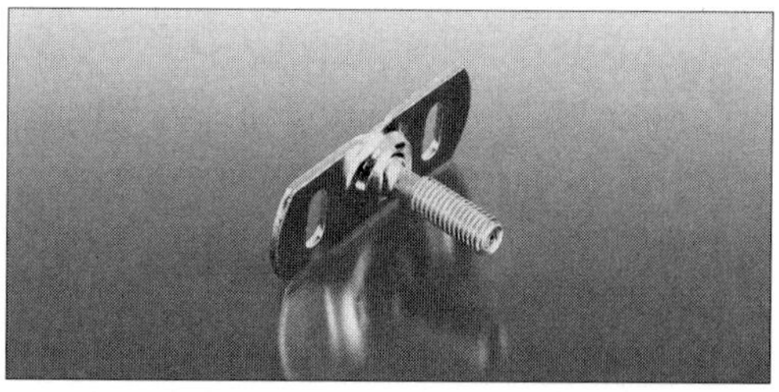

Front stabilizer
Finish: steel, zinc-plated

Cat. No.	546.78.230

Packing: 1 pc.
inside cabinet height of 1235 mm = 1 pc.
inside cabinet height of 1463 mm = 2 pc.
inside cabinet height of 1780 mm = 3 pc.
inside cabinet height of 2080 mm = 3 pc.

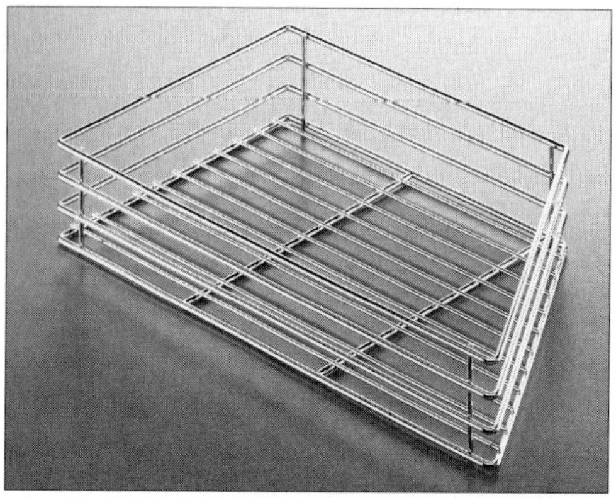

Hanging wire baskets
size: 228 x 467 x 74 mm
(width x depth x height)
Finish: steel

for angle		chrome-plated	plastic-coated white, RAL 9010
55°	right	545.60.226	545.60.726
	left	545.60.235	545.60.735
45°	right	545.60.224	545.60.724
	left	545.60.234	545.60.734

Packing: 1 pc.

Dimensions in mm
Inches are approximate

Tall Unit Fittings

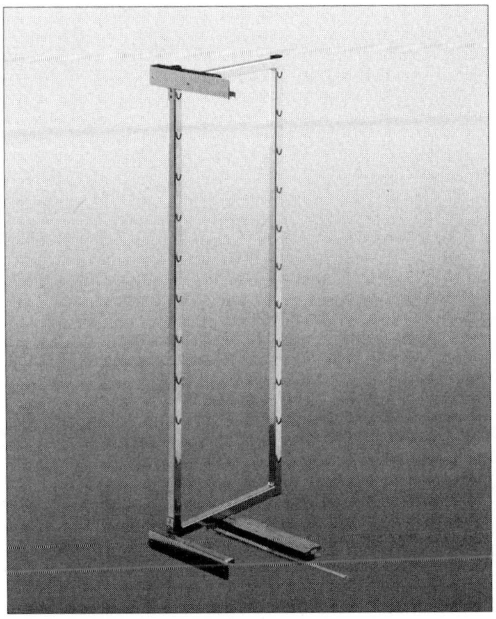

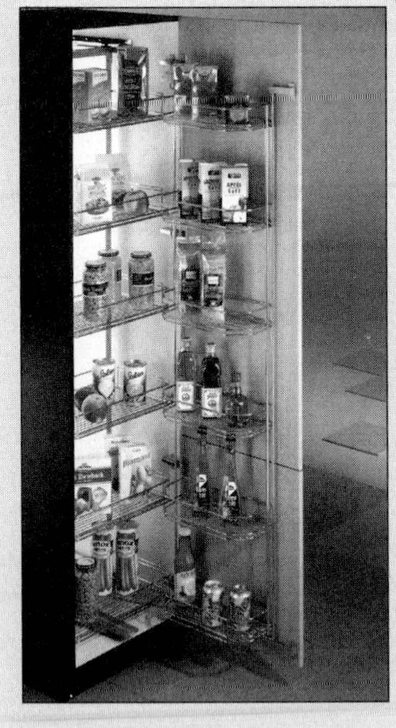

- As the cabinet door is opened, the door panel swings out and the back pullout shelf comes to the front.

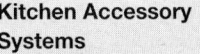

Tandem-Pullout

Inside height:
starting from 1200 mm (47¼) (4-shelf)
starting from 1700 mm (67) (6-shelf)
Inside width:
450 mm cabinet: starting from 412 mm (16¼)
500 mm cabinet: starting from 462 mm (18¼)
Inside depth:
minimum 500 mm (19¾)

Pullout Frame
for left or right mounting
Finish: Steel, epoxy coated white RAL 9010

fits cabinet Width mm (inch)	Height mm (inch) 1200 (47¼)	1700 (67)
450 (17¾)	545.94.741	545.94.742
500 (19¾)	545.94.751	545.94.752

Packing: 1 pc.

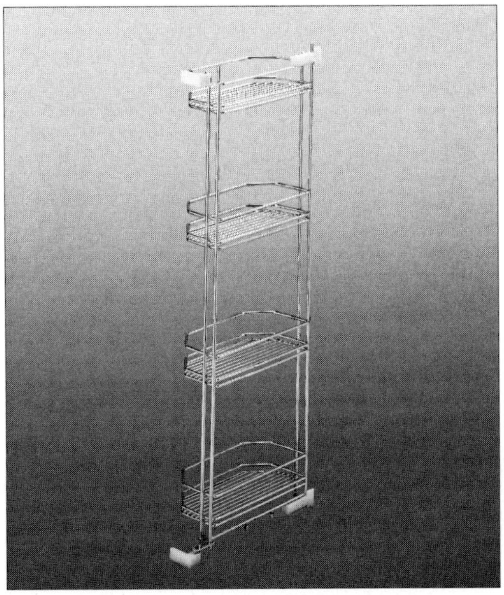

Door Shelf
for left and right mounting
1200 mm comes with 4 shelves, 1700 mm with 6 shelves fixed
Finish: Steel, chrome-plated

fits cabinet Width mm (inch)	Height mm (inch) 1200 (47¼)	1700 (67)
450 (17¾)	545.94.261	545.94.262
500 (19¾)	545.94.271	545.94.272

Packing: 1 pc.

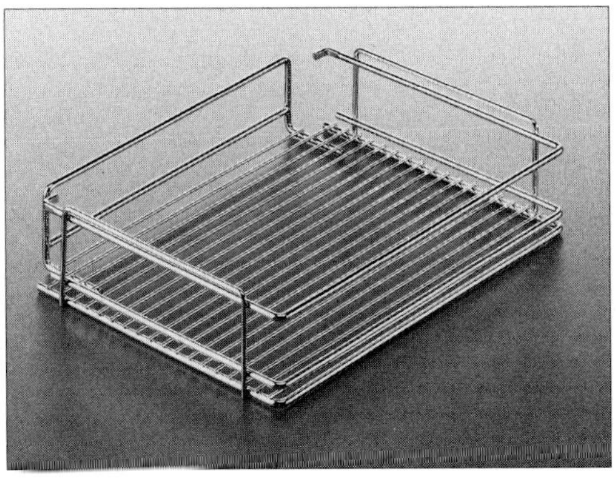

Storage Basket, for pullout frame.
Finish: Steel, chrome-plated

fits cabinet width mm (inch)	W x D x H	Cat. No.
450 (17¾)	375 x 300 x 80	545.95.240
500 (19¾)	425 x 300 x 80	545.95.250

Packing: 1 pc.

Dimensions in mm
Inches are approximate

HÄFELE

Gourmet Pantry Unit

Benefits:
- Large storage capacity in a small space
- Easy access
- Baskets individually height adjustable

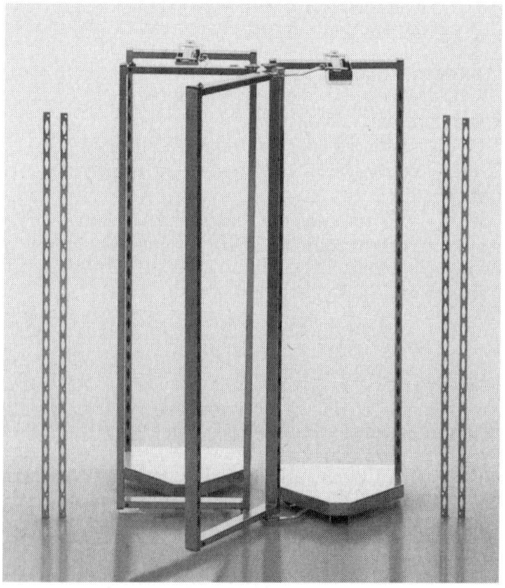

Gourmet pantry unit frames set.
Including:
- 2 swivel frames,
- 2 extension frames,
- 2 upper runners with stop,
- 2 lower runners,
- 2 upper bearing brackets,
- 2 lower bearing brackets with ball-bearings,
- 2 upper and 2 lower lever arms,
- 2 upper and 2 lower safety covers,
- 2 door catches for the swivel frames,
- 4 door rails, 1500 mm, and all accessories for the assembly. Screws for installing the unit in the cabinet are not included.

Finish: steel, epoxy-coated

Cat. No.	white	545.92.700
	silver	545.92.200

Packing: 1 set

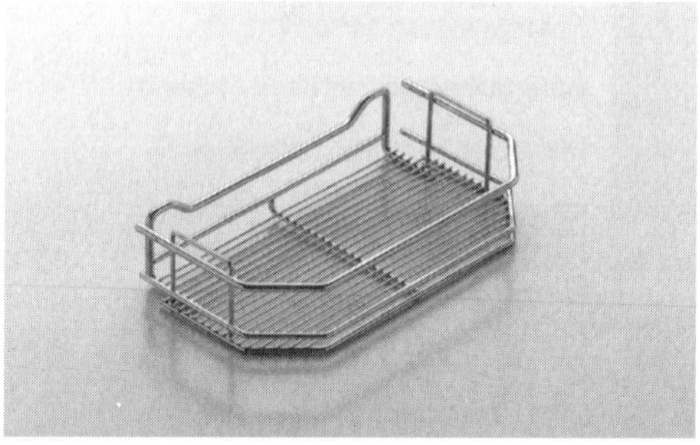

Storage baskets, for swivel and extension frames
Size: (W x D x H) 368 x 205 x 74 mm
Finish: steel, chrome-plated

Cat. No.	545.93.207

Packing: 1 pc.

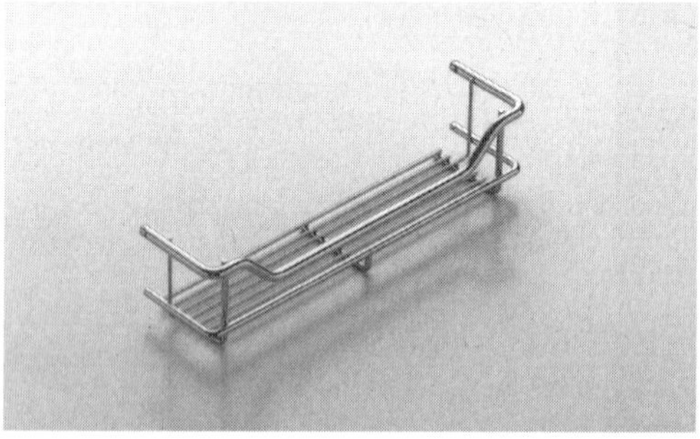

Storage basket, for standard rails
Size: (W x D x H) 300 x 75 x 75 mm
Finish: steel, chrome-plated

Cat. No.	520.81.213

Packing: 1 pc.

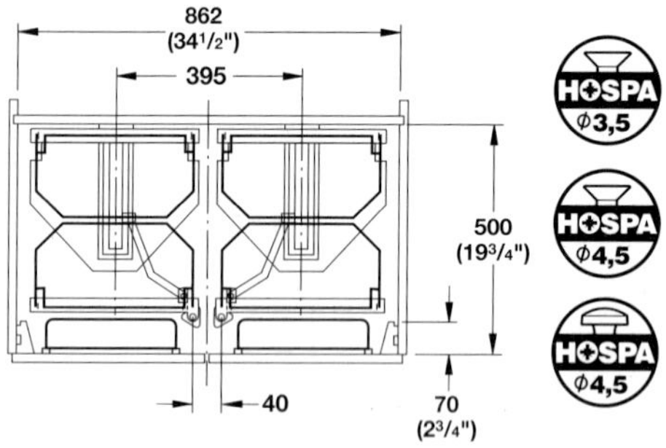

Fits cabinets with:
Inside width: 862 mm (34")
Inside height: 1270 mm (50")
Inside depth: 500 mm (19⅝")

Note: Please use door hinges with 125° opening angle.

Ordering suggestion:

1 set	Gourmet pantry Cat. No. 545.92.700/200
20 pcs.	Baskets, large Cat. No. 545.93.207
10 pcs.	Baskets, small Cat. No. 520.81.213

Cabinet closed

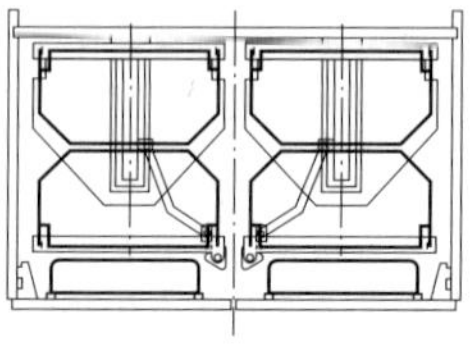

Doors opened

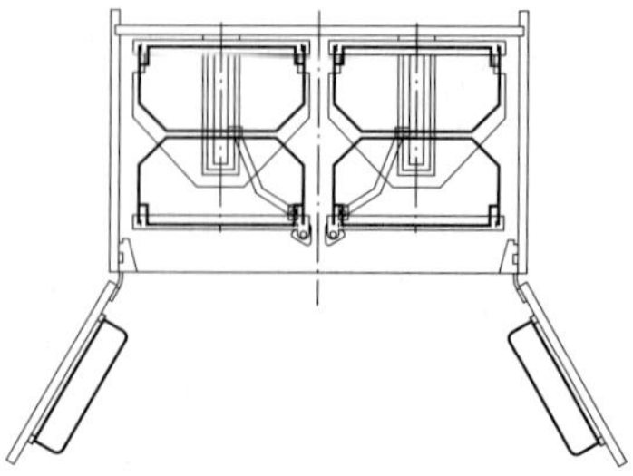

Swivel frame turned out, extension frame pulled forward automatically

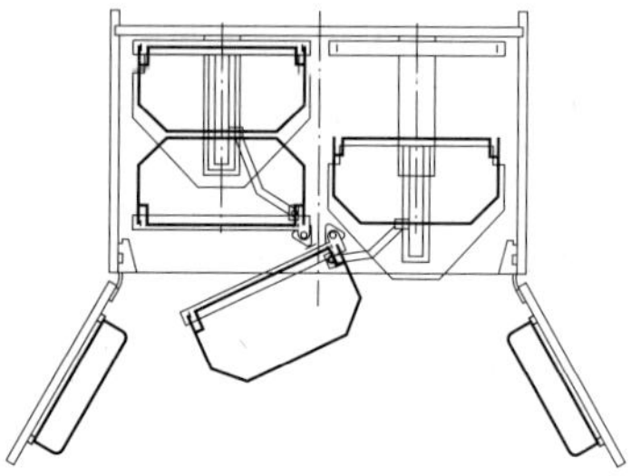

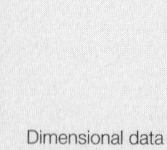

Dimensional data not binding.
We reserve the right to alter specifications without notice.

Dimensions in mm
Inches are approximate

Rota Store

HÄFELE

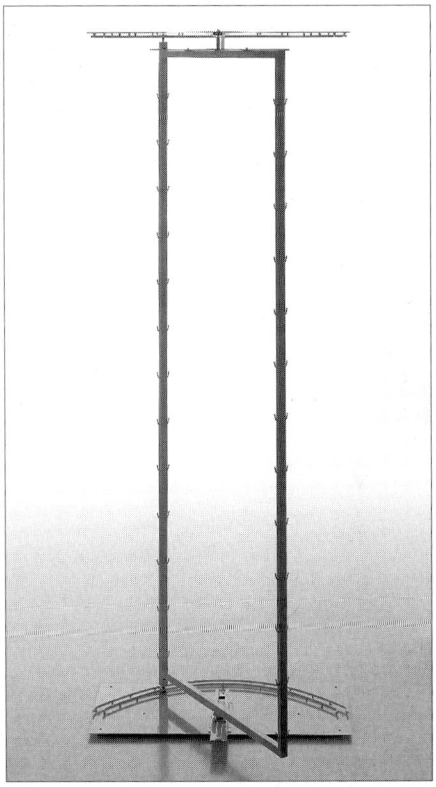

Revolving fitting, fits cabinets with an inside width of 984 mm (38¾")
Load capacity: 100 kg (220 lbs.)
Dimensions: 960 x 570 x 2026 mm
Finish: steel, silver epoxy coated

Cat. No.	805.51.202

Packing: 1 pc.

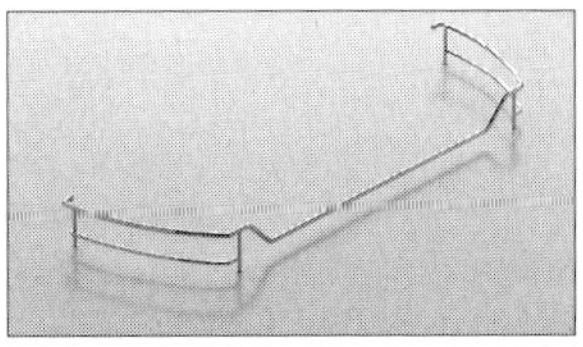

Fence for bottom shelf
One set required for bottom of frame
Dimensions: 935 x 255 x 68 mm
Finish: steel, chrome-plated polished

Cat. No.	805.52.218

Packing: 1 set (2 pcs.)

Fence – four sided shelves
Can be used any location except very bottom of frame.
Dimensions: 935 x 265 x 127 mm
Finish: steel, chrome-plated polished

Cat. No.	805.52.209

Packing: 1 pc.

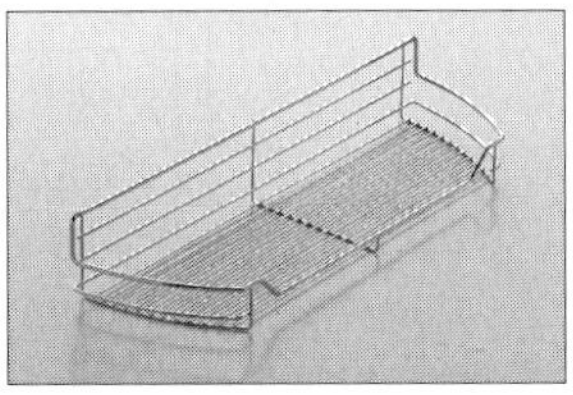

Basket, hook-on, flat
Dimensions: 935 x 265 x 127 mm
Finish: steel, chrome-plated polished

Cat. No.	805.52.227

Packing: 1 pc.

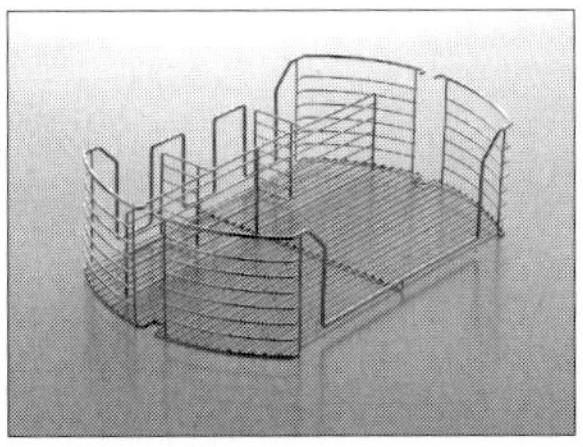

Functional basket, hook-on, high with dividers
Dimensions: 935 x 545 x 260 mm
Finish: steel, chrome-plated polished

Cat. No.	805.52.236

Packing: 1 pc.

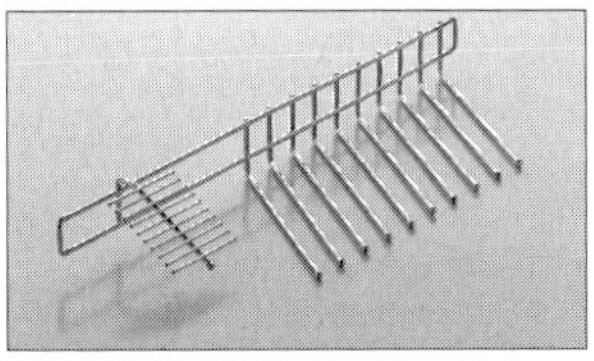

Tie and Trousers Rack
Dimensions: 935 x 277 x 110 mm
Finish: steel, chrome-plated polished

Cat. No.	805.52.245

Packing: 1 piece

Kitchen Accessory Systems **5**

- Hooks along length of frame allows mounting of shelves and baskets at almost any height.
- All dimensions are shown in the following order: width x depth x height

Dimensional data not binding. We reserve the right to alter specifications without notice.

Dimensions in mm
Inches are approximate

HÄFELE

Metal Rail System

Straight rod and corner rods are inserted through the holes in the posts and are "spliced" inside the post holes.

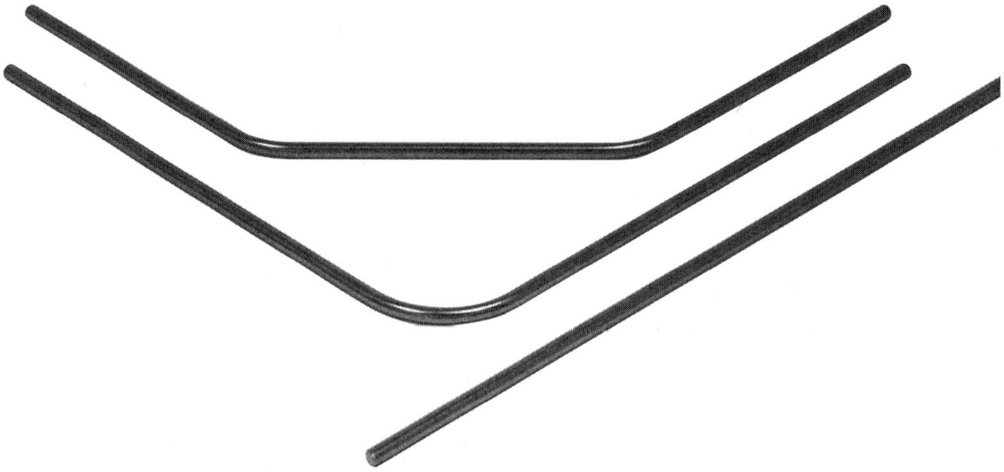

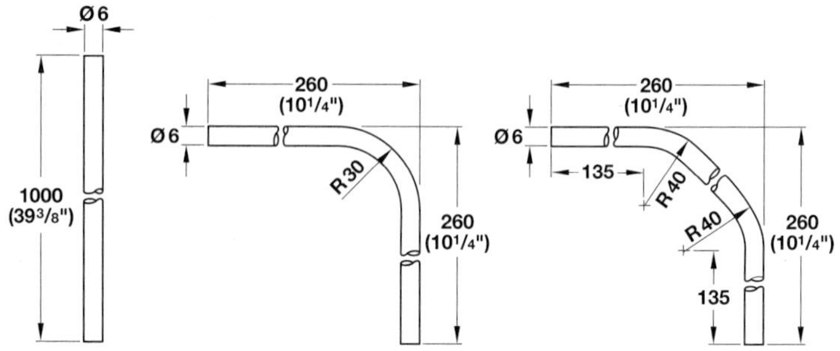

Finish:	**Rod, 1000 mm**	**Corners 90°**	**Corners135°**
Steel chrome polished	522.15.219	522.16.216	522.16.225
Brass gold-plated polished	522.15.817	522.16.814	522.16.823
Brass brass, antique	522.15.111	522.16.118	522.16.127

Packing: 1 pc.

5 Kitchen Accessory Systems

Posts, knock-in

Finish: Zinc

color	Gallery post	End post
chrome polished	522.17.213	522.17.222
gold-plated polished	522.17.811	522.17.820
brass antique	522.17.115	522.17.124

Packing: 10 pcs.

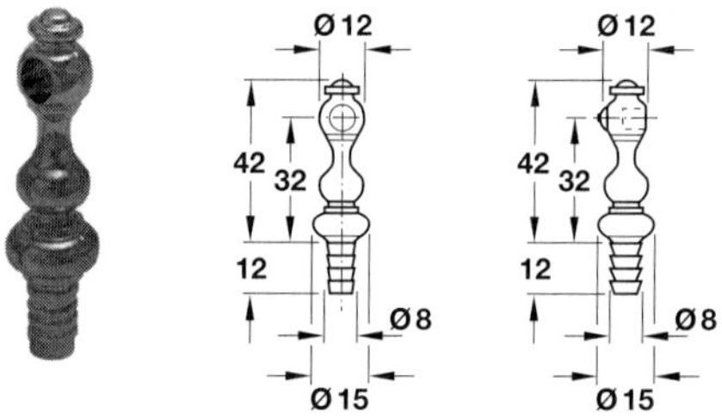

Dimensional data not binding.
We reserve the right to alter specifications without notice.

Dimensions in mm
Inches are approximate

Kitchen Railing System

HÄFELE

Tubular Rail Set, 16 mm diameter
Includes: 1500 mm tube, two end caps, four posts, four s hooks, four adapters and one dowel connector.

- Individual pieces can be ordered separately on preceding pages.

flat end cap

Finish	Cat. No.
gold polished	522.05.035
antique bronze	522.05.133
chrome polished	522.05.231
nickel matt	522.05.633
white epoxy	522.05.731
brass polished	522.05.839

Packing: 1 set

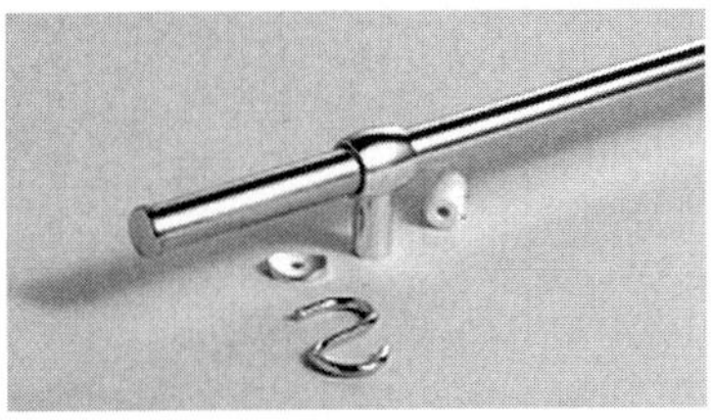

profiled end cap

Finish	Cat. No.
gold polished	522.06.032
antique bronze	522.06.130
chrome polished	522.06.238
nickel matt	522.06.630
white epoxy	522.06.738
brass polished	522.06.836

Packing: 1 set

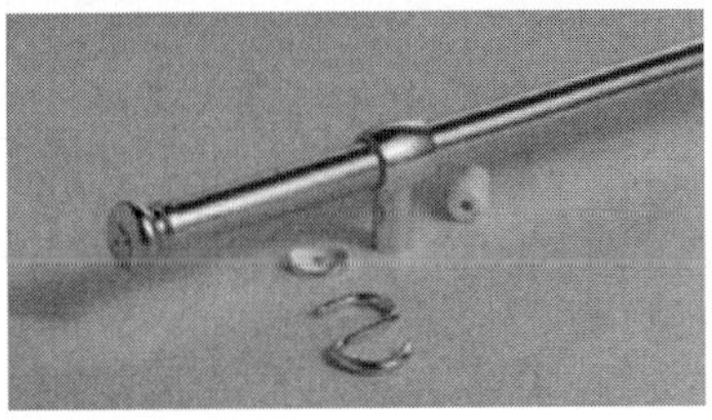

Elbow Section Set
consists of one elbow, two tube supports, two adapters and two dowel connectors

90° elbow

Finish	Cat. No.
gold polished	522.07.011
antique bronze	522.07.119
chrome polished	522.07.210
nickel matt	522.07.612
white epoxy	522.07.717
brass polished	522.07.818

Packing: 1 set

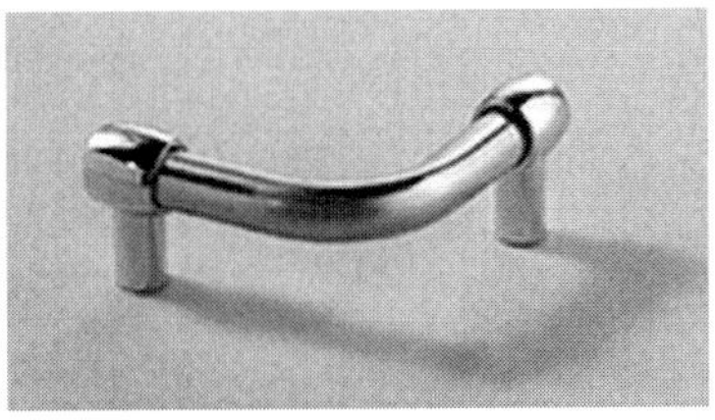

135° elbow

Finish	Cat. No.
gold polished	522.07.020
antique bronze	522.07.128
chrome polished	522.07.229
nickel matt	522.07.621
white epoxy	522.07.726
brass polished	522.07.827

Packing: 1 set

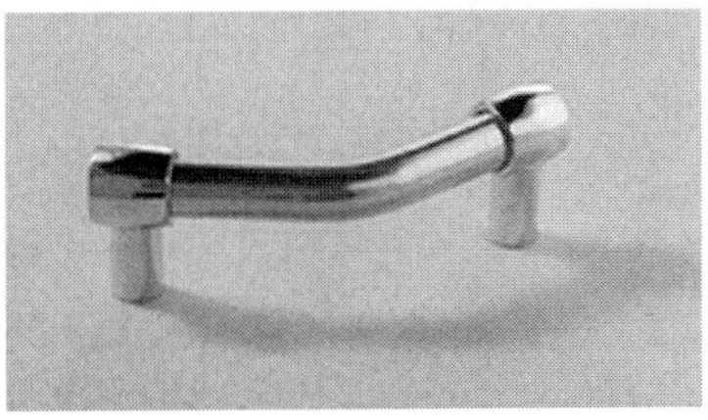

Dimensions in mm
Inches are approximate

HÄFELE

Kitchen Rail System

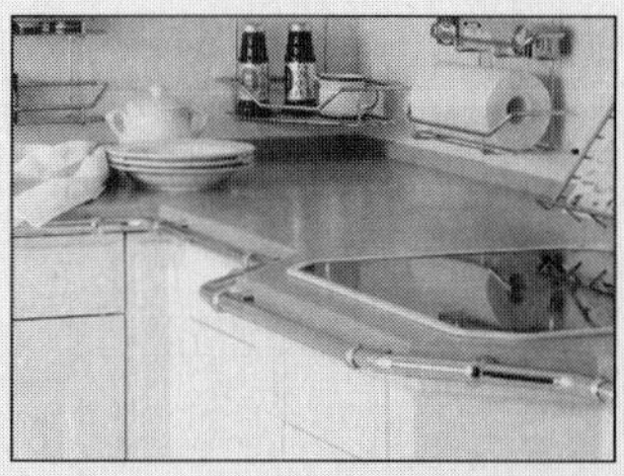

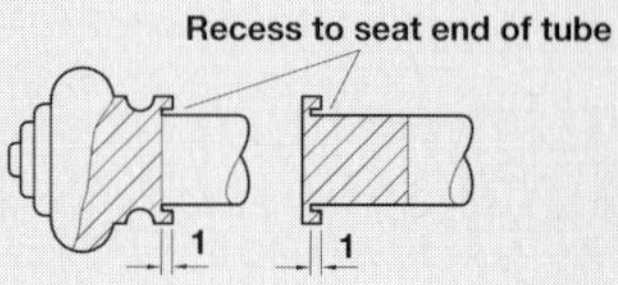

The recess which accommodates the end cap ensures a neatly concealed joint for decorative end-caps

Installed along the front of the countertop

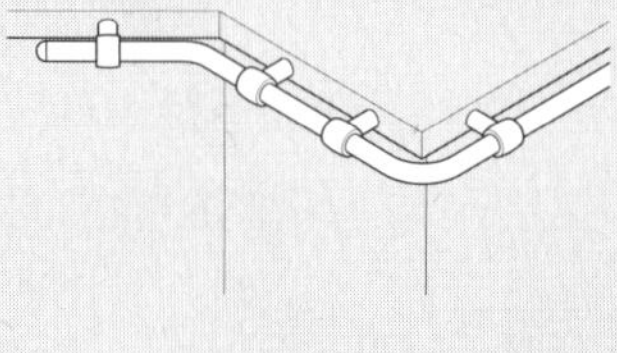

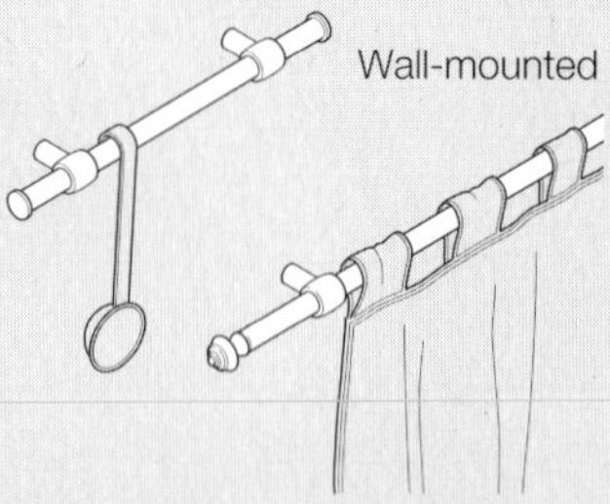

Installed on top of the countertop

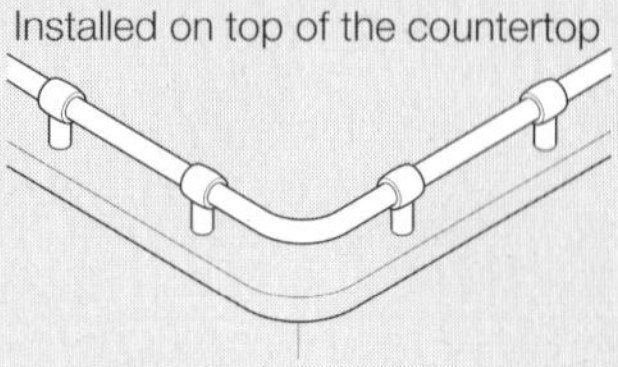

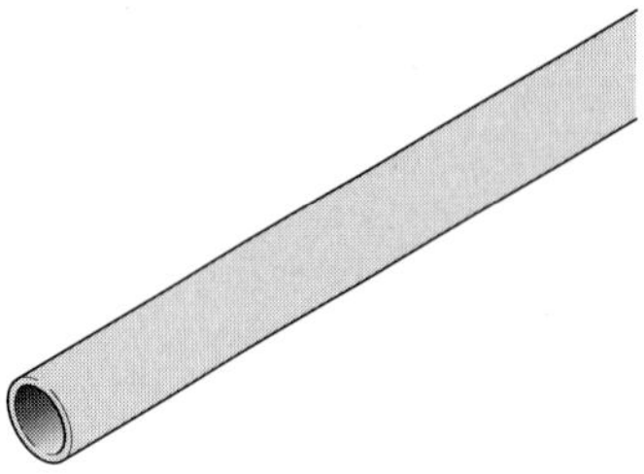

Tubular rail, 16 mm dia.
Length 1500 mm, seamless tubing

Finish	Cat. No.
steel, gold polished	522.00.035
steel, nickel-plated matt	522.00.630
steel, chrome-plated polished	522.00.236
brass, gold colored matt	522.00.530
brass, polished	522.00.830
steel, plastic-coated, white RAL 9010	522.00.730
steel, antique bronze	522.00.130

Packing: 1 pc.

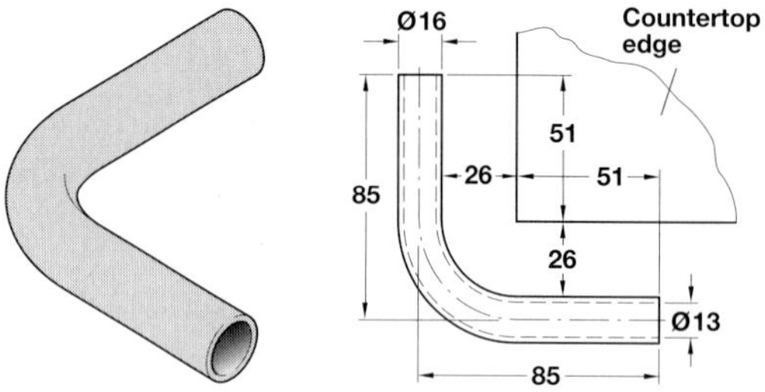

Elbow section, 90°, 16 mm dia.
seamless tubing

Finish	Cat. No.
steel, gold polished	522.01.019
steel, nickel-plated matt	522.01.617
steel, chrome-plated polished	522.01.215
brass, gold colored matt	522.01.510
brass, polished	522.01.813
steel, plastic-coated, white RAL 9010	522.01.715
steel, antique bronze	522.01.117

Packing: 1 pc.

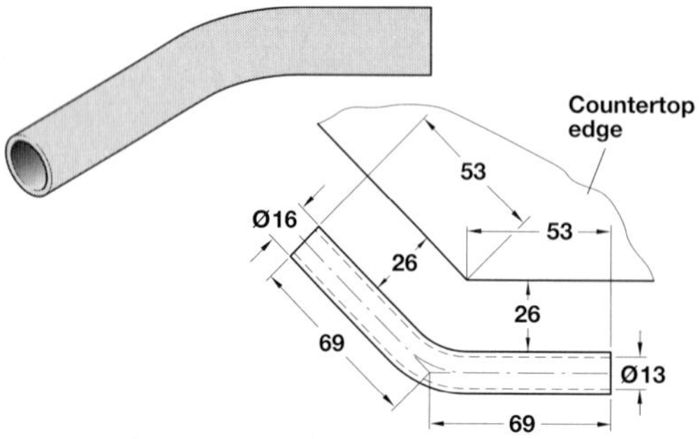

Elbow section, 135°, 16 mm dia.
seamless tubing

Finish	Cat. No.
steel, gold polished	522.01.028
steel, nickel-plated matt	522.01.626
steel, chrome-plated polished	522.01.224
brass, gold colored matt	522.01.520
brass, polished	522.01.822
steel, plastic-coated, white RAL 9010	522.01.724
steel, antique bronze	522.01.126

Packing: 1 pc.

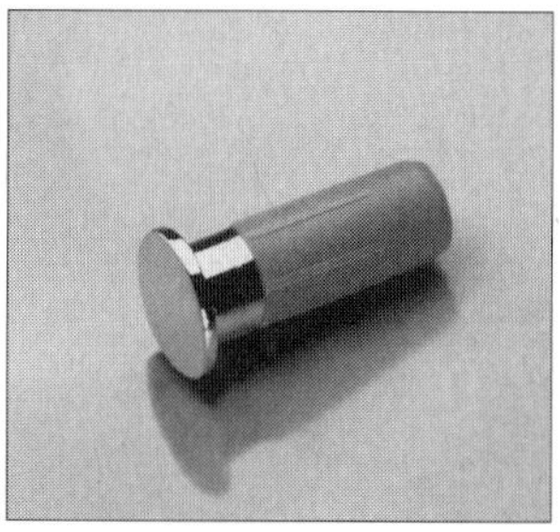

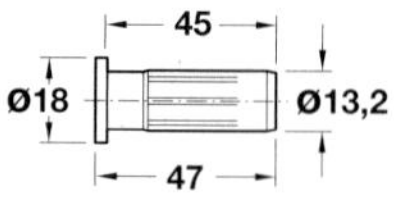

Decorative end-cap, with flat head plugs into kitchen rails.
Finish: brass

Color	Cat. No.
gold polished	522.03.022
nickel-plated matt	522.03.620
chrome-plated polished	522.03.228
gold colored matt	522.03.520
polished	522.03.826
white RAL 9010, plastic-coated	522.03.728
antique bronze	522.03.120

Packing: 1 pc.

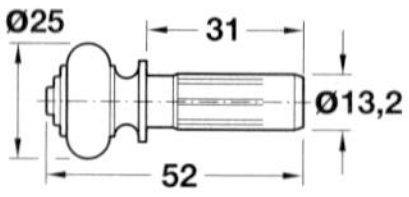

Decorative end-cap, with profile-style head plugs into kitchen rails.
Finish: brass

Color	Cat. No.
nickel-plated matt	522.03.639
chrome-plated polished	522.03.237
gold colored matt	522.03.530
polished	522.03.835
white RAL 9010, plastic-coated	522.03.737
antique bronze	522.03.139

Packing: 1 pc.

Dimensions in mm
Inches are approximate

Dimensional data not binding.
We reserve the right to alter specifications without notice.

Kitchen Rail System

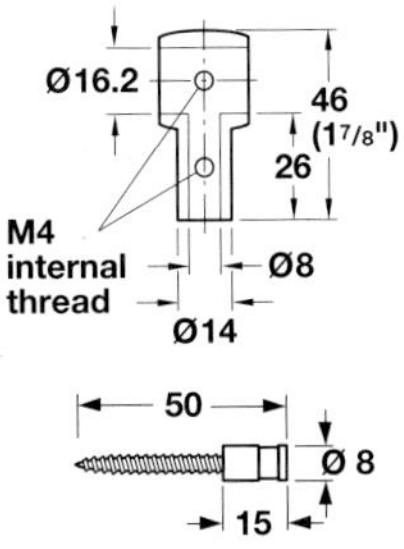

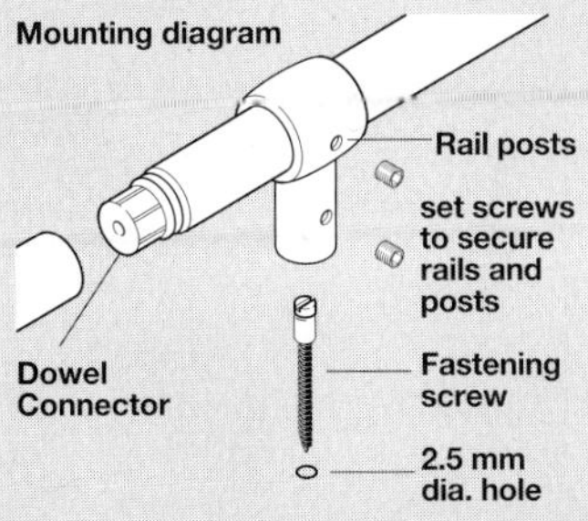

Railing posts

Press-fits over fastening screw (included),
with M4 set screw
and Allen key to secure rail
Finish: zinc

Color	Cat. No.
gold polished	522.02.016
nickel-plated matt	522.02.614
chrome-plated polished	522.02.212
gold colored matt	522.02.510
brass-plated polished	522.02.810
white RAL 9010, plastic-coated	522.02.712
antique bronze	522.02.114

Packing: 1 pc.

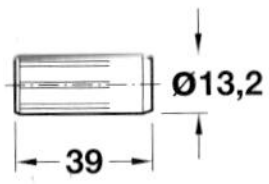

Dowel connector

Plugs into kitchen rails and elbow sections
Finish: plastic

Cat. No.	520.72.090

Packing: 1 and 10 pcs.

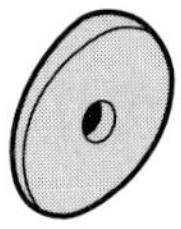

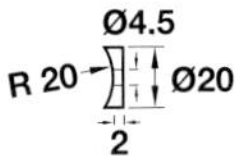

Adapter

Fits front of countertops edges (R = 20)
Finish: zinc

Color	Cat. No.
nickel-plated matt	522.02.687
chrome-plated polished	522.02.285
brass colored matt	522.02.589
polished	522.02.883
white RAL 9010, plastic-coated	522.02.785
antique bronze	522.02.187

Packing: 1 pc.

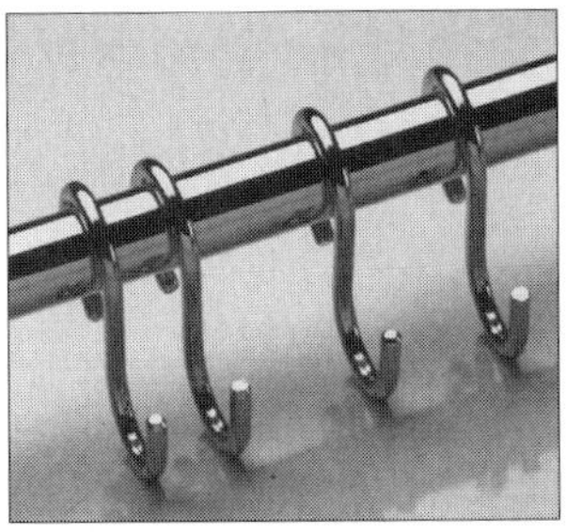

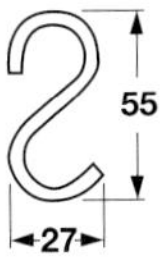

S-hooks

for railing
Finish: steel

Color	Cat. No.
gold polished	522.04.001
nickel-plated matt	522.04.609
chrome-plated polished	522.04.207
gold colored matt	522.04.501
polished	522.04.805
white RAL 9010, plastic-coated	522.04.707
antique bronze	522.04.109

Packing: 4 pcs.

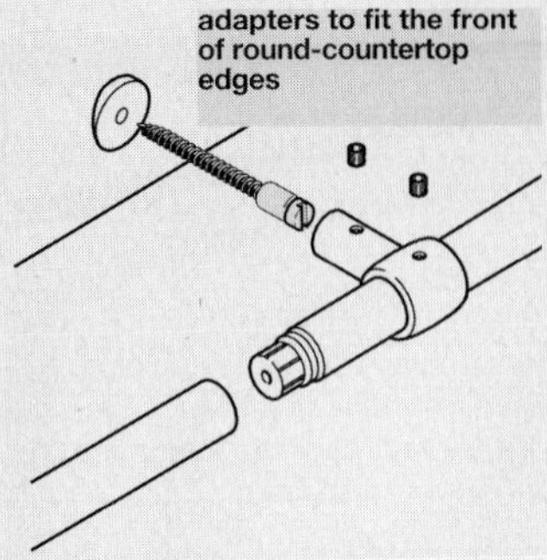

Dimensions in mm
Inches are approximate

Dimensional data not binding.
We reserve the right to alter
specifications without notice.

HÄFELE

Backsplash Railing System

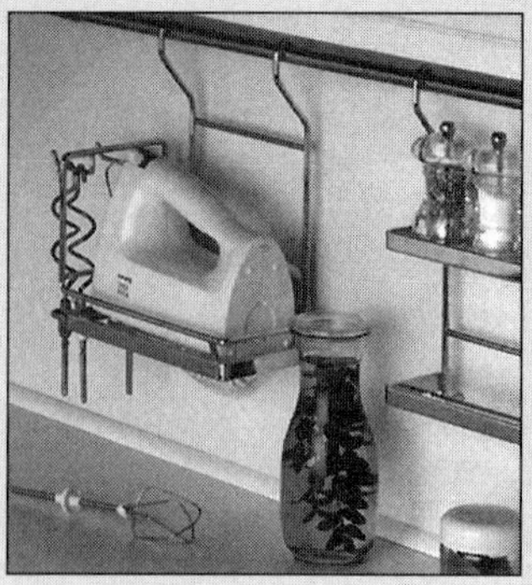

Dimensions are in the following order: Width x Height x Depth

For 16 mm dia. tubing

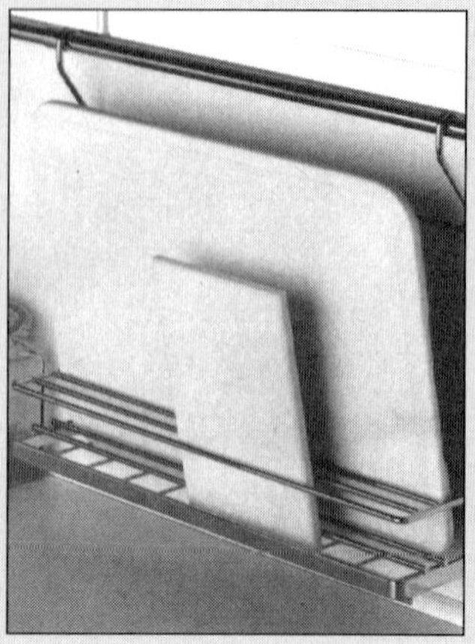

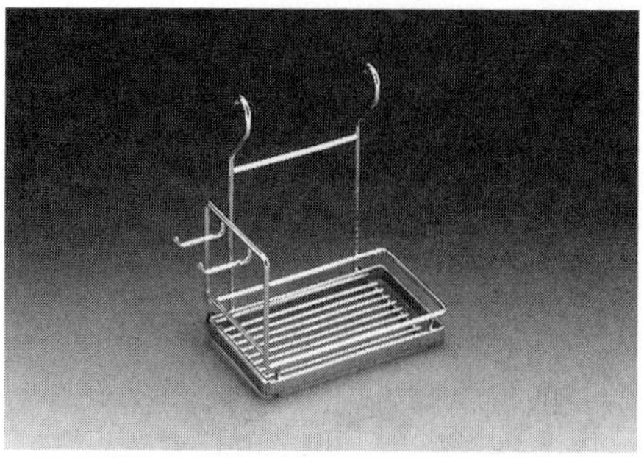

Mixer holder
with hooks for mixing utensils
Size: 280 x 145 x 270 mm
Finish: steel, protective covers black plastic

Color	Cat. No.
chrome-plated matt	521.19.472
chrome-plated polished	521.19.276
gold-plated polished	521.19.874

Packing: 1 pc.

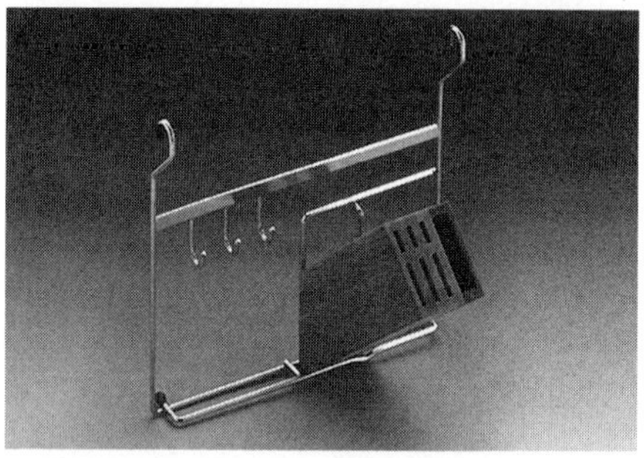

Knife holder
with knife block and hooks
Size: 350 x 230 x 350 mm
Finish: steel, protective covers black plastic

Color	Cat. No.
chrome-plated matt	521.19.409
chrome-plated polished	521.19.203
gold-plated polished	521.19.801

Packing: 1 set

The knife block consists of matt lacquered beech wood. Separates from the knife holder for cleaning.

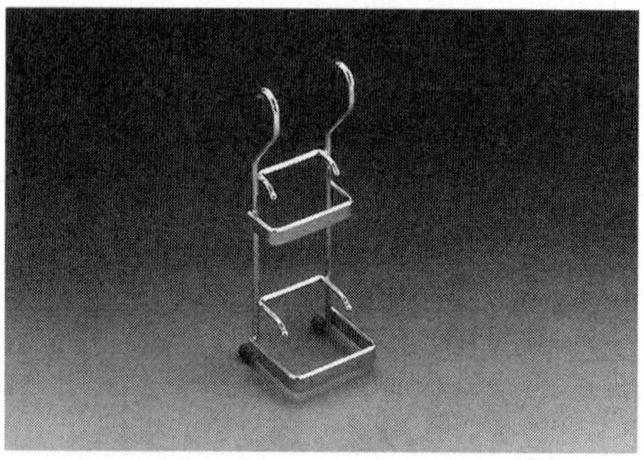

Lid holder
Size: 92 x 80 x 275 mm
Finish: steel, protective covers black plastic

Color	Cat. No.
chrome-plated matt	521.19.481
chrome-plated polished	521.19.285
gold-plated polished	521.19.883

Packing: 1 pc.

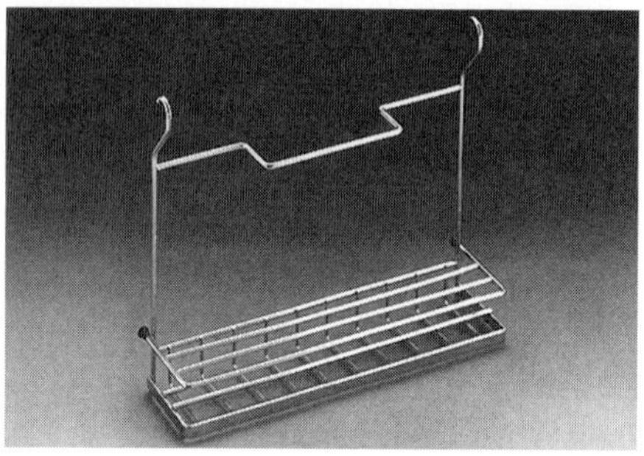

Cutting board holder
Size: 420 x 110 x 350 mm
Finish: steel, protective covers black plastic

Color	Cat. No.
chrome-plated matt	521.19.418
chrome-plated polished	521.19.212
gold-plated polished	521.19.810

Packing: 1 pc.

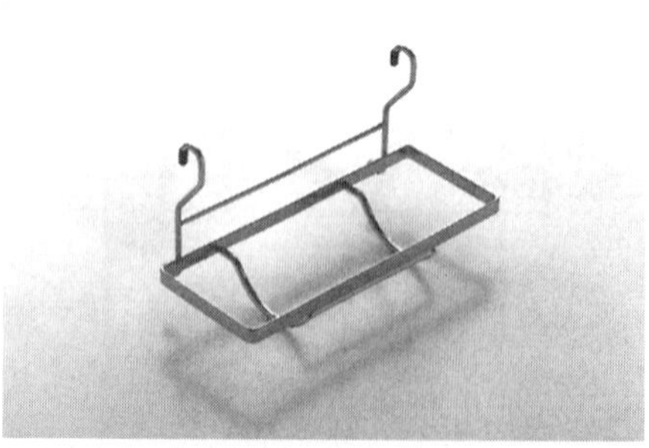

Paper towel holder
Size: 325 x 155 x 180 mm
Finish: steel, protective covers black plastic

Color	Cat. No.
chrome-plated matt	521.19.534
chrome-plated polished	521.19.338
polished gold-plated	521.19.936

Packing: 1 pc.

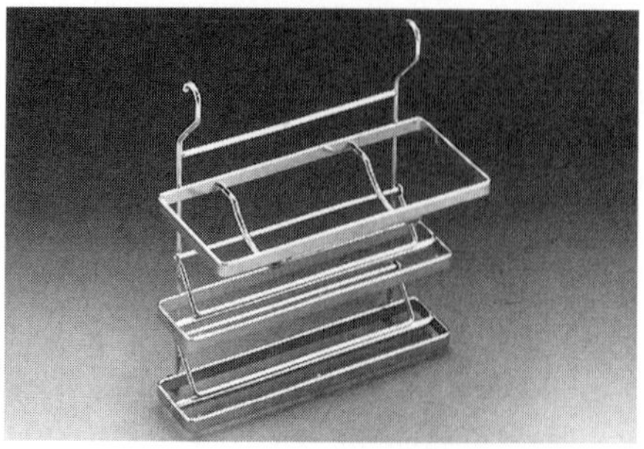

Paper towel/kitchen wrap holder
with serrated edges on both lower holders
(for aluminum foil, grease-papers, cling-wrap, etc.)
Size: 325 x 155 x 365 mm
Finish: steel, protective covers black plastic

Color	Cat. No.
chrome-plated matt	521.19.436
chrome-plated polished	521.19.230
gold-plated polished	521.19.838

Packing: 1 pc.

Dimensional data not binding. We reserve the right to alter specifications without notice.

Backsplash Railing System

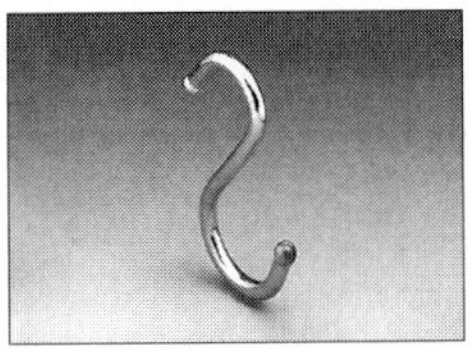

S-Hooks

For 16 mm railing system
Dimensions: single hook, 6 x 27 x 55 mm
Finish: steel, electroplated

Color	Cat. No.
chrome-plated polished	522.04.207
gold-plated polished	522.04.001

Packing: 4 pcs.

For 16 mm dia. tubing

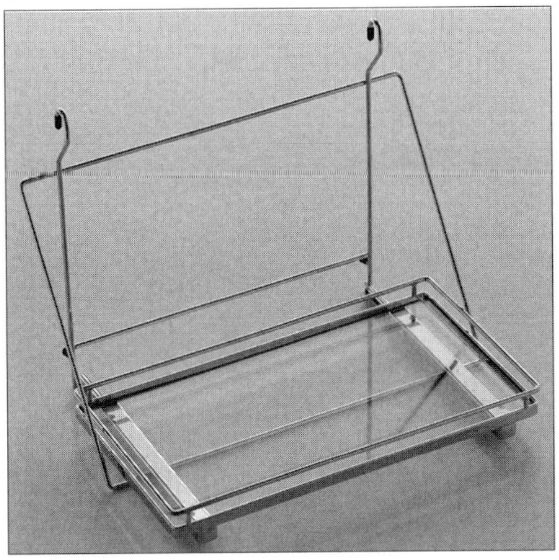

Coffee maker shelf

glass surface
Dimensions: 480 x 275 x 370 mm
Extended length: 150 mm
Finish: steel, protective covers black plastic

Color	Cat. No.
matt chrome-plated matt	521.19.507
chrome-plated polished	521.19.301
gold-plated polished	521.19.909

Packing: 1 pc.

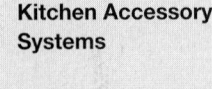

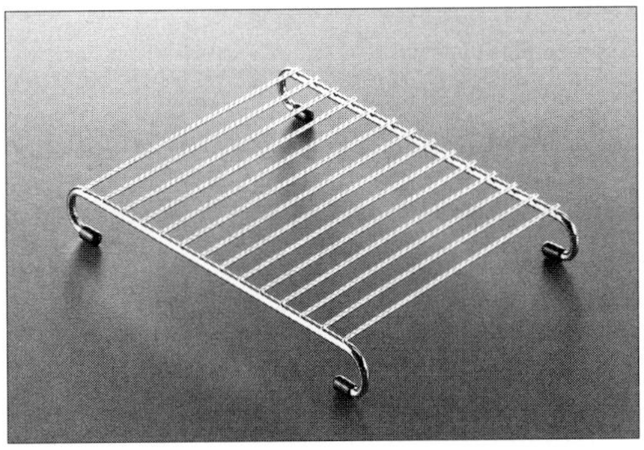

Trivet

Size: 200 x 300 x 35 mm
Finish: steel, protective covers black plastic

Color	Cat. No.
chrome-plated matt	521.19.570
chrome-plated polished	521.19.370

Packing: 1 piece

Dimensions are in the following order: Width x Depth x Height

Dimensional data not binding. We reserve the right to alter specifications without notice.

Dimensions in mm
Inches are approximate

HÄFELE

Backsplash Railing System

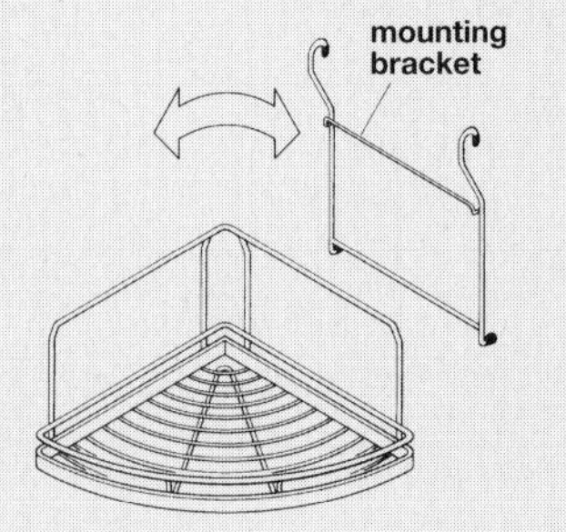

For16 mm dia. tubing

5 Kitchen Accessory Systems

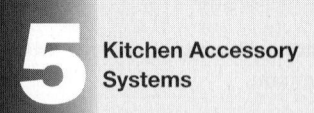

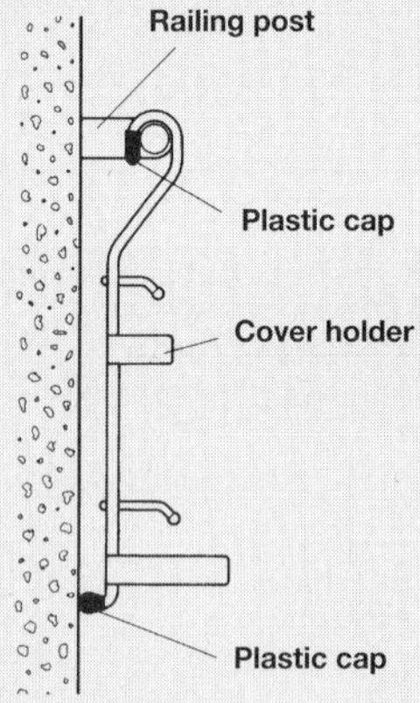

To prevent unintentional movement and marring of the wall and railing, all backsplash railing accessories feature plastic caps on wire ends.

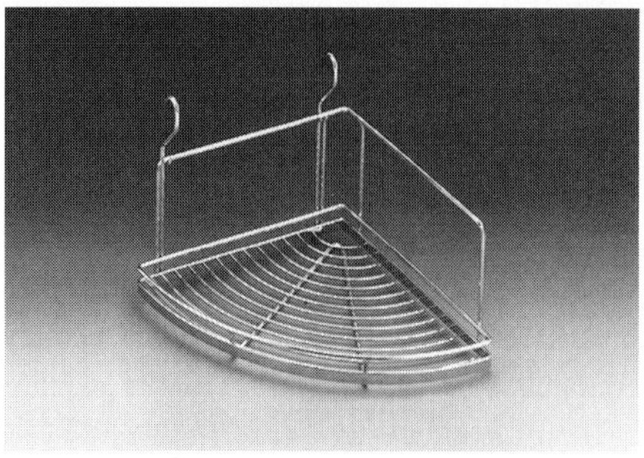

Corner shelf
with separate mounting bracket
Size: 320 x 340 x 275 mm
Finish: steel, protective covers black plastic

Color	Cat. No.
chrome-plated matt	521.19.490
chrome-plated polished	521.19.294
gold-plated polished	521.19.892

Packing: 1 piece

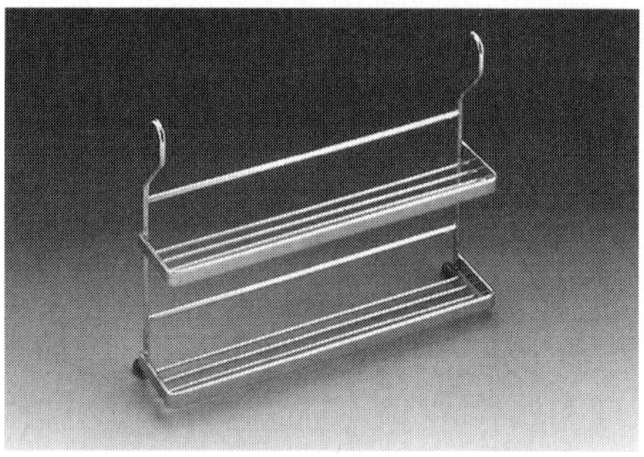

Spice rack, 2 tier
Size: 350 x 90 x 275 mm
Finish: steel, protective covers black plastic

Color	Cat. No.
chrome-plated matt	521.19.427
chrome-plated polished	521.19.221
gold-plated polished	521.19.829

Packing: 1 piece

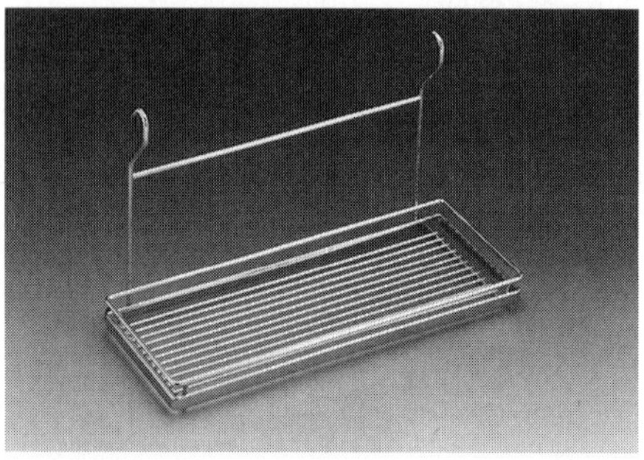

Multi-purpose shelf
Size: 455 x 185 x 270 mm
Finish: steel, protective covers black plastic

Color	Cat. No.
chrome-plated matt	521.19.463
chrome-plated polished	521.19.267
gold-plated polished	521.19.865

Packing: 1 piece

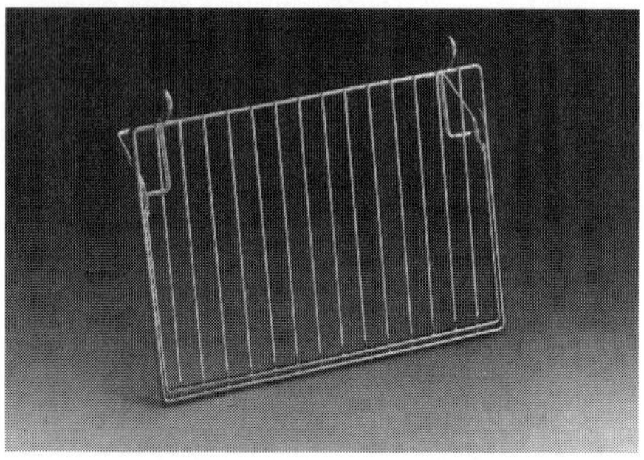

Cook book shelf
with slanted support and page holder
Size: 450 x 50 x 360 mm
Finish: steel, protective covers black plastic

Color	Cat. No.
chrome-plated matt	521.19.445
chrome-plated polished	521.19.249
gold-plated polished	521.19.847

Packing: 1 piece

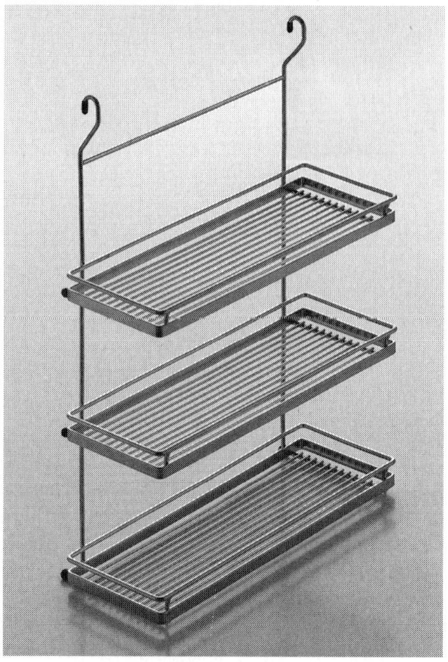

Multi-all purpose shelf, 3 tier
Size: 455 x 180 x 630 mm
Finish: steel, protective covers black plastic

Color	Cat. No.
chrome-plated matt	521.19.543
chrome-plated polished	521.19.347
gold-plated polished	521.19.945

Packing: 1 piece

Shelf Standard System

Slotted Standards accept individual accessories
Standard is screw-mounted.
Length: 1500 mm (59)

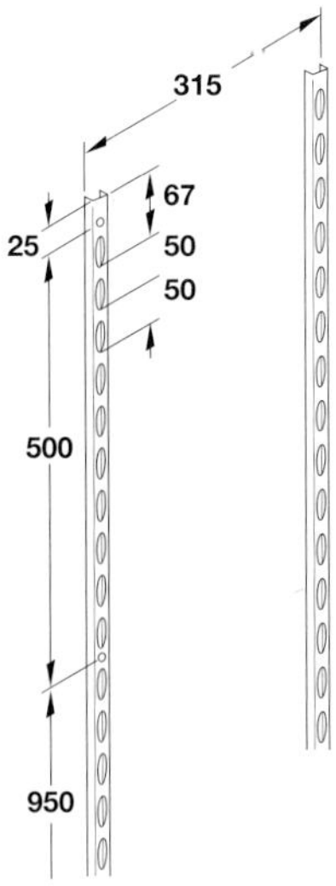

Finish: steel, epoxy coated

Cat. No.	white	520.80.707
	sliver	520.80.207

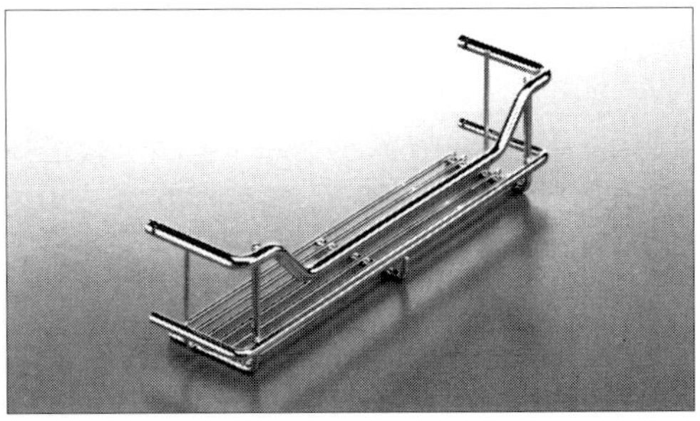

Wire basket, clip-on
300 x 75 x 75
Finish: steel wire, chrome-plated

Cat. No.	520.81.213

Packing: 1 pc.

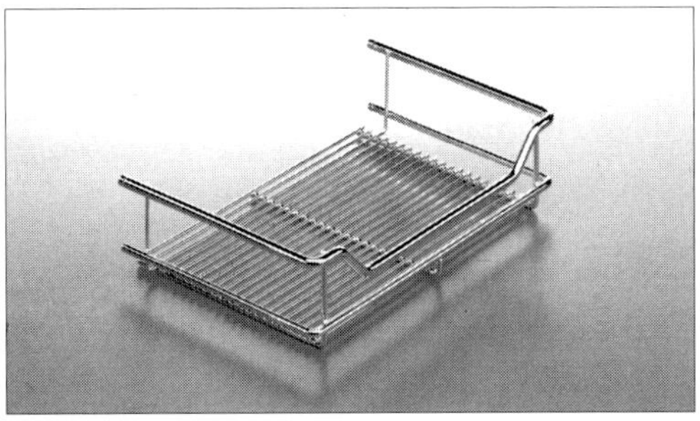

Wire basket, clip-on
300 x 200 x 75
Finish: steel wire, chrome-plated

Cat. No.	520.81.222

Packing: 1 pc.

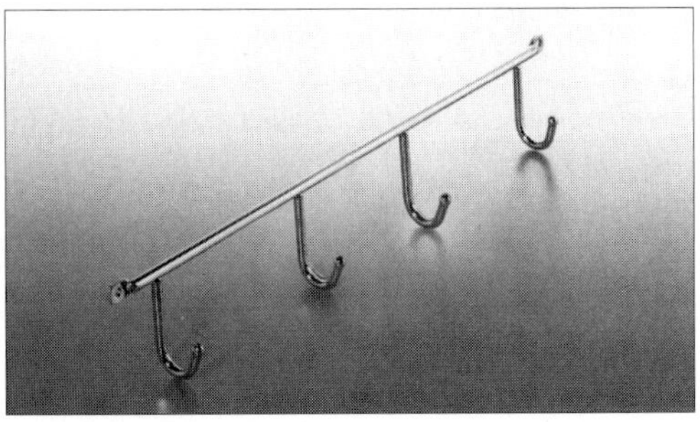

Hook rail, clip-on
300 x 33 x 52
Finish: steel wire, chrome-plated

Cat. No.	520.82.229

Packing: 1 pc.

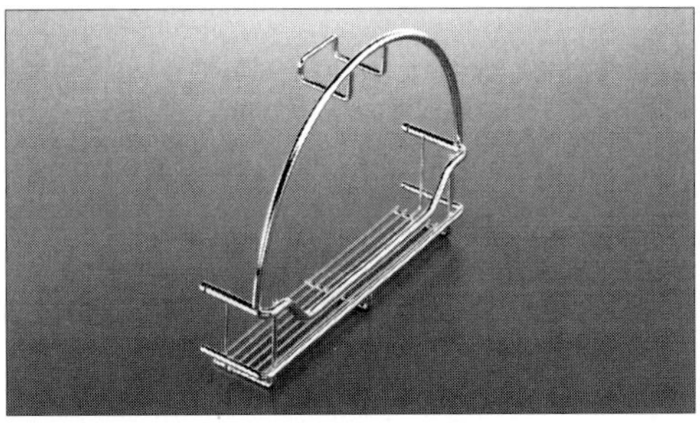

Vacuum hose rack, clip-on
300 x 75 x 235
Finish: steel wire, chrome-plated

Cat. No.	520.82.201

Packing: 1 pc.

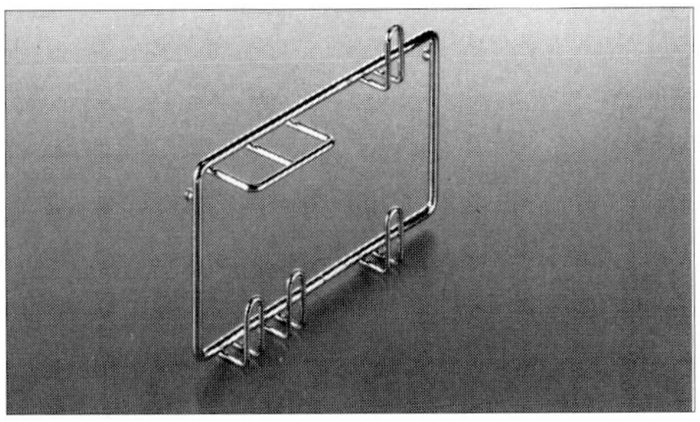

Vacuum tube and nozzle holder
300 x 60 x 190
Finish: steel wire, chrome-plated

Cat. No.	520.82.210

Packing: 1 pc.

Dimensions in mm
Inches are approximate

HÄFELE

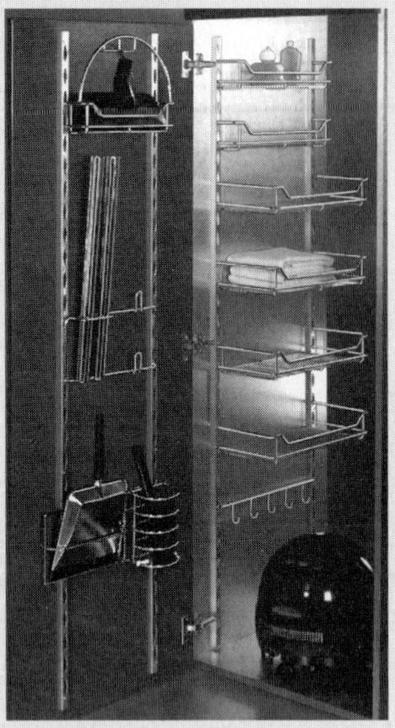

Dimensions are in the following order:
width x depth x height

Kitchen Accessory Systems 5

Featuring special clip-on accessories, this shelf standard system provides storage space for cleaning supplies and equipment such as vacuum cleaner accessories.
With an installation width of only 315mm (12⅜), this space–saving system can be mounted on cabinet side panels or doors.
Thanks to the special clip-on attachment system for the accessories, the layout can be rearranged at any time.

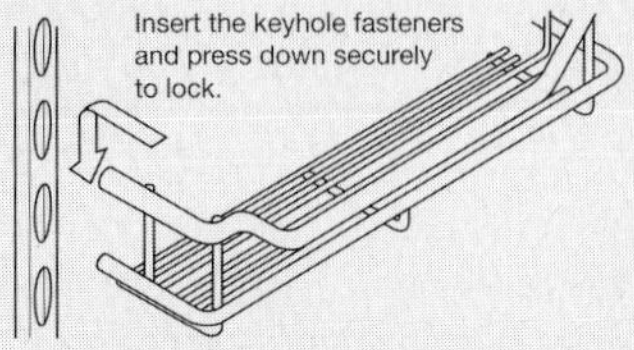

Insert the keyhole fasteners and press down securely to lock.

The specified installation width 315 mm of the system is measured at the outside edges of the supporting standards.

Dimensional data not binding.
We reserve the right to alter specifications without notice.

HÄFELE

Shelf Standard System

The system shown here uses the 520.80. series **Shelf Standards** but with installed width of 415 mm (16¼)

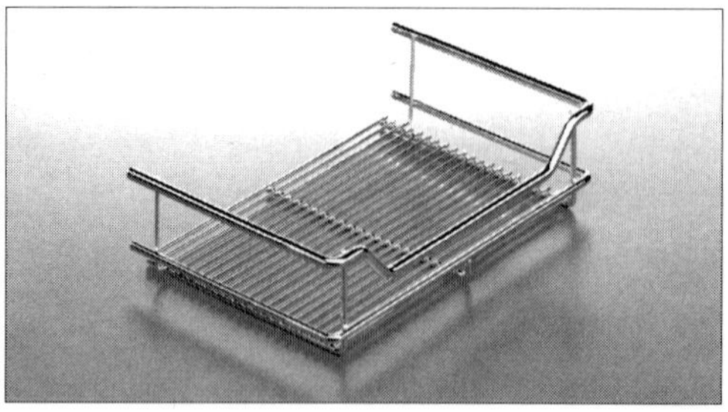

Wire basket, clip-on
400 x 200 x 75

Finish: steel wire, chrome-plated

Cat. No.	520.81.240

Packing: 1 pc.

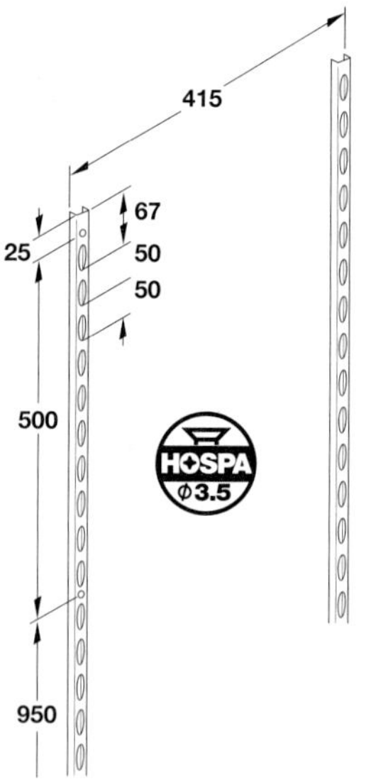

Dimensions are in the following order:
width x depth x height

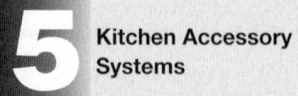

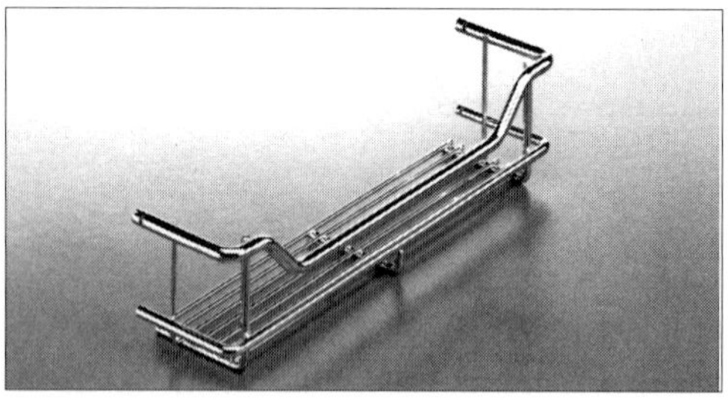

Wire basket, clip-on
400 x 75 x 75

Finish: steel wire, chrome-plated

Cat. No.	520.81.231

Packing: 1 pc.

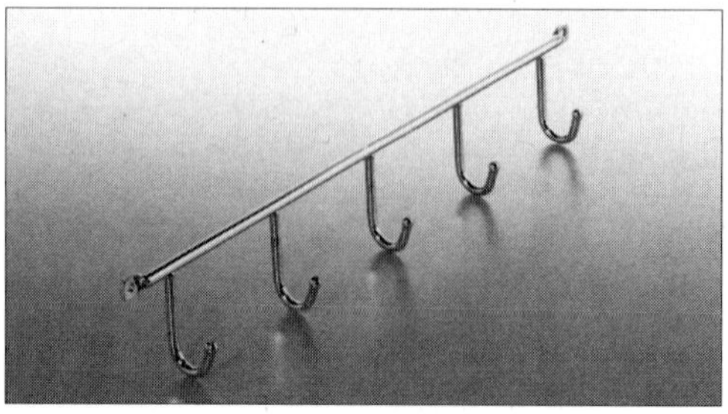

Hook rail, clip-on
400 x 33 x 52

Finish: steel wire, chrome-plated

Cat. No.	520.82.238

Packing: 1 pc.

Dimensions in mm
Inches are approximate

Kitchen Cabinet Accessories

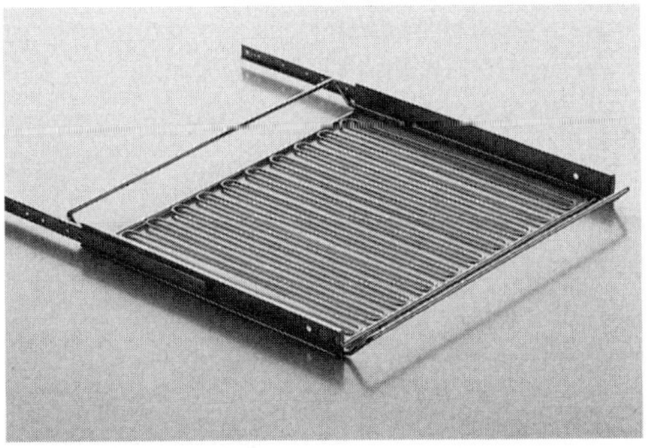

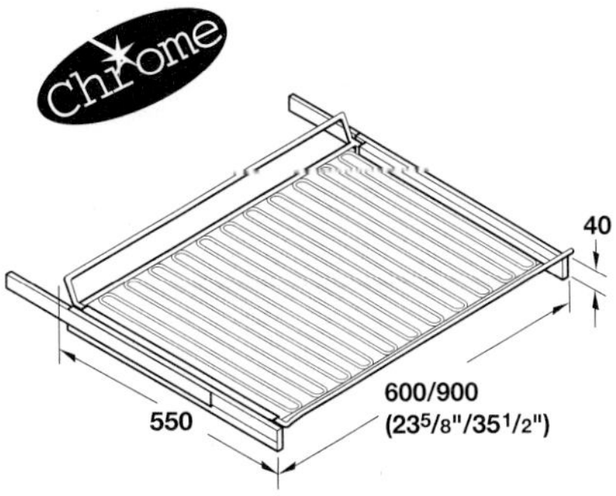

- For installation under range tops or in open areas between two cabinets

Oven Rack Extension
with integrated safety rail at front and rear.
Packed ready for installation complete with guides and stainless steel guide covers.
Finish grating: steel wire, chrome-plated
guide: galvanized steel
guide cover: stainless steel

Installed width mm (inch)	Cat. No.
600 (23 5/8")	545.39.212
900 (35 1/2")	545.39.221

Packing: 1 pc.

Bottle Caddy, 8 bottle capacity
Stands on floor of storage drawer within wire fence
Dimensions: 225 x 410 x 297 mm (8 7/8" x 16 1/8" x 11 5/8")
Finish grating: steel, chrome-plated

Cat. No.	545.45.229

Packing: 1 pc.

Kitchen Accessory Systems **5**

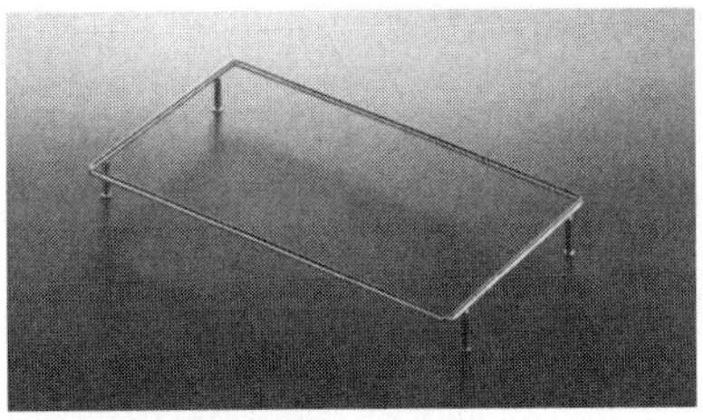

Wire fence for bottle caddy
Screw-mounted to drawer base
Dimensions: 240 x 430 x 40 mm (9 3/8" x 17" x 1 1/2")
Finish: steel, chrome plated

Cat. No.	545.45.238

Packing: 1 pc.

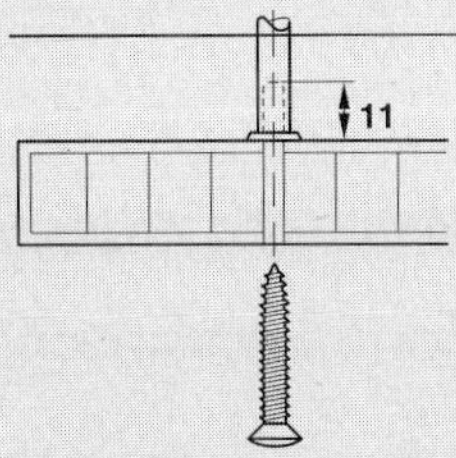

Wire fences are secured to wooden shelves with **raised head screws** Size: Ø 4.2 x 32 mm
Finish: steel, galvanized

Cat. No.	023.27.460

Packing: 100 pcs.

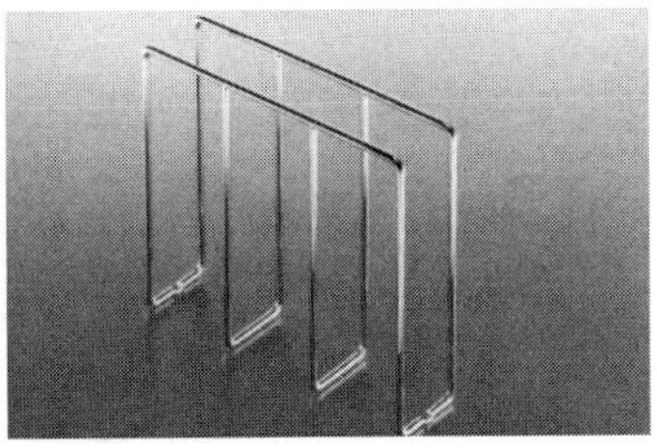

Baking rack support
Screw-mounted to cabinet base
Dimensions: 75 x 300 x 250 mm (3" x 10" x 12")
Finish: steel, chrome plated

Cat. No.	540.42.200

Packing: 1 pc.

Dimensions in mm
Inches are approximate

Dimensional data not binding.
We reserve the right to alter specifications without notice.

HÄFELE

Cabinet Accessories

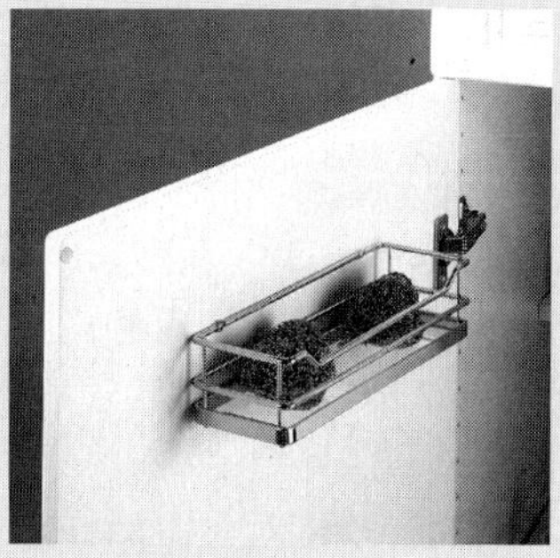

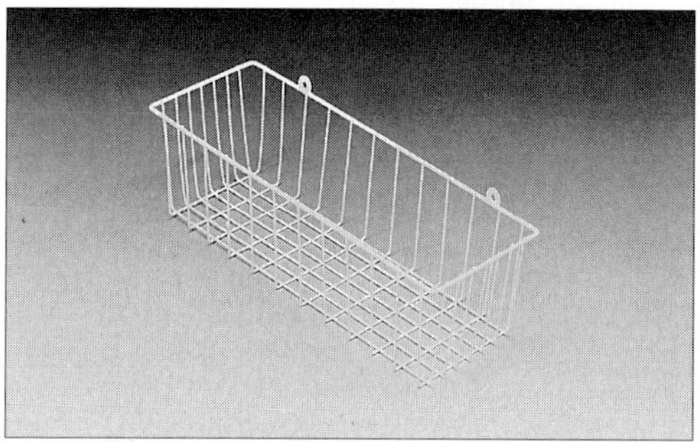

Multi-purpose basket
with screw-mounting eyes
Finish: steel wire, plastic-coated, white

width x depth x height	Cat. No.
340 x 120 x 100 mm	540.31.006

Packing: 1 pc.

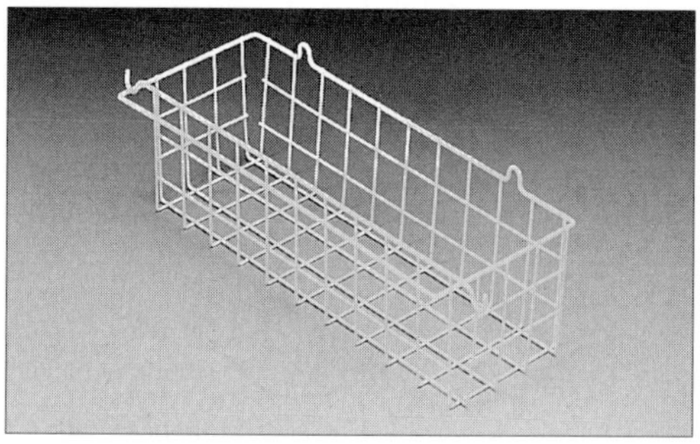

Multi-purpose basket
with hook-in eyes
Finish: steel wire, plastic-coated, white

width x depth x height	Cat. No.
380 x 140 x 120 mm	540.33.000

Packing: 1 pc.

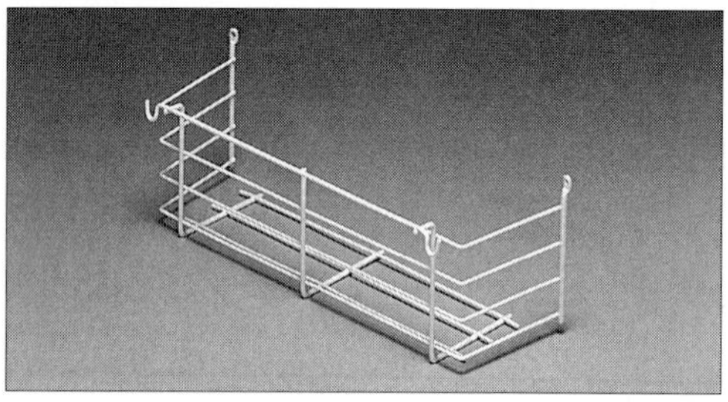

Multi-purpose basket, three-sided
with screw-mounting eyes
Finish: steel wire, plastic-coated, white

width x depth x height	Cat. No.
330 x 115 x 110 mm	540.30.705

Packing: 1 pc.

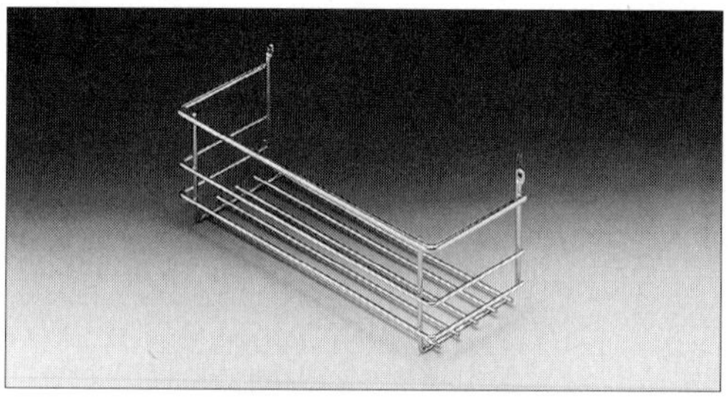

Multi-purpose basket, three-sided
with screw-mounting eyes
Finish: steel wire, chrome-plated

width x depth x height	Cat. No.
312 x 101 x 112 mm	540.36.207

Packing: 1 pc.

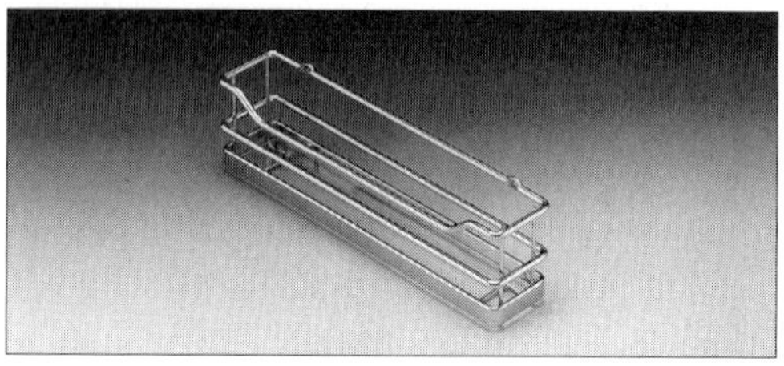

Holder for small packages and bags
screw-mounted, with plexiglas liner
Finish: steel wire, chrome-plated

width x depth x height	Cat. No.
260 x 50 x 63 mm	543.21.210

Packing: 1 pc.

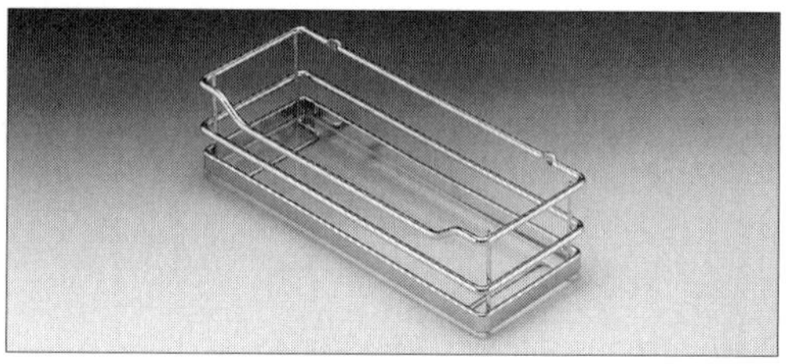

Door basket
screw-mounted, with plexiglas liner
Finish: steel wire, chrome-plated

width x depth x height	Cat. No.
260 x 90 x 63 mm	543.21.229

Packing: 1 pc.

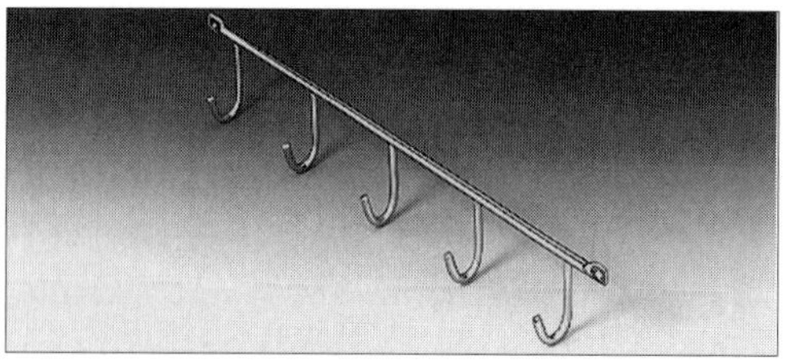

Hookrail with five hooks
screw attachment to side panels
Finish: steel wire, chrome-plated

width x depth x height	Cat. No.
350 x 30 x 50 mm	520.04.207

Packing: 1 pc.

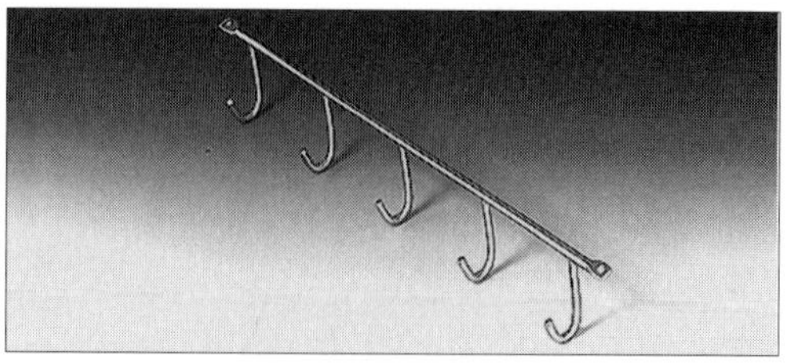

Hookrail with five hooks
screw attachment to underside of wall unit
Finish: steel wire, chrome-plated

width x depth x height	Cat. No.
350 x 30 x 50 mm	520.04.252

Packing: 1 pc.

Dimensions in mm
Inches are approximate

Cabinet Accessories

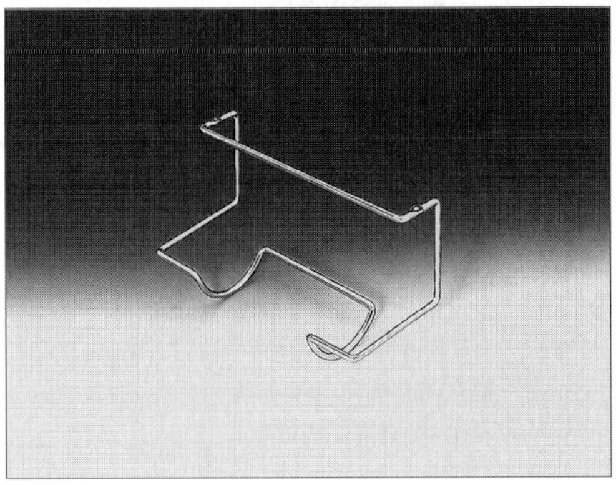

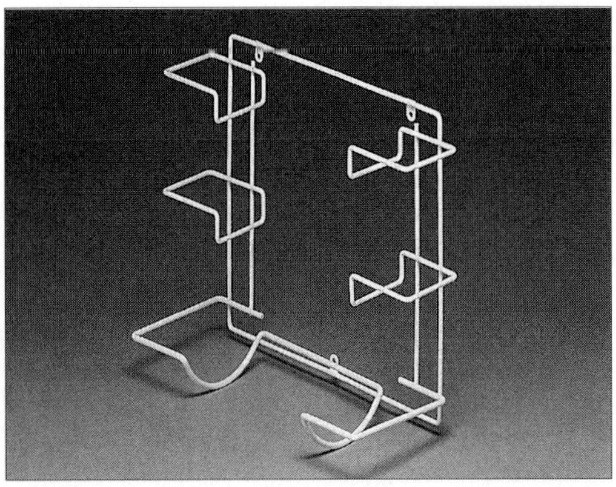

Kitchen roll holder
undercabinet screw-mounted
paper roll loads from front possible

Finish: steel wire, chrome-plated

width x depth x height	Cat. No.
300 x 135 x 165 mm	521.06.206

Packing: 1 pc.

Kitchen wrap/paper towel holder
strap for screw-mounted

Finish: steel wire, plastic-coated, white

width x depth x height	Cat. No.
330 x 130 x 320 mm	500.06.865

Packing: 1 pc.

Kitchen wrap/paper towel dispenser
for screw-mounted
(junior rolls only)

Finish: plastic, white

width x depth x height	Cat. No.
380 x 66 x 259 mm	500.11.704

Packing: 1 pc.

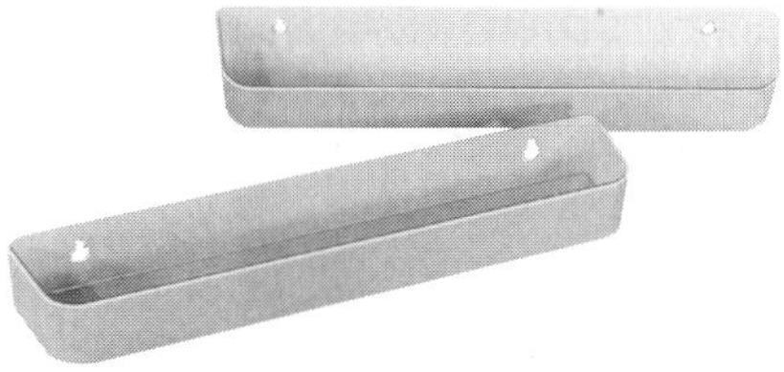

Door trays
for hook-over screws

Finish: polystyrene, white

width x depth x height	Cat. No.
390 x 80 x 45 mm	500.09.704

Packing: 1 pc.

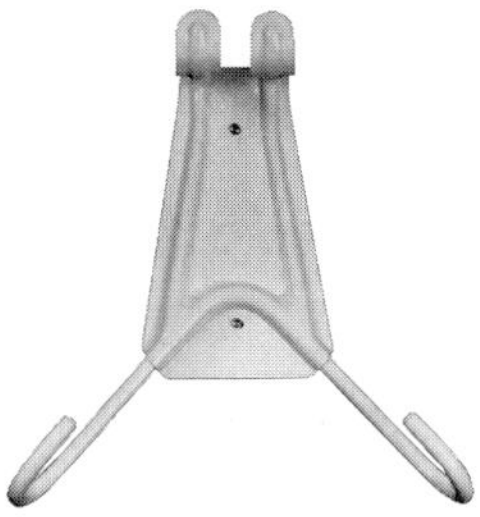

Combo wall mount
screw-mounted
Holds ironing-board and iron.

Finish: steel plate, round tube, white

width x depth x height	Cat. No.
345 x 90 x 325	520.14.758

Packing: 1 piece

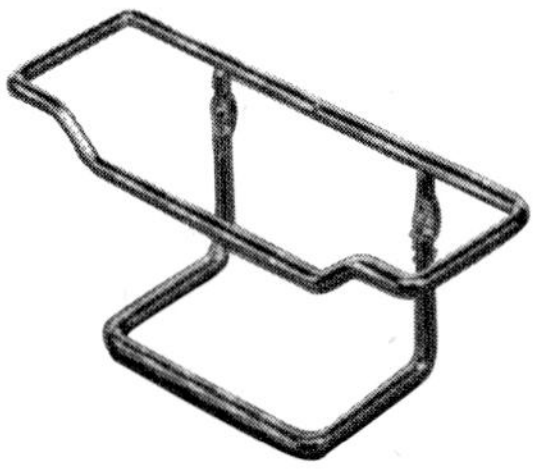

Coffee filter holder
screw-mounted

Finish: steel wire, chrome-plated

width x depth x height	Cat. No.
165 x 60 x 62 mm	543.21.238

Packing: 1 pc.

Dimensional data not binding.
We reserve the right to alter specifications without notice.

Dimensions in mm
Inches are approximate

HÄFELE

Cabinet Accessories

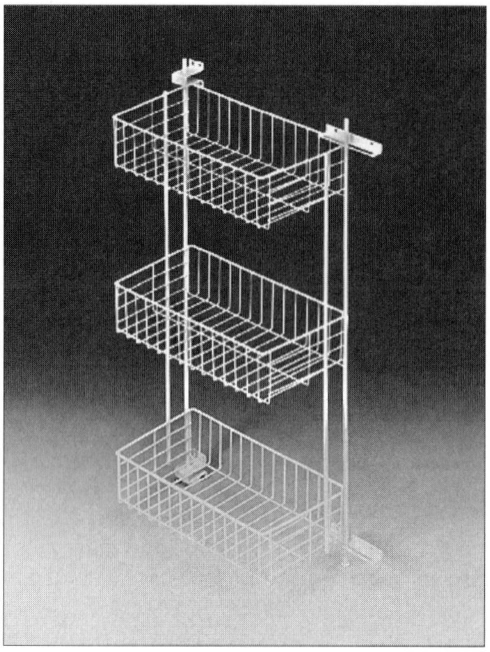

Pivotable storage basket
optional screw-mounted on left or right,
complete with hinges and 2 follower brackets

Finish: steel, plastic-coated, white

width x depth x height	Cat. No.
352 x 186 x 686 mm (13⁷/₈ x 7³/₈ x 27")	541.64.000

Packing: 1 pc.

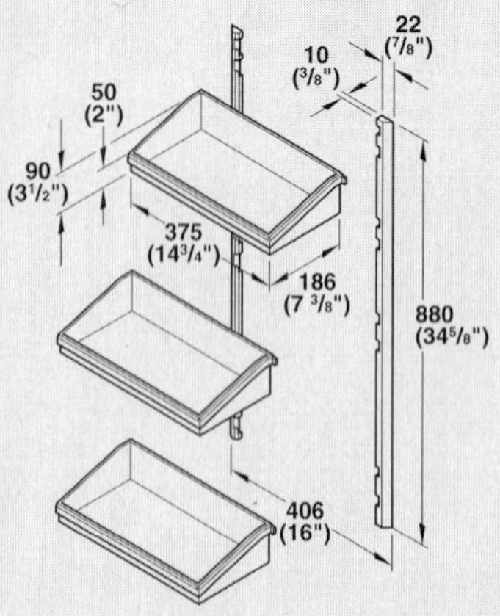

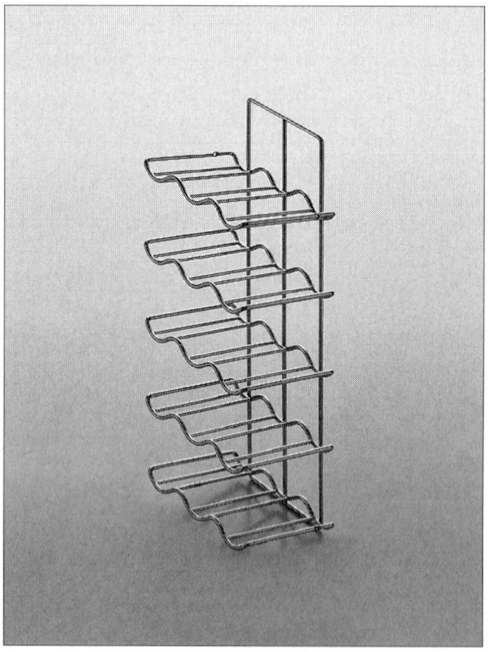

Wine rack
Capacity: 15 bottles
screw-mounted to side panel of cabinet

Finish: steel, chrome-plated

width x depth x height	Cat. No.
260 x 185 x 635 mm (10¹/₄ x 7¹/₄ x 25")	541.92.200

Packing: 1 pcs.

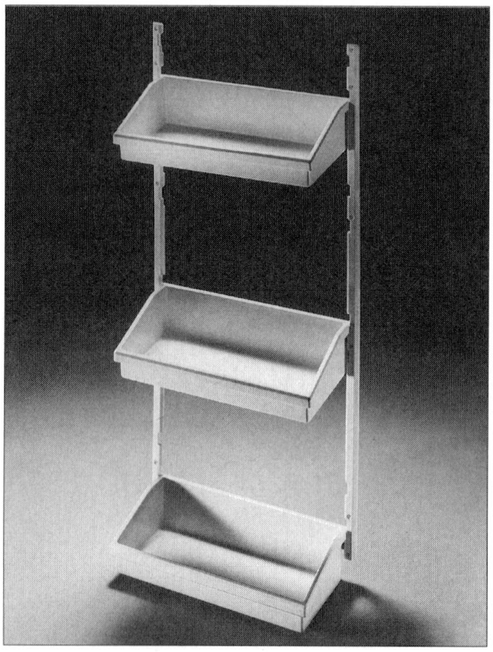

Hook-on standards
screw-mounted on the cabinet wall

Finish: plastic, white

Cat. No.	500.10.725

Packing: 1 pair

Trays
hooks onto the standards

Finish: plastic, white

Cat. No.	500.10.716

Packing: 3 pcs.

Dimensional data not binding.
We reserve the right to alter specifications without notice.

Dimensions in mm
Inches are approximate

Cabinet Accessories

HÄFELE

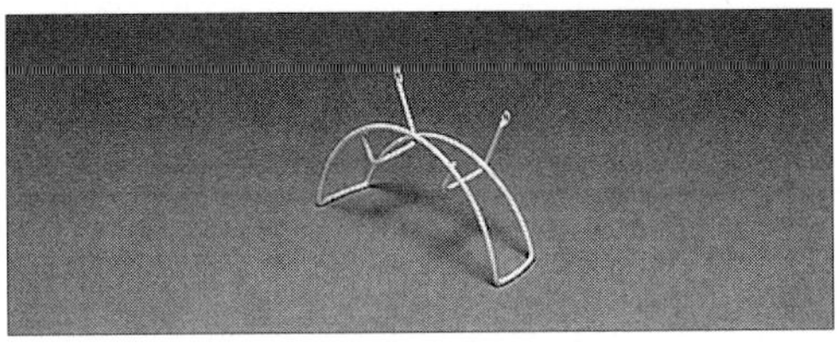

Hose and cable holder for vacuum cleaner
single pieced, with screw-mounted eyes
Finish: steel, plastic-coated, white

width	Cat. No.
220 mm	520.16.707

Packing: 1 pc.

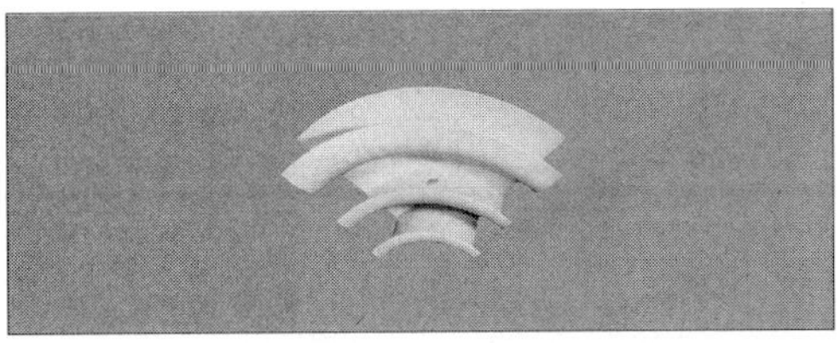

Hose and cable holder for vacuum cleaner
with three trays, screw-mounted
Finish: plastic, white

width x depth x height	Cat. No.
210 x 65 x 125 mm	520.13.706

Packing: 1 and 40 pcs.

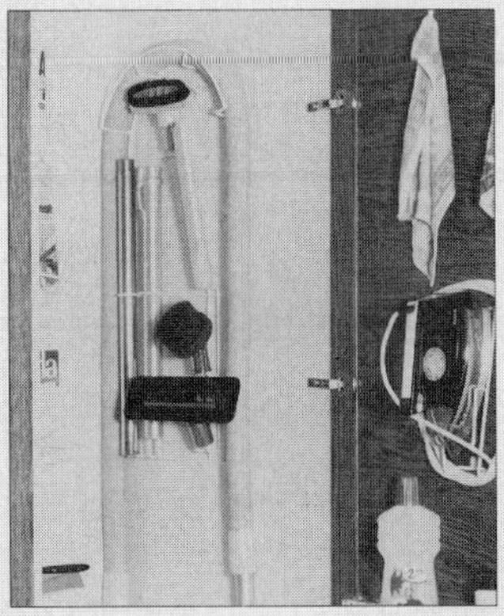

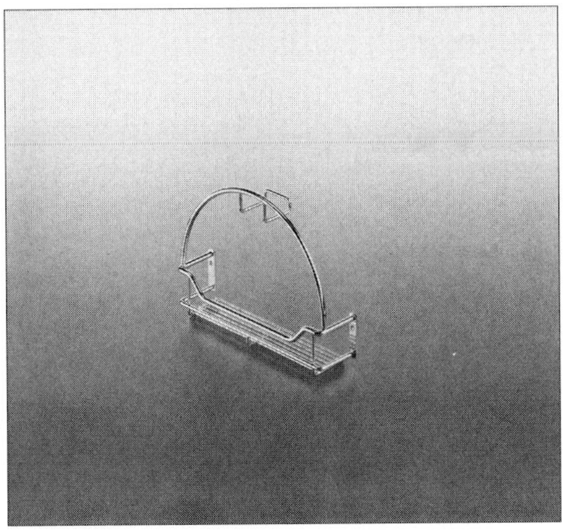

Hose and cable holder
screw-mounted to cabinet sidewall
Finish: steel, chrome-plated

width x depth x height	Cat. No.
310 x 78 x 224 mm	520.19.200

Packing: 1 pc.

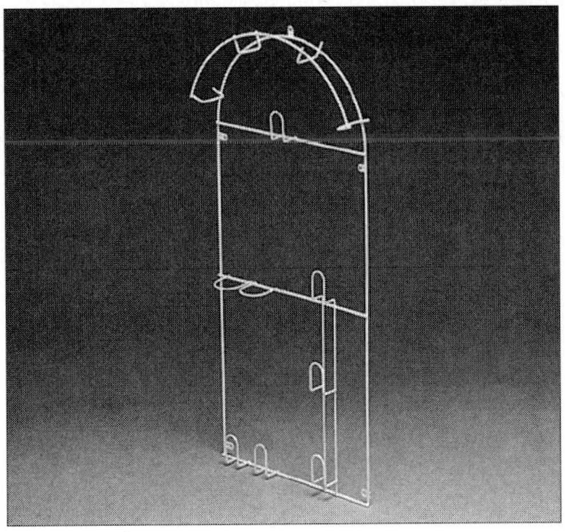

Hose and cable holder for vacuum cleaner
accessories, and screw-mounted eyes
Finish: steel, plastic-coated, white

width x depth x height	Cat. No.
305 x 60 x 680 mm	520.17.704

Packing: 1 pc.

Kitchen Accessory Systems

5

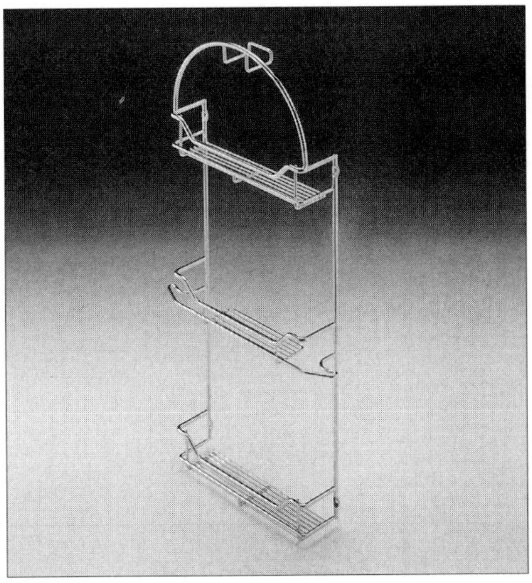

Hose and appliance holder
for vacuum cleaner accessories
with screw-mounted eyes
Finish: steel, chrome-plated

width x depth x height	Cat. No.
390 x 83 x 765 mm	541.68.204

Packing: 1 pc.

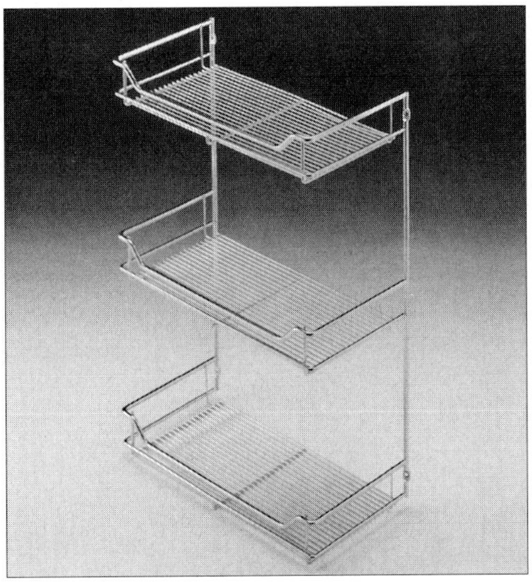

Shelving for interior cabinet
with screw-mounted eyes
Finish: steel, chrome-plated

width x depth x height	Cat. No.
405 x 210 x 625 mm	541.67.207

Packing: 1 pc.

Dimensions in mm
Inches are approximate

Dimensional data not binding.
We reserve the right to alter specifications without notice.

HÄFELE

Cabinet Spice Racks

- Spice racks can be mounted inside the door or on the side panel of the cabinet.

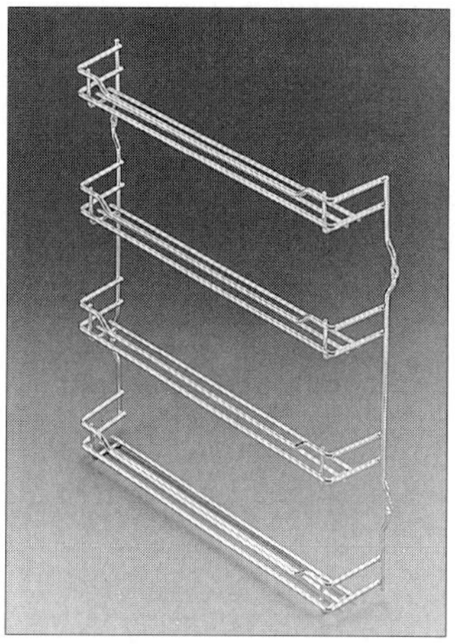

Spice rack
with screw-mounting eyes
Finish: steel wire, chrome-plated

width x depth x height	No. of shelves	Cat. No.
244 x 66 x 404 mm	4	543.19.260
390 x 66 x 404 mm	4	543.19.280
531 x 66 x 283 mm	3	543.19.250

Packing: 1 pc.

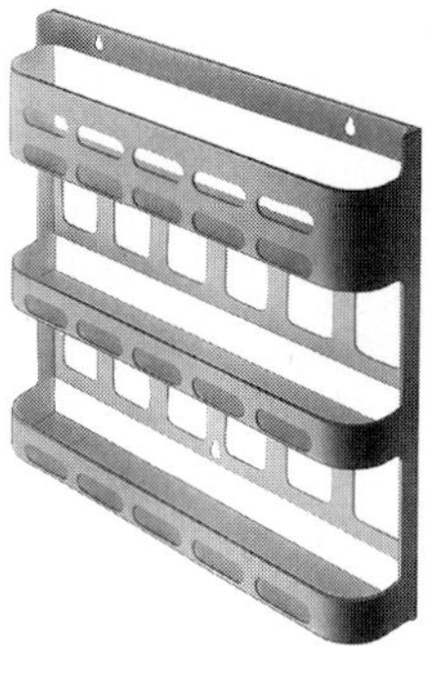

Spice rack
screw-mounted inside the door or on a wall
Finish: plastic, white

width x depth x height	Cat. No.
380 x 70 x 350 mm	543.14.706

Packing: 1 and 5 pcs.

Dimensional data not binding. We reserve the right to alter specifications without notice.

Dimensions in mm
Inches are approximate

Storage Systems for Upper Cabinets

HÄFELE

Chrome

Cabinet storage systems to be built into narrow cabinets.
- Minimum installation dimensions:
  Inside width 262 mm (10 1/2")
  Inside depth 275 mm (10 3/4")
  Inside height when using the follower fitting:
  420 mm (16 1/2") or 630 mm (24 3/4")
- Larger dimensions can be made to work by cutting the 16 mm (5/8") or 19 mm (3/4") thick back panel as desired.
- The follower fitting connects the movable back panel

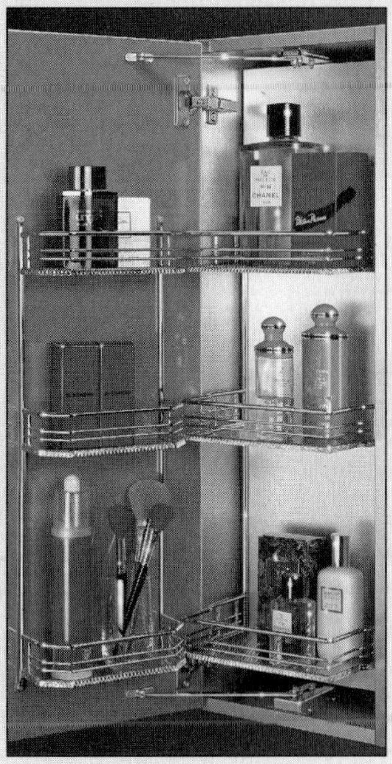

Installation instructions are included.

- Can be used for left hand or right hand doors.
- Door or pull-out shelf can be used alone.
- Opening the cabinet door makes the pull-out shelves slide-out.

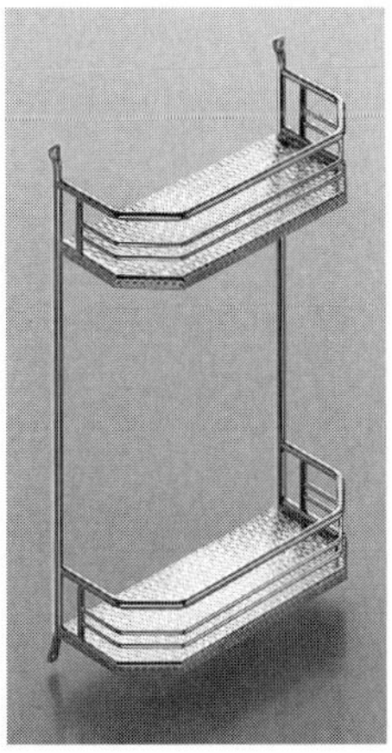

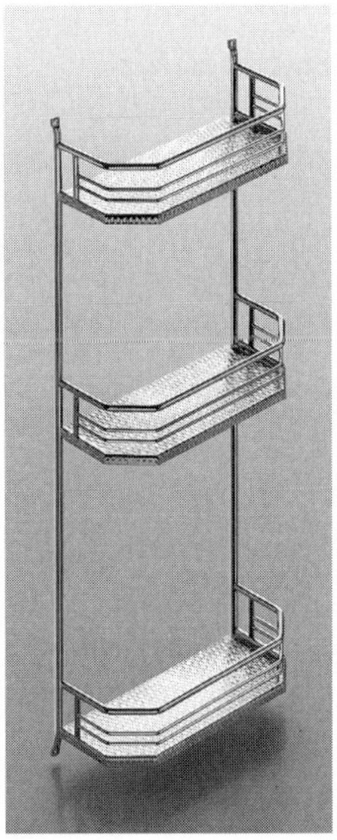

Door-mounted shelves
Shelf liners are made of textured metal.
Can be screw-mounted on the inside of the cabinet door.
Can be combined with the pull-out shelf and the follower fitting.
Finish: steel, chrome-plated
Width: 210 mm
Depth: 90 mm
Height: **360** mm
Number of shelves: 2

Cat. No.	543.23.232

Packing: 1 pc.

Width: 210 mm
Depth: 90 mm
Height: **570** mm
Number of shelves: 3

Cat. No.	543.23.214

Packing: 1 pc.

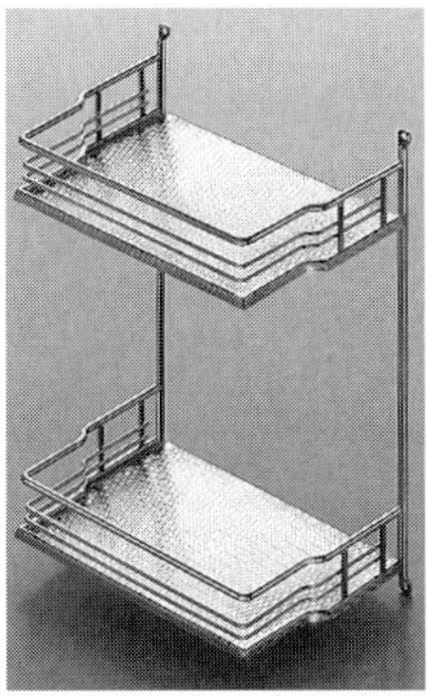

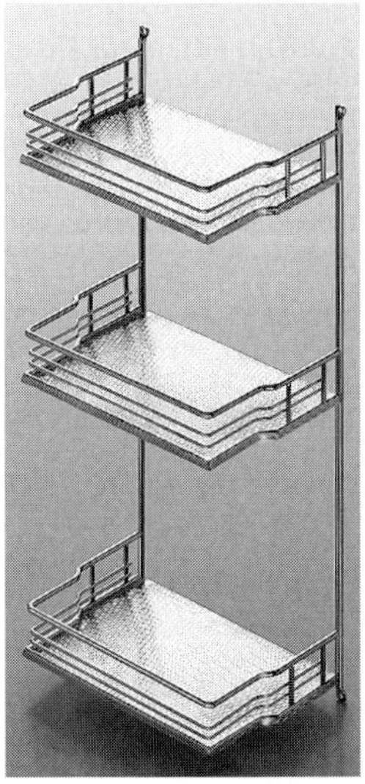

Pull-out shelves
Shelf liners are made of textured metal.
Can be screw-mounted onto a 2-part (movable) back panel. Can be combined with the door-mounted shelves and the follower fitting.
Finish: steel, chrome-plated
Width: 255 mm
Depth: 155 mm
Height: **360** mm
Number of shelves: 2

Cat. No.	543.23.241

Packing: 1 pc.

Width: 255 mm
Depth: 155 mm
Height: **570** mm
Number of shelves: 3

Cat. No.	543.23.223

Packing: 1 pc.

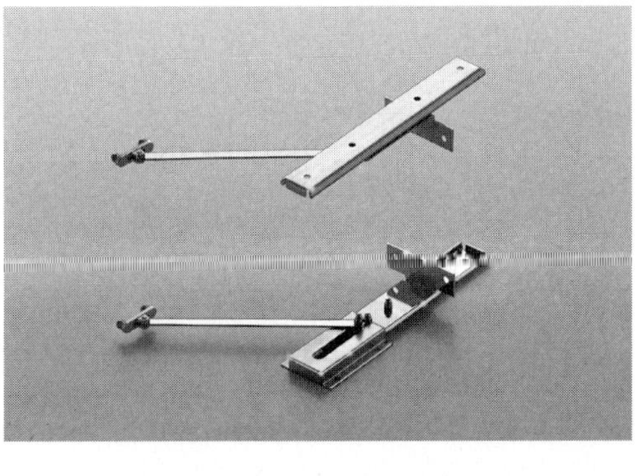

Follower fitting
for the pull-out shelves.
With welded angle brackets for mounting onto the rear panel.
Finish: visible parts: steel, chrome-plated
guide runners: steel, zinc-plated
front cover for guides: plastic, chrome-plated

Cat. No.	543.23.296

Packing: 1 set

Dimensions in mm
Inches ar approximate

Dimensional data not binding.
We reserve the right to alter specifications without notice.

HÄFELE

Revolving Shelf Fitting Systems

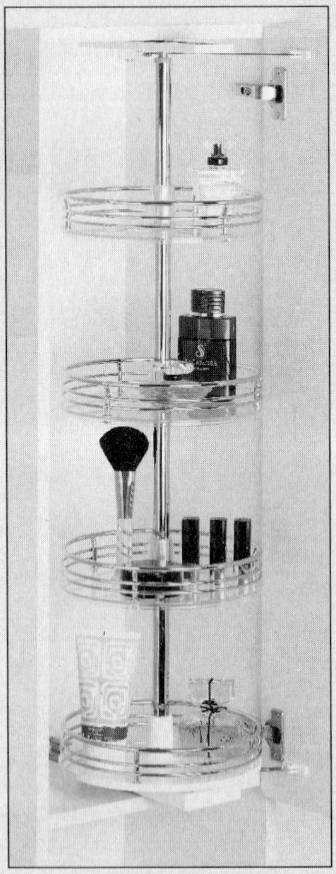

- When the cabinet door is opened the revolving shelf slides forward for easy access.

5 Kitchen Accessory Systems

- Clear shelves allow items in upper units to be seen.

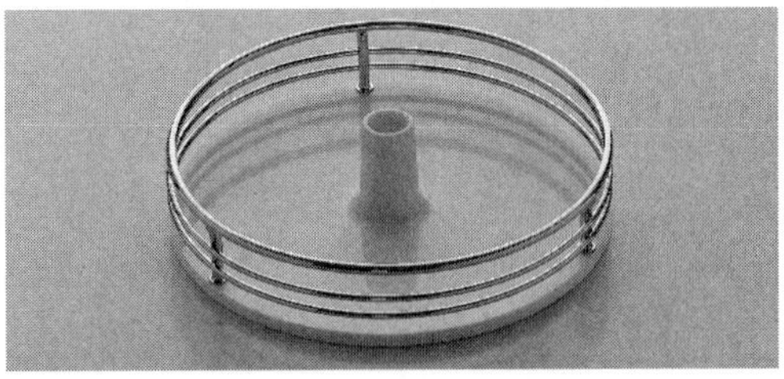

Revolving shelf, unit is particularly suitable for narrow cabinets 268 mm (10 1/2") wide with a inside depth of min. 260 mm (10 1/4"). Its design allows easy removal of smaller items. For use in kitchen or bath.

Revolving Shelf, white, with chrome fence
Finish:
Shelf: Plastic, white
Fence: Steel, chrome plated

Cat. No.	547.54.700

Packing: 1 pc.

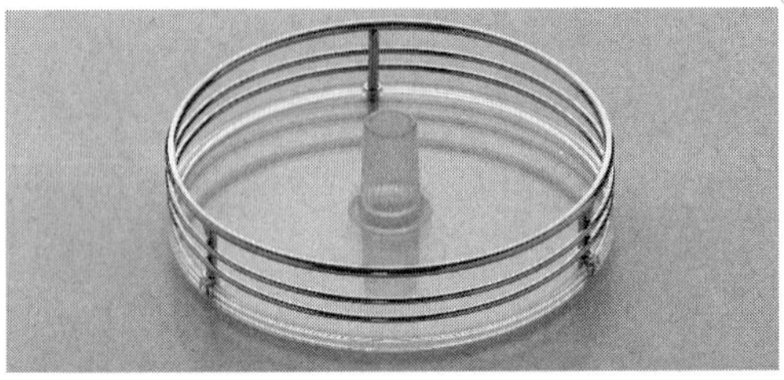

Revolving Shelf, clear, with chrome fence
Finish:
Shelf: Plastic, clear
Fence: Steel, chrome-plated

Cat. No.	547.54.406

Packing: 1 pc.

*The revolving shelves are supplied complete with bearing disc and securing pin made of steel, bright galvanized.

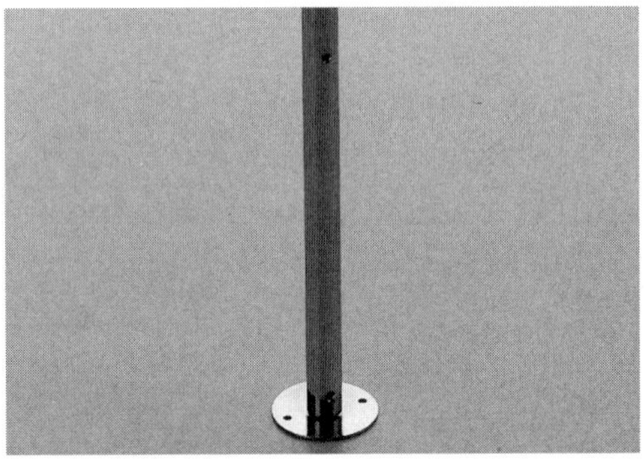

Posts for revolving shelves
Finish: Steel, chrome-plated; upper bearing sleeve, plastic, white

Post length mm (inch)	Installed length A mm (inch)	For shelf no.	Cat. No.
560 (22)	596 (23 1/2)	2	547.53.212
785 (31)	820 (32 1/4)	3	547.53.221
860 (33 7/8)	896 (35 1/4)	3	547.53.230
1185 (46 5/8)	1221 (48)	5	547.53.249

Packing: 1 pc.

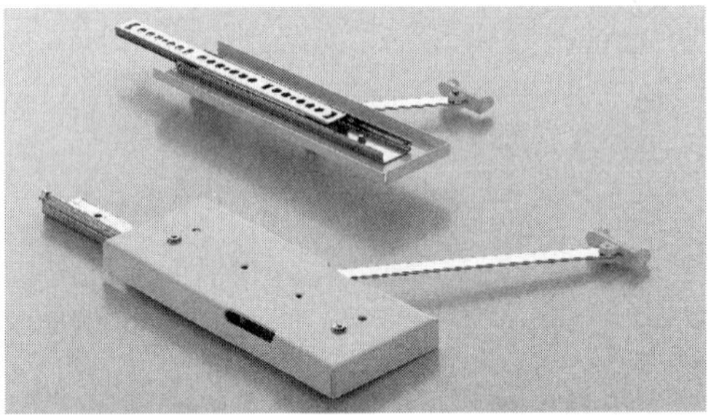

Pull-Out Fitting for Revolving Shelf Unit,
Includes: upper and lower runner, with all accessories.
Finish:
Runners: Steel, galvanized
Cover: Steel, plastic-coated, white, RAL 9010

Cat. No.	547.53.703

Packing: 1 Set

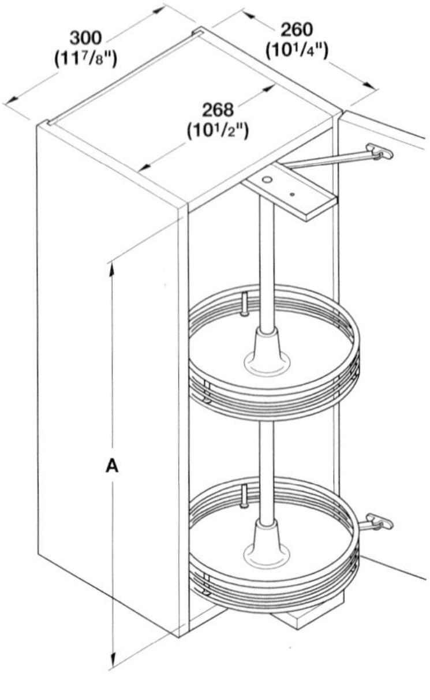

Installed height = inside cabinet height less 34 mm. If necessary, the axle can be shortened appropriately for shorter height.

Dimensions in mm
Inches are approximate

Dimensional data not binding. We reserve the right to alter specifications without notice.

Kitchen Gallery System

HÄFELE

8 Jar Spice Set, filled
contains seven superb quality freeze dried spices and herbs including thyme, paprika, curry, pepper, steak, oregano, nutmeg, and marjoram.

Installed length: 400 mm (16")
Finish: container-glass, clear
top, post caps-plastic, white
rod-steel, chrome plated

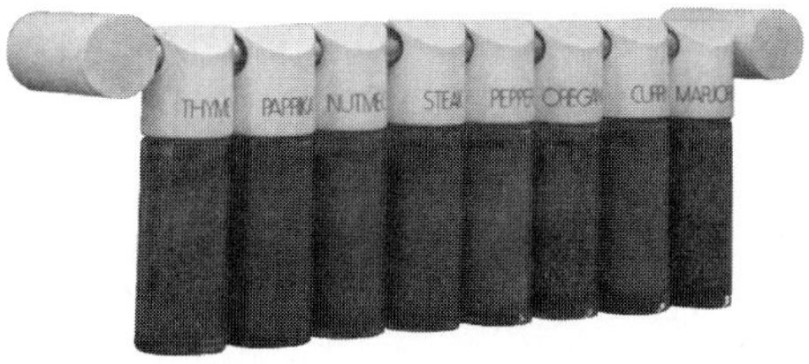

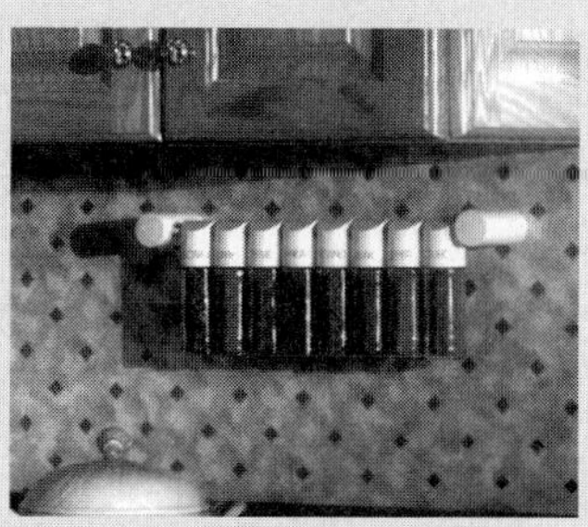

- Use under cabinets, behind doors and walls.
- Convenient and organized.
- No more rummaging about kitchens or in cabinets for items.

Cat. No.	521.40.735

Packing: 1 set

Spice glass, empty (not shown)

Cat. No.	521.40.002

Packing: 1 each

3 Cannister Storage Rack
Installed length: 350 mm (14")
Finish: cannister – plastic, clear
top, post caps – plastic, white
rod – steel, chrome plated

Cat. No.	521.40.726

Packing: 1 set

- Rod can also be mounted under cabinets or inside cabinet doors.
- Complete with mounting hardware.

Coffee Filter Paper Holder & Storage Cannister
Installed length: 350 mm (14")
Finish: Cannister – plastic, clear
top, post caps – plastic, white
rod – steel, chrome plated

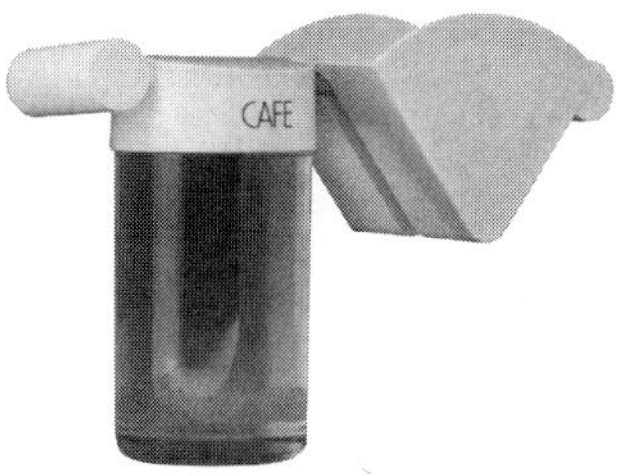

Cat. No.	521.40.717

Packing: 1 set

Dimensional data not binding. We reserve the right to alter specifications without notice.

Dimensions in mm
Inches are approximate

Cabinet Accessories

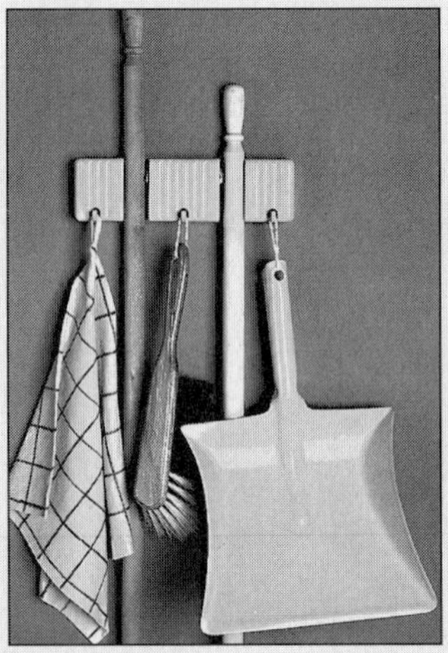

Broomstick holder
screw-mounted

Finish: spring steel, bright galvanized, rubber rollers

width x depth x height	Cat. No.
51 x 40 x 50 mm	520.10.009

Packing: 10 and 50 pcs.

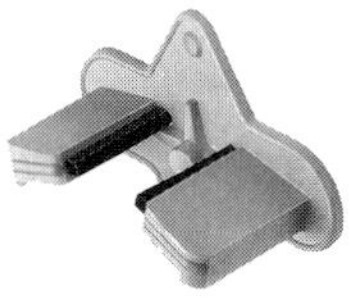

Broomstick holder
screw-mounted

Finish: plastic, white

width x depth x height	Cat. No.
86 x 40 x 71 mm	520.11.202

Packing: 10 and 50 pcs.

Broomstick holder
with **two** holders, screw-mounted.
Additional injection molded hooks for hanging cloths, rags etc.

Finish: plastic, white
rubber-coated jaws

width x depth x height	Cat. No.
250 x 32 x 70 mm	520.42.707

Packing: 1 pc.

Broomstick holder
with **four** holders, for concealed screw-mounting.

Finish: plastic housing, white
hooks: steel, nickel-plated, rubber-coated, with mounting hardware

width x depth x height	Cat. No.
318 x 27 x 75 mm	495.01.126

Packing: 1 pc.

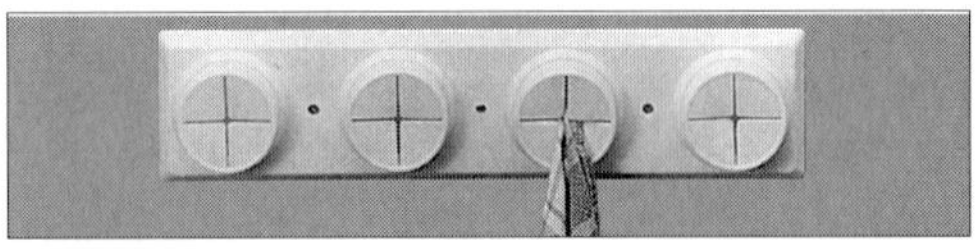

Towel holder
Holds towels in the cross-slots in the front of the rosette.

Finish: plastic, white

width x depth x height	Cat. No.
235 x 23 x 54 mm	520.02.409

Packing: 1 and 50 pcs.

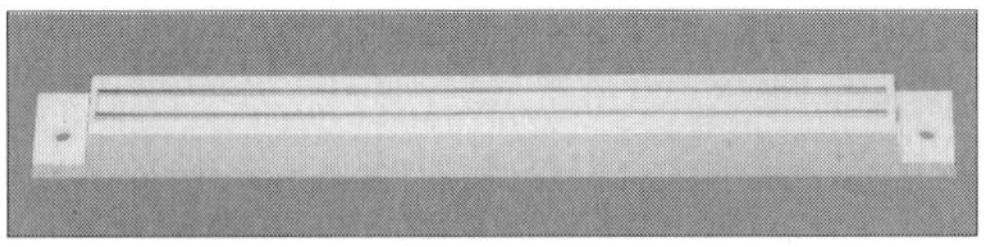

Magnetic rail
screw-mounted, for metal kitchen utensils

Finish: plastic, white

width x depth x height	Cat. No.
262 x 20 x 25 mm	520.41.700

Packing: 1 pc.

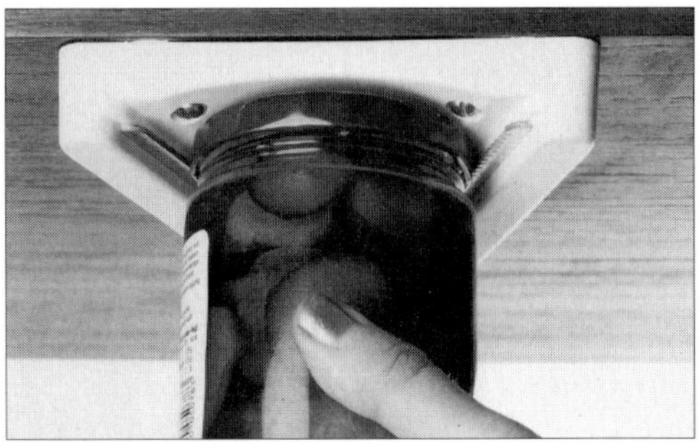

Jar opener
screw-mounted under shelves
Opens all sizes of jar lids

Finish: plastic, white
hardened steel jaws

width x depth x height	Cat. No.
138 x 153 x 25 mm	520.64.703

Packing: 1 pc.

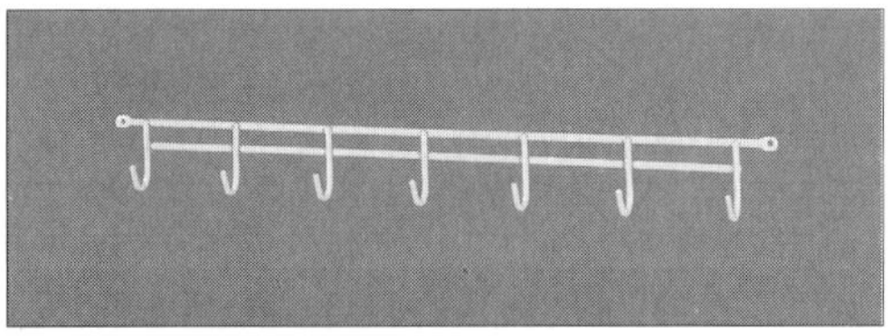

Hook rack with mounting screw eyes
screw-mounted to side panels

Finish: steel, epoxy-coated, white

Length		Cat. No.
290 mm	5 hook	520.05.713
42 mm	7 hook	520.05.722

Packing: 1 pc.

Dimensions in mm
Inches are approximate

Cabinet Fittings

Bottle holder grommets
for insertion in round openings of ø100 mm
height to lower edge: 70 mm
Finish: plastic

Color	Cat. No.
white	520.39.700
black	520.39.602

Packing: 1 pc.

Bottle holder grommets
for insertion in round opening
height to lower edge: 24 mm
Finish: plastic

Aperture	Color	Cat. No.
Ø 95 mm	white	520.39.719
	black	520.39.611
Ø 105 mm	white	520.39.728
	black	520.39.620

Packing: 1 pc.

Ultrahold
Dimensions: 18" (4 hooks) and 36" (8 hooks) length

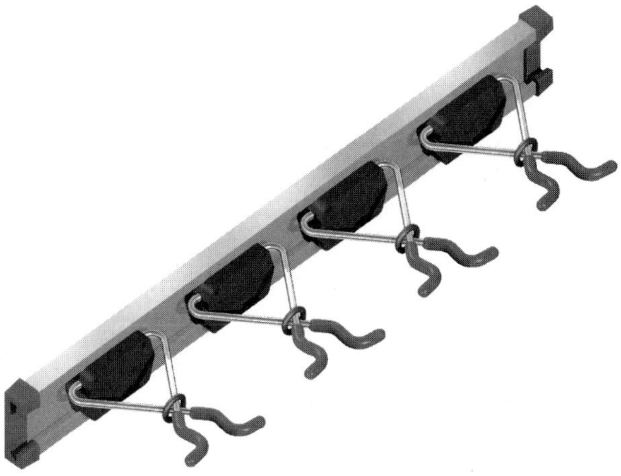

Finish: Rail: aluminum, anodized; Clip: steel

Cat. No.		
Cat. No.	18"	888.00.015
	36"	888.00.024

Packing: 1 pc.

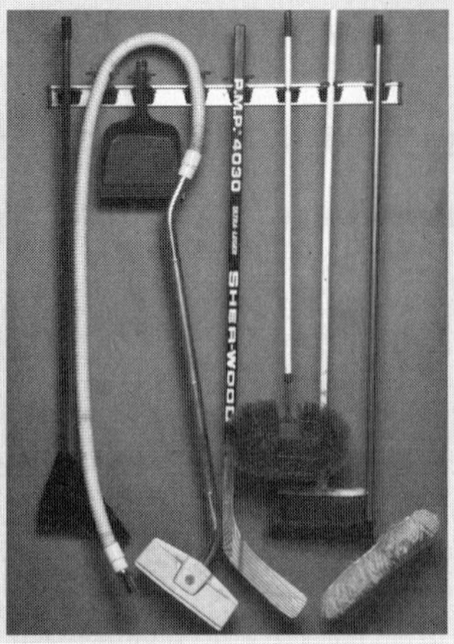

- Use in kitchen pantry, garage storage, workshop, office, storage room.
- Aluminum rail
- Will not rust
- Non-slip covering on hooks
- Will virtually hold anything
- Adjustable sliding clamp
- May be removed from rail and fastened independently to wall.
- Each clamp holds up to 20 lbs.

HÄFELE

E-Z Pull-Down Shelf Mechanism

- Use in kitchens, offices, hospitals, and upper cabinets.
- Fits from 12" to 33" wide cabinets.
- Optional light springs allow use for lighter loads of 7kg (16 lbs.)
- Shelving unit pivots down to user allowing easier access to upper shelf.
- Sturdy steel construction.
- Blends into cabinetry.
- Mounting instructions and hardware provided.

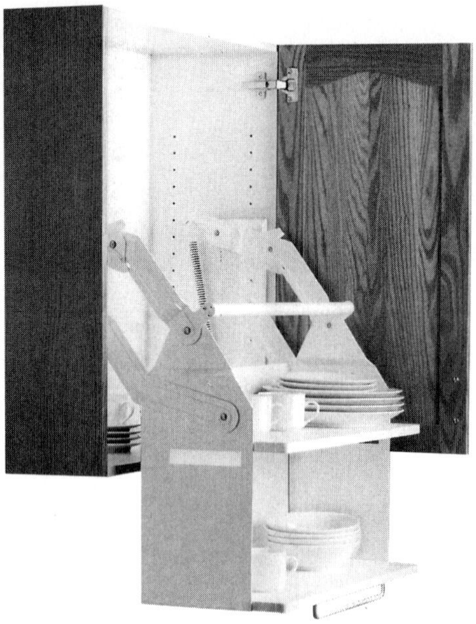

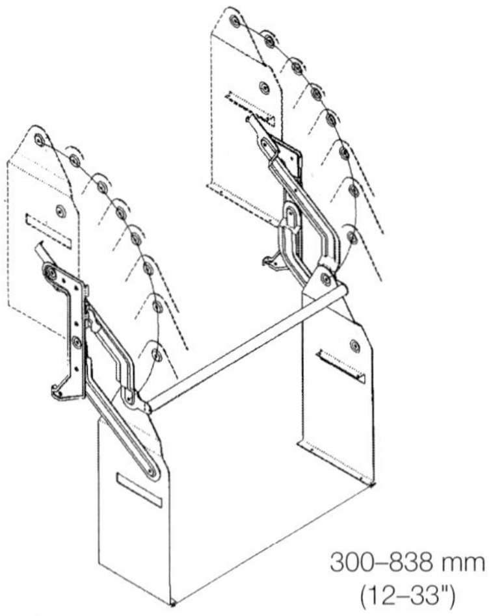

Minimum 635 mm (25") high , depth 279–305 mm (11"–12"), width 300–838 mm (12"–33"), with spring for weight capacity of 7–13kg (16–30 lbs.)
Material: steel
Finish: white, epoxy-coated

Cat. No.	504.56.700

Packing: 1 set

Optional light spring for weight capacity under 7kg (16 lbs.)
Finish: steel, zinc-plated

Cat. No.	504.56.790

Packing: 1 set

Shelves are not supplied. These are cut-to-width of interior cabinet less 2¾" x interior cabinet depth less 1/4". Depth of shelves cannot exceed 305 mm (12"). It is recommended in deeper cabinets that adjustable shelves be used behind the mechanism as fixed storage. Back panel and stabilizer bar supplied can be cut-to-size.

Not recommended for cabinets wider than 838 mm (33"), or total loads greater than 13kg (30 lbs.) or cabinets deeper than 300 mm (12"). Cabinet must be securely fastened to wall.

For face frame applications blocking is required before installation.

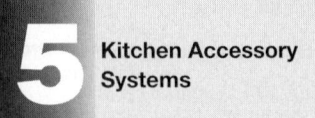

5 Kitchen Accessory Systems

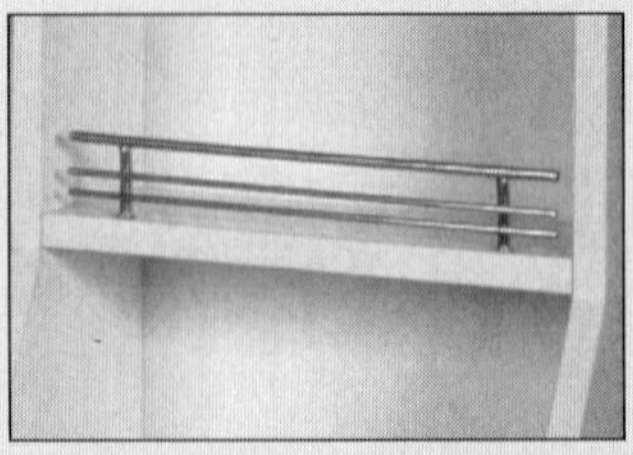

Optional fence for installation at front of shelves to prevent items from falling off.

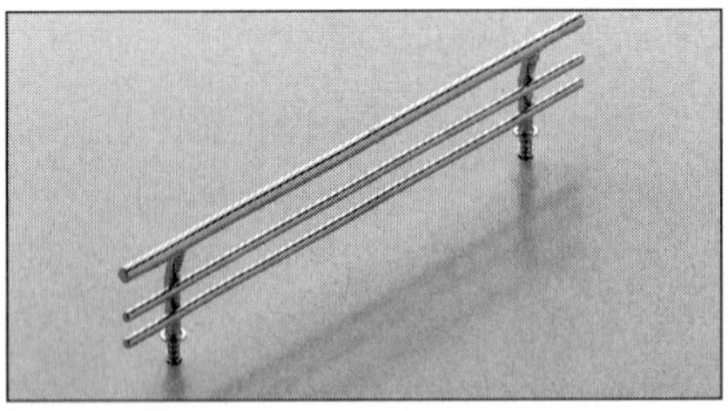

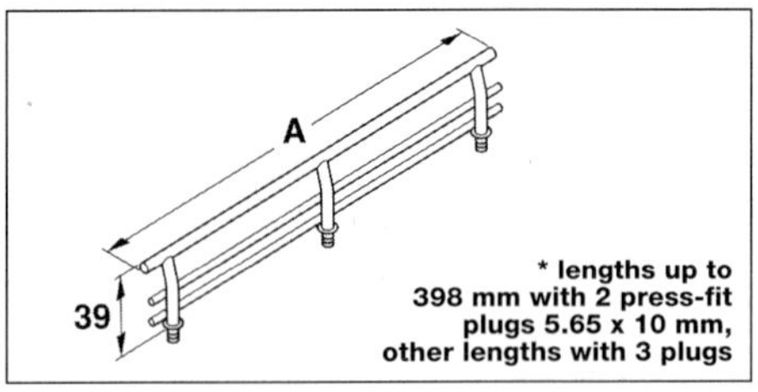

Fence for wooden shelves press-fit in 5 mm dia. drilled holes.
Finish: steel, chrome-plated

Length		Cat. No.
248 mm*	(9¾")	547.51.218
298 mm*	(11¾")	547.51.227
348 mm*	(13¾")	547.51.236
398 mm*	(15¾")	547.51.245
448 mm	(17⅝")	547.51.254
548 mm	(21½")	547.51.263

Packing: 2 pcs.

Dimensional data not binding.
We reserve the right to alter specifications without notice.

Dimensions in mm
Inches are approximate

Ergoflex Adjustable Counter Top Mechanisms

HÄFELE

Slab-End Frame Style, for adjustable workstations.

Adjustment range: 12" (23 -35" in height)

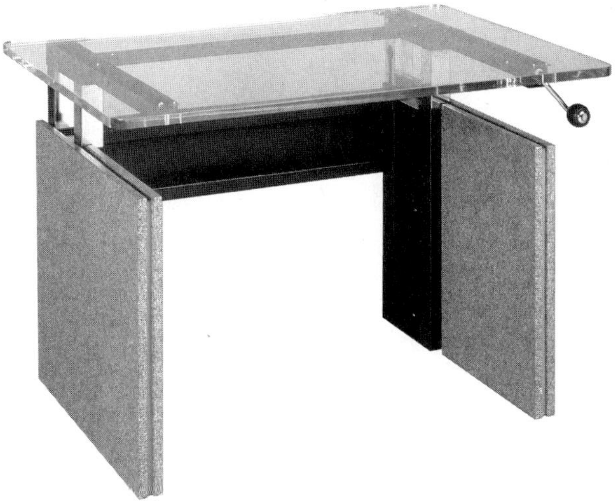

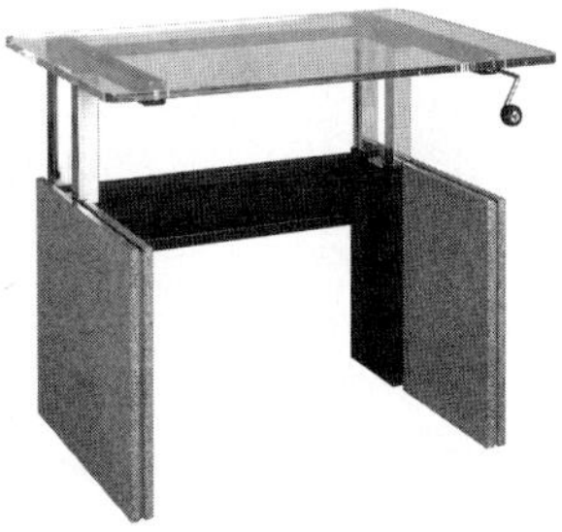

Finish: frame, steel, epoxy powder-coated black or gray
Elevation tubes, steel chrome-plated

	Size: for countertop sizes	black	light gray
Cat. No.	24" Deep x specify*	639.01.34X	639.01.54X
	30" Deep x specify*	639.01.36X	639.01.56X

Packing: 1pc.

***Must specify width between side panels**

Frame is not available with panels or top as shown.

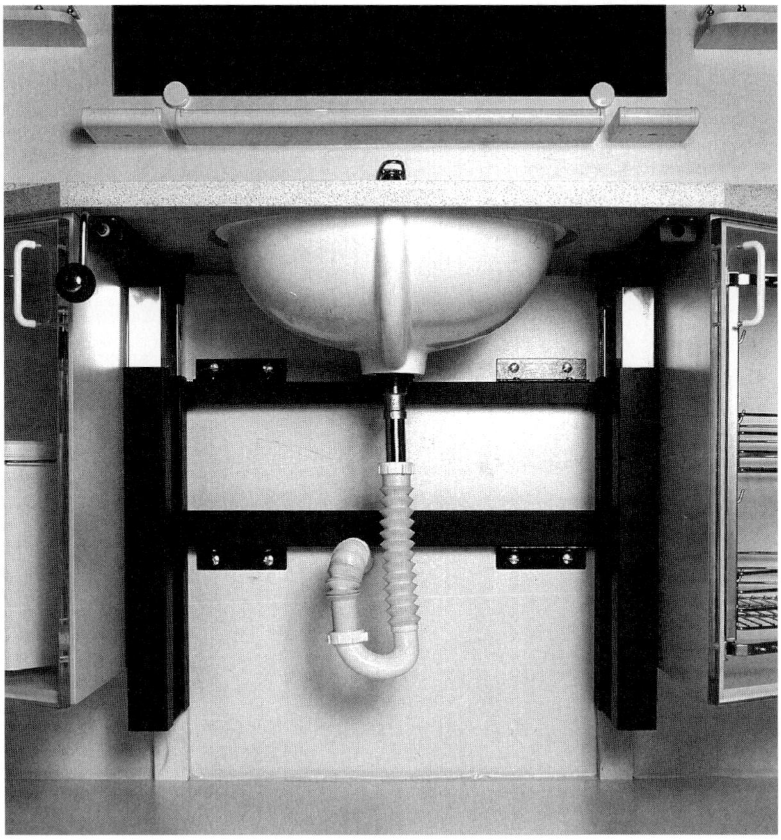

Free Standing C-Frame Style
- All steel construction shipped RTA. Only 6 screws required for assembly.
- 8 bearings in each leg column for effortless movement - even under heavy loads.
- All mechanical components are "Molybonded" to eliminate the need for lubrication.
- Gas cylinder assisted to aid lifting even the heaviest loads.
- Unique "Flexdrive" provides adjustment range of 12" (23-35"). Approximately 8 turns of the ergonomic handle moves the work surface 1".
- Epoxy powder coated to provide superior protection and ensure long lasting appearance.
- Weight capacity - 350 lbs.

Conform to the following technical standards:
- ANSI/BIFMA X5.5-1983 "Tests for Desk Products"
- BSI 4875: Part 5: 1985 "Strength and Stability of Furniture"
- Australian Standards Association AS 3590.2 - 1990 "Screen Based Workstations Part 2: Workstation Furniture"

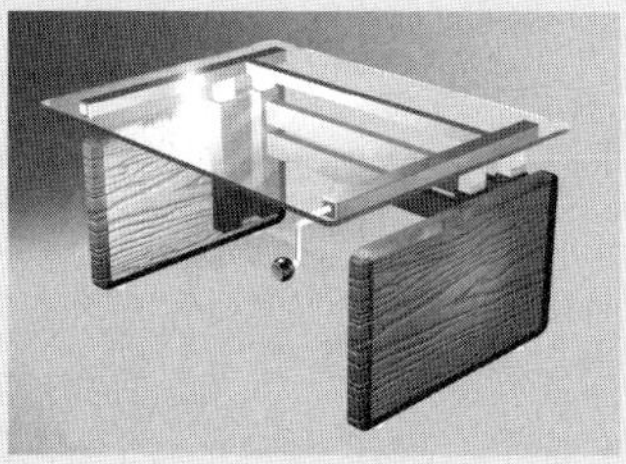

HÄFELE

Laundry Hampers

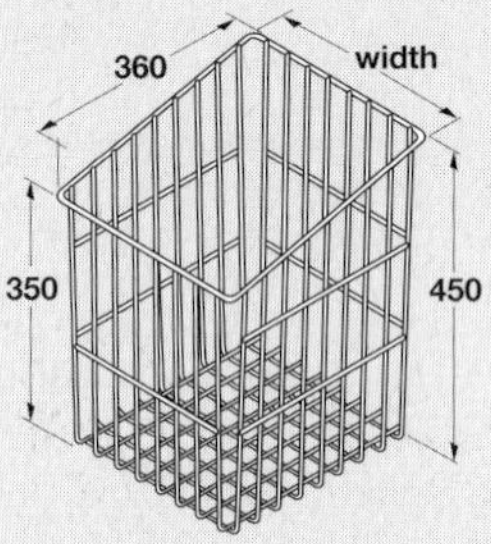

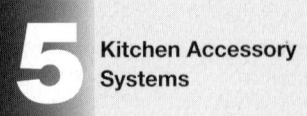

Laundry hamper, three-sided with mounting brackets
Dimensions: 300 mm x 240 mm x 400 mm (w x d x h)
Finish: steel wire, epoxy-coated, white

Cat. No.	540.05.711

Packing: 1 pc.

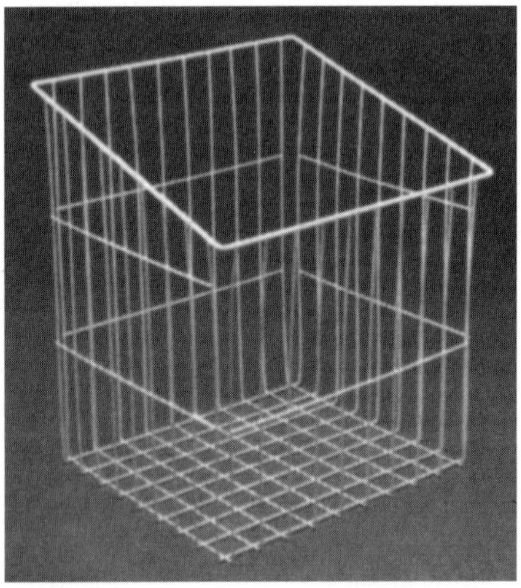

Hook-on hamper, slanted
for hanging on mounting bracket
Finish: steel wire, epoxy-coated, white

Min. inside Cabinet width mm	(inch)	Width mm	(inch)	Cat. No.
343	(13½")	318	(12½")	540.09.755
419	(16½")	394	(15½")	540.09.764
495	(19½")	470	(18½")	540.09.773

Packing: 1 pc.

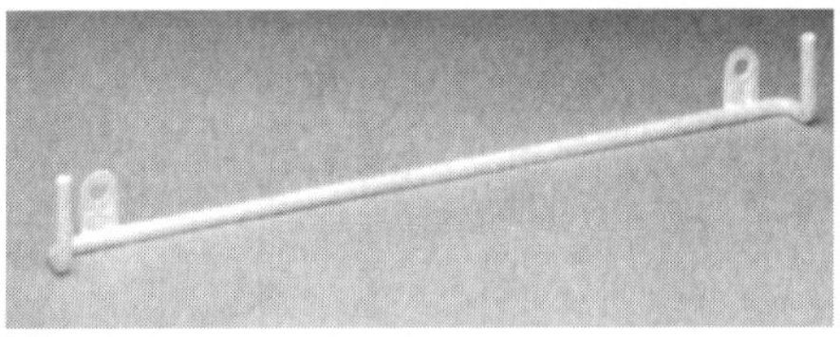

Mounting bracket for laundry hamper
for screw-mounted with Hospa 4.0 mm
Dimensions: 230 mm (9 1/16") x 16 mm (5/8") x 26 mm (1") w x d x h
Space between holes: 190 mm (7½")
Finish: steel, epoxy-coated, white

Cat. No.	540.06.996

Packing: 1 pc.

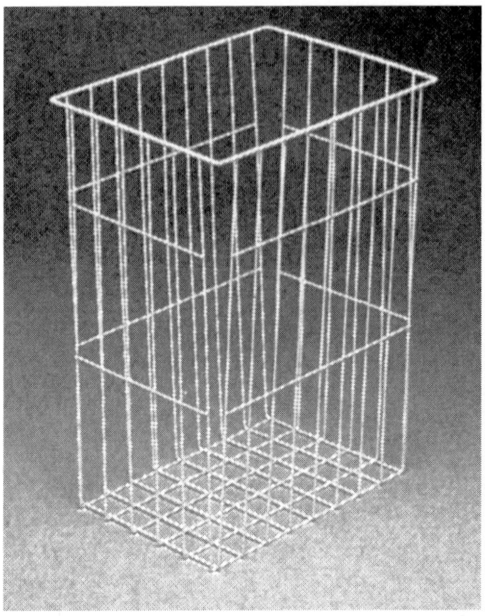

Laundry hamper, four-sided
Finish: steel wire, epoxy-coated, white

Width mm (inch)	Height mm (inch)	Depth mm (inch)	Cat. No.
340 (13 3/8")	250 (10")	450 (17¾")	540.06.736
395 (15½")	480 (18 7/8")	520 (20½")	540.06.754

Packing: 1 pc.

Dimensions in mm
Inches are approximate

Dimensional data not binding.
We reserve the right to alter specifications without notice.

Laundry Hampers

Chrome

HÄFELE

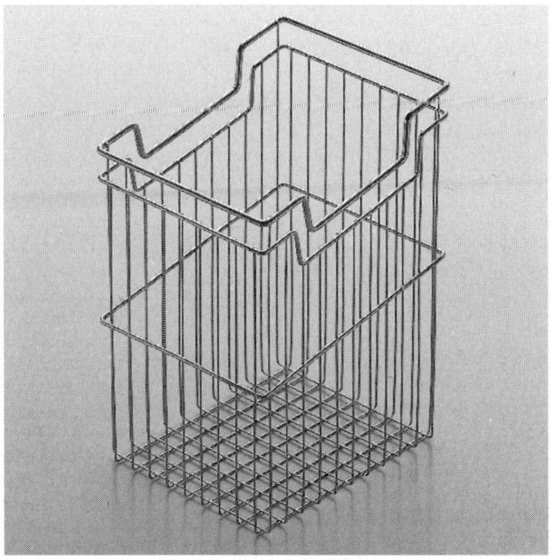

Laundry Hamper , with lowered handles
for hanging on mounting rail
Finish: steel, chrome-plated

For cabinet width: **300 mm (11¾)**
Capacity: 23.5 liters (6 gal.)
Hamper width: 235 mm (9¼")
Hamper depth: 285 mm (11¼")
Height: rear 365 mm (14⅜")/front 420 mm (16½")

Cat. No.	540.02.112

Packing: 1 pc.

For cabinet width: **450 mm (17¾)**
Capacity: 39 liters (10 gal.)
Hamper width: 385 mm (15¼")
Hamper depth: 285 mm (11¼")
Height: rear 365 mm (14⅜")/front 420 mm (16½")

Cat. No.	540.02.121

Packing: 1 pc.

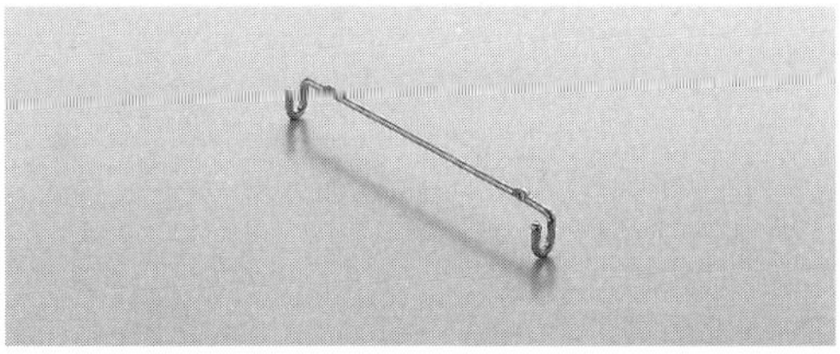

Mounting Bracket, for laundry basket,
for screw mounted with Hospa 4.0 mm
Width: 214 mm
Spacing between holes: 160 mm
Finish: steel, chrome-plated

Cat. No.	540.02.194

Packing: 1 pc.

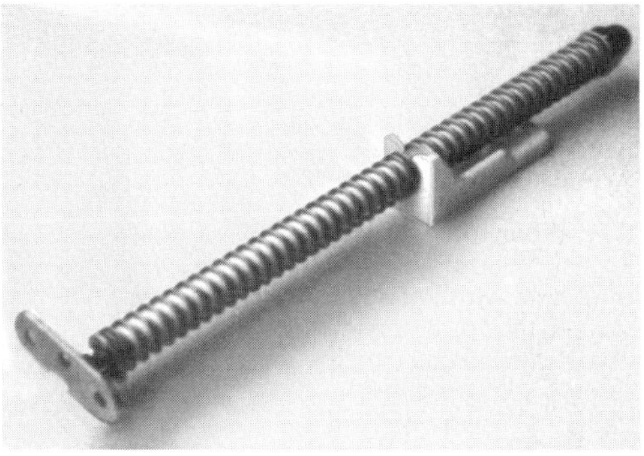

Flap stay »FLAP-EX«
completely assembled, includes:
- 1 screw-on angular bracket, steel, nickel-plated
  1 round rod with plastic sleeve, 2 washers
  2 spiral springs: front =126 mm long
  rear = 90 mm long

1 screw-on bearing, packed loose: plastic, white

Cat. No.	365.52.708

Packing: 10 pcs.

Kitchen Accessory Systems 5

The door is opened under spring tension by approx. 27° by simply applying pressure directly to the door itself. Refer to page 3.105 for additional information.

Laundry Hamper, mobile
Capacity appr: 73 liters (19 gal.)
Dimensions: (L x W x H) = 455 x 400 x 535 mm
(18 x 15¾ x 21")
Finish: steel, chrome-plated, twin-wheel castors
in black plastic

Cat. No.	540.01.204

Packing: 1 pc.

Dimensions in mm
Inches are approximate

HÄFELE

Baskets and Accessories

Chrome

- Multi-purpose baskets mount between two panels as shown above.

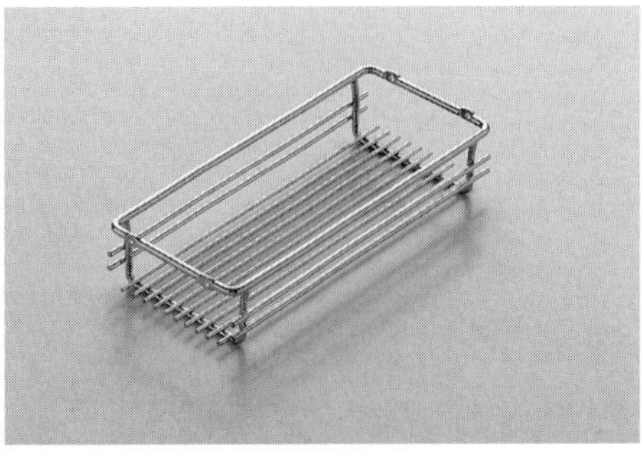

Multi-purpose basket
for base cabinet with
minimum width of 150 mm (5 7/8)
Width: 107 mm (4 1/4")
Length: 250 mm (9 7/8")
Height: 50 mm (2")
Finish: steel, chrome-plated

Cat. No.	547.50.211

Packing: 1 pc.

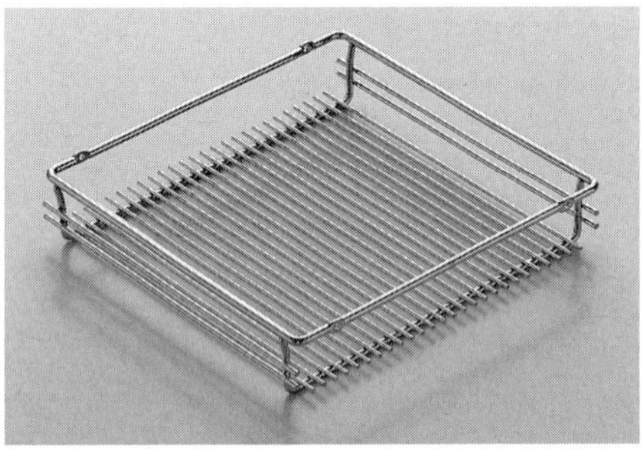

Multi-purpose basket
for base cabinet with
minimum width of 300 mm (11 3/4)
Width: 257 mm (10 1/8")
Depth: 250 mm (9 7/8")
Height: 50 mm (2")
Finish: steel, chrome-plated

Cat. No.	547.50.220

Packing: 1 pc.

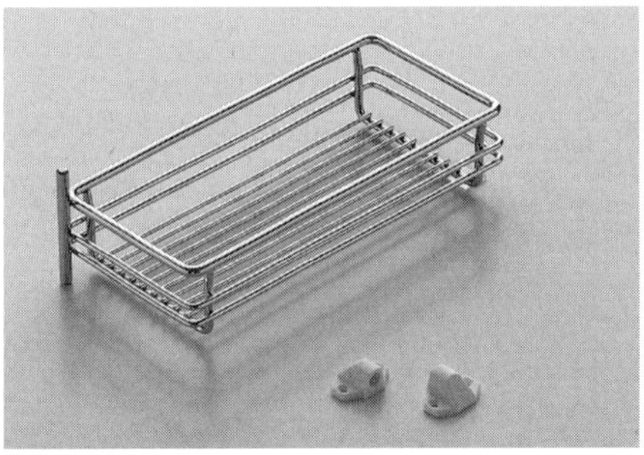

Swivel basket
for installation in wall units with a
minimum width of 300 mm (11 3/4")
Handed for mounting on right or left side panel.
Swivel radius: 250 mm (9 7/8")
Length: 240 mm (9 1/2")
Width: 110 mm (4 3/8")
Height: 50 mm (2")
Finish: steel, chrome-plated

Cat. No.	left	547.52.215
	right	547.52.206

Packing: 1 pc.

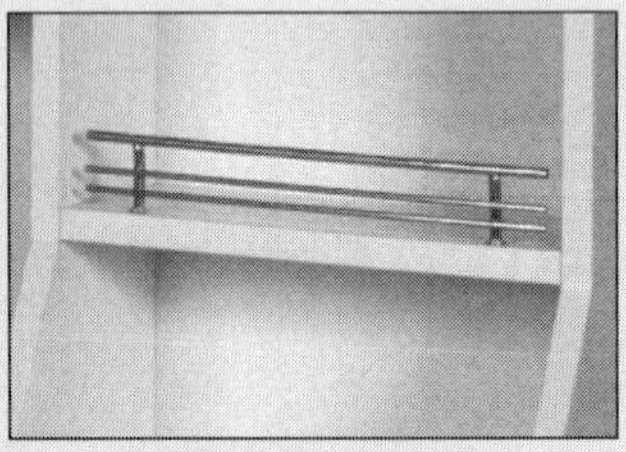

Press fit plugs
Ø 5.65 mm x 10 mm

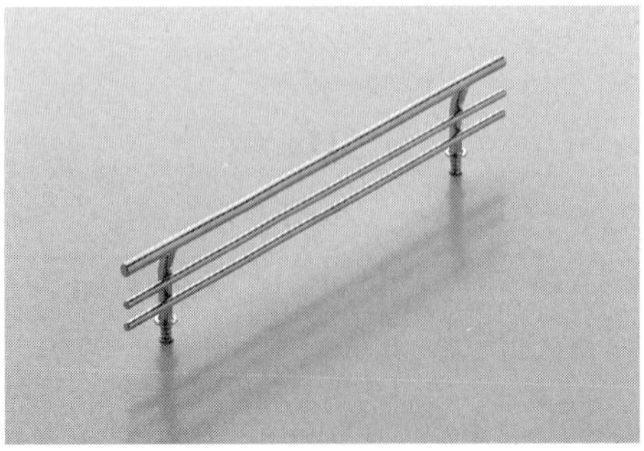

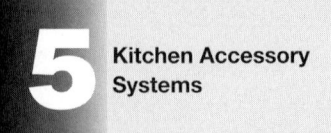

Fence
for wood shelves
press-fit
5 mm dia. holes
Height: 39 mm (1 1/2")
Finish: steel, chrome-plated

Length mm	# Press fit plugs	Cat. No.
248 (9 3/4")	2	547.51.218
298 (11 3/4")	2	547.51.227
348 (13 3/4")	2	547.51.236
398 (15 3/4")	2	547.51.245
448 (17 5/8")	3	547.51.254
548 (21 1/2")	3	547.51.263

Packing: 2 pcs.

Dimensional data not binding.
We reserve the right to alter specifications without notice.

Dimensions in mm
Inches are approximate

Swing-up Fitting

HÄFELE

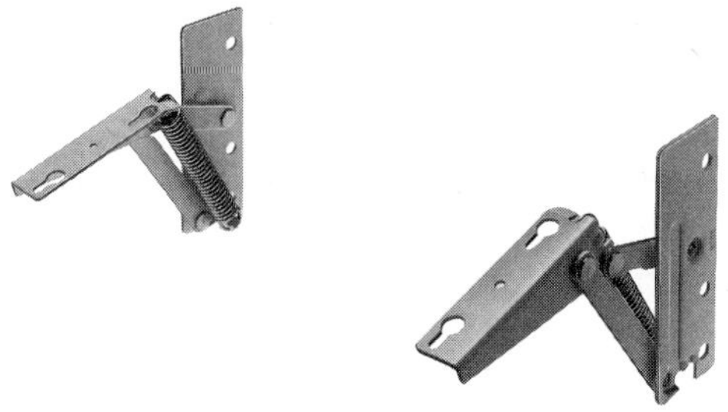

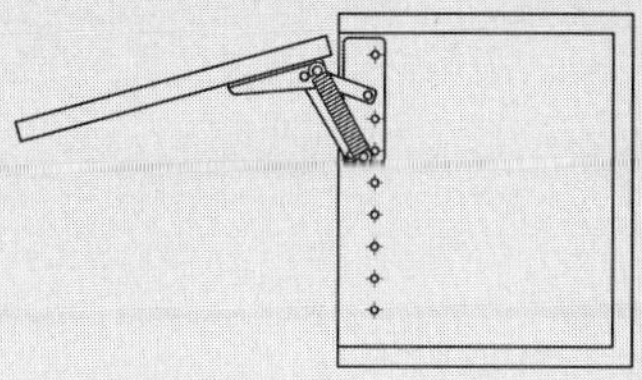

Doors swing up automatically when lifted and are securely held open. Opening angle is 76°. Self operating from 17°. The spring action holds doors tight when closed.

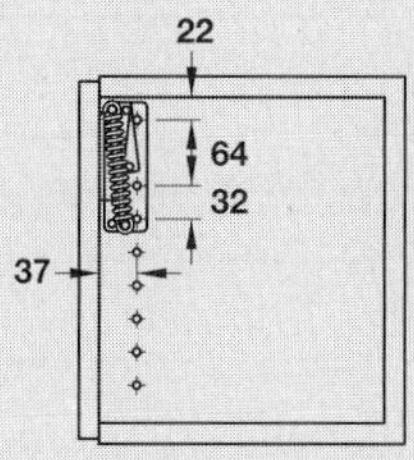

Swing-up Fitting, Swingtop
Finish: steel, epoxy-coated white; Spring: nickel-plated

		Cat. No.
with spring	left	504.48.774
without spring	right	504.48.765
	left only	504.48.792

Packing: 10 pcs.

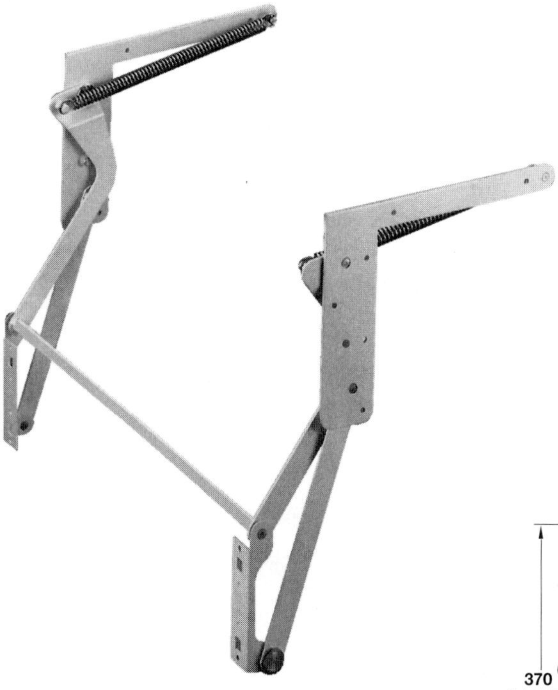

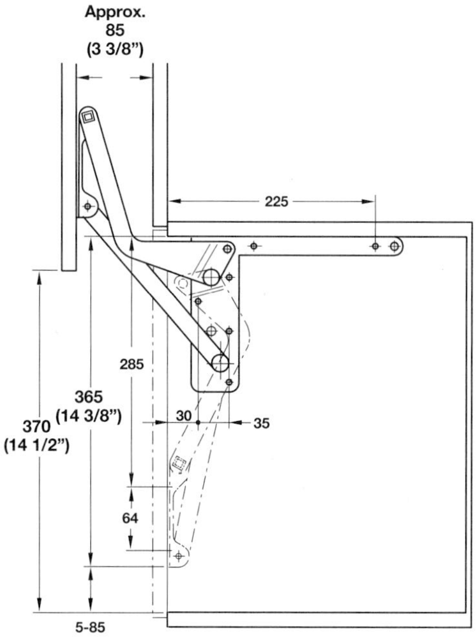

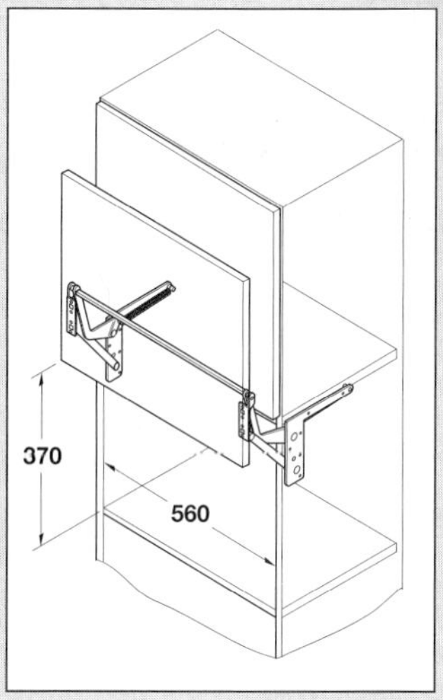

- For concealed installation of small appliances in tall kitchen cabinets.
- Dimensions for door flap:
  Width: max. 600 mm(23 5/8")
  Height: max. 450 mm(18")
  Thickness: max. 19 mm(3/4")

Swing Up Fitting Frontlift
Finish: steel, epoxy-coated RAL 9010

Cat. No.	504.39.775

Packing: 1 pc.

Dimensional data not binding. We reserve the right to alter specifications without notice.

Dimensions in mm
Inches are approximate

HÄFELE

Swing-Up Fittings

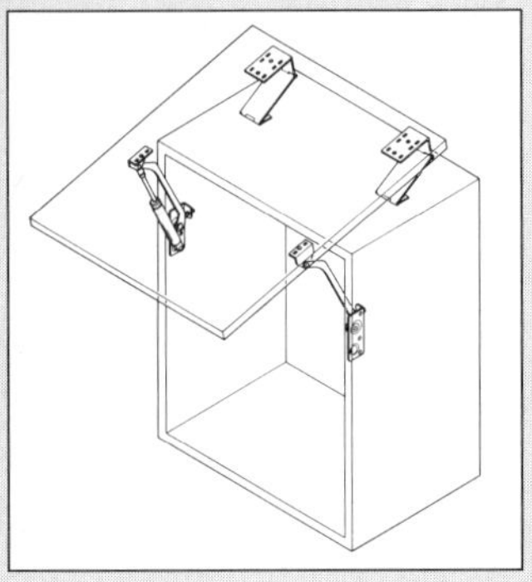

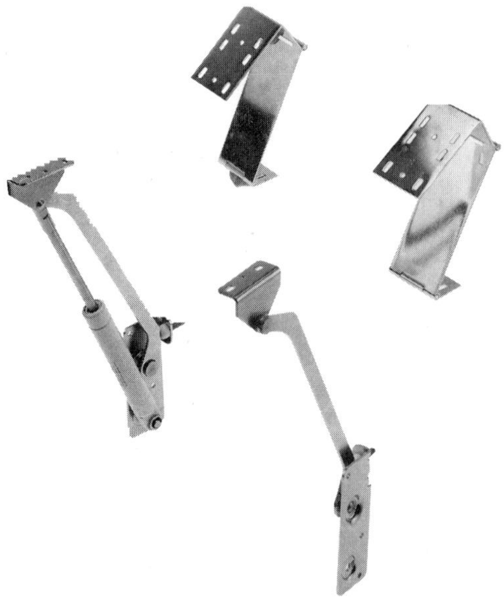

Toplift swing-up hardware

System includes 2 double-jointed hinges and 2 guide arms, and a gas cylinder.
Finish: steel, chrome-plated;
Gas cylinder: white, epoxy-coated

cabinet door width	Handing	Force	Cat. No.
600 mm (23 5/8")	left	250 N	504.35.017
	right	w/o gas cylinder	
1000 mm (39")	left	250 N	504.35.026
	right	250 N	

Packing: 1 and 10 sets

Cabinet door width specifications provided are based on an average door height.

Replacement gas cylinder

250 N	504.35.919
350 N	504.35.928

Packing: 1 pc.

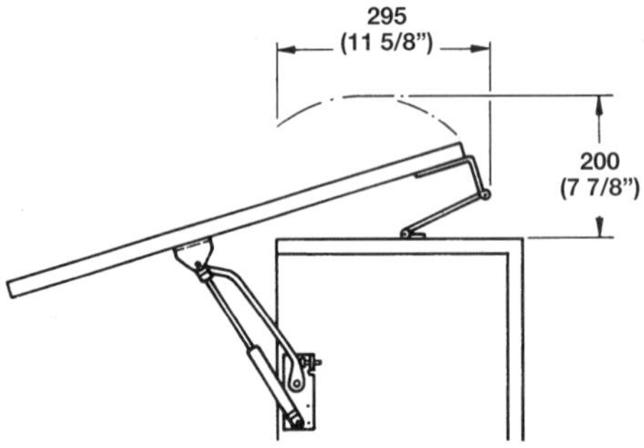

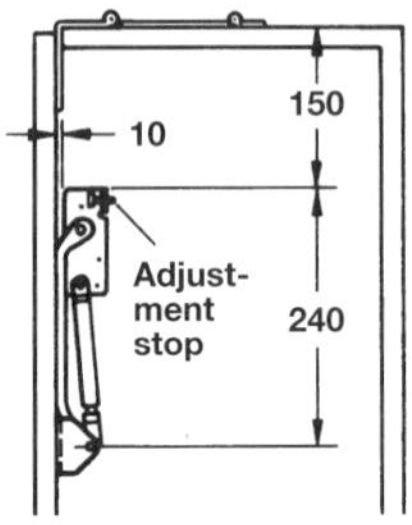

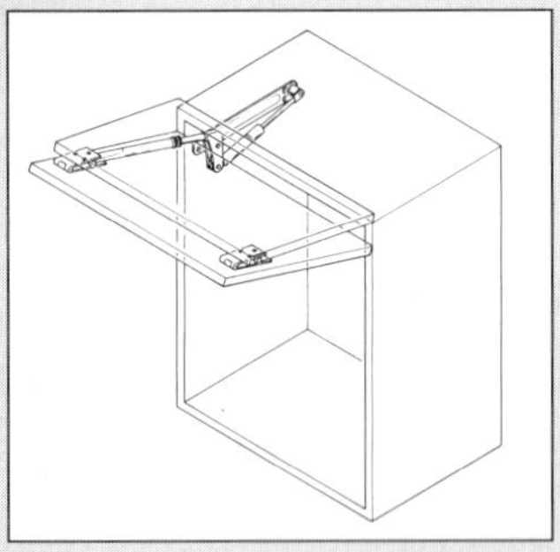

Automatic fold-up door hardware

System includes 1 mounting plate, 1 gas cylinder, 1 double-jointed lever, 1 guide arm, 2 hinges and 1 bearing pin. Cabinet door width specifications provided are based on an average door height.
Finish: steel, nickel-plated and cream-white enameled

cabinet door width	Handing	Force	Cat. No.
400 – 500 mm (16-20")	non-handed left	390 N	504.40.018
500 – 600 mm (20-23 5/8")	or right	460 N	504.40.027

Packing: 1 set

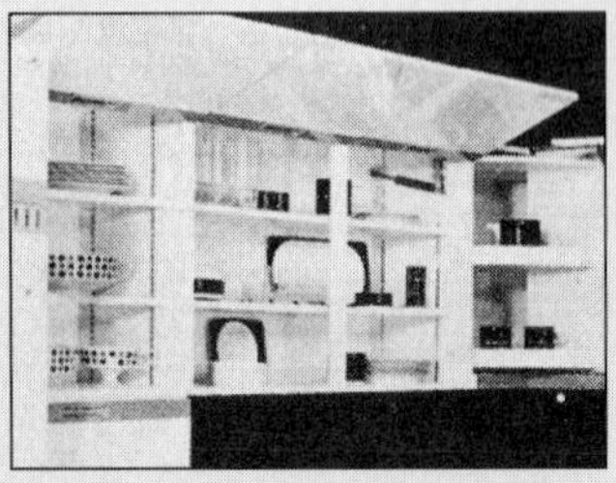

Cabinet doors are height-adjustable to allow alignment with adjacent cabinets.

Replacement gas cylinder

390 N	504.40.483
460 N	504.40.492

Packing: 1 pc.

The two cabinet door panels are joined by hinges. As the door swings up, the lower panel automatically folds up against the upper. A built-in gas cylinder drives the actual upward swing.

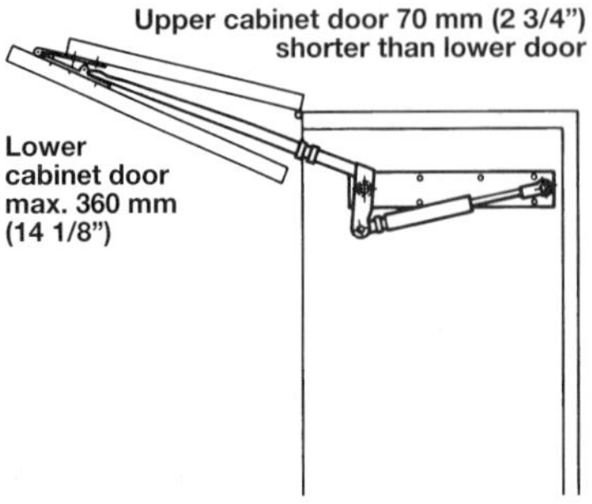

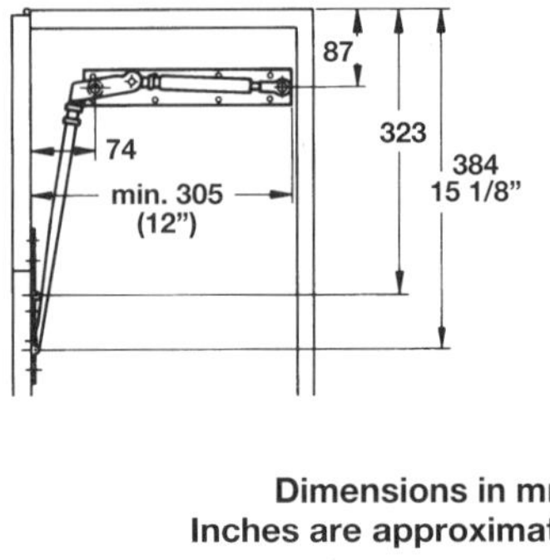

Dimensional data not binding.
We reserve the right to alter specifications without notice.

Dimensions in mm
Inches are approximate

Ventilation Grills

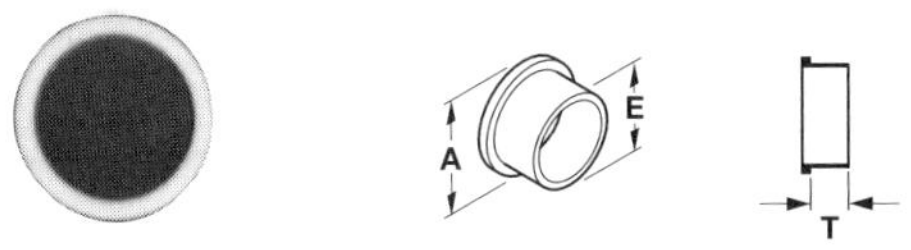

Air ventilation grommets, recess-mounted
Finish: plastic

Dimensions (mm) A	E	T	color	Cat. No.
ø38	ø34	15	white	571.27.714
			black	571.27.312
ø49	ø45	15	white	571.27.723
			black	571.27.321

Packing: 50 pcs.

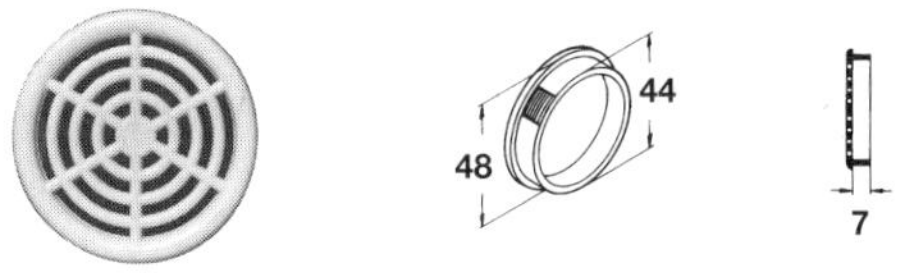

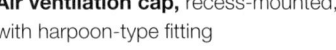

Air ventilation cap, recess-mounted,
with harpoon-type fitting
Finish: plastic

Cat. No.	white	571.09.707
	brown	571.09.109

Packing: 50 pcs.

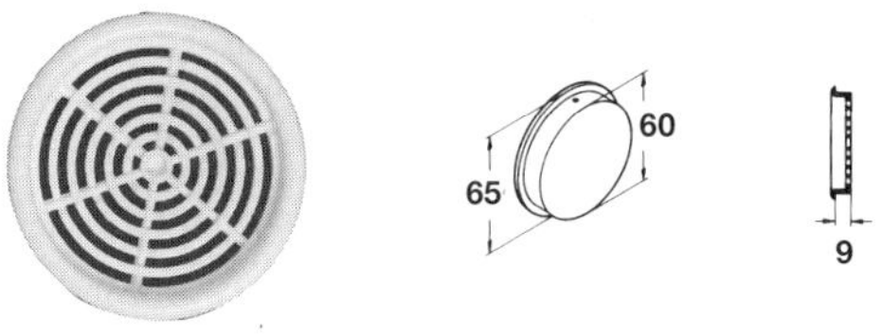

Air ventilation cap, recess-mounted
Finish: plastic

Cat. No.	white	571.03.723
	brown	571.03.125

Packing: 50 pcs.

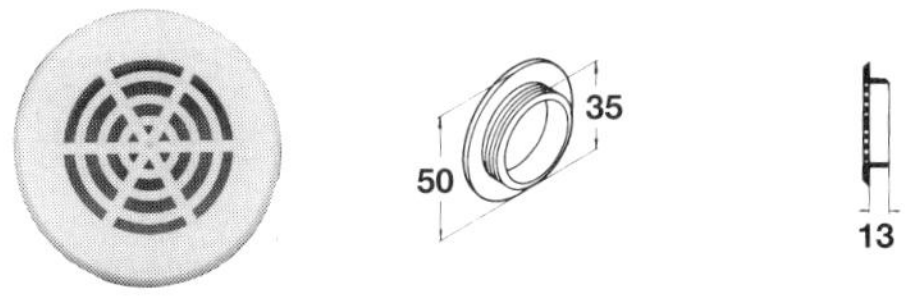

Air cap, recess-mounted,
with harpoon-type fastening
Finish: plastic, white

Cat. No.	571.10.700

Packing: 100 pcs.

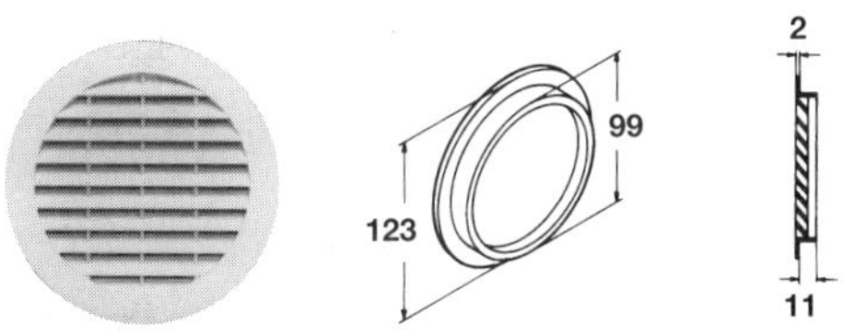

Air ventilation cap, recess-mounted, with flanged rim
Finish: plastic, white

Ventilation area cm²	Cat. No.
50.0	571.67.718

Packing: 10 pcs.

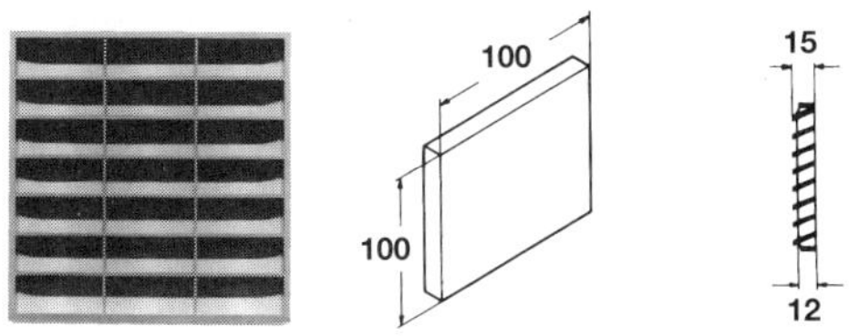

Air ventilation cap, recess-mounted, without flanged rim
Finish: plastic, black

Ventilation area cm²	Cat. No.
81.3	571.62.302

Packing: 10 pcs.

HÄFELE

Ventilation Grills

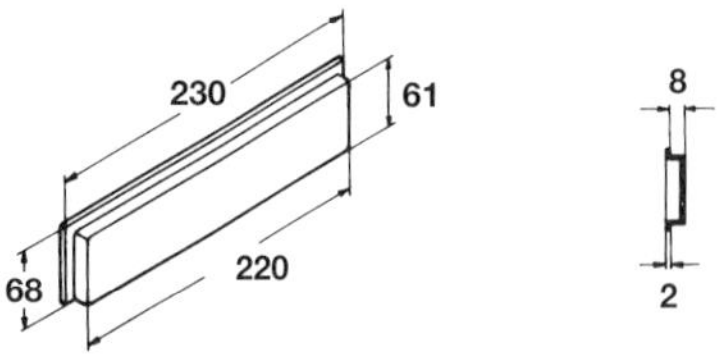

Air ventilation grill with flanged rim
Finish: plastic, chrome-plated

Ventilation area cm^2	Cat. No.
42.24	571.54.248

Packing: 50 pcs.

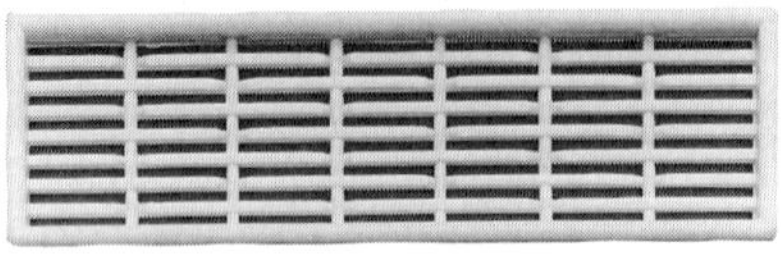

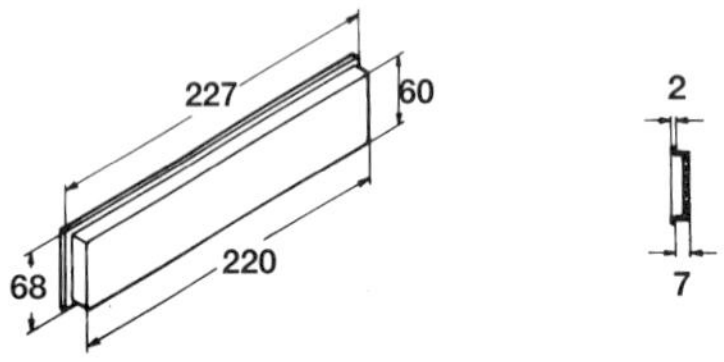

Air ventilation grill with flanged rim
Finish: plastic, white

Ventilation area cm^2	Cat. No.
60	571.55.343

Packing: 50 pcs.

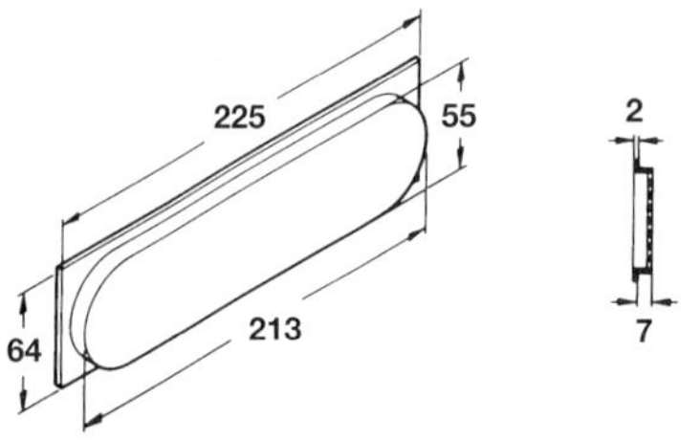

Air ventilation grill with flanged rim, with oval recess section, no holes, mounted by adhesive
Finish: plastic, bright and chrome-plated

Ventilation area cm^2	Cat. No.
45.0	571.52.208

Packing: 50 pcs.

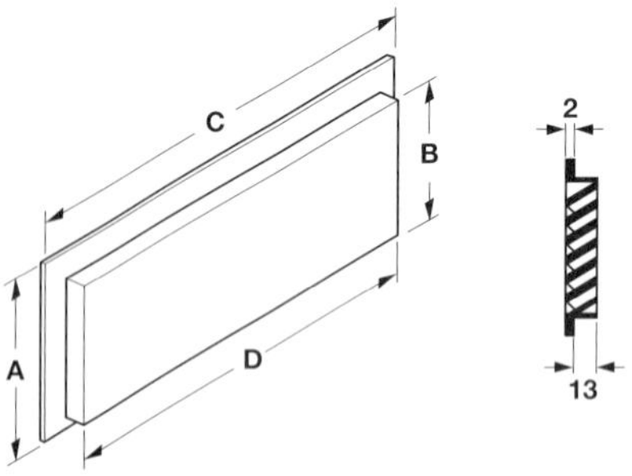

Air ventilation grill with flanged rim
Finish: plastic, white

Dimensions (mm)				Ventilation area	Cat. No.
A	B	C	D	cm^2	
108	84	254	230	100.0	571.64.726
120	96	299	275	150.0	571.64.735
132	108	338	314	200.0	571.64.744

Packing: 10 pcs.

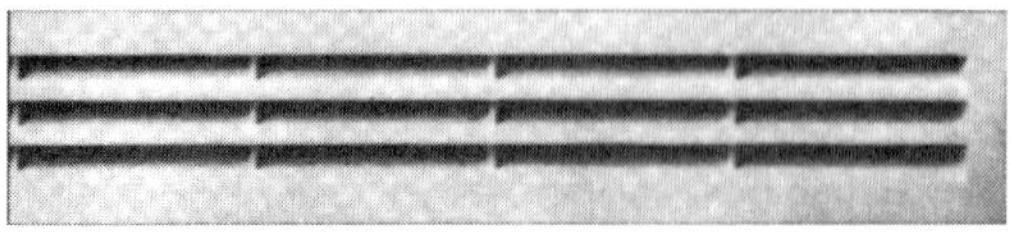

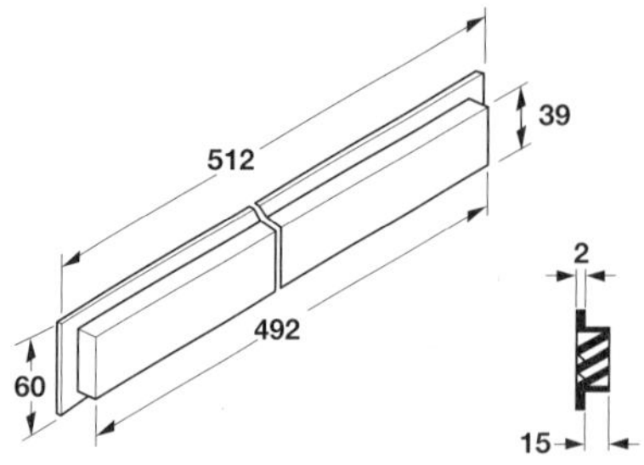

Ventilation grill with flanged rim
Finish: plastic, white

Ventilation area cm^2	Cat. No.
90.0	571.70.706

Packing: 1 and 10 pcs.

Counter Top Supports

- Panel thicknesses up to 40 mm

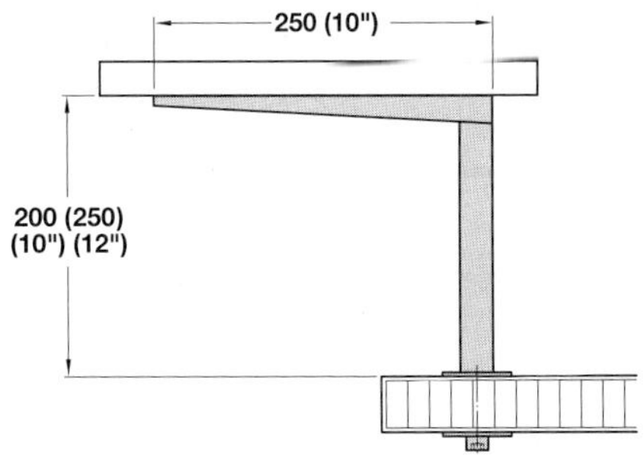

Counter top support
with 25 x 25 mm support
Finish: steel, chrome-plated, polished

Height x depth	Cat. No.
200 x 250 mm	505.11.218
250 x 250 mm	505.11.236

Packing: 1 pc. (incl. mounting hardware)

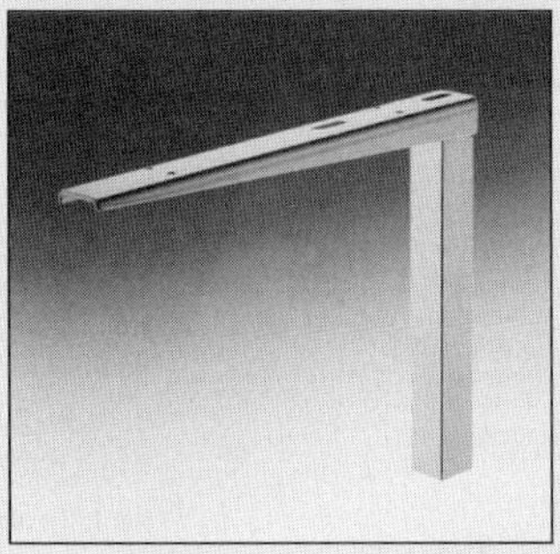

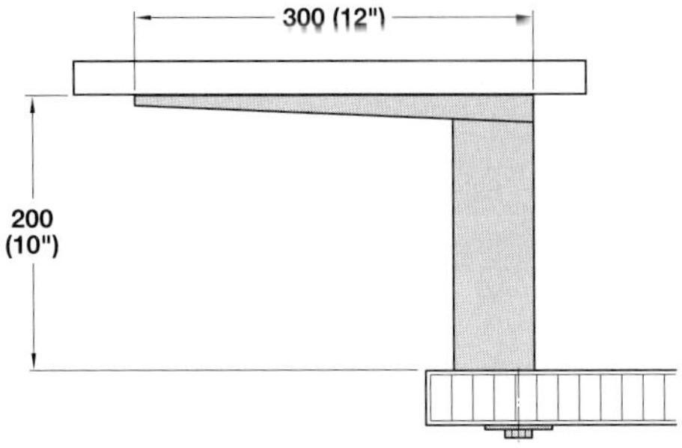

Counter top support
with 25 x 60 mm support
Finish: steel, chrome-plated, polished

Cat. No.	505.12.206

Packing: 1 pc. (incl. mounting hardware)

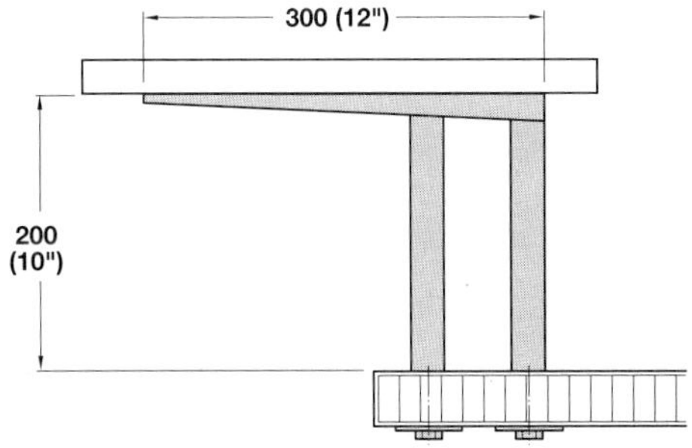

Counter top support
with two 25 x 25 mm supports
Finish: steel, chrome-plated, polished

Cat. No.	505.13.203

Packing: 1 pc. (incl. mounting hardware)

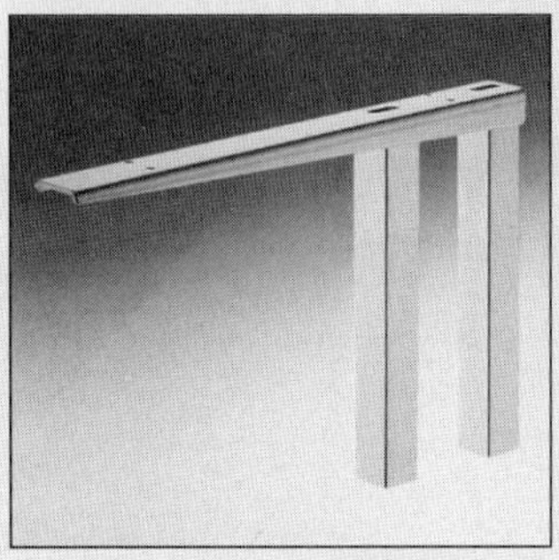

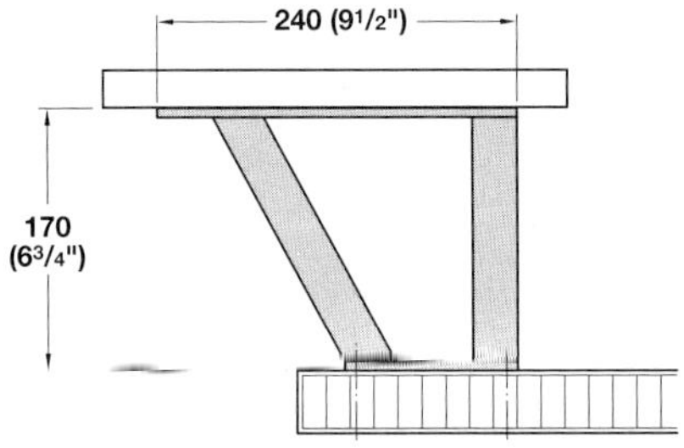

Counter top support
frame type
Finish: light alloy, silver-colored matt anodized

Cat. No.	505.10.908

Packing: 1 pc.

Dimensional data not binding. We reserve the right to alter specifications without notice.

Dimensions in mm
Inches are approximate

HÄFELE

Countertop Supports

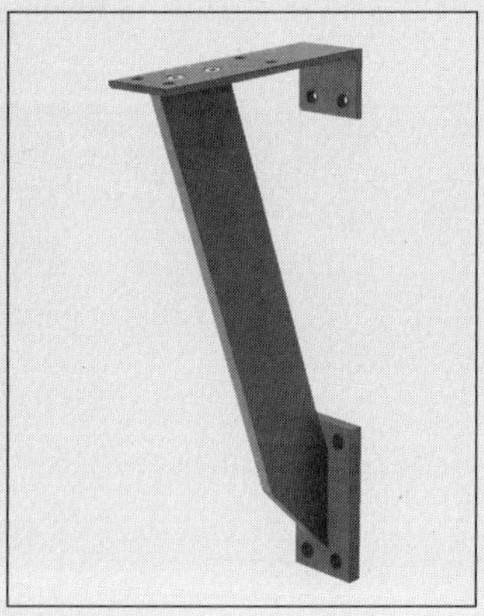

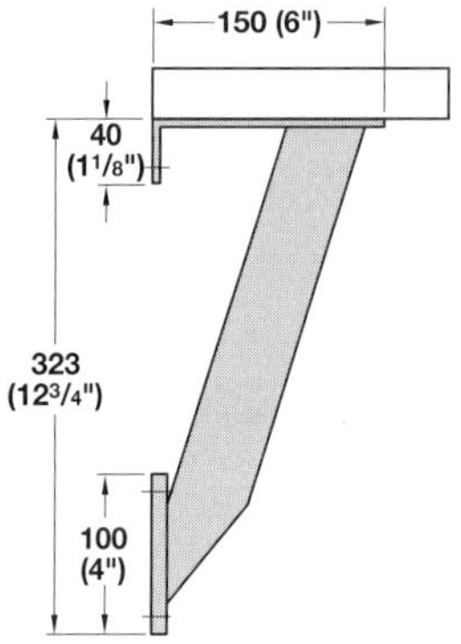

Countertop support
side-mounted
Finish: aluminum

Color	Cat. No.
silver, matt anodized	505.14.956

Packing: 1 pc. (incl. mounting hardware)

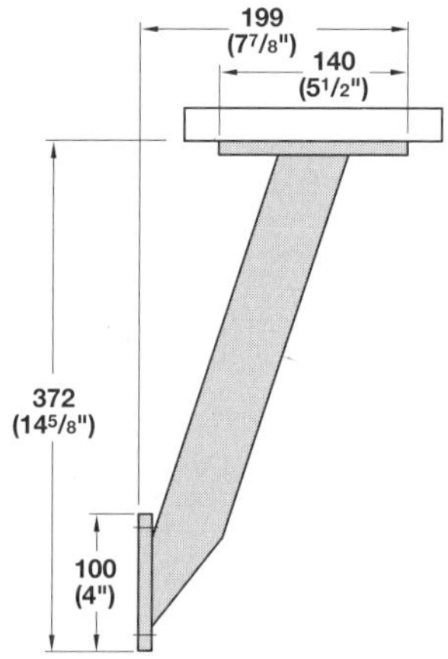

Countertop support
side-mounted
Finish: aluminum

Color	Cat. No.
silver, matt anodized	505.14.916

Packing: 1 pc. (incl. mounting hardware)

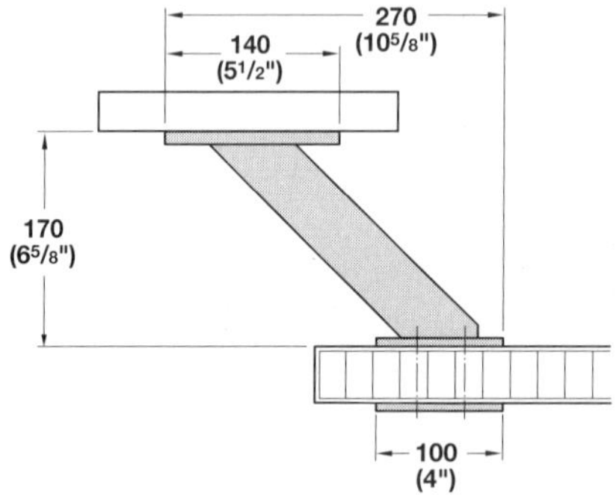

Countertop support
mounted on the countertop
Finish: aluminum

Color	Cat. No.
silver, matt anodized	505.14.926

Packing: 1 pc. (incl. mounting hardware)

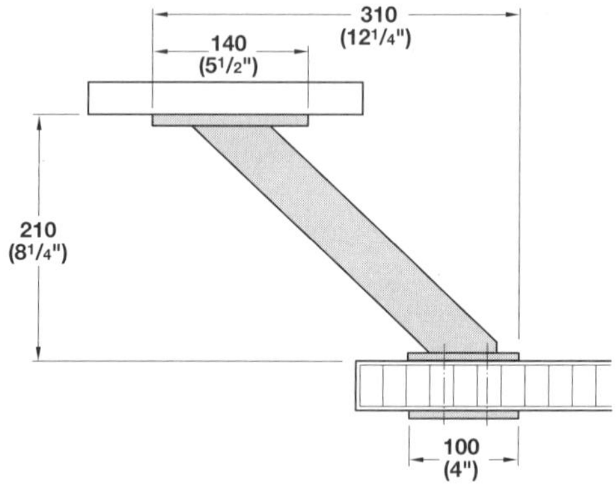

Countertop support
mounted on the countertop
Finish: aluminum

Color	Cat. No.
silver, matt anodized	505.14.936

Packing: 1 pc. (incl. mounting hardware)

Dimensions in mm
Inches are approximate

Product Guide - Furniture Support Systems

HÄFELE

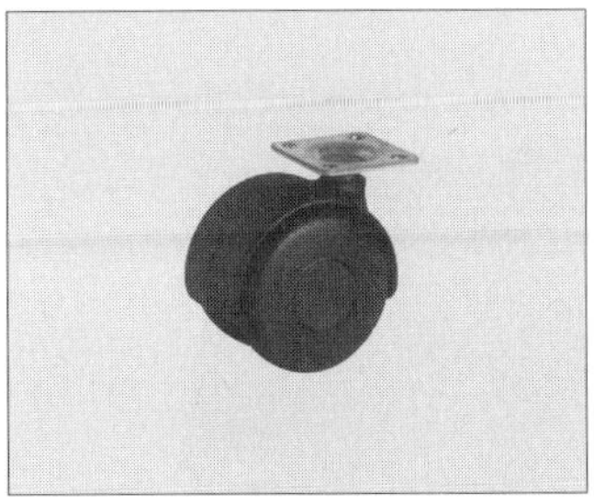

Furniture Casters
Pages **6.2 - 6.13**

Furniture Glides
Pages **6.13 - 6.17**

Levelers
Pages **6.18 - 6.23**

Base Cabinet Levelers
Pages **6.24 - 6.26**

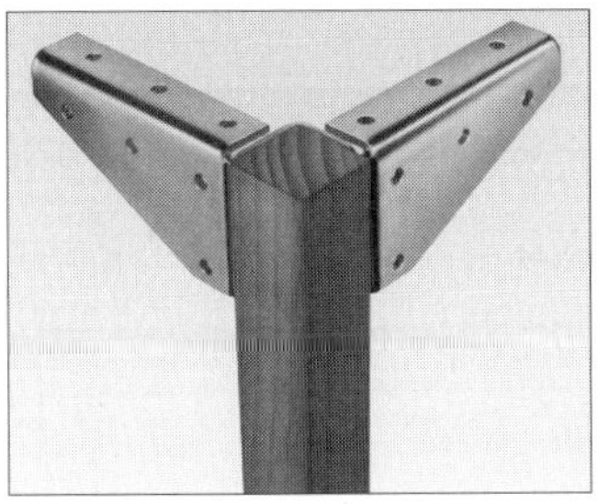

Accessories for Tables
Pages **6.27 - 6.31**

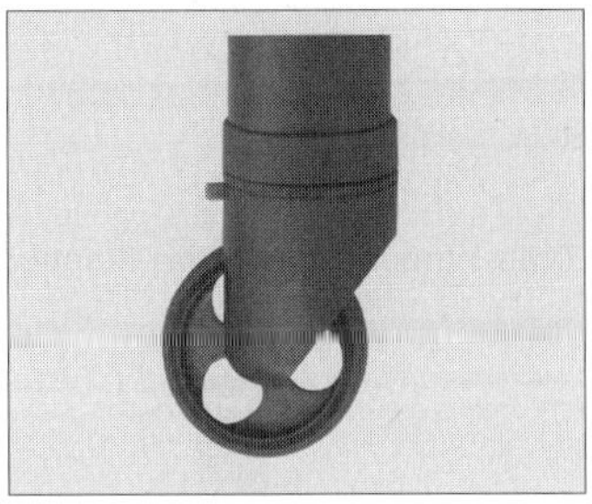

Table Legs
Pages **6.32 - 6.33**

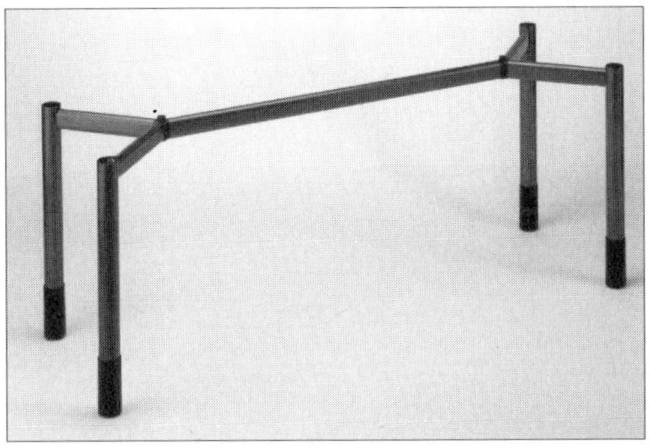

IDEA-Table Support System
Pages **6.34 - 6.39**

ERGOFLEX - Adjustable Work Surface Mechanisms
Pages **6.40 - 6.41**

Monitor Suspension System
Pages **6.42 - 6.43**

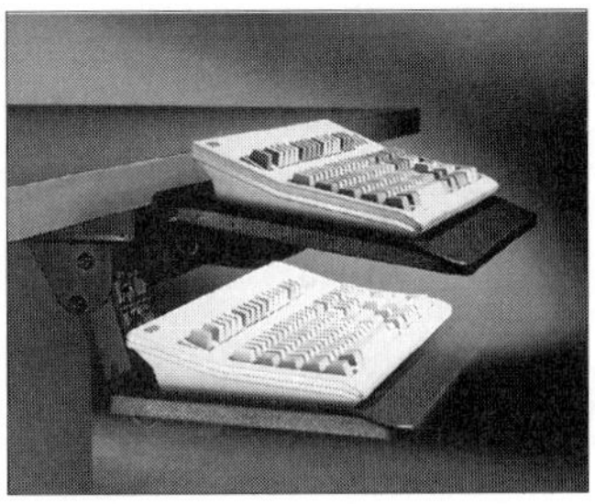

Keyboard Support Mechanisms
Pages **6.44 - 6.47**

Monitor Supports
Pages **6.48 - 6.49**

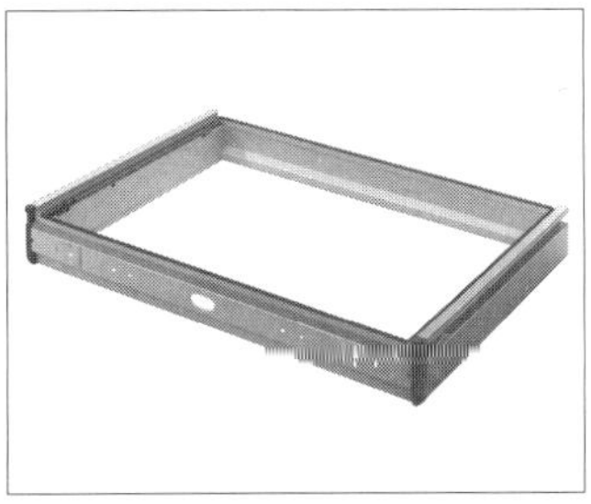

Filing Frame System
Pages **6.53 - 6.55**

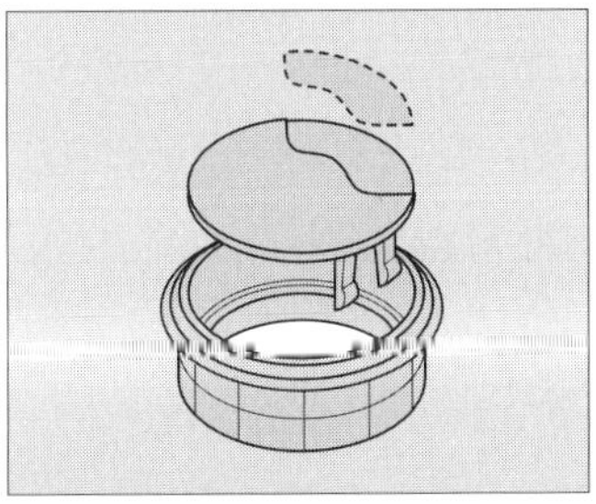

Cable Management
Pages **6.58 - 6.60**

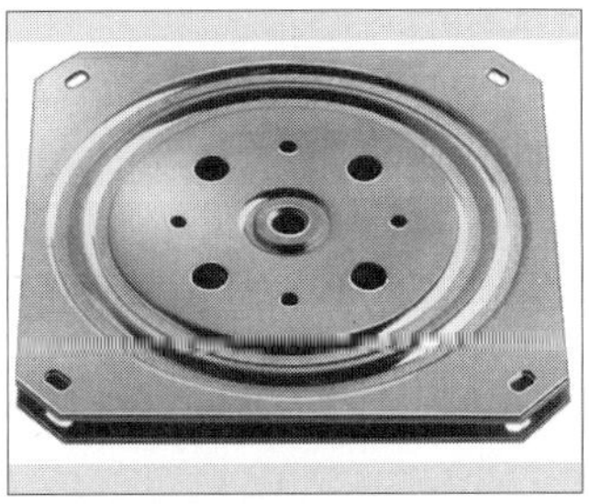

Turntables
Pages **6.61 - 6.63**

Dimensional data not binding.
We reserve the right to alter specifications without notice.

Twin-Wheel Casters – 40 mm

With well-spaced wheels, these twin-wheel casters combine exceptionally smooth running with an easy castering action. Incorporating a hard, abrasion-proof surface, they are particularly suitable for soft floor coverings such as carpets.

Caster Features

 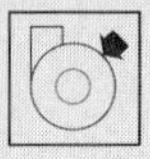 Free-running or with brake

 Plastic hood and wheel

 Wheel diameter **40mm**

 Hard wheel surface, particularly suitable for soft floor coverings (e.g. carpets).

Load carrying capacity – 50 kg.

Plastic press-fit socket permitting their install- action in narrow wooden legs.

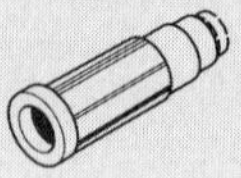

Free-running model

With brake

Twin-Wheel Caster with Plastic Socket

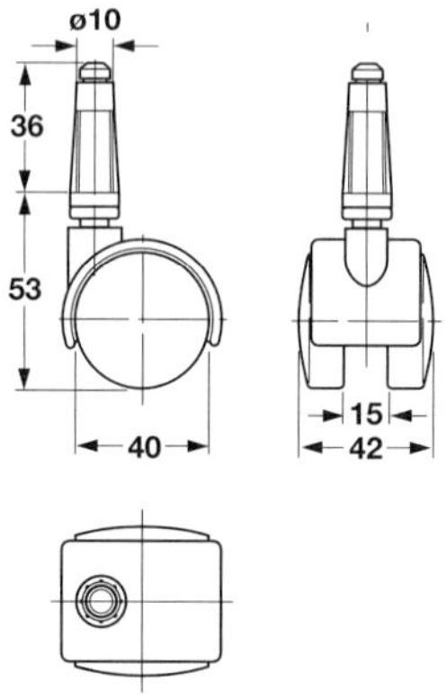

Without brake

Finish: plastic, black matt

Cat. No.	660.44.353

Packing: 100 pcs.

With brake

Finish: plastic, black matt

Cat. No.	660.43.356

Packing: 100 pcs.

Twin-Wheel Caster with Mounting Plate

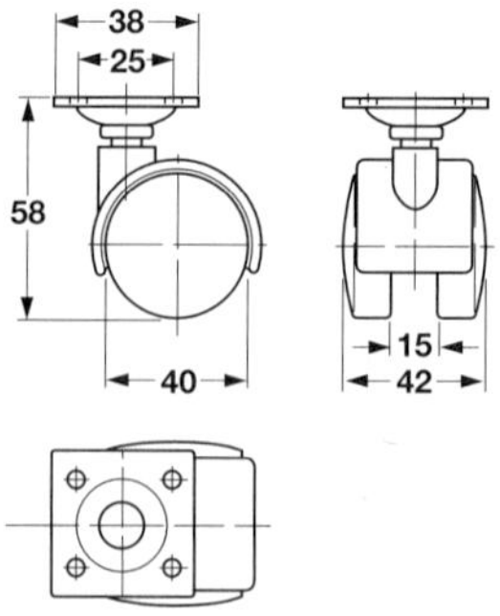

Without brake

Finish: plastic, black matt

Cat. No.	660.44.344

Packing: 100 pcs.

With brake

Finish: plastic, black matt

Cat. No.	660.43.347

Packing: 100 pcs.

Dimensions in mm

Twin-Wheel Casters – 50mm

Free-running model

With brake

With well-spaced wheels, these twin-wheel castors combine exceptionally smooth running with an easy castering action. Incorporating a hard, abrasion-proof surface finish, they are particularly suitable for soft floor coverings such as carpets.

Caster Features

Free-running or with brake

Plastic hood and wheel

Wheel diameter **50mm**

Hard wheel surface, particularly suitable for soft floor coverings (e.g. carpets).

Load carrying capacity – 60 kg

Twin-Wheel Caster with Plastic Socket

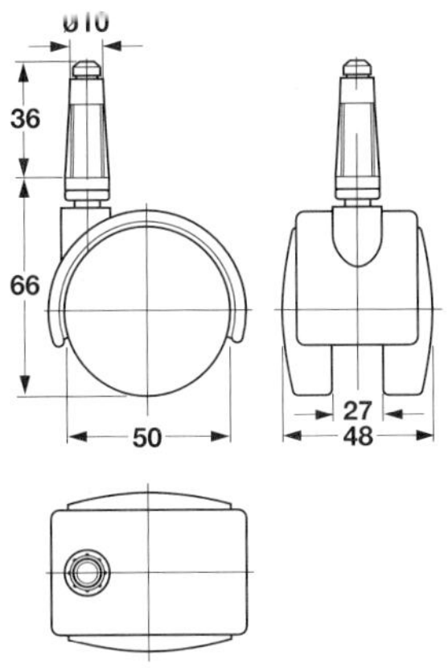

Without brake

Finish: plastic, black matt

Cat. No.	660.44.380

Packing: 100 pcs.

With brake

Finish: plastic, black matt

Cat. No.	660.43.383

Packing: 100 pcs.

Plastic press-fit socket permitting their install- ation in narrow wooden legs.

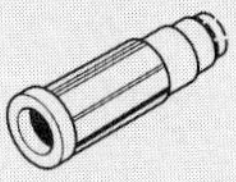

Furniture Support Systems, Office and Computer Furniture Accessories **6**

Twin-Wheel Caster with Mounting Plate

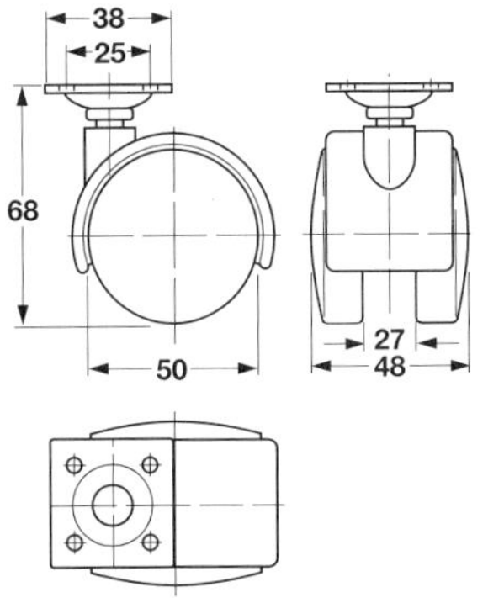

Without brake

Finish: plastic hood and wheels

Cat. No. black matt	660.44.371

Packing: 100 pcs.

With brake

Finish: plastic, black matt

Cat. No.	660.43.374

Packing: 100 pcs.

Dimensions in mm

Dimensional data not binding. We reserve the right to alter specifications without notice.

Dimensions in mm

HÄFELE

Large Twin-wheel Casters

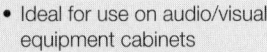

- Ideal for use on audio/visual equipment cabinets
- Use wherever maximum stability and strength are required
- Will work on soft as well as hard flooring surfaces

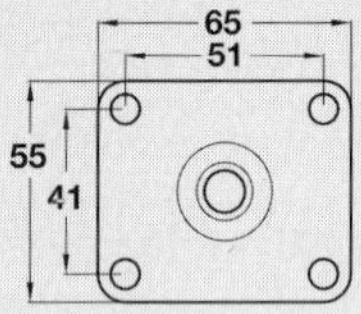

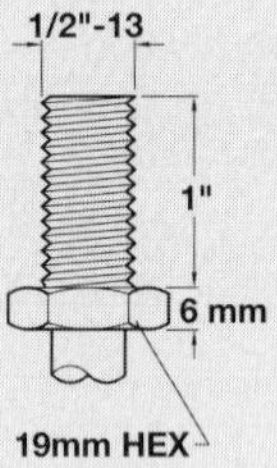

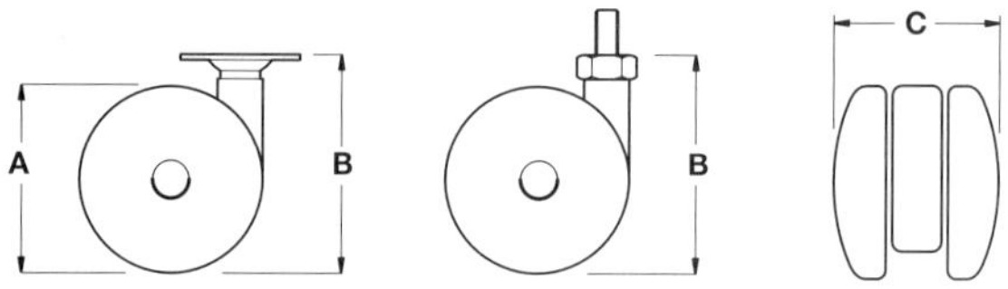

With Brake

Finish: nylon, black

Top Plate Mount Size Ø	Cat. No.	A	B	C	Load Cap. (kg/pc.)
3" (76 mm)	660.58.321	73 mm	90 mm	63 mm	80
4" (102 mm)	660.58.341	100 mm	117 mm	74 mm	100
5" (127 mm)	660.58.361	123 mm	145 mm	80 mm	120
Stem Mount					
3" (76 mm)	660.58.322	73 mm	85 mm	63 mm	80
4" (102 mm)	660.58.342	100 mm	112 mm	74 mm	100
5" (127 mm)	660.58.362	123 mm	140 mm	80 mm	120

Packing: 1 pc.

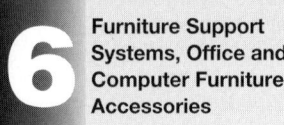

6 Furniture Support Systems, Office and Computer Furniture Accessories

Top Plate Mount   Bolt Stud Mount

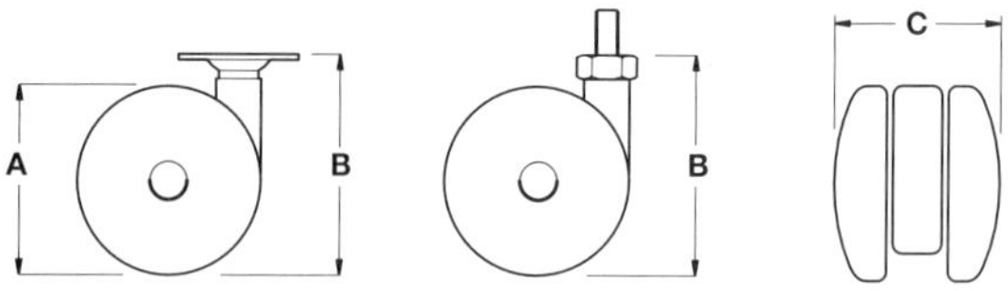

Without Brake

Finish: nylon, black

Top Plate Mount Size Ø	Cat. No.	A	B	C	Load Cap. (kg/pc.)
3" (76 mm)	660.57.321	73 mm	90 mm	63 mm	80
4" (102 mm)	660.57.341	100 mm	117 mm	74 mm	100
5" (127 mm)	660.57.361	123 mm	145 mm	80 mm	120
Stem Mount					
3" (76 mm)	660.57.322	73 mm	85 mm	63 mm	80
4" (102 mm)	660.57.342	100 mm	112 mm	74 mm	100
5" (127 mm)	660.57.362	123 mm	140 mm	80 mm	120

Packing: 1 pc.

Dimensions in mm

Furniture Casters

HÄFELE

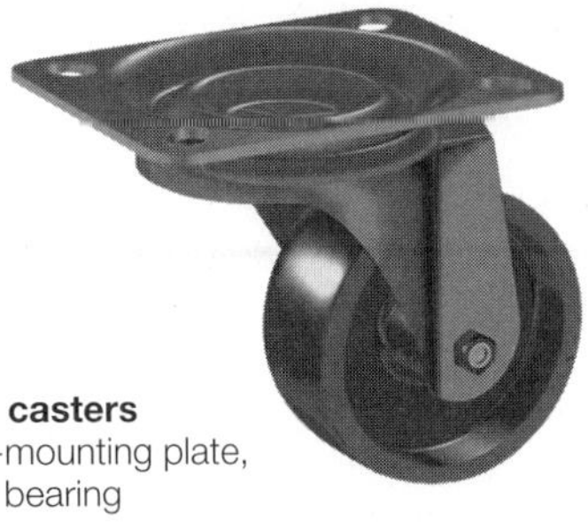

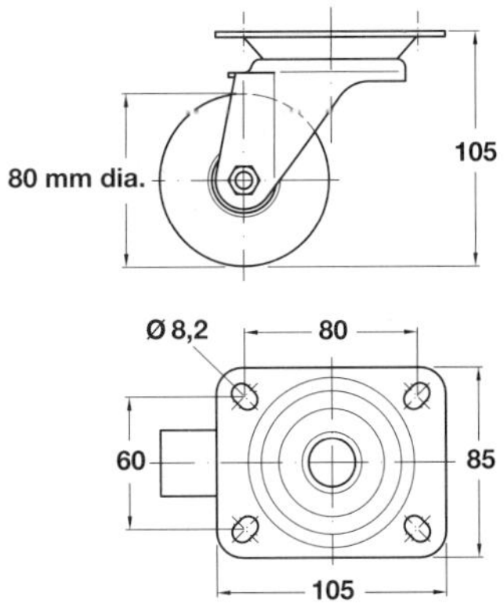

Swivelling casters
with screw-mounting plate,
double ball bearing

Finish:
housing: steel, black or chrome
wheel: high quality polyamide with friction bearing, or natural beech wood

approx. load capacity each caster	120 kg	100 kg	100 kg
wheel width	40mm	30 mm	30 mm
color: housing/wheel	black/black	black/beech	chrome-plated/beech
Cat. No.	661.26.300	661.26.330	661.26.230

Packing: 4 pcs.

Industrial Style Casters:
- Wheels natural beech or black polyamide
- Housing black or chrome

The **wooden wheel** can be easily removed for surface treatment.

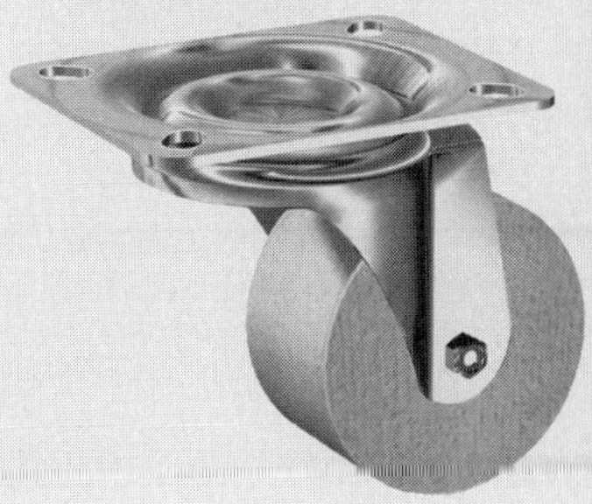

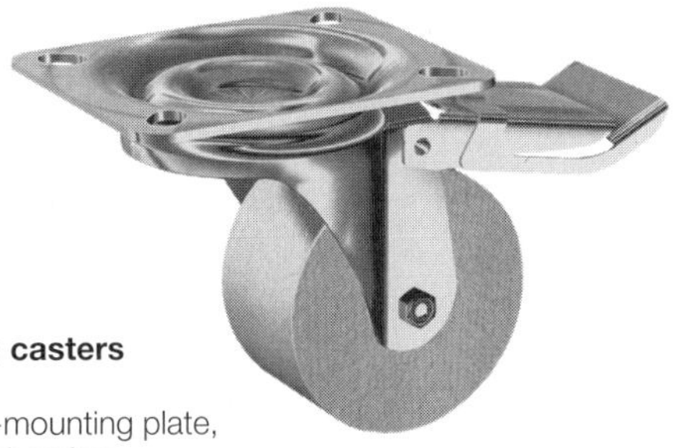

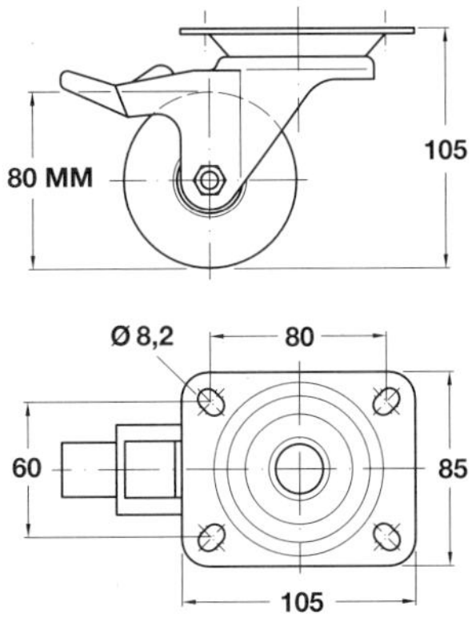

Swivelling casters
with brake
and screw-mounting plate,
double ball bearing

Finish:
housing: steel, black or chrome
wheel: high quality polyamide with friction bearing, or natural beech wood

approx. load capacity each caster	120 kg	100 kg	100 kg
wheel width	40 mm	30 mm	30 mm
color: housing/wheel	black/black	black/beech	chrome-plated/beech
Cat. No.	661.27.300	661.27.330	661.27.230

Packing: 4 pcs.

Furniture Support Systems, Office and Computer Furniture Accessories

6

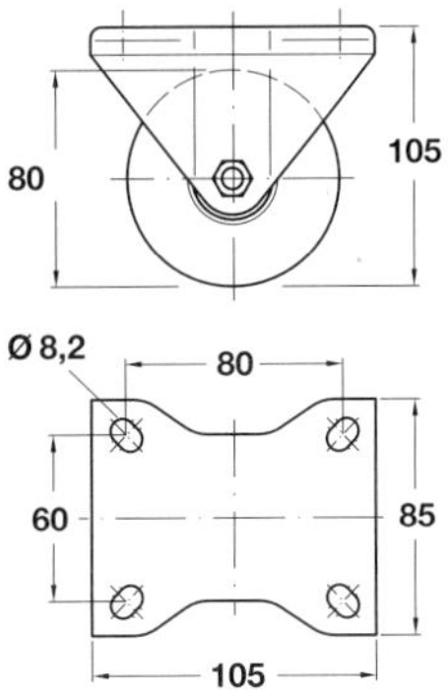

Dimensions in mm

Fixed caster
with screw-mounting plate,
Finish:
housing: steel, black or chrome
wheel: high quality polyamide with friction bearing, or natural beech wood

approx. load capacity each caster	120 kg	100 kg	100 kg
wheel width	40mm	30 mm	30 mm
color: housing/wheel	black/black	black/beech	chrome-plated/beech
Cat. No.	661.28.300	661.28.330	661.28.230

Packing: 4 pcs.

Dimensions in mm

Dimensional data not binding.
We reserve the right to alter specifications without notice.

Casters for Furniture and Special Applications

Coal Box casters
screw-on
mounting plate, free-running
Finish:
housing: steel plate, zinc plated
wheel: plastic, black

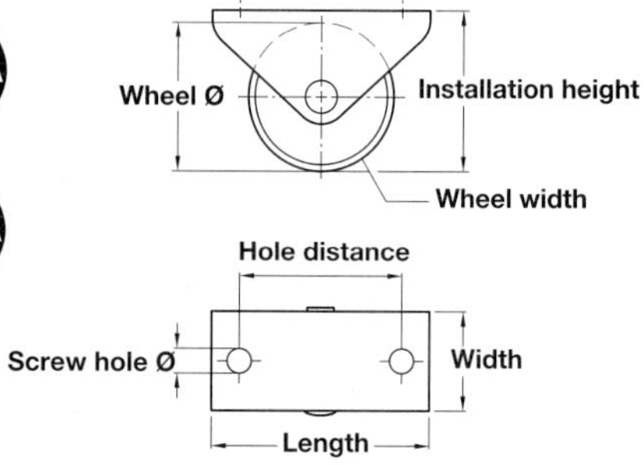

- Suitable for all low level storage boxes
- When mounted upside down they can be used as a conveyor system for transporting heavy loads.

Wheel Ø	**15 mm**	**25 mm**	**30 mm**	**45 mm**
Load capacity per caster	15 kg	20 kg	25 kg	35 kg
Installation height	17.5 mm	28 mm	32 mm	48.5 mm
Mounting plate Length x width	30 x 17 mm	40 x 17 mm	45 x 20 mm	67 x 27 mm
Hole distance	20 mm	30 mm	35 mm	54 mm
Wheel width	13 mm	13 mm	15 mm	19 mm
Screw hole Ø	4 mm	4.3 mm	5 mm	5.2 mm
Cat. No.	661.23.322	661.23.304	661.23.313	661.25.906

Packing: 100 pcs.

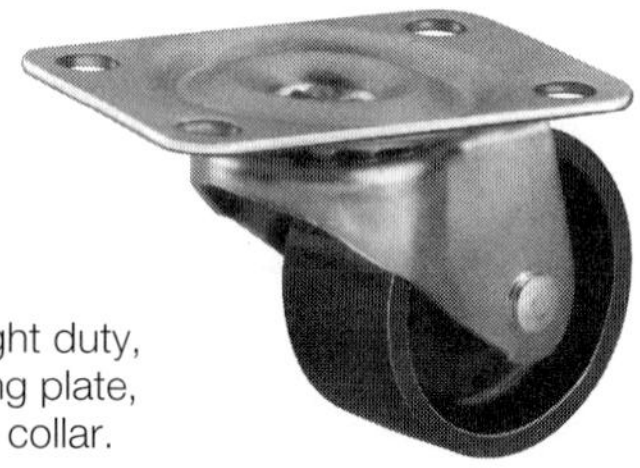

- The plastic wheels run in friction bearings.
- Hard wheel surface, suitable for soft floor coverings. (e.g. carpets)
- Abrasion-proof.

Swivel caster, light duty,
screw-on mounting plate,
ball bearing in the collar.
Free-running
Finish:
housing: steel, zinc-plated
wheel: plastic, black

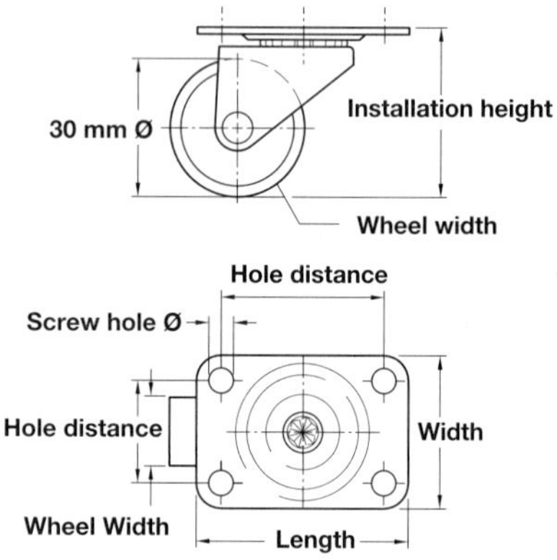

Wheel Ø	**30 mm**
Load capacity per caster	15 kg
Installation height	36 mm
Mounting plate Length x width	48 x 33 mm
Hole distance	36 x 22 mm
Wheel width	15 mm
Screw hole Ø	5.3 mm
Cat. No.	662.03.852

Packing: 20 pcs.

6 Furniture Support Systems, Office and Computer Furniture Accessories

Swivel caster,
screw-on mounting
plate, double ball bearing
in the ring mount, free-running
Finish:
housing: steel, zinc-plated
wheel: plastic, black

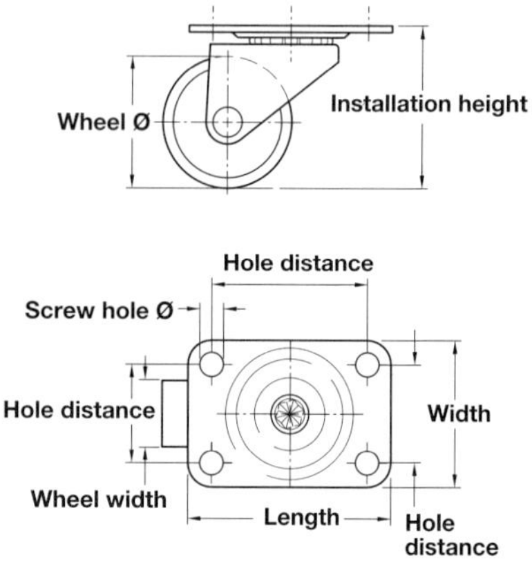

Wheel Ø	**30 mm**	**40 mm**
Load capacity per caster	30 kg	35 kg
Installation height	48 mm	63 mm
Mounting plate Length x width	38 x 38 mm	45 x 45 mm
Hole distance	30 x 30 mm	33 x 33 mm
Wheel width	15 mm	18 mm
Screw hole Ø	4.3 mm	5.3 mm
Cat. No.	662.03.861	662.03.870

Packing: 1 pc.

Dimensional data not binding. We reserve the right to alter specifications without notice.

Dimensions in mm

Casters for Furniture and Special Applications

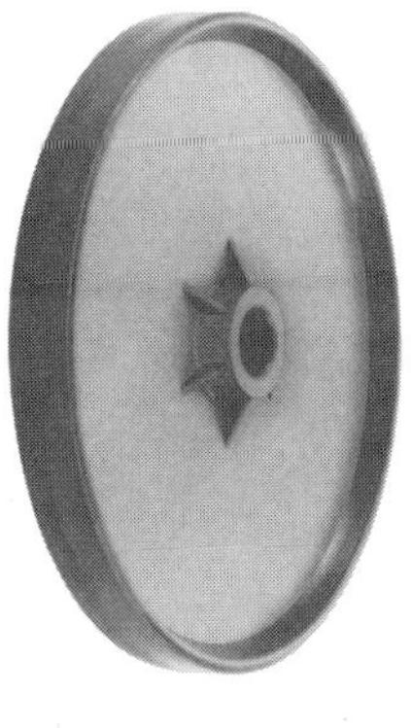

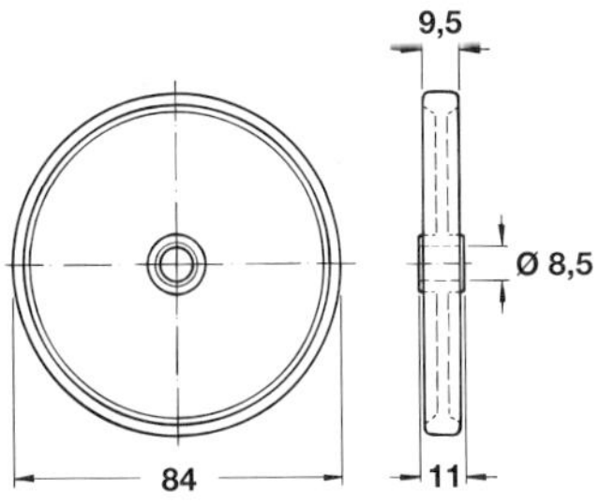

Bed Box wheel
Load capacity per wheel approx. 40 kg
Finish: plastic

Color	Cat. No.
brown	660.97.103
white	660.97.701

Packing: 100 pcs.

- Good running characteristics on deep piled carpets due to the wide running surface and large wheel diameter.
- Particularly suited for under-bed storage boxes.

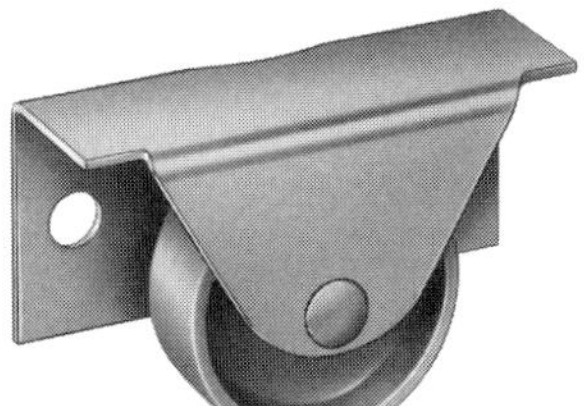

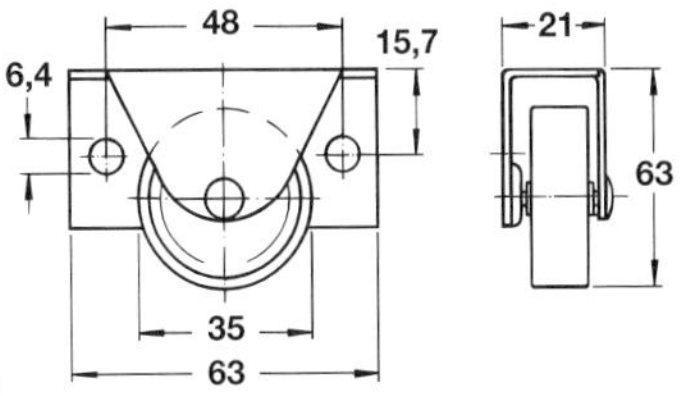

HOSPA Φ4.0

Bed Box caster
with screw-on mounting plate
Load capacity per caster 40 kg
Finish: housing: steel, zinc-plated
wheel: plastic, white

Cat. No.	660.98.904

Packing: 500 pcs.

- This bedbox caster features a wide tread for easy movement on carpeted floors.
- The side mounting facility and low height make this caster particularly suitable for installation in situations with limited clearance.

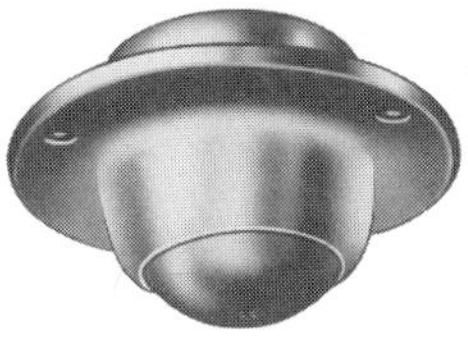

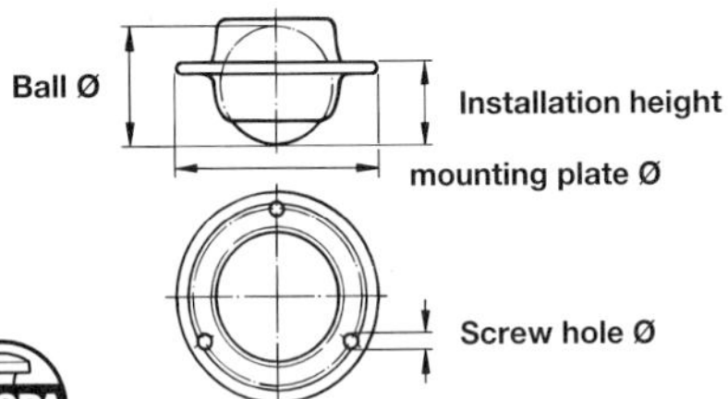

HOSPA Φ3.0

Ball casters
with screw-on mounting plate
Finish: housing: steel, yellow chromate
with reinforced base
ball: steel, chrome-plated

- The ball casters can be moved in any direction.
- When mounted upside down they can be used as a conveyor system for transporting heavy loads.

Ball Ø	13 mm	20 mm	25 mm
Approx. load capacity of each caster	6 kg	12 kg	17 kg
Installation height	10 mm	15 mm	20 mm
Mounting plate Ø	25 mm	35 mm	45 mm
Screw hole Ø	2 mm	3 mm	3 mm
Cat. No.	661.02.210	661.02.230	661.02.250

Packing: 100 pcs.

Dimensional data not binding.
We reserve the right to alter specifications without notice.

Dimensions in mm

HÄFELE

Single Wheel Casters

Roller Caster
with cast zinc press-fit socket
Ø 13 x 25 mm
Load carrying capacity:
approximately 75 kg per caster

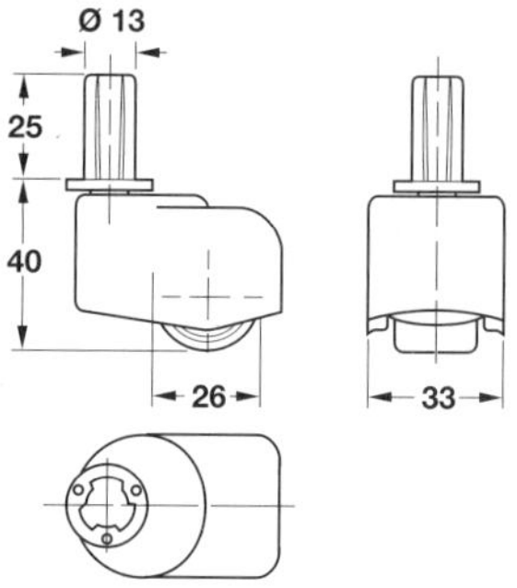

Finish: plastic housing and roller, matt black

Cat. No.	661.31.324

Packing: 100 pcs.

Roller Caster
with mounting plate
38 x 38 mm
Load carrying capacity:
approximately 75 kg per caster

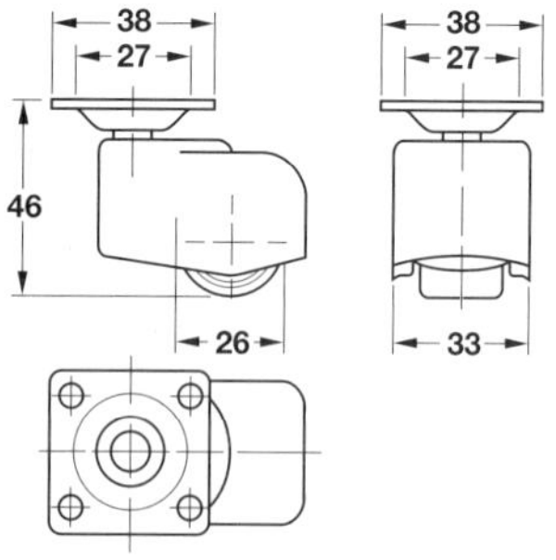

Finish: plastic housing and roller, matt black

Cat. No.	661.31.315

Packing: 100 pcs.

Roller Caster
with threaded stem
M 10 x 15 mm
Load carrying capacity:
approximately 75 kg per caster

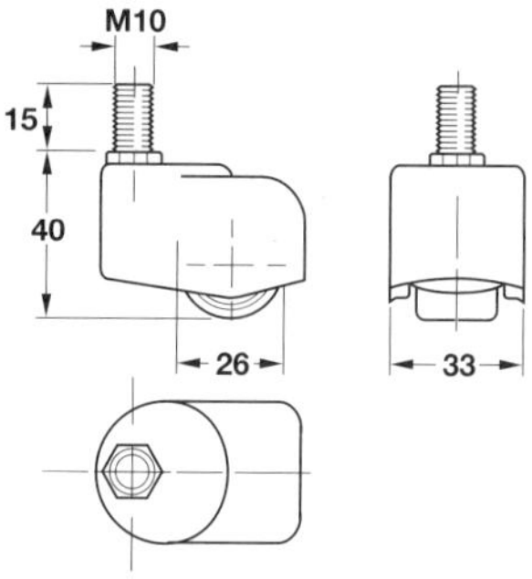

Finish: plastic housing and roller, matt black

Cat. No.	661.31.333

Packing: 100 pcs.

Press-fit sockets incorporate three holes for fixing pins.

For models
with threaded stem
Square plugs with M 10 internal thread
For knock-in installation in 25 x 25 mm and 30 x 30 mm square tubes, 1.5-2 mm thick steel.

Finish: plastic, black

Size	25 x 25 mm	30 x 30 mm
Cat. No.	652.11.627	652.11.636

Packing: 100 pcs.

For models
with threaded stem
Knock-in, M 10 nuts with four prongs
For use in mounting threaded bolt casters under wooden bases

Finish: steel, unfinished

Cat. No.	031.00.301

Packing: 500 pcs.

Dimensional data not binding.
We reserve the right to alter specifications without notice.

Dimensions in mm

Double Wheel Casters

HÄFELE

Roller Caster
with cast zinc press-fit socket
Ø 13 x 25 mm
Load carrying capacity:
approximately 90 kg per caster

Finish: plastic housing and roller, matt black

Cat. No.	661.32.321

Packing: 100 pcs.

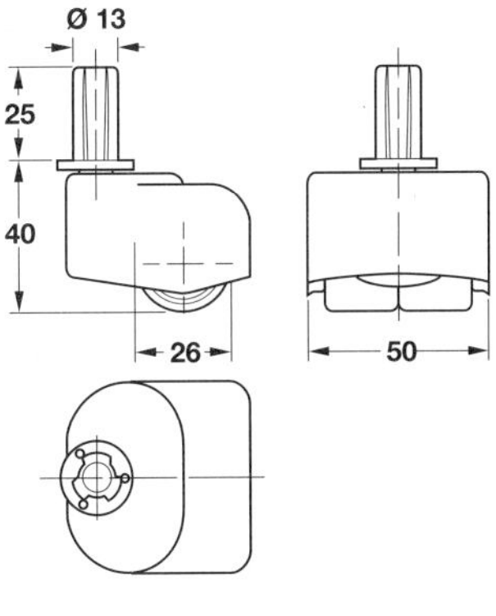

Press-fit sockets incorporate three holes for fixing pins.

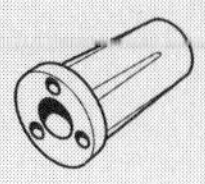

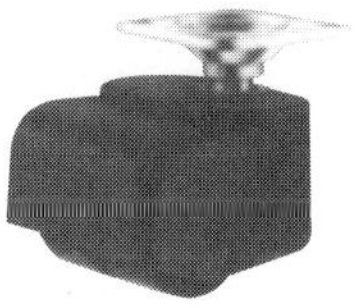

Roller Caster
with mounting plate
38 x 38 mm
Load carrying capacity:
approximately 90 kg per caster

Finish: plastic housing and roller, matt black

Cat. No.	661.32.312

Packing: 100 pcs.

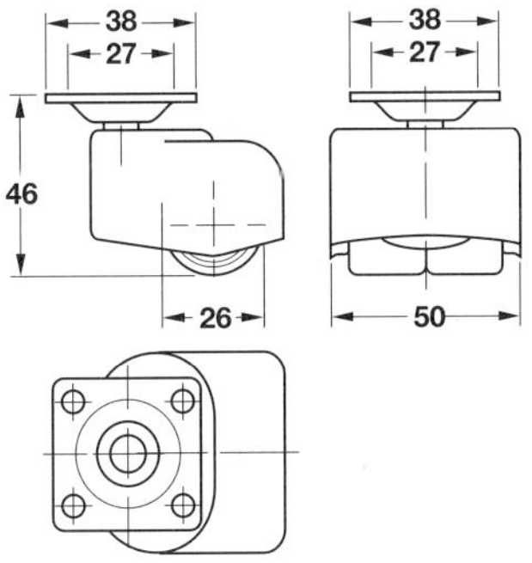

Roller Caster
with threaded stem
M 10 x 15 mm
Load carrying capacity:
approximately 90 kg per caster

Finish: plastic housing and roller, matt black

Cat. No.	661.32.330

Packing: 100 pcs.

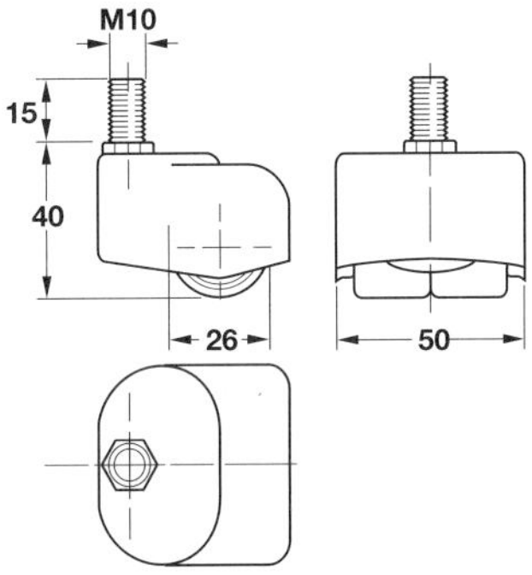

Dimensions in mm

Brass Casters

Screw Caster

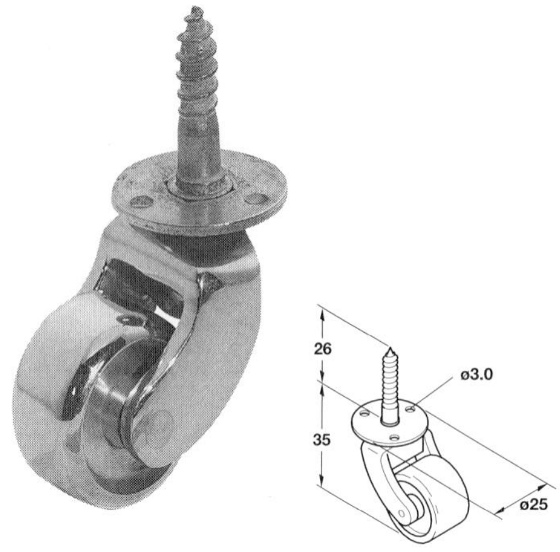

Polished and lacquered

Cat. No.	663.19.819

Packing: 1 set (4 pcs.)

Screw Caster

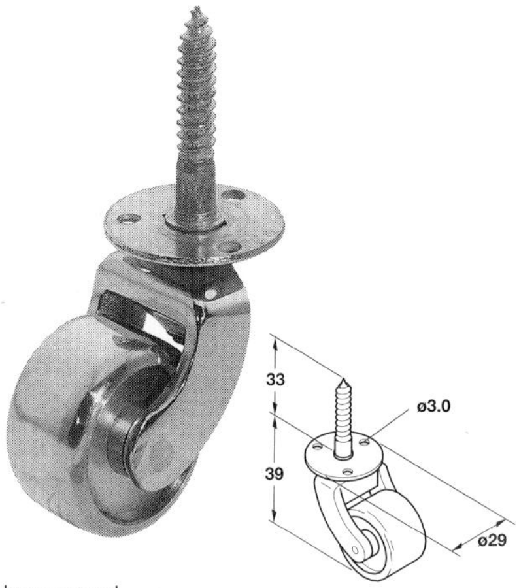

Polished and lacquered

Cat. No.	663.19.828

Packing: 1 set (4 pcs.)

Screw Caster

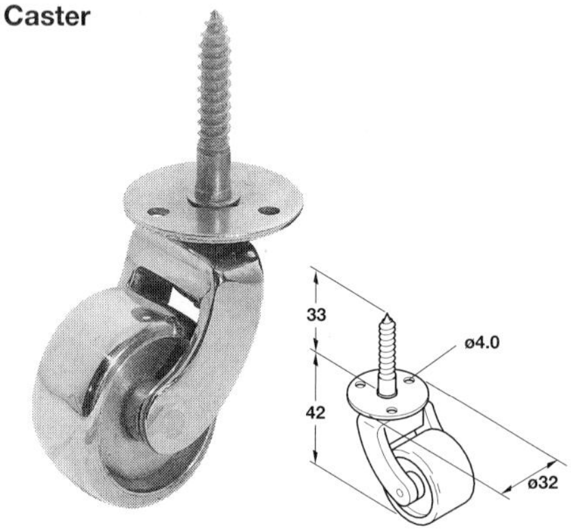

Polished and lacquered

Cat. No.	663.19.837

Packing: 1 set (4 pcs.)

Cup Caster

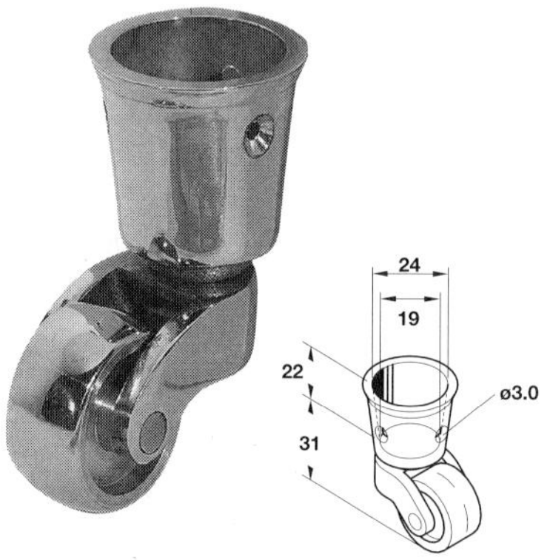

Polished and lacquered

Cat. No.	663.18.812

Packing: 1 set (4 pcs.)

Cup Caster

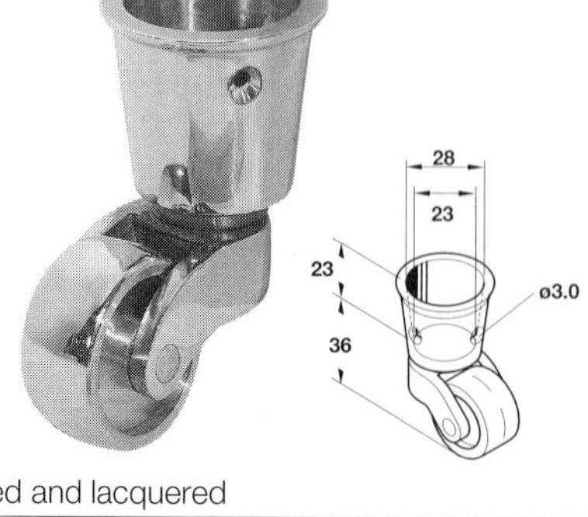

Polished and lacquered

Cat. No.	663.18.821

Packing: 1 set (4 pcs.)

Cup Caster

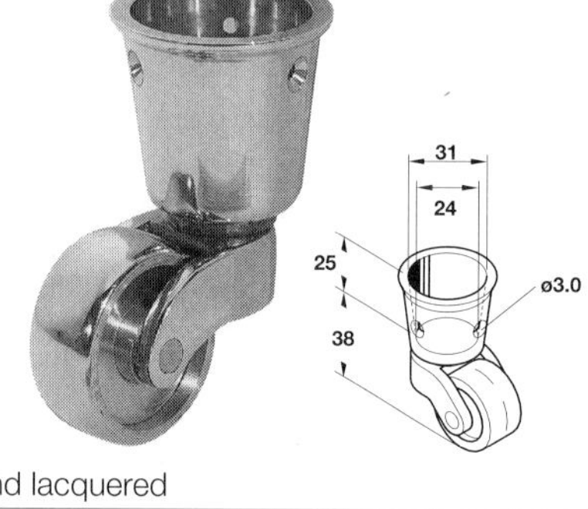

Polished and lacquered

Cat. No.	663.18.830

Packing: 1 set (4 pcs.)

Dimensions in mm

Brass Claw Casters

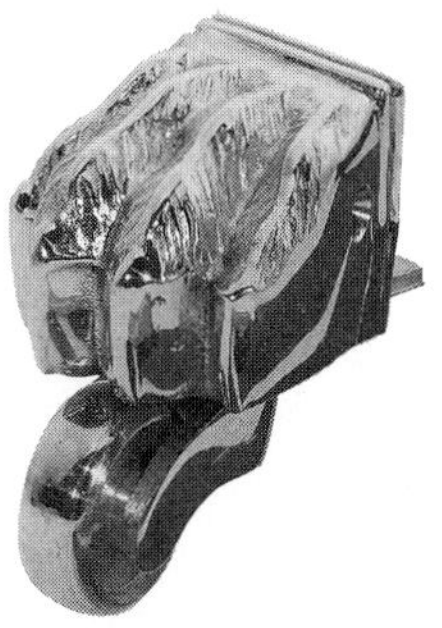

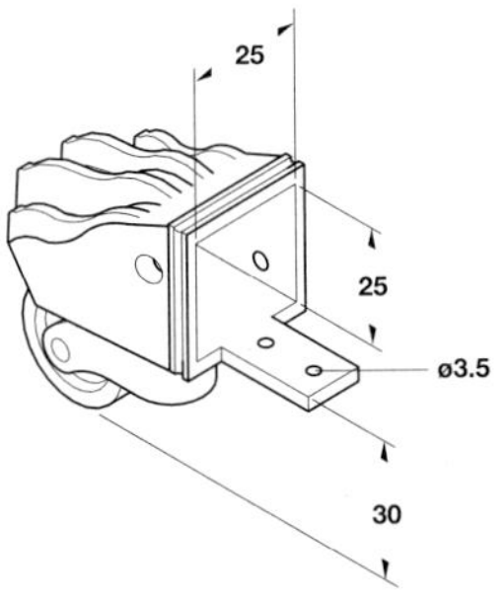

Polished and lacquered

Cat. No.	663.20.812

Packing: 1 set (4 pcs.)

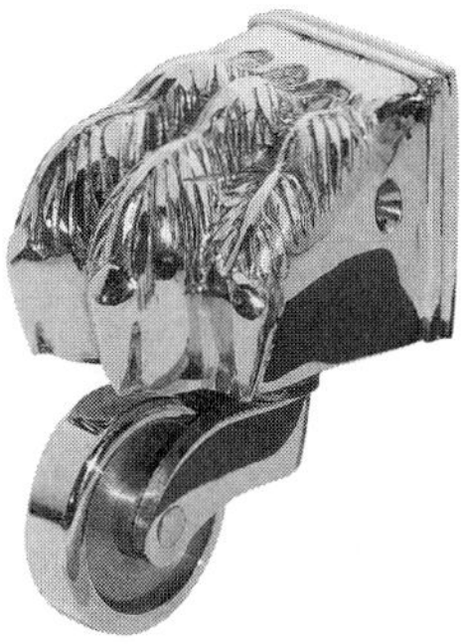

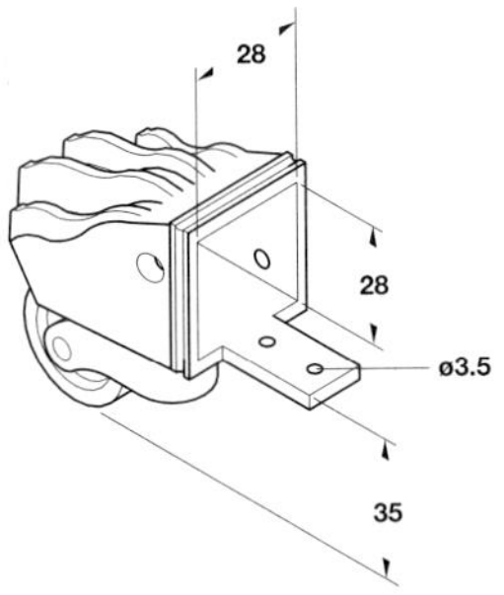

Polished and lacquered

Cat. No.	663.20.821

Packing: 1 set (4 pcs.)

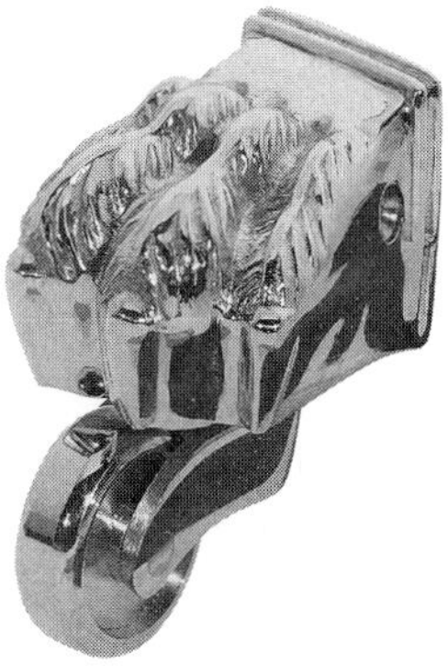

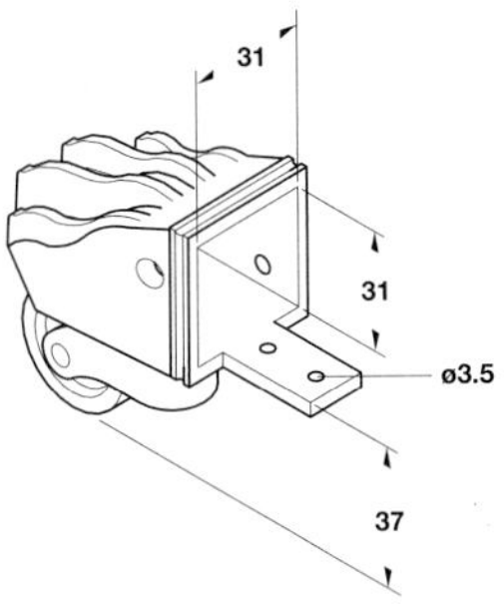

Polished and lacquered

Cat. No.	663.20.830

Packing: 1 set (4 pcs.)

Dimensions in mm

HÄFELE

Rolling Star Casters

Approximately 190 small stainless steel balls roll along the surface of the roller with minimum friction. When weight is placed on the roller, a galvanized spring proves its flexibility.

- Works without maintenance.
- Insensitive to dirt even under maximum stress.
- Rollers leave no traces.
- Ball bearing roller is made with the high grade plastic material POM (Polyoxmethylene).
- Maximum abrasion resistance provides long life.
- When the roller is loaded, a galvanized steel spring provides flexibility.
- Exterior sleeve and the super - sonically sealed lid are made of PP (Polypropylene).
- Smooth running action with little noise.

6 Furniture Support Systems, Office and Computer Furniture Accessories

Rolling Star With Spring, 14 kg.

This is a solid design, suitable for heavy upholstery. This spring is fixed at: 14 kg.

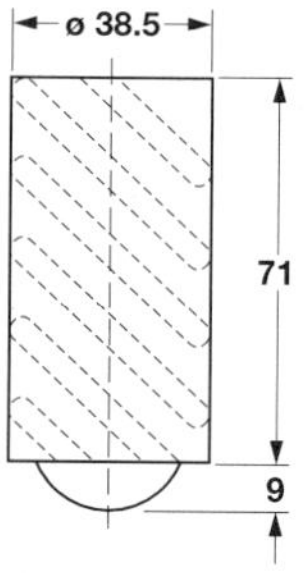

Finish: Case: POM, white
Ball: PP, white
Spring: steel, galvanized

Cat. No.	661.03.026

Packing: 20 pcs.

Optional Mounting Sleeve for above

This can be pushed into ø 42 mm hole and screwed to the underside of the frame.

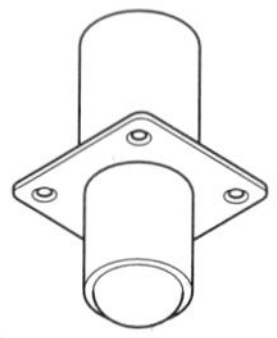

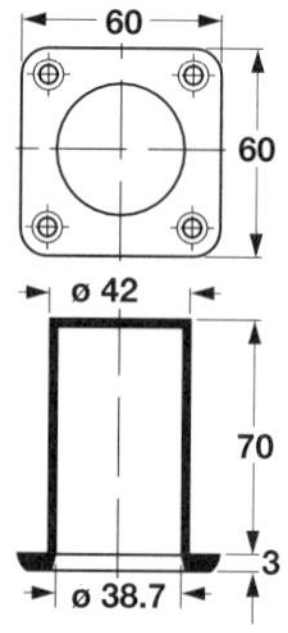

Finish: plastic, black

Cat. No.	661.03.320

Packing: 20 pcs.

Rolling Star With Spring, 6.5 kg.

Due to its small dimensions this caster can easily be used in existing chairs. The spring is fixed at: 6.5 kg.

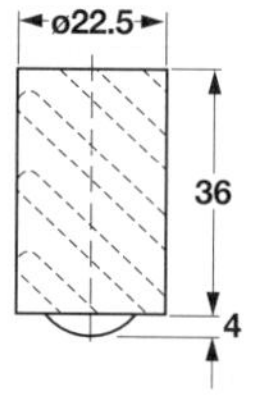

Finish: Case: POM, white
Ball: PP, white
Spring: steel, galvanized

Cat. No.	661.03.017

Packing: 20 pcs.

Rolling Star Without Spring

This fixed model is suitable for heavy furniture. Maximum load carrying capacity is 40 kg.

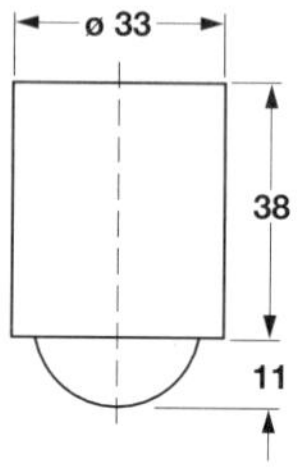

Finish: Case: POM, white
Ball: PP, white

Cat. No.	661.03.035

Packing: 20 pcs.

Optional Mounting Sleeve for above

This can be screw-mounted to the underside of the furniture.

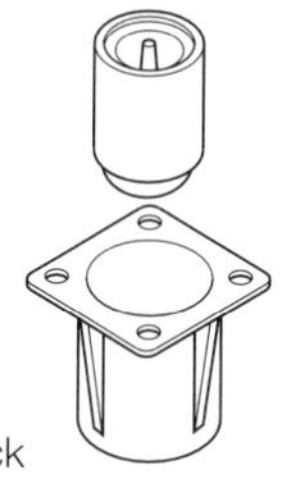

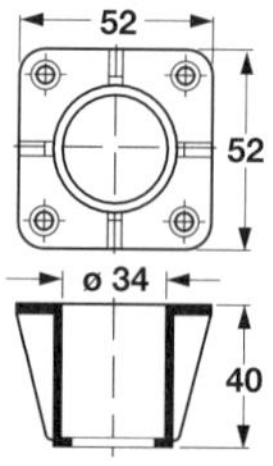

Finish: plastic, black

Cat. No.	661.03.339

Packing: 20 pcs.

Rolling Star Without Spring

Best used in small furniture or tables. Maximum load carrying capacity is 15 kg.

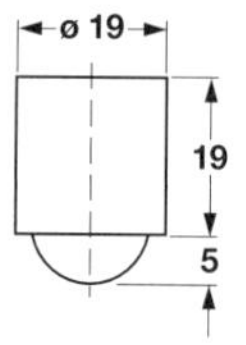

Finish: Case: POM, white
Ball: PP, white

Cat. No.	661.03.008

Packing: 20 pcs.

Dimensional data not binding. We reserve the right to alter specifications without notice.

Dimensions in mm

Roller-Mini Casters

Roller-Mini Swivel Caster

Allows furniture to be moved and swiveled in a discreet and elegant manner. Only 7 mm from floor they truly make any furniture movable; loud speakers, book cases, drum tables, etc…

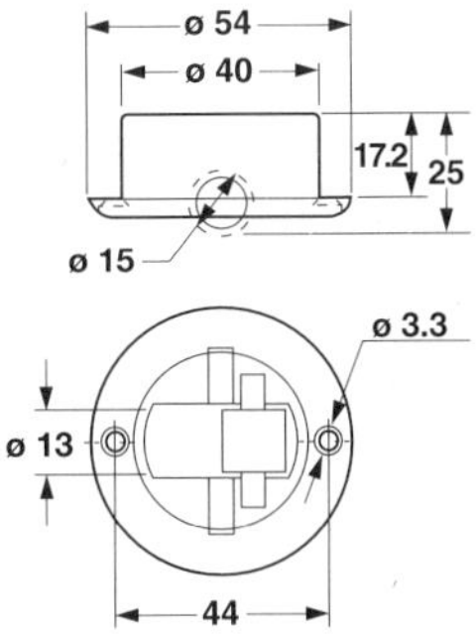

Finish: plastic, black

Cat. No.	661.04.309

Packing: 250 pcs.

Roller-Mini Fixed Caster

Same design as above in a fixed version.
Allows only one direction or movement as the swivel position is now stationary.

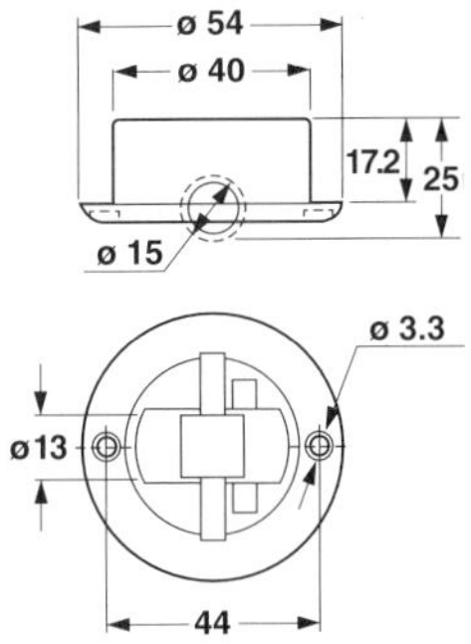

Finish: plastic, black

Cat. No.	661.04.318

Packing: 250 pcs.

Roller-Mini Combined Glide/Swivel Caster

For those applications that normally would require a glide, such as carpeting, we now can offer a caster (combined) with a glide! When used on hard surfaces. the caster wheel is used, on carpeting the glide is used. An elegant solution to a difficult problem.

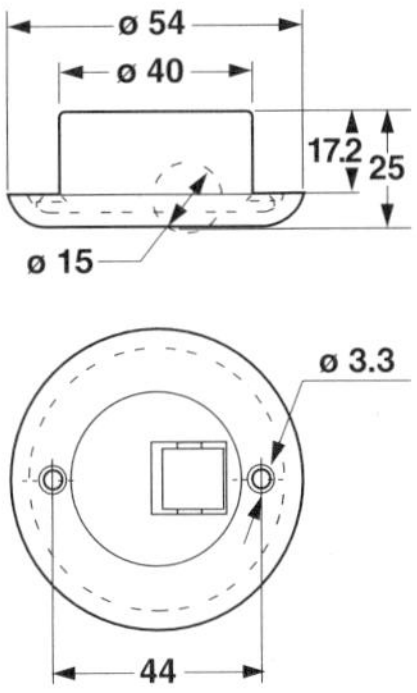

Finish: plastic, black

Cat. No.	661.04.327

Packing: 250 pcs.

Furniture Support Systems, Office and Computer Furniture Accessories 6

Dimensional data not binding.
We reserve the right to alter specifications without notice.

Dimensions in mm

HÄFELE

Furniture Glides

Glide
Finish: felt, gray
plastic housing, natural colored

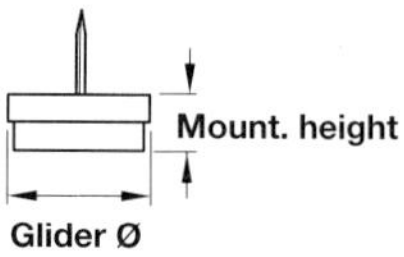

Glider Ø	**20 mm**	**24 mm**	**30 mm**
Mount. height	10 mm	10 mm	10 mm
Cat. No.	650.20.206	650.20.242	650.20.304

Packing: 100 and 1000 pcs.

Glide
Finish: plastic, white

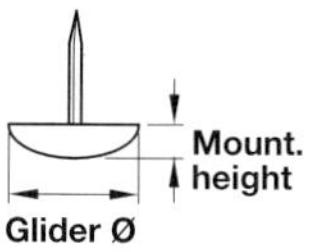

Glider Ø	**10 mm**	**13 mm**	**16 mm**	**19 mm**	**22 mm**	**25 mm**
Mount. height	5 mm	5 mm	5 mm	5 mm	5 mm	5 mm
Cat. No.	650.02.100	650.02.137	650.02.164	650.02.191	650.02.226	650.02.250

Packing: 100 and 1000 pcs.

Glide
with 2 nails
Finish: plastic, white

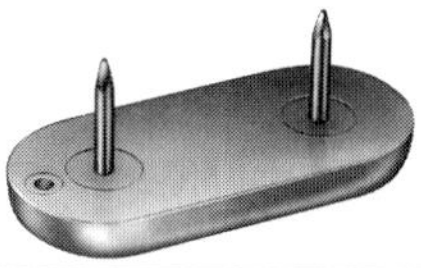

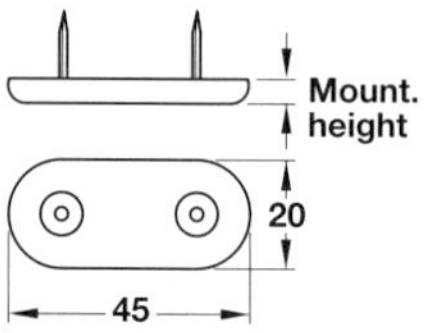

Size	**45 x 20 mm**
Mount. height	5 mm
Cat. No.	650.05.450

Packing: 100 pcs.

Glide
with 3 knock in teeth
Finish: steel, nickel-plated

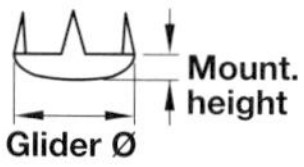

Glider Ø	**13 mm**	**15 mm**	**18 mm**	**20 mm**
Mount. height	3.5 mm	4 mm	4 mm	4.5 mm
Cat. No.	650.03.134	650.03.152	650.03.189	650.03.205

Packing: 100 and 1000 pcs.

Glide
Finish: steel, nickel-plated

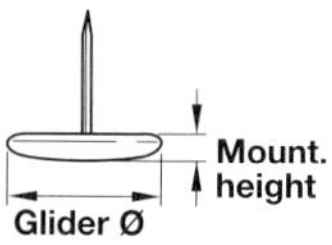

Glider Ø	**13 mm**	**15 mm**	**18 mm**	**20 mm**	**23 mm**	**25 mm**	**30 mm**
Mount. height	3.5 mm	3.5 mm	3.5 mm	3.5 mm	4.5 mm	4.5 mm	4.5 mm
Cat. No.	650.01.130	650.01.158	650.01.185	650.01.201	650.01.238	650.01.256	650.01.309

Packing: 100 and 1000 pcs.

Glide
with intermediate rubber layer
Finish: steel, nickel-plated,
rubber, black

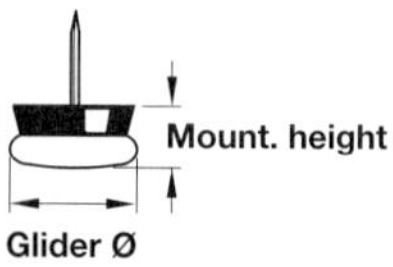

Glider Ø	**18 mm**	**20 mm**	**23 mm**	**25 mm**	**30 mm**
Mount. height	8 mm	8 mm	8.5 mm	8.5 mm	9 mm
Cat. No.	650.11.181	650.11.207	650.11.225	650.11.252	650.11.305

Packing: 500 pcs.

Glide
with intermediate rubber layer
Finish: plastic, white,
rubber, black

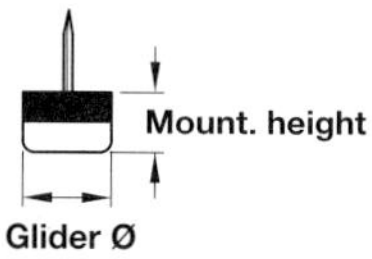

Glider Ø	**15 mm**	**20 mm**	**25 mm**	**30 mm**
Mount. height	10 mm	10 mm	10 mm	10 mm
Cat. No.	650.04.159	650.04.202	650.04.257	650.04.300

Packing: 100 pcs.

Dimensional data not binding.
We reserve the right to alter
specifications without notice.

Dimensions in mm

HÄFELE

Furniture Glides

Facilitate the mobility of upholstered furniture without inducing excessive movement. Screw mounted or knocked in (and screw reinforced).
Interlocking glides can also be fitted with Connecta fasteners, enabling separate upholstered articles to be linked together in rows or groups.

Glide With Screw-Hole

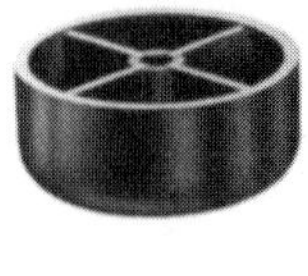

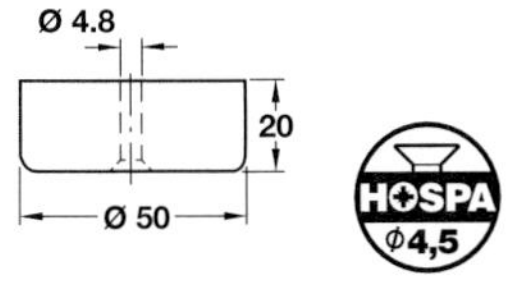

Finish: plastic, black

Cat. No.	635.80.316

Packing: 100 pcs.

Glide With Screw-Hole

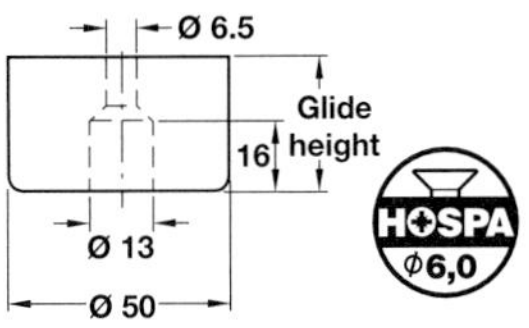

Finish: plastic, black

Cat. No.	30 mm height	635.80.334
	40 mm height	635.80.343

Packing: 100 pcs.

Glide With Moulded Plug

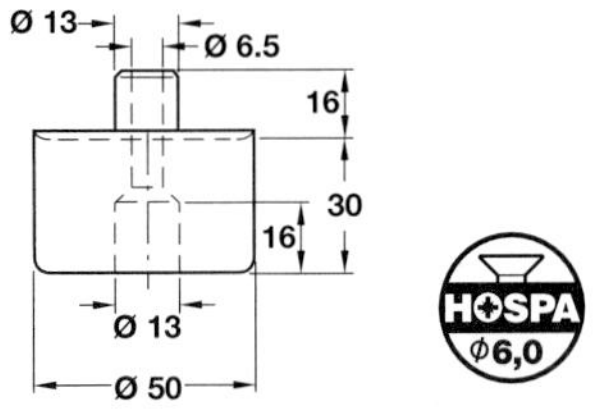

Finish: plastic, black

Cat. No.	635.82.338

Packing: 100 pcs.

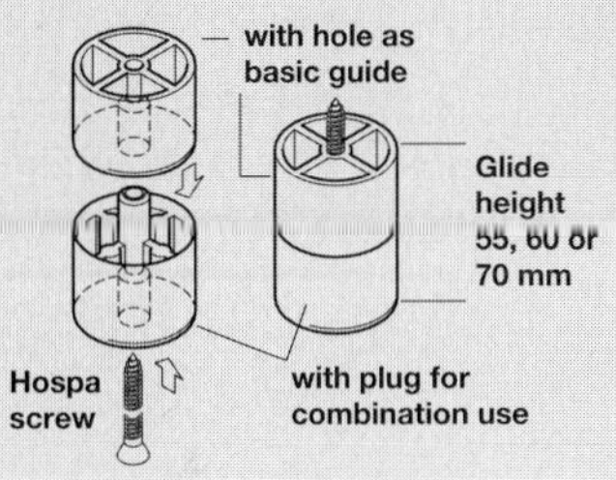

The 30 and 40 mm glides can be doubled up with the 30mm plug-in model to obtain glide heights of 60 and 70 mm. Whether alone or combined, they can be linked together with Connecta fasteners.

Furniture Support Systems, Office and Computer Furniture Accessories 6

Connecta Fastener

Connecta fastener enable articles of upholstered furniture to be linked together in rows or groups. The plugs fit securely into the apertures in the glides, but can be subsequently withdrawn if required. The glides can be spaced between 85 and 175 mm apart in 5 mm intervals.

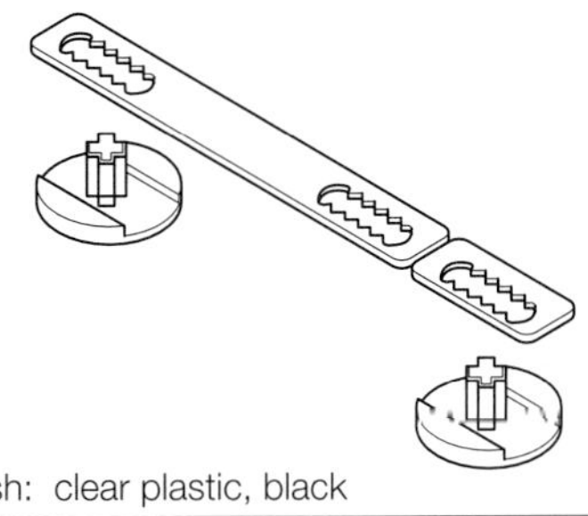

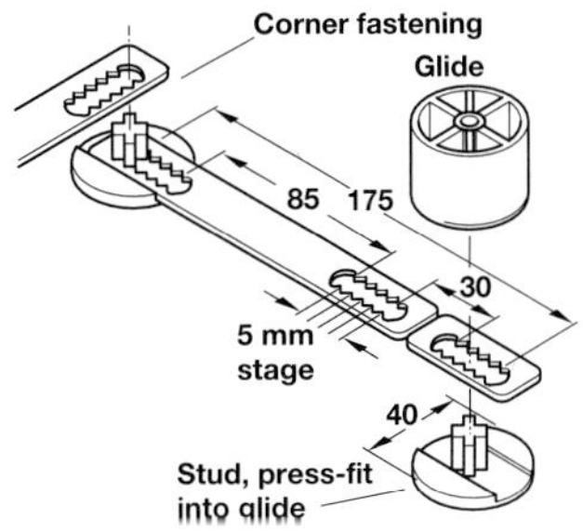

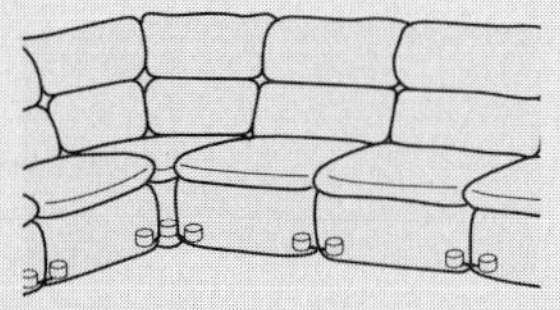

The illustration above demonstrates the use of Connecta fasteners to obtain a seating group with a corner module. The corner arrangement employs one stud to secure two fasteners at right angles to each other.

Finish: clear plastic, black

Cat. No.	635.82.258

Packing: 100 pcs.

Dimensions in mm

HÄFELE

Furniture Glides

Furniture glides are economically priced yet meet all the requirements of a high quality furniture glide. Minimal contact pressure due to flat base, combined with easy movement because of radiused edges. Available in three different heights, these glides are especially suitable for upholstered furniture.

Furniture glide, height 25 mm

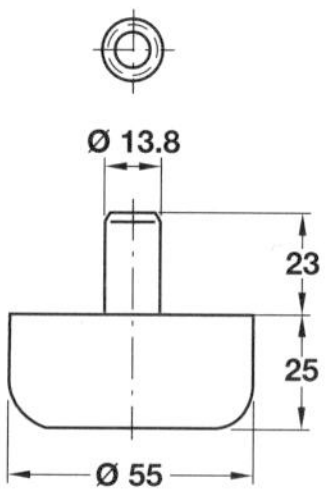

Finish: plastic, black

Cat. No.	635.87.315

Packing: 100 pcs

Furniture glide, height 32 mm

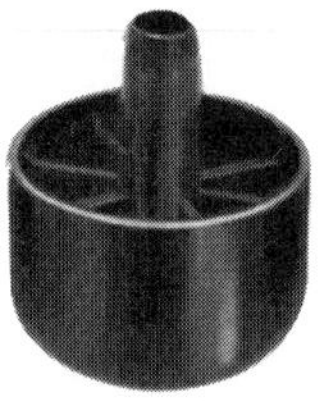

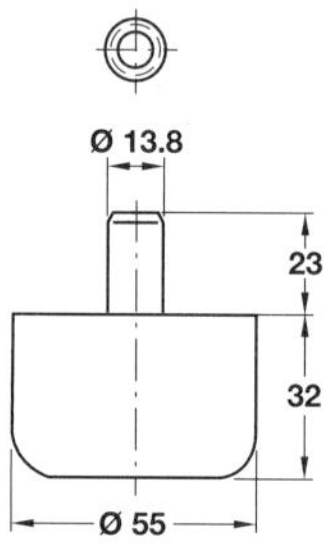

Finish: plastic, black

Cat. No.	635.87.324

Packing: 100 pcs

Furniture glide, height 52 mm

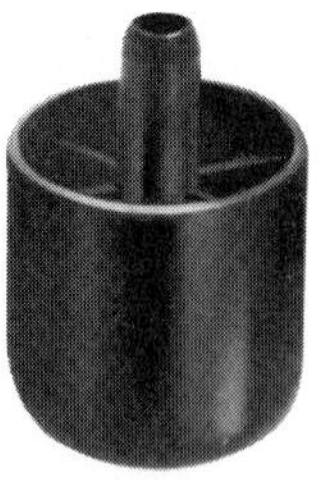

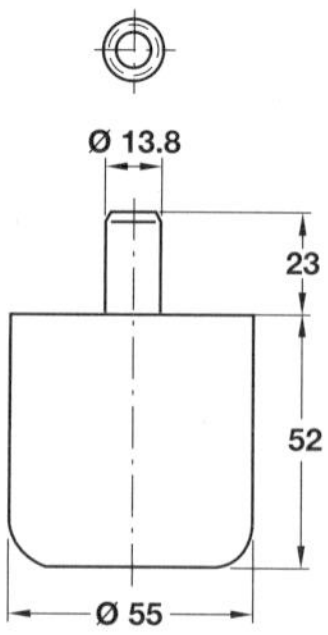

Finish: plastic, black

Cat. No.	635.87.333

Packing: 100 pcs

Connecting link
For combining individual chairs into rows or groups. Adjustment in 5 mm increments.

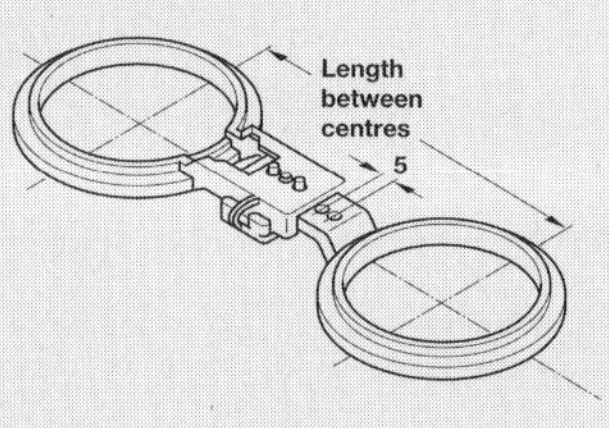

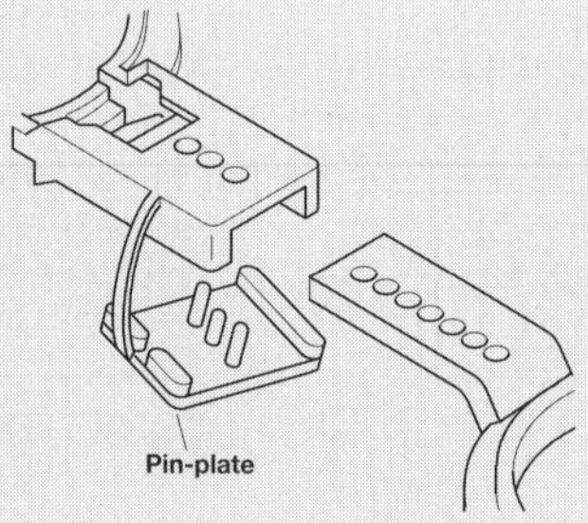

Finish: plastic, black

Size (mm)	130 - 180
Cat. No.	635.87.397

Packing: 100 pcs

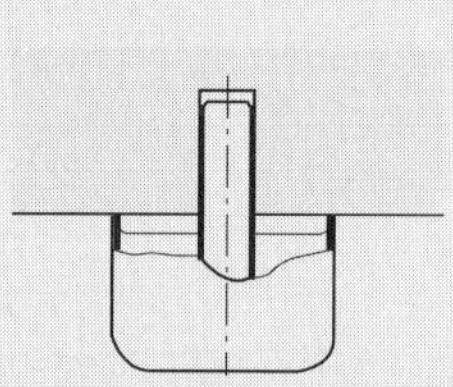

The molded, press-fit stem ensures that the glide fits close against the furniture, thus preventing any unwanted twisting.

Dimensional data not binding. We reserve the right to alter specifications without notice.

Dimensions in mm

Adjustable Furniture Glides

HÄFELE

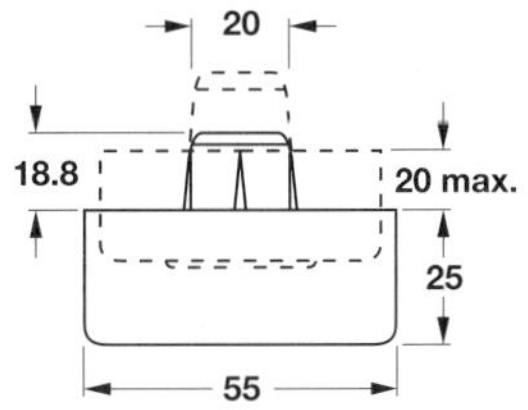

Two section furniture foot
Ø 55 mm diameter, 25 mm high height adjustable by + 20 mm, for 20mm diameter holes,
dowel length 18.8 mm
Finish: plastic, black

	min. height 25 mm
	max. height 45 mm
Cat. No.	635.92.320

Packing: 100 pcs.

Adapter
20 mm high
Finish: plastic, black

Cat. No.	635.92.382

Packing: 100 pcs.

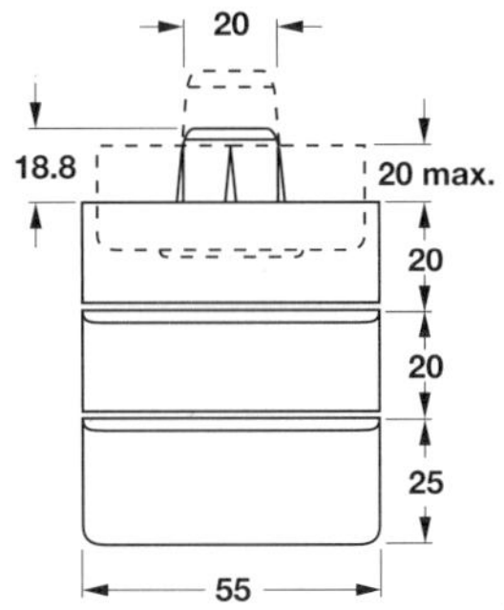

The 55 mm diameter furniture foot is simply knocked into place and can be height adjusted by 20 mm.

The furniture feet are easily adjusted using an 8 mm hex key through the base of the furniture. This is a particular advantage for large units.

An additional cover cap is no longer needed due to the design of the foot.

Furniture Glide
A vertically adjustable glide featuring an extra-large contact area which prevents the furniture sinking into the floor covering and provides effortless movement.

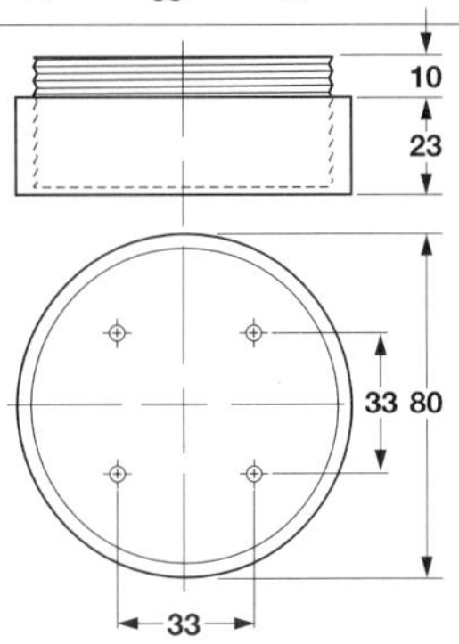

Finish: plastic, charcoal gray

Cat. No.	635.83.308

Packing: 20 pcs.

Furniture Glide Features:
- All-plastic
- Glide diameter ø 80 mm, vertical adjustment 23-33 mm
- Hard surface, particularly suitable for soft floor coverings (e.g. carpets).
- Abrasion-proof, easy on carpeting.

Base Leveler-Knock-in Mount
Bore a Ø 40 mm hole into your base unit. A 13.5 mm hole allows access to the top of the leveling bolt. An M5 hex key is required for adjustment. Foot plate swivels to allow for uneven surfaces.

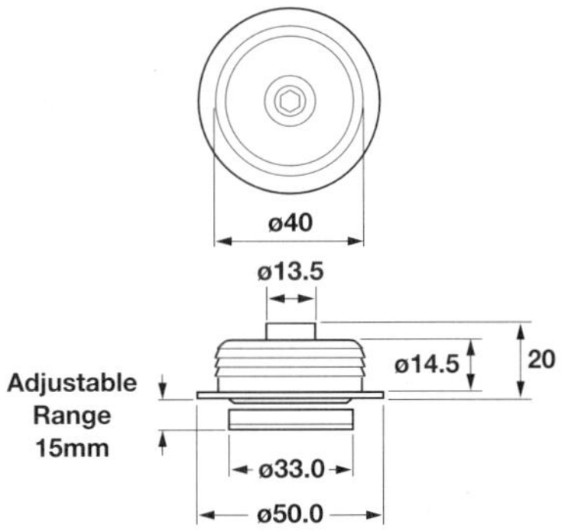

Finish: plastic, black; steel, zinc-plated

Cat. No.	635.79.304

Packing: 1 pc.

Furniture Support Systems, Office and Computer Furniture Accessories

6

Base Leveler With Extensions
Same construction as above except with the additional extensions for greater adjustment ranges.
An M4 hex key is required for adjustment.
Foot plate swivels for uneven surface adjustment.

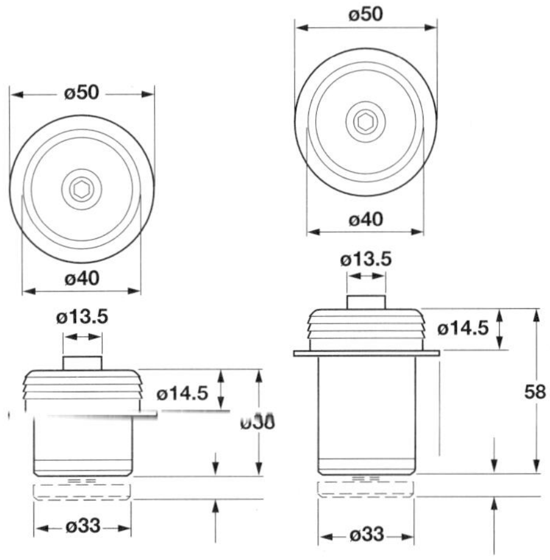

Finish: plastic, black; steel, zinc-plated

Length	Cat. No.
30 mm	635.79.313
50 mm	635.79.322

Packing: 1 pc.

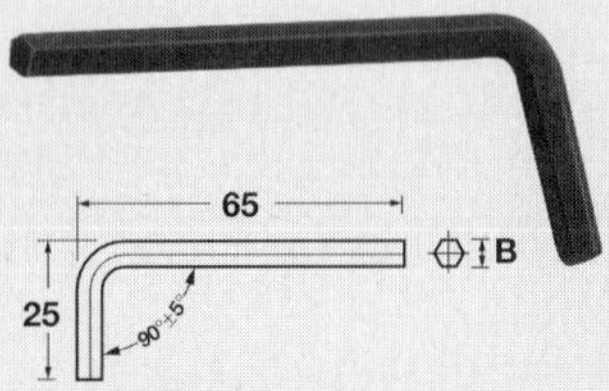

Size	Cat. No.
M4	008.28.044
M5	008.28.062

Packing: 1000 pcs.

Dimensional data not binding. We reserve the right to alter specifications without notice.

Dimensions in mm

HÄFELE

Cabinet Levelers

- Used to clamp cabinets, shelves against ceiling.
- Point presses into ceiling to eliminate slipping.

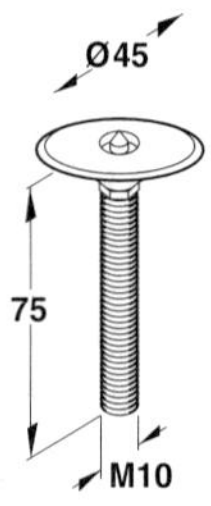

M 10 Top Clamping Screw
with adjustable ceiling plate
Finish: steel, galvanized
Plate: plastic

Color	Cat. No.
white	637.01.717
brown	637.01.119

Packing: 100 pcs.

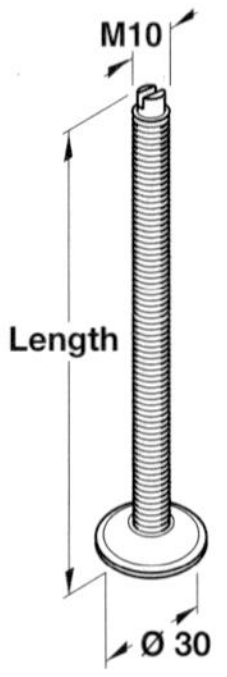

M 10 Base Adjusting Screw
with adjustable baseplate
Finish: steel, galvanized

Length	Cat. No.
60 mm	637.02.009
70 mm	637.02.018
80 mm	637.02.027
90 mm	637.02.036
100 mm	637.02.045
120 mm	637.02.054

Packing: 100 pcs.

Protective Cap
snaps over baseplate
Finish: plastic, white

Cat. No.	637.02.090

Packing: 100 pcs.

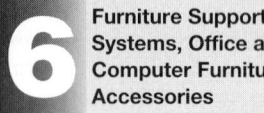

6 Furniture Support Systems, Office and Computer Furniture Accessories

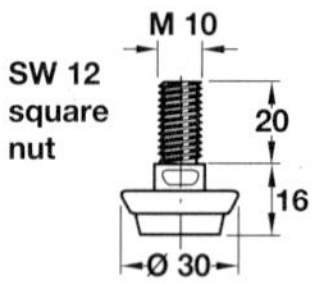

M10 Adjustment Screw

Finish: steel, nickel-plated with black rubber base

Cat. No.	651.02.909

Packing: 20 pcs.

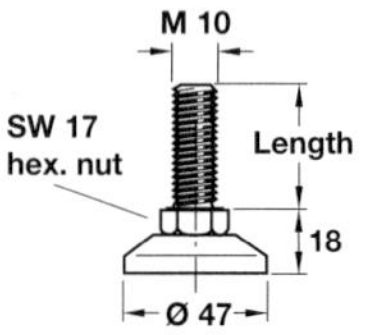

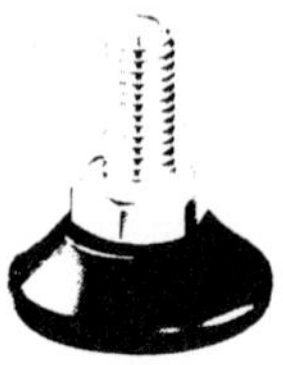

M10 Adjustment Screw, with fixed foot

Finish: Screw: steel, zinc-plated
Foot: plastic, black

Length	Cat. No.
30 mm	651.01.304
50 mm	651.01.500

Packing: 100 pcs

Dimensional data not binding. We reserve the right to alter specifications without notice.

Dimensions in mm

Cabinet Levelers

HÄFELE

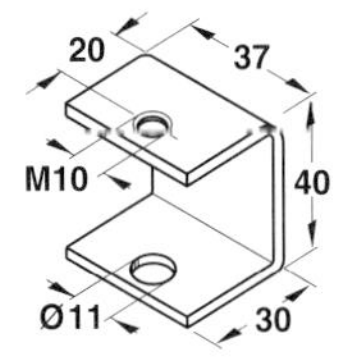

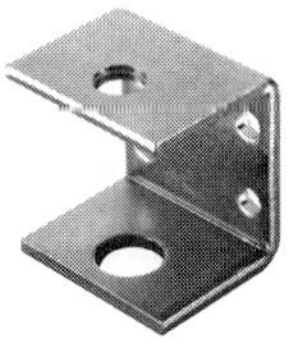

Screw-mount Bracket
Finish: steel, galvanized

Cat. No.	637.07.004

Packing: 100 pcs.

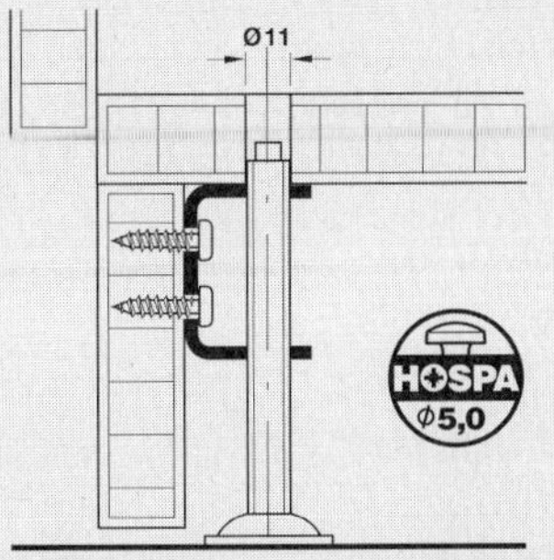

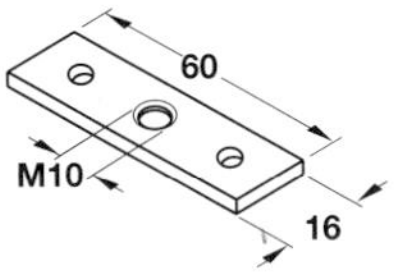

Screw-mount Plate
Finish: steel, galvanized

Cat. No.	637.09.008

Packing: 100 pcs.

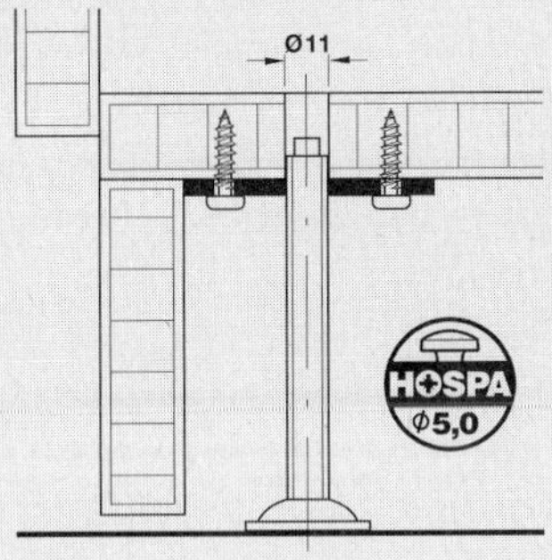

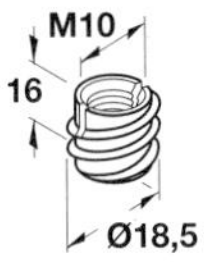

Threaded Socket
Finish: steel, unfinished

Cat. No.	030.00.502

Packing: 100 pcs.

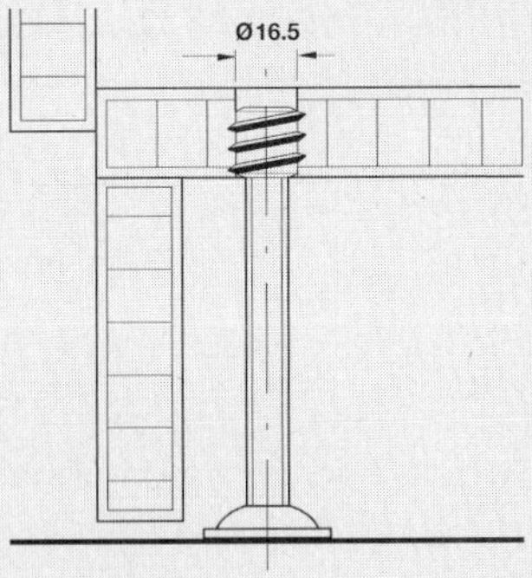

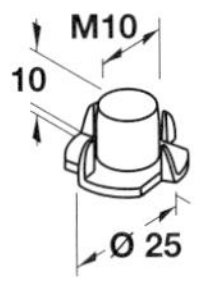

T-Nut
Finish: steel, unfinished

Cat. No.	031.00.301

Packing: 100 pcs.

Glides
Press-fit into square tubes, 1.5-2 mm gauge

Finish: plastic, black

Size	Cat.No.
20 x 20 mm	652.12.615
25 x 25 mm	652.12.624
30 x 30 mm	652.12.633

Packing: 100 pcs

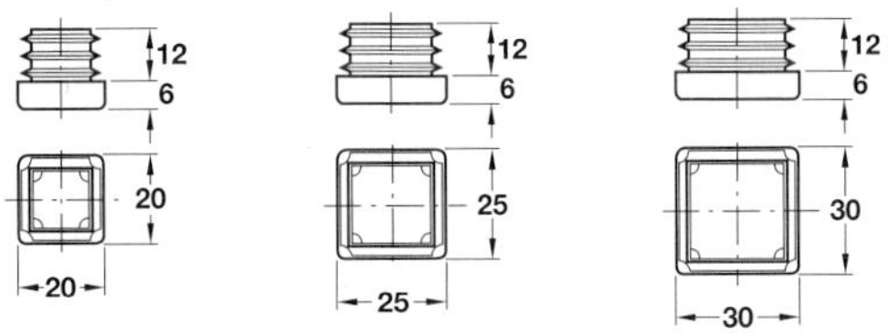

Furniture Support Systems, Office and Computer Furniture Accessories

6

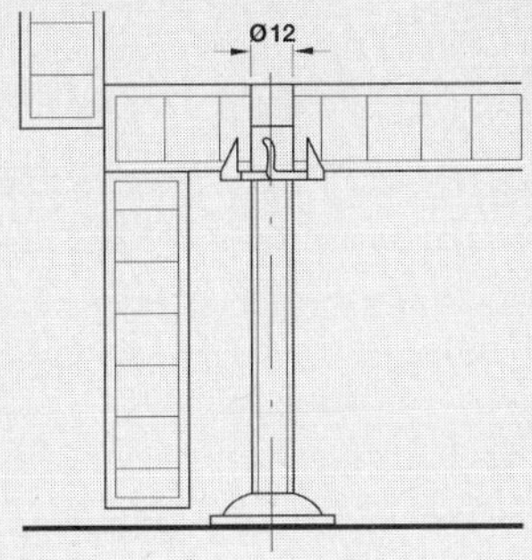

Glides With M10 Internal Thread
Press-fit into square tubes, 1.5-2 mm gauge

Finish: plastic, black

Size	Cat. No.
25 x 25 mm	652.11.627
30 x 30 mm	652.11.636

Packing: 100 pcs

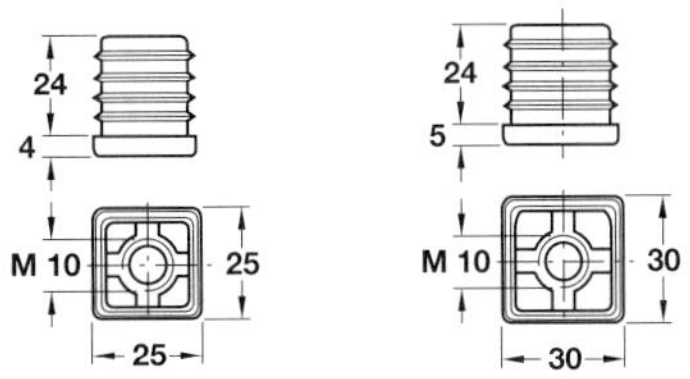

Dimensions in mm

Dimensional data not binding. We reserve the right to alter specifications without notice.

HÄFELE

Cabinet Levelers

Adjustable from above through hole in cabinet bottom and from below with an open-ended wrench.

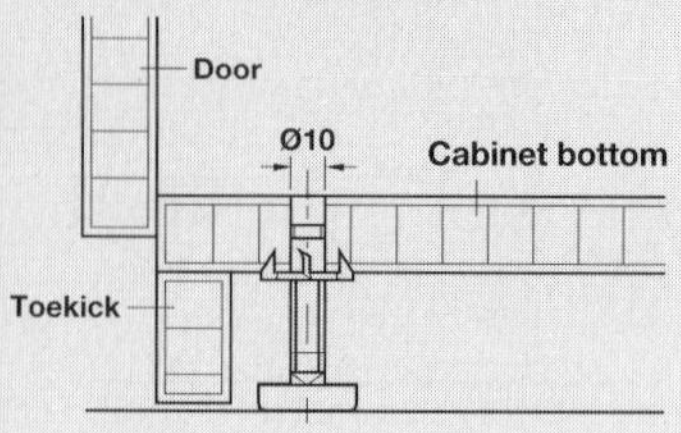

Base leveler screw

M8 X 45, with T-nut and plastic cap.

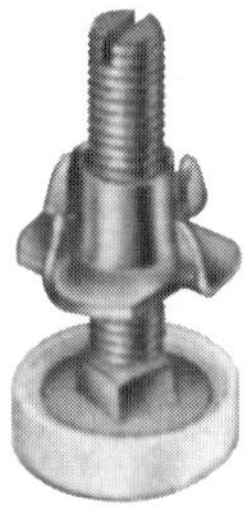

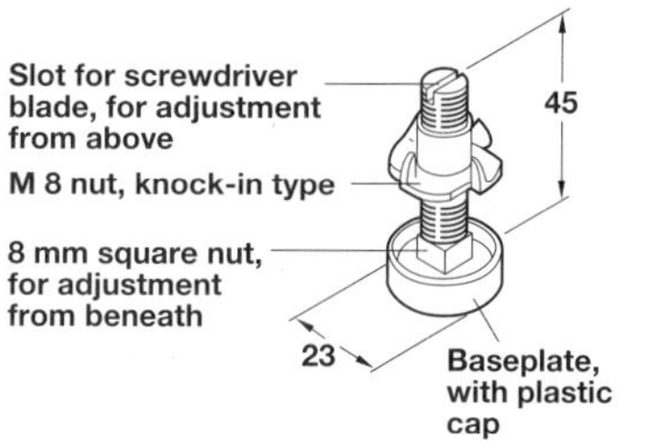

Finish: steel, zinc-plated; plastic, white

Cat. No.	637.05.000

Packing: 100 pcs.

Base leveler

Screw type

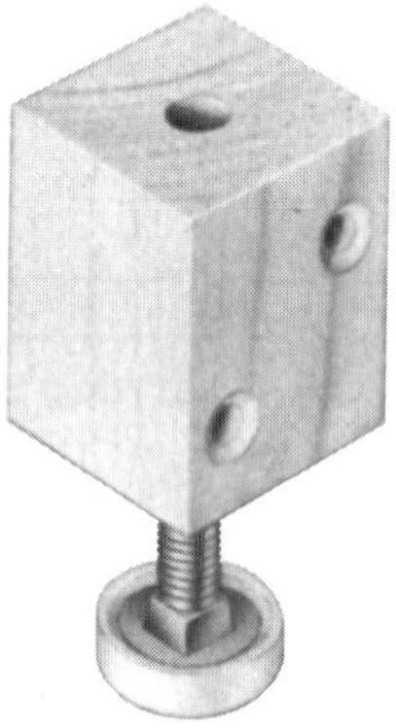

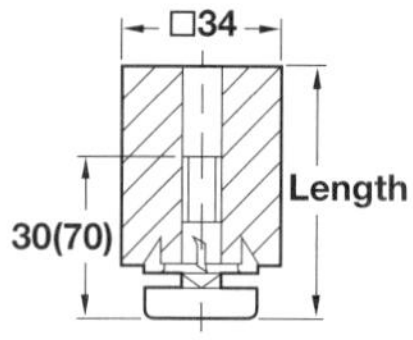

Adjustable from above through hole in cabinet floor and from below with an open-ended wrench.

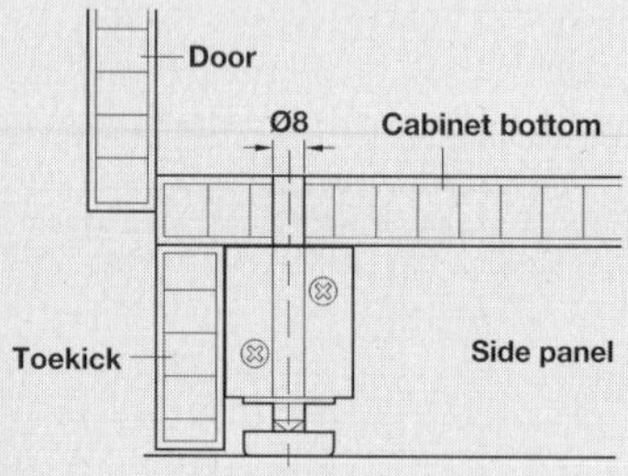

With 30 mm long screw x M 8
Mounting block: wood
Finish: steel, zinc-plated; plastic cap, white

Cat. No.	Length 55 mm	637.12.229

With 70 mm long screw x M 8
Mounting block: wood
Finish: steel, zinc-plated; plastic cap, white

Cat. No.	Length 80 mm	637.12.265
	Length 100 mm	637.12.283

Packing: 100 pcs.

Base leveler

1/4-20 x 20 spindle, plastic beige cap Minimum installation height: 7.5 mm Adjustment range: +15 mm

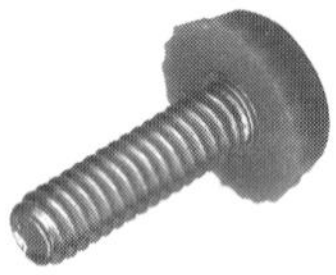

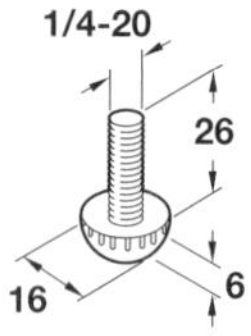

Finish: steel, zinc-plated; plastic, beige

Cat. No.	637.05.108

Packing: 500 pcs.

6 Furniture Support Systems, Office and Computer Furniture Accessories

Base leveler

1/4-20 x 22 spindle, black cap

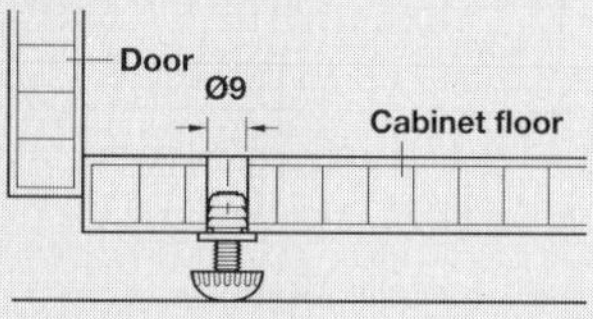

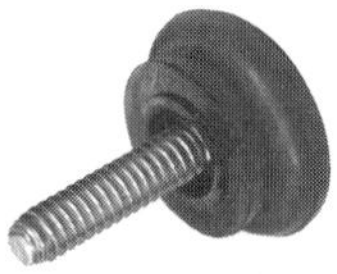

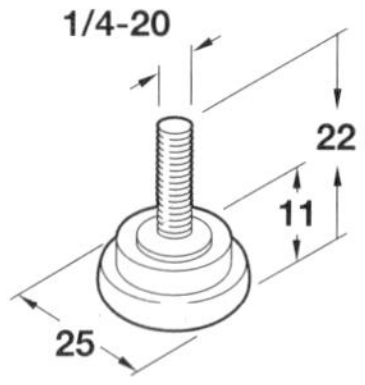

Finish: steel, zinc-plated; plastic, black

Cat. No.	651.04.332

Packing: 500 pcs.

Knock-in stem

1/4-20 x 11

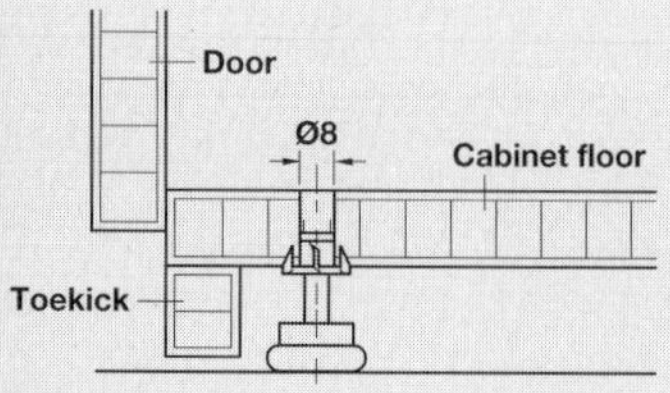

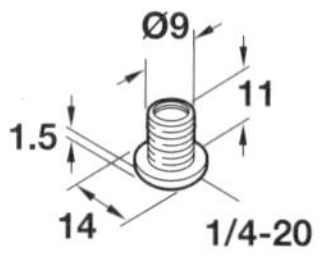

Finish: brass

Cat. No.	039.02.065

Packing: 500 pcs.

T-nut

1/4-20 x 10

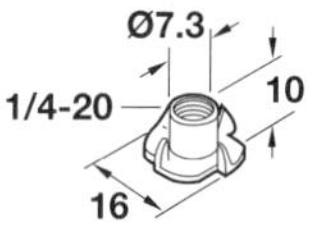

Finish: steel, zinc-plated

Cat. No.	031.05.968

Packing: 100 pcs.

Dimensional data not binding. We reserve the right to alter specifications without notice.

Dimensions in mm

Cabinet Levelers

HÄFELE

Base leveler

with press-fit plugs
Minimum installation height: 50mm
Adjustment range: +20mm
M8 bolt
Base plate with plastic cap

Finish: polyamid, black; steel, zinc-plated

Catalog No.	Length	Packing
637.11.320	60	500
637.11.348	80	300
637.11.366	100	100

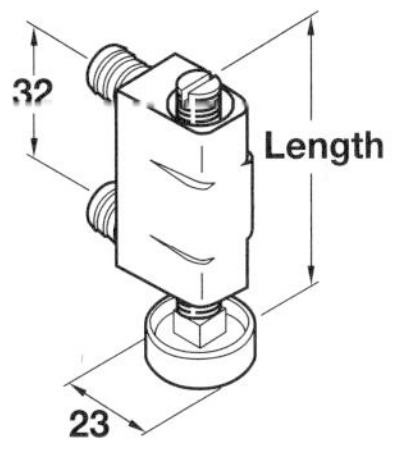

Adjustable from above through hole in cabinet bottom and from below with an open-ended wrench.

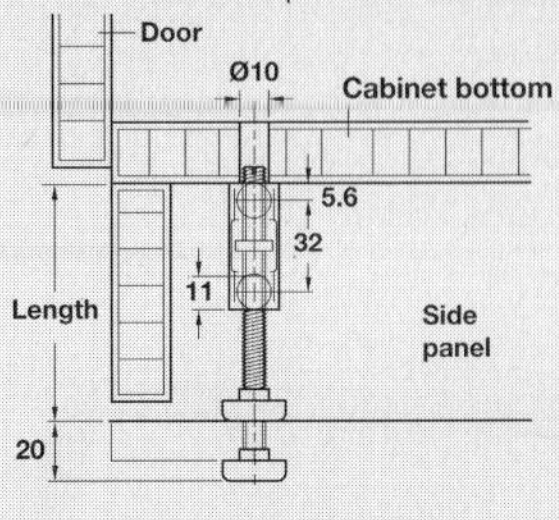

Base leveler, with supporting bracket

Screw-mounted
Minimum installation height: 100mm
Adjustment range: +20mm
M10 X 100 bolt
with swivelling base plate

Finish: steel galvanized

Cat. No.	637.30.941

Packing: 100 pcs.

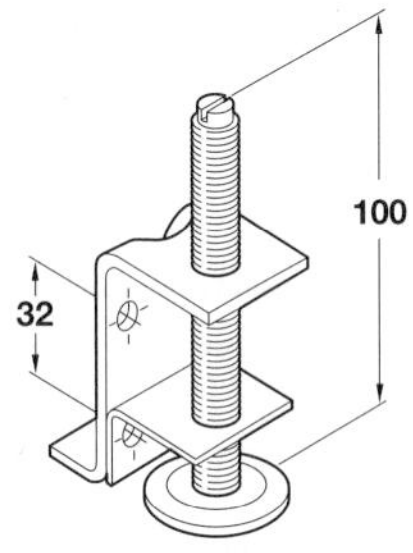

Supporting bracket for side panel
L x W = 30 x 14 mm

Easily mounted and requiring only a Ø 12 mm hole in the cabinet bottom for adjustment.

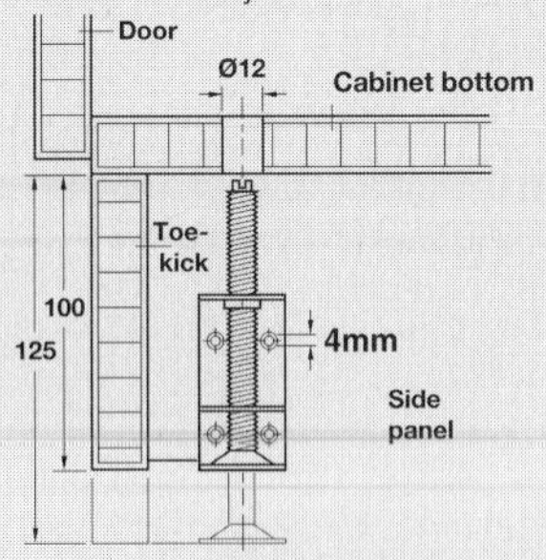

Protective cap, for swivelling base plate

Finish: white plastic

Cat. No.	637.02.090

Packing: 500 pcs.

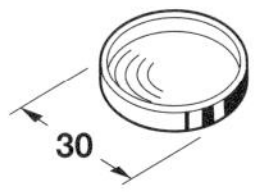

Heavy duty base leveler, with supporting bracket

Screw-mounted
Minimum installation height: 70mm
Load-bearing capacity: 200 kg
Adjustment range: +45 mm
M12 X 65 bolt
with M5 mm Allen socket head

Finish: steel, zinc-plated

Cat. No.	637.67.900

Packing: 1 pc.

HOSPA Φ5,0

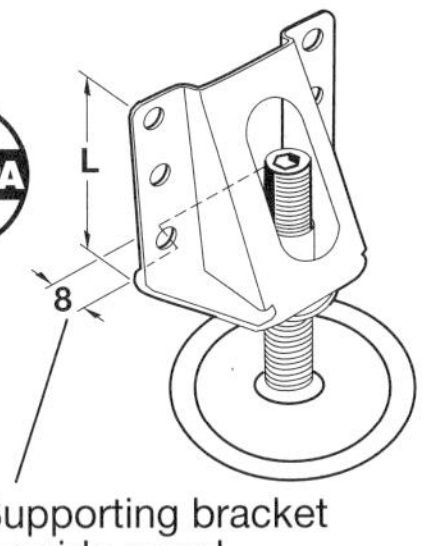

Supporting bracket for side panel
L x W = 58 x 15 mm

Easily mounted and requiring only a Ø 15 mm hole in the cabinet bottom for adjustment.

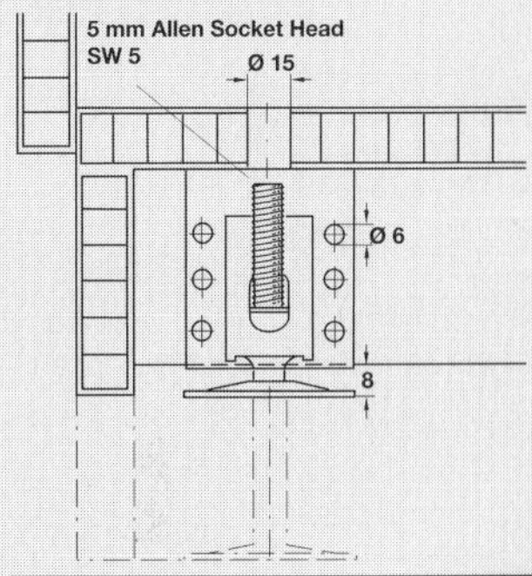

Base Leveler with Corner Support

M4 hex key required to adjust the 70 mm threaded bolt. Foot plate swivels to allow for uneven surfaces.

- Provides 65 mm of adjustment while adding support to the side panel.
- Effectively serves as corner brace and panel support.
- Load capacity 150 kg

Finish: steel, zinc-plated

Cat. No.	637.37.904

Packing: 1 set = 2L and 2R

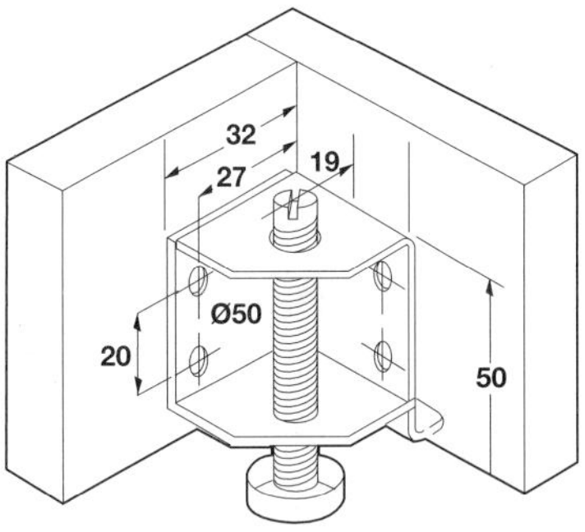

Furniture Support Systems, Office and Computer Furniture Accessories

6

Refer to page 6.17 for hex keys.

Base Leveler with supporting bracket

Groove or screw-on mounted.
Threaded bolt M 10 x 65 mm
with hexagon socket M5 and swiveling base plate dia. 50 mm.
Min. installation height: 75 mm
Adjustment range: + 30 mm
Load capacity 150 kg

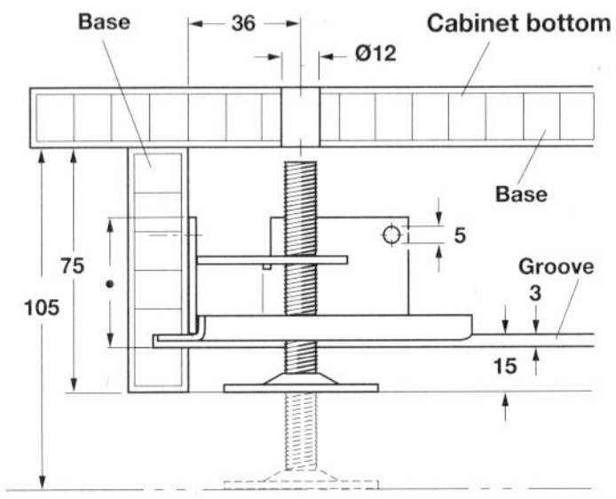

Top View

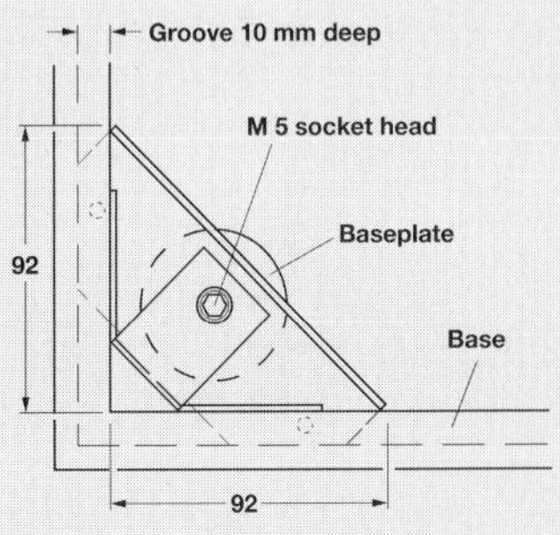

Finish: steel, galvanized.

Cat. No.	637.33.900

Packing: 12 and 50 pcs.

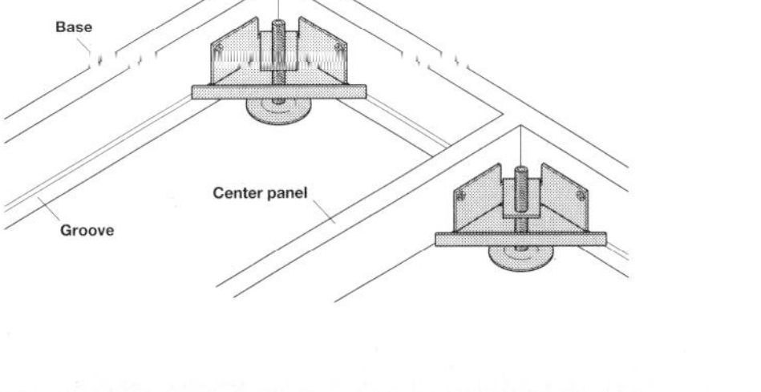

Dimensional data not binding. We reserve the right to alter specifications without notice.

Dimensions in mm

Call 1-800-423-3531 anywhere in the US and Canada

Height-Adjustment Fittings

Particularly suitable for office furniture walls. The adjustment part is designed to operate by means of an allen key. Minimum thickness of material required 19 mm.

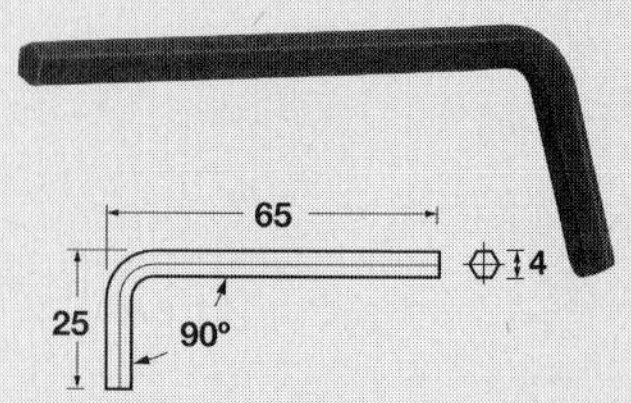

Allen key - M4

Cat. No.	008.28.044

Packing: 1 pc.

Adjustment Fitting

To adjust the height of partitions, screens and cabinets.

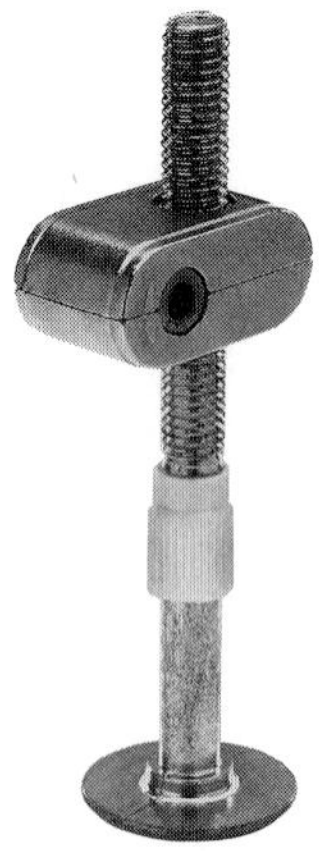

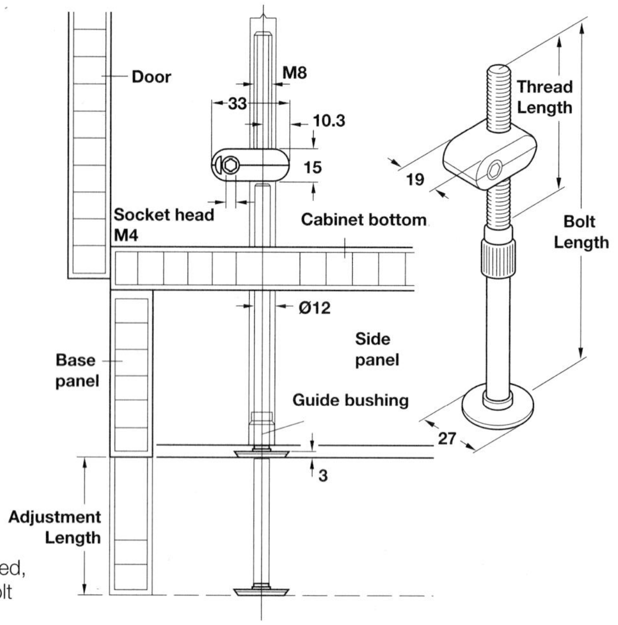

Finish: zinc-alloy adjustment fitting, nickel plated, plastic guide bushing, galvanized threaded bolt M 8 with Ø 27 mm flat foot.

Bolt length	thread length	adjustment length	Catalog No.
100 mm	50 mm	35 mm	637.33.719
160 mm	70 mm	55 mm	637.33.746
200 mm	80 mm	80 mm	637.33.764

Packing: 50 pcs.

Adjustment leveler

Minimum installation height: 80 mm
Adjustment range: 36 mm
Dynamic load capacity: 260 kg/pc.
Static load capacity: 400 kg/pc.

Drilling diagram

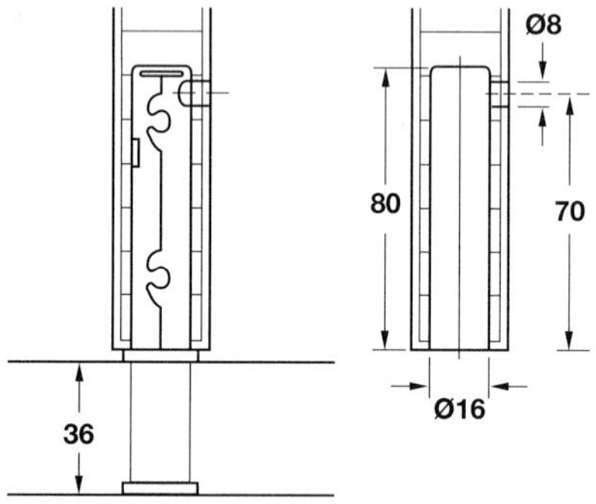

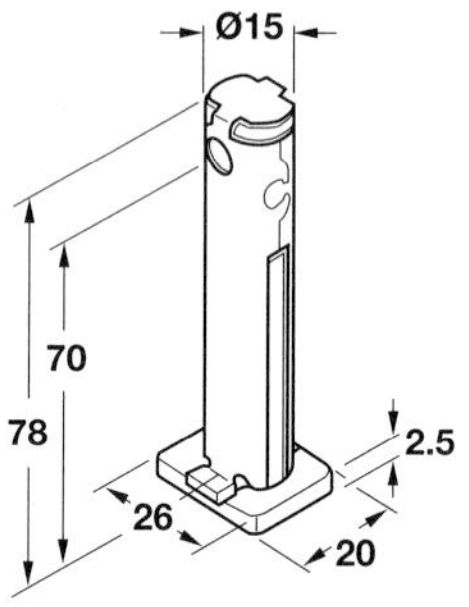

Easily mounted and requires only a Ø 8 mm hole in the panel for adjustment.

Finish: steel, zinc die-cast

Cat. No.	637.13.002

Packing: 150 pcs.

6 Furniture Support Systems, Office and Computer Furniture Accessories

The adjustment feature is easy to operate and is driven by a "#2 Phillips" screwdriver.

Dimensional data not binding. We reserve the right to alter specifications without notice.

Dimensions in mm

Self-Adjusting Furniture Levelers

HÄFELE

Tabloplan Table Stabilizing Fitting
compensates automatically for floor irregularities up to 10 mm.

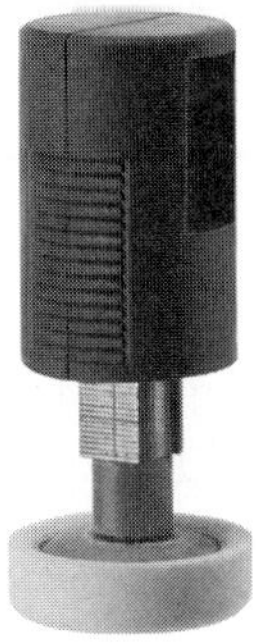

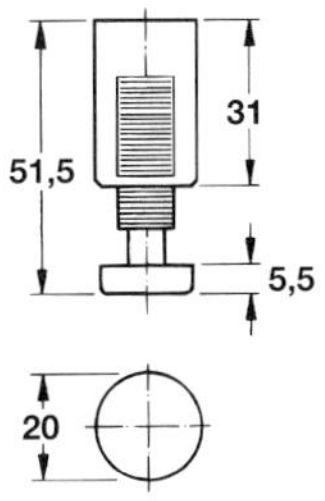

Drilling Diagram **Useful compensating range– up to 10 mm (no tools required)**

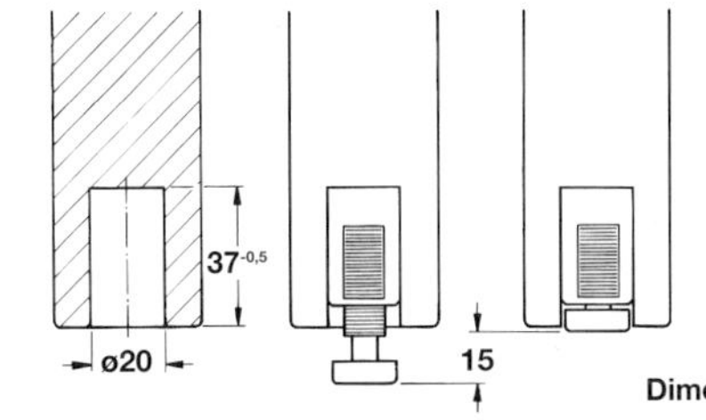

Dimensions in mm

Finish: brown plastic housing with metal foot; steel baseplate, zinc-plated; with white plastic cap.

Cat. No.	651.32.103

Packaging: 1 pc.

Function

1. Lift the table at the corner where the Tabloplan is fitted. The baseplate will now be fully extended.
2. Now press down firmly on the table top, causing the baseplate to retract fully into the table leg.
3. Apply weight to the other three table legs so that the table is level. The Tabloplan baseplate will now extend under spring pressure until it comes into contact with the floor, where it locks into place under the weight of the table.

These three steps can be repeated again and again, any time the table is moved. The fitting is made to withstand high loadings and can be used with heavy tables, e.g. with table tops made of glass, marble, tiles, etc.

- Fast, easy way to level without the use of tools
- Concealed when installed
- Installation requires drilling only a single hole.

Super Level Table Glide

Automatic self adjusting leveler for tables weighing 25 to140 pounds. 1/4 - 20 threaded stud. Attachment to 1/4 - 20 insert with 3/16" size allen wrench.

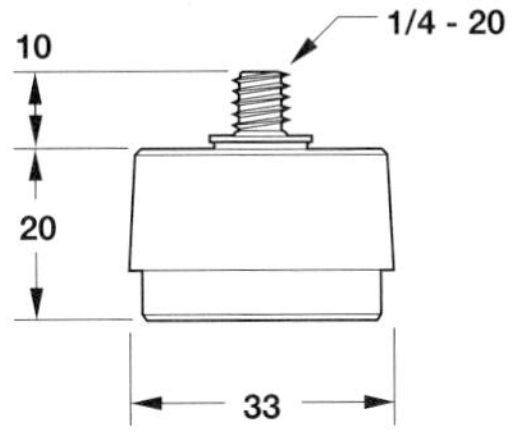

Finish: Housing: nylon, black
Spring: stainless steel
Stud: steel, heat treated

Cat. No.	651.30.332

Packing: 25 pcs.

- Unique leveler uses only the tables weight to stop it from wobbling.
- Tables can be moved without worrying about re-adjustment as the leveler adjusts itself automatically to any uneven floor surface.
- Stainless steel spring housed within a precision engineered nylon body.

Furniture alignment wedges

Plastic strips can be broken off from 1 mm to 8 mm to level furniture.

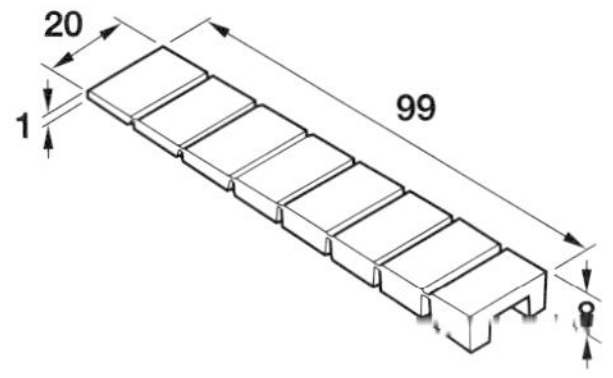

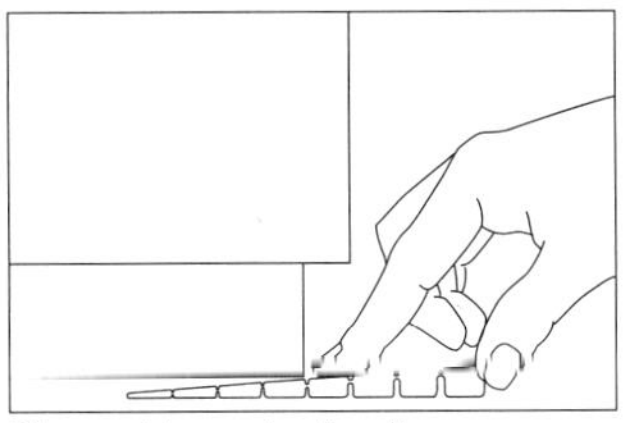

Place strip under furniture,

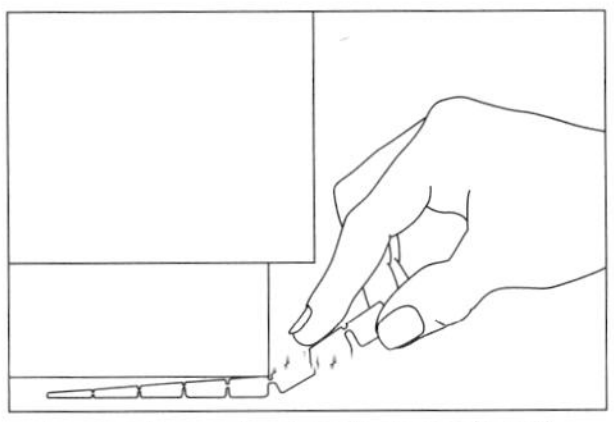

when aligned, simply break off.

Finish: plastic

Cat. No.	Brown 006.90.900	White 009.90.920

Packing: 100, 250

Dimensions in mm

HÄFELE

Base Cabinet Levelers

The base levelers shown on this page gives the manufacturer a wide choice of bases, levelers and toekick-clips.

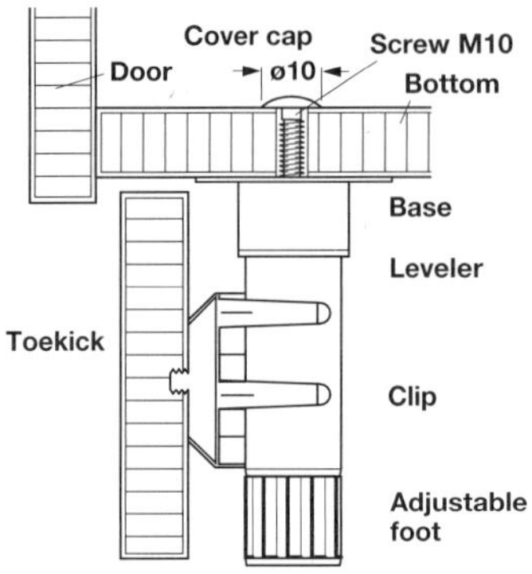

All bases and levelers are for a toekick-height of 100 mm (4")

Base, for levelers

Mounts through the bottom of the cabinet, includes a steel screw M10 and a cover cap, white.

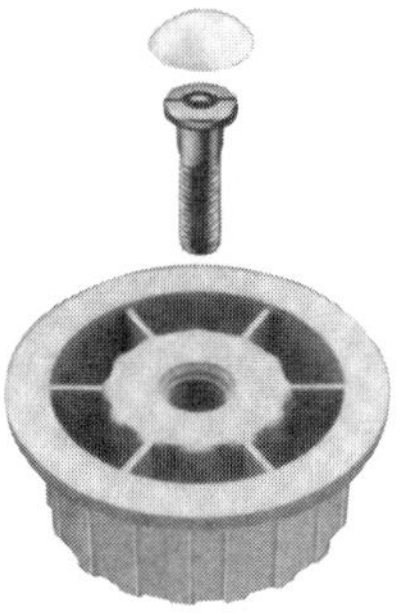

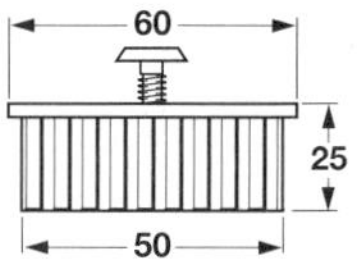

Finish: plastic, black

Cat. No.	637.31.028

Packing: 100 pcs. each

Base, for levelers

Screw-mounts to the bottom of the cabinet

HOSPA Φ4.0

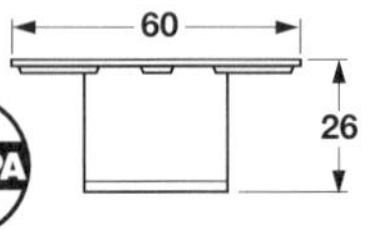

Finish: steel, zinc-plated; plastic, black

Cat. No.	637.31.019

Packing: 100 pcs.

Leveler, for bases

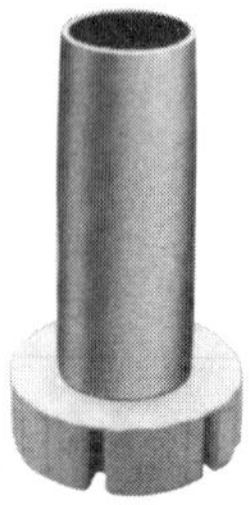

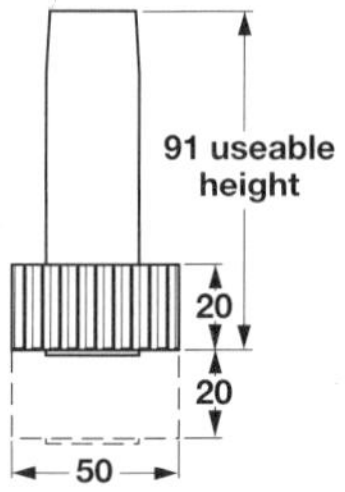

Finish: steel, zinc-plated; plastic foot, black

Cat. No.	637.32.918

Packing: 100 pcs.

Leveler, for bases

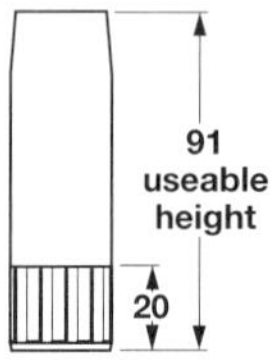

Finish: steel, zinc-plated; plastic foot, black

Cat. No.	637.31.911

Packing: 100 pcs.

Leveler Extensions

used only with this leveler

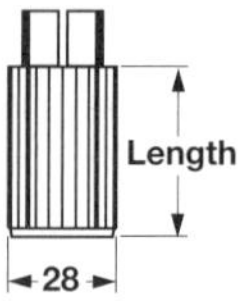

Finish: plastic, black

Length	for heights from:	to:	Cat. No.
40	140	160	637.31.715
50	150	170	637.31.724

Packing: 100 pcs.

Toekick-clip, for levelers

Screw-mounted

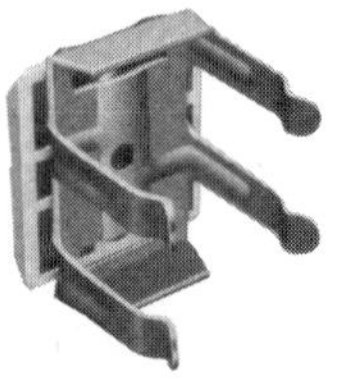

HOSPA Φ3,5

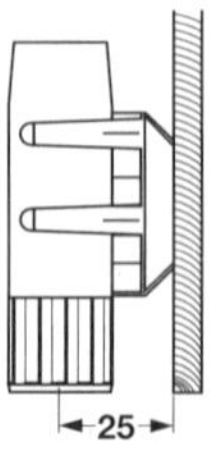

Finish: steel, zinc-plated; plastic, black

Cat. No.	637.31.984

Packing: 100 pcs.

Toekick-clip, for levelers

Groove mounting

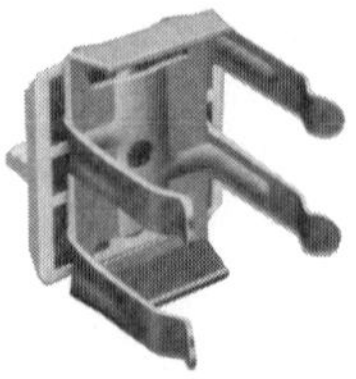

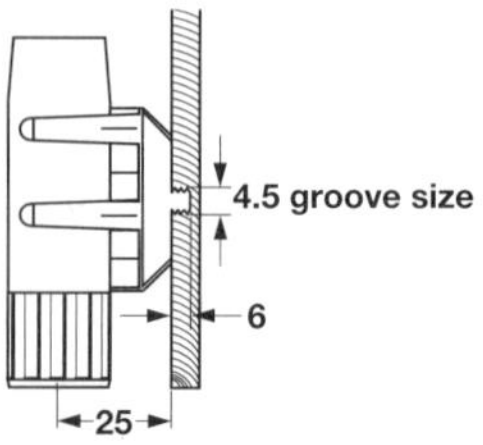

Finish: steel, zinc-plated; plastic, black

Cat. No.	637.31.993

Packing: 100 pcs.

6 Furniture Support Systems, Office and Computer Furniture Accessories

Dimensional data not binding. We reserve the right to alter specifications without notice.

Dimensions in mm

Base Cabinet Levelers

Adjustable Foot
2 part

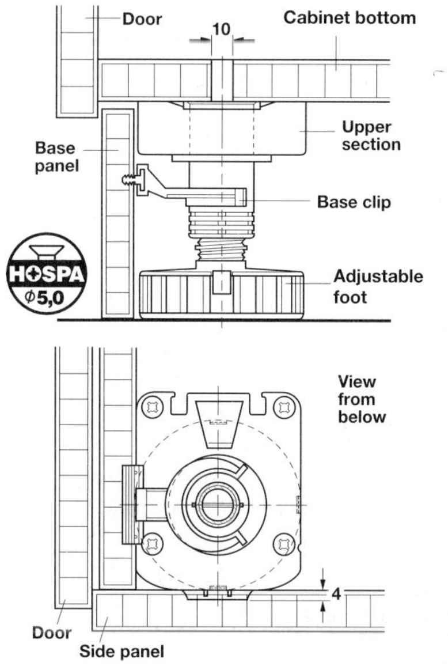

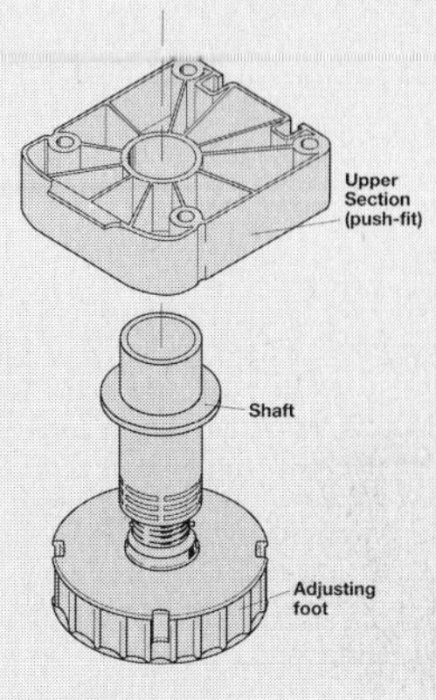

Finish: plastic, black

Base height	Adjustment range		Cat. No.
80	-5	+15	637.39.293
100	-5	+15	637.39.300
120	-5	+15	637.39.328
150	-5	+15	637.39.355

Packing: 4 pcs.

Base Clip, 2-part
Groove-mounted to base panel

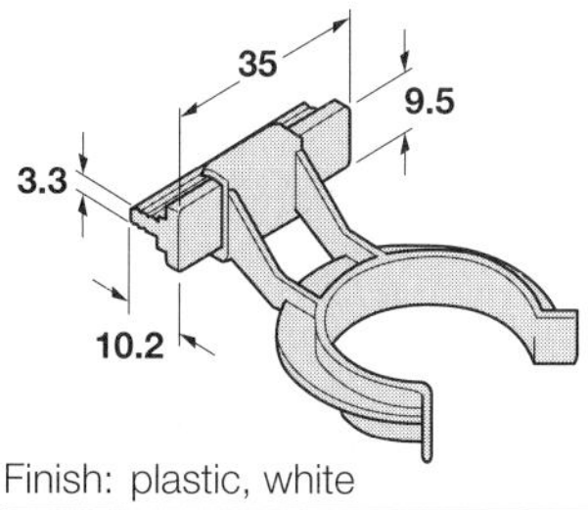

Finish: plastic, white

Cat. No.	637.39.051

Packing: 10 pcs.

Base Clip, 2-part
Screw-mounted to base panel

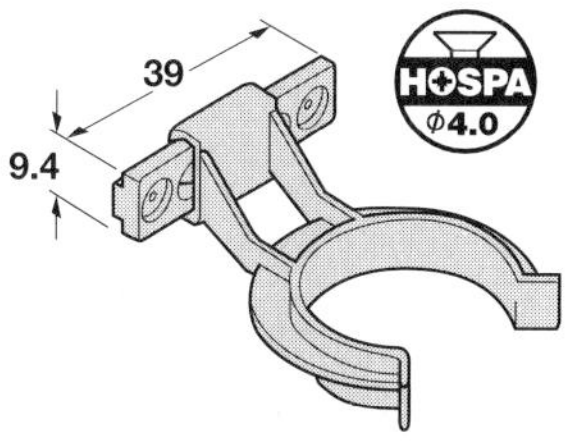

Finish: plastic, white

Cat. No.	637.39.060

Packing: 10 pcs.

Base Drawer Retainer, suitable for use together with the base adjusting foot for **150 mm** high base.

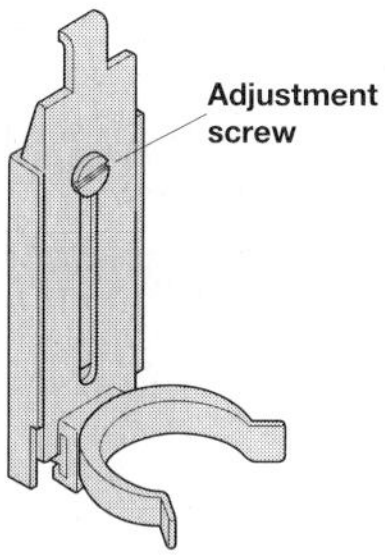

Finish: zinc alloy, clip: plastic, white

Cat. No.	637.39.097

Packing: 10 pcs.

Furniture Support Systems, Office and Computer Furniture Accessories

6

Base Panel Clip
Provides for installation of **13 mm** or **16 mm** thick base panels

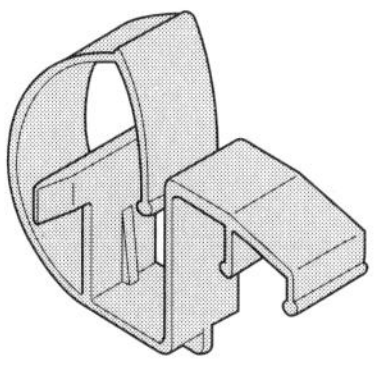

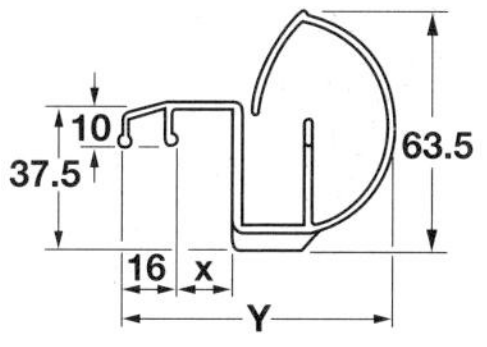

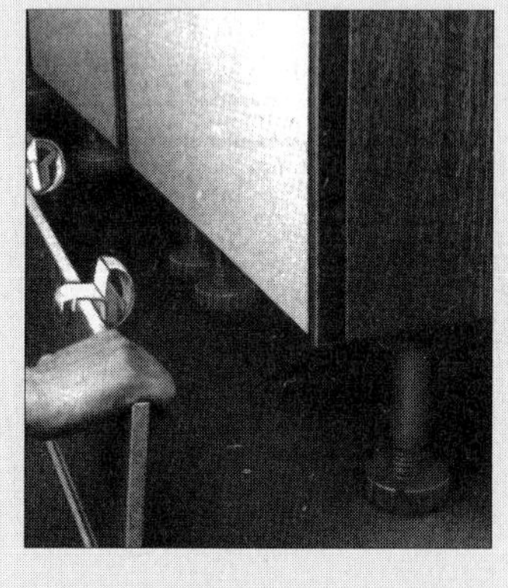

Finish: plastic, white

Wood thickness	Cat. No.
13 mm	637.30.015
16 mm	637.39.024

Packing: 20 and 500 pcs.

Minimum height for base panel:
base height minus 20 mm
Maximum height for base panel:
base height minus 2 mm

Dimensional data not binding. We reserve the right to alter specifications without notice.

Dimensions in mm

HÄFELE

Base Cabinet Levelers

Upper section/glide and shaft installed separately.

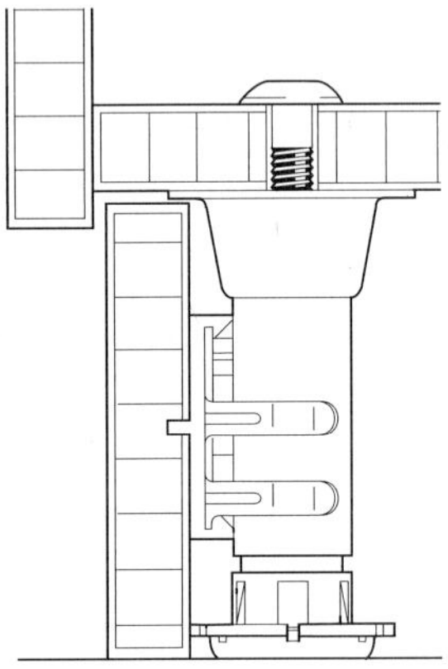
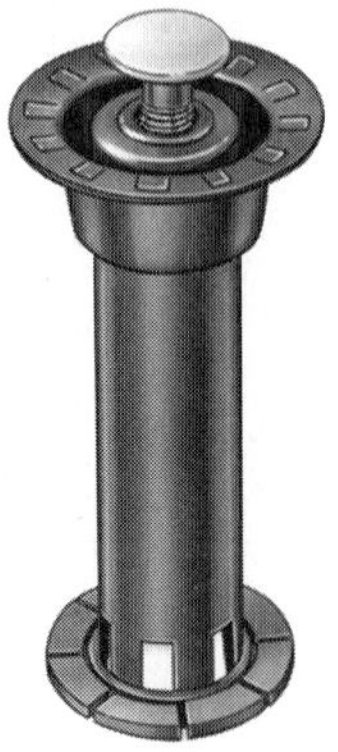

Adjuster 2-part
Finish: steel, zinc-plated
M10 attachment screw with cap
Finish: plastic, white

Toekick height	Cat. No.
100-120 mm	637.19.219
120-140 mm	637.19.228
150-170 mm	637.19.237

Packing: 20 pcs.

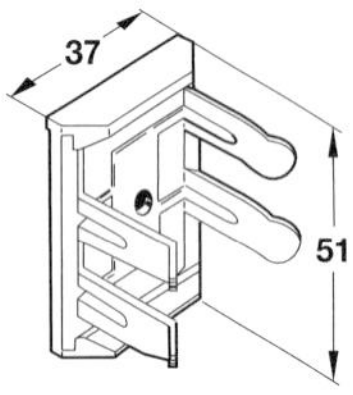

Panel Clip, 2 part screw mounted to toekick panel with steel spring
Finish: plastic, black

Cat. No.	637.19.906

Packing: 20 pcs.

Attachment options:
3 Hospa screws can be used in place of M10 screw.

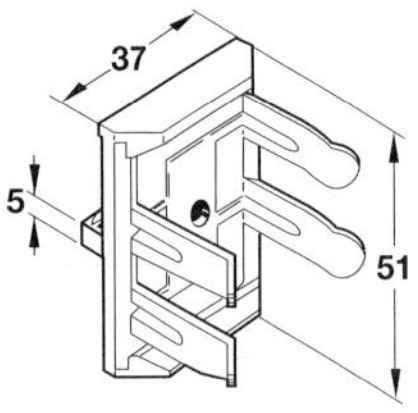

Panel Clip, 2 part groove mounted to toekick panel
Finish: plastic, black

Cat. No.	637.19.915

Packing: 20 pcs.

Cap
Finish: plastic, white

Cat. No.	637.45.791

Packing: 20 pcs.

Attachment Screw - M10
Finish: steel, zinc-plated

Cat. No.	637.45.997

Packing: 100 pcs.

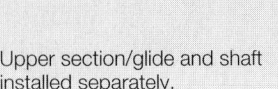

6 Furniture Support Systems, Office and Computer Furniture Accessories

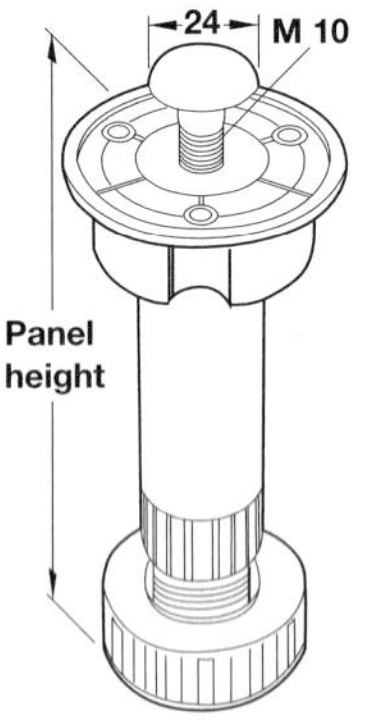

Adjuster 2-part
Finish: plastic, black

Toekick height	Adj. range	Cat. No.
80	-5 + 10	637.45.308
100	-5 + 10	637.45.326
120	-5 + 10	637.45.344
150	-5 + 10	637.45.371

Packing: 100 pcs.

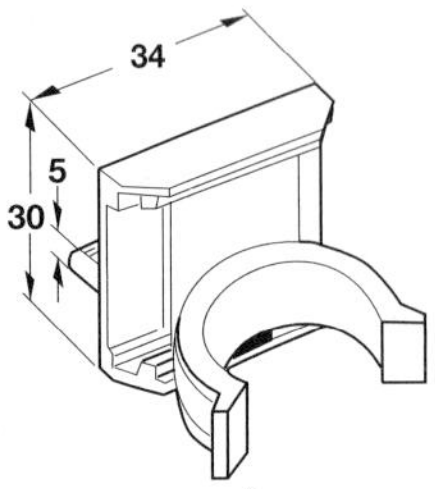

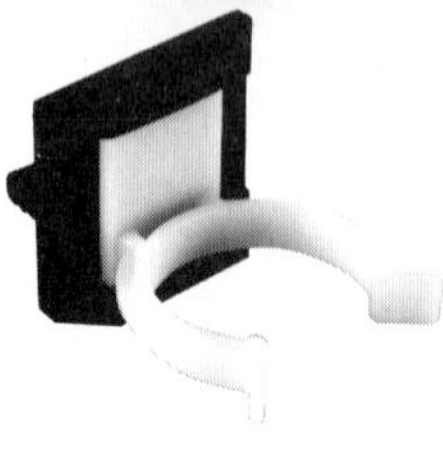

Panel Clip, 2-part
groove-mounted to toekick panel
Finish: plastic, black

Cat. No.	637.45.915

Packing: 100 pcs.

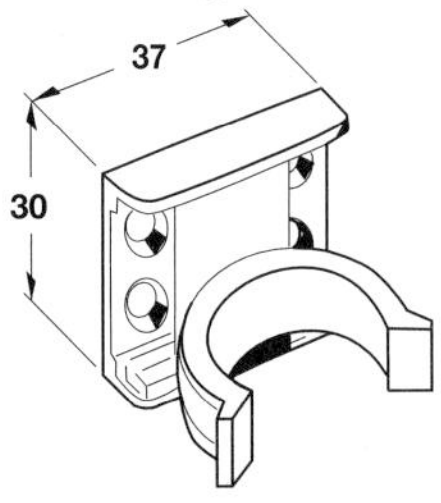

Panel Clip, 2-part
screw-mounted to toekick panel
Finish: plastic, black

Cat. No.	637.45.906

Packing: 100 pcs.

Dimensions in mm

Dimensional data not binding. We reserve the right to alter specifications without notice.

Furniture Support Fittings

HÄFELE

Angle fitting

Finish: steel, nickel-plated

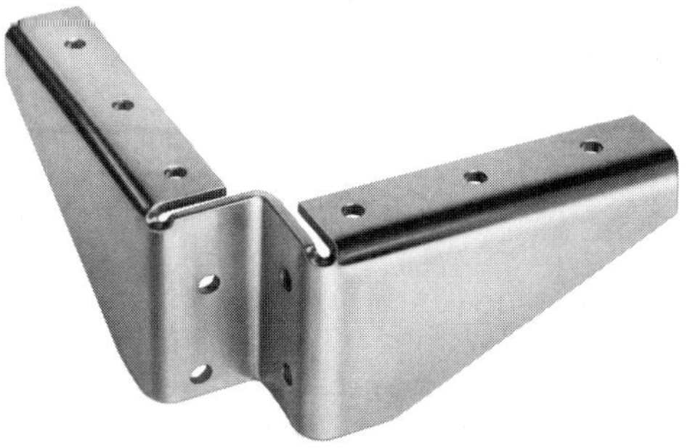

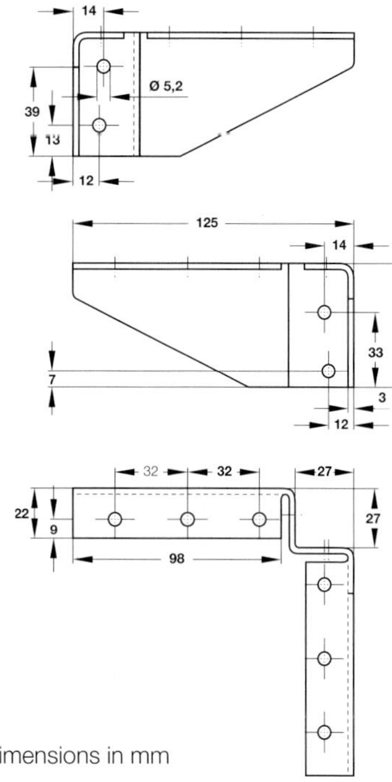

HOSPA Φ5,0

SYSTEM VARIANTA 32

Cat. No.	641.01.720

Packing: 20 pcs.

Dimensions in mm

Angle fitting

with additional side holes for screw-mounting to apron.
Finish: steel, nickel-plated

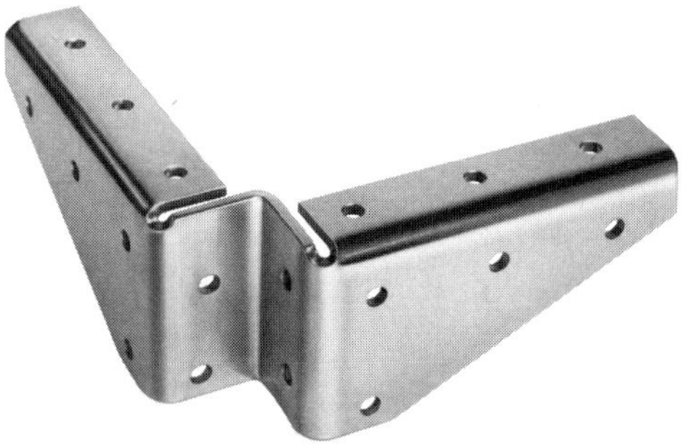

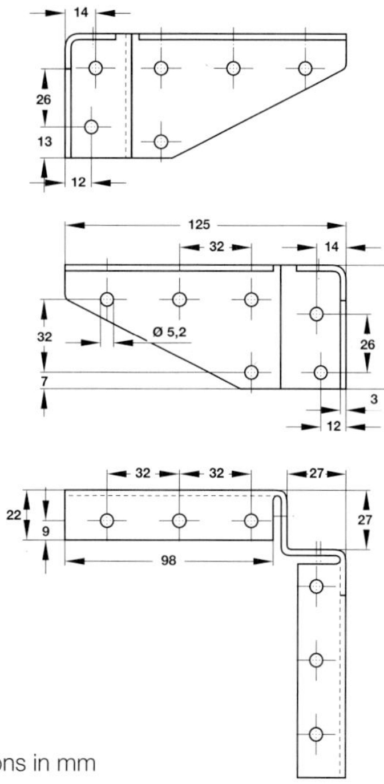

HOSPA Φ5,0

SYSTEM VARIANTA 32

Cat. No.	641.01.711

Packing: 20 pcs.

Dimensions in mm

Corner Brace

For simple and economical attachment of table legs to frame.
The ends of the brace are set into grooves in the frame.
The table leg is secured using the center hole.

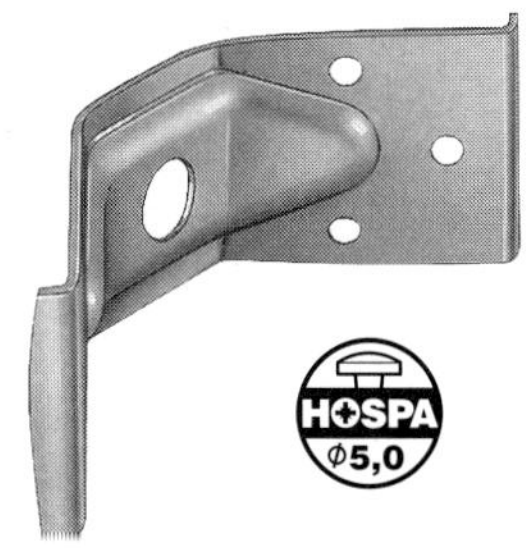

HOSPA Φ5,0

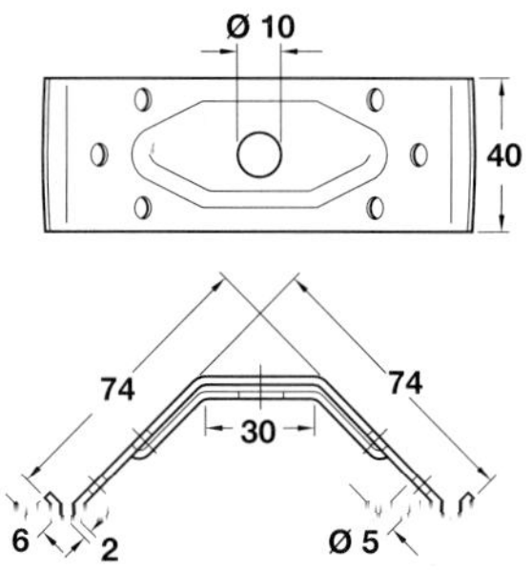

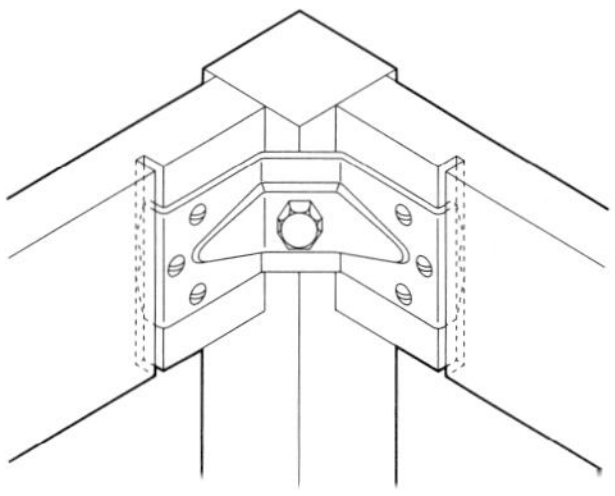

Finish: steel, galvanized

Cat. No.	641.00.901

Packing: 250 pcs.

Dimensions in mm

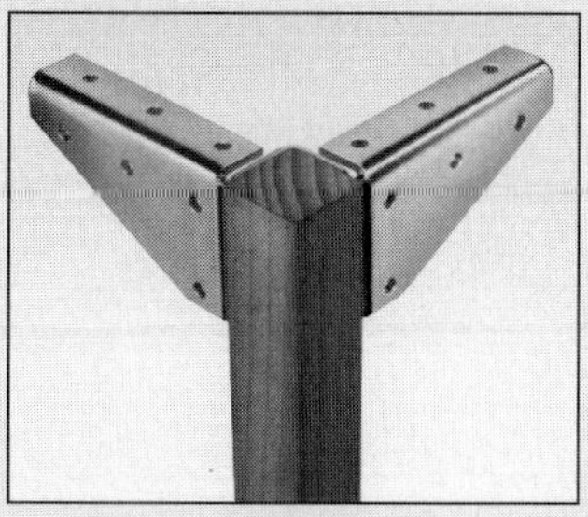

Angle fittings for sturdy corner connections on all types of tables, frames, cabinets, work benches, shelving, mobile tables, etc.

Advantages:
- Knee space under the tabletop for tables without enclosing frames
- Application with wood, metal, plastic

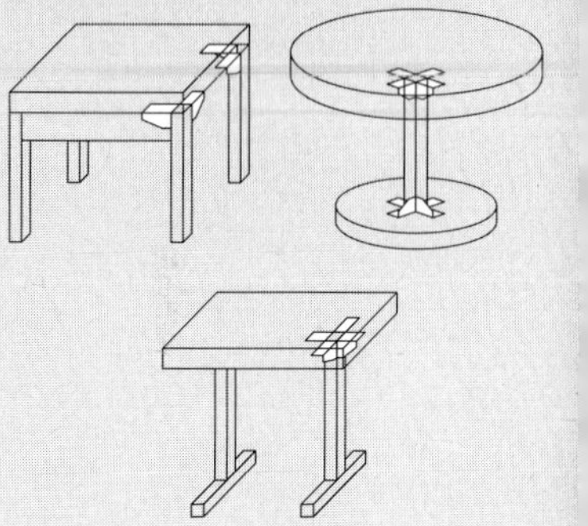

Furniture Support Systems, Office and Computer Furniture Accessories **6**

Table designed to make use of corner braces can be stored, packed and transported in RTA form.

Dimensional data not binding. We reserve the right to alter specifications without notice.

HÄFELE

"Click Catch" Table Connector

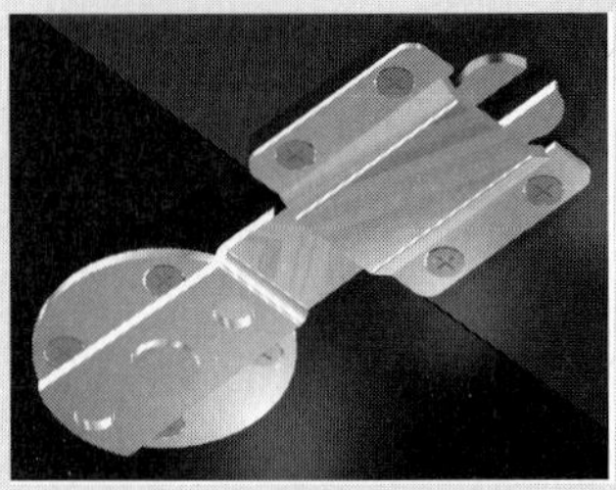

For joining free-standing tables or table leaves

1 Complete Set = 1 male and 1 female piece.

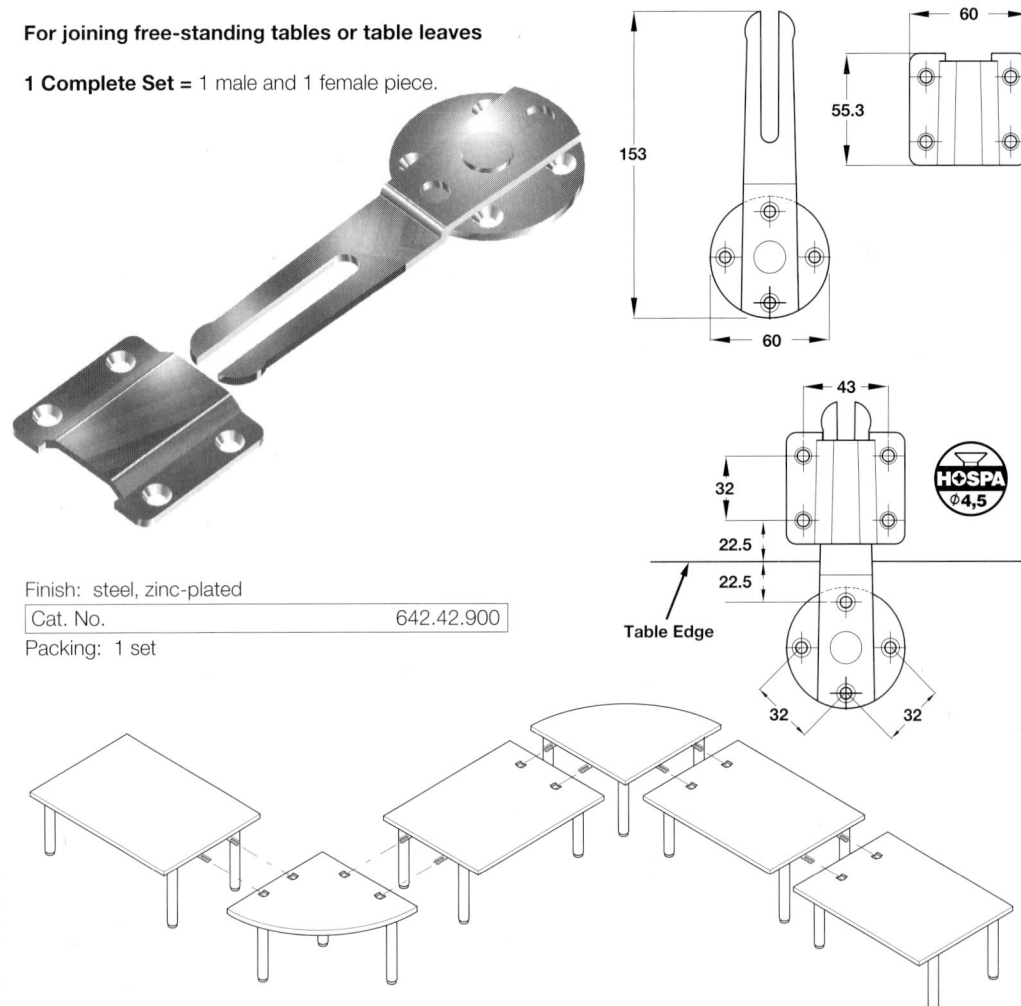

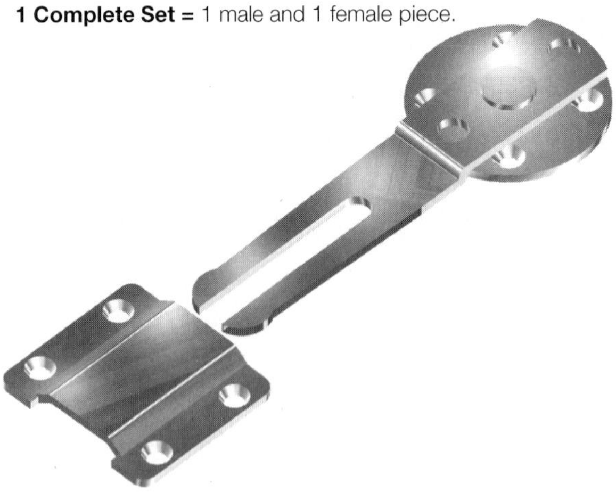

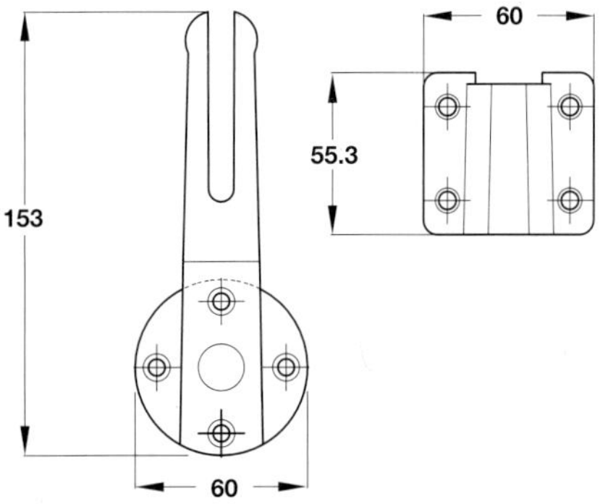

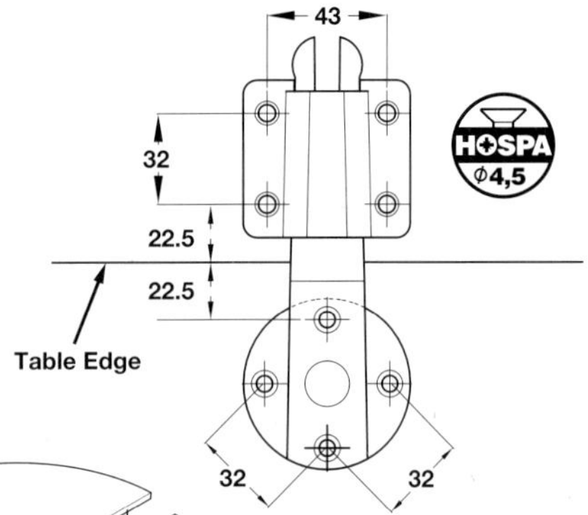

- Simply clicks together. No tool required for tightening.
- Extremely thin design. Does not interfere with leg movement.

Finish: steel, zinc-plated

Cat. No.	642.42.900

Packing: 1 set

- Male portion rotates 360° with stops every 90°.
- Completely concealed under table top.

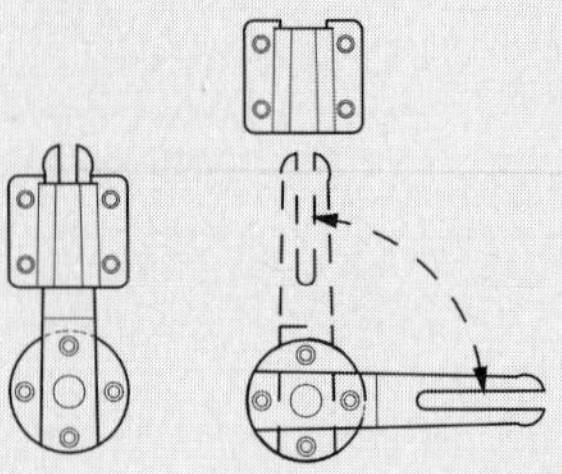

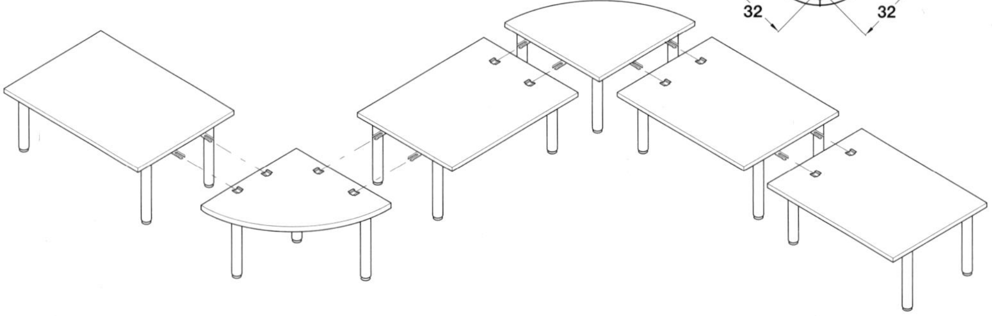

Ganging Device Connector

Flat Connector

With attachment plate for horizontal mounting.

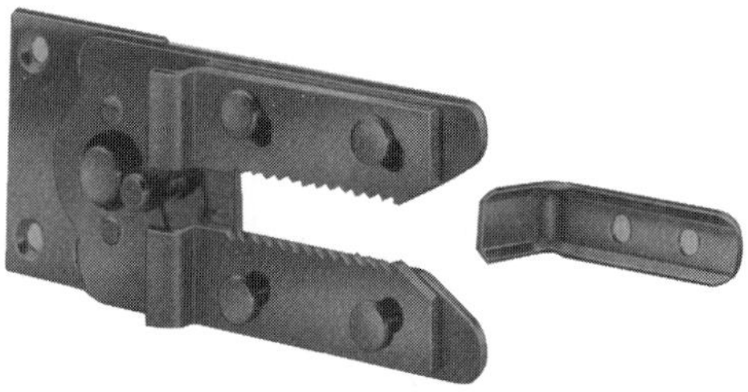

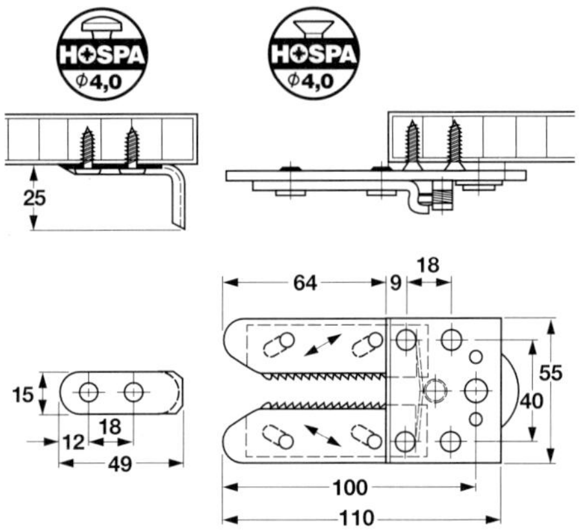

Finish: steel, zinc-plated

Cat. No.	635.88.910

Packing: 10 pcs.

Angle Connector

For vertical attachment on side.

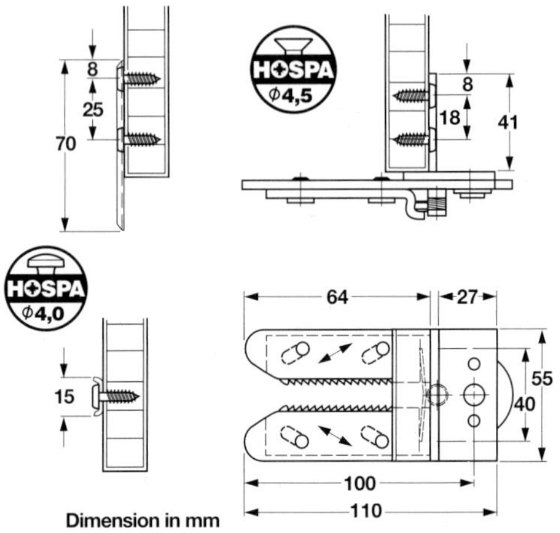

Finish: steel, zinc-plated

Cat. No.	635.89.917

Packing: 10 pcs.

Dimension in mm

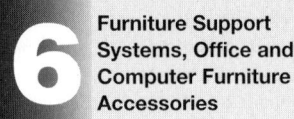

6 **Furniture Support Systems, Office and Computer Furniture Accessories**

This hardware is used to connect modular upholstered furniture to form seating rows or groups. The hardware is easily connected to the bottom of the upholstered pieces and connects to the corresponding angle bracket. When not in use the device can be pivoted under the upholstery pieces. Specify flat or angle mounting.

Dimensional data not binding. We reserve the right to alter specifications without notice.

Accessories for Extending Tables

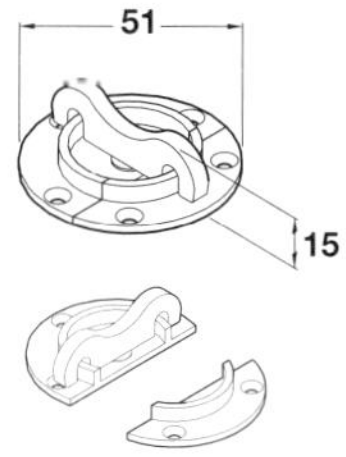

Round Table Catch – Small
Screw-mounted to underside of table top, joins table top panels together.

Finish: brass

Cat. No.	642.39.818

Packing: 1 pc.

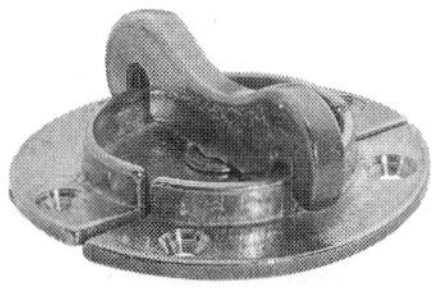
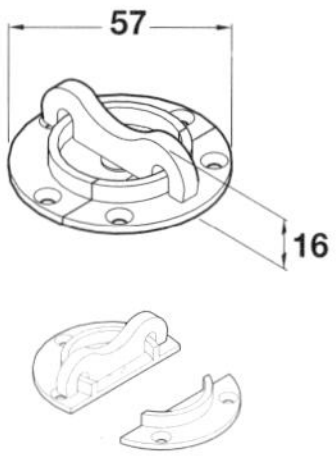

Round Table Catch – Large
Screw-mounted to underside of table top, joins table top panels together.

Finish: brass

Cat. No.	642.39.827

Packing: 1 pc.

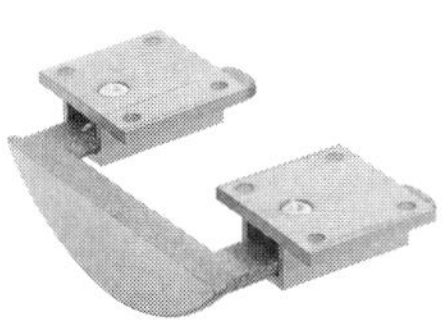
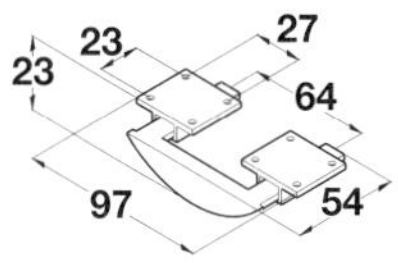

Table Fork
Attachment underneath table top to join two separate sections firmly together.

Finish: brass

Cat. No.	642.38.802

Packing: 1 pc.

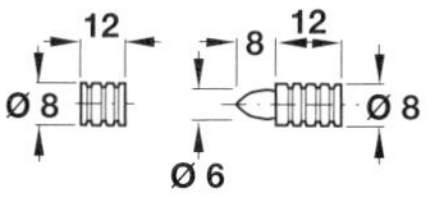

Peg and sleeve connector
Pressed into holes Ø 8 mm
Finish: steel, yellow chromated

Cat. No.	642.51.243

Packing: 100 pcs.

HOSPA Φ3,0
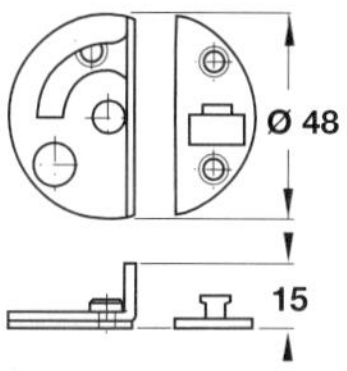

Swivel bolt
Recessed or screw-mounted underneath the table top, joins the leaves together
Finish: steel, zinc-plated

Cat. No.	642.48.924

Packing: 100 pcs.

HOSPA Φ3,0
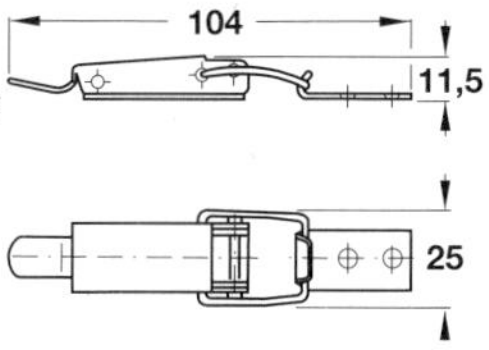

Spring clips
Screw-mounted underneath the table top
Finish: steel, zinc-plated

Cat. No.	380.52.925

Packing: 100 pcs.

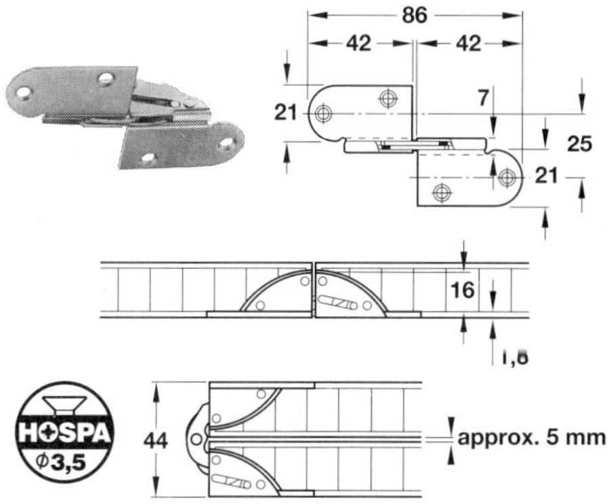

HOSPA Φ3,5

Folding table hinges – recessed
Finish: steel, yellow chromated

Table top thick-ness	Recess Depth	Hinge Size length x width	Cat. No.
19mm	16	85x47	341.30.508
22mm	19	85x51	341.30.526

Packing: 100 pcs.

Furniture Support Systems, Office and Computer Furniture Accessories 6

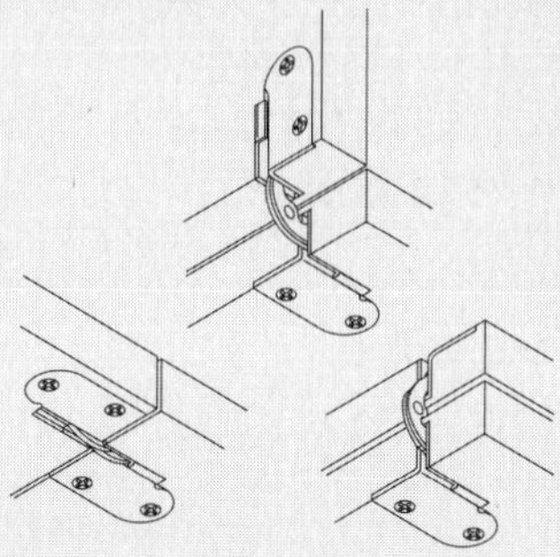

Hinges for other table top thickness are shown on page 3.148.

Dimensional data not binding. We reserve the right to alter specifications without notice.

Dimensions in mm

HÄFELE

Folding Table Fittings

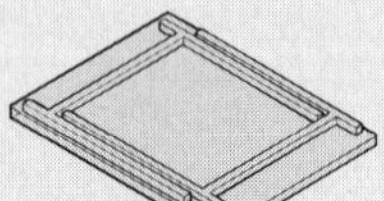

- The sides are folded by pressing the hinged strut. The mechanism effectively prevents play in the locking fitting.
- When folded, the sides are held securely in place by the locking springs.
- The erect table is protected from inadvertent folding by the safety catches of the retaining springs, which press the hinged strut firmly into the locating groove of the locking feature.

Folding table fitting, H-type legs
Square steel tube, 30 x 30 x 1.5 mm
Legs with plastic end caps.
Hinged struts lock in position, both open and closed.

Minimum table top length:	950 mm	(37 1/2")
Leg width:	610 mm	(24")
Leg height:	720 mm	(28 3/8")
Table top thickness:	40 mm	(1 1/2")

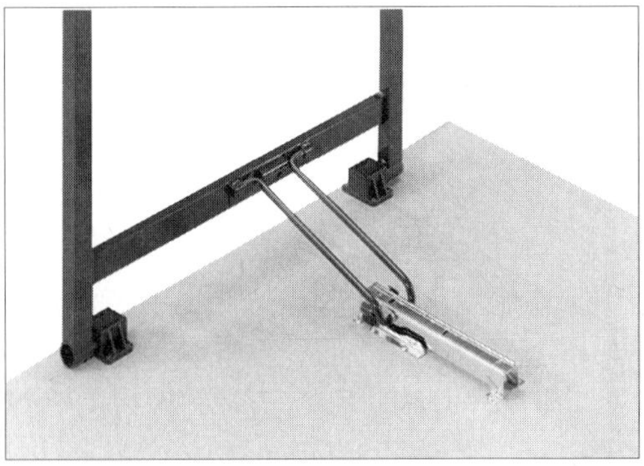

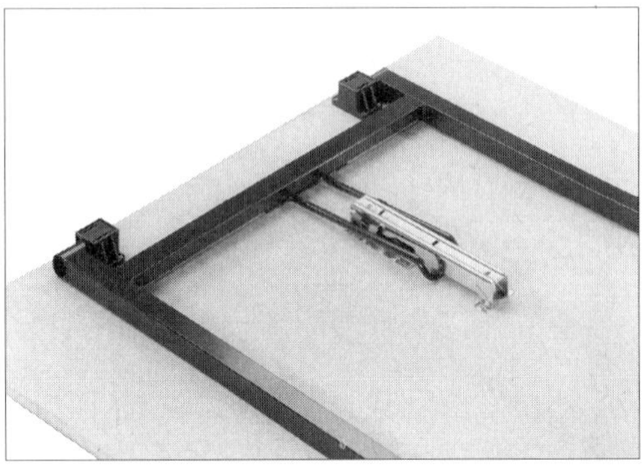

Finish:
steel, brown RAL 8014,
Epoxy coated
Latch and release fitting: Steel, zinc-plated
Pivot fitting: PVC, brown RAL 8019

Cat. No.	642.83.101

Packing: 1 set

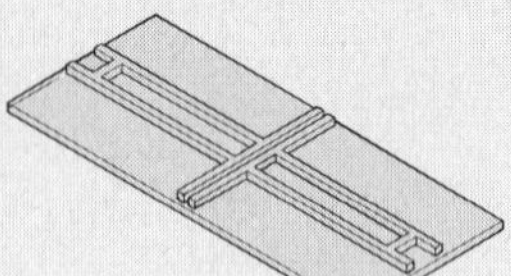

Folding table fitting, T-type legs
Square steel tube, 30 x 30 x 1.5 mm
Feet with glides.
Hinged struts lock in position, both opened and closed.

Minimum table length:	1530 mm	(51 1/4")
Leg width:	610 mm	(24")
Leg height:	720 mm	(28 3/8")
Table top thickness:	40 mm	(1 1/2")

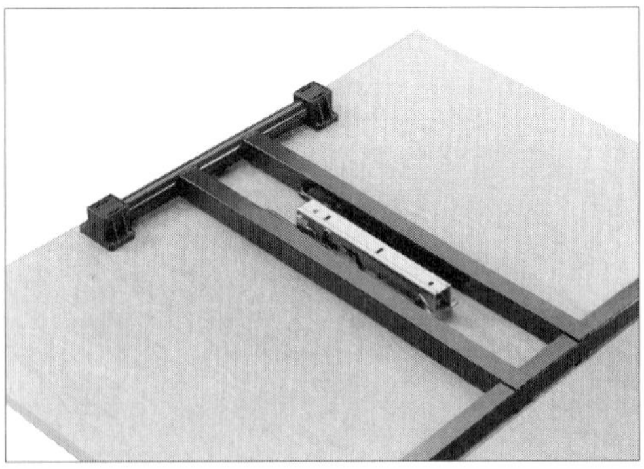

Finish:
steel, brown RAL 8014, epoxy coated
Latch and release fitting: Steel, zinc-plated
Pivot fitting: PVC, brown RAL 8019

Cat. No.	642.84.108

Packing: 1 set

6 Furniture Support Systems, Office and Computer Furniture Accessories

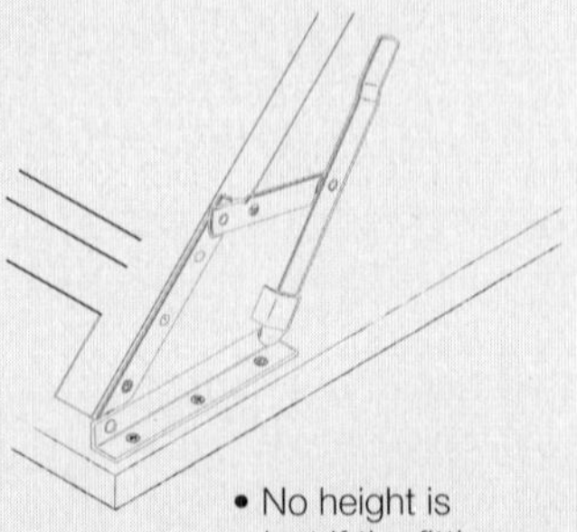

- No height is lost if the fitting is mounted on the side of the table leg.

Folding fitting for tables and benches
for 38 x 38 mm legs
Locks in position, open and closed

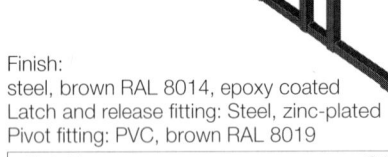

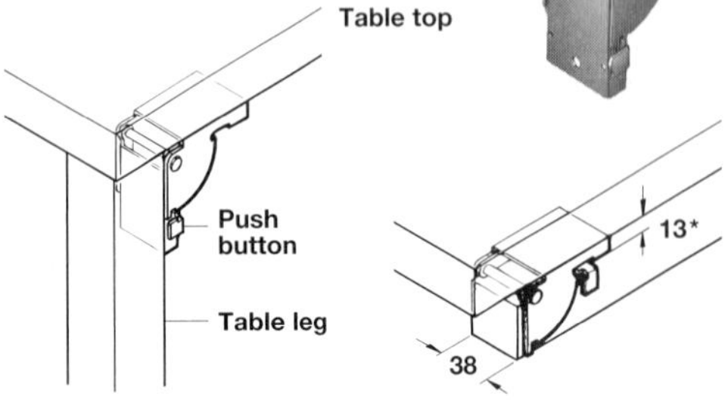

* **Installation height of folded fitting**

Finish: steel, galvanized

Cat. No.	642.90.919

Packing: 50 pair

Folding bracket for tables and benches
L-steel support 25 x 25 x 3 mm
Supporting arm length 200 mm

HOSPA Φ4,5

Dimensions in mm

Finish: steel, black lacquered

Cat. No.	642.81.300

Packing: 1 pair

Dimensional data not binding. We reserve the right to alter specifications without notice.

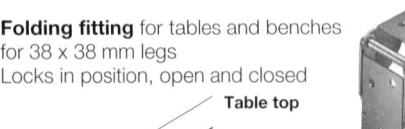

Drop-Leaf Table Fitting

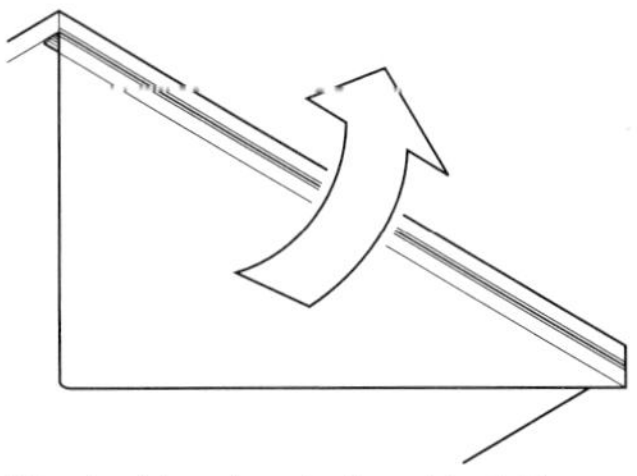

The leaf is retracted and held in place by the ball catch.

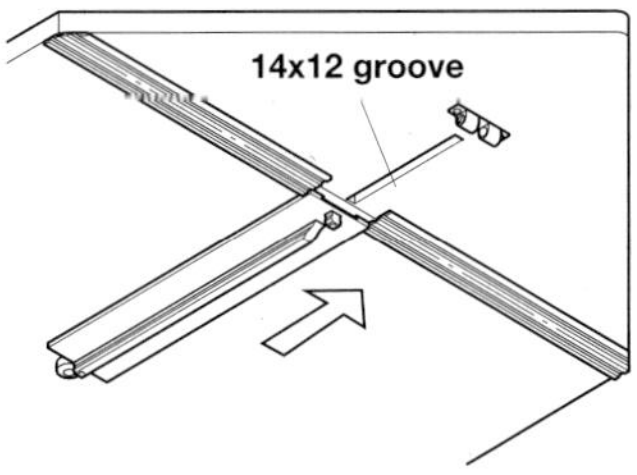

The leaf is extended. The sliding support must also be extended.

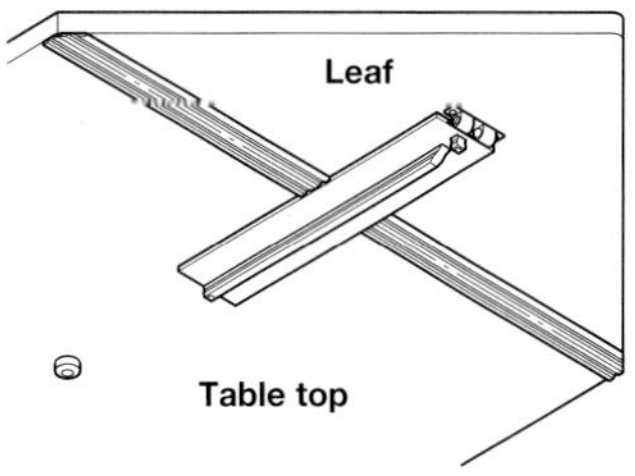

The table top rests on the extended sliding support.

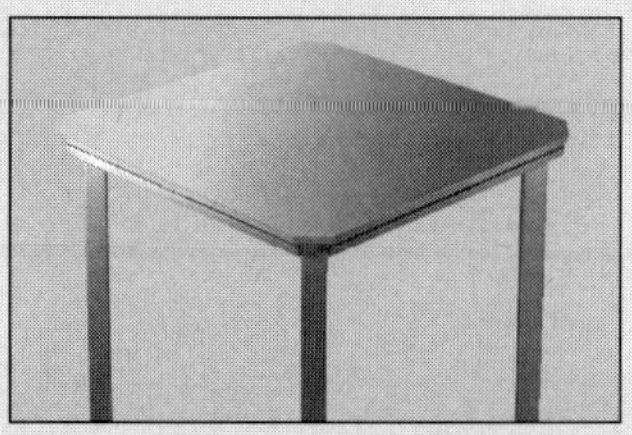

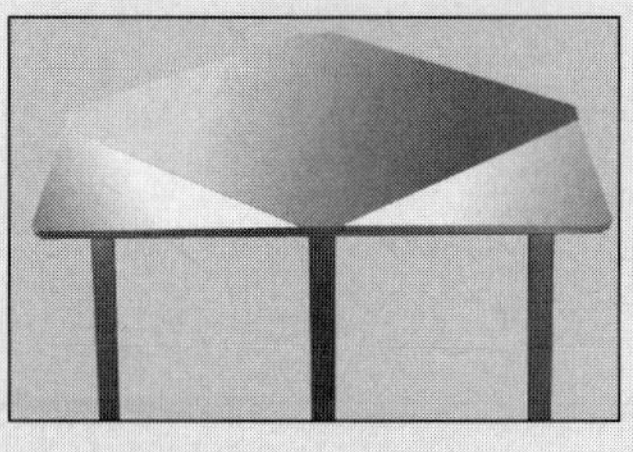

The table can be enlarged and modified.

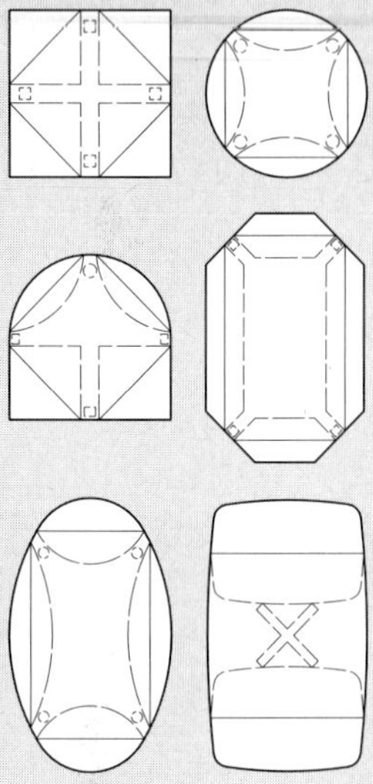

Drop-leaf table fitting
consist of:
1 sliding support, 360 mm long
Finish: aluminum, silver anodized
1 guide profile, 180 mm long
Finish: aluminum, silver anodized
2 flexible hinges, each 500 mm long
Finish: plastic, natural-colored
1 double ball catch, unfinished brass
1 stop buffer, rubber

Cat. No.	642.40.008

Packing: 1 set

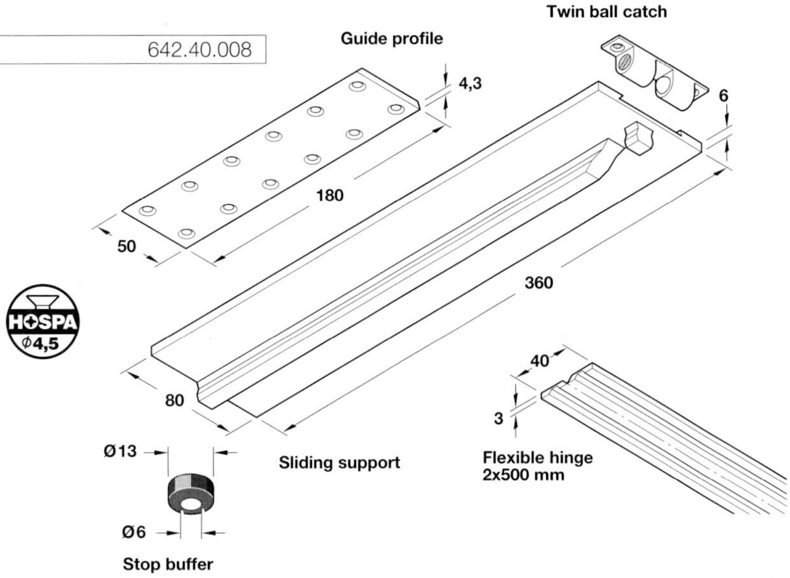

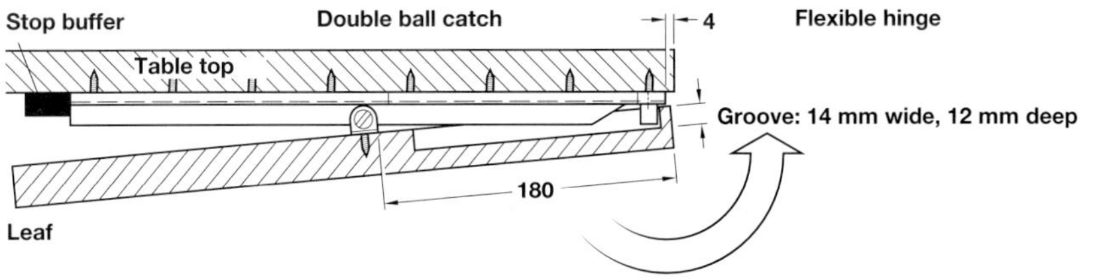

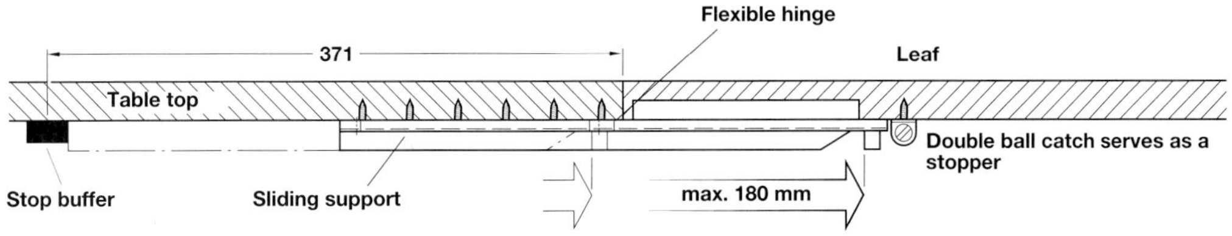

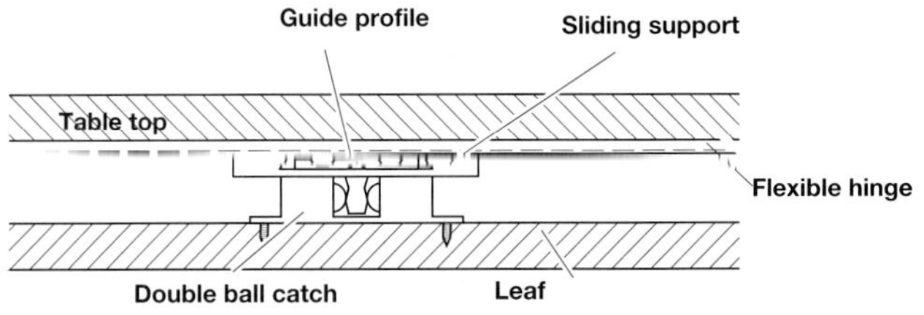

Furniture Support Systems, Office and Computer Furniture Accessories **6**

Possible table edge profiles

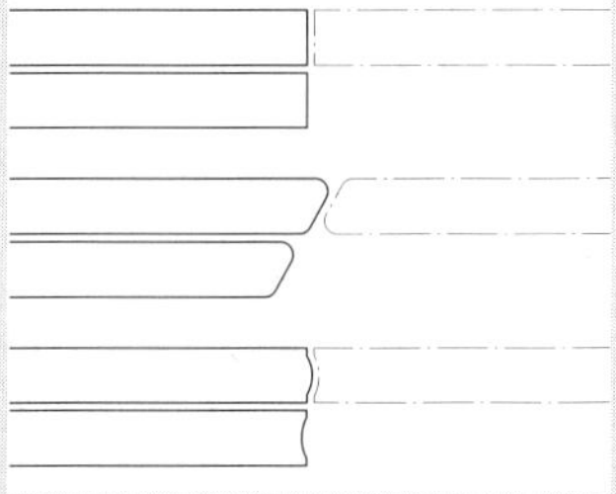

Dimensional data not binding. We reserve the right to alter specifications without notice.

HÄFELE

Table Legs

Rondella Table Legs, with adjustable foot. Secured to underside of table top with mounting plates. Adjustment range: +20 mm

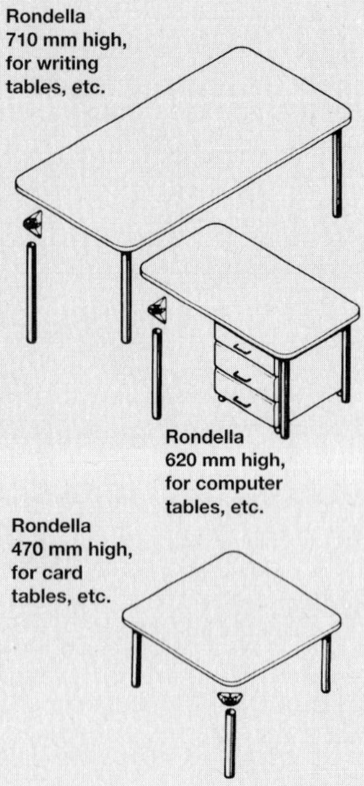

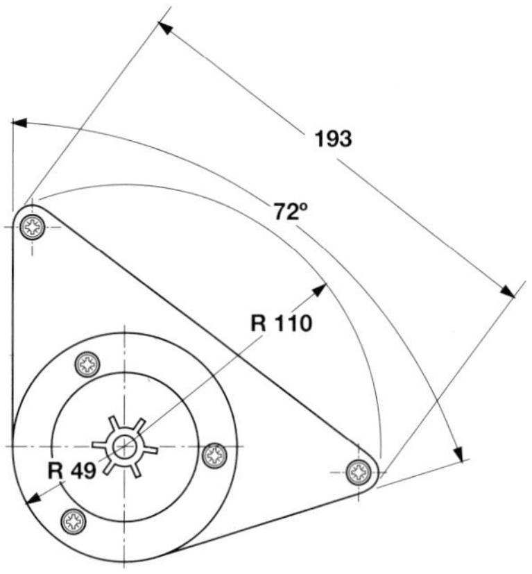

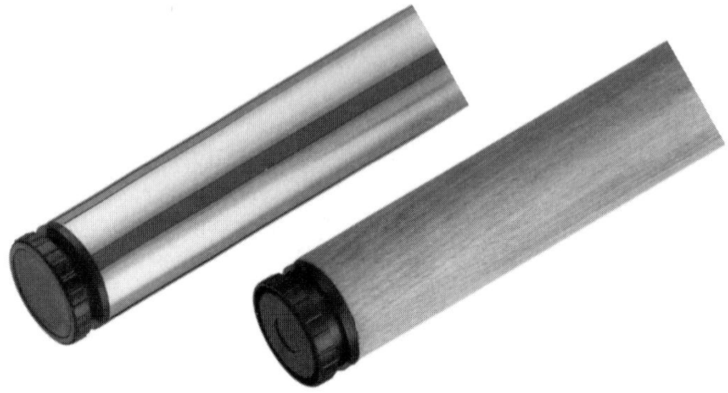

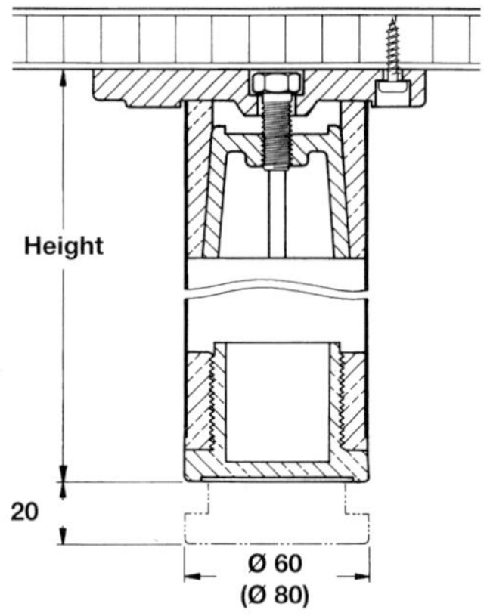

Finish: steel tube, electro-plated, with black plastic foot, zinc die-cast mounting plate.

	Diameter	Height	Finish	
Cat. No.	60 mm	470 mm	chrome	635.06.249
	60 mm	620 mm	chrome	635.06.267
	60 mm	710 mm	raw	635.06.070
	60 mm	710 mm	chrome	635.06.276
	60 mm	710 mm	satin, steel	635.11.071
	60 mm	710 mm	gray, metallic	635.11.571
	60 mm	710 mm	oak, unfinished	635.06.472
	60 mm	710 mm	white, gloss	635.06.776
	60 mm	710 mm	brass, bright	635.06.874
	60 mm	710 mm	black, gloss	635.06.374
	60 mm	710 mm	black, matt	635.11.375
	80 mm	710 mm	chrome	635.07.273
	80 mm	710 mm	white, gloss	635.07.773
	80 mm	710 mm	black, matt	635.12.372

Packing: 1 set (4 legs and mounting plates.)

Table Legs

Rondella Table Leg, with locking caster.
Secured to underside of table top with mounting plate.
Dynamic weight rating: 150 kg

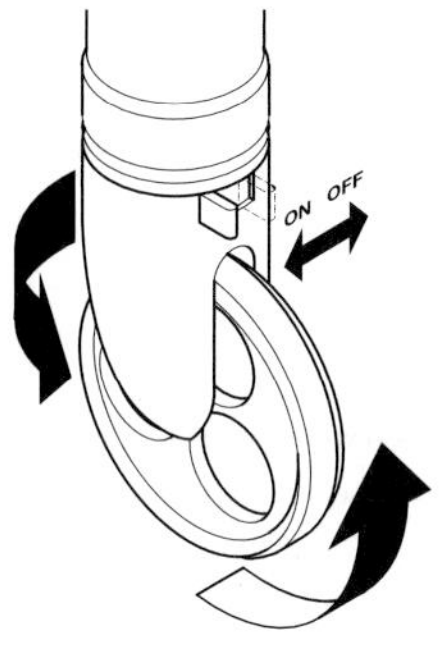

Lock secures wheel in both rotation and swivel.

Finish: steel tube, epoxy powder-coated, black plastic rubberized wheel, zinc die-cast mounting plate.

	Diameter	Height	Finish	
Cat. No.	60 mm	710 mm	black matt	635.16.370

Packing: 1 pcs.

Rondella Table Leg with Locking Caster
- Provides elegant mobility to your tables.
- Unique locking mechanism secures wheel in both rotation and swivel.
- Rubberized surface on wheel insures a quiet and smooth operation.

Modesty panel clips for Ø 60 mm legs. Allows a modesty panel to be easily attached to a Ø 60 mm leg.

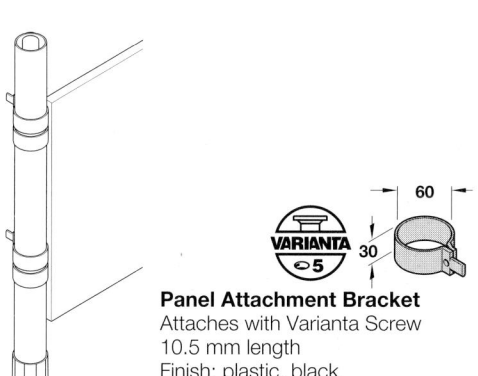

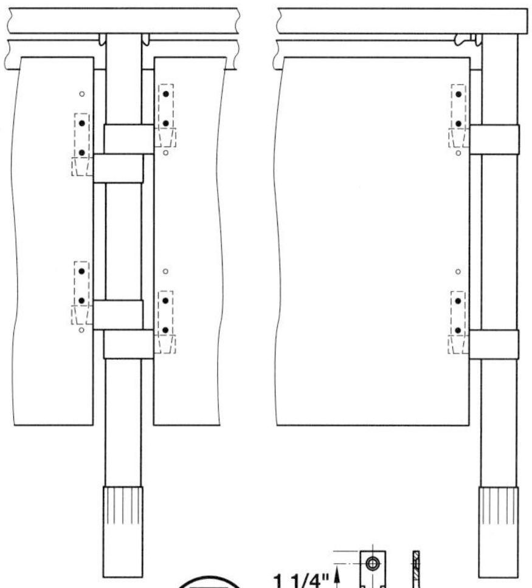

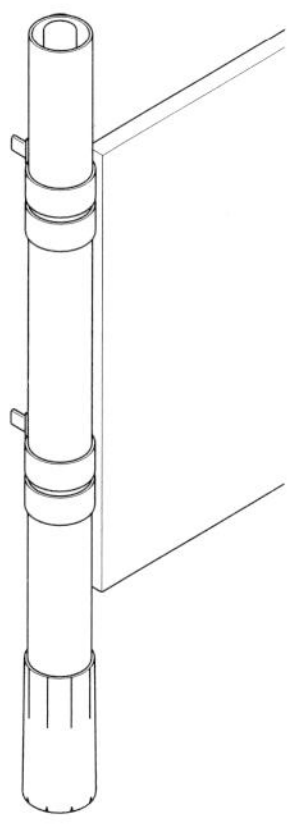

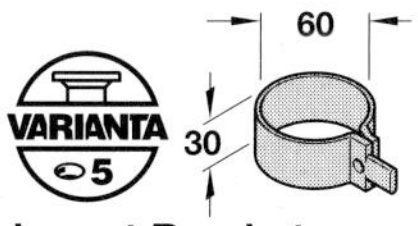

Panel Attachment Bracket
Attaches with Varianta Screw
10.5 mm length
Finish: plastic, black

Cat. No.	654.34.390

Packing: 16 pcs.

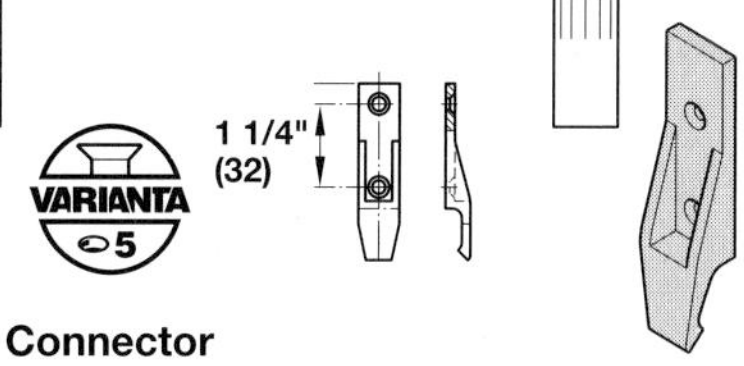

Keku Panel Connector
Finish: plastic, black

Cat. No.	262.49.357

Packing: 200 pcs.

Furniture Support Systems, Office and Computer Furniture Accessories

6

Recommended Modesty Panel Height 15 3/4"

Table Length	Distance A
36"	**29 3/8"**
42"	**35 3/8"**
48"	**41 3/8"**
54"	**47 3/8"**
60"	**51 3/8"**
66"	**59 3/8"**
72"	**66 3/8"**

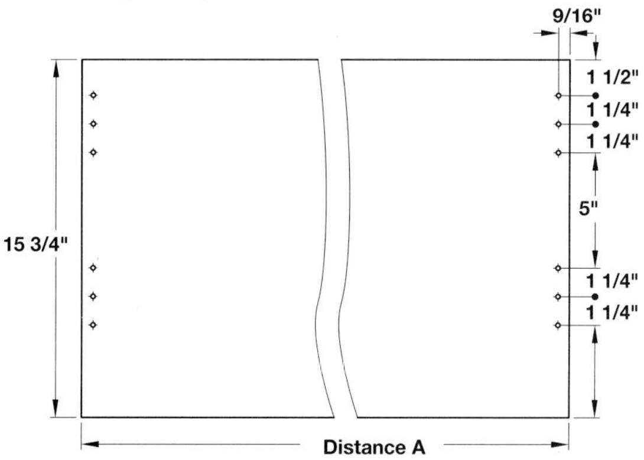

Dimensional data not binding.
We reserve the right to alter specifications without notice.

Dimensions in mm

HÄFELE

Idea Table Support System

- Comes ready to assemble
- Numerous configuration options possible.
- 6" Module provides flexible application of various top sizes
- Speedy assembly and disassembly, e.g. 36" x 72" table frame assembles in about 3 minutes.
- Meets DIN and most ergonomic requirements.
- Extremely stable. Low vibration characteristics.
- Not limited to just the office environment. Ideally suited to the home office as well.

The problems associated with table support systems that are welded or screwed together are well known: limitations caused by different types/models; lack of flexibility; high expense associated with packaging, shipping and assembly.

The Idea system meets the challenge for new, intelligent concepts to solve these problems. In addition, Idea protects the health of the users.

Idea is a modular system featuring individual components offering maximum flexibility and individual customization.

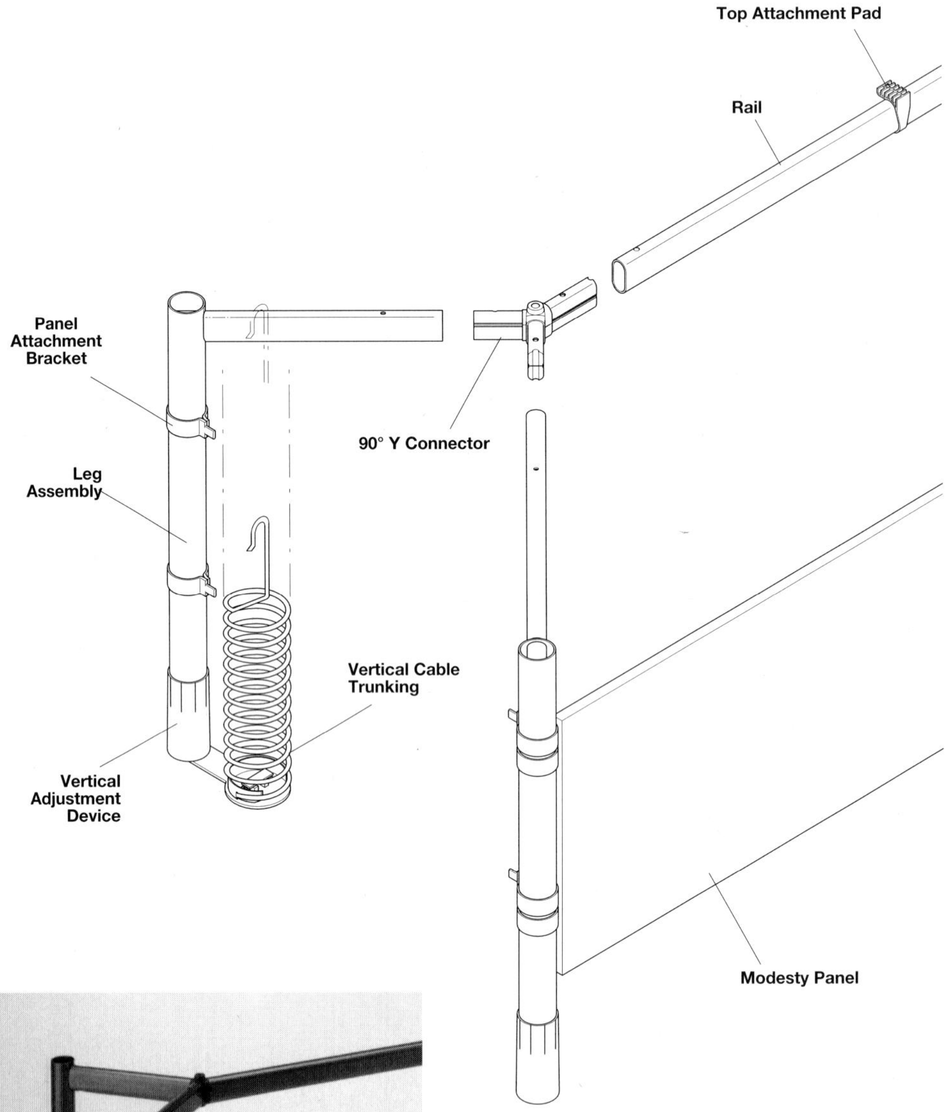

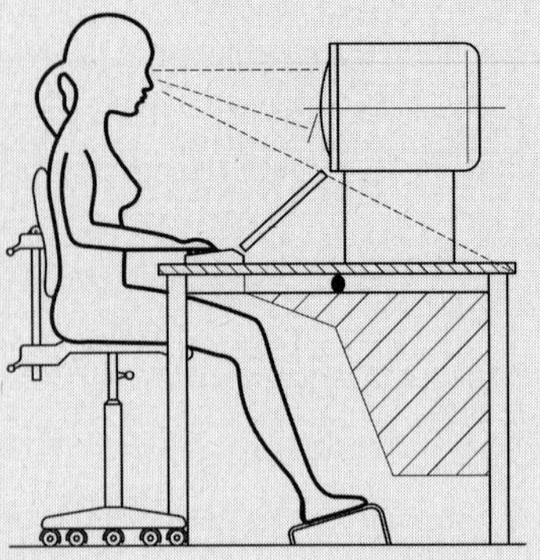

Idea-System designed by **IDE**Architects Ltd.

Dimensional data not binding. We reserve the right to alter specifications without notice.

Idea Table Support System

Based on a 6" module, individual components can be used to configure tables in a variety of ways, e.g. at a 90° angle or 45° angle.

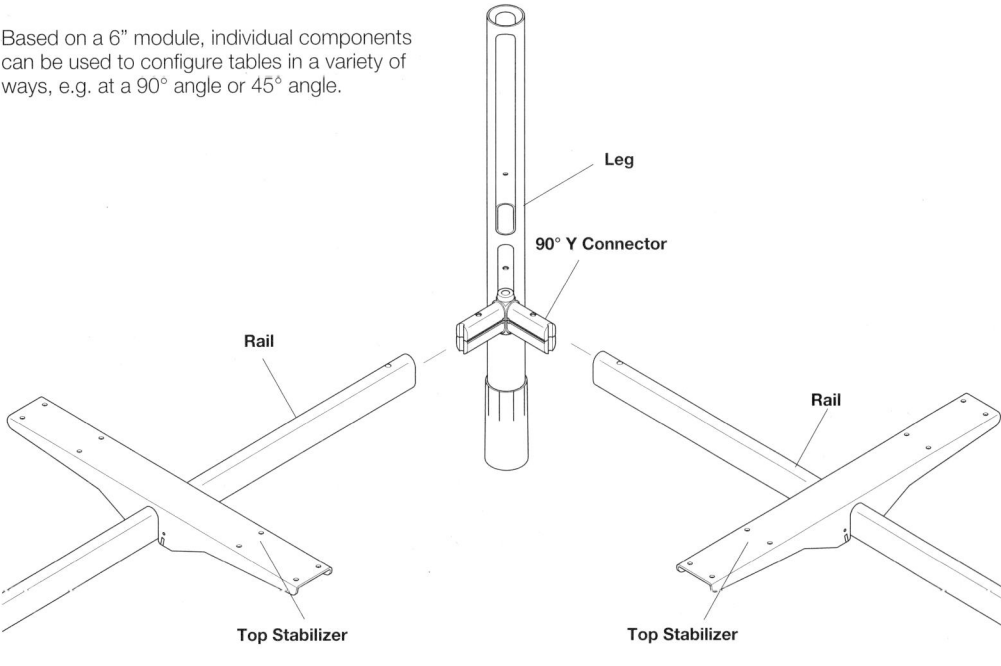

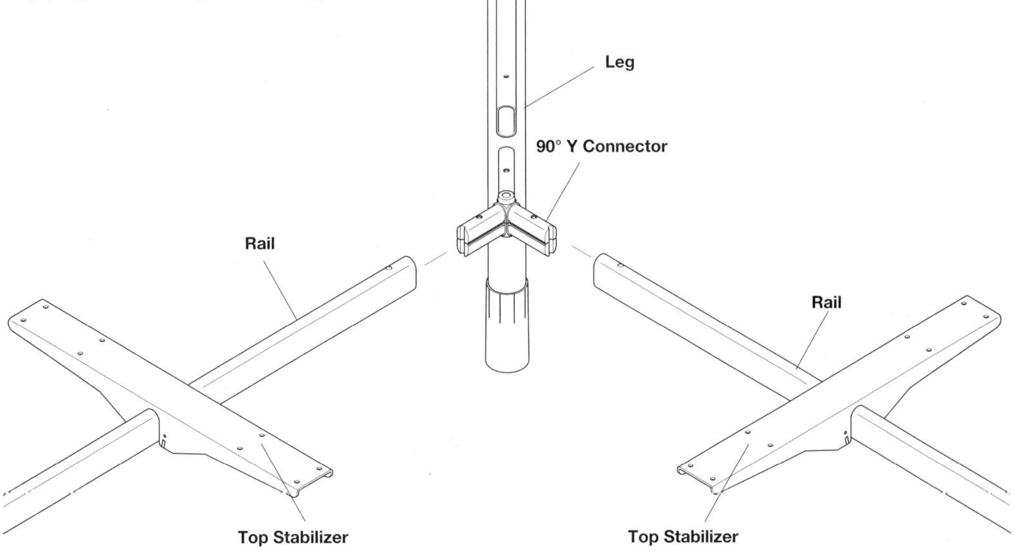

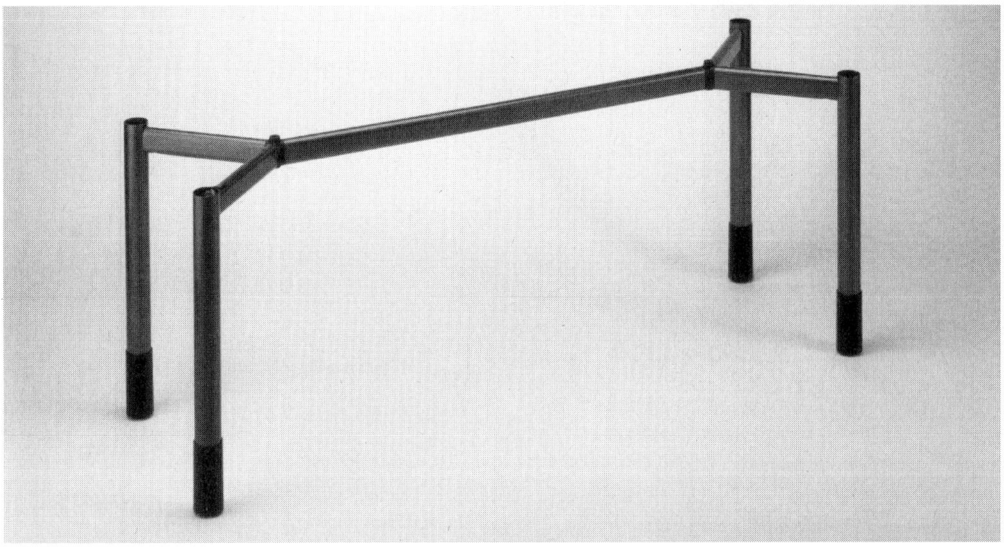

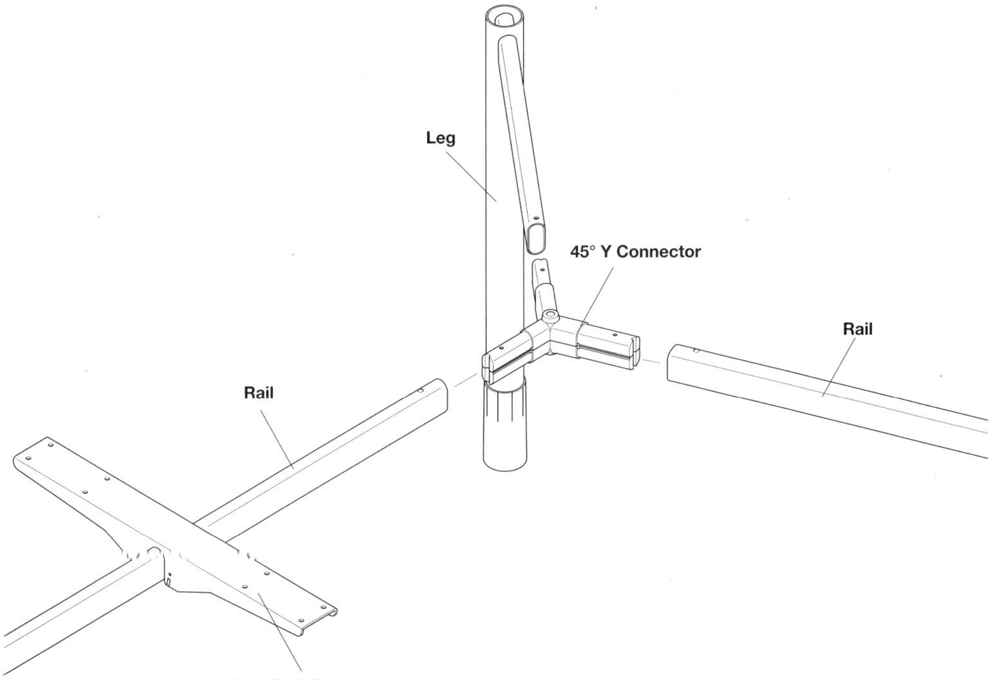

Dimensions in mm

HÄFELE

The Idea System. . .

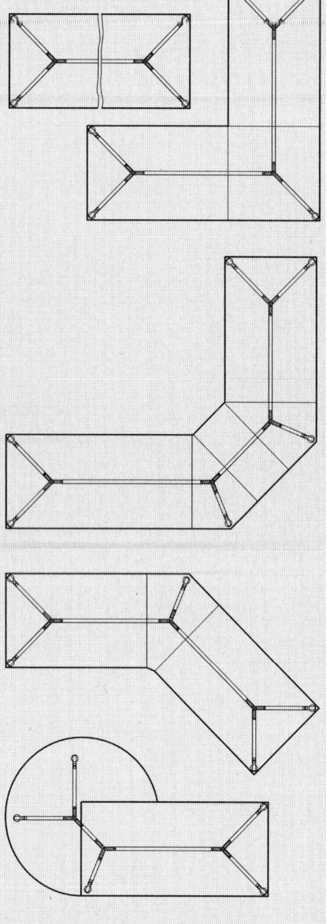

...offers many unique configuration possibilities.

HÄFELE

Idea Table Support System

Integrated Height Adjuster

- **Adjustment range 4¼" (110) mm, 26⅞"-30⅛" (683-765 mm)**
- Adjusts without tools. Screwdriver may be used to assist.
- Can be adjusted under load
- Each turn equivalent to .196" (5 mm) on the vertical scale
- Adjustment locks safely by use of clamp ring and tightening sleeve
- Base plate remains stationary during adjustment
- Stylish sleeve hides adjustment feature

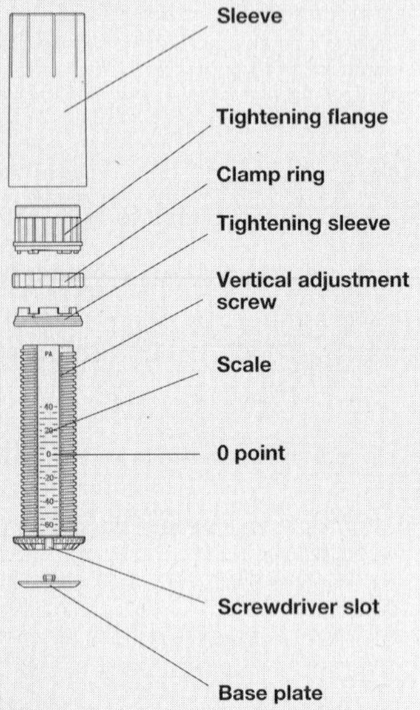

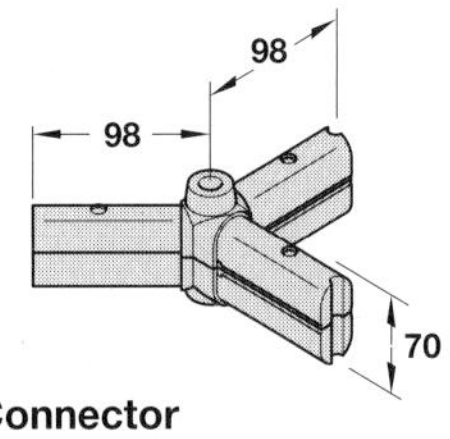

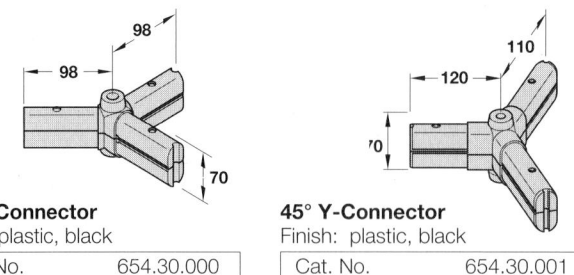

90° Y-Connector
Finish: plastic, black

Cat. No.	654.30.000

Packing: 1 pc.

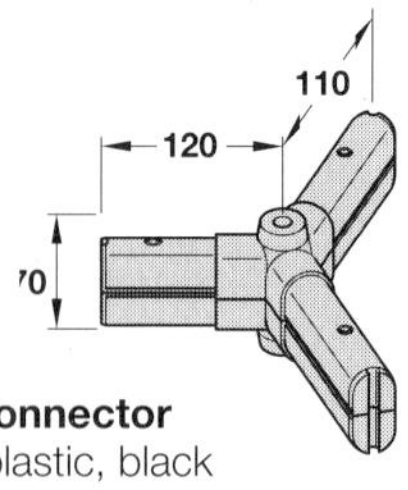

45° Y-Connector
Finish: plastic, black

Cat. No.	654.30.001

Packing: 1 pc.

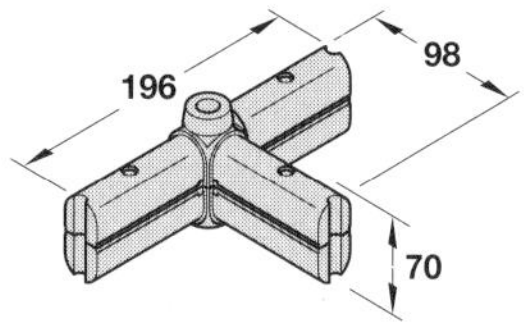

T-Connector
Finish: plastic, black

Cat. No.	654.30.020

Packing: 1 pc.

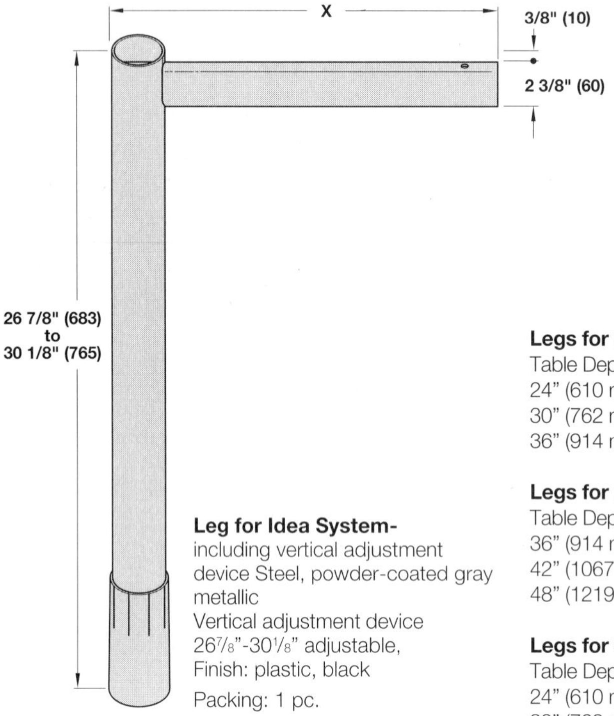

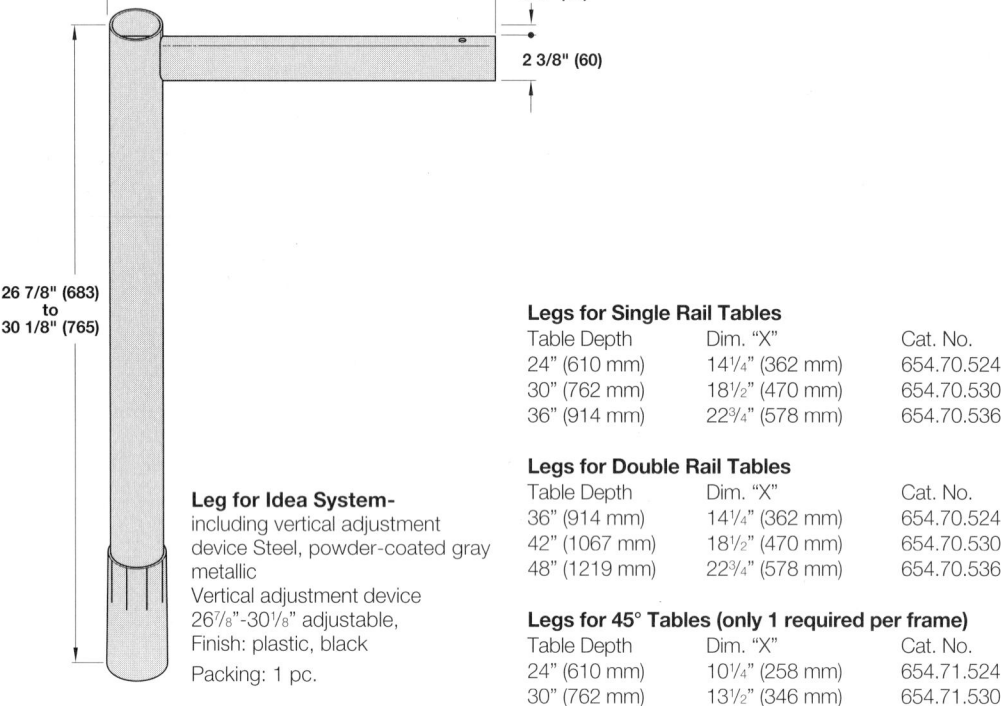

Leg for Idea System-
including vertical adjustment device Steel, powder-coated gray metallic
Vertical adjustment device 26⅞"-30⅛" adjustable,
Finish: plastic, black
Packing: 1 pc.

Legs for Single Rail Tables

Table Depth	Dim. "X"	Cat. No.
24" (610 mm)	14¼" (362 mm)	654.70.524
30" (762 mm)	18½" (470 mm)	654.70.530
36" (914 mm)	22¾" (578 mm)	654.70.536

Legs for Double Rail Tables

Table Depth	Dim. "X"	Cat. No.
36" (914 mm)	14¼" (362 mm)	654.70.524
42" (1067 mm)	18½" (470 mm)	654.70.530
48" (1219 mm)	22¾" (578 mm)	654.70.536

Legs for 45° Tables (only 1 required per frame)

Table Depth	Dim. "X"	Cat. No.
24" (610 mm)	10¼" (258 mm)	654.71.524
30" (762 mm)	13½" (346 mm)	654.71.530

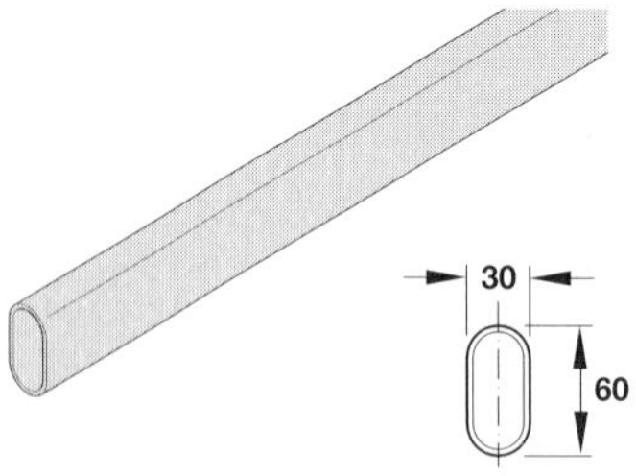

Rail
Finish: Steel, powder-coated gray metallic
Packing: 1 pc.
See table on next page for ordering

Idea Table Support System

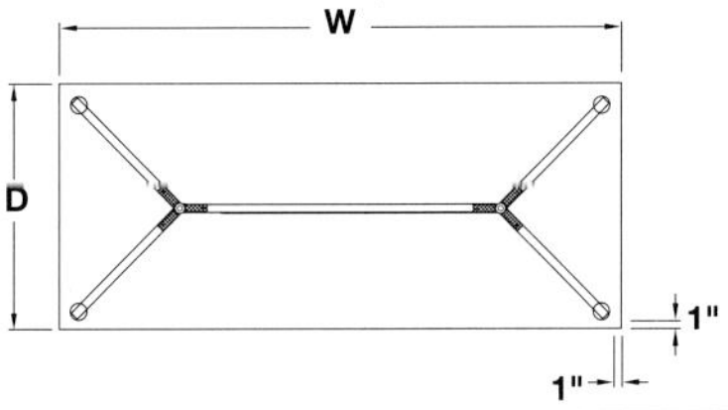

Single Rail Tables	Table Depth **"D"** 24"	30"	36"
Order Leg Style	654.70.524	654.70.530	654.70.536
Packing: 1 pc.			
Table Width **"W"**		**Order Rail Style**	
36"	654.72.510	-	-
42"	654.72.542	654.72.510	-
48"	654.72.548	654.72.542	654.72.510
54"	654.72.554	654.72.548	654.72.542
60"	654.72.560	654.72.554	654.72.548
66"	654.72.566	654.72.560	-
72"	654.72.572	654.72.566	-
78"	654.72.578	654.72.572	-
84"	654.72.584	654.72.578	-
90"	654.72.590	654.72.584	-
96"	654.72.596	654.72.590	

Packing: 1 pc.

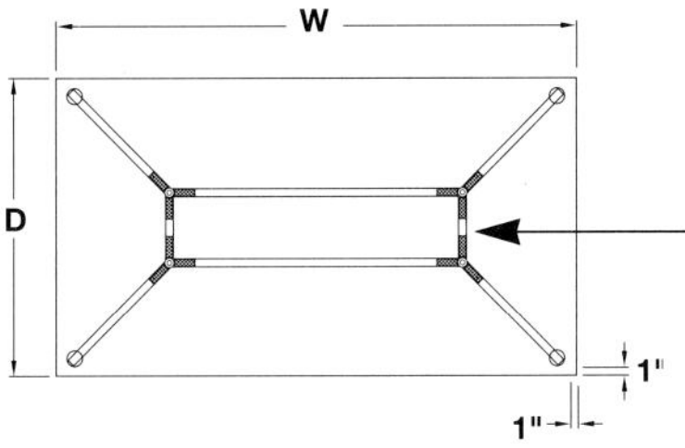

***Note: all Double Rail Tables require 2 pieces-654.72.510 to complete assembly.**

Double Rail Tables	Table Depth **"D"** 36"	42"	48"
Order Leg Style	654.70.524	654.70.530	654.70.536
Packing: 1 pc.			
Table Width **"W"**		**Order Rail Style**	
36"	654.72.510	-	-
42"	654.72.542	654.72.510	-
48"	654.72.548	654.72.542	654.72.510
54"	654.72.554	654.72.548	654.72.542
60"	654.72.560	654.72.554	654.72.548
66"	654.72.566	654.72.560	654.72.554
72"	654.72.572	654.72.566	654.72.560
78"	654.72.578	654.72.572	654.72.566
84"	654.72.584	654.72.578	654.72.572
90"	654.72.590	654.72.584	654.72.578
96"	654.72.596	652.72.590	654.72.584

Packing: 1 pc.

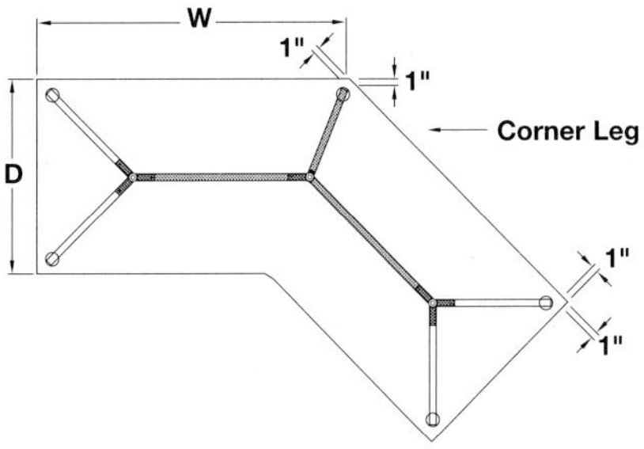

45° Tables	Table Depth **"D"** 24"	30"
Order Leg Style	654.71.524	654.71.530
Packing: 1 pc.		
Table Width **"W"**	**Order Rail Style**	
42"	654.73.542	654.74.542
48"	654.73.548	654.74.548
54"	654.73.554	654.74.554
60"	654.73.560	654.74.560

Packing: 1 pc.

Examples:

To order an Idea frame for a 30" x 60" work surface size you would order:
- 4 pc - 654.70.530-Leg
- 1 pc - 654.72.554-Rail
- 2 pc - 654.30.000-90° Connector

For a double rail system, 42" x 72" top size you would order:
- 4 pc - 654.70.530-Leg
- 2 pc - 654.72.510-Rail
- 2 pc - 654.72.566-Rail
- 4 pc - 654.30.000-Connector

For a 45° table as illustrated, 30" deep x 54" x 54" you would order:
- 4 pc - 654.70.530-Leg
- 1 pc - 654.71.530-Leg
- 2 pc - 654.74.554-Rail
- 2 pc - 654.30.000-90° Connector
- 1 pc - 654.30.001-45° Connector

Dimensional data not binding. We reserve the right to alter specifications without notice.

HÄFELE

Idea Table Support System Accessories

Screw for Top Stabilizer

Screw
M6 x 12 mm with internal M4 socket, used with insert.
Finish: steel, nickel-plated

Cat. No.	020.46.612

Packing: 100 pieces

Insert with internal M6 thread
10 x 12 mm
Finish: steel, unfinished

Cat. No.	030.00.351

Packing: 1000 pcs.

Or

Varianta Screws
Varianta Special
Cylinder Head Cross-slot PZ 2
Finish:
steel, nickel-plated

Length	Cat. No.
10.5 mm	013.20.716
13.5 mm	013.20.724
16.0 mm	013.20.743

Packing: 1000 pcs.

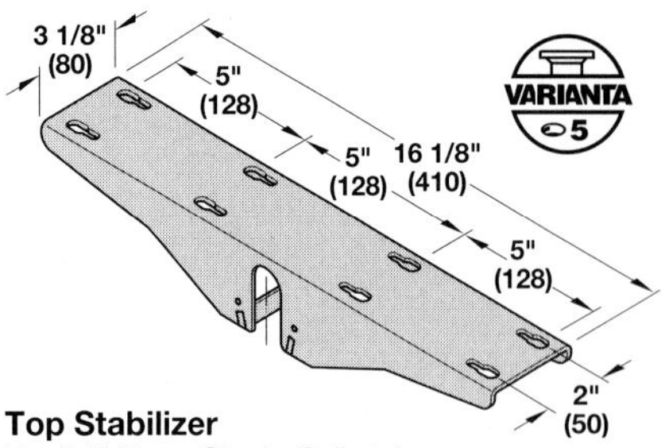

Top Stabilizer
For 24" Deep Single Rail styles
Finish: steel, powder-coated, gray metallic

Cat. No.	654.44.501

Packing: 1 pc.

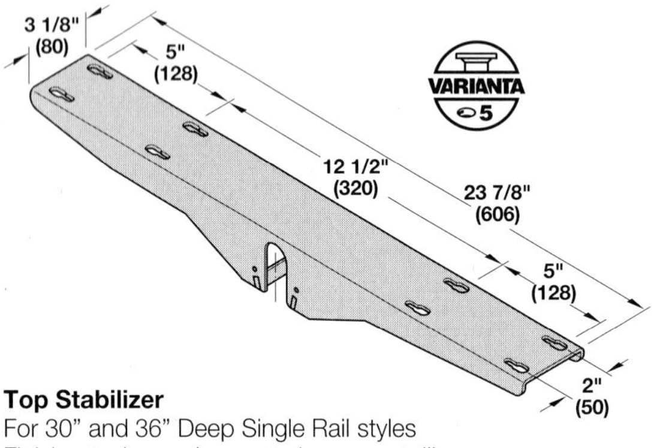

Top Stabilizer
For 30" and 36" Deep Single Rail styles
Finish: steel, powder-coated, gray metallic

Cat. No.	654.44.500

Packing: 1 pc.

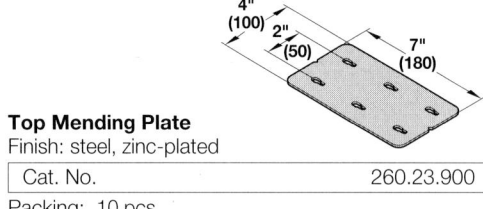

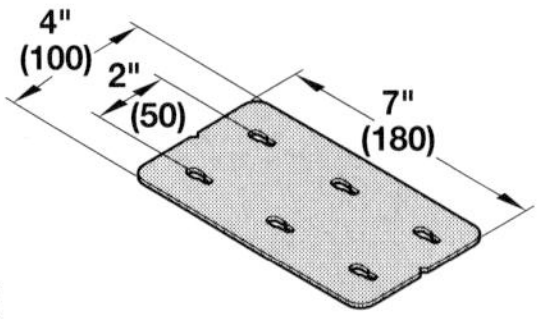

Top Mending Plate
Finish: steel, zinc-plated

Cat. No.	260.23.900

Packing: 10 pcs.

Measurements in mm

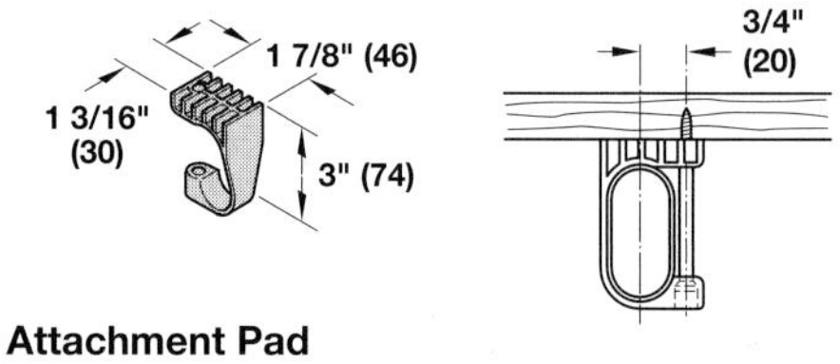

Top Attachment Pad
Finish: plastic, black

Cat. No.	654.34.510

Packing: 10 pcs.

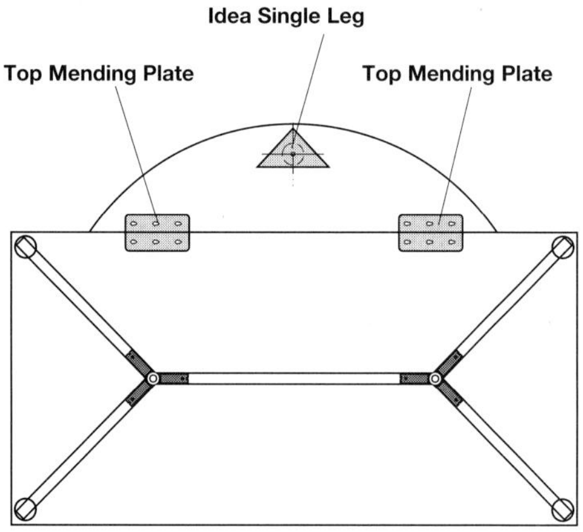

Bolt
for attaching top through connector or top attachment pad

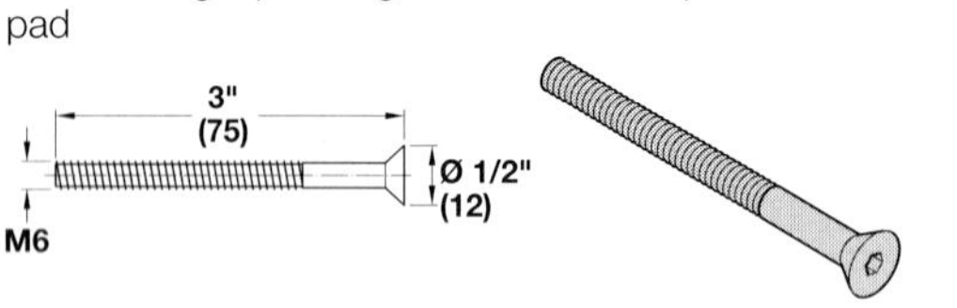

Countersunk, flat head
with socket SW4 for use with insert below
Finish: steel, zinc-plated

Cat. No.	032.48.930

Packing: 500 pcs.

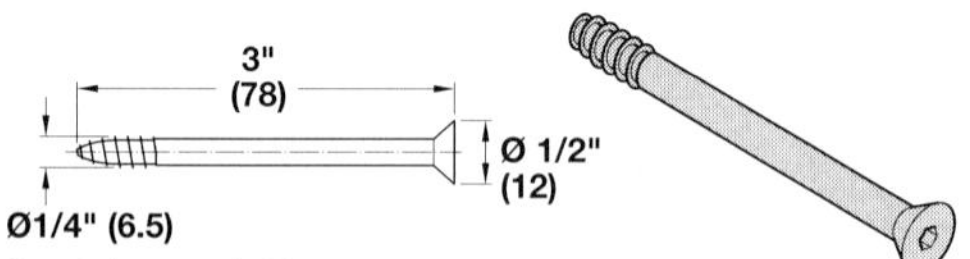

Countersunk Screw
with SW4 socket and **Special Thread**
for Ø 5 mm hole
Finish: steel, zinc-plated

Cat. No.	023.01.978

Packing: 1000 pcs.

Insert with M6 internal thread, 10 x 12 mm
Finish: steel, unfinished

Cat. No.	030.00.351

Packing: 1000 pcs.

Special High Speed Drill, Ø5 mm for Idea System

Cat. No.	001.24.500

Packing: 1 pc.

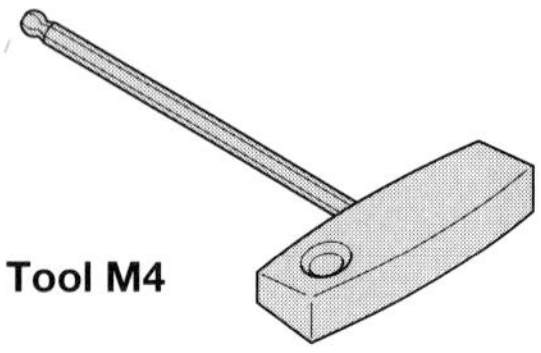

Idea Table Assembly Tool M4

Finish: Handle; plastic, black
Shaft; hardened steel

Cat. No.	006.32.140

Packing: 1 pc.

6 Furniture Support Systems, Office and Computer Furniture Accessories

Dimensional data not binding.
We reserve the right to alter specifications without notice.

Idea Table Support System Accessories

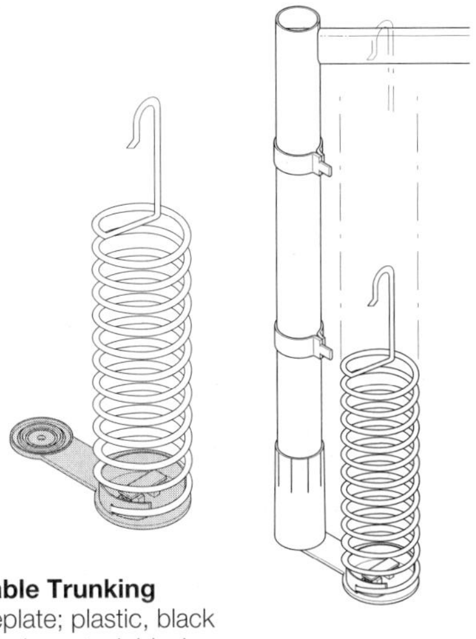

This base-plate allows placing the vertical cable trunking option at any position on the frame by simply positioning over the plastic base-plate.

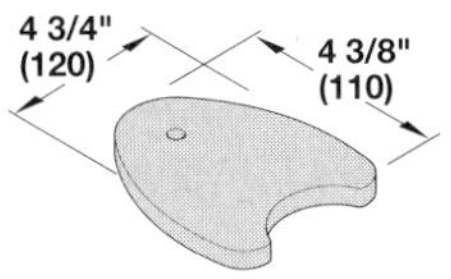

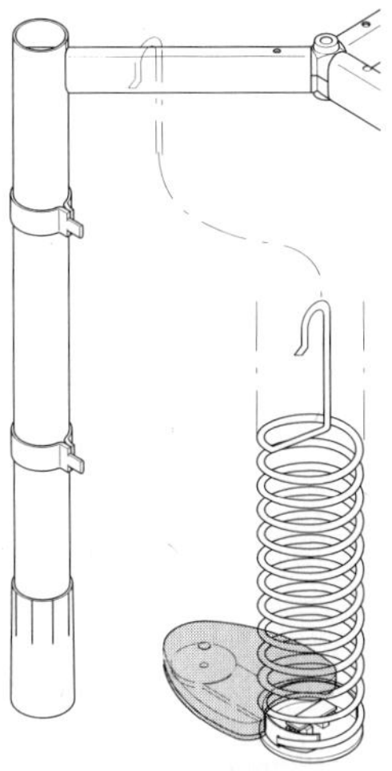

Vertical Cable Trunking
Finish: Baseplate; plastic, black with Steel Spring; steel, black

Cat. No.	654.52.300

Packing: 1 pc.

Finish: epoxy powder-coated, gray metallic

Cat. No.	654.52.370

Packing: 1 pc.

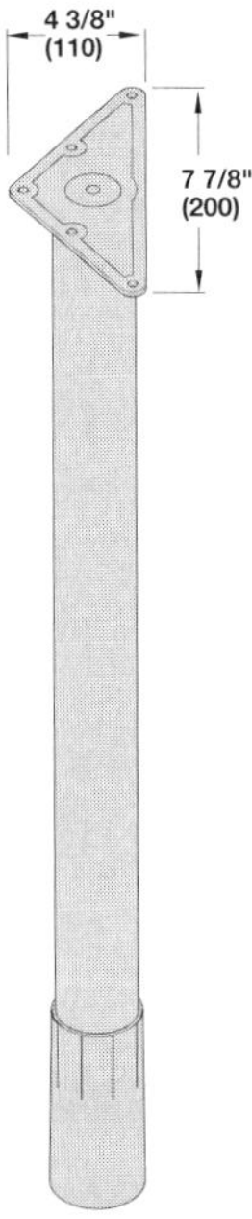

Single Leg for Idea
Leg for Idea System with steel attachment plate, powder-coated, gray metallic including **Adjustment Device** 26 7/8" -30 1/8" (650 - 760 mm), plastic, black

Cat. No.	654.39.570

Packing: 1 pc.

Mounting Screws for panel attachment bracket
Varianta Special
Cylinder -head with Cross-slot PZ2
Finish:
steel, nickel-plated

Length	Cat. No.
10.5 mm	013.20.716

Packing: 100 and 1000 pcs.

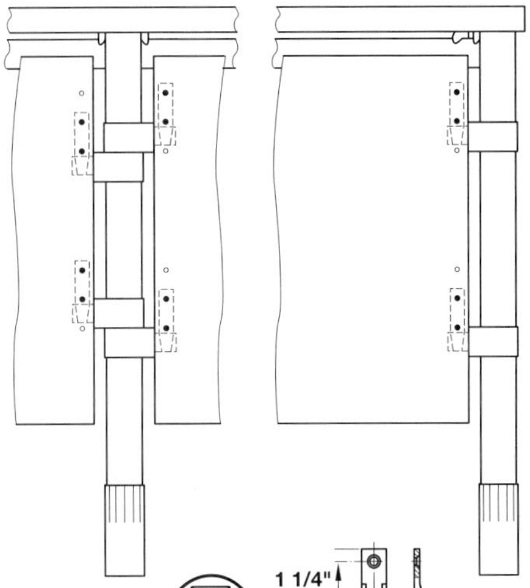

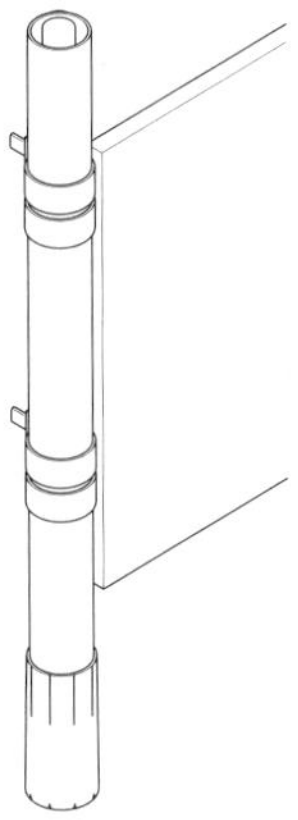

Furniture Support Systems, Office and Computer Furniture Accessories 6

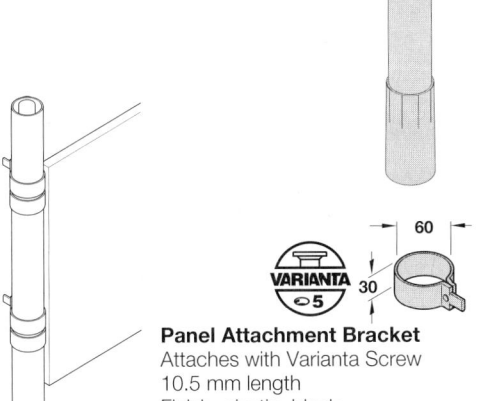

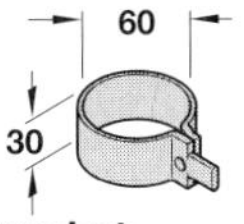

Panel Attachment Bracket
Attaches with Varianta Screw 10.5 mm length
Finish: plastic, black

Cat. No.	654.34.390

Packing: 16 pcs.

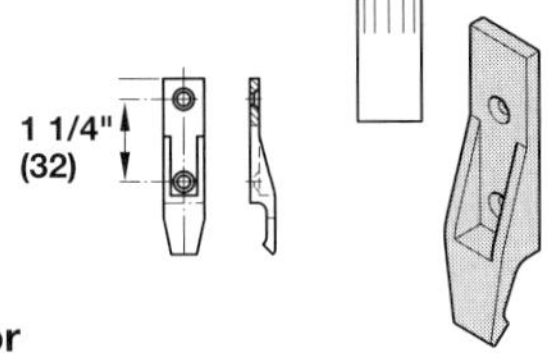

Keku Panel Connector
Finish: plastic, black

Cat. No.	262.49.357

Packing: 200 pcs.

Screws for panel connector
Varianta Special
Flat-head with Cross-slot PZ2
Finish:
steel, nickel-plated

Length	Cat. No.
10.5 mm	013.15.715
13.5 mm	013.15.724
16.0 mm	013.15.733

Packing: 100 and 1000 pcs.

Recommended Modesty Panel Height 15 3/4"

Table Length	Distance A
36"	**29 3/8"**
42"	**35 3/8"**
48"	**41 3/8"**
54"	**47 3/8"**
60"	**51 3/8"**
66"	**59 3/8"**
72"	**66 3/8"**

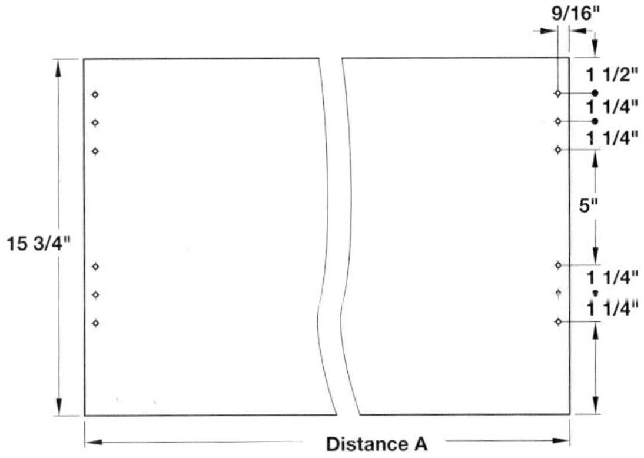

Dimensional data not binding. We reserve the right to alter specifications without notice.

HÄFELE

Free Standing C-Frame Style

- All steel construction shipped RTA form. Only 6 screws required for assembly.
- 8 bearings in each leg column for effortless movement - even under severe loading.
- All mechanical components are "Molybonded" to eliminate the need for lubrication.
- Gas cylinder assisted to aid lifting even the heaviest loads.
- Unique "Flexdrive" provides adjustment range of 12" (23-35"). Approximately 8 turns of the ergonomically designed handle moves the work surface 1".
- Epoxy powder-coated to provide superior protection and ensure long lasting appearance.
- Weight capacity - 350 lbs.

Both products conform to the following technical standards:

- ANSI/BIFMA X5.5-1983 "Tests for Desk Products"
- BSI 4875: Part 5: 1985 "Strength and Stability of Furniture"
- Australian Standards Association AS 3590.2 - 1990 "Screen Based Workstations Part 2: Workstation Furniture"

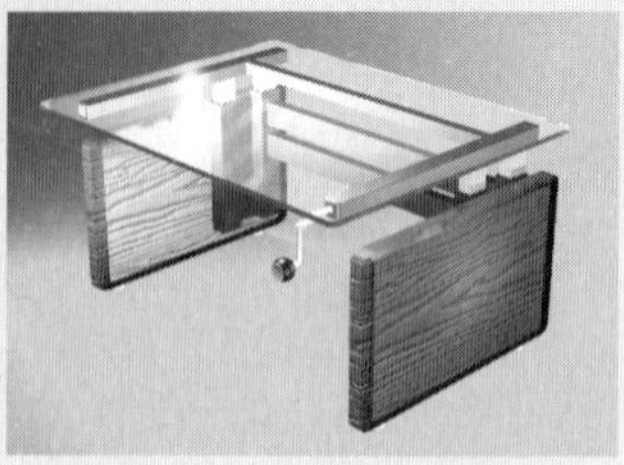

Slab-End Frame Style

- Same unique features as found in our C-frame style.
- Width is variable, depending upon your individual requirements.
- Can be used in many applications, e.g. study carrels, traditional style desks, even kitchen cabinets!

Dimensional data not binding. We reserve the right to alter specifications without notice.

Ergoflex Adjustable Work Surface Mechanisms

Free Standing C-Frame Style, for adjustable workstations.

Adjustment range: 12" (23 -35" in height)

Finish: frame, steel, epoxy powder coat black or gray
Elevation tubes, steel chrome-plated

	To Fit Work Surface Size	black	light gray
Cat. No.	24" D x 30" W	639.60.300	639.60.500
	24" D x 36" W	639.60.310	639.60.510
	24" D x 42" W	639.60.320	639.60.520
	24" D x 48" W	639.60.330	639.60.530
	24" D x 60" W	639.60.340	639.60.540
	30" D x 30" W	639.60.350	639.60.550
	30" D x 36" W	639.60.360	639.60.560
	30" D x 42" W	639.60.370	639.60.570
	30" D x 48" W	639.60.380	639.60.580
	30" D x 60" W	639.60.390	639.60.590

Packing: 1pc.

Slab-End Frame Style, for adjustable workstations.

Adjustment range: 12"

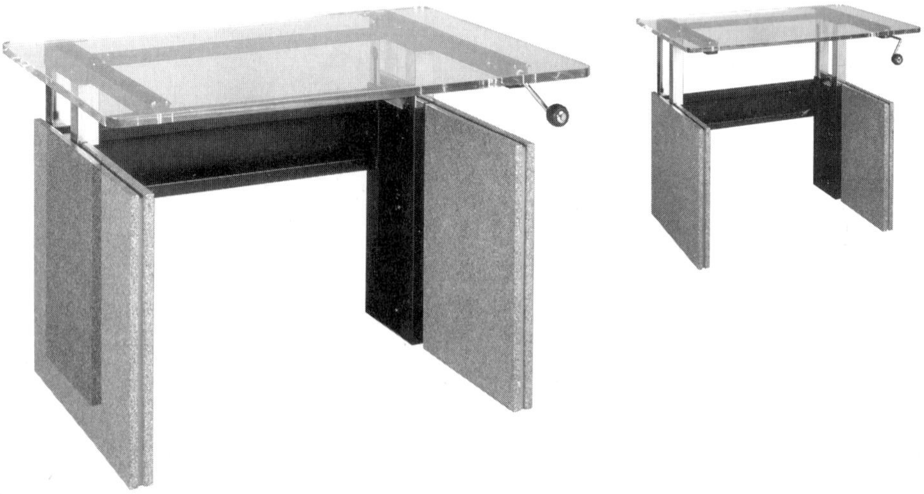

Finish: frame, steel, epoxy powder coat black or gray
Elevation tubes, steel chrome-plated

	Size: for work surface sizes	black	light gray
Cat. No.	24" Deep x specify*	639.01.34X	639.01.54X
	30" Deep x specify*	639.01.36X	639.01.56X

Packing: 1pc.

***Must specify width between side panels.**

Frame is not available with panels or top as shown.

HÄFELE

Ergoflex Adjustable Work Surface Mechanisms

Splay C-Frame Style, for adjustable workstations.
Adjustment range:
12" (23 -35" in height)

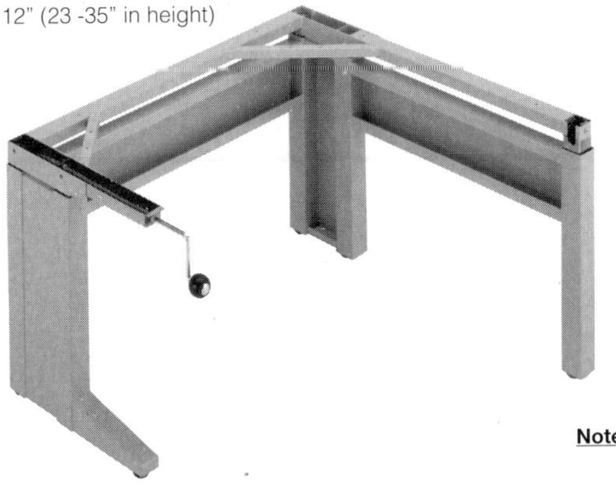

Note: Table Top Dimensions

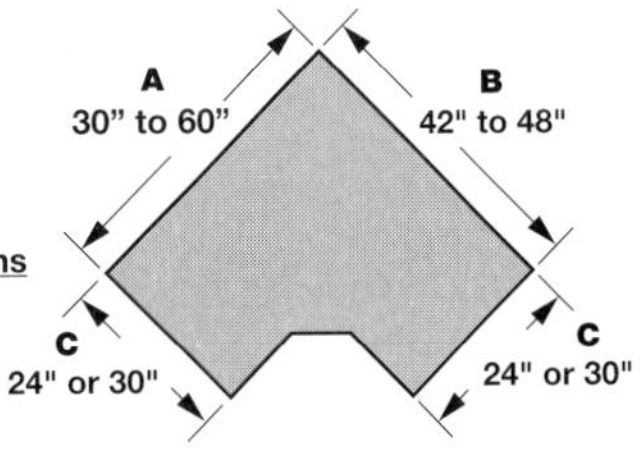

Finish: frame, steel, epoxy powder coat black or gray
Elevation tubes, steel chrome-plated

Cat. No.	Depth C	Width A	Crank position	black	gray
	24"	30"	RH	639.61.300	639.61.500
	24"	30"	LH	639.61.301	639.61.501
	30"	30"	RH	639.61.350	639.61.550
	30"	30"	LH	639.61.351	639.61.551
	24"	36"	RH	639.61.310	639.61.510
	24"	36"	LH	639.61.311	639.61.511
	30"	36"	RH	639.61.360	639.61.560
	30"	36"	LH	639.61.361	639.61.561
	24"	42"	RH	639.61.320	639.61.520
	24"	42"	LH	639.61.321	639.61.521
	30"	42"	RH	639.61.370	639.61.570
	30"	42"	LH	639.61.371	639.61.571
	24"	48"	RH	639.61.330	639.61.530
	24"	48"	LH	639.61.331	639.61.531
	30"	48"	RH	639.61.380	639.61.580
	24"	60"	RH	639.61.381	639.61.581
	24"	60"	LH	639.61.340	639.61.540
	24"	60"	RH	639.61.341	639.61.541
	30"	60"	LH	639.61.390	639.61.590
	30"	60"	RH	639.61.391	639.61.591

Packing: 1 pc.

Right Angle C-Frame Style, for adjustable workstations.
Adjustment range: 12" (23 -35" in height)

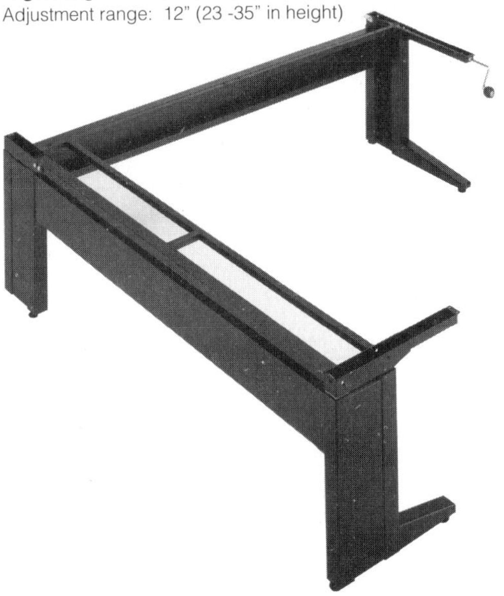

Note: Table Top Dimensions

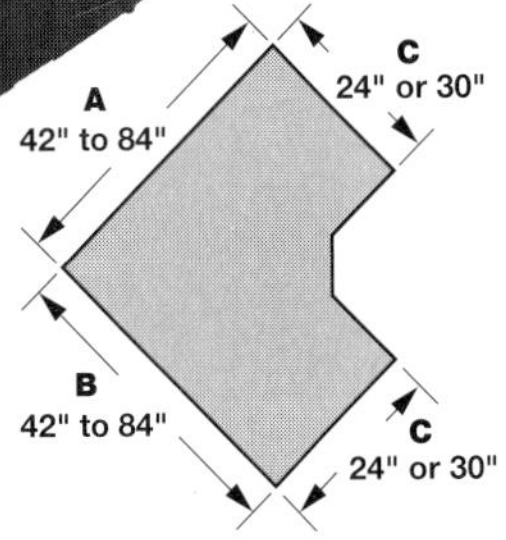

Finish: frame, steel, epoxy powder coat black or gray
Elevation tubes, steel chrome-plated

Work Surface size **A**	Work Surface Size **B**	Work Surface Size **C**	Cat. No.
42" to 84"	42" to 84"	24"	639.03.SPEC.77
42" to 84"	42" to 84"	30"	639.03.SPEC.77

Packing: 1pc.

Splay C-Frame Style
- Same basic functions as standard model.
- Allows for easy application of corner unit.
- No legs protrude into foot well area.
- Fixed dimension of 39" allows for splay width of 42" or 48". Other side can be up to 84".
- Available in 24" and 30" depths.
- Meets or exceeds BIFMA specifications.
- Shipped unassembled to facilitate delivery. Simple assembly is all that's required.

Ordering note: specify top size, frame color, and hand when ordering.

Both products conform to the following technical standards:
- ANSI/BIFMA X5.5-1983 "Tests for Desk Products"
- BSI 4875: Part 5: 1985 "Strength and Stability of Furniture"
- Australian Standards Association AS 3590.2 - 1990 "Screen Based Workstations Part 2: Workstation Furniture"

Right Angle C-Frame Style
- Same basic functions as standard model.
- Allows the largest possible table size - 84" x 84" with 36" deep returns.
- 2 gas pistons assist the lifting of large loads — up to 350 lbs.
- Handing must be specified.
- Shipped unassembled to facilitate delivery. Simple assembly is all that's required.
- Meets or exceeds BIFMA specifications.

Ordering note: specify top size, frame color, and hand when ordering.

HÄFELE

Integrated Suspension System

The Nova Integrated Suspension System positions the monitor at a comfortable viewing angle, thereby reducing the risks of cumulative trauma disorders (CTD), while increasing valuable workspace.

Finish: Steel, black epoxy powder coat.
Glass: tinted and tempered.
Plastic, black.

For **standard** monitors
set consists of:

- Suspension frame for monitor
- Keyboard tray with locking slides
- Adjustable feet for free-standing option
- Tinted and tempered glass (1/4" thick) viewing surface
- Glare shield
- Complete mounting instructions.

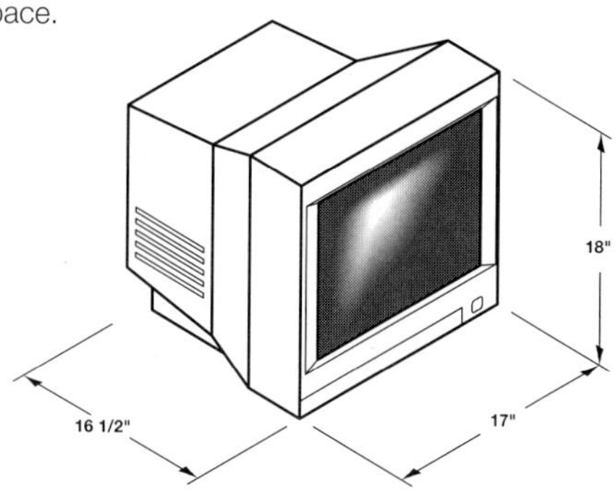

Designed to fit monitors with these maximum dimensions.

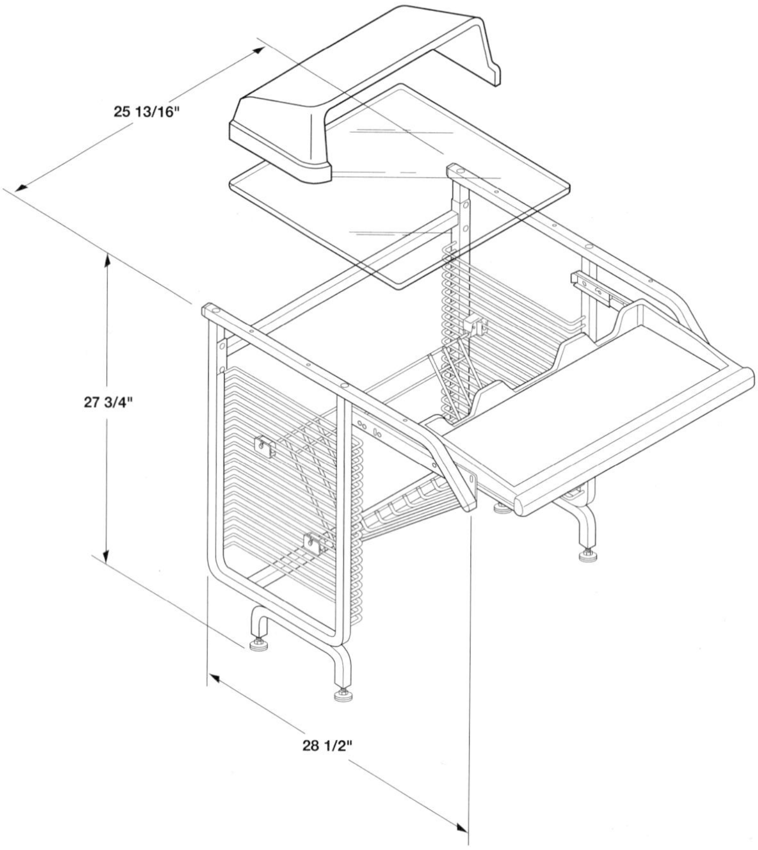

Cat. No.	639.90.303

Packing: 1 set

CPU Holder

Easily attaches to horizontal rungs of unit. Adjustable in width from 3 3/4" to 6 3/4".

Finish: Steel, black epoxy powder coat.

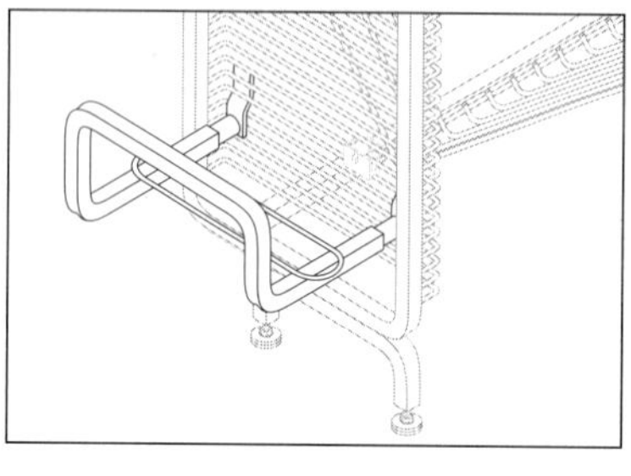

Cat. No.	639.89.391

Packing: 1 set

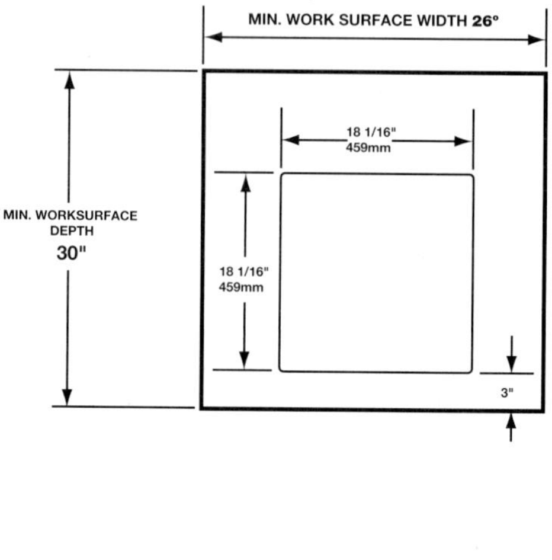

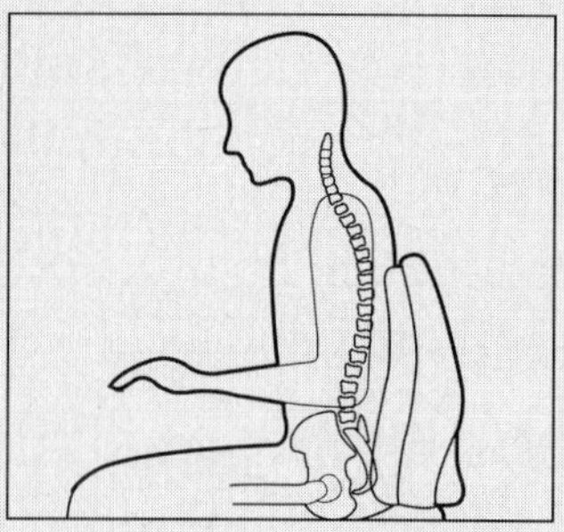

Alleviation-Encourages an upright posture which helps alleviate the growing number of musculo-skeletal complaints.

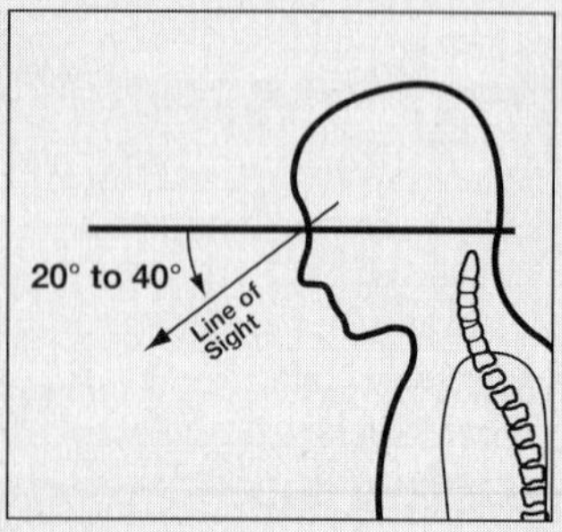

Declination- The natural tendency to look down, "preferred declination of the line of sight." The suspension system achieves a comfortable angle without moving the head.

6 **Furniture Support Systems, Office and Computer Furniture Accessories**

- Enhances eye contact - allows a direct line of sight.
- Assures privacy - the recessed monitor provides security for sensitive material.
- Saves space - removes the cpu, monitor and keyboard and frees up the most critical part of the workspace.
- Manages wires - hides unsightly computer cables. This also keeps them from being accidently disconnected.
- Lowers costs - eliminates the need for a separate computer workstation. This saves office space.

Dimensional data not binding. We reserve the right to alter specifications without notice.

Integrated Suspension System

Unlike any other system found, the computer and its components are housed entirely within the unit to provide maximum desktop space.

Finish: Steel, black epoxy powder coat.
Glass: tinted and tempered.
Plastic, black.

For **oversized** monitors set includes:

- Suspension frame for monitor
- Keyboard tray with locking slides
- Adjustable feet for free-standing option
- Tinted and tempered glass (1/4" thick) viewing surface
- Glare shield
- Complete mounting instructions.

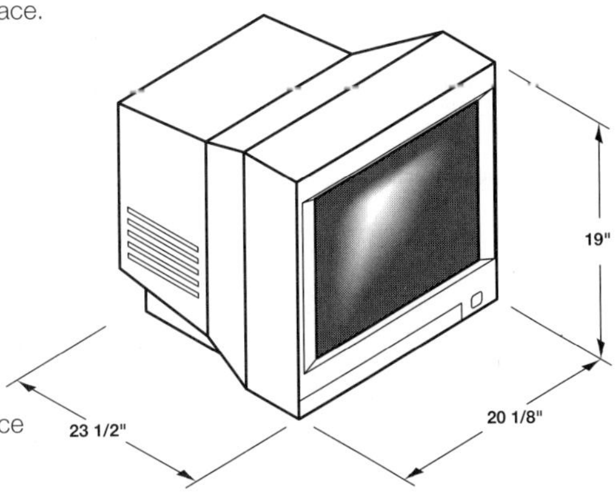

Designed to fit monitors with these maximum dimensions.

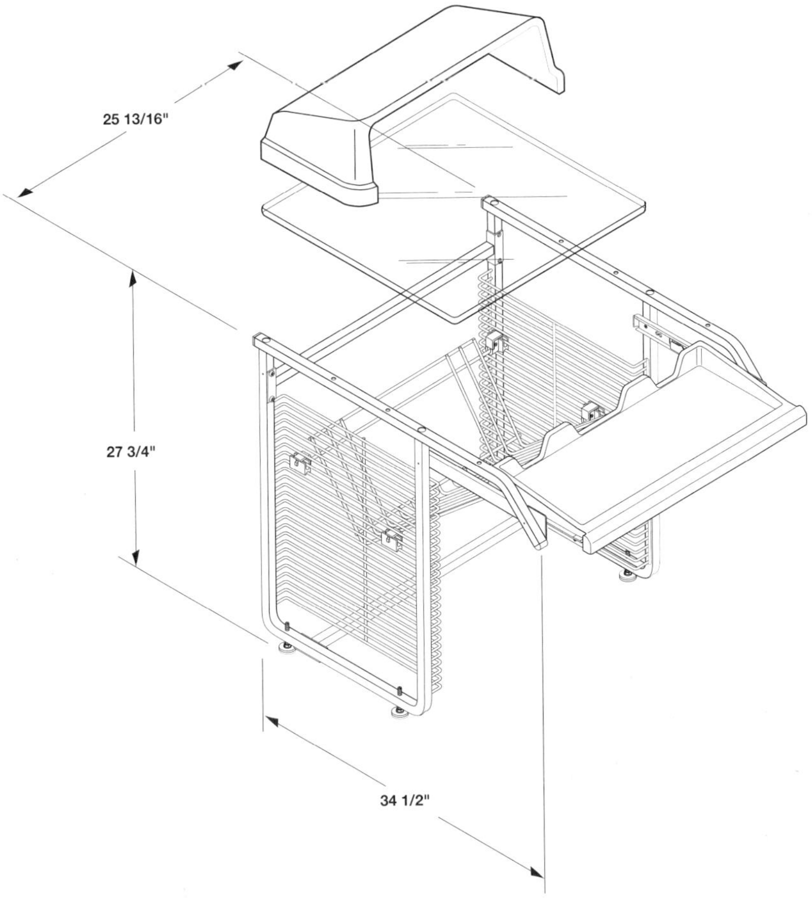

Cat. No.	639.89.300

Packing: 1 set

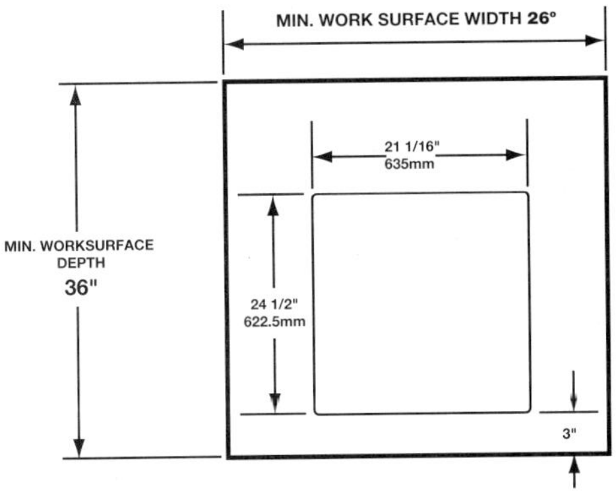

HÄFELE

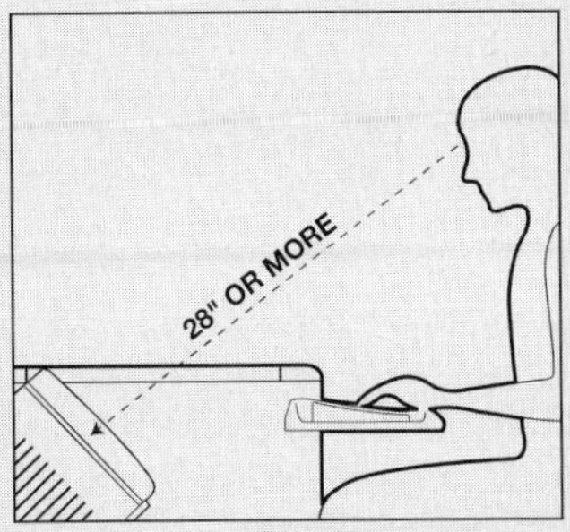

Accommodation - The eye has a “resting point of accommodation,” the distance at which the eye experiences the least amount of strain. Most people prefer a distance of approximately 31". The suspension system positions the monitor 28" to 32" from the eye.

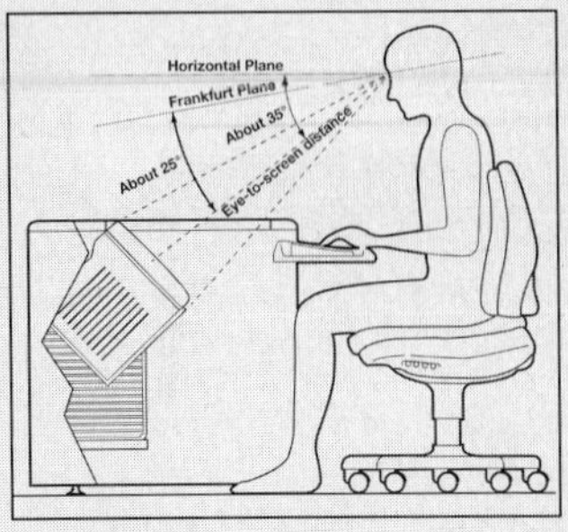

Technology Integration - The Nova suspension system offers a solution to the problems faced in today's workplace reduced risk ergonomics.

Furniture Support Systems, Office and Computer Furniture Accessories 6

Dimensional data not binding. We reserve the right to alter specifications without notice.

HÄFELE

Keyboard Mechanisms

SwingLift™ Keyboard Arm, for dual surface, sit/stand workstations.

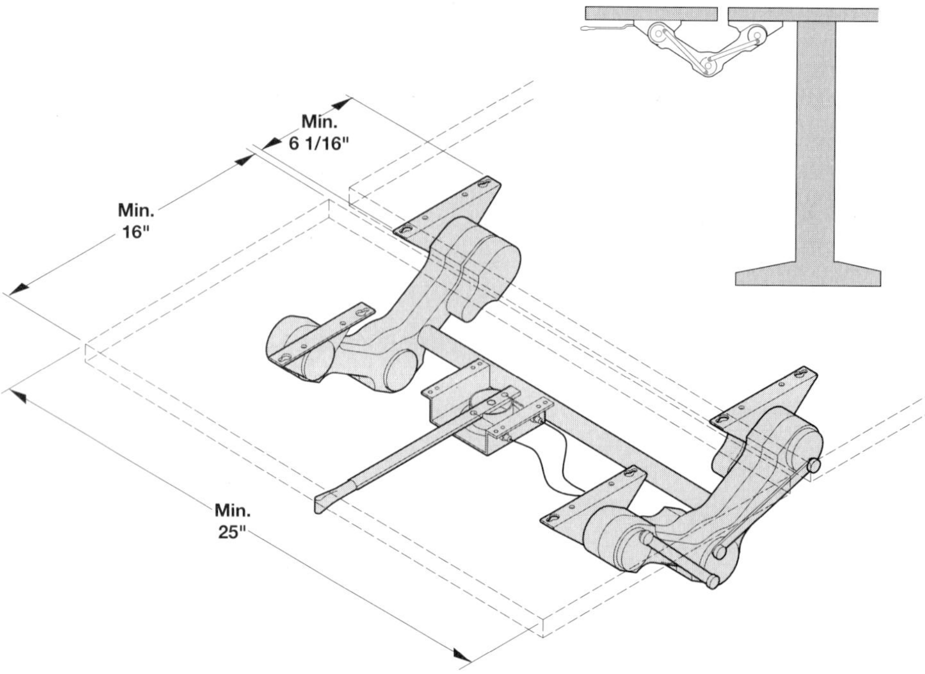

Finish: steel, black; plastic, black

Cat. No.	639.87.300

Packing: 1 pc.

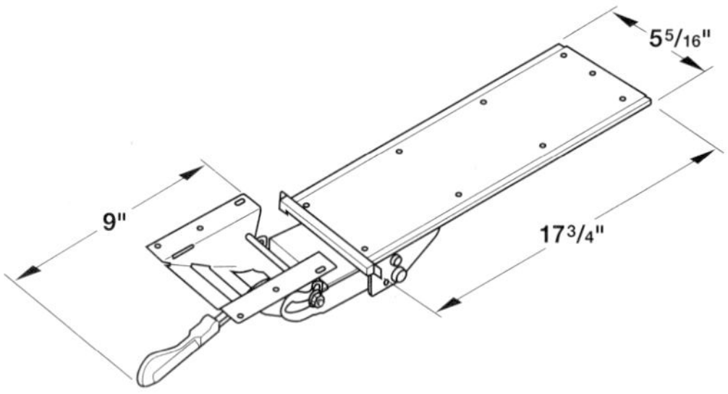

Lever activated, spring assisted keyboard arm
Material: steel
Finish: epoxy powder-coated, black

Cat. No.	639.86.300

Packing: 1 piece

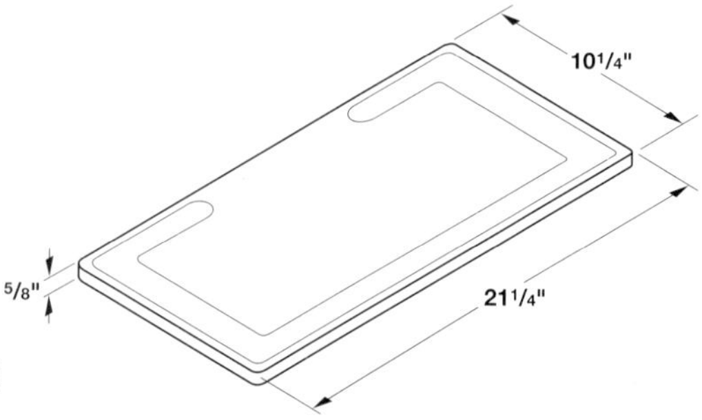

Keyboard tray, contoured surface, soft touch vinyl
Material: MDF; foam, vinyl covered
Finish: black

Cat. No.	639.86.310

Packing: 1 piece

Swing Lift™ Keyboard Arm

- Simultaneous tilt and height adjustment. Controlled by a single lever actuator.
- Internal gear system permits infinite height adjustment range of 13 1/2" (5 1/2" below - 8" above), tilt range of 20° (10° positive - 10° negative).
- Smooth shrouds on all working parts - no obtrusive springs are exposed.
- One size mechanism suitable for surfaces from 30" to 48" wide.
- Shipped totally assembled and ready to mount.
- Exceeds BIFMA and ANSI standards for strength and Human Factors Criteria.
- Load 57kg (125 lbs).
  Will counter-balance 16kg (35 lbs)

- Single lever locks and unlocks height and tilt adjustments. Can be adjusted 5 3/4" easily and quickly, even the physically challenged.
- 10 lbs. of spring pressure keeps keyboard tray from dropping during adjustments.
- Slides in and out on formed steel track with little effort.
- Provides 8" of infiinte height adjustment and 30° of tilt (15° towards and 15° away from user).
- Low profile, just 2 1/2" high, won't interfere with knees.
- Mounting instructions included.

Dimensional data not binding.
We reserve the right to alter specifications without notice.

Keyboard Mechanisms

HÄFELE

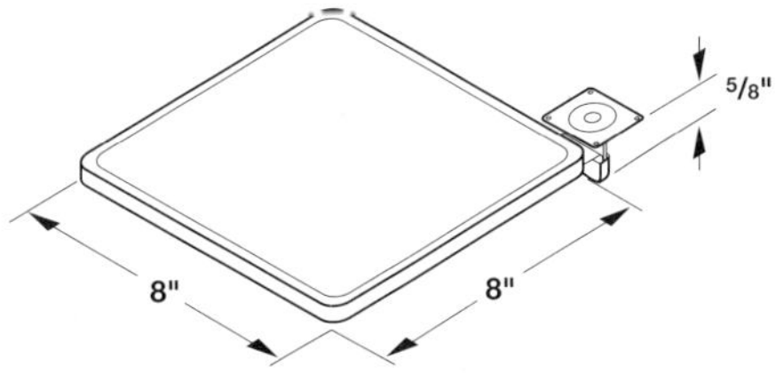

Tilt/Swivel computer mouse pad
Easily mounts to keyboard tray or any other work-surface.
Material: steel, Mylar surface, black
Finish: epoxy powder-coated, black

Cat. No.	639.86.330

Packing: 1 piece

- Swivels out of way when not in use.
- Tilts a total of 30° so that pad remains level even when tray is tilted.
- Surface allows for smooth movement of mouse ball.
- Can be mounted for left or right hand users.

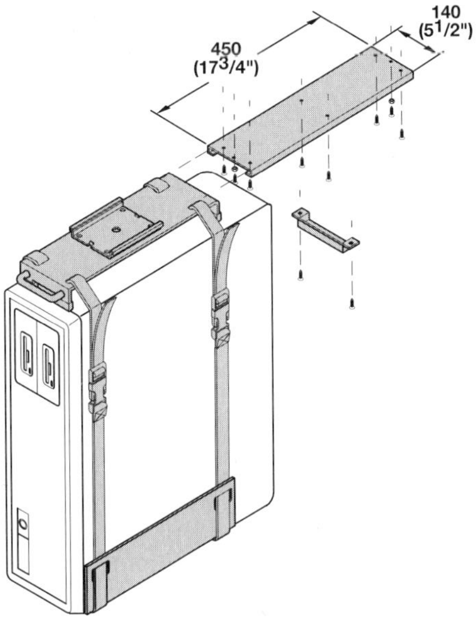

CPU holder
Material: steel, nylon straps
Finish: black, epoxy powder-coated, black

Cat. No.	639.70.300

Packing: 1 piece

- Unique strap design can be adjusted to fit popular sizes of computers. Positive locking strap clamps keep CPU's firmly in place.
- When mounted below the work-surface, its slide track provides 5 1/2" of travel for ease of accessibility. Front and back bumpers prevent over travel.
- 360° swivel provides easy access to connections on the rear of CPU.
- Easy to install using instructions included.
- Holds CPUs up and away from shoes, dust, moisture, vacuum cleaners or mops.

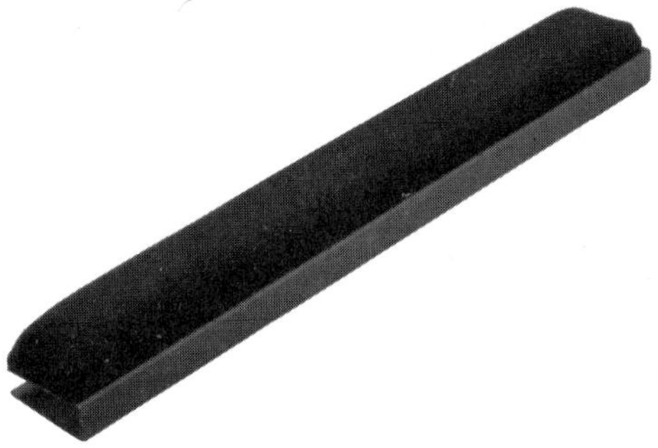

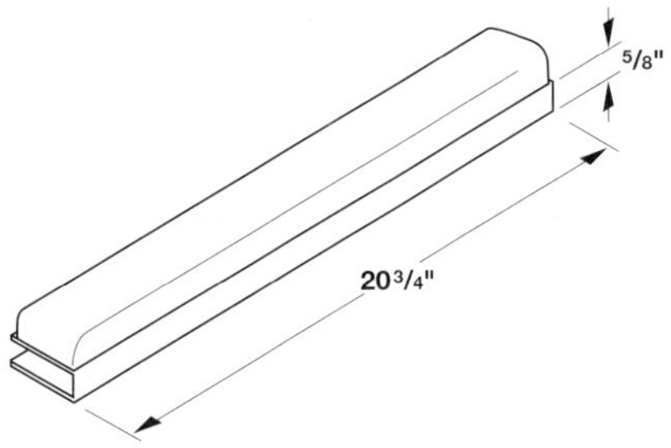

Clip-on wrist rest
Material: plastic/foam/cloth covered
Finish: Color: black

Cat. No.	639.86.320

Packing: 1 piece

- foam filled to relieve wrist pressure
- Fabric covered for greater comfort
- Easily clips onto tray

Dimensional data not binding. We reserve the right to alter specifications without notice.

Keyboard Mechanisms

Fully Articulated Keyboard Arm

- Low-profile
- Ball-bearing slides guide mechanism
- Locks in extended position
- Keyboard rotates 360° for maximum adjustibility
- 15° tilt, lever activated
- 6" of spring assited height adjustment
- Designed to accept optional keyboard tray
- Meets or exceeds BIFMA standards.

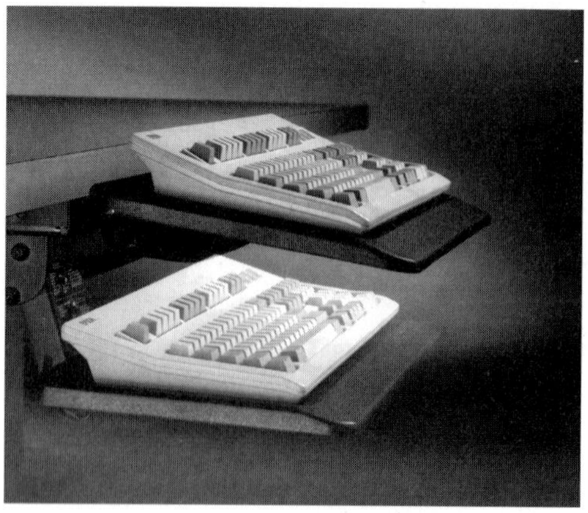

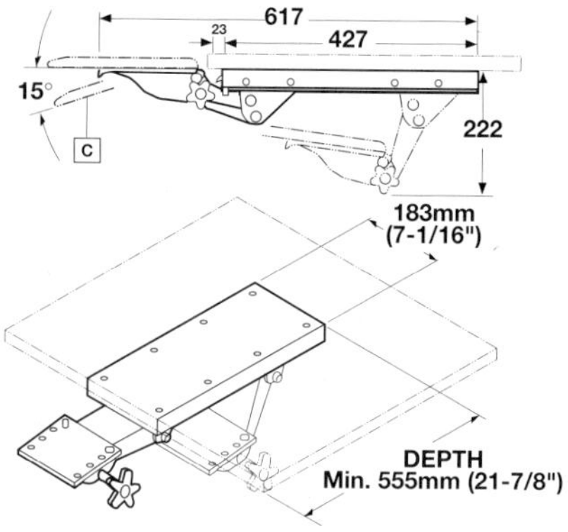

Finish: plastic, black; steel, black

Cat. No.	639.96.305

Packing: 1 pc.

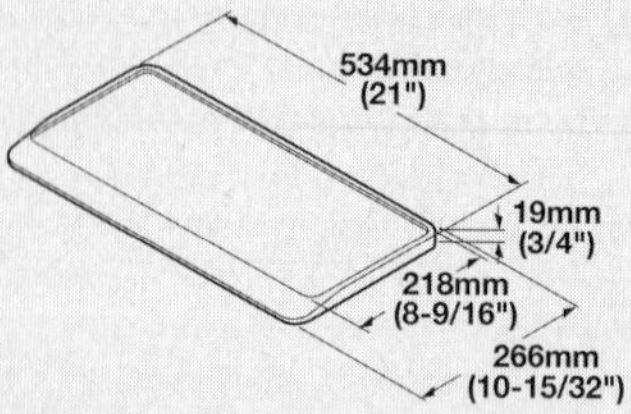

Optional Keyboard Tray suitable for fully articulated keyboard arm

Cat. No.	Color
639.96.396	black
639.96.592	gray

Packing: 1 pc.

Retractable Keyboard Arm

- Low-profile
- Plastic/metal slide
- Keyboard can be tilted 15° Adjustable keyboard clamp – no tray or shelf required
- Meets or exceeds BIFMA standards.

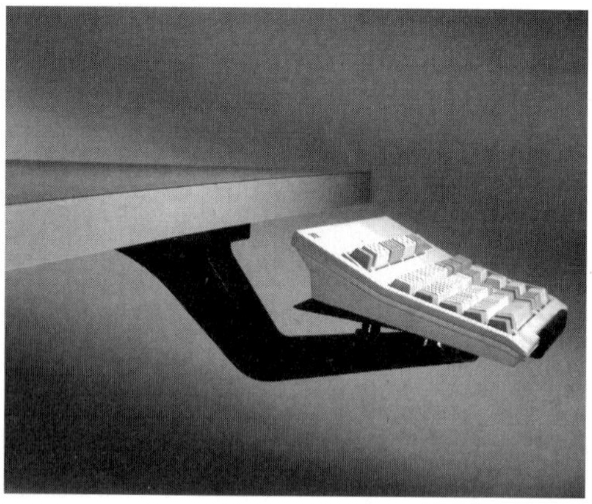

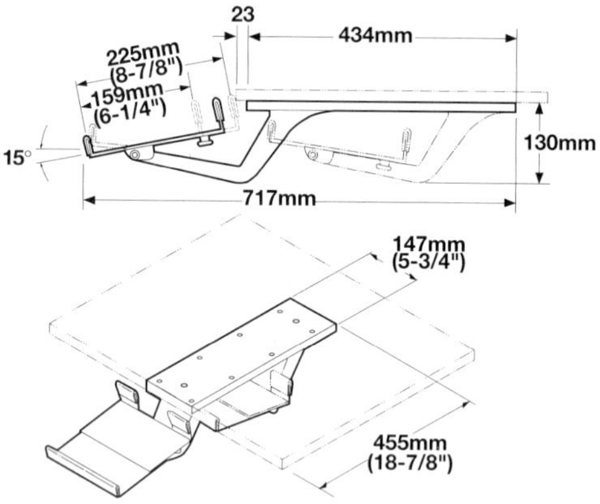

Finish: steel, powder coated, black

Cat. No.	639.95.308

Packing: 1 pc.

6 Furniture Support Systems, Office and Computer Furniture Accessories

K-Board Computer Keyboard

- Moves to new vertical position without use of knobs or levers.
- Dual locking mechanism assures stability.
- Can be integrated into worksurface or mounted below.
- Two widths provide maximum adaptability.
- Spring assisted to prevent accidental lowering of keyboard.

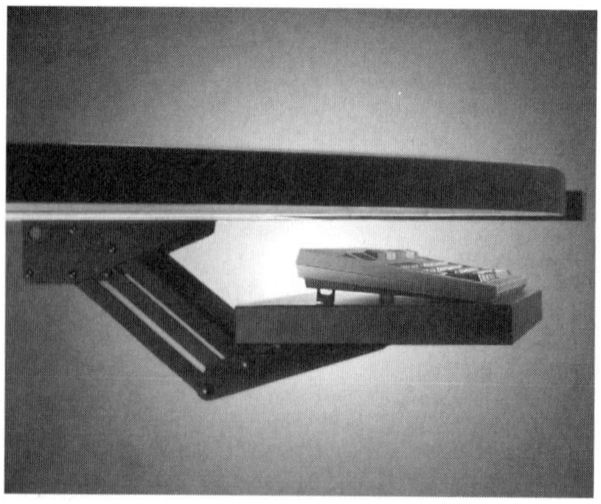

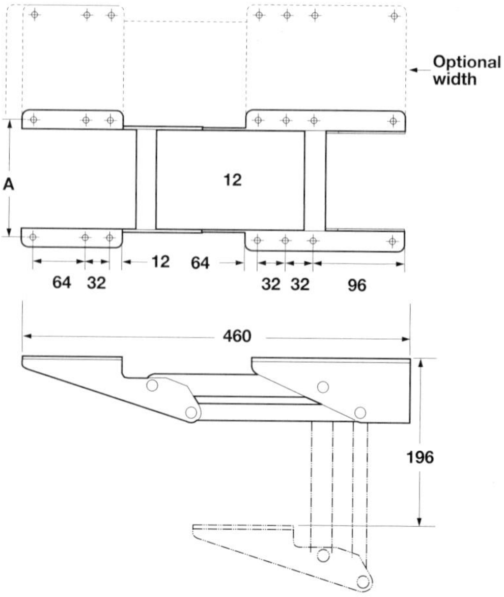

Finish: steel, black powder-coated

Dimension A	Cat. No.
142	639.97.302
630	639.97.330

Packing: 1 pc.

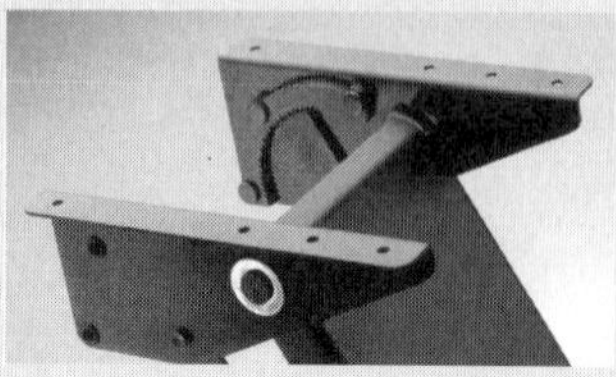

Detail of adjustment mechanism.

Dimensional data not binding. We reserve the right to alter specifications without notice.

Dimensions in mm

Lap Top Computer Security Drawer

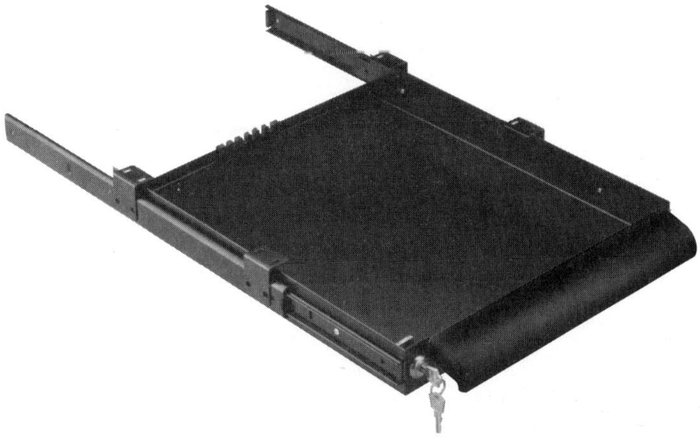

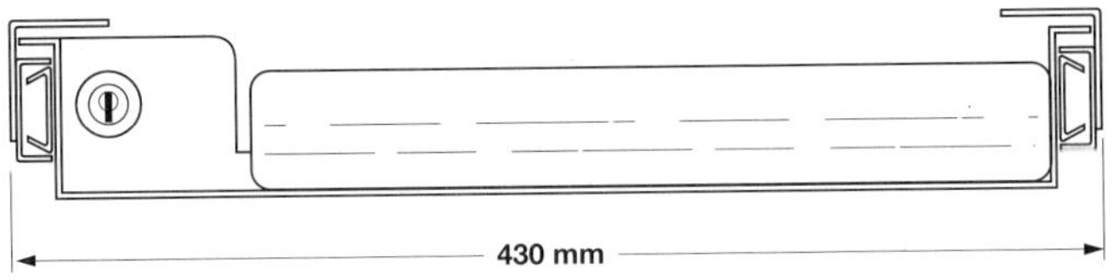

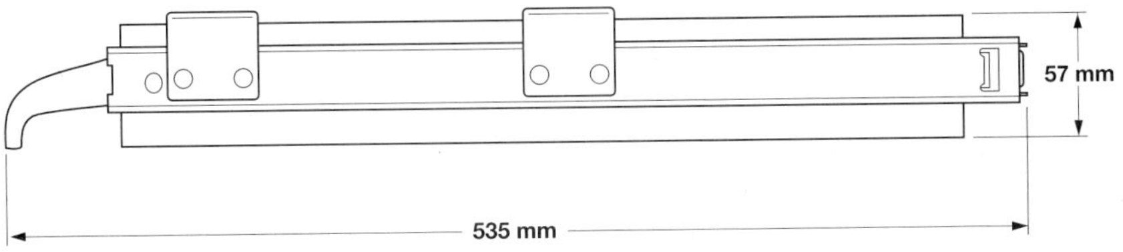

Finish: steel, epoxy powder-coated, black;
foam wrist rest, black

Cat. No.	429.82.350

Packing: 1 pc.

Extending Keyboard Shelf

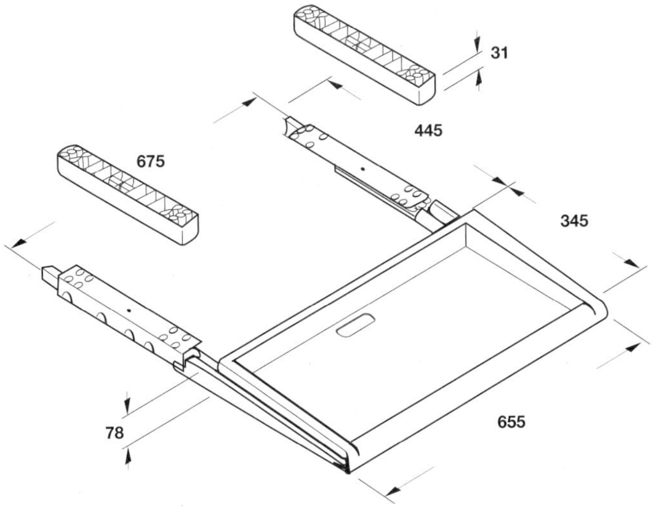

Finish: tray and spacers: plastic
mounting brackets: steel, galvanized
Runners: steel, zinc-plated

Color	Cat. No.
gray	429.80.512
black	429.80.316

Packing: 1 set

Dimensions in mm

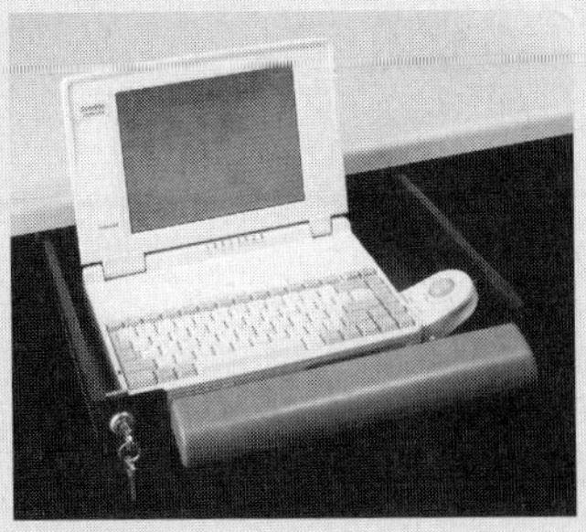

Lap Top Computer Security Drawer
- Secures laptop computer while providing convenient storage.
- Constructed of strong 18 ga. cold rolled steel
- Protected by durable black epoxy powder coat
- Smooth rolling ball bearing slides with hold out detent prevents drawer from moving while in use.
- Cable organizer keeps power and data cables neatly in place when computer is removed. Simply reconnect cables when you return lap top to drawer.
- Integral foam wrist rest enhances comfort
- Lock with 2 keys deters theft and unauthorized use.
- Mounting instructions, template and mounting screws are included for easy installation.

Easily installed beneath any desk, this keyboard shelf consists of a plastic tray with integral runners and accepts any flat keyboard measuring 590 mm wide x 285 mm deep x 25-60 mm high.

HÄFELE

Ergoarm Monitor Suspension System

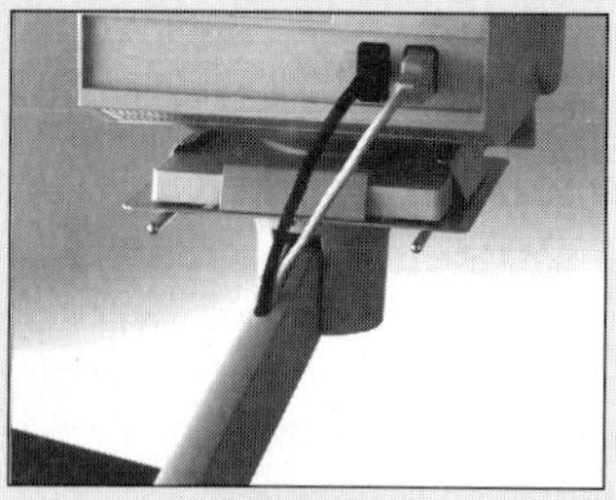

The Ergoarm's efficient cable ducting conceals all cables neatly within the arm.

The cushioned surface monitor plate is fitted with a retractable handle providing convenient storage for your keyboard.

- Allows total flexibility of placement. Can easily be moved from desk to desk.
- Provides ultimate focal length adjustment, monitor height, tilt and swivel.
- Counter balanced

- Optimize valuable desk space.
- Removes monitor from work surface safely on a cushioned lipped plate.
- Maximize working comfort and efficiency.
- Enables you to position the monitor exactly for individual needs.
- Monitor height, tilt and swivel can be adjusted with a light touch from a seated position due to the unique counter balanced system.
- Eliminates cable clutter
- Conceals all cables neatly within its arm.
- Provides a grommet for additional cords e.g. telephone, calculator, lighting.

Dimensional data not binding. We reserve the right to alter specifications without notice.

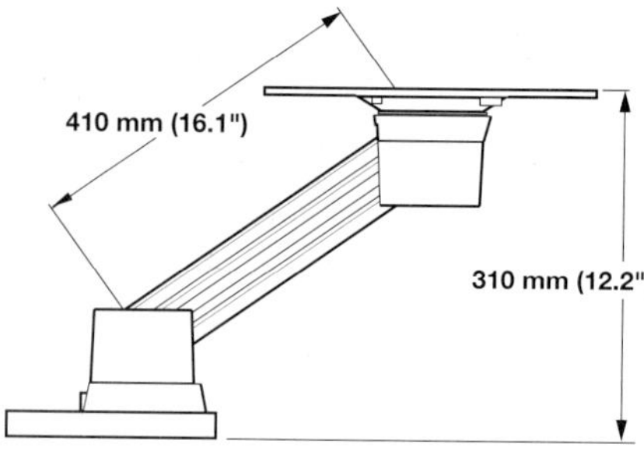

Ergoarm Monitor Stand,
with moveable surface mount, non-rotating arm
Weight capacity: **9-22 kg (20-48 lbs)**

Monitor plate dimensions: 349 mm x 349 mm (13¾" x 13¾")

Monitor tilt 25°

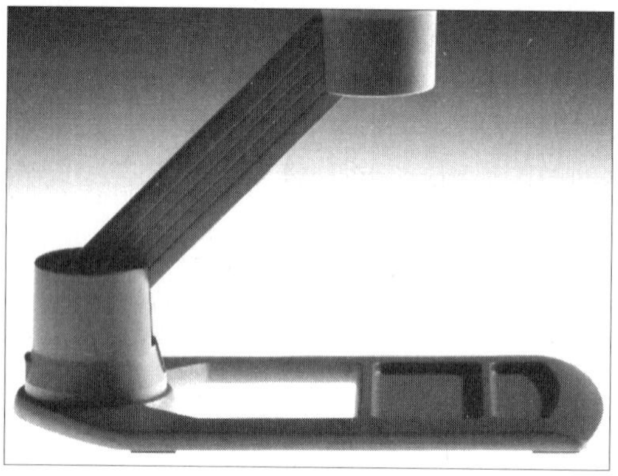

Finish:
arm: steel, epoxy powder-coated
housing: plastic

	Cat. No.
gray	639.98.532
black	639.98.336

Packing: 1 pc.

Ergoarm Monitor Stand,
with dual pupose mount. A Ø 60 mm (2⅜") hole is required for mounting.
Weight capacity: **9-22 kg (20-48 lbs)**

Monitor plate dimensions: 349 mm x 349 mm (13 3/4" x 13 3/4")

Monitor rotation 360°
Monitor tilt 25°
Arm rotation 360°

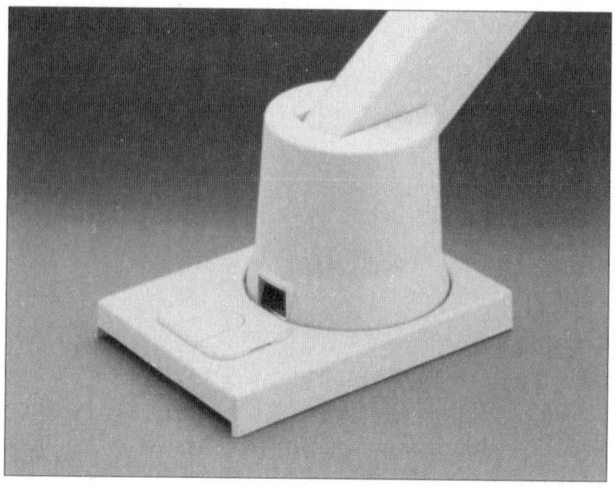

Finish:
arm: steel, epoxy powder-coated
housing: plastic

	Cat. No.
gray	639.98.540
black	639.98.340

Packing: 1 pc.

Dimensions in mm

The Desktop Liberators

HÄFELE

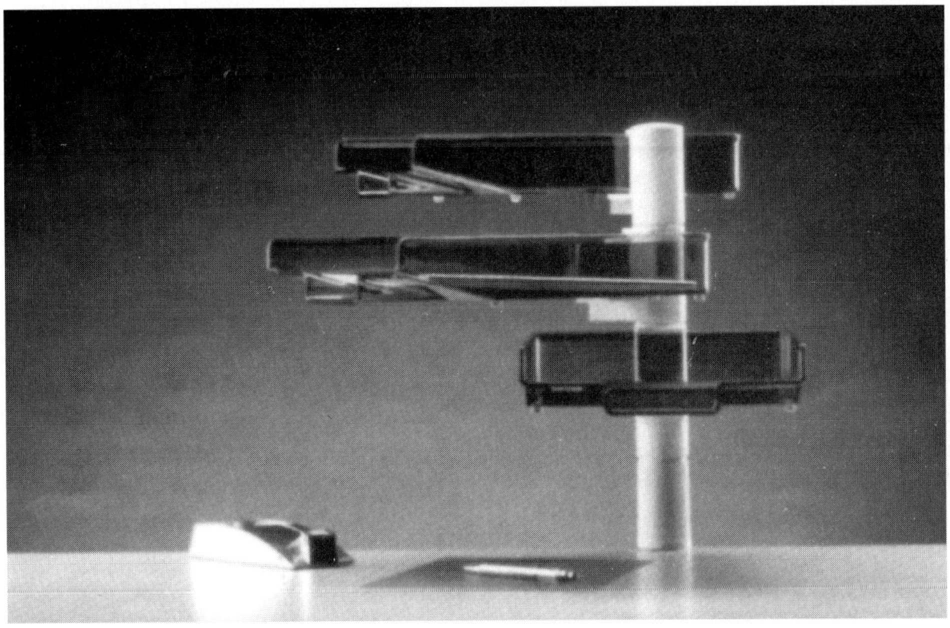

Letter Trays
- Load capacity = 3 kg per tray
- Swivels 360°
- Extension: min. 27 mm, max. 37 mm

Letter Trays
2- 4 tray sets, clamps to work surface with clamp supplied.
Approximately 21 to 72 mm
Total height: 2 trays: 320 mm,
3 trays: 410 mm,
4 trays: 500 mm
Paper size: 240 x 340 mm
Finish: plastic, steel

color	2 tray set	3 tray set	4 tray set
charcoal	818.63.227	818.63.236	818.63.245
light gray	818.63.729	818.63.738	818.63.747

Packing: 1 pc.

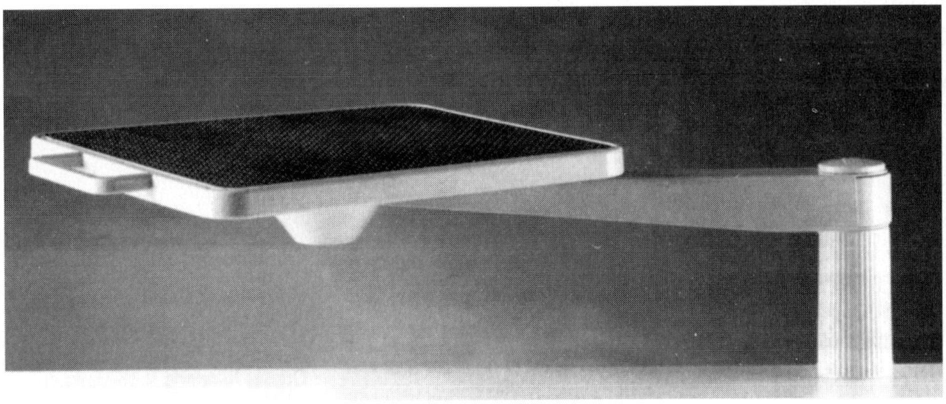

Monitor Swing
- Load capacity = 12 kg
- Swivels 360° both at post and under monitor.
- Projection over desktop = 400 mm
- Height above desktop = 95 mm

Monitor Swing
for monitor support, clamps to work surface for thicknesses from 16-76 mm. Clamps supplied.
Fits monitors up to approximately 170 x 260 mm
Finish: plastic, steel

color	Cat. No.
light gray	818.60.520
charcoal	818.60.220

Packing: 1 pc.

HÄFELE

The Desktop Liberators

Tele-swing
- Load capacity = 4 kg
- Swivels 360°
- Projection over desktop = 550 mm
- Height above desktop = 130 mm

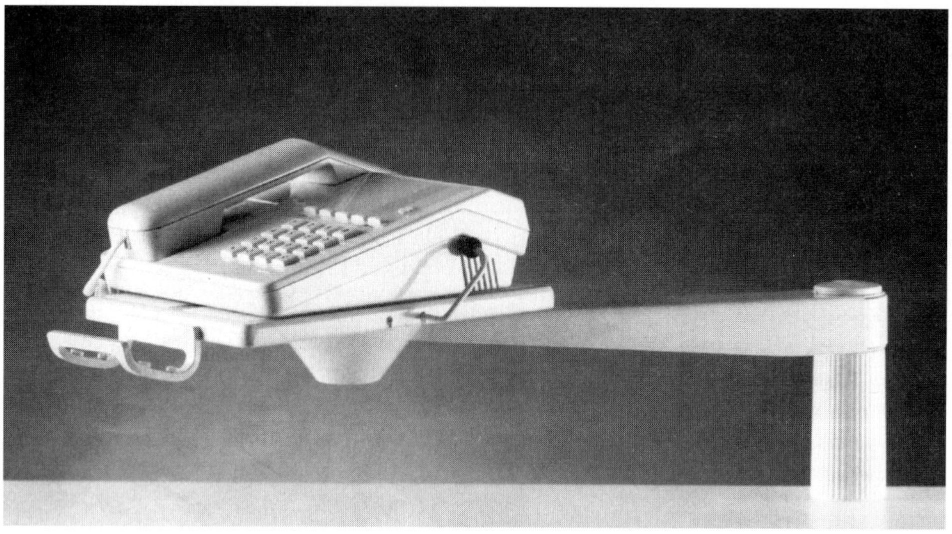

Tele-swing
for telephone with wire support, clamps to work surface for thicknesses from 16 to 74 mm. Clamp supplied.

Total height: 210 mm
Plate dimensions: 173 x 260
Finish: plastic, steel

color	Cat. No.
charcoal	818.61.220
light gray	818.61.520

Packing: 1 pc.

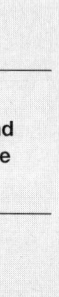

Telephone Stand
- Load capacity = 4 kg
- Swivels 360°
- Projection over desktop = 550 mm
- Height above desktop = 130 mm

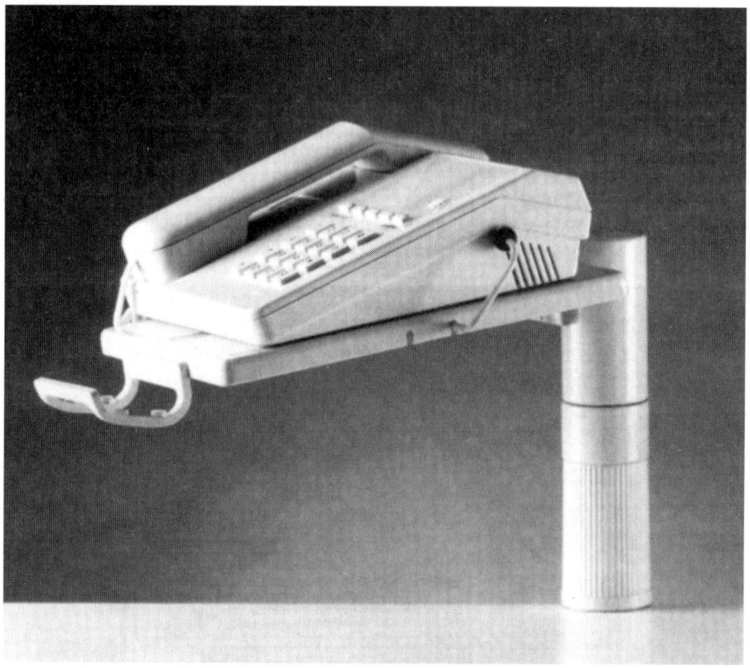

Telephone Stand
for telephone and wire support, clamps to work surface for thicknesses from 16 to 74 mm. Clamp supplied.
Fits large and small telephones up to approximately 170 x 260 mm
Total height: 210 mm
Plate dimensions: 173 x 260
Finish: plastic, steel

color	Cat. No.
light gray	818.62.704
charcoal	818.62.202

Packing: 1 pc.

Dimensional data not binding. We reserve the right to alter specifications without notice.

Dimensions in mm

Pencil Drawers/Inserts

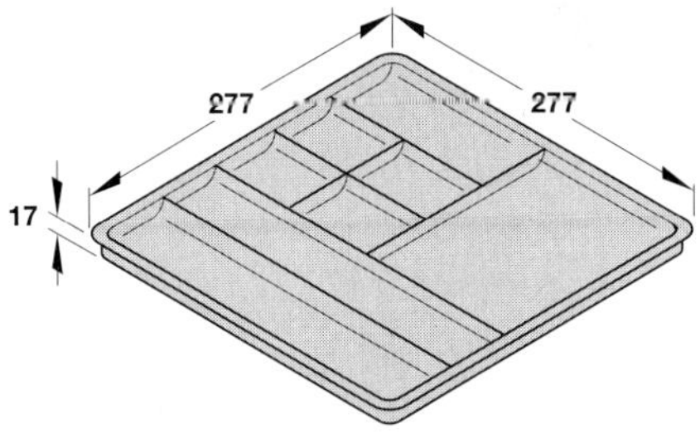

Utensil tray, 8 compartments
Finish: plastic, charcoal gray

Cat. No.	818.03.054

Packing: 1 pc.

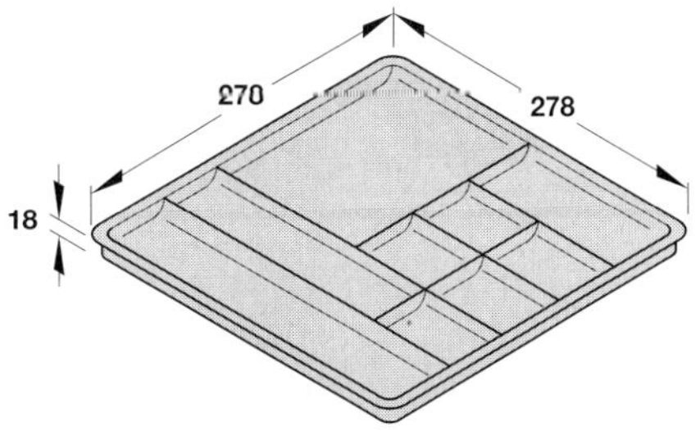

Utensil tray, 9 compartments
Finish: plastic, charcoal gray

Cat. No.	818.02.011

Packing: 1 pc.

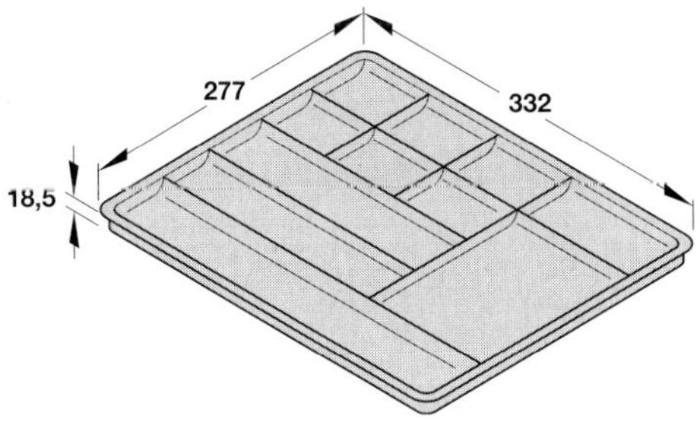

Utensil tray, 11 compartments
Finish: plastic, charcoal gray

Cat. No.	818.04.051

Packing: 1 pc.

Pencil Drawer

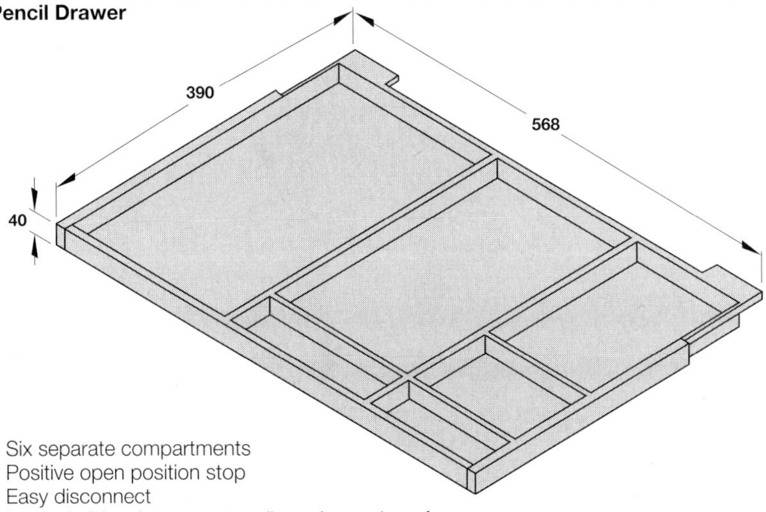

- Six separate compartments
- Positive open position stop
- Easy disconnect
- Integral slides that mount easily under work surface
- Screws included

Finish: textured plastic, gray or black

Cat. No.	gray	429.57.504
	black	429.57.308

Packing: 1 set

Drawers only
Finish: textured plastic

Cat. No.	gray	429.57.522
	black	429.57.326
	beige	429.57.424

Packing: 100 pcs.

Slides only
Finish: textured plastic

Cat. No.	gray	429.57.531
	black	429.57.335
	beige	429.57.433

Packing: 100 pairs

Pencil drawer extended:

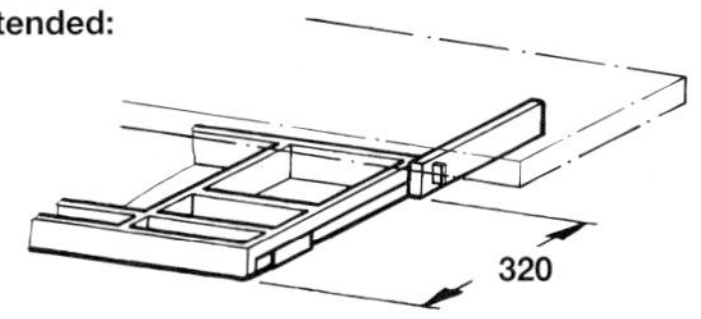

Pencil drawer retracted:

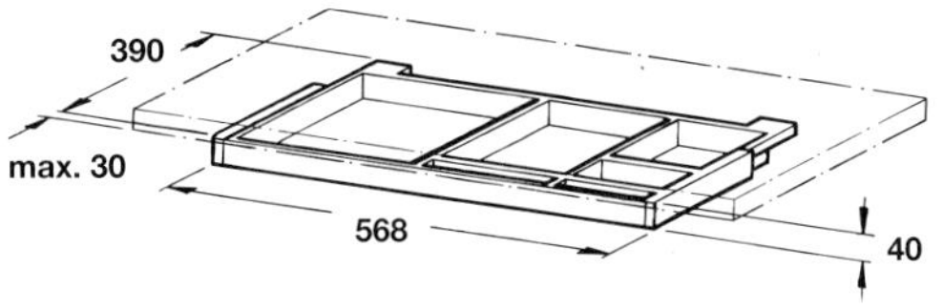

Dimensions in mm

The utensil trays fit...

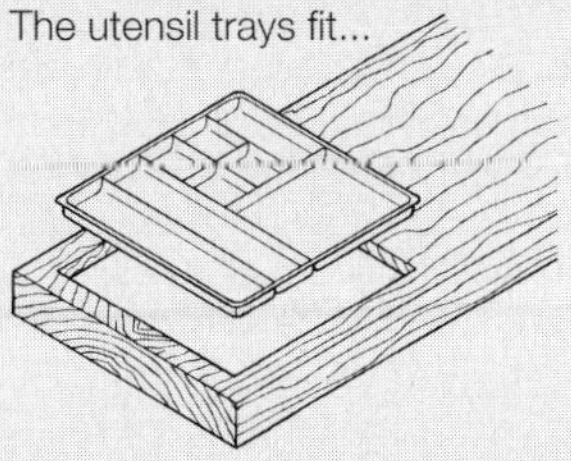

...in special openings of wood...

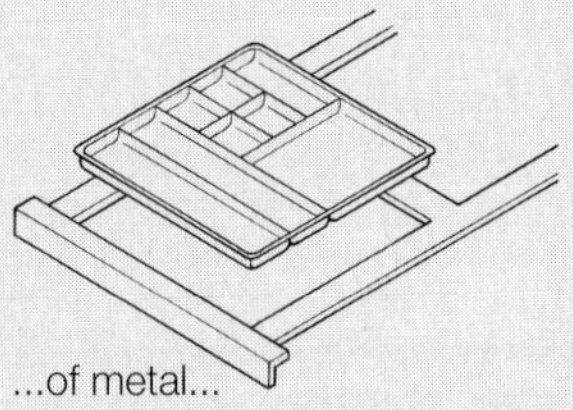

...of metal...

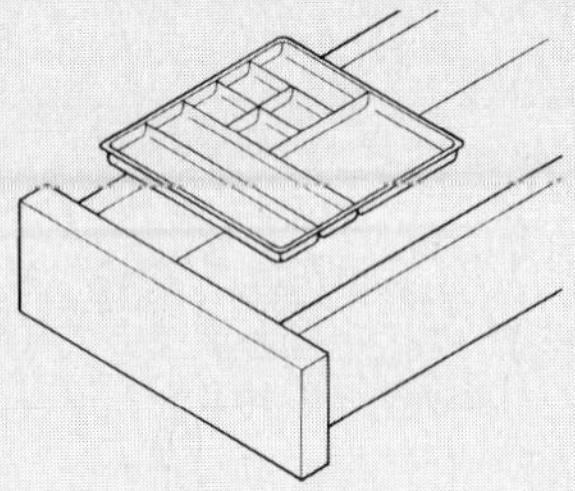

Furniture Support Systems, Office and Computer Furniture Accessories 6

Dimensional data not binding. We reserve the right to alter specifications without notice.

HÄFELE

Filing Tray Housings

This filing tray housing can be installed in a custom-made desk compartment or as a freestanding unit. It is particularly suitable for domestic filing purposes or for preliminary sorting.

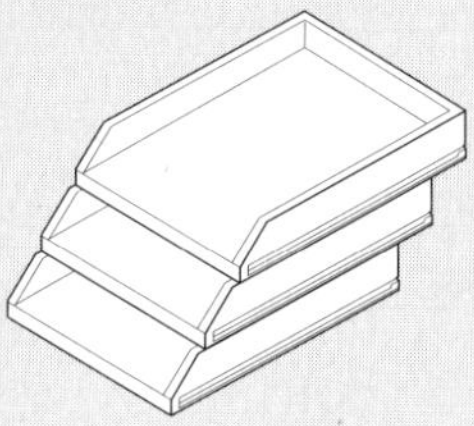

- This filing tray housing is designed so that it can be combined in rows or built up into complete filing systems.

- Based on the modular princple, the individual units can be joined together vertically and horizontally with the metal clips supplied with the housing.

Filing tray housing, with 5 trays.

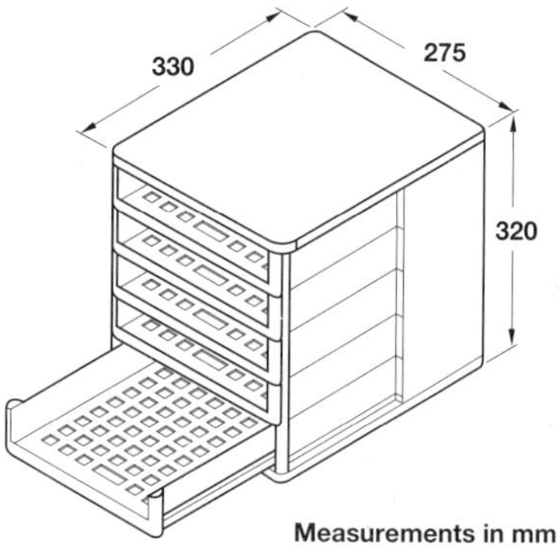

Measurements in mm

Finish: antistatic, impact-resistant, plastic, black-brown

Cat. No.	818.50.160

Packing: 1 pc.

Filing tray housing, built-in type, with 5 trays.

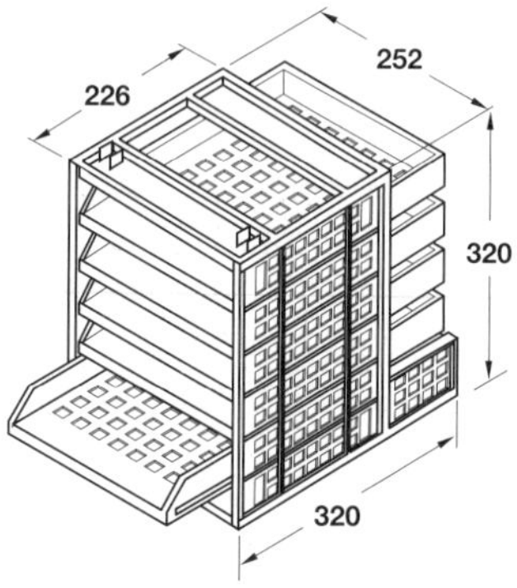

Measurements in mm

Finish: impact-resistant, plastic

Color	Catalog No.
white-gray	818.50.517
beige	818.50.419
black-brown	818.50.115

Packing: 1 pc.

Dimensional data not binding. We reserve the right to alter specifications without notice.

Dimensions in mm
Inches are approximate

Variant-S 386 File Drawer System

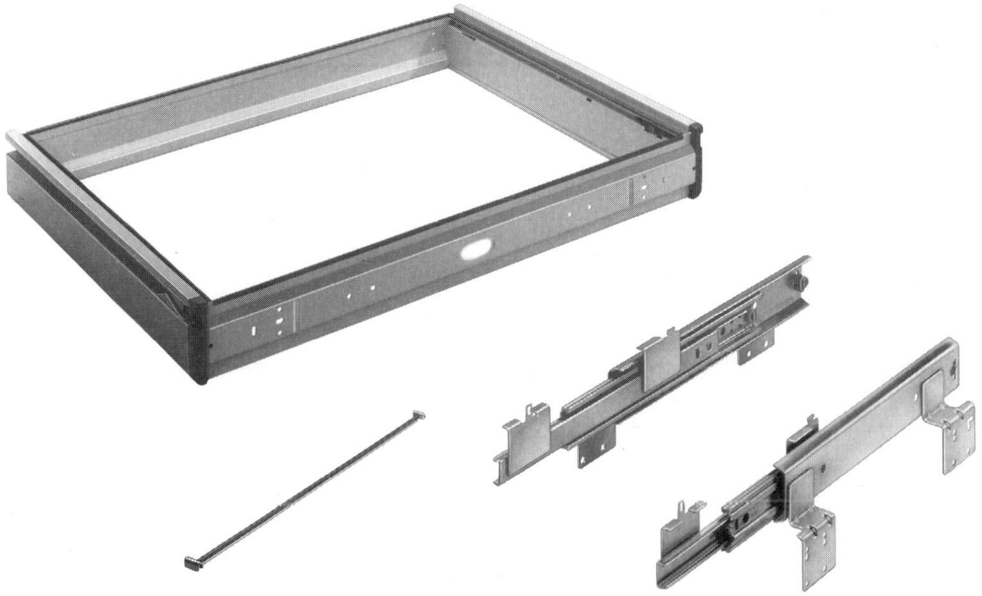

HÄFELE

Variant-S 386

- Steel frame filing system
- Pre-drilled, ready for installation
- Frame sides completely conceal drawer slides
- Plastic edge protection and corner mouldings
- 32 mm compatible
- Shipped RTA to save on costly freight charges. Also conserves on storage space.
- Convenient handle hole eliminates need for additional handle.
- Spring clip system for easy mounting of slides
- Epoxy coated steel

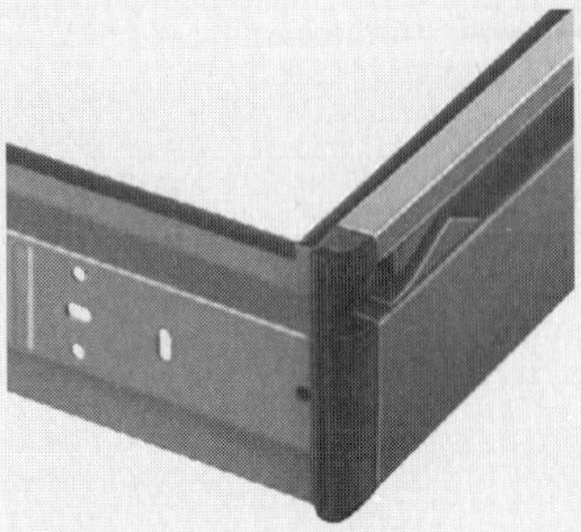

Filing Options

	30"	36"	42"
Letter Size Arranged front to back	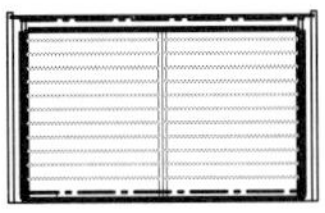	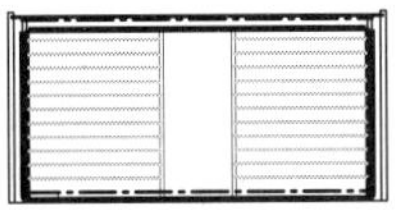	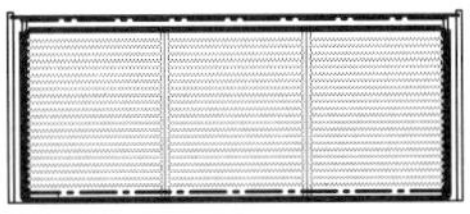
Legal Size Arranged front to back		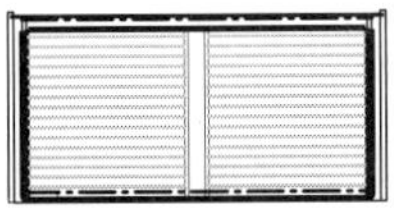	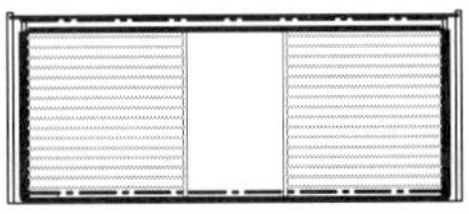
Letter Size Arranged side to side	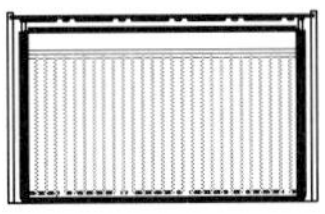	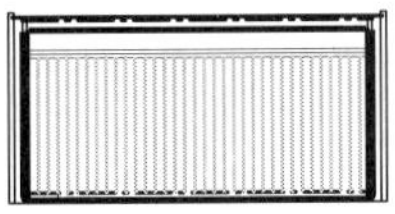	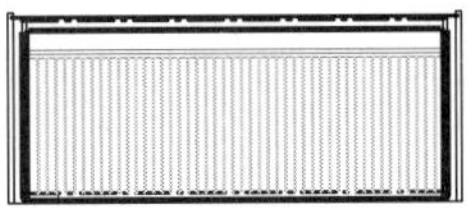
Legal Size Arranged side to side	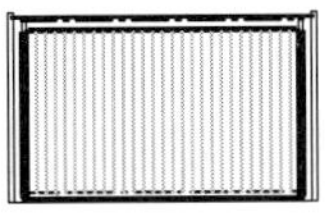	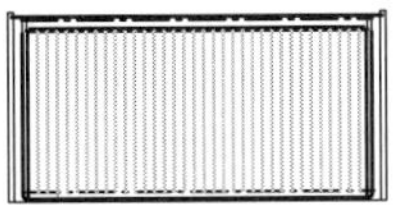	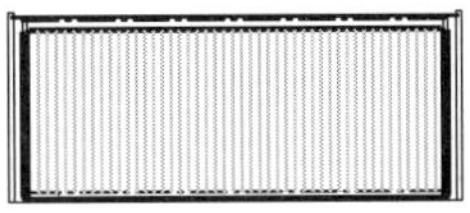

Frame Widths

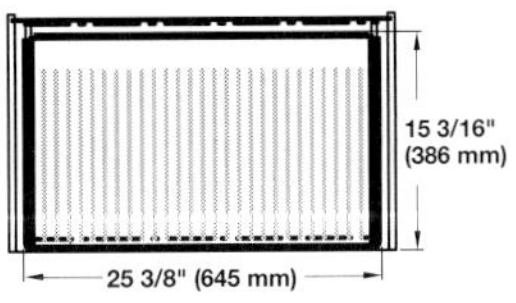

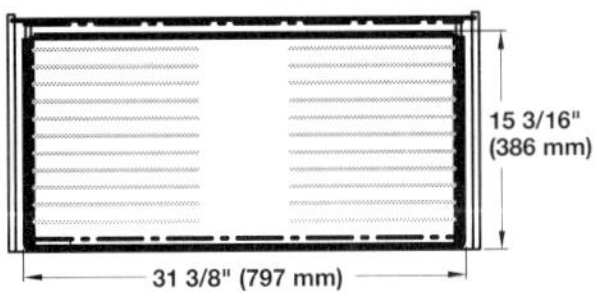

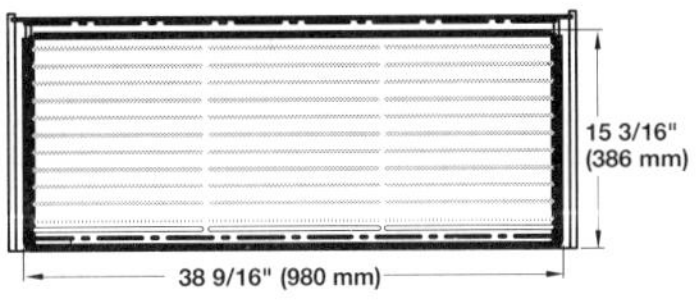

Dimensions in mm

Furniture Support Systems, Office and Computer Furniture Accessories 6

HÄFELE

Variant-S 386 File Drawer System

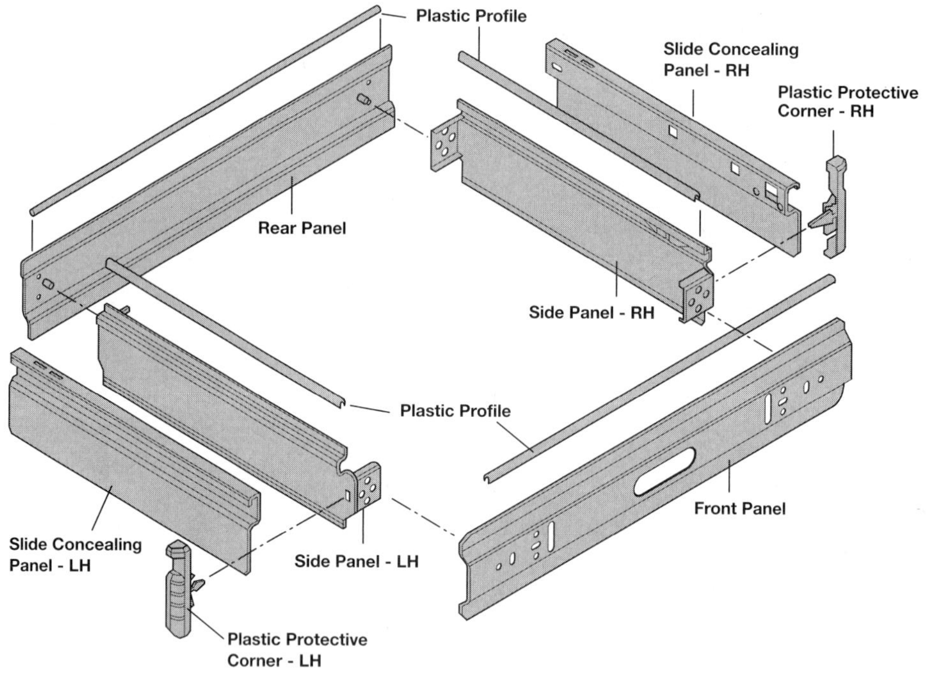

Drawer front mounting screws, 5 mm dia.

Length	Cat. No.
14 mm	013.10.149

Packing: 200 pcs.

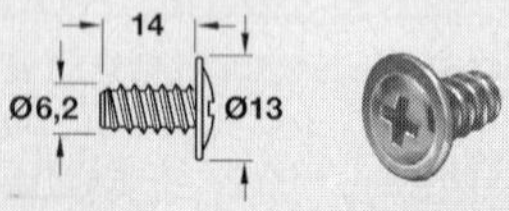

Variant Frame Filing System

Three widths are available for a variety of filing solutions. With each kit, the following parts are included:

1	Front Panel
1	Back Panel
1	Side Panel, left hand
1	Slide Concealing Panel, left hand
1	Side Panel, right hand
1	Slide Concealing Panel, right hand
2	Plastic Profiles for front and back panels
2	Plastic Profiles for Side Panels
1	Plastic Protective Corner Right Hand
1	Plastic Protective Corner Left Hand
**2	Cross Bars 386 mm
*1	Cross Bar 642 mm

Slides are ordered separately. See drawer slides.

*** 36" option includes the same parts but with:**
1 pc. - 794 mm cross bar

****42" option includes the same part but with:**
1 pc. - 973 mm crossbar and

4 pcs. - 386 mm crossbars

Finish: steel, black RAL 9011

Option	Dim. A	Dim. B	Cat. No.
30"	700 mm	645 mm	425.25.331
36"	852 mm	797 mm	425.25.332
42"	1035 mm	980 mm	425.25.333

Packing: 1 pc

6 Furniture Support Systems, Office and Computer Furniture Accessories

Front panel supports:
Use on both sides of frame for maximum stability

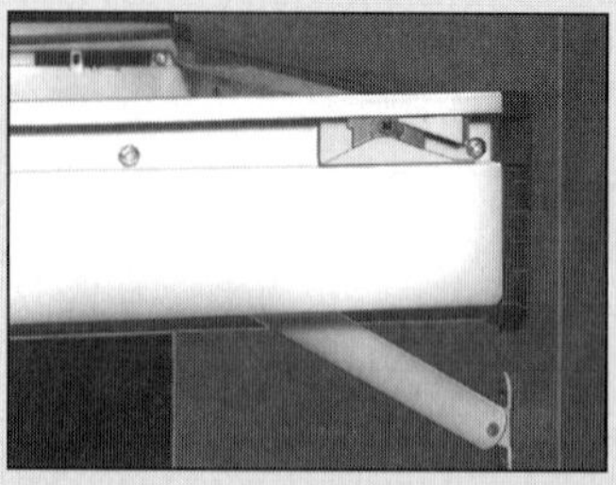

Finish:

Drawer front heights from 192 mm	
Black RAL 9011	424.00.939

Packing: 1 pair

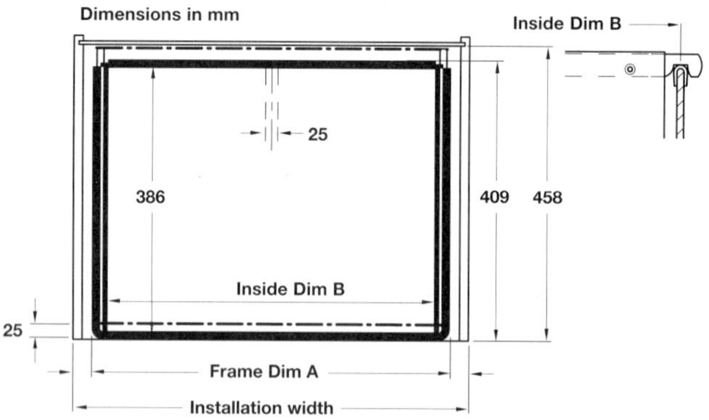

Variant-S 386 Front Panel

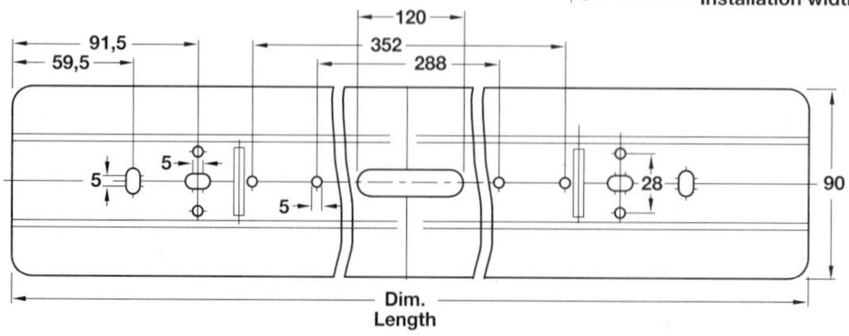

Dimensions in mm

Dimensional data not binding. We reserve the right to alter specifications without notice.

Variant-S 386 File Drawer System

HÄFELE

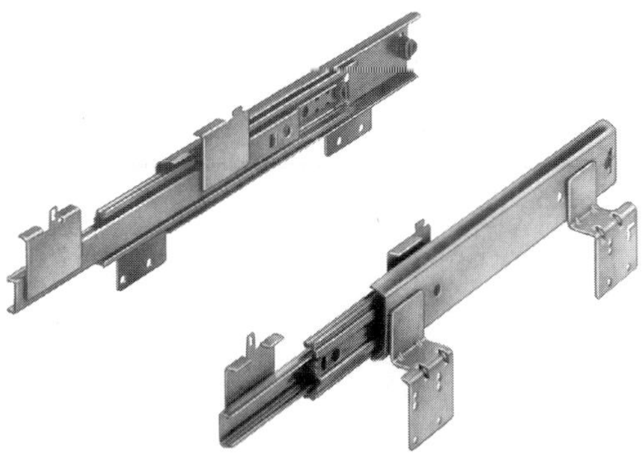

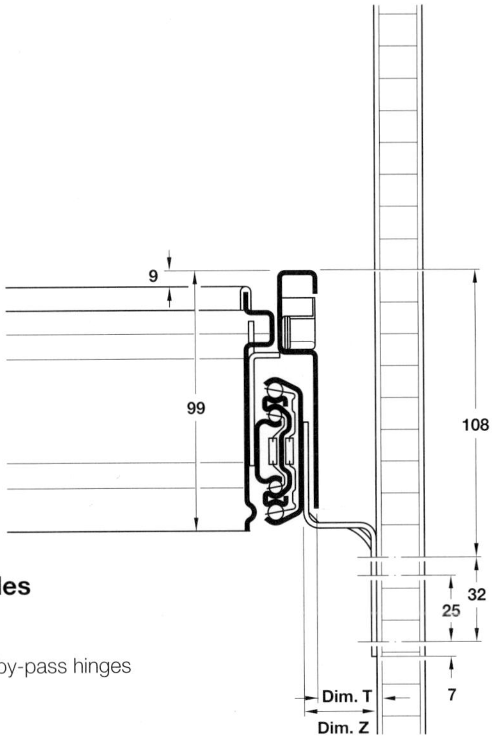

Drawer slides for Variant-S 386

- 1" over travel
- 150 lb. capacity
- Hold-in detent
- Z-shaped mounting bracket. Available to accommodate 2 different inside widths

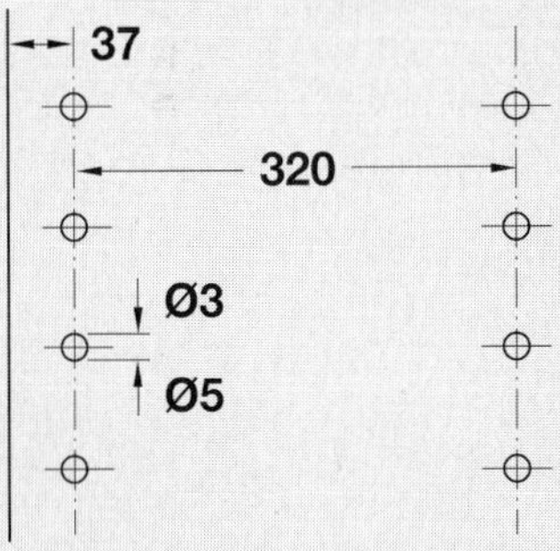

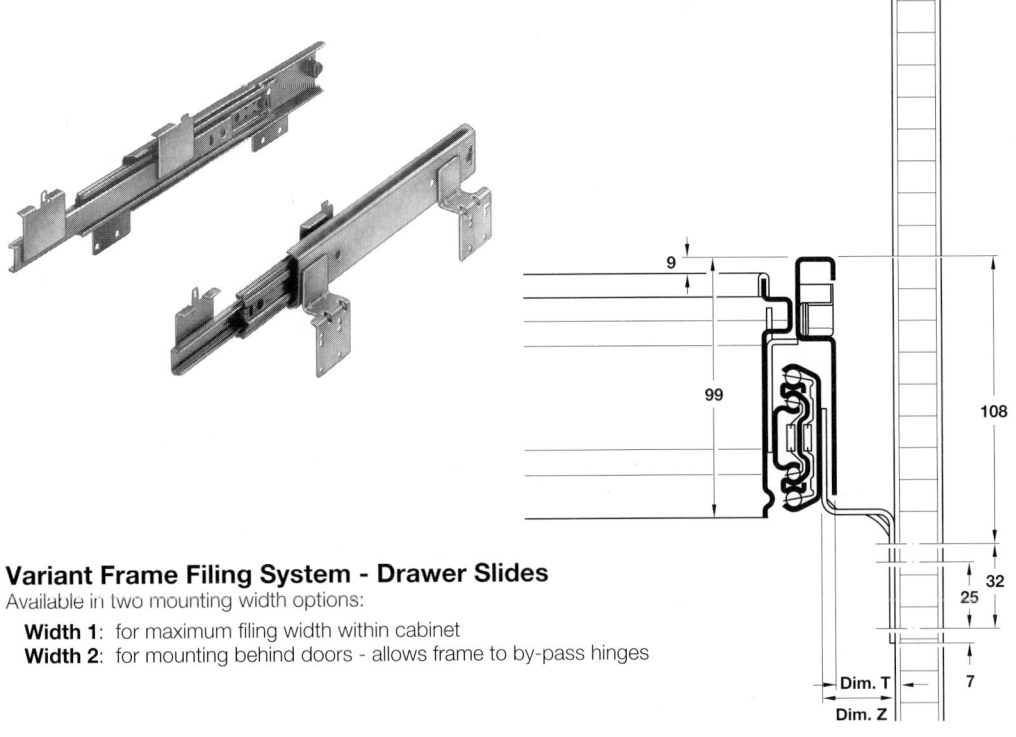

Variant Frame Filing System - Drawer Slides

Available in two mounting width options:

Width 1: for maximum filing width within cabinet
Width 2: for mounting behind doors - allows frame to by-pass hinges

Finish: steel, zinc plated

	installation width			Dim.	Dim.	
	30" option	**36" option**	**42" option**	**T**	**Z**	**Cat. No.**
width 1	707 mm	859 mm	1045 mm	3.5	9.5	424.19.300
width 2	742 mm	894 mm	1077 mm	21	27	424.19.330

Packing: 1 pair

SYSTEM VARIANTA 32

Flush mounting

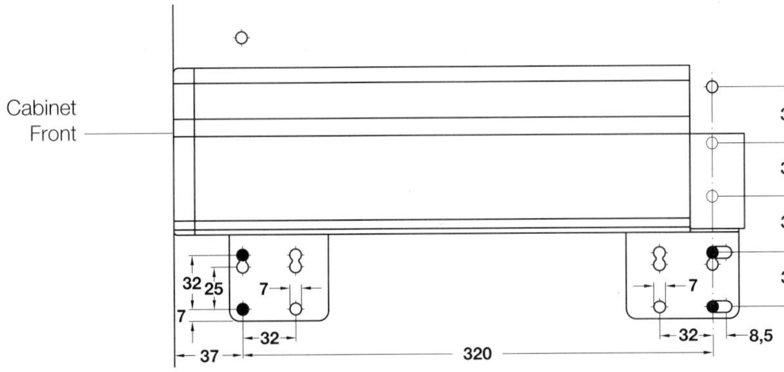

Backset mounting

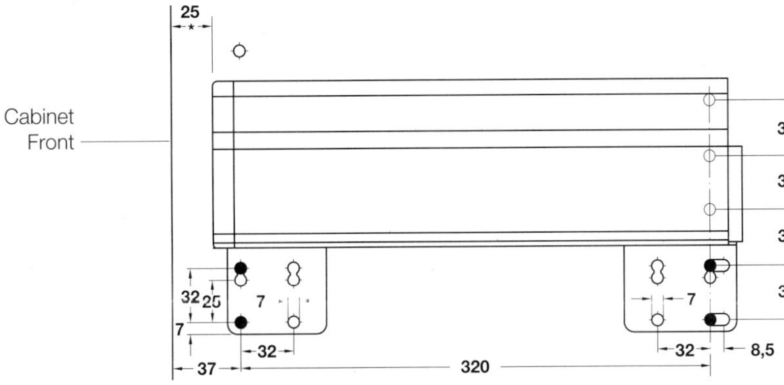

Furniture Support Systems, Office and Computer Furniture Accessories

6

- Two positions available for positioning of slides. Flush mounting for attachment of drawer faces or with a 25 mm backset for mounting behind doors.

Dimensional data not binding. We reserve the right to alter specifications without notice.

Dimensions in mm

Office Furniture Fittings

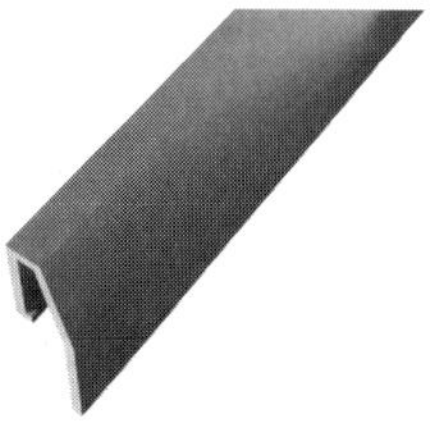

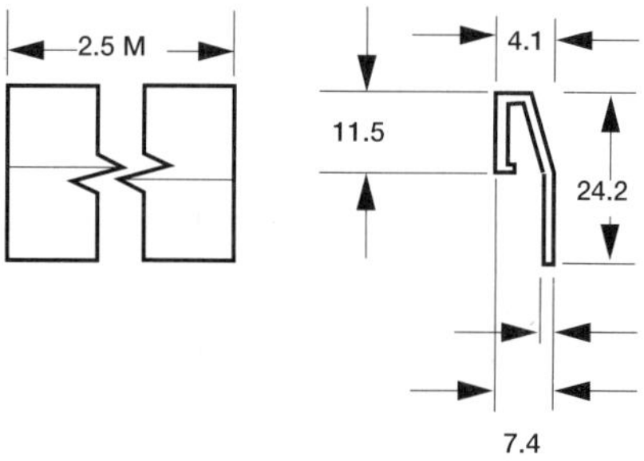

Hanging file rail - aluminum
- Available in four anodized finishes
- No holes provided - allows you to place them where needed
- Shipped in 2.5 meter lengths

Finish: aluminum, anodized

Finish	Cat. No.
satin silver	422.71.901
satin gold	422.71.803
black	422.71.303
antique bronze	422.71.107

Packing: 2.5 meters

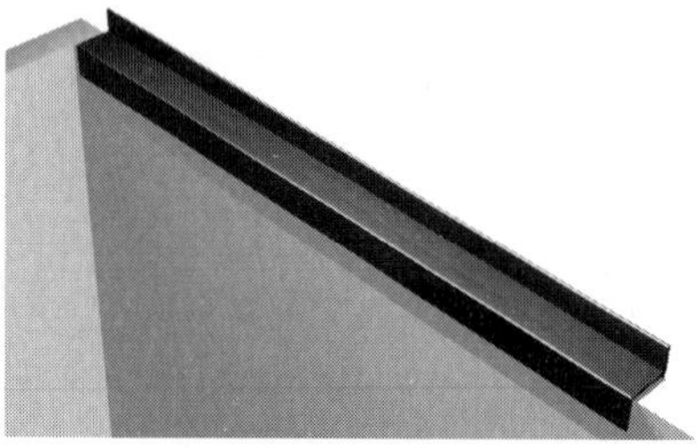

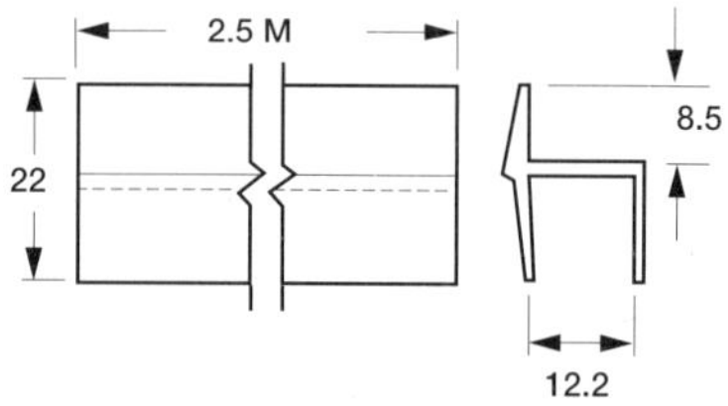

Hanging file rail - plastic
- Economical file rail system
- Can be snapped on ½" drawer sides
- Requires no glue or staples
- 2.5 meter lengths

Finish: plastic

Cat. No.	Black	422.72.391
	White	422.73.790

Packing: 100 pcs.

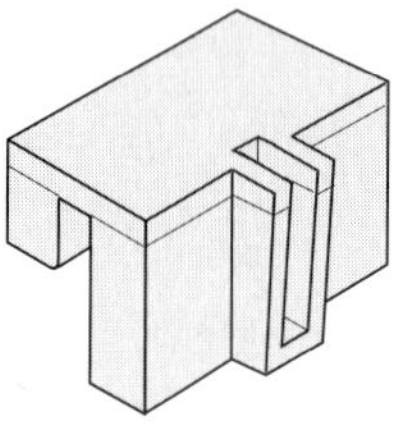

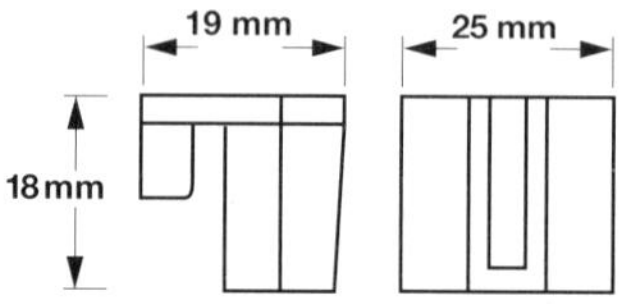

Hanging file rail clip

Allows files to be hung at 90° angle to rails.

Finish: plastic

Cat. No.	Black	422.73.300
	White	422.73.700

Packing: 10 pcs.

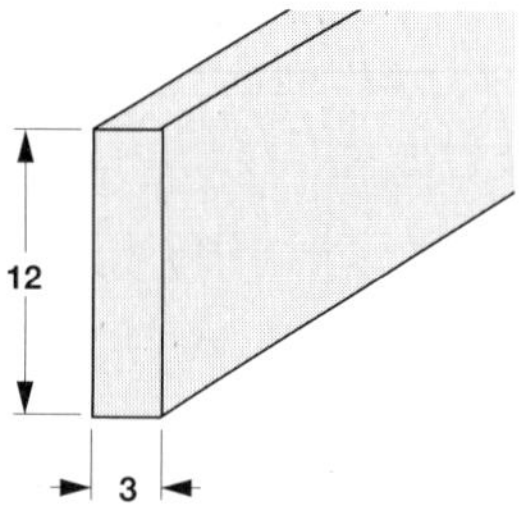

Hanging file cross rail

Fits in clip above. Easily cut to length for your application.

Finish: aluminum, unfinished

Cat. No.	422.74.900

Packing: 1 pc.

Paper Slot Grommets

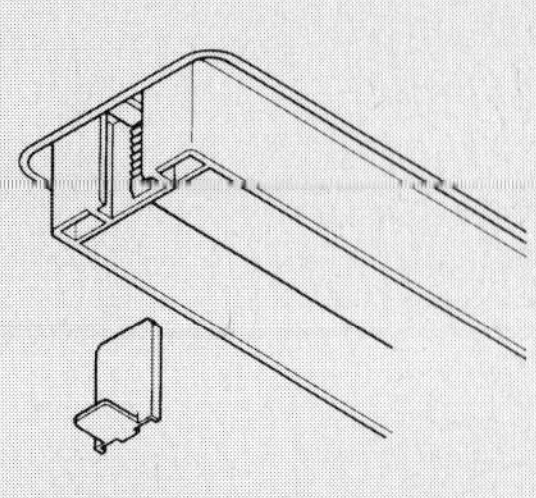

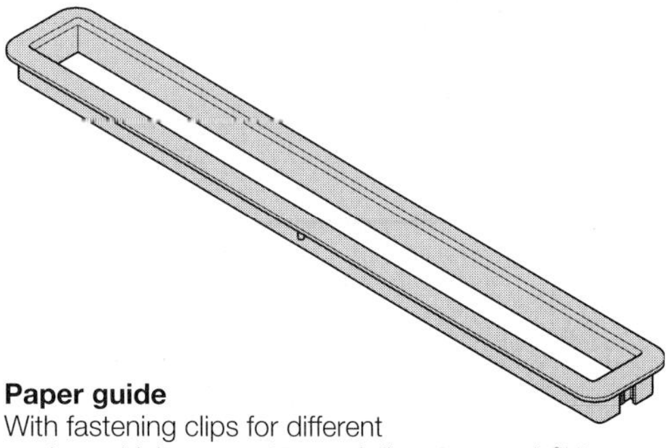

Paper guide

With fastening clips for different worktop thicknesses 25 mm (1") to 35 mm (1⅜").

Finish: plastic

Color	Cat. No.
brown	429.98.176
black	429.98.372

Packing: 1 set

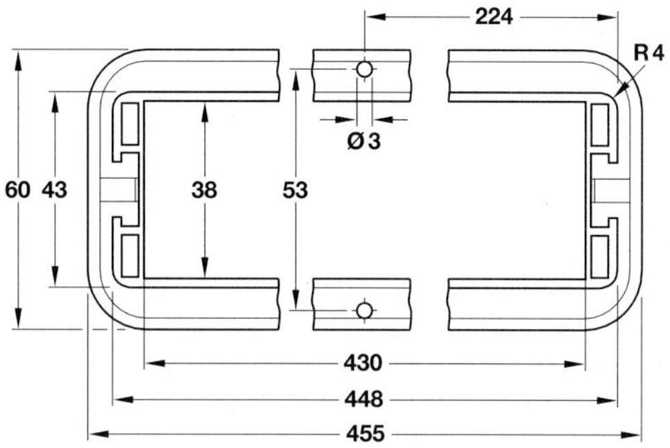

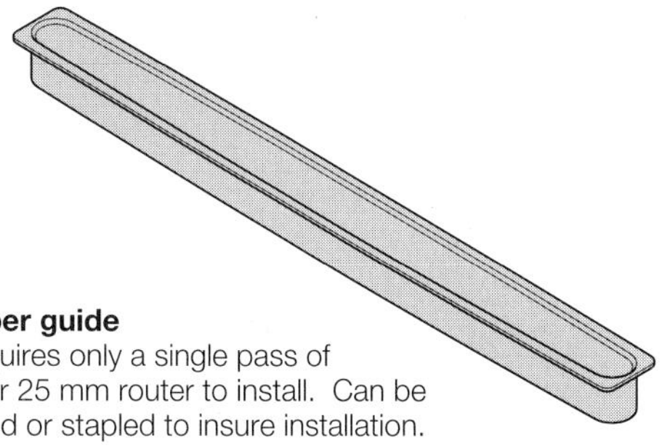

Paper guide

Requires only a single pass of 1" or 25 mm router to install. Can be glued or stapled to insure installation.

Finish: plastic

Color	Cat. No.
light gray	429.98.596
white	429.98.792
brown	429.98.194
black	429.98.390

Packing: 1 pc.

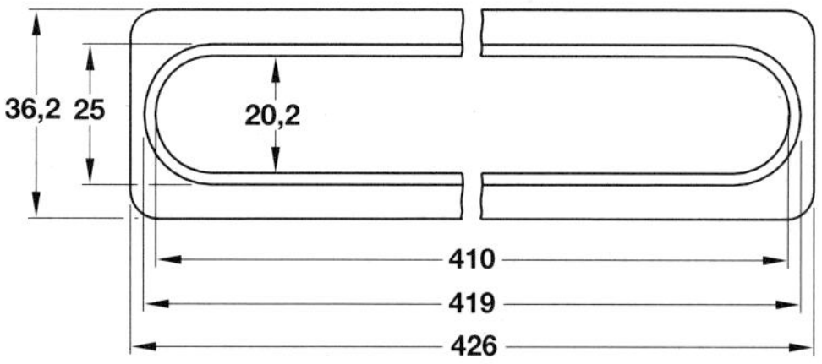

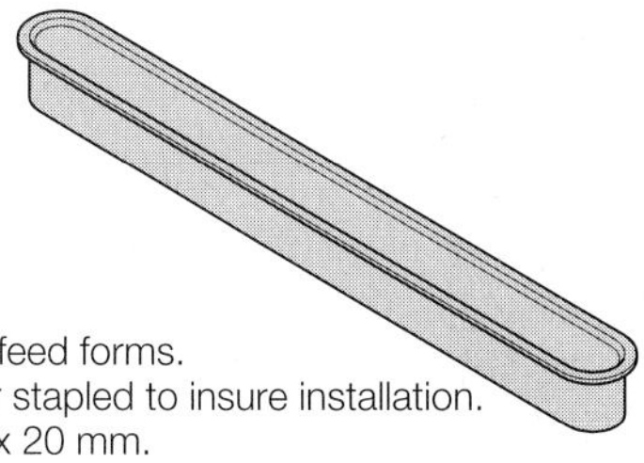

Paper guide

For continuous-feed forms.
Can be glued or stapled to insure installation.
Paper size 310 x 20 mm.

Finish: plastic

Color	Cat. No.
light gray	429.98.514
brown	429.98.112
black	429.98.318

Packing: 1 pc.

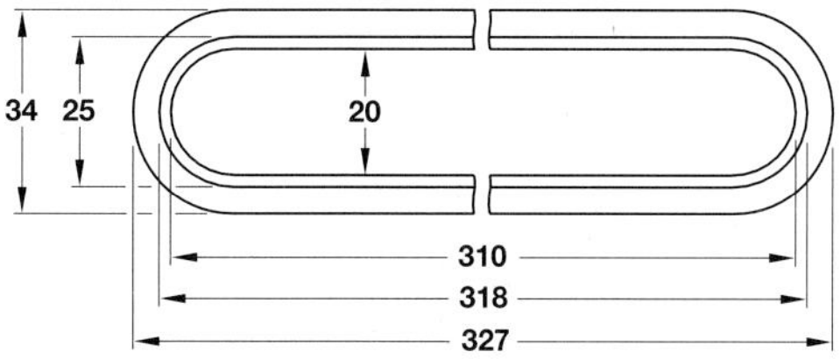

Cable Grommets

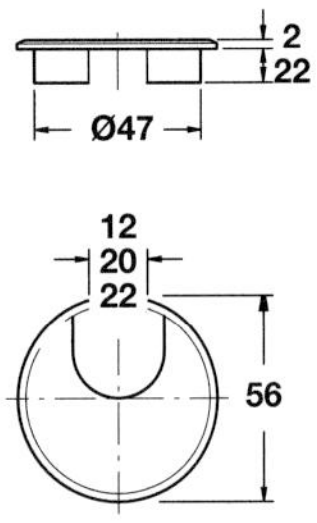

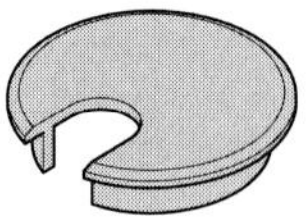

Cover with cut-out for cables, one-piece, round for press-fitting or glueing into **Ø 63 mm** (2 1/2") holes,

Finish: zinc die-cast

	Cat. No.		
Finish	40x12 x46	40x12x46	40x12x46
Chrome pol.	429.94.212	429.94.221	429.94.258
Brass pol.	429.94.810	429.94.829	429.94.856
Bronze ant.	429.94.114	429.94.123	429.94.150
Black	429.94.310		
Brass ant.	429.94.025		

Packing: 10 pcs.

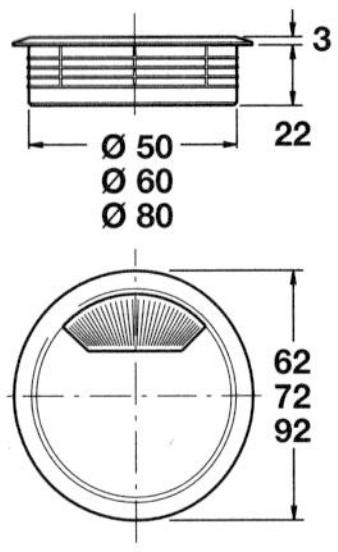

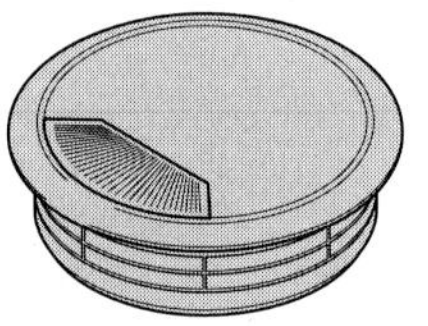

Cable set two-piece, round, with spring closure
Finish: plastic

	Cat. No.		
Finish	50 mm dia.	60 mm dia.	80 mm dia.
white	429.99.735	429.99.726	429.99.744
gray	429.99.539	429.99.520	429.99.548
beige	429.99.431	429.99.422	429.99.440
almond	429.99.039	429.99.020	429.99.048
brown	429.99.137	429.99.128	429.99.146
black	429.99.333	429.99.324	429.99.342
chrome matt	429.97.222	429.97.231	429.97.240
brass matt	429.97.526	429.97.535	429.97.544

Packing: 10 pcs.

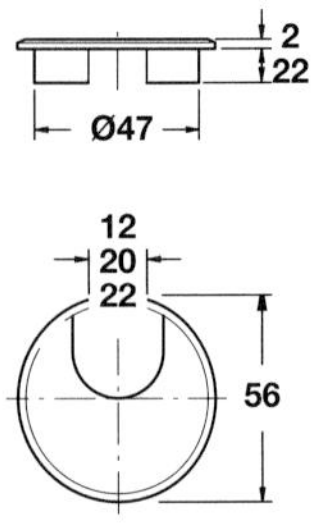

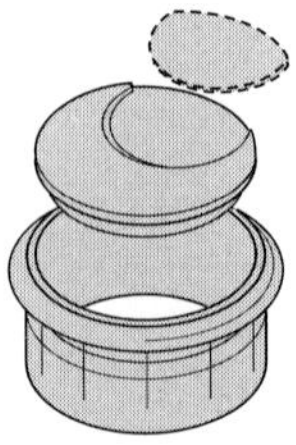

Cable set two-piece, round, with break-away tab in cover cap.

Finish: plastic

Finish	Cat. No.
almond	429.93.019
brown	429.93.117
black	429.93.313

Packing: 10 pcs.

Dimensions in mm

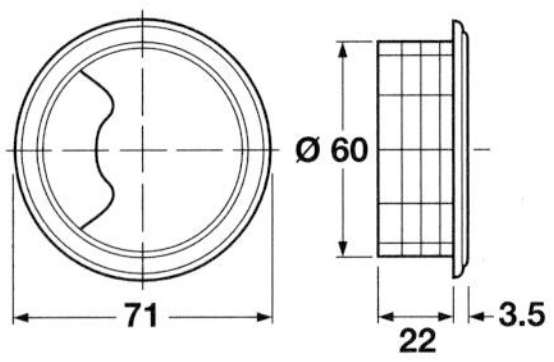

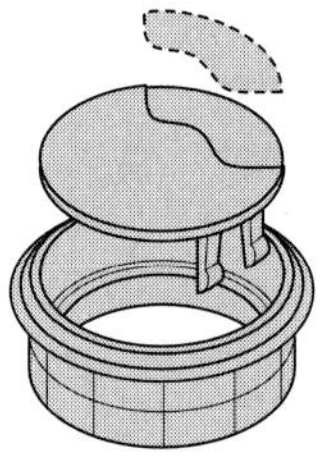

Cable set, two-piece, with break-away tab cover cap.

Finish: plastic

Finish	Cat. No.
almond	429.93.028
brown	429.93.126
black	429.93.322

Packing: 10 pcs.

Dimensional data not binding. We reserve the right to alter specifications without notice.

Cable Grommets

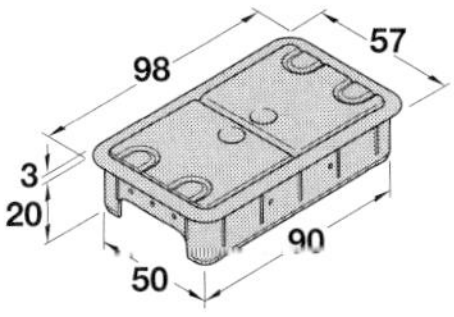

Cable set, three-piece, rectangular, inserts in desk top
Includes:
1-frame
2-hinged covers, that can be removed for inserting plugs. Two cable holes can be broken out of each cover.

Finish: plastic

Color	Cat. No.
chrome colored	428.98.260
white	428.98.715
light gray	428.98.519
beige	428.98.411
brown	428.98.117
black	428.98.313

Packing: 10 pcs.

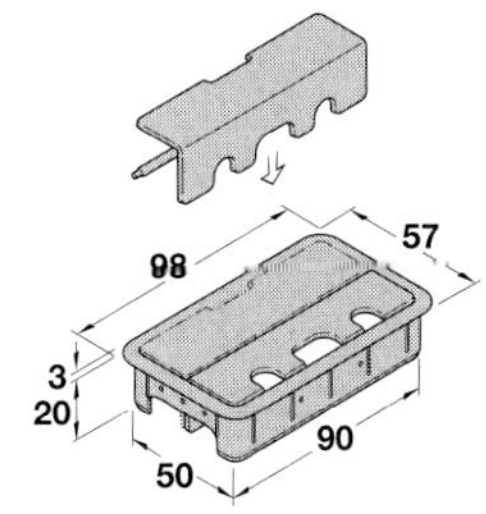

Cable set, three-piece, rectangular, inserts in desk top
Includes:
1-frame
2-angular profiles, with or without cable apertures for inserting in the frame.

Finish: plastic

Color	Cat. No.
chrome colored	428.98.279
white	428.98.724
light gray	428.98.528
beige	428.98.420
sepia brown	428.98.126
black	428.98.322

Packing: 10 pcs.

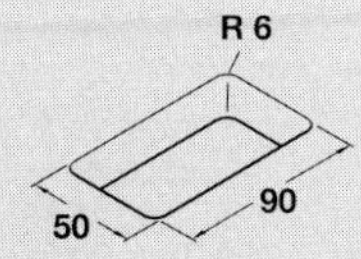

Hole diagram

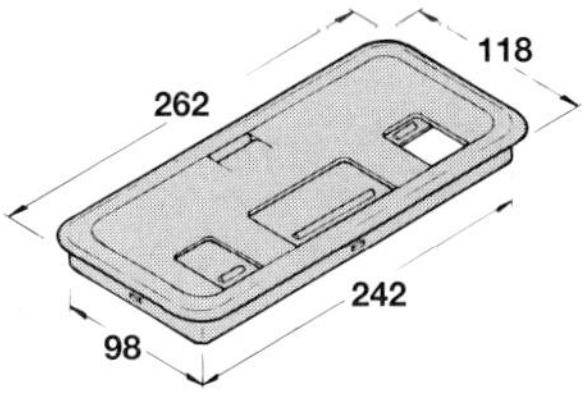

Cable set, two-piece, rectangular, inserts in desk top
Includes:
1-frame
1-cover with three sliding openings for cable insertion

Finish: plastic

Color	Cat. No.
white	429.99.771
light gray	429.99.575
brown	429.99.173

Packing: 5 pcs.

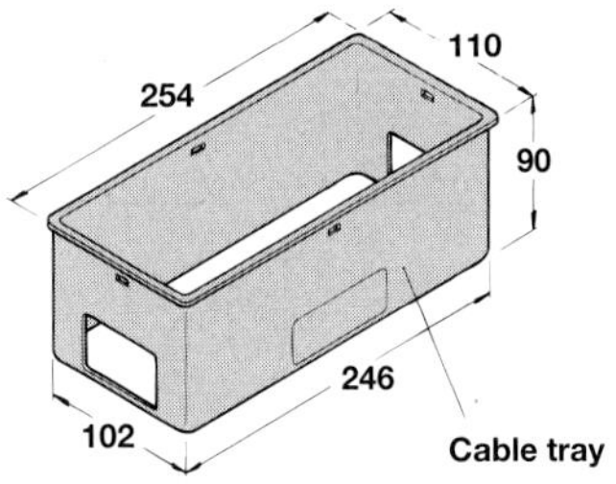

Cable tray,
clips into cable set shown opposite
Finish: plastic, black

Cat. No.	429.99.388

Packing: 5 pcs.

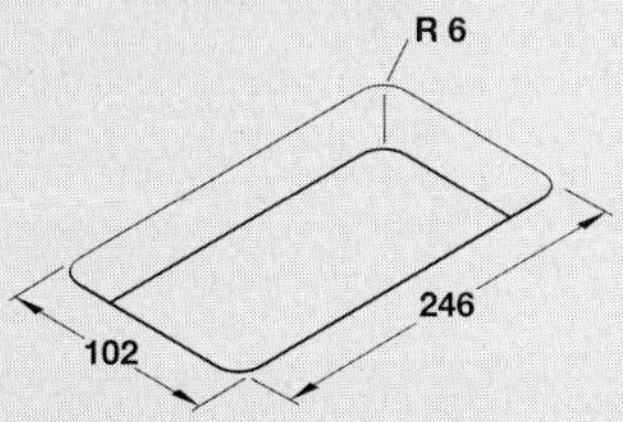

Hole diagram for cable set and cable tray

Furniture Support Systems, Office and Computer Furniture Accessories **6**

Cable trunking
Self adhesive tape factory applied.
Provides efficient cable concealment.
Finish: plastic, black, pressure sensitive tape

Cat. No.	829.15.302

Packing: 2.5 meter pc.

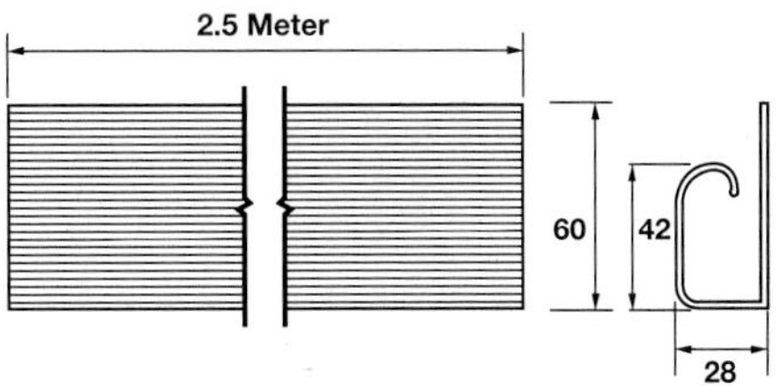

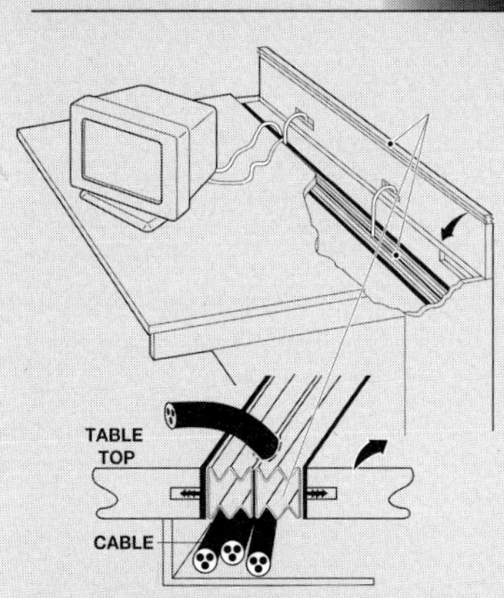

- Eliminates unsightly holes and caps. Provides the user with the flexibility of moving electrical equipment anywhere along the surface without tangling wires.

PVC Continuous Cord Grommet
Made of flexible PVC, it attaches to surfaces 19 mm thick by fitting into a single 3 mm routed groove.
Finish: PVC

Color	Cat. No.
brown	829.14.109
gray	829.14.501
black	829.14.305

Packing: 1.6 meter pc.

Dimensional data not binding.
We reserve the right to alter specifications without notice.

Dimensions in mm

HÄFELE

Electrical Management

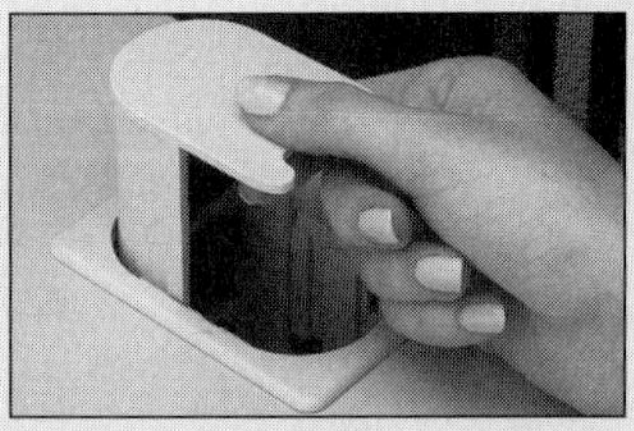

Pull up

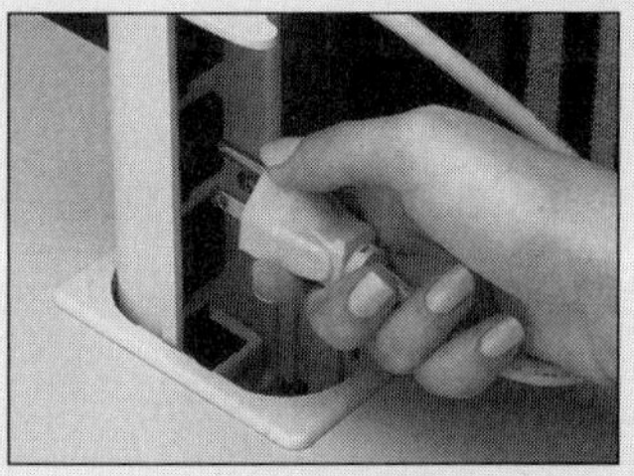

Plug in

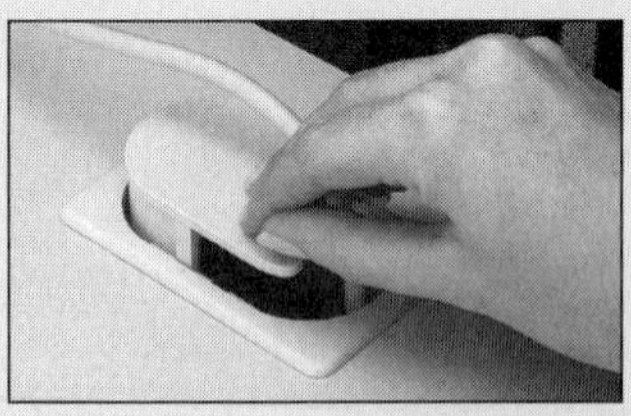

Push down

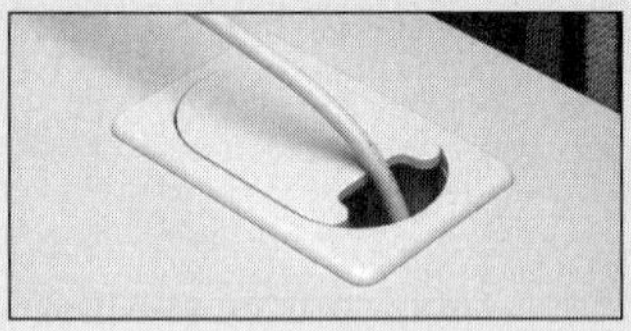

Closed position

6 Furniture Support Systems, Office and Computer Furniture Accessories

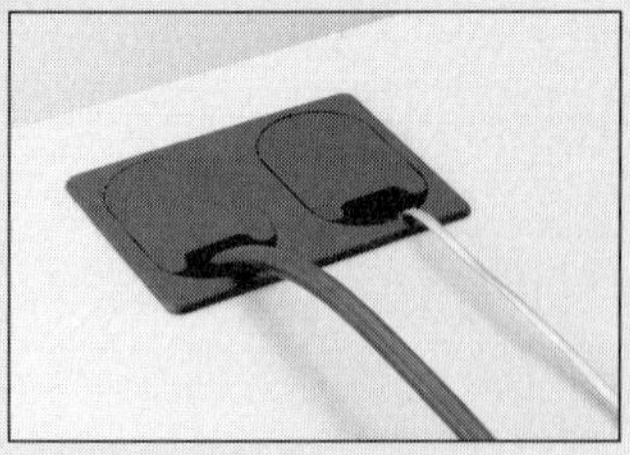

- UL and CSA listed
- Complete with mounting instructions and template
- Blank covers outlet opening for additional outlets that can be locally obtained.
- Allows versatility of multiple voice/data connections. Uses either Amp or Panduit modules.

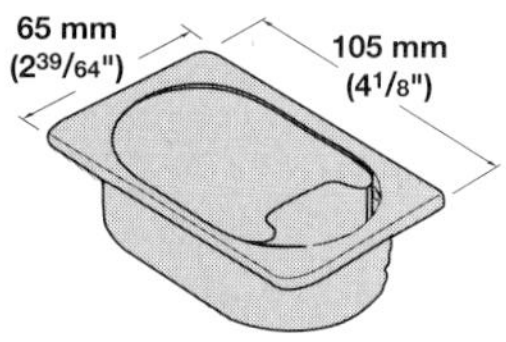

Grommet kit permits you to route power, communication or data cables through a work surface. Allows you to add power center at later date.
Finish: plastic

Cat. No.	white	428.97.700
	black	428.97.300

Packing: 1 pc.

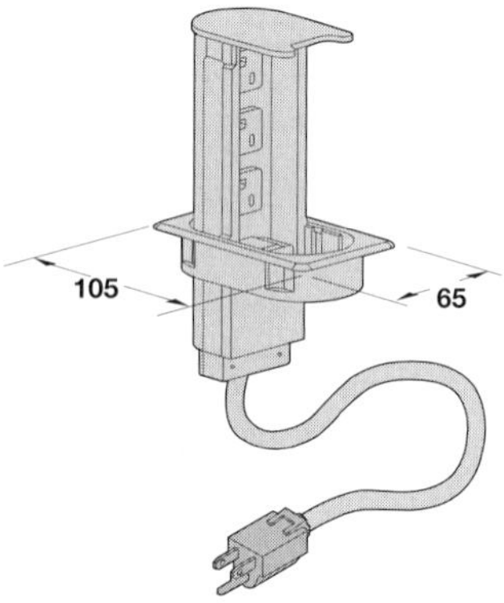

Retractable power center complete with grommet/cover kit. No unsightly power cords, plugs or outlets to look at. Equipped with 30 amp circuit breaker, 3 simplex outlets and 6 ft. power cord
Finish: plastic

Cat. No.	white	822.50.710
	black	822.50.310

Packing: 1 set

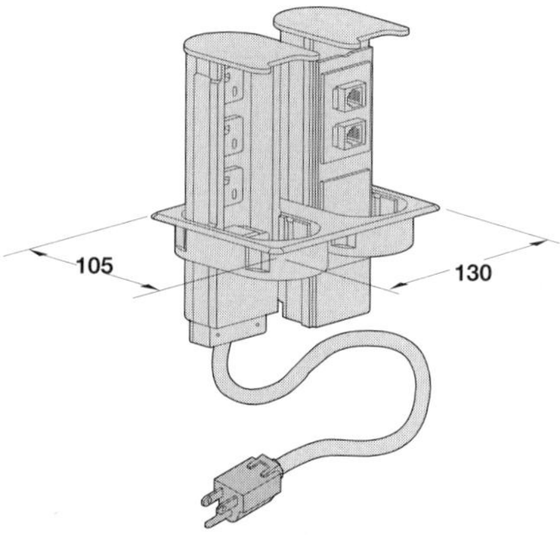

Retractable communication center
Includes 3 simplex outlets, 30 amp circuit breaker, 6 ft. power cord, 2 pcs - RJ 45 outlets ready for installation.

Finish: plastic

Cat. No.	white	822.50.720
	black	822.50.320

Packing: 1 set

Dimensional data not binding. We reserve the right to alter specifications without notice.

Dimensions in mm

Turntables

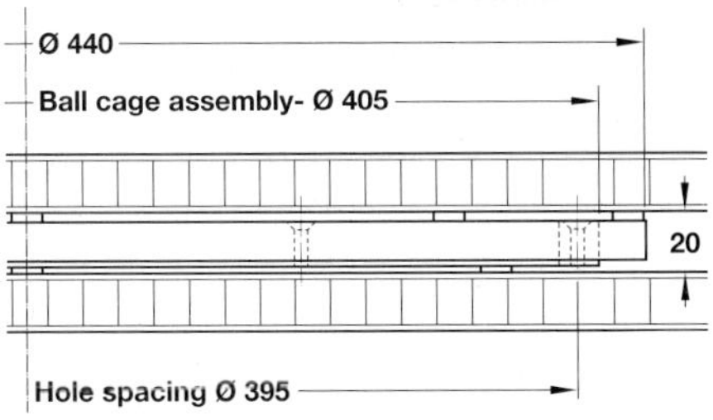

Turntable, extra heavy duty
For large surfaces.
Rotates 360°, ball-bearing mounted
Load capacity: 100 kg
Finish: ABS-plastic

Cat. No.	646.19.101

Packing: 1 pc.

Load capacity: 150 kg
Finish: Aluminum

Cat. No.	646.20.024

Packing: 1 pc.

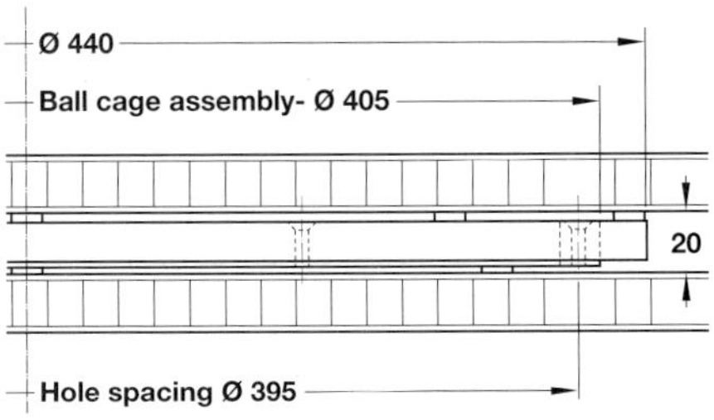

Turntable, extra heavy duty
To satisfy high quality application.
Rotates 360°, ball-bearing mounted
Load capacity: 100 kg
Finish: Aluminum

Cat. No.	646.20.006

Packing: 1 pc.

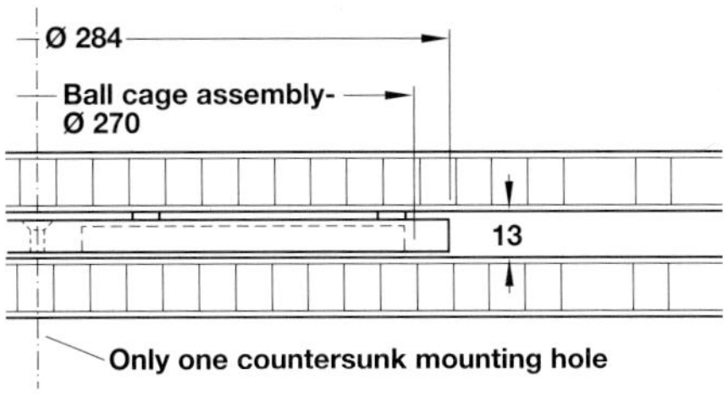

Turntable
Particularly suitable for electronic furniture. Quiet ball-bearing rotation 360° on 8 balls.
Load capacity: 50 kg
Finish: ABS-plastic

Cat. No.	646.21.307

Packing: 1 pc.

Dimensions in mm

Turntables

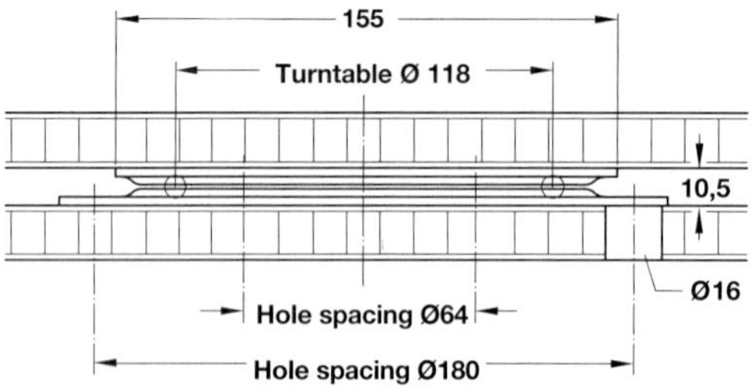

Turntable
rotates 360°, ball-bearing mounted
Load capacity: 150 kg
Finish: steel, galvanized

Cat. No.	646.18.908

Packing: 1 pc.

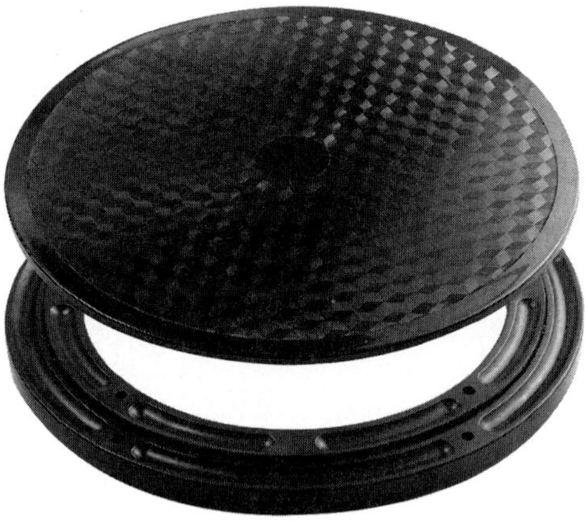

Turntable 646.16.002:
Ø 176 mm opening, ideal for inserting cables

Turntable 646.19.316:
- with round plate, suitable **for non-fastened mounted.** The turntable has 5 slip-proof plastic suction supports.
- or **screw mounted,** for shelves etc. In this case remove the round plate and the suction supports.

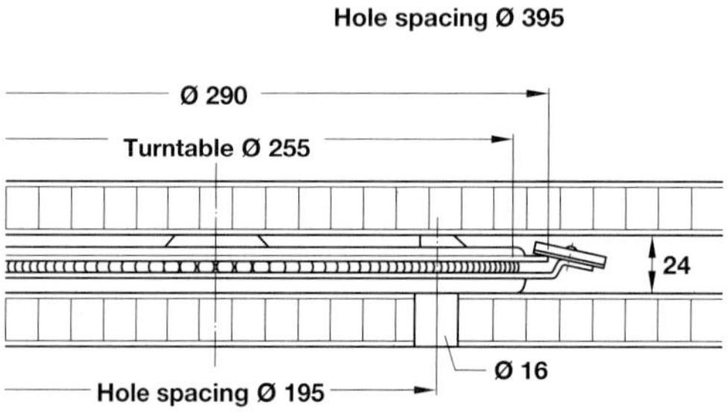

Turntable
rotates 360°, ball-bearing mounted
Load capacity: 150 kg
Finish: steel, galvanized

Cat. No.	646.16.002

Packing: 1 pc.

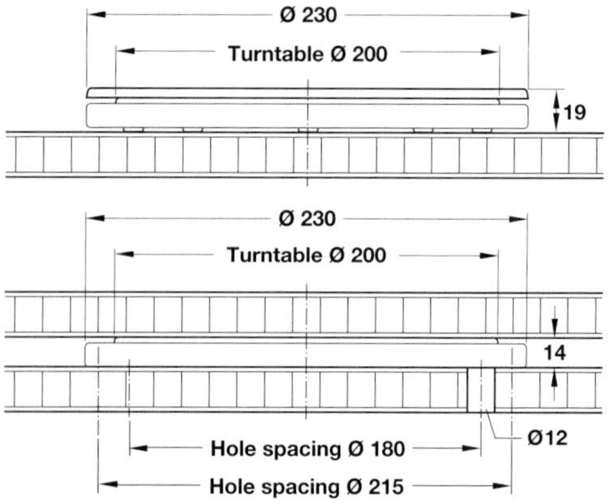

Turntable
rotates 360°, ball-bearing mounted
Load capacity: 150 kg
Finish: plastic, black

Cat. No.	646.19.316

Packing: 1 pc.

Dimensional data not binding. We reserve the right to alter specifications without notice.

Dimensions in mm

Turntables

HÄFELE

Dimensions in mm

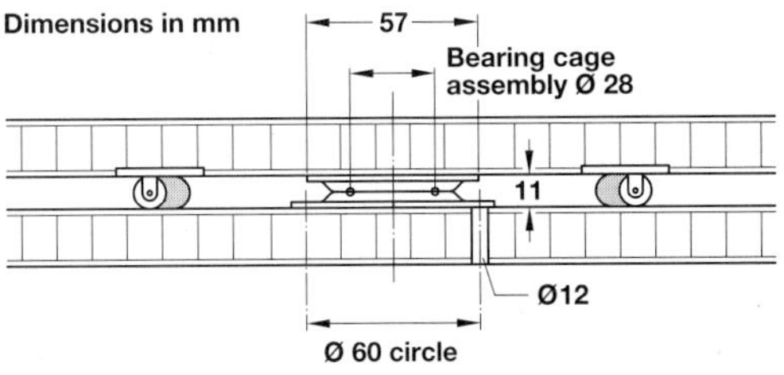

Turntable
rotates 360°, ball-bearing mounted
load capacity: 50 kg
Finish: steel, zinc-plated

Cat. No.	646.12.102

Packing: 30 pcs.

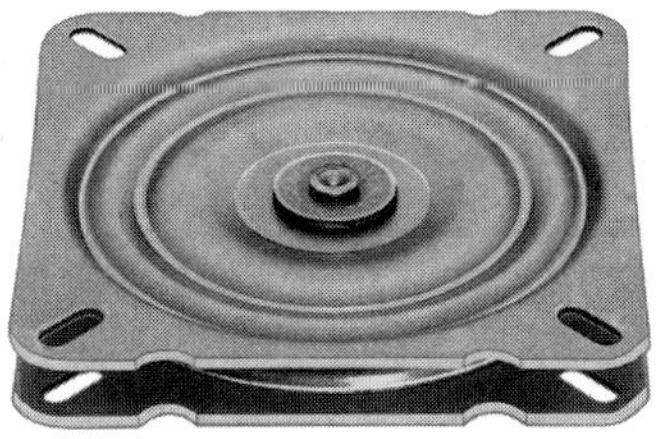

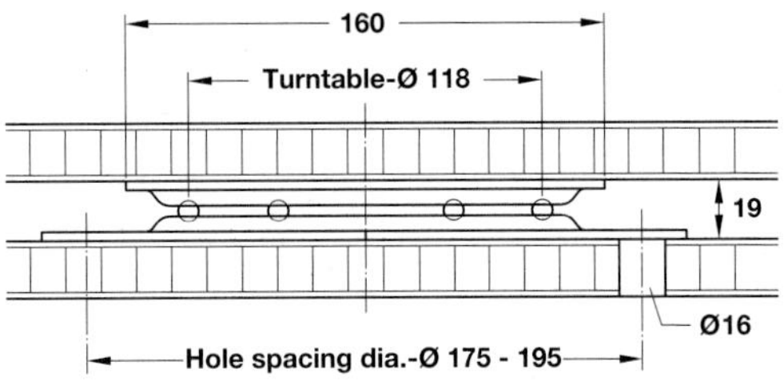

Turntable
rotates 360°, ball-bearing mounted
load capacity: 50 kg
Finish: steel, unfinished

Cat. No.	646.14.062

Packing: 1 pc.

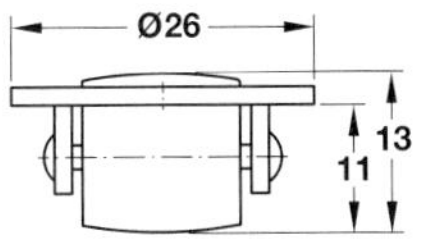

Roller
Finish: sheet metal, with plastic wheel

Cat. No.	646.11.016

Packing: 100 pcs.

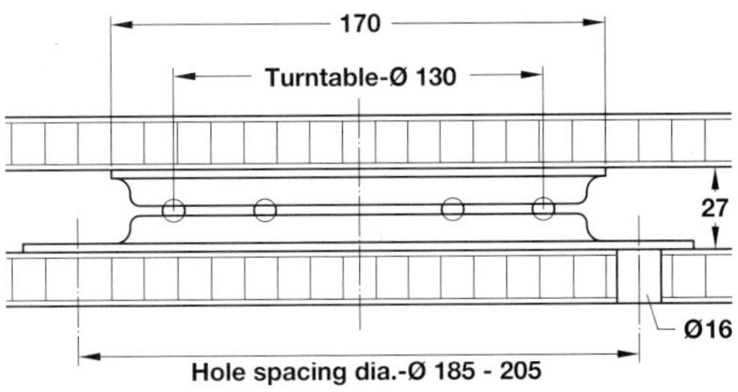

Turntable
rotates 360°, ball-bearing mounted
Load capacity: 100 kg
Finish: steel, unfinished

Cat. No.	646.15.014

Packing: 1 pc.

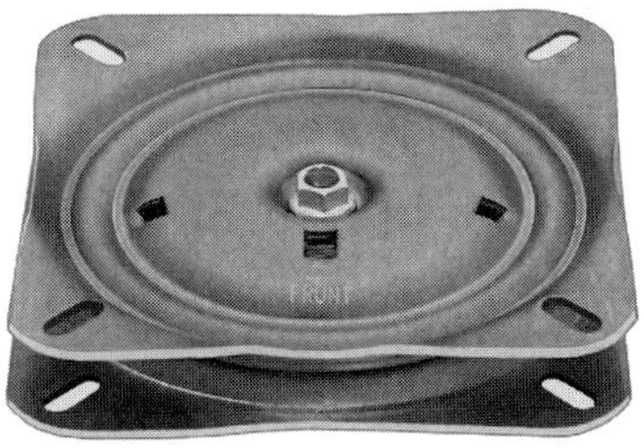

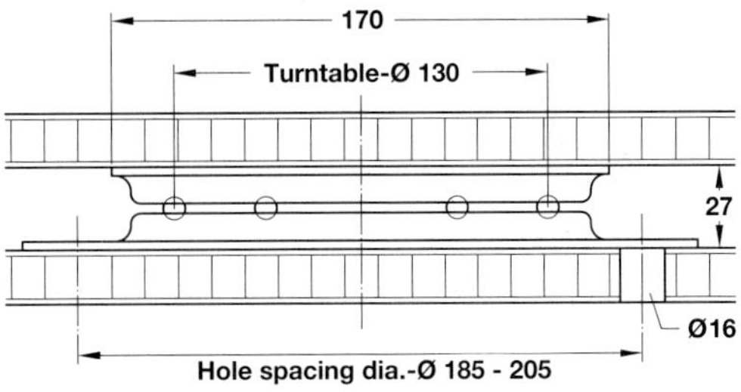

Turntable, rotates 90° to the right and left sides, ball-bearing mounted.
After turning, a steel spring returns the turntable to its original position.
It is recommended to install additional stops.
Load capacity: 100 kg
Finish: steel, unfinished

Cat. No.	646.15.023

Packing: 1 pc.

HÄFELE

Metric Conversion Chart

Length

For our purposes, the basic metric units of *length* are the **millimeter and the meter.**

To convert inches to millimeters, multiply inches x 25.4

Inches	To	Millimeters
1/16"		1.59 mm
1/8"		3.18 mm
3/16"		4.76 mm
1/4"		6.35 mm
3/8"		9.53 mm
1/2"		12.70 mm
5/8"		15.88 mm
3/4"		19.05 mm
7/8"		22.23 mm
1"		25.40 mm
2"		50.80 mm
4"		101.60 mm
6"		152.40 mm
8"		203.20 mm
10"		254.00 mm
12"		304.80 mm
16"		406.40 mm
18"		457.20 mm
21"		533.40 mm
24"		609.60 mm
27"		685.80 mm
30"		762.00 mm
33"		838.20 mm
36"		914.40 mm
39"		990.60 mm
48"		1219.20 mm

To convert millimeters to inches, divide millimeters by 25.4

Millimeters	To	Inches
1 mm		1/16"
3 mm		1/8"
6 mm		1/4"
8 mm		5/16"
10 mm		3/8"
12 mm		1/2"
16 mm		5/8"
19 mm		3/4"
22 mm		7/8"
25.4 mm		1"
32 mm		1 1/4"
100 mm		4"
305 mm		12"
500 mm		19 3/4"
1000 mm		39 3/8"

*Inches are expressed to the nearest 16th.

To convert meters to feet, multiply meters by 3.3

Meters	To	Feet
1 meter		3' 3 3/8"
2 meters		6' 6 3/4"
2.5 meters		8' 2 1/2"
4 meters		13' 1 1/2"
6 meters		19' 8 1/4"

Weight

The basic metric unit of *weight* is the **kilogram.**

To convert kilograms to pounds, multiply kilograms x 2.2

Kilograms	To	Pounds
1 kg		2.2 lbs.
10 kg		22 lbs.
50 kg		110 lbs.

Volume

The basic metric unit of *volume* is the **liter.**

To convert liters to gallons, multiply liters x 0.26

Liters	To	Gallons
1 liter		0.26 gallons
4 liter		1 gallon
15 liter		4 gallons

Product Guide - Store Fixture Systems

HÄFELE

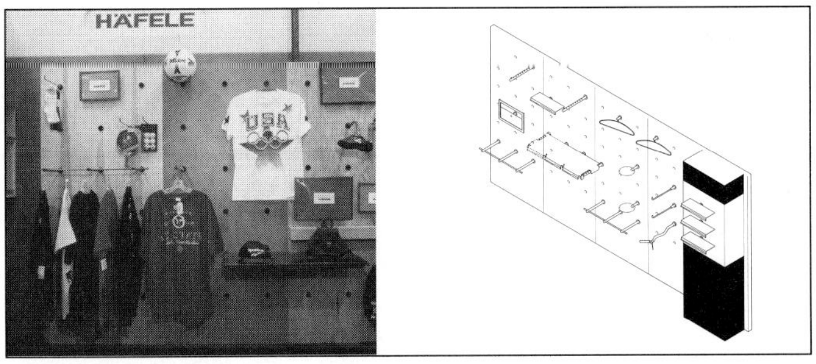

System A Display System
Pages **7.2 - 7.5**

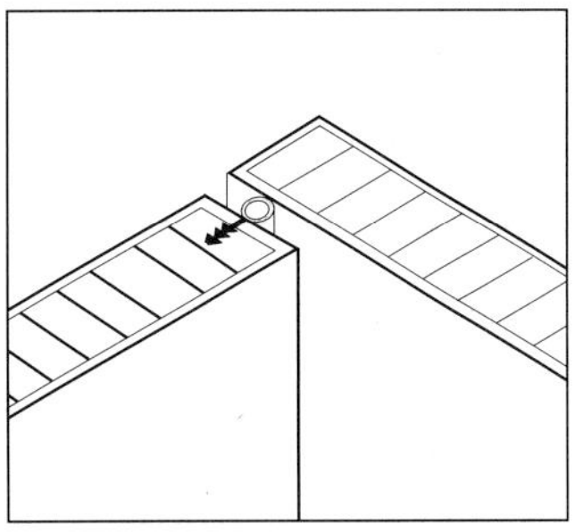

Door Profile Strips
Pages **7.17**

System M Display System
Pages **7.6**

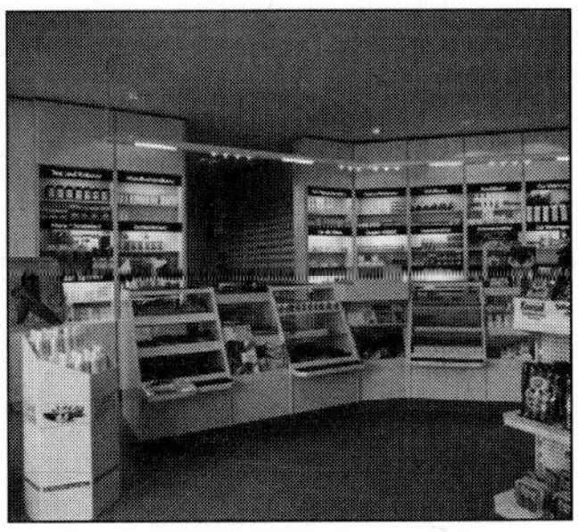

Pharmacy System
Pages **7.14**

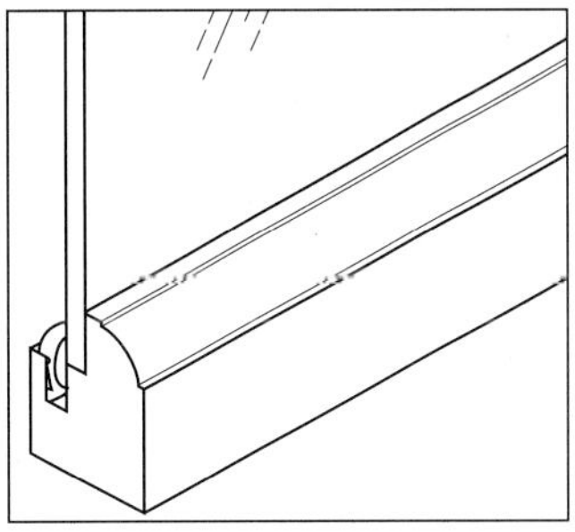

Glass Retaining Profile
Pages **7.18**

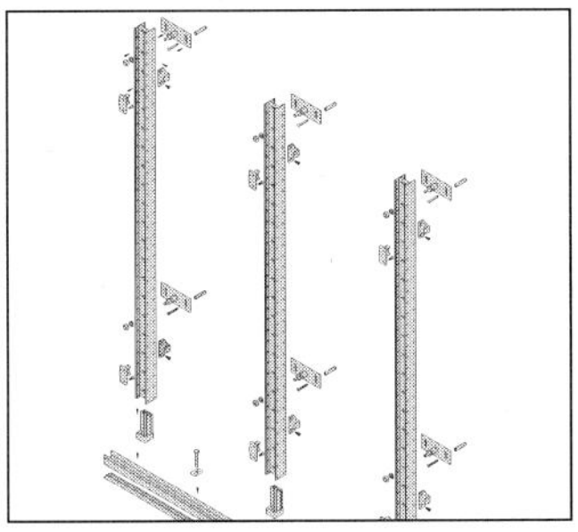

Keku R Wall System
Pages **7.7 - 7.13**

HÄFELE

System A

By installation of attachment plates on 300mm center to centers, all hardware components can be rearranged at anytime.

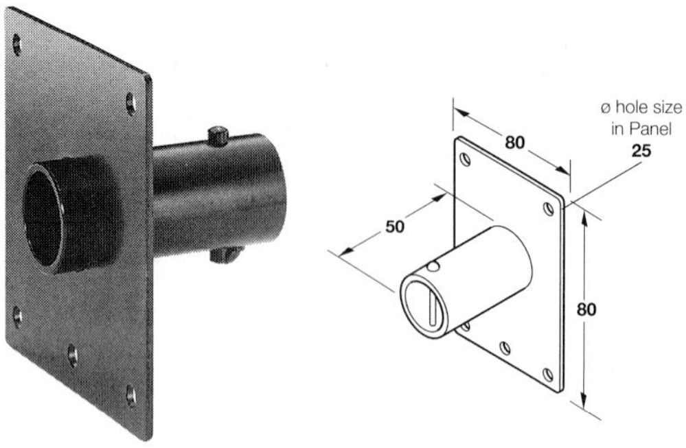

Attachment plate with self locking pin
for screw mounting to back of panel
Finish: steel, epoxy-coated black

Cat. No.	790.40.301

Packing: 1 pc.

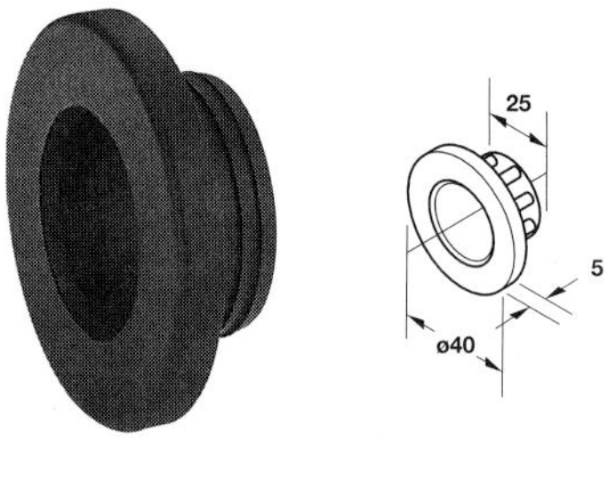

Cover grommet for attachment plate
Finish: plastic black

Cat. No.	790.40.310

Packing: 1 pc.

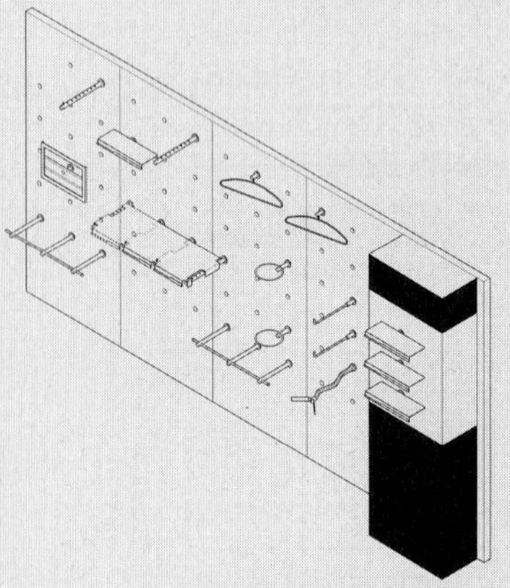

Hardware can be utilized on walls...

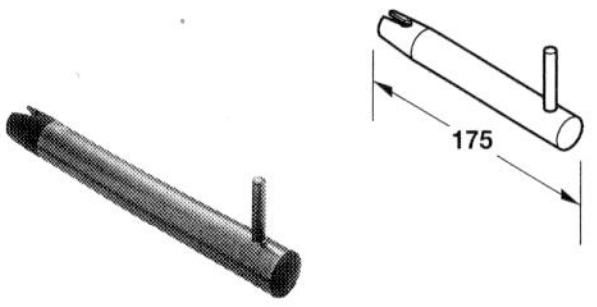

Bag holder
Finish: steel, epoxy-coated silver RAL 9007

Cat. No.	790.42.433

Packing: 1 pc.

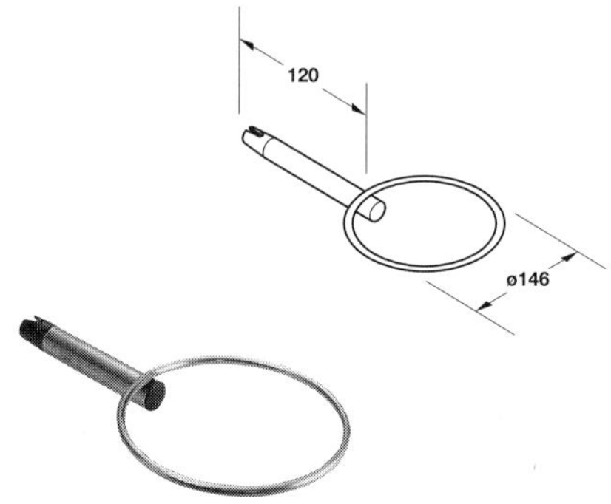

Ball support
Finish: steel, epoxy-coated silver RAL 9007

Cat. No.	790.42.430

Packing: 1 pc.

7 **Store Fixtures**
Profiles
Retainers

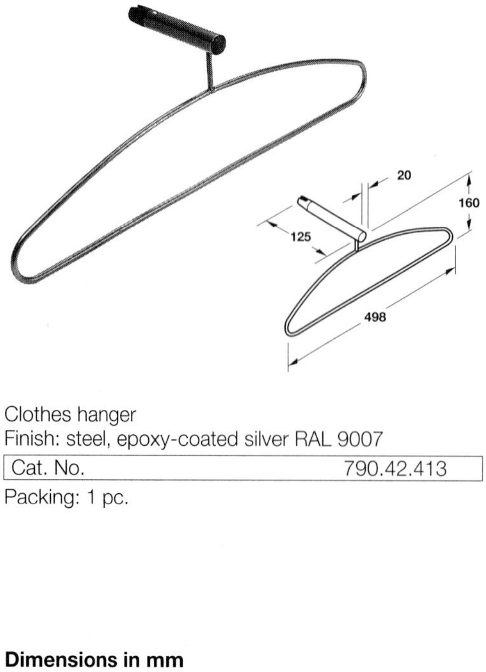

Clothes hanger
Finish: steel, epoxy-coated silver RAL 9007

Cat. No.	790.42.413

Packing: 1 pc.

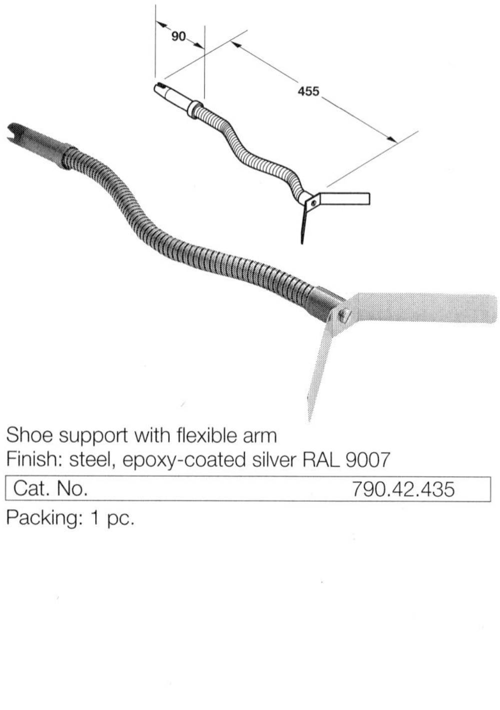

Shoe support with flexible arm
Finish: steel, epoxy-coated silver RAL 9007

Cat. No.	790.42.435

Packing: 1 pc.

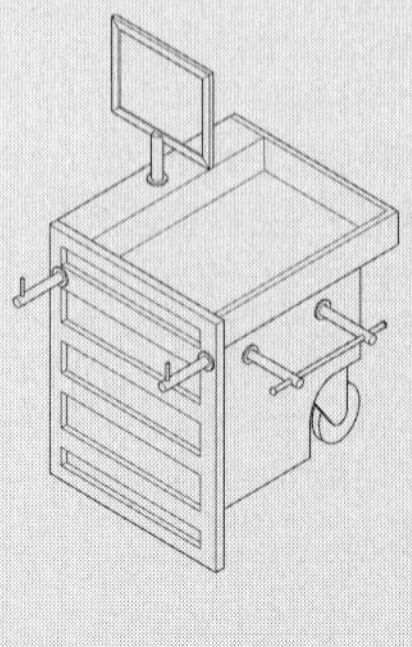

on carts or free-standing kiosks.

Dimensional data not binding.
We reserve the right to alter specifications without notice.

Dimensions in mm

System A

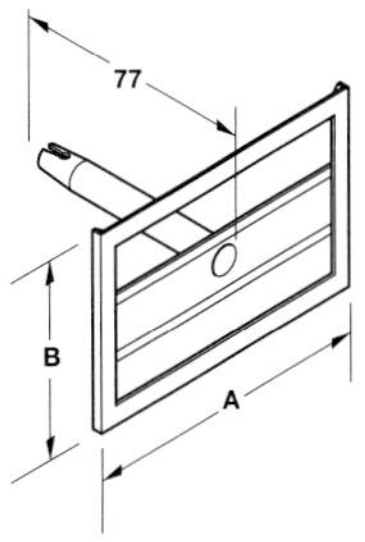

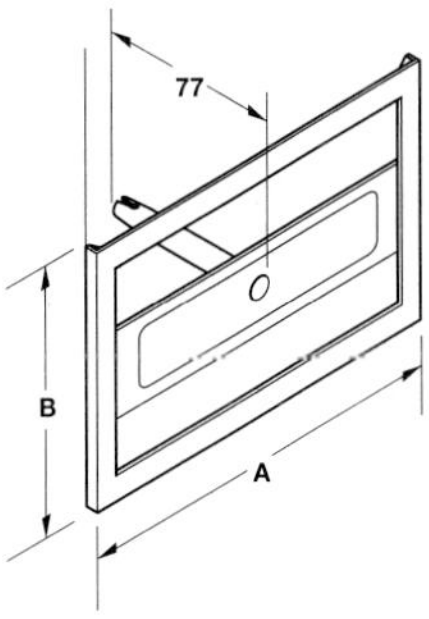

Sign-holder for horizontal mounting
Finish: steel, epoxy-coated silver RAL 9007

Size A x B	Window Size	Sign Size	Cat. No.
300 x 210	267 x 180	295 x 208	790.42.441
422 x 298	390 x 267	415 x 295	790.42.442

Packing: 1 pc.

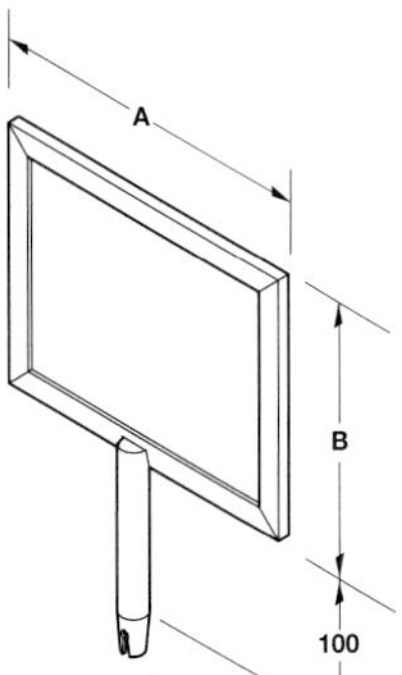

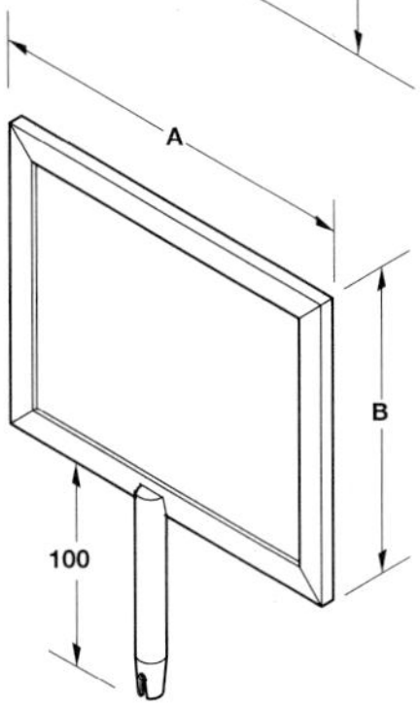

Sign-holder for vertical mounting
Finish: steel, epoxy-coated silver RAL 9007

Size A x B	Window Size	Sign Size	Cat. No.
300 x 210	267 x 180	295 x 210	790.42.443
422 x 300	390 x 267	418 x 295	790.42.444

Packing: 1 pc.

Dimensions in mm

HÄFELE

By installation of attachment plates on 300mm center to centers, all hardware components can be rearranged at anytime.

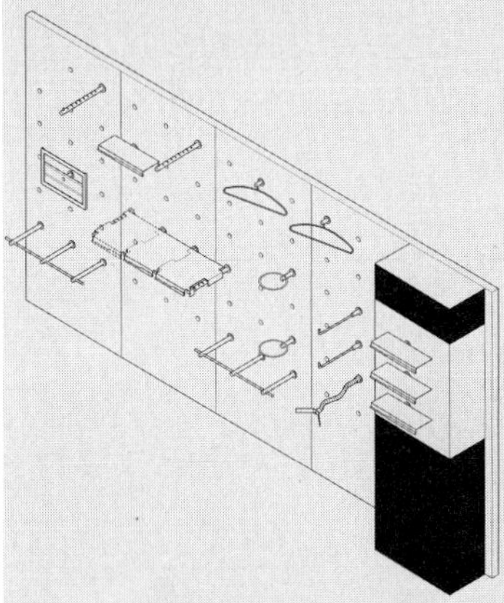

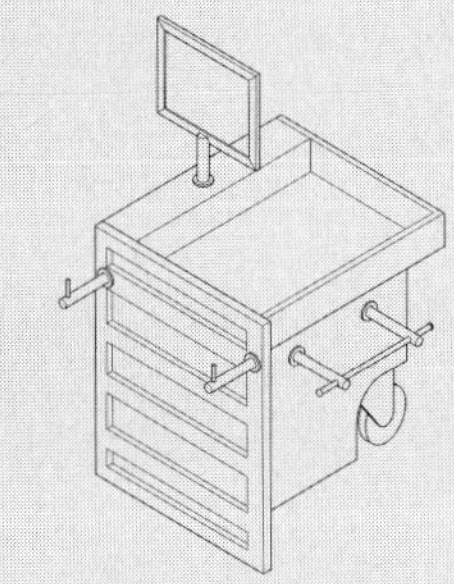

on carts or free-standing kiosks.

Dimensional data not binding.
We reserve the right to alter specifications without notice.

HÄFELE

System A

By installation of attachment plates on 300mm center to centers, all hardware components can be rearranged at anytime.

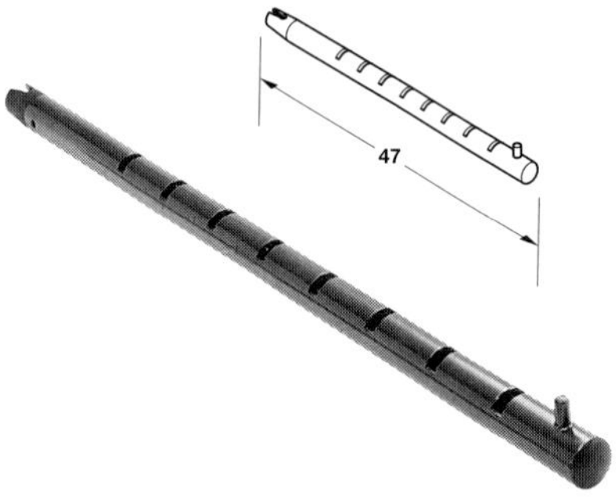

Rail is slotted for clothes hanger or as support for modular shelf 790.42.422
Finish: steel, epoxy-coated silver RAL 9007

Cat. No.	790.42.411

Packing: 1 pc.

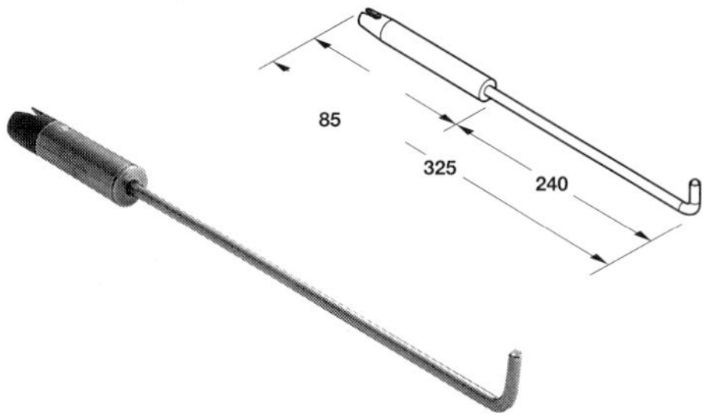

Peg hook-holder
Finish: steel, epoxy-coated silver RAL 9007

Cat. No.	790.42.431

Packing: 1 pc.

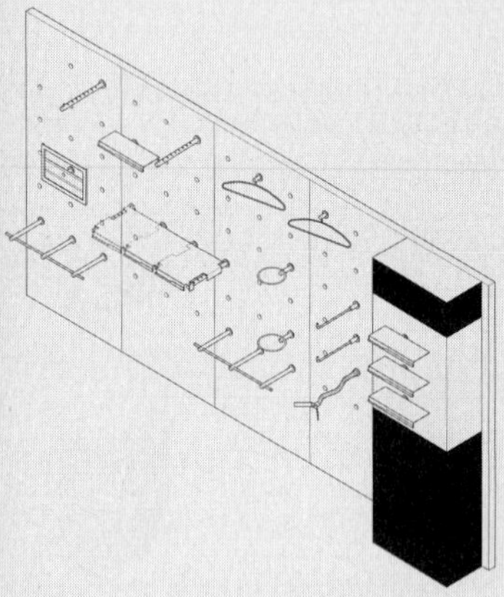

Hardware can be utilized on walls...

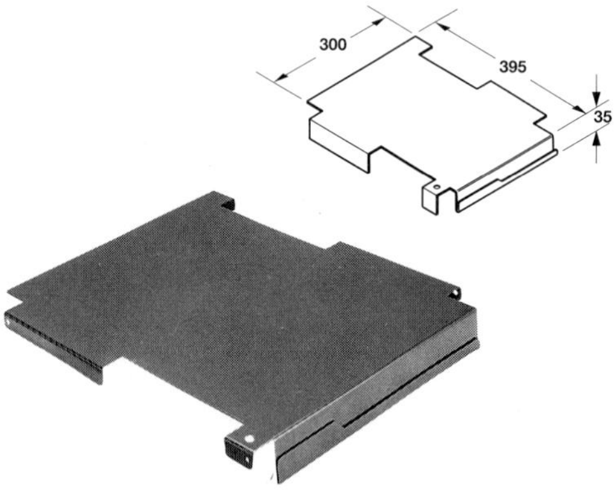

Modular shelf requires rod 790.42.411 for support
Finish: steel, epoxy-coated silver RAL 9007

Cat. No.	790.42.422

Packing: 1 pc.

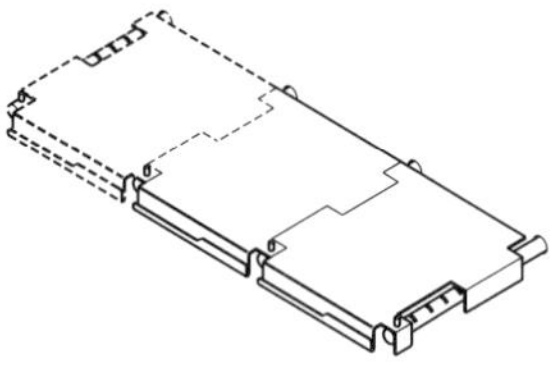

Shelves interlock to prevent sliding.
This application shows three shelves with four rods.

7 Store Fixtures Profiles Retainers

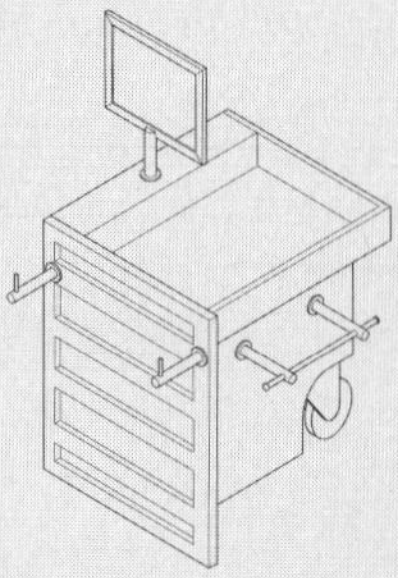

on carts or free-standing kiosks.

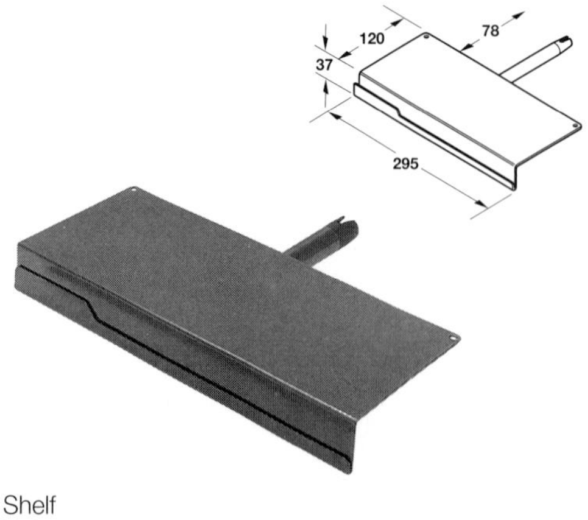

Shelf
Finish: steel, epoxy-coated silver RAL 9007

Cat. No.	790.42.421

Packing: 1 pc.

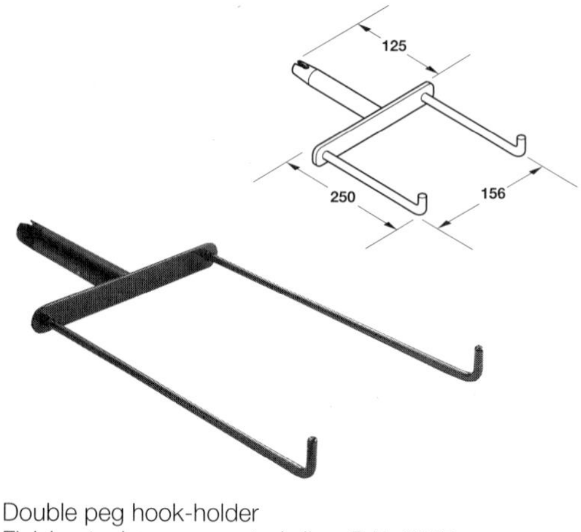

Double peg hook-holder
Finish: steel, epoxy-coated silver RAL 9007

Cat. No.	790.42.434

Packing: 1 pc.

Dimensional data not binding.
We reserve the right to alter specifications without notice.

Dimensions in mm

System A

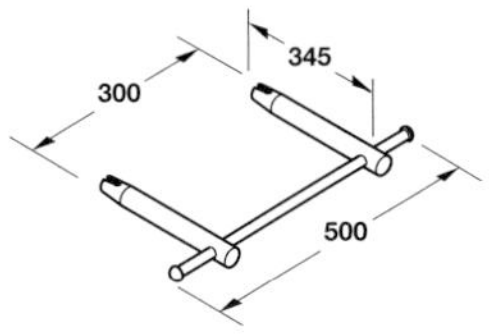

Support for hanging clothes
Finish: steel, epoxy-coated silver RAL 9007

Cat. No.	790.42.401

Packing: 1 pc.

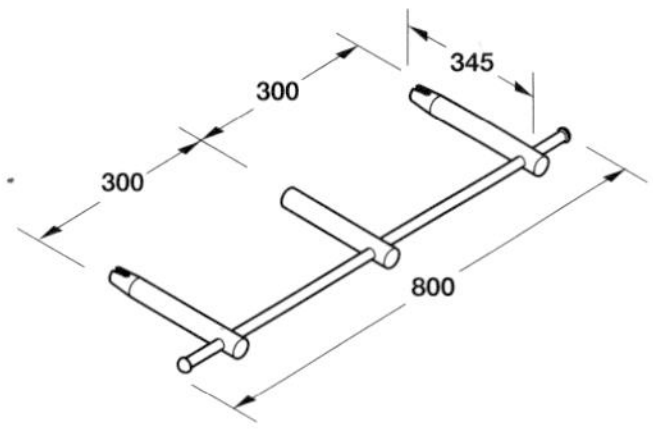

Support for hanging clothes
Finish: steel, epoxy-coated silver RAL 9007

Cat. No.	790.42.402

Packing: 1 pc.

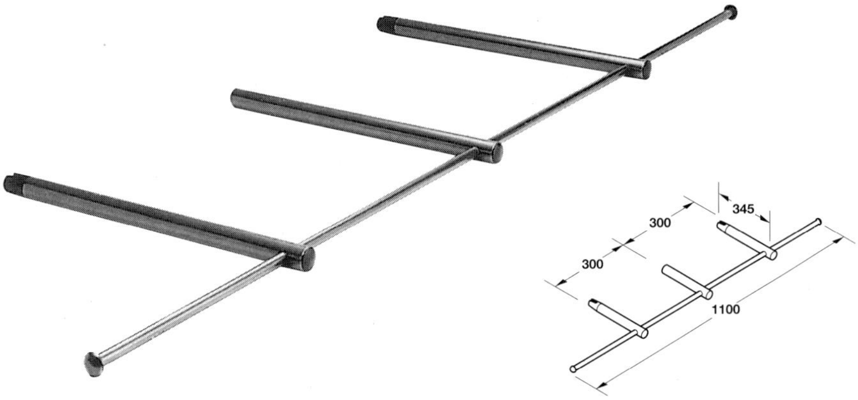

Support for hanging clothes
Finish: steel, epoxy-coated silver RAL 9007

Cat. No.	790.42.403

Packing: 1 pc.

By installation of attachment plates on 300mm center to centers, all hardware components can be rearranged at anytime.

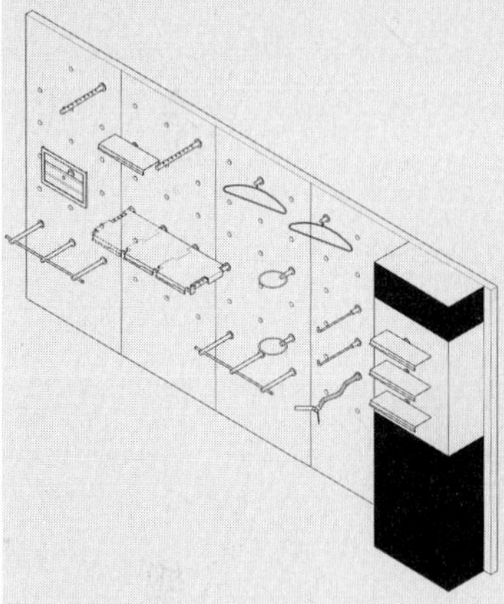

Hardware can be utilized on walls...

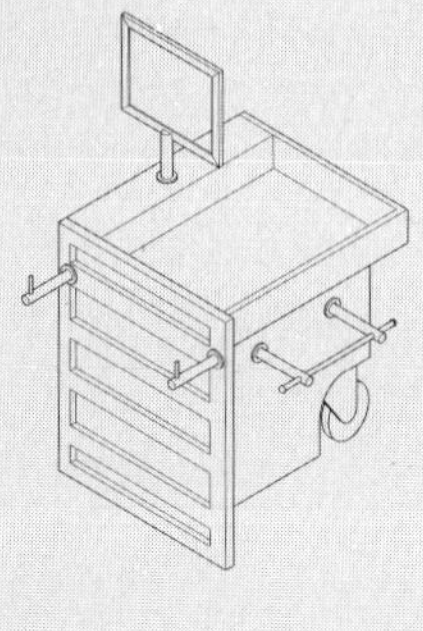

on carts or free-standing kiosks.

Dimensional data not binding.
We reserve the right to alter specifications without notice.

HÄFELE

System M

SYSTEM M - the display system where the merchandise support hardware adapts to the product... not the other way around. It's a sure way to show what you have.

What can **SYSTEM M** hold? There's no limit to your imagination... the display fixture hardware can be produced in different shapes, colors, sizes and from different materials.

For further information on this innovative new concept in merchandising contact Häfele today.

Keku R Interior Finishing System

HÄFELE

Wall Paneling Hardware

These structural materials consist of aluminum profiles. They can be used for the installation of wall panels, ceiling panels and partitions.

- The profiles are connected using various accessories.
- ASR slide-on, hang-in and coupling fitting
- Can be used as desired and screw-mounted into the profiles' holes
- Different kinds of panels can be clipped onto these fittings. The clip-on technique allows for easy installation and removal, if necessary.

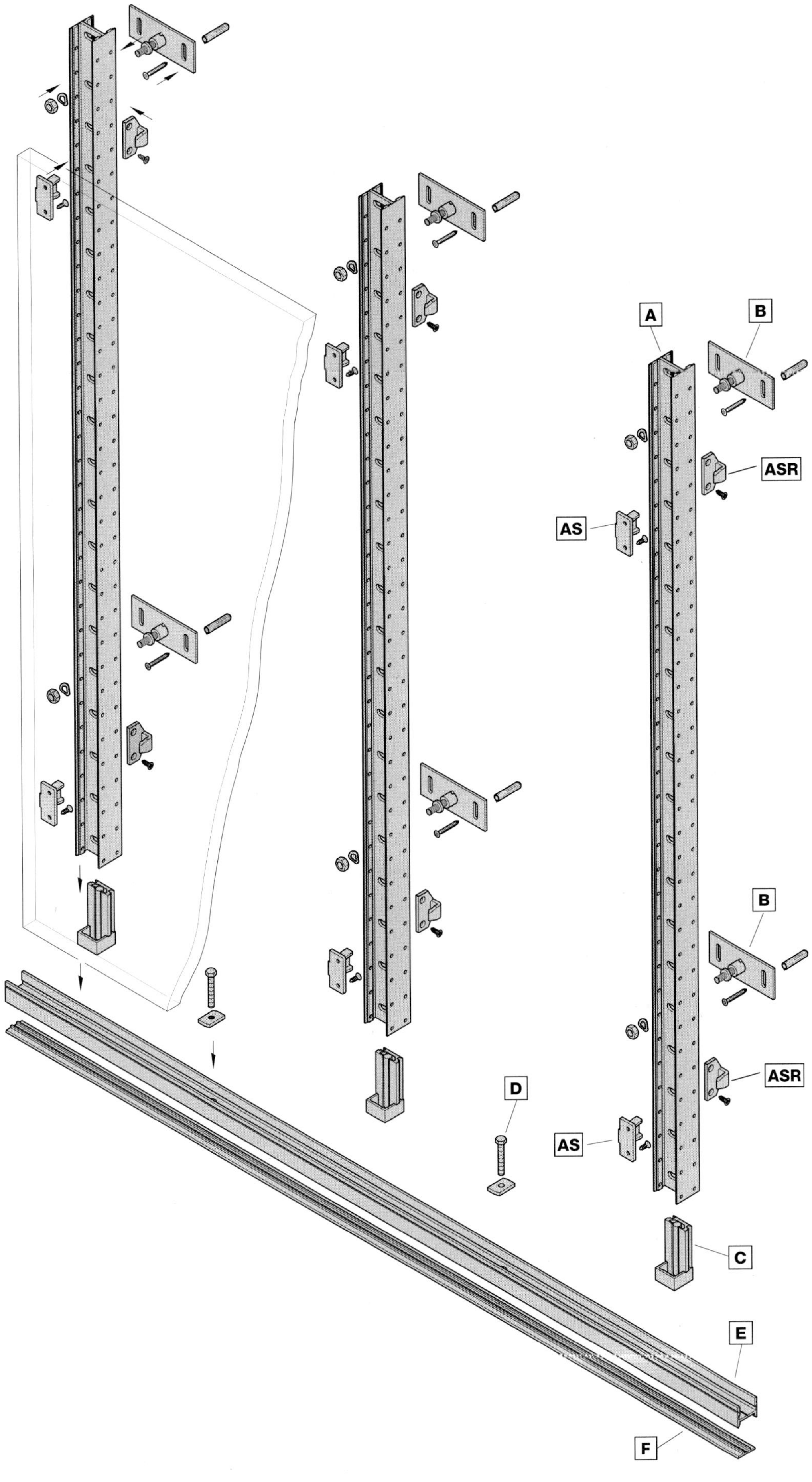

HÄFELE

Keku R Interior Finishing System

Applications:
- Wall paneling
- Ceiling paneling
- Light-weight partitions
- Booths for trade shows
- Store fixtures

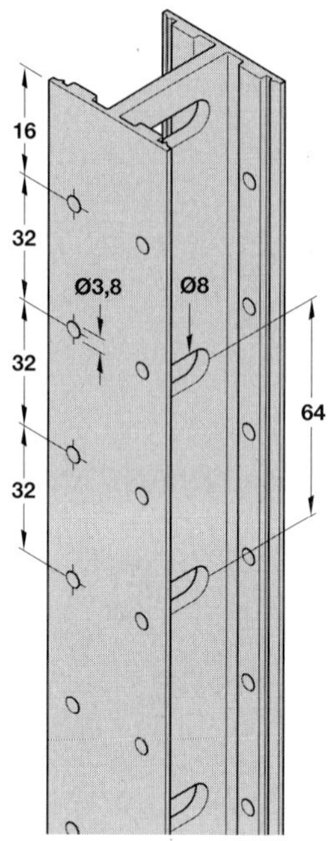

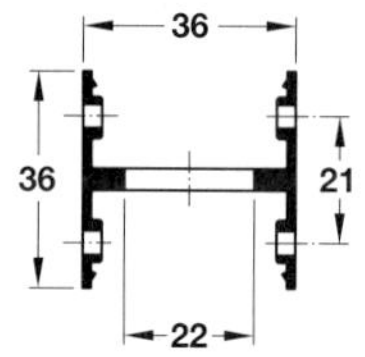

A Support Profile, H-shape
With system holes for screw-mounting of 32 mm fittings.
Finish: aluminum, unfinished

Cat. No.	782.10.000

Packing: 6 meter lengths

Wall mounting:

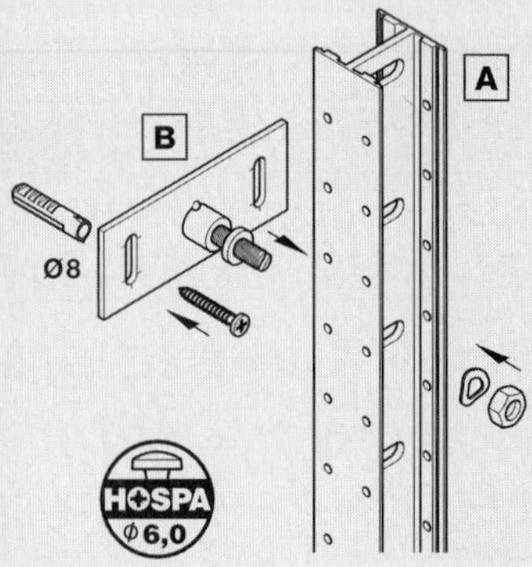

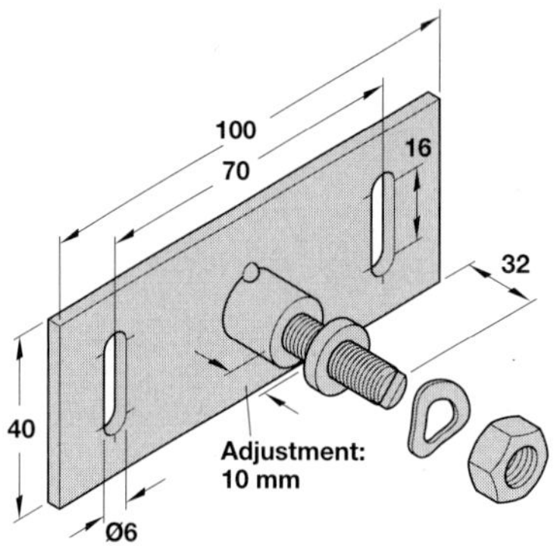

B Wall or ceiling fastener
For support A, adjustable in 3 directions with attached M6 screw, spring washer and hex nut
Finish: steel, zinc-plated

Cat. No.	782.00.900

Packing: 1 and 10 pcs.

Structural construction materials for wall paneling

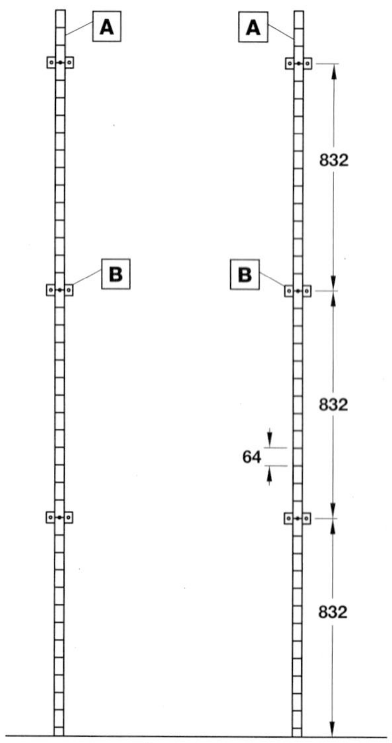

Horizontal cross section

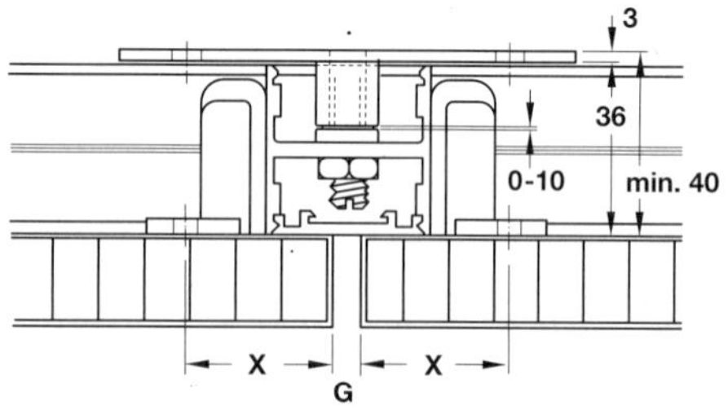

Distance X: between the edge of the panel to the center of the hole.

Gap	Distance X
0 mm	37.0 mm
5 mm	34.5 mm
10 mm	32.0 mm
15 mm	29.5 mm
20 mm	27.0 mm
25 mm	24.5 mm

Maximum gap width: 26 mm

Dimensions in mm

Keku R Interior Finishing System

HÄFELE

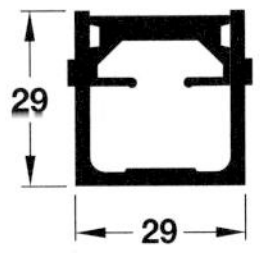

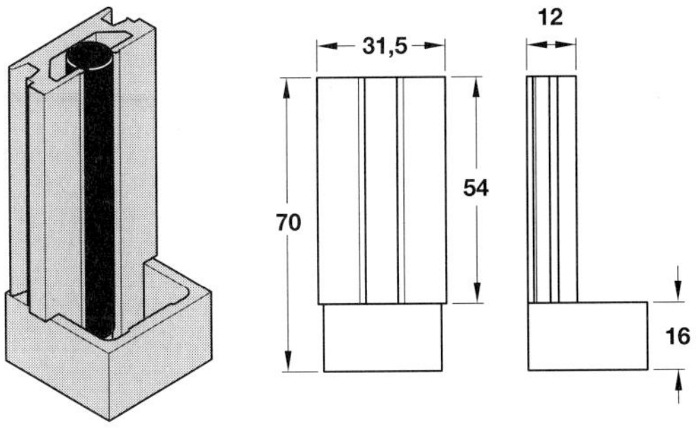

C **90° Degree Profile Connector**
To connect support profiles **A** to floor/ceiling profiles **E**

Finish: aluminum, unfinished

Cat. No.	782.15.000

Packing: 1 and 10 pcs.

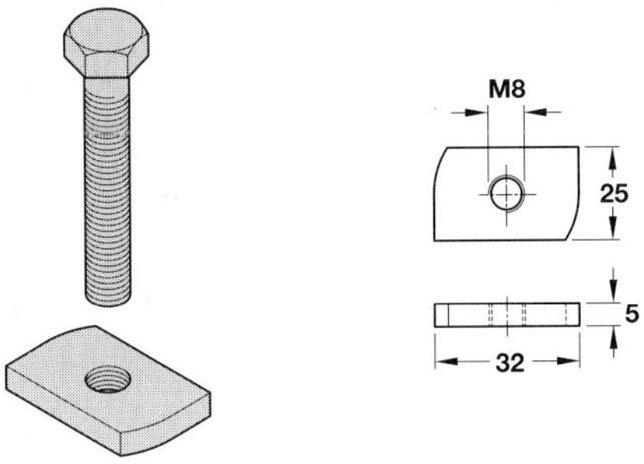

D **Adjustment Screw,** 30 mm long.
To align and level the frame system.
Includes: M8 screw and tenon block
Finish: Screw: steel, chromatized
Tenon block: aluminum, unfinished

Cat. No.	782.16.000

Packing: 1 and 10 pcs.

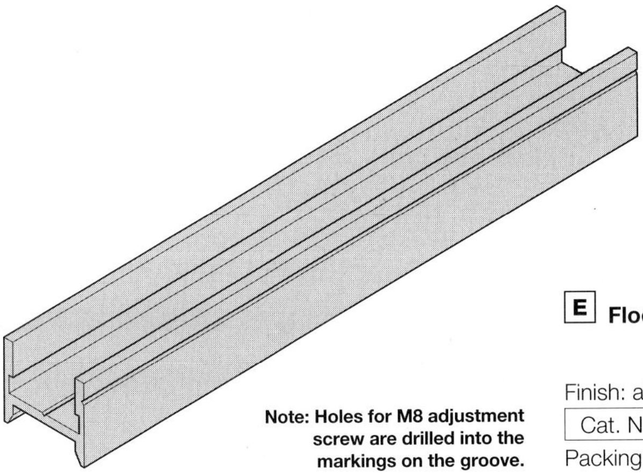

Note: Holes for M8 adjustment screw are drilled into the markings on the groove.

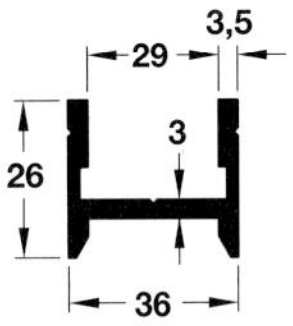

E **Floor/ceiling Profile,** U-shaped.

Finish: aluminum, unfinished

Cat. No.	782.11.000

Packing: 6 meter

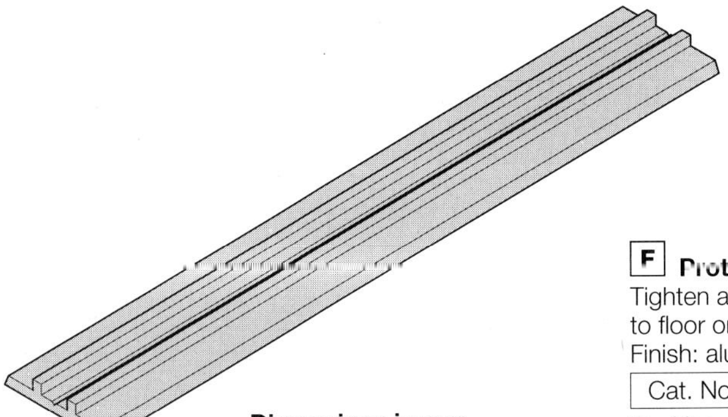

Dimensions in mm

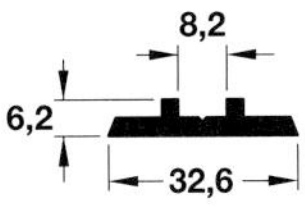

F **Protecting Profile**
Tighten and adjust the frame system without damage to floor or ceiling.
Finish: aluminum, unfinished

Cat. No.	782.12.000

Packing: 3 meter

Connecting the floor/ceiling profiles to the support profiles

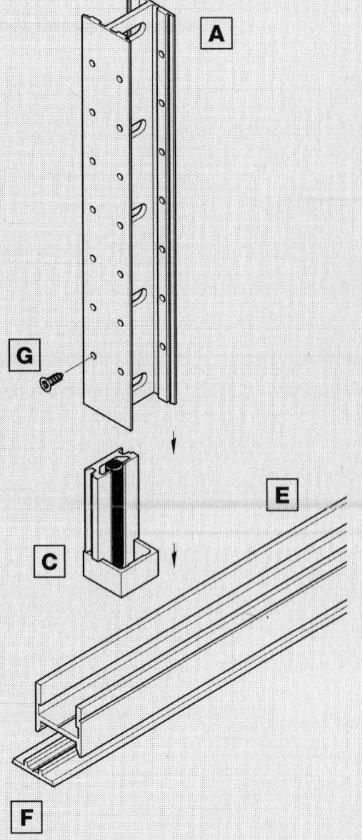

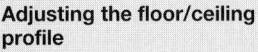

Adjusting the floor/ceiling profile

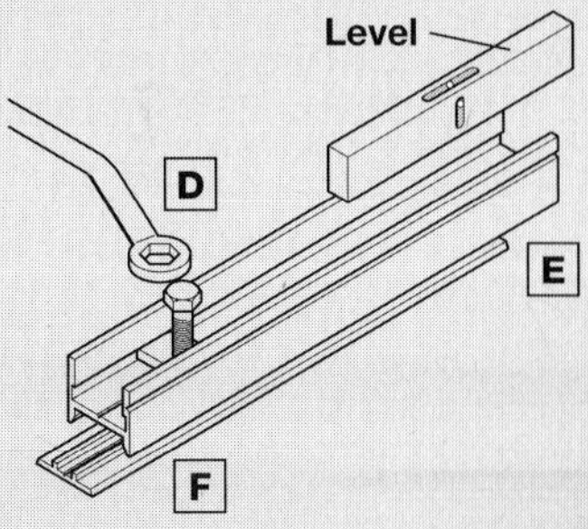

Store Fixtures
Profiles
Retainers

7

G **System Screw,** Ø 4 mm
with Phillips head PZ 2
self-tapping, to fasten all fittings and connectors.

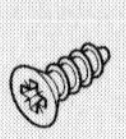

Finish:
steel, nickel-plated

Length	Cat. No.
10 mm	782.17.900

Packing: 100 pcs.

Dimensional data not binding.
We reserve the right to alter specifications without notice.

HÄFELE

Keku R Interior Finishing System

Gap profile H just clips on

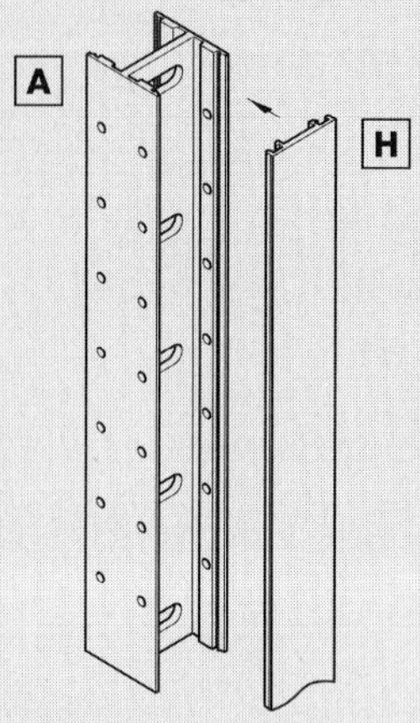

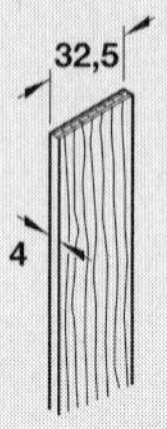

To match paneling, gap profiles can also be made from wood.

The gap profile with slots can only be used in connection with the gap profile securing element I

- Press the securing element into the gap profile with slots.
- Press the gap profile with the securing element into the support profile A
- Secure assembly using screw G
- No matter how long the gap profile is, mount 1 securing element on top of the gap profile

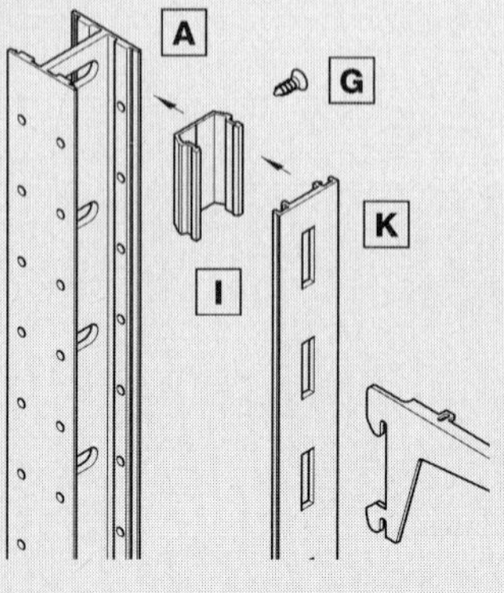

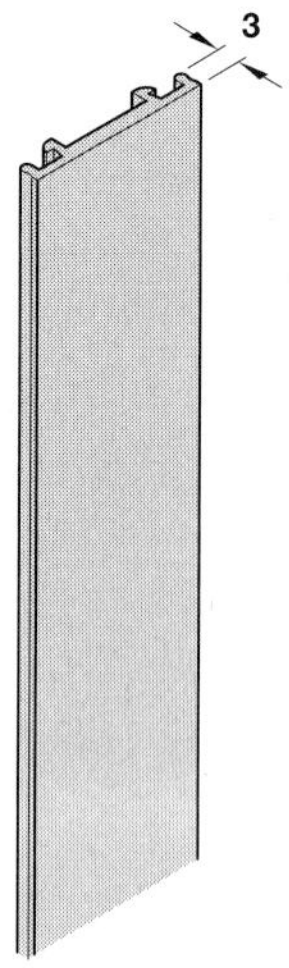

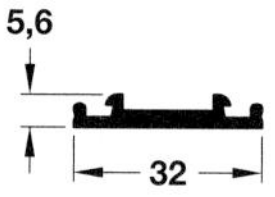

H Gap Profile

To cover visible gaps
Finish: aluminum, unfinished

Cat. No.	782.13.000

Packing: 3 meters

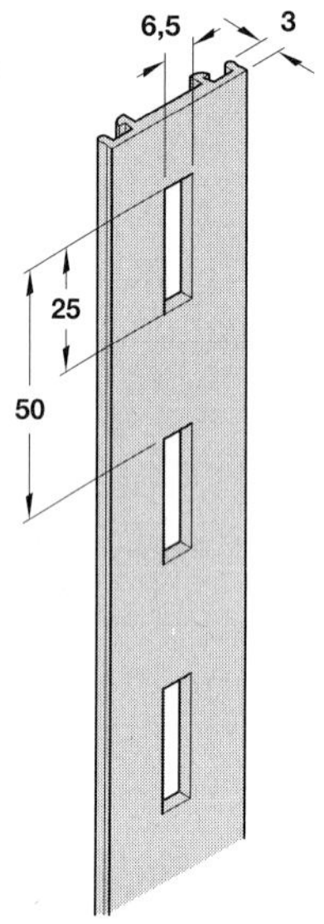

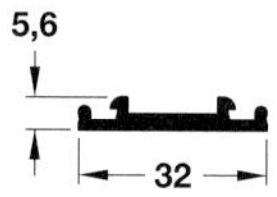

K Gap Profile with Slots

To hang merchandise or shelf support brackets

Finish: aluminum, unfinished

Cat. No.	782.14.000

Packing: 3 meters

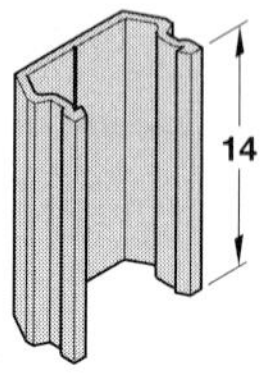

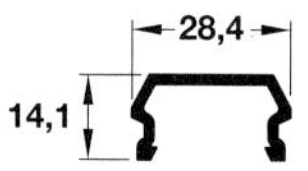

I Securing Element for Gap Profile

For gap profile with holes K
Finish: aluminum, unfinished

Cat. No.	782.15.090

Packing: 1 and 10 pcs.

Dimensional data not binding.
We reserve the right to alter specifications without notice.

Dimensions in mm

Keku R Interior Finishing System

HÄFELE

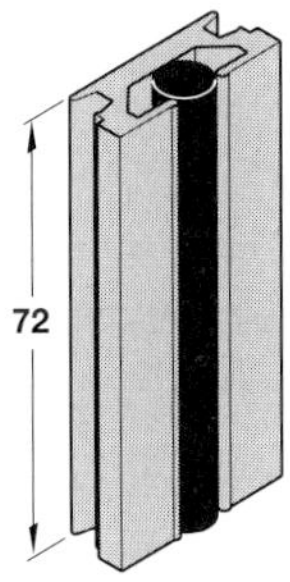

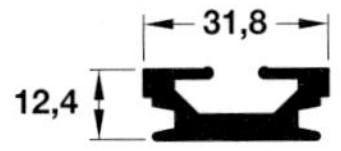

L Vertical Connector

Add length to support profiles A
or to floor/ceiling profiles E
Finish: aluminum, unfinished

Cat. No.	782.15.010

Packing: 1 and 10 pcs.

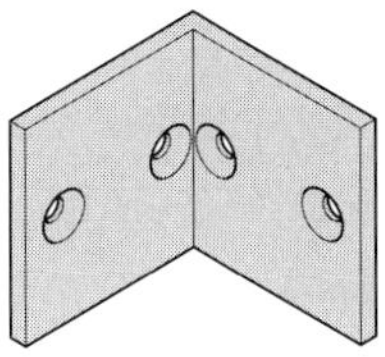

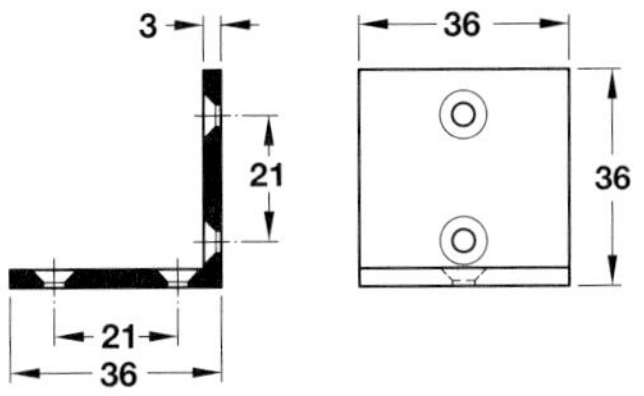

M 90° Degree Angle Bracket

Connect 2 support profiles at a 90° degree angle, using 4 system screws G
Finish: aluminum, unfinished

Cat. No.	782.15.020

Packing: 1 and 10 pcs.

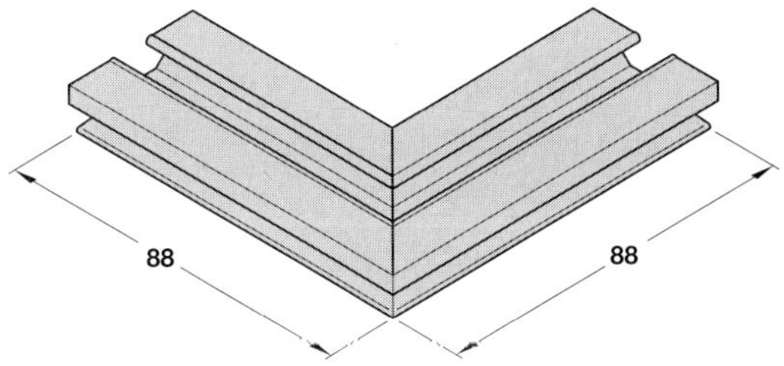

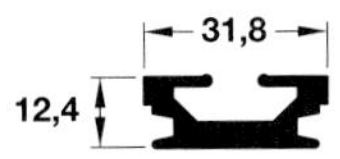

N Miter Connector

Connect profiles A and E at a mitered angle, for corners.
Finish: aluminum, unfinished

Cat. No.	782.15.050

Packing: 1 and 10 pcs.

Dimensions in mm

Vertical connections for floor/ceiling profiles and support profiles.

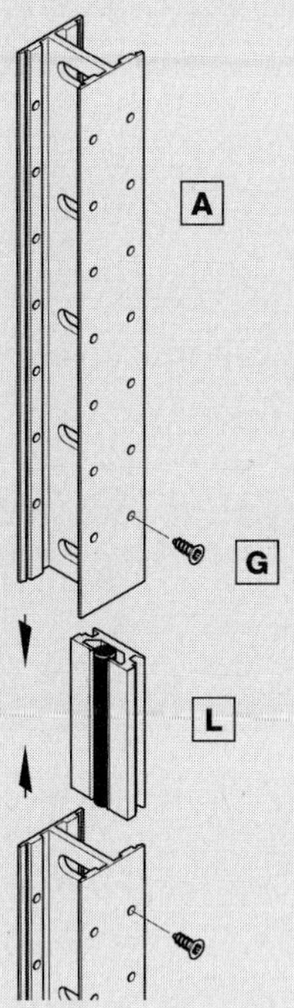

Making a corner with two support profiles.

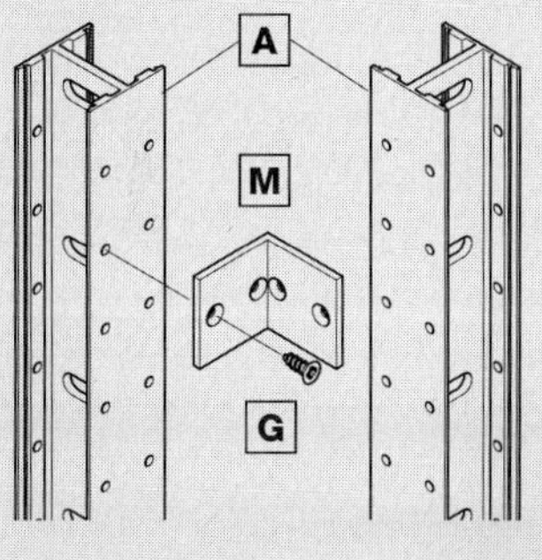

Store Fixtures
Profiles
Retainers

7

Making a 90° degree mitered corner using 2 floor/ceiling profiles or support profiles.

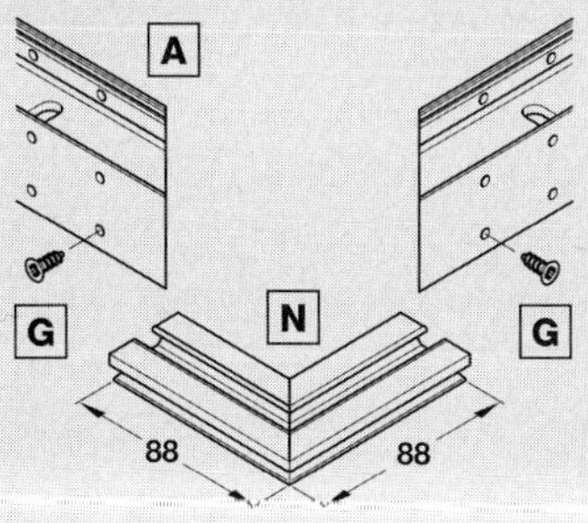

Dimensional data not binding.
We reserve the right to alter specifications without notice.

HÄFELE

Keku R Interior Finishing System

Horizontal connections on support profiles

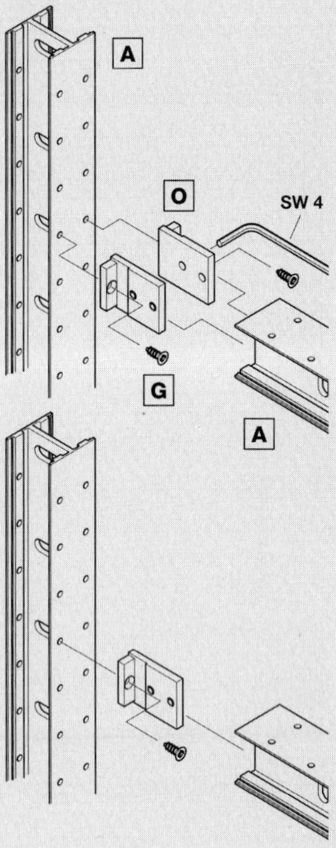

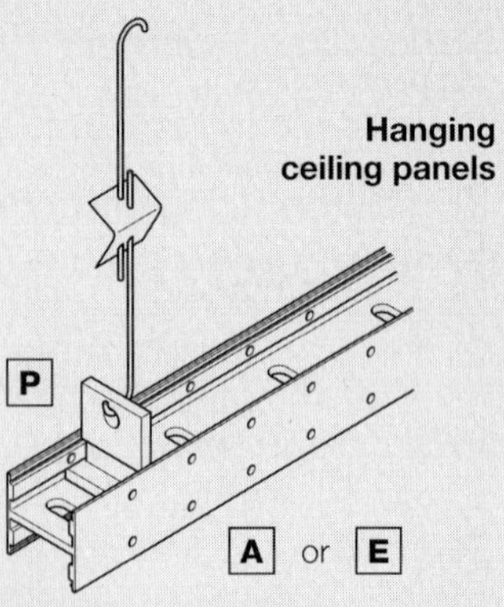

7 Store Fixtures
Profiles
Retainers

G System screw, Ø 4 mm
with Phillips head PZ 2
self-tapping, to fasten
all fittings and connectors.

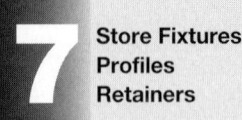

Finish:
steel, nickel-plated

Length	Cat. No.
10 mm	782.17.900

Packing: 100 pcs.

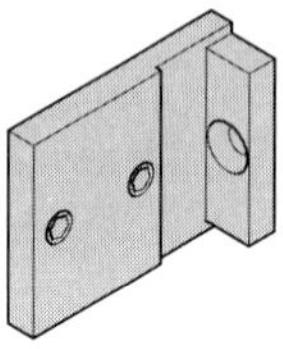

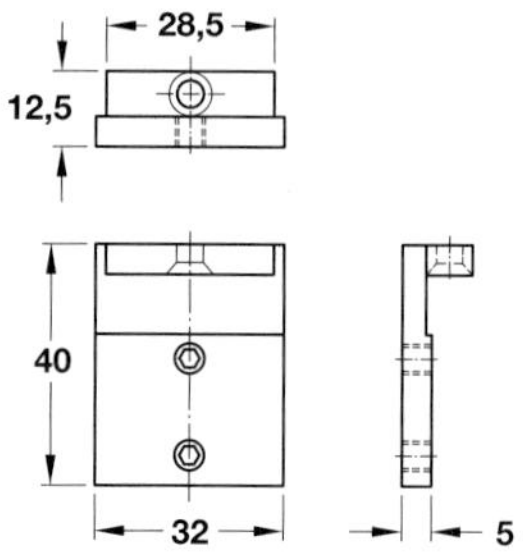

O Horizontal Connector
For T-shaped, horizontal braces on
support profiles A
Finish: aluminum, unfinished

Cat. No.	782.15.030

Packing: 1 and 10 pcs.

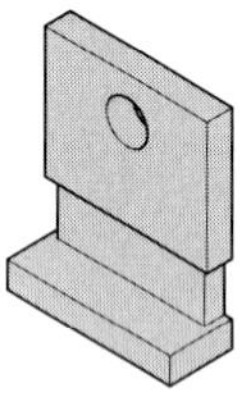

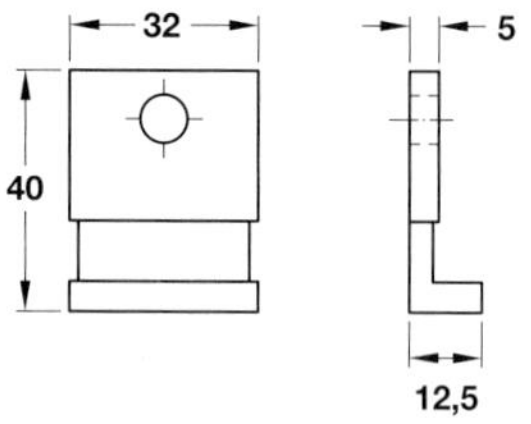

P Slide-in Connector
To hang support profiles A
or for hanging ceiling panels from E
Finish: aluminum, unfinished

Cat. No.	782.15.040

Packing: 1 and 10 pcs.

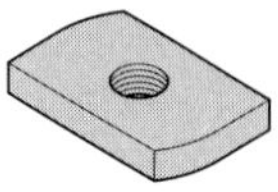

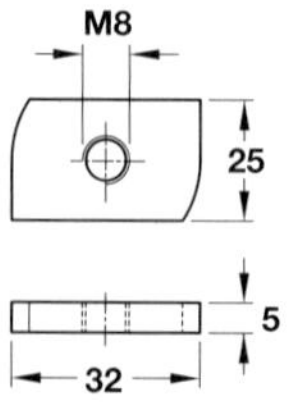

Q Tenon Block
Used for hanging and spacing applications
together with an M8 threaded rod.
Finish: aluminum, unfinished

Cat. No.	782.16.010

Packing: 1 pc.

Dimensional data not binding.
We reserve the right to alter
specifications without notice.

Dimensions in mm

Keku R Interior Finishing System

HÄFELE

Macrolon is temperature resistant, -100° C to +135° C

AS Panel Component
Screw-mounted to panels.
(Order frame component separately)

HOSPA Φ4,0 VARIANTA ⊘3 VARIANTA ⊘5

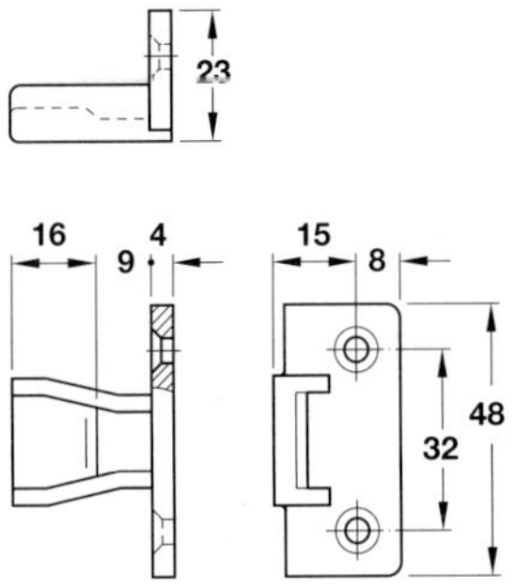

Finish: macrolon, black

Mounted with:	Cat. No.
Hospa-screws	262.50.359
Varianta-screws	262.50.358

Packing: 200 pcs.

ASR Frame Component
Screw-mounted to frame

HOSPA Φ4,0 VARIANTA ⊘3 VARIANTA ⊘5

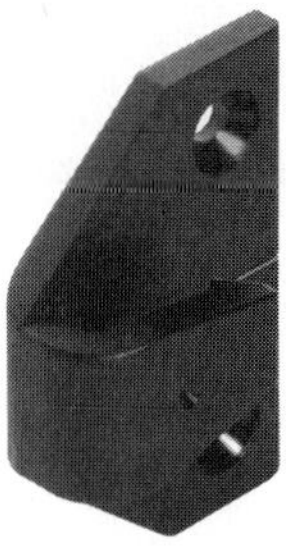

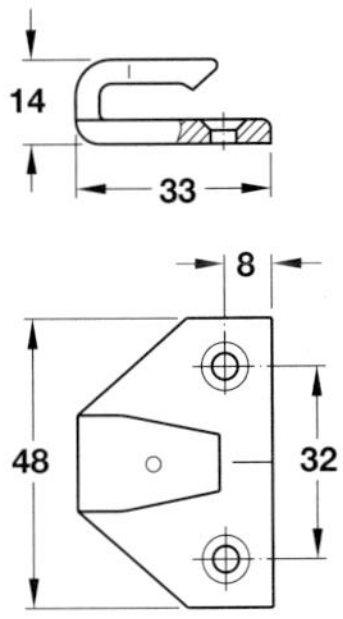

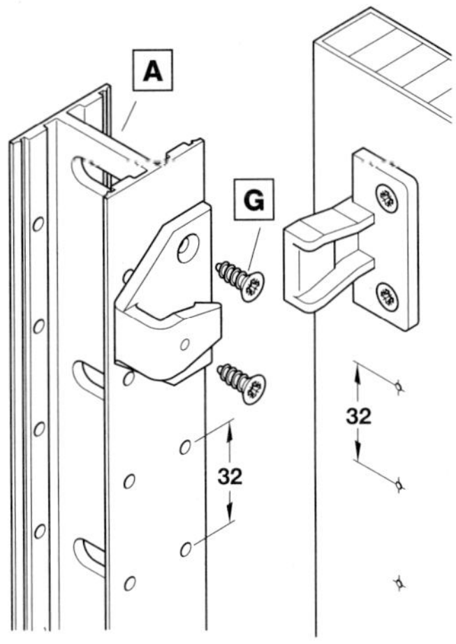

Finish: macrolon, black

Mounted with:	Cat. No.
Hospa-screws	262.50.390
Varianta-screws	262.50.391

Packing: 200 pcs.

Attachment screws:
Varianta-flat head screws with PZ 2 cross-slot.
Finish:
Steel, nickel-plated

VARIANTA ⊘3 VARIANTA ⊘5

length (mm)	Cat. No. Ø 3 mm	Ø 5 mm
10.5	013.15.617	013.15.715
13.5	013.15.626	013.15.724
16.0	013.15.635	013.15.733

Packing: 100 and 1000 pcs.

Note:
Do not use chemical solutions and aggressive lubricants on load-bearing plastic fittings.

G **System screw,** Ø 4 mm
with Phillips head PZ 2
self-tapping, to fasten
all fittings and connectors.

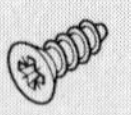

Finish:
steel, nickel-plated

Length	Cat. No.
10 mm	782.17.900

Packing: 100 pcs.

Dimensions in mm

HÄFELE

Pharmacy Shop Fitting System "PHARMA-ORG"

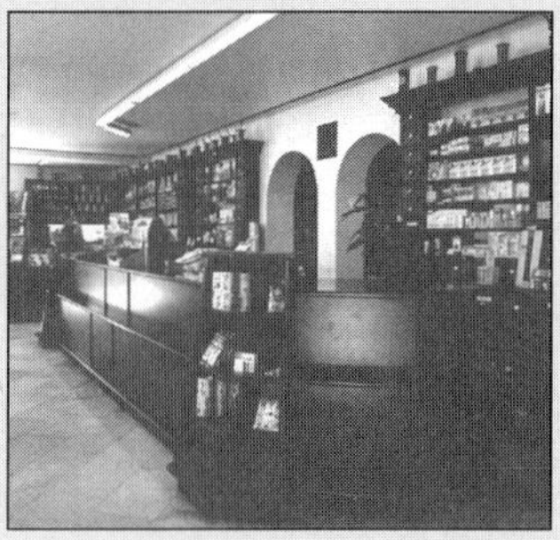

The pharmacies pictured on this page are just a few reference examples of the wide variety of pharmacies that have been equipped with Häfele pharma-org systems.

7 Store Fixtures
Profiles
Retainers

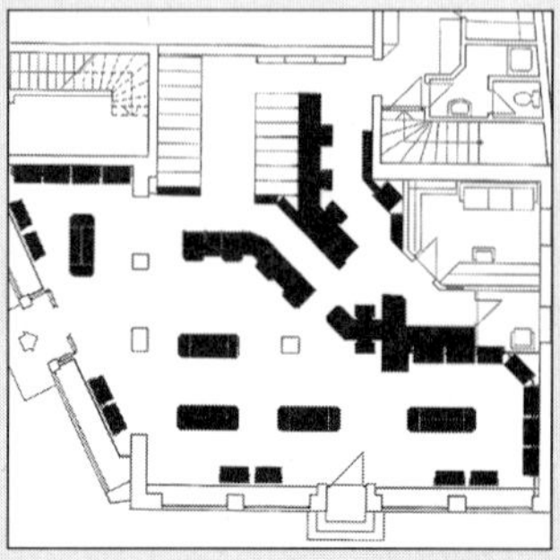

Dimensional data not binding.
We reserve the right to alter specifications without notice.

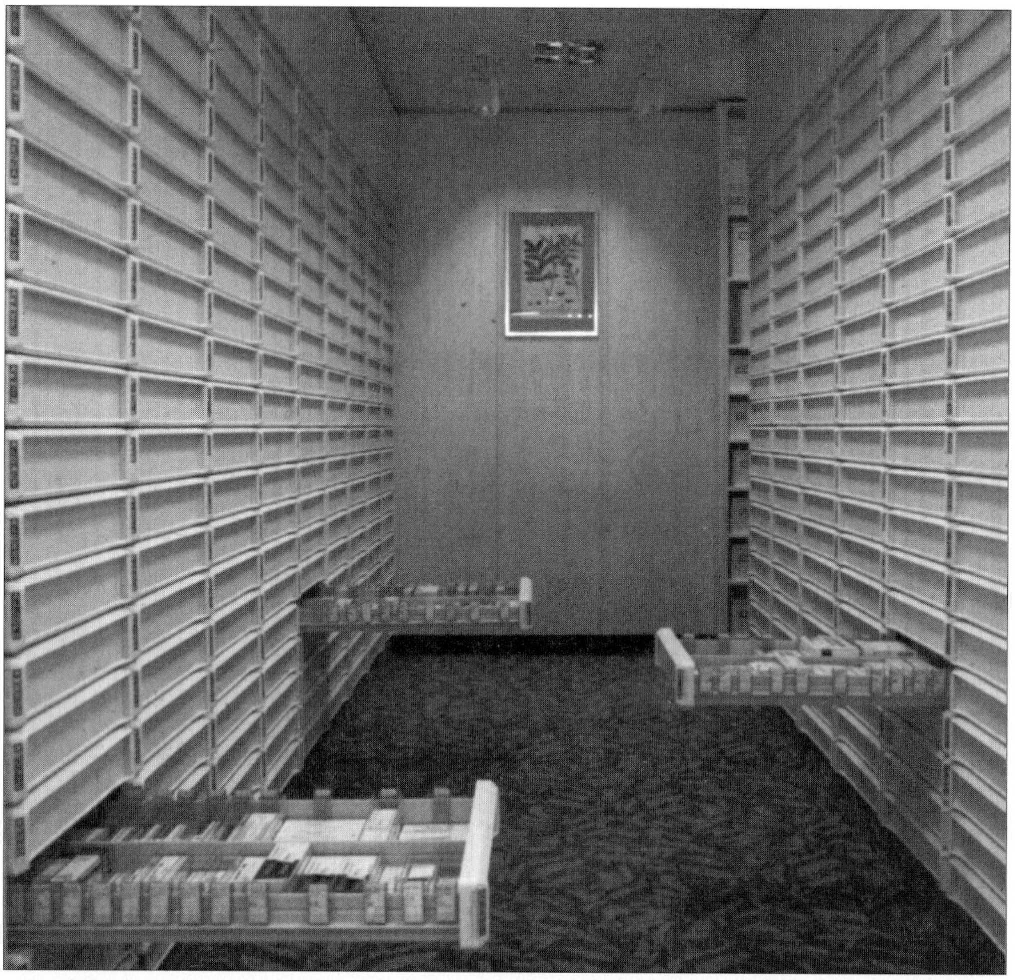

We are glad to provide information about Pharma-Org pharmacy systems. Please contact us and request a set of detailed planning guidelines.

Metallic Plastic Trim (NTP)

HÄFELE

Decorative Metallic Plastic Trim w/pressure-sensitive acrylic adhesive.

Clean surface thoroughly. Make sure surface is smooth as irregularities in substrate can show through. Clean with solvent such as alcohol, not acetone or lacquer thinner. Can be machined & cut with standard woodworking tools.

Impact modified plastic w/scratch-resistant metallized and lacquered surface.

Width		Finish		
Inch	mm	Pol. Chrome	Pol. Brass	Black Polished
1/4"	9mm	751.90.108	751.90.804	751.90.304
1/2"	13mm	751.90.117	751.90.813	751.90.313
5/8"	16mm	751.90.126	751.90.822	751.90.322
3/4"	19mm	751.90.135	751.90.831	751.90.331
7/8"	22mm	751.90.144	751.90.840	751.90.340
1"	25mm	751.90.153	751.90.859	751.90.359
1 1/4"	32mm	751.90.162	751.90.868	751.90.368
1 1/2"	38mm	751.90.171	751.90.877	751.90.377
2"	51mm	751.90.180	751.90.886	751.90.386
3"	76mm	751.90.199	751.90.895	751.90.395

Packing: 1 roll (width x 250 feet)

Dimensions in mm

HÄFELE

Cabinet/Furniture Profiles

Cabinet profile
Plastic, concealed mounting The profile is simply pushed onto the mounting clip. The profile is suitable for e.g. cabinets, office furnitures, kitchen.

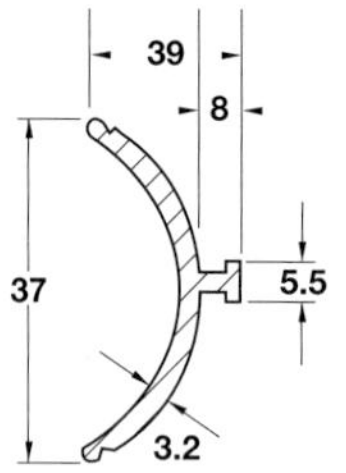

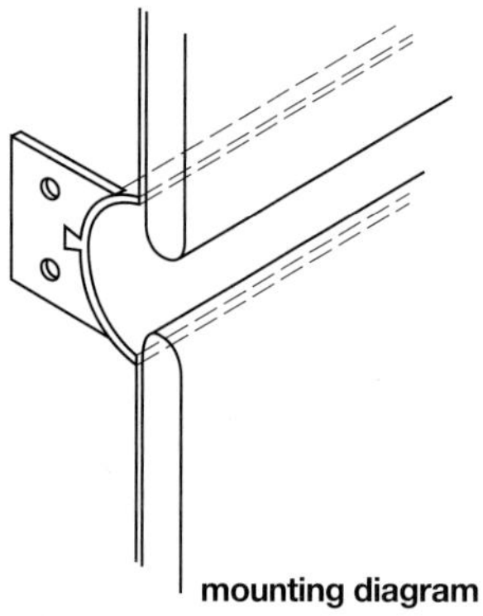

mounting diagram

Cabinet trim profile
fastened with the mounting clip

Finish: PVC, white and PVC, aluminum covering

Cat. No.	white	713.50.706
	gold, polished	713.51.801
	silver, polished	713.51.909

Packing: lengths of 2.5 m

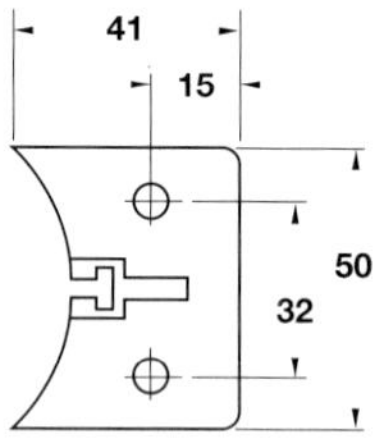

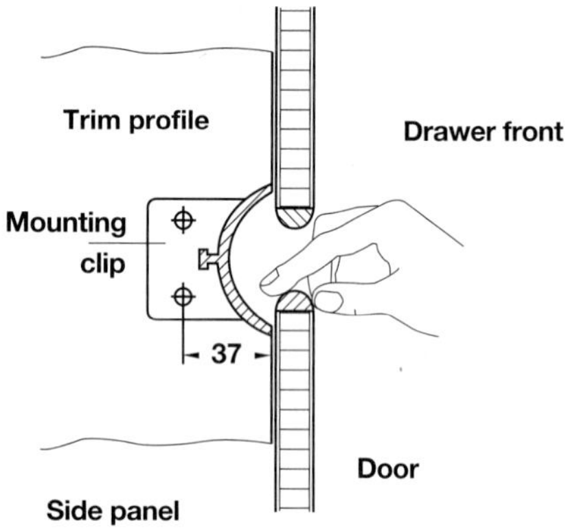

Mounting clip
screw-mounted

Finish: plastic, white

Cat. No.	713.50.797

Packing: 1 pc.

Corner trim profile for 16 mm panels.
You can easily dress up your design with decorative trims. End caps are to be used to give a finished look. This profile is fastened by use of the mounting block. The mounting block can be used with the Häfele Minifix system (see page **2.92** from this catalog).

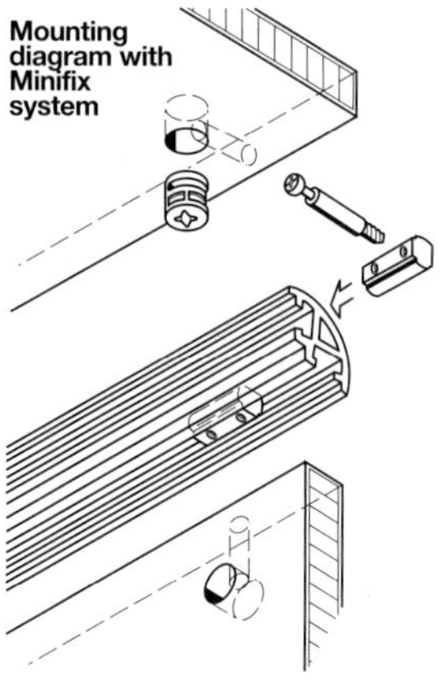

Corner trim profile

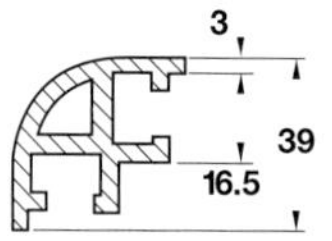

Finish: aluminum, polished; bright gold, anodized

Cat. No.	755.90.813

Packing: lengths of 2.5 m

End cap
for corner trim profile

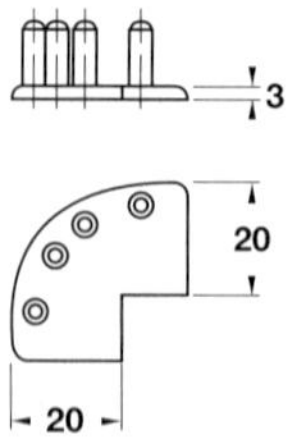

Finish: plastic, metallized; bright gold

Cat. No.	713.91.810

Packing: 100 pcs.

Mounting block, with fixing screw

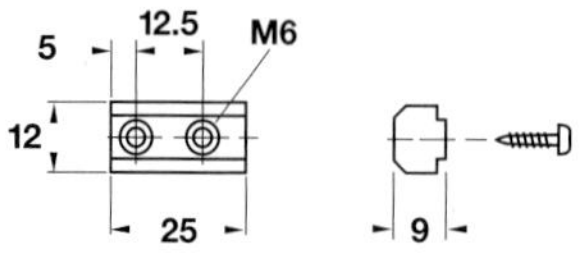

Finish: nylon, white

Cat. No.	755.91.016

Packing: 100 pcs.

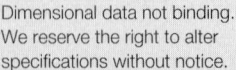

Dimensions in mm

Profile Strips

Door sealing profile with soft PVC lip; self adhesive.
Finish: plastic

Cat. No.	white	716.60.707
	brown	716.60.109
	beige	716.60.403

Packing: 2.5 meters

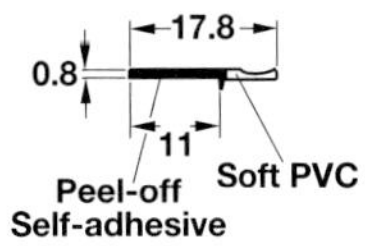

Door sealing profile with soft PVC lip; self adhesive.
Finish: plastic

Cat. No.	white	716.60.716
	brown	716.60.118
	beige	716.60.412

Packing: 2.5 meters

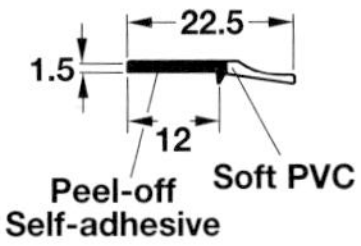

Closure strip
Finish: plastic

Cat. No.	white	716.57.488
	brown	716.51.486

Packing: 5 meters

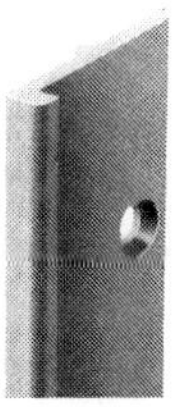

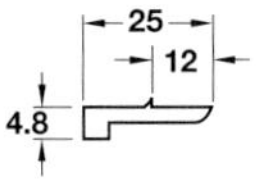

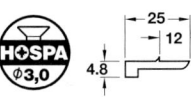

Stop Strip screw-mounted
Finish: plastic

Cat. No.	white	239.92.750
	gray	239.92.550
	brown	239.92.150

Packing: 2.5 meters

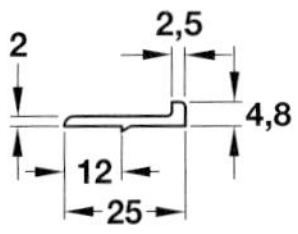

Ideal for:
- Wardrobe locks, Espagnolette locks…wherever a lock or sealing strip is needed.

Stop Strips screw-mounted with self-hinged cover
Finish: plastic

Cat. No.	white	239.93.750
	gray	239.93.550
	brown	239.93.150
	black	239.93.350

Packing: 2.5 meters

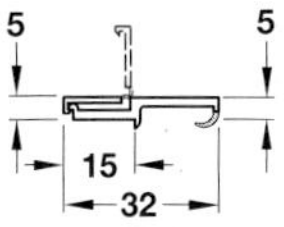

Stop Strips screw-mounted with self-hinged cover
Finish: plastic

Cat. No.	white	239.93.780
	gray	239.93.580
	brown	239.93.180
	black	239.93.380

Packing: 2.5 meters

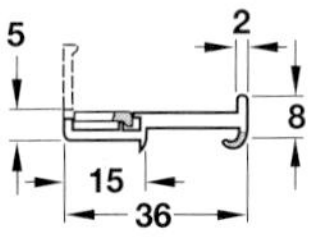

Stop Strips with pressure sensitive adhesive
Finish: plastic

Cat. No.	white	239.91.700
	gray	239.91.500
	brown	239.91.100
	black	239.91.300

Packing: 2.5 meters

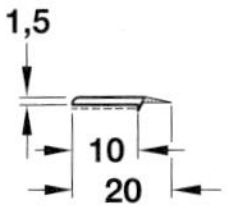

Stop Strips screw-mounted
Finish: plastic

Cat. No.	white	239.90.700
	brown	239.90.100

Packing: 2.5 meters

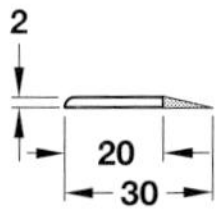

Dimensions in mm

HÄFELE

- Installs easily and quickly
- Retains glass while eliminating rattle
- Clear and frosted finish eliminates unsightly moulding
- No staples, screws or glue required.

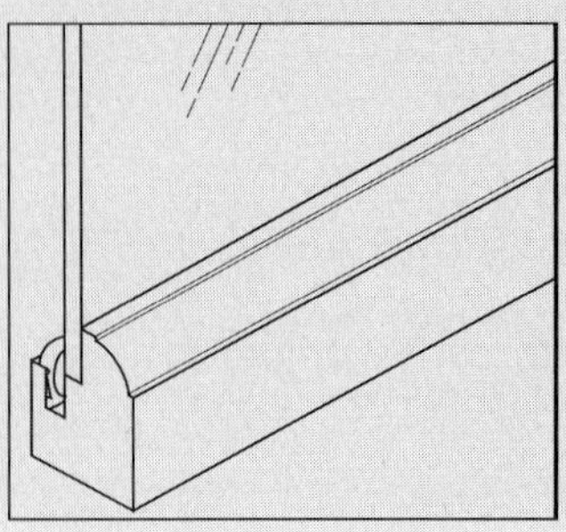

Panel Retainer

For glass doors
Finish: Vinyl

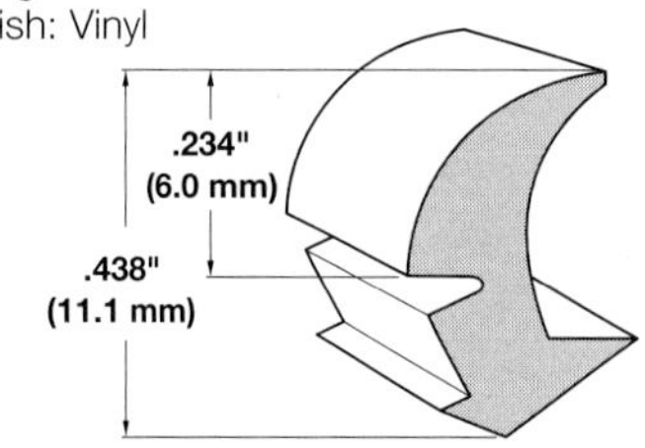

Finish	Cat. No.
frosted	706.60.516
clear	706.60.418

Packing: 1-500' roll (127 m)

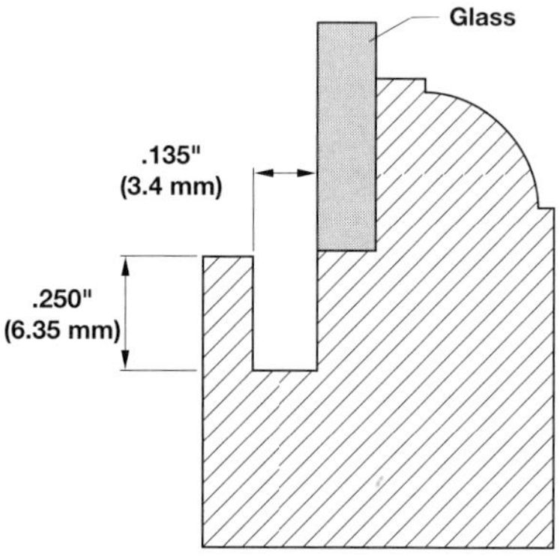

- Larger height allows for greater tolerance in glass squareness dimensions.

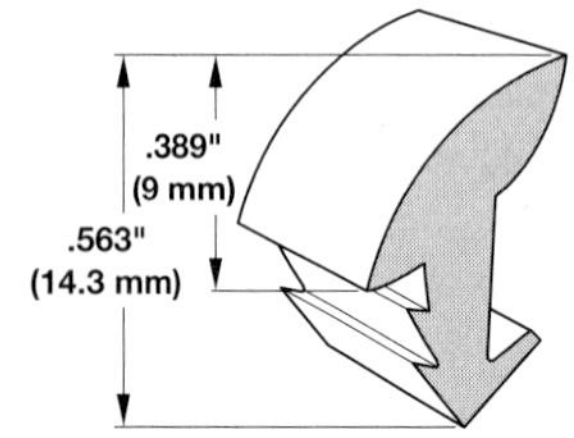

Finish: vinyl

Finish	Cat. No.
frosted	706.62.510
clear	706.62.412

Packing: 1-500' roll (127 m)

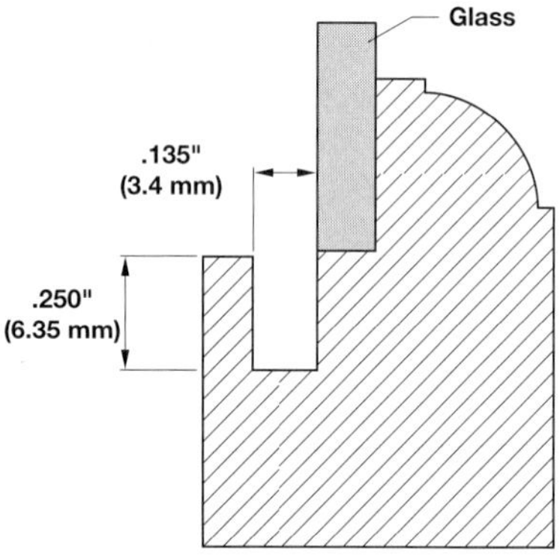

- Larger base dimension allows for greater tolerance in moulding machining.

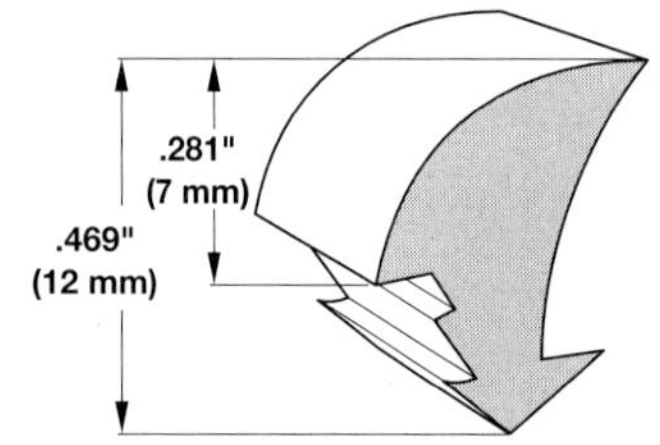

Finish: vinyl

Finish	Cat. No.
frosted	706.61.513
clear	706.61.415

Packing: 1-500' roll (127 m)

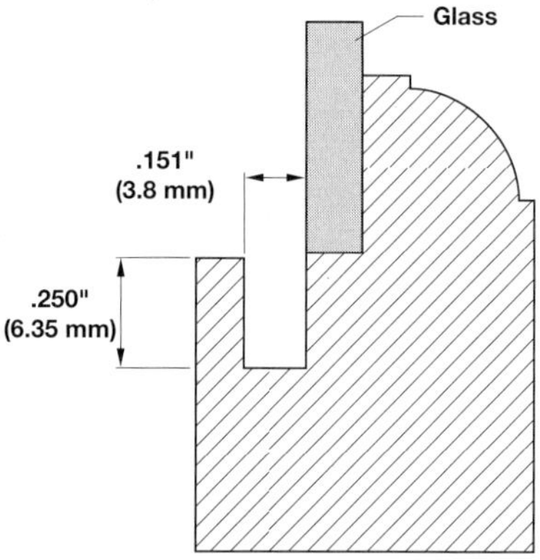

7 Store Fixtures
Profiles
Retainers

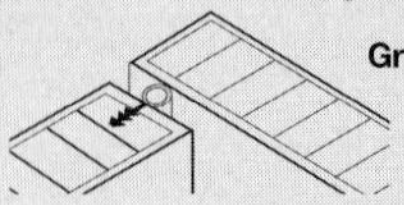

Edge sealing profiles, plastic. Groove mounted in edge of the side panel.

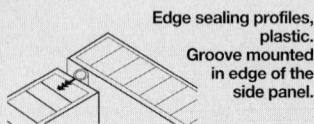

Edge sealing profile

with serrated strip for groove mounting in cabinet side panel.
Finish: plastic (hard and soft PVC)

Color	Cat. No.
white	716.99.708
brown	716.99.100

Packing: rolls of 100 m

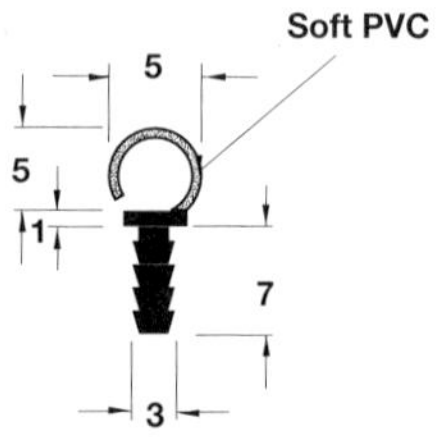

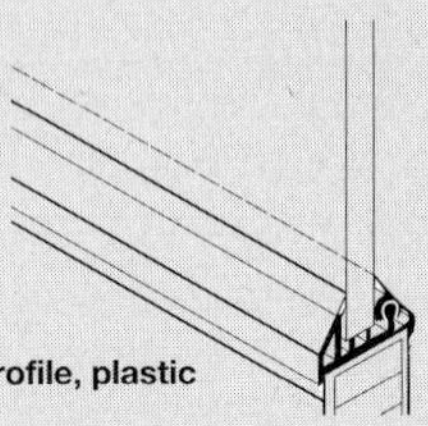

Glass profile, plastic

Glass profile, 2-part

Finish: plastic (hard and soft PVC)

Color	Cat. No.
white	706.77.708
brown	706.77.100

Packing: lengths of 2.5 m each

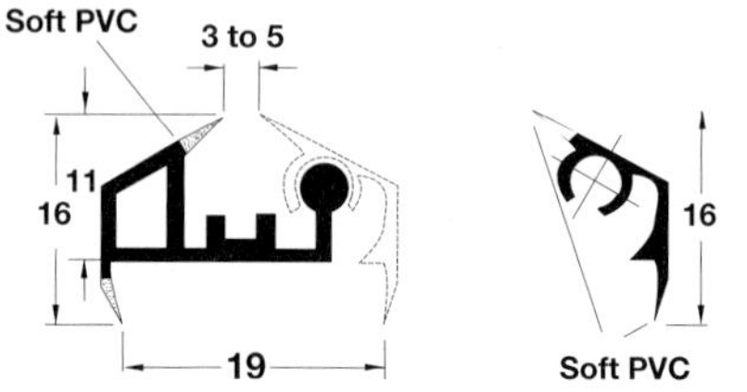

Dimensions in mm

Dimensional data not binding.
We reserve the right to alter specifications without notice.

Product Guide – Furniture Interior Accessories

HÄFELE

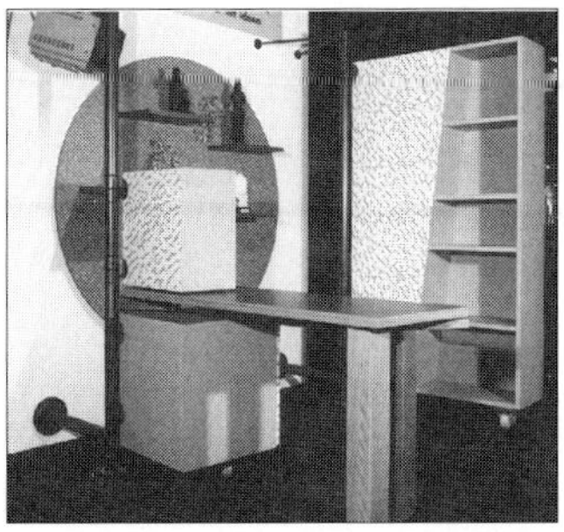
Cabinet Rotation System
Page **8.2 - 8.3**

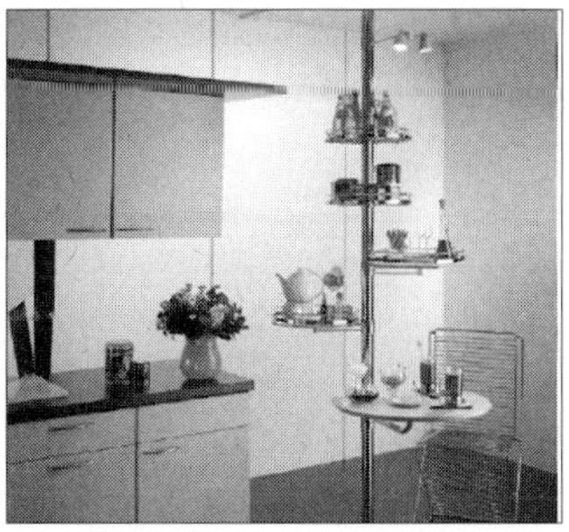
Multi-Purpose Pole Storage
Page **8.4 - 8.21**

Audio/Video Storage
Page **8.22 - 8.28**

Wardrobe Rails
Page **8.29 - 8.33**

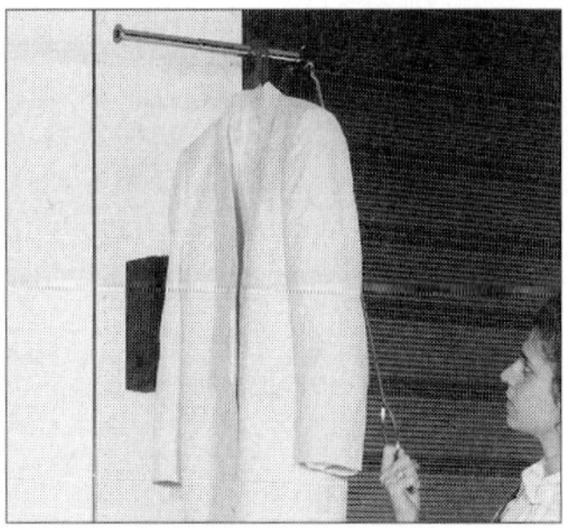
Wardrobe Lifts
Page **8.34 - 8.35**

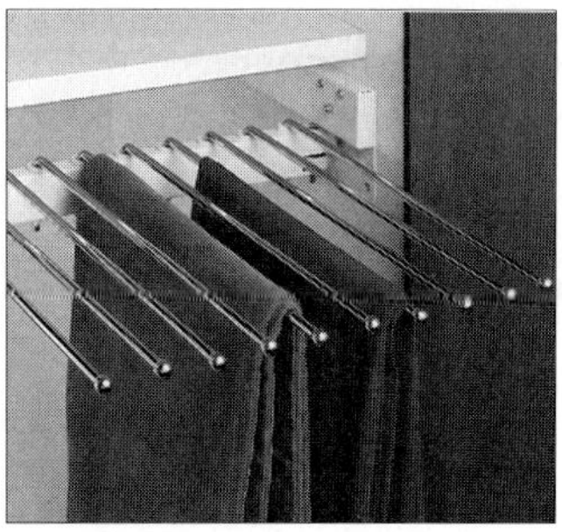
Wardrobe Accessories
Page **8.36 - 8.46**

Wire Basket Storage
Page **8.41**

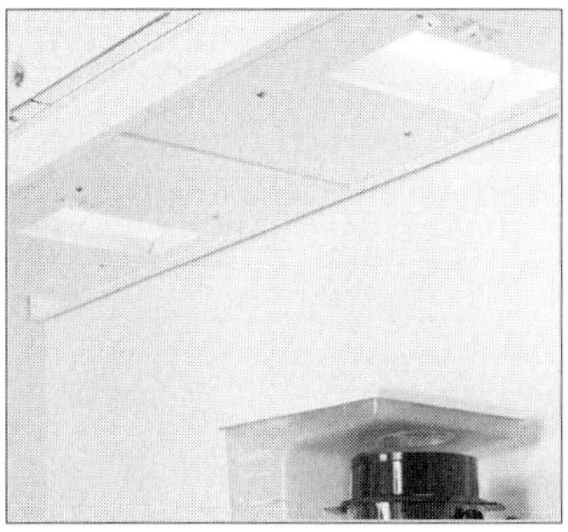
Flourescent Undercabinet Lighting
Page **8.47 - 8.48**

Halogen Lighting Systems
Page **8.49 - 8.59**

Undercabinet Halogen Systems
Page **8.60 - 8.62**

Cable Lighting Systems
Page **8.63 - 8.71**

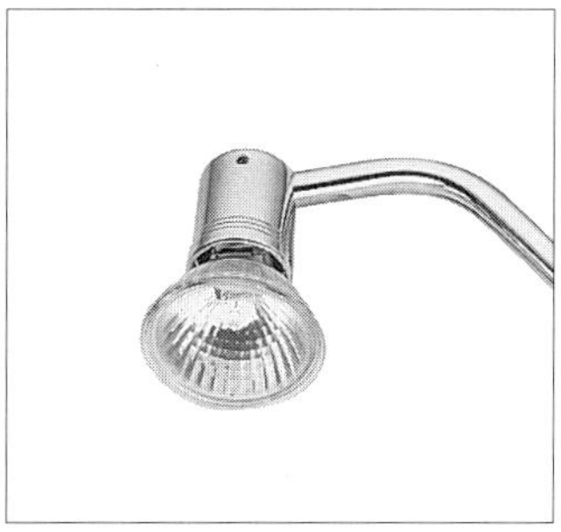
Cornice Lighting
Page **8.72 - 8.73**

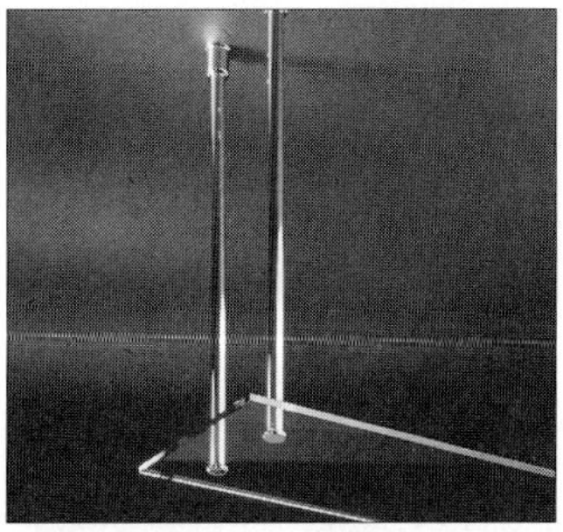
Shelf Suspension System
Page **8.74**

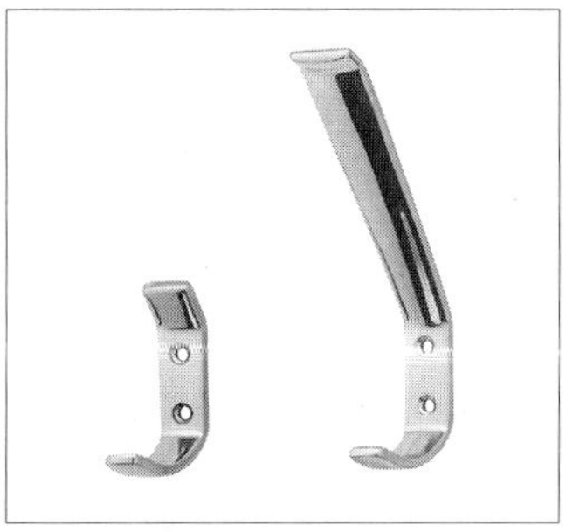
Utility Hooks
Page **8.75 - 8.79**

Decorative Hardware 1

Lock, Catches, RTA and PAS® Fittings Shelf Supports Bed Fittings 2

Hinges Flap and Lid Stays Associated Fittings 3

Sliding Door Hardware Drawer Slides Television Supports 4

Kitchen Accessory Systems 5

Furniture Support Systems, Office and Computer Furniture Accessories 6

Store Fixtures Profiles Retainers 7

Interior Accessories Wardrobe Accessories Storage Systems Furniture Lighting 8

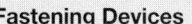

Fastening Devices 0

HÄFELE

Cabinet Rotation System

Application Examples

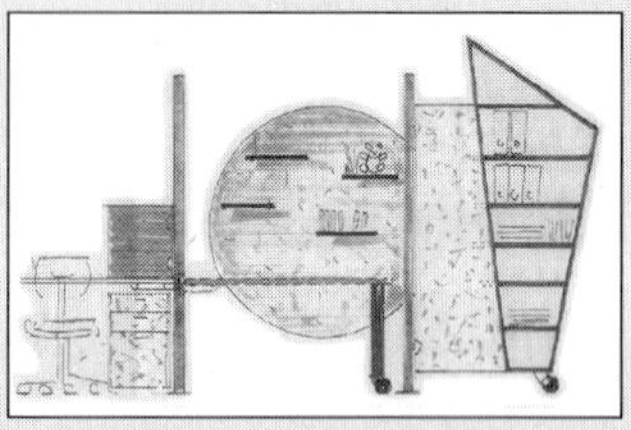

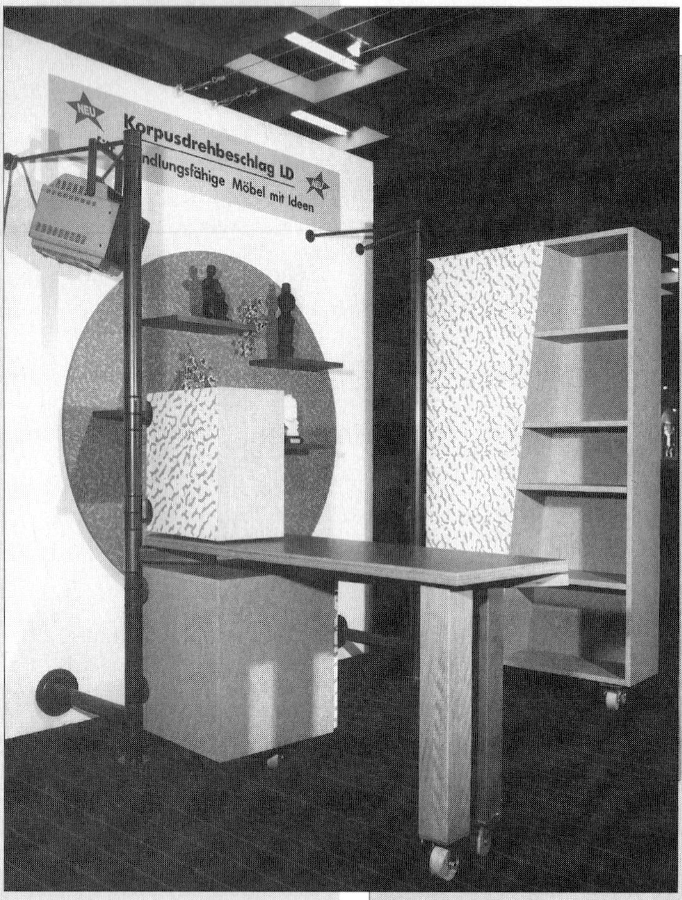

Dimensional data not binding.
We reserve the right to alter specifications without notice.

Cabinet Rotation System LD

HÄFELE

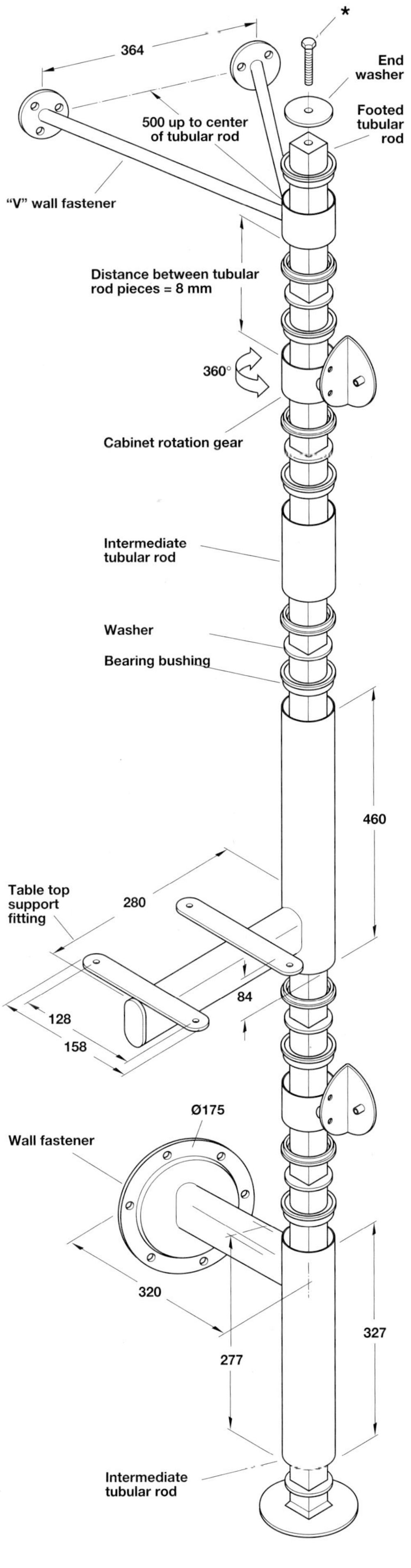

Dimensions in mm

Footed tubular rod

For the different tube elements to be threaded onto

Square tube: 30 x 30 mm
Foot: Ø 110 mm
Height: 2054 mm (80 7/8")

Finish: steel, plastic-coated, metallic gray

Cat. No.	815.50.500

Packing: 1 pc.

Wall fastener

For wall distance 320 mm (middle of tube to wall)

Tube: 60 mm
Oval tube: 60 x 30 mm

Finish: steel, plastic-coated, metallic gray

Cat. No.	815.51.500

Packing: 1 pc.

"V" wall fastener

For a wall distance of 500 mm (middle of tube to wall)

Finish: steel, plastic-coated, metallic gray

Cat. No.	815.51.510

Packing: 1 pc.

Cabinet rotation gear

For fastening cabinets that can be rotated

Finish: steel, plastic-coated, metallic gray

Cat. No.	815.52.500

Packing: 1 pc.

Table top support fitting

Finish: steel, plastic-coated, metallic gray

Cat. No.	815.52.510

Packing: 1 pc.

End washer

With M8 x 40 screws, DIN 912
Diameter: 53.6 x 3 mm

Finish: steel, zinc-plated black

Cat. No.	815.54.320

Packing: 1 pc.

Bearing bushings

To be put into the tubular rod elements
Diameter: 62 mm

Finish: plastic, black

Cat. No.	815.54.300

Packing: 1 pc.

Washer

To be used between the bearing bushings

Finish: plastic, black

Cat. No.	815.54.310

Packing: 1 pc.

Intermediate tubes

Diameter: 60 x 1.5 mm

Finish: steel, plastic-coated, metallic gray

Length	Cat. No.
46 mm (1 3/4")	815.53.501
76 mm (3")	815.53.502
130 mm (5 1/8")	815.53.503
190 mm (7 1/2")	815.53.504
204 mm (8")	815.53.505
248 mm (9 3/4")	815.53.506
327 mm (12 7/8")	815.53.507
355 mm (14")	815.53.508
396 mm (15 5/8")	815.53.509
450 mm (17 3/4")	815.53.510
460 mm (18 1/8")	815.53.511
657 mm (25 7/8")	815.53.512
1164 mm (45 3/4")	815.53.513

Packing: 1 pc.

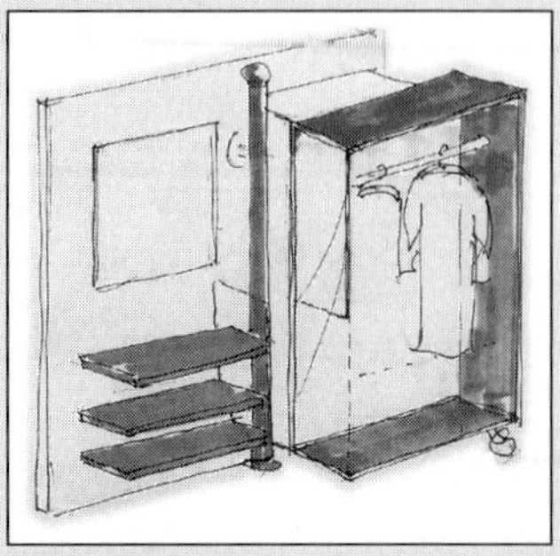

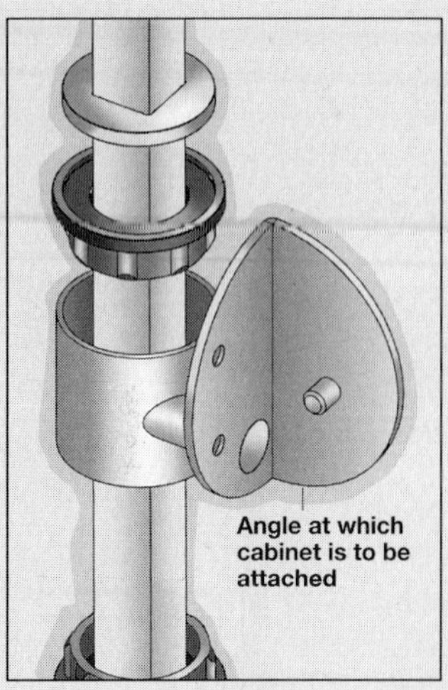

* Do not attach rotating elements at the very beginning, i.e. to the foot; nor at at the very end, i.e. the end washer.

* When tightening the screws the tubular elements will be tightened against each other.

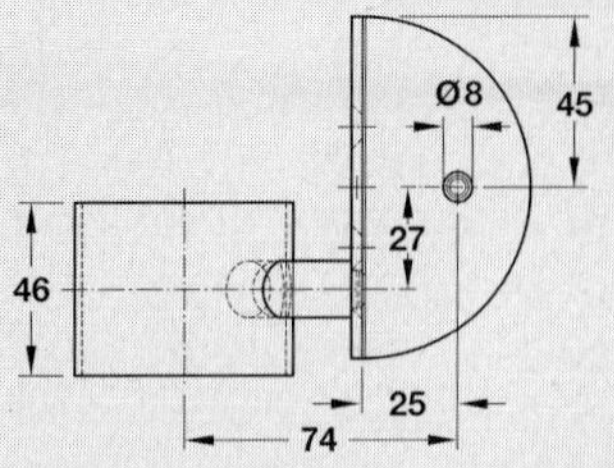

HÄFELE

Multi-Purpose Pole Mount System, Ø 50 mm

- Attachments feature continuous adjustment to desired height
- Wide selection of attachments for custom configuration

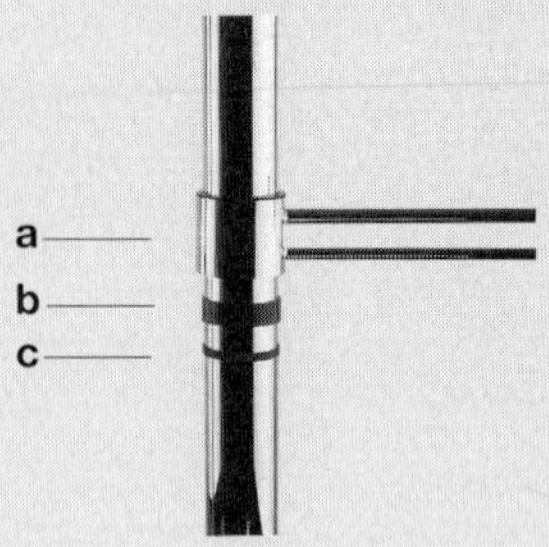

Retaining ring (c) holds the bearing ring (b) in position. Bearing ring supports the pivot arm (a).

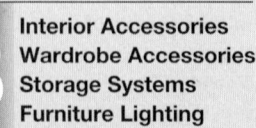

Pole, Ø 50 mm
with bottom bearing mount, trim ring and top trim cap
Finish: steel, chrome-plated

Overall length	Cat. No.
1208 mm	815.00.212
1825 mm	815.00.218
2625 mm	815.00.226
3020 mm	815.00.230

Packing: 1 pc.

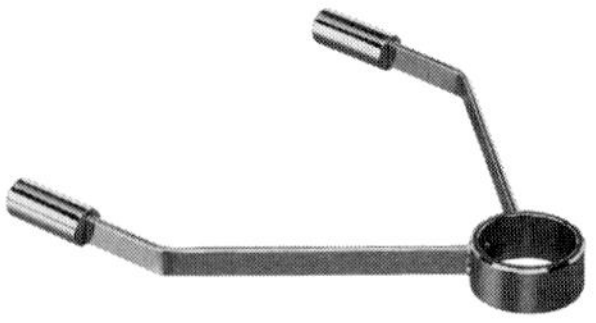

Mounting bracket, for wall attachment
250 x 310 x 24 mm (W x D x H)
Finish: steel, chrome-plated

Cat. No.	815.02.200

Packing: 1 pc.

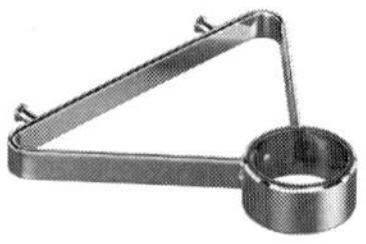

Mounting bracket, for cabinet attachment
192 x 160 x 24 mm (W x D x H)
Finish: steel, chrome-plated

Cat. No.	815.02.210

Packing: 1 pc.

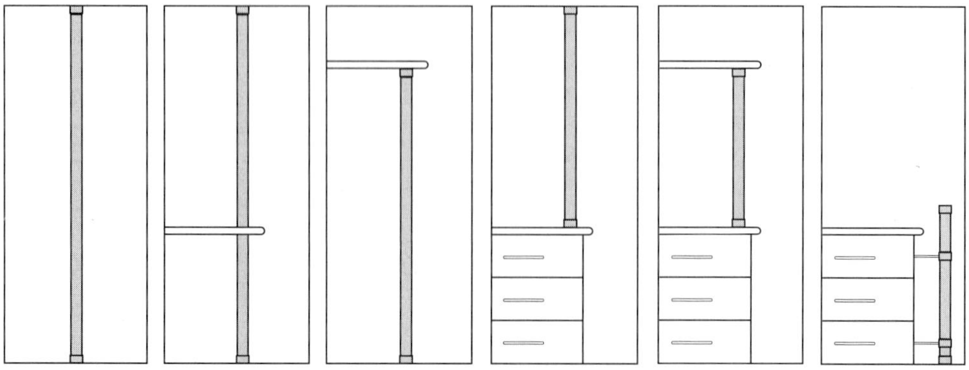

Dimensional data not binding. We reserve the right to alter specifications without notice.

Dimensions in mm

Multi-Purpose Pole Mount System, Ø 50 mm

HÄFELE

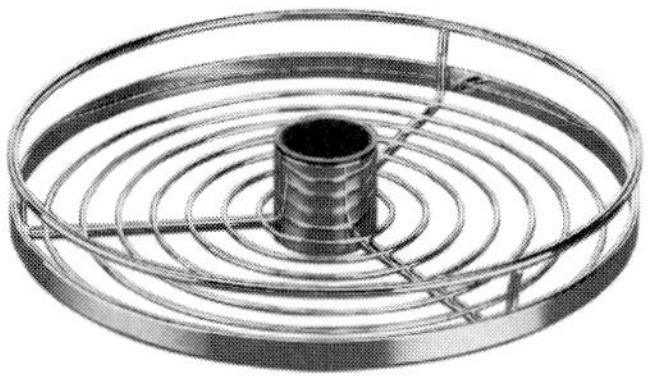

Revolving wire basket, round
Ø 360 mm, Height: 50 mm
Finish: steel, chrome-plated

Cat. No.	815.04.200

Packing: 1 pc.

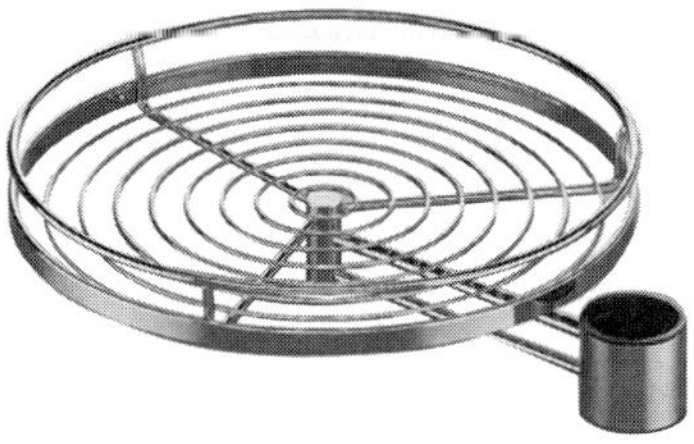

Swivelling basket, round with swivel arm
Ø 360 mm, Height: 90 mm
Finish: steel, chrome-plated

Cat. No.	815.04.210

Packing: 1 pc.

Swivelling basket, round, with wood bottom and swivel arm Ø 360 mm, Height: 100 mm
Finish: steel, chrome-plated, bottom: beech

Cat. No.	815.04.211

Packing: 1 pc.

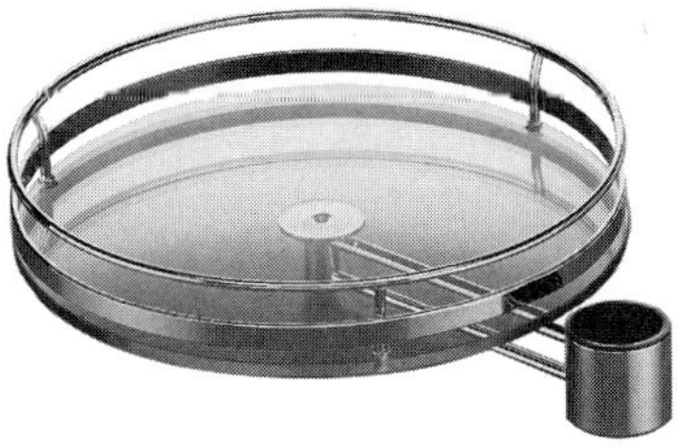

Swivelling basket, round, with glass bottom and swivel arm Ø 364 mm, Height: 100 mm
Finish: steel, chrome-plated

Cat. No.	815.04.212

Packing: 1 pc.

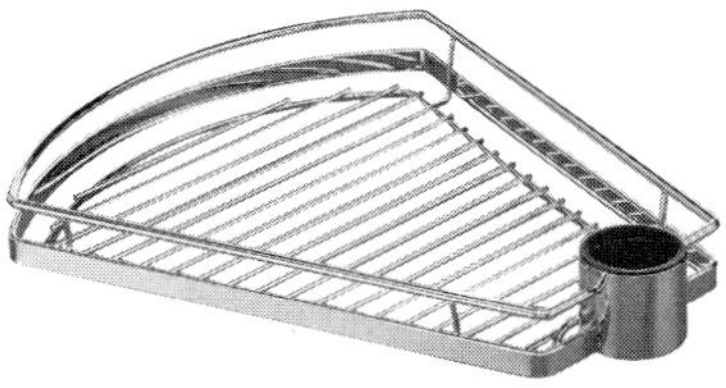

Swivelling basket, with wire bottom
355 x 420 x 50 mm (W x D x H)
Finish: steel, chrome-plated

Cat. No.	815.04.220

Packing: 1 pc.

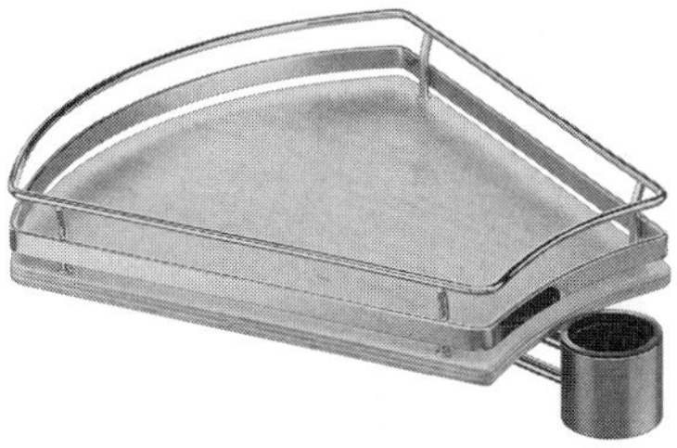

Swivelling basket, with wood bottom and swivel arm,
353 x 372 x 100 mm (W x D x H)
Finish: steel, chrome-plated, bottom: beech

Cat. No.	815.04.221

Packing: 1 pc.

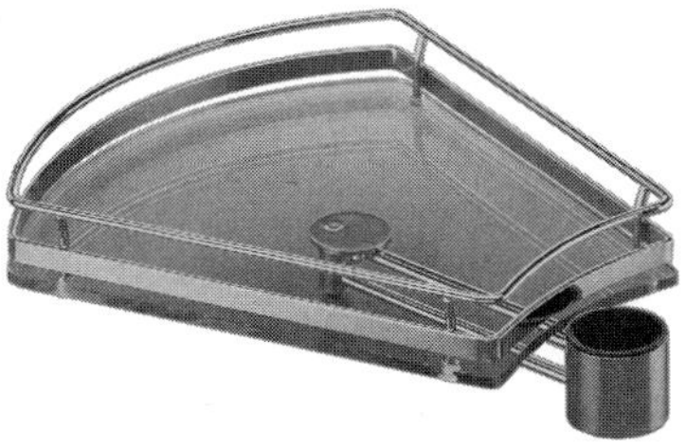

Swivelling basket, with glass bottom and swivel arm,
358 x 376 x 100 mm (W x D x H)
Finish: steel, chrome-plated

Cat. No.	815.04.222

Packing: 1 pc.

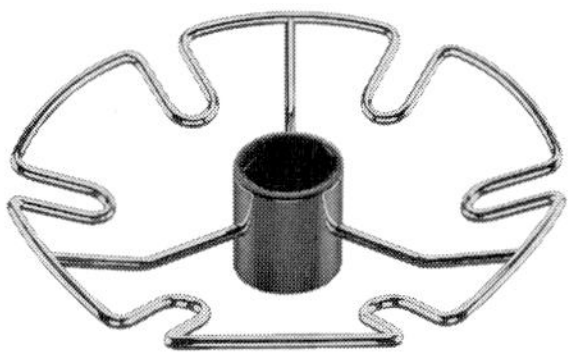

Glass rack for 6 glasses,
Ø 300 mm, Height: 52 mm
Finish: steel, chrome-plated

Cat. No.	815.05.200

Packing: 1 pc.

Dimensions in mm

- For use with 50mm diameter pole
- Retaining ring and bearing ring come with all baskets and racks for fastening to the pole.

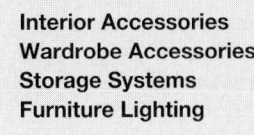

Multi-Purpose Pole Mount System, Ø 50 mm

- Accessories for use with 50mm diameter pole

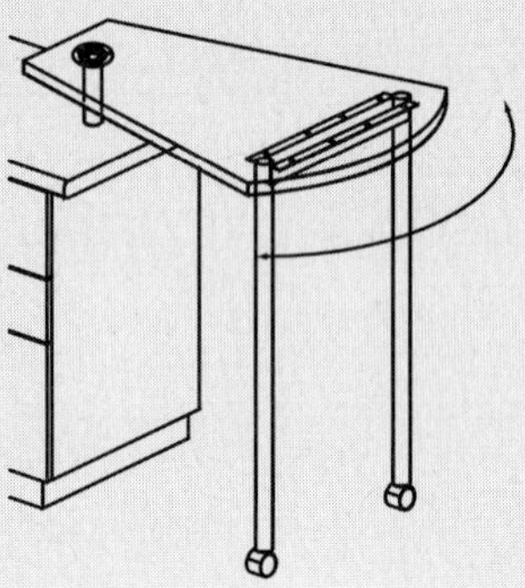

Bistro table, with wood surface and adjustment ring, swivel-mounted, Ø 600 mm, Height: 170 mm, Wood thickness: 16 mm
Finish: steel, chrome-plated, table top: beech

Cat. No.	815.06.200

Packing: 1 pc.

Foot rest ring with adjustment ring
Ø 360 mm, Height: 120 mm
Finish: steel, chrome-plated

Cat. No.	815.06.210

Packing: 1 pc.

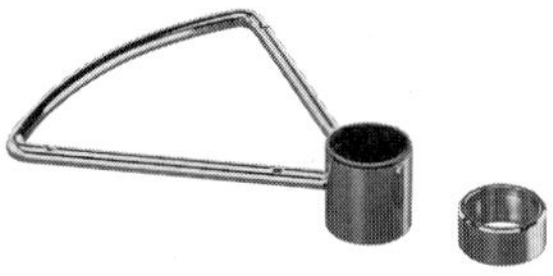

Swivel arm featuring adjustment ring for table top
256 x 290 x 50 mm (W x D x H)
Finish: steel, chrome-plated

Cat. No.	815.03.200

Packing: 1 pc.

Table top mount featuring pivot bearing for mounting on countertop
Length: 185 mm
Finish: steel, chrome-plated

Cat. No.	815.03.220

Packing: 1 pc.

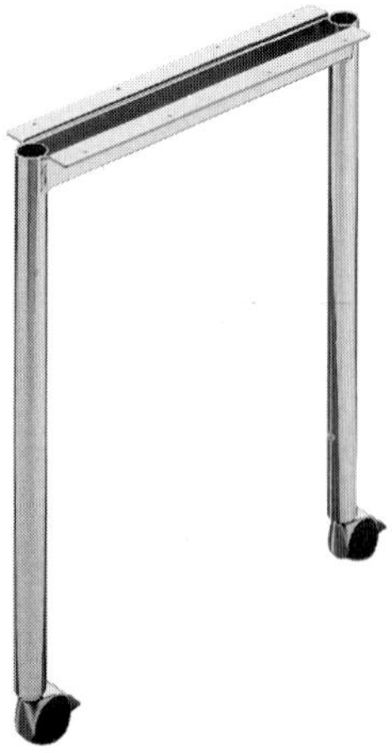

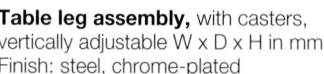

Table leg assembly, with casters, vertically adjustable W x D x H in mm
Finish: steel, chrome-plated

W x D x H in mm	Cat. No.
545 x 116 x 670 - 770	815.07.202
545 x 116 x 1035 -1135	815.07.205

Packing: 1 pc.

Wire chair
475 x 570 x 930 mm (W x D x H)
Finish: steel, chrome-plated

Cat. No.	815.06.240

Packing: 1 pc.

Dimensional data not binding. We reserve the right to alter specifications without notice.

Dimensions in mm

Multi-Purpose Pole Mount System, Ø 50 mm

HÄFELE

Mount with trim ring for table top
310 x 185 x 27 mm (W x D x H)
Finish: steel, chrome-plated

Cat. No.	815.03.210

Packing: 1 pc.

Adapter mount for slanted ceilings
Finish: steel, chrome-plated

Cat. No.	815.02.220

Packing: 1 pc.

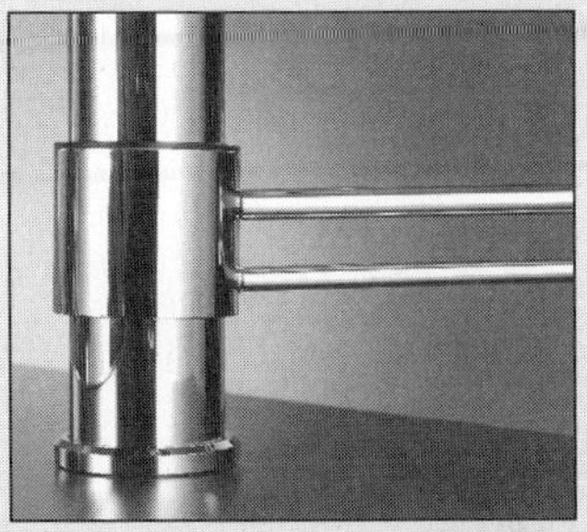

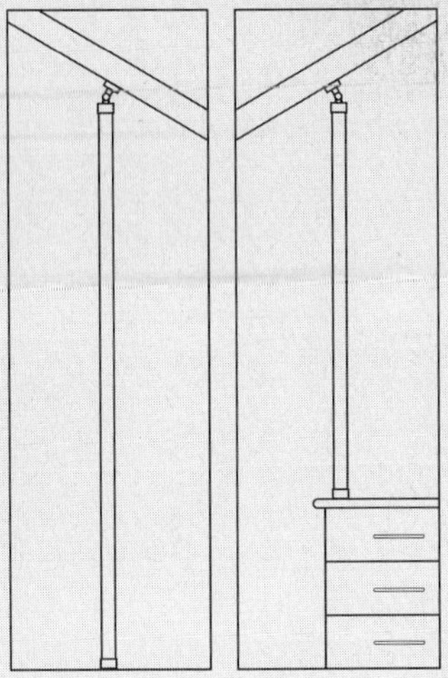

- Accessories for use with 50mm diameter pole

Support for pole-mounted table-top, featuring adjustment ring and trim
Ø 360 mm, Height: 120 mm
Finish: steel, chrome-plated

Cat. No.	815.06.230

Packing: 1 pc.

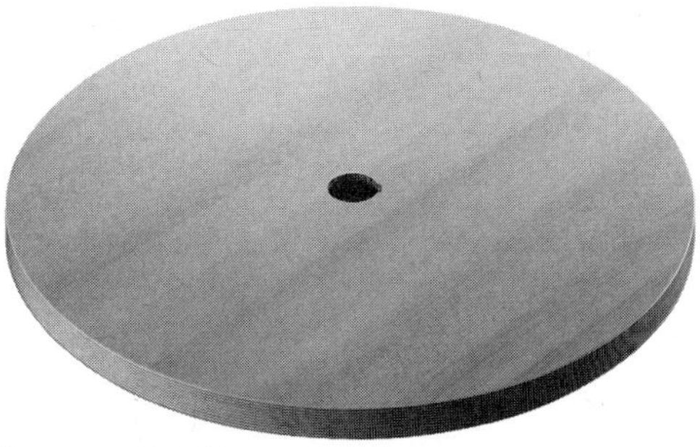

Pole-mount table
Ø 700 mm, wood thickness: 30 mm
Finish: Particle board, plastic-coated
Beech pattern

Cat. No.	815.06.231

Packing: 1 pc.

Table top
Wood thickness: 30 mm
Finish: Particle board, plastic-coated
beech pattern

Cat. No.	815.06.220

Packing: 1 pc.

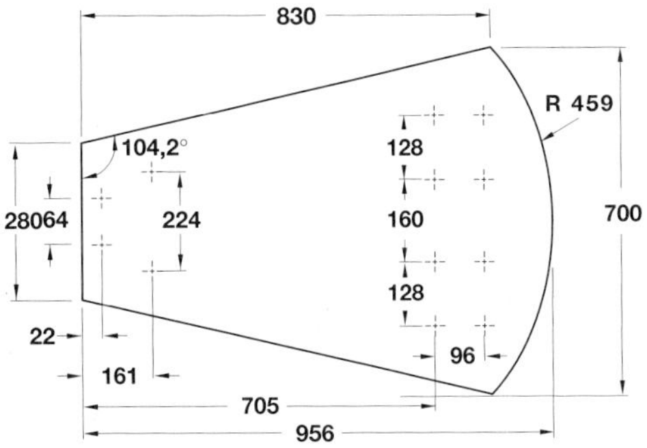

Hole - Ø 5 mm

Dimensions in mm

Dimensional data not binding.
We reserve the right to alter specifications without notice.

HÄFELE

Multi-Purpose Pole Mount System, Ø 50 mm

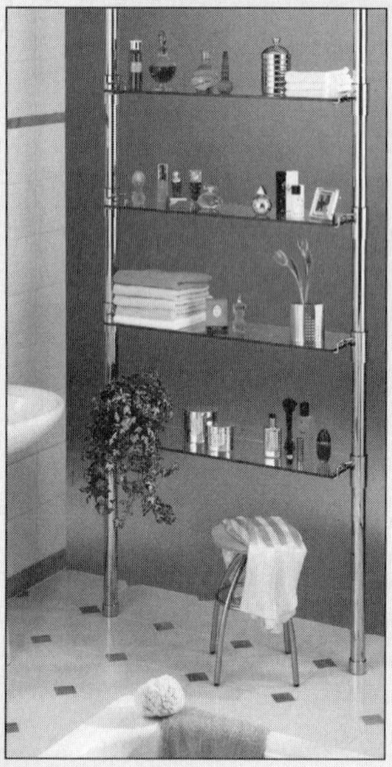

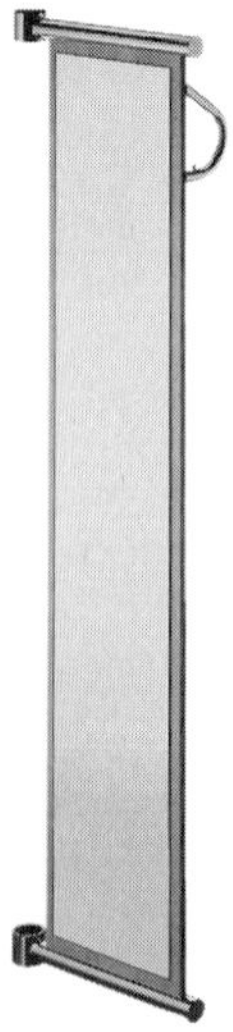

Dressing mirror with clothes hanger hook
460 x 360 x 1630 mm (W x D x H)
Finish: bracket: steel, chrome-plated
border: beech pattern

Cat. No.	815.08.221

Packing: 1 pc.

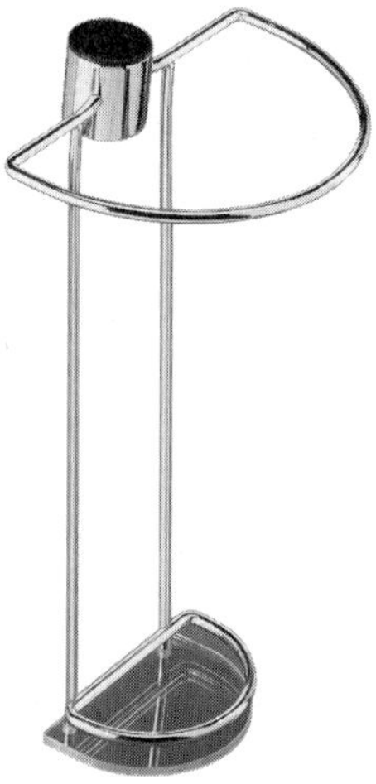

Umbrella stand
280 x 220 x 415 mm (W x D x H)
Finish: steel, chrome-plated

Cat. No.	815.08.240

Packing: 1 pc.

Glass-bottom shelf,
small Ø 260 mm
Finish: steel, chrome-plated

Cat. No.	815.08.210

Packing: 1 pc.

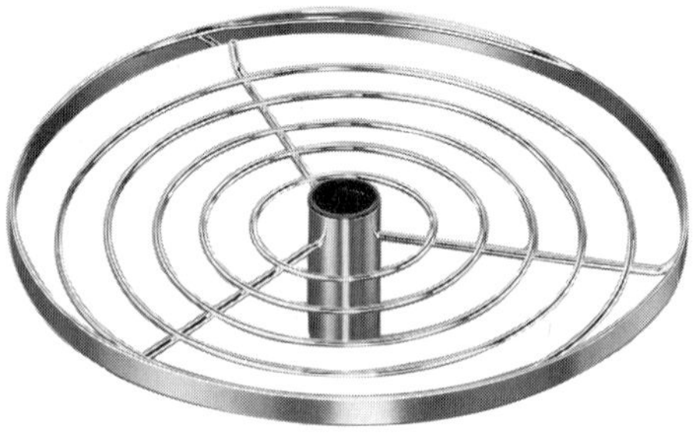

Round shelf
round Ø 550 mm
Finish: steel, chrome-plated

Cat. No.	815.08.211

Packing: 1 pc.

Support for wood or glass shelf,
200 x 100 x 100 (W x D x H)
Finish: bracket: steel, chrome-plated

Cat. No.	815.08.200

Packing: 1 pc.

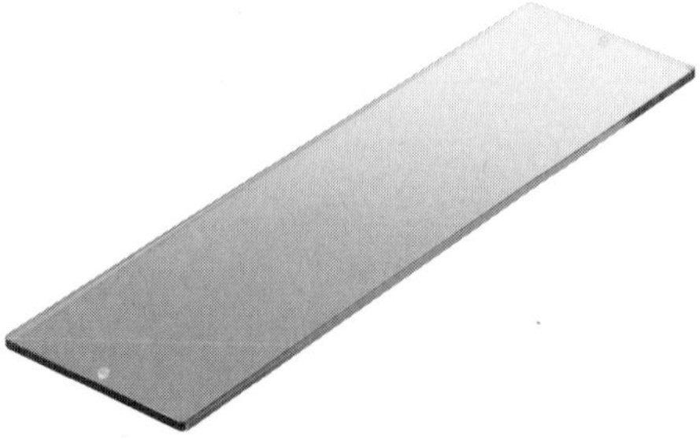

Glass Shelf
thickness: 8 mm
Finish: tempered glass

W x D	Cat. No.
300 x 850 mm	815.08.030
400 x 850 mm	815.08.040

Packing: 1 pc.

- Accessories for use with 50mm diameter pole

Dimensions in mm

Multi-Purpose Pole Mount System, Ø 50 mm

HÄFELE

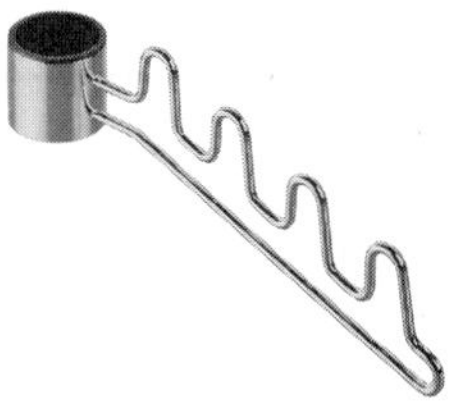

Clothes rack
320 x 110 x 60 (W x D x H)
Finish: steel, chrome-plated

Cat. No.	815.08.230

Packing: 1 pc.

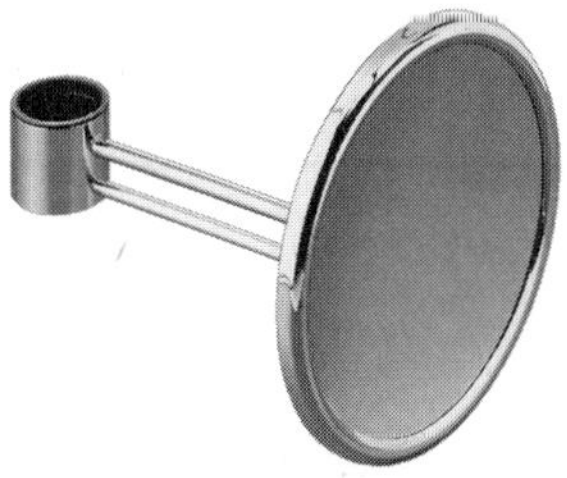

Cosmetic mirror
Ø 230 mm
Finish: bracket: steel, chrome-plated
mirror frame: plastic, chrome-colored

Cat. No.	815.08.220

Packing: 1 pc.

Hair drier holder
85 x 165 x 53 (W x D x H)
Finish: steel, chrome-plated

Cat. No.	815.08.232

Packing: 1 pc.

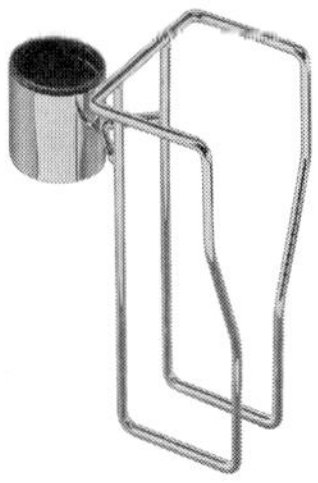

Tissue box holder
128 x 170 x 210 mm (W x D x H)
Finish: steel, chrome-plated

Cat. No.	815.08.234

Packing: 1 pc.

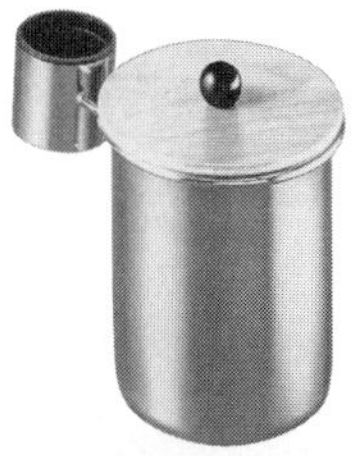

Multi-purpose container
Ø 150 mm, Height: 180 mm
Finish: bracket: steel, chrome-plated
container: stainless steel
lid: beech

Cat. No.	815.08.233

Packing: 1 pc.

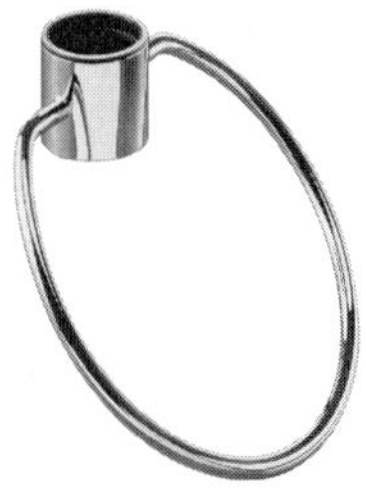

Hand towel ring
235 x 210 x 170 mm
Finish: steel, chrome-plated

Cat. No.	815.08.231

Packing: 1 pc.

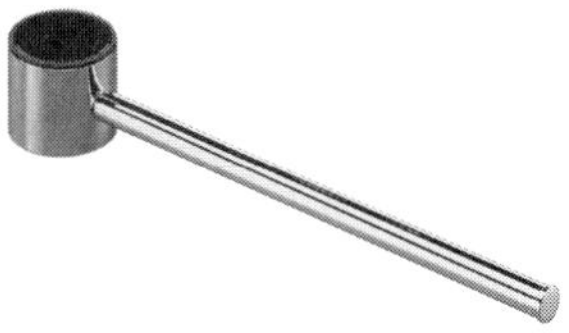

Swivel rod, Ø 16 mm
Length: 360 mm
Height: 50 mm
Finish: steel, chrome-plated

Cat. No.	815.05.210

Packing: 1 pc.

S-hooks for swivel rod, Ø 16 mm,
Finish: steel, chrome-plated

Cat. No.	522.04.207

Packing: 4 pc.

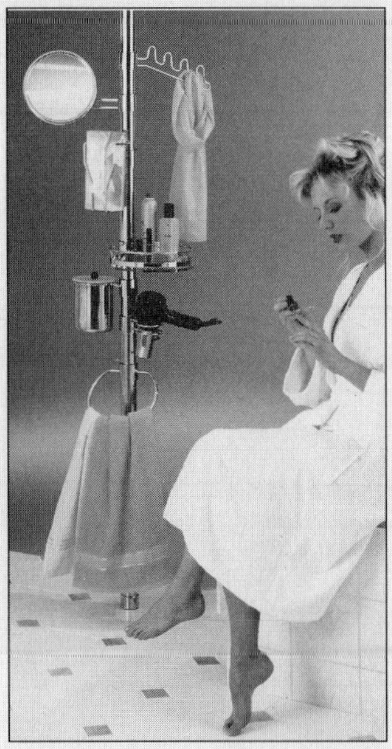

- Accessories for use with 50mm diameter pole

Dimensional data not binding.
We reserve the right to alter specifications without notice.

Dimensions in mm

HÄFELE

Multi-Purpose Pole Mount System, Ø 45 mm and Ø 65 mm

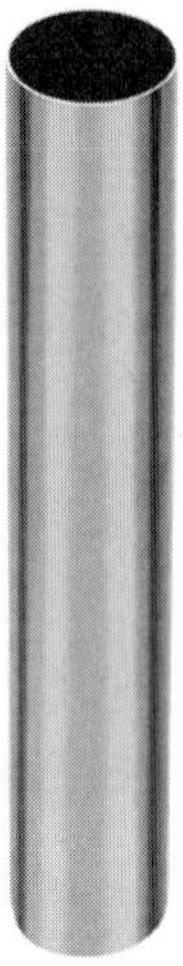

Pole
Finish: steel, chrome-plated

Length	Cat. No. Ø 45 mm	Cat. No. Ø 65 mm
820 mm	815.40.208	815.20.208
1300 mm	815.40.213	815.20.213
1800 mm	815.40.218	815.20.218
2500 mm	815.40.225	815.20.225
3000 mm	815.40.230	815.20.230

Packing: 1 pc.

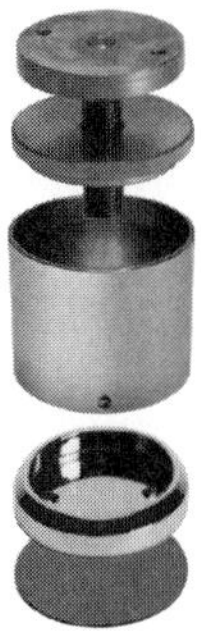

Pole attachment hardware
- for floor and ceiling
- for table top and ceiling
- for floor and under table top

Finish: brass, chrome-plated

for pole Ø	Cat. No.
65 mm	815.22.210
45 mm	815.42.210

Packing: 1 pc.

Pole attachment hardware
for floor, ceiling and pre-drilled table top
Finish: brass, chrome-plated

for pole Ø	Cat. No.
65 mm	815.22.211
45 mm	815.42.211

Packing: 1 pc.

Pole attachment hardware
for free-standing pole with pre-drilled table top
Finish: brass, chrome-plated

for pole Ø	Cat. No.
65 mm	815.22.212
45 mm	815.42.212

Packing: 1 pc.

Pole attachment hardware
for attaching predrilled table top to pole
Finish: brass, chrome-plated

for pole Ø	Cat. No.
65 mm	815.22.207
45 mm	815.42.207

Packing: 1 pc.

Pole attachment hardware
for ceiling
Finish: brass, chrome-plated

for pole Ø	Cat. No.
65 mm	815.22.201
45 mm	815.42.201

Packing: 1 pc.

Dimensions in mm

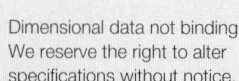

Dimensional data not binding.
We reserve the right to alter specifications without notice.

Multi-Purpose Pole-Mount System, Ø 45 mm and Ø 65 mm

Pole attachment hardware, for floor
Finish: brass, chrome-plated

for pole Ø	Cat. No.
65 mm	815.22.202
45 mm	815.42.202

Packing: 1 pc.

Adjustment ring, with washer
Finish: brass, chrome-plated

for pole Ø	Cat. No.
65 mm	815.22.203
45 mm	815.42.203

Packing: 1 pc.

Flange
for table top
Finish: brass, chrome-plated

for pole Ø	Cat. No.
65 mm	815.22.205
45 mm	815.42.205

Packing: 1 pc.

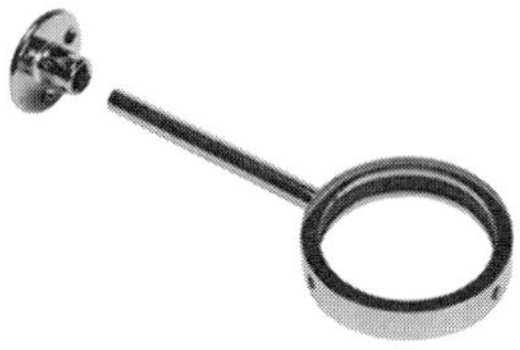

Mounting bracket, for cabinet attachment*
for freestanding pole
Finish: brass, chrome-plated

for pole Ø	Cat. No.
65 mm	815.22.206
45 mm	815.42.206

Packing: 1 pc.

Adjustment ring, cylindrical
for multi-tier installation
Finish: brass, chrome-plated

for hole Ø	Cat. No.
65 mm	815.22.204
45 mm	815.42.204

Packing: 1 pc.

Mounting set
with flange and ring for drilled work surface
Finish: brass, chrome-plated

for pole Ø	Cat. No.
65 mm	815.22.214
45 mm	815.42.214

Packing: 1 pc.

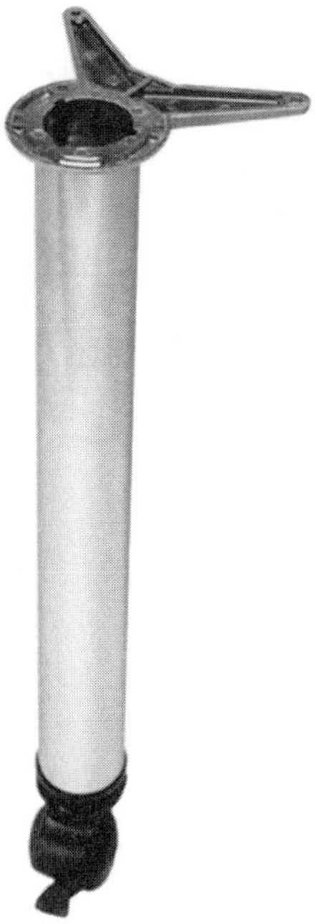

Table leg, featuring caster
Height: adjustable, 650-675 mm
Finish: table leg: steel, chrome-plated
castor: plastic black

Cat. No.	815.27.200

Packing: 1 pc.

Dimensions in mm

HÄFELE

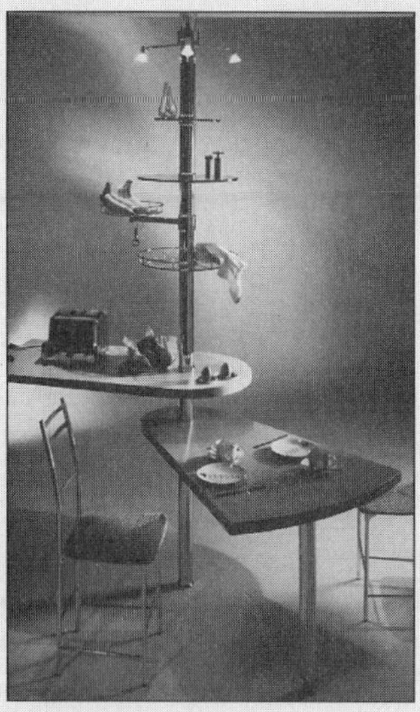

* We recommend using two attachments.

- Accessories for use with 45 and 65mm diameter pole

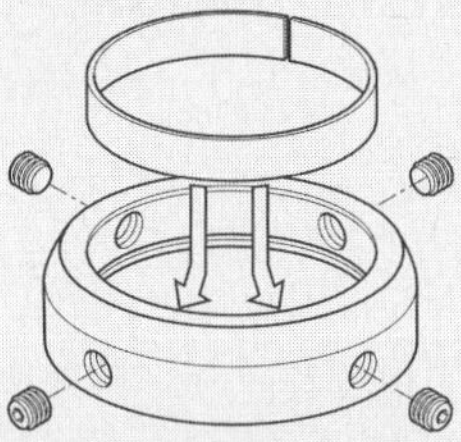

Each pole system attachment features a concentric spring ring on the inside to prevent damage to pole by attachment screws.

Dimensional data not binding. We reserve the right to alter specifications without notice.

HÄFELE

Multi-Purpose Pole-Mount System, Ø 45 mm and Ø 65 mm

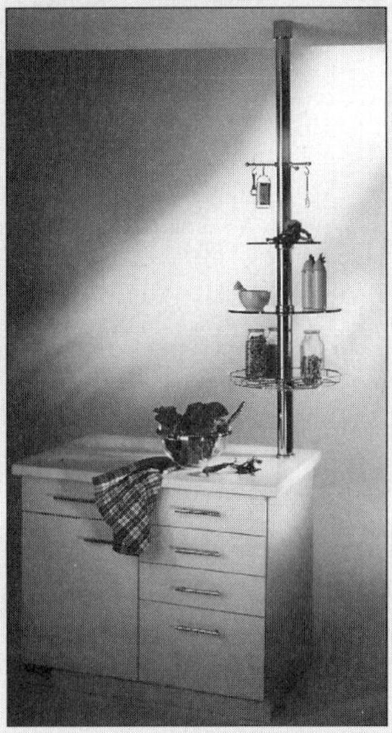

• Accessories for use with 45 & 65mm diameter pole

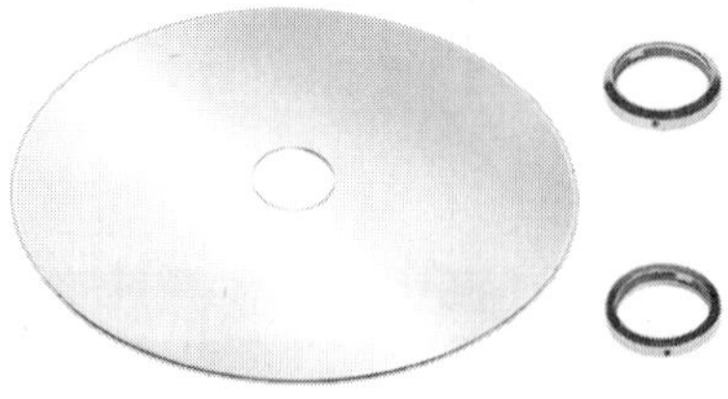

Glass shelf, for use as standalone attachment*
glass thickness 10 mm complete with pole attachment hardware

	Cat. No.	
Size	Pole Ø 45 mm	Pole Ø 65 mm
Ø 300 mm	815.46.000	815.26.000
Ø 450 mm	815.46.010	815.26.010

Packing: 1 pc.

*Not suitable for revolving baskets

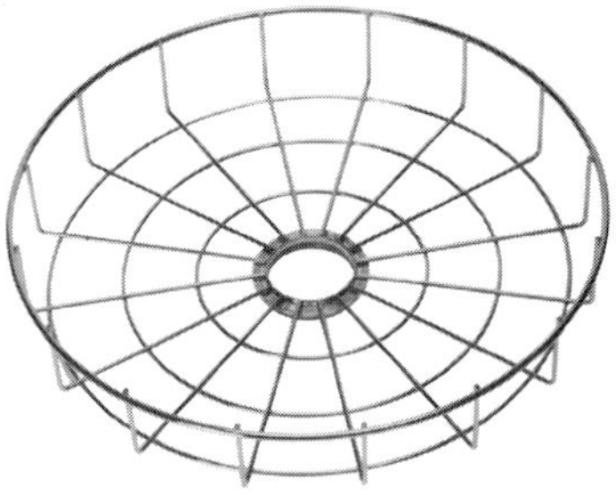

Revolving wire basket, Ø 450 mm without glass plate
Finish: steel, chrome-plated

	Cat. No.	
Height	Pole Ø 45 mm	Pole Ø 65 mm
40 mm	815.44.200	815.24.200
70 mm	815.44.210	815.24.210

Packing: 1 pc.

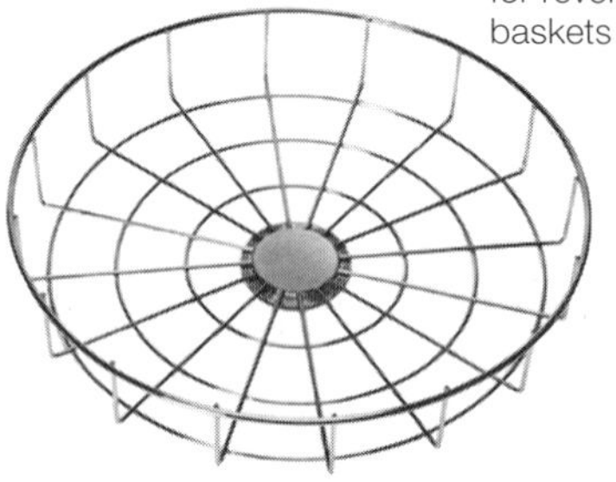

Revolving wire basket, Ø 450 mm
without hole, closed center
used as finish basket without glass plate
Finish: steel, chrome-plated

	Cat. No.	
Height	Pole Ø 45 mm	Pole Ø 65 mm
70 mm	815.44.220	815.24.220

Packing: 1 pc.

Glass plate, Ø 425 mm
without hole

Glass Thickness	for Revolving Wire Basket	Cat. No.
5 mm	815.24.220/815.44.220	815.24.000

Packing: 1 pc.

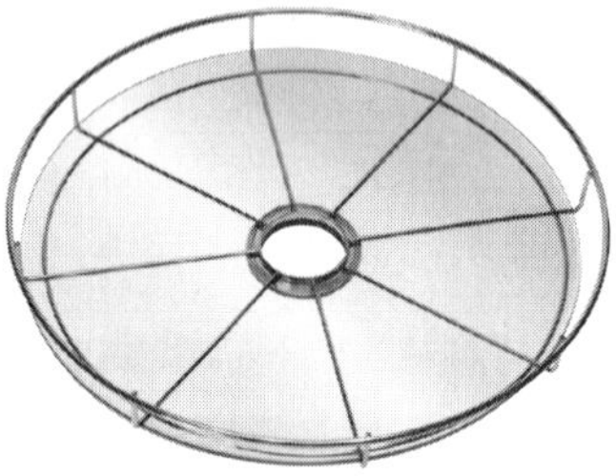

Revolving wire basket, Ø 450 mm complete with glass plate, 815.24.001 and mounting hardware
Finish: steel, chrome-plated

Height	for Pole Ø	Cat. No.
40 mm	65 mm	815.24.201

Packing: 1 pc.

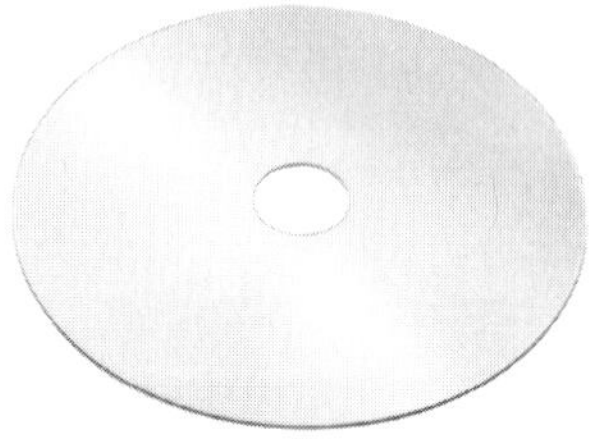

Replacement glass plate, Ø 425 mm
with Ø 70 mm hole

Glass Thickness	for Revolving Wire Basket	Cat. No.
5 mm	815.24.201	815.24.001

Packing: 1 pc.

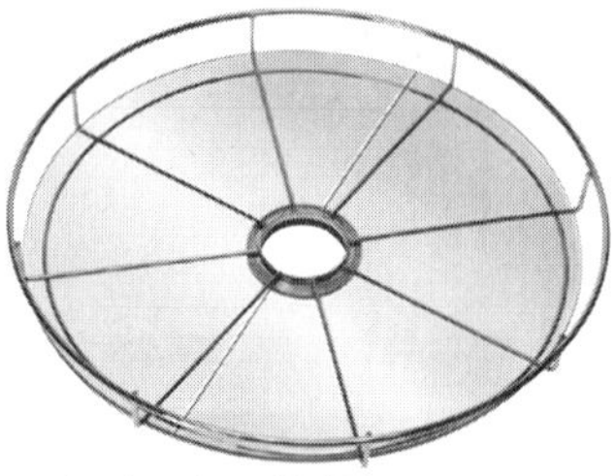

Revolving wire basket, Ø 450 mm
complete with two-piece glass plate 815.24.002
Finish: steel, chrome-plated

	Cat. No.	
Height	Pole Ø 45 mm	Pole Ø 65 mm
40 mm	815.44.222	815.24.222

Packing: 1 pc.

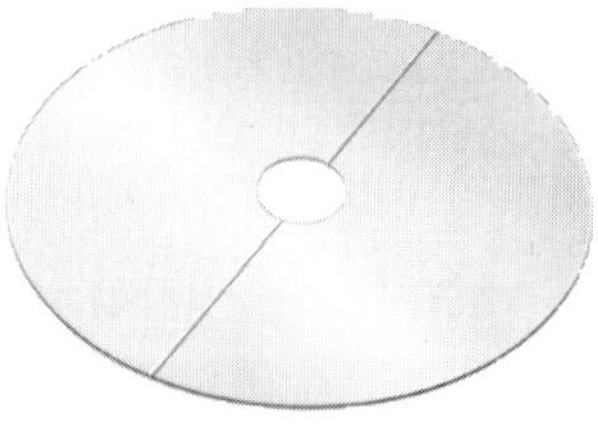

Replacement glass plate, Ø 425 mm
two-piece

Glass Thickness	for Revolving Wire Basket	Cat. No.
5 mm	815.24.222	815.24.002
5 mm	815.44.222	815.44.002

Packing: 1 pc.

Dimensions in mm

Multi-purpose Pole-mount System Ø 45

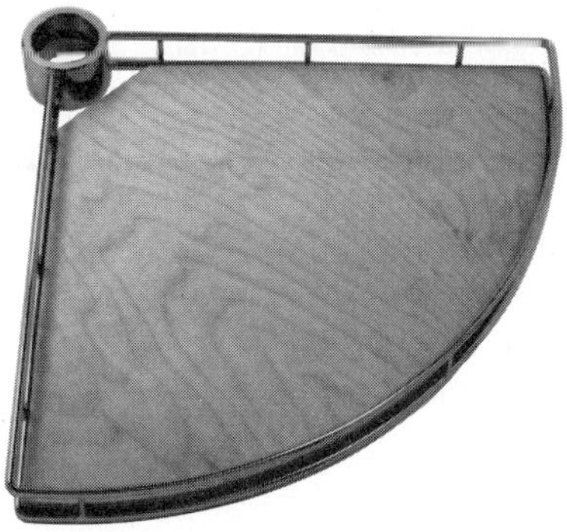

Swivel Basket with wood shelf,
500 x 360 x 38 mm (W x D x H),
complete with pole fastener hardware
Finish: Steel, chrome-plated,
Shelf: wood, plastic-coated

for Pole-Ø	color	Cat. No.
45 mm	decorative beech	815.44.242
45 mm	white	815.44.243

Packing: 1 pc.

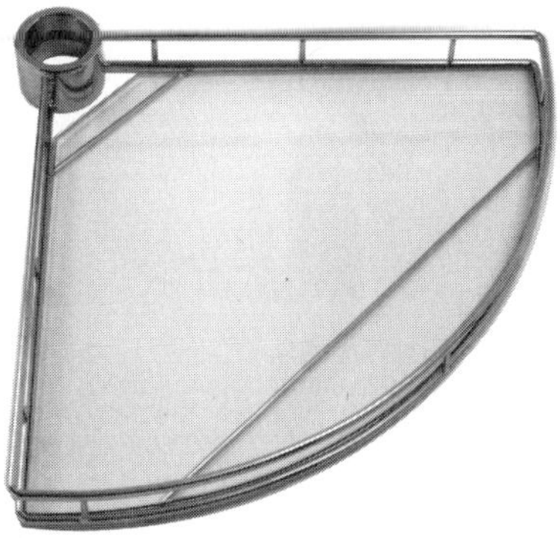

Swivel Basket with glass shelf,
500 x 360 x 38 mm (W x D x H),
complete with pole fastener hardware
Finish: Steel, chrome-plated

for Pole-Ø	Cat. No.
45 mm	815.44.241

Packing: 1 pc.

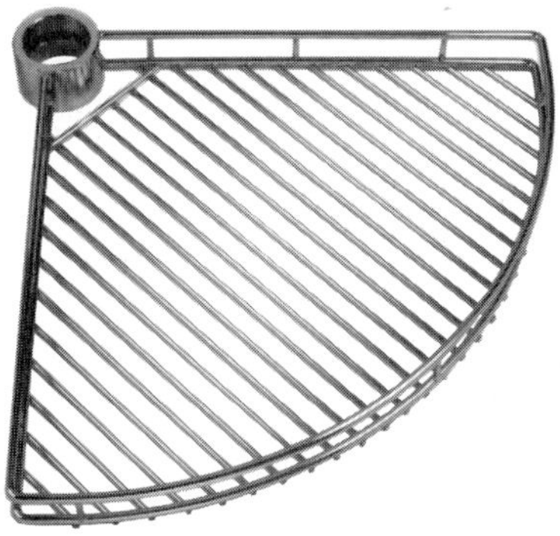

Swivel basket
500 x 360 x 38 mm (B x T x H),
complete with pole fastening hardware
Finish: Steel, chrome

for Pole-Ø	Cat. No.
45 mm	815.44.240

Packing: 1 Pc.

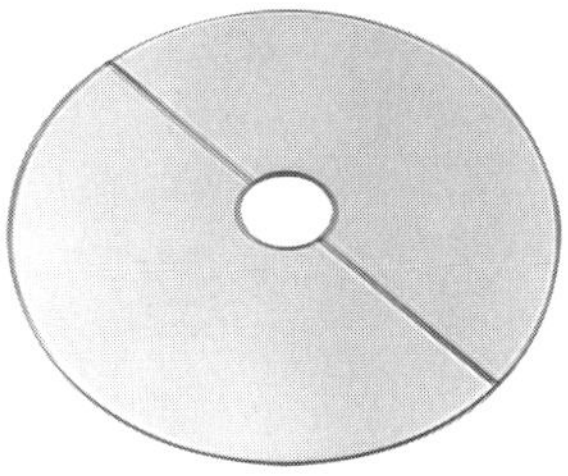

Replacement glass plate, Ø 275 mm,
2-piece, for Wire Baskets 815.44.230

for Pole-Ø	Glass thickness	Cat. No.
45 mm	5 mm	815.44.003

Packing: 1 Pc.

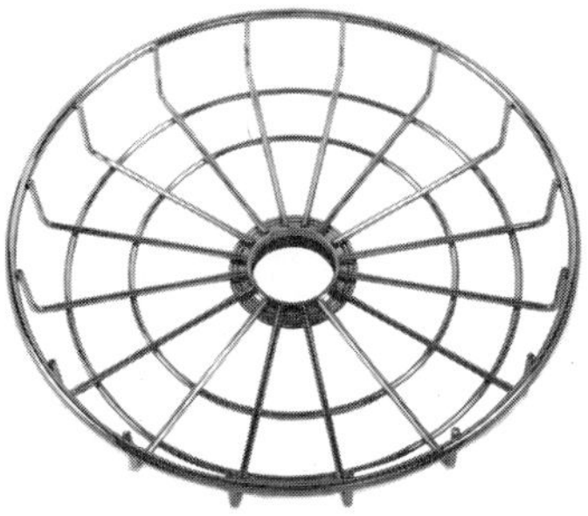

Revolving Wire Basket, Ø 300 mm
with glass plate complete with pole fastener hardware
Finish: steel, chrome-plated

for Pole-Ø	Height:	Cat. No.
45mm	40 mm	815.44.230

Packing: 1 Pc.

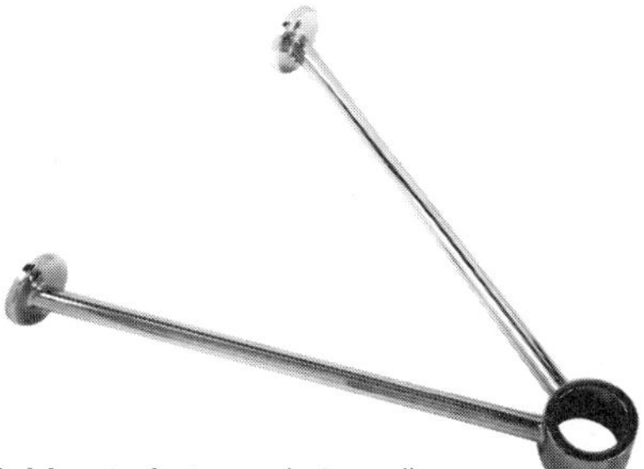

Pole Holder, to fasten pole to wall,
drilling distance: 280 mm, depth: 330 mm,
complete with pole fastener hardware
Finish: Steel, chrome-plated

for Pole-Ø	Cat. No.
45 mm	815.42.209

Packing: 1 pc.

Dimensional data not binding.
We reserve the right to alter
specifications without notice.

HÄFELE

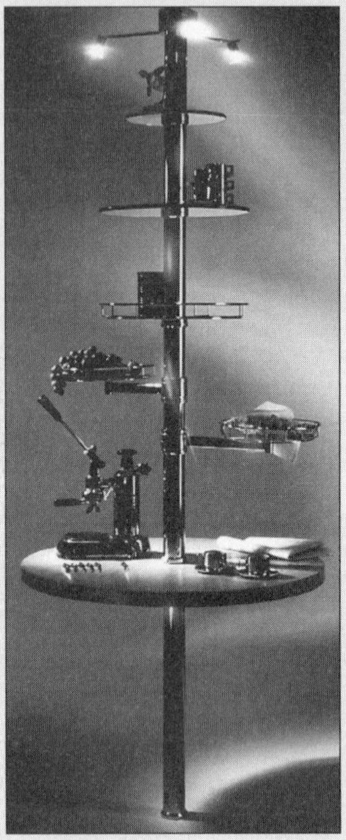

• Accessories for use with 45 and 65mm diameter pole

Multi-Purpose Pole Mount System, Ø 45 mm and Ø 65 mm

Table top
Wood thickness 15 mm
Complete with pole attachment hardware
Finish: wood, plastic-coated
white

	Cat. No.	
Diameter	Pole-Ø 45 mm	Pole-Ø 65 mm
300 mm	815.46.700	–
460 mm	815.46.710	815.26.710

beech, natural

	Cat. No.	
Diameter	Pole-Ø 45 mm	Pole-Ø 65 mm
300 mm	815.46.300	–
460 mm	815.46.310	815.26.310

Packing: 1 pc.

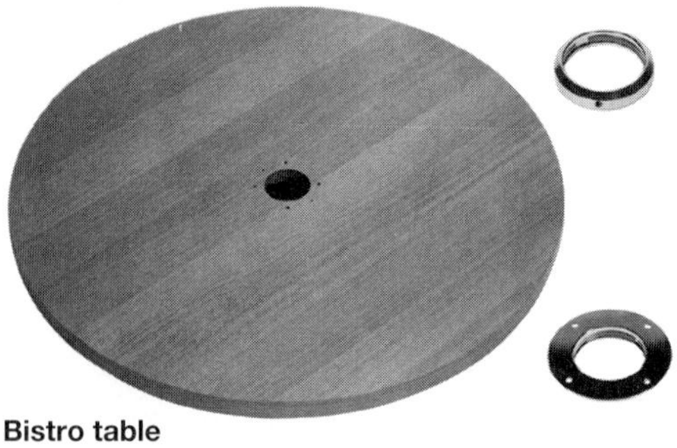

Bistro table
wood thickness 38 mm
complete with pole attachment hardware
Finish: wood, plastic-coated
white

for Pole-Ø	Diameter	Cat. No.
45 mm	650 mm	815.46.720
65 mm	825 mm	815.26.720

beech, natural

for Pole-Ø	Diameter	Cat. No.
45 mm	650 mm	815.46.320
65 mm	825 mm	815.26.320

Packing: 1 pc.

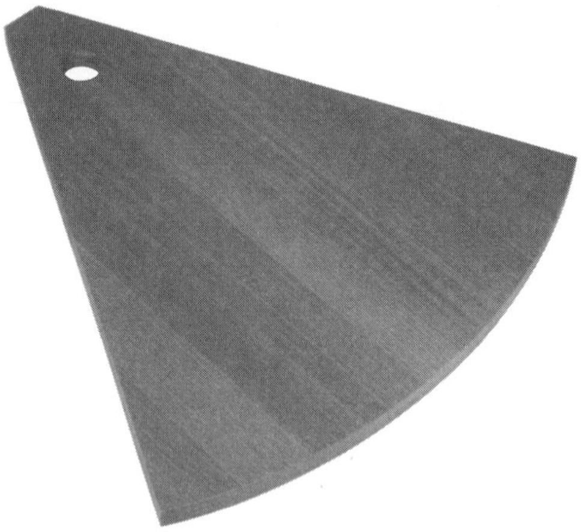

Work Table, without accessories
880 x 950 x mm (W x D x H)
Finish: wood, plastic coated

for Pole-Ø	color	Cat. No.
45 mm	decorative beech	815.46.330
45 mm	white	815.46.730
65 mm	decorative beech	815.26.330
65 mm	white	815.26.730

Packing: 1 pc.

Upper End Cap,
plug in if pole doesn't end in ceiling
Finish: plastic, black

for Pole-Ø	Cat. No.
45 mm	815.42.220

Packing: 1 pc.

Fastener Set, for do-it-yourself tables
Finish: brass, chrome-plated

for Pole-Ø	Cat. No.
45 mm	815.42.208
65 mm	815.22.208

Packing: 1 pc.

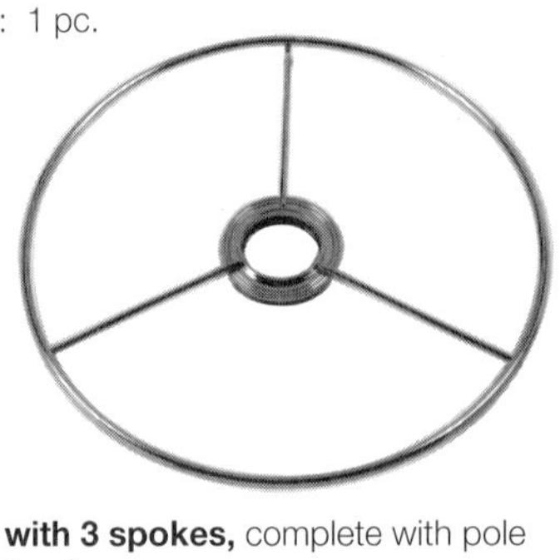

Railing with 3 spokes, complete with pole fastener hardware
Use in combination with tabletop 815.46.300/310/700/710 or glass bottom 815.46.000/010

for Pole-Ø	diameter	Cat. No.
45 mm	300 mm	815.46.200
45 mm	450 mm	815.46.201

Packing: 1 Pc.

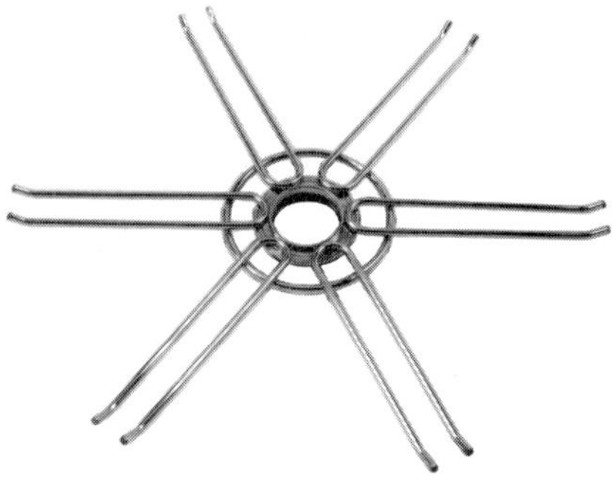

Glass Holder, Ø 390 mm,
complete with pole fastener hardware
Finish: Steel, chrome

for Pole-Ø	Cat. No.
45 mm	815.48.211

Packing: 1 Pc.

Multi-Purpose Pole Mount System, Ø 45 mm and Ø 65 mm

Basket support
with 1 extension arm which accommodates a revolving basket
Finish: brass, chrome-plated

Length of oval tube	for Pole Ø	Cat. No.
approx. 300 mm	65 mm	815.25.230
	45 mm	815.45.230

Packing: 1 pc.

Basket support
with 3 extension arms to accommodate revolving baskets
Finish: brass, chrome-plated

Length of oval tube	for Pole Ø	Cat. No.
approx. 300 mm	65 mm	815.25.220
	45 mm	815.45.220

Packing: 1 pc.

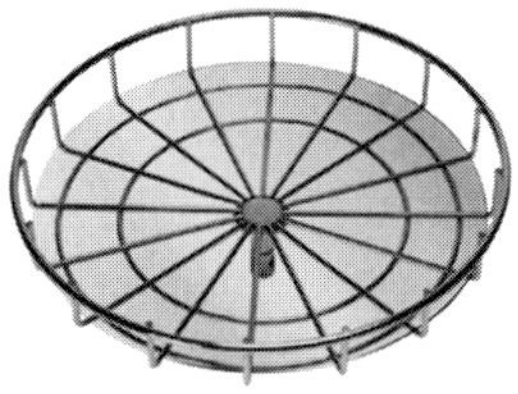

Revolving basket, ∅ 300 mm
to be used on support 815.25.230/220 or 815.45.230/220. Height: 70 mm
Complete with pole-mounting hardware
Finish: steel, chrome-plated

	Cat. No.
without Glass plate	815.25.240
with Glass plate 5 mm	815.25.241

Packing: 1 pc.

Wooden Tray with railing,
to be used on support arm 815.45.230 or 815.45.220
Wood thickness: 16 mm, 385 x 395 x 53 mm (W x D x H)
Finish: wood, plastic coated,
Railing: steel chrome-plated

for Pole-Ø	color	Cat. No.
45 mm	decorative beech	815.44.390
45 mm	white	815.44.790

Packing: 1 Pc.

Foot ring base, ∅ 450 mm
Complete with pole mounting hardware
Finish: steel, chrome-plated

Cat. No.	for Pole Ø 65 mm	815.26.290

Packing: 1 pc.

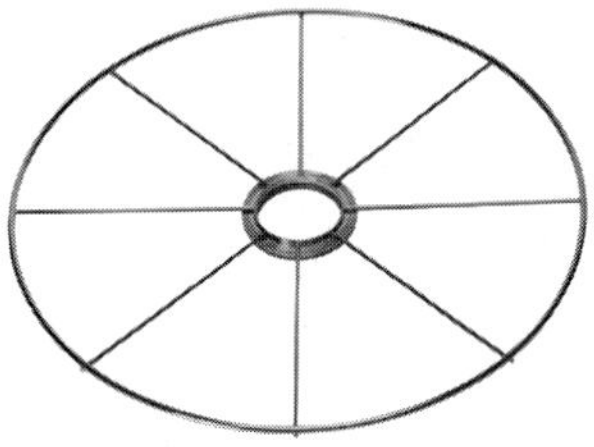

Umbrella stand, ∅ 450 mm
Complete with pole mounting hardware
Finish: steel, chrome-plated

Cat. No.	for Pole Ø 65 mm	815.25.250

Packing: 1 pc.

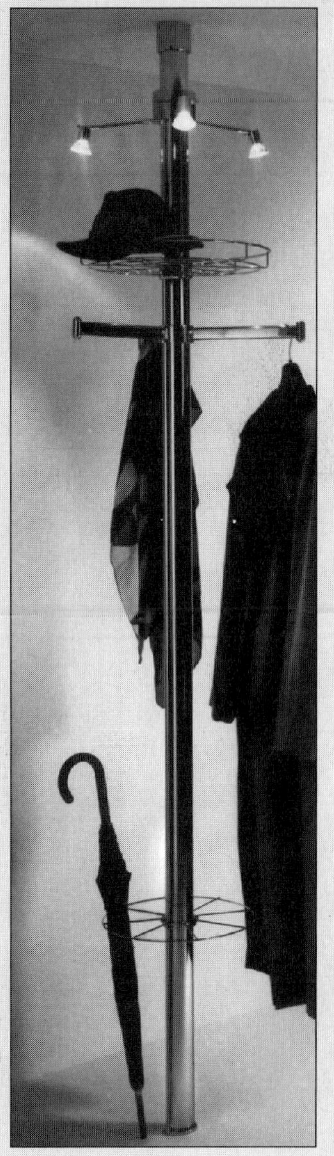

- Accessories for use with 45 and 65mm diameter pole

Dimensions in mm

HÄFELE

Multi-Purpose Pole Mount System, Ø 45 mm and Ø 65 mm

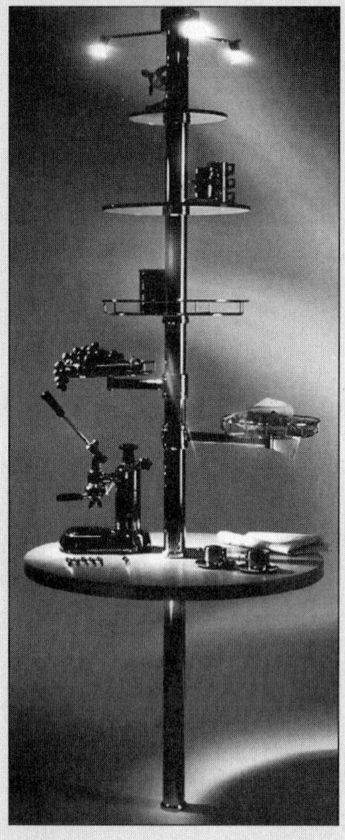

- Accessories for use with 45 and 65mm diameter pole

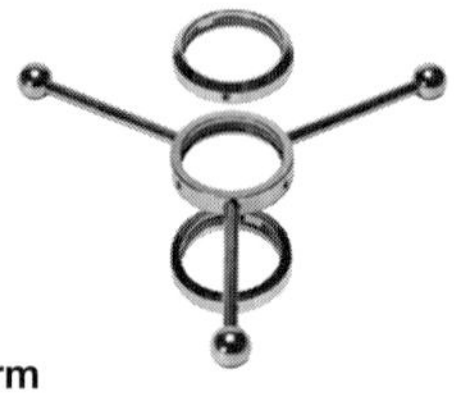

Extension arm
with 3 rods, Ø 10 mm, complete with pole attachment hardware
Finish: brass, chrome-plated

	Cat. No.	
Length of rod	for Pole Ø 45	for Pole Ø65
approx. 100 mm	815.45.201	815.25.201
approx. 300 mm	815.45.204	–
approx. 400 mm	–	815.25.204

Packing: 1 pc.

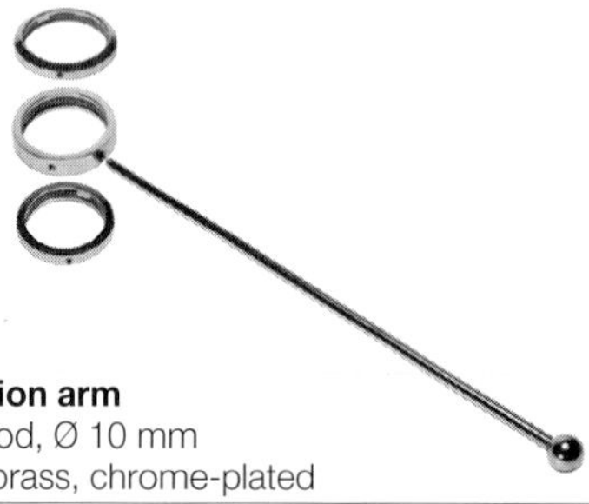

Extension arm
with 1 rod, Ø 10 mm
Finish: brass, chrome-plated

Length of rod	for Pole Ø	Cat. No.
approx. 400 mm	65 mm	815.25.214
approx. 300 mm	45 mm	815.45.214
approx. 100 mm	45 mm	815.45.211

Packing: 1 pc.

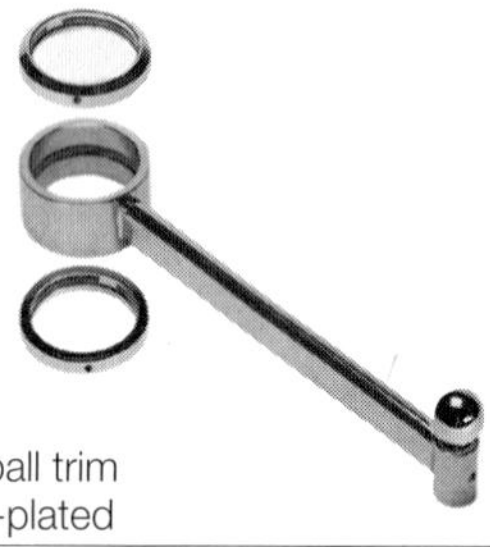

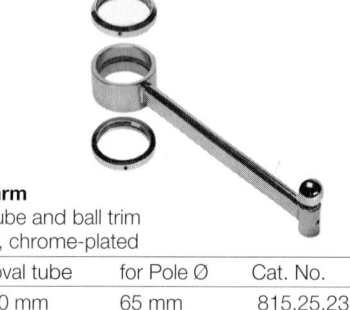

Extension arm
with 1 oval tube and ball trim
Finish: brass, chrome-plated

Length of oval tube	for Pole Ø	Cat. No.
approx. 300 mm	65 mm	815.25.231
	45 mm	815.45.231

Packing: 1 pc.

Clothes rack
with 3 oval tubes and ball trim
Finish: brass, chrome-plated

Length of oval tubes	for Pole-Ø	Cat. No.
approx. 300 mm	65 mm	815.25.221
	45 mm	815.45.221

Packing: 1 pc.

S-Hook
for extension arms
Finish: steel wire, chrome-plated

Cat. No..	815.25.260

Packing: 5 pcs.

Multi-purpose Pole-mount System, Ø 45 and 65 mm

HÄFELE

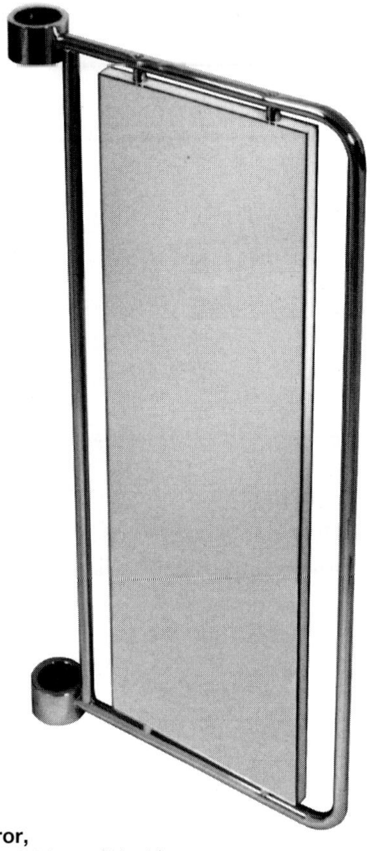

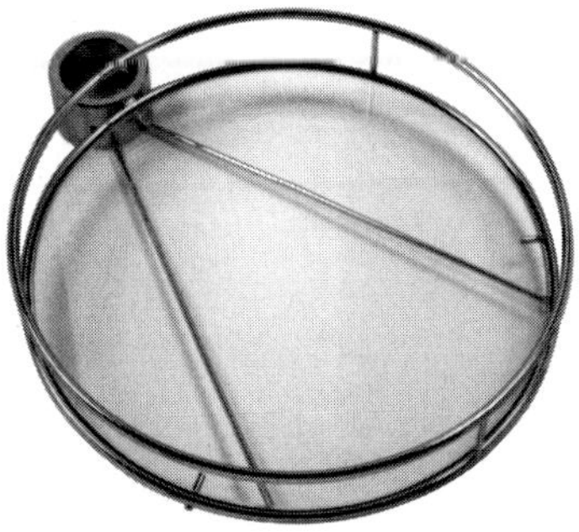

Glass Shelf with rail,
complete with pole fastening hardware
Finish: steel, chrome-plated

for Pole-Ø	Cat. No.
45 mm	815.48.200

Packing: 1 Pc.

Mirror,
342 x 804 mm (W x H)
(Mirror: 230 x 725 mm),
complete with pole fastening hardware
Finish: Steel, chrome-plated

for Pole-Ø	Cat. No.
45 mm	815.48.250

Packing: 1 pc.

Make-up Mirror, Ø 190 mm,
with arm, Length: 265 mm,
complete with pole fastening hardware
Finish: Arm: steel chrome-plated
mirror frame: Aluminum

for Pole-Ø	Cat. No.
45 mm	815.48.212

Packing: 1 Pc.

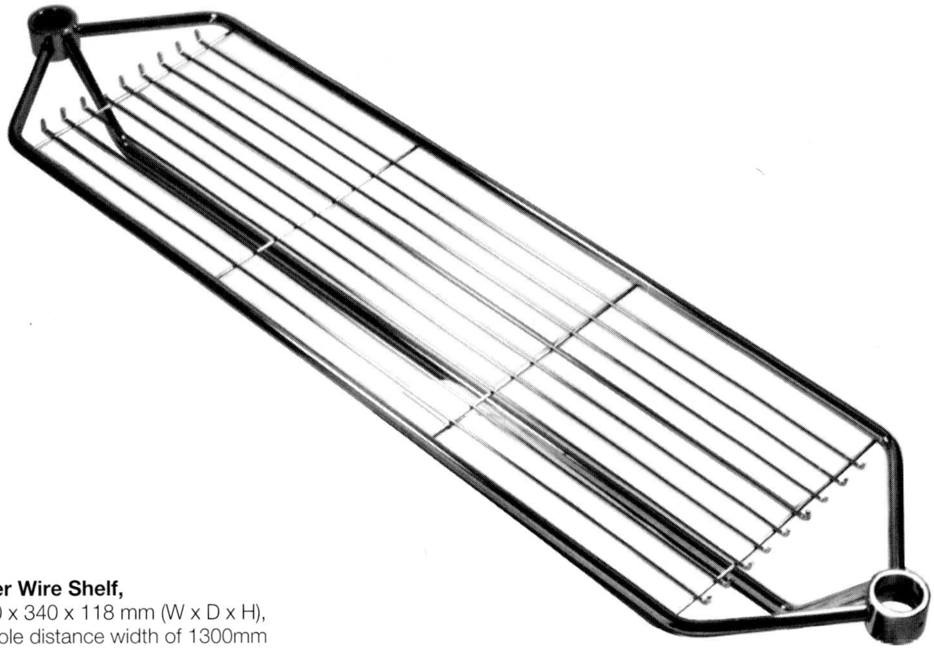

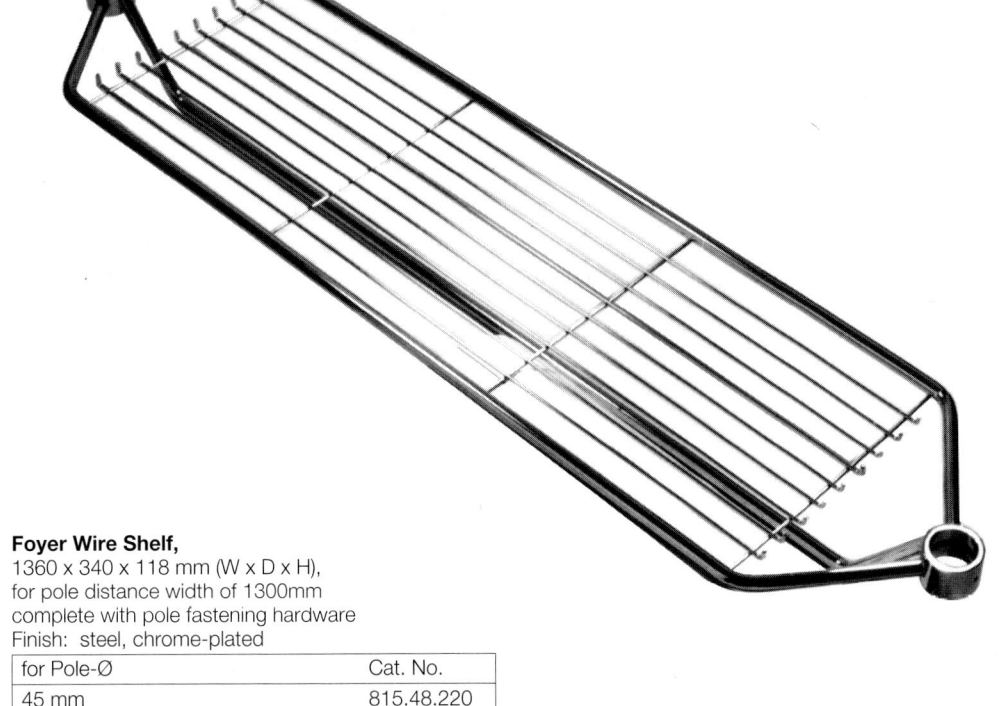

Foyer Wire Shelf,
1360 x 340 x 118 mm (W x D x H),
for pole distance width of 1300mm
complete with pole fastening hardware
Finish: steel, chrome-plated

for Pole-Ø	Cat. No.
45 mm	815.48.220

Packing: 1 Pc.

HÄFELE

Multi-purpose Pole-mount System, Ø 45

Paper Towel holder,
to be hung on slatted frame 815.48.240
Size: 300 x 130 x 50 mm (W x D x H)
Finish: steel, chrome-plated

for Pole-Ø	Cat. No.
45 mm	815.48.262

Packing: 1 Pc.

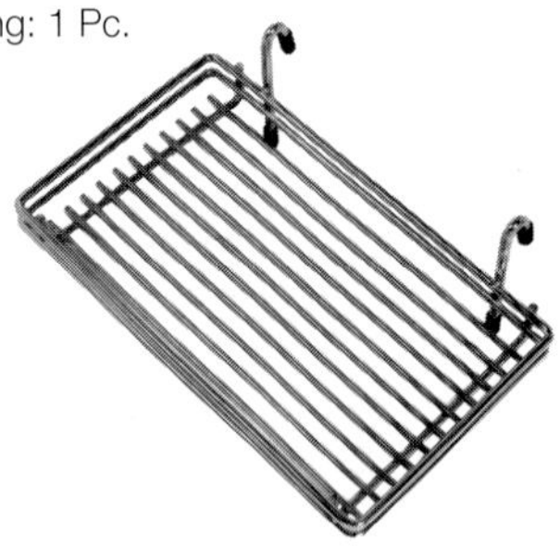

Wire Baskets, to be hung on slatted frame 815.48.240
Finish: steel, chrome-plated

for Pole-Ø	Size	Cat. No.
45 mm	260 x 100 x 32	815.48.260
45 mm	260 x 150 x 32	815.48.261

Packing: 1 Pc.

Slatted Frame
342 x 804 mm (W x H), to be used to hang up baskets 815.48.260/261 and paper towel holder 815.48.262 complete with pole fastening hardware
Finish: Steel, chrome-plated

for Pole-Ø	Cat. No.
45 mm	815.48.240

Packing: 1 pc.

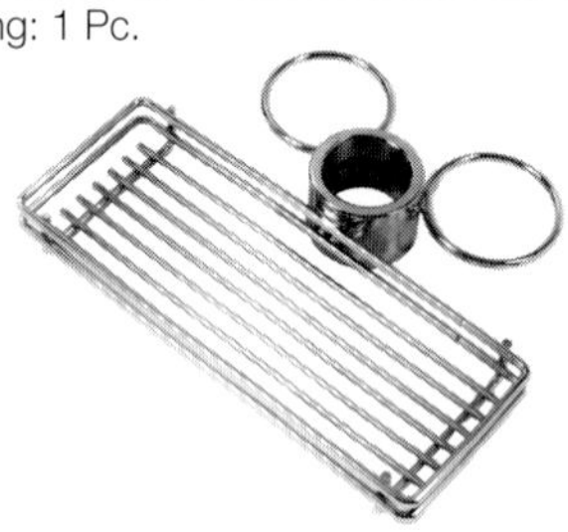

Shelf basket, with 2 cup holders,
Tray size: 260 x 100 x 32 mm (W x D x H),
Inner diameter of cup holders: approx. 65 mm,
complete with pole fastening hardware
Finish: steel, chrome-plated

for Pole-Ø	Cat. No.
45 mm	815.48.230

Packing: 1 Pc.

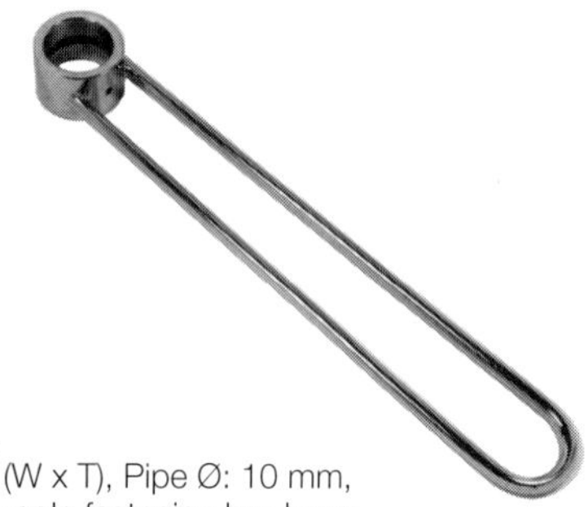

Towel Rack,
380 x 60 mm (W x T), Pipe Ø: 10 mm,
complete with pole fastening hardware
Finish: Steel, chrome-plated

for Pole-Ø	Cat. No.
45 mm	815.48.210

Packing: 1 pc.

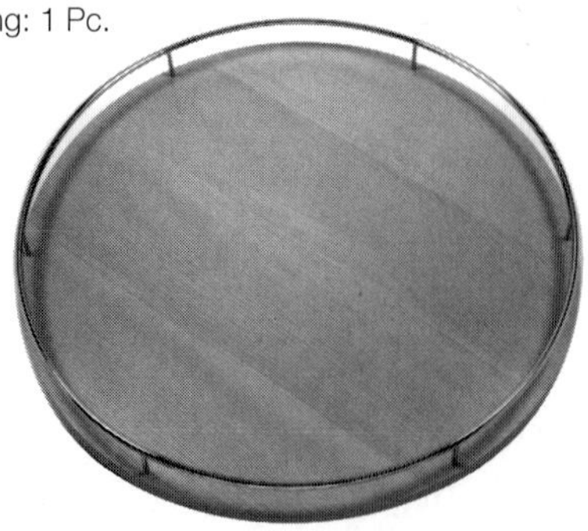

Wooden Shelf with railing **for Pole-Ø 45 mm,**
to be set up on support arm 815.45.230 or 815.45.220
Wood thickness: 15 mm, Height: 50 mm
Finish: wood, plastic-coated
Railing: Steel, chrome-plated

Size	decorative beech	white
Ø 310 mm	815.45.371	815.45.771
Ø 460 mm	815.45.372	815.45.772

Packing: 1 pc.

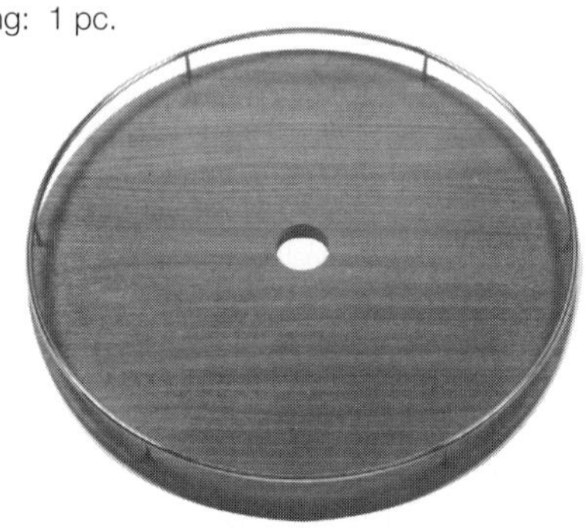

Wooden Shelf with railing, **for Pole-Ø 45 mm,**
Wood thickness: 15 mm,
complete with pole fastening hardware
Finish: wood, plastic-coated
Railing: Steel, chrome-plated

Size	decorative beech	white
Ø 310 mm	815.44.371	815.44.771
Ø 460 mm	815.44.372	815.44.772

Packing: 1 pc.

Multi-purpose Pole-mount System, Ø 20 mm

HÄFELE

Pole, Ø 20 mm
Finish: steel, chrome-plated

Length	Cat. No.
600	815.30.206
1000	815.30.210
1200	815.30.212
1500	815.30.215

Packing: 1 pc.

All fastening elements on the pole have a spring-action ring inside in order to avoid damaging the pole with fastening screws.

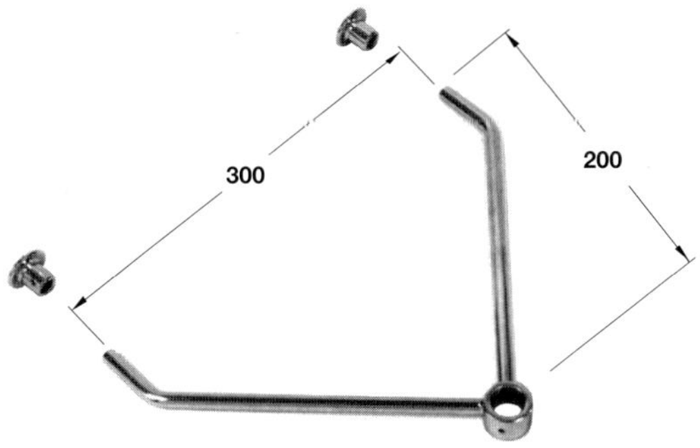

Wall Brace, horizontal
Finish: steel, chrome-plated

Cat. No.	815.32.210

Packing: 1 pc.

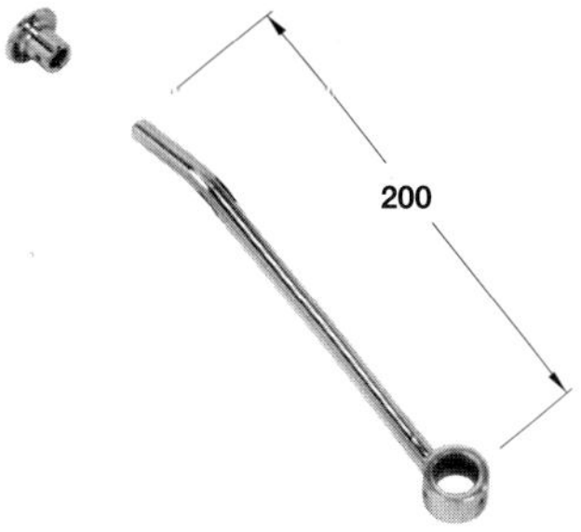

Support Brace, vertical
Finish: steel, chrome-plated

Cat. No.	815.32.220

Packing: 1 pc.

Pole Fastener, for the ceiling
Finish: brass, chrome-plated

Cat. No.	815.32.201

Packing: 1 pc.

Pole Fastener, for the floor
Finish: brass, chrome-plated

Cat. No.	815.32.202

Packing: 1 pc.

End Cap
Finish: brass, chrome-plated / Plastic

Cat. No.	815.32.204

Packing: 1 pc.

Adjustment Ring
Finish: brass, chrome-plated

Cat. No.	815.32.203

Packing: 1 pc.

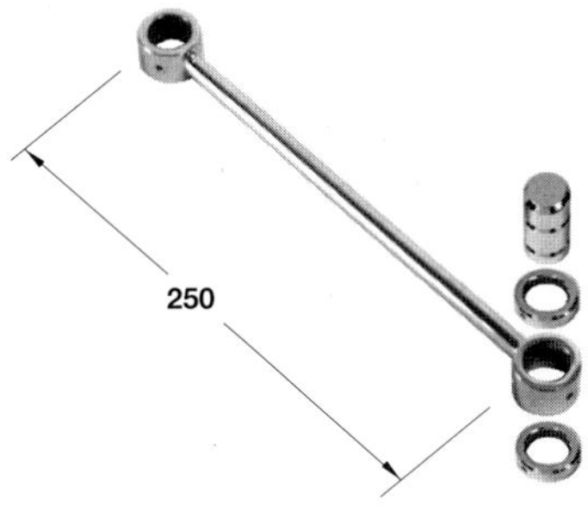

Support Arm, Ø 10 mm
complete with pole fastening hardware
Finish: steel, chrome-plated/brass, chrome-plated

Cat. No.	815.36.230

Packing: 1 pc.

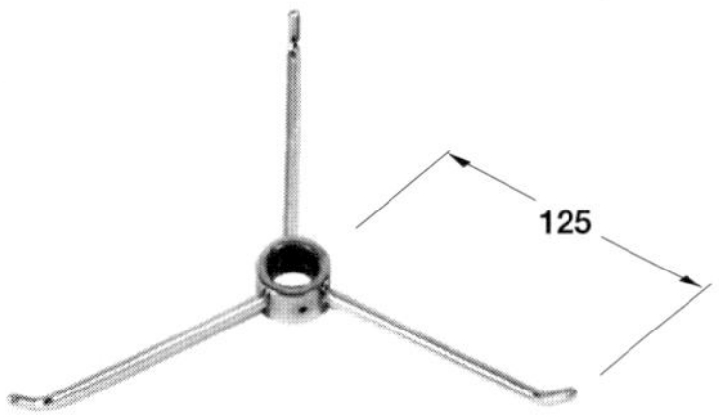

Measurements in mm

3-way Extension Bracket
complete with pole fastening hardware
Finish: steel, chrome-plated

Cat. No.	815.35.201

Packing: 1 pc.

Dimensional data not binding.
We reserve the right to alter specifications without notice.

HÄFELE

Multi-purpose Pole-mount System, Ø 20 mm

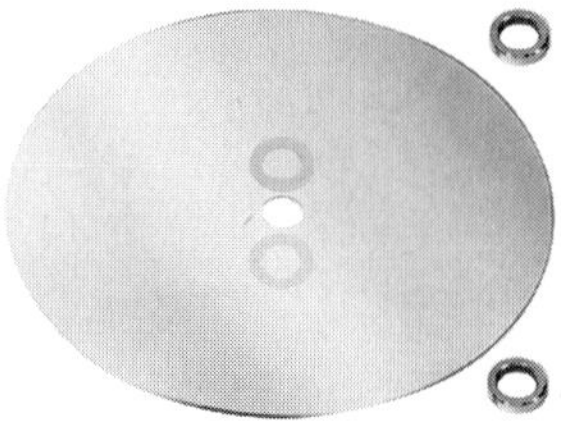

Glass Shelf, sold as a single unit*
Glass thickness: 10 mm, Ø 22 mm hole
complete with pole fastening hardware

Size	Cat. No.
Ø 300 mm	815.36.000

Packing: 1 pc.

*not suitable for rotating baskets

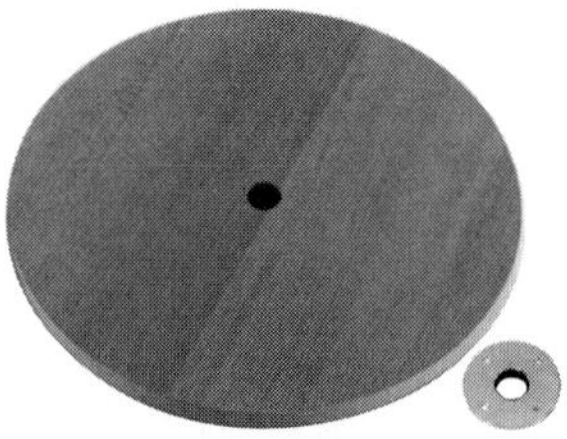

Wooden Shelf, Ø 310 mm
Wood thickness: 15 mm, Ø 22 mm hole
complete with pole fastening hardware
Finish: wood, plastic coated

color	Cat. No.
decorative beech	815.36.310
white	815.36.710

Packing: 1 pc.

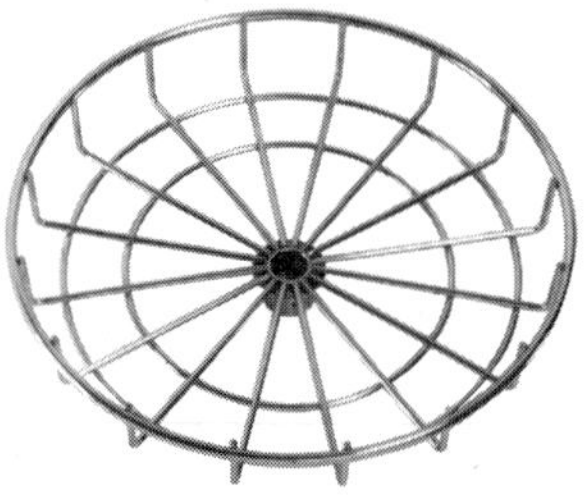

Revolving Basket, Ø 300 mm, fine mesh without glass shelf, complete with pole fastening hardware
Finish: steel, chrome-plated

Cat. No.	815.34.200

Packing: 1 pc.

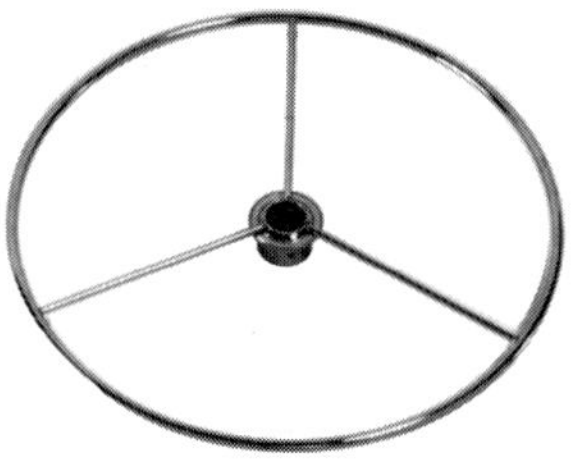

Railing, Ø 300 mm
to be used in combination with glass shelf or wood shelf
Finish: steel, chrome-plated

Cat. No.	815.36.220

Packing: 1 pc.

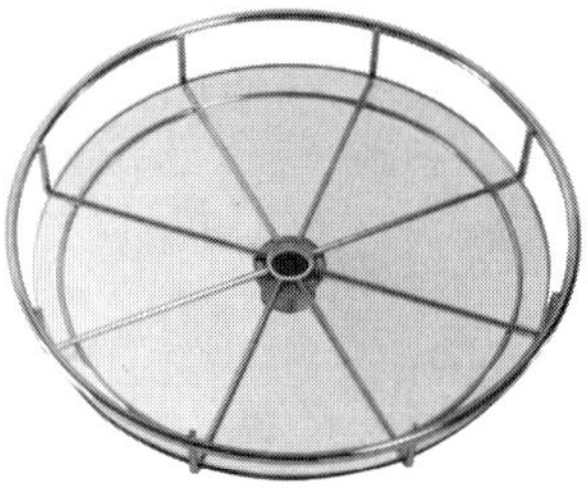

Revolving Basket, Ø 300 mm, coarse mesh with glass shelf 815.34.001, complete with pole fastening hardware
Finish: steel, chrome-plated

Cat. No.	815.34.211

Packing: 1 pc.

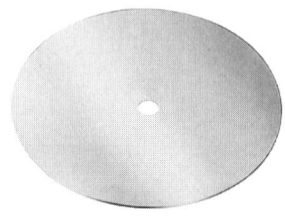

Replacement Glass Shelf, Ø 275 mm
Glass thickness: 5 mm, Ø 22 mm hole

Cat. No.	815.34.001

Packing: 1 pc.

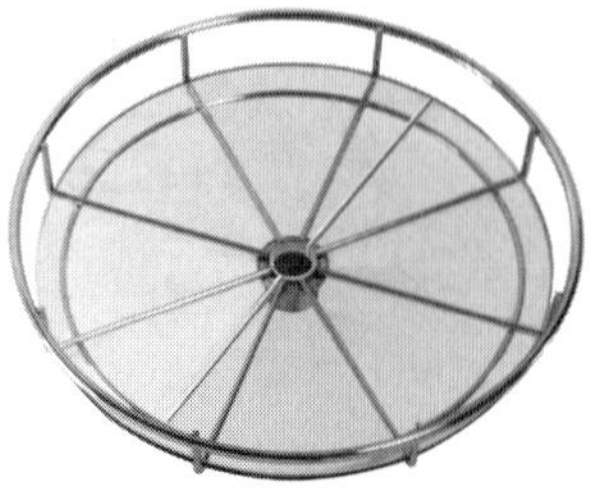

Revolving Basket, Ø 300 mm, coarse mesh with 2 p-part glass shelf 815.34.002, complete with pole fastening hardware
Finish: steel, chrome-plated

Cat. No.	815.34.212

Packing: 1 pc.

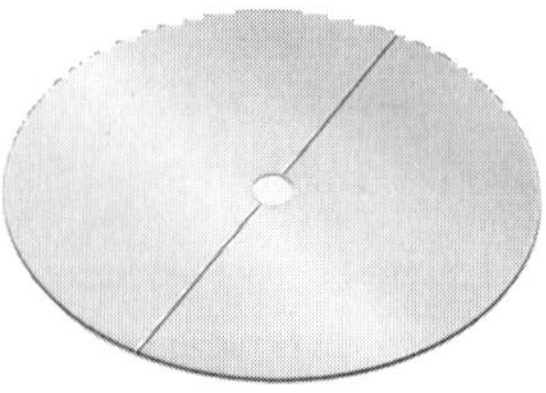

2-part Glass Shelf, Ø 275 mm, 2-parts
Glass thickness: 5 mm, Ø 22 mm hole

Cat. No.	815.34.002

Packing: 1 pc.

Multi-purpose Pole-mount System, Ø 20 mm

HÄFELE

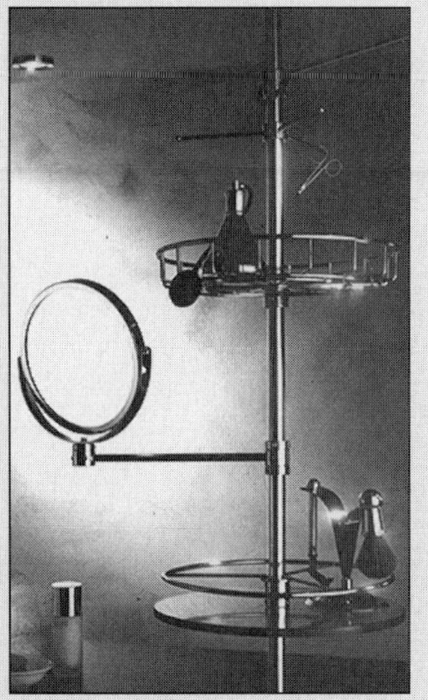

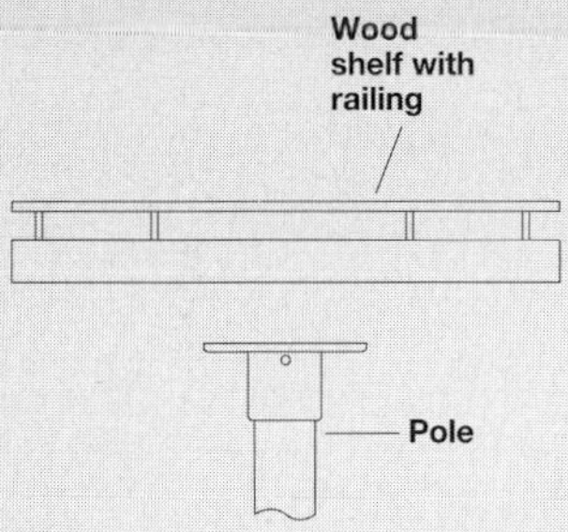

Wooden Shelf
Wood thickness: 15 mm, Ø 310 mm
for use with support arm or column top
Finish: wood, plastic coated

color	Cat. No.
decorative beech	815.36.332
white	815.36.732

Packing: 1 pc.

Wooden Shelf, with railing
Wood thickness: 15 mm, Ø 310 mm
for use with support arm or column top
Finish: wood, plastic coated
Railing: steel, chrome-plated

color	Cat. No.
decorative beech	815.36.333
white	815.36.733

Packing: 1 pc.

Make-up Mirror, Ø 190 mm
for use with support arm
Finish: brass, chrome-plated

Cat. No.	815.36.231

Packing: 1 pc.

HÄFELE

Audio-Video Media Storage Systems

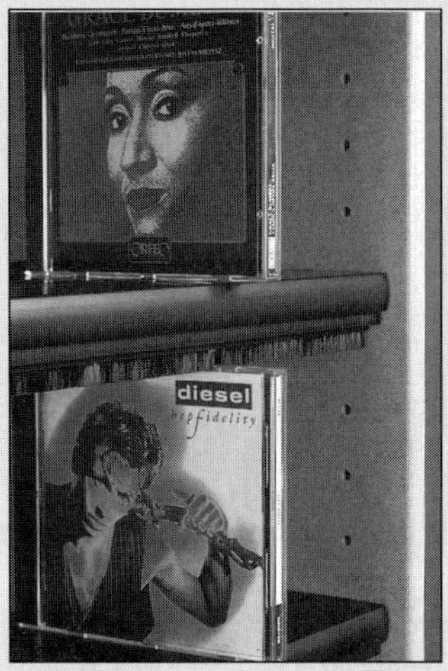

Advantages

- Flexible system allows for 1 single system to store CD, MC, DAT and VHS cassettes
- Space saving cassettes are stored next to each other without gaps
- Easy access to cassettes, easy return of cassettes
- The brush profile allows for unlimited browsing and flipping through
- Single or double CD's can be placed anywhere
- User can easily label as desired on the profile's front
- Standard hole distances for 32 mm make the system easy to use in furniture production

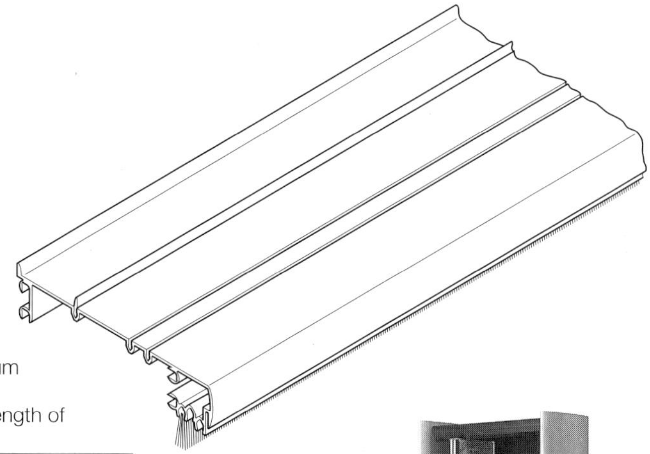

FileBrush® Shelf System
Shelf system for
CD, MC, DAT and VHS cassettes
consists of:
1 shelf made of black anodized aluminum
1 mounting profile, black plastic
1 brush profile, 1 or 2 parts for a total length of 2600 mm

Cat. No.	810.54.300

Packing: 2600 mm (1 set)

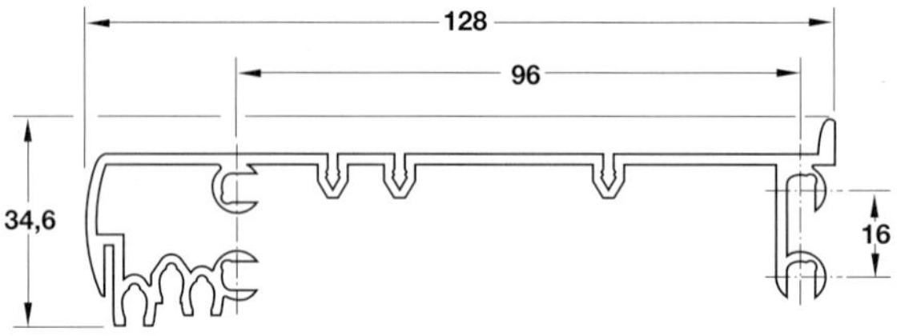

Dimensions in mm

Drill diagrams for FileBrush Shelf Systems

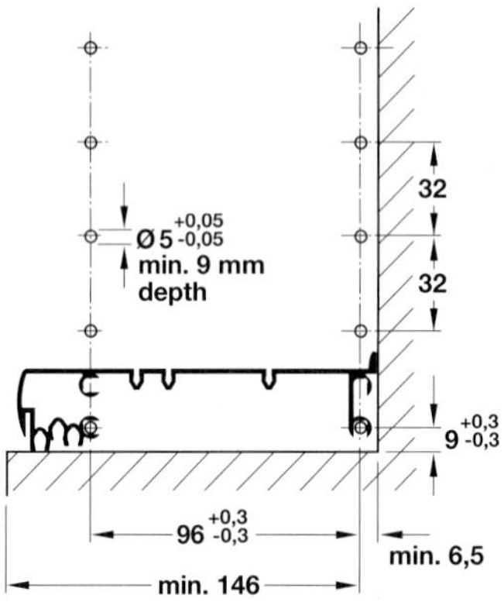

Bottom shelf = FileBrush®, Profile 6

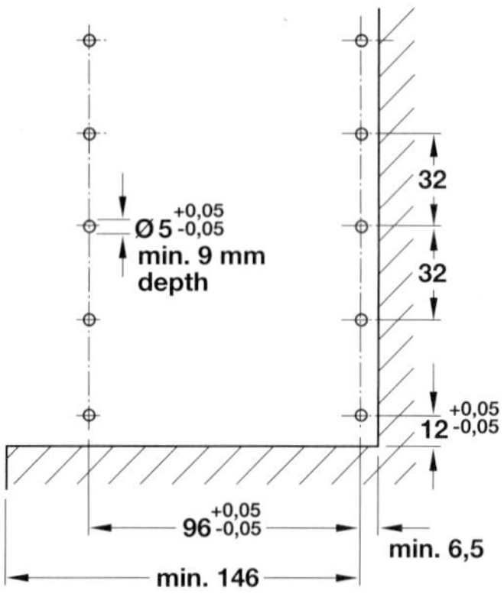

Bottom shelf = Regular panel

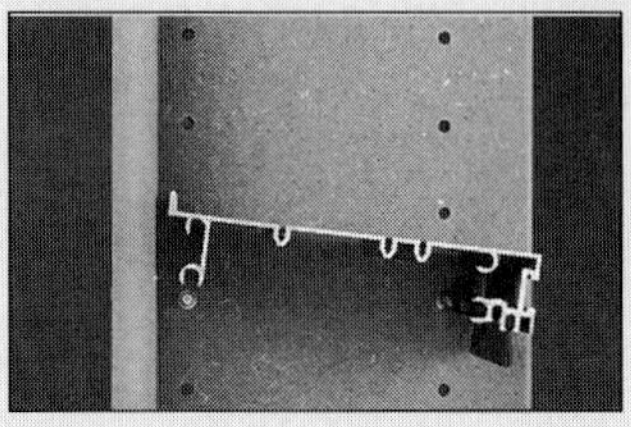

For fastening different shelf heights

Shelf supports, Ø 5 mm

Finish: steel, zinc-plated

Cat. No.	282.43.905

Packing: 500 and 1000 pcs.

Distances
Depending on cassette type, from the upper edge of the shelf to upper edge of next shelf

DAT	112 mm
MC	144 mm
CD	160 mm
VHS	224 mm

Groove for the mounting profile to mark depth limit (for CD's, the mounting profile is not necessary

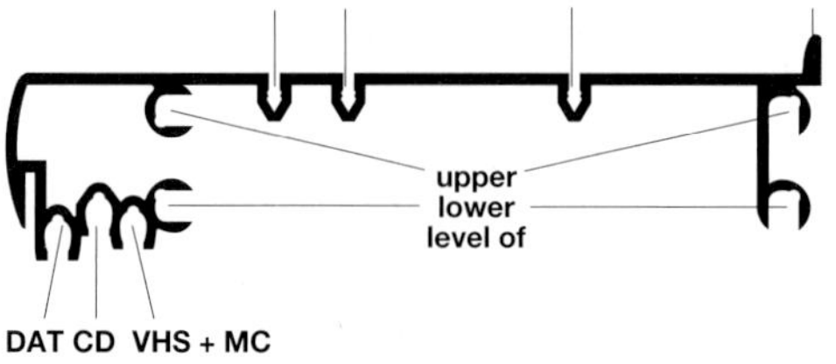

Groove for brush profile

8
Interior Accessories
Wardrobe Accessories
Storage Systems
Furniture Lighting

Dimensions in mm.

Audio/Video Media Storage Systems

For Compact Disks, Audio and Video Tape Storage
Organizes all three major Audio/Video/Game media formats and are designed especially for single row applications and "Library" style drawers.

Universal Rail System
This system uses two edge rails as the basic supports. Additional center rails may be used for a variety of storage options as shown in the chart below. Note: each slot holds two Audio Tapes.

Mounting Options - Countersunk screws and ⅝" 2-sided tape squares included.

Capacities For Universal Rail System						
Installed Width		Rails Required		Maximum Capacity (If only one type used)		
Inch	mm	Edge	Center	CD	AUDIO	VIDEO
6 13/16"	173	2		24	16	-
7 3/16"	202	1	1	24	16	10
12 1/2"	318	2	1	48	32	10
18 1/8"	461	2	2	72	48	20
23 13/16"	605	2	3	96	64	20
29 1/2"	749	2	4	120	80	30

Universal-Vertical Rail System
This system uses two edge rails only. May be mounted to individual shelves utilizing Euro-slides or the cantilever slide - 810.80.300. Note: each slot holds two Audio Tapes.

Mounting - Flat head screws included.

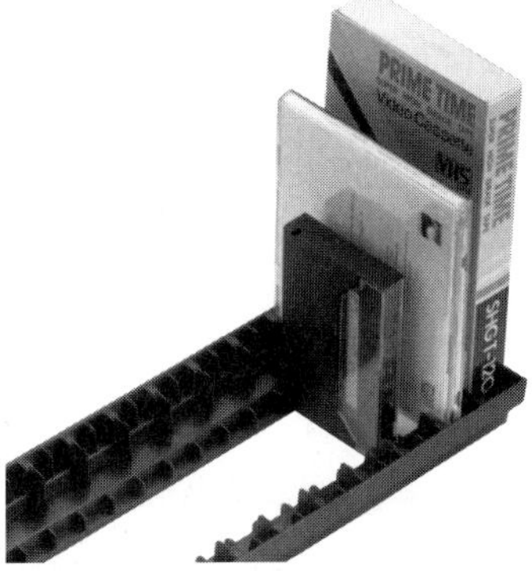

Capacities For Universal-Vertical Rail System				
Installed Width		Maximum Capacity (If only one type used)		
Inch	mm	CD	AUDIO	VIDEO
5¼"	133	22	16	11

Universal-Flip Storage System
This system uses two edge rails as the basic supports. Additional center rails, along with tubing, may be used for a variety of storage options explained below. Center rails can be snapped in and moved to instantly change its storage capabilities.

Mounting - Flat head screws securing the edge pins included; tubing with edge pins and screws included; soft roller slides with screws.

Capacities For Universal-Flip Storage System						
Minimum Installed Width		Rails Required		Capacity (If only one type used)		
Inch	mm	Edge	Center	CD	AUDIO	VIDEO
5 3/8"	132.5	2		22	10	10

If 18" wide unit is used, the following media is accommodated;
66 CD's vertical
20 VHS tapes horizontal or 30 vertical
30 Audio tapes (more with additional rails)
CD's and Video's can also be stored in the same row providing both are in the upright position. Combinations of the above are possible.

*** Accommodates 8mm video tape, DAT, Sega® and Nintendo® game cartridges.**

Dimensions in mm.
Inches are approximate.

Dimensional data not binding.
We reserve the right to alter specifications without notice.

HÄFELE

Audio/Video Media Storage Systems

Sample Configurations
Shown on this page are just a few of the many possible configurations using the Universal Storage Systems.

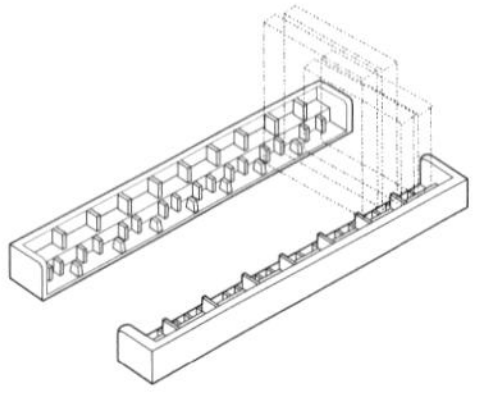

810.77.312 -Edge Rails

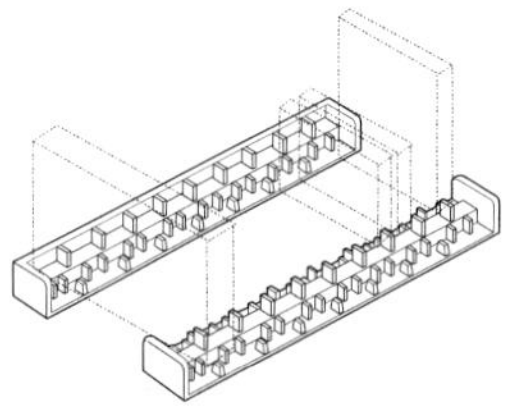

810.77.312- Edge Rails
810.77.321 -Center Rail

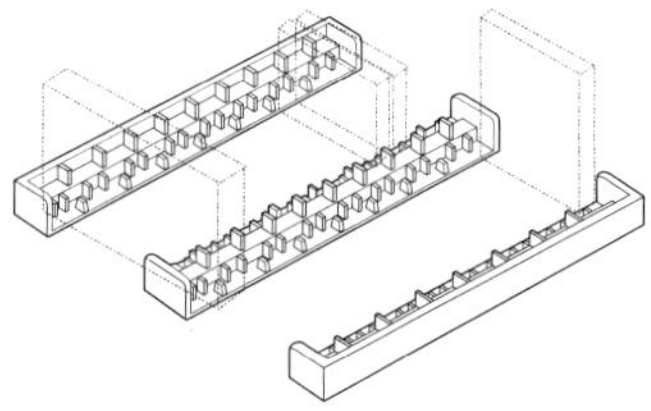

810.77.312- Edge Rails
810.77.321 -Center Rail

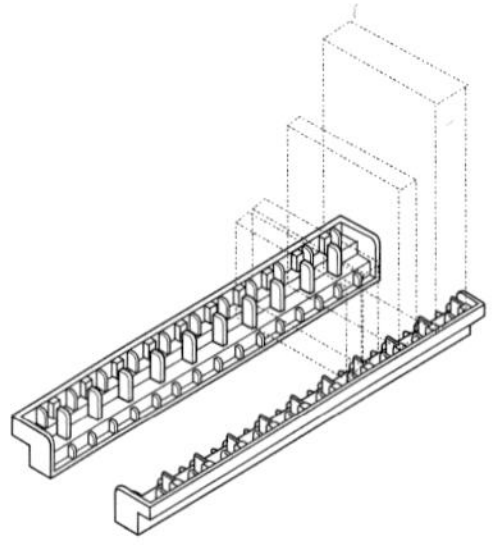

810.77.330 -Edge Rails

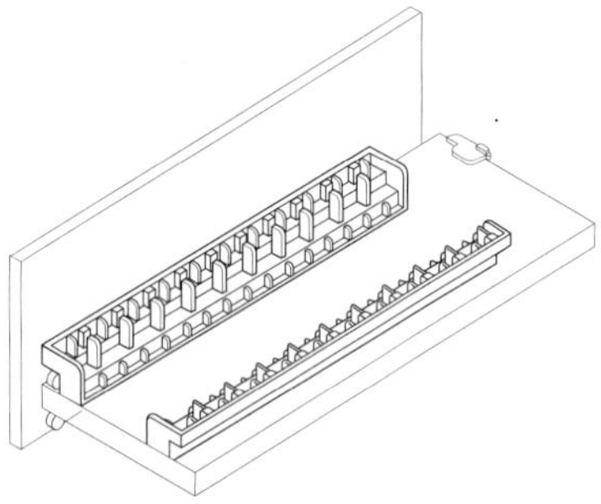

810.77.330 -Edge Rails
810.80.300 - Cantilever Shelf Slide

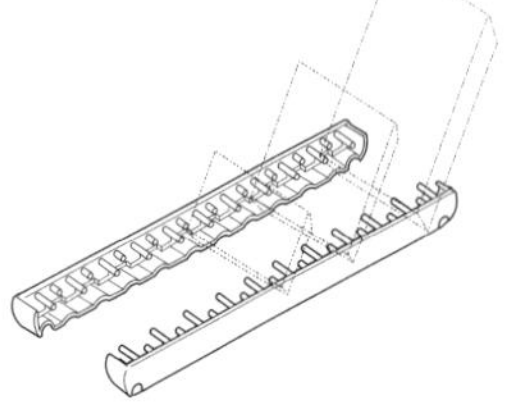

810.78.319- Edge Rails

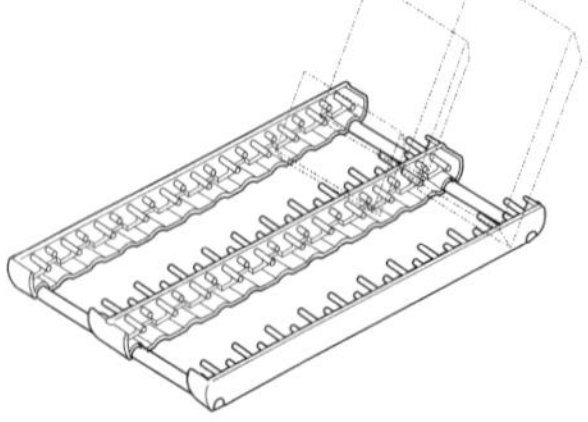

810.78.319 Edge Rails
810.78.328 Center Rail
810.79.307 Tube (Cut to length)

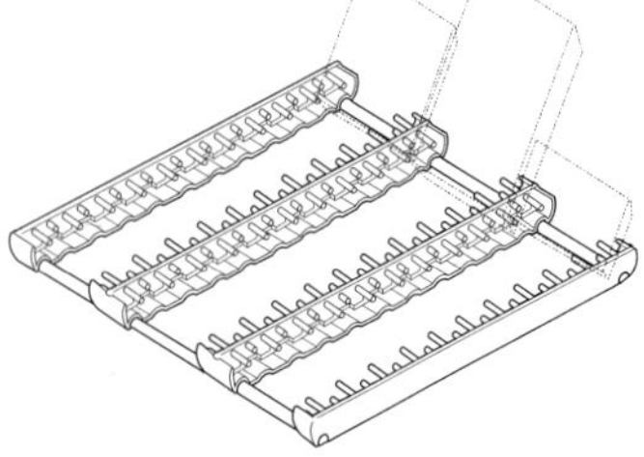

810.78.355-18" Kit

8 Interior Accessories
Wardrobe Accessories
Storage Systems
Furniture Lighting

Audio/Video Media Storage Systems

HÄFELE

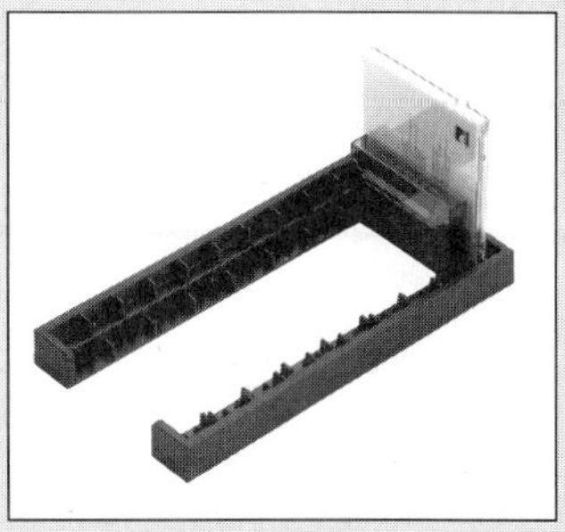

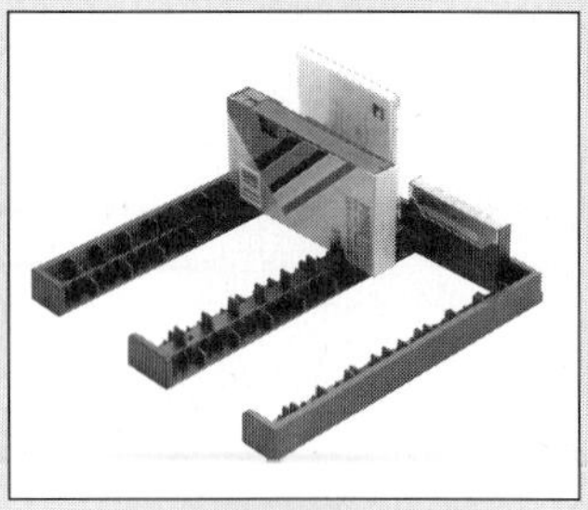

Universal Edge Rail for Compact Disk, Audio and Video Tape Storage
Width: 1.5"(38.1mm),
Height: 1.2"(30.4mm) ,
Length: 12.5"(317.5mm)
Note: Will only store VHS tapes when used in combination with center rail.

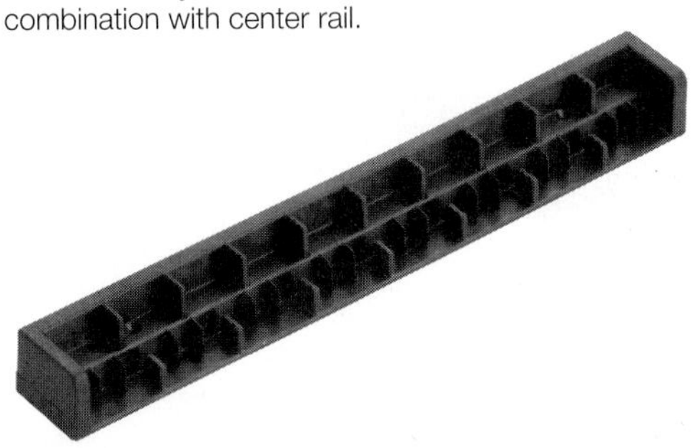

Finish: plastic, black

Cat. No.	810.77.312

Packing: 1 pair, with screws and tape in polybag.

Universal Center Rail for Compact Disk, Audio and Video Tape storage
Width: 2"(50.8mm) , Height: 1.2"(30.4mm) ,
Length: 12.5"(317.5mm)

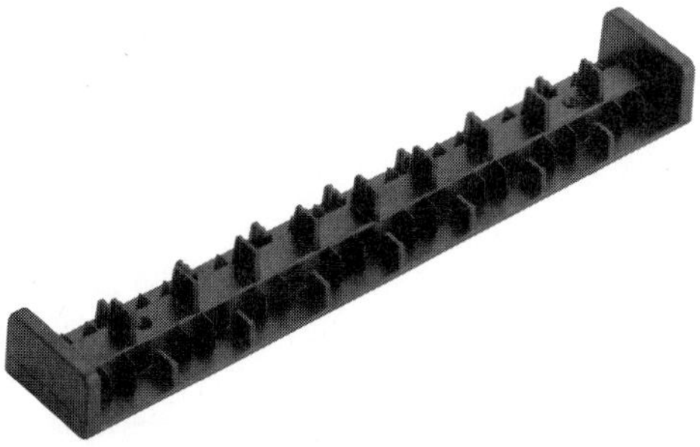

Finish: plastic, black

Cat. No.	810.77.321

Packing: 1 pc, with screws and tape in polybag.

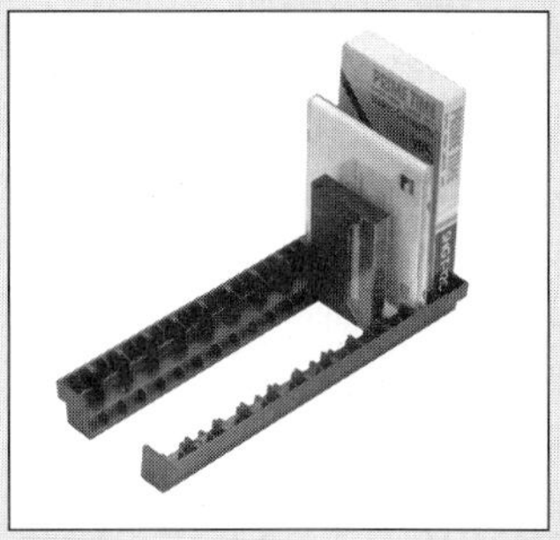

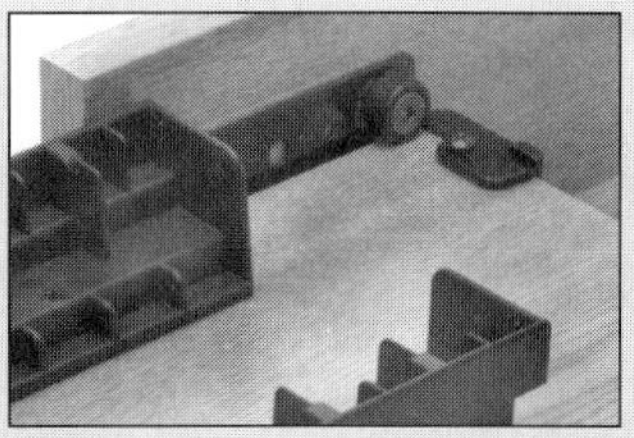

Universal-Vertical Rail for Compact Disk, Audio and Video Tape Storage
Width: 1.4"(35.5mm)
Height: 1.3"(33.7mm)
Length: 12.5"(317.5mm)

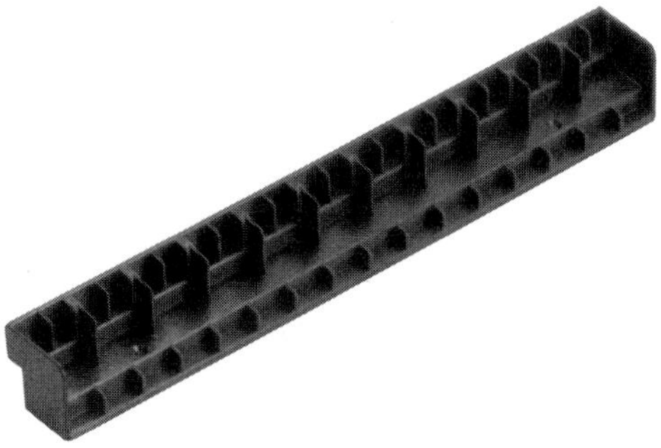

Universal-Vertical Storage

- Allows installation in openings as narrow as 5.3" wide.
- Indented to hide slides rollers.
- 32mm System compatible.

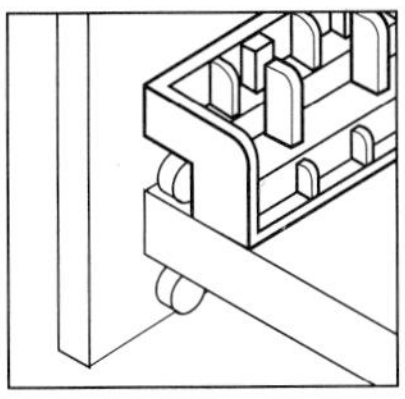

Roller mount

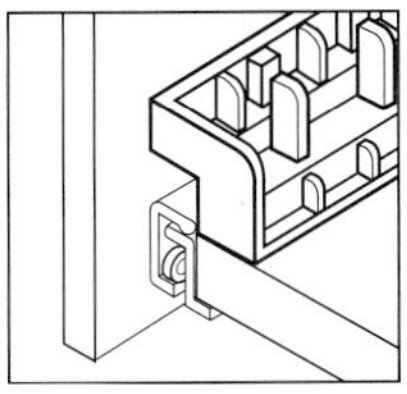

Euro-slide mount

Finish: plastic, black

Cat. No.	810.77.330

Packing: 1 pair with screws in polybag.

Cantilever Shelf Slide for Vertical Compact Disk, Audio and Video Tape storage system.
Width: 3.4"(86mm)
Height: 2.25"(57mm)
Length: 4.5"(114mm)

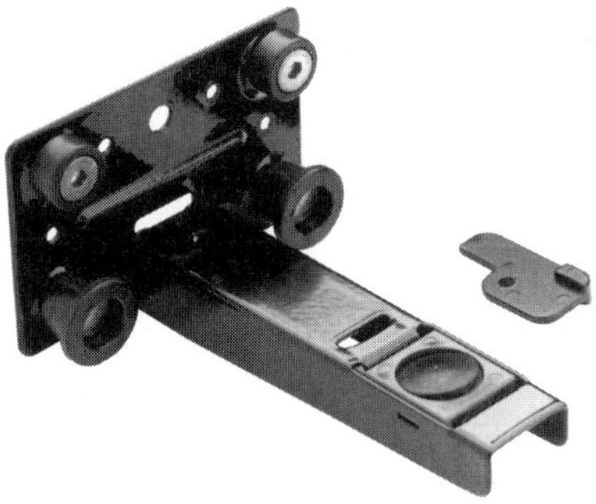

Cantilever Shelf Slide

- 32mm System compatible.
- Shelf Length = Desired Extension Length + 100mm.
- Easily adds storage to new or existing home enter tainment centers.
- Top rollers are adjustable to accept panel thickness of 18.3 to 19.8mm.
- Stop prevents accidental removal of shelf.
- Only one required per shelf.

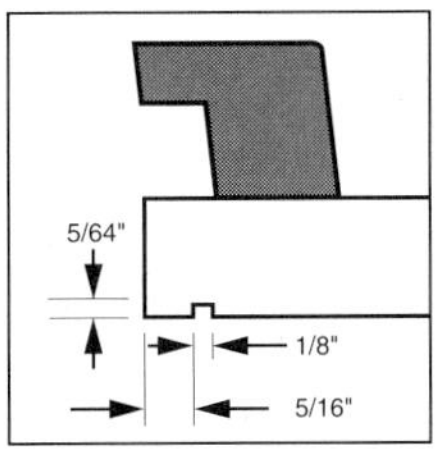

Shelf is grooved on bottom to accept guide rollers — see chart. Additional screw can be installed in groove to form front stop if required.

Finish: steel, black; plastic, black; zinc die-cast, black

Cat. No.	810.80.300

Packing: 1 set, w/stop and screws in polybag.

Dimensions in mm.
Inches are approximate.

HÄFELE

Audio/Video Media Storage Systems

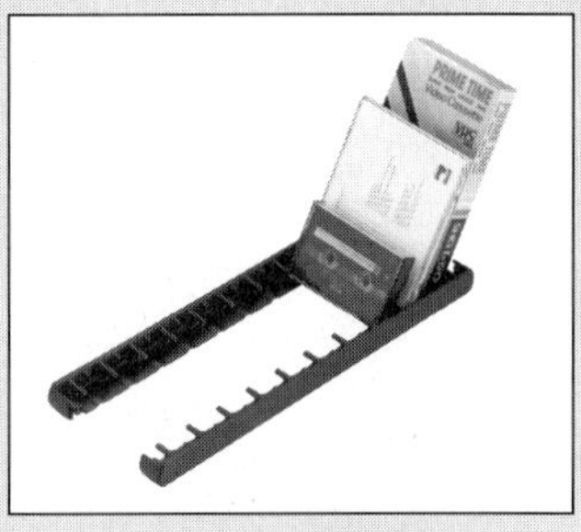

- Media can be "flipped" to facilitate viewing.
- Easily adjusted by consumer to accommodate a wide combination of media.
- Unique mounting system conceals fastening materials
- Will adapt to variety of mounting options and sizes.

- Used to expand edge rail capacity.
- Snaps onto tube in any position to accommodate media variety.
- Easily cut to required length.

- Provides storage for all three types in an 18" space.
- Packaged as complete set including all mounting hardware and instructions.

Can be used in a wide variety of applications — in a drawer, behind a door or simply mounted on the wall near your workstation.

Universal-Flip Edge Rail for Compact Disk, Audio and Video Tape storage.

Width: 1.03"(26mm)
Height: 1.03"(26mm)
Length: 15.9"(404mm)

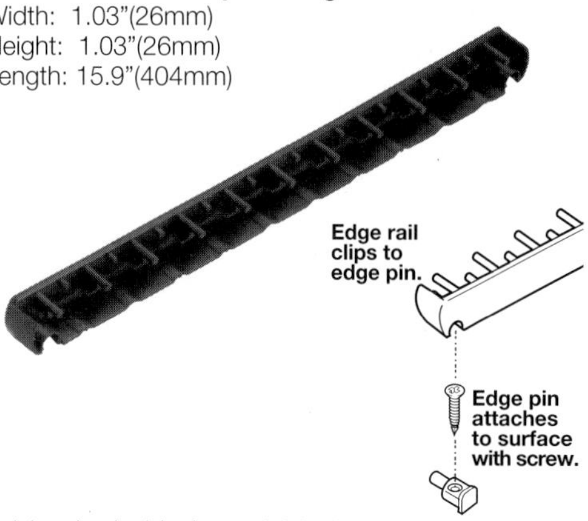

Finish: plastic, black; steel, black

Cat. No.	810.78.319

Packing: 1 set w/edge pins, screws & tape in polybag.

Universal-Flip Center Rail for Compact Disk, Audio and Video Tape storage

Width: 1.9"(48.2mm)
Height: 1.03"(26mm)
Length: 15.9"(404mm)

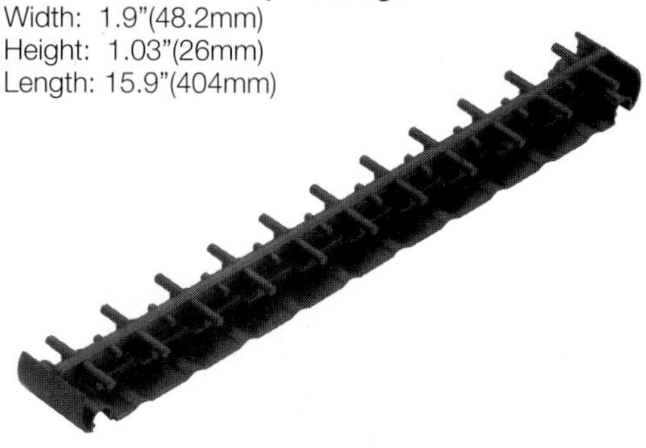

Finish: plastic, black

Cat. No.	810.78.328

Packing: 1 pc.

Connecting Tube for Flip Storage System

9.6mm diameter, 1 meter length.

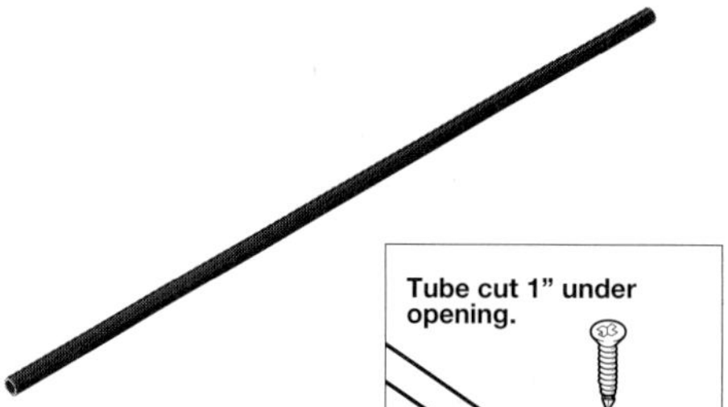

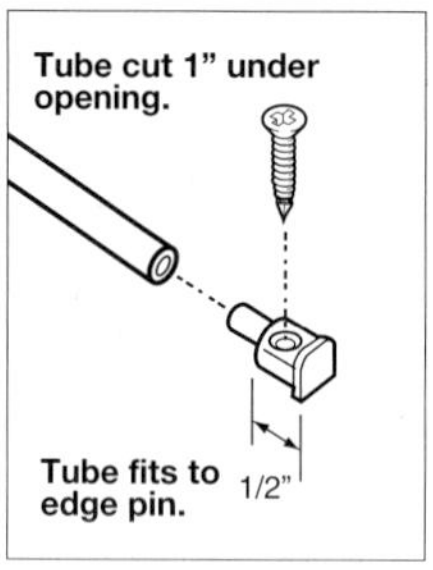

Finish: aluminum, black

Cat. No.	810.79.307

Packing: 1 pc.

Universal-Flip Storage Set for Compact Disks, Audio and Video Tape Storage-18"

Set consists of:

- 2- Edge Rails
- 2- Center Rails
- 4- Edge Pins
- 4- Screws
- 2- Tubes -17"

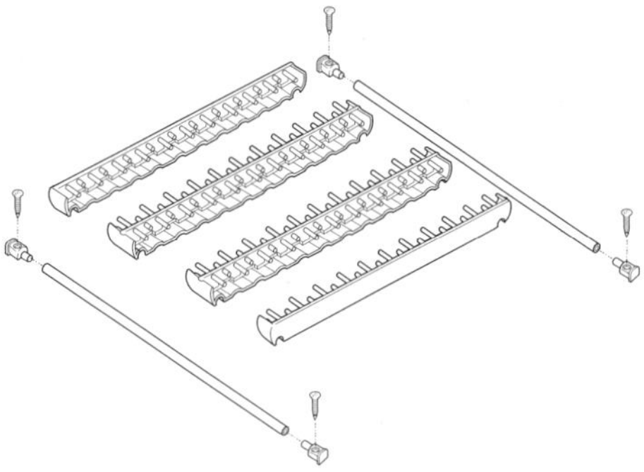

Finish: plastic, black; aluminum tubing, black; steel, black

Cat. No.	810.78.355

Packing: 1 set in polybag

Stores $3^1/_2$" or $5^1/_4$" computer disks

Quick access to the most often used disks is provided by this unique product. By simply mounting the "bridge", using two screws, you can now snap the side panels into the preset positions for $3^1/_2$" and $5^1/_4$" (with or without sleeves) disks. Storage capacity is 16 disks. Poly packed including screws.

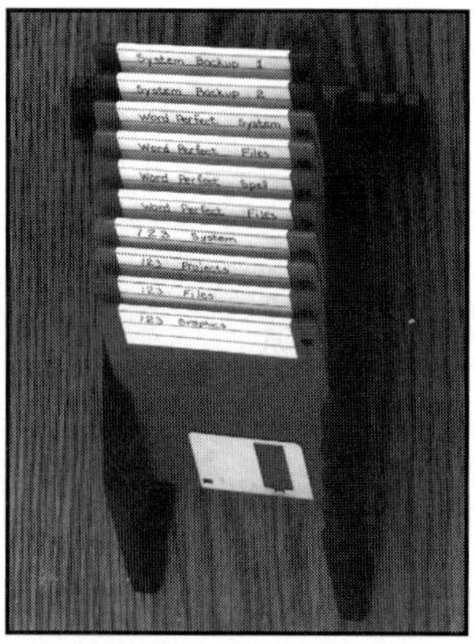

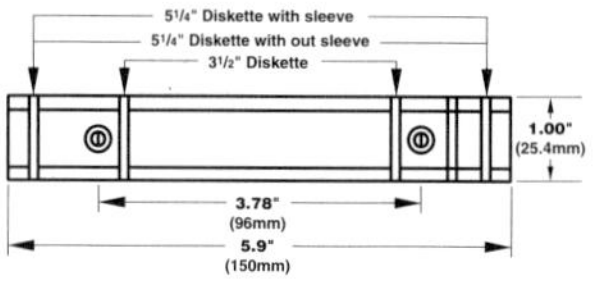

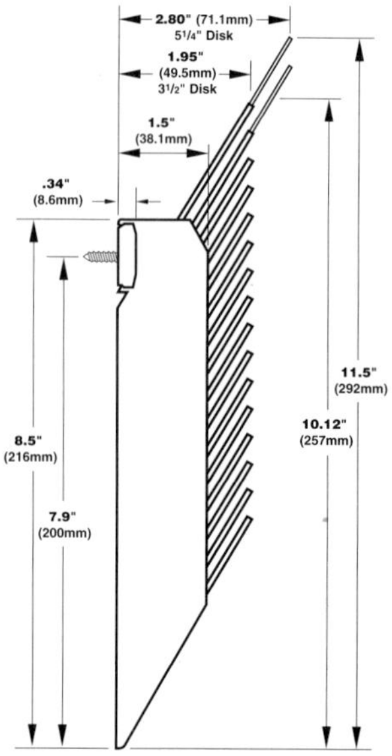

Finish: plastic, black

Cat. No.	810.68.304

Packing: 100 sets

**Dimensions in mm.
Inches are approximate.**

Dimensional data not binding. We reserve the right to alter specifications without notice.

Audio/Video Media Storage Systems

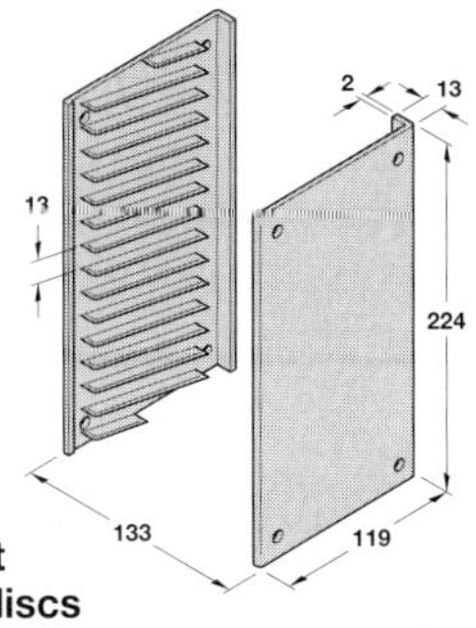

Screw-mounted compact disc holder for **13 single discs**
Finish: plastic, black

Cat. No.	810.64.324

Packing: 50 pairs

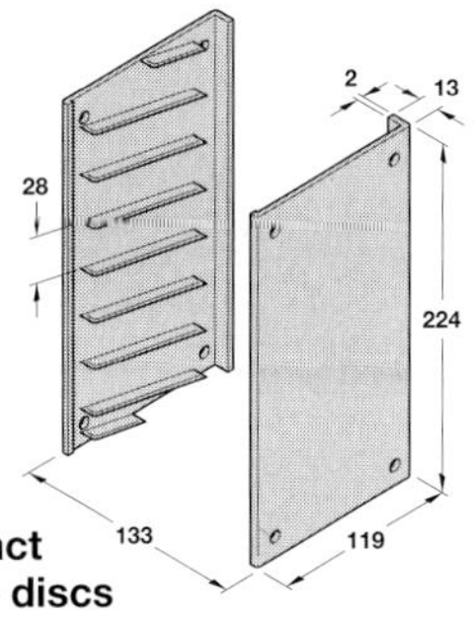

Screw-mounted compact disc holder for **6 double discs**
Finish: plastic, black

Cat. No.	810.64.333

Packing: 50 pairs

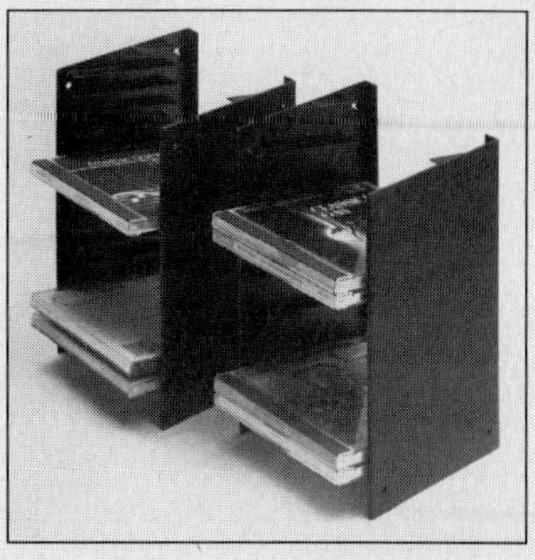

The width of the compact disc dictates the installation width, the installation height is optional, as the elements can be stacked or shortened by sawing off as desired.

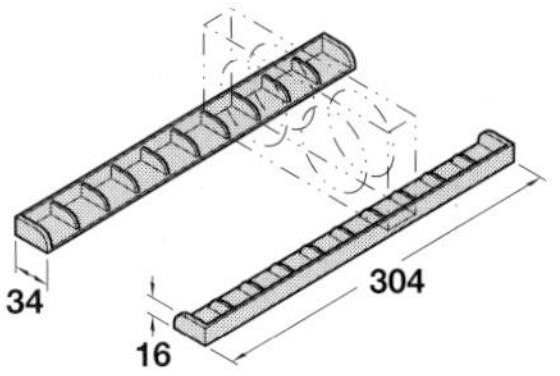

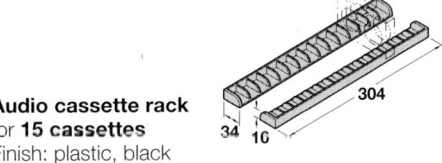

Video cassette rack
for **10 cassettes**
Finish: plastic, black

Cat. No.	810.58.326

Packing: 100 pair

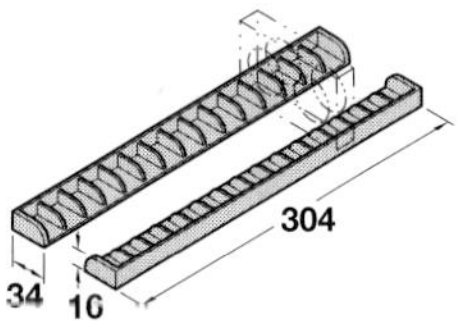

Audio cassette rack
for **15 cassettes**
Finish: plastic, black

Cat. No.	810.58.317

Packing: 100 pair

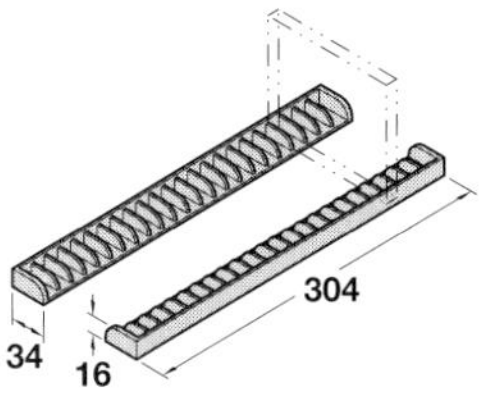

CD rack
for **23 CDs**
Finish: plastic, black

Cat. No.	810.58.335

Packing: 100 pair

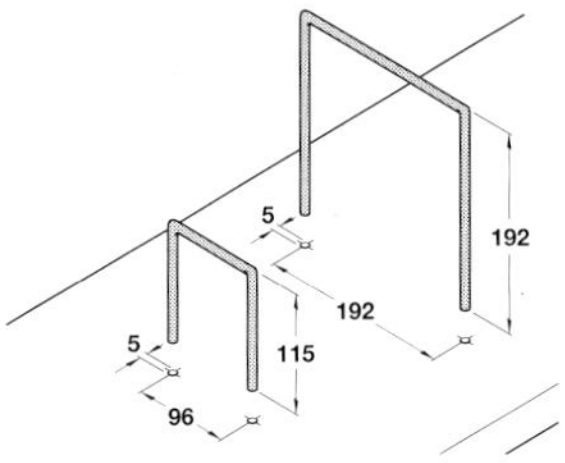

Dividers
fit in Ø 5 mm holes
Finish: steel, zinc-plated

for records, books: 192 x 192 mm

Cat. No.	810.69.920

Packing: 100 pcs.

for compact discs: 115 x 96 mm

Cat. No.	810.69.910

Packing: 200 pcs.

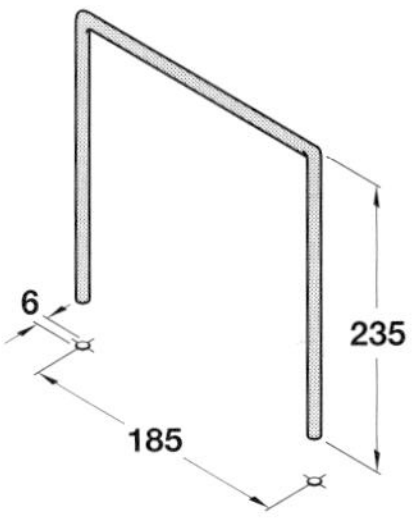

Record Divider
retangular
Finish: steel

Cat. No.	chrome	771.80.217
	brass	771.80.815
	black	771.80.315

Packing: 1 pc.

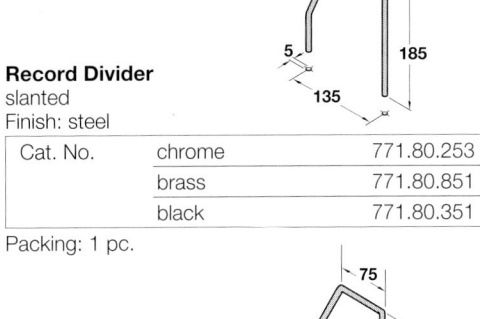

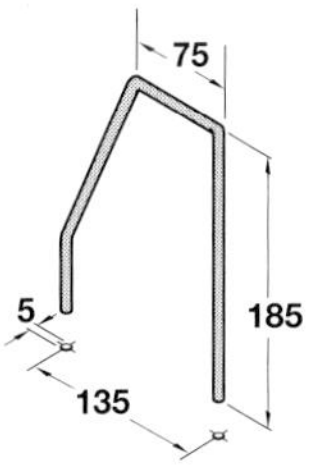

Record Divider
slanted
Finish: steel

Cat. No.	chrome	771.80.253
	brass	771.80.851
	black	771.80.351

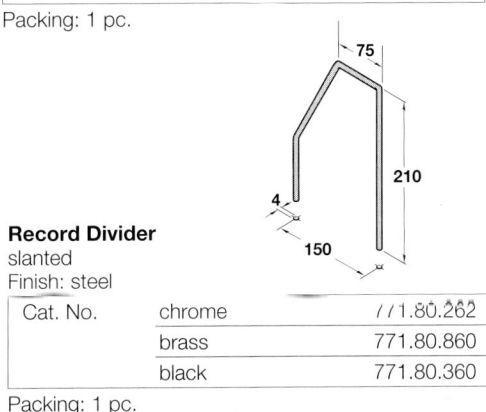

Packing: 1 pc.

Interior Accessories
Wardrobe Accessories
Storage Systems
Furniture Lighting
8

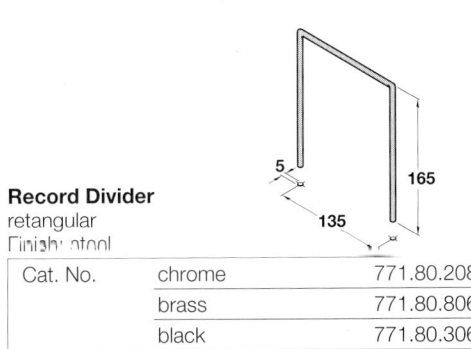

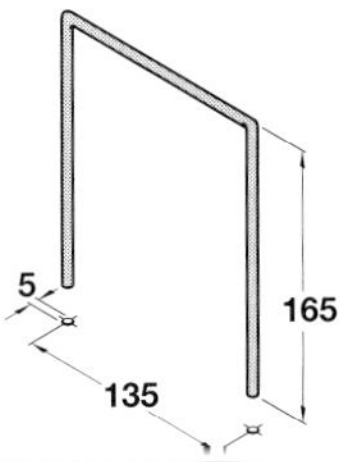

Record Divider
retangular
Finish: steel

Cat. No.	chrome	771.80.208
	brass	771.80.806
	black	771.80.306

Packing: 1 pc.

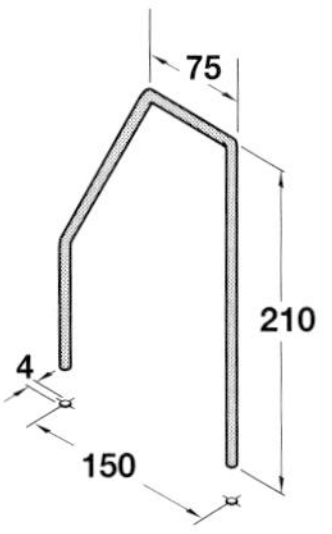

Record Divider
slanted
Finish: steel

Cat. No.	chrome	771.80.262
	brass	771.80.860
	black	771.80.360

Packing: 1 pc.

Dimensions in mm.

Dimensional data not binding. We reserve the right to alter specifications without notice.

HÄFELE

Hi-Fi and VCR Cabinet Accessories

The oversized rim of these trays can be shortened to the minimum dimensions indicated by the dashed lines.

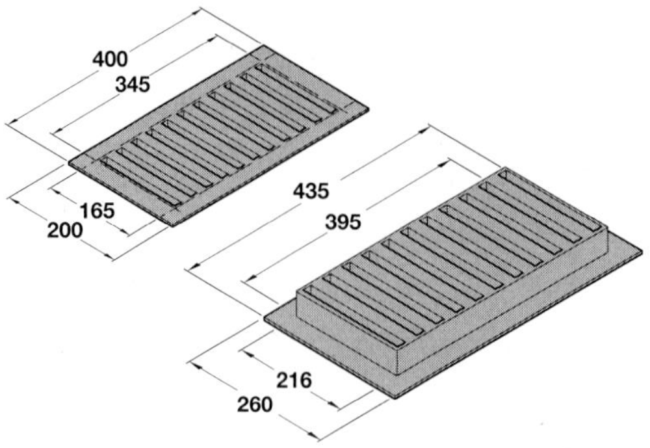

Compact disc tray

for assembly in drawers etc.Trays swaged from 2 mm thick plastic plates, with oversized rim.

for **11 compact discs**, height: 30 mm
Finish: polystyrene, black, leather grain

Cat. No.	810.61.314

Packing: 1 piece

Insert with bottom border, for **11 compact discs**, height: 30 mm
Finish: polystyrene, black, leather grain

Cat. No.	810.62.311

Packing: 1 piece

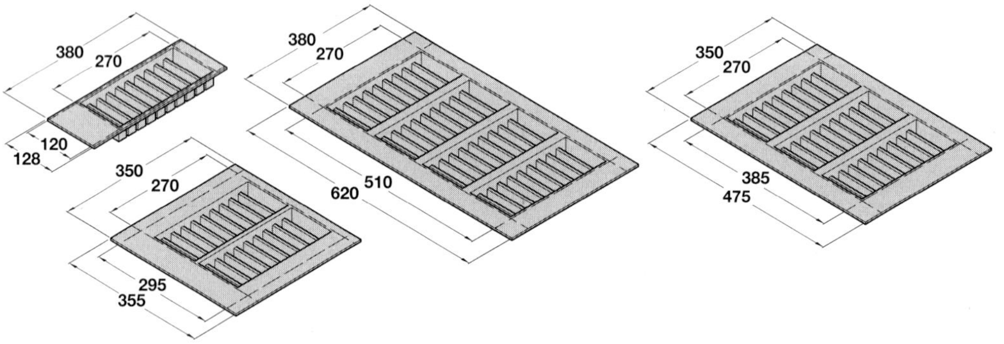

Music cassette trays

for assembly in drawers etc.
Trays swaged from 2 mm thick plastic plates, with oversized rim.
height: 32 mm
Finish: polystyrene, black, leather grain

Max. cassettes	Cat. No.
10	810.56.313
20	810.56.322
30	810.56.331
40	810.56.340

Packing: 1 piece

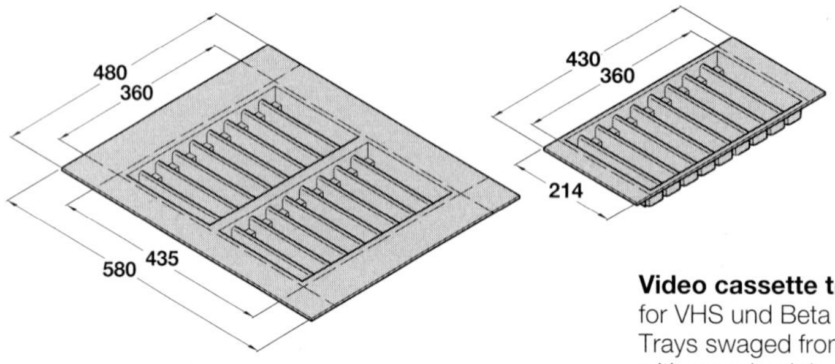

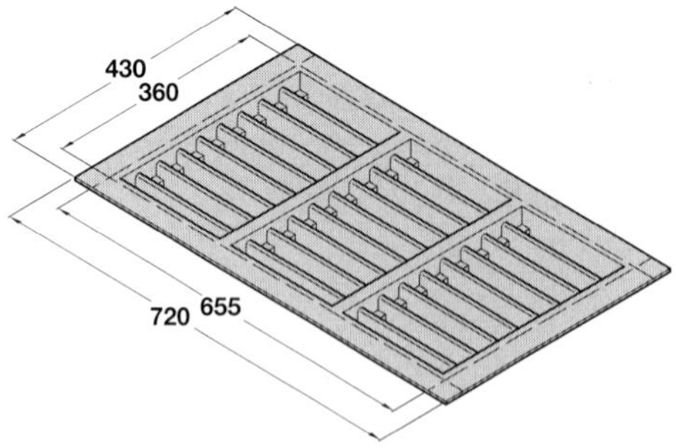

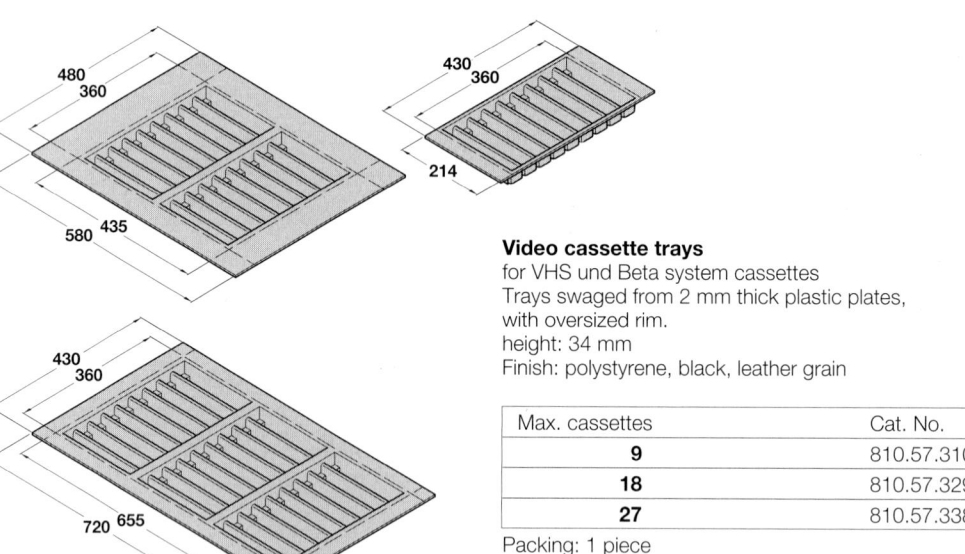

Video cassette trays

for VHS und Beta system cassettes
Trays swaged from 2 mm thick plastic plates, with oversized rim.
height: 34 mm
Finish: polystyrene, black, leather grain

Max. cassettes	Cat. No.
9	810.57.310
18	810.57.329
27	810.57.338

Packing: 1 piece

Pop-Out CD Storage Rack

- allows storage of 20 CD's in a compact pop-out storage unit.
- The exclusive "spring back" feature, provided by two polyester covered 6 ply elastic cords, delivers the selected CD to your hand at the touch of your fingertip.

HOSPA ϕ4,0

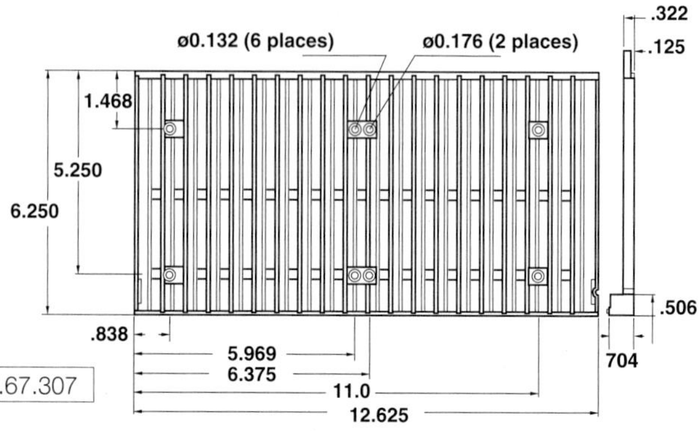

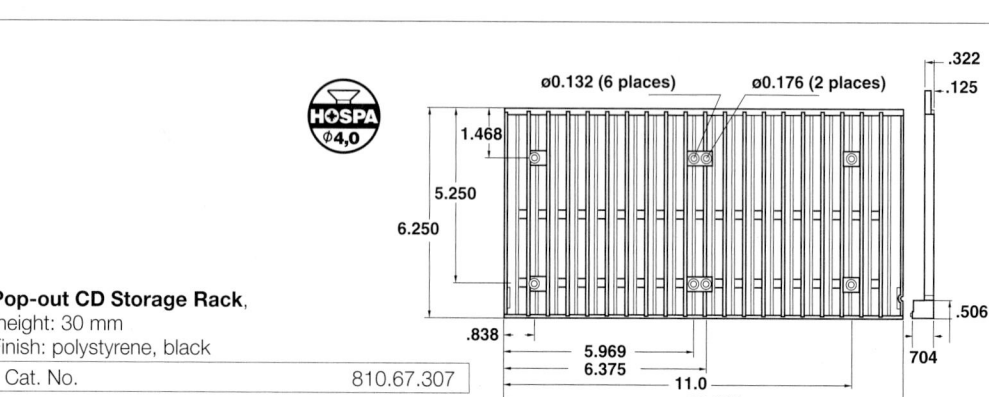

Pop-out CD Storage Rack,
height: 30 mm
Finish: polystyrene, black

Cat. No.	810.67.307

Packing: 100 sets

Dimensions in mm

Dimensional data not binding.
We reserve the right to alter specifications without notice.

Oval Wardrobe Rails

HÄFELE

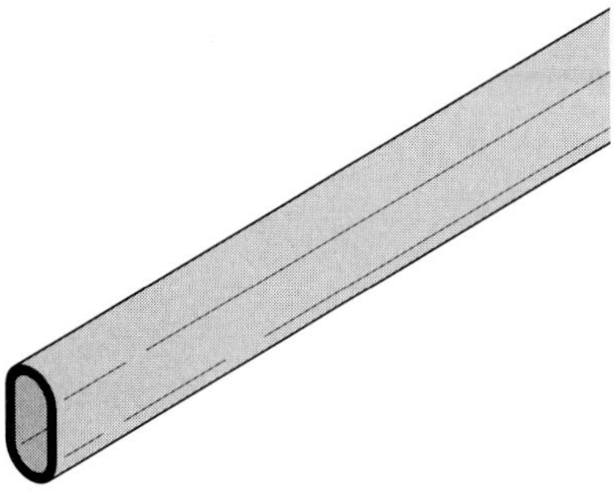

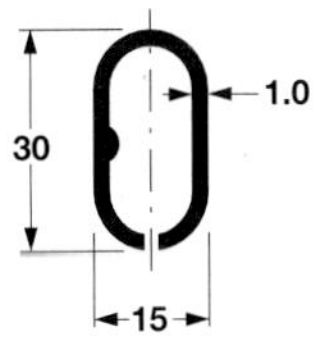

Oval wardrobe rail, welded
Finish: Steel,

Material thickness mm	Finish	Cat. No.
1.0	chrome-plated	801.13.220
	brass-plated	801.06.805
	PVC, white	801.13.702

Packing: 50 meters in 2.5 meter lengths

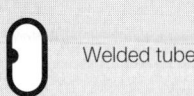

Welded tube

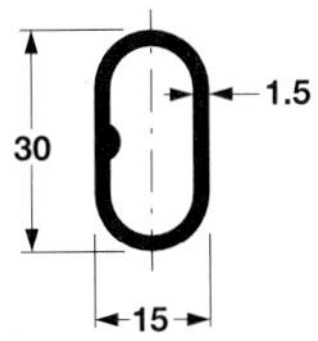

Oval wardrobe rail, welded
Finish: steel, chrome-plated

Material thickness mm	Cat. No.
1.5	801.09.226

Packing: 50 meters in 2.5 meter lengths

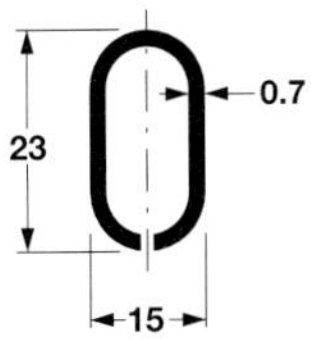

Oval-Mini wardrobe rails, rolled
with butted seam
Finish: steel, nickel-plated

Material thickness mm	Cat. No.
0.7	801.02.172

Packing: 25 meters in 2.5 meter lengths

* Precut lengths:

- Minimum order, 100 pcs
- In addition to the Cat. No., the length and finish must be specified

Rolled tube
with butted seam

Dimensions in mm

HÄFELE

Oval Wardrobe Rail Supports

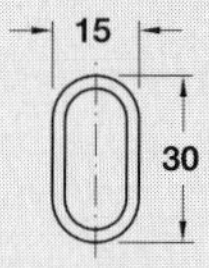

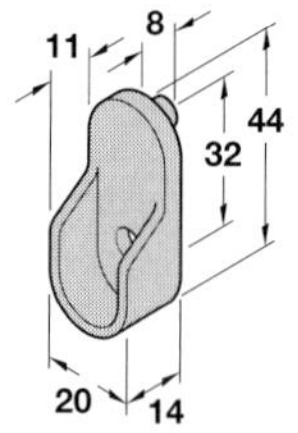

Wardrobe rail support, for insertion in Varianta 32 system holes, with 2 pins for Ø 5 mm holes and an additional screw hole
Finish: zinc die cast

Color	Cat. No.
nickel-plated	803.33.722
chrome	803.33.210
brass-plated	803.33.520
white	803.33.830

Packing: 200 pcs.

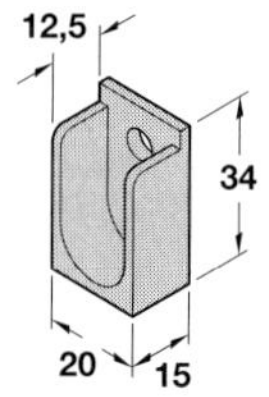

Wardrobe rail support
for screw-mounting on side panel
Finish: plastic

Color	Cat. No.
natural	803.25.720
chrome-plated	803.25.220
black	803.25.328

Packing: 200 pcs.

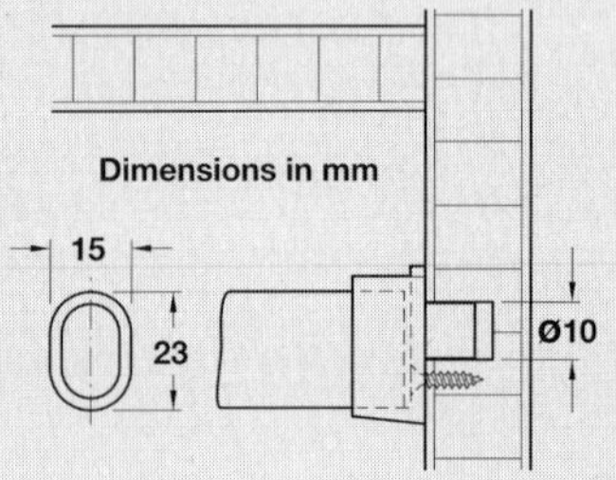

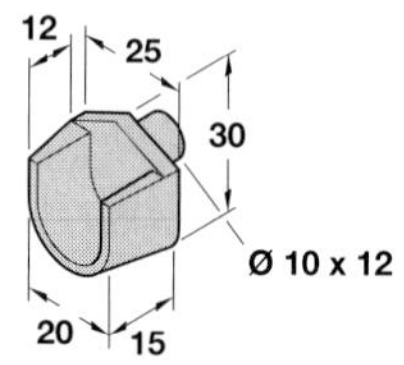

Wardrobe rail support, for Oval-Mini wardrobe rail with Ø 10 mm mounting pin and additional screw hole for mounting on the side panel
Finish: plastic, white

Cat. No.	803.22.747

Packing: 200 pcs.

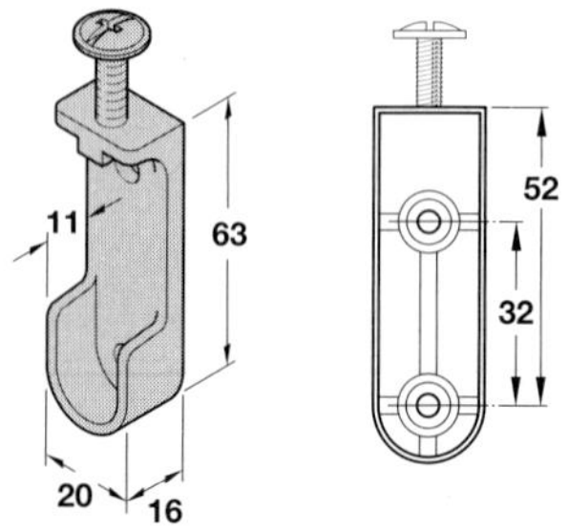

Wardrobe rail support, for screw-mounting under a shelf, with M6 x 28 mm mounting screw and 2 screw holes for panel fastening
Finish: zinc die cast nickel-plated

Cat. No.	803.32.720

Packing: 200 pcs.
with mounting screws

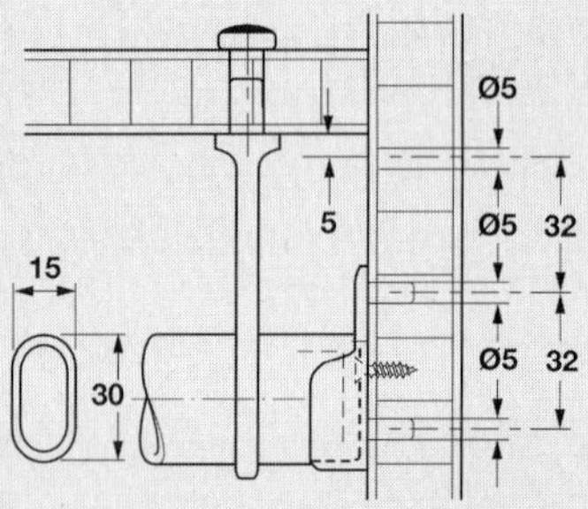

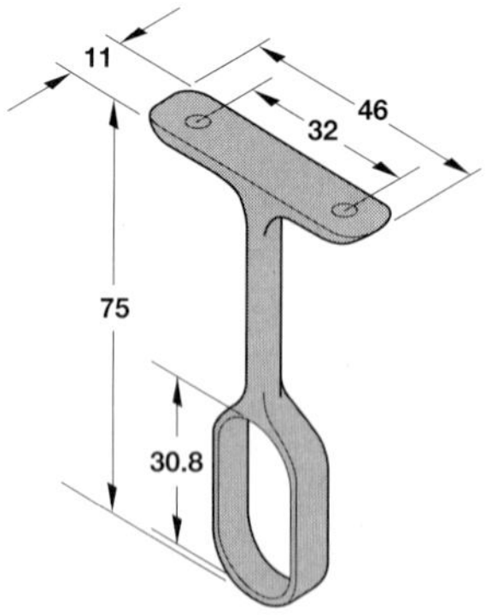

Oval Center Bracket, surface mount
for 15 x 30 mm rail
Finish: zinc die cast

Cat. No.	chrome-plated	802.04.208
	brass-plated	802.04.500

Packing: 100 pcs.

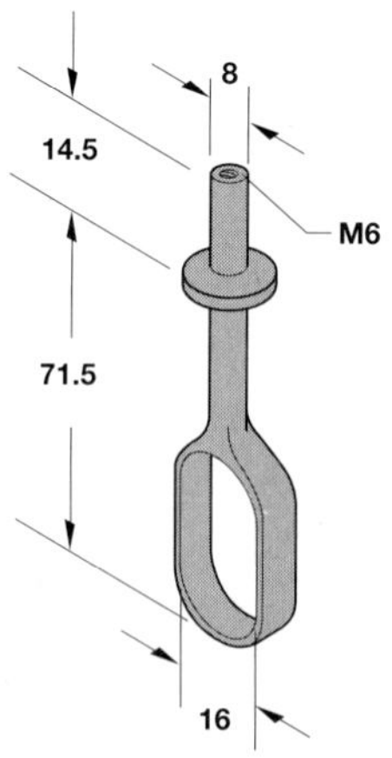

Oval Center Bracket, top mount
for 15 x 30 mm rail, mounts with M6 screw.
Finish: zinc die cast

Cat. No.	chrome-plated	802.03.201
	brass-plated	802.03.809

Packing: 100 pcs. with mounting screw

Ø 18 mm Wardrobe Rails and Supports

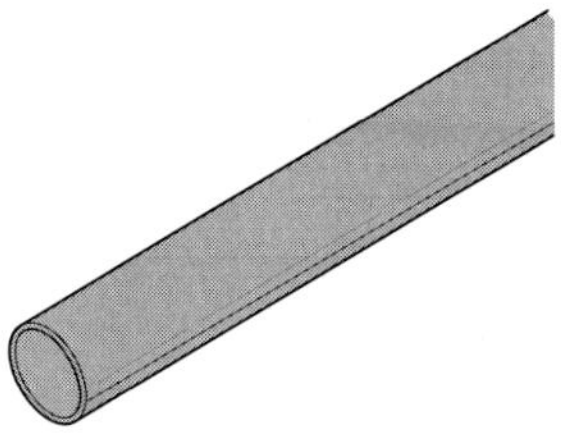

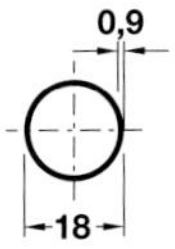

Wardrobe rail, round, welded
with plastic coating
Finish: steel

Color	Cat. No.
white	801.17.700
black	801.17.602

Packing: 25 meters in 2.5 meter lengths

Also available in precut lengths in minimum quantities of 200 pcs.

Cat. No.	801.17.XX*

* In addition to the Cat. No., the length and type must be specified.

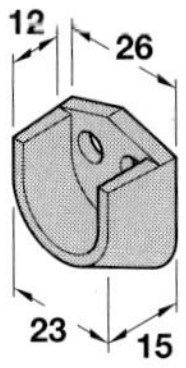

Wardrobe rail support
for mounting on the side panel
Finish: plastic

Color	Cat. No.
white	803.27.724
black	803.27.322

Packing: 100 pcs.

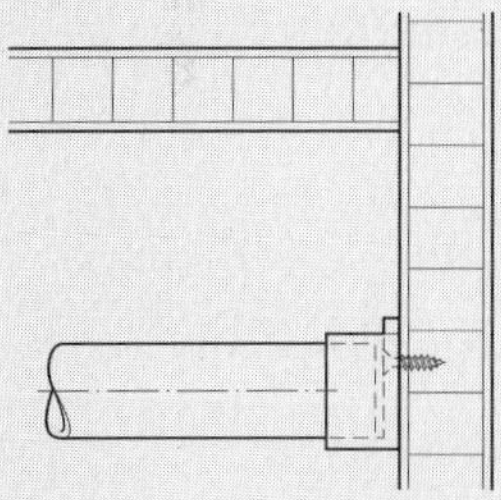

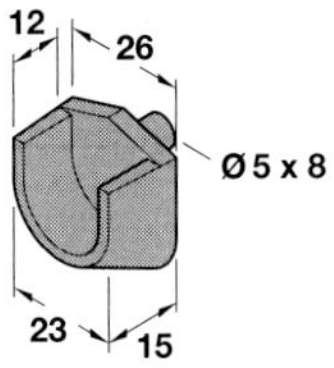

Wardrobe rail support
with Ø 5 mm mounting pin and additional screw hole for mounting on the side panel
Finish: plastic

Color	Cat. No.
white	803.28.721
black	803.28.329

Packing: 100 pcs.

Ø 20 mm Wardrobe Rails and Supports

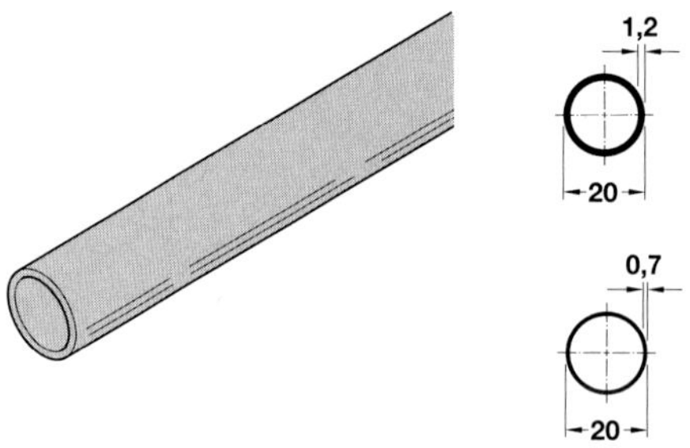

Wardrobe rail, round, welded
with plastic coating
Finish: steel, white plastic coated

Cat. No.	801.15.037

Packing: 5 meters

Wardrobe rail, round, with butted seam
Finish: steel, nickel-plated

Cat. No.	801.01.177

Packing: 25 meters in 2.5 meter lengths

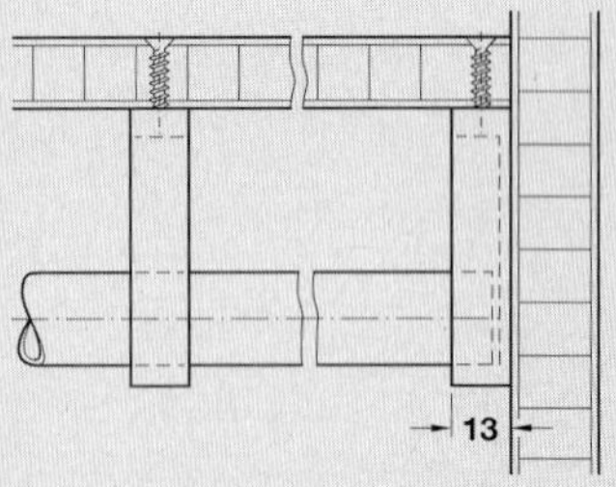

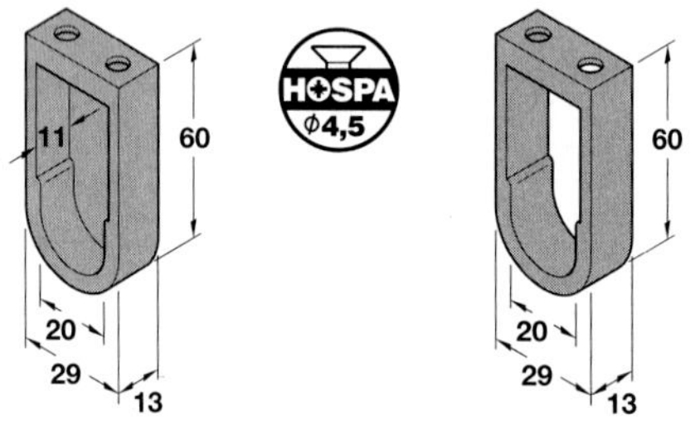

Wardrobe rail support and center support
for screw-mounting under a shelf
Finish: plastic, white

	Rail support	Center support
Cat. No.	803.23.735	803.23.771

Packing: 50 and 1000 pcs.

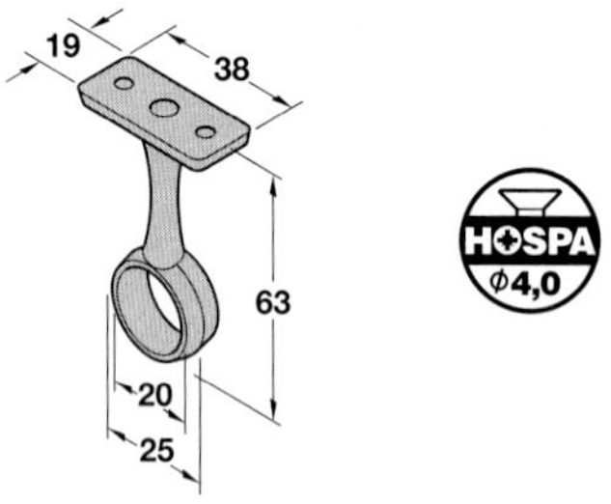

Wardrobe center support
for screw-mounting under a shelf
with setscrew to secure the wardrobe rail
Finish: zinc die-cast, chrome-plated

Cat. No.	802.02.220

Packing: 10 pcs.

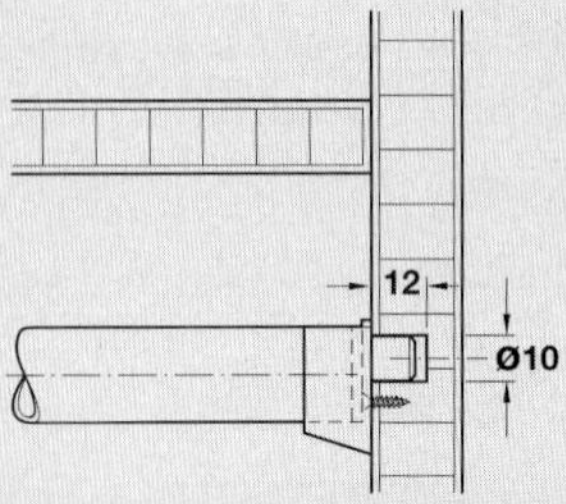

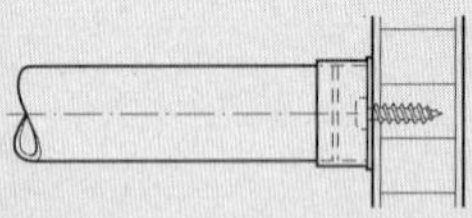

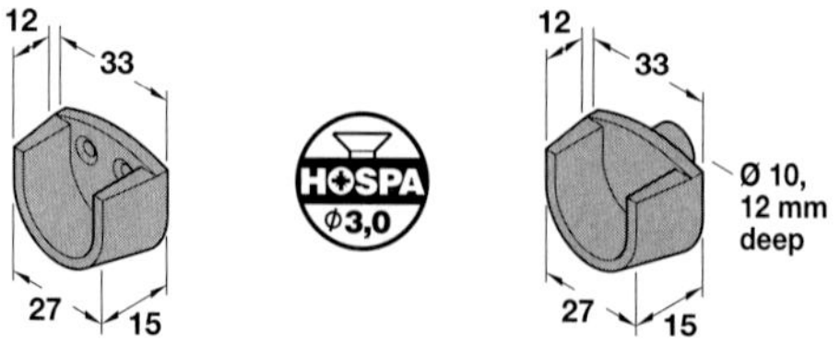

Wardrobe rail support, for mounting on side panel
Finish: plastic, white

	Screw-mounted	with Ø 10 mm mounting pin and additional screw hole
Cat. No.	803.21.731	803.22.738

Packing: 200 pcs.

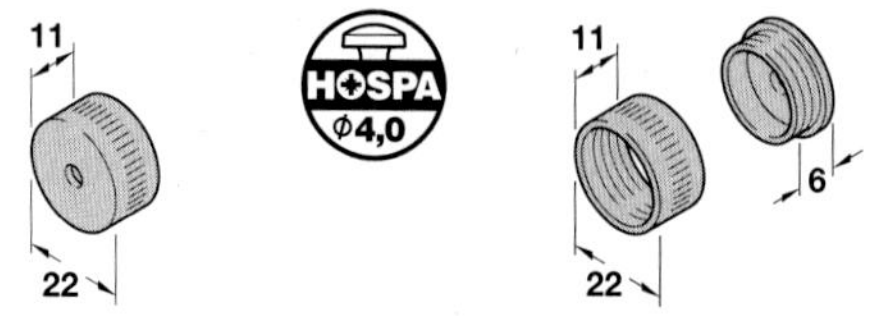

Wardrobe support set, 2-piece
1 support fixed, 1 threaded 2-piece support
(the sleeve is premounted on the rail and then
screwed onto the screw-mounted support)
Finish: brass, nickel-plated

Cat. No.	803.51.702

Packing: 50 pairs

Dimensions in mm

Ø 25 mm Wardrobe Rails and Supports

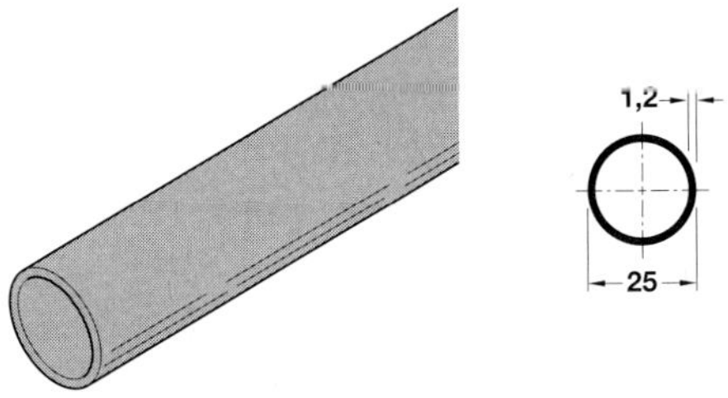

Wardrobe rail, round, welded
Finish: steel

Color	Cat. No.
nickel-plated, polished	801.12.205
brass-plated, polished	801.12.803

Packing: 25 meters in 2.5 meter lengths

HOSPA Φ3,0

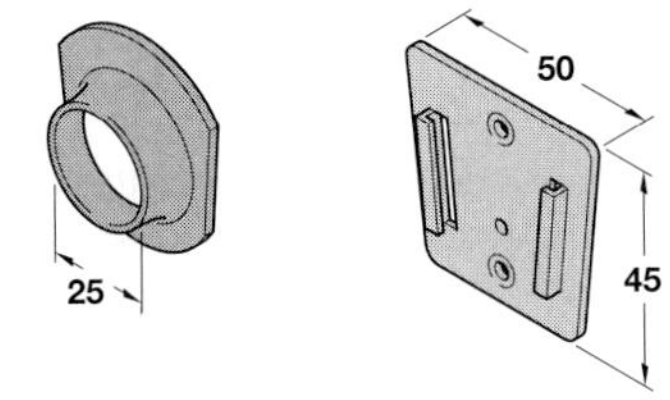

Wardrobe rail support, concealed, 2-piece
for screw-mounting on side panel
Finish: steel

Color	Cat. No.
nickel-plated	803.18.743
brass-plated	803.18.547

Packing: 50 pcs.

HOSPA Φ4,5

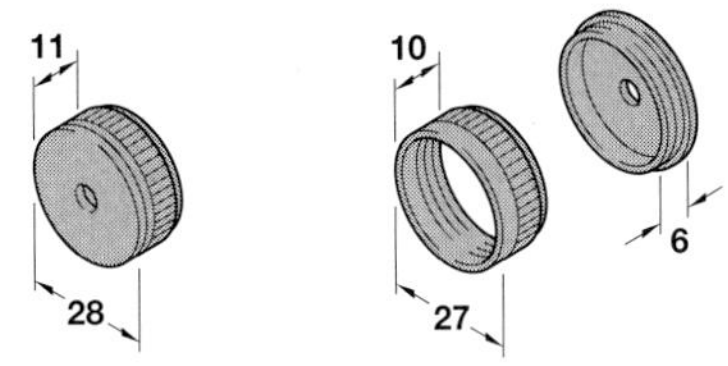

Wardrobe support set, 2-piece
1 support fixed, 1 threaded 2-piece support (the sleeve is premounted on the rail and then screwed onto the screw-mounted support)
Finish: brass

Color	Cat. No.
nickel-plated	803.51.757
brass, polished	803.51.855

Packing: 25 pairs

HOSPA Φ4,0

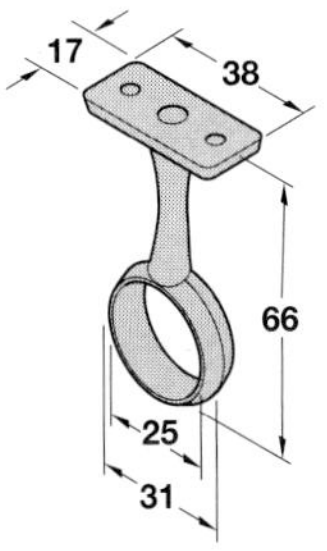

Wardrobe center support
for screw-mounting under a shelf
Finish: zinc die cast

Color	Cat. No.
nickel-plated	802.02.250
brass-plated	802.02.525

Packing: 10 pcs.

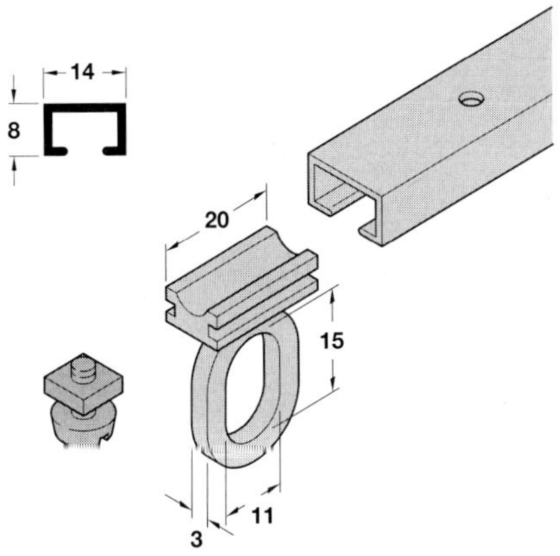

Wardrobe track
with Ø 4 mm screw holes for screw-mounting under a shelf
Finish: aluminum, unfinished

Cat. No.	804.22.055

Packing: 5 meters

Ring for track
Finish: polyethylene, natural

Cat. No.	804.23.007

Packing: 1000 pcs.

End stop for track
Finish: steel, galvanized

Cat. No.	804.24.004

Packing: 10 pcs.

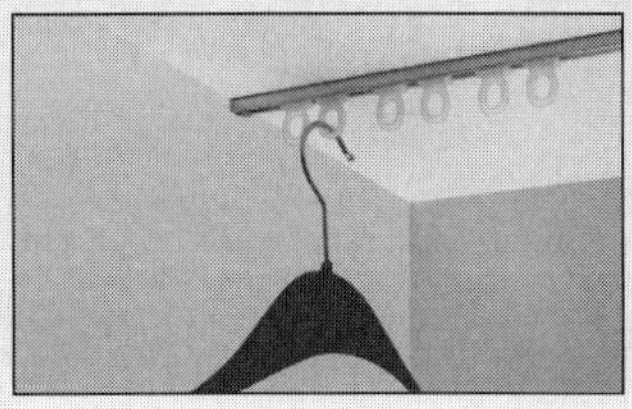

Dimensional data not binding.
We reserve the right to alter specifications without notice.

Dimensions in mm

HÄFELE

Wardrobe Accessories

Wardrobe Lift
for attachment to wardrobe sides with screws
Weight capacity: **10 kg**
Height: 845 mm (33 1/4")
Wardrobe tube: Ø 22 mm, with adjustment feature for different widths of wardrobes.

Finish: arm: steel, nickel-plated
Housing: plastic, black

for inside wardrobe widths (mm)	Cat. No. nickel/ black
450 - 600 (17 3/4" - 23 5/8")	805.20.314
600 - 830 (23 5/8" - 32 3/4")	805.20.341
830 - 1150 (32 3/4" - 45 1/2")	805.20.305

Packing: 1 set

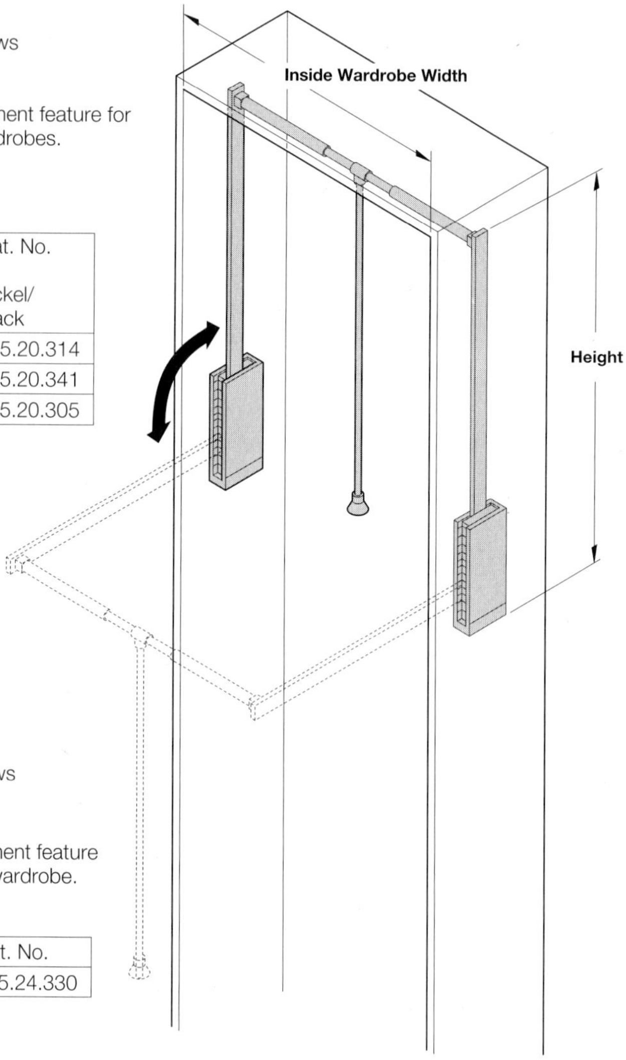

Wardrobe Lift
for attachment to wardrobe sides with screws
Weight capacity: **15 kg**
Height: 1028 mm (40 1/2")
Wardrobe tube: Ø 22 mm, with adjustment feature for different widths of wardrobe.
Finish: arm: steel, nickel-plated
Housing: plastic, black

for inside wardrobe widths	Cat. No.
870 - 1190 mm (34 1/4" - 46 1/8")	805.24.330

Packing: 1 set

Measurements in mm

8
Interior Accessories
Wardrobe Accessories
Storage Systems
Furniture Lighting

Dimensions in mm.
Inches are approximate.

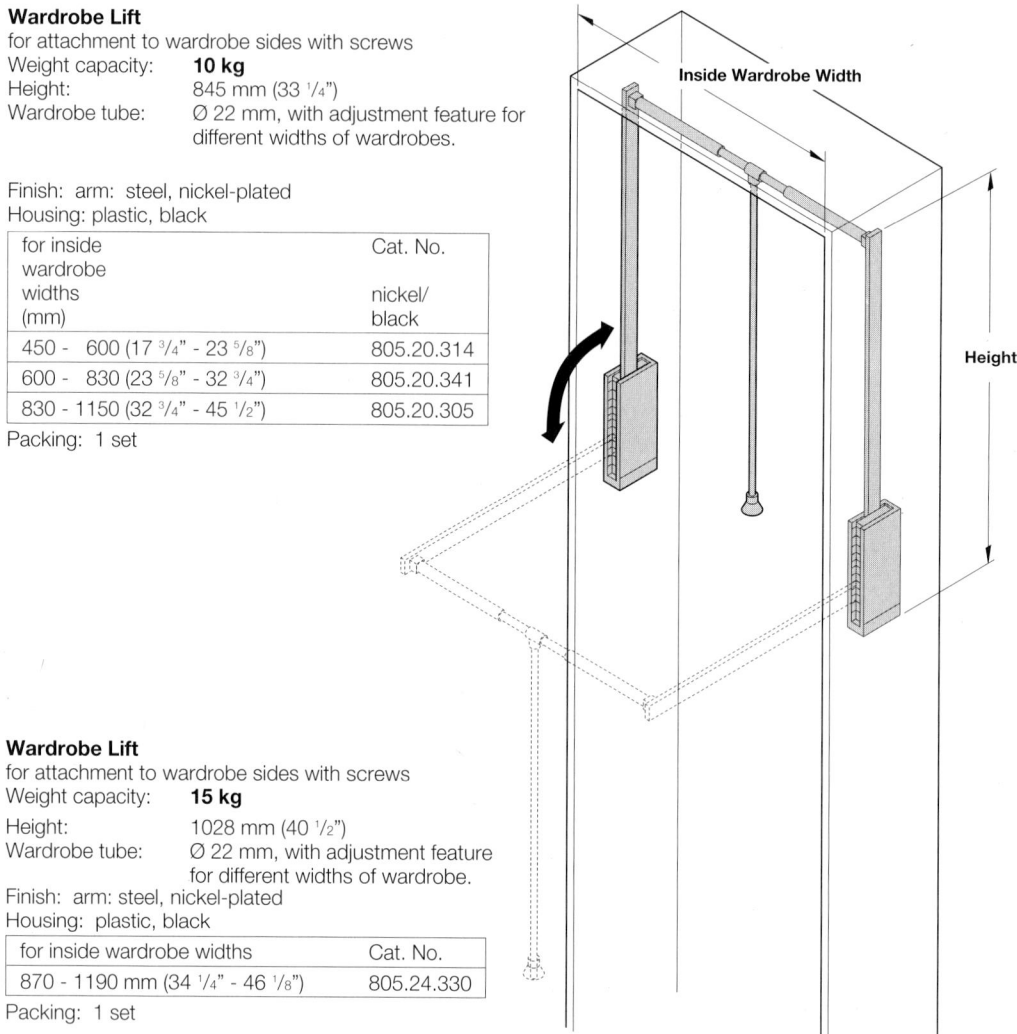

Wardrobe Accessories

Wardrobe lift - single sided
for attachment to wardrobe side panels
Weight capacity: **5 kg**
Width adjustment from 350 – 450 mm (13 3/4" - 17 3/4")

Finish: Arm: steel, nickel-plated
housing: plastic, black

	Cat. No.
left	805.22.210
right	805.22.200

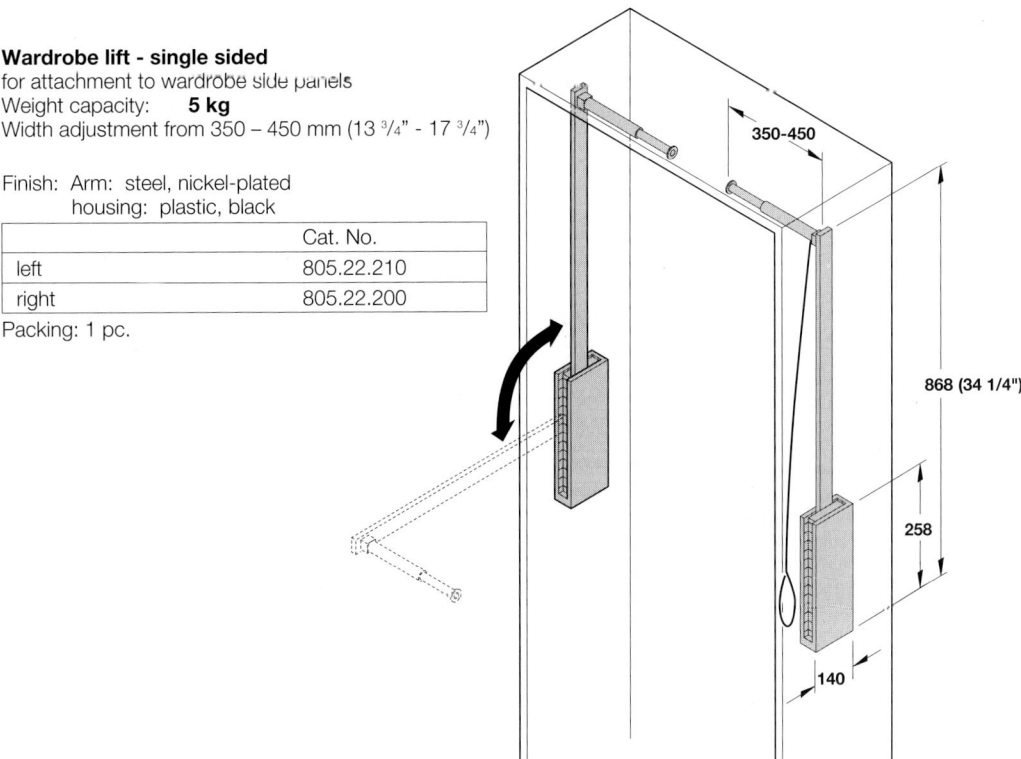

Packing: 1 pc.

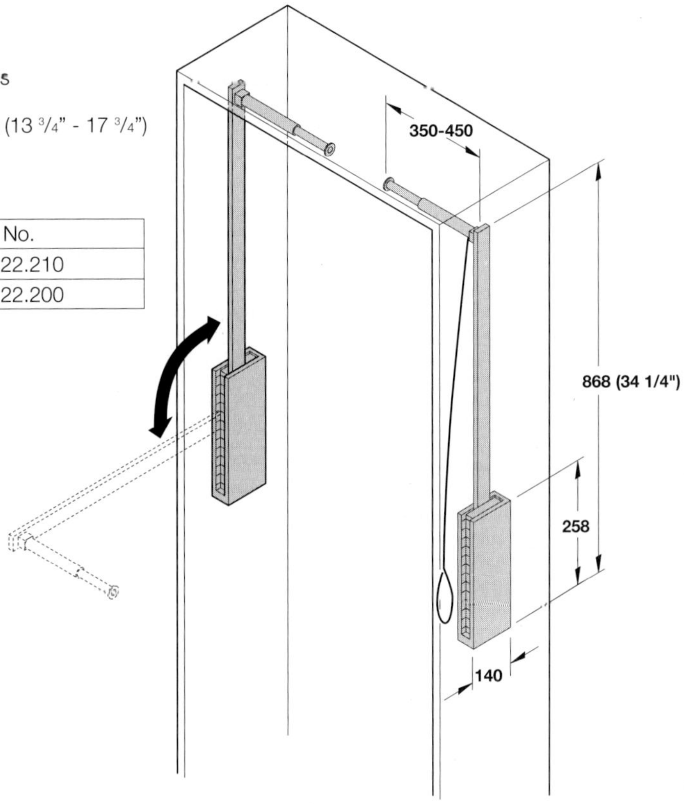

Measurements in mm

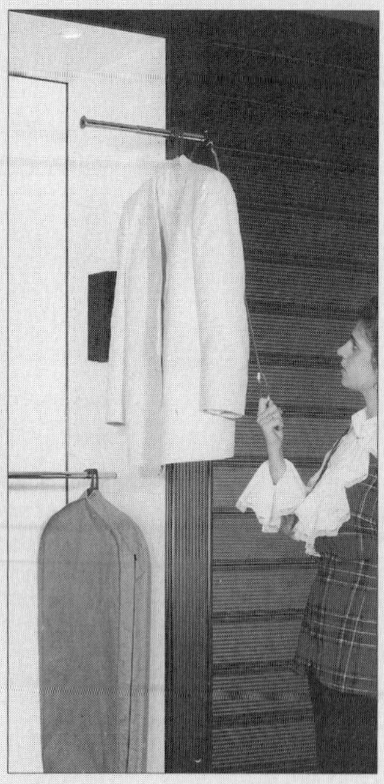

Clothes Lift for attachment to wall or back panel with Ø 22 mm wardrobe arm and lift rod.
Weight capacity: **5 kg**
Finish: Housing: plastic, black
Arm and lift rod: Steel, nickel-plated

Cat. No.	805.28.310

Packing: 1 piece (Screws included)

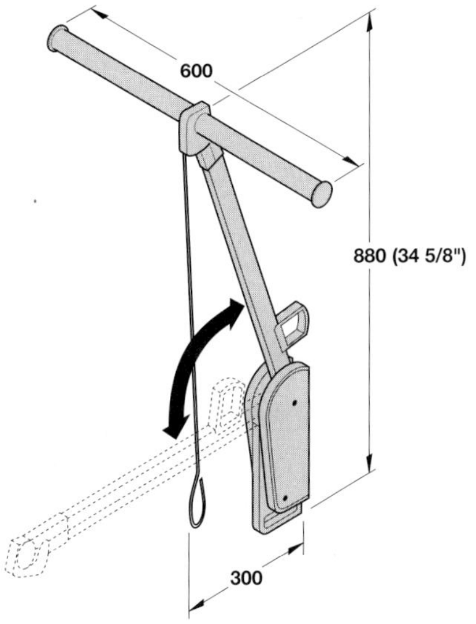

Dimensions in mm.
Inches are approximate.

Dimensional data not binding.
We reserve the right to alter specifications without notice.

HÄFELE

Wardrobe Accessories

How the adjustment feature works
- Adjust to desired width
- Twist both rods in opposite directions, and the eccentric inside the adjustment element hold tubes in position.

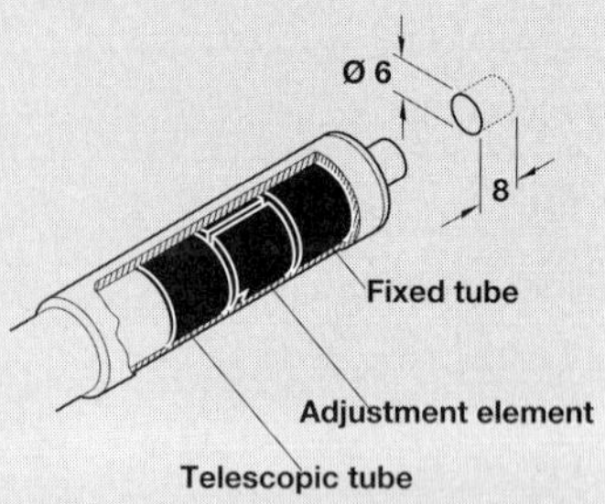

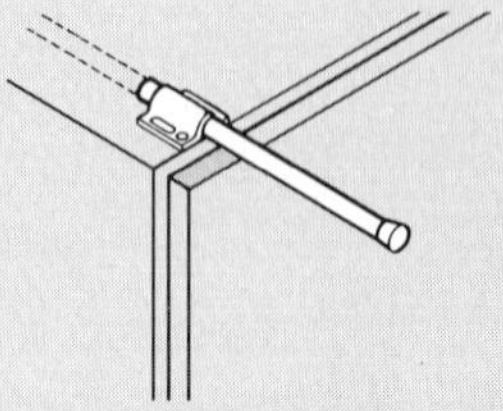

- Extra heavy duty rod will hold clothing in excess of 50 lbs.
- Up to 10" of clothing and garment bag.
- Can be mounted on top, bottom or projecting corner wall.
- Convenient holder for cleaning, laundry or garment bag.
- Eliminate scratches on doors caused by garment bags.
- Ideal for residential as well as hotel & motel use.

Telescopic Wardrobe Tube
for lower part of wardrobe with dowels for side panel attachment and adjustment feature for different widths of wardrobe.
Rod: Ø 22 mm
Dowels: Ø 6 mm

Finish: Rod: Steel, nickel-plated
Dowels and adjustment element: plastic, black

Range of adjustment	Cat. No.
380 - 620 mm (15" - 24 1/2")	805.20.387
680 -1200 mm (26 3/4" - 47 1/4")	805.20.396

Packing: 1 pc.

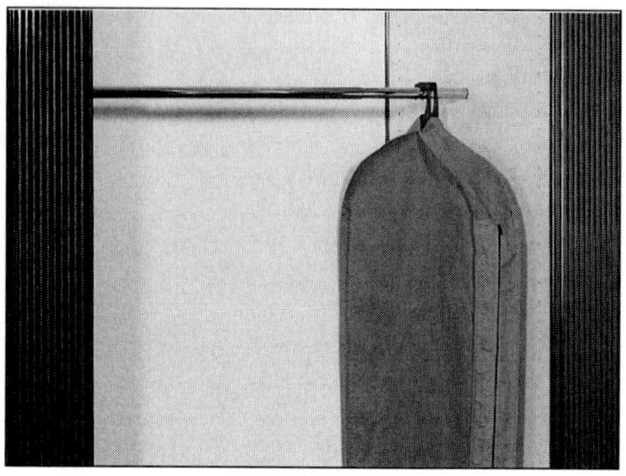

Pull-out Rod, for clothes hangers
to be screwed on the top of the wardrobe.
Length: 225 mm
Tube Ø: 13 mm
Finish: Aluminum, gold anodized with white plastic end caps

Cat. No.	808.61.203

Packing: 25 pcs. (screws included)

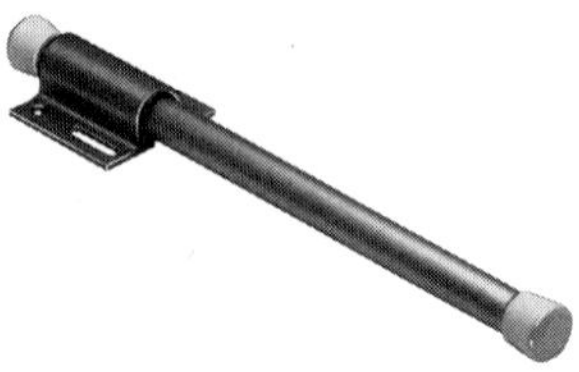

Garment Bag Valet®

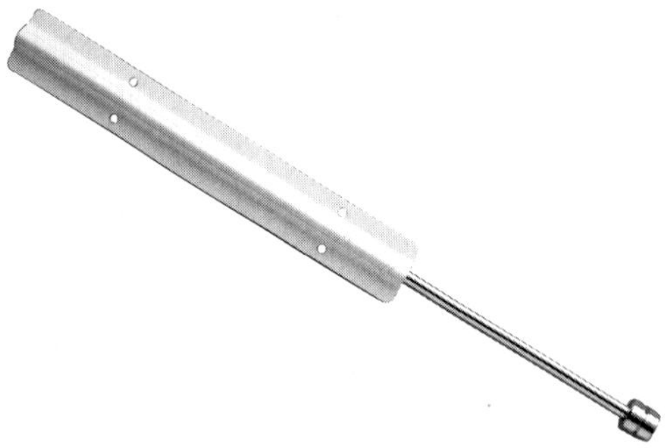

Finish: Steel, epoxy-coated white

Cat. No.	808.68.700

Packing: 24 pcs.

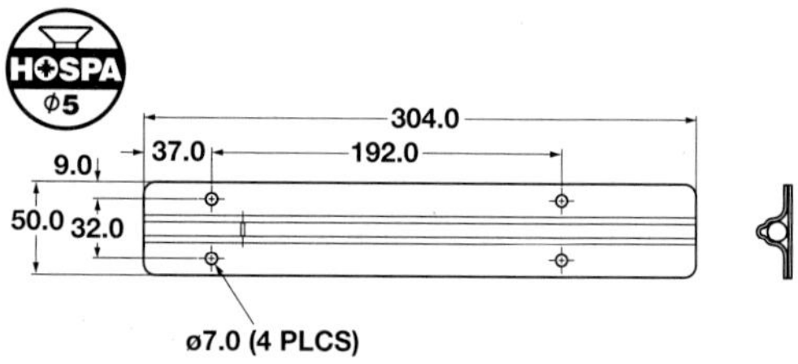

Can be mounted on top or bottom of shelf as well as side-mounted. Back plate prevents damage to drywall.

Dimensions in mm.
Inches are approximate.

Wardrobe Fittings

HÄFELE

- mounted under the cabinet top
- retractable

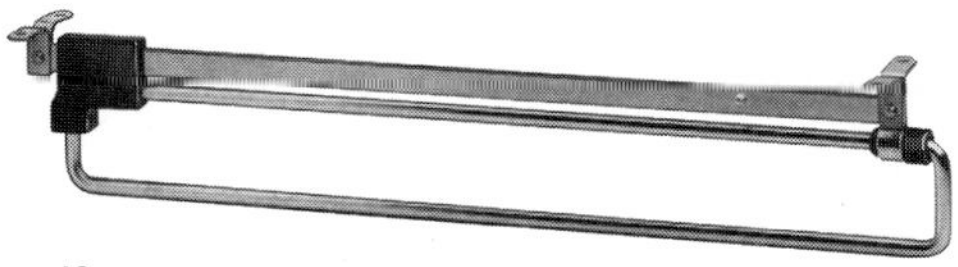

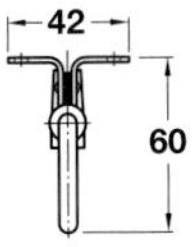

HOSPA Φ4,0

Wardrobe rail
with plastic runner
Finish: steel, nickel-plated

Length		Load capacity	Cat. No.
260 mm	(10 1/4")	8 kg	805.01.702
310 mm	(12 1/4")	6 kg	805.01.711
360 mm	(14 1/4")	5 kg	805.01.720
410 mm	(16 1/8")	4 kg	805.01.739

Packing: 10 pcs.

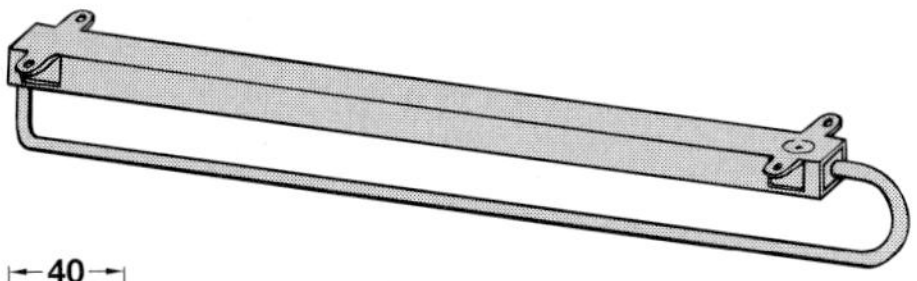

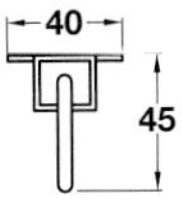

HOSPA Φ3,0

Wardrobe rail
Finish: track: steel, epoxy-coated
rail: steel, nickel-plated

Length		Load capacity	Cat. No.
245 mm	(9 5/8")	10 kg	805.12.250
295 mm	(11 5/8")	10 kg	805.12.303
345 mm	(13 1/2")	10 kg	805.12.358
395 mm	(15 1/2")	10 kg	805.12.401
445 mm	(17 1/2")	10 kg	805.12.456

Packing: 5 pcs.

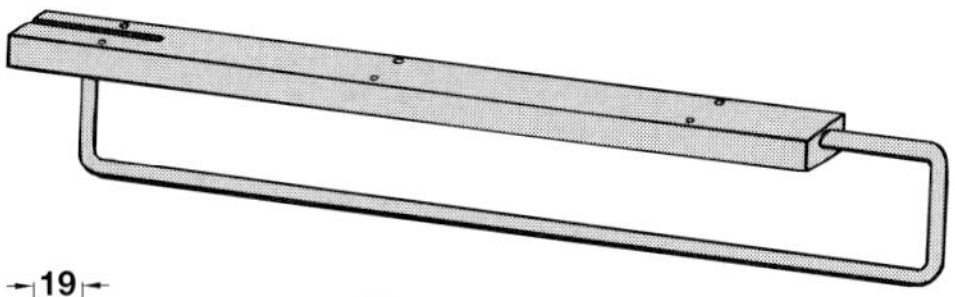

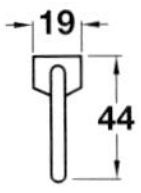

HOSPA Φ3,5

Wardrobe rail
Finish: track: plastic, white
rail: steel, nickel-plated

Length		Load capacity	Cat. No.
305 mm	(12")	6 kg	805.02.718
355 mm	(14")	5 kg	805.02.727
405 mm	(16")	5 kg	805.02.736

Packing: 10 pcs.

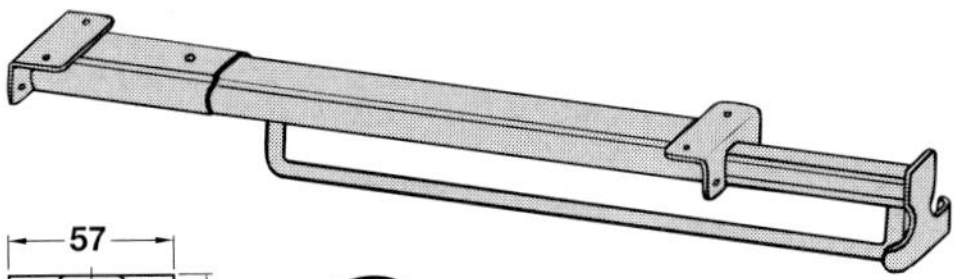

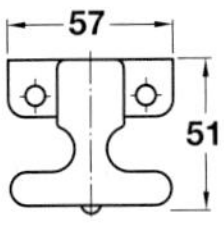

HOSPA Φ4,5

Wardrobe rail
ball-bearing runner system with cover plate
Finish: steel, chrome-plated

Length		Load capacity	Cat. No.
254 mm	(9 5/8")	40 kg	805.14.254
305 mm	(11 5/8")	40 kg	805.14.307
406 mm	(16")	40 kg	805.14.405
508 mm	(20")	40 kg	805.14.503

Packing: 1 piece

Interior Accessories
Wardrobe Accessories
Storage Systems
Furniture Lighting
8

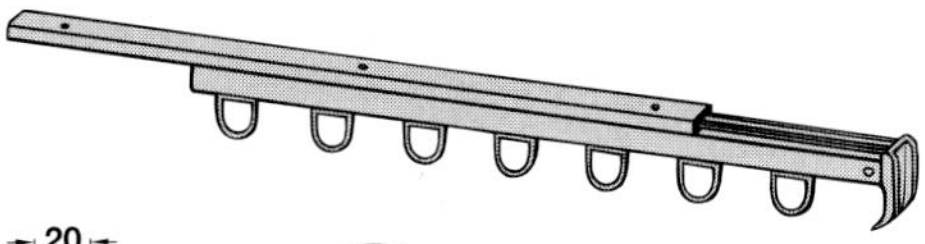

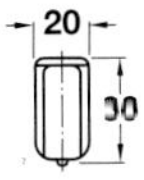

HOSPA Φ3,0

Wardrobe rail
with sliding rings and cover plate
Finish: aluminum, matt
plate and rings: plastic, white

Length		Load capacity	Cat. No.
305 mm	(12")	30 kg	805.04.301
355 mm	(14")	30 kg	805.04.356
405 mm	(16")	35 kg	805.04.409
455 mm	(18")	35 kg	805.04.454

Packing: 1 pc.

Dimensions in mm.
Inches are approximate.

Dimensional data not binding.
We reserve the right to alter specifications without notice.

HÄFELE

Wardrobe Fittings

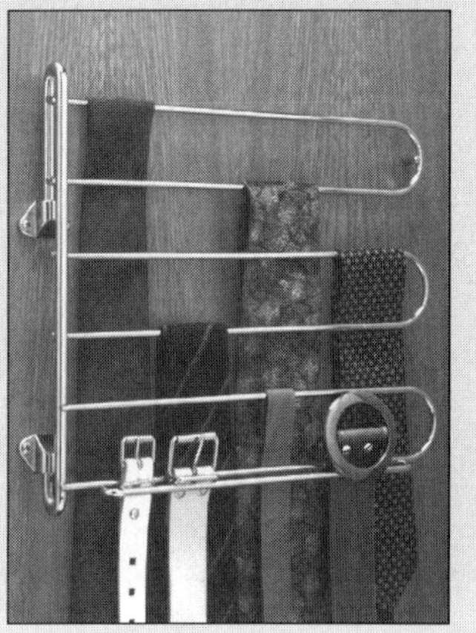

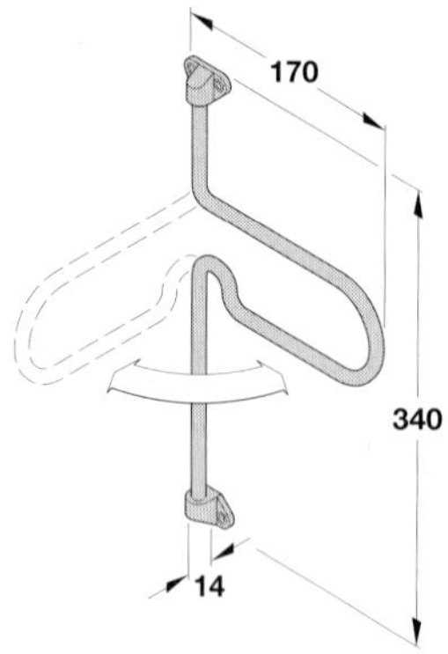

Swing Wardrobe rail, pivotable
for screw-mounting
180° pivoting range
Finish: steel, chrome-plated
mounts: zinc die cast, chrome-plated

Cat. No.	805.40.209

Packing: 1 piece (including screws)

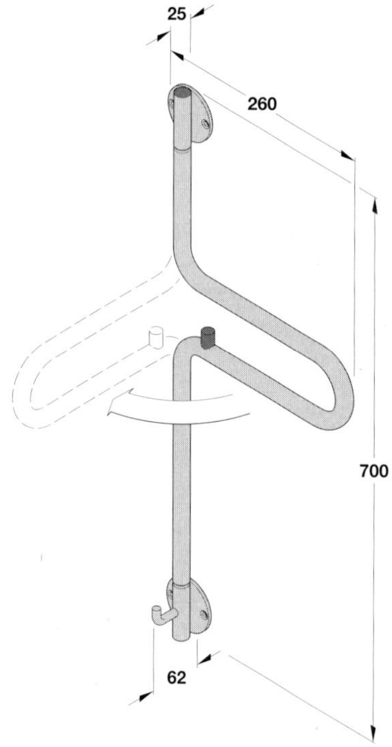

Swing wardrobe rail, pivotable
for screw-mounting
180° pivoting range
Finish: steel, chrome-plated
mounts: plastic, black

Cat. No.	805.40.254

Packing: 1 piece (including screws)

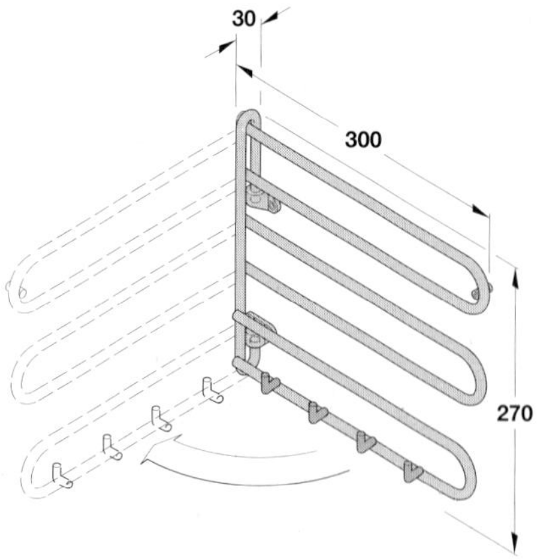

Tie and belt holder, pivotable
for screw-mounting
90° pivoting range
Holders are offset
Finish: steel, chrome-plated
mounts: zinc die cast, chrome-plated

Cat. No.	807.16.212

Packing: 1 piece (including screws)

Dimensions in mm

Rota Store

HÄFELE

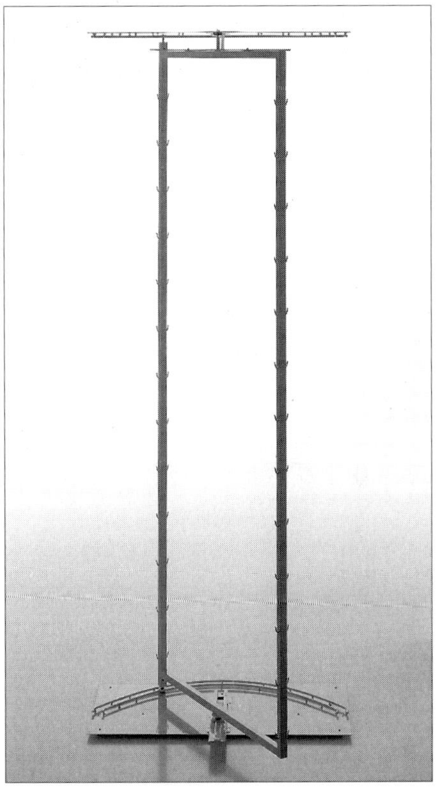

Revolving fitting, fits cabinets with an inside width of 984 mm (38¾")
Load capacity: 100 kg (220 lbs.)
Dimensions: 960 x 570 x 2026 mm
Finish: steel, silver epoxy-coated

Cat. No.	805.51.202

Packing: 1 pc.

Fence for bottom shelf
One set required for bottom of frame
Dimensions: 935 x 255 x 68 mm
Finish: steel, chrome-plated polished

Cat. No.	805.52.218

Packing: 1 set (2 pcs.)

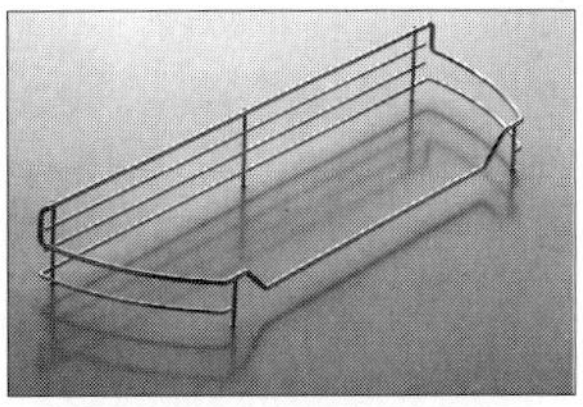

Fence – four sided shelves
Can be used any location except very bottom of frame.
Dimensions: 935 x 265 x 127 mm
Finish: steel, chrome-plated polished

Cat. No.	805.52.209

Packing: 1 pc.

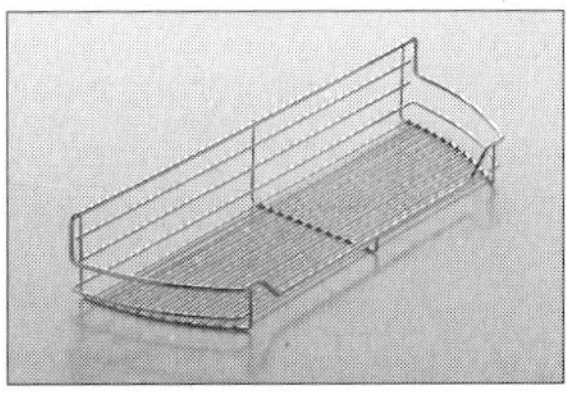

Basket, hook-on, flat
Dimensions: 935 x 265 x 127 mm
Finish: steel, chrome-plated polished

Cat. No.	805.52.227

Packing: 1 pc.

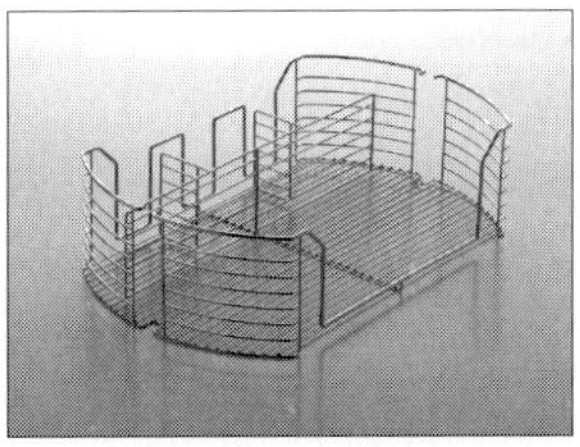

Functional basket, hook-on, high with dividers
Dimensions: 935 x 545 x 260 mm
Finish: steel, chrome-plated polished

Cat. No.	805.52.236

Packing: 1 pc.

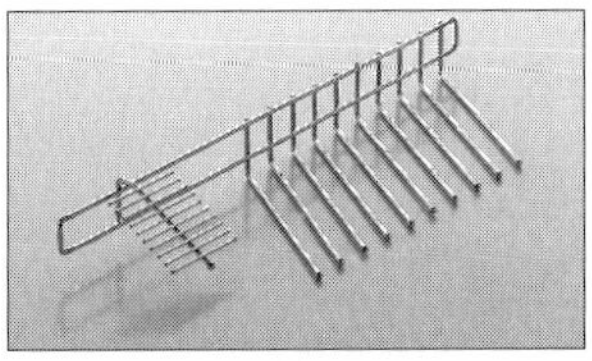

Tie and Trousers Rack
Dimensions: 935 x 277 x 110 mm
Finish: steel, chrome-plated polished

Cat. No.	805.52.245

Packing: 1 piece

Dimensions in mm
Inches are approximate

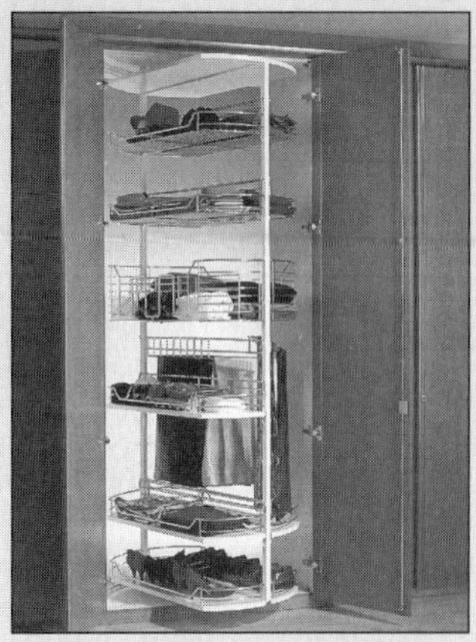

- Hooks along length of frame allows mounting of shelves and baskets at almost any height.
- All dimensions are shown in the following order: width x depth x height

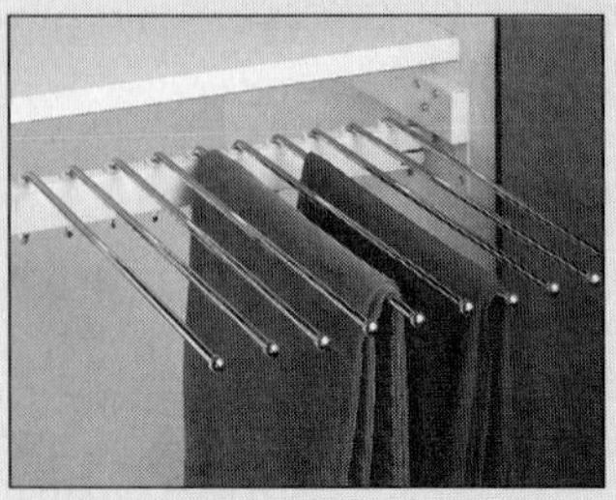

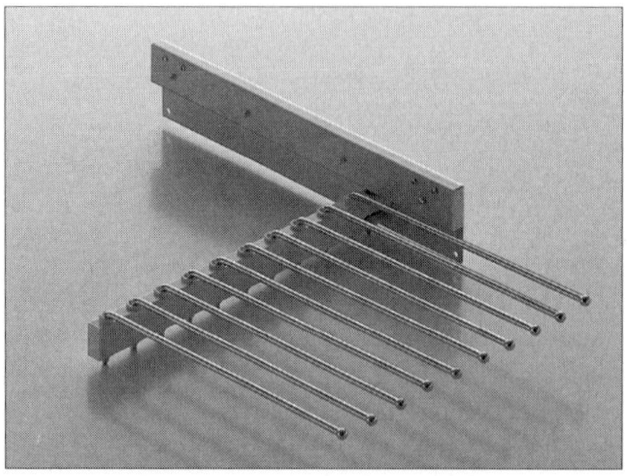

Trousers swivel pull out, for 10 pairs of trousers
to be used on the left or right
width: 465 mm
depth: 505 mm
height: 100 mm
Finish: steel, chrome-plated polished
Guide-cover: steel
plastic-coated, white

Cat. No.	805.45.204

Packing: 1 piece

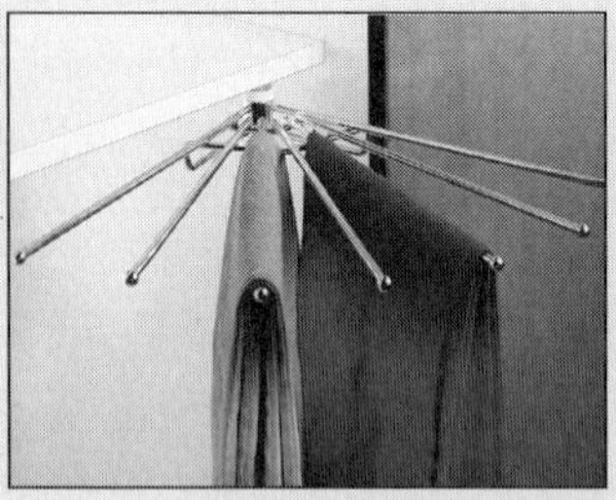

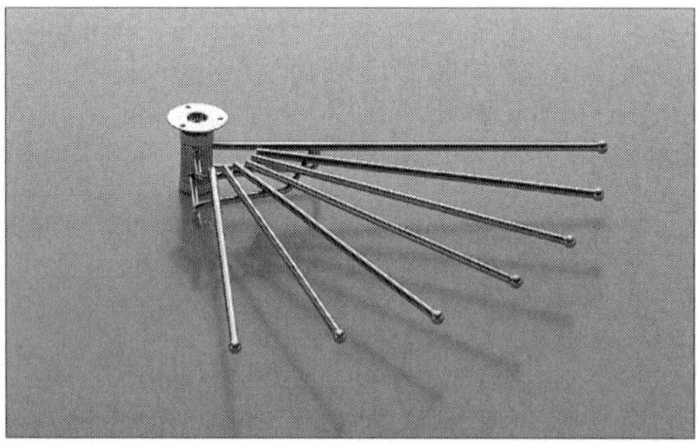

Trousers holder for 7 pairs of trousers, swivelling
to be used on the left or right
width: 430 mm
depth: 430 mm
height: 75 mm
Finish: steel, chrome-plated polished

Cat. No.	805.46.201

Packing: 1 piece

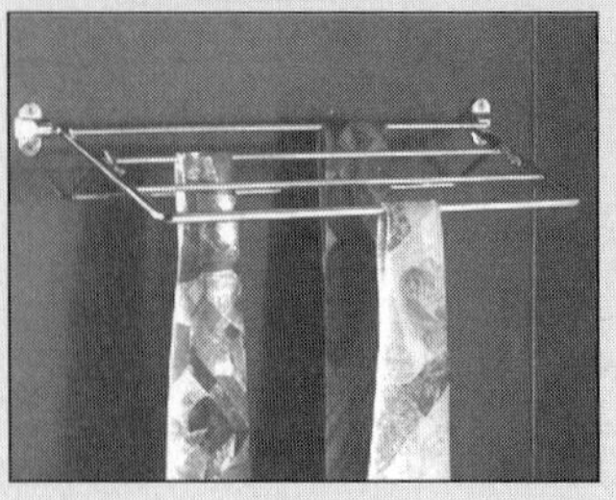

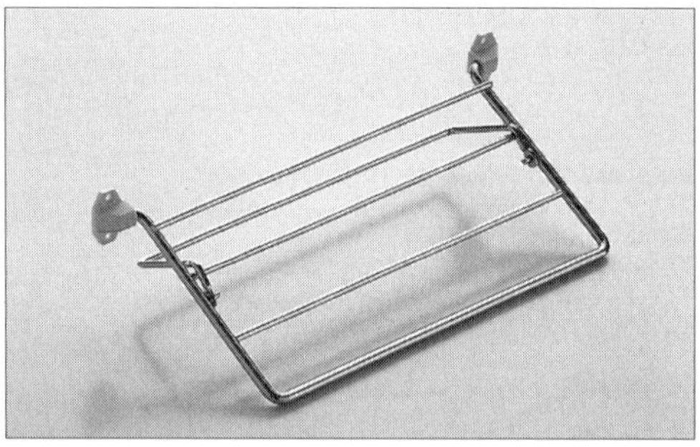

Tie holder, foldaway
width: 320 mm
depth: 160 mm
height: 25 mm
Finish: steel, chrome-plated polished

Cat. No.	807.17.200

Packing: 1 piece

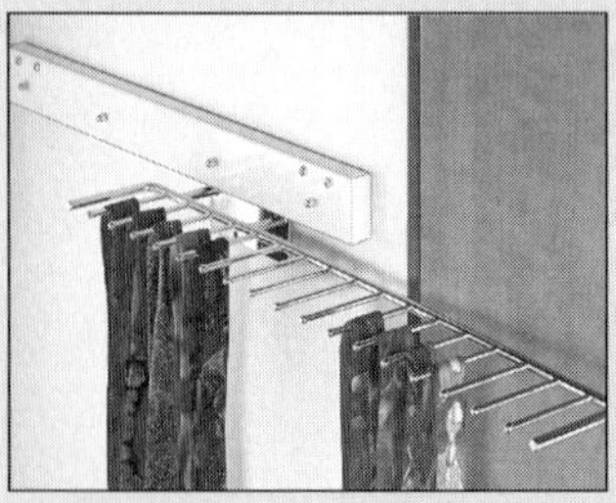

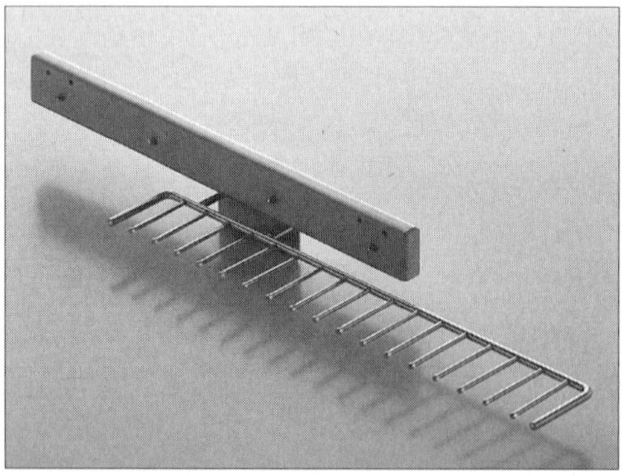

Tie pull out for 17 ties
to be used on the left or right
width: 130 mm
depth: 540 mm
height: 90 mm
Finish: steel, chrome-plated polished
Guide-cover: steel
plastic-coated, white

Cat. No.	807.41.206

Packing: 1 piece

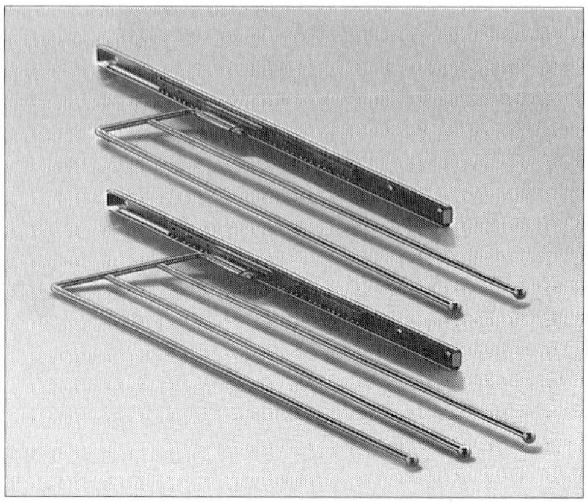

Tie extension, inifinitely adjustable, swivelling
for left, right or upper mounting
Finish: steel, chrome-plated polished

2-armed
width: 102 mm
depth: 495 mm

Cat. No.	510.37.220

Packing: 1 piece

3-armed
width: 145 mm
depth: 495 mm

Cat. No.	510.37.239

Packing: 1 piece

Wire Basket Pull Outs

Wire basket with steel rim for 24" inside cabinet width, with use of optional 423.35 slides only.

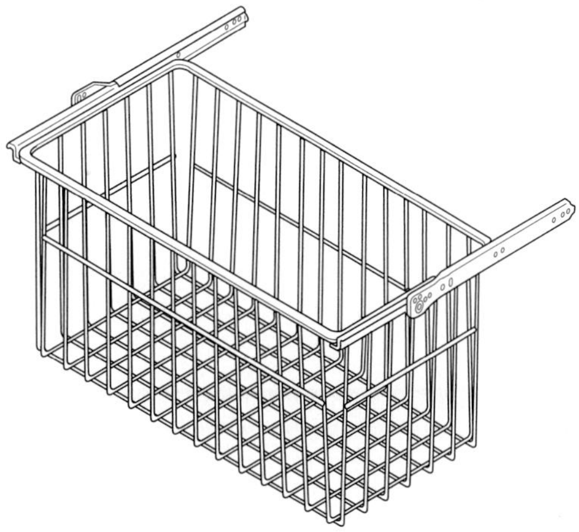

586 (23") width x 300 ($11\frac{7}{8}$") depth

Height mm	Packing	Cat. No.
200 ($7\frac{7}{8}$")	10 pcs.	540.41.717
300 ($11\frac{7}{8}$")	10 pcs.	540.41.726
500 ($19\frac{7}{8}$")	5 pcs.	540.41.735

586 (23") width x 350 ($13\frac{7}{8}$") depth

Height mm	Packing	Cat. No.
100 (4")	10 pcs.	540.41.646
200 ($7\frac{7}{8}$")	10 pcs.	540.41.655
300 ($11\frac{7}{8}$")	5 pcs.	540.41.664
500 ($19\frac{7}{8}$")	5 pcs.	540.41.673

586 (23") width x 400 ($15\frac{3}{4}$") depth

Height mm	Packing	Cat. No.
100 (4")	10 pcs.	540.41.744
200 ($7\frac{7}{8}$")	10 pcs.	540.41.753
300 ($11\frac{7}{8}$")	5 pcs.	540.41.762
500 ($19\frac{7}{8}$")	5 pcs.	540.41.771

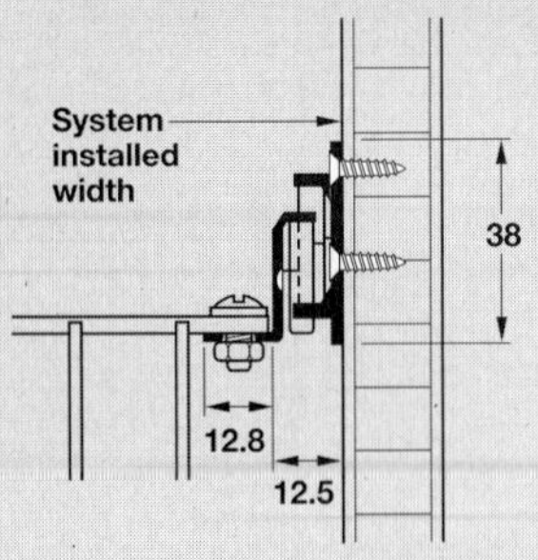

Screws and nuts for attaching baskets to rollers

M4 Screw x 10mm Length

Cat. No.	022.35.109

Packing: 100 and 1000 pcs.

M4 Nuts

Cat. No.	034.11.943

Packing: 100 pcs.

Six screws and nuts required per basket

Softroller Slider
for basket Catalog No. 540.41.
Load-Bearing Capacity: 30kg (66lbs.)/pair
Finish: Steel, epoxy-coated, white
rollers, nylon, white

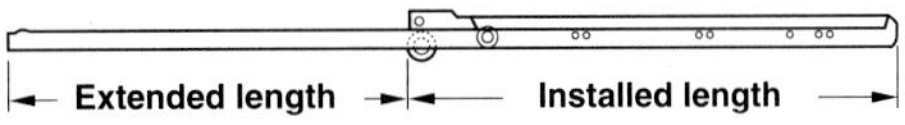

Installed length	300 mm	350 mm	400 mm
Extension length	212 mm	262 mm	312 mm
Cat. No. (non self-closing)	423.35.311	423.35.366	423.35.419
Cat. No. (self-closing)	423.36.318	423.36.363	423.36.416

Packing: 20 pairs

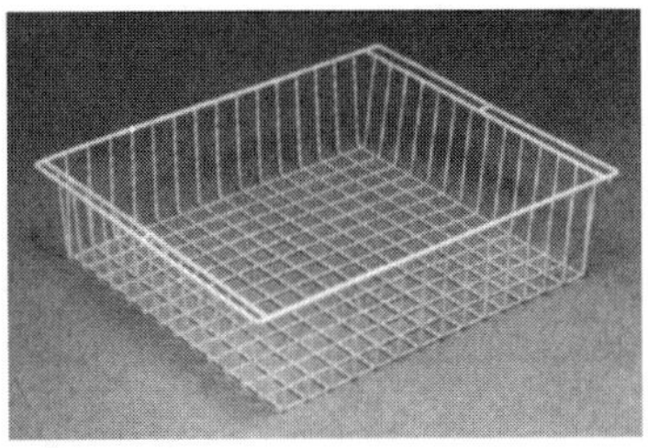

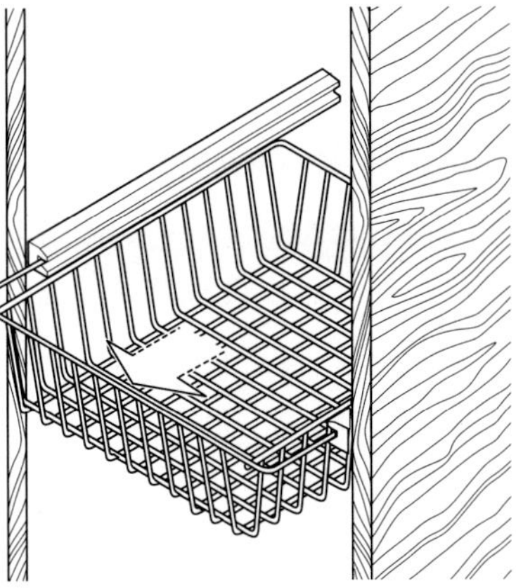

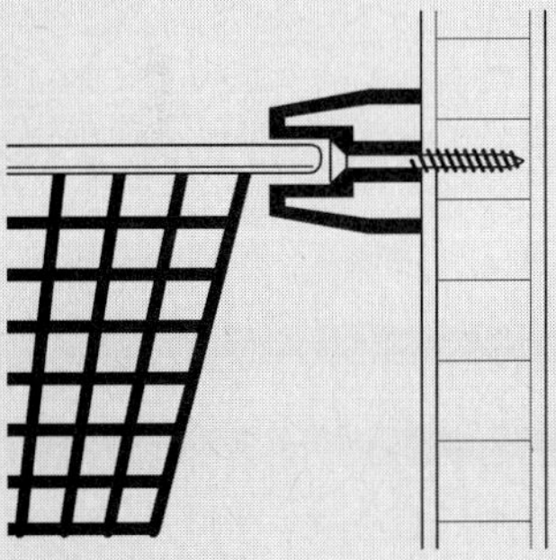

Wire basket with rim for use with 430.34 series track
Height: 120 mm ($4\frac{3}{4}$")
Finish: steel wire, epoxy-coated, white

Width mm	Depth mm	Cat. No.
380 (15")	430 (17")	540.46.025
430 (17")	430 (17")	540.46.052
450 ($17\frac{3}{4}$")	450 ($17\frac{3}{4}$")	540.46.061
530 ($20\frac{7}{8}$")	430 (17")	540.46.007
380 (15")	450 ($17\frac{3}{4}$")	540.46.089
495 ($19\frac{1}{2}$")	500 ($19\frac{5}{8}$")	540.46.098

Packing: 1 pc.

• Baskets can be slid out from cabinets with doors due to extra width of guide rail track.

Tracks for wire baskets Cat. No. 540.46 series
Length: 430 mm (17")
Finish: plastic, white

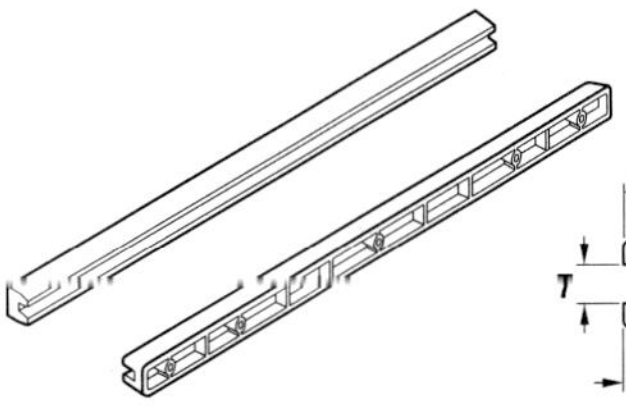

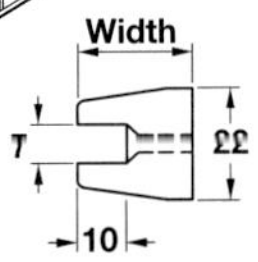

Width	Cat. No.
26 mm	430.34.726
24 mm	430.34.724
18 mm	430.34.718

Packing: 1 pair

Dimensions in mm
Inches are approximate

HÄFELE

Cabinet Fittings

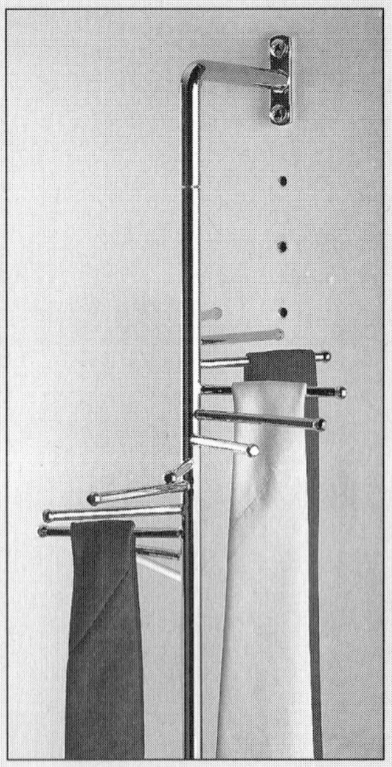

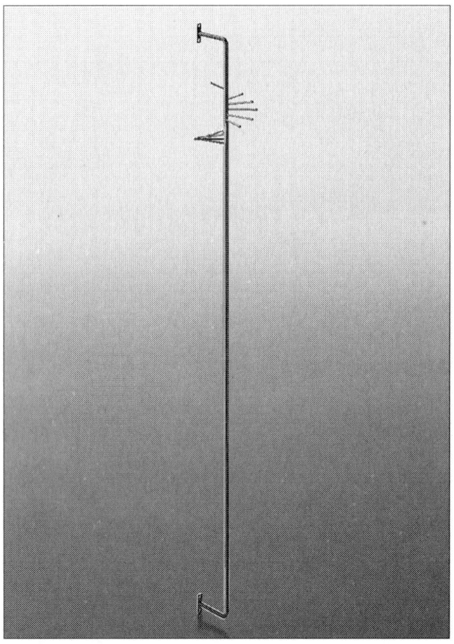

Tie holder, rotating
width: 160 mm
depth: 135 mm
height: 1325 mm
Finish: steel, chrome-plated polished

Cat. No.	807.40.218

Packing: 1 piece

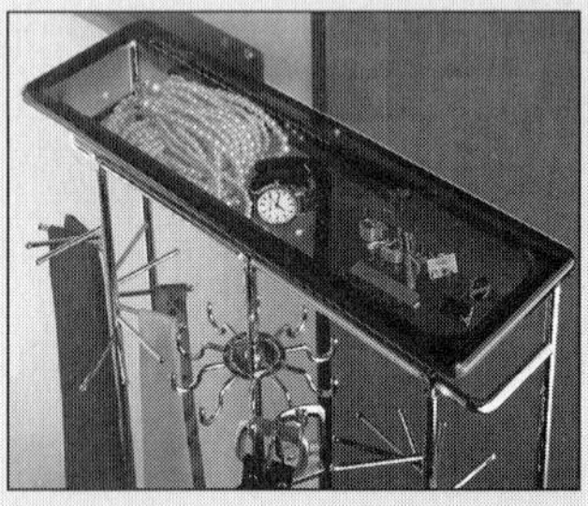

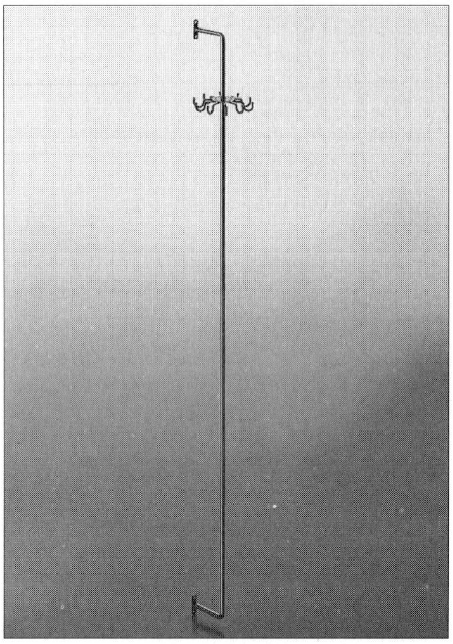

Combi-holder, rotating, for belts, scarves, etc.
width: 160 mm
depth: 135 mm
height: 1325 mm
Finish: steel, chrome-plated polished

Cat. No.	807.40.227

Packing: 1 piece

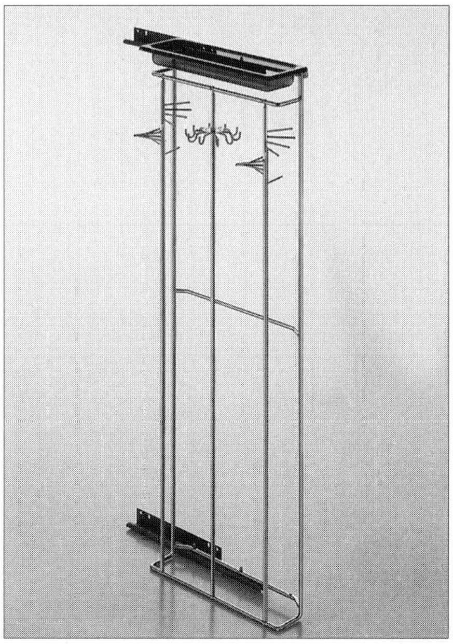

Wardrobe pull out
consisting of:
2 guides with frame
1 storage tray
3 swivel elements
width: 200 mm
depth: 480 mm
height: 1270 mm
Finish: steel, chrome-plated polished

Cat. No.	805.50.205

Packing: 1 piece

Cabinet Fittings

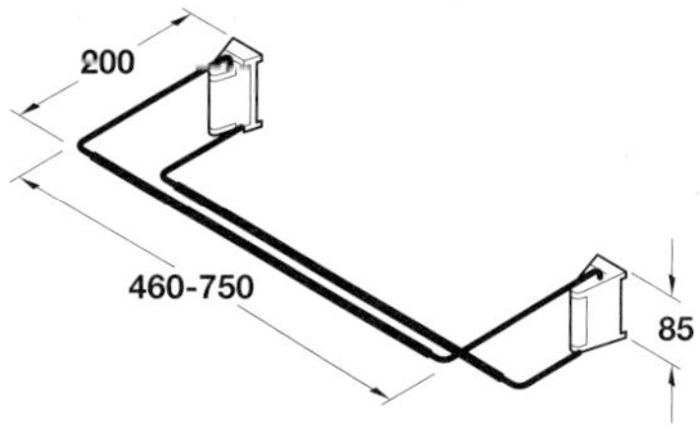

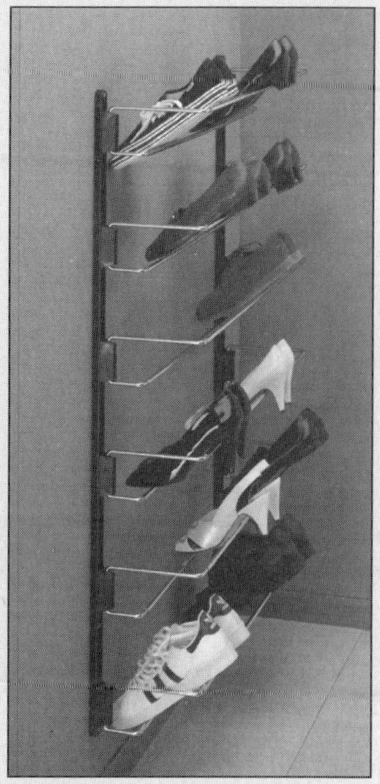

Shoe holder
for screw-mounting
extendible from 460 - 750 mm

Finish: steel, chrome-plated
mounting parts: plastic, black

Cat. No.	892.12.206

Packing: 6 pcs.

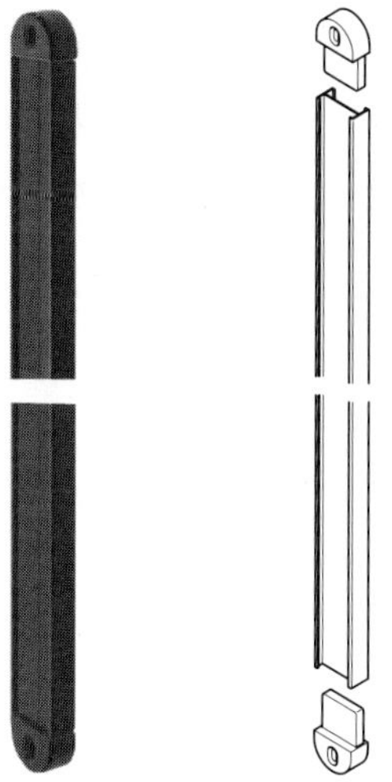

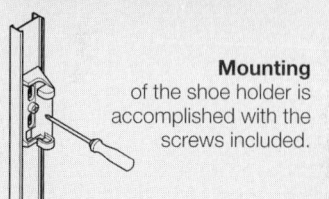

Mounting of the shoe holder is accomplished with the screws included.

Wall rack for above
height adjustable
entire length: 1120 mm (including end caps)

Finish: rail: aluminum, black oxidized
end caps: plastic, black

Cat. No.	892.12.390

Packing: 1 pc.

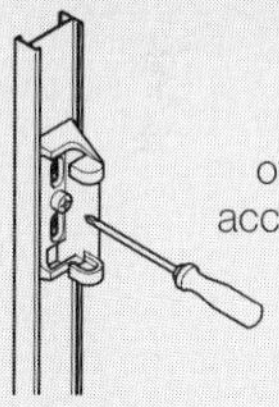

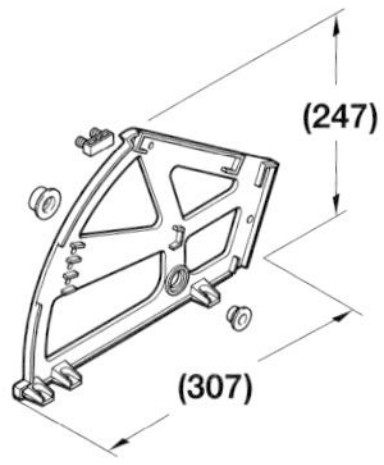

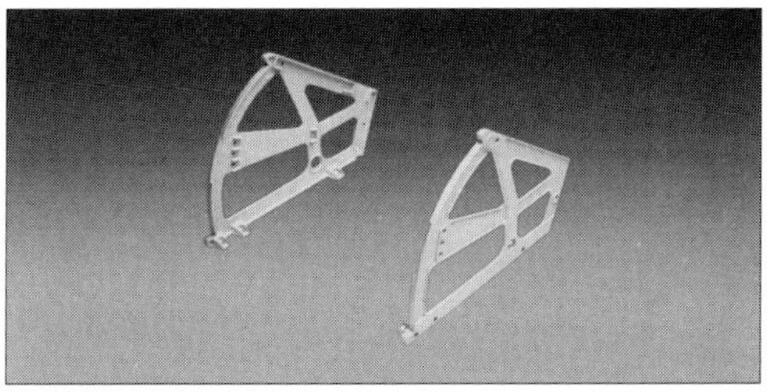

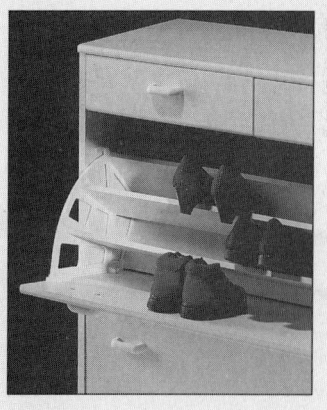

Tilt fitting
for installation in shoe cabinets, 3 sections

Finish: plastic, white

	Cat. No.
for 3 partitions	892.14.737

Packing: 1 pair, incl. mounting material

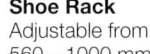

Shoe Rack
Adjustable from
560 – 1000 mm

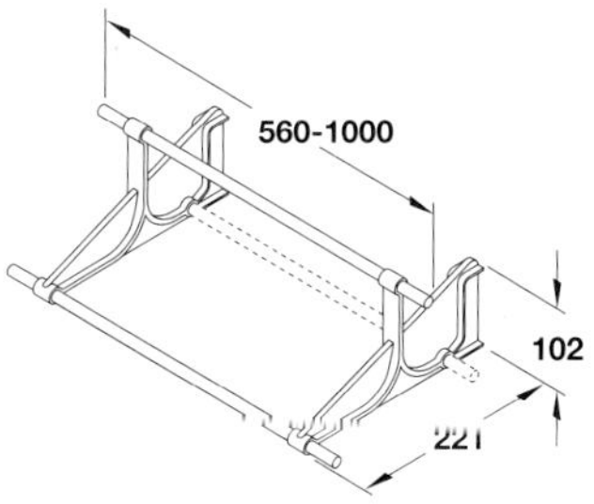

Finish: rod: steel, nickel-plated
Plastic: black

Cat. No.	892.11.200

Packing: 1 pc.

Dimensions in mm

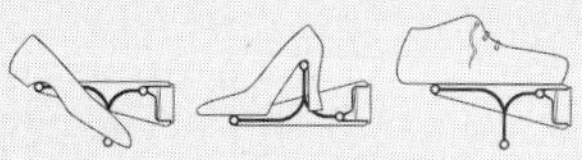

Dimensional data not binding.
We reserve the right to alter specifications without notice.

HÄFELE

Belt and Tie Racks

Tie Rack
- Organizes ties
- Choice of stationary mounted or pull-out slide model.

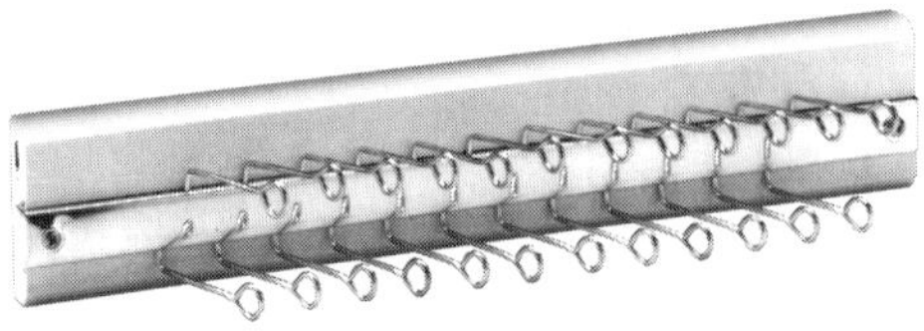

Tie rack without slide
Dimensions: High x deep (incl. hooks): 51 x 70 mm
Length: 348 mm (13 3/4")

Finish: Rail: PVC white
Hooks: steel electroplated

Cat. No.	brass	807.30.801
	chrome	807.30.703

Packing: 1 pc.

Tie rack with slide
Dimensions: High x deep (incl. hooks): 63 x 70 mm

Finish: Rail: PVC white
Hooks: steel electroplated

No. Tie Hooks	Finish	Length	Cat. No.
20	Brass	293 mm	807.33.850
24	Brass	348 mm	807.33.802
20	Chrome	293 mm	807.33.250
24	Chrome	348 mm	807.33.204

Belt Rack
- 6 hooks for belts
- Choice of stationary mounted or pull-out slide model.

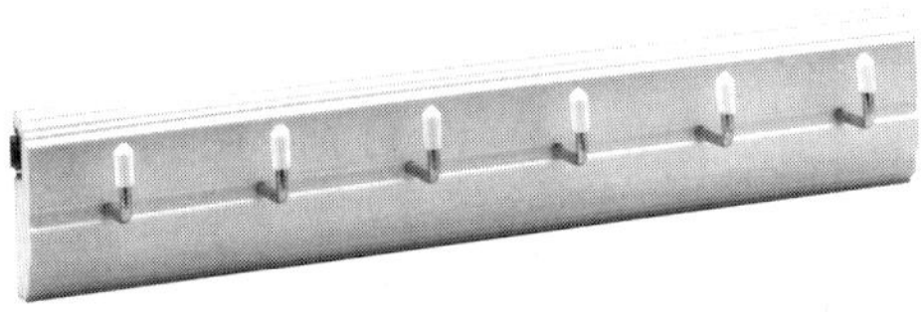

6 Hook belt rack - without slide
Dimensions: High x deep (incl. hooks): 51 x 47 mm
Length: 348 mm (13 3/4")

Finish: Rail: PVC white
Hooks: steel electroplated

Cat. No.	brass	807.31.808
	chrome	807.31.700

Packing: 1 pc.

6 Hook belt rack with slide
Dimensions: High x deep (incl. hooks): 63 x 70 mm

Finish: Rail: PVC white
Hooks: steel electroplated

	Length	348mm	293mm
Catalog No.	brass	807.33.811	807.33.830
	chrome	807.33.213	807.33.240

Packing: 1 pc.

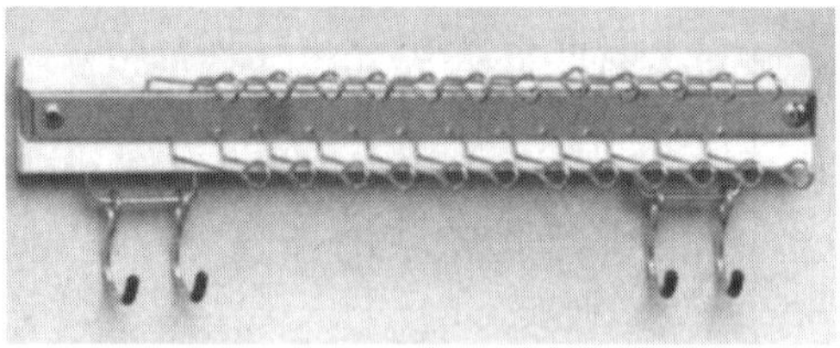

24 hook Tie Rack, 4 hook Belt Rack without slide
Dimensions: High x deep (incl. hooks): 51 x 70 mm
Length: 384 mm

Finish: Rail: PVC white
Hooks: steel brass-plated

Cat. No.	white/brass	807.30.810

Packing: 1 pc.

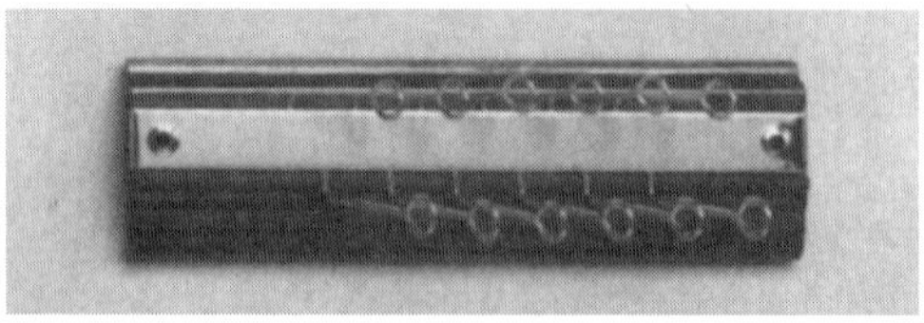

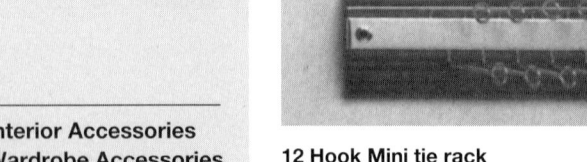

12 Hook Mini tie rack
This rack can be screw-mounted to the side wall of the closet or back of the door.
Includes mounting screws.

Dimensions:
High x deep (incl. hooks): 62 x 63 mm
Length: 222 mm (8 3/4")

Finish: Rail: poplar stained
Hooks: steel electroplated

Cat. No.	dark red oak/brass	807.30.856

Packing: 1 pc.

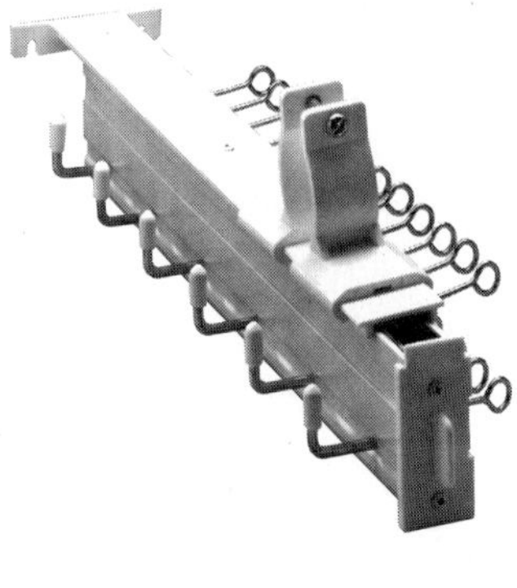

24 hook Tie Rack, 6 hook Belt Rack with slide
Dimensions: High x deep (incl. hooks): 120 x 100 mm
Length: 364 mm (14 1/2")

Finish: Rail: PVC white
Hooks: steel brass-plated

Catalog No.	white/brass	807.33.820

Packing: 1 pc.

8
Interior Accessories
Wardrobe Accessories
Storage Systems
Furniture Lighting

Dimensional data not binding. We reserve the right to alter specifications without notice.

Dimensions in mm. Inches are approximate.

Drawer Trays

HÄFELE

- Optional drawer fronts and slides can be mounted directly to the trays.
- Lined with brushed gray nylon for a plush feel.
- Will fit a standard 24" opening.

Jewelry tray features a single, large compartment and nine small compartments, one of which is specially designed for rings.
Dimensions: width x depth x height
584 x 356 x 50 mm (23" x 14" x 2")

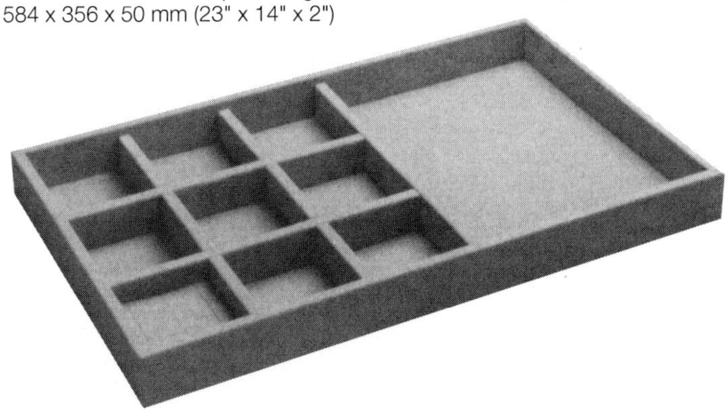

Finish: nylon, gray

Cat. No.	811.03.504

Packing: 1 pc.

Belt tray features a single, long compartment and four smaller compartments. The four inch depth makes this tray ideal for storing belts, scarves, underwear, socks, watches and other accessories.
Dimensions: width x depth x height
584 x 356 x 100 mm (23" x 14" x 4")

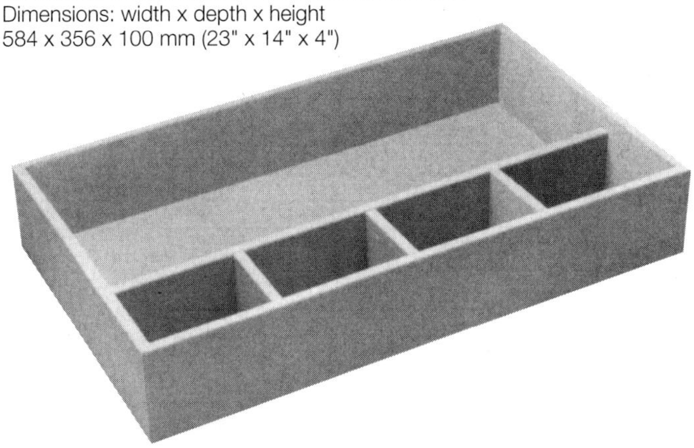

Finish: nylon, gray

Cat. No.	811.03.513

Packing: 1 pc.

Valet tray for storage of watches, jewelry and other accessories.
Dimensions: width x depth x height
279 x 203 x 32 mm (11" x 8" x 1¼")

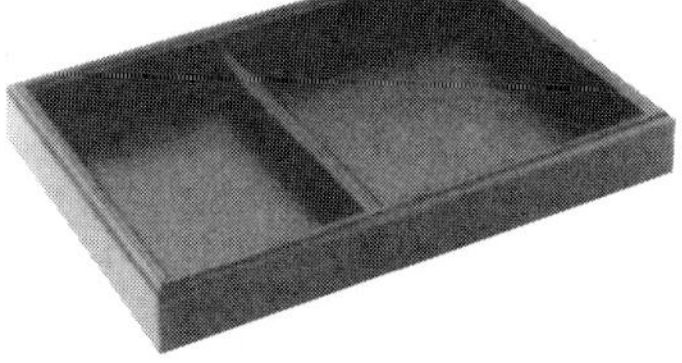

Finish: bonded leather, black

Cat. No.	811.03.326

Packing: 1 pc.

Dimensions in mm.
Inches are approximate.

Dimensional data not binding.
We reserve the right to alter specifications without notice.

HÄFELE

Silverware Holders Insert

Assembly instructions:
1. Line the drawer base with self-adhesive felt.
2. Mount the holders (silverware must lie at right angle to drawer movement).
3. Knife holders: adjoining knives must always face in opposite directions (see photo below).

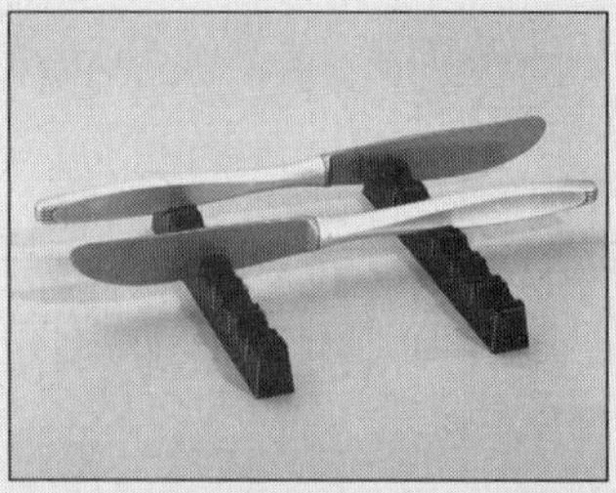

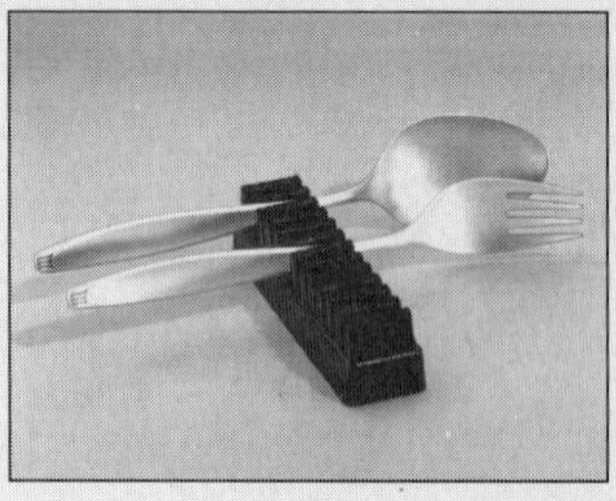

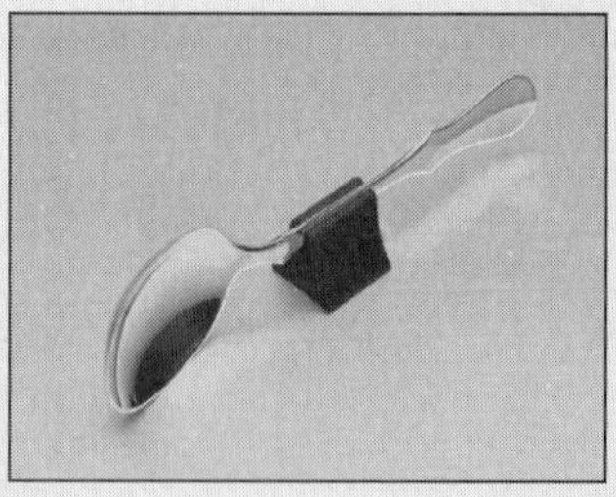

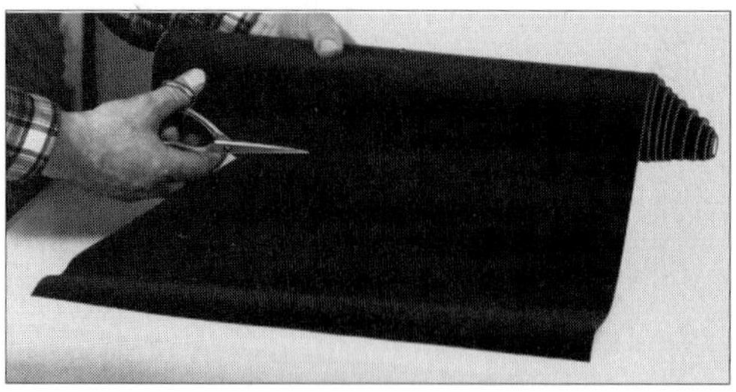

Felt cloth
for lining the drawer bottom
Size: 100 x 45 cm
Finish: brown, self-adhesive

Cat. No.	891.21.193

Packing: 1 roll

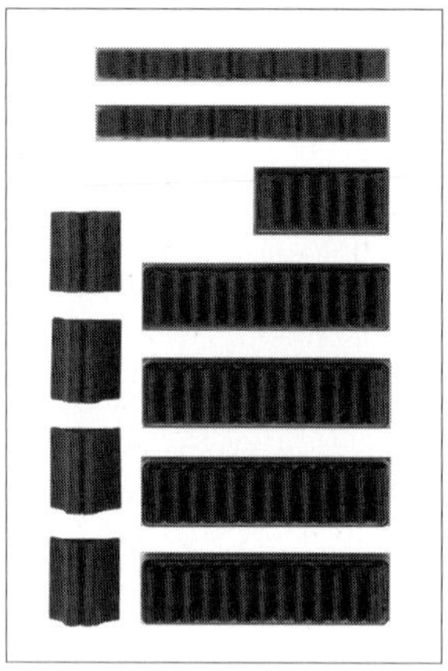

Silverware holders, assorted set
Finish: plastic, brown
with felt overlay, brown; self-adhesive

Quantity	Cat. No.:
for **50** pieces (12 knives, forks, spoons, teaspoons each; 2 large individual items)	891.21.111
for **70** pieces (12 knives, forks, spoons, teaspoons, pastry forks each; 6 small and 4 large individual items)	891.21.120
for **90** pieces (24 knives, forks each; 12 spoons, teaspoons, pastry forks each; 6 large individual items)	891.21.139

Packing: 1 set

Mini Flourescent Undercabinet Lighting

HÄFELE

Surface mounted, mini flourescent light, 8 watt/110 volt
Screw mounted with integral rocker switch, plug connector and lamp.

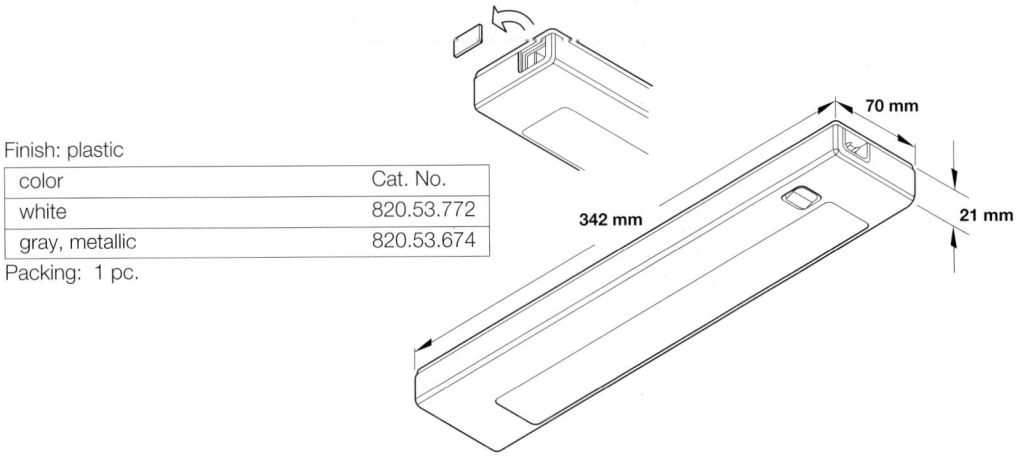

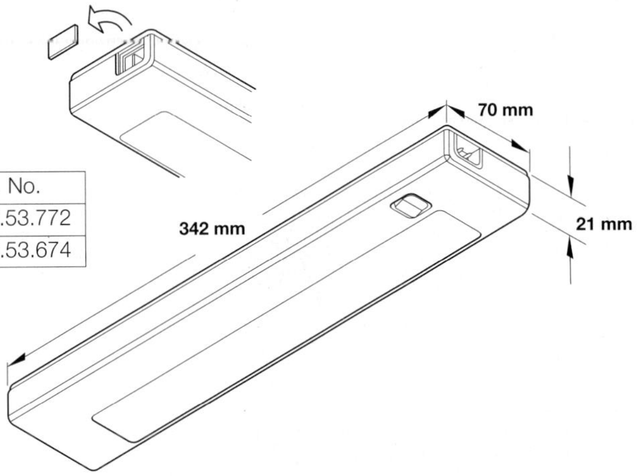

Finish: plastic

color	Cat. No.
white	820.53.772
gray, metallic	820.53.674

Packing: 1 pc.

The ends of the lamps are fitted with the plug connectors, suitable for the electric lead shown below.

Replacement Bulb

Cat. No.	820.53.923

Packing: 1 pc.

Application of surface lights - maximum 10 lights per connection

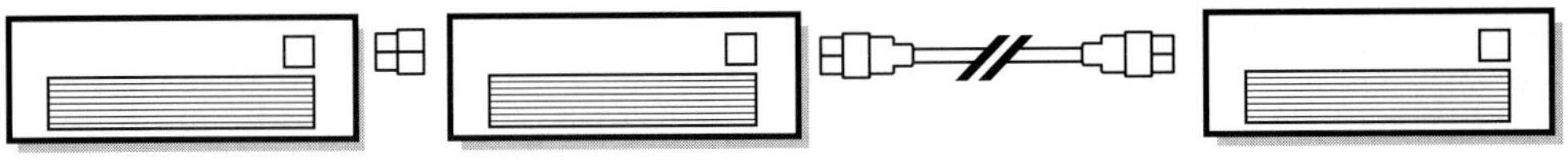

Adaptor
for installing endless lights

Finish: plastic, white

Cat. No.	820.54.804

Packing: 1 pc.

Connector Lead,
for use between lights

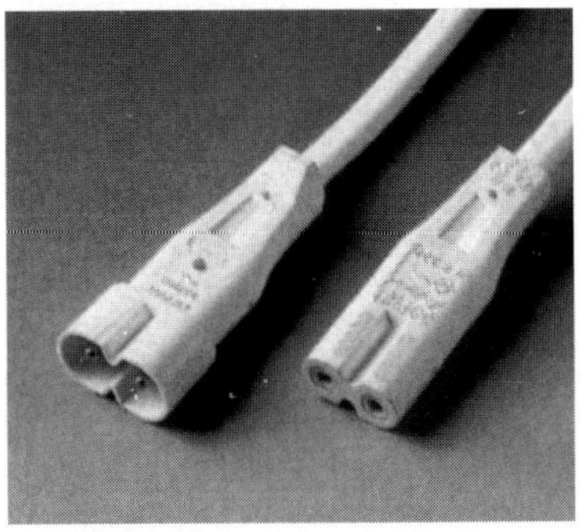

Finish: plastic, white

Length	Cat. No.
300 mm	820.54.813
600 mm	820.54.822
1000 mm	820.54.831

Packing: 1 pc.

Supply Lead, with **US plug** (shown here with European plug) for connectors from light to wall outlet

Finish: plastic, white

Cat. No.	820.61.810

Packing: 1 pc.

HÄFELE

Built-in Kitchen Lighting Systems - Fluorescent

- Provides more efficient task lighting directly on the work surface.
- Fixture uses a 13 watt twin tube compact fluorescent lamp.
- Offers a convenient outlet and switch eliminating unnecessary receptacles in backsplash areas.
- Select from a variety of closure panels to accommodate 15" through 42" wide frameless cabinetry (can be adapted to framed cabinetry with installation modification and blocking).
- Panels completely enclose the bottom of the panel recess, protect the main housing, and provide an aesthetically pleasing "flush" appearance.
- Prewired and assembled to be mounted into cabinet recess 13/4" high.
- Integral space compartment for connection to power supply. Wiring is suitable to allow fixtures in adjacent cabinets to be wired together through the cabinet.

Undercover light fixture housing 120 Volt
Contains ballast, convenience receptacle, switch and reflector plate.
Order closure panel and lamp separately.
Finish: steel, baked white enamel

Cat. No.	white	821.20.705

Packing: 1 pc.

Closure panel
Finish: steel, baked white enamel with fastening screws.
One each required for each housing ordered.

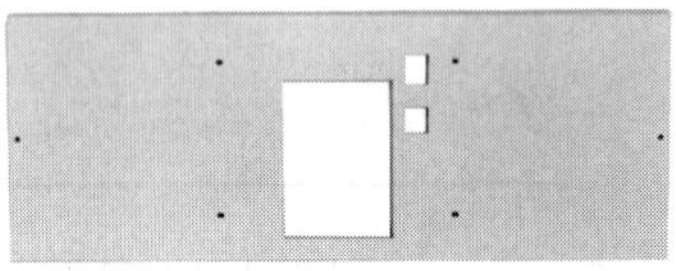

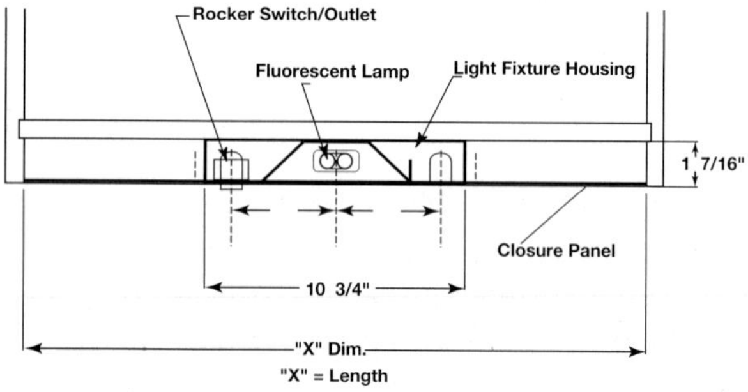

Size (x) length x depth	Cat. No.
13 3/8 x 10 3/8	821.21.702
16 3/8 x 10 3/8	821.21.711
19 3/8 x 10 3/8	821.21.720
22 3/8 x 10 3/8	821.21.739
25 3/8 x 10 3/8	821.21.748
28 3/8 x 10 3/8	821.21.757
31 3/8 x 10 3/8	821.21.766
34 3/8 x 10 3/8	821.21.775
37 3/8 x 10 3/8	821.21.784
40 3/8 x 10 3/8	821.21.793

Packing: 1 pc.

Dulux® S - Twin Tube Compact Fluorescent Lamp
Color temperature: 5000 K daylight
One each required for each housing ordered.

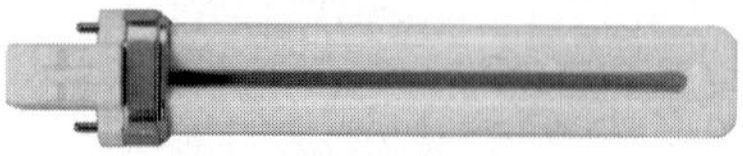

Cat. No.	13 watt	821.20.018

Packing: 1 pc.

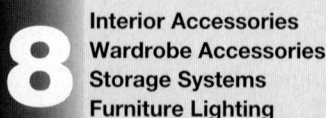

8 Interior Accessories
Wardrobe Accessories
Storage Systems
Furniture Lighting

UL LISTED

Dimensional data not binding.
We reserve the right to alter specifications without notice.

Halogen Lighting for Furniture & Cabinetry

Finishes

Lacquered or electroplated for long lasting finish that prevents discoloring.

white

black

chrome

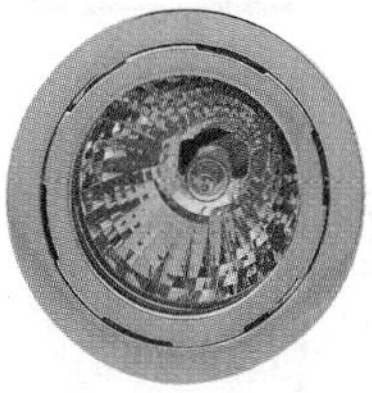

gold

Mounting Applications

Complete Mounting and Installation Instructions included with each Lamp.

Recessed mounted

Almost concealed in top shelf. Requires 58mm x 14mm hole drilling.

Surface mounted

Screw-mount to horizontal surface. Requires only one hole for cable.

Swivel-mounted

Allows light angle to be adjusted

Light distribution patterns

The halogen lamp reflectors featured on the following pages are designed to produce a light emission angle of 28°.

The diagrams below indicate light intensities (measured in lux) at distance up to 3 meter.

10 W lamp, G4 base

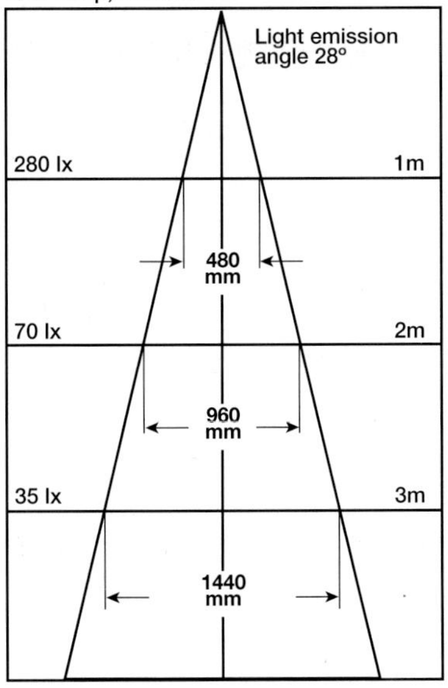

20 W lamp, G4 base

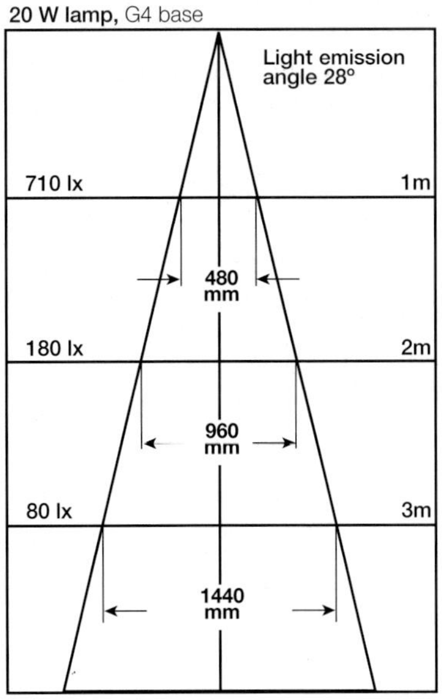

Halogen lamps have become an important component of modern lighting systems.

- Compact size.
- Minimal power consumption-highly economical.
- Easy connections--no electrician required. All wiring supplied with modular plugs which snap together. Once installed, the plugs feature a locking clip to prevent the wires from coming loose.
- CSA® & UL® Listed, Class II Low Voltage Halogen System 100% tested before shipment.
- Standards require a distance of at least 300 mm (12") between light source and combustible material. Minimum distance is marked on the fixture as follows D→0.3M . Complete mounting instructions are supplied with each light and transformer.

- Halogen light is similar to natural sunlight. Halogen color temperature (2900° Kelvin to 3100° Kelvin) makes its color purity at 12 volts superior to standard 120 volt lamps. Colors are seen as they really are.
- Long life span of bulb - up to 2000 hours.
- Halogen lamps function according to a cycle in which halogen gas continuously "cleans" heat vaporized tungsten from the wall of the lamp and redeposits it on the filament. Because of this cyclical cleaning action, quartz halogen lamps can perform at 97% of original output at the end of the bulb's life, while incandescent bulbs darkened by tungsten deposits, are reduced to 60% of original output.
- Lights come standard with 2000 mm (78") wires which allow flexible placement of lights.
- Protective glass lens twists off for easy access to the bulb. The lens shield ultraviolet B radiation.

- Transformers feature electronic short circuit protection. If a short is detected, it shuts down automatically until the short is corrected then restarts itself. Emits no audible noise–sound rating A+. The transformer is moisture and shock-resistant. Energy efficient–if lights are turned off transformer senses no load and turns itself off.
- Extension cables, switches and dimmers are available which all plug into the lights. Dimmer handles transformers up to 200 watts and are connected to the primary side. If halogen lights must be dimmed, they should be operated at full voltage for a few hours each week to allow the halogen cycle to occur long enough so that the bulb walls are cleaned off.

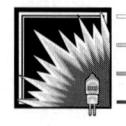

Low-Voltage Halogen Lights for Furniture and Cabinetry

HÄFELE

c UL   UL LISTED

Recess-mounted, 12 volt halogen lamp
Includes 2000 mm lead with plug contacts.
Finish: plastic with glass lens

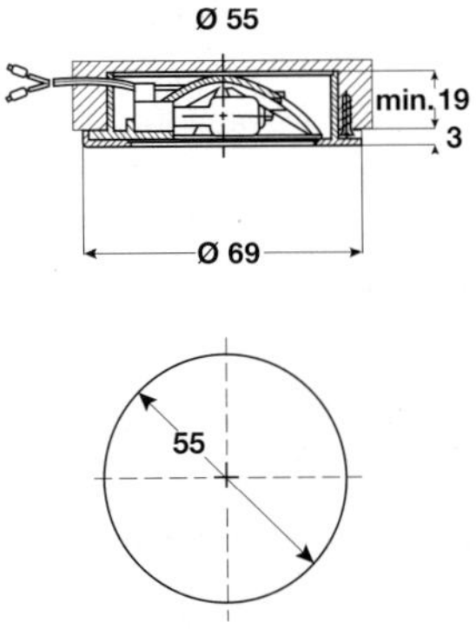

Color	10 watt/clear lens	20 watt/clear lens
white	823.94.710	823.94.720
black	823.94.310	823.94.320
gold	823.94.810	823.94.820
chrome	823.94.210	823.94.220

Packing: 1 pc.

Surface mounted ring for Halogen Lamp
Finish: plastic with fastening screws for optional surface mounting of 823.94 light.

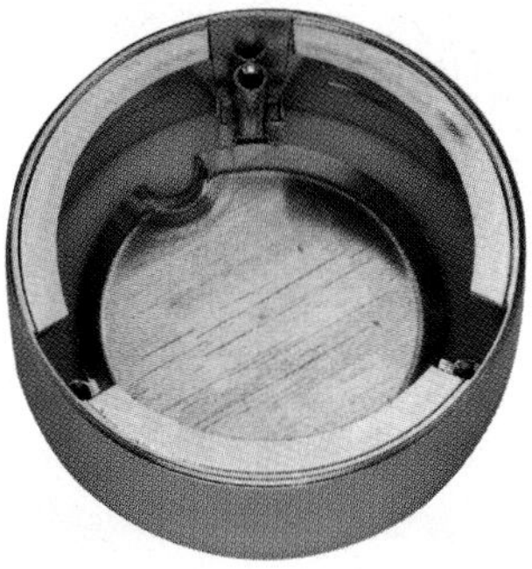

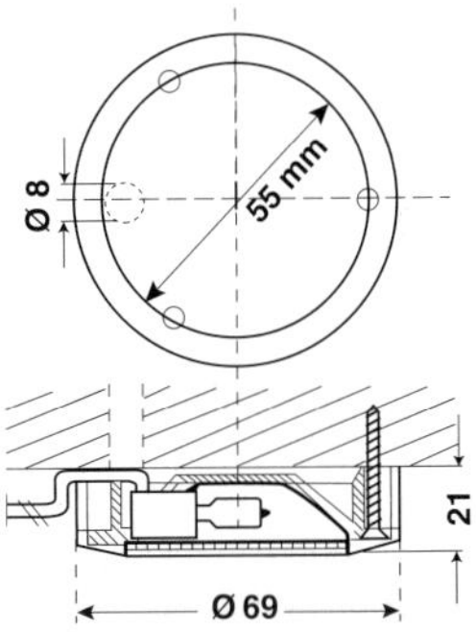

Color	Cat. No.
white	823.94.790
black	823.94.390
gold	823.94.890
chrome	823.94.290

Packing: 1 pc.

- Recess-Mounted.
- Press fit into installation hole. No screws required.
- Use with Häfele power supply only.
- Lens covers twist off for easy access for bulb replacement.
- Can be used surface-mount with optional ring.
- Mounting instruction provided with each light.
- Complete with bulb installed.
- Replacement G4 bulbs available.

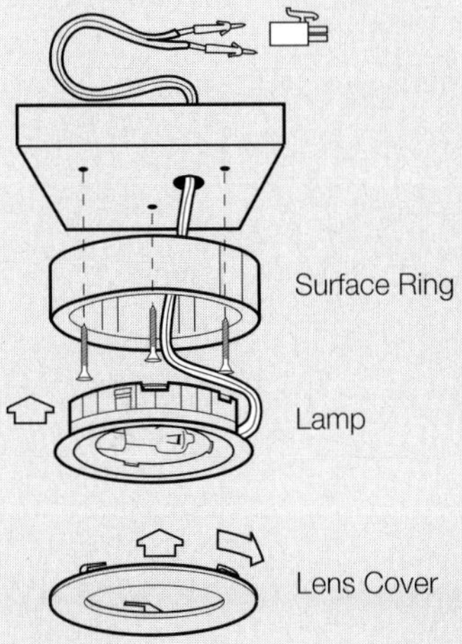

Dimensional data not binding.
We reserve the right to alter specifications without notice.

HÄFELE

Low-Voltage Halogen Lights for Furniture and Cabinetry

- Use with Häfele power supply only.
- Lens covers twist off for easy access for bulb replacement.
- Complete with bulb installed.
- Mounting instructions provided with each light.
- Replacement G4 lamps available

Recess-mounted, 12 volt halogen lamp
Includes 2000 mm lead with plug contacts.
Finish: plastic with glass lens and fastening screws.

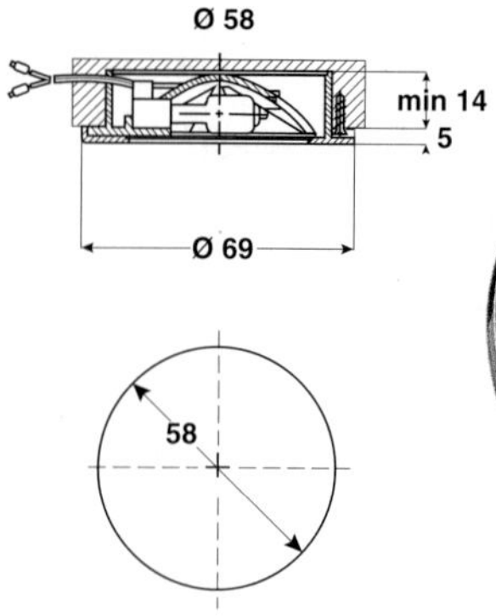

Color	10 watt/frosted lens	20 watt/clear lens
white	823.29.735	823.29.744
black	823.29.333	823.29.342
gold	823.29.833	823.29.842
chrome	823.29.235	823.29.244

Packing: 1 pc.

Surface mounted, 12 volt halogen lamp
Includes 2000 mm lead with plug contacts.
Finish: plastic with glass lens and fastening screws.

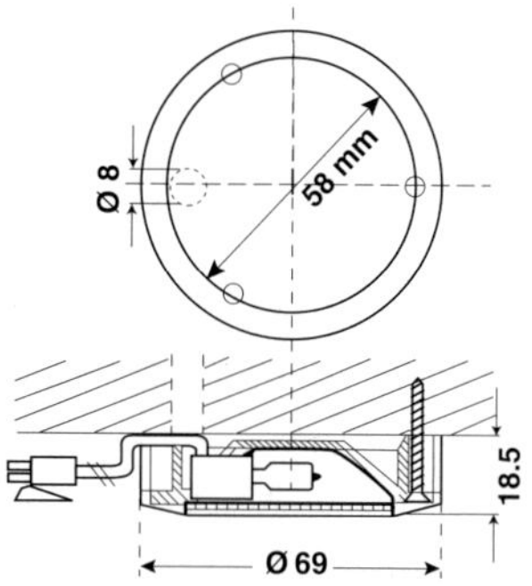

Color	10 watt/frosted lens	20 watt/clear lens
white	823.59.715	823.59.724
black	823.59.313	823.59.322
gold	823.59.813	823.59.822
chrome	823.59.215	823.59.224

Packing: 1 pc.

HÄFELE

Low-Voltage Halogen Lights for Furniture and Cabinetry

Cool to the touch, recess-mounted 12 volt halogen lamp 10 watt

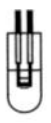

Includes 2000 mm lead with plug-contacts
Material: plastic with clear glass lens

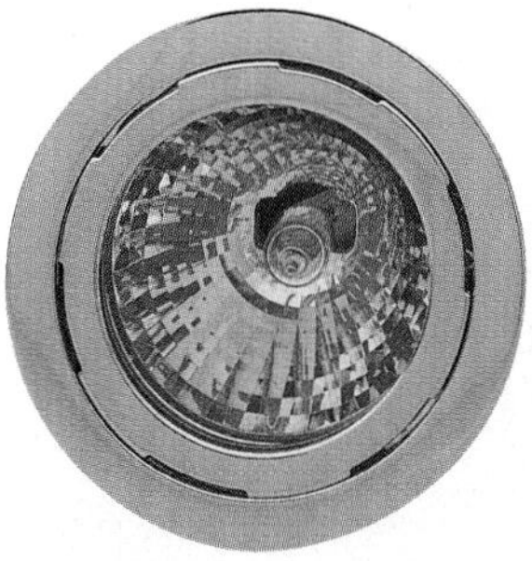

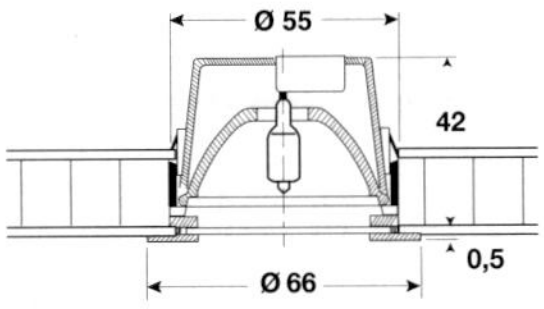

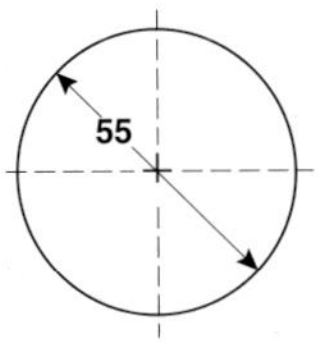

Color	Cat. No. 12 volt/10 watt
white	823.48.701
black	823.48.301
chrome	823.48.201
gold	823.48.801

Packing: 1 pc.

Recessed mounted, 12 volt halogen lamp

Includes 2000 mm lead with plug contacts.
Finish: plastic with glass lens

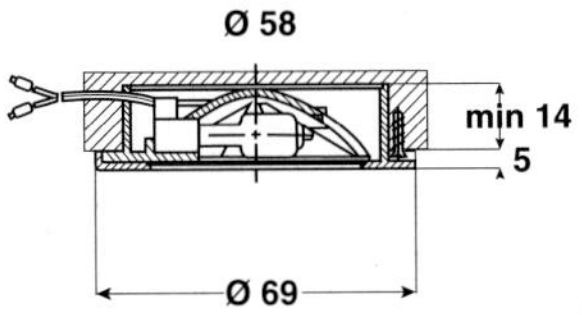

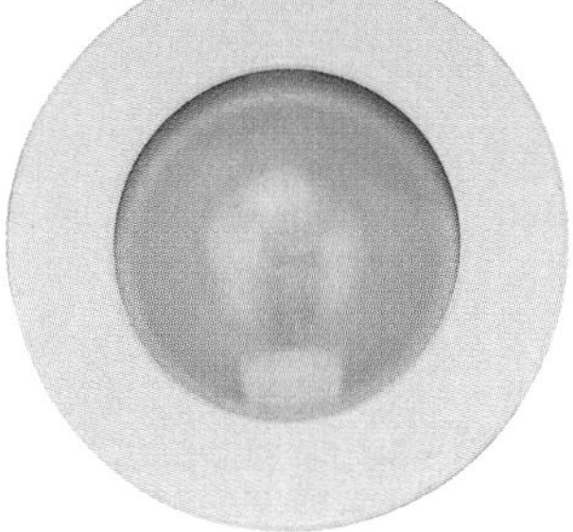

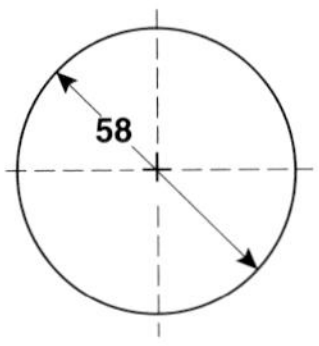

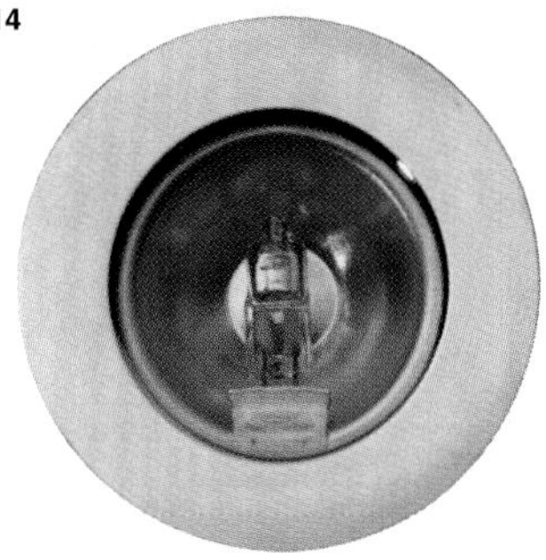

Color	10 watt/frosted lens	20 watt/clear lens
white	823.29.750	823.29.760
black	823.29.350	823.29.360
gold	823.29.850	823.29.860
chrome	823.29.250	823.29.260

Packing: 1 pc.

Surface mounted ring for Halogen Lamp
Finish: plastic with fastening screws for optional surface mounting of 823.29 lights.

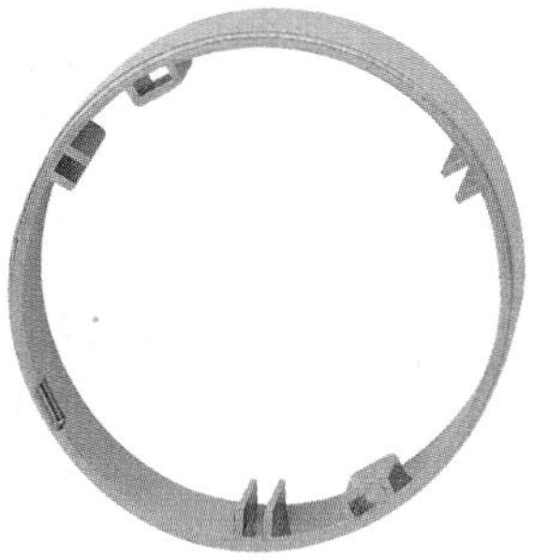

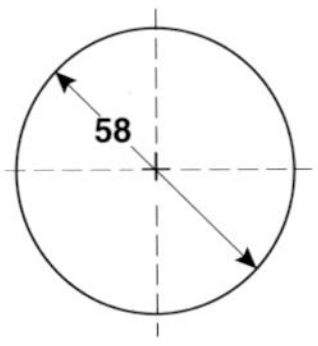

Color	Catalog No.
white	823.29.781
black	823.29.381
gold	823.29.881
chrome	823.29.281

Packing: 1 pc.

c UL UL LISTED

- Use with Häfele power supply only.
- Lens covers twist off for easy access for bulb replacement.
- Replacement G4 lamps available.
- Complete with bulb installed
- Mounting instructions provided with each light.

HÄFELE

Low Voltage Halogen Lights for Furniture and Cabinetry

- Use with Häfele power supply only.
- Lens covers twist off for easy access for bulb replacement.
- Cover available to prevent back light from washing walls or ceilings.
- Complete with bulb installed
- Mounting instructions provided with each light.
- Replacement G4 lamps available

Swivel light, adjustable 12 volt halogen lamp-10 watt
Includes 2000 mm lead with plug-contacts
Material: plastic with frosted glass lens

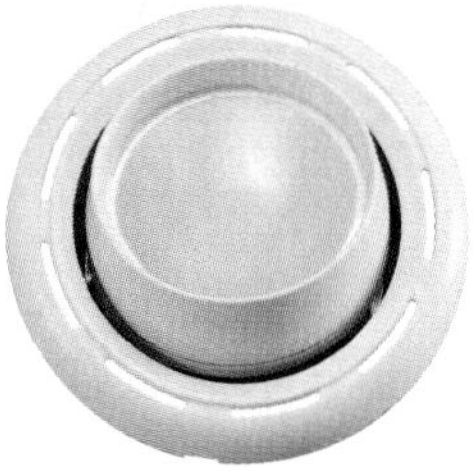

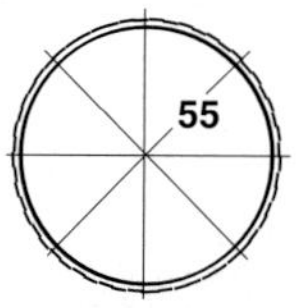

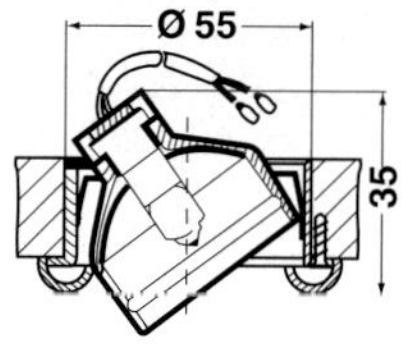

Color	Cat. No. 12 volt/10 watt
white	823.18.714
black	823.18.312
chrome	823.18.214
gold	823.18.812

Packing: 1 pc.

Mounted light, adjustable, 12 volt halogen lamp-10 watt
Includes on/off switch, 2000 mm lead with plug-contacts and fastening screws
Material: plastic with frosted glass lens with fastening screws

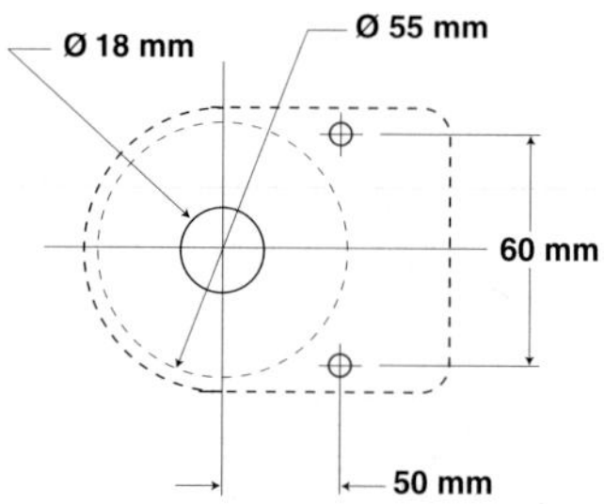

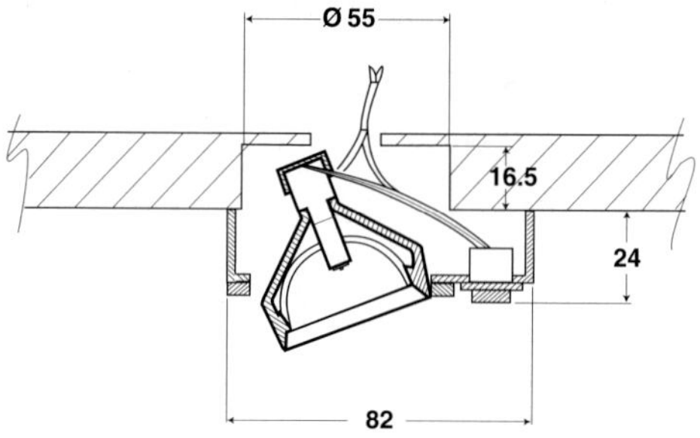

Color	Cat. No. 12 volt/10 watt
white	823.19.711
black	823.19.319
chrome	823.19.211
gold	823.19.819

Packing: 1 pc.

Swivel light, adjustable, 12 volt halogen lamp
Includes 2000 mm lead with plug-contacts
Material: plastic with glass lens with fastening screws

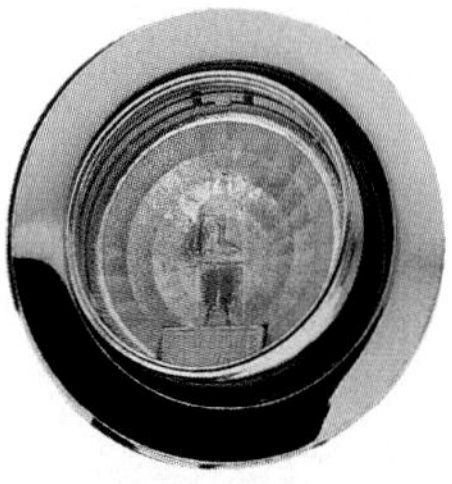

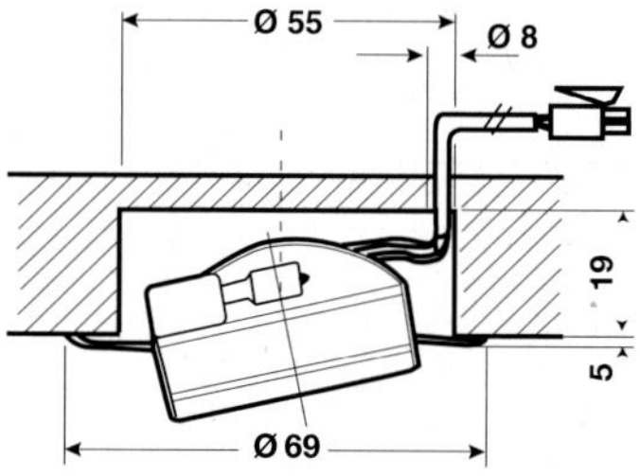

Color	Cat. No. 10 watt frosted lens	Cat. No. 20 watt clear lens
white	825.16.701	825.16.702
black	825.16.301	823.16.302
chrome	825.16.201	823.16.202
gold	825.16.801	823.16.802

Packing: 1 pc.

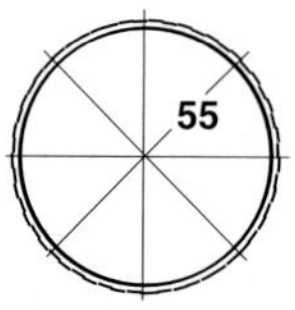

Switches

HÄFELE

Wireless switch outlet
Finish: plastic, white
To be used only with Power Supply transformer with two pronged electrical plug.

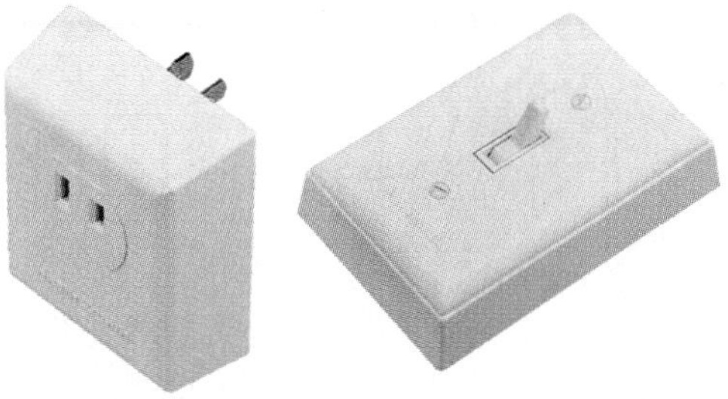

RF Channel	Catalog No.
A	820.66.700
B	820.66.710
C	820.66.720

Packing: 1 set

- Add switched lighting control to any outlet.
- Modular no wiring required
- Receiver plugs into 120 volt wall outlet
- Controls up to 500 watts of incandescent lighting
- Transmitter range - up to 50 ft. Different RF channels so that more than one outlet can be used in the same house
- 9 volt battery required for transmitter - typically lasts one year.
- For indoor use only

Switch
for connection to end of transformer or mounting block
Requires 7/8" (22mm) diameter hole for switch.
Finish: black

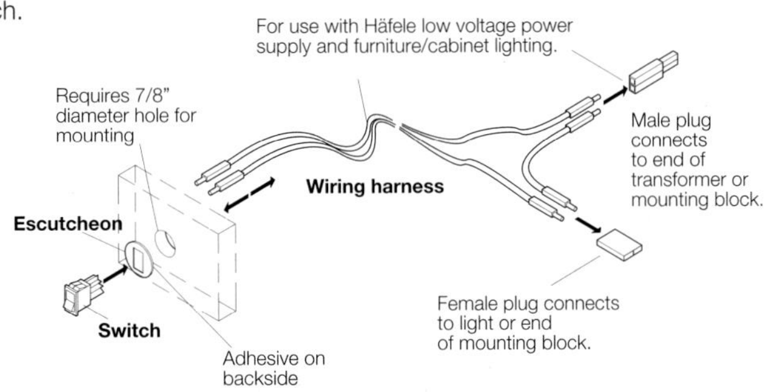
For use with Häfele low voltage power supply and furniture/cabinet lighting.
Requires 7/8" diameter hole for mounting
Wiring harness
Male plug connects to end of transformer or mounting block.
Escutcheon
Switch
Adhesive on backside
Female plug connects to light or end of mounting block.

Length	Catalog No.
1 meter	823.78.318
2 meter	823.78.327

Packing: 1 pc.

- On-Off switch
- Can control group of lights or individual light.

CSA® UL LISTED

Micro mini switch
Connection is made by attachment to one of the secondary wires of the lamp. Switch 34 x 33 x 16mm with 7mm travel.
Finish: plastic

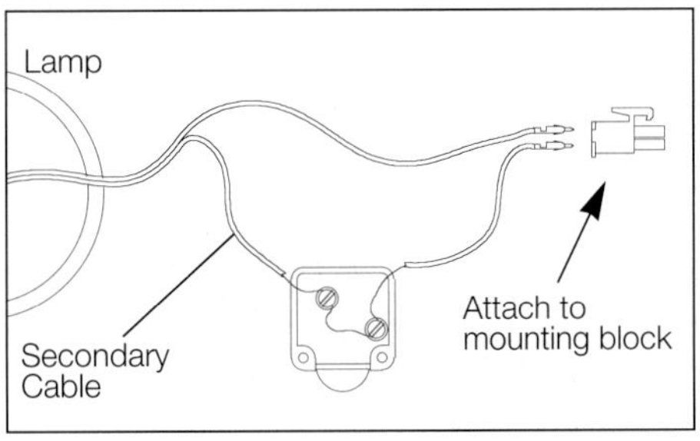
Lamp
Secondary Cable
Attach to mounting block

Finish	Catalog No.
plastic, black	823.28.381

Packing: 1 pc.

- For use behind cabinet doors.
- When door is opened, light turns on automatically.

HÄFELE

Switches and Cables

- Accepts up to three 60 watt transformers
- No electrician required for installation
- Four position touch light - 25%, 50%, 100% light, and off
- Connect touch wire to metal hinge, knob, etc. to operate or use optional touch pad.

Touch Switch
120 volt 13' cord with 4' touch wire
Finish: plastic, black
To be used only with Power Supply Transformer with two pronged electrical plug.

•Minimum of 20 watt light recommended.

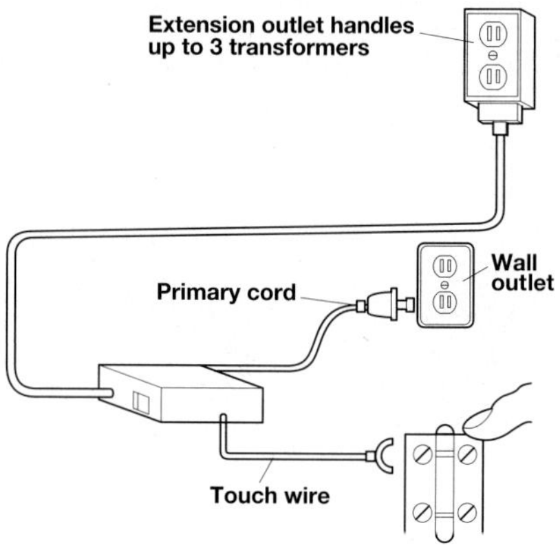

Cat. No.	820.99.312

Packing: 1 pc.

- Touch pad is used to replace touchwire on 820.99.312 touch dimmer.
- Touch pad can be placed in any convenient location ie: under cabinet, set on counter, on shelf. Do not attach to metal surface.

Touch Pad for connection to touch switch 820.99.312.
Pad 51 mm diameter x 12 mm high.
Can be recessed in hole 45 x 7 mm.
Complete with 8' wire.
Finish: plastic, black

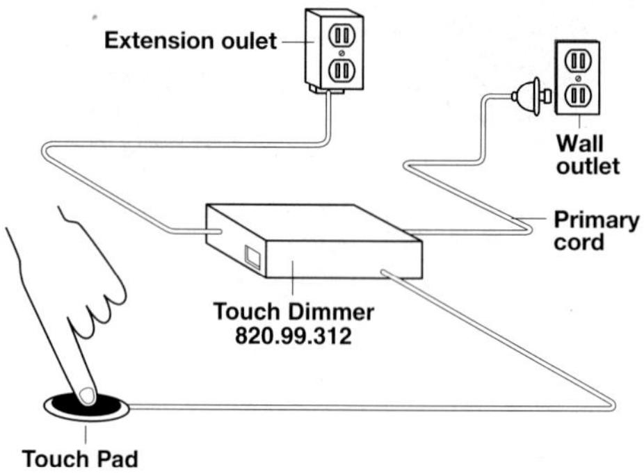

Cat. No.	820.99.390

Packing: 1 pc.

- To extend connection from lamp to transformer.

Secondary extension cable
Finish: black

Length	Cat. No.
2000 mm	823.28.327

Packing: 1 pc.

Transformers

Electronic Transformer
Primary: 120V
Secondary: Max 60 watt - Min 20 watts-11.5V
45mm wide x 70mm high x 24mm deep.

Secondary cord with AMP socket, transformer plugs into wall outlet - **requires** mounting block 823.24.418 for hook-up of more than one light.
Finish: plastic

Wattage	Secondary cord length	Electrical Plugs	Color	Cat. No.
20 watts	10 feet	2 prong	black	823.24.450
20 watts	1 foot	2 prong	black	823.24.455
60 watts	10 feet	2 prong	black	823.24.460
60 watts	10 feet	2 prong	white	823.24.480

Packing: 1 pc.

Electronic Transformer
Primary: 120 Volt, 2-pronged electrical plug
Secondary: Max 60 watt - Min 20 watts - 11.5V
68mm long x 38mm wide x 30mm high.

13' primary cord with AMP socket and 4" secondary cord and adhesive tape for fitting to shelves - requires mounting block 823.24.418 for hook-up of more than one light.

Cat. No.	823.24.436

Packing: 1 pc.

Mounting Block
for connection of up to six lights not exceeding 60 watts
Finish: plastic, black

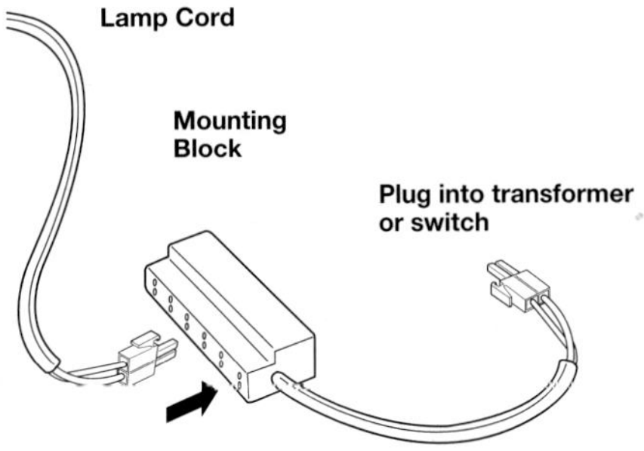

Cat. No.	823.24.418

Packing: 1 pc.

HÄFELE

- UL® and CSA® Listed Tested safe power source for use with Häfele lights.
- Electronic short circuit protection feature. When short is detected, automatically turns off. Upon correction of problem transformer automatically restarts.
- 100% factory tested
- Modular plugs - No electrician or hard wiring required.
- Radio frequency interference protection.
- Emits no audible noise- Sound rating A+
- Energy efficient - If lights are turned off, transformer senses no signal and automatically turns off.
- Moisture and shock resistant.
- Soft start circuitry maximizes lamp life.
- Mounting instructions included.

LISTED

HÄFELE

Accessories for Halogen

- Use with swivel lights to prevent back light from washing walls or ceilings.

Cover for swivel light 823.18, and 823.19
Finish: plastic, black

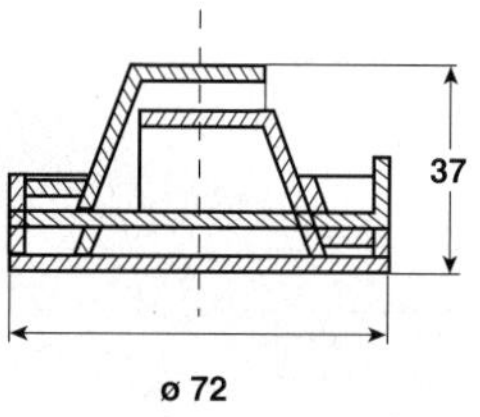

Finish	Catalog No.
plastic black	823.21.015

Packing: 1 set

Spare lamps
Halogen lamp with base G4

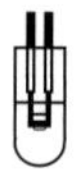

Caution: Replace lamps with same wattage only.

Finish: glass, clear

Size	Catalog No.
12V/10 watt	821.80.014
12V/20 watt	821.80.112

Packing: 1 pc.

Drill bits for lamps
Finish: steel, carbide-tipped

Size	Catalog No.
22mm dia.	001.06.258
55mm dia.	001.07.513
58mm dia.	001.07.522

Packing: 1 pc.

HÄFELE

Low-Voltage Halogen Lights for Recreational Vehicles

Recess-mounted RV, 12 volt halogen lamp
Includes 300 mm lead with plug contacts.
Finish: plastic with clear glass lens

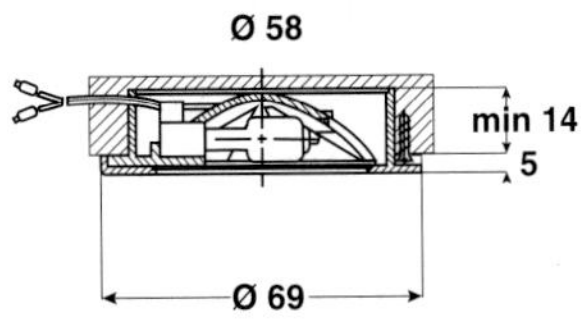

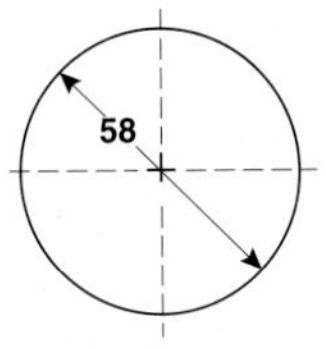

Mounting instructions include information for installation. Fixtures used in RV ceiling or in open air alcove requiring a minimum of 4" from the edge of the fixture to any side wall or surface and a minimum 12" spacing between fixtures.

	Cat. No.
Color	12 volt/10 watt
white	823.93.730
black	823.93.330
gold	823.93.830
chrome	823.93.230

Packing: 1 pc.

C UL LISTED

UL LISTED

For use in recreational vehicles, ie. motor homes, coaches or boats.

- Twist off lens covers. Easy access to bulbs.
- Electroplated or lacquered cover rings. Prevent fading or peeling of finish for longer lasting wear.
- Glass shield with cover ring. No loose parts - lamp complete with all accessories.
- UL® Listed for U.S. and Canada. Tested for public safety to **UL 234** for recreational vehicles.
- 100% tested before shipment. Reliable light system.

HÄFELE

- Each handsomely designed unit plugs easily into a thin, continuous track which can be cut to any desired length.
- Installation is quick and simple.
- No electrician is needed.
- Installation height is only 22 mm (7/8 in.)
- Each lamp can be switched individually
- Glass lens provided with each lamp.
- Low power consumption
- Halogen low voltage system

UL LISTED

c UL LISTED

- UL listed Class 2 transformer has soft start circuitry and employs electronic short circuit protection vital to lamp life.
- Radio frequency interference protection

8 **Interior Accessories**
Wardrobe Accessories
Storage Systems
Furniture Lighting

Spare Lamps
Halogen Lamp with base G4.
12V/20 Watt

Cat. No.	821.80.112

Packing: 1 pc.

Dimensional data not binding. We reserve the right to alter specifications without notice.

Built-in Kitchen Lighting Systems - Halogen

A Low voltage supply track

Length: 1000 mm (39 3/8 in.) including mounting accessories

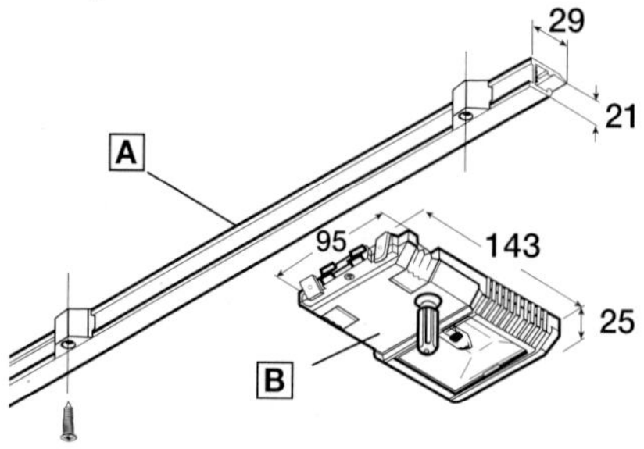

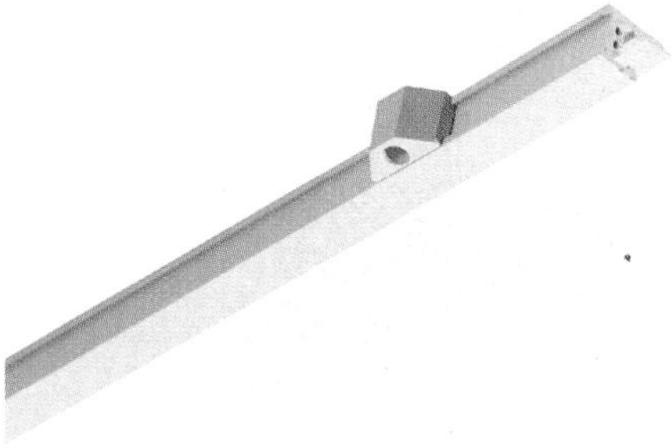

Cat. No.	white	532.83.702

Packing: 1 pc.

B Low voltage halogen lamp, 12 volts/20 watts

Housing of heat-resistant plastic reflector of anodized aluminum, diffuser of safety glass and 20W halogen bulb.

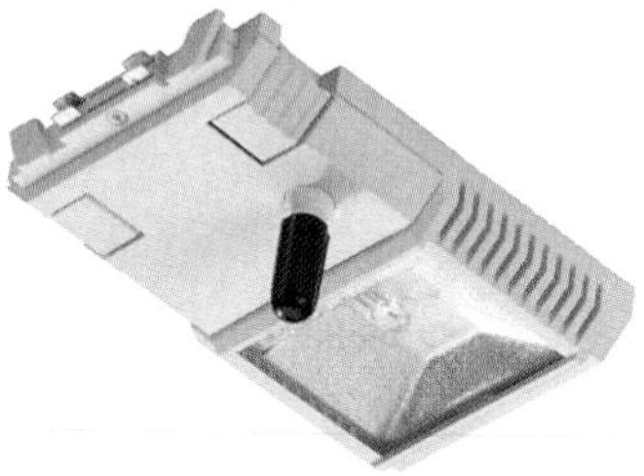

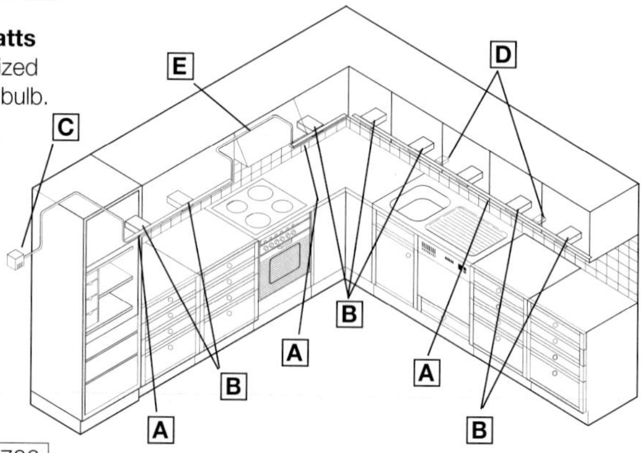

Cat. No.	white	532.85.706

Packing: 1 pc.

C Electronic safety transformer for 1-3 Sunlight lamps

Primary input 120V with 20' secondary lead and connector.
Secondary input min. 10VA -max. 60VA - 11.5V
45mm wide x 70mm high x 24mm deep

Catalog No.	white	823.24.470

Packing: 1 pc.

D Connector, locking type

For linear connection of low-voltage supply track sections.

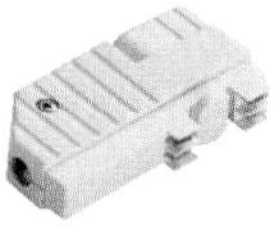

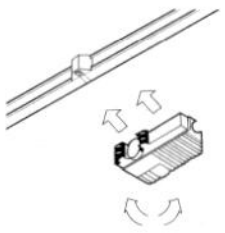

Linear installation of two supply tracks using connector type **D**.

Cat. No.	white	532.84.709

Packing: 1 pc.

E Connecting lead, flexible type

With end-plugs for connection of low-voltage supply track sections.

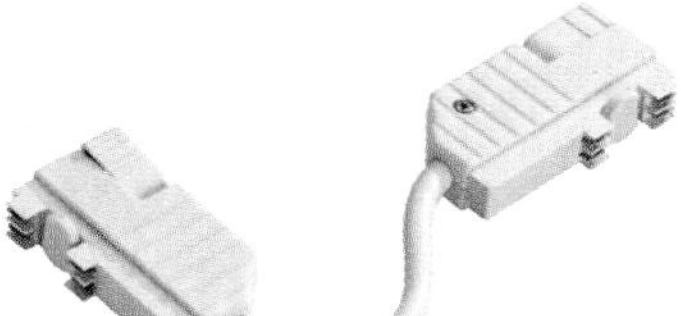

Color	Length	Catalog No.
white	250 mm	532.84.718
white	2500 mm	532.84.727

Packing: 1 pc.

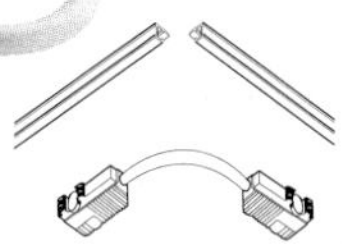

Corner layout two supply tracks connected with connecting lead **E**.

HÄFELE

Low-Voltage Halogen Light Bars

Halogen Light Bar/110 volt /20 watts, Hardwire
Dimensions: 9" length x 2" width x 1 1/4" depth , 12V/20 watt (1 x 20w Lamp)

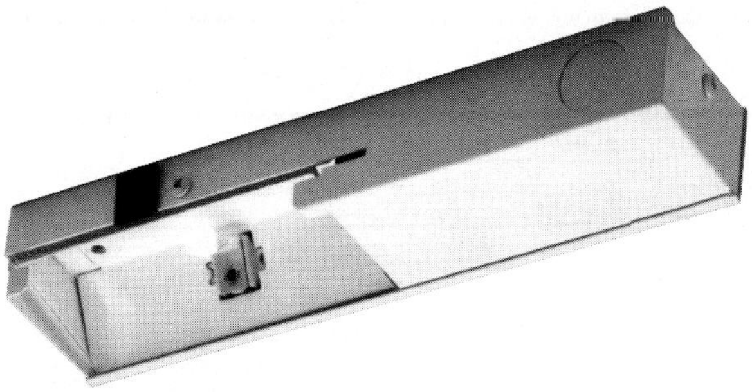

Finish: steel epoxy-coated/glass clear

Finish	Catalog No.
white epoxy	820.29.710
black epoxy	820.29.310

Packing: 1 pc.

Halogen Light Bar/110 volt/40 watts, Hardwire
Dimensions: 18" length x 2" width 1 1/4" depth, 12V/40 watt (2 x 20 watt bulbs)

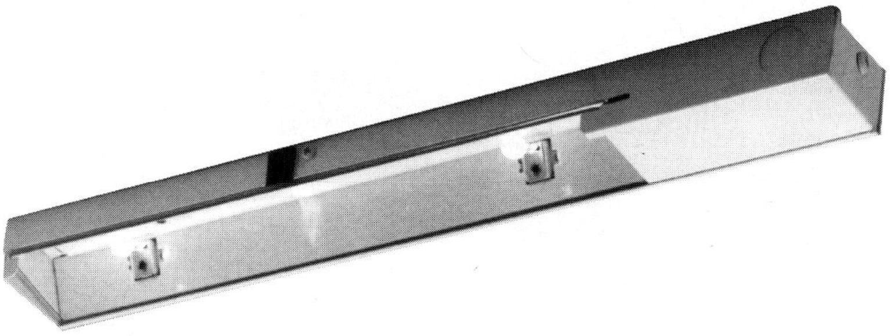

Finish: steel epoxy-coated/glass clear

Finish	Catalog No.
white epoxy	820.29.720
black epoxy	820.29.320

Packing: 1 pc.

Halogen Light Bar/110v/60 watts, Hardwire
Dimensions: 27" length x 2" width x 1 1/4" depth 12V/60 watt (3 x 20 watt bulbs)

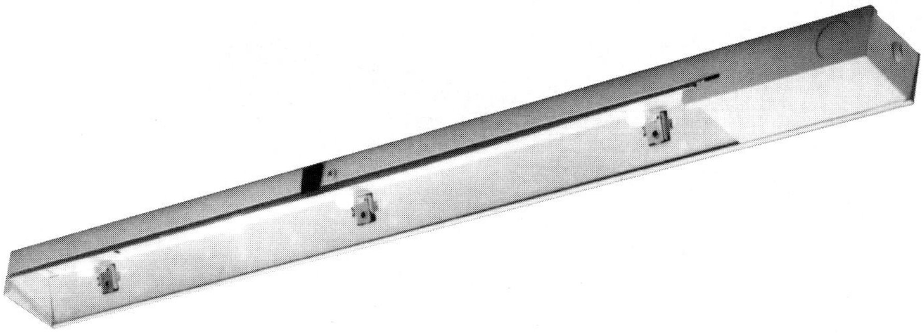

Finish: steel epoxy-coated/glass clear

Finish	Catalog No.
white epoxy	820.29.730
black epoxy	820.29.330

Packing: 1 pc.

- For hardwiring to power source by an electrician.
- To be mounted on wood surfaces only
- Whiter light/brighter colors
- Halogen energy efficient
- Surface mounted-no drilling required
- Applications for residential, commercial and industrial use. Use under kitchen cabinets, home planning centers, display cases, entertainment centers, medical & laboratory furniture, workshops, etc.

SA® UL LISTED

Spare Lamps
Halogen Lamp with base G4
12 volt/20 watt

Catalog No.	821.80.112

Packing: 1 pc.

HÄFELE

- With 6' cord and plug-no electrician needed
- To be mounted on wood surfaces only
- Whiter light/brighter colors
- Halogon onorgy officiont
- Surface mounted-no drilling required
- Applications for residential, commercial and industrial use. Use under kitchen cabinets, home planning center, display cases, entertainment centers, medical and laboratory furniture, workshops, etc.

LISTED

Low-Voltage Halogen Light Bars

Halogen Light Bar/110 volt /20 watts
Dimensions: 9" length x 2" width x 1 1/4" depth , 12V/20 watt (1 x 20w Lamp)

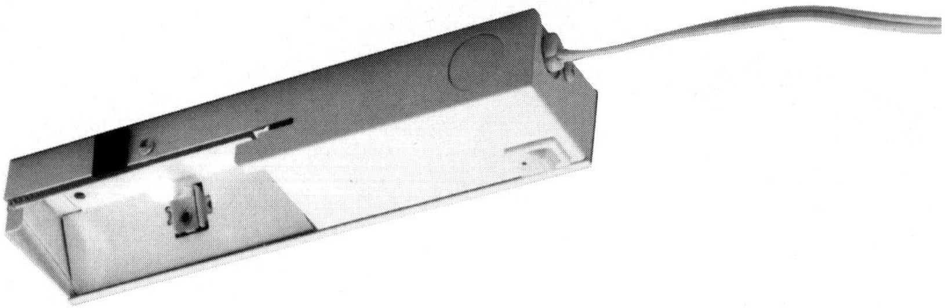

Finish: steel epoxy-coated/glass clear

Finish	Catalog No.
white epoxy	820.28.715
black epoxy	820.28.313

Packing: 1 pc.

Halogen Light Bar/110 volt/40 watts
Dimensions: 18" length x 2" width 1 1/4" depth, 12V/40 watt (2 x 20w Lamps)

Finish: steel epoxy-coated/glass clear

Finish	Catalog No.
white epoxy	820.28.724
black epoxy	820.28.322

Packing: 1 pc.

Halogen Light Bar/110V/60 Watt
Dimensions: 27" length x 2" width x 1 1/4" depth 12V/60 watt (3 x 20w Lamps)

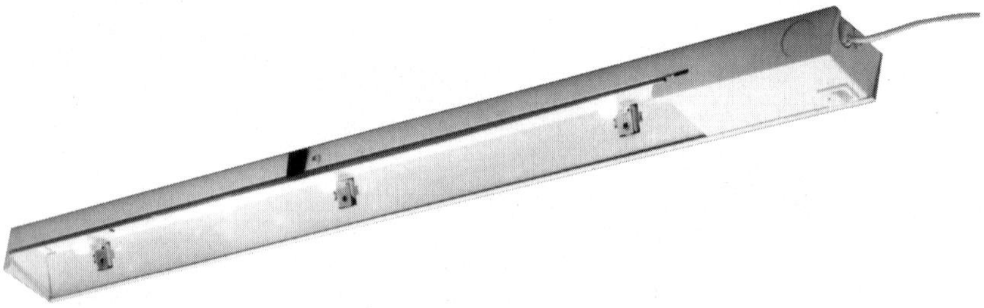

Finish: steel epoxy-coated/glass clear

Finish	Catalog No.
white epoxy	820.28.733
black epoxy	820.28.331

Packing: 1 pc.

Spare Lamps
Halogen Lamp with base G4

Cat. No.	821.80.112

Packing: 1 pc.

Cable and Radius Light Systems

HÄFELE

Cable and Radius Lights

Lights use bare wires which offer low profile fixtures that appear to float in air, almost disappearing in space. Cable lighting is fast becoming a popular alternative to conventional track lighting because of simple installation.

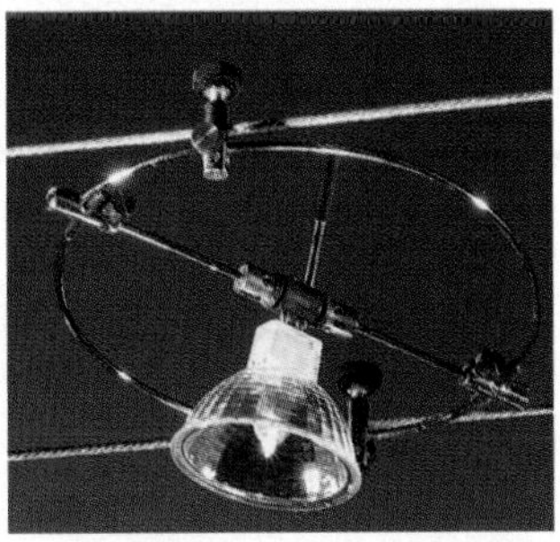

- Fixtures can be positioned anywhere on the cable.
- No ceiling is required to hook up cable lights.
- Quick and easy installation, wires can be strung just about anywhere.
- Light hard to reach places.
- Bare wires provide a nice clean look.
- Bare wires may be touched, as they carry only 12 volts.
- Multiple layers of light can be achieved.

MR16 Quartz Halogen Lamps

- Glass front lens protects lamp, as well as dichroic reflector from dust and finger prints.
- Produce up to three times more light than regular lamps using the same number of watts.
- Savings up to 50% on energy costs as compared to standard line voltage systems.
- Long lamp life thus replacement costs are lower.
- Small size lamp (2")

Halogen Light

- Quartz halogen lamps give off a much whiter light than regular incandescent.
- Whiter light means greatly improved color rendition.
- The small light source allows you more control of the beam and accurate focusing.
- Color temperature remains constant throughout lamp life.
- Cooler beam emits less heat, allowing you to use near heat sensitive objects such as food or flowers.

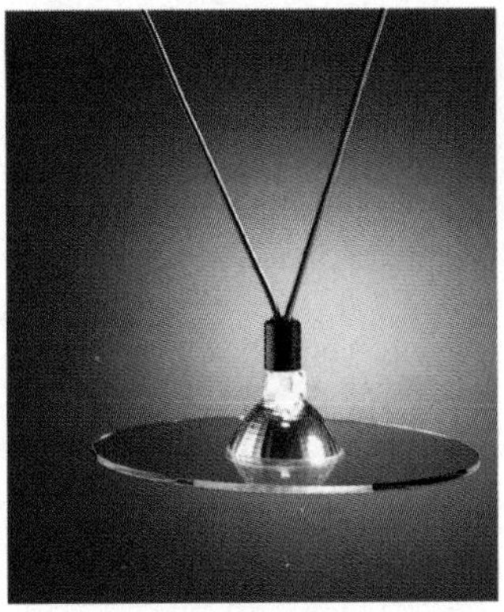

HÄFELE

Cable Lighting System, Low-Voltage Halogen for Cable and Radius Systems

Pivot cable light
Fixture may be secured to horizontal and vertical cables, for 5 1/2" cable separation.

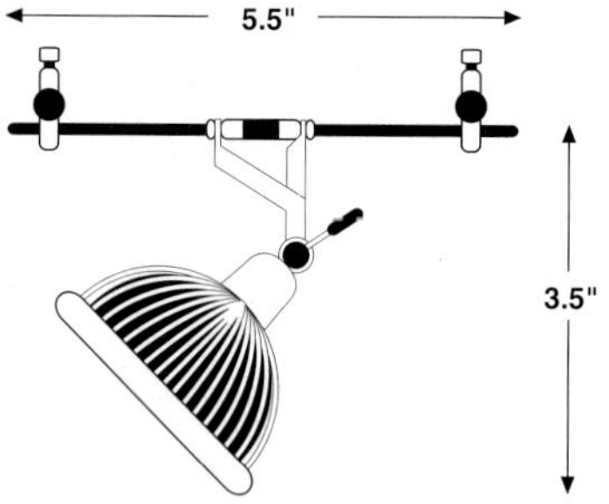

Finish: Steel chrome plated

Catalog No.	823.51.200

Packing: 1 pc. (Bulb not included)

Circular cable light
Fixture may be secured to horizontal and vertical cables.

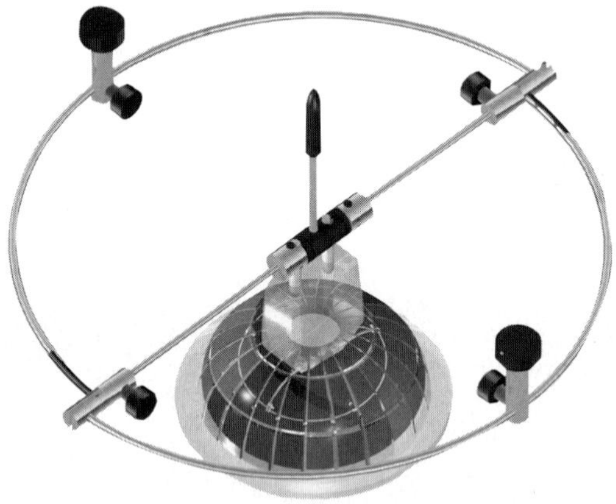

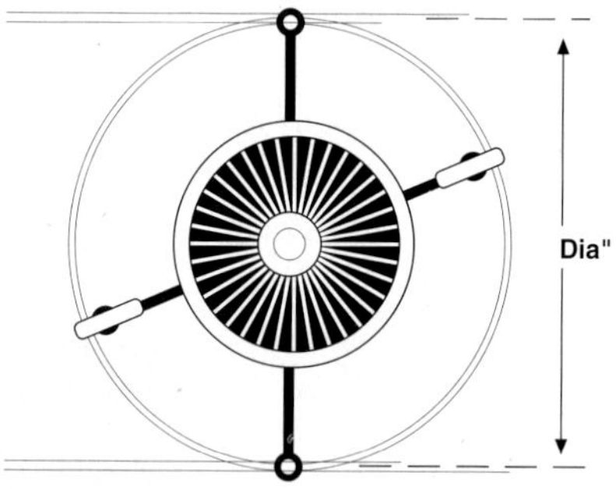

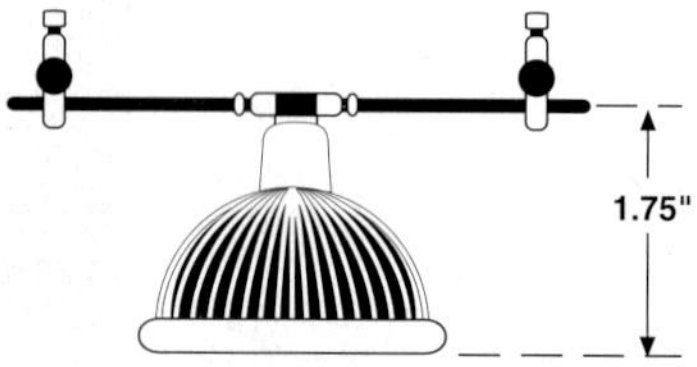

Finish: Steel chrome plated

Diameter	Cable Separation	Cat. No.
5.5"	5.5"	823.52.216
8"	8"	823.52.207

Packing: 1 pc. (Bulb not included)

- Lamp head rotates 360° on its vertical axis
- Accepts up to 50 watt bulb MR16 (not included)
- Direct light to highlighted area
- Locks into place, fastening securely to cable
- Optional back light shield and louver lens holder for bulb.

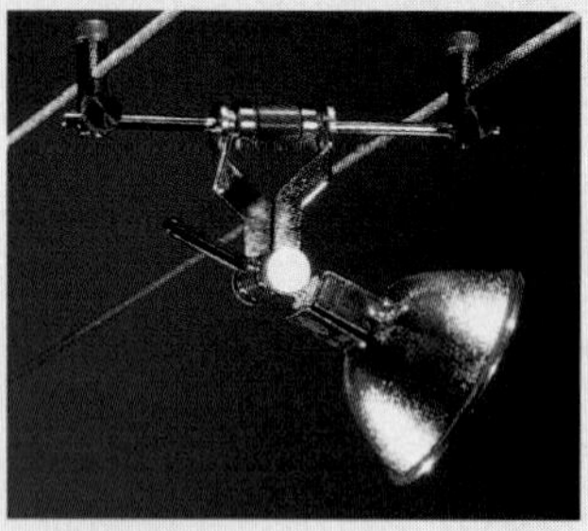

LISTED

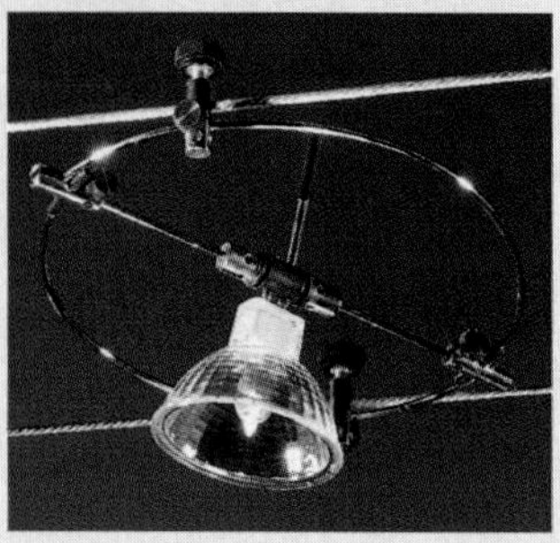

- Rotates 350° between parallel cables and its lamp rotates 360° about axis
- Locks into place, fastening securely to cable
- Accepts up to a 50 watt bulb MR16 (not included)
- Optional backlight shield and louver lens holder for bulb.

Dimensional data not binding. We reserve the right to alter specifications without notice.

HÄFELE

Cable Lighting System
Low-Voltage Halogen Light

Hanging light, glass clear with 50W bulb
Diameter: 6"
Complete with 6 feet of light gray cable for suspension (cut to desired length).
Fixture may be secured to horizontal cable only, min. 2" to max. 36" separation.

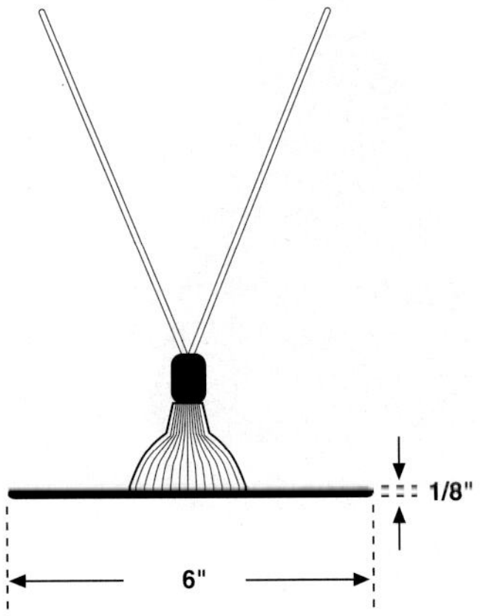

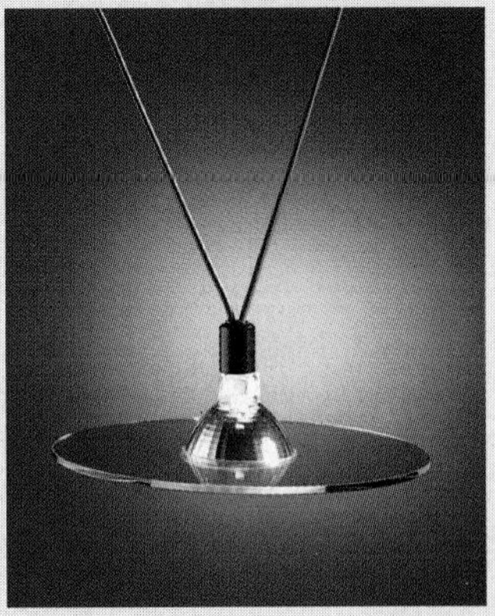

- Glass disc sits atop the exposed 50 watt bulb.

Finish: glass clear, cable gray

Catalog No.	823.53.302

Packing: 1 pc. (with 50 watt MR16 bulb included)

Hanging light, opaque glass shade with 50W bulb
Dimensions: Max. 5' wires connect to parallel steel rods 21 1/2" long complete with 6' of black cable for suspension (cut to desired length)

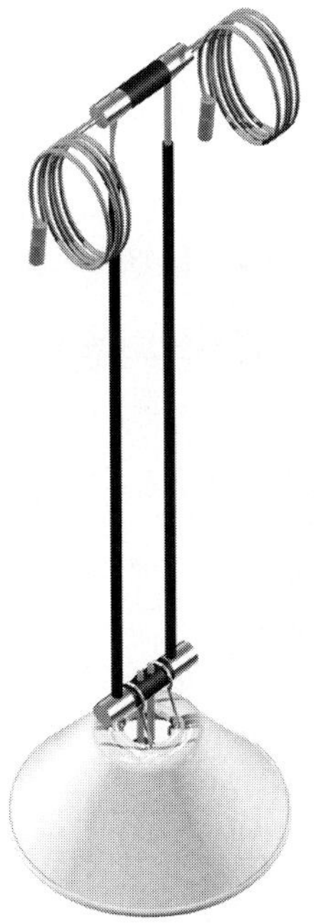

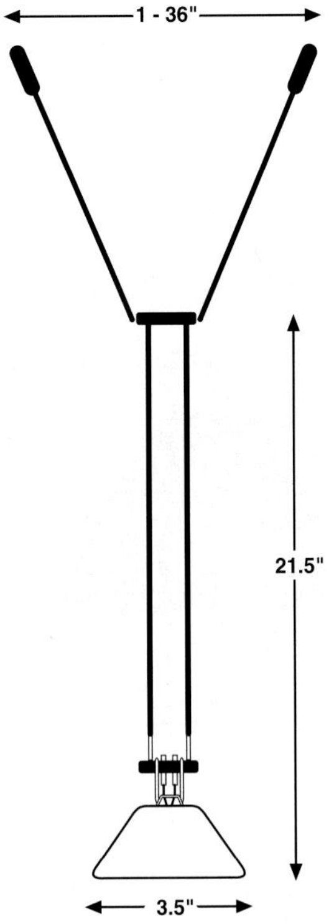

Finish: glass opaque white/rods steel chrome plated with black sleeves

Catalog No.	823.50.203

Packing: 1 pc. (with 50 watt MR16 bulb included)

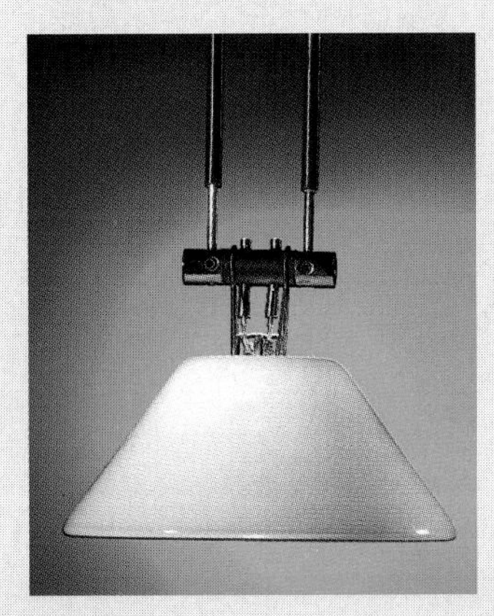

Spare lamp for light 823.50.203
Bi-Pin 50 Watt
Finish: glass clear

Cat. No.	823.50.290

Packing: 1 pc.

Interior Accessories
Wardrobe Accessories
Storage Systems
Furniture Lighting
8

HÄFELE

Cable and Radius Light Pendents

- Pendent Lights cable can be field cut to desired length.
- We recommend using standoffs every two fixtures or every 10 feet due to weight of pendents.

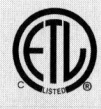

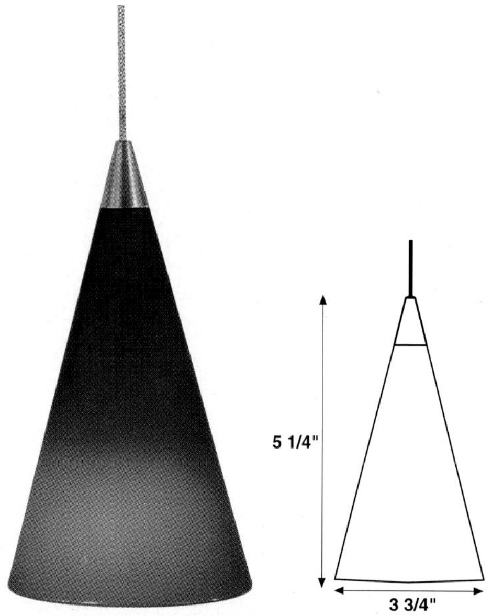

Cone Pendant complete with 50 watt bi-pin bulb and six feet of chrome cable for suspension
Finish: glass

Color	Cat. No.
Green	824.58.000
White	824.58.700
Apricot	824.58.910
Red	824.58.900
Cobalt	824.58.800

Packing: 1 pc

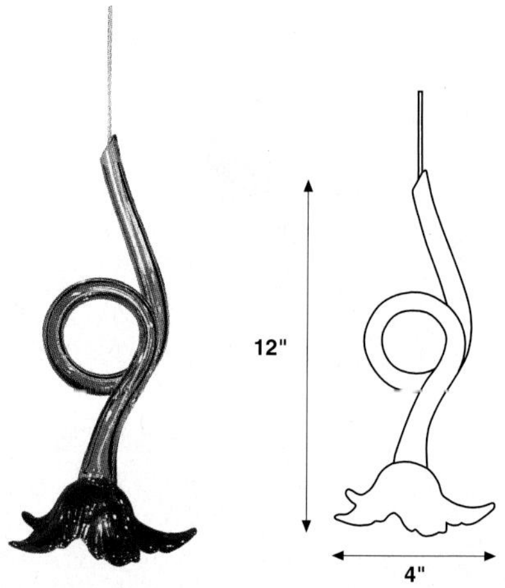

Flower Stem Pendent on a curved glass stem complete with 35 watt bi-pin bulb and six feet of chrome cable for suspension.
Finish: stem; Murano glass, green
Shade: Murano glass, blue

Cat. No.	824.59.800

Packing: 1 pc

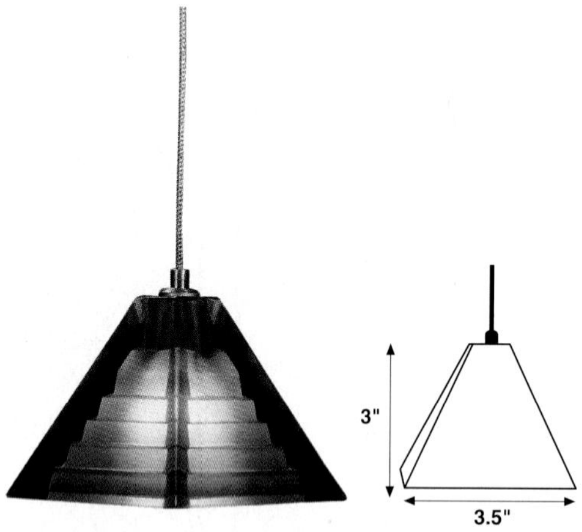

Pyramid Pendent complete with 50 watt bi-pin bulb and six feet of chrome cable for suspension.
Finish: Murano glass

Color	Cat. No.
Cobalt	824.58.801
Green	824.58.001
Light Blue	824.58.811
Amber	824.58.111
Frost	824.58.411
Amethyst	824.58.920

Packing: 1 pc

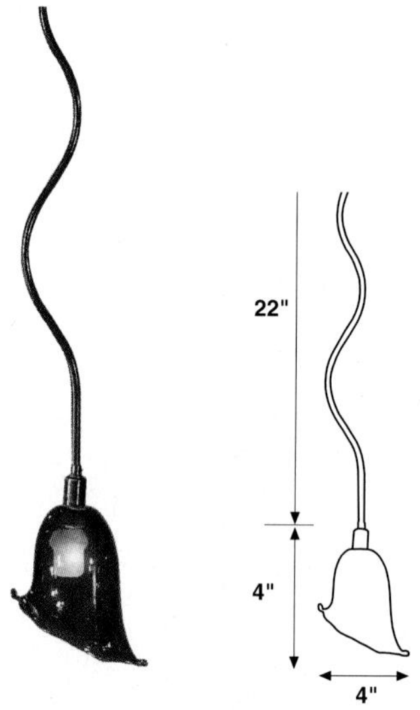

Flower Stem Pendent complete with 35 watt bi-pin bulb and six feet of chrome cable for suspension.
Finish: stem; steel, green, lacquered
Shade: Murano glass, red

Cat. No.	824.59.900

Packing: 1 pc

Cable Light System
Low Voltage Halogen Accessories

HÄFELE

Mesh backlight shield
- Use over MR16 bulb
- Cuts down on glare from back of bulb
- Egg crate cuts glare from front of bulb

- Protective glass lens safety feature

- Round or cone glass shield shield fit over MR16 bulbs.

Mesh backlight shield, MR16
No. 823.56.303, Louver Holder required for use.

Finish: steel black

Catalog No.	823.56.312

Packing: 1 pc.

Egg crate louver lens, MR16
No. 823.56.303, Louver Holder required for use.

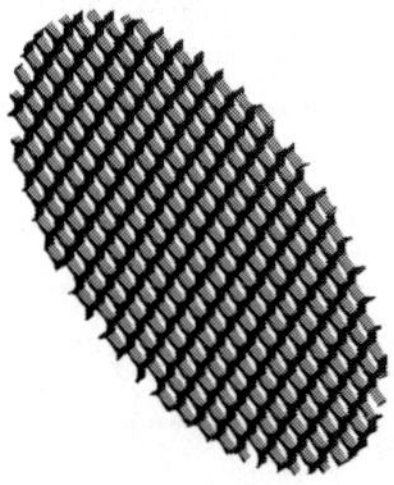

Finish: aluminum black

Catalog No.	823.56.321

Packing: 1 pc.

Louver lens holder, MR16

Finish: aluminum black

Catalog No.	823.56.303

Packing: 1 pc.

MR16 Bulb

Finish: glass, clear lens

Wattage	Beam	Cat. No.
50W	38°	823.56.009
20W	35°	823.56.080

Packing: 1 pc.

Round glass shield, MR 16
Complete with Louver Lens Holder

Finish: Murano glass

Color	Cat. No.
Frost	824.57.410
Amber	824.57.110
Cobalt	824.57.800
Green	824.57.000

Packing: 1 pc.

Cone glass shield, MR 16

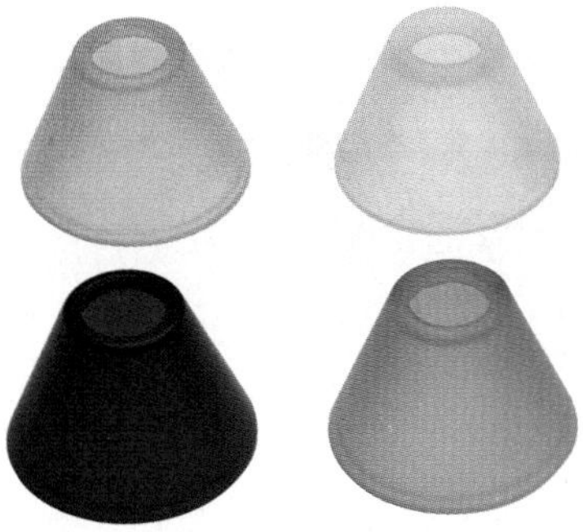

Finish: Spanish glass

Color	Cat. No.
Frost	824.57.411
Colbalt	824.57.801
Rose	824.57.901
Green	824.57.001

Packing: 1 pc.

HÄFELE

- Surface mounted transformer
- Can be mounted to wall or ceiling.
- Standard with a pair of 24" long, 12 volt low voltage softwire leads with connector.
- With debuzzing dimming coil which prevents buzzing when using a low voltage dimmer.

Cable Light System Low-Voltage Halogen Transformer for Cable and Radius Systems

Transformer for cable lights 12 Volt / 120 Volt Primary
Dimmable with magnetic low voltage dimmer. Transformer must be mounted within 2 ft. of cable light system. Complete with 24" long low voltage softwire and connectors, and 12' cord and inline switch 24" from the plug.

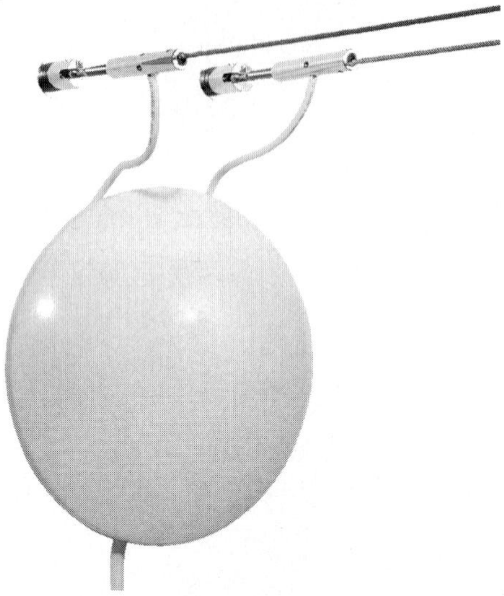

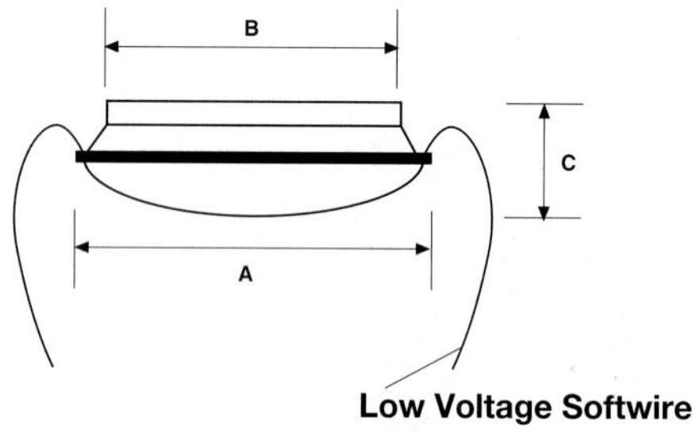

Finish: steel, white

Dimension, A x B x C	Watts	Catalog No.
6 1/2 x 2 1/4 x5	150	824.60.700
9 x 3 x 7	300	824.60.710

Packing: 1 pc.

Insulated connector
for connecting cables when two transformers are used and cables are connected end to end.
Finish: plastic, clear

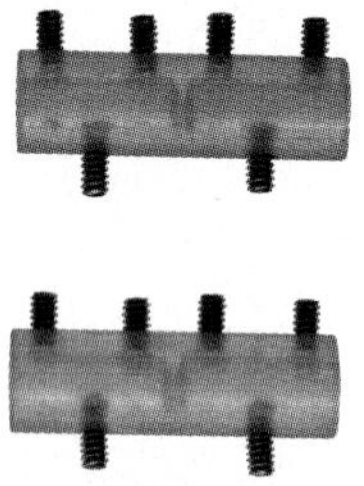

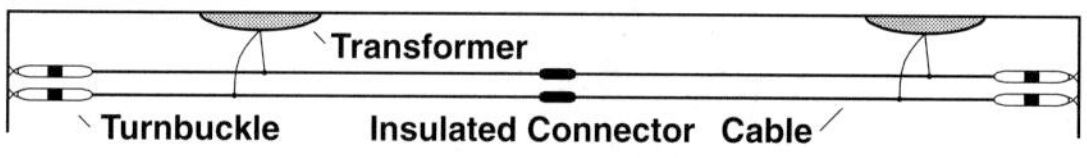

Catalog No.	823.57.390

Packing: 1 pair

Dimensional data not binding. We reserve the right to alter specifications without notice.

Cable Light Accessories for Cable Light Systems

HÄFELE

- For custom cable lengths, order cable by the foot and turnbuckles separately.

Cable and mounting hardware set
Includes 4 wall-mount turnbuckles and two-20 foot cables.

Finish: Silver plated wire with kynar core, turnbuckles brass, chrome-plated

Cat. No.	823.55.208

Packing: 1 set

Cable # 10 gauge, sold by the foot for up to 300 watt maximum.
Finish: Tin-plated copper, with kynar core.

Cat. No.	823.57.900

Packing: per foot

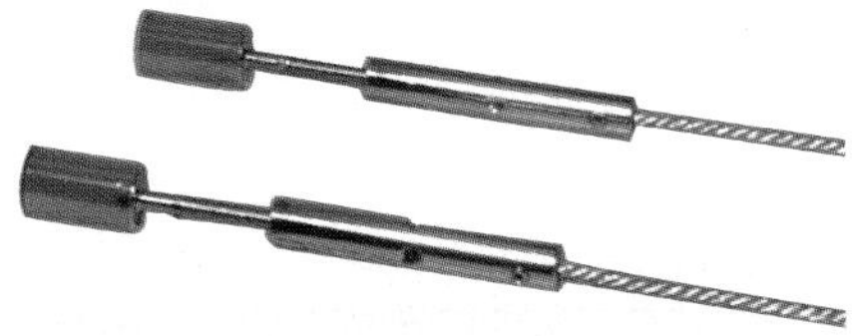

Turnbuckles for cable runs of less than 20 ft.
Can be mounted to wall or ceiling (cable drops 1" from ceiling)
Dimensions: 4-5" long x 3/8" dia.
Finish: stainless steel, chrome

Cat. No.	823.58.200

Packing: 1 pair (2 pcs.)

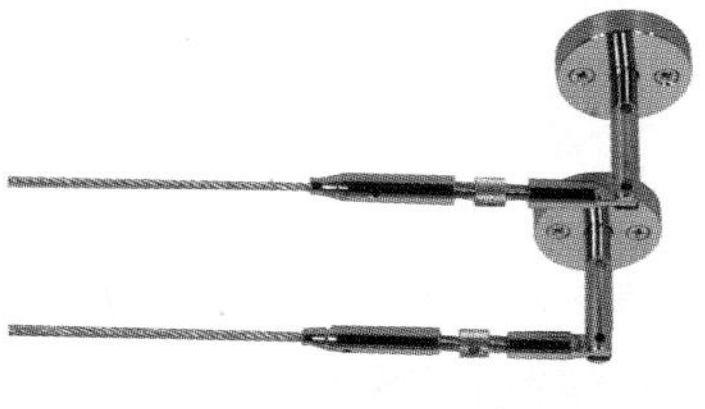

Turnbuckles, heavy duty for cable runs over 20 ft.
Can be mounted to wall or ceiling (cable drops 2 1/2" from ceiling)
Dimensions: 5 1/2"-6 1/2" x 3/8" dia.
Finish: stainless steel, chrome

Cat. No.	824.52.200

Packing: 1 pair (2 pcs.)

HÄFELE

Adjustable Cable Post Support for Cable Light Systems

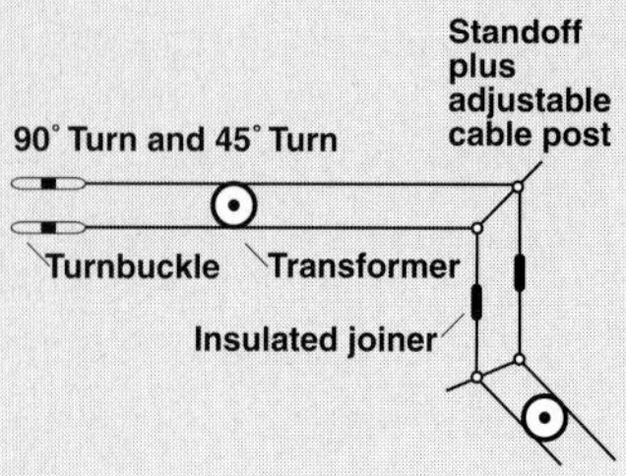

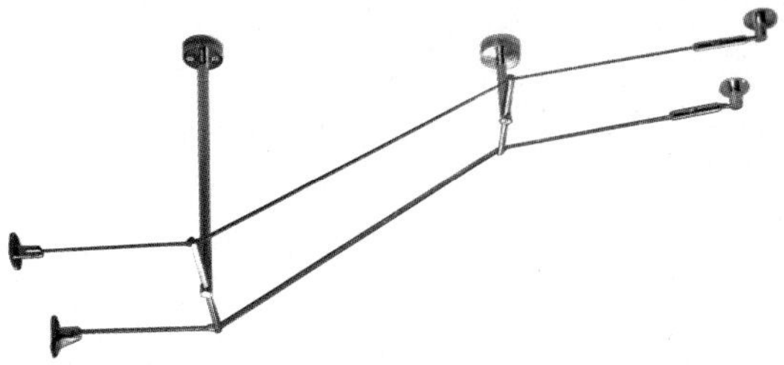

Double Standoff
Cantilevered double standoff to drop cable off the ceiling and maintain separation. NOTE: Use the 5" drop to run cable beneath transformer mounted to ceiling.
Finish: brass chrome-plated

	Cable Separation	
Drop	5 1/2"	8"
1"	823.53.201	823.53.205
2 1/2"	823.53.202	823.53.206
5"	823.53.203	823.53.207
12"	823.53.204	823.53.208

1Packing: 1 pc.

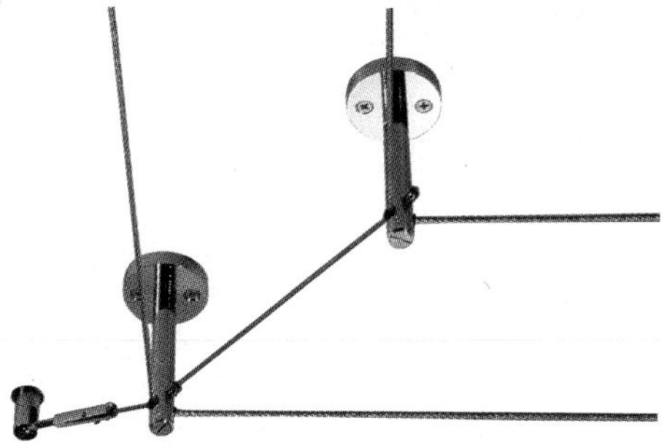

Standoff with Turn Support provides tension for clean turns. Can be used for cable separation from 2" to 24".

Drop	Cat. No.
1"	824.54.201
2 1/2"	824.54.202
5"	824.54.203
12"	824.54.204

Packing: 1 set

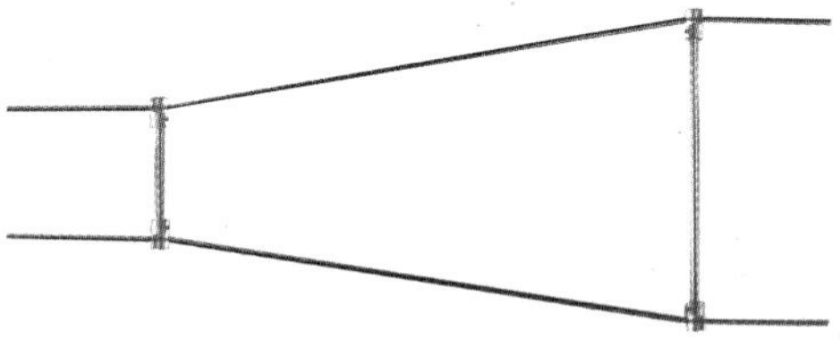

Cable Separator changes cable separation from 1" to 8". Can be field cut to desired length.
Finish: brass chrome-plated

Catalog No.	824.51.201

Packing: 1 pair

Support for long or heavy runs. Consists of 12 feet of cable for suspension and horizontal rod is 12" long Both can be field cut to desired length.
Finish: brass chrome-plated

Catalog No.	824.50.201

Packing: 1 pc.

8 Interior Accessories
Wardrobe Accessories
Storage Systems
Furniture Lighting

Cable Light-
Radius Wire System

HÄFELE

• Radius wire uses the same light and transformers as Cable wire system.

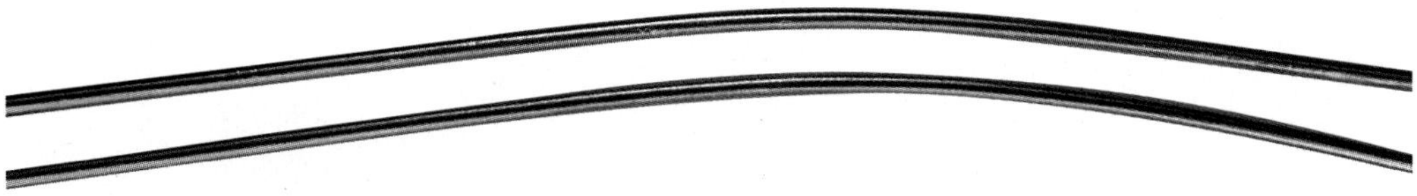

Conductors hand bendable #10 gauge wire.
Load: 350 watts maximum at 12 volts
Length: 8 feet
Finish: copper wire, chrome plated

Catalog No.	824.56.201

Packing: 1 pair

• Standoffs recommended every 18" to 36".

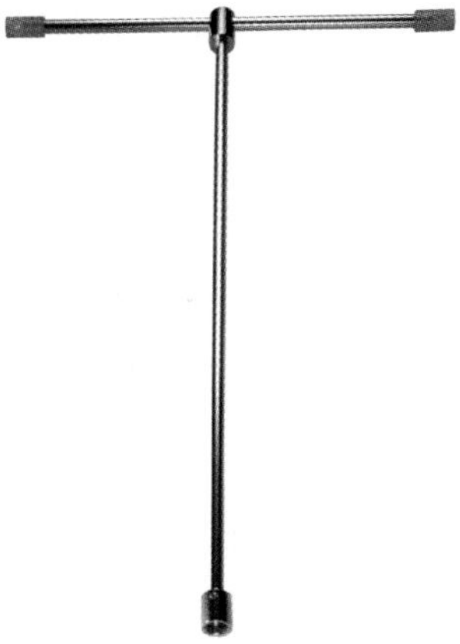

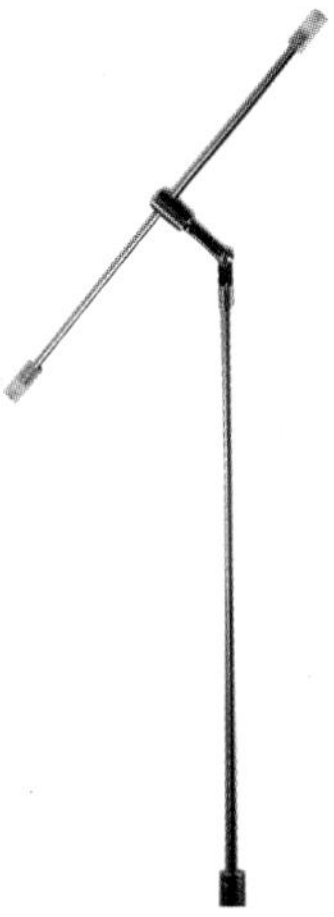

Standoff Supporter for Radius wire. Screws hold wires secure. 8" wire separation, may be field cut to as small as 1" wide x 1" high.
Finish: crossbar, brass chrome-plated
support, steel chrome-plated

Height	Cat. No.
12"	824.55.201
24"	824.55.202

Packing: 1 pc

Tiltable Standoff for Radius wire. Flexible joint to allow wire to be tilted to desired angle and secured. 8" wire separation, May be field cut to as small as 1" wide x 3 1/2" high.
Finish: stainless steel chrome

Height	Cat. No.
12"	824.55.211
24"	824.55.212

Packing: 1 pc

Insulated connector
for connecting cables when two transformers are used and cables are connected end to end.
Finish: plastic, clear

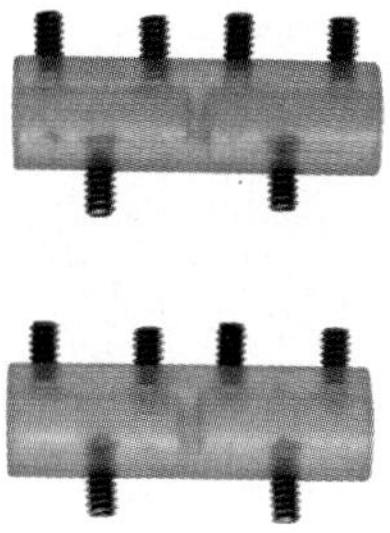

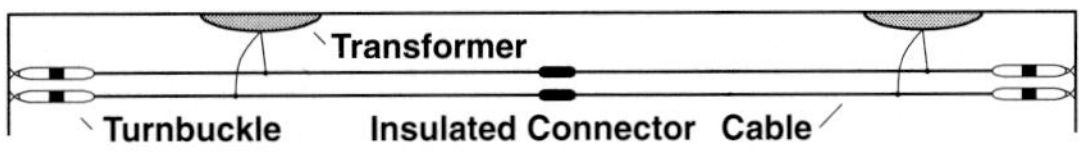

Catalog No.	823.57.390

Packing: 1 pair

HÄFELE

Halogen-Cornice Lights

Cornice Lights
Complete with:
- 2000 mm length cable
- amp plug
- halogen lamp MR16/20 watts

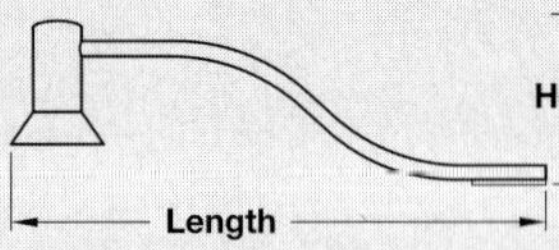

c UL UL LISTED

- Cornice lights are intended for mounting above cabinets to shine down and "wash" the area below.
- Multiple fixtures should be spaced minimum 12" (300 mm) apart on center.

Spare lamp for light 823.50.203
Bi-Pin 50 Watt
Finish: glass clear

Cat. No.	823.50.290

Packing: 1 pc.

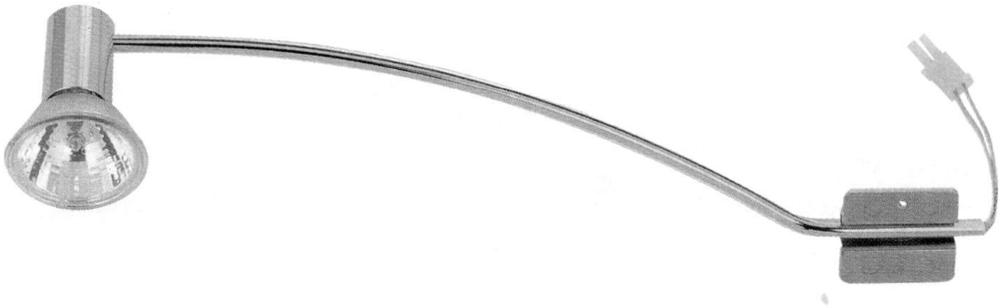

Cornice Light, with fixed head
Rod Ø 6 mm
Finish: steel

Length: **330 mm**
Height: **95 mm**

	Cat. No. **12V / 20W**
black, powder-coated	824.12.332
chrome polished, plated	824.12.232
gold polished, plated	824.12.832

Packing: 1 pc.

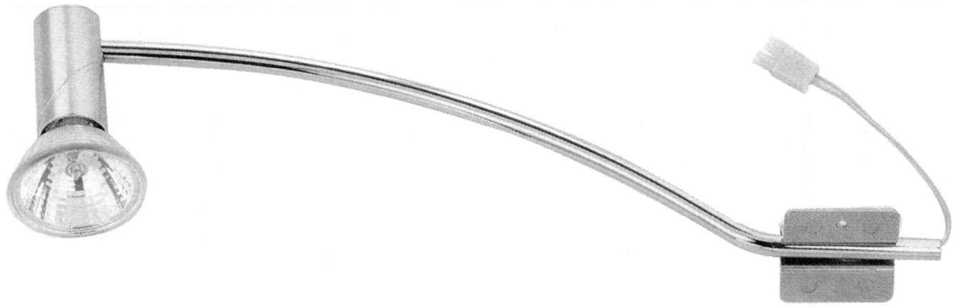

Cornice Light, with adjustable head
Rod Ø 8 mm
Finish: steel

Length: **330 mm**
Height: **99 mm**

	Cat. No. **12V / 20W**
black, powder-coated	824.12.342
chrome polished, plated	824.12.242
gold polished, plated	824.12.842

Packing: 1 pc.

Halogen-Cornice Lights

HÄFELE

Cornice Lights
Complete with:
- 2000 mm length cable
- amp plug
- halogen lamp MR16/20 watts

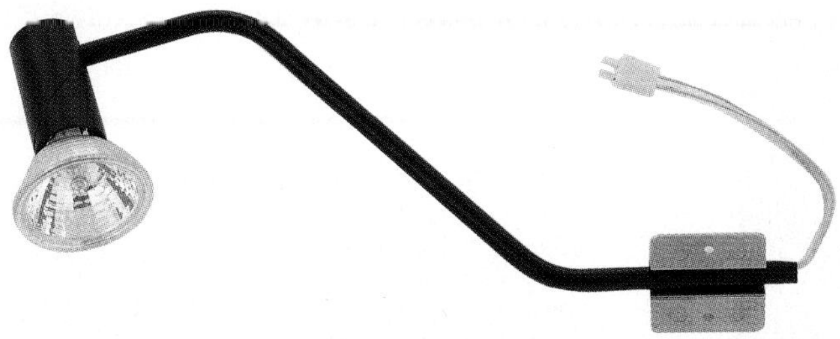

Cornice Light, with adjustable head
Rod Ø 8 mm
Finish: steel

Length: **275 mm**
Height: **115 mm**

	Cat. No. **12V / 20W**
black, powder-coated	825.22.302
chrome polished, plated	825.22.202
gold polished, plated	825.22.802

Packing: 1 pc.

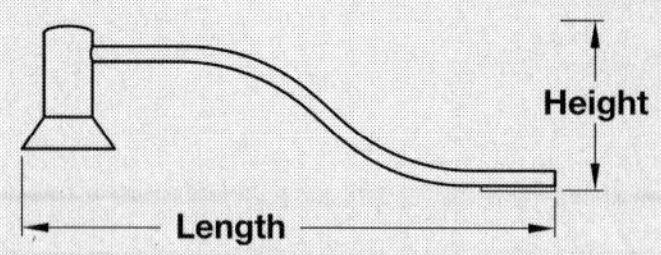

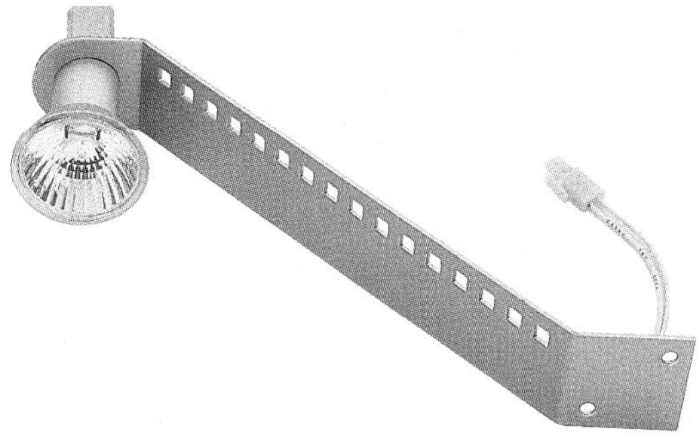

c UL UL LISTED

Cornice Light, with fixed head
Finish: steel, epoxy-coated

Length: **225 mm**
Height: **147 mm**

	Cat. No. **12V / 20W**
metallic, gray	824.11.502
silver, gray	824.11.002

Packing: 1 pc.

- Cornice lights are intended for mounting above cabinets to shine down and "wash" the area below.
- Multiple fixtures should be spaced minimum 12" (300 mm) apart on center.

HÄFELE

Shelf Suspension Systems

• For shelves suspended from the ceiling.

Beta shelf suspension system
Complete with 1 threaded rod M8X1000, 1 tube Ø 20 x 896 mm, 1 upper sleeve, 1 centering ring, 1 sleeve nut, 1 rubber clamping ring.
Load carrying capacity: 50 kg (110 lbs.)
Finish: steel/brass, surface-threaded

Color	Cat. No.
bright chrome	828.50.208
bright gold	828.50.806
white RAL 9010	828.50.708

Packing: 1 pc.

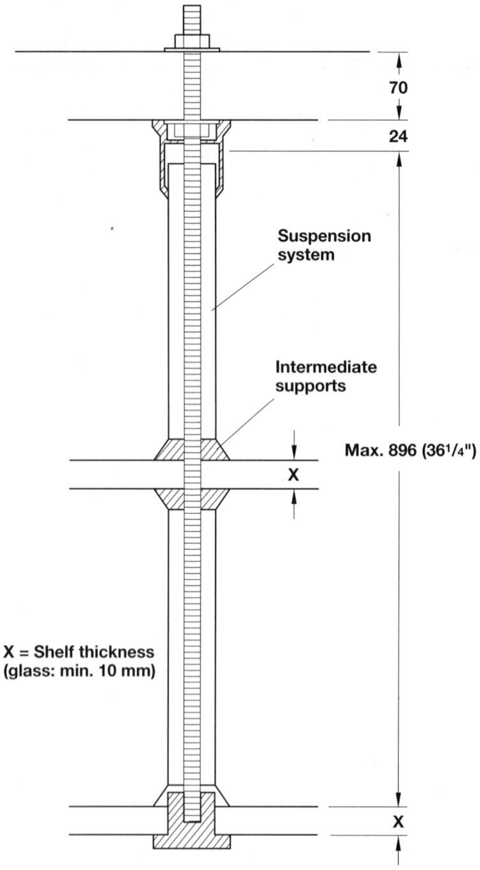

Intermediate supports
for additional ceiling shelves to the Beta Suspension System.
Finish: brass electroplated or epoxy-coated

Color	Cat. No.
chrome polished	828.50.210
brass polished	828.50.810
white	828.50.710

Packing: 1 pc.

Coat Hooks

HÄFELE

W x D x H =
width x depth x height

Coat hook, stainless steel, brushed, matt

Size: W x D x H	Cat. No.
20 x 40 x 60	842.34.050

Packing: 1 pc., including fixing materials

Hat & coat hook, stainless steel, brushed, matt

Size: W x D x H	Cat. No.
20 x 72 x 150	842.34.000

Packing: 1 pc., including fixing materials

Hat & coat hook, stainless steel, brushed, matt

Size: W x D x H	Cat. No.
25 x 52 x 110	842.34.010

Packing: 1 pc., including fixing materials

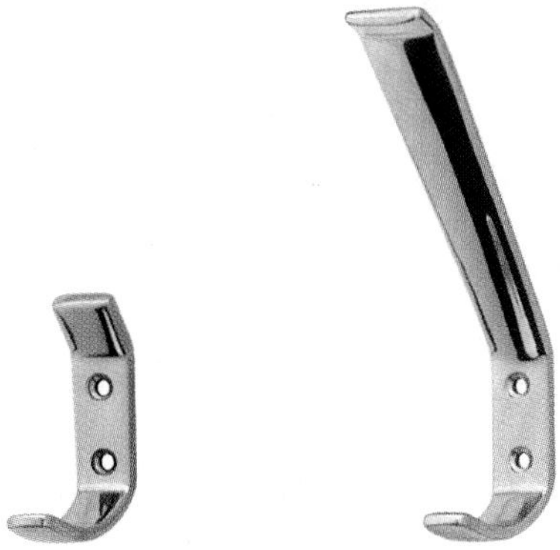

Coat hook, brass, polished

Size: W x D x H	Cat. No.
18 x 56 x 66	885.04.858

Packing: 1 pc., including fixing materials

Hat & coat hook, brass, polished

Size: W x D x H	Cat. No.
23 x 88 x 133	885.04.803

Packing: 1 pc., including fixing materials

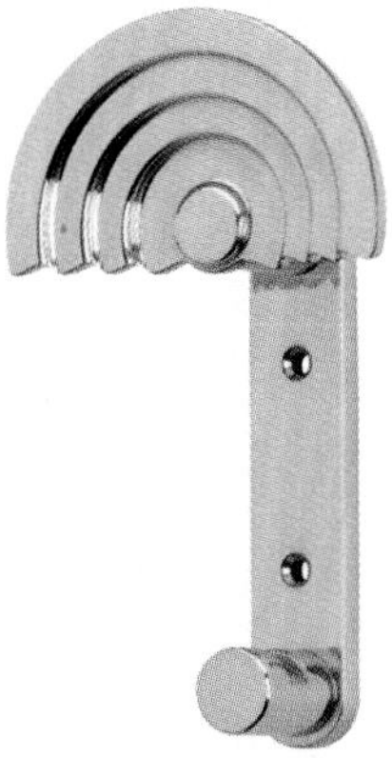

Hat & coat hook, brass, polished

Size: W x D x H	Cat. No.
86 x 57 x 148	842.17.800

Packing: 1 pc., including fixing materials

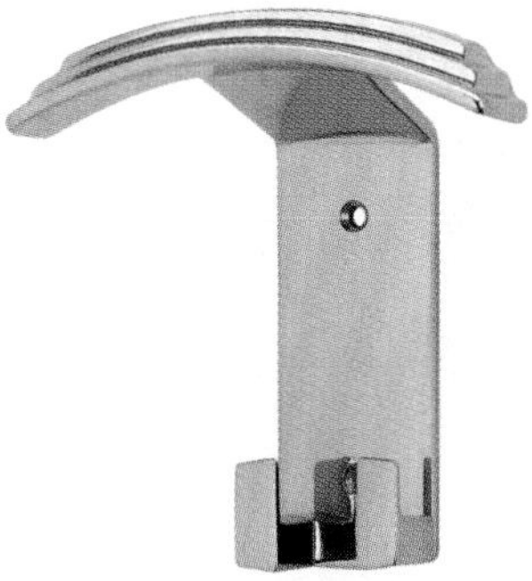

Hat & coat hook, brass, polished

Size: W x D x H	Cat. No.
120 x 65 x 125	842.16.800

Packing: 1 pc., including fixing materials

Dimensions in mm

HÄFELE

W x D x H =
width x depth x height

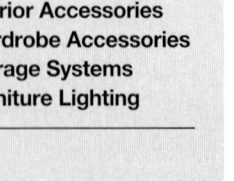

Coat Hooks

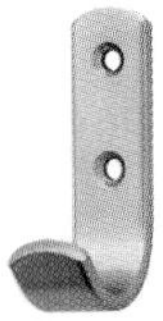

Coat hook,
Size: W x D x H 18 x 35 x 62
Finish: anodized aluminum

Cat. No.	silver colored	842.01.909
	gold colored	842.01.605

Packing: 10 pcs.

Hat & Coat hook,
Size: W x D x H 18 x 93 x 158
Finish: anodized aluminum

Cat. No.	silver colored	842.02.906
	gold colored	842.02.602

Packing: 1 pc.

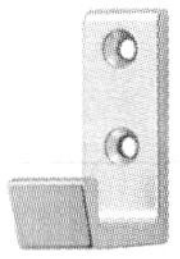

Coat hook, silver colored, anodized aluminum

Size: W x D x H	Cat. No.
17 x 41 x 47	842.20.959

Packing: 2 pcs.

Coat hook, polished aluminum

Size: W x D x H	Cat. No.
53 x 53 x 62	846.52.808

Packing: 50 pcs.

Coat hook, polished aluminum

Size: W x D x H	screw	Cat. No.
13 x 22 x 30	3.0	845.00.809
18 x 29 x 40	3.0	845.01.806
20 x 35 x 42	3.5	845.02.803

Packing: 10 pcs.

Coat hook, polished aluminum

Size: W x D x H	screw	Cat. No.
44 x 23 x 33	3.0	845.10.805
53 x 25 x 40	3.0	845.11.802
60 x 32 x 50	3.5	845.12.809

Packing: 10 pcs.

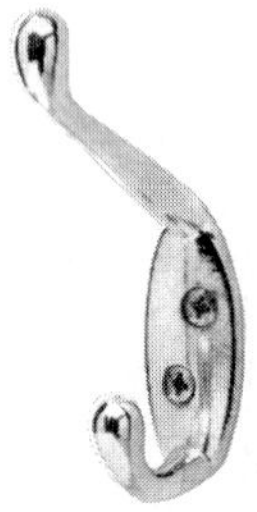

Coat hook,
Size: W x D x H 25 x 55 x 89
Finish: zinc

Cat. No.	chrome-polished	885.06.209
	brass-polished	885.06.807

Packing: 50 pcs.

Dimensions in mm

HEWI Closet Accessories

Wardrobe tube, 33 mm diameter
Length: 1000 mm, can be cut to any length, complete with 1 screw-mounted steel rosette and 1 plug-in rosette.
Finish: nylon, with steel core in the tube rosette diameter 70 mm

Cat. No.	804.51.1..

Packing: 1 pc.

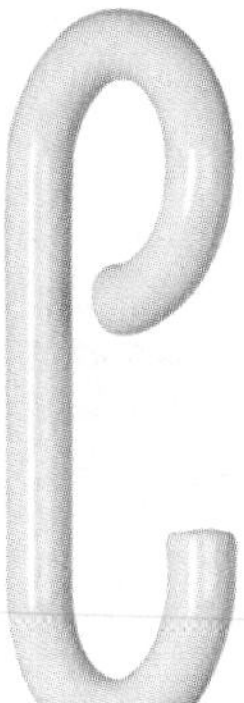

Double wardrobe hook, 13 mm diameter
to be screw-mounted onto wardrobe tubes up to 33 mm diameter. Height: 95 mm
Finish: Nylon

Cat. No.	804.54.1..

Packing: 1 pc.

Theft-proof wardrobe hook, 15 mm diameter
Slides onto wardrobe tubes up to 40 mm diameter. Height: 170 mm
Finish: Nylon

Cat. No.	804.55.1.

Packing: 1 pc.

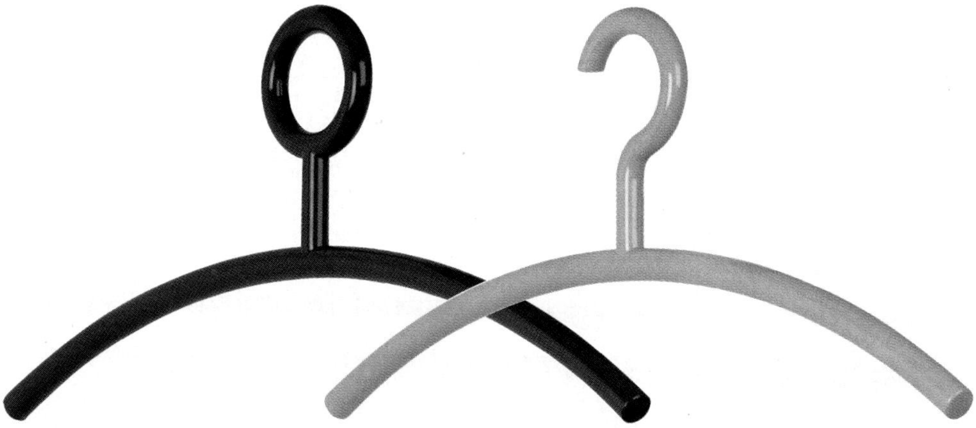

Theft-proof clothes hanger, 15 mm diameter
slides onto wardrobe tubes up to 40 mm diameter
Length: 450 mm
Finish: Nylon

Cat. No.	804.57.1..

Packing: 1 pc.

Clothes hanger, 15 mm diameter
hangs onto wardrobe tubes up to 40 mm diameter
Length: 450 mm
Finish: Nylon

Cat. No.	804.56.1..

Packing: 1 pc.

Ordering tip: replace the decimals (. .) in the catalog number with the color number of your choice.

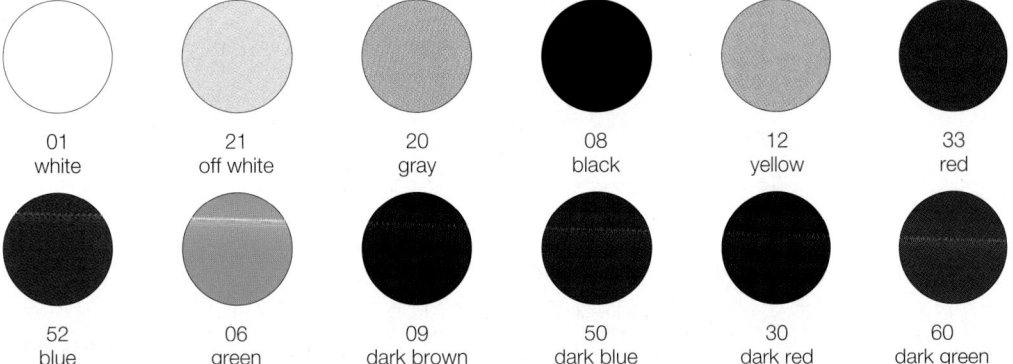

01	21	20	08	12	33
white	off white	gray	black	yellow	red
52	06	09	50	30	60
blue	green	dark brown	dark blue	dark red	dark green

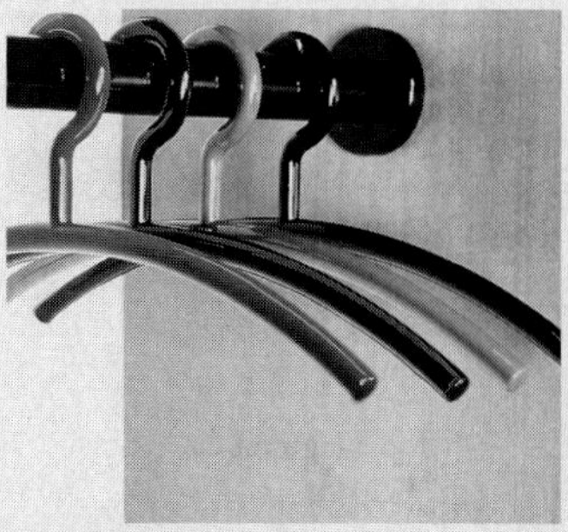

Wardrobe tube 804.51.1. . is also available in special versions:

* lengths from 1,001 to 2,000 mm
* 40 mm diameter for lengths from 100 to 2,500 mm

Ordering instructions:
When ordering, please replace the periods (..) at the end of Cat. No. with the color number of your choice.

Dimensional data not binding.
We reserve the right to alter specifications without notice.

HÄFELE

HEWI Hooks, Nylon Ceiling Hooks

W x D x H = width x depth x height

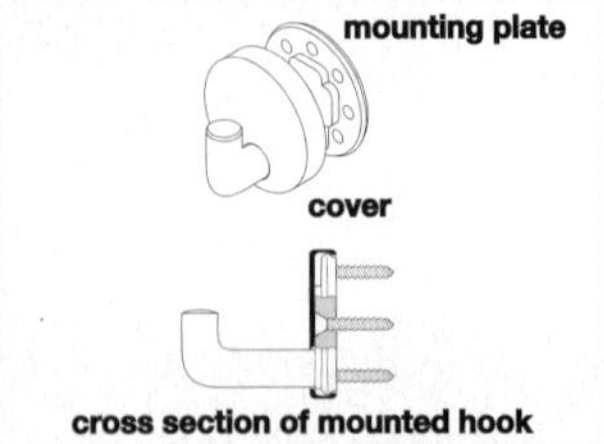

- mounting screws are hidden
- the covers are clipped onto the mounting plate

Hospa particle board screws pan head with Phillips head PZ 2 3.0 diameter

Finish: steel, nickel-plated

Length	Cat. No.
13 mm	015.71.526
15 mm	015.71.535
17 mm	015.71.544

Packing: 1000 pcs.

Hospa particle board screws pan head with Phillips head PZ 2 4.0 diameter

Finish: steel, nickel-plated

Length	Cat. No.
13 mm	015.71.811
15 mm	015.71.820
17 mm	015.71.839

Packing: 1000 pcs.

Hospa particle board screws pan head with Phillips head PZ 2 5.0 diameter

Finish: steel, nickel-plated

Length	Cat. No.
20 mm	015.72.078
30 mm	015.72.096

Packing: 1000 pcs.

Hospa particle board screws counter-sunk head with Phillips head PZ 2 4.0 diameter

Finish: steel, nickel-plated

Length	Cat. No.
15 mm	015.31.826
17 mm	015.31.835
20 mm	015.31.844

Packing: 1000 pcs.

Ordering instructions:
When ordering, please replace the periods (..) at the end of Cat. No. with the color number of your choice.

Double hook, 11 mm diameter
Finish: Nylon, unbreakable
Rosette diameter 50 mm, depth 43 mm

Cat. No.	842.62.2..

Packing: 1 or 10 pcs.

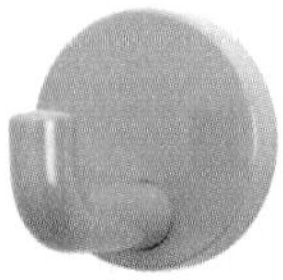

Hook, 15 mm diameter
Finish: Nylon, unbreakable

Rosette Ø	x depth	size of screws	Cat. No.
40 mm	x 135 mm	3.0	842.61.1..
50 mm	x 145 mm	4.0	842.61.2..
60 mm	x 165 mm	5.0	842.61.3..
70 mm	x 100 mm	5.0	842.61.4..

Packing: 1 or 10 pcs.

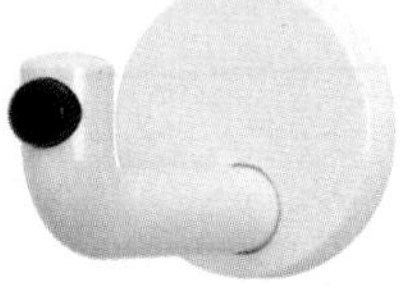

Hook with door buffer,
diameter 20 mm
Finish: Nylon, unbreakable
Buffer: rubber black
Rosette diameter 70 mm, depth 105 mm

Cat. No.	842.63.4..

Packing: 1 or 10 pcs.

Hook, double, 15 mm diameter
Finish: Nylon, unbreakable

width	x depth	x height	Cat. No.
50 mm	x 87 mm	x 136 mm	842.80.0..
90 mm	x 87 mm	x 165 mm	842.84.0..

Packing: 1 or 10 pcs., fixing materials included

Ceiling hook, 11 mm diameter
Finish: Nylon, unbreakable

Rosette Ø	x height	size of screw	Cat. No.
40 mm	x 40 mm	3.0	842.64.1..
50 mm	x 50 mm	4.0	842.64.2..

Packing: 1 or 10 pcs.

Ceiling hook, triple, rotates, 11 mm diameter
Finish: Nylon, unbreakable
Rosette diameter 50 mm, height: 70 mm

Cat. No.	842.65.2..

Packing: 1 or 10 pcs.

Dimensions in mm

HÄFELE

W x D x H =
width x depth x height

Plastic Coat Hooks

Coat hook, Finish: plastic, white

Size: W x D x H	Cat. No.
23 x 40 x 70	843.18.703

Packing: 20 pcs.

Hat & coat hook, Finish: plastic, white

Size: W x D x H	Cat. No.
23 x 98 x 160	843.17.706

Packing: 20 pcs.

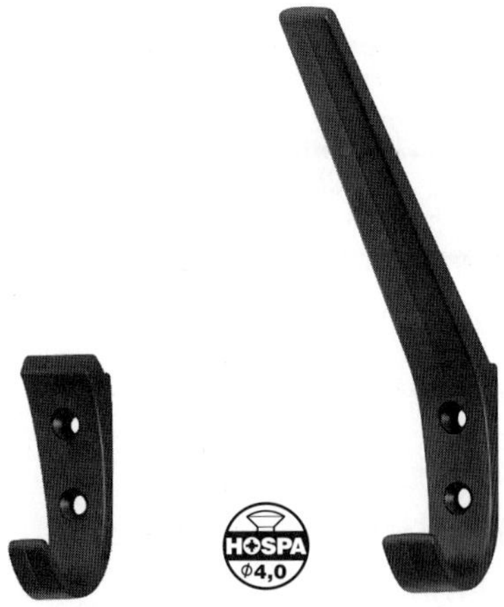

Coat hook, Finish: plastic, black

Size: W x D x H	Cat. No.
23 x 40 x 70	843.18.605

Packing: 20 pcs.

Hat & coat hook, Finish: plastic, black

Size: W x D x H	Cat. No.
23 x 98 x 160	843.17.608

Packing: 20 pcs.

HEWI Nylon Hooks

Coat hook

Size: W x D x H	Cat. No.
20 x 36 x 67	842.50.1..

Packing: 1 pc. or 10 pcs.

Hat & coat hook

Size: W x D x H	Cat. No.
28 x 93 x 165	842.51.1..

Packing: 1 pc. or 10 pcs.

Ordering instructions:
When ordering, please replace the periods (..) at the end of Cat. No. with the color number of your choice.

Dimensions in mm

HÄFELE

Metric Conversion Chart

Length

For our purposes, the basic metric units of *length* are the **millimeter and the meter.**

To convert inches to millimeters, multiply inches x 25.4

Inches	To	Millimeters
1/16"		1.59 mm
1/8"		3.18 mm
3/16"		4.76 mm
1/4"		6.35 mm
3/8"		9.53 mm
1/2"		12.70 mm
5/8"		15.88 mm
3/4"		19.05 mm
7/8"		22.23 mm
1"		25.40 mm
2"		50.80 mm
4"		101.60 mm
6"		152.40 mm
8"		203.20 mm
10"		254.00 mm
12"		304.80 mm
16"		406.40 mm
18"		457.20 mm
21"		533.40 mm
24"		609.60 mm
27"		685.80 mm
30"		762.00 mm
33"		838.20 mm
36"		914.40 mm
39"		990.60 mm
48"		1219.20 mm

To convert millimeters to inches, divide millimeters by 25.4

Millimeters	To	Inches
1 mm		1/16"
3 mm		1/8"
6 mm		1/4"
8 mm		5/16"
10 mm		3/8"
12 mm		1/2"
16 mm		5/8"
19 mm		3/4"
22 mm		7/8"
25.4 mm		1"
32 mm		1 1/4"
100 mm		4"
305 mm		12"
500 mm		19 3/4"
1000 mm		39 3/8"

*Inches are expressed to the nearest 16th.

To convert meters to feet, multiply meters by 3.3

Meters	To	Feet
1 meter		3' 3 3/8"
2 meters		6' 6 3/4"
2.5 meters		8' 2 1/2"
4 meters		13' 1 1/2"
6 meters		19' 8 1/4"

Weight

The basic metric unit of *weight* is the **kilogram.**

To convert kilograms to pounds, multiply kilograms x 2.2

Kilograms	To	Pounds
1 kg		2.2 lbs.
10 kg		22 lbs.
50 kg		110 lbs.

Volume

The basic metric unit of *volume* is the **liter.**

To convert liters to gallons, multiply liters x 0.26

Liters	To	Gallons
1 liter		0.26 gallons
4 liter		1 gallon
15 liter		4 gallons

Product Guide - Fastening Devices

HÄFELE

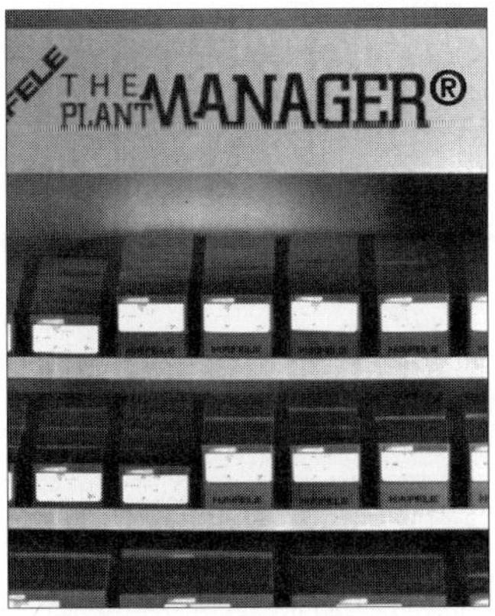

The Plant Manager®
Page **0.2**

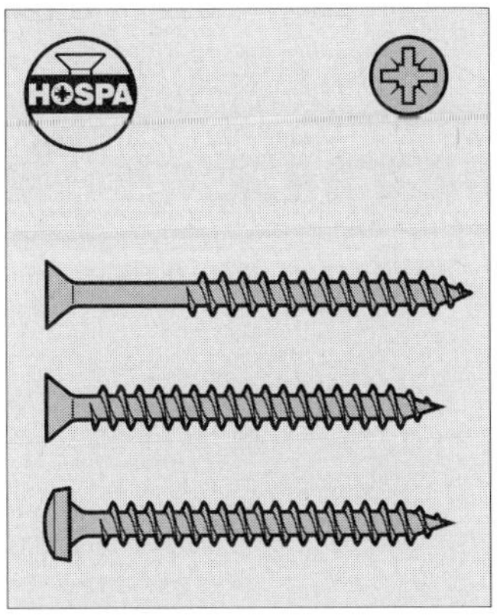

Hospa Screws
Pages **03 - 0.4**

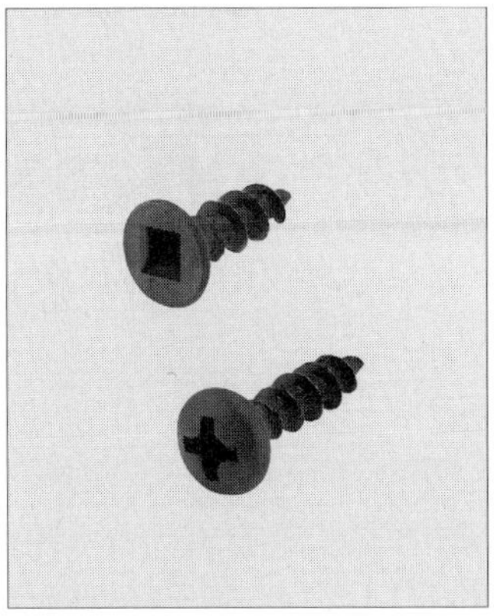

Zip-R Screws
Page **0.5 - 0.6**

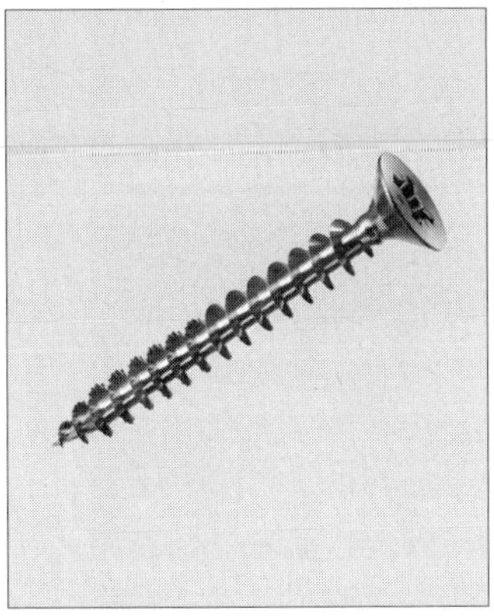

Specialty Screws
Page **0.7**

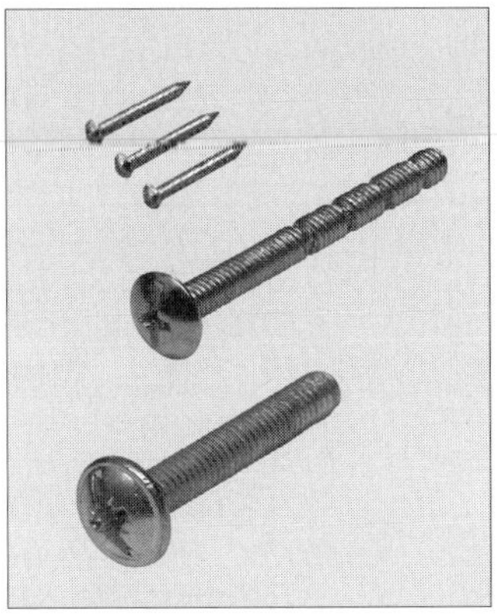

Decorative Screws and Fittings
Page **0.8 - 0.9**

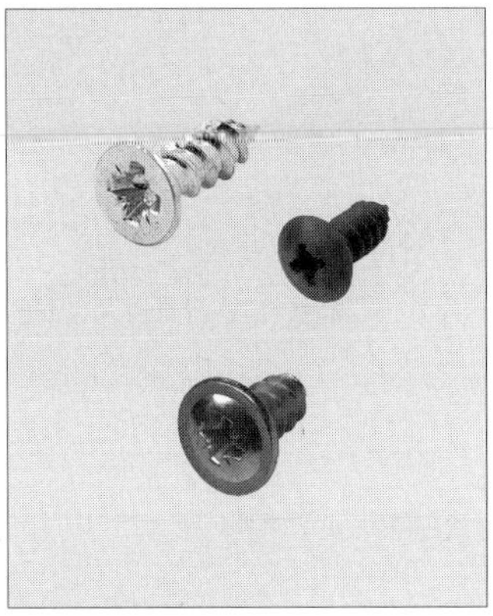

Screws for Drawer Slides & fronts
Page **0.10**

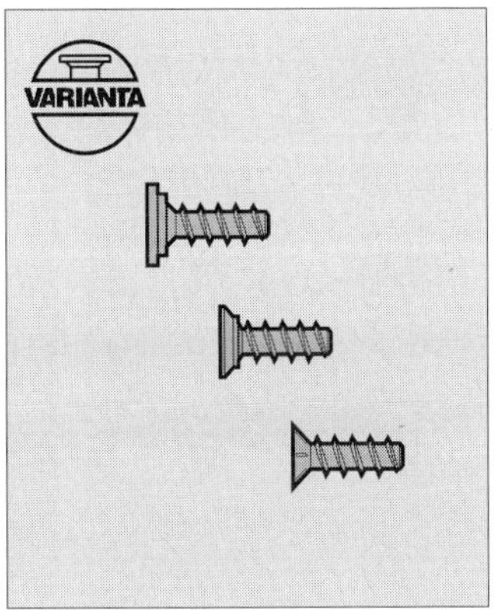

Varianta Screws
Page **0.11**

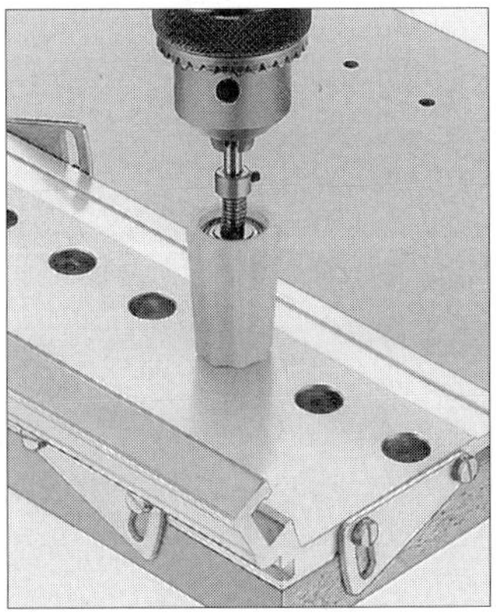

Unitool 32 mm Jig
Page **0.12**

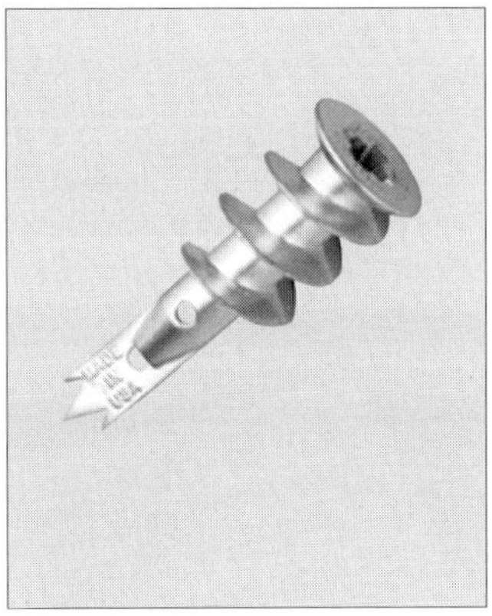

Wall Anchors
Page **0.13**

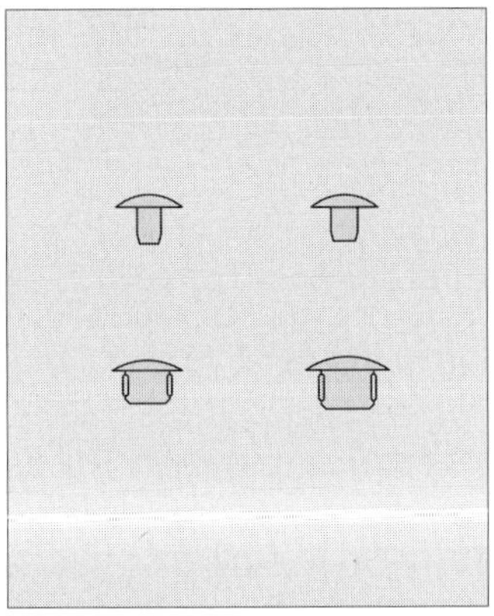

Cover Caps
Page **0.14**

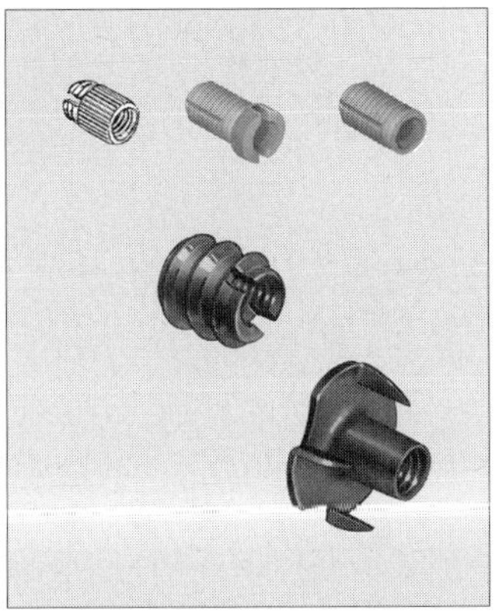

Threaded Inserts
Page **0.15 - 0.16**

THE PLANT MANAGER®
HÄFELE

Maximize Your Productivity

The Rack

- Slant-design keeps cartons in position for easy access.
- Cartons can be opened while in rack.
- Keeps hardware centrally organized and within view.
- Dimensions are - 34 1/2" W x 16" D x 6' H.
  Plant Manager® Rack No. 732.15.069.PM

Cartons

- Consistent packaging
- Locking feature prevents accidental spilling.
- Flip-top design
- Perfect for transporting to work site
- Smaller quantities better for inventory control and fast turnaround.

Labels

- Displays drawing of each part for fast identification.
- Color coded for easy ordering and referencing to catalog.
- Detachable portion permits error-free ordering.

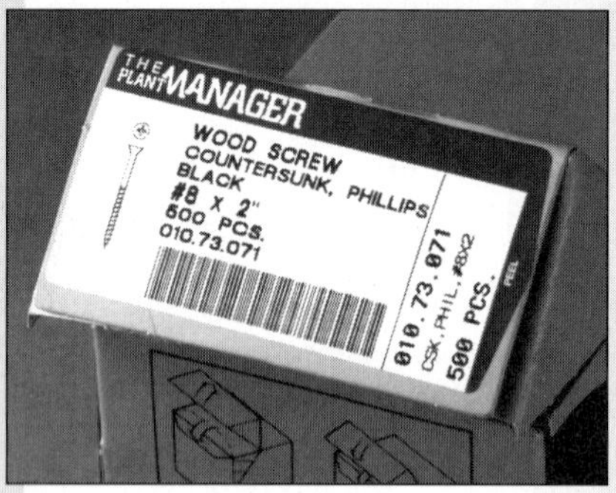

Order Form

- Color coded label from box attaches to order form.
- Information can be filled in and faxed directly
- Provides immediate error-free service

There's no simpler way to increase your productivity than with the Plant Manager System®. The Plant Manager Rack is uniquely designed to organize fasteners for easy access and inventory control. The cartons are designed to assist in the management of day to day use of the fasteners with helpful features such as the flip top and roll-out front for easy access. A unique locking feature allows the box to be transported without fear of spillage. Each carton has a label with a drawing of the fastener and information such as type of fastener, recess, coating, box quantity and more. Another special feature of the label is its patented tear-off tab. This tab features the article number and other detailed information. When you are ready to reorder, just tear this tab off, apply it to the supplied reorder form and fax it in. Simple and easy, error-free ordering, delivered when you need it.

Hospa Screws

HÄFELE

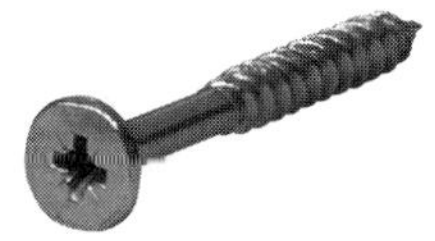

Designed especially for particle board applications. With a 40° thread pitch, these screws readily penetrate particle board, even length wise, without splitting.

Hospa Countersunk Screws Pozi Recess ø x length Metric	Inches	Zinc-Plated Steel Cat. Number	Box Qty.	Zinc-Plated Steel Short Thread Cat. Number	Box Qty.	Nickel-Plated Steel Cat. Number	Box Qty.
3.0 x 13	#5 x 1/2	015.31.326	1000	Piano hinge screw with small head Ø 5 mm			
3.0 x 15	#5 x 9/16	015.31.335	1000			015.35.333	1000
3.0 x 17	#5 x 5/8	015.31.344	1000				
3.0 x 13	#5 x 1/2	015.31.522	1000				
3.0 x 15	#5 x 9/16	015.31.531	1000				
3.0 x 17	#5 x 5/8	015.31.540	1000				
3.0 x 20	#5 x 3/4	015.31.559	1000				
3.0 x 25	#5 x 1	015.31.577	1000	015.31.577	1000		
3.0 x 30	#5 x 1 1/8	015.31.586	1000	015.41.582	1000		
3.5 x 13	#6 x 1/2	015.31.620	1000				
3.5 x 15	#6 x 9/16	015.31.639	1000			015.35.637	1000
3.5 x 17	#6 x 5/8	015.31.648	1000			015.35.646	1000
3.5 x 20	#6 x 3/4	015.31.657	1000			015.35.655	1000
3.5 x 25	#6 x 1	015.31.675	1000				
3.5 x 30	#6 x 1 1/8	015.31.684	1000				
3.5 x 35	#6 x 1 3/8	015.31.693	1000				
3.5 x 40	#6 x 1 1/2	015.31.700	500				
3.5 x 45	#6 x 1 3/4	015.31.719	500				
3.5 x 50	#6 x 2	015.31.728	500				
4.0 x 15	#8 x 9/16	015.31.826	1000			015.35.824	1000
4.0 x 17	#8 x 5/8	015.31.835	1000			015.35.833	1000
4.0 x 20	#8 x 3/4	015.31.844	1000				
4.0 x 25	#8 x 1	015.31.853	1000				
4.0 x 30	#8 x 1 1/8	015.31.862	1000				
4.0 x 35	#8 x 1 3/8	015.31.871	500	015.41.877	500		
4.0 x 40	#8 x 1 1/2	015.31.880	500	015.41.886	500		
4.0 x 45	#8 x 1 3/4	015.31.899	500				
4.0 x 50	#8 x 2	015.31.906	500	015.41.902	500		
4.0 x 60	#8 x 2 3/8			015.41.920	200		
4.0 x 70	#8 x 2 3/4			015.41.939	200		
4.5 x 17	#9 x 5/8	015.31.915	1000				
4.5 x 20	#9 x 3/4	015.31.924	1000				
4.5 x 25	#9 x 1	015.31.933	1000				
4.5 x 30	#9 x 1 1/8	015.31.942	1000				
4.5 x 35	#9 x 1 3/8	015.31.951	500				
4.5 x 40	#9 x 1 1/2	015.31.960	500	015.41.966	500		
4.5 x 45	#9 x 1 3/4	015.31.979	500				
4.5 x 50	#9 x 2	015.31.988	200	015.41.984	200		
4.5 x 60	#9 x 2 3/8			015.42.007	200		
5.0 x 20	#10 x 3/4	015.32.074	1000				
5.0 x 25	#10 x 1	015.32.083	500				
5.0 x 30	#10 x 1 1/8	015.32.092	500				
5.0 x 35	#10 x 1 3/8	015.32.109	500				
5.0 x 40	#10 x 1 1/2	015.32.118	500				
5.0 x 45	#10 x 1 3/4	015.32.127	200				
5.0 x 50	#10 x 2	015.31.997	200				
5.0 x 60	#10 x 2 3/8	015.32.145	500	015.42.141	200		
5.0 x 70	#10 x 2 3/4			015.42.169	200		
5.0 x 80	#10 x 3 1/4			015.42.178	100		
5.0 x 90	#10 x 3 1/2			015.42.187	100		
5.0 x 100	#10 x 4			015.42.196	100		
6.0 x 50	#13 x 2			015.42.347	200		
6.0 x 60	#13 x 2 3/8			015.42.356	200		
6.0 x 70	#13 x 2 3/4			015.42.365	100		
6.0 x 90	#13 x 3 1/2			015.42.383	100		
6.0 x 100	#13 x 4			015.42.392	100		

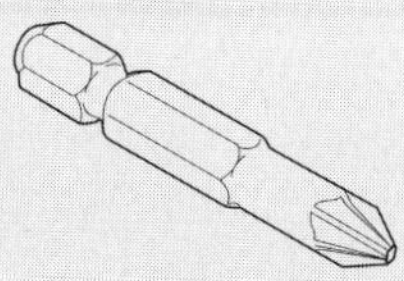

Bits Cross-slot PZ hardened tool steel Hexagon shank, 1/4".

Cat. No.	Size	Length
006.37.301.PM	1	25mm
006.37.310.PM	2	25mm
006.37.329.PM	3	25mm
006.37.276.PM	1	50mm
006.37.285.PM	2	50mm
006.37.294.PM	3	50mm

Packing: 25 pcs.

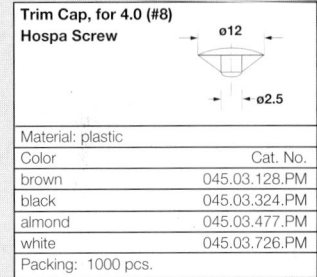

Trim Cap, for 4.0 (#8) Hospa Screw

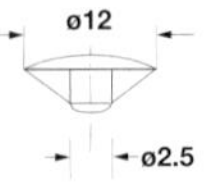

Material: plastic	
Color	Cat. No.
brown	045.03.128.PM
black	045.03.324.PM
almond	045.03.477.PM
white	045.03.726.PM
Packing: 1000 pcs.	

Cup Washer For Countersunk Screws — **Nickel Plated**

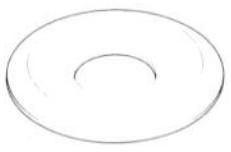

Cat. No.	for size
045.17.711	3.5 (#6)
045.17.739	4.0 (#8)
Packing: 1000 pcs.	

Fastening Devices **0**

Dimensional data not binding. We reserve the right to alter specifications without notice.

Hospa Screws

Manufactured especially for particle board applications. With a 40° thread pitch, these screws readily penetrate particle board, even length wise without splitting.

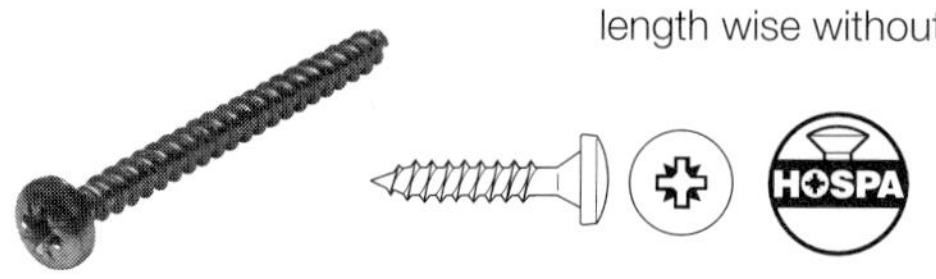

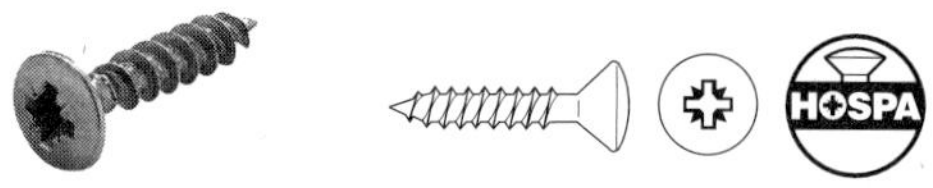

Hospa Panhead Screws

Zinc-plated steel

Pozi Recess

Cat. No.	ø x length Metric	Inches	Box Qty.
015.71.526	3.0 x 13	#5 x 1/2	1000
015.71.535	3.0 x 15	#5 x 9/16	1000
015.71.544	3.0 x 17	#5 x 5/8	1000
015.71.553	3.0 x 20	#5 x 3/4	1000
015.71.571	3.0 x 25	#5 x 1	1000
015.71.624	3.5 x 13	#6 x 1/2	1000
015.71.633	3.5 x 15	#6 x 9/16	1000
015.71.642	3.5 x 17	#3.5 x 5/8	1000
015.71.651	3.5 x 20	#6 x 3/4	1000
015.71.679	3.5 x 25	#6 x 1	1000
015.71.688	3.5 x 30	#6 x 1 1/8	1000
015.71.697	3.5 x 35	#6 x 1 3/8	1000
015.71.811	4.0 x 13	#8 x 1/2	1000
015.71.820	4.0 x 15	#8 x 9/16	1000
015.71.839	4.0 x 17	#8 x 5/8	1000
015.71.848	4.0 x 20	#8 x 3/4	1000
015.71.857	4.0 x 25	#8 x 1	1000
015.71.866	4.0 x 30	#8 x 1 1/8	1000
015.71.875	4.0 x 35	#8 x 1 3/8	500
015.71.884	4.0 x 40	#8 x 1 1/2	1000
015.71.893	4.0 x 45	#8 x 1 3/4	500
015.71.900	4.5 x 13	#9 x 1/2	1000
015.71.919	4.5 x 15	#9 x 9/16	1000
015.71.991	4.5 x 17	#9 x 5/8	1000
015.71.928	4.5 x 20	#9 x 3/4	1000
015.71.937	4.5 x 25	#9 x 1	1000
015.71.955	4.5 x 35	#9 x 1 3/8	500
015.72.078	5.0 x 20	#10 x 3/4	1000
015.72.096	5.0 x 30	#10 x 1 1/8	500
015.72.130	5.0 x 50	#10 x 2	200

Hospa Raised Head Countersunk Screws

Nickel-plated steel

Pozi Recess

Cat. No.	ø x length Metric	Inches	Box Qty.
015.55.531	3.0 x 15	#5 x 9/16	1000
015.55.540	3.0 x 17	#5 x 5/8	1000
015.55.559	3.0 x 20	#5 x 3/4	1000
015.55.577	3.0 x 25	#5 x 1	1000
015.55.586	3.0 x 30	#5 x 1 1/8	1000
015.55.639	3.5 x 15	#6 x 9/16	1000
015.55.648	3.5 x 17	#6 x 5/8	1000
015.55.657	3.5 x 20	#6 x 3/4	1000
015.55.675	3.5 x 25	#6 x 1	1000
015.55.684	3.5 x 30	#6 x 1 1/8	1000
015.55.693	3.5 x 35	#6 x 1 3/8	1000
015.55.844	4.0 x 20	#8 x 3/4	1000
015.55.853	4.0 x 25	#8 x 1	1000
015.55.862	4.0 x 30	#8 x 1 1/8	1000
015.55.871	4.0 x 35	#8 x 1 3/8	500
015.55.880	4.0 x 40	#8 x 1 1/2	500

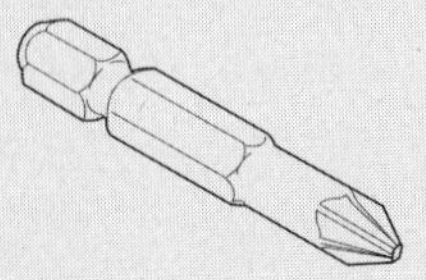

Bits Cross-slot PZ hardened tool steel
Hexagon shank, 1/4".

Cat. No.	Size	Length
006.37.301.PM	1	25mm
006.37.310.PM	2	25mm
006.37.329.PM	3	25mm
006.37.276.PM	1	50mm
006.37.285.PM	2	50mm
006.37.294.PM	3	50mm

Packing: 25 pcs.

Cup Washer For Countersunk Screws — Nickel-Plated

Cat. No.	for size
045.17.711	3.5 (#6)
045.17.739	4.0 (#8)

Packing: 1000 pcs.

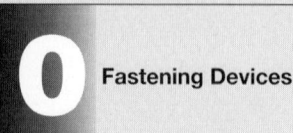

Rear Panel Screw: designed for tap-in or screw-in assembly with #1 Phillips. Removal of panel can be easily accomplished without damage.

Hardened Steel Black Oxide Finish

Rear Panel Push Screw

Truss-head/Phillips with No. 1 recess.

Cat. No.	ø x length	Box Qty.
016.14.300	#2 x 3/4	1000

Trim Head Screw: finishing screw, with very small head for fastening without the obvious appearance of the fastener head.

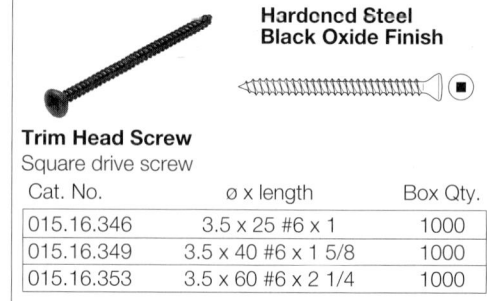

Hardened Steel Black Oxide Finish

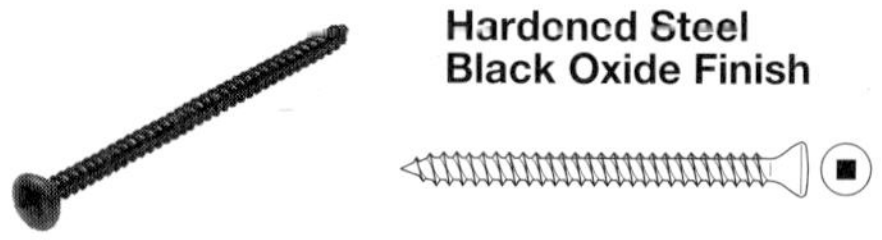

Trim Head Screw

Square drive screw

Cat. No.	ø x length	Box Qty.
015.16.346	3.5 x 25 #6 x 1	1000
015.16.349	3.5 x 40 #6 x 1 5/8	1000
015.16.353	3.5 x 60 #6 x 2 1/4	1000

Face Frame Screw: specially designed for face frame application, Type 17Auger point eliminates wood splitting while providing ease of installation.

Hardened Steel Black Oxide Finish

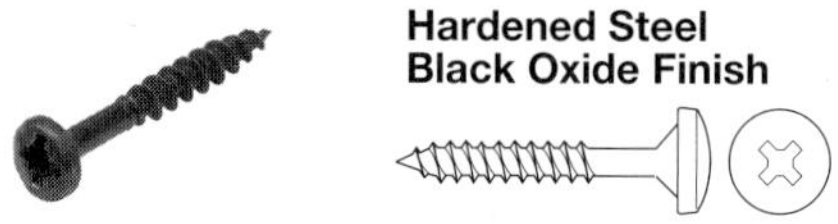

Face Frame Type 17 - Waxed

Panhead, Phillips Drive, recess

Cat. No.	ø x length	Box Qty.
015.17.348	3.5 x 32 #6 x 1 1/4	1000
015.17.349	3.5 x 40 #6 x 1 1/2	1000

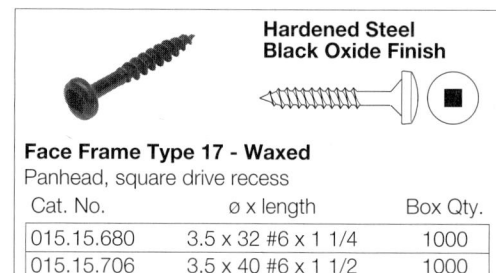

Hardened Steel Black Oxide Finish

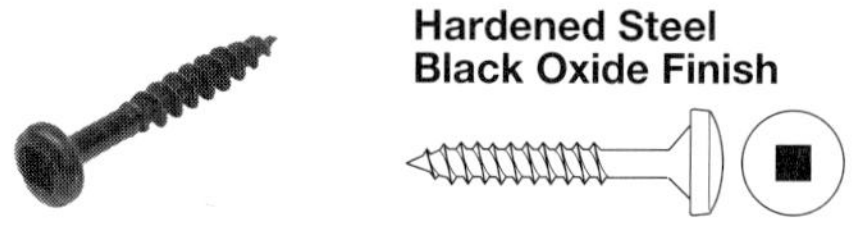

Face Frame Type 17 - Waxed

Panhead, square drive recess

Cat. No.	ø x length	Box Qty.
015.15.680	3.5 x 32 #6 x 1 1/4	1000
015.15.706	3.5 x 40 #6 x 1 1/2	1000

Zip-R Countersunk and Panhead Screws

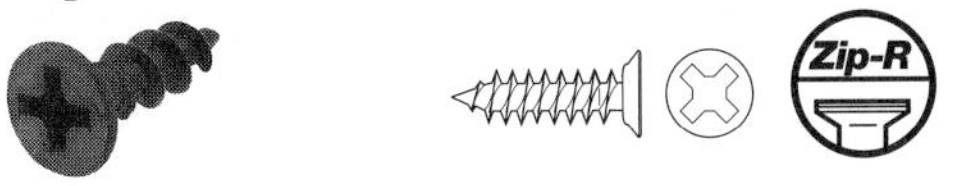

Deep Thread Countersunk Screws

Steel, Black Oxide

Phillips Recess

Cat. No.	ø x length Metric	Inches	Box Qty.
010.73.041	3.5 x 12	#6 x 1/2	1000
010.73.042	3.5 x 15	#6 x 9/16	1000
010.73.043	3.5 x 16	#6 x 5/8	1000
010.73.045	3.5 x 20	#6 x 3/4	1000
010.73.046	3.5 x 25	#6 x 1	1000
010.73.047	3.5 x 30	#6 x 1 1/8	1000
010.73.048	3.5 x 32	#6 x 1 1/4	1000
010.73.049	3.5 x 40	#6 x 1 1/2	1000
010.73.050	3.5 x 45	#6 x 1 3/4	1000
010.73.051	3.5 x 50	#6 x 2	1000
010.73.061	4.0 x 12	#8 x 1/2	1000
010.73.063	4.0 x 16	#8 x 5/8	1000
010.73.065	4.0 x 20	#8 x 3/4	1000
010.73.066	4.0 x 25	#8 x 1	1000
010.73.067	4.0 x 30	#8 x 1 1/8	1000
010.73.068	4.0 x 32	#8 x 1 1/4	1000
010.73.079	4.0 x 35	#8 x 1 3/8	1000
010.73.069	4.0 x 40	#8 x 1 1/2	500
010.73.070	4.0 x 45	#8 x 1 3/4	1000
010.73.071	4.0 x 50	#8 x 2	500
010.73.073	4.0 x 60	#8 x 2 1/4	500
010.73.074	4.0 x 65	#8 x 2 1/2	500
010.73.075	4.0 x 70	#8 x 2 3/4	500
010.73.076	4.0 x 75	#8 x 3	500

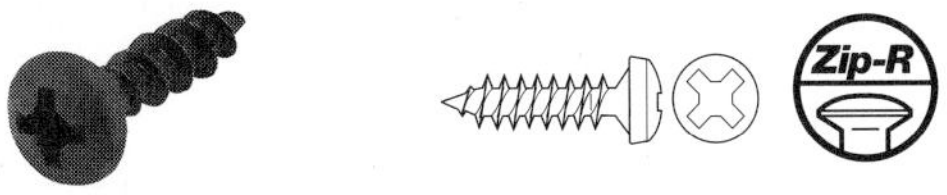

Deep Thread Panhead Screws

Steel, Black Oxide

Phillips Recess

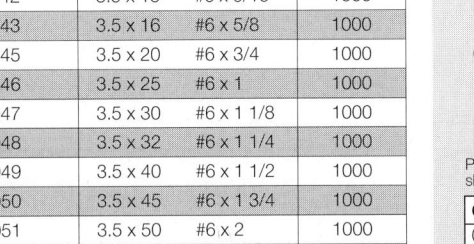

Cat. No.	ø x length Metric	Inches	Box Qty.
010.83.041	3.5 x 12	#6 x 1/2	1000
010.83.042	3.5 x 15	#6 x 9/16	1000
010.83.043	3.5 x 16	#6 x 5/8	1000
010.83.045	3.5 x 20	#6 x 3/4	1000
010.83.046	3.5 x 25	#6 x 1	1000
010.83.047	3.5 x 30	#6 x 1 1/8	1000
010.83.048	3.5 x 32	#6 x 1 1/4	1000
010.83.049	3.5 x 40	#6 x 1 1/2	1000
010.83.050	3.5 x 45	#6 x 1 3/4	1000
010.83.051	3.5 x 50	#6 x 2	1000
010.83.061	4.0 x 12	#8 x 1/2	1000
010.83.063	4.0 x 16	#8 x 5/8	1000
010.83.065	4.0 x 20	#8 x 3/4	1000
010.83.066	4.0 x 25	#8 x 1	1000
010.83.067	4.0 x 30	#8 x 1 1/8	1000
010.83.068	4.0 x 32	#8 x 1 1/4	1000
010.83.099	4.0 x 35	#8 x 1 3/8	1000
010.83.069	4.0 x 40	#8 x 1 1/2	500
010.83.070	4.0 x 45	#8 x 1 3/4	1000
010.83.071	4.0 x 50	#8 x 2	500
010.83.073	4.0 x 60	#8 x 2 1/4	500
010.83.074	4.0 x 65	#8 x 2 1/2	500
010.83.075	4.0 x 70	#8 x 2 3/4	500
010.83.076	4.0 x 75	#8 x 3	500

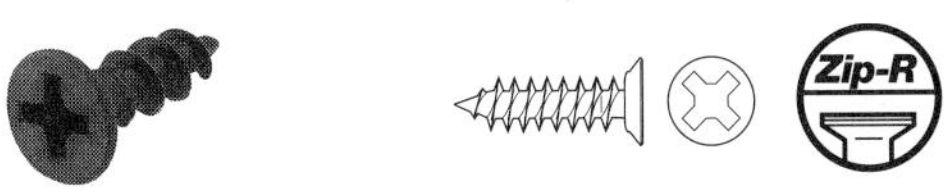

Deep Thread Countersunk Screws

Steel, Zinc-plated

Phillips Recess

Cat. No.	ø x length Metric	Inches	Box Qty.
010.73.941	3.5 x 12	#6 x 1/2	1000
010.73.942	3.5 x 15	#6 x 9/16	1000
010.73.943	3.5 x 16	#6 x 5/8	1000
010.73.945	3.5 x 20	#6 x 3/4	1000
010.73.946	3.5 x 25	#6 x 1	1000
010.73.947	3.5 x 30	#6 x 1 1/8	1000
010.73.948	3.5 x 32	#6 x 1 1/4	1000
010.73.949	3.5 x 40	#6 x 1 1/2	1000
010.73.950	3.5 x 45	#6 x 1 3/4	1000
010.73.951	3.5 x 50	#6 x 2	1000
010.73.961	4.0 x 12	#8 x 1/2	1000
010.73.963	4.0 x 16	#8 x 5/8	1000
010.73.965	4.0 x 20	#8 x 3/4	1000
010.73.966	4.0 x 25	#8 x 1	1000
010.73.967	4.0 x 30	#8 x 1 1/8	1000
010.73.968	4.0 x 32	#8 x 1 1/4	1000
010.73.979	4.0 x 35	#8 x 1 3/8	1000
010.73.969	4.0 x 40	#8 x 1 1/2	500
010.73.070	4.0 x 45	#8 x 1 3/4	1000
010.73.971	4.0 x 50	#8 x 2	500
010.73.973	4.0 x 60	#8 x 2 1/4	500
010.73.974	4.0 x 65	#8 x 2 1/2	500
010.73.975	4.0 x 70	#8 x 2 3/4	500
010.73.976	4.0 x 75	#8 x 3	500

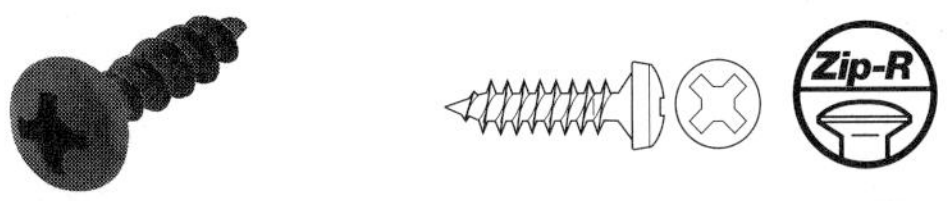

Deep Thread Panhead Screws

Steel, Zinc-plated

Phillips Recess

Cat. No.	ø x length Metric	Inches	Box Qty.
010.83.941	3.5 x 12	#6 x 1/2	1000
010.83.942	3.5 x 15	#6 x 9/16	1000
010.83.943	3.5 x 16	#6 x 5/8	1000
010.83.945	3.5 x 20	#6 x 3/4	1000
010.83.946	3.5 x 25	#6 x 1	1000
010.83.947	3.5 x 30	#6 x 1 1/8	1000
010.83.948	3.5 x 32	#6 x 1 1/4	1000
010.83.949	3.5 x 40	#6 x 1 1/2	1000
010.83.950	3.5 x 45	#6 x 1 3/4	1000
010.83.951	3.5 x 50	#6 x 2	1000
010.83.961	4.0 x 12	#8 x 1/2	1000
010.83.963	4.0 x 16	#8 x 5/8	1000
010.83.965	4.0 x 20	#8 x 3/4	1000
010.83.966	4.0 x 25	#8 x 1	1000
010.83.967	4.0 x 30	#8 x 1 1/8	1000
010.83.968	4.0 x 32	#8 x 1 1/4	1000
010.83.999	4.0 x 35	#8 x 1 3/8	1000
010.83.969	4.0 x 40	#8 x 1 1/2	500
010.83.970	4.0 x 45	#8 x 1 3/4	1000
010.83.971	4.0 x 50	#8 x 2	500
010.83.973	4.0 x 60	#8 x 2 1/4	500
010.83.974	4.0 x 65	#8 x 2 1/2	500
010.83.975	4.0 x 70	#8 x 2 3/4	500
010.83.976	4.0 x 75	#8 x 3	500

HÄFELE

Zip-R Screws

High-quality screw for wood to wood applications. Extra deep threads and case hardened body provide ease of installation in all types of wood.

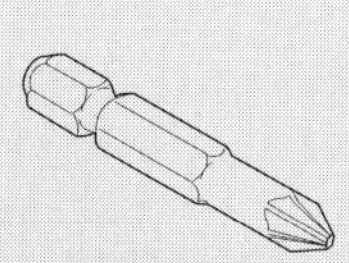

Phillips Bit hardened tool steel Hexagon shank, 1/4".

Cat. No.	Size	Length
006.40.270.PM	1	25mm
006.40.280.PM	2	25mm
006.40.290.PM	3	25mm
006.40.271.PM	1	50mm
006.40.281.PM	2	50mm
006.40.291.PM	3	50mm

Packing: 25 pcs.

Trim Cap, for Phillips Recess

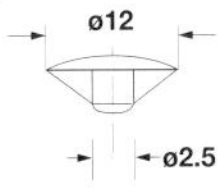

Material: plastic

Color	Cat. No.
white	045.22.700.PM
almond	045.22.400.PM
dove gray	045.22.500.PM
black	045.22.300.PM
oak	045.22.410.PM

Packing: 500 pcs.

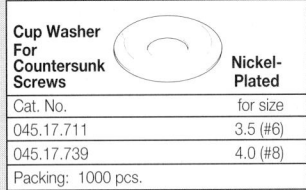

Cup Washer For Countersunk Screws **Nickel-Plated**

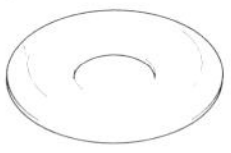

Cat. No.	for size
045.17.711	3.5 (#6)
045.17.739	4.0 (#8)

Packing: 1000 pcs.

Dimensional data not binding. We reserve the right to alter specifications without notice.

HÄFELE

Zip-R Countersunk and Panhead Screws

Zip-R Screws
High quality screw for wood to wood to wood applications. Extra deep threads and case hardened body provides ease of installation in all types of wood.

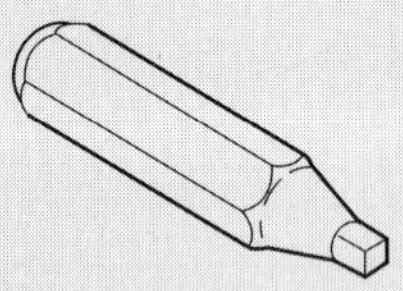

Square Drive Bits hardened tool steel Hexagon shank, 1/4".

Cat. No.	Size	Length
006.37.874.PM	1	25mm
006.37.883.PM	2	25mm
006.37.892.PM	3	25mm
006.37.810.PM	1	50mm
006.37.829.PM	2	50mm
006.37.838.PM	3	50mm

Packing: 25 pcs.

Cover Caps for Square Recess Countersunk Screws for 4.0 (#8) and 4.5 (#9)

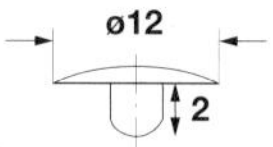

Cat. No.	for size
045.15.100.PM	Brown
045.15.306.PM	Black
045.15.404.PM	Almond
045.15.502.PM	Dove Gray
045.15.708.PM	White

Packing: 500 pcs.

Cup Washer For Countersunk Screws — **Nickel-Plated**

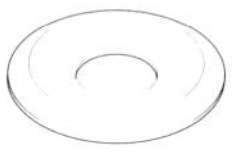

Cat. No.	for size
045.17.711	3.5 (#6)
045.17.739	4.0 (#8)

Packing: 1000 pcs.

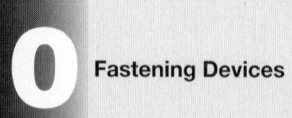

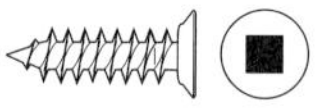

Deep Thread Countersunk Screws
Steel, Black Oxide
Square Recess

Cat. No.	ø x length Metric	Inches	Box Qty.
010.72.041	3.5 x 12	#6 x 1/2	1000
010.72.042	3.5 x 15	#6 x 9/16	1000
010.72.043	3.5 x 16	#6 x 5/8	1000
010.72.045	3.5 x 20	#6 x 3/4	1000
010.72.046	3.5 x 25	#6 x 1	1000
010.72.047	3.5 x 30	#6 x 1 1/8	1000
010.72.048	3.5 x 32	#6 x 1 1/4	1000
010.72.049	3.5 x 40	#6 x 1 1/2	1000
010.72.050	3.5 x 45	#6 x 1 3/4	1000
010.72.051	3.5 x 50	#6 x 2	1000
010.72.061	4.0 x 12	#8 x 1/2	1000
010.72.063	4.0 x 16	#8 x 5/8	1000
010.72.065	4.0 x 20	#8 x 3/4	1000
010.72.066	4.0 x 25	#8 x 1	1000
010.72.068	4.0 x 32	#8 x 1 1/4	1000
010.72.069	4.0 x 40	#8 x 1 1/2	500
010.72.070	4.0 x 45	#8 x 1 3/4	1000
010.72.071	4.0 x 50	#8 x 2	500
010.72.073	4.0 x 60	#8 x 2 1/4	500
010.72.074	4.0 x 65	#8 x 2 1/2	500
010.72.075	4.0 x 70	#8 x 2 3/4	500
010.72.076	4.0 x 75	#8 x 3	500

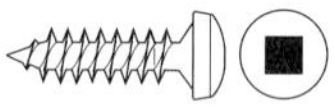

Deep Thread Panhead Screws
Steel, Black Oxide
Square Recess

Cat. No.	ø x length Metric	Inches	Box Qty.
010.82.041	3.5 x 12	#6 x 1/2	1000
010.82.042	3.5 x 15	#6 x 9/16	1000
010.82.043	3.5 x 16	#6 x 5/8	1000
010.82.045	3.5 x 20	#6 x 3/4	1000
010.82.046	3.5 x 25	#6 x 1	1000
010.82.048	3.5 x 32	#6 x 1 1/4	1000
010.82.049	3.5 x 40	#6 x 1 1/2	1000
010.82.050	3.5 x 45	#6 x 1 3/4	1000
010.82.051	3.5 x 50	#6 x 2	1000
010.82.061	4.0 x 12	#8 x 1/2	1000
010.82.063	4.0 x 16	#8 x 5/8	1000
010.82.065	4.0 x 20	#8 x 3/4	1000
010.82.066	4.0 x 25	#8 x 1	1000
010.82.068	4.0 x 32	#8 x 1 1/4	1000
010.82.069	4.0 x 40	#8 x 1 1/2	500
010.82.070	4.0 x 45	#8 x 1 3/4	1000
010.82.071	4.0 x 50	#8 x 2	500
010.82.073	4.0 x 60	#8 x 2 1/4	500
010.82.074	4.0 x 65	#8 x 2 1/2	500
010.82.075	4.0 x 70	#8 x 2 3/4	500
010.82.076	4.0 x 75	#8 x 3	500

Screws -Stainless Steel, Cap Socket and Rear Panel

HÄFELE

Countersunk Screw	Stainless steel Pozi Recess

Cat. No.	ø x length Metric	Inches	Box Qty.
014.70.631	3.5 x 16	#6 x 5/8	200
014.70.677	3.5 x 25	#6 x 1	200
014.70.846	4.0 x 20	#8 x 3/4	200
014.70.864	4.0 x 32	#8 x 1 1/4	200
014.70.908	4.0 x 50	#8 x 2	200
014.71.156	5.0 x 70	#10 x 2 3/4	200

Stainless Steel Screw
Made of marine steel - perfect for applications where rust is not allowed.

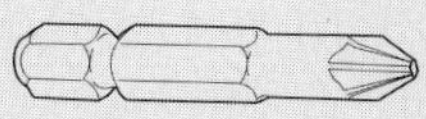

Bits Cross-slot PZ hardened tool steel Hexagon shank, 1/4".

Cat. No.	Size	Length
006.37.301.PM	1	25mm
006.37.310.PM	2	25mm
006.37.329.PM	3	25mm
006.37.276.PM	1	50mm
006.37.285.PM	2	50mm
006.37.294.PM	3	50mm

Packing: 25 pcs.

Screw with Cap Socket	Zinc-plated steel Pozi Recess

Cat. No.	ø x length Metric	Inches	Box Qty.
015.01.935	4.5 x 25	#9 x 1	1000
015.01.944	4.5 x 32	#9 x 1 1/4	1000
015.01.953	4.5 x 35	#9 x 1 3/8	500
015.01.962	4.5 x 40	#9 x 11/2	500
015.01.971	4.5 x 45	#9 x 1 3/4	500
015.01.980	4.5 x 50	#9 x 2	200
015.02.003	4.5 x 60	#9 x 2 3/8	200
015.02.021	4.5 x 70	#9 x 2 3/4	200
015.02.049	4.5 x 80	#9 x 3 1/8	200

Cap Socket Screw
A self-countersinking screw used in applications requiring the screw to be deeply countersunk and a cover cap used. The 5 mm drilled hole allows a special cover cap to be installed for a flush surface.

Trim Cap to press-fit
for Screw with Cap Socket.
Material: plastic

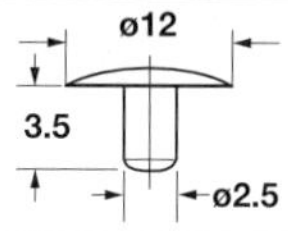

Color	Cat. No.
white	045.18.709.PM
brown	045.18.101.PM
black	045.18.307.PM
pine	045.18.209.PM

Packing: 500 pcs.

Rear Panel Screws	Zinc-plated steel Pozi Recess

Cat. No.	ø x length Metric	Inches	Box Qty.
016.10.573	3.0 x 25	#5 x 1	1000
016.10.644	3.5 x 17	#6 x 5/8	1000
016.10.671	3.5 x 25	#6 x 1	1000
016.10.680	3.5 x 32	#6 x 1 1/4	1000
016.10.699	3.5 x 35	#6 x 1 3/8	1000
016.10.831	4.0 x 17	#8 x 5/8	1000
016.10.840	4.0 x 20	#8 x 3/4	1000
016.10.859	4.0 x 25	#8 x 1	1000
016.10.868	4.0 x 32	#8 x 1 1/4	1000
016.10.877	4.0 x 35	#8 x 1 3/8	500
016.10.886	4.0 x 40	#8 x 1 1/2	500

Rear Panel Screw
Unique screw with a flange extension head for extra grip requirements such as on rear panels of cabinets.

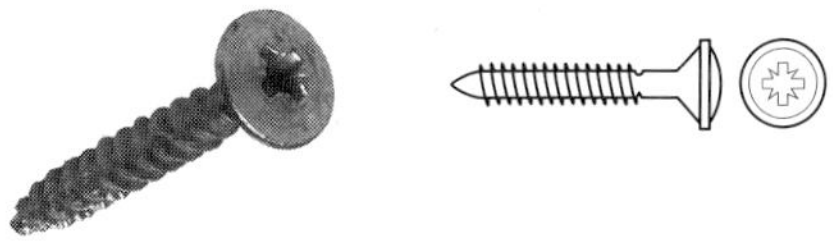

HÄFELE

Screws for Decorative Hardware

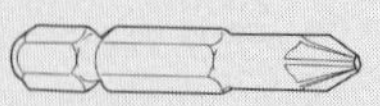

Phillips Bit hardened tool steel Hexagon shank, 1/4".

Cat. No.	Size	Length
006.40.270.PM	1	25mm
006.40.280.PM	2	25mm
006.40.290.PM	3	25mm
006.40.271.PM	1	50mm
006.40.281.PM	2	50mm
006.40.291.PM	3	50mm

Packing: 25 pcs.

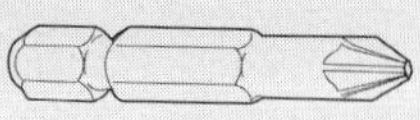

Bits Cross-slot PZ hardened tool steel Hexagon shank, 1/4".

Cat. No.	Size	Length
006.37.301.PM	1	25mm
006.37.310.PM	2	25mm
006.37.329.PM	3	25mm
006.37.276.PM	1	50mm
006.37.285.PM	2	50mm
006.37.294.PM	3	50mm

Packing: 25 pcs.

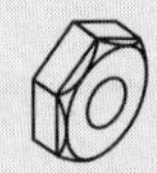

Hexagon Nut for M4 Screw

Cat. No.	Box Qty.
034.11.943	100

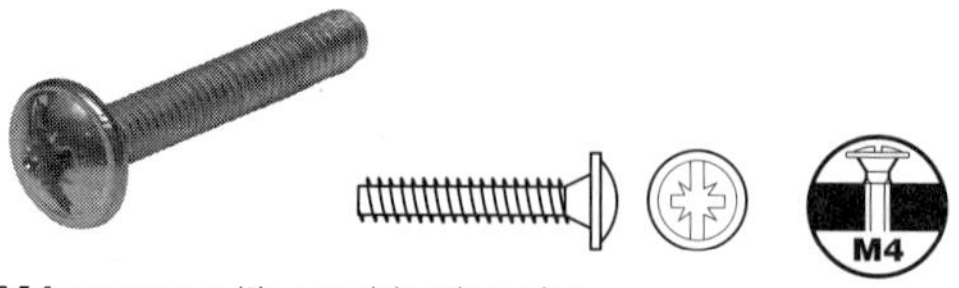

M4 screw, with combination slot
Finish: zinc plated

Cat. No.	ø x Length Metric	Box Qty.
022.35.081	M4 x 8	100 or 1000
022.35.090	M4 x 9	100 or 1000
022.35.109	M4 x 10	100 or 1000
022.35.127	M4 x 12	100 or 1000
022.35.154	M4 x 15	100 or 1000
022.35.181	M4 x 18	100 or 1000
022.35.207	M4 x 20	100 or 1000
022.35.225	M4 x 22	100 or 1000
022.35.234	M4 x 23	100 or 1000
022.35.252	M4 x 25	100 or 1000
022.35.289	M4 x 28	100 or 1000
022.35.305	M4 x 30	100 or 1000
022.35.350	M4 x 35	100 or 1000
022.35.387	M4 x 38	100 or 1000
022.35.403	M4 x 40	100 or 1000
022.35.458	M4 x 45	100 or 1000
022.35.501	M4 x 50	100 or 1000
022.35.609	M4 x 60	100 or 1000

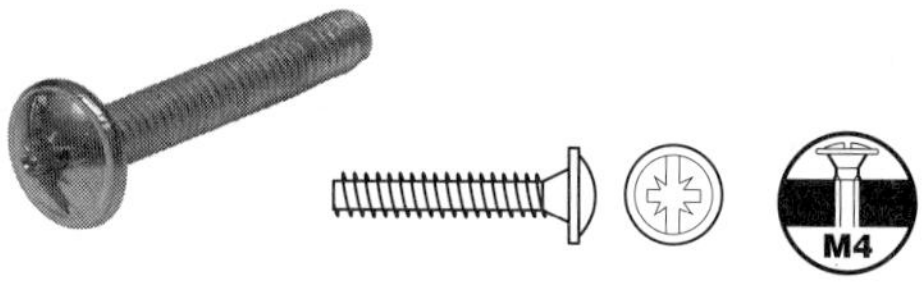

M4 Screw, with combination slot
Finish: nickel-plated

Cat. No.	ø x Length Metric	Box Qty.
022.34.157	M4 x 15	1000
022.34.255	M4 x 25	1000
022.34.308	M4 x 30	1000

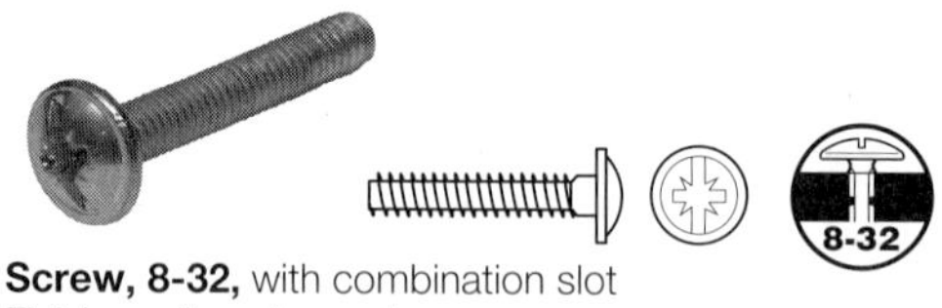

Screw, 8-32, with combination slot
Finish: yellow chromate

Cat. No.	ø x Length Metric	Box Qty.
022.25.229	8-32 x 22	100 or 1000
022.25.256	8-32 x 25	100 or 1000
022.25.327	8-32 x 32	100 or 1000
022.25.381	8-32 x 38	100 or 1000
022.25.452	8-32 x 45	100 or 1000

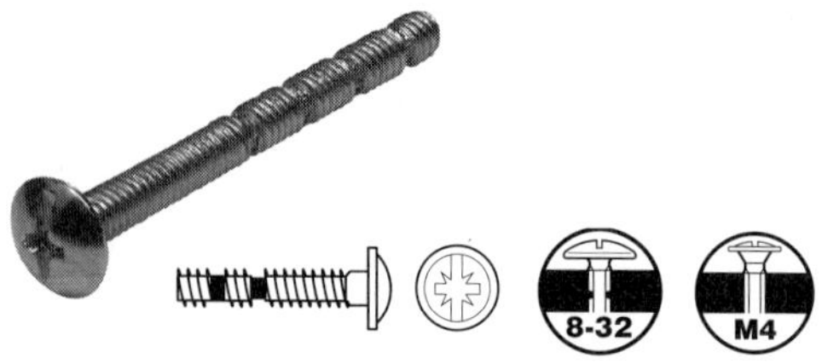

Break-Off Screw

Cat. No.	ø x Length Metric	Box Qty.
Break-Off Screw 8-32 yellow chromate		
022.25.881	8-32 x 1 3/4 x 3/4	100 or 1000
Break-Off Screw M4 zinc-plated		
022.35.887	M4 x 1 3/4 x 3/4	100 or 1000

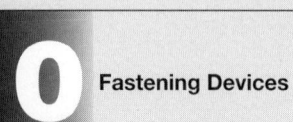

Dimensional data not binding. We reserve the right to alter specifications without notice.

Screws for Decorative Hardware

HÄFELE

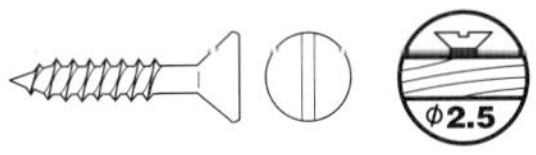

Countersunk wood screws
Finish: brass, unfinished

Cat. No.	ø x Length Metric
011.00.214	2.5 x 12
011.00.232	2.5 x 16
011.00.241	2.5 x 20

Packing: 200 pcs.

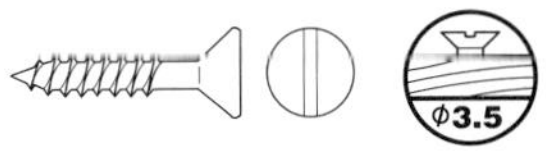

Countersunk wood screws
Finish: brass, nickel-plated

Cat. No.	ø x Length Metric
011.04.525	3.5 x 16
011.04.534	3.5 x 20
011.04.543	3.5 x 25

Packing: 200 pcs.

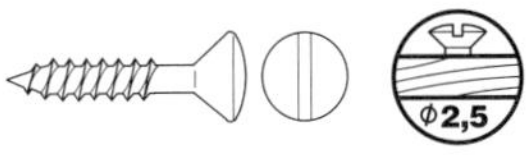

Raised Head Countersunk wood screws
Finish: brass, unfinished

Cat. No.	ø x Length Metric
011.20.216	2.5 x 12
011.20.234	2.5 x 16
011.20.243	2.5 x 20

Packing: 200 pcs.

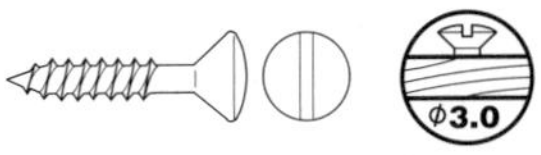

Raised Head Countersunk wood screws
Finish: brass, nickel-plated

Cat. No.	ø x Length Metric
011.24.410	3.0 x 12
011.24.438	3.0 x 16
011.24.447	3.0 x 20

Packing: 200 pcs.

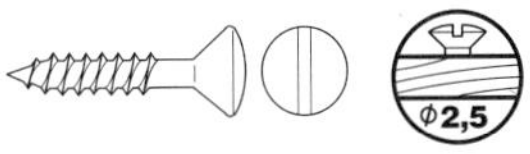

Raised Head Countersunk wood screws
Finish: brass, nickel-plated

Cat. No.	ø x Length Metric
011.24.214	2.5 x 12
011.24.232	2.5 x 16
011.24.241	2.5 x 20

Packing: 200 pcs.

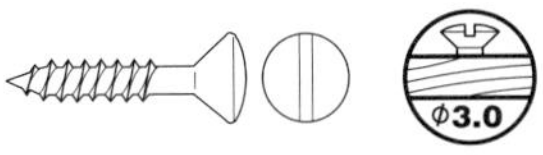

Raised Head Countersunk wood screws
Finish: brass, unfinished

Cat. No.	ø x Length Metric
011.20.412	3.0 x 12
011.20.430	3.0 x 16
011.20.449	3.0 x 20

Packing: 200 pcs.

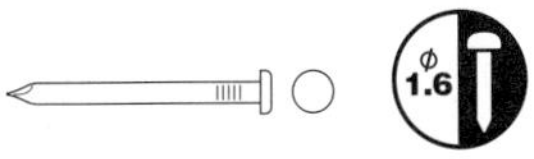

Round-head Metal Pins Ø 1.6 mm
Finish: steel, brass-plated

Cat. No.	ø x Length Metric
076.40.191	1.6 x 15

Packing: 2150 pcs.

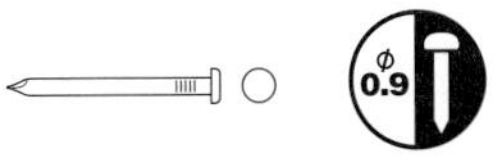

Round-head Metal Pins Ø .9 mm
Finish: steel, nickel-plated

Cat. No.	ø x Length Metric
076.40.217	.9 x 11

Packing: 7400 pcs.

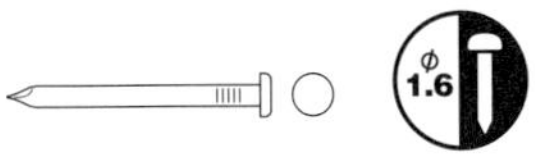

Round-head Metal Pins Ø 1.6 mm
Finish: steel, nickel-plated

Cat. No.	ø x Length Metric
076.40.299	1.6 x 15

Packing: 2000 pcs.

Round-head Metal Pins Ø .9 mm
Finish: steel, brass-plated

Cat. No.	ø x Length Metric
076.40.119	.9 x 11

Packing: 7400 pcs.

Dimensional data not binding.
We reserve the right to alter specifications without notice.

HÄFELE

Screws for Drawer Slides and Drawer Fronts

Specially designed for ball-bearing type slides.

Hospa Special Screws for Accuride® Slides
Panhead with Phillips Recess

Cat. No.	Finish	ø x length mm	ø x length Inches	Box Qty.
013.09.900	zinc	4.0 x 11	#8 x 7/16	200
013.09.300	black	4.0 x 11	#8 x 7/16	200
013.09.700	white	4.0 x 11	#8 x 7/16	200
013.03.706	white	4.0 x 13	#8 x 1/2	200
013.03.304	black	4.0 x 13	#8 x 1/2	200
013.03.902	zinc	4.0 x 13	#8 x 1/2	200

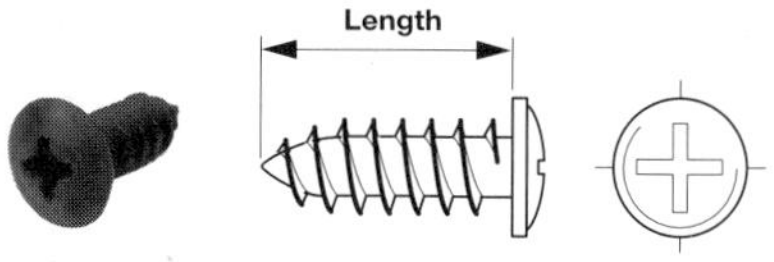

Specially designed screw for epoxy slides.

Hospa Special Screw for Epoxy Slides
Countersunk head with Phillips Recess
Finish: steel, zinc-plated

Cat. No.	ø x length mm	ø x length inches	Box Qty.
010.79.041	3.5 x 13	#6 x 1/2"	200 pcs.

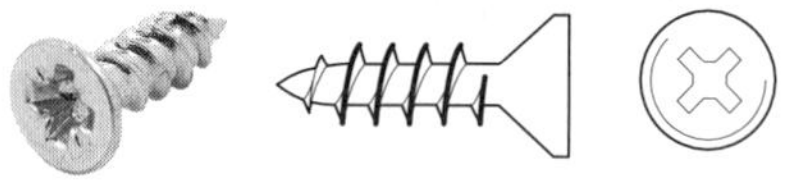

Large head screw with flat washer for attachment of drawer face to drawer box.

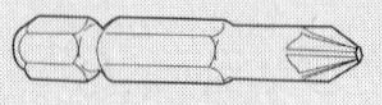

Phillips Bit hardened tool steel Hexagon shank, 1/4".

Cat. No.	Size	Length
006.40.270.PM	1	25mm
006.40.280.PM	2	25mm
006.40.290.PM	3	25mm
006.40.271.PM	1	50mm
006.40.281.PM	2	50mm
006.40.291.PM	3	50mm

Packing: 25 pcs.

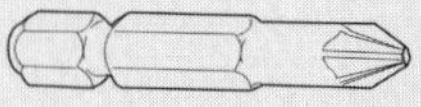

Bits Cross-slot PZ hardened tool steel Hexagon shank, 1/4".

Cat. No.	Size	Length
006.37.301.PM	1	25mm
006.37.310.PM	2	25mm
006.37.329.PM	3	25mm
006.37.276.PM	1	50mm
006.37.285.PM	2	50mm
006.37.294.PM	3	50mm

Packing: 25 pcs.

Truss Head Screw for Drawer Front Applications
Phillips Recess
Finish: zinc-plated steel

Cat. No.	ø x length mm	ø x length Inches	Box Qty.
013.13.917	4.0 x 15	#8 x 9/16	1000
013.13.935	4.0 x 25	#8 x 1	1000
013.13.944	4.0 x 32	#8 x 1 1/4	500
013.13.971	4.0 x 48	#8 x 1 7/8	500

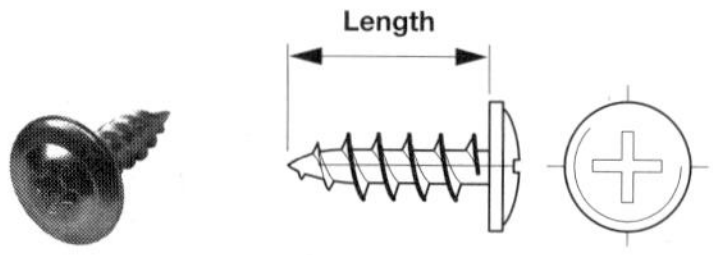

Washer Head Screw for 5 mm System Hole
Pozi Recess
Finish: zinc-plated steel

Cat. No.	ø x length mm	Box Qty.
013.10.149	6.3 x 14.0	200
013.10.283	6.3 x 28.0	500

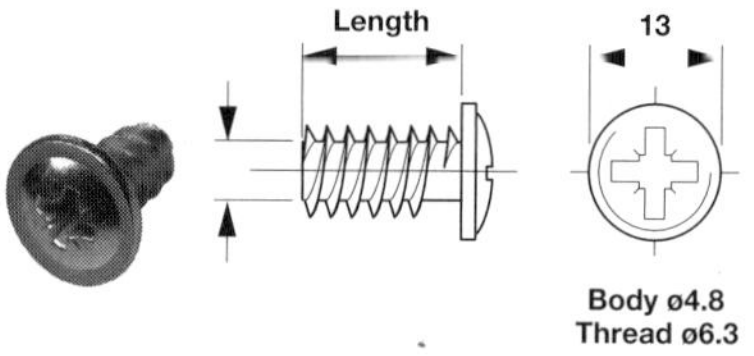

Varianta System Screws

Varianta System Screws
Designed for use in the 32 mm system, these screws fit either 5 mm or 3 mm holes for application of slides, hinge plates or other hardware.

Varianta For Hardware (3 mm)

Varianta special screws with cross-slots, size 2
Material: steel

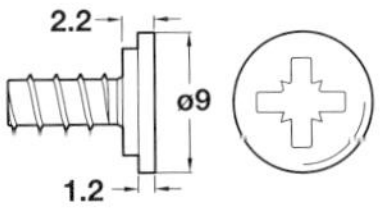

VARIANTA ⌀3

Core Dia.	Outside Dia.	Head Dia.	Length	Finish	Cat. No.	Box Qty.	Fits Hole
2.8	4.2	9.0	10.5	zinc-plated	013.20.814	500	3 mm
2.8	4.2	9.0	13.5	zinc-plated	013.20.832	500	3 mm
2.8	4.2	9.0	16.0	zinc-plated	013.20.841	500	3 mm
2.8	4.2	9.0	10.5	nickel-plated	013.20.618	500	3 mm
2.8	4.2	9.0	13.5	nickel-plated	013.20.636	500	3 mm
2.8	4.2	9.0	16.0	nickel-plated	013.20.645	500	3 mm

Bulk Quantity Boxes Cat. No.	Box Qty.
012.20.814	5000
012.20.832	5000
012.20.841	5000
012.20.618	5000
012.20.636	5000
012.20.645	5000

Varianta For Hardware (5 mm)

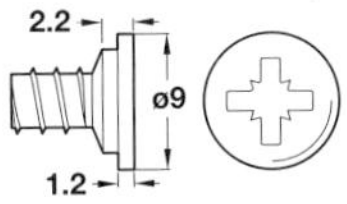

VARIANTA ⌀5

Core Dia.	Outside Dia.	Head Dia.	Length	Finish	Cat. No.	Box Qty.	Fits Hole
4.6	6.2	9.0	10.5	zinc-plated	013.20.912	500	5 mm
4.6	6.2	9.0	13.5	zinc-plated	013.20.930	500	5 mm
4.6	6.2	9.0	16.0	zinc-plated	013.20.949	500	5 mm
4.6	6.2	9.0	10.5	nickel-plated	013.20.716	500	5 mm
4.6	6.2	9.0	13.5	nickel-plated	013.20.734	500	5 mm
4.6	6.2	9.0	16.0	nickel-plated	013.20.743	500	5 mm
4.6	6.2	9.0	10.5	bronzed	013.20.118	500	5 mm

Bulk Quantity Boxes Cat. No.	Box Qty.
012.20.912	5000
012.20.930	5000
012.20.949	5000
012.20.716	5000
012.20.734	5000
012.20.743	5000
012.20.118	5000

Varianta For Hinge Mounting Plates (3 mm)

with countersunk head and cross-slots, size 2
Material: steel

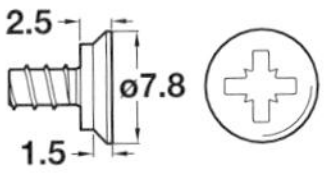

VARIANTA ⌀3

Core Dia.	Outside Dia.	Head Dia.	Length	Finish	Cat. No.	Box Qty.	Fits Hole
2.8	4.2	7.8	10.5	nickel-plated	013.15.617	500	3 mm
2.8	4.2	7.8	13.5	nickel-plated	013.15.626	500	3 mm
2.8	4.2	7.8	16.0	nickel-plated	013.15.635	500	3 mm
2.8	4.2	7.8	10.5	bronzed	013.15.019	500	3 mm

Bulk Quantity Boxes Cat. No.	Box Qty.
012.15.617	5000
012.15.626	5000
012.15.635	5000
012.15.019	5000

Varianta For Hinge Mounting Plates (5 mm)

with countersunk head and cross-slots, size 2
Material: steel

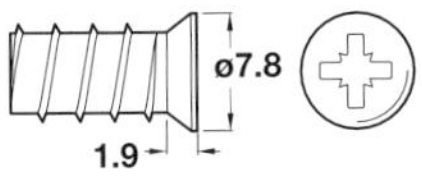

VARIANTA ⌀5

Core Dia.	Outside Dia.	Head Dia.	Length	Finish	Cat. No.	Box Qty.	Fits Hole
4.6	6.2	7.8	10.5	nickel-plated	013.15.715	500	5 mm
4.6	6.2	7.8	13.5	nickel-plated	013.15.724	500	5 mm
4.6	6.2	7.8	16.0	nickel-plated	013.15.733	500	5 mm
4.6	6.2	7.8	10.5	bronzed	013.15.117	500	5 mm

Bulk Quantity Boxes Cat. No.	Box Qty.
012.15.715	5000
012.15.724	5000
012.15.733	5000
012.15.117	5000

Varianta For Hardware (5 mm)

Varianta special screws with **flat head** and cross-slots, size 2, Material: steel

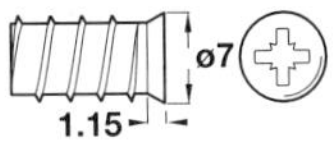

VARIANTA ⌀5

Core Dia.	Outside Dia.	Head Dia.	Length	Finish	Cat. No.	Box Qty.	Fits Hole
4.8	6.0	7.0	8	nickel-plated	013.14.719	500	5 mm
4.8	6.0	7.0	10.5	nickel-plated	013.14.718	500	5 mm
4.8	6.0	7.0	13.5	nickel-plated	013.14.727	500	5 mm
4.8	6.0	7.0	16.0	nickel-plated	013.14.736	500	5 mm

Bulk Quantity Boxes Cat. No.	Box Qty.
012.14.719	5000
012.14.718	5000
012.14.727	5000
012.14.736	5000

Dimensional data not binding. We reserve the right to alter specifications without notice.

HÄFELE

Variantool®-N Series Drilling Jig

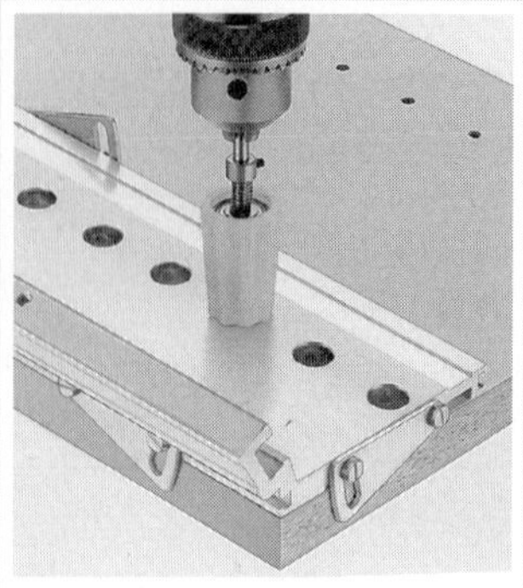

An ideal addition to the other Unitool drilling jigs. For drilling line holes and group holes according to ...

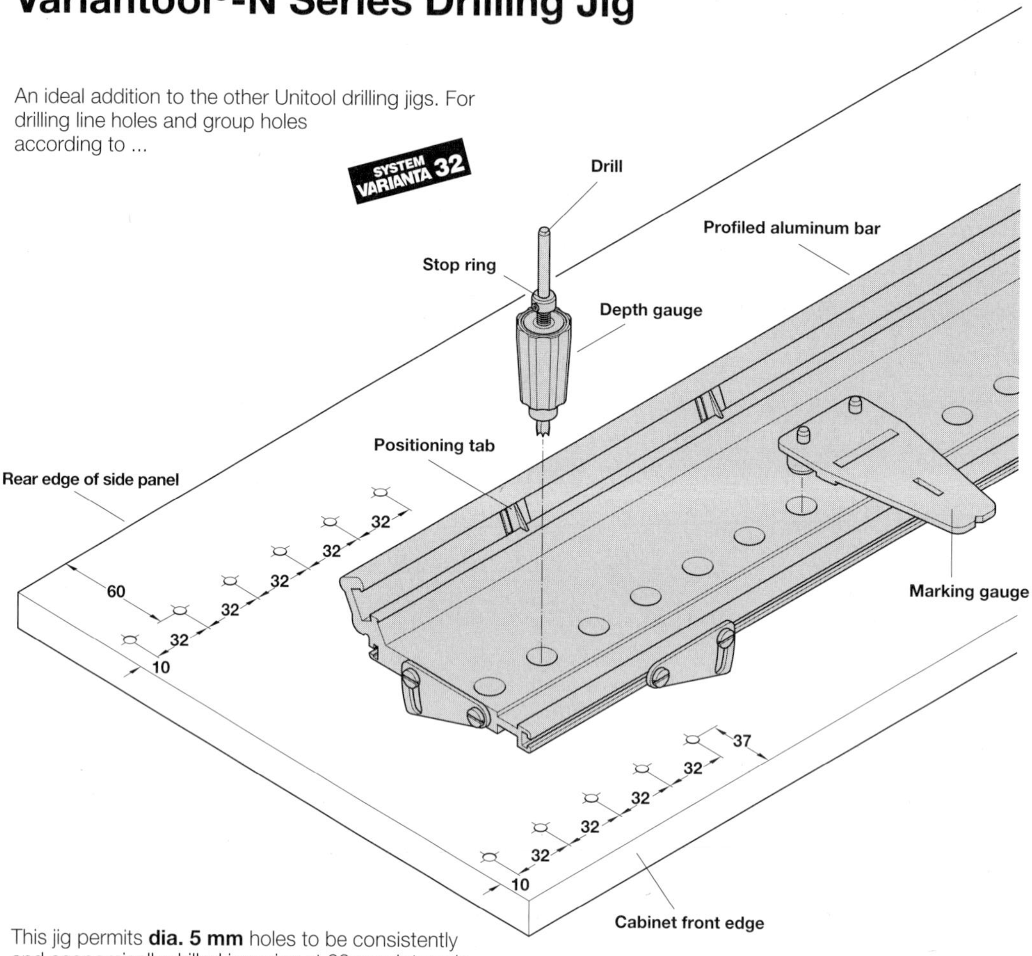

This jig permits **dia. 5 mm** holes to be consistently and economically drilled in series at 32 mm intervals. Holes can be drilled in lines or groups at **37 mm** inset distance from the front edge of the side panel or **60 mm** from the rear edge.
In the latter case, the jig is simply repositioned along the rear edge without being turned around.
Integral sliding positioning tabs ensure consistent drilling locations.

Variantool-N drilling jig for manual drilling of holes at 32 mm intervals
Includes:
1 profiled aluminum bar E6-treated
Dimensions: 1172 x 120 x 10 mm for 37 holes at 32 mm intervals (other system intervals also available on application), with 8 adjustable stop plates providing inset distances of 37 and 60 mm
1 locating pin for **dia. 5 mm** holes
5 positioning tabs and
1 marking gauge (plastic)

*Cat. No.	001.27.015

Packing: 1 set

* Necessary for a complete system.

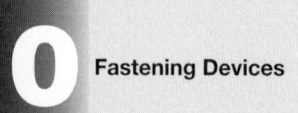

Accessories (to be ordered separately):

Depth gauge. Material: plastic, with 2 ball-bearings, stop-ring, coil spring, and Allen key for drill-bits with dia. 5 mm shanks

*Cat. No.	001.28.710

Packing: 1 pc.

Drill bit with centering tip
shank dia. 5 mm, length 110 mm

*Cat. No. **dia. 5 mm** carbide	001.24.498

Packing: 1 pc.

Spare Locating Pin

Cat. No.	001.27.024

Packing: 1 pc.

Spare Marking Guage

Cat. No.	001.27.060

Packing: 1 pc.

Installing of drill-bit in depth gauge:

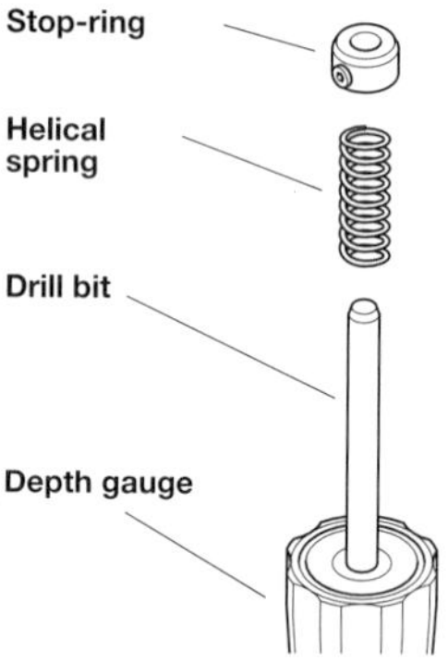

1. Insert 5 mm dia. bit into depth gauge from below.
2. Push coil spring and stop-ring onto bit shank.
3. Set drilling depth by adjusting stop-ring after trial operation.

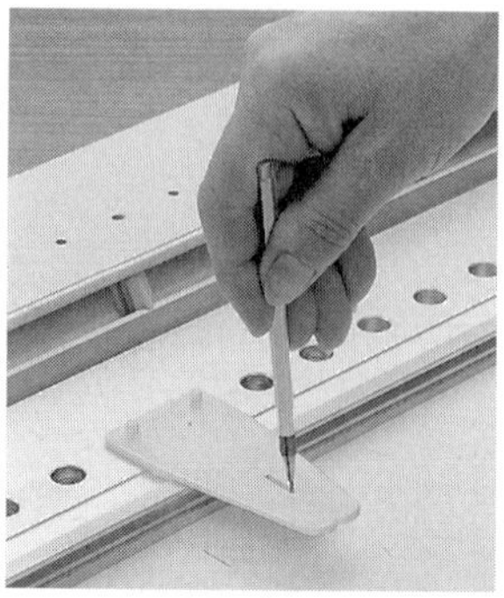

If intermediate drilling positions are required between the 32 mm series-drilled holes, e.g. for concealed hinges, the position can be transferred to the corresponding workpiece from the drilling jig or the appropriate 5 mm dia. line hole.

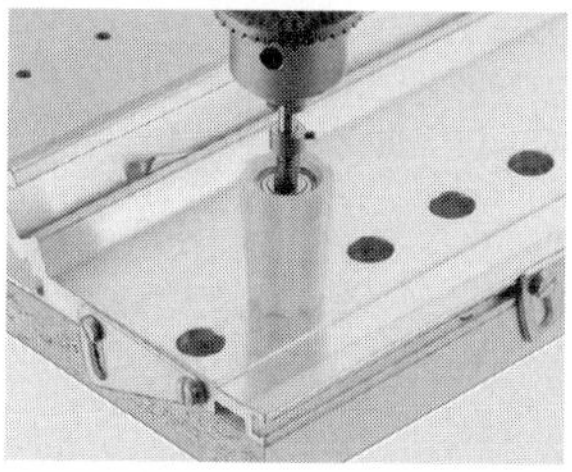

If more holes are required than the jig provides, it can be repositioned lengthwise and located by installing the locating pin in a previously drilled hole.

Wall Anchors

HÄFELE

E-Z Anchors®
A One-Piece Self-Drilling Anchor

- **Fast!** Self-Drilling, one-step installation.
- **Easy!** All you need is a #2 Phillips screwdriver.
- **Removable!** Unlike other mounting hardware, you can take the E-Z Anchor out of the wall as easily as you put it in.
- **Secure!** The deep threads hold fast in 3/8", 1/2" or 5/8" gypsum wallboard. Holds up to 70 lb. shear strength.*
- **Neat!** The unique point cuts clearly into wall and the head sits flush.
- **Corrosion Resistant!** E-Z Anchor will not rust, stain or streak.

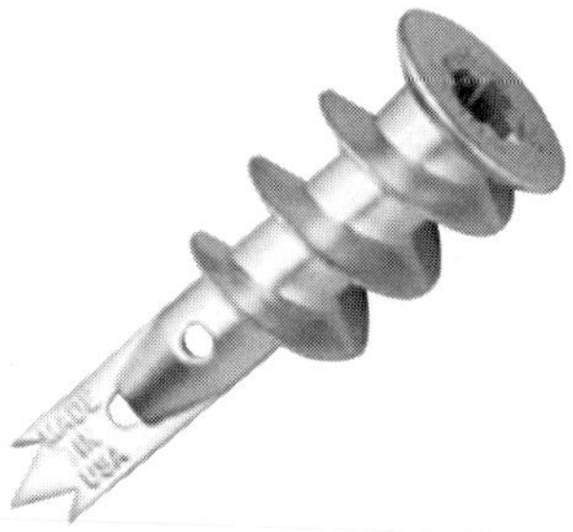

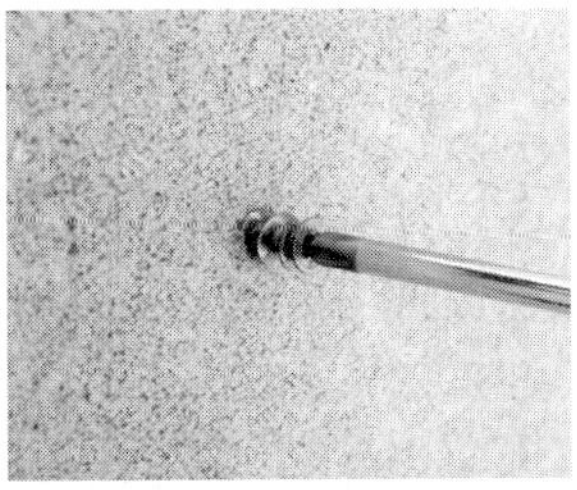

Place #2 Phillips screwdriver or cordless (#2 Phillips bit) into recess of either plastic or zinc E-Z Anchor.

Press into gypsum wall-board, while turning the anchor clockwise until it is seated flush with the wall.

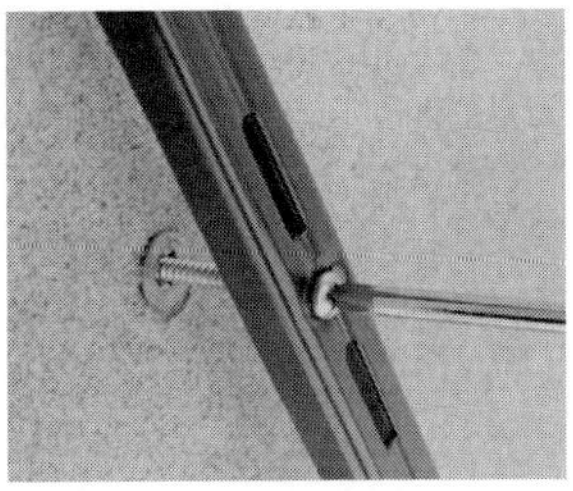

Insert screw with #2 Phillips screwdriver (or bit). #8 screws are recommended.

Cat. No.	Finish	Box Qty.
051.18.025	zinc-plated steel (heavy duty)	100 pcs./box
051.18.034	white plastic (medium duty)	100 pcs./box

*Depends on material strength.

E-Z Toggles
A Self-Drilling Toggle That's Trouble-free

Now you can mount heavy objects to gypsum wallboard without drilling, cutting, hammering or hunting for studs. With just a #2 Phillips screwdriver you can install the E-Z Toggle® bolt and you're ready to go. Holds up to 120 lb. shear strength.*

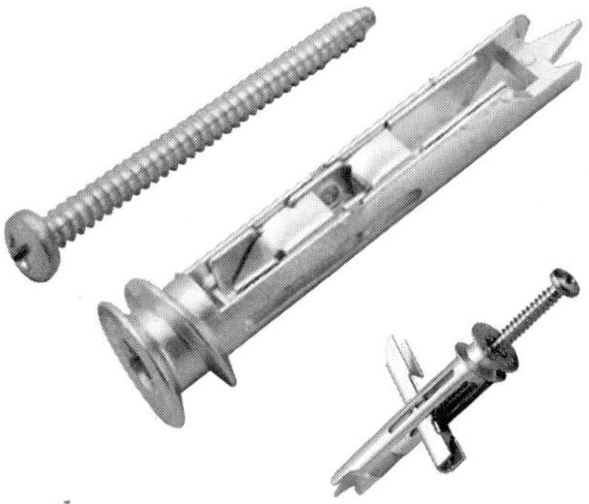

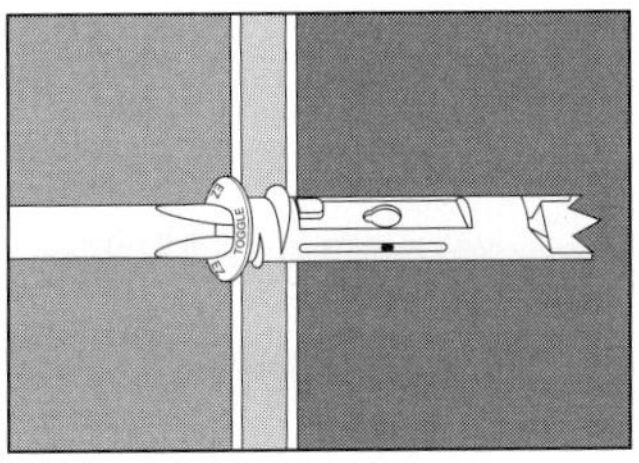

*Depends on material strength.

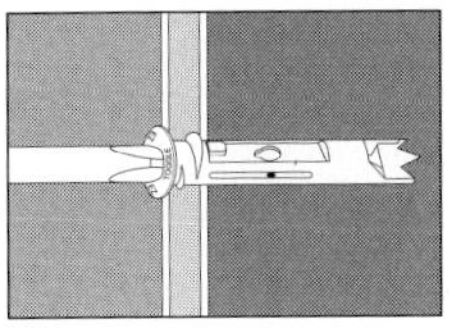

Simply screw E-Z Toggle into the wall.

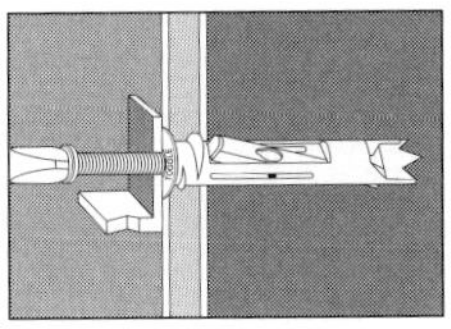

Place the fixture and insert the screw provided.

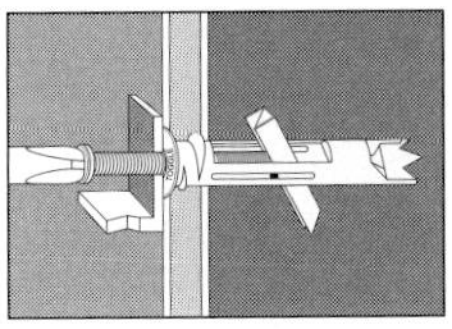

As screw turns, clamp engages.

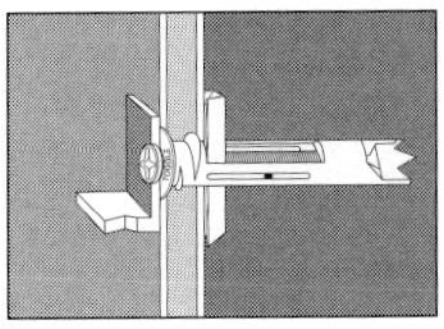

Keep turning until tight.

Cat. No.	Description	Size	Material	Box Qty.
051.17.911	Toggle w/sheet metal screw (For thickness: 0-1/2")	#8 x 2 1/8" 4mm x 54mm	zinc-plated steel	50 pcs./box
051.17.920	Toggle w/**flanged head** sheet metal screw (For thickness: 0-1/2")	#8 x 2 1/8" 4mm x 54mm	zinc-plated steel	50 pcs./box

Dimensional data not binding. We reserve the right to alter specifications without notice.

HÄFELE

Cover Caps

Snap Caps with washers

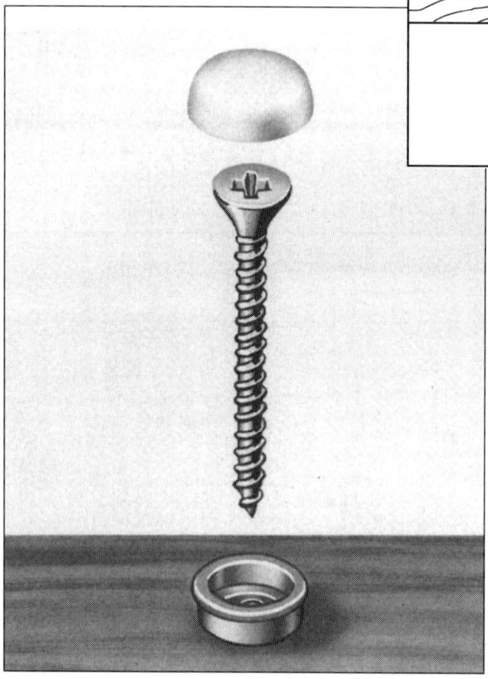

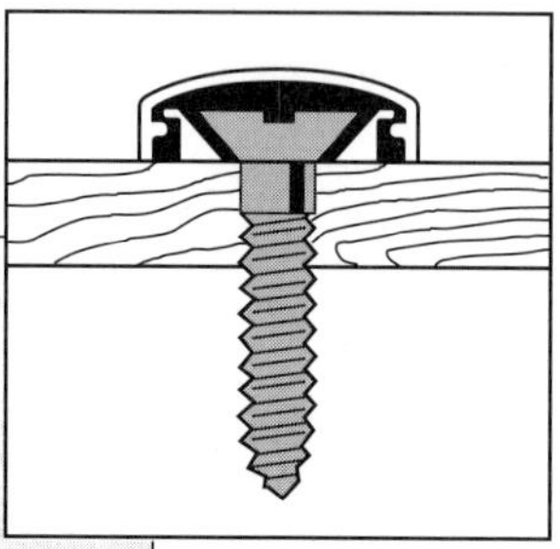

Installation of countersunk screw with washer and snap cap.

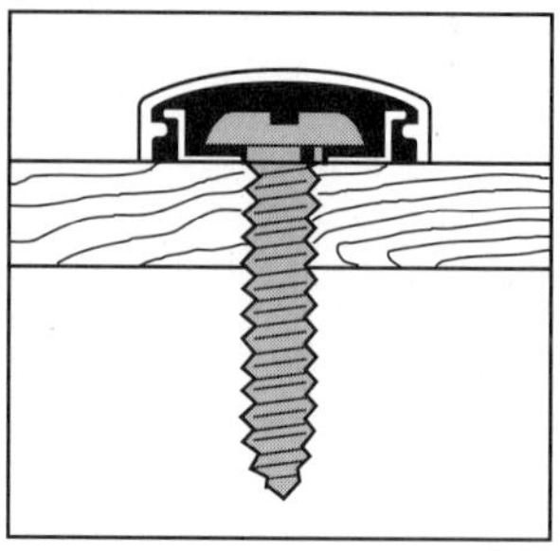

Installation of panhead screw with washer and snap cap.

Washers for screws up to **Ø 4 mm**
Finish: plastic

Cat. No.	countersunk	045.06.030
	panhead	045.08.034

Packing: 1000 pcs.

Cover Caps for washers
Finish: plastic

Cat. No.	white	045.06.709
	beige	045.06.405
	brown	045.06.101
	black	045.06.307

Packing: 1000 pcs.

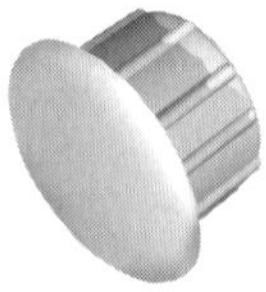

Cover Caps
Ribbed or slightly tapered for tighter grip
Finish: plastic

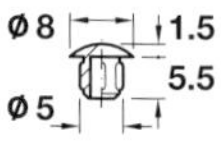

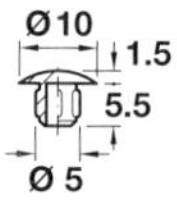

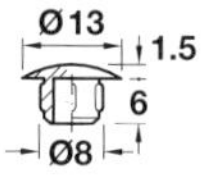

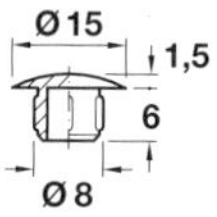

Cat. No.	white	RAL 9010	045.10.712	045.10.721	045.00.789	045.00.770
	light brown	RAL 8007	045.10.212		045.00.289	045.00.270
	dark brown	RAL 8014	045.10.114		045.00.181	045.00.172
	black	RAL 9005	045.10.310	045.10.329	045.00.387	045.00.378
	almond	RAL 1013		045.10.623		

Packing: 500 pcs.

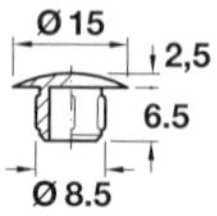

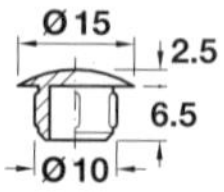

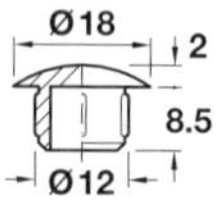

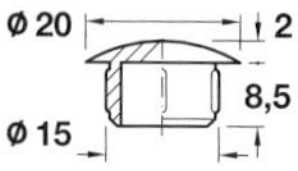

Cat. No.	white	RAL 9010	045.00.725	045.00.743	045.00.734	045.00.798
	light brown	RAL 8007			045.00.234	
	dark brown	RAL 8014			045.00.136	
	black	RAL 9005	045.00.323	045.00.341	045.00.332	045.00.396
	almond	RAL 1013				

Packing: 500 pcs.

Threaded Inserts

HÄFELE

T-nuts
4 -pronged
Finish: steel, unfinished

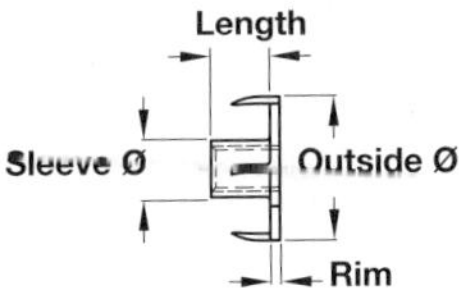

Internal thread	M 4	M 5	M 6	M 8	M 10
Outside Ø	15	18	19	22,5	26
Sleeve Ø	5.5	6.5	7.5	10	11.5
Length	7.5	8	8	9.5	11
Rim	1	1	1.3	1.5	2
Cat. No. unfinished	031.00.249	031.00.258	031.00.267	031.00.285	031.00.301
Packing in pcs.	1000	1000	1000	500	500

Screw-in sockets
with screwdriver slot
Finish: steel, unfinished

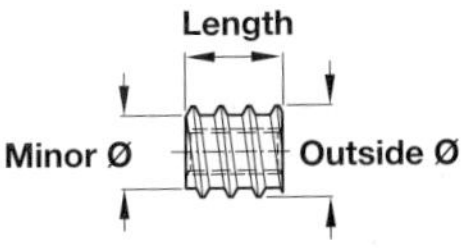

Internal thread	M 4	M 4		M 5
Outside Ø	8	8		10
Minor Ø	5.5	5.5		7
Length	8	10		10
Cat. No.	030.00.100	030.00.119		030.00.208
Packing in pcs.	1000	100		100

Internal thread	M 6	M 6	M 6	M 6
Outside Ø	10	12	12	12
Minor Ø	7	9	9	9
Length	12	11	13	15
Cat. No.	030.00.351	030.00.306	030.00.315	030.00.324
Packing in pcs.	1000	1000	100	1000

Internal thread	M 8	M 8		M 10
Outside Ø	14	16		18.5
Minor Ø	11.5	12		15
Length	15	18		15
Cat. No.	030.00.404	030.00.422		030.00.502
Packing in pcs.	100	100		100

Glue-in sockets
with grooves
Finish: nylon, natural
colored

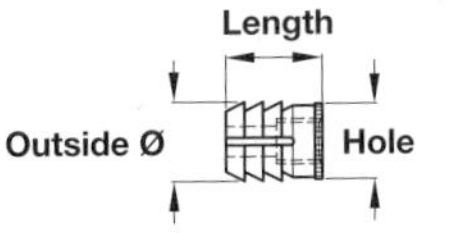

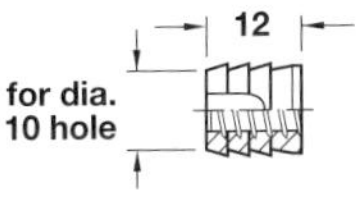

Internal thread	M 4	M 4	M 4		M 5
Outside Ø	8.5	8.5	11		11
Hole Ø	8	8	10		10
Length	8	10	10		13
Cat. No.	039.33.140	039.33.042	039.33.239		039.33.051
Packing in pcs.	1000	1000	1000		100

Internal thread	M 6	M 6	M 6	M 6	M 8
Outside Ø	8.5	11	11	11	11.2
Hole Ø	8	10	10	10	9.5
Length	11	9	11	13	12
Cat. No.	039.33.462	039.33.364	039.33.266	039.33.060	039.33.186
Packing in pcs.	5000	1000	5000	5000	100

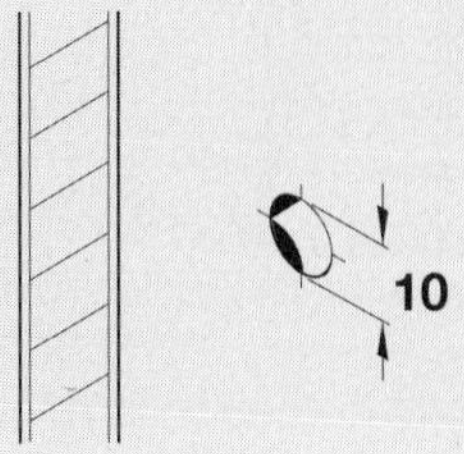

Dimensions in mm

HÄFELE

Threaded Inserts

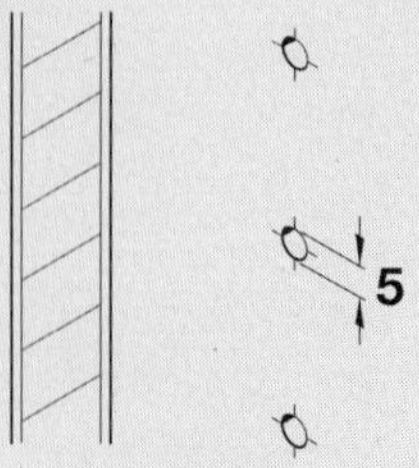

The SYSTEM VARIANTA 32 offers many advantages as a design principle for knock-down furniture.

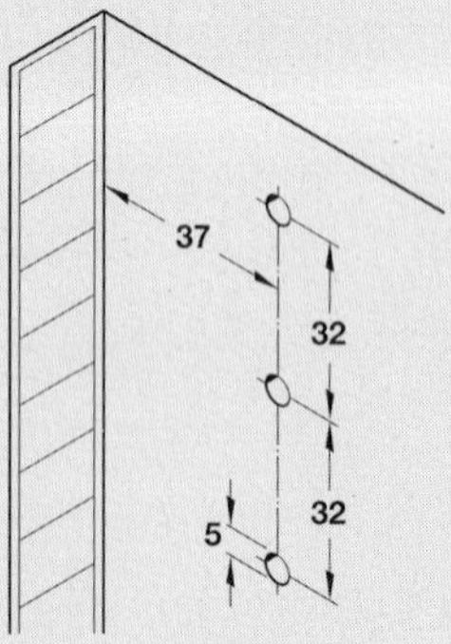

Many types of RTA fittings can be installed using series-drilled holes at 32 mm intervals on a line 37 mm from the panel face edge.

All the adjoining sleeves can be used with Ø 5 mm hole based on this system.

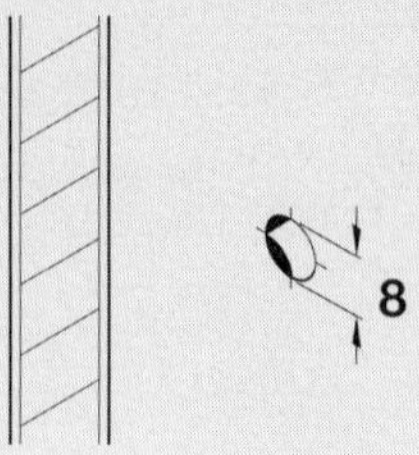

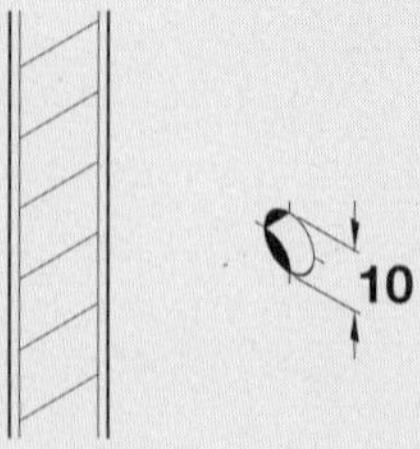

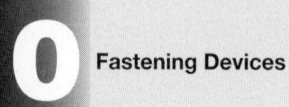

Spreading sleeve
with M4 internal thread, milled surface.
Finish: brass

Cat. No.	051.45.004

Packing: 3000 pcs.

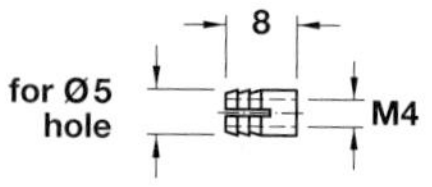

Spreading dowels with collar
Finish: nylon, natural-colored

Length	9 mm	12 mm
Cat. No.	340.43.000	340.43.019
Packing in pcs.	500	1000

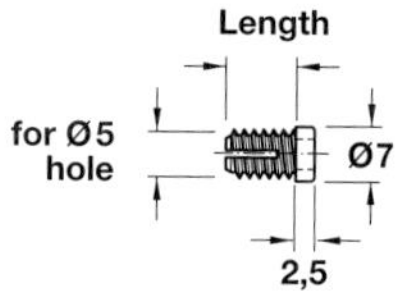

Spreading dowels with collar
Finish: nylon, natural-colored

Cat. No.	042.98.033

Packing: 1000 pcs.

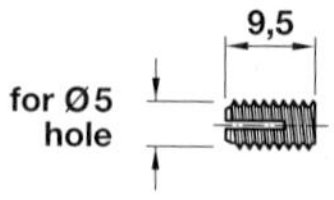

Spreading sleeve without collar
Finish: nylon, natural-colored

Cat. No. 9 mm long	042.98.051

Packing: 5000 pcs.

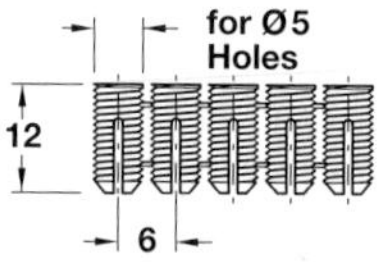

Strip of 20 spreading dowels integrally injection moulded.

Spreading dowels
with M6 internal thread
Finish: brass

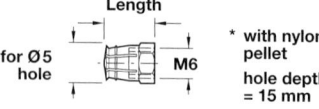

Length	9 mm	12 mm*
Cat. No.	039.00.267	039.00.061
Packing in pcs.	2000	1000

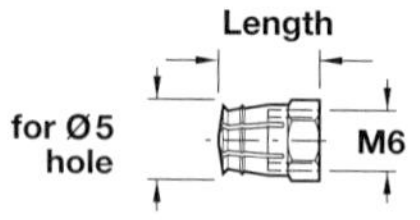

* with nylon pellet
hole depth = 15 mm

Spreading dowels
with M6 internal thread
Finish: nylon, natural-colored

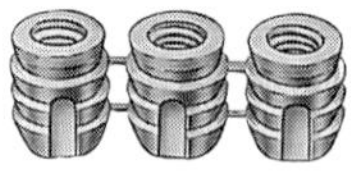

Cat. No.	039.34.067

Packing: 1000 pcs.

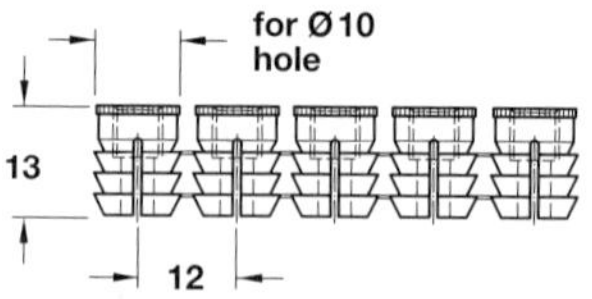

Knock-in dowels

Spreading dowels
with M6 internal thread
Finish: nylon, natural-colored

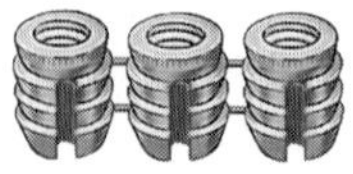

Cat. No.	039.35.064

Packing: 1000 pcs.

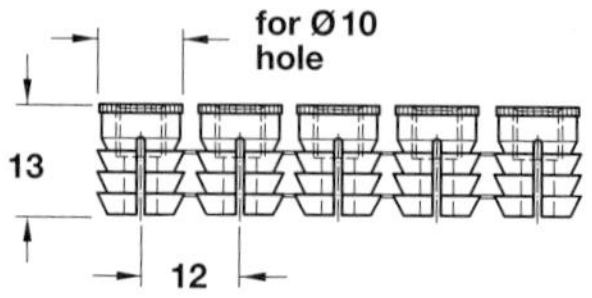

Spreading dowels, integrally injection moulded.
Glue not required.
Requires minimum bolt thread of 7.5 mm to expand

Glued dowel, with special internal thread in Ø 10 mm holes.

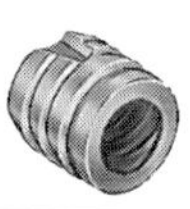

Finish: plastic

Cat. No.	039.32.050

Packing: 5000 pcs.

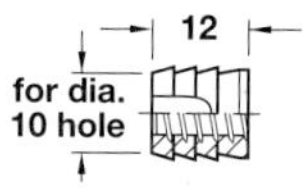

Dimensional data not binding. We reserve the right to alter specifications without notice.

Index - by product type

Index - by product type

Index - by product type

P

R

S

T

U

V

W, X

Cat. No. Page No.

1

Cat. No. Page No.

Cat. No. Page No.

Cat. No. Page No.

Cat. No.	Page No.

4

5

8

0

0

0

Important

This catalog is intended for exclusive use by the recipient. No part of this publication may be distributed in any form to direct competitors of Häfele. Häfele retains complete ownership of this catalog.

Häfele reserves the right to demand the return of this catalog in any case where it is employed for purposes of unfair competition.

Reproduction of this catalog, either wholly or in part, or reprinting of any drawing or copying of the layout, are strictly forbidden.

The technical data and dimensions contained in the drawings are non-binding and are subject to design improvement.

Häfele accepts no liability for any typographical or other type of error which may occur in the production of this catalog.

All merchandise is furnished subject to Häfele's official Terms and Conditions of Sale.

STANDARD TERMS AND CONDITIONS OF SALE

HÄFELE

1. Exclusive Terms.

All orders, whether through the catalog or otherwise, shall be governed by the following terms and conditions. These terms and conditions shall constitute the complete Agreement between the purchaser of the goods (herein called "Buyer") and Häfele America Co. (herein called "Seller") and shall supersede all prior and contemporaneous oral and written statements of any kind whatsoever made by the parties and their representatives.

2. Acceptance.

Buyer's orders shall not constitute contracts of sale unless accepted in writing by an authorized agent of Seller at its home office in Archdale, North Carolina or its offices in Carson, California or San Francisco, California or Arlington Heights, Illinois. Seller's acceptance of any order is expressly conditioned upon Buyer's assent to the terms and conditions contained in this Agreement. Any added, varied, or conflicting terms in Buyer's Purchase Order or elsewhere are hereby objected to and shall not bind Seller, unless expressly agreed to in a writing signed at Seller's home office in Archdale, North Carolina, by a duly authorized officer of Seller in a document making specific reference to this Agreement and specifically stating that it "amends" this Agreement. Buyer shall notify Seller in writing, as soon as practicable after receipt of Seller's acceptance of Buyer's order, of any objection to the terms of this Agreement. Buyer's failure to notify Seller of any objection shall conclusively indicate Buyer's assent to and acceptance of all terms and conditions herein. Buyer expressly accepts the terms and conditions herein at the exact moment Seller commences performance on any purchase order requiring or providing for Seller to commence performance prior to Buyer's receipt of Seller's written acknowledgment.

3. Prices.

Seller has the right to change, without notice, any prices and/or specifications contained in its catalog or any other writing that does not expressly prohibit such change. Buyer agrees to pay for all samples priced in excess of $10 on the date of shipment.

4. Taxes.

Any applicable federal, state, local or other government tax or charge on the sale or shipment of the goods covered by this Agreement shall be added to the price and paid by Buyer. Buyer agrees to hold harmless Seller from all such taxes, including interest and penalties thereon, and any costs and expenses in connection therewith.

5. Shipment, Freight and Delivery.

Except as otherwise provided, all prices are F.O.B. Seller's warehouses, Archdale, North Carolina or Carson, California, depending on the location from which the goods are shipped. The decision as to place of shipment shall be solely that of Seller.

6. Terms.

Except as otherwise provided, payment terms are net thirty (30) days from date of Seller's invoice. Statements are issued monthly and a late payment charge of one and one half percent (1.5%) per month (but not in excess of the legal maximum) will be added to all past due balances. Buyer shall have no right of set-off.
Buyer's cancellation of orders for any items referred to in the catalog is subject to a service charge to cover the costs of initial processing and/or production of the order. Orders for items which are not referred to in the Seller's catalog are not subject to cancellation by Buyer. Orders for an amount of less than $100 are subject to a service charge of $20.

7. Financial Responsibility.

Shipments and deliveries of all items shall at all times be subject to approval of Seller's Credit Department. Seller at any time may require payment in advance or satisfactory security or guarantee that invoices will be promptly paid when due. Prior to credit approval orders will only be shipped on the basis of payment in advance. Buyer should submit a completed credit application with its initial order to expedite credit approval. In addition to and without limiting Seller's existing rights and remedies, Seller reserves the right to withhold further deliveries and/or terminate this or any other contract with Buyer, if Buyer fails to comply with the terms of this or any other Agreement. Upon Seller's termination of this Agreement, all unpaid amounts Buyer owes Seller shall become immediately due and payable.

8. Buyer's Agreement to Defend.

Buyer agrees to defend, protect and save Seller harmless against all suits at law or in equity and from all costs of suit, legal fees and expenses, damages, claims and demands arising out of or awarded in connection with any goods: (a) sold or supplied to Buyer by Seller that are not maintained and operated in accordance with recommended procedures, or (b) sold or supplied to Buyer by Seller to meet Buyer's specifications, requirements or instructions.

9. Notice of Accident or Malfunction.

Buyer shall notify Seller promptly and in any event within thirty (30) days of any accident or malfunction involving goods manufactured or sold by Seller. Buyer agrees to protect, defend and save Seller harmless (as provided in paragraph 8), in the event that Buyer fails to give such notice to Seller and to so cooperate.

10. Warranty.

Except as otherwise provided, Seller warrants for a period of ninety (90) days from the date of shipment that the goods supplied to Buyer shall be of good materials and workmanship. Seller further warrants for a period of ninety (90) days that the goods supplied by Buyer, when properly installed and used, are fit for the ordinary purpose or purposes indicated in the catalog and will conform to the catalog or to any other specifications supplied by Seller. Seller makes no warranty with respect to the following: (a) materials not manufactured by Seller, the use of which is suggested by Seller's general recommendations, application or installation procedures, or otherwise; (b) goods sold by Seller to Buyer for other than resale; and (c) all display items sold by Seller to Buyer.

THE FOREGOING WARRANTIES ARE EXCLUSIVE, AND IN LIEU OF ALL OTHER WARRANTIES, EXPRESS OR IMPLIED, WRITTEN OR ORAL, INCLUDING BUT NOT LIMITED TO, ANY IMPLIED WARRANTY OF MERCHANTABILITY OR FITNESS FOR ANY PARTICULAR PURPOSE. SELLER DOES NOT ASSUME, NOR AUTHORIZE ANY REPRESENTATIVE OR OTHER PERSON TO ASSUME FOR IT, ANY OBLIGATION OR LIABILITY OTHER THAN AS EXPRESSLY SET FORTH HEREIN.

11. Limitation of Remedies.

Seller's obligations under the above warranties (contained in Section 10) are conditioned upon Seller actually receiving notice from Buyer of the alleged defect within ninety (90) days from date of shipment and the allegedly defective goods revealing an actual defect upon examination by Seller. Seller shall not be liable for any labor or other expenses incurred by Buyer in the removal, repair or replacement of the goods or any component part claimed to be defective nor shall Seller be liable for any expenses incurred by the Buyer in order to remedy any defect. Seller shall not be liable for any consequential, special or contingent damages or expenses, arising directly or indirectly from any defect in the goods or from Buyer's use or inability to use such goods. The discharge of Seller's warranty obligation hereunder shall constitute fulfillment of all liabilities of Seller to Buyer, whether based on contract, negligence or otherwise. The remedies set forth herein shall be the exclusive remedies available to the Buyer and in lieu of all other remedies, and the liability of Seller, whether in contract, in tort, warranty or otherwise, shall not exceed the price of the goods sold, supplied or furnished by Seller. Any suit or action arising out of or relating to this Agreement or the breach thereof, must be commenced within one (1) year after the cause of action has accrued. The foregoing shall not limit the time within which any suit or action must be brought to collect an amount agreed to be paid by Buyer or to enforce a judgment or to collect any amount awarded to Seller. The sole purpose of the stipulated exclusive remedy shall be to provide Buyer with a credit or replacement for, or repair of, defective parts in the manner provided herein. This exclusive remedy shall not be deemed to have failed of its essential purpose so long as Seller is willing to credit Buyer's account or repair or replace the defective part(s) in the manner prescribed herein.

12. Shortages and Returns.

Any claim for shortage must be made by Buyer within ten (10) days from the date of shipment. Any shortage claim not made within said period shall be conclusively deemed waived by Buyer. Goods shall only be returned to Seller if requested by Seller in writing. The return of other than defective goods will subject Buyer to a handling charge of no less than twenty dollars ($20.00) and no more than twenty percent (20%) of the price of the returned goods. Seller shall not be liable for any damage to goods during shipment. The Buyer shall make any claim for damages due to shipment directly to the carrier.

13. Defaults or Delays.

Seller shall not be liable for any default or delay in the production or delivery of all or any goods resulting either directly or indirectly from (a) accidents to, or breakdowns or mechanical failure of Seller's plant, machinery or equipment; strikes or other labor troubles; labor shortages; fire; flood; wars; acts of the public enemy, acts of God; delays of suppliers; delays in transportation or lack of transportation facilities; embargos; shortages of, or reductions in, energy sources; priorities, allocations, limitations, restrictions or other acts required or requested by Federal, state or local governments, or any subdivision, bureau or agency thereof; or (b) any cause beyond the control of Seller. In no event shall Seller be liable for any consequential, special or contingent damages arising out of Seller's default or delay in filling Buyer's order.

14. Governing Law.

All orders are executed by both Buyer and Seller with reference to the laws of the State of North Carolina and the rights of all parties and the construction and effort of every provision of this Agreement shall be subject to and construed according to the laws of the State of North Carolina.

15. Binding Effect.

The provisions of any order shall bind and inure to the benefits of Seller and Buyer and their respective successors and permitted assigns. However, neither this Agreement, nor any part thereof or right thereunder, may be assigned by Buyer without the prior written consent of Seller.

16. Waiver.

The right of either party to require strict performance by the other party of any or all terms and conditions of this Agreement shall in no way be affected or impaired by prior waiver, forbearance, or course of dealing.

17. Interpretation.

Whenever possible, each provision of this Agreement will be interpreted in such a manner as to be effective and valid under applicable law, but if any provision of the Agreement should be prohibited or invalid under appropriate law, that provision will be deemed deleted and the remaining provisions of the Agreement will remain in full force and effect. The subject headings of the sections of this Agreement are included for the purpose of convenience only and will not affect construction or interpretation of any of its provisions.